NON-LEAGUE CLUB DIRECTORY 1997

EDITOR TONY WILLIAMS

ISBN 1-869833-38-4

Published by Tony Williams Publications Ltd.
Printed by Hillman Printers (Frome) Ltd.
Typeset by Formatvisual Ltd., Aski pre-press, Typecast, Keith Rye & T.W. Publications

Distributed by Tony Williams Publications Ltd., Helland, North Curry, Taunton TA3 6DU.
Tel: 01823 490080 Fax: 01823 490281

Cover photograph, with Barry Hayles of Stevenage Borough and David Harlow of Farnborough Town, **by Andrew Chitty.**

INTRODUCTION

Our regular readers will know that this Directory attempts to feature the complete non-League Pyramid of football competitions, especially highlighting the clubs who compete in the Football Association's Umbro Trophy and Carlsberg Vase knock-out competitions.

At the very top, the Vauxhall Conference, which has its usual comprehensive section, is the national Semi-Professional league linking the Nationwide Football League with the heart of the 'pyramid' i.e. the Unibond, Dr. Martens and ICIS football leagues with their 'families' of feeder leagues - these are displayed at the back of the book.

This year's Directory lists clubs within these three 'families' while the County section includes competitions below them in the Pyramid.

There is a contents section on Page 5 and at the back of the book, along with the regional pyramids and index of leagues you will also find a comprehensive index of clubs.

Hopefully the readers, who have not fully understood the Pyramid before, will be able to see how the country is split and how it is possible for the smallest clubs to gradually develop their facilities and improve their team and move through the Pyramid. Existing Conference clubs Welling United and Farnborough Town have been able to rise from parks' football right through to the brink of the Football League. Our Feeder Pyamids show how the book is laid out and where the various leagues stand in terms of seniority.

Sadly there are still many clubs whose secretaries do not find time to keep us up to date with changes of personnel once a year. We have tried to chase them for facts and photos and many league secretaries have been very helpful, but sometimes we have had to go to print without vital information. We apologise to supporters of clubs who may suffer in this way. However, we must not forget to thank the vast majority of club officials who are so helpful.

The County section, which includes clubs and leagues below the pyramid, has extra background information this year on the County Cups and another exciting new feature is Steve Whitney's fascinating Tranfer Records near the back of the book.

We know the minority sections appreciate their coverage and we will continue to include Scottish, Welsh, Schools, Youth, Sunday, Amateur Football Alliance, Channel Islands, Isle of Man and Women's football.

Hopefully we have managed to concentrate on the heart of non-League football with the top players, including the England team and the Conference, highlighted and all levels below the pyramid recognised in their own right.

We will react to your suggestions and hopefully the year ahead will give us much more chance of planning and checking as we improve our technology and consolidate as a publishing company.

Please keep in touch with us all year through 'Team Talk' and thank you once again for your support which has enabled us to come through a difficult time with very limited resources.

T.W.

ACKNOWLEDGEMENTS

League Secretaries must dread the close season when they have to compile their own handbooks and log all their club changes of personnel, colours and facilities and also get pestered by people like us wanting the previous seasons details for our books. Their willingness to help and their efficiency is greatly appreciated every year.

Club Secretaries who in general are 'honorary servants' of their clubs are also tremendous when it comes to sending in changes for their club pages. Most of them are really enthusiastic and keen to ensure their clubs' supporters will not be disappointed with their section of the book. To all of you who made the effort - thank you very much.

A number of new contributors really pulled out the stops this year with special thanks to Rob Grillo for the League Tables from around Yorkshire and the brilliant contributions from Mark Jones, Peter Gorringe, Jonathon Rouse and Leslie G. Moore.

New ideas and improvements will always be welcome and thanks for your enthusiasm.

Our Sponsors this year are ICIS who have certainly contributed greatly to senior pyramid football and we are thrilled they have chosen to be involved with the Directory. They have much to offer the game at our level and I am sure their quality products are already greatly appreciated by the clubs and especially the ICIS League.

The staff at The Football Association have once again been most helpful all year and our special thanks go to the hard working teams in the Competitions, Publications and Press departments.

Our Photographic Team seems to get larger and more enthusiastic every year. We have never been able to offer fees for photos in the Directory or Team Talk but we greatly appreciate their supurb work and their enthusiastic loyalty. We apologise if any credit lines have been missed but thank you again for all your efforts.

There is a new group of helpers this year known as **'The Team Talk Team'**, they are encouraging clubs to send in news, articles and photos for the magazine and the Directory. We hope they are enjoying their first season and we certainly appreciate their help.

Character Graphics, Hillman Printers and all our typesetters are aware this is a very difficult book to produce. We really thank all of the production 'team' for their patience, co-operation and expertise.

TW

CONTENTS

Only the major leagues are listed in this section. The full list will be found in the index of leagues on page 1066.

EDITORIAL

Looking back on the year's football at semi-professional level the highlights were probably the two excellent England performances against The Republic of Ireland and Holland and the two Wembley Finals which were a credit to the clubs battling for the FA Umbro Trophy and FA Carlsberg Vase. Indeed Macclesfield who were pushed all the way by their neighbours Northwich Victoria were outstanding as were Brigg Town who beat a neat Clitheroe side with a stylish display. Sky TV showed the football world the quality of Conference clubs but perhaps they were influencial in limiting the Wembley attendance to its all time smallest. The Vase Final was also contested by two northern clubs with modest support so the old 'chestnut' regarding the pros and cons of playing the finals at Wembley was a matter of some comment once again.

Personally I think every player and club official still considers a trip to Wembley as something very special to treasure, but I do think we should consider a Trophy\Vase weekend or even just a Saturday at the end of the season when non-League supporters from all over the country could watch both finals and enjoy an annual get together in London.

Sadly Tony Jennings has stepped down as England's Semi-Professional International manager as he is now looking after Carshalton Athletic in the ICIS League and felt he would not be able to find the time to watch enough Conference football and complete his 'duties' at his club, his work and, of course, his family. Tony with Ron Reid's support instigated two excellent England performances which are reported in this Directory. He will be missed but he hands over the squad in very good shape, so let's hope this team, that represents a huge section of England's national sport, will eventually get the competition or tournament it deserves.

Didn't Euro96 show what a good influence football can have on the whole country? When we were winning and playing well, the songs, the atmosphere and the whole feeling of happiness and exhileration lifted us all into a much friendlier, more pleasant race of people. People smiled and talked to each other in shops and public transport, they worked with a smile on their faces and certainly at our level of the game there are far more club managers trying to produce winning sides through passing football rather than the 'route one' craze we have suffered for much of the last ten years.

The influence of some spectacular Premier football well presented on Sky TV and the glorious stadia that are eventually being responsible for a new geneation of fans, who don't miss standing behind the goal, all give the game a new image. More people are certainly attending Premier League matches and hopefully the love of the game will spread down and town clubs in this pyramid will accordingly set their playing standards higher and also continue to improve their facilities.

Competition for promotion has never been more intense at probably every level of pyramid football. The Conference, although disappointed that for the third year their champions failed to gain Football League acceptance, has produced some excellent clubs and surely this season will see a really good representative side gain promotion and take its rightful place up there in the Nationwide League. Stevenage Borough, Woking, Kidderminster Harriers or Macclesfield would all feel at home in Division Three.

The three senior feeder leagues have the look of very well contested competitions this season and some real quality can be found in their Premier Divisions as results in the FA Cup show every year. Sadly for them only one club can go up from each 'family' however good their record, as poor Halesowen Town found out last year. You can produce record breaking form and still miss promotion. A number of sad stories have resulted in clubs being disbanded with Leicester United being the most senior of these. I wonder if the County FAs or even the Football Association themselves are able to protect or help clubs that may get into the wrong hands. It's a difficult 'political' matter, but there are times when help is needed and many long serving supporters and members are often powerless to protect their clubs.

This Directory is the nineteenth since the series started as a little pocket book in 1973. As those of you who read Team Talk will know we are still reeling from a recession which saw us extend to seven staff publishing over twenty books plus the monthly magazine. A well documented disaster hit us as little publishers and we had to repay bookshops for books the shops failed to sell (and hard backed books did not sell in the recession!). So we could not continue to employ so many people or publish so many titles. We were reduced to three and just published two annuals - this Directory and the

Courage Rugby Union Club Directory and of course Team Talk which has gone from strength to strength. This year should prove to be the last in which we will have had to work under severe pressure.

One aspect of our Non-League Club Directory has been highlighted this year Many club officials prefer to give us **this** season's team photo with new players, their details and, of course, often new sponsors. As club officials do not rely on this Directory for league or cup rules or features then a later publishing date giving **all clubs** a better chance of supplying up-to-date team photos and information may be prefered rather than rushing it out during the summer. What do you think?

Finally, some good news - the FA's Pyramid Committee is set up to help the semi-professional leagues to develop in harmony while promoting the interests of clubs and leagues alike. The two main points of contention appear to be the Conference officials being keen to lift their competition away from the rest of non-League football, and the fact that geographically the ICIS and Dr. Martens Leagues could surely help some clubs by amending their league boundaries to accommodate all in a more sensible constitution. It will be interesting to hear the views of the FA Pyramid Committee?

Well, we hope you enjoy the Directory and are having a great season. Please let me know about any ideas you would like discussed in Team Talk and best wishes to you all for another good year of football. Thank you for your support.

Tony Williams

* * * * *

Once again the completion of the Non-League club Directory has been a mammoth task. A huge team of helpers have contributed but as mentioned above we will have to make a policy decision regarding the time of publication for next year. Club officials seem happier to supply the new season's team photo in August along with up to date playing squads and clubs' administrative changes, so perhaps we should officially publish the book in October on a regular basis? We will see but hopefully you will enjoy this edition and our thanks go to everyone who helped. TW.

Editor

Tony Williams

House Editor: Keith Rye

Editorial Team: George Brown, Steve Whitney, Tony Williams, Bill Mitchell.

Editorial Address: Tony Williams Publications, Helland, North Curry, Taunton, Somerset TA3 6DU. Tel: 01823 490080 Fax: 01823 490281.

Photographers: Peter Barnes, Andrew Chitty, Keith Clayton, Alan Coomes, Graham Cotterill, Paul Dennis, Tim Durrant, Keith Gillard, Garry Letts, Peter Lirettoc, Eric Marsh, Rob Monger, Ian Morsman, Dennis Nicholson, Kevin Rolfe, Francis Short, Colin Stevens, Roger Turner, Alan Watson, Gordon Whittington, Martin Wray.

Contributors: Mike Ford - 'Bureau of Non-League Football' (League Tables & County Cup Results), Mandy Sabat & Steve Clark (Football Association), Nick Robinson (Icis League), Dennis Strudwick (Dr Marten's League), Duncan Bayley (Unibond League League), Wally Goss (A.F.A.), Mike Simmonds (Schools Football), Jeremy Biggs, Trevor Bailey (Sunday Football), Bob Morrison - 'First XI Sports Agency', Dudley Jackson, Stewart Davidson (Scottish Football), Bill Berry - 'Non-League Traveller' (League & Club Addresses), Robert Errington, Gareth Davies (North Wales Football), Rob Kelly, Peter Bentley, Mike Wilson, Leslie G Moore (Ten Year Records), Richard Ralph, Andy Molden, Steve Layzell, Jon Weaver, John Bullen, Rex Bennett (Channel Islands), Mike Odgers & Dave Deacon (Cornish Football), Dave Edmunds, Steve Davies, Colin Timbrell, Paul Gardner, Mike Amos, Arthur Clark, Alan Turvey, Keith Masters, David Halford, Rod Harrington, Cathy Gibb (Womens' Football), Rob Grillo, Mark Jones, Peter Goringe, Jonathon Rouse, William Hughes, Andy Snowley, Dave Dorey & Keith Dixon.

All League Secretaries & Officials - names accompany relevant pieces

All Club Secretaries & Officials who completed questionnaires

ICIS
SPORTSWEAR

Who are ICIS?

ICIS Sportswear is the forerunner in mail-order-direct supply to football clubs offering the unique opportunity of purchasing top quality football gear at the most competitive prices possible.

Formely known as New Olympic sportswear the staff at ICIS Sportswear have been manufacturing garments for over 20 years to companies such as Umbro, Adidas, Marks & Spencer and Next.

Now that the company is under new ownership, it has decided to go its own way and develop its own brand, hence the recent sponsorship of one of the oldest football leagues in the world.

The company factory is situated in Aspatria, Cumbria whilst the offices which deal with all orders has moved nearer to its main market area in the south at Chesham, Buckinghamshire.

The Companys Managing Director Bill Wilson who has been involved in football at all levels has a firm commitment towards quality. He feels that every soccer club deserves the best quality sportswear and equipment available and sees no reason why this should be the exclusive right of professional clubs.

Sponsorship

As a sign of its support for the amateur game ICIS is now in the 2nd year of sponsoring the largest football league (The Isthmian League) in the pyramid system.

In addition to this sponsorship ICIS are now the main kit suppliers to the other two pyramid feeder Leagues, the Northern Premier League (Unibond) and the Southern League (Dr Martens) for the next 3 years.

The newly developed ICIS 'Pro' football is also the official matchball to the ICIS and Unibond Leagues.

The quality of ICIS products has been recognised by competitors and users alike and the range is still increasing with several new products being launched this year.

The range and quality.

A wide choice of over 200 design/colourways are available ex-stock. Furthermore, we offer the larger club the opportunity to design its own kit.

All the manufacturing is carried out to the very highest standards without any cutting of corners. They have now developed their own fabric which is superior to the majority of competitors in weight (150gsm) and feel with their own brand name running through it for distinction and endorsement.

All the shirts are cut generously to reflect the the loose fitting fashion of the modern game whilst remaining flexible to cater for any special requests.

The Future.

▼ The intention is to continue the traditional principles of quality, value for money and improved service - The ultimate goal being a one stop shop for football.

▼ A continued support of amateur football stretching to the very grassroots of the game which is youth football.

▼ To form an exclusive club which benefits its customers via special offers, increased product range and close customer involvement.

▼ To provide a more extensive range of leisurewear consistent with the quality of the football kits already available.

In 1994 everyone said "Who are ICIS ?"

.... **now you know.**

ICIS
SPORTSWEAR

AWARDS 1995-96

* * * * *

PLAYER OF THE YEAR

Barry Hayles

* * * * *

INDIVIDUAL MERIT AWARDS

Arthur Clark
Paul Fairclough
Leon Shepherdson

* * * * *

REGIONAL CLUB AWARDS

NORTH EAST
Brigg Town

NORTH WEST
Macclesfield Town

MIDLANDS
Halesowen Town

EAST of ENGLAND
Rushden & Diamonds

HOME COUNTIES NORTH
Stevenage Borough

HOME COUNTIES SOUTH
Dartford

WEST of ENGLAND
Torpoint Athletic

WALES
Barry Town

F.A. CUP
Cinderford Town

* * * * *

PLAYER OF THE YEAR

PLAYER OF THE YEAR

Barry Hayles

(Stevenage Borough & England)

Scoring goals is a special art. To be prolific at the top of your level of football needs talent and to carry on scoring for England means you have very real quality. For someone who has come up through 'the ranks', Barry really has proved to all those who have worked with him at club and country level, that he has goalscoring ability way above the average semi-professional player. If Stevenage Borough can keep him and he stays fit, then few will bet against the champions holding on to the title and Barry to finish top scorer in The Conference.

INDIVIDUAL MERIT AWARDS

Arthur Clark

When I was running the Rothmans side of the sponsorship of the Northern League I remember Arthur Clark was voted in as chairman by one vote from Stan Bradly and was then voted onto the FA Council. He has always been a tremendous supporter of all North Eastern football and has fought their corner in many political battles. Whether you agree with his views or not, you must respect his intense loyalty and as a colleague in the old Rothmans Northern League days I know what a dedicated football man Arthur is.

Paul Fairclough

He is not everyones 'cup of tea' - his performances on the bench are sometimes a little over the top, but you cannot take away anything from the results and achievements recorded. Paul has built a superb squad at a level where competition is intense. He has spotted quality players at lower levels and pursuaded senior players to join him. The results have proved him right and there is no one who has worked harder for success.

Leon Shepherdson

Do you remember little Stamco in the Sussex County League? A works team who developed, took on a new identity, found sponsors, built a brilliant ground with atmosphere and quality, attracted well known players, won the majority of their games and were accepted by the Dr. Martens League and were the first Sussex League club to gain promotion? You do? Well the inspiration behind a very well administered team was Leon Shepherdson, and his example should be an inspiration to all ambitious enthusiasts at small clubs.

REGIONAL CLUB AWARDS 1995-96

Brigg Town
NORTH EAST

Usually playing to crowds of about 100, Brigg built a side on a shoestring that must have been the envy of all the Vase clubs. To only concede goals on the way to Wembley and then turn on a quality display when it mattered, showed just what the management had achieved. A sound defence gave confidence to the whole side and in the end their performance was as good as any in a Vase Final.

Macclesfield
NORTH WEST

The disappointment of winning the Conference and not going up could have crippled many a club. But Sammy McIlroy's drive and enthusiasm, backed by an excellent board of directors produced another squad battling in the Conference (4th Place) and going all the way to Wembley where they produced a superb performance to win an excellent game and bring credit to non-League football, the competition and of course themselves.

Halesowen Town
MIDLANDS

According to the Beazer Homes League table on the 1st January, 1996, Halesowen Town were lying in fourth position, sixteen points behind the leaders Rushden & Diamonds. On 13th April Gloucester City and Cheltenham Town had been overtaken and there were just three points between 'Yeltz' and the leaders. In a run of twenty-six games only one match had been lost, but quite incredibly their super form did not bring promotion to the Conference. They must surely start as favourites this season.

Rushden & Diamonds
EAST OF ENGLAND

It's all very well having money, but you still have to produce the results. Everyone wanted to beat 'The Diamonds' last season, and, although at one time promotion looked too easy, a brilliant run of results by Halesowen Town and a little flutter of 'the butterflies' gave the end of season an exciting 'twist'. The club has been built quite brilliantly to possess the best of facilities and the best of players. What an exciting time for those who were with the original Rushden and Irthlingborough Diamonds clubs.

Stevenage Borough

HOME COUNTIES NORTH

They did it and they did it in style. The club have come a long way, developing facilities and playing strength all the time. Sadly the political problems sometimes overshadowed the superb performances on the field where a side of quality deservedly won our strongest competition in style. Hopefully with the backroom 'team' playing equally well, the future will be just as exciting.

Dartford

HOME COUNTIES SOUTH

They only came second in the Kent League, but they gained promotion back to the Southern (Dr. Martens) League and what a wonderful achievement that was. Especially for the hundreds of loyal fans who had stuck by them in an enforced exile. All of us at the 'Directory' and 'Team Talk' were thrilled as we know just how many real supporters the club has and how overjoyed they will be with this come back.

Torpoint Athletic

WEST OF ENGLAND

There are not many footballing heroes emerging from the West Country these days, but Torpoint Athletic's FA Carlsberg Vase 'run' last season lifted the whole area. Super away support backed a quality side and it was so good to see the real joy of everyone involved as the little South Western League club knocked over more fancied opposition. Hopefully they can keep it going, as it can only be good for the game and the 'deep West'.

Barry Town

WALES

Winning The League of Wales championship was a good performance, but probably expected. To reach the Cup Final was also fine although the penalties went against them. But to enter Europe with such style was magnificent and put all these achievements together, in a ground developed superbly and you have a club that can only go forward with pride.

Cinderford Town

F.A. CUP

They have been given this award ahead of Gravesend & Northfleet who certainly did well to beat Swansea City but had their reward with a glamourous day at Villa Park. Little Cinderford beat 'senior' clubs, Gloucester City, Bath City and Bromsgrove Rovers before losing to Gravesend after a replay. They made a host of new friends at the ties played at their homely little ground and the publicity for the town and the club certainly put Cinderford on the map.

PROMOTION AND RELEGATION 1996/97

(R) = Relegated (P) = Promoted

LEAGUE	CLUBS JOINING (From)	Clubs Leaving (To)
GMVC 22	Rushden & Diamonds (Beazer) Hayes (ICIS)	Dagenham & Redbridge (ICIS) Runcorn (Unibond)
UNIBOND Premier 22 + 1 = 23	Lancaster City *(P)* Alfreton Town *(P)* Runcorn (GMVC)	Droylsdon *(R)* Matlock Town *(R)*
First Division 21+1+2=22	Stocksbridge Park Steels (NCEFL) Flixton (CNWCFL)	Fleetwood Town (Disbanded)
ICIS Premier 22 22	Dagenham & Redbridge (GMVC) Oxford City *(P)* Heybridge Swifts *(P)* Staines Town *(Pro)*	Hayes (GMVC) Molesey *(R)* Walton & Horsham *(R)* Worthing *(R)*
Division One 22	Canvey Island *(P)* Croydon *(P)* Hampton *(P)*	Wembley *(R)* Barking *(R)* Ruislip Manor(Spartan League)
Division Two 22	Horsham *(P)* Leighton Town *(P)* Windsor & Eton*(P)*	Saffron Waldon Town (Essex League.) Newbury Town (Disbanded Mid-Season)
Division Three 21-4=17	Braintree Town (Dr Martens Southern)	Cove (Combined Counties) Harefield United (Spartan Lge.)
DR MARTENS Premier 22	Nuneaton Borough *(P)* Kings Lynn *(P)* Sittingbourne *(P)* Ashford Town *(P)*	Rushden & Diamonds (GMVC) Stafford Rangers (Rel Midland Division) VS Rugby (Rel Midland Div) Ilkeston Town (Rel Midland Div)
Midland Division 22	Shepshed Dynamo (Midlands Allnce.) Raunds Town (United Counties Lge.)	Buckingham Town (T Southern Division) Bury Town *(R)* Bridgenorth Town (Rel Mid Alliance.)
Southern Division 22	Dartford (Kent League) Cirencester Town (Hellenic League) St Leonards Stamcroft (Sussex Co Lge)	Braintree Town (ICIS Div Three) Poole Town *(R)* (Previously known as Stanco)

LEAGUE	CLUBS JOINING (From)	Clubs Leaving (To)
CNWCFL Division One 22	Vauxhall GM *(P)* Atherton Collieries *(P)*	Flixton (P Unibond First Div.) Skelmersdale Utd. *(R)*
Division Two 18+2=20	Colne FC (New Club) Garswood United (P Mid-Cheshire Lge.) Leek C S O B (P Midland League)	
NCEFL Premier 20	Selby Town *(P)* Pontefract Collieries *(P)*	Stocksbridge Park Steels (P Unibond) Goole Town (Disbanded)
Division One 16-2+1=15	Glapwell (Central Midlands League)	
UNIJET SUSSEX Division One 20	Saltdean United *(P)* Selsey *(P)*	St Leonards Stamcroft (Dr Martens) Crowborough Athletic. *(R)*
Division Two 18	Crawley Down Village *(P)*	
Division Three 16	Anstey Rangers Uckfield Town	Lindfield Rangers
COMBINED COUNTIES Premier Division 22-2=20	Corinthian Casuals (Spartan League) Cove (ICIS Division Three)	Peppard (T Chiltonian Premier) DCA Basingstoke (T Chiltonain Premier) Eton Wick (T Chiltonian Prmr.) Horley Town *(R)*
CHARRINGTON Chiltonian Premier 16+2=18	DCA Basingstoke (T Combined Co) Eton Wick (T Division Combined Co) Peppard (T Combined Counties)	Chalfont Wasps *(R)*
Division One 11-2+6=15	AFC Wallingford Res. *(Pro D2)* Penn & Tylers Green Res *(Pro D2)* Englefield Green Rovers (T Surrey County Intermediate Lge. (Western) Eton Wick Res. (T Combined Counties Reserve Section) Peppard Res. (T Combined Counties Reserve Section)	Martin Baker Sports Res *(R)* Cippenham Village *(R)*
ESSEX SENIOR Premier Div. 15	Ilford Saffron Walden Town (ICIS D2)	Maldon Town (Jewson Eastern Co) Romford (Merged with Collier Row)

LEAGUE	CLUBS JOINING (From)	Clubs Leaving (To)
SPARTAN Premier Division 16-3+4=17	Harefield United (ICIS) Ruislip Manor (ICIS) Islington St Mary's *(P)* Woodford Town *(P)*	Willesden Hawkeye Corinthian Casuals (T Combined Co) Woolwich Town (Tufnel Park now Haringey Borough)
Division One 14-7+2=9	Classic Inter *(P)* A C Milla *(P)*	AFC Blackheath Beckton United Metpol Chigwell Lewisham Elms Farreh (Withdrew Mid-Season)
Division Two 10-4+3=9	Doddinghurst Ouds United Leyton Sports	AFC Blackheath Res. Woodford '94 (Withdrew Mid-Season)
MIDLANDS ALLIANCE 20-3+3=20	Bridgenorth Town (Beazer Midland) Bloxwich Town (Endsleigh Mid Comb) Pelsall Villa (Bank's Brewery)	Shepshed Dynamo (Dr Martens Midland) Bolehall Swifts (Endsleigh Mid Comb) Armitage (Disbanded Mid-Season)
BANKS' BREWERY Premier 19-2+1=18	Wolverhampton United *(P)*	Pelsall Villa (P Midland Alliance) Lichfield City

Division One

Last seasons 21 Club Division – 4 Split into Division One North (13) & Division One South (14) Plus 10 New Clubs

	CLUBS JOINING (From)	Clubs Leaving (To)
	Goodyer FC Rocester Res.	Hinckley Athletic Res. Moxley Rangers

Division One North
13 inc:5 new clubs

Blakenall Res; Corestone Services; Heath Hayes (Mid Lge); Sporting Khalsa; Wolverhampton Casuals Res (Mid Comb 2).

Division One South
14 inc:5 new clubs

Bustleholme FC; Cradley Town Res; Kington Town; Leominster Town; Smethwick Rangers.

LEAGUE	CLUBS JOINING (From)	Clubs Leaving (To)
ENDSLEIGH MIDLAND Premier 20	Bolehall Swifts (Midland Alliance) Richmond Swifts *(P)* Kenilworth Town *(P)* Bilston Community College *(P)* David Lloyd F.C. Worcester Athletico	Bloxwich Town (Midland Allnce.) Chelmsley Town *(R)* Northfield Town *(R)* Ansells Oulton Royals (Previously Upton Town)
Division One 17-6+7=18	Continental Star *(P)* Cheslyn Hay *(P)* Brownhills Town *(P)* Leicester YMCA (Leic's District Lge) Yardley	Kings Norton Ex-Servicemen Fairfield Villa *(R)* Badsey Rangers *(R)*

LEAGUE	CLUBS JOINING (From)	Clubs Leaving (To)
Division Two 18-8+6=16	Feckenham *(P)* Richmond Swifts *(P)* Tipton Sports & Social *(P)* Birmingham Vaults *(P)*	Bromsgrove Rangers Coleshill Town Res. Wolverhampton Casuals Res (Banks) Wellesbourne Res. Rugby Town (Withdrew Mid Season)
Divison Three 18-8+2=12	Kenilworth Town Res. Tipton Town Res.	Studley United Kings Heath Res Tipton Rovers Park Rangers (Disbanded)
CENTRAL MIDLANDS Supreme 17-4+3=16	Dunkirk *(P)* Graham Street Prims*(P)* Nuthall *(P)*	Glapwell (NCEFL) Oldham United (Disbanded) Rossington (Demoted) Kiverton Park (Disbanded)
Premier Division 18-3+3=18	Grimethorpe M W (Sheffield Co) Holbrook (New Club)	
SHEFFIELD Premier 14-3+3=14	Ecclesfield Red Rose *(P)* Parkgate Res. *(P)* Wombwell Town *(P)*	Grimethorpe MW (Central Midlands) Throstles Ridgeway *(R)*
Division One 13-5+6=14	Kiveton Sports Wickersley Old Boys *(P)* The Wetherby *(P)*	Woodsetts Sports *(R)* Yorkshire Main *(R)* Worksop Town Res *(P)*
Division Two 14-5+6=15	Sheffield Lane Top Sheffield Res Queens Hotel Wombwell Main Norton Woodsetts	Sheffield Abbeydale Kiveton Park Res.
WEST LANCS 18-3+3=18	Lensil *(P)* Kirkham & Wesham *(P)* Tempest United *(P)*	BAe Canberra *(R)* Vernon Carus *(Resigned)* Colne RBL (Withdrawn Mid-Season)
Division Two 18-4+4=18	Miltonthorpe Corinthians Glaxa F.C. Harlingden St Mary's	Chlorley Motors *(Resigned)*
NOTTS ALLIANCE Senior 16-2+2=16	Ollerton Town *(P)* Awsworth Villa *(P)*	Barford United *(R)* G P T FC *(R)*
First Division 16-2+2=16	Beeston Town *(P)* Attenborough (P)	Pelican Res *(R)* Radcliffe Olympic *(R)*
Second Division 16-3+3=16	Magdale Amateurs	G P T Res (Resigned)

The Football Association CHALLENGE CUP

1995-96 (non-league) Review

Not a vintage year,

but some vintage performances.

Top: *Steve Porter and Alan Brett were Canvey Island's goalscorers against Brighton & Hove Albion. Photo: Eric Marsh.*

Bottom: *Jimmy Jackson (left) and Peter Mortley, the goalscorers, celebrate after Gravesend & Northfleet's victory against Colchester United. Photo: Roger Turner.*

Welling winger Steve Barnes hurdles the Wick defender's tackle during his side's 2-0 victory in the 1st Qualifying Round of the FA Cup. Photo: Keith Gillard.

Gravesend & Northfleet's Dave Powell (white shorts) is well policed by Godalming & Guidford's Tony Ford (No.8) during their 1st Qualifying Round tie. Photo: Alan Coomes.

F.A. CHALLENGE CUP

SECTION 1

Preliminary Round - 26th Aug.

	Liversedge	1v4	Blackpool (Wren) Rovers
	Guisborough Town	1v0	Gretna
	Willington	0v0	Dunston Fed. Brewery
r	Dunston F. B.	5v2	Willington
	Prudhoe Town	1v3	Consett

1st Qualifying Round - 9th Sept.

	Durham City	1v1	Blackpool (Wren) Rovers
r	Blackpool (Wren) R.	1v5*	Durham City
	Barrow	3v0	Consett
	Gateshead	3v2	Dunstan F.B.
	Guisborough Town	1v0	Murton

2nd Qualifying Round - 23rd Sept.

	Durham City	2v1	Guisborough Town
	Gateshead	2v2	Barrow
r	Barrow	1v0	Gateshead

3rd Qualifying Round - 7th Oct.

	Barrow	1v1 Att: 1413	Durham City
r	Durham City	0v1 Att: 764	**Barrow**

SECTION 2

Preliminary Round - 26th Aug.

	South Shields	3v4	Pickering Town
	Netherfield	10v1	Evenwood Town
	RTM Newcastle	1v2	Harrogate Railway
	Brandon United	1v4	Chester-Le-Street Town

1st Qualifying Round - 9th Sept.

	Lancaster City	2v1	Pickering Town
	Tow Law Town	3v3	Chester-le-Street Town
r	Chester-le-Street T.	1v3	Tow Law Town
	Bishop Auckland	2v1	Harrogate Railway
	Netherfield	2v4	Peterlee Newtown

2nd Qualifying Round - 23rd Sept.

	Lancaster City	3v0	Peterlee Newtown
	Bishop Auckland	2v1	Tow Law Town

3rd Qualifying Round - 7th Oct.

	Bishop Auckland	0v1 Att: 298	**Lancaster City**

SECTION 3

Preliminary Round - 26th Aug.

	Seaham Red Star	1v2	Billingham Town
	Esh Winning	3v1	Stockton
	Workington	8v1	Hebburn
	Alnwick Town	1v3	Glasshoughton Welfare
	Whitley Bay	3v0	Easington Colliery

1st Qualifying Round - 9th Sept.

	Whitby Town	0v1	Billingham Town
	Spennymoor United	1v0	Glasshoughton Welfare
	Whitley Bay	1v2	Workington
	Esh Winning	1v2	West Auckland Town

2nd Qualifying Round - 23rd Sept.

	Billingham Town	1v0	West Auckland Town
	Workington	2v4	Spennymoor United

3rd Qualifying Round - 7th Oct.

	Spennymoor United	6v1 Att: 337	Billingham Town

SECTION 4

Preliminary Round - 26th Aug.

	Tadcaster Albion	1v1	Bedlington Terriers
r	Bedlington Terriers	3v0	Tadcaster Albion
	Ryhope CA	2v2	Morpeth Town
r	Morpeth Town	3v1*	Ryhope CA
	Shotton Comrades	1v1	Shildon
r	Shildon	2v1	Shotton Comrades
	Washington	1v0	Garforth Town
	Darlington Cleve. S.	0v3	Billingham Synthonia

1st Qualifying Round - 9th Sept.

	Harrogate Toon	1v2	Bedlington Terriers
	Blyth Spartans	6v0	Garforth Town
	Billingham Synthonia	3v1	Shildon
	Morpeth Town	1v2	Whickham

2nd Qualifying Round - 23rd Sept.

	Bedlington Terriers	1v0	Whickham
	Billingham Synthonia	0v2	Blyth Spartans

3rd Qualifying Round - 7th Oct.

	Blyth Spartans	3v1 Att: 648	Bedlington Terriers

SECTION 5

Preliminary Round - 26th Aug.

	Prescot AFC	3v0	Atherton Collieries
	Chadderton	0v1	Eastoood Town
	Lincoln United	3v2	Stocksbridge Park Steels
	Burscough	2v2	Northallerton 1994
r	Northallerton 1994	1v2	Burscough
	Eccleshill United	0v2	Atherton LR

1st Qualifying Round - 9th Sept.

	Frickley Athletic	0v0	Prescot AFC
r	Prescot AFC	2v2*	Frickley Athletic
2r	Prescot AFC	0v1	Frickley Athletic
	Northwich Victoria	5v0	Burscough
	Atherton LR	2v3	Lincoln United
	Eastwood Town	2v1	Buxton

2nd Qualifying Round - 23rd Sept.

	Frickley Athletic	2v4	Eastwood Town
	Lincoln United	1v4	Northwich Victoria

3rd Qualifying Round - 7th Oct.

	Northwich Victoria	0v0 Att: 742	Eastwood Town
r	Eastwood Town	1v2* Att: 640	**Northwich Victoria**

SECTION 6

Preliminary Round - 26th Aug.

	Arnold Town	2v0	Maine Road
	Glossop North End	1v2	Nantwich Town
	Radcliffe Borough	3v2	Alfreton Town
	Sheffield	w/o	Caernarfon Town
	Belper Town	2v3	Worksop

1st Qualifying Round - 9th Sept.

	Gainsborough Trinity	2v0	Arnold Town
	Morecambe	7v0	Sheffield
	Worksop	4v0	Radcliffe Borough
	Nantwich Town	3v0	Droylsden

2nd Qualifying Round - 23rd Sept.

	Gainsborough Trinity	5v0	Nantwich Town
	Worksop	2v3	Morecambe

3rd Qualifying Round - 7th Oct.

	Morecambe	6v2 Att: 807	Gainsborough Trinity

SECTION 7

Preliminary Round - 26th Aug.

	North Ferriby Utd.	2v4	Heanor Town
	Maltby MW	3v3	Mossley
r	Mossley	4v0	Maltby MW
	Leigh RMI	2v0	Flixton
	Brigg Town	1v1	Clitheroe
r	Clitheroe	1v0	Brigg Town

1st Qualifying Round - 9th Sept.

	Bamber Bridge	4v1	Heanor Town
	Leek Town	1v1	Clitheroe
r	Clitheroe	2v2	Leek Town
2r	Clitheroe	0v0*	Leek Town
3r	Leek Town	1v0	Clitheroe
	Guiseley	3v0	Leigh RMI
	Mossley	1v0	Hallam

2nd Qualifying Round - 23rd Sept.

	Bamber Bridge	0v2	Mossley
	Guiseley	4v0	Leek Town

3rd Qualifying Round - 7th Oct.

	Guiseley	6v1	Mossley
		Att: 608	

SECTION 8

Preliminary Round - 26th Aug.

	Farsley Celtic	2v2	Oldham Town
r	Oldham Town	0v2	Farsley Celtic
	Blidworth MW	0v0	Rossendale United
r	Rossendale United	3v0	Blidworth MW
	St Helens Town	1v2	Bootle
	Winterton Rangers	2v0	Darwen
	Denaby United	4v0	Hucknall Town

1st Qualifying Round - 9th Sept.

	Chorley	2v2	Farsley Celtic
r	Farsley Celtic	1v2	Chorley
	Hyde United	6v0	Winterton Rangers
	Denaby United	3v0	Bootle
	Rossendale United	1v4	Colwyn Bay

2nd Qualifying Round - 23rd Sept.

	Chorley	1v2	Colwyn Bay
	Denaby United	1v2	Hyde United

3rd Qualifying Round - 7th Oct.

	Hyde United (at Curzon Ashton)	1v2	**Colwyn Bay**
		Att: 414	

SECTION 9

Preliminary Round - 26th Aug.

	Trafford	2v1	Fleetwood
	Crook Town	3v2	Kimberley Town
	Ossett Town	3v2	Castleton Gabriels
	Armthorpe Welfare	1v1	Bradford Park Avenue
r	Bradford Park Ave.	1v0	Armthorpe Welfare

1st Qualifying Round - 9th Sept.

	Warrington Town	2v2	Trafford
r	Trafford	4v3*	Warrington Town
	Knowsley United	0v0	Bradford Park Avenue
r	Bradford Park Ave.	3v2	Knowsley
	Accrington Stanley	2v1	Ossett Town
	Crook Town	1v1	Curzon Ashton
r	Curzon Ashton	2v1	Crook Town

2nd Qualifying Round - 23rd Sept.

	Trafford	1v2	Curzon Ashton
	Accrington Stanley	1v2	Bradford Park Ave.

3rd Qualifying Round - 7th Oct.

	Bradford Park Ave.	2v1	Curzon Ashton
		Att: 202	

SECTION 10

Preliminary Round - 26th Aug.

	Goole Town	2v2	Great Harwood Town
r	Gt Harwood Town	3v2	Goole Town
	Ossett Albion	1v3	Hatfield Main
	Immingham Town	1v1	Rossington Main
r	Rossington Main	1v4	Immingham Town
	Louth United	4v0	Harworth CI
	Salford City	1v2	Newcastle Town

1st Qualifying Round - 9th Sept.

	Matlock Town	5v2	Gt Harwood Town
	Marine	4v0	Louth United
	Newcastle Town	5v0	Immingham Town
	Hatfield Main	0v2	Ilkeston Town

2nd Qualifying Round - 23rd Sept.

	Matlock Town	1v2	Ilkeston Town
	Newcastle Town	0v1	Marine

3rd Qualifying Round - 7th Oct.

	Marine	0v0	Ilkeston Town
		Att: 499	
r	Ilkeston Town	1v2*	**Marine**
		Att: 801	

SECTION 11

Preliminary Round - 26th Aug.

	Pontefract Collieries	4v1	Oakham United
	Hinckley Athletic	1v1	Ashton United
r	Ashton United	1v3	Hinckley Athletic
	Thackley	5v2	Cheadle Town
	Yorkshire Amateur	2v4	Borrowash Victoria

1st Qualifying Round - 9th Sept.

	Congleton Town	3v1	Pontefract Collieries
	Winsford United	1v0	Borrowash Victoria
	Emley	6v0	Thackley
	Hinckley Athletic	3v1	Kidsgrove Athletic

2nd Qualifying Round - 23rd Sept.

	Congleton Town	1v1	Hinckley Athletic
r	Hinckley Athletic	1v0	Congleton Town
	Emley	1v1	Winsford United
r	Winsford United	2v1	Emley

3rd Qualifying Round - 7th Oct.

	Winsford United	3v2	Hinckley Athletic
		Att: 236	

SECTION 12

Preliminary Round - 26th Aug.

	Bilston Town	0v0	Blakenall
r	Blakenall	2v1*	Bilston Town
	Redditch United	2v2	Bridgnorth Town
r	Bridgnorth Town	1v4	Redditch United
	Desborough Town	0v0	Rocester
r	Rocester	2v4	Desborough Town
	Shifnal Town	0v0	Willenhall Town
r	Willenhall Town	0v1	Shifnal Town
	West Mids. Police	1v1	Raunds Town
r	Raunds Town	3v2	West Midlands Police

1st Qualifying Round - 9th Sept.

	Halesowen Town	3v2	Blakenall
	Telford United	4v0	Shifnal Town
	Raunds Town	3v0	Desborough Town
	Redditch United	1v3	Moor Green

2nd Qualifying Round - 23rd Sept.

	Halesowen Town	3v0	Moor Green
	Raunds Town	1v2	Telford United

3rd Qualifying Round - 7th Oct.

	Telford United	4v1	Halesowen Town
		Att: 905	

Shaun Philbean (white shorts) crashes to the ground after getting his head to the ball. He just managed to see it go into the Corinthian Casuals net. Photo: Peter Lirettoc.

First half action from the FA Cup Preliminary Round match between Tonbridge Angels and Croydon Athletic. Photo: Dennis Nicholson.

SECTION 13

Preliminary Round - 26th Aug.

	Stourport Swifts	0v1	Armitage
	Chasetown	2v1	Halesowen Harriers
	Tamworth	3v1	Hinckley Town
	Westfields	1v1	Corby Town
r	Corby Town	7v5	Westfields
	Wellingborough T.	0v4	Bolehall Swifts

1st Qualifying Round - 9th Sept.

	Atherstone United	2v2	Armitage
r	Armitage	3v3*	Atherstone
2r	Armitage	5v3	Atherstone
	Hednesford Town	3v1	Corby Town
	Bolehall Swifts	0v1	Tamworth
	Chasetown	1v3	Solihull Borough

2nd Qualifying Round - 23rd Sept.

	Armitage	2v3	Solihull Borough
	Tamworth	1v2	Hednesford Town

3rd Qualifying Round - 7th Oct.

	Hednesford Town	2v2	Solihull Borough
		Att: 1013	
	Solihull Borough	1v2	**Hednesford Town**
		Att: 421	

SECTION 14

Preliminary Round - 26th Aug.

	Shepshed Dynamo	0v1	Grantham Town
	Stapenhill	1v2	Lye Town
	Northampton Spencer	2v2	Cogenhoe United
r	Cogenhoe United	1v0	Northampton Spencer
	Pelsall Villa	1v1	Dudley Town
r	Dudley Town	1v0	Pelsall Villa
	Brierley Hill Town	0v0	Sandwell Borough
r	Sandwell Borough	5v3	Brierley Hill Town

1st Qualifying Round - 9th Sept.

	Rushden & Diamonds	4v1	Grantham Town
	Gresley Rovers	1v2	Dudley Town
	Sandwell Borough	2v1	Cogenhoe United
	Lye Town	1v2	Eastwood Hanley

2nd Qualifying Round - 23rd Sept.

	Rushden & Diamonds	1v0	Eastwood Hanley
	Sandwell Borough	2v1	Dudley Town

3rd Qualifying Round - 7th Oct.

	Sandwell Borough	1v6	**Rushden & Diamonds**
		Att: 250	

SECTION 15

Preliminary Round - 26th Aug.

	Pershore Town	1v1	Evesham United
r	Evesham United	3v2	Pershore Town
	Newport Pagnell T.	0v2	Boldmere St Michaels
	Leicester United	0v0	Barwell
r	Barwell	1v1*	Leicester United
2r	Barwell	3v4	Leicester United
	Wednesfield	2v2	Banbury Utd (1989)
r	Banbury Utd (1989)	0v3	Wednesfield

1st Qualifying Round - 9th Sept.

	Stourbridge	2v2	Evesham United
r	Evesham United	3v0	Stourbridge
	Paget Rangers	1v0	Wednesfield
	VS Rugby	1v2	Leicester United
	Boldmere St Michaels	1v2	Bedworth United

2nd Qualifying Round - 23rd Sept.

	Evesham United	2v0	Bedworth United
	Leicester United	3v2	Paget Rangers

3rd Qualifying Round - 7th Oct.

	Leicester United	0v1	**Evesham United**
		Att: 169	

SECTION 16

Preliminary Round - 26th Aug.

	Oldbury United	4v0	Darlaston
	Long Buckby	2v1	Stewarts & Lloyds
	Knypersley Victoria	0v3	Stratford Town
	Rothwell Town	2v0	Rushall Olympic

1st Qualifying Round - 9th Sept.

	Racing Club Warwick	1v0	Oldbury United
	Stafford Rangers	6v1	Rothwell Town
	Burton Albion	4v0	Stafford Town
	Long Buckby	2v1	Sutton Coldfield Town

2nd Qualifying Round - 23rd Sept.

	R.C. Warwick	2v0	Long Buckby
	Burton Albion	1v1	Stafford Rangers
r	Stafford Rangers	2v3	Burton Albion

3rd Qualifying Round - 7th Oct.

	Burton Albion	2v0	R C Warwick
		Att: 867	

SECTION 17

Preliminary Round - 26th Aug.

	East Thurrock Utd.	1v1	Tiptree United
r	Tiptree United	6v2	East Thurrock Utd.
	Gorleston	1v5	Diss Town
	Halstead Town	1v1	Stamford AFC
r	Stamford AFC	3v3*	Halstead Town
2r	Stamford AFC	1v2	Halstead Town
	Wisbech Town	4v0	Tring Town
	Eynesbury Rovers	4v1	Witham Town

1st Qualifying Round - 9th Sept.

	Sudbury Town	3v0	Tiptree United
	Boston United	1v2	Wisbech Town 4
	Eynesbury Rovers	7v1	Halstead Town
	Diss Town	0v2	Heybridge Swifts

2nd Qualifying Round - 23rd Sept.

	Sudbury Town	2v1	Heybridge Swifts
	Eynesbury Rovers	3v3	Wisbech Town
r	Wisbech Town	6v1	Eynesbury Rovers

3rd Qualifying Round - 7th Oct.

	Wisbech Town	1v0	Sudbury Town
		Att: 705	

SECTION 18

Preliminary Round - 26th Aug.

	Wroxham	0v0	Canvey Island
r	Canvey Island	3v1	Wroxham
	Spalding United	2v3	Harwich & Parkeston
	Kings Lynn	3v0	Wivenhoe Town
	Newmarket Town	0v1	Boston Town
	Basildon United	1v2	Saffron Walden Town

1st Qualifying Round - 9th Sept.

	Cambridge City	2v3	Canvey Island
	Bishop's Stortford	2v2	Boston Town
r	Boston Town	5v2	Bishop's Stortford
	Saffron Walden Town	0v2	Kings Lynn
	Harwich & Parkeston	0v1	Braintree Town

2nd Qualifying Round - 23rd Sept.

	Canvey Island	2v0	Braintree Town
	Kings Lynn	5v1	Boston Town

3rd Qualifying Round - 7th Oct.

	Kings Lynn	1v0	Canvey Island
		Att: 1737	

F.A. CHALLENGE CUP

SECTION 19

Preliminary Round - 26th Aug.

	Aveley	0v0	Stowmarket Town
r	Stowmarket Town	3v4	Aveley
	Gt. Yarmouth Town	2v1	Bourne Town
	Burnham Ramblers	1v3	Holbeach United
	Bury Town	1v2	Collier Row
	March Town United	1v0	Fakenham Town

1st Qualifying Round - 9th Sept.

	Billericay Town	2v0	Aveley
	Chelmsford City	1v0	Collier Row
	March Town United	0v3	Holbeach United
	Gt. Yarmouth Town	2v1	Mirrlees Blackstone

2nd Qualifying Round - 23rd Sept.

	Billericay Town	2v0	Gt Yarmouth Town
	Holbeach United	0v0	Chelmsford City
r	Chelmsford City	3v1*	Holbeach United

3rd Qualifying Round - 7th Oct.

	Chelmsford City	1v1	Billericay Town
		Att: 2074	
	Billericay Town	2v1	Chelmsford City
		Att: 1704	

SECTION 20

Preliminary Round - 26th Aug.

	Leyton Pennant	2v2	Clacton Town
r	Clacton Town	0v4	Leyton Pennant
	East Ham United	0v7	Sudbury Wanderers
	Hertford Town	2v1	Ware
	Cheshunt	0v1	Wealdstone
	Tufnell Park	1v0	Potton United

1st Qualifying Round - 9th Sept.

	Arlesey Town	3v0	Leyton Pennant
	Grays Athletic	2v2	Wealdstone
r	Wealdstone	4v3	Grays Athletic
	Tufnell Park	2v2	Hertford Town
r	Hertford Town	5v1	Tufnell Park
	Sudbury Wanderers	3v1	Watton United

2nd Qualifying Round - 23rd Sept.

	Arlesey Town	1v2	Sudbury Wanderers
	Hertford Town	1v0	Wealdstone

3rd Qualifying Round - 7th Oct.

	Hertford Town	0v2	**Sudbury Wanderers**
		Att: 205	

SECTION 21

Preliminary Round - 26th Aug.

	Felixstowe Town	1v1	Burnham
r	Burnham	2v3	Felixstowe Town
	Bedford Town	1v4	Edgware Town
	Hillingdon Borough	2v0	Cornard United
	Hornchurch	3v0	Bowers United
	Biggleswade Town	0v4	Berkhamsted Town

1st Qualifying Round - 9th Sept.

	Purfleet	4v0	Felixstowe Town
	Dagenham & Redb'.	4v0	Hornchurch
	Berkhamsted Town	3v2	Hillingdon Borough
	Edgware Town	0v1	Chesham United

2nd Qualifying Round - 23rd Sept.

	Purfleet	3v1	Chesham United
	Berkhamsted Town	1v2	Dagenham & Redb'

3rd Qualifying Round - 7th Oct.

	Dagenham & Redb'	1v1	Purfleet
		Att: 718	
r	Purfleet	2v1	Dagenham & Redbridge
		Att: 683	

SECTION 22

Preliminary Round - 26th Aug.

	Lowestoft Town	2v2	Chalfont St Peter
r	Chalfont St Peter	4v1	Lowestoft Town
	Haverhill Rovers	0v1	Hampton
	Uxbridge	4v0	Kempston Rovers
	Brook House	0v0	Welwyn Garden City
r	Welwyn Garden City	0v2	Brook House
	Northwood	3v2	Ford United

1st Qualifying Round - 9th Sept.

	Boreham Wood	1v0	Chalfont St Peter
	Stevenage Borough	0v0	Brook House
r	Brook House	1v5	Stevenage Borough
	Northwood	0v5	Uxbridge
	Hampton	1v2	Staines Town

2nd Qualifying Round - 23rd Sept.

	Boreham Wood	0v1	Staines Town
	Uxbridge	0v1	Stevenage Borough

3rd Qualifying Round - 7th Oct.

	Stevenage Borough	2v0	Staines Town
		Att: 1176	

SECTION 23

Preliminary Round - 26th Aug.

	Hadleigh United	1v0	Southall
	Soham Town Rangers	1v1	Stotfold
r	Stotfold	4v1	Soham Town Rangers
	Tilbury	1v2	Woodbridge Town
	Brimsdown Rovers	0v2	Barton Rovers
	Harefield United	0v1	Hoddesdon Town

1st Qualifying Round - 9th Sept.

	Romford	1v0	Hadleigh United
	St Albans City	4v1	Barton Rovers
	Hoddesdon Town	0v2	Woodbridge Town
	Stotfold	2v1	Hemel Hempstead

2nd Qualifying Round - 23rd Sept.

	Romford	4v1	Stotfold
	Woodbridge Town	1v1	St Albans City
r	St Albans City	2v0	Woodbridge Town

3rd Qualifying Round - 7th Oct.

	St Albans City	3v1	Romford
		Att: 648	

SECTION 24

Preliminary Round - 26th Aug.

	Metropolitan Police	7v0	Viking Sports
	Concord Rangers	2v1	Wooton Blue Cross
	Clapton	2v1	Leighton Town
	Flackwell Heath	1v0	Potters Bar Town
	Barking	1v0	Royston Town

1st Qualifying Round - 9th Sept.

	Baldock Town	2v1	Metropolitan Police
	Hendon	8v0	Flackwell Heath
	Barking	1v3	Clapton
	Concord Rangers	0v3	Hayes

2nd Qualifying Round - 23rd Sept.

	Baldock Town	0v1	Hayes
	Clapton	2v3	Hendon

3rd Qualifying Round - 7th Oct.

	Hendon	0v3	**Hayes**
		Att: 376	

SECTION 25

Preliminary Round - 26th Aug.

	Bedfont	0v0	Langford
r	Langford	1v1*	Bedfont
2r	Bedfont	0v4	Langford
	Hanwell Town	2v4	Wingate & Finchley
	Harlow Town	2v3	Thamesmead Town
	Milton Keynes	0v4	Leatherhead
	Bracknell Town	0v0	Kingsbury Town
r	Kingsbury Town	0v0*	Bracknell Town
2r	Kingsbury Town	1v1*	Bracknell Town
3r	Bracknell Town	3v2	Kingsbury Town

1st Qualifying Round - 9th Sept.

	Wembley	3v0	Langford
	Harrow Borough	2v1	Leatherhead
	Bracknell Town	1v1	Thamesmead Town
r	Thamesmead Town	2v3*	Bracknell Town
	Wingate & Finchley	2v3	Ruislip Manor

2nd Qualifying Round - 23rd Sept.

	Wembley	3v0	Ruislip Manor
	Bracknell Town	2v1	Harrow Borough

3rd Qualifying Round - 7th Oct.

	Bracknell Town	4v1	Wembley
		Att: 169	

SECTION 26

Preliminary Round - 26th Aug.

	Three Bridges	0v5	Camberley Town
	Corinthian-Casuals	3v0	Stamco
	Lewes	2v1	Lancing
	Dartford	3v1	Egham Town
	Fisher 93	0v0	Merstham
r	Merstham	0v2	Fisher 93

1st Qualifying Round - 9th Sept.

	Walton & Hersham	4v0	Camberley Town
	Farnborough Town	1v0	Dartford
	Fisher 93	7v0	Lewes
	Corinthian Casuals	2v5	Margate

2nd Qualifying Round - 23rd Sept.

	Walton & Hersham	2v2	Margate
r	Margate	0v1	Walton & Hersham
	Fisher 93	1v4	Farnborough Town

3rd Qualifying Round - 7th Oct.

	Farnborough Town	3v2	Walton & Hersham
		Att: 761	

SECTION 27

Preliminary Round - 26th Aug.

	Tonbridge	3v1	Croydon Athletic
	Croydon	5v2	Dorking
	Folkestone Invicta	1v1	Peacehaven & Telscombe
r	Peacehaven & Tels.	4v1	Folkestone Invicta
	Shoreham	4v2	Corinthian
	Epsom & Ewell	0v4	Tooting & Mitcham Utd

1st Qualifying Round - 9th Sept.

	Ashford Town	2v0	Tonbridge
	Chertsey Town	2v2	Shoreham
r	Shoreham	1v3	Chertsey Town
	Tooting & Mitcham	0v0	Peacehaven & Telscombe
r	Peacehaven & Telsc'	0v1	Tooting & Mitcham
	Croydon	2v3	Hastings Town

2nd Qualifying Round - 23rd Sept.

	Ashford Town	3v1	Hastings Town
	Tooting & Mitcham	2v2	Chertsey Town
r	Chertsey Town	1v2	Tooting & Mitcham U.

3rd Qualifying Round - 7th Oct.

	Tooting & Mitcham	0v1	**Ashford Town**
		Att: 540	

SECTION 28

Preliminary Round - 26th Aug.

	Littlehampton Town	1v1	Southwick
r	Southwick	1v0	Littlehampton Town
	Chatham Town	3v1	Whyteleafe
	Banstead Athletic	3v1	Burgess Hill Town
	Bognor Regis Town	4v3	Whitehawk
	Raynes Park Vale	3v0	Canterbury City

1st Qualifying Round - 9th Sept.

	Dulwich Hamlet	7v1	Southwick
	Dover Athletic	1v2	Bognor Regis Town
	Raynes Park Vale	1v2	Banstead Athletic
	Chatham Town	1v1	Ramsgate
r	Ramsgate	0v2	Chatham Town

2nd Qualifying Round - 23rd Sept.

	Dulwich Hamlet	2v1	Chatham Town
	Banstead Athletic	0v3	Bognor Regis Town

3rd Qualifying Round - 7th Oct.

	Bognor Regis Town	4v2	Dulwich Hamlet
		Att:780	

SECTION 29

Preliminary Round - 26th Aug.

	Redhill	3v0	Tunbridge Wells
	Chipstead	0v4	Horsham
	Wick	3v2	Portfield
	Herne Bay	1v1	Horsham YMCA
r	Horsham YMCA	1v4	Herne Bay

1st Qualifying Round - 9th Sept.

	Erith & Belvedere	4v1	Redhill
	Bromley	3v1	Herne Bay
	Welling United	2v0	Wick
	Horsham	0v5	Sittingbourne

2nd Qualifying Round - 23rd Sept.

	Erith & Belvedere	2v2	Sittingbourne
r	Sittingbourne	6v1	Erith & Belvedere
	Welling United	2v2	Bromley
r	Bromley	3v3*	Welling United
2r	Welling United	1v2	Bromley

3rd Qualifying Round - 7th Oct.

	Bromley	1v1	Sittingbourne
		Att: 692	
r	**Sittingbourne**	3v2*	Bromley
		Att: 1030	

SECTION 30

Preliminary Round - 26th Aug.

	Sheppey United	2v0	Arundel
	Slade Green	0v2	Langney Sports
	Whitsable Town	3v2	Hailsham Town
	Crowborough Athletic	1v3	Godalming & Guildford

1st Qualifying Round - 9th Sept.

	Carshalton Athletic	3v1	Sheppey United
	Gravesend & N'fleet.	7v0	Godalming & Guildford
	Molesey	4v1	Whitstable Town
	Langney Sports	1v3	Windsor & Eton

2nd Qualifying Round - 23rd Sept.

	Carshalton Athletic	4v3	Windsor & Eton
	Molesey	0v6	Gravesend & N'fleet

3rd Qualifying Round - 7th Oct.

	Gravesend & N'fleet	2v1	Carshalton Athletic
		Att: 685	

Paul Fagin, Camberley Town's No. 3, attempts to clear his goalmouth but Mark Arcard of Three Bridges seems to have other ideas, during their Preliminary Round tie. Photo: Roger Turner.

Jason Goodlife, Hayes No.6, gets his head to this corner against Concord Rangers in their 1st Qualifying Round tie. Photo: Martin Wray.

Robbie Pearce (white shirt) takes on two Dulwich Hamlet defenders in Bognor's 4-2 3rd Qualifying Round win at Nyewood Lane. Photo courtesy Bognor Regis Observer.

SECTION 31

	Home	Score	Away
Preliminary Round - 26th Aug.			
	Bicester Town	0 v 1	Ringmer
	Aldershot Town	5 v 0	Selsey
	Steyning Town	3 v 0	Cove
	Buckingham Town W/O		*
	Thatcham Town	2 v 1	Oakwood
* Newbury Town withdrawn by F.A.			
1st Qualifying Round - 9th Sept.			
	Wokingham Town	3 v 1	Ringmer
	Worthing	1 v 1	Buckingham Town
r	Buckingham Town	0 v 0*	Worthing
2r	Worthing	2 v 2*	Buckingham Town
3r	Buckingham Town	6 v 1	Worthing
	Thatcham Town	5 v 1	Steyning Town
	Aldershot Town	4 v 0	Pagham
2nd Qualifying Round - 23rd Sept.			
	Wokingham Town	1 v 2	Aldershot Town
	Thatcham Town	0 v 1	Buckingham Town
3rd Qualifying Round - 7th Oct.			
	Buckingham Town	0 v 1	**Aldershot Town**
		Att: 916	

SECTION 32

	Home	Score	Away
Preliminary Round - 26th Aug.			
	Hungerford Town	5 v 0	Poole Town
	Abingdon Town	3 v 2	Andover
	Totton AFC	3 v 1	Fleet Town
	Witney Town	5 v 0	BAT Sports
	Thame United	4 v 0	Maidenhead United
1st Qualifying Round - 9th Sept.			
	Salisbury City	5 v 2	Hungerford Town
	Oxford City	1 v 1	Witney Town
r	Witney Town	3 v 1*	Oxford City
	Thame United	1 v 1	Totton AFC
r	Totton AFC	0 v 4	Thame United
	Abingdon Town	2 v 3	Newport (IoW)
2nd Qualifying Round - 23rd Sept.			
	Salisbury City	1 v 3	Newport (IoW)
	Thame United	1 v 1	Witney Town
r	Witney Town	2 v 3	Thame United
3rd Qualifying Round - 7th Oct.			
	Thame United	1 v 1	Newport (IoW)
		Att: 308	
r	**Newport (IoW)**	3 v 1	Thame United
		Att: 863	

SECTION 33

	Home	Score	Away
Preliminary Round - 26th Aug.			
	Bournemouth	0 v 4	Wimborne Town
	Westbury United	2 v 2	Basingstoke Town
r	Basingstoke Town	5 v 1	Westbury United
	Fareham Town	1 v 1	Weymouth
r	Weymouth	3 v 2	Fareham Town
	Lymington AFC	0 v 2	Calne Town
	Bemerton Heath H.	2 v 3	Ryde
1st Qualifying Round - 9th Sept.			
	Dorchester Town	2 v 2	Wimborne Town
r	Wimborne Town	0 v 2	Dorchester Town
	Waterlooville	5 v 0	Calne Town
	Ryde	1 v 1	Weymouth
r	Weymouth	2 v 1	Ryde
	Basingstoke Town	2 v 1	Havant Town
2nd Qualifying Round - 23rd Sept.			
	Dorchester Town	2 v 0	Basingstoke Town
	Weymouth	1 v 0	Waterlooville
3rd Qualifying Round - 7th Oct.			
	Weymouth	2 v 3	**Dorchester Town**
		Att: 2527	

SECTION 34

	Home	Score	Away
Preliminary Round - 26th Aug.			
	Brockenhurst	0 v 0	Swanage T. & Herston
r	Swanage T. & Herston	1 v 1*	Brockenhurst
2r	Brockenhurst	1 v 0	Swanage T. & Herston
	Melksham Town	1 v 2	Bridport
	Welton Rovers	2 v 0	Odd Down
	Gosport Borough	2 v 0	Eastleigh
	Chippenham Town	0 v 0	Paulton Rovers
r	Paulton Rovers	1 v 1*	Chippenham Town
2r	Chippenham Town	0 v 2	Paulton Rovers
1st Qualifying Round - 9th Sept.			
	Newport AFC	5 v 0	Brockenhurst
	Trowbridge Town	8 v 1	Gosport Borough
	Paulton Rovers	1 v 1	Welton Rovers
r	Welton Rovers	2 v 1	Paulton Rovers
	Bridport	0 v 3	Merthyr Tydfil
2nd Qualifying Round - 23rd Sept.			
	Newport AFC	3 v 3	Merthyr Tydfil (24th)
r	Merthyr Tydfil	1 v 2	Newport AFC
	Welton Rovers	1 v 2	Trowbridge Town
3rd Qualifying Round - 7th Oct.			
	Trowbridge Town	2 v 0	Newport AFC
		Att: 623	

SECTION 35

	Home	Score	Away
Preliminary Round - 26th Aug.			
	Devizes Town	1 v 1	Bristol Manor Farm
r	Bristol Manor Farm	3 v 1	Devizes Town
	Glastonbury	1 v 5	Tuffley Rovers
	Clevedon Town	1 v 5	Mangotsfield United
	Worcester City	1 v 2	Yate Town
	Forest Green Rovers	4 v 0	Exmouth Town
1st Qualifying Round - 9th Sept.			
	Gloucester City	8 v 0	Bristol Manor Farm
	Cheltenham Town	5 v 0	Yate Town
	Forest Green Rovers	2 v 1	Mangotsfield United
	Tuffley Rovers	0 v 4	Cinderford Town
2nd Qualifying Round - 23rd Sept.			
	Gloucester City	0 v 1	Cinderford Town
	Forest Green Rovers	3 v 0	Cheltenham Town
3rd Qualifying Round - 7th Oct.			
	Forest Green Rovers	1 v 1	Cinderford Town
		Att: 335	
r	Cinderford Town	1 v 1*	Forest Green Rovers
		Att: 624	
2r	Forest Green Rovers	1 v 3	**Cinderford Town**
		Att: 671	

SECTION 36

	Home	Score	Away
Preliminary Round - 26th Aug.			
	Backwell United	0 v 1	Elmore
	Saltash United	3 v 2	Torrington
	Weston-super-Mare	7 v 0	St Blazey
	Barnstaple Town	2 v 0	Minehead
	Falmouth Town	3 v 0	Frome Town
1st Qualifying Round - 9th Sept.			
	Bideford	2 v 2	Elmore
r	Elmore	2 v 6	Bideford
	Tiverton Town	9 v 0	Barnstaple Town
	Falmouth Town	1 v 1	Weston-super-Mare
r	Weston-super-Mare	5 v 0	Falmouth Town
	Saltash United	1 v 2	Taunton Town
2nd Qualifying Round - 23rd Sept.			
	Bideford	4 v 2	Taunton Town
	Weston-super-Mare	1 v 1	Tiverton Town
r	Tiverton Town	1 v 0	Weston-super-Mare
3rd Qualifying Round - 7th Oct.			
	Tiverton	4 v 1	Bideford
		Att: 653	

4TH ROUND QUALIFYING

SATURDAY 21ST OCTOBER

Home	Score	Away
Ashford Town Warillo 19, Arter 87.	2v0 Att: 2016	Aldershot
Aylesbury United Pluckrose 51(p).	1v3 Att: 1480	Stevenage Borough Crawshaw 30p, 63p, Browne 86
Billericay Town Prue 52.	1v1 Att: 1106	Wisbech Town Munns 15.
r Wisbech Town Massingham 25, Munns 54.	2v0 Att: 1220	Billericay Town
Blyth Spartans Ditchburn 77, Pyle 84p	2v0 Att: 775	Guiseley
Burton Albion Keast 3, Davies 63, Hadley 68.	3v1 Att: 1008	Bracknell Town Wilson 42.
Cinderford Town Hamilton 24, Hill 25, Smith 71.	3v2 Att: 730	Bath City Birkby 50, Mings 55.
Farnborough Town Stemp 24, Boothe 89.	2v1 Att: 1409	Yeovil Town Patmore 66.
Gravesend & N'fleet Munday 40p	1v1 Att: 814	Marlow Gubbins 41og
r Marlow Clarke 19, McDonnell 65, 70.	3v3* Att: 767	Gravesend & N'fleet Gibbs 67, Lamb 82, Blewden 90.
Hayes Kellman 6,47,87, Pearce 50.	4v1 Att: 420	Sudbury Wanderers
Hitchin Town Burns 33, Williams 46.	2v1 Att: 1147	St Albans City Mudd 5.
Kettering Town	0v0 Att: 2427	Bromsgrove Rovers
r Bromsgrove Rovers Clarke 48, Skelding 67p	2v2* Att: 1246	Kettering Town Scott 52, Alford 85.
Canvey Island Collins 4og, Ustace 90.	2v0 Att: 537	Hednesford Town
Kingstonian Warden 16, Nebin 17, Fisher 41.	3v1 Att: 780	Trowbridge Town Benbow 68.
Macclesfield Town	0v1 Att: 1707	Northwich Victoria Duffy 80.

Dominic Feltham (light shirt) fires home Sutton United's fourth goal in their 4th Round Qualifying tie against Crawley Town. Photo: Peter Lirettoc.

Dave Kelman, Hayes No.9 (stripes) makes a great contact with his head to give Hayes their first goal in their 4-0 victory over Sudbury Wanderers in this 4th Qualifying Round clash. Photo: Andrew Chitty.

	Home	Score	Away
	Marine Grant 5, Blackhurst 22.	2 v 0 Att: 626	Bradford P.A.
	Newport IoW Ritchie 88p	1 v 1 Att: 1061	Bashley Lovell 90
r	Bashley Lovell 74, Sales 85	2 v 3 Att: 558	Newport (IoW) Fearon 5, Gee 85, Ritchie 90.
	Nuneaton Borough Drewitt 15p, Statham 52,69, Hackett 66, Anderson 81, Straw 84p.	6 v 1 Att: 1415	Evesham United Yates 17.
	Purfleet Crown 90.	1 v 1 Att: 794	Rushden & Diamonds Hannigan 6.
r	Rushden & Diamonds Watkins 43, Collins 47, Wilkins 67	3 v 1 Att: 2800	Purfleet Donovan 49.
	Runcorn Taylor 11, Bignall 80.	2 v 1 Att: 901	Halifax Town Worthington 67.
	Sittingbourne Walker 3.	1 v 2 Att: 1232	Dorchester Town Evans 48, Pickard 71.
	Spennymoor United DeBont 90.	1 v 0 Att: 621	Lancaster City
	Stalybridge Celtic Burke 24, Wheeler 54.	2 v 2 Att: 617	Colwyn Bay Nicholas 31,63.
r	Colwyn Bay Donnelly 15,34, Roberts 44.	3 v 0 Att: 613	Stalybridge Celtic
	Sutton United Hynes 4, 24, Feltham 26p, 85.	4 v 1 Att: 1637	Crawley Town Pates 84.
	Telford United Langford 13,80, Myers 66.	3 v 0 Att: 898	Southport
	Tiverton Town Everest 87.	1 v 4 Att: 1101	Bognor Regis Town Miles 11,82,88, Rice 72.
	Winsford United	0 v 3 Att: 714	Barrow Brown 14, Parker 34, Hoskin 53.
	Witton Albion Cowley 33, Watson 39, 63.	3 v 2 Att: 931	Morecambe Burns 53p, 57.
	Yeading	0 v 2 Att: 473	Slough Town Bushay 43, 71.

1ST ROUND PROPER

SATURDAY 11TH NOVEMBER

Barrow 2 v 1 Nuneaton Borough

Morton 26, Dobie 39. Att: 2869 Simpson 27

BARROW: Todhunter, Brown (sub Kennedy 45), Deegan, Speak, Kennedy J., Harold, Parker, Humphries, Dobie, Morton, Hoskin. Subs: Ventre.

NUNEATON: Hayward, Donald, Luby, Statham, Williams, Crowley, Anderson, Carr, Straw, Drewitt (sub Donnelly 85), Simpson. Subs: Clamp, Culpin.

Referee: K. Lynch (Knaresborough).

There is a new air of optimism at Barrow these days but their 26th minute opening goal from Morgan was quickly neutralized by Nuneaton's Simpson. Dobie put the 'Bluebirds' back in front before half time and a tight game finished without further goals.

Bradford City 4 v 3 Burton Albion

Showler 16,25, Robson 29, Ormondroyd 88. Att: 4920 Rhodes 27p, Stride 34,41.

BURTON: Acton, Davies, Devaney, Gretton, Keast, Redfern, Rhodes, Smith M., Smith R., Williams, Stride. Subs: Hadley, Freeman.

Referee: J. Winter (Middlesbrough).

What a great effort by Burton Albion! A thrilling first half brought six goals with Albion recovering from a two goal deficit and it was then only a very late winner from the experienced Ormondroyd that squeezed Bradford City through. Full marks to the Beazer club to frighten such tough opponents.

Runcorn 1 v 1 Wigan Athletic

Bignall 55. Att: 2844 Martinez 38.

RUNCORN: Morris, Bates, Ruffer, Ellis, Byrne, Brady, Clowes (sub Taylor 54), Doherty N., Farrington, Bignall, Smith. Subs: Warder, Doherty.

Referee: S. Baines (Chesterfield).

A local 'derby' at Runcorn resulted in a predictable scoring draw. Wigan with their continental connection were attractive opposition but once again Runcorn proved themselves to be one of non-league football's best cup fighters. Martinez scored first for Wigan in the first half and Bignall equalized ten minutes into the second half.

Replay

Wigan Athletic 4 v 2 Runcorn

Leonard 41, Diaz 42, Martinez 48, Thompson 74og. Att: 3224 Ruffer 25, Smith 28p.

RUNCORN: Thompson, Bates (sub Doherty 80 sub McInerney 84), Warder, Ellis, Byrne, Ruffer, Taylor, Doherty N., Farrington (sub Clowes 74), Bignall, Smith.

Referee: S. Baines (Chesterfield).

Two up after half an hour, Runcorn and their fans must have had the feeling it was going to be their night. But two goals in a minute, in that energy sapping and most psychological of periods just before half time, took the steam out of the Conference club and Martinez then gave Wigan the lead three minutes after the break before an unfortunate 'own goal' sealed Runcorn's fate.

Northwich Victoria 1 v 3 Scunthorpe

Cooke 82. Att: 2685 Ford 55, McFarlane 66,86.

NORTHWICH: Greygoose, Burgess, Jones, Tinson, Simpson, Walters, Williams, Butler, Cooke, Clayton (sub Vicary 60), Duffy. Sub: ??

Referee: S. Lodge (Barnsley).

Another non-league 'hope' not allowed to threaten on the day was Northwich Victoria who were kept under control by visiting Scunthorpe and only had a late goal through Cooke as some consolation. All the goals came in the second half when full time fitness gave the League team a slight edge.

Shrewsbury Town 11 v 2 Marine

Draper 3 og, Spink 39, 48,65, Withe 40, Scott 41, Whiston 47,58, Evans 55, Stevens 82, Dempsey 86. Att: 2845 Penman 53, Rowlands 68.

MARINE: O'Brien, Baines, Procter, Murray, Draper, Ward (sub Moss 74), Lundon (sub Hollywood 77), Rowlands, Grant, Penman, Rooney. Sub: Odger.

Referee: P. R. Richard (Preston).

Not many people will believe this but at half time Marine had looked every bit as good as the in form Shrewsbury side and were unlucky to be two goals down. They had every hope of getting back in the game but a couple of early mistakes put the game out of reach and you have read about the rest. Marine did manage to score two good goals!

Telford United 2 v 1 Witton Albion

Foster 13, Langford 86. Att: 1277 Watson 24.

TELFORD: Goodwin, Gardiner (sub Langford 84), Fowler, Ramsey, Foster, Niblett, Myers, Clarke, Gray, Bignot, Robinson. Subs: Elitts, Tansley.

WITTON: Macauley, Oakes, McNeilis, Albiston, Pritchard B., Ranson, Rodwell, Rose, Thomas (sub Camden 88), Morley (sub Pritchard D. 85), Watson. Sub: Cowley.

Referee: R. Dilkes (Mossley).

The only Conference club to go through on the day was Telford United, one of the non-league F.A. Cup giant killers of the eighties. They met old colleagues Witton Albion, now in the Unibond League, and worked hard to hold on to a 2-1 victory. The winner from Langford coming in the last four minutes.

Bury 0 v 2 Blyth Spartans

Att: 3076 Bond 20, Ditchburn 67.

BLYTH: O'Connor, Sokoluk, Curry, Walker, Teasdale, Telford, Gamble, Raffell, Ditchburn, Hays, Bond. Subs: Palmer, Adams, Craggs.

Referee: R. A. Hart (Darlington).

The 'new' Blyth Spartans are making some headlines for themselves now, having previously lived in the shadows of their famous predecessors of the seventies. A goal in each half, from Bond and Ditchburn, certainly gave the Northumberland club the 'result of the round' against a powerful Bury side.

Altrincham 0 v 2 Crewe Alexandra
Att: 3062 Adebola 63, Unsworth 82.
ALTRINCHAM: Collings, Cross, Heesom, France, Hardy, Reid, Terry, Whalley, Zumrutel (sub Royle 85), Anderson, Sharratt. Subs: John, Oliver.
Referee: D. Allison (Leicester).

This fixture had brought good memories for Altrincham supporters and their management team who remembered Crewe featuring among 'Alty's' F.A. Cup victims in the eighties. The new Crewe are made of different stuff, however, and a solid professional performance gave them two second half goals and a passage through to the Second Round.

Spennymoor Utd. 0 v 1 Colwyn Bay
Att: 824 Nicholas 51.
SPENNYMOOR: Swan, O'Hara (sub Goodrick 79), Skedd (sub Watson 85), Coatsworth, Saunders, Healy, Alderson, Ainsley, Gorman, Ludlow (sub Cowell 62), Veart.
COLWYN BAY: Mann, Roberts R., McCosh, Harley, Woods (sub Dulson 45), Price, Nicholas, Roberts G., Drury, Donnelly, Rigby. Subs: Cunningham, Armour.
Referee: U. Rennie (Sheffield).

A surprise win for the North Wales club in an all Unibond clash. Favourites Spennymoor probably found it difficult to raise their game in front of a small crowd and against Premier colleagues. The Welshmen will have been thrilled to hang on to a Nicholas goal scored just after half time.

Hereford United 2 v 1 Stevenage Borough
White 56, Cross 62. Att: 3321 Crawshaw 42.
STEVENAGE: Gallagher, Webster, Mutchell, Sodje, Nugent, Barrowcliff, Beevor (sub Berry 75), Browne, Crawshaw (sub Venables 52), Lynch, Hayles. Sub: Wilmot.
Referee: G. Ashby (Worcester).

A tinge of disappointment for the much fancied Conference side who were tipped by many to get at least a draw. Stevenage did score first but their League opponents, Hereford United, had suffered at the feet of non-league clubs in recent years so maybe they were just that bit more determined. However, look out for the Herts club in this season's F.A.Trophy and, of course, the Conference Championship.

Kingstonian 5 v 1 Wisbech Town
Wingfield 52, 77, Att: 1396 McLaughlin 10.
Riley 55, Warden 63, Akuamoah 67.
KINGSTONIAN: Root, Brooker (sub Jasper 74), Riley, Finch, Nebberling, Fisher, Warmington, Luckett (sub Stevens 79), Warden, Akumoah, Wingfield (sub Kane 85).
WISBECH: Cross, Shelton, Lindsay, Munns, Slade, Parrot, Massinghams (sub Garner 23), McLaughlin, De Ath (sub Wales 79), Gallagher, Topkiss. Sub: Hudson.
Referee: A. Butler (Sutton-in-Ashfield).

Wisbech Town enjoyed a famous cup run in the fifties and have certainly lifted their supporters' spirits this season but after trailing to a first half goal, their powerful hosts retaliated in style. Kingstonian scoring five times in 25 minutes to set up another home tie in Round Two.

Canvey Island 2 v 2 Brighton & Hove A.
Porter 34, Brett 81. Att: 3403 McDougald 16, 38.
CANVEY ISLAND: Keeley, Lee, Martin (sub Blakeborough 80), Joscelyn, Porter, Brett, Pennyfather, Pizzey, Britnell, Jones, Mahoney (sub Harding 72). Sub: Desborough.
Referee: M. Bailey (Cambridge).

By playing on the Sunday, Canvey Island certainly attracted more media attention and the two exciting equalizers against a pretty desperate Brighton club really lifted the crowd and created a splendid atmosphere. You felt that Albion were really pleased to have survived!

Replay

Brighton & Hove A. 4 v 1 Canvey Island
Byrne 45, 68 Att: 7008 Pennyfather 68.
McDougald 47, Smith 78.
CANVEY ISLAND: Keeley, Lee, Joscelyne, Blakeborough (sub Martin 78), Porter, Brett, Pennyfather, Pizzey, Mahoney, Jones, Harding. Subs: Hall, Finning.
Referee: M. Bailey (Cambridge).

Despite Brighton's horrific financial plight, very few people imagined Canvey Island would reach the second round but the first goal didn't come until the part timers' legs were tiring at the end of the first half. Three more plus a reply from Pennyfather for Canvey provided good second half entertainment for the excellent 7,008 attendance.

Rushden & Diamonds 1 v 3 Cardiff City
Hannigan 46. Att: 4212 Dale 24,71 Jarman 28.
RUSHDEN: Benstead, Wooding, Ashby, Peake (sub Spooner 81), Smith N., Hannigan, Kirkup, Betterworth, Nuttell (sub Watkins 81), Wilkin, Collins. Sub: Lilwall.
Referee: S. Dunn (Bristol).

Maybe because of their glorious ground, their league position as Beazer leaders and the media build up, Diamonds became 'the favourites' in this tie and this gave Cardiff City much more reason to concentrate on producing a special performance. Two first half goals virtually tied the game up, and although Hannigan got one back just after half time, a second from Dale saw the Welsh side safely through.

Oxford United 9 v 1 Dorchester Town
Ford M 9, Wood 33, 70, Att: 3819 Killick 90p
Rush 56, Ford B 57,
Moody 63,69,82, Beauchamp 82.
DORCHESTER: Veysey, Coates, Morgan, Tallon, Reeve, Wilkinson, Richardson, Taylor, Killick, Pickard (sub Milner 84), Evans (sub Jordan 73). Sub: Oliver.
Referee: M. Bodenham (East Looe, Cornwall).

It was 'just one of those days' for Dorchester Town who went in at half time only two goals down. However, a second half blitz gave Oxford an afternoon to remember and one in which Dorchester goalkeeper Veysey managed to salvage some personal pride with a string of excellent saves. And, if ever there was a 'consolation' goal, it must have been Tommy Killick's 90th minute penalty!

The players run on to the field, with plenty of media attention, for Canvey Island's historic 1st Round match against Brighton & Hove Albion. Photo: Eric Marsh.

The Gravesend & Northfleet players and supporters celebrate after beating Colchester United at Stonebridge Road. Photo: Roger Turner.

Kidderminster Harriers 2 v 2 Sutton United
Hughes 33, Webb 80p. Att: 2513 Hynes 50, Vansittart 60.
KIDDERMINSTER: Steadman, Hodson, Bancroft, Weir, Brindley, Yates, Shepherd, Webb, May, Davies, Hughes. Subs: Eades, Dearlove, Rose.
SUTTON: McCann, Gates, Benning, Marchant, Costello, Green, Payne, Haynes, Vansittart, Feltham, Dack. Subs: Pritchard, Shephard, Roberts.
Referee: G. Poll (Tring).

Tradition is very important in the F.A. Cup and both Kidderminster Harriers and Sutton United have plenty to fall back on! In this tie the visiting Icis club will be the happier with the draw although it was a late Webb penalty that kept 'Kiddie' in contention.

Replay
Sutton United 1 v 1* Kidderminster Harriers
Sutton United won 3-2 on kicks from the penalty mark.
Payne 46. Att: 1804 Casey 13.
SUTTON: McCann, Gates, Golley, Marchant, Costello, Green, Payne, Hynes, Vansittart, Feltham, Dack. Subs: Hall, Roberts, Shepherd.
KIDDERMINSTER: Steadman, Hodson, Bancroft, Weir, Brindley, Yates, Webb, Casey, May (sub Shepherd 57), Davies (sub Dearlove 115), Hughes. Sub: Rose.
Referee: S. Dunn (Bristol).

Harriers had Kim Casey, the veteran goalscoring ace back in the side and his thirteenth minute goal seemed to have given Sutton too much to do. But a lapse by the midlanders defence just after half time gave Payne an equalizer and although Sutton never looked like scoring again, a penalty shoot out was reached and the home side won 3-2 amid much excitement.

Barnet 2 v 2 Woking
Primus 44, Devine 45. Att: 3034 Hay 1, Steele 19.
WOKING: Batty, Tucker, Timothy (sub Wye 88), Fielder, Brown, Crumplin, Thompson, Ellis, Steele, Hay, Walker. Subs: Peters, Girdler.
Referee: M. Fletcher ((West Midlands).

Two early goals from Hay and Steele put Woking in command at Underhill but full marks to Barnet who came back to equalize before the interval and managed to hold on despite having two players sent off in the second half

Replay
Woking 2 v 1* Barnet
Hay 22, Steele 103. Att: 3535 Hodges 2.
WOKING: Batty, Tucker, Wye, Fielder, Brown, Timothy (sub Alexander 97), Thompson, Ellis, Steele, Hay, Walker. Subs: Peters, Girdler.
Referee: M. Fletcher (West Midlands).

A goal after two minutes from Hodges, was just what Barnet needed to settle their cup tie nerves but Hay equalized after 22 minutes and both sides could and should have wrapped the game up in ordinary time. Barnet's penalty miss was the most obvious chance but the lively Steele clinched the tie for Woking in the 103rd minute enabling his side to eliminate Barnet for the second consecutive year.

Gravesend & Northfleet 2 v 0 Colchester United
Jackson 35, Mortley 70. Att: 3120
GRAVESEND: Turner, Walker, Lamb, Gubbins, Mortley, Jackson, Best (sub Gooding 57), Cotter (sub Bourne 58), Blewden, Munday, Powell. Sub: Gibbs.
Referee: G. R. Pooley (Bishop Stortford).

Gravesend can't have known whether to laugh or cry when they heard the Second Round draw! A fine victory over Colchester United has given them a difficult tie at Cinderford. But it does mean that one Beazer club will be in the big draw.

Hitchin Town 2 v 1 Bristol Rovers
Conroy 1, Burns 9. Att: 3001 Archer 22
HITCHIN: Sylvester, McMenamin, Covington, Burke, Bone, Scott, Burns, Conroy, Williams, Cooper, Gillard. Subs: Roberts, Gittings, Ryan.
Referee: I. Hemley (Ampthill, Beds.).

Hereford United last season, Bristol Rovers this year. For a club not doing too well in the Icis Premier, Hitchin Town covered themselves with glory with another excellent cup display. Conroy's first minute goal set the game alight and another from Burns within ten minutes made life very difficult for Rovers.

Newport (I.o.W.) 1 v 1 Enfield
Fearon 4. Att: 1818 Abbott 34.
NEWPORT: Wickens, Hughes, Leader, Phillips, Male (sub Bartlett 85), Gee, Ritchie, Webb, Soares, Fearon (sub Barsdell 80), Simpkins. Sub: Newnham.
ENFIELD: Pape, Blackford, May, Hoddle, Terry, Rideout, Adams, Sayer, Abbott, Nolan (sub Cooper 70), Gentle (sub Flemming 51). Sub: Carstairs.
Referee: S. Bennett (Swancombe).

The neutrals will have been cheering the little Isle of Wight club in this tie but Enfield are a powerful and very professional outfit these days and a hard fought draw was a credit to both sides. Newport are certainly putting themselves well and truly on the football 'map' these days and their fans will be enjoying their escapades in the national competitions.

Replay
Enfield 2 v 1 Newport (I.o.W.)
Abbott 1, 77p. Att: 2034 Leader 65.
ENFIELD: Pape, Blackford, May, Hoddle, Terry, Kerr, Ridout, Sayer, Abbott, Nolan (sub Richardson 60), Gentle. Subs. Flemming, Adams.
NEWPORT: Simpkins, Wickens, Hughes, Leader, Phillips, Male, Gee, Ritchie (sub Bardell 78), Puckett, Soares (sub Webb 86), Fearon. Sub: Hughes.
Referee: S. G. Bennett (Dartford).

Another great battling performance by Beazer Southern Division club Newport brought more pride to the Isle of Wight. But ace goalscorer Gary Abbott ruined their night with a first minute goal and a winning penalty with just thirteen minutes to go, after Leader had equalised. Enfield now entertain Woking in a truly fascinating meeting of the Non-League 'form teams'.

Bognor Regis Town 1 v 1 Ashford Town
Birmingham 85. Att: 2200 Allon 36.

BOGNOR: Matthews, Pullen P, Beazeley, Pearce D (sub Easterland 83), Mariner, Pullen M., Rutherford, Birmingham, Rice, Cormack, Miles (sub Pearce R. 45). Sub: Kilpatrick.
ASHFORD: Munden, White, Lemoine A., Pearson, Warrilow, Wynter, Wheeler, Allon, Arter, Stanton (sub Caruthers 74), Ross. Subs: Lemoine M., Griffiths.
Referee: P. Taylor (Cheshunt).

Ashford Town will be well pleased with a draw at Bognor where Jack Pearce's Icis Division One side had been enjoying a great start to the season. In fact it was only a late equalizer by the highly rated Birmingham that gave 'The Rocks ' a second chance.

Replay
Ashford Town 0 v 1 Bognor Regis Town
Att: 2542 Pearce D 58.

ASHFORD: Munden, Morris, Lemoine A., Pearson, Allon, Wynter, Wheeler, Carruthers (sub Stanton 59), Arter, White (sub Griffiths 70, sub Lemoine M. 75)), Ross.
BOGNOR: Matthews, Pullen P, Beazeley, Pearce R (sub Pearce D 45), Easterland, Pullen M, Rutherford, Birmingham, Rice, Cormack (sub Ford 70), Miles. Sub: Kilpatrick.
Referee: P. Taylor (Cheshunt).

It's often easier to play away in cup football. The pressure is off as the home team are usually favourites, your supporters expect less and shout more away from home, and even your admin team have less to do and can enjoy the occasion. So maybe it wasn't a surprise that Bognor snatched a victory at Ashford despite a delayed start because of power failure. Pearce scored the all important goal to give The Icis League their sixth club through to the second round.

Slough Town 0 v 2 Plymouth Argyle
Att: 3013 Harvey 61og, Heathcote 77.

SLOUGH: Preddie, Honour, Clement, Paris, Baron, Harvey, Catlin, Bushay (sub Clee 85), West, Pickett (sub Crake 74), Fiore (sub Blackman 74).
Referee: P. A. Durkin (Portland).

Plymouth Argyle concentrate very hard against non-league opposition away from home and they certainly have had some practice in recent seasons! They produced the goods again at Slough Town and full marks go to them for a very professional performance.

Brentford 1 v 1 Farnborough Town
Bent 7. Att: 4711 Senior 50.

FARNBOROUGH: MacKenzie, Baker S., Stemp, Coney, McAvoy, Robson, Boothe, Harlow, Senior, Denny, Baker K.. Subs: Juryeff, Turkington, Rowe.
Referee: B. Knight (Orpington).

Experience told for Farnborough when Trevor Senior made space for himself in the box and crashed in a fine left foot volley to equalize young Bent's first ever goal for Brentford. Farnborough weren't at their best but they achieved a fine result.

Replay
Farnborough Town 0 v 4 Brentford
Att: 3581 Smith 32, Taylor 52, 76, Bent 72

FARNBOROUGH: MacKenzie, Bakes S., Stemp, Coney (sub Horton 9), Day (sub Juryeff 59), Robson, Boothe, Harlow, Senior, Denny, Baker K. Sub: Rowe.
Referee: B. Knight (Orpington)

The injury to skipper Coney didn't help the Farnborough cause but Brentford showed great determination to dominate the match throughout. Two first half goals made a comeback very difficult and, as 'Borough' threw everything into attack, their more composed Division Two visitors hit back with two more excellent goals before missing a penalty. Bright spot for Farnborough was David Harlow's hard work in mid field.

Cinderford Town 2 v 1 Bromsgrove Rovers
Price 32, Hill 50. Att: 1850 Skelding 80p

CINDERFORD: Price (sub Harris 52), Bowes, Wilton, Vauxhall, Howells, Cole, Hamilton, Crouch, Hill (sub Townsend 77), Thomas, Smith. Sub: Criddle.
BROMSGROVE: Taylor, Scelding, Brighton, Richardson, Randal, Dowling (sub Carter 63), Smith, Crocutt, Crisp, Dale, Radburn (sub Power 77). Sub: Glasser.
Referee: J Rushton (Stoke).

What a year for Cinderford Town! Gloucester City, Bath City and now Bromsgrove Rovers have been eliminated and it wasn't until Skelding's 80th minute penalty that the home crowd had any real worries. Chris Price was again a hero and the locals can't wait for another home cup day with fellow Beazer members Gravesend & Northfleet as visitors.

Northampton Town 1 v 0 Hayes
Warburton 67. Att: 5389

HAYES: Meara, Wilkinson, Stevens, Kelly W., Cox, Denton, Baker (sub Brady 70), Kellman, Kelly T. (sub Knight 77), Pearce (sub Hyatt 77), Goodlisse.
Referee: P. Jones (Quorn).

A tough battle at Northampton's beautiful new ground saw The Cobblers through with a second half goal from Warburton. Hayes fought hard and their excellent cup record in recent years ensured that Northampton didn't get through without a tough contest.

OTHER RESULTS

Hull City	0	v	0	Wrexham
(R) Wrexham	0	v	0*	Hull City
Wrexham won 3-1 on kicks from the penalty mark.				
Blackpool	2	v	1	Chester City
Scarborough	0	v	2	Chesterfield
Mansfield Town	4	v	2	Doncaster Rovers
Carlisle United	1	v	2	Preston North End
York City	0	v	1	Notts County
Burnley	1	v	3	Walsall
Hartlepool	2	v	4	Darlington
Rochdale	5	v	3	Rotherham United
Stockport County	5	v	0	Lincoln City
Wycombe Wanderers	1	v	1	Gillingham
(R) Gillingham	1	v	0	Wycombe Wanderers
Fulham	7	v	0	Swansea City
Bournemouth AFC	0	v	0	Bristol City
(R) Bristol City	0	v	1	Bournemouth AFC
Torquay United	1	v	0	Leyton Orient
Swindon Town	4	v	1	Cambridge City

SECOND ROUND PROPER

SATURDAY 2ND DECEMBER

Barrow 0 v 4 **Wigan Athletic**
Att: 3,500 Diaz, Black 2, Martinez.

BARROW: Deegan, Speak, Harold, Parker, J Kennedy (sub E Kennedy 77), Todhunter (sub Foley 77), Kenny, Humphries, Hoskin, Dobie, Morton. Sub: Ventre.

Once again it was Wigan Athletic's Spanish connection that swung this cup tie away from part time opposition. Barrow manfully held their visitors until twelve minutes into the second half when Diaz strode through the home defence to start a four goal burst over just fourteen minutes. Tony Black scored two and Martinez the other to give Wigan a comfortable victory.

Stockport County 2 v 0 **Blyth Spartans**
Eckhardt, Raffell og. Att: 5,693

BLYTH SPARTANS: O'Connor, Curry, Hays,Raffell, Gamble, Ditchburn, Bond, Proctor, Moat, Pyle (sub Pearson 77), Walker (sub Telford 69). Sub: Teasdale.
Referee: R Furnandiz (Doncaster).

The distinctive name - Blyth Spartans - conjures up images of heroic F.A. Cup triumphs by the part timers in the North East but sadly Stockport County proved too experienced for the Unibond club on this occasion. A goal after three minutes and an own goal before half time settled the issue but a two goal deficit at Edgeley Park is no disgrace.

Telford United 0 v 2 **Notts County**
Att: 2,831 Gallagher, Legg.

TELFORD: Goodwin, Gardiner (sub Gray 54), Fowler, Wilcox, Niblett, Kearney, Myers, Clarke, Adams, Bignot, Langford. Subs: Robinson, Tansley.
Referee: T. West (Hull).

Telford United's great 80s F.A. Cup record may have lifted hopes as they prepared to entertain Notts County. Although a goal in each half seemed to give the visitors a comfortable win, Telford certainly appeared to have deserved a penalty when they were only a single goal in arrears. A goal then and who knows ....

Blackpool 2 v 0 **Colwyn Bay**
Preece, Quinn. Att: 4,581

COLWYN BAY: Roberts R., McCosh, Mann, Harley, Woods, Price, Nicholas (sub Dulson 72), Roberts G, Drury, Donnelly, Rigby (sub Morgan 72). Sub: Cunningham.
Referee: S Mathieson (Stockport).

A very impressive and disciplined performance by one of the real remaining minnows was achieved by Colwyn Bay. They held the Seasiders until the 52nd minute and continued to fight hard until Blackpool made the game safe with a second goal. On a day when no non-league side scored against Endsleigh League opposition, this was probably the best performance from the part timers.

Adam Beazeley, Adie Miles, Daren Pearce, Marc Rice and Rob Eastland (L-R) salute the fans after Bognor's 0-4 defeat at Peterborough. Photo courtesy of the Bognor Regis Observer.

Colin Luckett of Kingstonian bends this free kick over the Plymouth Argyle wall but unfortunately didn't manage to score. Photo: Gary Letts.

Hereford United 2 v 0 Sutton United
White 2. Att: 2,908

SUTTON UNITED: McCann, Benning, Marchant, Costello, Golley, Payne, Haynes, Vansittart (sub Lemprienc 54), Feltham, Dack. Subs: Roberts, Shephard.
Referee: P Rejer (Tipton).

Hereford United have had some very unhappy experiences against part-time opposition in recent years so full marks to them for holding the traditionally dangerous Sutton United at bay. Again it was a goal in each half that sunk the visitors with both coming from the experienced Steve White in his eighteenth Football League season. Sutton did hit the cross bar twice and they had Goley sent off for a second bookable offence after 55 minutes. It certainly wasn't their day and Hereford deservedly went into the Third Round draw.

Gillingham 3 v 0 Hitchin Town
Fortune-West 2, Ratcliffe. Att: 7,142

HITCHIN TOWN Sylvester, McMenamin, Covington, Burke, Bone, Scott, Burns, Conroy (sub Roberts 72), Williams, Thompson (sub Ryan 75), Gillard. Sub: Wilson.
Referee: M Pearce (Portsmouth).

A half time score of 0-0 was encouraging for Hitchin Town who were facing a very confident Gillingham whose 'new' team and managemnet had rewarded a brave young chairman and attracted inspired and noisy support from an excellent 7,142. The massive Fortune-West made his mark in the second half with two goals and an assist and left Hitchin wondereing what might have been if their two first half near misses from Gillard had gone in.

Peterborough Utd. 4 v 0 Bognor Regis Town
Farrell 3, Ebdon Att: 5,004

BOGNOR REGIS: Matthews, Pullen P, Beazeley, Pearce D (sub Kilpatrick 74), Pullen M, Birmingham, Rutherford, Rice, Easterland, Miles (sub Cormack 67).
Referee: P Danson (Blaby, Leics.)

So far this season Bognor Regis Town have swept all opposition away in the F.A. Cup and the F.A. Trophy but Peterborough United proved to be a little different! A first half hat trick by Farrell virtually won the match but all credit to this excellent Icis Division One side who never stopped trying to play good attractive football and although they conceded a fourth, Jack Pearce's boys were close to scoring a couple of their own.

Cinderford Town 1 v 1 **Gravesend & Northfleet**
Thomas. Att: 2,067 Blewden.

CINDERFORD TOWN: Bowes, Price (sub Smith 46), Wilton, Boxall, Howells, Cole, Hamilton, Criddle (sub Townsend 64), Hill, Thomas, Harris. Sub: Wilband.
GRAVESEND & NORTHFLEET: Turner, Walker, Lamb, Gubbins, Motley, Jackson, Bourne, Cotter, Blewden, Munday (sub Reynolds 83(, Powell (sub Wilson 75). Sub: Gibbs.
Referee: D Orr (Iver, Bucks.).

What a thriller! Having beaten opposition from the Conference, the little Beazer Homes Southern Division club were, unfortunately (for them), considered 'favourites' to beat Beazer Premier, Gravesend & Northfleet so there wasn't the same aura of giant-killing potential surrounding the game. A tough, well balanced first half didn't produce a goal but just after the break Blewden beat two defenders and slipped a neat shot past Bowles to give Gravesend the lead. With the home support lifting them Cinderford piled on the pressure and it was the result of consistent pressure following a free kick that Thomas dived into a crowded penalty area and headed a dramatic equaliser with just tem minutes to go. Needless to say the last minutes drained both sets of supporters as the tension mounted but neither side could force a winner and a replay at Gravesend would decide who enjoyed a magical day in The Third Round.

REPLAY

Gravesend & Northfleet 3 v 0 **Cinderford Town**
Best, Munday, Powell. Att: 2700

GRAVESEND & NORTHFLEET: Turner, Walker, Gubbins (sub Gibbs 15), Mortley, Lamb, Munday, Blewden, Jackson, Cotter (sub Gooding 76), Powell, Best. Sub: Bourne.
CINDERFORD TOWN: Bowles, Cole, Bloxall, Howells, Wilton, Price (sub Townsend 70), Crouch, Thomas, Hamilton (sub Criddle 65), Smith (sub Harris 59), Hill.
Referee: D Orr (Iver, Bucks.).

A massive prize awaited the winner of this battle of the non-league minnows. The winners were to play Aston Villa of the Premier League and could expect massive gate receipts and a day to remember for the rest of their lives if the tie was switched to Villa Park. Within six minutes the senior Beazer Homes club (Gravesend are in the Premier to Cinderford's Southern Division) scored through Grant Best and those of us watching Sky TV's football programme were informed that they were proud of Grant as he worked for their football unit. Two more goals, from Munday and Powell in the second half left Cinderford with wonderful memories of their cup run but frustration for Chris Price and Brian Godfrey (assistant manager), two of their experienced members who had enjoyed playing spells with Villa. Danny Hill had a great effort well saved by Turner but on the night the Beazer Premier club proved just too strong and Gravesend will be smothered with publicty as their date with the Villa comes nearer. Perhaps Beazer Homes will build them a new stand to show their gratitude!

Enfield 1 v 1 **Woking**
Gentle. Att: 3,477 Walker.

ENFIELD: Pape, Blackford, May, Richardson (sub Flemming 83), Terry, Kerr, Rideout, Sayer, Abbott, Carstairs, Gentle. Sub: Hoddle, Nolan.
WOKING: Batty, Tucker, Wye, Fielder, Brown, Crumplin, Thompson, Ellis, Timothy, Hay, Walker. Subs: Dowe, Alexander, Girdler.
Referee: A P D'urso (Billericay).

Two very classy non-league sides showed each other the utmost respect in a tense first half which included very little flowing football. Enfield were the more direct but were frustratingly caught offside too often and the class of Kevan Brown and Colin Holder stood out. In fact the central defensive pairing of Enfield was just as impressive as Andy Kerr and Steve Terry also took control of matters in their penalty area and the game seemed to be at stalemate when Justin Gentle managed to avoid the offside trap. He raced through the middle onto a fine through ball from David May,held off a challenge and lobbed an excellent goal over the advancing Laurence Batty with just a minute to go before half time. At this stage Enfield had to be favopurites as Woking were obviously missing the suspended Scott Steele and their attack just hadn't worried the home defence. But ill discipline probably prevented victory as a quite unnecessary late tackle by Carstairs left Enfield 40 minutes to negotiate with only ten men. Gradually Woking got on top, they moved the ball from wing to wing stretched the home side and the evergreen Clive Walker's class became more and more apparent. So it was no surprise when he picked a loose ball up 35 yards out, beat two men, cut into the penalty area and scored with a low cross shot passed Andy Pape. There were ten minutes remaining and Enfield's ten men were up against it as Walker hit the crossbar with a screamer and Woking piled on the pressure until the final whistle. The second half had all the ingredients of a good cup tie and two of non-league football's most experienced cup battlers certainly should feel proud of their contributions to an excellent contest played on a superb surface.

REPLAY

Woking 2 v 1 **Enfield**
Hay 2. Att: 2253 Abbott
(at Wycombe Wanderers F.C.)

WOKING: Batty, Tucker, Wye, Fielder, Brown, Timothy, Thompson, Ellis, Steele, Hay, Dowe. Subs: Girdler, Kilner, Alexander.
ENFIELD: Pape, Blackford, May, Carstairs (sub Nolan 46), Terry, Kerr, Rideout, Sayer (sub Adams 65), Abbott, Richardson (sub Flemming 80), Gentle.
Referee: A D'Urso (Billericay).

The news that Clive Walker was unfit for this replay lifted Enfield but a tense battle was settled in the second half when the Icis side was reduced to ten men after May was sent off for a violent foul in the 52 minute. Woking took the lead through

Cinderford goalkeeper Russ Bowles gets down well here to make a superb save from Gravesend & Northfleet's Mickey Cotter. Photo: Keith Gillard.

Darren Hay seven minutes later and although the high scoring Abbott of Predator fame equalised within a minute, it was Hay again who won the match with a well placed shot from a clever Scott Steele pass. So Woking reached the Third Round once again and will carry the Conference banner to Swindon Town who will prove difficult opposition. But so were West Bromwich Albion!

SUNDAY 3RD DECEMBER

Kingstonian 1 v 2 **Plymouth Argyle**
Warden. Att: 2,961 Leadbitter, Littlejohn.

KINGSTONIAN: Root, Finch, Warmington, Nebbeling, Riley, Brooker, Fisher, Luckett (sub Stevens 85), Wingfield (sub Bolton 80), Warden, Akulamoah. Sub: Jasper.

With no goals scored by the part timers against full time opposition on Saturday it was left to Kingstonian to hit the back of the net with an excellent header from Jon Warden just before half time. Plymouth Argyle had taken an early lead after eight minutes, when Leadbitter had scored through a crowd of players, but'K's'hit back to produce wave after wave of attacking play inspired by the running of Phil Wingfield who did everything but score as the Icis club dominated preceedings until half time. Warden's equaliser was thoroughly deserved and with Curtis Warmington marshalling the defence well, Kingstonian continued to hold their own and nearly scored a second when Kevin Blackwell (a goalkeeper with an excellent non-league pedigree) saved well from Brooker. It was the ex-Sheffield United striker from the F.A.School at Lilleshall, Adrian Littlejohn who showed his class with a great winner in the last five minutes but Kingstonian had impressed a lot of people and given Sky viewers an excellent game to enjoy.

OTHER RESULTS

Rochdale	2	v	2	Darlington
(R) Darlington	0	v	1	Rochdale
Scunthorpe United	1	v	1	Shrewsbury Town
(R) Shrewsbury Town	2	v	1	Scunthorpe United
Bradford City	2	v	1	Preston North End
Crewe Alexandra	2	v	0	Mansfield Town
Wrexham	3	v	2	Chesterfield
Torquay United	1	v	1	Walsall
(R) Walsall	8	v	4*	Torquay United
Fulham	0	v	0	Brighton & H.A.
(R) Brighton & H.A.	0	v	0*	Fulham
Fulham won 4-1 on kicks from the penalty mark				
Oxford United	2	v	0	Northampton Town
Swindon Town	2	v	0	Cardiff City
Bournemouth AFC	0	v	1	Brentford

THIRD ROUND PROPER

SATURDAY 2ND DECEMBER

Gravesend & Northfleet 0 v 3 **Aston Villa**
at Villa Park **Att:** 26,021

Report by Tony Williams
Referee: K Cooper (Pontypridd).

A visit to one the country's most famous football clubs is the dream of every semi-professional club as they set out on each seasons F.A. Cup campaign. This year it was Gravesend & Northfleet who grabbed the headlines but after a solid home victory over Colchester United in the First Round they must have been disappointed with an away tie at little Cinderford Town who had already beaten two Conference sides at The Causeway. But 'Fleet' kept their nerve, drew away, learnt that Villa awaited the winners and duly prevented 'Cinders' from going to the ball. The colourful welcome they received at Villa Park will long be remembered and frustratingly it wasn't until afterwards that the players actually realised that they could have done even better than the three goal defeat which was certainly 'respectable'.

A second minute mistake by their goalkeeper gave Draper a goal and might have opened up the floodgates - but it didn't and Fleet settled down to play some excellent football. A goal before half time when Colin Blewden and Mickey Cotter kept Bosnich the busier keeper, would certainly have sharpened up the Premier side who were happy to coast along to a victory without showing up the part timers. This can be a dangerous tactic however however, as once into that mood it is sometimes very difficult to move up a gear. But it was not to be and despite resolute defending by Peter Mortley and his men, another quick goal after the interval by Milosevic virtually killed off the tie and Aston Villa achieved a painless passage through to the Fourth Round without shattering the pride of their visitors, despite a third goal through Johnson after 72 minutes.

Everyone seemed to be happy - Aston Villa were through, Gravesend & Northfleet's players had played at Villa Park and produced some excellent football and collected momentoes and memories of a special occasion, while their supporters had enjoyed a never to be forgotten day. There were just those nagging thoughts - if only we had realised they weren't that good. . . if only we hadn't let in an early goal. . . . if we had scored when we were playing well just before half time. But that's the F.A. Cup!

Gravesend & Northfleet: Turner, Walker (sub Harrop 78 mins), Lamb, Gubbins, Mortley, Jackson, Gibbs, Cotter (sub Best 77 mins), Blewden, Munday, Powell (sub Gooding 75 mins).

The Gravesend & Northfleet team at Villa Park prior to their 3rd Round match against Aston Villa. Photo: Keith Gillard.

Gravesend & Northfleet's Colin Blenden gets in his shot despite the prescence of Villa's Andy Townsend. Photo: Keith Gillard.

Report by Francis Short

Swindon Town 2 v 0 Woking

Att: 10,322

Woking's Cup run came to an end at the County Ground where, despite an accomplished performance and a number of good chances, Swindon's greater fluency with the ball and the top level experience of several of their players ultimately swung the match in their favour.

38-year-old Clive Walker led the Woking attack in what was the Conference side's first choice team, while Swindon were able to call on Culverhouse, Bodin and Paul Allen, with leading scorer Steve Finney starting on the bench alongside former Liverpool star, and now manager, Steve McMahon. McMahon did not have to wait too long to enter the action, replacing the injured Taylor on 38 minutes, but by then his side were already a goal to the good, Wayne Allison controlling a cross from Kevin Horlock and drilling a shot passed Batty after 17 minutes. Despite enjoying plenty of possession, Woking found it hard to get behind a well-organised defence, with Walker and Hay frequently being caught offside, and Fraser Digby's only real alarm before the break was in holding on to a fierce long range free-kick from Colin Fielder.

Swindon began the second half in positive fashion, Ling tormenting the Woking defence with a number of mazy runs from midfield, but this was merely the prelude to Woking's best spell, which manager Geoff Chapple was to describe as "our magic twenty minutes". Walker brought two fine saves out of Digby in quick succession, and Thompson fired a shot just wide after a penetrating run, but perhaps the best opportunity of all was created by Darren Hay, who took the ball almost into the six-yard box but wasted it, shooting against a defender when a pass across goal may have brought that crucial equaliser.

As it was, Woking were left to rue their failure to turn their domination into a goal, as nine minutes from time, a speculative shot from Bodin on the corner of the Woking area, which he later admitted was intended as a cross, flew over the stranded Batty and into the net to seal the victory.

The large Woking contingent, left unprotected from the torrential rain which swept across the ground in the later stages, gave their side a good reception at the end, and both Walker and Chapple were quick to pay tribute to Swindon's style of play afterwards.

Woking: Batty, Tucker, Fielder, Brown, Crumplin, L Wye, Thompson, Ellis, Steele, Hay, Walker Subs not used: Dowe, Timothy, Alexander.

Referee: J. Bushton (Burton)

1995-96 REVIEW

FIRST ROUND QUALIFYING

Saturday October 14th

Home	Score	Away
Harrogate Town	1v4	Grantham Town
	Att: 191	
Farsley Celtic	3v1	Bedworth United
	Att: 159	
Droylsden	0v3	Matlock Town
	Att: 173	
Atherstone United	2v1	Lincoln United
	Att: 278	
Accrington Stanley	2v2	Bradford (Park Ave.)
	Att: 415	
r Bradford P. A.	2v3*	Accrington Stanley
	Att: 258	
Atherton LR	1v2	Chorley
	Att: 298	
Sutton Coldfield T	1v1	Bilston Town
	Att: 116	
r Bilston Town	4v4*	Sutton Coldfield T.
	Att: 85	
2r Bilston Town	2v1	Sutton Coldfield T.
	Att: 154	
R. C. Warwick	1v0	Warrington Town
	Att: 130	
Bridgnorth Town	1v1	Leigh RMI
	Att: 90	
r Leigh RMI	7v0	Bridgnorth Town
	Att: 37	
Winsford United	1v1	Paget Rangers
	Att: 183	
r Paget Rangers	0v2	Winsford United
	Att: 124	
Curzon Ashton	4v3	Worksop Town
	Att: 170	
Knowsley United	3v2	Moor Green
	Att: 80	
Alfreton Town	5v0	Congleton Town
	Att: 202	
Workington	1v1	Leicester United
	Att: 286	
r Leicester United	5v0	Workington
	Att: 125	
Barrow	3v0	Hinckley Town
	Att: 1119	
Stourbridge	1v2	Frickley Athletic
	Att: 126	
Lancaster City	3v0	Solihull Borough
	Att: 173	
Fleetwood	2v1	Whitley Bay
	Att: 119	
Tamworth	v	Caernarfon Town
Walkover for Tamworth - Caernarfon T. withdrawn		
Radcliffe Borough	3v1	Redditch United
	Att: 107	
Erith & Belvedere	0v6	Basingstoke Town
	Att: 112	
Leyton Pennant	0v1	Fleet Town
	Att: 66	
Hastings Town	2v2	Havant Town
	Att: 392	

Dulwich Hamlet's Dave Patullo gets in a powerful header against Carshalton's Francis Vine (white shirt). Photo: Alan Coomes.

Worthing 'keeper Dean Beale under pressure from Thame's Nigel Mott while Dennis Gascoyne gets his header in. Worthing;s No.3, Neil Kerton looks on. Photo: Andrew Chitty.

	Home	Score	Away	Att
[r]	Havant Town	1v0	Hastings Town	Att: 141
	Chertsey Town	9v0	Poole Town	Att: 328
	Bury Town	1v2	Trowbridge Town	Att: 107
	Buckingham Town	1v1	Braintree Town	Att: 65
[r]	Braintree Town	1v0	Buckingham Town	Att: 102
	Carshalton Athletic	1v1	Dulwich Hamlet	
[r]	Dulwich Hamlet	1v1*	Carshalton Athletic	Att: 292
[2r]	Dulwich Hamlet	1v3	Carshalton Athletic	Att: 301
	Ruislip Manor	3v1	Cinderford Town	Att: 142
	Barton Rovers	1v3	Crawley Town	Att: 331
	Salisbury City	2v0	Fisher 93	Att: 319
	Weston-super-Mare	2v6	Bognor Regis Town	Att: 226
	Yate Town	3v2	Witney Town	Att: 156
	Ashford Town	0v2	Sudbury Town	Att: 569
	Billericay Town	0v4	Wembley	Att: 261
	Fareham Town	2v4	Maidenhead United	Att: 90
	Barking	0v0	Baldock Town	Att: 136

	Home	Score	Away	Att
[r]	Baldock Town	3v2*	Barking	Att: 136
	Forest Green Rovers	1v2	Sittingbourne	Att: 101
	Abingdon Town	1v1	Bishop's Stortford	Att: 182
[r]	Bishop's Stortford	5v1	Abingdon Town	Att: 182
	Berkhamsted Town	1v2	Purfleet	Att: 98
	Newport (IoW)	1v3	Chesham United	Att: 462
	Kings Lynn	1v2	Uxbridge	Att: 833
	Staines Town	2v1	Wokingham Town	
	Weymouth	4v0	Tonbridge	Att: 714
	Hendon	2v2	Waterlooville	Att: 179
	Waterlooville	0v1	Hendon	Att: 110
	Whyteleafe	1v2	Tooting & Mitcham U	Att: 161
	Harrow Borough	1v1	Marlow	Att: 244
[r]	Marlow	1v4	Harrow Borough	Att: 261
	Worthing	1v1	Thame United	Att: 372
[r]	Thame United	2v0	Worthing	Att: 152
	Bashley	1v1	Margate	Att: 220
[r]	Margate	1v2	Bashley	Att: 157

2nd ROUND QUALIFYING

Saturday November 4th

Home	Score	Away	Att
Barrow	0v1	Winsford United	Att: 1222
Tamworth	3v1	Netherfield	Att: 409
Bilston Town	5v2	Leicester United	Att: 100
Alfreton Town	2v2	Dudley Town	Att: 260
r Dudley Town	2v0	Alfreton Town	Att: 183
Gt. Harwood Town	3v2	Frickley Athletic	Att: 105
Atherstone United	1v3	Accrington Stanley	Att: 422
Radcliffe Borough	2v0	Fleetwood	Att: 136
Eastwood Town	0v1	Chorley	Att: 231
Grantham Town	1v3	Farsley Celtic	Att: 303
Leigh RMI	0v2	Matlock Town	Att: 90
Emley	2v1	R C Warwick	Att: 225
Curzon Ashton	1v1	Lancaster City	Att: 278
r Lancaster City	3v0	Curzon Ashton	Att: 206
Nuneaton Borough	3v2	Knowsley United	Att: 1017
Carshalton Athletic	5v1	Weymouth	Att: 379
Braintree Town	4v0	Harrow Borough	Att: 203
Chertsey Town	2v2	Chesham United	Att: 518
r Chesham United	2v3	Chertsey Town	Att: 397
Staines Town	3v1	Havant Town	Att: 207
Walton & Hersham	0v0	Oxford City	Att: 193
r Oxford City	5v2	Walton & Hersham	Att: 196
Trowbridge Town	1v0	Bishop's Stortford	Att: 361
Clevedon Town	0v4	Worcester City	Att: 420
Crawley Town	0v1	Bashley	Att: 609
Evesham United	0v2	Aldershot Town	Att: 465
Newport AFC	2v1	Fleet Town	Att: 679
Tooting & Mitcham	2v1	Baldock Town	Att: 174
Basingstoke Town	0v2	Uxbridge	Att: 165
Purfleet	6v1	Corby Town	Att: 88
Wembley	1v1	Ruislip Manor	Att: 85
r Ruislip Manor	1v2	Wembley	Att:
Bognor Regis Town	2v2	Sittingbourne	Att: 400
r Sittingbourne	1v2	Bognor Regis Town	Att: 674
Hendon	3v0	Gravesend & N'fleet	Att: 291
Salisbury City	2v2	Sudbury Town	Att: 332
r Sudbury Town	2v2	Salisbury City	Att:
2r Sudbury Town	3v2	Salisbury City	Att: 249
Yate Town	1v2	Heybridge Swifts	Att: 163
Maidenhead Utd	0v5	Thame United	Att: 93

BELOW: *Action with Radcliffe Borough (dark shirts) attacking the Matlock defence. Photo: Colin Stevens.*

3rd ROUND QUALIFYING
Saturday November 25th

Spennymoor United 0v2 Nuneaton Borough
Att: 486 Straw, Donnelly.

Halesowen Town 0v0 Bilston Town
Att: 601

r Bilston Town 1v4* Halesowen Town
Hazlewood. Att: 307 Crisp, Snape, Wright 2.

Burton Albion 3v3 Bamber Bridge
Stride 2, Redfearn. Att: 964 Leaver 3.

r Bamber Bridge 2v3 Burton Albion
Allen, Edwards. Att: 502 Rhodes 2, Devaney.

Ashton United 1v1 Lancaster City
Clowes Att: 274 Flannery

r Lancaster City 0v2 Ashton United
Att: 228 Turner, Whittaker.

Bishop Auckland 0v0 Witton Albion
Att: 239

r Witton Albion 0v0* Bishop Auckland
Att: 461

2r Bishop Auckland 3v1* Witton Albion
Todd, Dobson, Banks. Att: 222 Watson.

Radcliffe Borough 3v1 Farsley Celtic
McCrae 2, Graham. Att: 155 Armitage

Emley 3v1 Gt. Harwood T.
Viner, Peltier, Reynolds. Att: 224 Smith

Chorley 3v1 Winsford United
Mayers 2, Leitch Att: 297 T Bishop

Stafford Rangers 1v1 Tamworth
Bywater Att: 647 Canning

r Tamworth 0v3 Stafford Rangers
Att: 741 Banks, Bertschin, Mitchell.

Matlock Town 1v0 Buxton
Evans Att: 516

Blyth Spartans 3v2 Gretna
McDonald 3. Att: 453 Townsley 2(1p)

Dudley Town 4v3 V S Rugby
Hall 3, Horne p Att: 283 Murphy, Martin, Green

Accrington Stanley 2v3 Gresley Rovers
Shaughnessy, Welsh Att: 547 Garner 2, Marsden

Leek Town 0v0 Boston United
Att: 370

r Boston United 2v0 Leek Town
Fee 2p Att: 819

Ilkeston Town 0v5 Gainsborough Trinity
Att: 626 Smith, Evans 3, Snodin

Chelmsford City 2v1 Yeading
Garvey, Kane Att: 828 Graham

Gloucester City 5v1 Aldershot Town
Milsom, Holmes 2, Adebowale, Webb Att: 1041 Sugrue

Boreham Wood 3v0 Heybridge Swifts
Joyce 2, A Samuels Att: 204

Bromley 1v1 Oxford City
Cherry Att: 183 Thomas

r Oxford City 3v2* Bromley
Charles, Morrisey, Brown. Att: 248 Coles, Cherry.

Worcester City 3v0 Aylesbury United
Norris, Ferguson, Williams Att: 868

Chertsey Town 0v1 Purfleet
Att: 266

Molesey 2v2 Staines Town
Lewis, Swift Att: 158 Riley, Grainger

r Staines Town 5v0 Molesey
Beeks 3, Williams 2. Att: 208

Carshalton Athletic 1v1 Braintree Town
Vines Att: 309 Metcalf

r Braintree Town 0v5 Carshalton Athletic
Att: 260 Bishop (og), Vines, Robson Salako, Brady.

St Albans City 4v2 Thame United
Daly 2, Driscoll, Howell Att: 407 Sheldrick, Barresi

Sutton United 0v1 Trowbridge Town
Att: 617 Cole

Wembley 2v0 Bashley
Granville, Sakhraoui Att: 116

Rothwell Town 3v2 Uxbridge
McGuire 2 (1p), Meads Att: 126 King, Gill

Dorchester Town 2v3 Hayes
Pickard, Kilgour Att: 515 Pearson, Kelly, Brady

Hitchin Town 1v2 Bognor Regis Town
Gillard Att: 394 Miles 2

Newport AFC 1v0 Grays Athletic
Jones. Att: 679

Cambridge City 2v0 Hendon
Tovey, Pincher Att: 234

Sudbury Town 2v0 Tooting & Mitcham U
Stafford, Thompson Att: 418

* After extra-time.

FIRST ROUND PROPER
Saturday 20th January 1996

Stalybridge Celtic 1v1 Gresley Rovers
Goodacre 57. Att: 638 O'Reilly 38.

r **Gresley Rovers 1v0 Stalybridge Celtic**
Marsden 90. Att: 603

Stafford Rangers 1v1 Guiseley
Mitchell 32. Att: 689 Norbury 51.

r **Guiseley 2v1 Stafford Rangers**
Norbury 36,53. Att: 365 Moore 85(p).

Colwyn Bay 3v3 Altrincham
Donnelly 13, 83, Roberts 73. Att: 596 Hughes 6, Terry 43(p), France 89.

r **Altrincham 2v0 Colwyn Bay**
Reid 30, France 55. Att: 527

Halifax Town 2v1 Southport
Johnson 2, Cochrane 8 Att: 966 Whittaker 27.

Ashton United 1v3 Blyth Spartans
Whittaker 12. Att: 535 Gamble 10, Proctor 58,80.

Dudley Town 4v2 Halesowen Town
Hall 37, Cooper 71, Horne 77, Piggott 85. Att: 769 Snape, Wright.

Macclesfield Town 1v0 Runcorn
Power 45. Att: 1401

Burton Albion 3v1 Telford United
Rhodes 88, Devaney 90 Att: 950 Gray 65.
Payne 90.

Gainsborough T. 4v1 Nuneaton Borough
Snodin 15, 40, 85, Morrow 27. Att: 867 Drewitt 43.

Morecambe 2v2 Emley
Coleman 50, Cain 66. Att: 656 Graham 10, Banks 85.

r **Emley 3v1 Morecambe**
David 35,67, McLean 43 Att: 412 McCluskie 48.

Hednesford Town 1v1 Northwich Vic.
McNally 45. Att: 935 Vicary 2.

r **Northwich Vic. 2v0 Hednesford Town**
Walters 60, Cooke 83. Att: 636

Kidderminster H. 0v0 Gateshead
Att: 1312

r **Gateshead 2v0 Kidderminster H.**
Robson 16, Cramman 76 Att: 383

Marine 0v0 Hyde United
Att: 467

r **Hyde United 0v0* Marine**
Att: 416

2r **Hyde United 3v0 Marine**
Nolan 15, Carroll 46, Rodney 59 (og). Att:

Boston United 1v1 Chorley
Brown 62. Att: 808 Hook 57.

r **Chorley 2v1 Boston United**
Trundle 63, Ross 73. Att: 294 Cook 56.

Bromsgrove Rov. 1v0 Bishop Auckland
Carter 22. Att: 999

Radcliffe Borough 3v2 Matlock Town
McCrae 18,60,88. Att: 241 Varadi 39, Cully 58.

Oxford City 1v2 Merthyr Tydfil
Herbert 44(p). Att: 352 Evans 75(p), Williams 90.

An aerial struggle at Sheepy Road as Atherstone United (dark shirts) defend a Lincoln United free kick. Photo: Martin Wray.

Worcester City defenders look on in despair as Bognor's Lee Cormack (just visible behind City 'keeper Melvin Watson) watches his header give the Rocks a 1-0 victory. Photo: Andrew Chitty.

Rothwell Town 2v2 **Welling United**
Beards 19, McGuire 88. Att: 238 Morah 89(p), Tierling 90.

[r] **Welling United** 3v0 **Rothwell Town**
Tierling 37, Morah 86, Wordsworth 88. Att: 312

Bognor Regis T. 1v0 **Worcester City**
Cormack 14. Att: 524

Dover Athletic 2v2 **Cheltenham Town**
Rogers 27, Darlington 38. Att: 904 Wring 47,90.

[r] **Cheltenham T.** 1v1* **Dover Athletic**
Banks 56. Att: 640 Leworthy 85.

[2r] **Dover Athletic** 1v0 **Cheltenham Town**
Rogers. Att: 654

Chelmsford City 0v1 **Newport AFC**
Att: 1130 Evans.

Gloucester City 5v0 **Staines Town**
Hallam 37,74, Phillips 63, Knight 83, Portway 88. Att: 748

Trowbridge Town 2v2 **Sudbury Town**
Mitchell 21, Ferns 39(p) Att: 319 McClean 37, Smith 68(p).

[r] **Sudbury Town** 1v1* **Trowbridge Town**
Brown 50. Att: 224 Lunt 71.

[2r] **Trowbridge T.** 1v1* **Sudbury Town**
Rolph (og) Att: 327 Smith

[3r] **Sudbury Town** 4v3 **Trowbridge Town**
Marean 2, French, Greaves. Benbow, Stafford (og),
Att: 386

Carshalton Athletic 3v1 **Woking**
Salako 31, Vines 51, Ugbah 70. Att: 1485 Steele 82.

Farnborough Town 1v1 **Slough Town**
Gavin 30. Att: 856 West 90.

[r] **Slough Town** 4v3 **Farnborough Town**
West 17 (p), 58, Baron 64,71. Att: 742 Harlow 5, Boothe 37, Gavin 76.

Rushden & Ds. 0v1 **Purfleet**
Att: 1906 Jeyes 61.

Kettering Town 1v1 **St Albans City**
Pope 68. Att: 1577 Clark 65.

[r] **St Albans City** 2v3* **Kettering Town**
Howell 45, Gurney 78. Att: 705 Ibrahim 25, Alford 54, Pope 100.

Cambridge City 1v2 **Boreham Wood**
Lockhart 72. Att: 287 Gentle 17,47.

Hayes 0v0 **Enfield**
Att: 502

[r] **Enfield** 2v2* **Hayes**
Abbott 47, Carstairs 119. Att: 436 Cox 2, Randall 97.

[2r] **Enfield** 2v2 **Hayes**
Abbott 24, Carstairs 47. Att: 392 Cox 38, O.G. 61.

[3r] **Hayes** 2v0 **Enfield**
Goodliffe 38, Randall 77. Att: 369

Stevenage Bor. 3v2 **Dagenham & Redbridge**
Bayles 11, Venables 16, Marshall 42. Att: 1348 Stringfellow 2, Prindiville

Wembley 2v1 **Kingstonian**
Bates 13,87. Att: 214 Bolton 18.

Sunday 21st January 1996

Bath City 1v1 **Yeovil Town**
Sugar 44. Att: 2225 Patmore 41.

[r] **Yeovil Town** 2v3* **Bath City**
Whale 13,20. Att: 2731 Cousins 60,86, Vernon 97.

SECOND ROUND PROPER

SATURDAY 10th FEBRUARY 1996

Home	Score	Away
Hyde United	4v1	**Welling United**
Kimmins 4	Att: 680	Henry
Guiseley	4v0	**Altrincham**
Norbury 2, Cook, Brockie	Att: 690	
Emley	1v2	**Gateshead**
Banks	Att: 668	Cramman 2
Bognor Regis T.	1v3	**Radcliffe Borough**
Cormack	Att: 539	Lunt 2, Kilner
Boreham Wood	2v1	**Dover Athletic**
Harrigan, Gentle	Att: 506	Restarick
Slough Town	1v2	**Kettering Town**
Pickett	Att: 1058	Scott, Gynn
Bath City	2v0	**Hayes**
Withey 2	Att: 699	
Macclesfield Town	2v1	**Purfleet**
Bradshaw, Payne	Att: 1003	Locke (og)
Blyth Spartans	1v2	**Gresley Rovers**
Young	Att: 626	O'Reilly, Garner
Carshalton Athletic	2v1	**Newport AFC**
Salako, Ugbah	Att: 682	Tucker
Stevenage Bor.	2v1	**Burton Albion**
Venables, Hayles	Att: 1362	Rhodes
Wembley	0v2	**Northwich Victoria**
	Att: 268	Butler, Cooke
Halifax Town	0v1	**Bromsgrove Rovers**
	Att: 887	Smith

TUESDAY 13th FEBRUARY

Home	Score	Away
Dudley Town	1v2	**Merthyr Tydfil**
Hall 13.	Att: 268	Jenkins 9, Evans 43.
Chorley	2v0	**Gainsborough Trin.**
Ross 42, 55.	Att: 425	

THURSDAY 15th FEBRUARY

Home	Score	Away
Sudbury Town	3v1	**Gloucester City**
McLean 1, Smith 40,83.	Att: 262	Hallam 65.

Steve Heffer of Borehamwood (white shirt) out-jumps Dover Athletic's No.2 Scott Linsey with looking on (from L-R) Nigel Down (Dover), Gary Nisbet (Borehamwood) and ex-England international Brian Stein now with Borheamwood. Photo: Clive Butchins.

Newport's Steve Lowndes fires in a shot past Carshalton Athletic's Phil Dawson (white shirt) during their Second Round tie in the FA Umbro Trophy. Photo: Alan Coomes.

A Gateshead (light strips) corner sets up this attack on the Radcliffe Borough goal during their Third Round tie at Stainton Park. Photo: Colin Stevens.

THIRD ROUND PROPER
Saturday 2nd March 1996

Home	Score	Away
Guiseley	1v2	**Gresley Rovers**
Norbury 79.	Att: 790	Evans 9, O'Reilly 29.
Merthyr Tydfil	1v1	**Northwich Victoria**
Summers 36.	Att: 528	Abel 9.
Hyde United	3v2	**Carshalton Athletic**
Carroll 26, Kimmins 68, Owen 79.	Att: 854	Clark 42, 81.
Macclesfield Town	1v0	**Sudbury Town**
Coates 19.	Att: 1140	
Boreham Wood	1v1	**Chorley**
Prutton 89.	Att: 525	Leitch 68.
Radcliffe Borough	1v2	**Gateshead**
Lunt 54.	Att: 716	Thompson 58, Kitchen 90.
Stevenage Bor.	3v0	**Kettering Town**
Smith 17, Hayles 85,87	Att: 2219	

SUNDAY 3rd MARCH

Home	Score	Away
Bath City	1v1	**Bromsgrove Rovers**
Clarke(og) 88.	Att: 1276	Brighton 70.

OPPOSITE: *Radcliffe Borough (dark strips) defend bravely against Gateshead but their efforts were in vain. Photo: Colin Stevens.*

Macclesfield's winning goal against Sudbury Town scored by Marc Coates just out of the picture.

F.A. UMBRO TROPHY

FOURTH ROUND PROPER

Saturday 23rd March 1996

3 HYDE UNITED
(Nolan 33 (p), Kimmins 47, Carroll 83.)
v Att: 2,012
(Venables 62, Hayles 90.)
2 STEVENAGE BOROUGH

0 GRESLEY ROVERS

v Att: 1,727
(Bradshaw 9, Towers 40.)
2 MACCLESFIELD TOWN

0 BROMSGROVE ROVERS

v Att: 1,807
(Cooke 54.)
1 NORTHWICH VICTORIA

3 CHORLEY
(Ross 44, Mayers 75, Trundle 89.)
v Att: 1,136
(Proudlock 64.)
1 GATESHEAD

Superb photo showing Stevenage Borough's Efetobor Sodje tackling Hyde United's Tony Carroll (white shorts). Photo: Colin Stevens.

Gresley Rovers' Tony Marsden was just wide of the mark with this spectacular overhead kick early in the first half of their quarter final tie against macclesfield Town. Photo: Tim Durrant.

SEMI-FINALS

Saturday 13th April 1996

			Att:
HYDE UNITED 1	v	**2 NORTHWICH VICTORIA**	Att: 1999
Varden 43.		Cooke 44, Humphreys 71.	
MACCLESFIELD TOWN 3	v	**1 CHORLEY**	Att:
Thorpe (og) 51, Coates 75, Power 87.		Hook 26.	

Saturday 20th April 1996

			Att:
NORTHWICH VICTORIA 1	v	**0 HYDE UNITED**	Att:
Abel 42.			
CHORLEY 1	v	**1 MACCLESFIELD TOWN**	Att:
Ross 36.		Sorvel 87.	

MACCLESFIELD TOWN v CHORLEY

By Gareth Thomas and Dave Swanton

Vauxhall Conference reigning champions Macclesfield were overwhelming favourites to make a return trip to Wembley seven years after their last visit, but for three-quarters of their first-leg semi-final against UniBond League Premier Division side Chorley, it didn't look as though the Silkmen would end up with a comfortable lead to take to Victory Park.

Macclesfield started slowly and created little as Chorley's busy engine-room of the experienced Dean Emerson and big-money signing from Bamber Bridge, Kenny Mayers, closed the Silkmen down well. The much sought-after Lee Trundle went closest to breaking the deadlock after 18 minutes when his shot following a mis-kick by goalkeeper Ryan Price went inches wide of the post. Howewevr, eight minutes later, the Magpies went in front when Steve Hook's glancing header from Dave McKearney's cross beat Price.

A Last desperate attempt - Chorley's Kenny Mayers tries to beat the Macclesfield defence with this overhead kick late in the match. Photo: Colin Stevens.

The goal stirred Macclesfield, and they almost drew level after 33 minutes when Phil Power, a former Chorley player, played a clever one-two with Marc Coates before seeing Simon Marsh in the Chorley goal make an excellent save.

Six minutes after the interval, Macc equalised, and the goal was a tragedy for veteran former Stockport defender Andy Thorpe, who diverted Darren Lyons' cross into his own net. Kenny Mayers had a chance to put the visitors back in front midway through the second half but then, with time running out, disaster struck the Lancashire outfit when another Lyons cross to the far post was finished impressively by Marc Coates and, as the Magpies rearguard began to fall apart, Phil Power crisply struck the third with just three minutes remaining to make his former club's chances of making Wembley very difficult.

After the 3-1 reversal at Moss Rose, Chorley attempted almost mission impossible at Victory Park in the second leg. However, the biggest crowd seen at the ground since their Conference days, were in carnival mood. The game started in disappointing fashion but the home side then began to cause a few problems for Macclesfield. Chorley made the semi-final interesting when ace-marksman Brian Ross put them ahead after 36 minutes with a super strike. That brought the tie back to within reach of the UniBond side but although they piled on the pressure in the second half and had chances to equalise, Macclesfield sealed victory when, after 87 minutes, Neil Sorvel scored to send the away fans delirious and end the Chorley dream.

Macclesfield's Neil Howarth about to tackle Brian Ross of Chorley. Photo: Colin Stevens.

Chorley's Mark Wright chases after Tony Hemmings of Macclesfield. Photo: Colin Stevens.

NORTHWICH VICTORIA v HYDE UNITED

The much-awaited semi-final between these two Cheshire neighbours served up two very entertaining and exciting encounters. The first-leg, played at Hyde's Ewen Fields, was a tense affair at first which burst into action towards the end of the first half.

Hyde, who had already played over 60 games this season, started off proceedings when, after 43 minutes, Paul Varden found himself in space in the six-yard box to flick Dave Nolan's header beyond Dean Greygoose and into the bottom corner of the net. But Hyde's celebrations were cut short seconds later when Ian Cooke latched on to a weak clearance and stunned the home crowd with a tremendous equaliser. The second half saw both sides have chances early on and Hyde's prolific front duo of Ged Kimmins and Tony Carroll were beginning to cause problems for an otherwise well-drilled Northwich back line. Despite all Hyde's efforts, the Vics continued to look the more assured side and it came as no real surprise when the visitors burst out of defence to grab the lead on 71 minutes. There seemed little danger when former England semi-professional captain Delwyn Humphreys received the ball close to the touchline but his angled drive appeared to deceive Arthur Williams in the Hyde goal as it flashed in at the near post. Hyde were now really up against it as their hopes of taking a lead into the second leg evaporated and, in the end, they looked a very tired team.

The second leg at the Drill Field saw the home side forced to bring in veteran goalkeeper Trevor Ball as a replacement for Dean Greygoose who had 12 stitches in a head wound received in the local derby againt Macclesfield on the previous Tuesday night. He was kept busy during the opening stages and got his angles right to deny Kimmins after the England striker had been freed by Dave Esdaille. But that was to be the hot-shot's last action as, after just 23 minutes, he limped off with a hamstring injury and was replaced by Julian Dowe. This seemed to fire the home side and it took a brilliant save from Williams to deny Cooke a certain goal from a point-blank header after 41 minutes. However, from the resulting corner, Vics took a 3-1 aggregate lead when veteran defender Graham Abel rose to powerfully head home Brian Butler's flag kick.

The second half saw Hyde, now with nothing to lose, power forward but the loss of the prolific Kimmins proved crucial, despite young Dowe's efforts. In the end, Northwich deserved their success over the two games, but it does make one wonder just what may have happened if Kimmins hadn't have been injured so early on.

Northwich Vic's Graham Abel gets up well to win the ball during his side's 2-1 1st leg victory at Hyde United. Photo: Colin Stevens.

Hyde's George Switzer about to get in his tackle on Vic's Delwyn Humphreys. Photo: Colin Stevens.

Ged Kimmins (dark shorts) of Hyde manages to get his chip over Vic's 'keeper, but, unfortunately for him, it just scraped the bar on its way over. Photo: Keith Clayton.

F.A. UMBRO TROPHY - AT A GLANCE

1st Rd.	2nd Rd.	3rd Rd.	4th Rd.	SEMI-FINAL	FINAL
Stafford R. 1,1					
Guiseley 1,2	Guiseley 4				
Colwyn Bay 3,0	Altrincham 0				
Altrincham 3,2		Guiseley 1			
Ashton Utd. 1		Gresley R. 2			
Blyth Spartans 1	Blyth Spartans 1				
Stalybridge C. 1,0	Gresley Rov. 2		Gresley Rovers 0		
Gresley Rov. 1,1				Macclesfield T. 3 1	
Rushden & Ds. 0			Macclesfield Town 2		
Purfleet 1	Purfleet 1				
Macclesfield T. 1	Macclesfield T. 2				
Runcorn 0		Macclesfield T. 1			
Trowbridge T. 2,1,1,3		Sudbury Town 0			
Sudbury T. 2,1,1,4	Sudbury Town 3				
Gloucester C. 5	Gloucester C. 1				
Staines T. 0					**MACCLESFIELD TOWN 3**
Cambridge C. 1					
Boreham Wood 2	Boreham Wood 2				
Dover Ath. 2,1,1	Dover Ath. 1				
Cheltenham T. 2,1,0		Boreham Wood 1,3			
Boston Utd. 1,1		Chorley 1,4			
Chorley 1,2	Chorley 2				
Gainsborough T. 4	Gainsborough T. 0		Chorley 3		
Nuneaton Bor. 1				Chorley 1 1	
Bornor Regis T. 1					
Worcester C. 0	Bognor Regis T. 1		Gateshead 1		
Radcliffe B. 3	Radcliffe B. 3				
Matlock T. 2		Radcliffe B. 1			
Morecambe 2,1		Gateshead 2			
Emley 2,3	Emley 1				
Kidderminster H. 0,0	Gateshead 2				
Gateshead 0,0					
Marine 0,0,0					
Hyde U. 0,0,3	Hyde Utd. 4				
Rothwell T. 2,0	Welling Utd. 1				
Welling U. 2,3		Hyde Utd. 3			
Carshalton A. 3		Carshalton Ath. 2			
Woking 1	Carshalton Ath. 2				
Chelmsford C. 0	Newport AFC 1		Hyde Utd. 3		
Newport AFC 1				Hyde United 1 0	
Stevenage B. 3			Stevenage B. 2		
Dagenham & R. 2	Stevenage B. 2				
Burton A. 3	Burton Alb. 1				
Telford U. 1		Stevenage Bor. 3			
Farnborough T. 1,3		Kettering T. 0			
Slough T. 1,4	Slough T. 1				
Kettering T. 1,3	Kettering T. 2				
St. Albans C. 1,2					**NORTHWICH VICTORIA 1**
Bath City 1,3					
Yeovil T. 1,2	Bath City 2				
Hayes 0,2,2,2	Hayes 0				
Enfield 0,2,2,0		Bath City 1,1			
Halifax T. 2		Bromsgrove R. 1,2			
Southport 1	Halifax T 0				
Bromsgrove R. 1	Bromsgrove R. 1		Bromsgrove R. 0		
Bishop Auck. 0				Northwich V. 2 1	
Dudley Town 4			Northwich V. 1		
Halesowen T. 2	Dudley T. 1				
Oxford C. 1	Merthyr T. 2				
Merthyr T. 2		Merthyr T. 1,2,0			
Wembley 2		Northwich V. 1,2,3			
Kingstonian 1	Wembley 0				
Hednesford T. 1,0	Northwich V. 2				
Northwich V. 1,2					

FINAL

MACCLESFIELD TOWN 3 v 1 NORTHWICH VICTORIA

Steve Payne 15, O.G. 28, Tony Hemmings 80. — Carwyn Williams 51.

SUNDAY 19th MAY 1996

	Macclesfield Town		Northwich Victoria
1	Ryan Price	1	Dean Greygoose
2	Cec Edey	2	Derek Ward
3	Mark Gardiner	3	Chris Duffy
4	Steve Payne	4	Dave Burgess
5	Neil Howarth (capt.)	5	Graham Abel
6	Neil Sorvel	6	Steve Walters
7	Darren Lyons	7	Carwyn Williams
8	Steve Wood	8	Brian Butler (capt.)
9	Marc Coates	9	Ian Cooke
10	Phil Power	10	Delwyn Humphries
11	Tony Hemmings	11	Darren Vicary

Substitutes

Kevin Hulme for Wood, 83 minutes
Paul Cavell for Hemmings, 88 minutes
Mark Bradshaw

Substitutes

Lee Steele for Abel, ?? minutes
Wes Simpson for Burgess, 87 minutes
Trevor Ball

Referee:

Mike D Reed (Birmingham FA)

Linesmen:

Ray J Oliver (Red) (Birmingham FA)
Paul A Vosper (Yellow) (Middlesex FA)

ATTENDANCE
8672

MANAGER
Sammy McIlroy

MANAGER
Brian Kettle

In an all-Cheshire final, which attracted a shamefully small crowd of only 8,672, Macclesfield at last managed to see their name back on the FA Trophy after they had been the first winners 26 years ago in 1970 (28,000 attended!) and well did they deserve their overdue second success in an excellent contest, which told fans that the FA Cup Final held in the same uncomfortable and over-priced stadium eight days earlier was not typical of the modern game. In fact, it was very much one of the better Trophy climaxes.

From the very first whistle the players settled down to a swift and skillful pattern of play with Macclesfield the superior side and after some near misses and an appeal for a penalty they took the lead in the fifteenth minute when Steve Payne ran in to head home Mark Gardiner's cleverly flighted free kick and Phil Power could have added to that lead soon afterwards during a defensive mix-up.

But, after some tentative attempts by Northwich to draw level, Macclesfield doubled their lead with less than 30 minutes on the clock and it was a tragedy for Dave Burgess, whose attempt to clear a cross from the brilliant Tony Hemmings went inside instead of outside Greygoose's left hand post.

Northwich had several chances to reduce the deficit before half-time but both Delwyn Humphreys and Ian Cooke missed gold-plated chances, the latter hitting a post when it would have been simpler to score. So Macclesfield's two-goal lead survived the first half.

On the resumption Phil Power headed over from a comparatively easy position, but, when it appeared that Victoria were just not up to it, they scored in 51 minutes thanks to a fine run and cross from Darren Vicary, which was collected by Carwyn Williams and neatly slipped past Ryan Price.

This clearly encouraged the men in green that all was not lost and they had numerous chances to draw level against a defence which began to look jittery. Humphreys, who for a second season running failed to live up to his fine reputation, was gifted a good chance almost exactly on the hour but shot wide.

The Northwich pressure continued but inevitably they exposed themselves at the back

MACCLESFIELD TRIUMPH AFTER A LONG WAIT

Report by Bill Mitchell

Photo: Ian Morsman

in their anxiety to draw level, which proved fatal to them with ten minutes left as the speedy Hemmings collected a clearance on half way and ran into the Victoria penalty area before sending an unstoppable shot past the desperate dive of Dean Greygoose.

That finished the gallant Northwich side and their cause was ruined by the 83rd minute dismissal of right back Derek Ward - but more of that later! There was a routine end to the match and the better team won. Their stars in a fine team effort were Hemmings (the game's outstanding player), Gardiner, Payne, Lyons, Wood and Power, who had also played for Northwich in the 1984 final.

The losers generally under-performed and appeared to be too shaky in defence. Darren Vicary, although short of pace, provided most danger to Macclesfield from the left flank and the Welshman Carwyn Williams also caused problems, while skipper Bryon Butler never wavered in his attempts to inspire his colleagues, but the others have played better.

The referee, Mike Reed of Birmingham, showed the yellow card on four occasions. Macclesfield's Gardiner (most harshly for an innocuous offence) and Coates ('handbags at dawn') were joined by Northwich's Derek Ward - twice for bad but by no means spiteful or malicious tackles on Hemmings. His second yellow card meant the humiliation of a long walk to the Wembley dressing rooms and it needed a heart of flint not to feel desperately sorry for him.

Mr Reed was correct in applying the letter of the law, but did he do justice to its spirit? On one of his lines he was helped by Ray Olivier, who was in charge earlier of the Oxford-Cambridge match at Fulham and deserved great praise for exactly gauging the mood of the game and conducted it accordingly. This was not a match which merited a red card, as such an action would give a misleading impression of a bad tempered encounter when quite the reverse was the case.

As a midlander Mr Reed will probably be familiar with the area's immortal bard William Shakespeare, so it might be appropriate to remind him of Portia's words from The Merchant of Venice, which go something like this:

The quality of mercy is not strained.
It droppeth as the gentle rain from heaven
Upon the place beneath. It is twice blest:
It blesseth him that gives and him that takes.

PAST F.A. TROPHY FINALS

1970 MACCLESFIELD TOWN 2 (Lyond, B Fidler) **TELFORD UNITED 0** Ref: K Walker
Macc: Cooke, Sievwright, Bennett, Beaumont, Collins, Roberts, Lyons, B Fidler, Young, Corfield, D Fidler.
Telford: Irvine, Harris, Croft, Flowers, Coton, Ray, Fudge, Hart, Bentley, Murray, Jagger. *Att: 28,000.*

1971 TELFORD UTD 3 (Owen, Bentley, Fudge) **HILLINGDON BORO. 2** (Reeve, Bishop) Ref: P Smith
Telford: Irvine, Harris, Croft, Ray, Coton, Carr, Fudge, Owen, Bentley, Jagger, Murray. *H'don:* Lowe, Batt, Langley, Higginson, Newcombe, Moore, Fairchild, Bishop, Reeve, Carter, Knox. *Att: 29,500.*

1972 STAFFORD RANGERS 3 (Williams 2, Cullerton) **BARNET 0** Ref: P Partridge
Staff: Aleksic, Chadwick, Clayton, Sargeant, Aston, Machin, Cullerton, Chapman, Williams, Bayley, Jones.
Barnet: McClelland, Lye, Jenkins, Ward, Embrey, King, Powell, Rerry, Flatt, Easton, Plume. *Att: 24,000.*

1973 SCARBOROUGH 2 (Leask, Thompson) **WIGAN ATHLETIC 1** (Rogers) aet Ref: H Hackney
Scarboro: Garrow, Appleton, Shoulder, Dunn, Siddle, Fagan, Donoghue, Franks, Leask (Barmby), Thompson, Hewitt. *Wigan:* Reeves, Morris, Sutherland, Taylor, Jackson, Gillibrand, Clements, Oats (McCunnell), Rogers, King, Worswick. *Att: 23,000.*

1974 MORECAMBE 2 (Richmond, Sutton) **DARTFORD 1** (Cunningham) Ref: B Homewood
M'cambe: Coates, Pearson, Bennett, Sutton, Street, Baldwin, Done, Webber, Roberts (Galley), Kershaw, Richmond. *D'ford:* Morton, Read, Payne, Carr, Burns, Binks, Light, Glozier, Robinson (Hearne), Cunningham, Halleday. *Att: 19,000.*

1975 MATLOCK TOWN 4 (Oxley, Dawson, T Fenoughty, N Fenoughy) **SCARBOROUGH 0** Ref: K Styles
Matlock: Fell, McKay, Smith, Stuart, Dawson, Swan, Oxley, N Fenoughy, Scott, T Fenoughty, M Fenoughty.
Scarborough: Williams, Hewitt, Rettitt, Dunn, Marshall, Todd, Houghton, Woodall, Davidson, Barnby, Aveyard. *Att: 21,000.*

1976 SCARBOROUGH 3 (Woodall, Abbey, Marshall(p)) **STAFFORD R. 2** (Jones 2) Ref: R Challis
S'boro: Barnard, Jackson, Marshall, H Dunn, Ayre (Donoghue), HA Dunn, Dale, Barmby, Woodall, Abbey, Hilley. *S'ford:* Arnold, Ritchie, Richards, Sargeant, Seddon, Morris, Chapman, Lowe, Jones, Hutchinson, Chadwick. *Att: 21,000.*

1977 SCARBOROUGH 2 (Dunn(p), Abbey) **DAGENHAM 1** (Harris) Ref: G Courtney
S'boro: Chapman, Smith, Marshall (Barmby), Dunn, Ayre, Deere, Aveyard, Donoghue, Woodall, Abbey, Dunn. *D'ham:* Hutley, Wellman, P Currie, Dunwell, Moore, W Currie, Harkins, Saul, Fox, Harris, Holder. *Att: 21,500.*

1978 ALTRINCHAM 3 (King, Johnson, Rogers) **LEATHERHEAD 1** (Cook) Ref: A Grey
A'cham: Eales, Allan, Crossley, Bailey, Owens, King, Morris, Heathcote, Johnson, Rogers, Davidson (Flaherty). *L'head:* Swannell, Cooper, Eaton, Davies, Reid, Malley, Cook, Salkeld, Baker, Boyle (Bailey). *Att: 20,000.*

1979 STAFFORD RANGERS 2 (A Wood 2) **KETTERING TOWN 0** Ref: D Richardson
S'ford: Arnold, F Wood, Willis, Sargeant, Seddon, Ritchie, Secker, Chapman, A Wood, Cullerton, Chadwick (Jones). *K'ring:* Lane, Ashby, Lee, Eastell, Dixey, Suddards, Flannagan, Kellock, Phipps, Clayton, Evans (Hughes). *Att: 32,000.*

1980 DAGENHAM 2 (Duck, Maycock) **MOSSLEY 1** (Smith) Ref: K Baker
D'ham: Huttley, Wellman, Scales, Dunwell, Mooore, Durrell, Maycock, Horan, Duck, Kidd, Jones (Holder).
M'ley: Fitton, Brown, Vaughan, Gorman, Salter, Polliot, Smith, Moore, Skeete, O'Connor, Keelan (Wilson).
Att: 26,000.

1981 BISHOP'S STORTFORD 1 (Sullivan) **SUTTON UNITED 0** Ref: J Worrall
S'ford: Moore, Blackman, Brame, Smith (Worrell), Bradford, Abery, Sullivan, Knapman, Radford, Simmonds, Mitchell. *Sutton:* Collyer, Rogers, Green, J Rains, T Rains, Stephens (Sunnucks), Waldon, Pritchard, Cornwell, Parsons. *Att: 22,578.*

1982 ENFIELD 1 (Taylor) **ALTRINCHAM 0** Ref: B Stevens
Enfield: Jacobs, Barrett, Tone, Jennings, Waite, Ironton, Ashford, Taylor, Holmes, Oliver (Flint), King.
A'cham: Connaughton, Crossley, Davison, Bailey, Cuddy, King (Whitbread), Allan, Heathcote, Johnson, Rogers, Howard. *Att: 18.678..*

1983 TELFORD UTD 2 (Mather 2) **NORTHWICH VICTORIA 1** (Bennett) Ref: B Hill
Telford: Charlton, Lewis, Turner, Mayman (Joseph), Walker, Easton, Barnett, Williams, Mather, Hogan, Alcock. *N'wich:* Ryan, Fretwell, Murphy, Jones, Forshaw, Ward, Anderson, Abel (Bennett), Reid, Chesters, Wilson. *Att: 22,071.*

1984 NORTHWICH VICTORIA 1 (Chesters) **BANGOR CITY 1** (Whelan) *Att: 14,200.* Ref: J Martin
Replay **NORTHWICH 2** (Chesters(p), Anderson) **BANGOR 1** (Lunn) *Att: 5,805* (at Stoke)
N'wich: Ryan, Fretwell, Dean, Jones, Forshaw (Power 65), Bennett, Anderson, Abel, Reid, Chesters, Wilson. *Bangor:* Letheren, Cavanagh, Gray, Whelan, Banks, Lunn, Urqhart, Morris, Carter, Howat, Sutcliffe (Westwood 105). *Same teams in replay.*

1985 WEALDSTONE 2 (Graham, Holmes) **BOSTON UNITED 1** (Cook) Ref: J Bray
W'stone: Iles, Perkins, Bowgett, Byatt, Davies, Greenaway, Holmes, Wainwright, Donnellan, Graham (N Cordice 89), A Cordice. *Boston:* Blackwell, Casey, Ladd, Creane, O'Brien, Thommson, Laverick (Mallender 78), Simpsom, Gilbert, Lee, Cook. *Att: 20,775.*

1986 ALTRINCHAM 1 (Farrelly) **RUNCORN 0** Ref: A Ward
A'cham: Wealands, Gardner, Densmore, Johnson, Farrelly, Conning, Cuddy, Davison, Reid, Ellis, Anderson. Sub: Newton. *Runcorn:* McBride, Lee, Roberts, Jones, Fraser, Smith, S Crompton (A Crompton), Imrie, Carter, Mather, Carrodus. *Att: 15,700.*

1987 KIDDERMINSTER HARRIERS 0 BURTON ALBION 0 *Att: 23,617.* Ref: D Shaw
Replay **KIDDERMINSTER 2** (Davies 2) **BURTON 1** (Groves) *Att: 15,685* (at West Brom)
K'minster: Arnold, Barton, Boxall, Brazier (sub Hazlewood in rep), Collins (sub Pearson 90 at Wembley), Woodall, McKenzie, O'Dowd, Tuohy, Casey, Davies. sub: Jones. *Burton:* New, Essex, Kamara, Vaughan, Simms, Groves, Bancroft, Land, Dorsett, Redfern, (sub Wood in replay), Gauden. Sub: Patterson.

1988 ENFIELD 0 TELFORD UNITED 0 *Att: 20,161.* Ref: L Dilkes
Replay **ENFIELD 3** (Furlong 2, Howell) **TELFORD 2** (Biggins, Norris(p)) *Att: 6,912* (at West Brom)
Enfield: Pape, Cottington, Howell, Keen (sub Edmonds in rep), Sparrow (sub Hayzleden at Wembley), Lewis (sub Edmonds at Wembley), Harding, Cooper, King, Furlong, Francis. *Enfield:* Charlton, McGinty, Storton, Nelson, Wiggins, Mayman (sub Cunningham in rep (sub Hancock)), Sankey, Joseph, Stringer (sub Griffiths at Wembley, Griffiths in rep), Biggins, Norris.

1989 TELFORD UNITED 1 (Crawley) **MACCLESFIELD TOWN 0** Ref: T Holbrook
Telford: Charlton, Lee, Brindley, Hancock, Wiggins, Mayman, Grainger, Joseph, Nelson, Lloyd, Stringer. Subs: Crawley, Griffiths. *Macclesfield:* Zelem, Roberts, Tobin, Edwards, Hardman, Askey, Lake, Hanton, Imrie, Burr, Timmons. Subs: Devomshire, Kendall. *Att: 18,102.*

1990 BARROW 3 (Gordon 2, Cowperthwaite) **LEEK TOWN 0** Ref: T Simpson.
Barrow: McDonnell, Higgins, Chilton, Skivington, Gordon, Proctor, Doherty (Burgess), Farrell (Gilmore), Cowperthwaite, Lowe, Ferris. *Leek:* Simpson, Elsby (Smith), Pearce, McMullen, Clowes, Coleman (Russell), Mellor, Somerville, Sutton, Millington. *Att: 19,011.*

1991 WYCOMBE W. 2 (Scott, West) **KIDDERMINSTER H. 1** (Hadley) Ref: J Watson
Wycombe: Granville, Crossley, Cash, Kerr, Creaser, Carroll, Ryan, Stapleton, West, Scott, Guppy (Hutchinson). *Kidderminster:* Jones, Kurila, McGrath, Weir, Barnett, Forsyth, Joseph (Wilcox), Howell (Whitehouse), Hadley, Lilwall, Humphries. *Att: 34,842.*

1992 COLCHESTER UTD 3 (Masters, Smith, McGavin) **WITTON ALBION 1** (Lutkevitch) Ref: K P Barratt
Colchester: Barrett, Donald, Roberts, Knsella, English, Martin, Cook, Masters, McDonough (Bennett 65), McGavin, Smith. *Witton:* Mason, Halliday, Coathup, McNeilis, Jim Connor, Anderson, Thomas, Rose, Alford, Grimshaw (Joe Connor), Lutkevitch (McCluskie). *Att: 27,806.*

1993 WYCOMBE W. 4 (Cousins, Kerr, Thompson, Carroll) **RUNCORN 1** (Shaughnessy) Ref: I J Borritt
Wycombe: Hyde, Cousins, Cooper, Kerr, Crossley, Thompson (Hayrettin 65), Carroll, Ryan, Hutchinson, Scott, Guppy. Unused sub: Casey. *Runcorn:* Williams, Bates, Robertson, Hill, Harold (Connor 62), Anderson, Brady (Parker 72), Brown, Shaughnessy, McKenna, Brabin. *Att: 32,968.*

1994 WOKING 2 (D Brown, Hay) **RUNCORN 1** (Shaw (pen)) Ref: Mr Paul Durkin
Woking: Laurence Batty, Mark Tucker, Lloyd Wye, Gwynne Berry, Kevan Brown, Andy Clement, Dereck Brown (Kevin Rattray 32), Colin Fielder, Scott Steele, Darran Hay (David Puckett 46), Clive Wilson. *Runcorn:* Arthur Williams, Jamie Bates, Paul Robertson, Nigel Shaw, Andy Lee, Garry Anderson, Karl Thomas, Joe Connor, Ian McInerney (Graham Hill 71), Ken McKenna, Gary Brabin. Unused sub: Neil Parker. *Att: 15,818*

1995 WOKING 2 (Steele, Fielder) **KIDDERMINSTER H. 1** (Davies) aet Ref: Mr D J Gallagher
Woking: Laurence Batty, Mark Tucker, Lloyd Wye, Colin Fielder, Kevan Brown, John Crumplin (Kevin Rattray 42), Shane Wye, Andrew Ellis, Scott Steele, Darran Hay (Richard Newberry 112), Clive Wilson. Sub: Tim Read (gk). Manager: Geoff Chapple.
Kidderminster: Kevin Rose, Simeon Hodson, Paul Bancroft, Paul Webb, Chris Brindley (Neil Cartwright 94), Richard Forsyth, John Deakin, Mark Yates, Delwyn Humphreys (Lee Hughes 105), Paul Davies, Jon Purdie. Sub: Mark Dearlove (gk). Manager: Graham Allner. *Att: 17,815.*

What a difference a win makes!

Above:
The Macclesfield players celebrate in the bath after the final. Photo: Ian Morsman.

Opposite:
Steve Payne and Tony Hemmings - the goalscorers with the spoils. Photo: Ian Morsman.

Below:
The Northwich players trudge off the field after losing the final. Photo: Alan Coomes.

F.A. Carlsberg VASE

1995-96 REVIEW

FIRST ROUND QUALIFYING

2nd September 1995

Ponteland United	4v3*	Billingham Town
Alnwick Town	1v1*	Ryhope CA
r) Ryhope CA	2v3*	Alnwick Town
Eppleton CW	2v2*	Seaton Delaval Amat.
r) Seaton Delaval A.	2v2*	Eppleton CW
2r Eppleton CW	0v2	Seaton Delaval A.
J. R. Boldon CA	2v3	Evenwood Town
West Allotment Celtic	1v0	North Shields Athletic
Harrogate Railway	0v0*	Shotton Comrades
r) Shotton Comrades	2v1	Harrogate Railway
Shirebrook Town	1v3	Cheadle Town
Salford City	2v1*	Sheffield
Castleton Gabriels	2v3*	Wythenshawe Amateur
Garforth Town	1v1*	Nuthall
r) Nuthall	3v2	Garforth Town
Maghull	2v3	Denaby United
Harworth CI	w/o	Priory (Eastwood)
Grove United	3v3*	Pontefract Collieries
r) Pontefract Collieries	0v1	Grove United
Heswall	2v1	Sandiacre Town
Tetley Walker	1v4	South Normanton Ath.
Rossington Main	2v3	Louth United
Maltby MW	4v2	Kimberley Town
Hallam	0v1	Selby Town
Kidsgrove Athletic	4v1	Formby
Hall Road Rangers	0v3	Nettleham
Glasshoughton Welf.	0v0*	Atherton Collieries
r) Atherton Collieries	3v3*	Glasshoughton Welf.
Glasshoughton Welf.	0v2	Atherton Collieries
Liversedge	3v0	Daisy Hill
Blackpool (Wren) Rovers	0v2	Newcastle Town
Eccleshill United	3v0	Worsbro Bridge MW
Long Eaton United	1v2*	Merseyside Police
Tadcaster Albion	1v2*	Ossett Town
Tividale	0v3	Stafford Town
Darlaston	4v2	Gedling Town
Match ordered to be replayed by F.A.		
r) Darlaston	3v2	Gedling Town
Cradley Town	1v0	Holwell Sports
Boldmere St Michaels	6v0	Knypersley Victoria
Wellingborough Town	6v0	Pegasus Juniors
Rushall Olympic	3v1	Highgate United
Shifnal Town	5v1	Northfield Town
Stourport Swifts	4v0	Brierley Hill Town
Chasetown	1v2	Bloxwich Town
Rocester	1v3	Northampton Spencer
Tiptree United	2v3	Sawbridgeworth Town
Cornard United	1v4	Witham Town

Roy Boan of Bedford Town (left) in a chase with Shane Duffy of Hanwell Town during their FA Carlsberg Vase 1st Qualifying Round match. Photo: Martin Wray.

Norwich United	2v5	Stamford AFC
Fakenham Town	2v0	Sudbury Wanderers
March Town United	4v0	Hullbridge Sports
Downham Town	2v3	Southend Manor
Haverhill Rovers	1v3	Harwich & Parkeston
Stwomarket Town	w/o	Brantham Athletic
Ford United	1v3	Tilbury
Kempston Rovers	0v1	Amersham Town
Milton Keynes	1v2	Edgware Town
Harlow Town	2v0	Beaconsfield Sycob
Hemel Hempstead	1v3	Stansted
Wealdstone	10v0	East Ham United
Hanwell Town	1v2	Bedford Town
Harpenden Town	1v4	Ware
Totternhoe	2v3	Feltham
Romford	2v1	Tufnell Park
Kingsbury Town	2v1	Rayners Lane
Clapton	4v2	Leverstock Green
Bedfont	2v3	Ramsgate
Ashford Town (Middx)	6v0	Southwick
East Grinstead	1v4	Folkestone Invicta
Crowborough Ath.	1v2	Lancing
Bracknell Town	2v0	Redhill
Horsham YMCA	2v1*	Epsom & Ewell
Merstham	1v4	Chichester City
Burgess Hill Town	3v0	Oakwood
Saltdean United	2v0	Sidley United
Chipstead	3v1*	Beckenham Town
Dartford	2v2*	Steyning Town
r) Steyning Town	0v4	Dartford
Eastbourne Town	0v1	Littlehampton Town
Portfield	2v0	Broadbridge Heath
Furness	1v1*	Sheppey United
r) Sheppey United	0v3	Furness
Langney Sports	3v2	Mile Oak
Newhaven	1v3	Canterbury City
Swindon Supermarine	2v1	Downton
Abingdon United	3v0	BAT Sports
Carterton Town	2v0	Swanage & Herston
Bemerton Heath Harl.	5v2*	Kintbury Rangers
Didcot Town	2v3	Totton AFC
Sherborne Town	5v3	Portsmouth Royal Navy
Brockenhurst	0v4	Ryde
Cowes Sports	1v2	Gosport Borough
Odd Down	1v0	Hallen
Crediton United	1v3	Glastonbury
Chippenham Town	2v0	Clyst Rovers
St Blazey	3v0	DRG AFC
Shortwood United	4v0	Ilfracombe Town
Exmouth Town	1v2*	Warminster Town
Fairford Town	2v3*	Backwell United
Bridgwater Town	2v0	Larkhall Athletic

Corinthian Casuals' goalkeeper Gary Brigden punches clear during a Saltdean United attack at Hill Park during their FA Vase 2nd Qualifying Round tie. Photo: Roger Turner.

SECOND ROUND QUALIFYING

30th September 1995

Home	Score	Away
Easington Colliery	4v2	West Allotment Celtic
Alnwick Town	1v2	Esh Winning
Seaton Delaval Amat.	1v5	Marske United
Pickering Town	3v4	Washington
Evenwood Town	1v3	Crook Town
Ashington	3v0	Darlington Cleveland Soc.
Penrith	0v1	Willington
Shotton Comrades	1v0	Morpeth Town
Annfield Plain	2v1	Norton & Stockton Anc.
Benfield Park	2v3	Whickham
Bedlington Terriers	5v1	Horden CW
Stockton	0v1	Ponteland United
Ferryhill Athletic	0v1	Yorkshire Amateur
Wythenshawe Amat.	3v2	Arnold Town
Oakham United	2v1	Blidworth MW
Flixton	2v1	Poulton Victoria
Darwen	0v3	Ossett Albion
Clitheroe	4v0	Immingham Town
Oldham Town	3v2	Prescot AFC
Liversedge	0v1	Newcastle Town
Denaby United	0v1	Ossett Town
Nettleham	1v1	Louth United
r) Louth United	0v1	Nettleham
Merseyside Police	2v3	North Ferriby United
Nantwich Town	3v0	Harworth CI
Selby Town	2v0	Armthorpe Welfare
Ashfield United	5v1	Heswall
Maltby MW	0v2	Nuthall
Salford City	3v0	Atherton Collieries
St Helens Town	4v0	Eccleshill United
Kidsgrove Athletic	3v0	Chadderton
Hatfield Main	7v1	Parkgate
Brigg Town	9v0	Rossendale United
Bootle	2v1	Grove United
Trafford	4v2	Staveley MW
Winterton Rangers	3v1	Rainworth MW
South Normanton A.	0v5	Hucknall Town
Heanor Town	2v2	Maine Road
r) Maine Road	5v2	Heanor Town
Borrowash Victoria	1v4	Cheadle Town
Stapenhill	1v4	West Midlands Police
Sandwell Borough	0v3	Lye Town
Long Buckby	4v1	Stourport Swifts
Shepshed Dynamo	4v0	Kings Heath
Darlaston	4v1	Northampton Spencer
Barwell	1v0	Stratford Town
Blakehall	1v0	Desborough Town
Rushall Olympic	3v1	Upton Town
Cradley Town	2v3	Halesowen Harriers
Shifnal Town	1v1	Bolehall Swifts
r) Bolehall Swifts	1v2	Shifnal Town
Anstey Nomads	4v1	Radford
Westfields	0v2	Brackley Town
Knowle	2v3	Pershore Town
Meir KA	0v5	Walsall Wood
Friar Lane OB	0v1	Oldbury United
Stafford Town	2v4	Willenhall Town
Stewarts & Lloyds	1v3	Boldmere St Michaels
Banbury United (1989)	2v2	Birstall United
r) Birstall United	1v2	Banbury United
Newport Pagnell T.	3v3	Wellingborough Town
r) Wellingborough T.	3v0	Newport Pagnell T.
Bloxwich Town	1v3	Wednesfield
Cogenhoe United	2v0	Barrow Town
Lowestoft Town	5v2	Mildenhall Town
Watton United	0v1	Stowmarket Town
Ipswich Wanderers	0v3	Gorleston
Warboys Town	2v0	March Town Utd
Brightlingsea United	w/o	Long Sutton Ath.
Felixstowe Town	1v2	Harwich & Parkeston
Maldon Town	3v1	Burnham Ramblers
Saffron Walden Town	1v2	Swaffham Town
Histon	1v3	Fakenham Town
Woodbridge Town	5v0	Chatteris Town
Soham Town Rangers	1v4	Ely City
Bourne Town	2v1	Gt Yarmouth Town
Holbeach United	1v4	Sawbridgeworth Town
Southend Manor	0v2	Newmarket Town
Stamford	0v1	St Neots Town
Gt Wakering Rovers	1v2	Clacton Town
Wroxham	7v3	Somersham Town
Eynesbury Rovers	2v2	Mirrlees Blackstone
r) Mirrlees Blackstone	2v1	Eynesbury Rovers
Witham Town	1v1	Spalding United
r) Spalding United	2v1	Witham Town
Hertford Town	3v1	Eton Manor
Kingsbury Town	0v1	Northwood

F.A. CARLSBERG VASE

Wooton Blue Cross	4v3	Hillingdon Borough
Brentwood	1v1	Welwyn Garden City
r) Welwyn G. C.	0v1	Brentwood
Harlow Town	5v4	East Thurrock United
Cockfosters	1v2	Edgware Town
Tilbury	2v1	Waltham Abbey
Hampton	3v0	Viking Sports
Brimsdown Rovers	0v4	Romford
Langford	3v2	London Colney
Shillington	2v4	Clapton
Bedford Town	1v0	Brook House
Concord Rangers	2v0	Potters Bar Town
Potton United	1v2	Aveley
Greenwich Borough	0v1	Chalfont St Peter
Letchworth Garden C.	w/o	Leighton Town
Flackwell Heath	1v0	Hornchurch
Wealdstone	1v1	St Margetsbury
r) St Margetsbury	0v2	Wealdstone
Cheshunt	1v0	Stansted
Eton Wick	2v6	Stotfold
Feltham	2v3	Biggleswade Town
Ware	3v0	Bowers United
Southall	1v3	Royston Town
Amersham Town	0v0	Hoddesdon Town
r) Hoddesdon Town	4v0	Amersham Town
Tring Town	2v4	Wingate & Finchley
Barkingside	2v1	Harefield United
Horsham	3v0	Crockenhill
Dartford	1v3	Furness
Ash United	0v6	Shoreham
West Wickham	2v0	Eastbourne United
Lancing	2v3	Corinthian
Windsor & Eton	2v2	Folkestone Invicta
r) Folkestone Invicta	4v5	Windsor & Eton
Ramsgate	1v2	Hassocks
Pagham	4v3	Arundel
Thamesmead Town	1v0	Chipstead
Ringmer	2v3	Whitstable Town
Worthing United	1v4	Littlehampton Town
Chichester City	1v0	Canterbury City
Herne Bay	1v0	Cray Wanderers
Slade Green	5v1	Leatherhead
Cove	0v2	Wick
Chatham Town	5v2	Camberley Town

Godalming & Guildford	1v0	Three Bridges
Horsham YMCA	0v0	Faversham Town
r) Faversham Town	3v4	Horsham YMCA
Croydon Athletic	0v0	Bracknell Town
r) Bracknell Town	4v3	Croydon Athletic
Hailsham Town	4v0	Portfield
Saltdean United	3v2	Corinthian-Casuals
Burgess Hill Town	3v1	Selsey
Cranleigh	3v1	Egham Town
Ashford T. (Middx)	2v1	Raynes Park Vale
Deal Town	2v1	Langney Sports
Netherene	3v1	Lewes
Bicester Town	1v1	Ryde
r) Ryde	3v1	Bicester Town
Totton AFC	2v1	Milton United
Gosport Borough	3v1	Calne Town
Lymington AFC	1v0	Carterton Town
Hungerford Town	3v1	Wantage Town
Swindon Supermarine	2v1	Thatcham Town
First Tower United	1v2	Bournemouth
Sandhurst Town	2v3	Peppard
Andover	3v1	Abingdon United
Petersfield Town	0v1	North Leigh
Westbury United	0v1	Bemerton Heath Harl.
Sherborne Town	3v1	Christchurch
St. Blazey	0v3	Chippenham Town
Endsleigh	0v1	Bridgwater Town
Minehead	0v1	Warminster Town
Almondsbury Town	1v2	Devizes Town
Chard Town	2v0	Dawlish Town
Shortwood United	3v1	Tuffley Rovers
Cirencester Town	1v0	Old Georgians
Backwell United	3v0	Bristol Manor Farm
Frome Town	1v2	Torpoint Athletic
Porthleven	0v0	Keynsham Town
r) Keynsham Town	4v2	Portleven
Bishop Sutton	2v2	Welton Rovers
r) Welton Rovers	0v1	Bishop Sutton
Newquay	0v3	Bridport
Brislington	0v2	Torrington
Truro City	6v2	Cadbury Heath
Odd Down	2v0	Glastonbury
Wellington Town	2v4	Liskeard Athletic
Harrow Hill	3v4	Bideford
Melksham Town	0v1	Saltash United

FIRST ROUND PROPER

Sat. 28th October

Home	Score	Away	Att
Flixton	3v0	Glossop North End	Att: 130
Crook Town	2v0*	Ashfield United	Att: 133
Oakham United	3v2	Washington	Att: 45
Eastwood Hanley	2v0	Shotton Comrades	Att: 82
Bedlington Terriers	4v0	Kidsgrove Athletic	Att: 110
Ponteland United	2v5*	Thackley	Att: 76
Hatfield Main	0v2	Selby Town	Att: 82
Esh Winning	2v5	Winterton Rangers	Att: 86
Easington Colliery	2v1*	Wythenshawe Amateur	Att: 58
Whickham	3v2	Marske United	Att: 50
Newcastle Town	3v1	Burscough	Att: 119
Ashington	0v3	North Ferriby United	Att: 152
Brigg Town	2v1	Stocksbridge Park Steels	Att: 79
Oldham Town	6v1	Annfield Plain	Att:
Ossett Town	7v3	Willington	Att: 64
Yorkshire Amateur	2v0	Cheadle Town	Att: 40
Trafford	2v1	St Helens Town	Att: 74
Brandon United	0v2	Ossett Albion	Att: 46
Salford City	0v1	Nuthall	Att: 34
Clitheroe	5v1	Bootle	Att:
Nettleham	2v0	Nantwich Town	Att: 59
South Shields	1v6	Maine Road	Att: 192
Hinckley Athletic	3v2	Wellingborough T.	Att:
Pelsall Villa	3v1	Halesowen Harriers	Att: 104
Anstey Nomads	2v1	Oldbury United	Att: 115
Oadby Town	2v5*	Boldmere St Michaels	Att: 88
West Midlands Police	2v4*	Pershore Town	Att: 36
Bloxwich Town	1v0	St Andrews	Att: 64
Rushall Olympic	2v1	Cogenhoe United	Att:
Boston Town	2v6*	Shepshed Dynamo	Att: 109
Blakenall	1v4	Lye Town	Att: 84
Brackley Town	3v0	Banbury United	Att: 220
Barwell	1v1*	Dunkirk	Att: 43
Dunkirk	0v2	Barwell	
Hucknall Town	2v1*	Shifnal Town	Att:
Darlaston	1v1*	Walsall Wood	Att: 102
r) Walsall Wood	0v1	Darlaston	Att:
Willenhall Town	1v0	Long Buckby	Att: 87
Harlow Town	2v1	Barkingside	Att: 52
Wroxham	2v0	Lowestoft Town	Att: 131
Brightlingsea United	0v1	Newmarket Town	Att: 84
Clapton	1v2	Leighton Town	Att: 58
Edgware Town	4v1*	Wingate & Finchley	Att: 206
Northwood	3v0	Stotfold	Att: 114
St Neots Town	1v4	Tilbury	Att: 150
Harwich & Parkeston	2v0	Warboys Town	Att: 231
Sawbridgeworth Town	1v0	Concord Rangers	Att: 55
Chalfont St Peter	3v1	Maldon Town	Att: 88
Royston Town	1v2	Cheshunt	Att: 79
Hadleigh United	4v2	Mirrlees Blackstone	Att: 77
Bourne Town	0v1	Bedford Town	Att: 221
Langford	3v1	Hoddesdon Town	Att: 90
Wealdstone	0v3	Hampton	Att: 333
Wooton Blue Cross	2v2*	Flackwell Heath	Att: 64
r) Flackwell Heath	1v2	Wooton Blue Cross	Att: 68
Romford	2v4	Fakenham Town	Att: 241
Halstead Town	1v2*	Wisbech Town	Att: 401
Swaffham Town	2v3	Brentwood	Att: 158
Gorleston	4v0	Biggleswade Town	Att: 173
Collier Row	8v1	Clacton Town	Att: 114
Spalding United	1v3	Ely City	Att: 131
Ware	4v2	Basildon United	Att: 100
Stowmarket Town	2v2*	Woodbridge Town	Att: 209
r) Woodbridge Town	2v1	Stowmarket Town	Att: 295
Aveley	2v1	Hertford Town	Att: 97
Thamesmead Town	1v0	Ashford Town (Middx)	Att: 71
Slade Green	5v1	Saltdean United	Att: 95

Home	Score	Away	Att
Burgess Hill Town	2v1	Bournemouth	Att: 117
Shoreham	1v0	Gosport Borough	Att: 131
Lymington AFC	3v0	Croydon	Att: 147
Cranleigh	3v2	Peppard	Att: 102
Banstead Athletic	1v0	Chatham Town	Att: 63
Andover	1v4	Furness	Att: 203
Corinthian	2v1	Totton AFC	Att: 48
Whitehawk	5v1	Littlehampton Town	Att: 95
Whitstable Town	4v0	Ryde	Att: 210
Netherene	3v4*	Bracknell Town	Att: 50
Stamco	1v2	Godalming & Guildford	Att:
Chichester City	2v0	Deal Town	Att: 80
Horsham YMCA	1v3	Wick	Att: 94
Pagham	1v2	Windsor & Eton	Att: 135
Horsham	6v3	Hassocks	Att: 217
West Wickham	0v3	Herne Bay	Att: 96
Tunbridge Wells	1v6	Hungerford Town	Att: 155

Home	Score	Away	Att
Eastleigh	2v1	Hailsham Town	Att: 131
Peacehaven & Telscombe	4v0	North Leigh	Att: 187
Falmouth Town	3v0	Liskeard Athletic	Att:
Paulton Rovers	2v0	Shortwood United	Att: 167
Backwell United	1v2	Bridport	Att: 85
Mangotsfield United	3v0	Truro City	Att: 185
Swindon Supermarine	1v2	Keynsham Town	Att: 67
Bideford	2v1	Tiverton Town	Att: 465
Chard Town	2v1	Saltash United	Att:
Elmore	1v4	Chippenham Town	Att: 52
Devizes Town	0v3	Bemerton Heath H.	Att: 66
Torpoint Athletic	3v1	Odd Down	Att: 80
Warminster Town	3v2	Barnstaple Town	Att: 130
Wimborne Town	2v1	Old Georgians	Att: 185
Bridgwater Town	1v2	Bishop Sutton	Att: 197
Torrington	3v0	Sherborne Town	Att: 81

Keynsham Town's last minute winner in their FA Carlsberg Vase First Round match against Swindon Supermarine. Photo: David Brassington.

SECOND ROUND PROPER

18th November 1995

Bye: Hungerford Town

Home	Score	Away	Att
Guisborough Town	1v1*	Crook Town	107
r) Crook Town	1v2	Guisborough Town	140
Yorkshire Amateur	1v1*	West Auckland Town	57
r) West Auckland T.	2v1*	Yorkshire Amateur	
Winterton Rangers	1v0	Northallerton 1994	70
Brigg Town	3v0	Tow Law Town	128
Selby Town	3v2	Billingham Synthonia	158
Shildon	1v2*	Mossley	116
Hebburn	2v1	Ossett Albion	53
Chester-le-Street Town	5v1	Whickham	85
North Ferriby United	7v2	Oldham Town	107
Durham City	4v1	Whitby Town	254
Clitheroe	2v1	RTM Newcastle	170
Seaham Red Star	2v1	Peterlee Newtown	40
Dunston FB	2v0	Cammell Laird	96
Prudhoe Town	2v0	Goole Town	48
Easington Colliery	2v1	Ossett Town	31
Murton	2v1	Consett	46
Thackley	0v1*	Bedlington Terriers	80
Nettleham	1v4	Pershore Town	81
Anstey Nomads	4v1	Shepshed Dynamo	300
Armitage	0v2*	Rushall Olympic	77
Nuthall	1v3	Boldmere St Michaels	50
Oakham United	1v4	Lye Town	45
Raunds Town	2v2*	Hinckley Athletic	120
r) Hinckley Ath.	0v3	Raunds Town	355
Willenhall Town	3v1	Newcastle Town	107
Flixton	5v1	Hucknall Town	118
Belper Town	3v1	Bloxwich Town	250
Trafford	3v0	Darlaston	112
Maine Road	1v4	Eastwood Hanley	66
Pelsall Villa	2v4	Barwell	110
Northwood	2v1	Ely City	146

First half action from a leafy Llimah Park as Anstey Nomads (white shorts) attack the Shepshed defence. Photo: Martin Wray.

Home	Score	Away	Att
Hampton	5v2	Ware	Att: 128
Brackley Town	2v3	Aveley	Att: 100
Diss Town	2v0	Herne Bay	Att: 429
Burgess Hill T.	3v2*	Wooton B.C.	Att: 110
Collier Row	5v4*	Woodbridge T.	Att: 164
Cheshunt	2v3	Bedford Town	Att:
Wisbech Town	2v3	Wivenhoe Town	Att: 538
Slade Green	2v0	Newmarket Town	Att: 86
Arlesey Town	1v2	Thamesmead Town	Att: 477
Metropolitan Police	1v3	Canvey Island	Att:
Furness	0v0*	Sawbridgeworth Town	
r) Sawbridgeworth T.	1v1*	Furness	Att: 60
(2R) Sawbridgeworth T.	1v2	Furness	Att: 118
Harwich & Parkeston	2v3	Tilbury	Att: 192
Langford	0v1	Whitstable Town	Att: 155
Wroxham	1v2	Brentwood	Att: 115
Whitehawk	3v1	Corinthian	Att: 89
Burnham	0v4	Windsor & Eton	Att: 176
Gorleston	3v2	Fakenham Town	Att: 216

Home	Score	Away	Att
Peacehaven & Telscombe	2v0	Harlow Town	Att: 214
Hadleigh United	0v2	Edgware Town	Att: 104
Leighton Town	1v1*	Chalfont St. Peter	Att: 149
r) Chalfont St. P.	2v0	Leighton Town	Att: 85
Keynsham Town	0v1	Chard Town	Att: 129
Lymington AFC	2v0*	Warminster Town	Att: 170
Paulton Rovers	2v0	Bideford	Att: 182
Bridport	2v0*	Bemerton Heath H.	Att: 190
Horsham	0v2	Falmouth Town	Att: 302
Torpoint Athletic	1v0	Eastleigh	Att: 127
Shoreham	1v2*	Chichester City	Att: 83
Dorking	2v2*	Bishop Sutton	Att: 56
r) Bishop Sutton	2v0	Dorking	Att: 81
Godalming & Guildford	2v5	Mangotsfield United	Att: 215
Wimborne Town	1v2	Torrington	
Cranleigh	0v2	Banstead Athletic	
Wick	0v1	Chippenham Town	Att: 180
Taunton Town	3v3*	Bracknell Town	Att: 377
r) Bracknell Town	1v2	Taunton Town	Att: 103

Jayme Sporton of Chichester City splits the Thamesmead Town defence with this cracking shot during their 4th Round FA Vase match. Photo: Andrew Chitty.

THIRD ROUND PROPER

SATURDAY 9TH DECEMBER 1995

Home	Score	Away
Winterton Rangers	0v4 Att: 104	Flixton
Rushall Olympic	0v4 Att: 100	Bedlington Terriers
Brigg Town	2v0 Att: 82	Guisborough Town
Hebburn	0v4 Att: 65	Durham City
Seaham Red Star	1v2 Att: 130	Belper Town
Prudhoe Town	1v2 Att:	Dunston F. B.
North Ferriby United	4v2* Att: 109	Eastwood Hanley
Chester-le-Street Town	1v3 Att: 145	Lye Town
Easington Colliery	2v3* Att: 65	Anstey Nomads
Boldmere St. Michaels	0v2 Att: 83	Trafford
Barwell	3v1 Att: 130	Mossley
Murton	3v5*	Selby Town
Clitheroe	6v0 Att: 210	West Auckland Town
Thamesmead Town	3v1* Att: 71	Brentwood
Willenhall Town	2v1 Att: 122	Chalfont St Peter
Whitstable Town	0v1 Att: 295	Peacehaven & Telscombe
Tilbury	2v4 Att: 158	Aveley
Slade Green	0v2 Att: 298	Diss Town
Northwood	0v1 Att: 158	Gorleston
Wivenhoe Town	3v1 Att: 113	Edgware Town
Raunds Town	1v1 Att: 196	Furness
abandoned after 105 minutes due to frozen pitch.		
r Furness	1v1* Att:	Raunds Town
2r Furness (at Raunds Town FC)	2v5 Att: 210	Raunds Town
Canvey Island	2v0 Att: 511	Bedford Town
Hampton	0v1 Att: 242	Collier Row
Taunton Town	4v0 Att: 408	Chippenham Town
Bridport	2v4* Att: 205	Windsor & Eton
Lymington AFC	4v0 Att: 177	Bishop Sutton
Whitehawk	0v2 Att: 108	Banstead Athletic
Burgess Hill Town	2v1 Att: 195	Pershore Town
Torpoint Athletic	4v2 Att: 111	Chard Town

Simon Pearce of Whitehawk gets clear of the Banstead Athletic defence to power a header towards goal during their FA Carlsberg Vase Third Round match. Photo: Roger Turner.

Paulton Rovers	2 v 0 Att: 275	Falmouth Town	Hungerford Town	0 v 0* Att: 175	Mangotsfield United
Torrington	1 v 2 Att: 157	Chichester City	r Mangotsfield Utd.	5 v 1 Att: 186	Hungerford Town

Above: Ian Stevens of Cowes Sports (stripes) shielding the ball from Nicky Gaoter of Gosport Borough.
Photo: Roger Turner.

Below: Pagham's record goalscorer, Mark Vickers, gets behind the Windsor & Eton defence but his shot was saved.
Photo: Graham Cotterill.

FOURTH ROUND PROPER

SATURDAY 13TH JANUARY 1996

North Ferriby United	2v3* Att: 204	Anstey Nomads
Lye Town	0v2 Att: 310	Barwell
Clitheroe	3v0 Att: 451	Willenhall Town
Trafford	0v0* Att: 151	Selby Town
r Selby Town	1v1* Att: 320	Trafford
2r Selby Town	0v3 Att: 550	Trafford
Flixton	2v0 Att: 180	Dunston F. B.
Durham City	2v3 Att: 570	Belper Town
Brigg Town	2v1* Att: 169	Bedlington Terriers
Burgess Hill Town	0v1 Att: 365	Collier Row
Windsor & Eton	0v1* Att: 278	Peacehaven & Telscombe
Diss Town	1v2* Att: 682	Banstead Athletic
Chichester City	1v3 Att: 235	Thamesmead Town
Wivenhoe Town	4v0 Att: 301	Aveley
Canvey Island	1v0 Att: 604	Gorleston
Raunds Town	4v1 Att: 290	Taunton Town
Lymington AFC	1v3 Att: 331	Torpoint Athletic

Saturday 20th January 1996

Paulton Rovers	0v3 Att: 360	Mangotsfield United

Chichester City's Dave Kelly (black shorts) sees his route to goal blocked by the Thamesmead defence. Photo: Graham Cotterill.

Above: Burgess Hill 'keeper Phil Reid manages to collect the ball despite close attention from a Collier Row forward during the first half at Leyland Park.

Both photos: Martin Wray.

Below: Collier Row (white) attacking the Burgess Hill goal. Talk about a tight match!

FIFTH ROUND PROPER

SATURDAY 3RD FEBRUARY 1996

Home	Score	Away
Raunds Town	2 v 0	Torpoint Athletic
Hill 8, Hardy 85.	Att: 296	
Wivenhoe Town	2 v 2*	Mangotsfield United
Howe 113, Gray 118	Att: 543	Winstone 96, Bright 119.
r) Mangotsfield Utd	3 v 0	Wivenhoe Town
Thompson 46, Rowlins 65, Bright 89.	Att: 446	
Banstead Athletic	2 v 3	Peacehaven & Telscombe
Liddle 15, Quamina 79.	Att: 315	Thomsett 43, Newman 58, Ingleden 90.
Collier Row	6 v 0	Anstey Nomads
Rogan 6, Munday 34(p) 89, Carrick 80, Dalarto 85, Parish 90.	Att: 448	
Brigg Town	1 v 0	Trafford
Elston.	Att: 320	
Flixton	3 v 1	Barwell
Bartholomew 44, Jackson 75, Byrne 86.	Att: 328	????
Thamesmead Town	1 v 2	Canvey Island
Burns 34.	Att: 811	Jones 76, Britnell 89.
Belper Town	0 v 3	Clitheroe
	Att: 754	Butcher 10, Rouile 24, Taylor 87.

Canvey Island's Kevin Lee (white shorts) thwarts Thamesmead's Henson Waithe during their FA Carlsberg Vase Fifth Round match. Photo: Keith Gillard.

Peacehaven striker Adie Chipper (stripes) is well outnumbered by Banstead defenders while 'keeper Hudson looks unconcerned. Photo: Mike Barry.

SIXTH ROUND PROPER

SATURDAY 24TH FEBRUARY 1996

Brigg Town 2v0 Collier Row
Stead 42, 88 Att: 566

Mangotsfield Utd 2v2* Raunds Town
Ewens 48(p), Bright 63. Att: 725 Hill 25, 87(p).

Clitheroe 1v0 Peacehaven & Telscombe
Westwell 58(p). Att: 850

Flixton 3v0 Canvey Island
Byrne 60, 62, Hall 75. Att: 860

SATURDAY 2ND MARCH

r) Raunds Town 0v1 Mangotsfield Utd
Att: 1200 Perrett 89.

Flixton's Neil Hall just fails to get his cross over during his side's 3-0 win against Canvey Island in the FA Carlsberg Vase Quarter Final. Photo: Colin Stevens.

A flying header from Raund's Shaun Keeble (No. 9) worries the Mangotsfield defence during their Quarter Final replay. Photo: Peter Barnes.

SEMI-FINAL

SATURDAY 16TH MARCH 1996

Brigg Town	0 v 0 Att: 1128	Flixton
Mangotsfield Utd. Thompson 44.	1 v 0 Att: 837	Clitheroe

SATURDAY 23RD MARCH 1996

Flixton	0 v 1 Att: 1540	Brigg Town Flounders 29.
Clitheroe Taylor 12, Butcher 115.	2 v 1* Att: 2000	Mangotsfield Utd.

The F.A. Carlsberg Vase seems to be encouraging more sophisticated football these days, or maybe the managers are using their heads more than their hearts when preparing their tactics. Whatever it is, many of the games played at the latter stages of this year's competition have been controlled, well planned affairs with little given away and all the clubs hoping to take advantage of the occasionally mistakes by the opposition. This is all very well but where has all the blood and thunder of traditional cup tie football gone?

I suspect the refereeing this season will have had something to do with it, as so many bookings are handed out for slightly mistimed tackles. Caution is now the key to winning. There is also a firm belief that playing away, against the home side which is expected to attack, offers chances on the break. So the home side doesn't attack so much either!

Certainly this season's first leg semi-finals followed that pattern. At Bristol the high scoring Mangotsfield side looked very inhibited. They set their stall out in the first minute with a very hard tackle by Minall on the Clitheroe star mid fielder Andy Rouine, who later showed why he had won the North West Counties Player of the Year last year and probably why he got 'the treatment' early on! Clitheroe in fact did start in lively fashion and their very small side certainly adapted better to the sticky conditions than the more powerful home side.

It appeared to be a case of both mid-fields cancelling each other out and few chances being set up. The powerful Rawlings brought a good save from Carlo Nash and at the other end centre backs Ewens and Thompson cleared some tricky free kicks. It looked like a goalless first half but the hard working Simon Winstone, who must have covered every inch of his right flank, sent over a perfect cross to the edge of the six yard area, where centre half Richard Thompson headed firmly home. It was a goal you would expect from a Football League centre forward and was a timely reminder of his days with Torquay United.

The second half was certainly more lively than the first period and both goalkeepers showed steady, clean handling under pressure. The game flowed from end to end and Thompson did clear off the line but there were no further scares as Clitheroe seemed content with a one goal deficit and, as the Mangotsfield manager Terry Rowles admitted afterwards, this was Mangotsfield's worst display so far and they would need to do a lot better in the second meeting.

Sadly for the West Country they couldn't manage to lift their game sufficiently although they certainly can count themselves unlucky not to have forced a replay. A tentative start by both sides didn't produce any attacks of note but after twelve minutes Andy Taylor, in his third season with the club, headed down and out of reach of the desperate Matthews and the sides were level. This seemed to settle the visitors and they created the better chances before half time. As in the first game Clitheroe's only six footer, Carlo Nash, was outstanding and it was his sound goalkeeping throughout that gave the home side the chance to stay in the game. In particular, two great saves from Matthew Rawlings inspired his team and must have given the visitors that dreaded feeling it just might not be their day!

The winning goal which took Clitheroe to Wembley will be added to the Vase folklore as it was a personal tragedy for Mangotsfield's captain who had played well in both games. He desperately lunged for a cross from Clitheroe's Gary Butcher and the ball ended up in the net. If he hadn't intercepted the cross it would have reached a waiting forward on the far post. It was a wholehearted effort by a committed player which ended in tragedy! The score was now 2-1 and time had run out for 'The Field'.

Congratulations go to Clitheroe who should have a lovely experience at Wembley, but poor Mangotsfield had a sad journey back to the West Country counting the costs of not making more of their home tie. They were very upset but Terry Rowles lifted them on the coach as he stressed how proud they should all be of their achievements since the side came together at

Action from the first leg between Mangotsfield and Clitheroe.

the beginning of the season. They are a very progressive club who will surely by moving up the pyramid very soon, and who knows? They could be enjoying some more cup excitement on the way.

The thought of two North West Counties teams reaching Wembley may have been an inspiration to all involved with that very well respected competition. And after the first legs it looked very much on the cards, as both their sides had returned home with creditable away performances. But what about the attendance at Wembley, and how about some North v West or East v West rivalry to spice up the final? We heard many such questions during the week leading up to the second legs and both ties certainly produced some drama before the North East v North West Wembley battle was confirmed.

The first leg when Brigg Town faced Flixton was another careful encounter with no chances being taken and both sides hoping to start the second meeting on equal terms. A dour first half at least got rid of the semi-final nerves and Brigg had to sort out the loss of influencial central defender Neill Buckley who suffered a badly twisted ankle after an awkward fall. If anything, 'The Zebras' were being caught in posssession playing their way out of trouble in their own half and Flixton did worry the home side just before half time.

However, with a half time pep talk still fresh, Brigg came out with a vengance and certainly bombarded Stephan Roberts and the Flixton rearguard with a succession of high balls into the penalty area. The keeper, who had played for Altrincham and Winsford previously, held firm and only once late in the game did he look in trouble. A shot-cum-lob from Graham Thompson, way out on the touch line, appeared to be dipping in just under the crossbar, until a scrambling Roberts just managed to flip it over the crossbar. Flixton kept the pressure on and from the second consecutive corner Mark Graves just failed to hit the target with a fierce shot. And so to Manchester where the battle was to be fought to a conclusion.

The Flixton side is full of well known players from the hot bed of football that is the North West. Many had experienced life with Conference clubs but for most of them this was the biggest game of their lives and

Early Flixton pressure as Bartholomew takes on the 'Zebras' defence in the opening moments of this FA Carlsberg Vase Semi Final. Photo: Martin Wray.

understandably it showed in the first half, when the expectations of the home supporters got through to the players. The Zebras from Brigg, however, felt a little less pressurised being away from home and they had in Andy Flounders a very experienced goalscorer. Nearly 200 Football League goals at a ratio better than one in two is certainly impressive. And it was the Zebras' top scorer who rose to the occasion after 30 minutes to score what probably was to turn out to be his club's most important goal ever. It was a delightful chip from the edge of the penalty area into the top corner of the net and it certainly takes Brigg to Wembley for a day the town will always remember. But there were plenty of heartstopping moments before the final whistle.

There was a frightening stoppage for seventeen minutes while Mark Elston had to be revived after swallowing his tongue following a clash of heads. The central defender had to go to hospital but was allowed home later. Inspired defending, especially by goalkeeper Rob Gawthorpe, kept Flixton at bay as they threw everything and everybody forward to get that vital equalizer. The tie enjoyed its best moments in a thrilling finish and full marks to the sporting Flixton club officials and players who accepted defeat so sportingly and wished the Zebras good luck at Wembley. John Mitchell, their Chairman, was thrilled with his team's efforts to get so far and hoped this would inspire them to achieve their ambition - promotion to the Unibond league.

At a regional meeting of the 'Team Talk Team' recently, a prospective member mentioned he had visited Brigg Town's very friendly club last month after a days work in the area and can't remember much about leaving! Sounds as if they deserve a Wembley trip but I wonder if they have finished celebrating yet?

The two communities, Clitheroe very close to Blackburn and Burnley and Brigg over the other side of the country near to Scunthorpe, will be enjoying a tremendous build up of excitement as the ladies prepare their Wembley outfits, the local media look for interviews, features, and photos and the poor managers try to cope with 'pre-Wembley football tension' when players want to avoid injury but games have to be won. Brigg Town's Ralph Clayton is a real character and he is helped by the old West Bromwich Albion and Scunthorpe United star John Kaye (incidentally, did John name the Brigg Town ground?), while Gary Butcher is the player manager at Clitheroe who shares the team responsibilities with Denis Underwood. They will have a tricky seven weeks in which to keep everyone happy and then they have got to pick their Wembley squads!

Clitheroe's managers, players and officials at Ewood Park where they were the guests of Blackburn Rovers.

Where it all began - the draw for the 1st Round being made at Carlsberg head office.

F.A. CARLSBERG VASE

FINAL

BRIGG TOWN 3 v O CLITHEROE

Carl Stead 37, 64; Simon Roach 87.

SUNDAY 12th MAY 1996

Brigg Town	Clitheroe
1 Rob Gawthorpe	1 Carlo Nash
2 Graham Thompson	2 Steve Lampkin
3 Steve Rogers	3 Neil Rowbotham
4 Mark Greaves	4 Neil Baron
5 Neil Buckley	5 Simon Westwell
6 Mark Elston	6 Andy Rovine
7 Carl Stead	7 Gary Butcher *
8 Dave McLean	8 Andrew Taylor
9 Nathan Stead	9 Chris Grimshaw
10 Andy Flounders	10 Andy Darbyshire
11 Simon Roach	11 Dennis Hill

Brigg Town Substitutes

David Mail
for Buckley, 19 minutes

Steve Clay
for Greaves, 84 minutes

Gavin McNally
for N Stead, 90 minutes

MANAGER
Ralph Clayton

Clitheroe Substitutes

Neil Otley
for Rowbotham, 73 minutes

Clive Dunn
for Hill, 60 minutes

Geoff Smith
for Taylor, 73 minutes

MANAGER
Denis Underwood
*Gary Butcher (Player/Manager)

Referee:

Stephen J Lodge
(Sheffield & Hallamshire FA)

Linesmen:

John P Devine (Red)
(North Riding FA)

Matthew D Messias (Yellow)
(North Riding FA)

ATTENDANCE
7340

The clubs were nicely balanced - Clitheroe, another North West club to give the area a tremendous Wembley year, as Macclesfield Town and Northwich Victoria were to follow in the Trophy final, faced Brigg Town breaking up the monopoly coming from the Northern Counties East.

The physically small side (only the excellent goalkeeper Carlo Nash was six foot) from The North West Counties League had reached Wembley by keeping the ball on the ground and using the width of the field with an attractive passing game. While Brigg were built around a big, strong defence, the determination of skipper Dave McLean and some inspirational flashes from the Stead boys, Nathan and Carl.

Right from the first whistle the two very different styles produced a fascinating battle. Clitheroe broke the Brigg off-side trap just twice in the first half and on the first occasion it was only a tremendous interception by Neil Buckley that saved the day. Then Andy Darbyshire bravely reached a through ball down the right just a fraction before the onrushing keeper Rob Gawthorpe. His shot from 30 yards was pulled across an empty net as he felt the full weight of a collision with keeper and defender who had done enough to prevent a calmer finish. This was a crucial moment as it kept the scores equal, poor Darbyshire was badly shaken and the Brigg defence became more and more confident. Sadly, Buckley, who had started the game brightly but was carrying an old injury, had to come off and was replaced by the vastly experienced David Mail. Not long after this Nathan Stead crashed in Brigg's first shot and one sensed Clitheroe may have missed their chance to take an important grip on the game.

Brigg's confidence was growing and their physical strength was beginning to tell, so it wasn't a surprise when, after a clearance from a corner, Carl Stead, showing similar skills to those raved about when Cantona had volleyed home in the Cup Final, breasted down a clearance and hammered home a glorious drive.

To their credit, Clitheroe stepped up the pace and continued to play good football but Brigg's extra power looked omminous. The experience and aerial skill of Andy Flounders was helping to keep the pressure on and half time came with

Clitheroe defending desperately and the best move of the match so far finishing with another fierce shot just wide.

Straight after half time David Mail had his header from a corner headed off the line by Steve Lampkin but all the time Gary Butcher, Clitheroe's player manager, was at the heart of most of his side's moves and if an equaliser was going to come you felt it would be from his inspiration.

Unfortunately the second goal came after more pressure had been put on the Clitheroe defence and the referee was perfectly placed to give what looked to those of us in the stand a rather harsh penalty. The confident Carl Stead stepped up to score with ease and Clitheroe's hopes were disappearing. Frustration showed as they battled to get back in the game. No one could be faulted for lack of determination, but the Lanacashire club had never really looked dangerous after that early period. Dennis Hill did have a good effort and Chris Grimshaw worked tirelessly but the longer the game went on the stronger the grip Brigg took on preceedings.

The third goal was a gem. A delightful piece of skill took Nathen Stead past two defenders and a sweet curling pass put the very skilfull Simon Roach away on another fine run. He cut inside to hammer a cross-cum-shot across goal and poor Steve Lampkin deflected the ball well out of his goalkeepers reach. The move had deserved to score anyway but the deflection was the last straw for Clitheroe. They had fought to the end, and had they taken an early lead, who knows what might have happened?

As it was the Brigg Town management could probably not have wished for a more complete performance. They had played fixtures at the rate of nearly one every other day during the seven weeks since the semi-final. They were carrying injuries and hadn't been able to field their first team very often. The Zebras looked a very good side and it was easy to understand why they only conceded two goals in ten Vase ties. Their back four were outstanding and it's difficult to remember Graham Thompson making a mistake. The driving force was the experienced skipper Dave McLean and all the attacking players showed their skills during a fine team effort. Managers Ralph Clayton and Tony Kaye must be very proud indeed and, when some highly paid southern Vase contenders consider the attendances and general funds of clubs like Brigg Town, it must make them wonder how such talent and attitude can be collected in one small club for so little.

Although the attendance was never going to be one of the biggest as neither of the northern clubs commanded great support, the oficial 'gate'of 7,340 was still larger than three of the very important play-off matches contested on the same day!

Finally a word of praise to Carlsberg who turned out to be wonderful sponsors. They showed a real interest in the competition right from the qualifying rounds, the draws, the man of the match awards, the build up to the semi-finals and the presentation of the Final. In and outside the stadium the Carlsberg presence was prominent but attractively displayed, they looked after the press, and their guests and even the P.A. announcer was enthusiastic! In the evening a wonderful night was had by all at a black tie West End dinner celebration for both Vase Finalists and the two Carlsberg Pub Cup teams. This is what sponsorship is all about and there is no doubt that the company covered themselves with glory and made a lot of new friends and 'probably' new Carlsberg Lager drinkers!

T.W.

PAST F.A. VASE FINALS

1975 Att: 9,500 **HODDESDON TOWN 2** v **1 EPSOM & EWELL** Ref: Mr R Toseland

Hoddesdon (Scorers: Sedgwick 2.)
Galvin, Green, Hickey, Maybury, Stevenson, Wilson, Bishop, Picking, Sedgwick, Nathan, Schofield.

Epsom & Ewell (Scorer: Wales)
Page, Bennett, Webb, Wales, Worby, Jones, O'Connell, Walker, Tuite, Eales, Lee.

1976 Att: 11,848 **BILLERICAY TOWN 1** v **0 STAMFORD** (aet) Ref: Mr A Robinson

Billericay (Scorer: Aslett)
Griffiths, Payne, Foreman, Pullin, Bone, Coughlan, Geddes, Aslett, Clayden, Scott, Smith.

Stamford
Johnson, Kwiatowski, Marchant, Crawford, Downs, Hird, Barnes, Walpole, Smith, Russell, Broadbent.

1977 Att: 14,000 **BILLERICAY TOWN 1** v **1 SHEFFIELD** aet Ref: Mr J Worrall

Billericay (Scorer: Clayden)
Griffiths, Payne, Bone, Coughlan, Pullin, Scott, Wakefield, Aslett, Clayden, Woodhouse, McQueen. Sub: Whettell.

Sheffield (Scorer: Coughlan og)
Wing, Gilbody, Lodge, Hardisty, Watts, Skelton, Kay, Travis, Pugh, Thornhill, Haynes. Sub: Strutt.

Replay Att: 3,482 **BILLERICAY TOWN 2** v **1 SHEFFIELD** at Nottingham Forest

Billericay (Scorers: Aslett, Woodhouse)
Griffiths, Payne, Pullin, Whettell, Bone, McQueen, Woodhouse, Aslett, Clayden, Scott, Wakefield.

Sheffield (Scorer: Thornhill)
Wing, Gilbody, Lodge, Strutt, Watts, Skelton, Kay, Travis, Pugh, Thornhill, Haynes.

1978 Att: 16,858 **NEWCASTLE BLUE STAR 2** v **1 BARTON ROVERS** Ref: Mr T Morris

Newcastle (Scorers: Dunn, Crumplin)
Halbert, Feenan, Thompson, Davidson, S Dixon, Beynon, Storey, P Dixon, Crumplin, Callaghan, Dunn. Sub: Diamond.

Barton Rovers (Scorer: Smith)
Blackwell, Stephens, Crossley, Evans, Harris, Dollimore, Dunn, Harnaman, Fossey, Turner, Smith. Sub: Cox.

1979 Att: 17,500 **BILLERICAY TOWN 4** v **1 ALMONDSBURY GREENWAY** Ref: Mr C Steel

Billericay (Scorers: Young 3, Clayden.)
Norris, Blacka;;er, Bingham, Whettell, Bone, Reeves, Pullin, Scott, Clayden, Young, Groom. Sub: Carrigan.

Almondsbury (Scorer: Price)
Hamilton, Bowers, Scarrett, Sulllivan, Tudor, Wookey, Bowers, Shehean, Kerr, Butt, Price. Sub: Kilbaine.

1980 Att: 11,500 **STAMFORD 2** v **0 GUISBOROUGH TOWN** Ref: Neil Midgeley

Stamford (Scorers: Alexander, McGowan.)
Johnson, Kwiatkowski, Ladd, McGowan, Bliszczak I, Mackin, Broadhurst, Hall, Czarnecki, Potter, Alexander. Sub: Bliszczak S.

Guisborough
Cutter, Scott, Thornton, Angus, Maltby, Percy, Skelton, Coleman, McElvaney, Sills, Dilworth. Sub: Harrison.

1981 Att: 12,000 **WHICKHAM 3** v **2 WILLENHALL** aet Ref: Mr R Lewis

Whickham (Scorers: Scott, Williamson, Peck og)
Thompson, Scott, Knox, Williamson, Cook, Ward, Carroll, Diamond, Cawthra, Robertson, Turnbull. Sub: Alton.

Willenhall (Scorers: Smith, Stringer)
Newton, White, Darris, Woodall, Heath, Fox, Peck, Price, Matthews, Smith, Stringer. Sub: Trevor.

1982 Att: 12,500 **FOREST GREEN ROVERS 3** v **0 RAINWORTH M.W.** Ref: Mr K Walmsey

Forest Green (Scorers: Leitch 2, Norman.)
Moss, Norman, Day, Turner, Higgins, Jenkins, Guest, Burns, Millard, Leitch, Doughty. Sub: Dangerfield.

Rainworth M.W.
Watson, Hallam, Hodgson, Slater, Sterland, Oliver, Knowles, Raine, Radzi, Reah, Cornerfield. Sub: Robinson.

1983 Att: 13,700 **V.S. RUGBY 1** v **0 HALESOWEN TOWN** Ref: Mr B Daniels

VS Rugby (Scorer: Crawley)
Burton, McGinty, Harrison, Preston, Knox, Evans, ingram, Setchell, Owen, Beecham, Crawley. Sub: Haskins.

Halesowen Town
Coldicott, Penn, Edmonds, Lacey, Randall, Shilvock, Hazelwood, Moss, Woodhouse, P Joinson, L Joinson. Sub: Smith

1984 (Att: 8,125) **STANSTED 3** v **2 STAMFORD** Ref: Mr T Bune

Stanstead (Scorers: Holt, Gillard, Reading.)
Coe, Williams, Hilton, Simpson, Cooper, Reading, Callanan, Holt, Reevs, Doyle, Gillard. Sub: Williams.

Stamford (Scorers: Waddicore, Allen.)
Parslow, Smitheringate, Blades, McIlwain, Lyon, Mackin, Genovese, Waddicore, Allen, Robson, Beech. Sub: Chapman.

1985 (Att: 16,715 **HALESOWEN TOWN 3** v **1 FLEETWOOD TOWN** Ref: Mr C Downey

Halesowen (Scorers: Moss 2, L Joinson)
Pemberton, Moore, Lacey, Randle (Rhodes), Sherwood, Heath, Penn, Woodhouse, P Joinson, L Joinson, Moss.

Southall
MacKenzie, James, McGovern, Croad, Holland, Powell (Richmond), Pierre, Richardson, Sweales, Ferdinand, Rowe.

1986 (Att: 18,340) **HALESOWEN TOWN 3** v **0 SOUTHALL** Ref: Mr D Scott

Halesowen (Scorers: Moss 2, L Joinson.)
Pemberton, Moore, Lacey, Randle (Rhodes), Sherwood, Heath, Penn, Woodhouse, P Joinson, L Joinson, Moss.

Southall
Mackenzie, James, McGovern, Croad, Holland, Powell (Richmond), Pierre, Richardson, Sweales, Ferdinand, Rowe.

1987 (Att: 4,254) **ST. HELENS 3** v **2 WARRINGTON TOWN** Ref: Mr T Mills

St Helens (Scorers: Layhe 2, Rigby.)
Johnson, Benson, Lowe, Bendon, Wilson, McComb, Collins (Gledhill), O'Neill, Cummins, Lay, Rigby. Sub: Deakin.

Warrington (Scorers: Reid, Cook.)
O'Brien. Copeland, Hunter, Gratton, Whalley, Reid, Brownville (Woodyer), Cook, Kinsey, Looker (Hill), Hughes.

1988 (Att: 15,000) **COLNE DYNAMOES 1** v **0 EMLEY** Ref: Mr A Seville

Colne Dynamoes (Scorer: Anderson)
Mason, McFafyen, Westwell, Bentley, Dunn, Roscoe, Rodaway, Whitehead (Burke), Diamond, Anderson, Wood (Coates).

Emley
Dennis, Fielding, Mellor, Codd, Hirst (Burrows), Gartland (Cook), Carmody, Green, Bramald, Devine, Francis.

1989 (Att: 26,487) **TAMWORTH 1** v **1 SUDBURY TOWN** aet Ref: Mr C Downey

Tamworth (Scorer: Devaney)
Bedford, Lockett, Atkins, Cartwright, McCormack, Myers, Finn, Devaney, Moores, Gordon, Stanton. Subs: Rathbone, Heaton.

Sudbury Town (Scorer: Hubbick)
Garnham, Henry, G Barker, Boyland, Thorpe, Klug, D Barker, Barton, Oldfield, Smith, Hubbick. Subs: Money, Hunt.

Replay (Att: 11,201) **TAMWORTH 3** v **0 SUDBURY TOWN** at Peterborough

Tamworth (Scorers: Stanton 2, Moores.)
Bedford, Lockett, Atkins, Cartwright, Finn, Myers, George, Devaney, Moores, Gordon, Stanton. Sub: Heaton.

Sudbury Town
Garnham, Henry, G Barker, Boyland, Thorpe, Klug, D Barker, Barton, Oldfield, Smith, Hubbick. Subs: Money, Hunt.

1990 (Att: 7,932) **YEADING 0** v **0 BRIDLINGTON TOWN** aet Ref: Mr R Groves

Yeading
Mackenzie, Wickens, Turner, Whiskey (McCarthy), Croad, Denton, Matthews, James (Charles), Sweates, Impey, Cordery.

Bridlington
Taylor, Pugh, Freeman, McNeill, Warburton, Brentano, Wilkes (Hall), Noteman, Gauden, Whiteman, Brattan (Brown).

Replay (Att: 5,000) **YEADING 1** v **0 BRIDLINGTON TOWN** at Leeds Utd FC

Yeading (Scorer: Sweales)
Mackenzie, Wickens, Turner, Whiskey, Croad (McCarthy), Schwartz, Matthews, James, Sweates, Impey (Welsh), Cordery.

Bridlington
Taylor, Pugh, Freeman, McNeill, Warburton, Brentano, Wilkes (Brown), Noteman, Gauden (Downing), Whiteman, Brattan.

1991 (Att: 11,314) **GRESLEY ROVERS 4** v **4 GUISELEY** aet Ref: Mr C Trussell

Gresley (Scorers: Rathbone, Smith 2, Stokes.)
Aston, Barry, Elliott (Adcock), Denby, Land, Astley, Stokes, K Smith, Acklam, Rathbone, Lovell (Weston).

Guiseley (Scorers: Tennison 2, Walling, A Roberts.)
Maxted, Bottomley, Hogarth, Tetley, Morgan, McKenzie, Atkinson (Annan), Tennison, Walling, A Roberts, B Roberts.

Replay (Att: 7,585) **GUISELEY 3** v **1 GRESLEY ROVERS** at Bramall Lane

Guiseley (Scorers: Tennison, Walling, Atkinson.)
Maxted, Annan, Hogarth, Tetley, Morgan, McKenzie (Bottomley), Atkinson, Tennison (Noteman), Walling, A Roberts, B Roberts.

Gresley (Scorer: Astley.)
Aston, Barry, Elliott, Denby, Land, Astley, Stokes (Weston), K Smith, Acklam, Rathbone, Lovell (Adcock).

1992 (Att: 10,772) **WIMBORNE TOWN 5** v **3 GUISELEY** Ref: Mr M J Bodenham

Wimborne (Scorers: Richardson, Sturgess 2, Killick 2.)
Leonard, Langdown, Wilkins, Beacham, Allan, Taplin, Ames, Richardson, Bridle, Killick, Sturgess (Lovell), Lynn.

Guiseley (Scorers: Noteman 2, Colville.)
Maxted, Atkinson, Hogarth, Tetley (Wilson), Morgan, Brockie, A Roberts, Tennison, Noteman (Colville), Annan, W Roberts.

1993 (Att: 9,061) **BRIDLINGTON TOWN 1** v **0 TIVERTON TOWN** Ref: Mr R A Hart

Bridlington Town (Scorer: Radford.)
Taylor, Brentano, McKenzie, Harvey, Bottomley, Woodcock, Grocock, A Roberts, Jones, Radford (Tyrell), Parkinson. Sub: Swailes.

Tiverton Town
Nott, J Smith, N Saunders, M Saunders, Short (Scott), Steele, Annunziata, K Smith, Everett, Daly, Hynds (Rogers).

1994 (Att: 13,450) **DISS TOWN 2** v **1 TAUNTON TOWN** Ref: Mr K. Morton

Diss Town (Scorers: Gibbs (p), Mendham.)
Woodcock, Carter, Wolsey (Musgrave), Casey (Bugg), Hartle, Smith, Barth, Mendham, Miles, Warne, Gibbs.

Taunton Town (Scorer: Fowler)
Maloy, Morris, Walsh, Ewens, Graddon, Palfrey, West (Hendry), Fowler, Durham, Perrett (Ward), Jarvis.

1995 Att: 13,670 **ARLESEY TOWN 2** v **1 OXFORD CITY** Ref: Mr G S Willard

Arlesey (Scorers: Palma, Gyalog.)
Young, Cardines, Bambrick, Palma (Ward), Hull, Gonsalves, Gyalog, Cox, Kane, O'Keefe, Marshall (Nicholls). Sub: Dodwell.

Oxford (Scorer: S Fontaine)
Fleet, Brown (Fisher), Hume, Shepherd, Muttock, Hamilton (Kemp), Thomas, Spittle, Sherwood, S Fontaine, C Fontaine. Sub: Torres.

F.A. CARLSBERG VASE - AT A GLANCE

3RD ROUND

Brigg Town 2
Guisborough 0

Rushall O. 0
Bedlington T. 4

Boldmere S M 0
Trafford 2

Murton 3
Selby T. 5*

Burgess H. T. 2
Pershore T. 1

Hampton 0
Collier Row 1

N Ferriby U. 4
Eastwood H. 2*

Easington C. 2
Anstey N. 3*

Winterton R. 0
Flixton 4

Prudhoe T. 1
Dunston F.B. 2

Chester-le-St. T 1
Lye Town 3

Barwell 3
Mossley 1

Torrington 1
Chichester C. 2

Thamesmead T. 3
Brentwood 1*

Canvey Is. 2
Bedford T. 0

Northwood 0
Gorleston 1

Wivenhoe T. 3
Edgware T. 1

Tilbury 2
Aveley 4

Paulton R. 2
Falmouth T. 0

Hungerford T 0* 1
Mang'field T 0* 5

Raunds T. 1 1* 5
Furness 1 1* 2

Taunton Town 4
Chippenham 0

Lymington AFC 4
Bishop Sutton 0

Torpoint Ath. 4
Chard Town 2

Hebburn 0
Durham City 4

Seaham R S 1
Belper Town 2

Clitheroe 6
W Auckland T 0

Willenhall T. 2
Chalfont S P 1

Slade Green 0
Diss Town 2

Whitehawk 0
Banstead Ath. 2

Bridport 2*
Windsor & E. 4

Whitsable T. 0
Peacehaven & T 1

4th ROUND

Brigg Town 2
Bedlington T. 1*

Trafford 0 1 0
Selby T. 0 1 3

Burgess H. T. 0
Collier Row 1

N Ferriby U 2
Anstey N. 3*

Flixton 2
Dunston FB 0

Lye Town 0
Barwell 2

Chichester C. 1
Thamesmead T. 3

Canvey Is. 1
Gorleston 0

Wivenhoe T. 4
Aveley 0

Paulton R. 0
Mang'field U. 3

Raunds Town 4
Taunton Town 1

Lymington 1
Torpoint Ath 3

Durham City 2
Belper Town 3

Clitheroe 3
Willenhall T. 0

Diss Town 1
Banstead Ath. 2*

Windsor & E. 0
Peacehaven & T. 1*

5th ROUND

Brigg Town 1
Trafford 0

Collier Row 6
Anstey N. 0

Flixton 3
Barwell 1

Thamesmead T. 1
Canvey Is. 2

Wivenhoe Town 2 0
Mangotsfield U. 2 3

Raunds Town 2
Torpoint Ath. 0

Belper Town 0
Clitheroe 3

Banstead Ath. 2
Peacehaven & T. 3

6th ROUND

Brigg Town 2
Collier Row 0

Flixton 3
Canvey I. 0

Mangotsfield U 2 1
Raunds Town 2 0

Clitheroe 1
Peacehaven & T. 0

SEMI-FINAL

Brigg Town 0 1
Flixton 0 0

Mangotsfield U.1 0
Clitheroe 0 2

FINAL

2nd Qual. Round - Brigg Town 9 Rossendale 0
1st Round - Brigg Town 2 Stocksbridge P.S.
2nd Round - Brigg Town 3 Tow Law Town 0

BRIGG TOWN 3

2nd Qual. Round - Clitheroe 4 Immingham Town 0
1st Round - Clitheroe 5 Bootle 1
2nd Round - Clitheroe 2 RTM Newcastle 1

CLITHEROE 0

Special Vase Moments

Above:
Carl Stead and Simon Roach, Brigg's scorers, with the Vase.
Photo: Alan Coomes

Opposite:
Brigg's driving force and skipper Dave McLean celebrates with the trophy.
Photo: Graham Cotteril

Below:
A tribute to Dunblane, a minute's silence before the kick-off in the semi-final between Brigg Town and Flixton.
Photo: Martin Wray.

F.A. YOUTH CUP 1995-96

EXTRA PRELIMINARY ROUND

	Home	Score	Away
	Guisborough Town	0 v 2	Hartlepool United
	Shotton Comrades	0 v 3	Carlisle United
	Marine	0 v 0	Rochdale
(R)	Rochdale	0 v 1	Marine
	Stalybridge Celtic	0 v 4	Southport
	Leigh RMI	0 v 9	Huddersfield Town
	Stockport County	3 v 0	Chorley
	Hinckley Athletic	2 v 1	Chesterfield
	Hinckley Town	v	Mansfield Town
	W/O for Mansfield Town - Hinckley Town withdrawn		
	Bilston Town	1 v 1	Lye Town
(R)	Lye Town	1 v 2	Bilston Town
	Brierley Hill Town	4 v 1	Pelsall Villa
	Rushden & Diamonds	1 v 1	Raunds Town
(R)	Raunds Town	1 v 5	Rushden & Diamonds
	Saffron Walden Town	v	Bury Town
	W/O for Bury Town - Saffron Walden T. withdrawn		
	Wivenhoe Town	10 v 0	March Town United
	Potters Bar Town	2 v 1	Berkhamsted Town
	St Albans City	4 v 3	Bedford Town
	Southend Manor	1 v 1	Collier Row
(R)	Collier Row	4 v 2	Southend Manor *
	Brook House	5 v 1	Clapton
	hayes	0 v 1	Enfield
	Staines Town	4 v 1	Newport Pagnell Town
	Hillingdon Borough	7 v 1	Hampton
	Tonbridge	4 v 0	Faversham Town
	Ashford Town	0 v 3	Thamesmead Town
	Tooting & Mitcham Utd.	3 v 1	Stamco
	Whitehawk	1 v 2	Bromley
	Horsham YMCA	1 v 2	Crawley Town
	Oakwood	4 v 2	Lewes
	Wokingham Town	0 v 1	Woking
	Walton & Hersham	6 v 1	Chipstead
	Romsey Town	3 v 2	Camberley Town
	Havant Town	0 v 2	Bognor Regis Town
	Abingdon Town	3 v 0	Aldershot Town
	Maidenhead United	5 v 0	Flackwell Heath
	Mangotsfield United	2 v 4	Forest Green Rovers
	Weston-super-Mare	2 v 0	Cheltenham Town

PRELIMINARY ROUND

	Home	Score	Away
	Hartlepool United	8 v 0	Harrogate Town
	Morecambe	1 v 1	Lancaster City
(R)	Lancaster City	3 v 0	Morecambe
	Darlington	2 v 1	Scarborough
	Darwen	1 v 0	Carlisle United
	Marine	1 v 2	Bolton Wanderers
	Chester City	4 v 0	Wigan Athletic
	Chadderton	1 v 1	Warrington Town
(R)	Warrington Town	2 v 2	Chadderton *
	(Chadderton Town won on kicks from the penalty mark, 5-3)		
	Trafford	0 v 1	Southport
	Huddersfield Town	4 v 0	Bury
	Immingham Town	3 v 1	Farsley Celtic
	Port Vale	6 v 1	Northwich Victoria
	Hall Road Rangers	2 v 2	Stockport County
(R)	Stockport County	0 v 2	Hall Road Rangers
	Hinckley Athletic	1 v 1	Lincoln City
(R)	Lincoln City	4 v 0	Hinckley Athletic
	Bedworth United	v	Leicester United
	W/O for Bedworth United - Leicester United withdrawn		
	Worksop Town	2 v 3	Birstall United
	Burton Albion	0 v 9	Mansfield
	Bilston Town	1 v 4	Nuneaton Borough
	Redditch United	2 v 2	Stourport Swifts
(R)	Stourport Swifts	0 v 1	Redditch United
	Stratford Town	1 v 0	Chasetown
	V.S. Rugby	3 v 2	Brierley Hill Town
	Rushden & Diamonds	3 v 0	Corby Town
	Bromsgrove Rovers	0 v 0	Banbury United
(R)	Banbury United	3 v 0	Bromsgrove Rovers
	Kidderminster Harriers	1 v 3	Kettering Town
	Worcester City	3 v 2	Daventry Town
	Bury Town	1 v 2	Wisbech Town
	Hitchin Town	5 v 1	Royston Town
	Braintree Town	0 v 1	Stevenage Borough
	Bishop's Stortford	2 v 5	Wivenhoe Town
	Potters Bar Town	5 v 1	Hemel Hemstead
	Hornchurch	2 v 0	Cheshunt
	Barnet	7 v 0	Wingate & Finchley
	Hoddesdon Town	1 v 2	St Albans City
	Collier Row	0 v 3	Basildon United
	Concord Rangers	v	Waltham Abbey
	W/O for Waltham Abbey - Concord Rangers withdrawn		
	Billericay Town	0 v 1	Tilbury
	Wembley	3 v 0	Canvey Island
	Brook House	1 v 6	Harefield United
	Northwood	7 v 0	Kingsbury Town
	Eton Manor	3 v 4	Leyton Pennant
	Viking Sports	0 v 0	Enfield
(R)	Enfield	9 v 0	Viking Sports
	Staines Town	0 v 2	Uxbridge
	Bedfont	1 v 2	Beaconsfield SYCOB
	Ruislip Manor	1 v 3	Windsor & Eton
	Bracknell Town	3 v 0	Hillingdon Borough
	Tonbridge	3 v 1	Dover Athletic
	Sittingbourne	3 v 0	Herne Bay
	Hastings Town	2 v 0	Chatham Town
	Gillingham	9 v 1	Thamesmead Town
	Tooting & Mitcham Utd.	3 v 3	Dartford
(R)	Dartford	1 v 2	Tooting & Mitcham Utd
	Redhill	2 v 1	Whyteleafe
	Three Bridges	0 v 3	Whitstable Town
	Sutton United	6 v 0	Bromley
	Crawley Town	1 v 3	Banstead Athletic
	Shoreham	9 v 0	Ringmer
	Carshalton Athletic	4 v 0	Peacehaven & Telscombe
	Southwick	6 v 1	Oakwood
	Woking	4 v 0	Raynes Park Vale
	Croydon	0 v 1	Leatherhead
	Kingstonian	2 v 1	Merstham
	Corinthian Casuals	2 v 5	Walton & Hersham
	Walton & Hersham removed for playing a suspended player - Corinthian Casuals re-instated.		
	Romsey Town	1 v 4	Farnborough Town
	Weymouth	2 v 1	Bashley
	Waterlooville	1 v 2	Eastleigh
	Bridport	0 v 2	Bognor Regis Town
	Abingdon Town	4 v 2	Marlow
	Thame United	1 v 6	Slough Town
	Basingstoke Town	v	Newbury Town
	Thatcham Town	0 v 3	Maidenhead United
	Forest Green Rovers	3 v 0	Chippenham Town
	Bristol Rovers	5 v 0	Oxford City
	Gloucester City	6 v 1	Yate Town
	Hereford United	5 v 1	Weston-super-Mare

FIRST ROUND QUALIFYING

	Home	Score	Away
	Darwen	3 v 3	Darlington
(R)	Darlington	5 v 0	Darwen
	Lancaster City	0 v 6	Hartlepool United
	Southport	3 v 0	Chadderton
	Chester City	1 v 2	Bolton Wanderers
	Hall Road Rangers	0 v 0	Port Vale
(R)	Port Vale	2 v 1	Hall Road Rangers *
	Immingham Town	1 v 9	Hudderfield Town
	Mansfield Town	6 v 2	Birstall United
	Bedworth United	2 v 0	Lincoln City
	V.S. Rugby	0 v 3	Stratford Town
	Redditch United	0 v 2	Nuneaton Borough
	Worcester City	1 v 5	Kettering Town
	Banbury United	1 v 2	Rushden & Diamonds
	Wivenhoe Town	2 v 0	Stevenage Borough
	Hitchin Town	7 v 1	Wisbech Town
	St Albans City	0 v 4	Barnet
	Hornchurch	2 v 4	Potters Bar Town
	Wembley	4 v 3	Tilbury
	Waltham Abbey	0 v 3	Basildon United
	Enfield	6 v 0	Leyton Pennant
	Northwood	1 v 9	Harefield United
	Bracknell Town	3 v 4	Windsor & Eton
	Beaconsfield SYCOB	2 v 5	Uxbridge
	Gillingham	7 v 0	Hastings Town
	Sittingbourne	6 v 0	Tonbridge
	Sutton United	4 v 0	Whitstable Town
	Redhill	0 v 4	Tooting & Mitcham Utd.
	Southwick	2 v 4	Carshalton Athletic
	Shoreham	2 v 4	Banstead Athletic
	Corinthian Casuals	2 v 2	Kingstonian
(R)	Kingstonian	3 v 1	Corinthian Casuals
	Leatherhead	1 v 2	Woking
	Bognor Regis Town	3 v 3	Eastleigh
(R)	Eastleigh	1 v 0	Bognor Regis Town *
	Weymouth	1 v 5	Farnborough Town
	Maidenhead United	2 v 2	Basingstoke Town
(R)	Basingstoke Town	1 v 2	Maidenhead United *
	Slough Town	5 v 1	Abingdon Town
	Hereford United	6 v 0	Gloucester City
	Bristol Rovers	1 v 2	Forest Green Rovers

SECOND ROUND QUALIFYING

	Home	Score	Away
	Darlington	2 v 2	Hartlepool United
(R)	Hartlepool United	1 v 1	Darlington

Hartlepool won on kicks from the penalty mark, 3-1.

	Home	Score	Away
	Southport	3 v 2	Bolton Wanderers
	Port Vale	1 v 1	Huddersfield Town
(R)	Huddersfield Town	5 v 0	Port Vale
	Mansfield Town	2 v 1	Bedworth United
	Stratford Town	0 v 1	Nuneaton Borough
	Kettering Town	0 v 7	Rushden & Diamonds
	Wivenhoe Town	3 v 2	Hitchin Town
	Barnet	5 v 0	Potters Bar Town
	Wembley	1 v 2	Basildon United
	Enfield	2 v 2	Harefield United
(R)	Harefield United	1 v 3	Enfield *
	Windsor & Eton	2 v 4	Uxbridge
	Gillingham	2 v 1	Sittingbourne
	Sutton United	4 v 1	Tooting & Mitcham Utd.
	Carshalton Athletic	2 v 4	Banstead Athletic
	Kingstonian	0 v 5	Woking
	Eastleigh	3 v 1	Farnborough Town
	Maidenhead United	0 v 3	Slough Town
	Hereford United	4 v 2	Forest Green Rovers

FIRST ROUND PROPER

	Home	Score	Away
	Rotherham United	1 v 0	Hartlepool United
	Southport	1 v 2	Burnley
	Tranmere Rovers	2 v 2	Wrexham
(R)	Wrexham	1 v 3	Tranmere Rovers
	Newcastle United	3 v 1	Blackpool
	Grimsby Town	3 v 4	Oldham Athletic
	Derby County	3 v 1	Scunthorpe United
	Preston North End	1 v 1	Huddersfield Town
(R)	Huddersfield Town	2 v 1	Preston North End *
	Everton	1 v 0	Notts County *
	Blackburn Rovers	2 v 0	Sheffield Wednesday
	Doncaster Rovers	1 v 0	Hull City
	Leeds United	3 v 1	Barnsley
	Basildon United	2 v 2	Chelsea
(R)	Chelsea	0 v 1	Basildon United
	Boreham Wood	0 v 3	Enfield
	Wivenhoe Town	0 v 1	Northampton Town
	Wycombe Wanderers	2 v 2	Watford
(R)	Watford	3 v 1	Wycombe Wanderers
	Shrewsbury Town	3 v 0	Cambridge United
	Wolverhampton Wanderers	5 v 6	Birmingham City
	Leicester City	10 v 0	Nuneaton Borough
	Walsall	1 v 1	Mansfield Town
(R)	Mansfield Town	0 v 1	Walsall
	Barnet	7 v 1	Leighton Town
	Boldmere St Michaels	4 v 1	Rushden & Diamonds
	Cambridge City	1 v 9	Luton Town
	Colchester United	2 v 4	Peterborough United
	Bournemouth AFC	1 v 2	Swansea City
	Torquay United	2 v 0	Welling United
	Southampton	1 v 1	Oxford United
(R)	Oxford United	1 v 2	Southampton
	Woking	5 v 1	CroydonAthletic
	Sutton United	1 v 2	Eastleigh
	Reading	0 v 2	Cardiff City
	Slough Town	2 v 4	Hereford United
	Gillingham	1 v 0	Fulham
	Dulwich Hamlet	0 v 0	Exeter City
(R)	Exter City	3 v 2	Dulwich Hamlet
	Uxbridge	1 v 2	Banstead Athletic
	Plymouth Argyle	1 v 4	Charlton Athletic

(Tie awarded to Plymouth - Charlton used an ineligible player)

SECOND ROUND

	Home	Score	Away
	Manchester City	3 v 0	Huddersfield Town
	leeds United	0 v 1	Middlesbrough
	Everton	1 v 3	Tranmere Rovers
	Oldham Athletic	3 v 2	York City
	Sheffield United	2 v 1	Newcastle United
	Sunderland	4 v 0	Crewe Alexandra
	Manchester United	3 v 1	Rotherham United
	Derby County	3 v 5	Doncaster Rovers
	Burnley	1 v 0	Stoke City
	Liverpool	4 v 2	Bradford City
	Blackburn Rovers	5 v 1	Nottingham Forest
	Ipswich Town	0 v 0	Walsall
(R)	Walsall	0 v 1	Ipswich Town
	Peterborough United	1 v 1	Norwich City
(R)	Norwich City	2 v 1	Peterborough United
	Barnet	0 v 4	Watford
	Birmingham City	5 v 0	Basildon United
	Tottenham Hotspur	4 v 1	Shrewsbury Town
	West Ham United	3 v 0	Aston Villa
	Leyton Orient	0 v 2	Enfield
	Leicester City	1 v 2	Luton Town
	Northampton Town	0 v 1	West Bromwich Albion
	Coventry City	1 v 2	Arsenal
	Boldmere St Michaels	2 v 1	Southend United
	Wimbledon	1 v 0	Brighton & Hove Albion
	Gillingham	1 v 3	Woking
	Brentford	4 v 0	Exeter City
	Swindon Town	0 v 2	Crystal Palace
	Plymouth Argyle	1 v 1	Eastleigh
(R)	Eastleigh	1 v 3	Plymouth Argyle
	Torquay United	0 v 1	Hereford United
	Swansea City	0 v 0	Portsmouth
(R)	Portsmouth	3 v 1	Swansea City
	Millwall	3 v 2	Southampton
	Queens Park Rangers	1 v 0	Cardiff City
	Bristol City	2 v 1	Banstead Athletic

THIRD ROUND

	Home	Score	Away
	Norwich City	2 v 1	Burnley
	Liverpool	5 v 0	Luton Town
	Boldmere St Michaels	0 v 3	Manchester City
	West Bromwich Albion	1 v 2	Sheffield United
	Blackburn Rovers	0 v 2	Tranmere Rovers
	Doncaster Rovers	0 v 5	Oldham Athletic
	Sunderland	1 v 4	Manchester United
	Ipswich Town	2 v 0	Middlesbrough
	Queens Park Rangers	2 v 0	Brentford
	Crystal Palace	7 v 0	Bristol City
	Portsmouth	1 v 2	Watford
	Hereford United	1 v 1	Enfield
(R)	Enfield	0 v 2	Hereford United
	Plymouth Argyle	2 v 1	Tottenham Hotspur
	Woking	0 v 3	West Ham United
	Arsenal	3 v 4	Wimbledon
	Millwall	5 v 2	Birmingham City

FOURTH ROUND

	Home	Score	Away
	Plymouth Argyle	0 v 2	Crystal Palace
	Hereford United	1 v 2	Manchester City
	Oldham Athletic	2 v 0	Millwall
	Liverpool	3 v 2	Sheffield United
	Manchester United	1 v 0	Norwich City
	Queens Park Rangers	1 v 4	West Ham United
	Wimbledon	2 v 2	Ipswich Town

(after abandoned tie, 0-0, 55 mins.)

	Home	Score	Away
(R)	Ipswich Town	1 v 2	Wimbledon
	Tranmere Rovers	1 v 1	Watford
(R)	Watford	4 v 1	Tranmere Rovers

FIFTH ROUND

Home	Score	Away
Liverpool	3 v 2	Manchester United
Oldham Athletic	1 v 2	West Ham United
Crystal Palace	2 v 0	Watford
Manchester City	1 v 3	Wimbledon

SEMI-FINALS

Home	Score	Away
Liverpool	4 v 2	Crystal Palace
Crystal Palace	3 v 3	Liverpool *
West Ham United	2 v 1	Wimbledon
Wimbledon	2 v 3	West Ham United

FINAL

West Ham United 0 v 2 Liverpool
Att: 15,386

Liverpool 2 v 1 West Ham United
Att: 20,600

F.A. SUNDAY CUP 1995-96

First Round (29th October 1995)

	Home	Score	Away
	Mitre	6 v 6	Stockton Roseworth Soc.
	W/O for Stockton R.S. - Mitre withdrawn		
	A3	v	Etnaward
	W/O for A3 - Etnaward withdrawn		
	Albion Sports	3 v 0	Nenthead
	Townley	3 v 3	Northwood *
(R)	Northwood	4 v 2	Townley
	Mode Force Boulevard	3 v 2	Boundary
	Lobster	0 v 4	Eden Vale
	Baildon Athletic	2 v 5	Seaton Sluice SC
	Bolton Woods	1 v 1	Dock *
(R)	Dock	1 v 1	Bolton Woods *
	(Dock win on kicks from the penalty mark, 3-2)		
	Manfast	0 v 1	Sandon
	Littlewoods Athletic	1 v 2	Clubmoor Nalgo *
	SDV	3 v 5	The Tiger *
	East Bowling Unity	0 v 2	Hartlepool Staincliffe Hotel
	BRNESC	2 v 3	Nicosia *
	Dudley & Weetslade	2 v 1	Britannia
	Croxteth & Gilmoss RBL	4 v 1	Fiddlers
	Caldway	3 v 2	Almithak
	Stanley Road	2 v 1	Walford Maritime *
	Salerno	8 v 1	Hartlepool Rovers
	Waterloo Social Club Blyth	v	Queens Park AFC
	W/O for Queens Park - Waterloo SCB withdrawn		
	Grosvenor Park	1 v 1	Courage *
(R)	Courage	1 v 2	Grosvenor Park
	Leicester City Bus	1 v 4	Sawston Keys
	Willen	1 v 0	BRSC Aidan
	Erdlington Cosmos Swan	8 v 1	Evesham WMC
	Altone Steels	1 v 6	Marston Sports
	Park Inn	5 v 0	Hemel Hempstead Social
	Girton Eagles	0 v 2	Slade Celtic
	Hanham Sunday	0 v 1	Celtic SC (Luton)
	Hundred Acre	v	Sun Kislingbury
	W/O for Hundred Acre - Sun K. withdrawn		
	Clifton Albion	1 v 1	Brookvale Athletic *
(R)	Brookvale Athletic	4 v 0	Clifton Albion
	Birmingham Celtic	1 v 2	Ouzavich
	St Clements Hospital	2 v 1	Watford Labour *
	Sandwell	2 v 1	Olympic Star
	dereham Hobbies	0 v 1	Roofwork
	Poringland Wanderers	2 v 1	St Joseph's (South Oxhey)
	Coach & Horses	1 v 0	Belstone
	Melton Youth Old Boys	2 v 2	Heathfield *
(R)	Heathfield	2 v 0	Melton Youth Old Boys
	Pitsea	3 v 1	Continental
	Holderness United	1 v 0	Bedfont Sunday
	Morden Nomads	2 v 2	St Joseph's (Bristol) *
(R)	St Joseph's (Bristol)	0 v 0	Morden Nomads *
	(Morden won on kicks from the penalty mark, 4-3)		
	Reading Borough	0 v 4	Fryerns Community
	Leavesden Sports & Social	6 v 1	Charlton Royals 89
	Inter Royalle	1 v 2	Forest Athletic
	Park Royals	1 v 0	Oakwood Sports
	British Rail SA	v	Caversham Park
	W/O for Caversham - British Rail SA withdrawn		
	Northfield Rangers	0 v 3	Cherry Tree (Warley)
	Cavaliers	0 v 1	Hallen United
	Ford Basildon	9 v 0	South Croydon
	Merton Admiral	v	Oxford Road Social
	W/O for Oxford RS - Merton A withdrawn		

Byes: Berner United, Microgen Breakspear & Shankhouse United.

Exemptions: Allerton, Capel Plough, Hammer, Hartlepool Lion Hotel, Humbledon Plains Farm, Lebeq Tavern, Lion Hotel, Lodge Cottrell, Newfield, Oakenshaw, Seymour, St Joseph's (Luton), Theale Sunday.

Second Round (19th November 1995)

	Home	Score	Away
	Park Inn	1 v 1	Hartlepool Lion Hotel *
(R)	Hartlepool Lion Hotel	2 v 1	Park Inn
	Seaton Sluice SC	5 v 1	Caldway
	Stanley Road	5 v 1	Newfield
	Lodge Cottrell	2 v 1	Brookvale Athletic
	Dudley & Weetslade	4 v 1	Eden Vale
	Sanden	0 v 1	Clubmoor Nalgo
	Croxteth & Gilmoss RBL	3 v 0	A3 *
	Stockton Roseworth Social	4 v 0	Dock
	Oakenshaw	0 v 2	Salerno
	Allerton	5 v 1	Northwood *
	Hartlepool Staincliffe Hotel	0 v 2	Shankhouse United
	Mode Force Boulevard	1 v 2	The Tiger *
	Humbledon Plains Farm	1 v 3	Nicosia
	Seymour	1 v 2	Martson Sports
	Lion Hotel	0 v 0	Queens Park AFC
(R)	Queens Park AFC	2 v 1	Lion Hotel *
	Albion Sports	4 v 2	Sandwell
	Microgen Breakspear	0 v 3	Slade Celtic
	Hundred Acre	2 v 0	Erdington Cosmos Swan
	Berner United	2 v 2	Cherry Tree (Warley) *
(R)	Cherry Tree (Warley)	1 v 2	Berner United
	Hammer	3 v 0	Roofwork
	Heathfield	4 v 0	Coach & Horses
	Poringland Wanderers	1 v 3	Sawston Keys
	Grosvenor Park	4 v 1	Fryerns Community
	Caversham Park	0 v 2	Ouzavich *
	Park Royals	2 v 1	Oxford Road Social
	Lebeq Tavern	3 v 1	Pitsea
	Morden Nomads	0 v 1	St Clements Hospital
	Hallen United	0 v 2	Capel Plough
	Willen	3 v 2	Theale Sunday
	Ford Basildon	6 v 2	Leavesden Sports & Social
	Forest Athletic	3 v 0	Holderness United
	Celtic SC (Luton)	0 v 0	St Joseph's (Luton) *
(R)	St Joseph's (Luton)	6 v 2	Celtic SC (Luton)

Third Round (10th December 1995)

	Home	Score	Away
	Queens Park AFC	2 v 1	Stanley Road
	Nicosia	3 v 1	Lodge Cottrell
	Marston Sports	6 v 2	Seaton Sluice SC
	Shankhouse United	0 v 7	Dudley & Weetslade
	Stockton Roseworth Social	2 v 1	Allerton
	Croxteth & Gilmoss RBL	5 v 1	Albion Sports
	The Tiger	1 v 3	Hartlepool Lion Hotel
	Salerno	1 v 0	Clubmoor Nalgo
	Forest Athletic	1 v 0	Berner United
	Willen	2 v 0	Hammer
	Ford Basildon	2 v 1	Hundred Acre
	St Clements Hospital	3 v 0	Heathfield
	Ouzavich	2 v 2	Lebeq Tavern *
(R)	Lebeq Tavern	5 v 1	Ouzavich
	Grosvenor Park	2 v 4	St Joseph's (Luton)
	Capel Plough	4 v 1	Slade Celtic
	Park Royals	4 v 1	Sawston Keys *

Fourth Round (14th January 1996)

Home	Score	Away
Croxteth & Gilmoss RBL	3 v 0	Stockton Roseworth Social
Nicosia	1 v 0	Marston Sports
Hartlepool Lion Hotel	2 v 1	Dudley & Weetslade
Salerno	1 v 0	Queens Park AFC
Lebeq Tavern	1 v 2	St Joseph's (Luton) *
Forest Athletic	1 v 6	Park Royals
Ford Basildon	0 v 3	Willen
St Clements Hospital	1 v 0	Capel Plough

Fifth Round (11th February 1996)

Home	Score	Away
Hartlepool Lion Hotel	0 v 4	Croxteth & Gilmoss RBL
Salerno	1 v 0	Nicosia
Park Royals	1 v 2	St Joseph's (Luton) *
St Clements Hospital	1 v 2	Willen

Semi-Final (17th March 1996)

Home	Score	Away	Venue
Croxteth & Gilmoss RBL	4 v 3	Salerno *	at Southport FC
St Joseph's (Luton)	2 v 0	Willen *	at Leighton T. FC

Final (5th May 1996) St Jospeh's (Luton) 2 v 1 Croxteth & Gilmoss RBL (at Northampton Town F.C.)

INTERNATIONAL and F.A. REPRESENTATIVE FOOTBALL

Two excellent victories for England's Semi-Professional International squad were achieved with style at two of our most distinguished grounds. So the image of our level of football at its best certainly received a timely and much appreciated boost.

With just a weekend (Saturday evening to Tuesday evening) in which to prepare their players, Tony Jennings and Ron Reid had to hope their original selections were sound, injuries were avoided before their weekend together and that the limited preparations and coaching proved useful.

Well, very few players pull out of England squads these days. The honour of playing for ones country is really appreciated and once at the training ground they proved to be keen, receptive players, with the intelligence and abilities to quickly grasp all that was put to them, thus proving that the selection was very sound!

The first international at Kidderminster Harriers, where the impressive new lounge, bar and entertainment boxes had just been opened, gave the team the stage on which to show off their new set pieces - and this they duly did as the match report describes.

Photo: Keith Clayton

Two of the outstanding successes on the International scene this year were Barry Hayles & Carl Alford. Photo: Keith Clayton.

Another equally impressive performance at Nene Park, the glorious home of Rushden and Diamonds, again made us all wish there was an annual tournament in which our England team could really be tested. We can only hope!

The outstanding successes of the international season were the strike force of Barry Hayles and Carl Alford backed up by a lively Ged Kimmins, the emergence of the young Lee Hughes and the captaincy of Paul Webb.

Sadly, Tony Jennings (photographed opposite) has had to stand down from the manager's job this season due to his committments at Carshalton Athletic and at the time of writing his replacement hasn't been announced.

The new man will again have a useful programme of FAXI representative games to help him decide upon his players and he will certainly have the basis of an excellent squad on which he can build.

ENGLAND 4 v 0 FAI NATIONAL LEAGUE

Everything about the build up seemed to point to a good day for Semi-Professional Football! Not one of Tony Jennings' 16-man-squad had to pull out through injuries after Saturday's games.

Tony and his assistant, Ron Reid, were really impressed with the attitude of the squad. Their keenness to listen, to practice the set plays and to concentrate, when given general tactical instructions, all gave the management the impression that the squad were thrilled to be representing their country and were taking it very seriously indeed. So the two days at Lilleshall were a success and the whole squad arrived at Kidderminster in great spirits.

The Harriers home at Aggborough was looking just great too. Over the last ten years the ground has been slowly developed and turned into a 'real' football ground. The open ends which were some way behind the goals overlooking a large track, have been smartly terraced, the track is no longer there and the roofs on both ends keep the noise in and create an excellent atmosphere. There are now more seats in a smart new stand and for the International match, the very impressive social faciities were being used for only the second time since the official opening on 22nd February.

Entertainment boxes and a large lounge for functions all fit into the usual friendly Harriers' environment quite naturally. For the Irish League game Graham Allner entertained a party in one of the boxes and Stevenage Borough took a box to watch their three players represent their country. It was a good party evening of which there should be a lot more!

So the ground looked smart, over 1,000 turned up, which is good for a friendly international, the players and management knew they were fit and well prepared and, as usual, the excellent pre match build up at the ground presented the game in a very professional manner. Chairman Dave Reynolds and his board were justly proud hosts, and it was obvious that the F.A. Chairman and Vice-Chairman of the Representative Committee, Terry Knight and Alan Turvey, were enjoying the occasion immensely.

New caps were won by five players in the original line up and right from the kick off 'new' England impressed. Within six minutes the set piece practice had paid off. A right footed inswinging corner from David Venables was headed on by Harriers young Lee Hughes and there was the powerful Carl Alford, crashing home a close range header. Very simple and very effective, but performed with consumate skill.

It soon became clear that the speed and all round skills of the home side were in a different class to those of the Irish League visitors. The Irish did cause a little trouble with inswinging free kicks from their left but in general there were few scares for the England defence, in which skipper Paul Webb and centre half Mark Smith were outstanding. In the fifties, when The Football League played representative matches against the Scottish League, The Irish League and The League of Ireland, the might of our First Division sent sides packed with full Internationals to play the part timers of both Irish leagues.

Well, times have obviously changed, and now the part timers of England are the England Semi-Professional International side and the obvious and best opposition would be a team from the very best of The Republic of Ireland's Premier Division. This would be a very good contest with home advantage probably being the deciding factor. But the Irish side in the Kidderminster game was unfortunately from their Division One, and maybe it is understandably difficult for the administrators to forget the old days, and accept that the best of our two countries' semi-pros are now probably very evenly matched.

England's attack was superbly led by Carl Alford in his first game for England. He recently turned down a very lucrative move to Rushden & Diamonds and on this form must soon be offered even better deals with League or Premier clubs. Not that Barry Hayles, another debutant was far behind and it was the Stevenage striker who smartly headed home a pinpoint cross from clubmate Venables after a lovely through ball from Ken Cramman had put the wingman away down the right. This goal came after twenty six minutes and before half time England were in a virtually unassailable position. David Venables once again was involved, this time setting Alford free on the right and the resultant hard low cross was turned into his own net by Irish centre back Stephen McGuinness as he raced back to cover.

The England attack all impressed, and Hayles and Hughes both had shots cleared off the line, while Alford was always dangerous in the air and crashed a couple of efforts against the woodwork. Venables and Cramman seemed to be involved with most attacks while the reliable Stott acted as the mid-field anchorman. All corners, free kicks and throw-ins were taken intelligently, with obvious thought and concentration on what had been planned at Lilleshall. Time and time again the moves worked and one was left wondering why full time professionals at some clubs can never get any set plays right after seasons of so called coaching, while these lads can respond to Tony Jennings and Ron Reid after just two days?

In the second half the urgency was naturally lacking, as the three goals gave the England lads a comfortable lead, but some excellent football was still played and when the front two came off for the last quarter of an hour we saw a spritely finish to the game with Ged Kimmins and Phil Power linking effectively, and Colin Rose also impressing on the right. In fact it was a deft pass from Power which gave Kimmins the chance for a debut goal, and the Hyde star lifted a neat lob over the keeper to give England a fine 4-0 victory.

In an article, which Tony Jennings and I prepared for the match programme, the attitude of potential England players was discussed. Playing for England is special and if players don't feel that way, they probably aren't the right ones to pull on those white shirts. In this case I feel sure that Tony and Ron will feel they made the right selections and the squad certainly gave the impresion they felt 'special'. They certainly looked it!

ENGLAND: Ryan Price (Macclesfield T.), Paul Webb (C) (Kidderminster Harriers), Nick Ashby (Rushden & Diamonds), Steve Stott (Rushden & Diamonds), Mark Smith (Stevenage Borough), Mark Tucker (Woking), David Venables (Stevenage Borough), Barry Hayles (Stevenage Borough), Carl Alford (Kettering T.), Ken Cramman (Gateshead), Lee Hughes (Kidderminster Harriers). Subs: Kevan Brown (Woking); Laurence Batty (Woking); Colin Rose (Witton Albion) for Venables; Ged Kimmins (Hyde Utd.) for Hayles; Phil Power (Macclesfield T.) for Alford.

ENGLAND 3 v 0 THE NETHERLANDS

Rushden & Diamonds' lovely new ground, Nene Park, was sparkling; it had been a clear spring day which had turned into a perfect evening for football and the two sets of international players looked superb in their traditional white and tangerine. The scene was set for a second impressive England performance in which a classy Dutch amateur side was soundly beaten.

If anything, England got on top too soon! As in their last International a carefully prepared set piece, practised in the morning under the guidance of manager Tony Jennings and his assistant Ron Reid, provided an exhilarating and very satisfying goal.

Nick Ashby shaped to take an outswinging free kick from near the corner on the left, but Lee Endersby actually sent over an inswinger that neatly cleared the first defender and was met first time by Steve Stott who, along with Kevan Brown, Barry Hayles and Carl Alford, had all lost their markers as planned (if ever there was a case for zonal marking in defence this was it!).The goal came after seven minutes and Steve's shot gave keeper Braaf no chance.

Just six minutes later two local 'Diamonds' combined to extend England's lead. Nick Ashby crossed for Carl Alford to volley smartly home and score his second goal at Nene Park since signing for Rushden for £85,000 in the previous week.

At this stage England were looking dangerous whenever they attacked and the cultured Dutch side had been losing their composure in defence. However, visiting left winger Van der Meent was causing some problems of his own with a series of long throws. Nick Ashby had already cleared an awkward situation after keeper Price had been beaten and crosses to the edge of the six yard box were causing all sorts of trouble as defenders seemed to be unsure who should accept responsibility.

Perhaps, it wasn't a surprise that a Dutch goal came in this spell but it was from a right wing cross which once again wasn't cleared, and the huge striker De Bruin was presented with a relatively easy tap in to reduce England's lead. It looked as if either side could score at will at this stage but, to give the respective managements credit, Holland brought on a new right back and England certainly tightened up at the back.

The Dutch change was perhaps a compliment to debutant Lee Endersby, the first representative of the ICIS Leaguie in the England squad this season. His excellent close ball control was causing all sorts of trouble down the left wing but it was a burst down the middle from the Harrow player which resulted in England's third goal after 33 minutes. His beautifully timed pass, slipped through to Barry Hayles, gave Stevenage's ace striker the simplest of chances which he put away with the grace and confidence of a natural goalscorer. He must surely have impressed the 30 odd club scouts watching the game.

With this two goal lead the game died a little, and the second half saw England contain a more resolute Holland side with comparative ease. If this period was less dramatic, it gave the highly impressive Ged Kimmins of Hyde United a chance to prove that England have THREE top class strikers who would surely do well in the full time game (and there's Phil Power who hasn't yet had much time to prove his quality as well at this level!).

Once again skipper Paul Webb was the perfect example of classy reliability.

Nick Ashby and Steve Stott certainly didn't let down their local supporters and Witton Albion's Colin Rose, playing his first full game in midfield, showed a quality that made up for the unfortunate loss, through injury, of the excellent Kenny Cramman.

For one so young, it was also good to see England's youngest ever semi-professional international, Lee Hughes, get stronger and stronger as the game developed and the class displayed by Mark Smith, once he had settled down to partner Kevan Brown at the heart of the defence, was really impressive.

Two conclusive victories with a goal tally of 7-1 must be satisfying for the management, the F.A. Staff and the committee responsible for the England team. But this should surely just be the warm up for a tournament of some kind. We have discussed this problem at length in Team Talk before and hopefully there will be some way found to give these players the competitive international matches they deserve.

ENGLAND: Ryan Price (Macclesfield Town); Paul Webb (Kidderminster Harriers) (captain), Mark Smith (Stevenage Borough), Kevan Brown (Woking), Nick Ashby (Rushden & Diamonds); Lee Hughes (Kidderminster Harriers), Colin Rose (Witton Albion), Steve Stott (Rushden & Diamonds), Lee Endersby (Harrow Borough); Barry Hayles (Stevenage Borough) and Carl Alford (Rushden & Diamonds). Subs: Ged Kimmins (Hyde United) for Alford 70 mins, Phil Power (Macclesfield Town) for Rose and David Venables (Stevenage Borough) for Endersby 84 mins.

F.A. REPRESENTATIVE MATCHES 1995-96

FA XI 0 v 2 NORTHEN PREMIER LEAGUE at Accrington Stanley FC (14th November 1995)

1 PAUL COLLINGS Altrincham
2 JAMIE BATES Runcorn
3 STEVE PRINDIVILLE Halifax Town
4 ALEX JONES Stalybridge Celtic
5 LEROY DOVE Southport
6 STEVE HAW Southport
7 STUART TERRY Altrincham
8 MARTIN McDONALD Macclesfield Town
9 MICHAEL MIDWOOD Halifax Town
10 MICK CARMODY Altrincham
11 CHRIS SHARRATT Altrincham

Subs:
DAVID GAMBLE (Southport) for 6
DARREN LYONS (Macclesfield Town) for 9
BRIAN BUTLER (Northwich Victoria) for 10
DEAN GREYGOOSE ( ) for 1

Team Manager:
JOHN KING (Altrincham)

FA XI 2 v 0 BRITISH STUDENTS at Hednesford Town FC (9th January 1996)

Scorers: Carty, Street.

1 DARREN STEADMAN Kidderminster Harriers
2 MARCUS BIGNOT Telford United
3 KEVIN COLLINS Hednesford Town
4 JOHN DEAKIN Kidderminster Harriers
5 WAYNE SIMPSON Hednesford Town
6 CRAIG GAUNT Bromsgrove Rovers
7 ADIE SMITH Bromsgrove Rovers
8 MARK YATES Kidderminster harriers
9 JOHN HUNT Bromsgrove Rovers
10 LEE HUGHES Kidderminster Harriers
11 JOE O'CONNOR Hednesford Town

Subs:
PAUL CARTY (Hednesford Town) for 2
NICK GOODWIN (Telford United) for 1
MARTIN MYERS (Telford United) for 7
PAUL DAVIES (Kidderminster Harriers) for 9
TYRONE STREET (Hednesford Town) for 10

Team Manager:
GRAHAM ALLNER (Kidderminster Harriers)

FA XI 1 v 0 COMBINED SERVICES at Mangotsfield United FC (16th January 1996)

Scorer: Holmes

1 TONY PENNOCK Yeovil Town
2 JERRY GILL Bath City
3 MICKY ENGWELL Yeovil Town
4 CHRIS BANKS Cheltenham Town
5 MARK FREEMAN Gloucester City
6 DARREN WRIGHT Cheltenham Town
7 KEITH KNIGHT Gloucester City
8 PAUL CHENOWETH Cheltenham Town
9 JASON EATON Cheltenham Town
10 TOMMY KILLICK Dorchester
11 DAVID HOLMES Gloucester City

Subs:
LEE FRANCIS (Yeovil Town) for 2
RUSSELL BOWLES (Cinderford Town) for 1
NICK DUNPHY (Cheltenham Town) for 4
LEE HOWELL (Cheltenham Town) for 9
DAVID WEBB (Gloucester City) not used

Team Manager:
Chris Robinson (Cheltenham Town)

FOUR NATIONS TOURNAMENTS 1979-87 and OTHER INTERNATIONALS

1979 (England)
Knock-out competition.

S/Final	England	5 v 1	Scotland
S/Final	Holland	3 v 0	Italy
3rd Place	Scotland	1 v 2	Italy
Final	England	1 v 0	Holland

1980 (Holland)	P	W	D	L	F	A	Pts
Scotland	3	2	1	0	7	2	5
England	3	2	0	1	6	5	4
Italy	3	0	2	1	2	4	2
Holland	3	0	1	2	3	7	1

1981 (Italy)	P	W	D	L	F	A	Pts
England	3	1	2	0	3	1	4
Italy	3	1	2	0	2	1	4
Scotland	3	0	3	0	2	2	3
Holland	3	0	1	2	2	5	1

1982 (Scotland)	P	W	D	L	F	A	Pts
Scotland	3	1	2	0	5	4	4
England	3	1	2	0	2	1	4
Italy	3	0	2	1	4	6	2
Holland	3	1	0	2	5	5	2

1983 (England)	P	W	D	L	F	A	Pts
England	3	3	0	0	10	1	6
Scotland	3	1	1	1	7	6	3
Holland	3	1	1	1	6	11	3
Italy	3	0	0	3	3	8	0

1984 (Italy)	P	W	D	L	F	A	Pts
Italy	3	2	1	0	4	1	5
England	3	1	1	1	5	4	3
Holland	3	1	1	1	8	8	3
Scotland	3	0	1	2	2	6	1

1985 (Holland)	P	W	D	L	F	A	Pts
Scotland	3	2	0	1	4	4	4
England	3	1	1	1	6	5	3
Italy	3	1	1	1	4	4	3
Holland	3	1	0	2	4	5	2

1986 (Scotland)

Competition cancelled - Italy withdrew.

1987 (Scotland)	P	W	D	L	F	A	Pts
Italy	3	2	1	0	6	3	5
England	3	2	0	1	7	3	4
Scotland	3	1	0	2	4	6	2
Holland	3	0	1	2	0	5	1

OVERALL FOUR NATIONS TROPHY RECORD

	P	W	D	L	F	A	Pts
England	23	13	6	4	45	21	32
Italy	23	7	9	7	27	31	23
Scotland	23	7	8	8	33	37	22
Holland	23	5	5	13	31	47	15

OTHER RESULTS

v WALES		Eng.	Wales
1984	Newtown	1	2
1985	Telford	1	0
1986	Merthyr	1	3
1987	Gloucester	2	2
1988	Rhyl	2	0
1989	Kidderminster	2	0
1990	Merthyr	0	0
1991	Stafford	1	2
1992	Aberystwyth	1	0
1994	Bangor	2	1
1995	Yeovil	1	0

v REPUBLIC OF IRELAND		Eng.	Ire.
1986	Kidderminster	2	1
1986	Nuneaton	2	1
1990	Dublin	2	1
1990	Cork	3	0
1996	Kidderminster	4	0

v GIBRALTAR		Eng.	Gib.
1982	Gibraltar	3	2
1995	Gibraltar	3	2

v FINLAND (under-21)		Eng.	Fin.
1993	Woking	1	3
1994	Aanekoski	0	2

v ITALY		Eng.	Italy
1989	La Spezia	1	1
1990	Solerno	0	2
1991	Kettering	0	0

v NORWAY (under-21)		Eng.	Nor.
1994	Slemmestad	1	2

v HOLLAND		Eng.	Hol.
1995	Amsterdam	0	0
1996	Rushden	3	1

ENGLAND'S Overall International Record

P	W	D	L	F	A
50	28	11	11	86	50

England Semi-Pro Caps 79-96 (Max 50)

Key: (I - Italy, S - Scotland, W - Wales, H - Holland, E - Eire, F - Finland, G - Gibralter, N - Norway)

Newly capped players during the 1995-96 season are boxed.

Gary Abbott (Welling) 87 I(s), S(s), 92 W(s) (3)
David Adamson (Boston Utd) 79 SH, 80 ISH (5)
Tony Agana (Weymouth) 86 E (1)
Carl Alford (Kettering T. & Rushden & Ds) 96 EH (2)
Ian Arnold (Kettering Town) 95 W(s)H (2)
Jim Arnold (Stafford Rangers) 79 SH (2)
Nick Ashby (Kettering & Rushden & Ds) 94 FN, 95 G 96 EH (5)
Noel Ashford (Enfield & Redbridge For.) 82 GHS, 83 IHS, 84 WHSI, 85 WI(s), 86 EE, 87 W(s), IHS, 90 WE, 91 I(s) (21)
John Askey (Macclesfield) 90 W, (1)
Paul Bancroft (Kidderminster H.) 89 IW, 90 IWE, 91 W (6)
Keith Barrett (Enfield) 81 HSI, 82 GIHS, 83 IHS, 84 W(s)HS, 85 IHS (16)
Laurence Batty (Woking) 93 F(s), 95 WHG (4)
Mark Beeney (Maidstone) 89 I(s) (1)
Graham Benstead (Kettering) 94 WFN(s) (3)
Jimmy Bolton (Kingstonian) 95 G (1)
Gary Brabin (Runcorn) 94 WFN (3)
Colin Brazier (Kidderminster) 87 W (1)
Stewart Brighton (Bromsgrove) 94 W (1)
Steve Brooks (Cheltenham) 88 W(s), 90 WE (3)
Derek Brown (Woking) 94 F(s)N (2)
Kevan Brown (Woking) 95 WHG 96 H (4)
Corey Browne (Dover) 94 F(s)N(s), 95 H(s) (3)
David Buchanan (Blyth) 86 E(s)E (2)
Brian Butler (Northwich) 93 F (1)
Steve Butler (Maidstone) 88 W, 89 IW (3)
Mark Carter (Runcorn & Barnet) 87 WIHS, 88 W, 89 IW, 90 IE, 91 IW(s) (11)
Kim Casey (Kidderminster) 86 WEE(s), 87 WI (5)
Paul Cavell (Redbridge) 92 W, 93 F (2)
Kevin Charlton (Telford) 85 WI (2)
Andrew Clarke (Barnet) 90 EE (2)
David Clarke (Blyth Spartans) 80 IS(s)H, 81 HSI, 82 IHS, 83 HS, 84 HSI (14)
Gary Clayton (Burton) 86 E (1)
Robert Codner (Barnet) 88 W (1)
John Coleman (Morecambe) 93 F(s) (1)
Darren Collins (Enfield) 93 F(s), 94 WFN (4)
Steve Conner (Dartford, Redbridge & Dagenham & R) 90 I, 91 IW, 92 W, 93 F (5)
David Constantine (Altrincham) 85 IHS, 86 W (4)
Robbie Cooke (Kettering) 89 W(s), 90 I (2)
Alan Cordice (Wealdstone) 83 IHS, 84 WS(s), I(s), 85 IHS (9)
Ken Cramman (Gateshead) 96 E (1)
Paul Cuddy (Altrincham) 87 IHS (3)
Paul Culpin (Nuneaton B) 84 W, 85 W(s) IHS (5)
Paul Davies (Kidderminster H.) 86 W, 87 WIS, 88 W, 89 W (6)
John Davison (Altrincham) 79 SH, 80 IS, 81 HSI, 82 GIHS, 83 IHS, 84 WHIS, 85 IHS, 86 WEE (24)
John Denham (Northwich Victoria) 80 H (1)
Peter Densmore (Runcorn) 88 W, 89 I (2)
Phil Derbyshire (Mossley) 83 H(s)S(s) (2)
Mick Doherty (Weymouth) 86 W(s) (1)
Lee Endersby (Harrow Bor.) 96 H (1)
Mick Farrelly (Altrincham) 87 IHS (3)
Steve Farrelly (Macclesfield) 95 H(s)G(s) (2)
Trevor Finnegan (Weymouth) 81 HS (2)
Richard Forsyth (Kidderminster) 95 WHG (3)
Paul Furlong (Enfield) 90 IEE, 91 IW (5)
John Glover (Maidstone Utd) 85 WIHS (4)
Mark Golley (Sutton Utd.) 87 H(s)S, 88 W, 89 IW, 92 W (6)
Phil Gridelet (Hendon & Barnet) 89 IW, 90 WEE (5)
Steve Guppy (Wycombe W.) 93 W (1)
Steve Hancock (Macclesfield) 90 W (1)
Barry Hayles (Stevenage Bor.) 96 EH (2)
Tony Hemmings (Northwich) 93 F (1)
Andy Hessenthaler (Dartford) 90 I (1)
Kenny Hill (Maidstone Utd) 80 ISH (3)
Mark Hine (Gateshead) 95 W(s)H (2)
Simeon Hodson (Kidderminster) 94 WFN (3)
Colin Hogarth (Guiseley) 95 WH (2)

Steven Holden (Kettering) 94 WFN(s), 95 HG (5)
Mark Hone (Welling) 90 I, 93 F, 94 W(s)F(s)N (5)
Gary Hooley (Frickley) 85 W (1)
Keith Houghton (Blyth Spartans) 79 S (1)
Barry Howard (Altrincham) 81 HSI, 82 GIHS (7)
Neil Howarth (Macclesfield) 95 H(s) (1)
David Howell (Enfield)
85 H(s)S(s), 86 WE, 87 WIHS, 88 W,
89 IW, 90 IEE (14)
Lee Hughes (Kidderminster) IH (2)
Delwyn Humphreys (Kidderminster H.)
91 W(s), 92 W, 94 WFN, 95 WH (7)
Steve Humphries (Barnet) 87 H(s) (1)
Nicky Ironton (Enfield) 83 H(s), 84 W (2)
Tony Jennings (Enfield)
79 SH, 80 ISH, 81 HSI, 82 GIHS (12)
Jeff Johnson (Altrincham)
81 SI, 82 GIHS, 83 IHS, 84 HSI,
84 IHS, 86 W(s)EE (18)
Tom Jones (Weymouth) 87 W (1)
Anton Joseph (Telford Utd. & Kidderminster H.)
84 S(s), 85 WIHS, 86 W(s), 87 WI(s)H,
88 W, 89 IW, 90 IEE (14)
Andy Kerr (Wycombe) 93 W (1)
Ged Kimmins (Hyde Utd.) 96 E(s)H(s) (2)
Mike Lake (Macclesfield) 89 I (1)
Andy Lee (Telford U. & Witton A.) 89 I(s), 91 IW (3)
David Leworthy (Farnborough) 93 W, 94 W (2)
Kenny Lowe (Barnet) 91 IW (2)
Martin McDonald (Macclesfield) 95 G(s) (1)
John McKenna (Boston Utd)
88 W(s), 90 IEE, 91 IW, 92 W (7)
Leroy May (Stafford R.) 95 G(s) (1)
Bobby Mayes (Redbridge) 92 W (1)
Paul Mayman (Northwich Vic) 80 IS (2)
Stewart Mell (Burton) 85 W (1)
Neil Merrick (Weymouth) 80 I(s)S (2)
Russell Milton (Dover) 94 FN (2)
Trevor Morley (Nuneaton) 84 WHSI, 85 WS(s) (6)
Les Mutrie (Blyth Spartans) 79 SH, 80 ISH (5)
Mark Newson (Maidstone U) 84 WHSI, 85 W (5)
Doug Newton (Burton) 85 WHS (3)
Paul Nicol (Kettering T) 91 IW, 92 W (3)
Steve Norris (Telford) 88 W(s) (1)
Eamon O'Keefe (Mossley) 79 SH (2)
Frank Ovard (Maidstone) 81 H(s)S(s)I(s) (3)

KEN CRAMMAN (Gateshead)

PAUL WEBB (Kidderminster Harriers)

DAVID VENABLES (Stevenage Borough)

Andy Pape (Harrow Bor. & Enfield) 85 W(s)HS, 86 W(s)E 87 WIHS, 88 W, 89 IW, 90 IWE (15)
Brian Parker (Yeovil Town) 80 S (1)
Trevor Peake (Nuneaton Bor) 79 SH (2)
David Pearce (Harrow Bor) 84 I(s) (1)
Brendan Phillips (Nuneaton Bor. & Kettering T.) 79 SH, 80 S(s)H (4)
Gary Philips (Barnet) 82 G (1)
Phil Power (Macclesfield T.) 96 E(s)H(s) (2)
Ryan Price (Stafford R. & Macclesfield) 92 W(s) 93 WF 96 EH (5)
Simon Read (Farnborough) 92 W(s) (1)
Andy Reid (Altrincham) 95 W (1)
Carl Richards (Enfield) 86 E (1)
Derek Richardson (Maidstone U) 83 I, 84 W, 86 E (4)
Ian Richardson (Dagenham & Red) 95 G (1)
Kevin Richardson (Bromsgrove) 94 WFN (3)
Paul Richardson (Redbridge) 92 W, 93 WF (3)
Terry Robbins (Welling) 92 W, 93 WF, 94 WFN (6)
Peter Robinson (Blyth S) 83 IHS, 84 WI, 85 W (6)
John Rogers (Altrincham) 81 HSI, 82 I(s)S (5)
Paul Rogers (Sutton) 89 W, 90 IE(2), 91 IW (6)
Colin Rose (Witton Alb.) 96 E(s)H (2)
Kevin Rose (Kidderminster) 94 F(s)N (2)
Brian Ross (Marine) 93 W(s)F(s), 94 W(s) 95 WH (5)
Neil Sellars (Scarboro) 81 HSI, 82 GH(s)S, 83 IHS (9)
Mark Shail (Yeovil T.) 93 W (1)
Peter Shearer (Cheltenham) 89 I(s) (1)
Paul Shirtliff (Frickley A. & Boston U.) 86 EE, 87 WIH, 88 W, 89 IW, 90 IWEE, 92 W, 93 WF (15)
Paul Showler (Altrincham) 91 I(s)W (2)
Gordon Simmonite (Boston Utd.) 79 S(s)H(s), 80 ISH (5)
Gary Simpson (Stafford R.) 86 EE, 87 IHS, 90 IWEE (9)
Wayne Simpson (Stafford) 94 FN(s) (2)
Glenn Skivington (Barrow) 90 IWE, 91 IW (5)
Alan Smith (Alvechurch) 82 GIS (3)
Ian Smith (Mossley) 80 ISH(s) (3)
Mark Smith (Stevenage Bor.) 96 EH (2)
Ossie Smith (Runcorn) 84 W (1)
Tim Smithers (Nuneaton), 85 W(s)I, 86 W (3)
Simon Stapleton (Wycombe) 93 W (1)
Mickey Stephens (Sutton), 82 GS(s), 86 WEE(s) (5)
Bob Stockley (Nuneaton Bor) 80 H (1)
Steve Stott (Kettering T. & Rushden & Ds) 95 WH(s)G 96 EH (5)
Peter Taylor (Maidstone) 84 HSI (3)
Steve Taylor (Bromsgrove R.) 95 G (1)
Shaun Teale (Weymouth) 88 W (1)
Stuart Terry (Altrincham) W (1)
Brian Thompson (Yeovil & Maidstone) 79 SH, 81 HSI, 82 IHS, 83 IHS, 84 WHSI (15)
Steve Thompson (Wycombe) 93 W (1)
Kevin Todd (Berwick Rangers) 91 W (1)
Mark Tucker (Woking) 96 E (1)
Tony Turner (Telford) 85 W (1)
David Venables (Stevenage Bor.) 94 W(s), 95 HG 96 EH(s) (5)
David Waite (Enfield) 82 G (1)
Paul Walker (Blyth) 86 WEE(s), 87 S(s) (4)
Mark Ward (Northwich Victoria) 83 S(s) (1)
John Watson (Wealdstone, Scarborough & Maidstone) 79 S(s)H, 80 ISH, 81 HSI, 82 IHS, 83 IHS, 84 W(s)HSI (18)
Liam Watson (Marine) 95 WH(s) (2)
Paul Watts (Redbridge Forest) 89 W, 90 IEE, 91 I, 92 W, 93 WF (8)
Paul Webb (Bromsgrove & Kidderminster) 93 F, 94 WFN(s) 95 WHG 96 EH (9)
Mark West (Wycombe W) 91 W (1)
Barry Whitbread (Runcorn & Altrincham) 79 SH, 80 ISH, 81 I (6)
Russ Wilcox (Frickley) 86 WE (2)
Colin Williams (Scarborough & Telford Utd.) 81 HS, 82 IHS (5)
Roger Willis (Barnet) 91 I(s) (1)
Paul Wilson (Frickley) 86 W (1)

GED KIMMINS (Hyde United)

G.M. VAUXHALL CONFERENCE

Founded: 1979

President: J C Thompson **Chairman:** W J King

Vice-Chairman: G E Smith

Chief Executive: P D Hunter

Secretary: J A Moules,
24 Barnehurst Road, Bexleyheath, Kent DA7 6EZ
Tel: 01322 521116 Fax: 01322 526793

STEVENAGE BOROUGH'S MARVELLOUS CAMPAIGN

In the end, Stevenage Borough's title-winning margin of eight points looks comfortable enough. However, it was never as easy as that and their success was only confirmed towards the latter weeks of the season. In fact, had Woking's away form been anything like their fortress-like home form, then it would have been the Cards who would have been celebrating. As it was, Borough became champions in only their second season in non-League football's top competition and after scoring 101 goals they were indeed worthy champions. Manager Paul Fairclough achieved success too without spending huge sums in the transfer market. In fact, only England semi-professional international midfielder Corey Browne cost the Hertfordshire club a fee. The only sad aspect of Borough winning the title is that, again, no club from the Vauxhall Conference will be promoted to the Football League. That is the third season in succession, and, with so many Conference clubs now having suitable facilities, it is vital that a club goes up next season, otherwise the powers that be may well decide to change the system.

Woking again enjoyed a great season, emulating their 1994/95 position as runners-up and going the whole campaign unbeaten at their Kingfield 'fortress'. Hednesford Town once again proved that the gap between the best sides in the Pyramid and the Conference is narrowing by finishing third in their first season whilst reigning champions Macclesfield Town dropped to fourth but had the consolation of their FA Umbro Trophy win at Wembley to compensate.

With the UniBond League unable to come up with a suitable promotion candidate, only two clubs were relegated. Both Dagenham & Redbridge and Runcorn had miserable campaigns and were rarely out of the bottom places. No doubt they will both be back.

This season the Vauxhall Conference welcomes Rushden & Diamonds and Hayes, champions of the Beazer Homes and ICIS leagues respectively. No doubt both will enjoy their first taste of the competition.

Steve Whitney

GM VAUXHALL CONFERENCE

FINAL LEAGUE TABLES 1995/96

		P	*W*	*D*	*L*	*F*	*A*	*Pts*
1.	Stevenage Borough	42	27	10	5	101	44	91
2.	Woking	42	25	8	9	83	54	83
3.	Hednesford Town	42	23	7	12	71	46	76
4.	Maclesfield Town	42	22	9	11	66	49	75
5.	Gateshead	42	18	13	11	58	46	67
6.	Southport	42	18	12	12	77	64	66
7.	Kidderminster Harr	42	18	10	14	78	66	64
8.	Northwich Victoria	42	16	12	14	72	64	60
9.	Morecambe	42	17	8	17	78	72	59
10.	Farnborough Town	42	15	14	13	63	58	59
11.	Bromsgrove Rovers	42	15	14	13	59	57	59
12.	Altrincham	42	15	13	14	59	64	58
13.	Telford	42	15	10	17	51	56	55
14.	Stalybridge Celtic	42	16	7	19	59	68	55
15.	Halifax Town	42	13	13	16	49	63	52
16.	Kettering Town	42	13	9	20	68	84	48
17.	Slough Town	42	13	8	21	63	76	47
18.	Bath City	42	13	7	22	45	66	46
19.	Welling United	42	10	15	17	42	53	45
20.	Dover Athletic	42	11	7	24	51	74	40
21.	Runcorn	42	9	8	25	48	87	35
22.	Dagenham & Redbridge	42	7	12	23	43	73	33

GM CONFERENCE RESULTS CHART 1995-96

HOME TEAM	1	2	3	4	5	6	7	8	9	10	11	12	13	14	15	16	17	18	19	20	21	22
1. Altrincham	*	1-2	3-0	3-1	2-2	2-2	1-1	3-2	2-1	1-3	1-1	0-4	3-0	3-4	2-2	0-1	1-0	1-0	0-2	1-0	1-0	2-0
2. Bath	2-0	*	0-1	0-2	2-1	2-1	0-1	2-1	1-0	3-1	1-1	1-1	3-2	0-3	3-0	3-1	4-0	0-4	1-2	0-3	1-1	0-3
3. Bromsgrove	0-0	4-1	*	2-0	3-0	1-2	3-1	0-1	1-4	3-2	2-1	1-0	1-0	1-1	2-0	0-0	4-1	1-1	1-1	0-2	1-1	2-1
4. Dagenham	1-0	0-1	2-2	*	3-0	2-2	0-4	1-1	1-2	1-2	4-2	3-0	2-2	0-3	2-3	1-3	1-2	4-1	1-2	1-1	1-1	0-0
5. Dover	1-4	1-0	0-2	0-1	*	1-3	1-1	3-2	1-3	2-1	2-1	2-3	2-3	0-1	4-2	0-1	0-1	1-3	1-2	1-0	2-1	4-3
6. Farnborough	1-1	0-0	1-0	2-0	3-2	*	2-3	0-0	1-3	1-1	3-1	6-1	3-1	0-1	0-1	0-1	1-0	1-1	2-2	2-1	0-1	0-2
7. Gateshead	2-3	3-1	1-0	2-0	1-1	1-1	*	3-2	0-3	1-1	4-1	0-1	3-0	1-1	1-0	2-1	2-2	1-0	2-2	1-2	1-1	0-1
8. Halifax Town	1-1	3-1	1-1	3-0	1-0	0-0	2-0	*	1-3	2-0	0-2	1-0	1-1	2-0	1-3	1-2	2-2	2-3	2-3	0-0	2-1	2-2
9. Hednesford T	2-1	2-1	4-2	0-0	2-2	4-1	0-1	3-0	*	1-0	1-3	0-1	1-2	2-1	2-0	3-1	2-1	0-1	2-1	4-0	1-1	2-1
10. Kettering T	4-2	3-0	2-2	2-0	2-2	0-2	1-0	1-2	2-0	*	2-0	2-2	2-3	2-2	4-0	2-0	1-1	1-6	1-2	0-3	1-3	3-0
11. Kidderminster	1-1	1-2	1-0	5-1	1-1	3-3	1-1	6-1	3-1	1-0	*	0-4	4-2	2-1	4-1	4-3	2-3	3-0	0-1	2-0	3-0	2-0
12. Macclesfield	2-3	0-1	2-1	3-1	0-1	1-0	1-0	7-0	1-1	1-1	0-2	*	2-0	0-0	1-0	1-1	3-1	1-0	0-0	1-0	2-1	3-2
13. Morecambe	7-0	1-0	4-1	2-2	3-1	2-3	2-3	0-1	0-1	5-3	3-1	2-4	*	2-2	3-1	1-2	4-3	2-0	1-0	2-0	1-0	4-5
14. Northwich Vic	2-1	2-2	2-2	1-0	1-2	1-3	1-2	1-1	0-2	6-2	5-2	1-2	2-1	*	4-3	0-3	1-2	1-0	1-3	2-0	1-2	3-0
15. Runcorn	0-1	1-0	0-0	2-0	1-3	0-3	1-1	0-1	2-2	4-2	0-1	0-0	1-3	3-4	*	4-3	1-1	0-1	0-8	2-3	1-3	2-3
16. Slough Town	1-2	1-1	2-3	5-0	3-2	1-1	1-2	2-3	0-2	1-2	5-4	2-2	1-1	1-1	0-1	*	2-5	2-1	2-6	1-2	0-0	2-3
17. Southport	1-2	2-1	1-2	2-1	0-0	7-1	1-0	0-0	2-2	6-1	0-2	2-1	1-1	2-1	1-1	2-0	*	5-3	0-1	3-2	2-0	2-2
18. Stalybridge	1-0	1-0	2-1	2-1	2-0	2-2	0-2	1-0	0-1	3-2	2-2	1-2	0-2	1-5	2-0	0-1	1-4	*	2-5	2-2	2-1	2-4
19. Stevenage B	1-1	2-0	3-3	1-0	3-2	0-0	1-1	2-0	1-0	5-1	4-1	4-0	1-1	5-1	4-1	3-1	1-3	2-2	*	0-1	4-1	4-0
20. Telford Utd	2-0	3-1	0-0	0-0	1-0	3-2	0-0	1-1	2-1	3-4	1-1	1-2	2-2	1-0	1-2	2-0	2-1	1-0	1-3	*	0-0	1-2
21. Welling Utd	1-1	2-1	5-2	0-0	1-0	0-1	1-2	0-0	1-1	1-0	0-0	1-2	1-0	1-1	1-1	0-3	0-1	1-1	0-3	3-1	*	1-2
22. Woking	2-0	2-0	1-1	2-2	1-0	2-1	2-0	2-0	3-0	1-1	0-0	3-2	3-0	0-0	2-1	3-0	4-0	2-1	4-1	5-1	3-2	*

G.M. Vauxhall Conference

TEN YEAR CLUB RECORD

	86/87	87/88	88/89	89/90	90/91	91/92	92/93	93/94	94/95	95/96
ALTRINCHAM	5	14	14	16	3	18	10	10	4	12
AYLESBURY UNITED	-	-	20	-	-	-	-	-	-	-
BARNET	2	2	8	2	1	-	-	-	-	-
BARROW	-	-	-	14	10	22	-	-	-	-
BATH CITY	10	20	-	-	20	9	7	12	12	18
BOSTON UNITED	6	16	3	18	18	8	22	-	-	-
BROMSGROVE ROVERS	-	-	-	-	-	-	2	18	13	11
CHELTENHAM TOWN	11	13	15	11	16	21	-	-	-	-
CHORLEY	-	-	17	20	-	-	-	-	-	-
COLCHESTER UNITED	-	-	-	-	2	1	-	-	-	-
DAGENHAM	15	22	-	-	-	-	-	-	-	-
DAGENHAM & REDBRIDGE	-	-	-	-	-	-	3	6	15	22
DARLINGTON	-	-	-	1	-	-	-	-	-	-
DOVER ATHLETIC	-	-	-	-	-	-	-	8	16	20
ENFIELD	4	12	13	22	-	-	-	-	-	-
FARNBOROUGH TOWN	-	-	-	21	-	5	21	-	14	10
FISHER ATHLETIC	-	15	18	19	22	-	-	-	-	-
FRICKLEY ATHLETIC	21	-	-	-	-	-	-	-	-	-
GATESHEAD	22	-	-	-	17	14	14	11	7	5
HALIFAX TOWN	-	-	-	-	-	-	-	13	8	15
HEDNESFORD	-	-	-	-	-	-	-	-	-	3
KETTERING TOWN	16	3	2	5	4	3	13	2	6	16
KIDDERMINSTER HARRIERS	12	7	5	13	13	19	9	1	11	7
LINCOLN CITY	-	1	-	-	-	-	-	-	-	-
MACCLESFIELD TOWN	-	11	7	4	7	13	18	7	1	4
MAIDSTONE UNITED	3	9	1	-	-	-	-	-	-	-
MERTHYR TYDFIL	-	-	-	9	9	4	16	20	20	-
MORECAMBE	-	-	-	-	-	-	-	-	-	9
NORTHWICH VICTORIA	17	17	10	15	12	11	11	15	10	8
NUNEATON BOROUGH	18	-	-	-	-	-	-	-	-	-
REDBRIDGE FOREST	-	-	-	-	-	7	-	-	-	-
RUNCORN	8	4	6	3	8	16	19	5	9	21
SCARBOROUGH	1	-	-	-	-	-	-	-	-	-
SLOUGH TOWN	-	-	-	-	19	20	5	21	-	17
SOUTHPORT	-	-	-	-	-	-	-	4	3	6
STAFFORD RANGERS	13	6	19	17	15	17	6	9	21	-
STALYBRIDGE CELTIC	-	-	-	-	-	-	12	14	18	14
STEVENAGE BOROUGH	-	-	-	-	-	-	-	-	5	1
SUTTON UNITED	7	8	12	8	21	-	-	-	-	-
TELFORD UNITED	9	5	16	12	6	6	15	17	19	13
WEALDSTONE	19	21	-	-	-	-	-	-	-	-
WELLING UNITED	20	19	11	6	11	12	20	16	17	19
WEYMOUTH	14	10	21	-	-	-	-	-	-	-
WITTON ALBION	-	-	-	-	-	10	17	22	-	-
WOKING	-	-	-	-	-	-	8	3	2	2
WYCOMBE WANDERERS	-	18	4	10	5	2	1	-	-	-
YEOVIL TOWN	-	-	9	7	14	15	4	19	22	-

SPALDING CHALLENGE CUP

First Round (2 Legs)

DAGENHAM & RED	0	v	3	SLOUGH TOWN
SLOUGH TOWN	3	v	0	DAGENHAM & RED
KIDDERMINSTER H	4	v	1	HEDNESFORD TOWN
HEDNESFORD TOWN	2	v	0	KIDDERMINSTER H
BATH CITY	0	v	3	FARNBOROUGH TOWN
FARNBOROUGH TOWN	3	v	2	BATH CITY
MORECAMBE	4	v	1	STALYBRIDGE CELTIC
STALYBRIDGE CELTIC	5	v	2	MORECAMBE

(Morecambe win on away goals rule)

TELFORD UNITED	1	v	2	NORTHWICH VICTORIA
NORTHWICH VICTORIA	0	v	3	TELFORD UNITED
WELLING UNITED	1	v	2	DOVER ATHLETIC
DOVER ATHLETIC	3	v	0	WELLING UNITED

Byes to Second Round:

Altrincham, Bromsgrove Rovers, Gateshead, Halifax Town, Kettering Town, Macclesfield Town, Runcorn, Southport, Stevenage Borough, Woking.

Second Round

BROMSGROVE ROVERS	3	v	1	TELFORD UNITED (AET)
FARNBOROUGH TOWN	1	v	3	DOVER ATHLETIC
GATESHEAD	4	v	0	HALIFAX TOWN
KETTERING TOWN	2	v	1	STEVENAGE BOROUGH (AET)
MACCLESFIELD TOWN	4	v	1	KIDDERMINSTER H
MORECAMBE	6	v	4	ALTRINCHAM
RUNCORN	1	v	5	SOUTHPORT
SLOUGH TOWN	3	v	0	WOKING

Third Round

DOVER ATHLETIC	0	v	1	BROMSGROVE ROVERS
KETTERING TOWN	2	v	0	SLOUGH TOWN
MORECAMBE	1	v	4	MACCLESFIELD TOWN
SOUTHPORT	2	v	1	GATESHEAD

Semi-Finals (2 Legs)

BROMSGROVE ROVERS	2	v	0	KETTERING TOWN
KETTERING TOWN	2	v	1	BROMSGROVE ROVERS
SOUTHPORT	4	v	4	MACCLESFIELD TOWN
MACCLESFIELD TOWN	2	v	1	SOUTHPORT

Final (2 Legs)

MACCLESFIELD TOWN	**1**	v	**1**	**BROMSGROVE ROVERS**
BROMSGROVE ROVERS	**3**	v	**1**	**MACCLESFIELD TOWN**

COMPLETE CONFERENCE TABLE 1979-1996

- Founder Member.

	Seasons	P	W	D	L	F	A	Pts
ALTRINCHAM #	17	704	299	181	224	1075	890	991
KETTERING TOWN #	17	704	281	188	235	1061	969	967
TELFORD UNITED #	17	704	276	175	253	966	956	941
RUNCORN	15	628	258	174	196	969	867	920
NORTHWICH VICTORIA #	17	704	248	197	259	976	955	883
KIDDERMINSTER HARRIERS	13	544	222	126	196	902	937	765
BATH CITY #	15	622	217	169	236	787	820	764
BOSTON UNITED #	14	578	222	136	220	881	911	740
BARNET #	12	494	209	114	174	759	658	688
STAFFORD RANGERS #	13	578	173	183	232	735	831	665
YEOVIL TOWN #	13	536	166	136	234	706	854	593
MAIDSTONE UNITED #	10	410	179	113	118	684	492	589
MACCLESFIELD TOWN	9	376	156	100	120	520	450	568
ENFIELD	9	376	169	80	127	672	541	553
WEYMOUTH #	10	410	164	102	144	603	553	524
WELLING UNITED	10	418	130	116	174	545	636	500
WYCOMBE WANDERERS	7	292	133	73	86	480	386	465
SCARBOROUGH #	8	328	136	101	91	471	393	450
GATESHEAD	9	378	119	101	165	476	607	445
WEALDSTONE #	8	328	113	99	116	444	443	387
BARROW #	9	370	108	103	159	452	575	387
CHELTENHAM TOWN	7	292	93	92	107	420	458	358
FRICKLEY ATHLETIC	7	290	108	69	113	432	458	337
NUNEATON BOROUGH #	7	286	104	79	103	425	408	333
MERTHYR TYDFIL	6	252	87	73	92	352	383	332
DAGENHAM	7	294	87	70	137	374	494	307
WORCESTER CITY #	6	244	93	58	93	347	376	288
SUTTON UNITED	5	208	76	59	73	352	305	287
WOKING	4	168	81	41	46	275	228	284
FARNBOROUGH TOWN	5	212	70	59	81	304	335	269
SLOUGH TOWN	5	210	68	45	97	274	351	249
BROMSGROVE ROVERS	4	168	59	56	63	246	241	233
STALYBRIDGE CELTIC	4	168	54	50	64	213	250	212
DAGENHAM & REDRIDGE	4	168	54	50	64	236	243	211
SOUTHPORT	3	126	57	33	36	202	165	204
COLCHESTER UNITED	2	84	53	20	11	166	75	179
HALIFAX TOWN	3	126	43	41	42	172	166	170
FISHER ATHLETIC	4	166	41	46	79	206	283	169
BANGOR CITY #	4	160	44	45	71	201	273	150
DOVER ATHLETIC	3	126	39	30	57	147	178	147
WITTON ALBION	3	126	34	40	52	162	188	142
DARTFORD	3	126	35	31	60	155	199	122
GRAVESEND & NORTHFLEET #	3	118	40	28	50	148	168	118
TROWBRIDGE TOWN	3	126	29	25	72	127	229	109
STEVENAGE BOROUGH	1	42	27	10	5	101	44	91
CHORLEY	2	82	26	12	44	99	138	90
DARLINGTON	1	42	26	9	7	76	25	87
LINCOLN CITY	1	42	24	10	8	86	48	82
A P LEAMINGTON #	3	118	21	32	65	119	234	78
HEDNESFORD TOWN	1	42	23	7	12	71	46	76
REDBRIDGE FOREST	1	42	18	9	15	69	56	63
MORECAMBE	1	42	17	8	17	78	72	59
AYLESBURY UNITED	1	40	9	9	22	43	71	36
REDDITCH UNITED #	1	38	5	8	25	26	69	18
(NEWPORT COUNTY - deleted record		29	4	7	18	31	62	19)

G.M. Vauxhall Conference

PREVIOUS SEASONS' TOP FOUR

Season	Max Pts	Champions Pts	Champions	Runners-up Pts	Runners-up	3rd Place Pts	3rd Place	4th Place Pts	4th Place
1979/80	76	56	Altrincham	54	Weymouth	49	Worcester C.	45	Boston Utd.
1980/81	76	54	Altrincham	51	Kettering T.	47	Scarborough	45	Northwich V.
1981/82	126	93	Runcorn	86	Enfield	77	Telford Utd.	71	Worcester C.
1982/83	126	84	Enfield	83	Maidstone U.	79	Wealdstone	72*	Runcorn
1983/84	105	70	Maidstone U.	69	Nuneaton Bor.	65	Altrincham	62*	Wealdstone
1984/85	105	62	Wealdstone	58	Nuneaton Bor.	57*	Dartford	57*	Bath City
1985/86	105	76	Enfield	69	Frickley Ath.	67	Kidderminster	63	Altrincham
1986/87	126	91	Scarborough	85	Barnet	73	Maidstone Utd.	70	Enfield
1987/88	126	82	Lincoln City	80	Barnet	75	Kettering Town	74	Runcorn
1988/89	126	84	Maidstone Utd.	76	Kettering Town	74	Boston Utd.	71	Wycombe W.
1989/90	126	87	Darlington	85	Barnet	70	Runcorn	66	Macclesfield T.
1990/91	126	87	Barnet	85	Colchester U.	82	Altrincham	80	Kettering T.
1991/92	126	94	Colchester Utd	94	Wycombe Wdrs	73	Kettering Town	68	Merthyr Tydfil
1992/93	126	83	Wycombe Wdrs	68	Bromsgrove R.	67	Dagenham & R.	66	Yeovil Town
1993/94	126	75	Kidderminster H.	72	Kettering T.	67	Woking	66	Southport
1994/95	126	80	Macclesfield	75	Woking	72	Southport	68	Altrincham

* Indicates position achieved through goal difference.

FOOTBALL LEAGUE MOVEMENTS

1987	Promoted to 4th Div.:	**Scarborough**	Relegated to Conference:	**Lincoln City**
1988	Promoted to 4th Div.:	**Lincoln City**	Relegated to Conference:	**Newport County**
1989	Promoted to 4th Div.:	**Maidstone United**	Relegated to Conference:	**Darlington**
1990	Promoted to 4th Div.:	**Darlington**	Relegated to Conference:	**Colchester United**
1991	Promoted to 4th Div.:	**Barnet**	No relegation from 4th Div.	
1992	Promoted to 4th Div.:	**Colchester United**	No relegation from 4th Div.	
1993	Promoted to 3rd Div.:	**Wycombe Wanderers**	Relegated to Conference:	**Halifax Town**
1994	No promotion to 3rd Div.		No relegation from 3rd Div.	
1995	No promotion to 3rd Div.		No relegation from 3rd Div.	
1996	No promotion to 3rd Div.		No relegation from 3rd Div.	

BOB LORD TROPHY

(also Drinkwise Cup)

	Winner	Runner-up
1979/80	Northwich Victoria	Altrincham
1980/81	Altrincham	Kettering Town
1981/82	Weymouth	Enfield
1982/83	Runcorn	Scarborough
1983/84	Scarborough	Barnet
1984/85	Runcorn	Maidstone United
1985/86	Stafford Rangers	Barnet
1986/87	Kettering Town	Hendon (Isthmian)
1987/88	Horwich RMI (NPL)	Weymouth
1988/89	Barnet	Hyde United (HFS)
1989/90	Yeovil Town	Kidderminster H.
1990/91	Sutton United	Barrow
1991/92	Wycombe Wdrs	Runcorn
1992/93	Northwich V.	Wycombe Wdrs
1993/94	Macclesfield T.	Yeovil Town
1994/95	Bromsgrove R.	Kettering T.

CHAMPIONSHIP SHIELD

Conference Champions v Trophy Winners

	Winner	Runner-up
1980	Northwich V	Altrincham
1981	Altrincham	Kettering T.
1982	runcorn	Weymouth
1983	Enfield	Runcorn
1984	Maidstone U.	Scarborough
1985	Runcorn	Wealdstone
1986	Stafford R.	Enfield
1987	Kidderminster H.	Scarborough
1988	Lincoln City	Enfield
1989	Maidstone Utd.	Telford Utd.
1990	Darlington	Barrow
1991	Wycombe W.	Barnet
1992	Wycombe W.	Colchester Utd
1993	Wycombe W.	Northwich Vics
1994	Woking	Kidderminster H.
1995	Macclesfield	Woking

CONFERENCE DIARY 1995-96

Compiled by Steve Whitney

1st - 21st August 1995

The league announces a new endorsement deal with Spalding Top-Flite Footballs. The deal, which will run for three years, includes amongst its benefits free provision of match balls and training balls. FA Umbro Trophy holders and Conference runners-up **Woking** are installed as 5-2 favourites to land the title by bokkmakers Ladbrokes. The Cards boss Geoff Chapple made few alterations to his squad, signing midfielder Carl Hoddle from Barnet as a replacement for Kevin Rattray, who was sold to Gillingham during the summer, and the ex-Manchester City defender Nicky Reid from Wycombe Wanderers. Second favourites and reigning champions **Macclesfield Town** were a little more active in the transfer market during the close season with six new players joining. Amongst the newcomers is the former England semi-professional international striker Paul Cavell and Yeovil Town forward Marc Coates, who is now resident in the North West and attending Manchester University. Joint favourites for the drop are **Telford United** and **Welling United**. Telford have a new player-manager in the former Manchester City, Wolves and Everton striker, Wayne Clarke. He made six new signings, including Bromsgrove Rovers attacker Brian Gray. Welling are also under new management in Kevin Hales, who succeeded Barnet-bound Terry Robbins. The Wings also saw the long-serving Nigel Ransom, Paul Collins and Steve Robinson depart and highly-rated winger Steve Finnan join Birmingham for £100,000. Of the Conference promotees, **Hednesford Town** look to be the best equipped and added the ex-Bromsgrove Rovers goalkeeper Scott Cooksey to an already strong squad. **Morecambe**, the UniBond League runners-up, stayed loyal to the previous season's squad as, in the main, did **Slough Town**. Brian Kenning is announced as the new boss at **Bromsgrove Rovers**, who have been shawn of a host of talented players in the summer, including both Steve Stott and Alan Judge, who have both joined Kettering Town whilst Steve Taylor was sold to Crystal Palace for £90,000. Kenning, however, uses some of the income to break the club's transfer record in signing Burton Albion midfielder Darren Grocutt for £12,500. Amongst the other big-money summer sales were Richard Forsyth (**Kidderminster Harriers** - Birmingham for £100,000), Steve Farrelly (**Macclesfield Town** - Rotherham for £20,000), **Leo Fortune-West** (**Stevenage Borough** - Gillingham for an undisclosed five-figure sum), Ian Richardson (Dagenham & Redbridge - Birmingham for £50,000) and Nick Ashby's move from **Kettering Town** to neighbours Rushden & Diamonds for £14,000. **Kidderminster Harriers** pay a 'susbantial' five-figure fee to sign striker Leroy May from Stafford Rangers. He will join an attack which also boasts former hero Kim Casey, a surprise re-signing from Solihull Borough.

22nd August - 3rd September 1995

Woking announce a whopping profit of £56,000 for the year ending 31 May 1995 and are awaiting the all-clear to start work on their new £1.35 million cantilver grandstand. **Bromsgrove Rovers** are the surprise early leaders, joining **Kettering Town** as the only remaining unbeaten sides after four games. **Dover Athletic**, who are already having to do without the services of Steve Restarick and Russell Milton, both in Japan playing in the World Student Games, suffer further blows when midfielder Junior Lewis is run over by a fork-lift truck and ace marksman David Leworthy sends his car through the wall of his garage and into his kitchen, suffering chest injuries into the bargain. Dover also sell goalkeeper Darren Williams to one of his previous clubs, **Dagenham & Redbridge**, who have lost the experienced Bob Bolder, who has retired. Spalding Footballs are to sponsor the League Cup, succeeding the Bob Lord Trophy. **Morecambe's** highly-rated midfielder Michael Knowles, who has already trialled with Liverpool, now attracts the attention of Blackburn Rovers.

4th - 17th September 1995

England semi-pro skipper Delwyn Humphreys signs for **Northwich Victoria** from **Kidderminster Harriers** for an undisclosed five-figure fee, ending a five year term at Aggborough Stadium. The last remaining unbeaten starts are relinquished when **Bromsgrove Rovers** and **Kettering Town** suffer their first defeats. Rovers are beaten 5-2 at **Welling United** while the Poppies lose 1-0 at **Kidderminster Harriers**. 18-year-old winger, Steve Barnes, notched a hat-trick in Welling's win over Bromsgrove whilst being watched by a host of Premiership and Endsleigh League scouts. Oldham Athletic join the band of League clubs to share Vauxhall Conference facilities with a one-year agreement to play their reserve team fixtures at **Stalybridge Celtic's** Bower Fold stadium. They join Newcastle United (Gateshead), Charlton (Welling United), Leeds (Halifax Town), Bristol Rovers (Bath City), Liverpool (Southport), Wolves (Telford United) and West Ham (Dagenham & Redbridge). Ten Vauxhall Conference clubs begin their FA Cup campaigns at the first qualifying round stage and all are handed home ties. Only **Dover Athletic**, beaten 2-1 at home by ICIS Leaguers Bognor Regis Town, are defeated although **Stevenage Borough** are surprisingly held to a goalless draw by little Spartan League outfit Brook House. Biggest winners of the day are **Morecambe**, who beat

Welling's Lee Tierling, signed from Woking during the season, (dark strip) gets to the ball first in the league match against Telford United. Photo: Keith Gillard.

Northern Counties East side Sheffield 7-0 with Mark Cereolo scoring a hat-trick. **Dover Athletic's** cup defeat and seven straight defeats saw the end of manager John Ryan's eight month reign at The Crabble. Senior players Nigel Donn and David Leworthy take over as caretaker managers. **Bromsgrove Rovers'** 19-year-old midfielder Stuart Whitehead joins Bolton Wanderers following a two-week trial at Burnden Park. **Dagenham & Redbridge** sack the experienced Roy McDonough as a player due to his poor disciplinary record. **Stevenage Borough** safely make the second qualifying round of the FA Cup by beating Brook House 5-1 in a replay. Meanwhile, a record crowd for the new Keys Park stadium of 2,480 see Conference newcomers **Hednesford Town** go top of the table with a 4-0 win over neighbours **Telford United.**

18th September - 1st October 1995

Dagenham & Redbridge sack manager Dave Cusack after a 3-0 home Spalding Cup defeat by **Slough Town**. Former Kettering Town boss, Graham Carr, is immediately installed as his successor following a brief term at Beazer Homes League side Weymouth. **Macclesfield Town** lift the J C Thompson Championship Shield with a 3-2 win over Trophy winners **Woking** at the Moss Rose. The second qualifying round of the FA Cup saw all but two of the nine Conference clubs in action drawn away from home. All survived, although both **Welling United** and **Gateshead** face replays after being held at home by Bromley and Barrow respectively. Graham Carr celebrates his first game in charge at **Dagenham & Redbridge** with a 2-1 win at Berkhamsted Town. **Dover Athletic** appoint the one-time Spurs and England player, Peter Taylor, as their new manager but he couldn't prevent them extending their losing sequence to nine - the longest run of consecutive defeats since 1987/88. **Hednesford Town** sell striker David Hanson to Leyton Orient for £50,000. The 26-year-old only joined the Pitmen in the summer from **Halifax Town**. Meanwhile, Hednesford manager John Baldwin is the first winner of the *Mail on Sunday* manager of the month award whilst **Farnborough Town** striker Chris Boothe wins the goalscorers award.

2nd - 15th October 1995

Reigning champions **Macclesfield Town** and runners-up **Woking** both receive major boosts by being awarded £250,000 each from the Sports Grounds Initiative. **Dover Athletic's** long run of defeats finally ends with a 1-1 draw at **Kidderminster Harriers. Slough Town** suffer a goalkeeping problem when both first choice Trevor Bunting and deputy Delroy Preddie are injured within the space of seven days and then loan signing from Rushden & Diamonds, Andy Lomas, suffers a groin strain on his debut. **Welling United** suffer a 2-1 home defeat by Kent neighbours Bromley in the replayed FA Cup second qualifying round tie at Park View Road. The third qualifying round sees **Morecambe's** John Coleman bag four of his side's six goals in their comfortable win over Gainsborough Trinity but **Dagenham & Redbridge** (at home to Purfleet), **Hednesford Town** (at home to Solihull Borough) and **Northwich Victoria** (also at home to Eastwood Town), all face replays. **Welling United** sell a second 19-year-old winger to Birmingham when Steve Barnes moves to St.Andrews for an initial £70,000. **Dover Athletic** finally break their duck by beating **Runcorn** 4-2 at The Crabble. It's all change at Victoria Road when manager Graham Carr signs four more new players for **Dagenham & Redbridge.** Dominic Crookes and Jon Davidson both join from **Telford United**, Deiniol Graham arrives from **Halifax Town** and Neil Matthews from Scunthorpe. The Daggers' miserable season continues, however, when ICIS League side Purfleet win the replayed FA Cup third qualifying round tie 2-1 but both **Hednesford Town** and **Northwich Victoria** safely negotiate their replays. The Vics lower **Kidderminster Harriers'** colours by beating the leaders 5-2 at the Drill Field. **Woking** moved menacingly into third place when a crowd of 2,081 witness a 2-0 win over **Altrincham** at Kingfield.

16th - 29th October 1995

Woking make a rare sorte into the transfer market by signing the experienced Steve Thompson from Wycombe Wanderers. The 32-year-old was a member of Wycombe's Conference and Trophy winning sides. **Farnborough Town** reward manager Alan Taylor with a new contract. He has overseen a run of ten wins from eleven games. **Telford United** unveil plans to re-locate from Buck's Head to a new purpose-built stadium. The fourth qualifying round of the FA Cup sees a few upsets with high-flying **Hednesford Town's** 2-0 defeat by ICIS League Second Division side Canvey Island top of the list. Beazer Homes League Southern Division Cinderford Town beat **Bath City** 3-2 while former Conference outfit Witton Albion defeat **Morecambe** in a five goal thriller at Wincham Park. Also out are **Halifax Town**, beaten 2-1 at **Runcorn** whilst **Kettering Town** and **Bromsgrove Rovers**, who drew 0-0 at Rockingham Road, and **Stalybridge Celtic**, held at home by Colwyn Bay, face replays. In the league, **Kidderminster Harriers** failed to take advantage of their rivals being in cup action by only drawing 1-1 at home to **Altrincham**, courtesy of a last minute goal from the prolific Paul Davies. Ian Arnold, **Kettering Town's** England semi-pro forward, returns to **Stalybridge Celtic** for a fee of £15,000. The ex-Carlisle player spent a loan spell at Bower Fold in 1994. **Runcorn's** 23-year-old left-back, Paul Robertson, joins Doncaster Rovers for an undisclosed five-figure fee. He joins former team-mate Gary Brabin at Belle Vue. **Woking's** Geoff Chapple is October's *Mail on Sunday* manager of the month and then sees his charges go top of the table after a 4-2 win against **Stalybridge Celtic** with veteran Clive Walker notching a hat-trick. Chapple also releases Carl Hoddle, who joins ICIS Leaguers Enfield. **Welling United**

suffer their seventh successive defeat in losing 2-1 at **Macclesfield Town. Stevenage Borough** sell 26-year-old midfielder Phil Simpson to Third Division Barnet for an undisclosed fee and replace him by securing **Dover Athletic's** Corey Browne on a permanent basis following a successful loan spell. **Stalybridge Celtic** go out of the FA Cup, being beaten 3-0 at Colwyn Bay, and **Bromsgrove Rovers** and **Kettering Town** will have to go to a third game following a 2-2 draw at the Victoria Ground.

30th October - 12th November 1995

Macclesfield Town make two impressive signings as they attempt to retain their title. Joining the Moss Rose outfit are winger Tony Hemmings from Wycombe Wanderers and goalkeeper Ryan Price from Birmingham City. Hemmings, previously with Northwich Victoria, joins on a free transfer whilst his ex-England semi-pro team-mate Price arrives initially on loan with a view to a permanent move. Moving out though is midfielder Martin McDonald, who joins **Southport** for a new club record fee of £20,000. McDonald is in the 'Port side which records one of the largest Conference wins of the decade, a 7-1 success over **Farnborough Town** at Haig Avenue. Another former England semi-pro player, midfielder Dereck Brown, returns to the Vauxhall Conference by joining **Welling United** from Walton & Hersham in a four-figure deal. **Bromsgrove Rovers** finally go through to the first round proper of the FA Cup by beating **Kettering Town** 2-1 in the second replay at Rocingham Road. Meanwhile, in the league, **Macclesfield Town** return to the top of the table with a 1-0 win at **Hednesford Town** in front of another 2,000-olus crowd at Keys Park whilst **Dover Athletic's** 2-1 defeat of **Kidderminster Harriers** sees **Dagenham & Redbridge** go back to the bottom. The Daggers are beaten 2-0 at **Kettering Town**. The Vauxhall Conference's top marksman for the past two seasons, **Gateshead's** Paul Dobson, leaves the International Stadium to join UniBond League neighbours Bishop Auckland for a four-figure fee. Dobson scored 51 goals in two seasons with the north east outfit. Another Wycombe Wanderers double winner, Simon Hutchinson, moves north to sign for **Macclesfield Town,** rejoining ex-Wanderer Tony Hemmings at Moss Rose. The first round proper of the FA Cup sees a shock when little Cinderford Town knock out **Bromsgrove Rovers** 2-1. **Farnborough Town** hold Second Division Brentford to a 1-1 draw at Griffin Park and **Woking** force a replay against Barnet at Underhill. **Runcorn's** Mike Bignall scores to take Wigan Athletic back to Springfield Park whilst **Kidderminster Harriers** were held to a 2-2 draw by ICIS League side Sutton United at Aggborough. There were defeats for **Stevenage Borough** at Hereford, **Slough Town** at home to Plymouth and **Northwich Victoria** against Scunthorpe and the only outright winners were **Telford United**, who overcame UniBond Leaguers Witton Albion 2-1 at Buck's Head.

13th - 26th November 1995

Woking extend their winning league sequence to seven straight wins with a 3-2 victory at **Slough Town.** In his first Vauxhall Conference start of the season, **Dagenham & Redbridge** striker Gary Bennett scores the fastest goal of the season, netting after just 15 seconds against **Halifax Town** but it wasn't enough to lift the Daggers off the foot of the table. **Telford United's** cup exploits have caused them to slip into the relegation zone along with **Bath City** and **Dover Athletic** whilst **Macclesfield Town's** excellent 4-0 away win at **Altrincham** takes them six points clear of **Woking. Runcorn's** poor run of form saw the end of John Carroll's four and a half year term as manager. The final straw was a humiliating 8-0 defeat at home to **Stevenage Borough** which followed a 4-2 FA Cup replay defeat at Wigan. There was little joy for the other Conference cup survivors either, as only **Woking**, who beat Barnet after extra-time, went through. **Kidderminster Harriers** lost at Sutton United on penalties after a 1-1 draw, **Farnborough Town** were comprehensively beaten by Brentford and Crewe won the Cheshire derby against **Altrincham** at Moss Lane. **Woking's** 100 per cent home record came to an end when they were held to a goalless draw by third placed **Kidderminster Harriers** in front of a crowd in excess of 2,200 at Kingfield. Alan Nicholls, the former England under-21 international and Cheltenham Town goalkeeper, died in a motorcycle accident shortly after assisting **Stalybridge Celtic** at **Dover Athletic**. The ex-Gillingham and Plymouth player had only signed for Celtic on loan the previous evening. **Welling United** celebrated their largest ever victory in senior football by hammering ICIS League Third Division side Southall 12-0 in the London Senior Cup.

27th November - 10th December 1995

Runcorn place the former Manchester City and England winger Peter Barnes in temporary charge of team affairs at Canal Street. Aylesbury United's record goalscorer, Cliff Hercules, joins **Slough Town** for a £10,000 fee. **Kidderminster Harriers'** nine-match unbeaten home sequence comes to an end when struggling **Bath City** win 2-1 at Aggborough. Meanwhile, twice player of the year, Chris Brindley, is transfer listed by manager Graham Allner. The 26-year-old has been with Harriers since 1992. Carl Alford's consolation goal for **Kettering Town** in their 2-1 defeat at lowly **Dover Athletic** was enough to win him the *Mail on Sunday's* goalscorers award for November. Alford now has 16 league goals to his credit. Leaders **Macclesfield Town** are brought down to earth with a bump as improving **Stevenage Borough** beat them 4-0 at Broadhall Way in front of a 2,00-plus crowd. **Telford United** finally bow out of the FA Cup when Notts County win 2-0 at Buck's Head. **Woking**, the only other Conference survivors in the second round, are held to a 1-1 draw by former

Conference outfit Enfield. Gary Robson, younger brother of Bryan, joins **Gateshead** from Bradford City. **Kidderminster Harriers** announce a big profit of £41,561 for the year ending 31 May 1995. **Altrincham** extend their run without success to ten games, their worst sequence for four years, with a 1-0 defeat by **Stalybridge Celtic. Woking** take advantage of **Macclesfield Town's** postponed game at **Welling United** to peg the gap at thre top to five points with a 3-2 win at **Runcorn. Dover Athletic** are back at the foot of the table after losing the basement battle against **Dagenham & Redbridge.**

11th December 1995 - 1st January 1996 Ambitious Beazer Homes League Premier Division leaders, Rushden & Diamonds, make a £100,000 bid for neighbouring **Kettering Town** duo Carl Alford and Steve Stott. The latter does make the move but the Conference's leading marksman declines the offer. Peter Barnes is given an entention to his temporary post at **Runcorn. Kidderminster Harriers'** prolific scorer Paul Davies equalls the all-time scoring Conference record with 172 goals. He pulled level with ex-Barnet and Runcorn striker Mark Carter by netting one of the three Harriers goals in the victory at **Hednesford Town. Woking** mark the end of 1995 by securing yet another home win, thus making them unbeaten at Kingfield throughout the year. Former Manchester City defender, Nicky Reid, leaves the club to join Third Division Bury. They also win through to the third round of the FA Cup after a Darran Hay double sinks Enfield in a replay. **Stevenage Borough** move into second place in the league after two successive away wins at **Dagenham & Redbridge** and **Morecambe.** For the third season in a row the Worcestershire derby between **Kidderminster Harriers** and **Bromsgrove Rovers** attracted the biggest Conference attendance of the season to date. A New Year's Day crowd of 4,481 watched Harriers return to the top four with a 1-0 victory. A few days earlier, on Boxing Day, Harriers and England semi-pro striker Leroy May scored one of the fastest goals in the hsitory of the Vauxhall Conference when he gave his side the lead at Rovers after only nine seconds. **Bath City** sell top scorer Dean Birkby to Yeovil Town for a £10,000 fee and **Farnborough Town** pay Kingstonian £7,500 for midfielder Phil Wingfield. Further transfers see **Altrincham** sign a new-look strike force in Mark Hughes from Runcorn and Dean Pritchard from Witton Albion, **Dagenham & Redbridge** add Ian Stringfellow from **Kettering Town** and **Welling United** make permanent the transfer of striker Ollie Morah from Cambridge United.

2nd - 14th January 1996 Eight clubs receive the Football League's approval that their grounds are satisfactory for promotion. However, only **Woking, Kidderminster Harriers**, and **Macclesfield Town** are in with a realistic chance of the title this season. The other clubs are **Bath City, Dover Athletic, Gateshead, Kettering Town** and **Southport. Woking** finally bow out of this season's FA Cup competition when they lost 2-0 at Second Division Swindon Town. **Runcorn** confirm the appointment of Peter Barnes as manager on a permanent basis. The ex-Manchester City, United, West Brom and England winger will combine his duties with the first-team with a role on the commercial and promotional side. **Gateshead** sign former Barnet and England semi-pro midfielder Kenny Lowe from Birmingham. Lowe returns to the International Stadium after a ten-year absence. **Dover Athletic** move out of the bottom three for the first time since August after a late winner against **Telford United. Slough Town** are getting themselves into trouble due to a nine-match unsuccessful home spell stretching back to 12th September. Local Lincolnshire club, AO Jaffa FC, withdraw their application to join the Conference after receiving setbacks to secure groundsharing agreements at both Notts County and Nottingham Forest! The league's top marksman, **Kettering Town's** Carl Alford, declines a £70,000 offer to join Second Division York City. **Gateshead** sign the mercurial John Burridge. The 44-year-old took the place of 42-year-old Steve Sherwood for the Spalding Cup tie against **Halifax Town.** Junior Hunter, the full-back released by **Kettering Town** just before Christmas, scores four times on his debut against **Morecambe** playing in attack. **Farnborough Town's** striker, Trevor Senior, announces his retirement from the game to take up the post of Football in the Community Officer at Beazer Homes club Dorchester Town.

15th - 28th January 1996 **Woking's** record breaking bid for a third consecutive FA Umbro Trophy success ended at the first round stage when Surrey neighbours Carshalton Athletic scored the shock of the day with a 3-1 win. There is also a shock for another former winner, **Telford United**, who are beaten at Burton Albion, whilst a number of others face tricky replays. **Altrincham** become the latest club to receive assistance from the Sports Grounds Initiative. The Robins are awarded a grant of £250,000 towards the redevelopment of Moss Lane. **Stevenage Borough's** march up the table hasn't gone unnoticed with a host of League scouts rumoured to be watching striker Barry Hayles and Nigerian defender Efetobor Sodje. **Morecambe** are beaten at Emley in their FA Umbro Trophy replay as are **Stalybridge Celtic** at Gresley Rovers. David Leworthy's 85th minute equaliser for **Dover Athletic** saves them at Cheltenham Town to force a third game. The whole league programme on January 27th is postponed due to bad weather.

Macclesfield Town's Phil Power (white shorts) trying to get passed the tackle from Mark Smith of Stevenage Borough. Photo: John Rooney.

Dagenham's Steve Connor gets in a powerful header above Woking's Clive Walker (stripes). Photo: Alan Coomes.

29th January - 11th February 1996

Veteran defender Glyn Creaser, who served both Barnet and Wycombe Wanderers with distinction for many years, joins the relegation battle at **Dagenham & Redbridge**, signing from Rushden & Diamonds. **Woking** opened their new £1.35 million stand before the home game against **Bromsgrove Rovers.** The 1-1 draw extended the Cards' home sequence to 23 games without defeat. **Stevenage Borough** narrow the gap at the top of the table to just one point after their 4-1 success against **Runcorn** and **Macclesfield Town's** 3-2 home defeat by neighbours **Altrincham.** Former **Kidderminster Harriers** midfielder Richard Forsyth becomes one of the most valuable recruits from the Vuaxhall Conference. After making his 30th appearances for Birmingham City, Harriers received a further payment for the 24-year-old, taking the total fee in excess of £100,000. England semi-pro manager, Tony Jennings, announces his squad for the international against the Republic of Ireland and includes potential new caps, Lee Hughes (**Kidderminster Harriers**), Kenny Cramman (**Gateshead**), Mark Smith (**Stevenage Borough**), Mark Tucker (**Woking**) and Carl Alford (**Kettering Town**). The second round of the FA Umbro Trophy sees exits for **Dover Athletic** at Boreham Wood, **Altrincham** at Guiseley, **Welling United** at Hyde United, **Halifax Town** against **Bromsgrove Rovers** and **Slough Town** at home by **Kettering Town.**

12th - 25th February 1996

Slough Town's home Trophy defeat by **Kettering Town** hastened the departure of the Rebels manager Dave Russell and his assistant Laurie Craker. The club's Football in the Community Officer, Brian McDermott, takes over in temporary charge. **Macclesfield Town** strengthen their squad by signing **Northwich Victoria** defender Darren Tinson for a 'substantial' five-figure fee. **Farnborough Town** spend again by signing Worthing's highly-rated young defender Spencer Mintram for a £5,000 fee. Carl Alford breaks the 20 league goal mark when scoring a 90th minute winner for **Kettering Town** in their 2-1 win at **Slough Town.** There is also an important win for **Dover Athletic**, who beat title contenders **Woking** by the odd goal in seven. Star striker David Leworthy scored all four goals for Dover. Brian McDermott is confirmed as the new manager of **Slough Town. Kidderminster Harriers'** striker Paul Davies finally breaks the all-time goalscoring record for the Vauxhall Conference. His 13th minute header against **Slough Town** was his 173rd Conference goal. The Vauxhall Conference re-presents its application for a 24 club constitution to the Football League. It was initially turned down following an FA appeal last year. The top of the table now sees **Stevenage Borough** and **Macclesfield Town** both level on 28 points.

26th February - 10th March 1996

Slough Town sign the former Arsenal and England defender Kenny Sansom. **Macclesfield Town** boss Sammy McIlroy rules himself out of the running for the vacant post at Burnley. **Woking's** Junior Hunter marks his remarkable transformation from full-back to striker by being named as February's *Mail on Sunday* goalscorer of the month. Hunter has now scored 13 league goals for the Cards. **Hednesford Town** make their first money signing of the season by paying a four-figure fee plus goalkeeper Richard Williams for Atherstone United midfielder Keith Russell. The third round of the FA Umbro Trophy sees all but **Kettering Town**, beaten in the all-Conference tie at **Stevenage Borough**, survive with two games going to replays. **Macclesfield Town** hammer **Halifax Town** 7-0 but still trail **Stevenage Borough** by four points. **Welling United**, renowned for producing young talent, see another, 16-year-old striker Richard Dimmock, come on as a substitute against **Kidderminster Harriers. Bromsgrove Rovers** progress in their Trophy replay against **Bath City** but the game between **Northwich Victoria** and **Merthyr Tydfil** goes to a third game after a 2-2 draw after extra-time at the Drill Field.

11th - 24th March 1996

Stevenage Borough striker Barry Hayles, who has overtaken Carl Alford as leading Conference scorer, attracts bids from Luton, Doncaster and an un-named Dutch First Division outfit. Meanwhile, Borough extend their unbeaten run to 17 games by defeating **Kidderminster Harriers** 4-1 at Broadhall Way. **Welling United's** teenage striker Richard Dimmock becomes the youngest player to score a Conference goal when he netted against **Morecambe. Runcorn** collected their first league victory of the year, beating **Farnborough Town** 1-0 at Cherrywood Road. After scoring 203 goals in 278 appearances, striker John Coleman leaves **Morecambe** to join UniBond League First Division promotion chasers Lancaster City. **Northwich Victoria** finally overcome former Conference outfit Merthyr Tydfil 3-0 in their FA Umbro Trophy second replay. **Runcorn**, 21st in the table, sack manager Peter Barnes and appoint the ex-Everton winger Ronnie Goodlass. **Halifax Town's** John Bird resigns after another heavy defeat, a 6-1 reversal at **Kidderminster Harriers**. Youth team boss George Mulhall assumes temporary charge. **Morecambe** appoint erstwhile Barrow manager Tony Hesketh as number two to Jimmy Harvey. There is a shock is the quarter-finals of the FA Umbro Trophy as leaders **Stevenage Borough** are beaten 3-2 at UniBond Leaguers Hyde United. **Gateshead** are also losers at another UniBond club, Chorley, but both **Macclesfield Town** and **Northwich Victoria** progress after wins away at Gresley Rovers and **Bromsgrove Rovers** respectively..

25th March - 8th April 1996 Graham Carr ends his six month term in charge of **Dagenham & Redbridge** after a 1-0 home defeat by fellow strugglers **Bath City.** Carl Alford finally makes a big money move, not into the League, but to Beazer Homes League Premier Division leaders Rushden & Diamonds who pay neighbours **Kettering Town** a new non-League record fee of £85,000 to secure his services. **Stevenage Borough's** 17-match unbeaten run is ended by second placed **Hednesford Town,** who win 2-1 at Keys Park. Transfer deadline day passes with the lowest amount of activity for ten years. Former Canal Street favourite Karl Thomas returns to strugglers **Runcorn** from Bangor City, who also add Stockport County forward Gavin Allen and Rhyl winger Tommy Murphy to their squad. **Northwich Victoria** sign promising striker Lee Steele from Bootle and ex-Wigan front man Paul Tait whilst title favourites **Stevenage Borough** add to their squad strength by signing **Slough Town** defender Alan Paris, former Borough striker Neil Trebble from Scarborough, Andy Ansah from Peterborough and veteran former England semi-pro skipper Dave Howell, the erstwhile coach at Birmingham. **Woking** narrow the gap at the top to four points by beating **Hednesford Town** 3-0 at Kingfield, thus leap-frogging the Pitmen into second place. Clive Walker bags two of the goals to take his tally of league goals to 16. **Dagenham & Redbridge** turn to old favourite Ted Hardy as manager for the fourth time. They move off the foot of the table with an Easter Monday win at **Bath City** but they and **Dover Athletic** are still nine points adrift of safety. **Bromsgrove Rovers** book their place in the Spalding Cup final for the second successive season after beating **Kettering Town** in the semi-final. They will meet **Macclesfield Town,** who beat **Southport** 6-5 on aggregate in their semi-final. A season's best attendance of 4,583 watch **Woking** defeat **Macclesfield Town** 3-2 at Kingfield on Easter Saturday but almost 4,000 saw the Cards lose the 'six-pointer' at Broadhall Way as **Stevenage Borough** strengthened their title aspirations with a 4-0 victory.

9th - 22nd April 1996 John Carroll, the former manager of **Runcorn,** takes over as the new boss at **Halifax Town.** He appoints his number two at Canal Street, Billy Rodaway, into a similar position at The Shay. **Northwich Victoria** and **Macclesfield Town** both take giant steps to Wembley when they open up first-leg leads in their FA Umbro Trophy semi-finals. The Vics take a 2-1 lead to the Drill Field against Hyde United and the Silkmen have a 3-1 advantage against another UniBond League side, Chorley. The title race is thrown wide open again as **Stevenage Borough** are held at home by **Stalybridge Celtic** whilst **Woking** win at **Gateshead.** Meanwhile, Borough's manager Paul Fairclough is linked with the managerial vacancy at Third Division Scunthorpe. **Halifax Town** receive a boost when Calderdale Council announce that they would not be selling The Shay for development after all. It would be kept as a local facility for sport and leisure. Another council, Tameside, give **Stalybridge Celtic** a boost by granting them £35,000 towards their £347,000 ground re-development plans. **Macclesfield Town** manager Sammy McIlroy is also linked with the vacancy at Scunthorpe, but is able to celebrate with his current charges as they draw 1-1 at Chorley to reach the final of the FA Umbro Trophy with a 4-2 aggregate win. It will be an all-Cheshire final as **Northwich Victoria** also get through on a 3-1 aggregate success over Hyde United. The gap at the top is again four points as this time **Woking** are held to a draw at **Halifax Town** and **Stevenage Borough** win at **Bath City.**

22nd April - End of Season The first relegation issue is settled as **Runcorn** end their 15-year term as a Conference club following a 3-2 home defeat by **Telford United.** The Spalding Cup final is evenly poised as **Bromsgrove Rovers** earn a 1-1 draw at **Macclesfield Town** in the first-leg. **Stevenage Borough** clinch the championship for the first time in their history and in only their second season in the top non-League competition. Borough's title success was confirmed after they had earned a 1-1 draw at home to **Morecambe** whilst challengers **Woking** went down 3-0 at **Northwich Victoria. Dagenham & Redbridge** confirmed their relegation from the Conference after losing 1-0 at champions **Stevenage Borough.** The Daggers are expected to return to the ICIS League next season and have already confirmed that Ted Hardy will remain in charge. **Bromsgrove Rovers** become the first side to successfully defend the Spalding Cup after a 3-1 second-leg win over **Macclesfield Town.** Rushden & Diamonds, champions of the Beazer Homes League, and Hayes, winners of the ICIS League, have both been confirmed as promotees for 1996/97. The UniBond League have no suitable promotion candidates so only two clubs will be relegated. Runners-up **Woking** become the first club since 1985 to complete a season without suffering a home defeat. **Hednesford Town** finish in third spot, thus becoming only the second promoted team in over a decade to earn a top three finish in their inaugural Conference campaign. **Stevenage Borough** striker, Barry Hayles, wins the *Mail on Sunday* goalscorer of the year award, netting 29 league goals, six ahead of Joe O'Connor of **Hednesford Town.** Second Division Bristol Rovers announce that they are to end their ten-year groundshare agreement with **Bath City** and move to the home of Bristol RUFC. **Macclesfield Town** lift the FA Umbro Trophy after a thrilling 3-1 victory over Cheshire neighbours **Northwich Victoria** at Wembley.

ALTRINCHAM

Formed: 1903

President:
Noel White

Vice President:
Bill King

Chairman:
Gerry Berman

Vice-Chairman
Len Rosenfield

Directors:
J.King,
C.Nash
I.Foden.
M.Harris
D.Keeling
R.Webb

Manager:
John King

Ass.Manager & Football Secretary:
Graham Heathcote

Commercial Director:
Rod Barry

Commercial Director/ Press Officer
Mark Harris

Physiotherapist:
Mandy Johnson

Trainer:
Les Attwood

After a nailbiting close season in which the club came within a whisker of closure, it was a relief just to be playing Conference football again just a month after manager John King became the owner of Altrincham FC. Having survived the threat of closure, the on-field priority was th ensure that the lack of preparation for the new campaign did not result in relegation, and throughout the season the fans had to remind themselves that existence was a very special achievement.

But, the season came as an anti-climax after the cup run and title challenge of 1994/95. The sale of Neil Morton to Barrow three days before the first fixture left the side short of strikepower, with partner Andy Green also allowed to leave for Holker Street before Christmas having netted just three goals after finishing the previous campaign as leading marksman. From the outset, the team suffered a dreadful run of red cards, and by the season's end had collected a full team's worth.

The first win came in injury time at Southport, where skipper Mike Carmody scored a screamer, and when the next four games brought maximum points, everyone thought the corner had been turned. Robins greatest constant was their inconsistency however, and nine matches followed without a win. The FA Cup brought frustration as opponents Crewe exercised their right to a postponement due to one of their players being called up for international duty. In the replay, Alty went out 0-2 at Moss Lane, and also lost a sizeable fee from *Match of the Day*, who would have covered the original game.

The turn of the year brought strikers Dean Pritchard and Mark Hughes to the club, whilst the season's high and low points came within a fortnight of each other in late January. First, league leaders Macclesfield Town were beaten at Moss Rose, and then Robins crashed out of the FA Trophy at Guiseley. Worse was yet to come, a record-equalling 0-7 humiliation following at Morecambe seven days later.

Mercifully, this was to prove the turning point and with the emergence of 'keeper Jerome John and the return after injury of Ricky Harris, the league was slowly climbed. A brief glimpse of true class arrived in the shape of former Bolton man Tony Kelly, but he quickly faded from the scene. Centre-back Paul France took the player of the year award for the second time in his career, whilst Stuart Terry finished as leading scorer. No predictions for 96/97, but the nucleus of a strong squad has already been assembled. **Mark Harris**

Altrincham FC: Back Row (L-R); Barry Butler, Paul France, Niell Hardy, Matt Dickens, Jerome John, Mark Maddocks, Paul Cain. Front; Ian Horrigan, Darren Heesom, Stuart Terry, Chris Sharratt, Mick Carmody, Neil Doherty, Darren Pybus, Steve Carroll

Altrincham

Match No.	Date	Comp.	Venue H/A	Opponents	Result	League Pos.	Goalscorers (Times if known)	Attendance
1	Aug 19	GMVC		Kettering Town	Lost 1-3		Bolland	969
2	22	GMVC		Telford United	Lost 0-2			840
3	26	GMVC		Dagenham	Lost 0-1			662
4	28	GMVC		Gateshead	Drew 1-1		Oliver	640
5	Sep 2	GMVC		Kidderminster H.	Drew 1-1		Green	881
6	5	GMVC		Southport	Won 2-1		Carmody, og	1127
7	9	GMVC		Bromsgrove Rovers	Won 3-0		Terry 2, Whalley	773
8	12	GMVC		Morecambe	Won 3-0		Allan, Hardy 2	755
9	16	GMVC		Slough Town	Won 2-1		Hardy, Sharratt	591
10	23	GMVC		Halifax Town	Won 3-0		Hardy, Green	1085
11	30	GMVC		Stevenage Borough	Drew 1-1		Green	1615
12	Oct 7	GMVC		Bath City	Lost 1-2		Terry	1057
13	14	GMVC		Woking Town	Lost 0-2			2081
14	21	GMVC		Kidderminster H.	Drew 1-1		Terry	2429
15	28	GMVC		Dover Athletic	Drew 2-2		Sharratt	929
16	Nov 4	GMVC		Welling United	Drew 1-1		Royle	623
17	18	GMVC		Macclesfield Town	Lost 0-4			1648
18	21	FAC 1		Crewe Alexandra	Lost 0-2			3062
19	25	GMVC		Kettering Town	Lost 2-4		Heesom, Terry	1369
20	28	CSC2		Warrington	Won 4-0		Terry, Green 2, Sharratt	273
21	Dec 2	GMVC		Runcorn	Drew 2-2		Terry 2p	707
22	5	SPT 2		Morecambe	Lost 4-6		Green, Hardy 2, Sharratt	503
23	9	GMVC		Stalybridge Celtic	Lost 0-1			654
24	16	GMVC		Telford United	Won 1-0		Hardy	633
25	26	GMVC		Northwich Victoria	Lost 1-2		France	1278
26	Jan 1	GMVC		Northwich Victoria	Lost 3-4		Sharratt 2, Butler	1076
27	6	GMVC		Bromsgrove Rovers	Drew 0-0			852
28	13	GMVC		Slough Town	Lost 0-1			648
29	20	FAT 1		Colwyn Bay	Drew 3-3		France, Terry 1p, Hughes	598
30	23	FAT 1R		Colwyn Bay	Won 2-0		France, Reid	527
31	30	GMVC		Macclesfield Town	Won 3-2		Terry 2p, Pritchard	1301
32	Feb 3	GMVC		Welling United	Won 1-0		Doherty	762
33	10	FAT 2		Guiseley	Lost 0-4			964
34	17	GMVC		Morecambe	Lost 0-7			n983
35	20	CSC SF		Witton Albion	Drew 1-1		Royle	460
36	24	GMVC		Farnborough Town	Drew 2-2		Pritchard 2	580
37	Mar 2	GMVC		Southport	Drew 1-1		Kelly	851
38	5	GMVC		Runcorn	Won 1-0		Terry	607
39	9	GMVC		Woking	Won 2-0		France, Butler	972
40	12	CSC SF		Witton Albion	Lost 1-2		France	481
41	16	GMVC		Halifax Town	Drew 1-1		Terry	755
42	27	GMVC		Gateshead	Won 3-2		France, Terry p, Hardy	357
43	30	GMVC		Stevenage Borough	Lost 0-2			838
44	Apr 6	GMVC		Hednesford Town	Lost 1-2		Doherty	1010
45	8	GMVC		Farnborough Town	Drew 1-1		Terry p	706
46	13	GMVC		Dover Athletic	Won 4-1		Harris 2, Doherty 2	1070
47	20	GMVC		Hednesford Town	Won 2-1		Hardy, Doherty	731
48	23	GMVC		Stalybridge Celtic	Won 1-0		France	608
49	27	GMVC		Bath City	Drew 2-2		Hardy 2	489
50	May 4	GMVC		Dagenham	Won 3-1		Hardy, Terry 2	748

Altrincham

1	2	3	4	5	6	7	8	9	10	11	12	14	Match No.
Collings	Anderson	Heesom	France	Bolland	Leitch	Terry	Whalley	Green	Cross	Cockram	Carmody	Kendall	1
Collings	Anderson	Bolland	France	Butler	O'Neill	Terry	Whalley	Green	Cross	Oliver	Cockram	Kendall	2
Collings	Anderson	Heesom	France	Butler	Cross	Terry	Whalley	Green	Carmody	Oliver	Allan	Hardy	3
Collings	Cross	Heesom	France	Butler	Oliver	Terry	Whalley	Green	Carmody	Sharratt	Hardy	Bolland	4
Collings	Cross	Heesom	France	Butler	Oliver	Terry	Whalley	Green	Carmody	Sharratt	Hardy	Bolland	5
Jones	Cross	Heesom	France	Butler	Hardy	Terry	Whalley	Green	Carmody	Sharratt	Oliver	Bolland	6
Collings	Cross	Oliver	France	Butler	Allan	Terry	Whalley	Hardy	Carmody	Sharratt	Royle	Heesom	7
Collings	Cross	Oliver	France	Butler	Allan	Terry	Whalley	Hardy	Carmody	Sharratt	Royle	Heesom	8
Collings	Cross	Heesom	France	Butler	Hardy	Terry	Whalley	Green	Carmody	Sharratt	Royle	Allan	9
Collings	Cross	Heesom	France	Butler	Hardy	Terry	Whalley	Green	Carmody	Sharratt	Royle	Bolland	10
Collings	Cross	Heesom	France	Butler	Hardy	Terry	Whalley	Green	Carmody	Sharratt	Royle	Oliver	11
Collings	Cross	Heesom	France	Butler	Hardy	Terry	Whalley	Green	Carmody	Sharratt	Royle	Oliver	12
Collings	Cross	Heesom	France	Butler	Hardy	Terry	Whalley	Green	Reid	Sharratt	Oliver	Anderson	13
Collings	Cross	Oliver	France	Butler	Reid	Terry	Whalley	Green	Carmody	Sharratt	Heesom	Royle	14
Collings	Cross	Oliver	France	Butler	Reid	Terry	Whalley	Green	Carmody	Sharratt	Heesom	Anderson	15
Collings	Cross	Heesom	France	Allan	Reid	Terry	Whalley	Royle	Carmody	Sharratt	Oliver	Anderson	16
Collings	Cross	Heesom	France	Hardy	Reid	Terry	Whalley	Royle	Carmody	Sharratt	Zumrutel	Daughtry	17
Collings	Cross	Heesom	France	Hardy	Reid	Terry	Whalley	Zumrutel	Anderson	Sharratt	Royle	Oliver	18
Collings	Cross	Heesom	France	Hardy	Reid	Terry	Challender	Zumrutel	Anderson	Sharratt	Green	Daughtry	19
John	Cross	Heesom	France	Hardy	Bolland	Terry	Zumrutel	Green	Anderson	Sharratt	Oliver	Royle	20
Collings	Cross	Heesom	France	Bolland	Daughtry	Terry	Challender	Green	Zumrutel	Sharratt	Hardy	Whalley	21
Collings	Cross	Heesom	France	Anderson	Daughtry	Terry	Whalley	Green	Hardy	Sharratt	Bolland	Zumrutel	22
Collings	Cross	Heesom	France	Oliver	Reid	Daughtry	Whalley	Zumrutel	Hardy	Sharratt	Royle	Clancy	23
Collings	Cross	Heesom	France	Oliver	Reid	Hall	Whalley	Royle	Hardy	Sharratt	Bolland	Clancy	24
Collings	Cross	Heesom	France	Reid	Hall	Terry	Hardy	Hughes	Carmody	Sharratt	Butler	Royle	25
Collings	Cross	Heesom	France	Reid	Hall	Terry	Royle	Hughes	Carmody	Sharratt	Hardy	Challender	26
John	Cross	Heesom	France	Reid	Challender	Terry	Hardy	Hughes	Butler	Sharratt	Hall	Royle	27
Collings	Cross	Heesom	France	Reid	Challender	Terry	Hardy	Hughes	Butler	Pritchard	Bolland	Clancy	28
Collings	Cross	Heesom	France	Reid	Challender	Terry	Hardy	Hughes	Butler	Royle	Anderson	Clancy	29
Collings	Cross	Heesom	France	Reid	Challender	Terry	Hardy	Hughes	Butler	Anderson	Royle	Clancy	30
Collings	Cross	Heesom	France	Reid	Anderson	Terry	Doherty	Pritchard	Hardy	Clancy	Royle	Bolland	31
Collings	Cross	Heesom	Butler	Anderson	Horrigan	Terry	Doherty	Pritchard	Hardy	Clancy	Royle	Bolland	32
Collings	Cross	Heesom	France	Anderson	Horrigan	Terry	Doherty	Challender	Hardy	Clancy	Royle	Bolland	33
John	Cross	Heesom	France	Butler	Anderson	Terry	Doherty	Hughes	Hardy	Pritchard	Challender	Horrigan	34
John	Cross	Heesom	France	Reid	Challender	Terry	Horrigan	Hughes	Hardy	Anderson	Bolland	Royle	35
John	Cross	Heesom	France	Reid	Butler	Terry	Doherty	Hughes	Kelly	Pritchard	Carmody	Horrigan	36
John	Cross	Heesom	France	Reid	Butler	Terry	Doherty	Pritchard	Carmody	Kelly	Hughes	Royle	37
John	Cross	Heesom	France	Reid	Butler	Terry	Doherty	Pritchard	Carmody	Kelly	Hughes	Royle	38
John	Cross	Heesom	France	Reid	Butler	Terry	Doherty	Pritchard	Harris	Kelly	Hughes	Hardy	39
John	Cross	Heesom	France	Reid	Butler	Terry	Hardy	Hughes	Harris	Kelly	Horrigan	Challender	40
John	Cross	Heesom	France	Reid	Butler	Terry	Harris	Pritchard	Carmody	Kelly	Hughes	Hardy	41
John	Cross	Heesom	Doherty	Reid	Butler	Terry	Doherty	Pritchard	Harris	Kelly	Carmody	Horrigan	42
John	Cross	Heesom	France	Reid	Butler	Terry	Doherty	Hardy	Carmody	Kelly	Horrigan	Doyle	43
John	Cross	Heesom	France	Reid	Butler	Terry	Harris	Hardy	Carmody	Kelly	Doherty	Armstrong	44
John	Cross	Heesom	France	Reid	Butler	Terry	Harris	Hardy	Carmody	Kelly	France	Armstrong	45
John	Cross	Heesom	France	Reid	Butler	Terry	Harris	Hardy	Carmody	Doherty	Armstrong	Doyle	46
John	Cross	Heesom	France	Reid	Butler	Terry	Harris	Hardy	Carmody	Doherty	Armstrong	Doyle	47
John	Cross	Heesom	France	Reid	Butler	Terry	Harris	Hardy	Carmody	Doherty	Armstrong	Anderson	48
John	Cross	Heesom	France	Horrigan	Butler	Terry	Harris	Hardy	Carmody	Doherty	Armstrong	Doyle	49
John	Cross	Heesom	France	Reid	Butler	Terry	Harris	Hardy	Carmody	Doherty	Armstrong	Doyle	50

JOHN KING

One of non-league football's most charismatic figures wrote a new chapter in his association with Altrincham F.C. when he became the outright owner of the club in June 1995, and is the only serving Conference manager to combine duties of manager and director.

John King returned to the club for his third spell as manager in February 1994, when his arrival sparked a massive revival in playing fortunes and kept the Robins in the Conference at the end of a season in which relegation had at one time looked certain.He started his playing career as a junior with Everton and Shrewsbury Town before goimg into non-league with Kirby Town,Wigan Athletic and Northwich Victoria.He then joined Altrincham in 1977 and began a highly successful spell at Moss Lane. One of the toughest competitors to have entered the non-league scene,John King skippered the Robins to two league titles,the F.A.Trophy and the Bob Lord Trophy, as well as featuring in the club's many F.A.Cup giantkilling exploits of the 70's and early 80's.

His career was cut short by an injury in the 1982 F.A.Trophy Final but he soon started his managerial career at South Liverpool before returning to Moss Lane as manager in January 1984. In 1986, he became the first man to captain and manage an Altrincham side to F.A.Trophy success, but left 24 hours after the game to take over at Runcorn, his victims at Wembley. Returning to Moss Lane in 1988, John almost steered the Robins into the Football League in the 1990-91 season,but gain left the club,this time for spells as manager of Barrow and then as assistant manager at Bury where he remained until answering the SOS to rescue his old club.

John King on the ice at Northwick in January 1996

Programme details:
36 pages for £1.20.
Editors- Mark Harris/ Terry Surridge

Any other club publications:
'Altrincham F.C.-Kingdom Come'
150 Page account of 1994-95 season and aftermath. £9.99 +p&p.

Local Newspapers:
Sale & Altrincham Messenger
Sale & Altrincham Express
Manchester Evening News

Local Radio Stations:
GMR (BBC)
Signal Radio

ALTRINCHAM - PLAYING SQUAD 1996-97

Player	Honours	Birthplace and date	Transfer Fees	Previous Clubs
GOALKEEPERS				
Jerome John		London 1976		West Ham Utd, Dulwich Hamlet
Matt Dickins		Sheffield 3/9/70		Sheffield U, Lincoln C, Blackburn R, Stockport Co
DEFENDERS				
George Shepherd	GMVC, DWC	Manchester 25/2/67		Manchester C, Bolton W, Hyde U, Macclesfield T
Andy Reid	ESP, CSC	Davyhulme 4/7/62		Everton, Witton A, Southport, Runcorn, Altrincham, Bury
Paul France		Holmfirth 10/9/68		Huddersfield, Bristol C, Burnley
Barry Butler		Farnworth 4/6/62		Atherton T, Chester C Barrow
Ian Horrigan		Liverpool		Liverpool, Prescot, Knowsley U, Conwy U, Barrow, Morecambe
Darren Heesom		Warrington 8/5/68		Burnley, Altrincham, Macclesfield T, Witton Alb, Hyde Utd, Barrow.
MIDFIELDERS				
Tony Kelly	FRT	Prescot 1/10/64		Liverpool, Prescot, Wigan, Stoke, WBA, Shrewsbury, Bolton, P.Vale, WiganWBoro,
Dean Pritchard		Rotherham 10/9/66		Ovenden West Riding, Emley, Accrington Stanley, Witton A
Mick Carmody		Huddersfield 9/2/66		Huddersfield, Emley, Tranmere R, Emley
Stuart Terry	ESP			Bangor City
Neil Hardy	DC	Manchester		Crewe Alexandra, Northwich Victoria
FORWARDS				
Chris Sharratt		West Kirby 13/8/70		Bangor C, Caernarfon, Stalybridge C, Wigan, Macclesfield T
Paul Williams	NIreland Int.	Sheffield 8/9/63		Distillery, Leeds, Nuneaton B, Preston, Newport Co, Sheff.U, St'port, WBA, Lincoln
Ricky Harris		Manchester 12/7/67		Ashton Utd, Altrincham, Hyde Utd, Runcorn, Hyde Utd
Neil Doherty		Preston		Bamber Bridge, Runcorn
Paul Cain		Liverpool		Local Football
Ian Doyle		Manchester		Local Football
Mark Hughes		Liverpool 19/12/68		Irlam T, Altrincham, Witton A, Congleton T, Buxton, Runcorn

Departures during season:
Andy Allan (Salford C), Neil Morton (Barrow), Steve O'Neill (Bamber B), Dave Cockram (Chorley), Andy Reid (Chorley - Loan), Soner Zumrutel (Released), Paul Daughtry (Released), Andy Green (Barrow), Neil Whalley (Witton A), Darren Oliver (Barrow), Mark Clancy (Trafford), Phil Bolland (Released), Greg Challender (Stalybridge C), Shaun Constable (Halifax T), Darren Royle (Winsford U - Loan).
Players on loan during season:
Derek Hall (Rochdale), Martin Jones (Tranmere).
Departures during close season: Paul Collings, Lee Anderson (Released), Steve Cross (Conwy U).

Moss Lane, Altrincham

ADDRESS:
Moss Lane, Altrincham, Cheshire WA15 8AP.

TELEPHONE NUMBER: 0161 928 1045. Fax: 0161 926 9934.

SIMPLE DIRECTIONS:
M6 junction 19; A556/M56 (Manchester Airport) to junction 7; signs Hale and Altrincham; through 1st traffic lights and 3rd right into Westminster Road and continue into Moss Lane. Ground on right.

CAPACITY: 3,500 **SEATED:** 1,000 **COVERED TERRACING:** Yes

RECORD ATTENDANCE:
10,275 - Altrincham Boys v Sunderland Boys - English Schools Shield 3rd Round 28.02.25.

CLUB SHOP:
Open on matchdays only; programmes, shirts, books & souvenirs.

SOCIAL FACILITIES:
Two snack bars on ground for pies, crisps, soft drinks and chocolate etc; bar under the stand open on match days only.

PREVIOUS GROUNDS:
Pollitts Field - 1903-1910

Altrincham Fact File

Nickname: The Robins

Club Sponsors:

Previous Leagues: Manchester League 1903-1911, Lancashire Combination 1911-1919, Cheshire County League 1919-1968, Northern Premier League 1968-1979.

Club colours: Red & white striped shirts, black shorts and white socks.

Change colours: Blue shirts with white trim,Blue shorts and socks.

Reserve team league: None.

Youth team league: None.

Midweek home matchday: Tuesday.

Record win: 9-2 v Merthyr Tydfil,Vauxhall Conference,Feb 1991.

Record defeat: Unknown.

Record transfer fee: £10,000 to Telford United for Ken McKenna - 1990.

Record transfer fee received: From Crewe Alexandra for Paul Edwards - 1988.

1995-96 Captain: Mick Carmody

1995-96 Top scorer: Stuart Terry

1995-96 Player of the Year: Paul France

Club record goalscorer: Jack Swindells 252 - 1965-71

Record appearances: John Davison 677 - 1971-86.

Past players who progressed to the Football League: Graham Barrow (Wigan Athletic, 1981), Eddie Bishop (Tranmere Rovers, 1988), Frank Carrodus (Manchester City, 1969), Tim Carke (Shrewsbury Town 1993), Peter Conning (Rochdale, 1986), Robert Dale (Bury, 1951), Nicky Daws (Bury, 1992), Paul Edwards (Crewe, 1988), Brian Green (Exeter City, 1962), John Hughes (Stockport County, 1976), Steve Johnson (Bury, 1977), Joe Kennedy (West Brom, 1948), Andy Kilner (Stockport County, 1990), Stan March (Port Vale, 1959), Charlie Mitten (Halifax Town, 1965), Brian Phillips (Middlesbrough, 1954), Andy Reid (Bury, 1992), Eric Robinson (West Brom, 1957), John Rogers (Wigan Athletic, 1982), Paul Showler (Barnet, 1991), Nelson Stiffle (Chesterfield, 1954), Jeff Street (Barrow, 1969), Clive Freeman (Doncaster Rovers 1993).

Club Honours: Alliance Premier League Champions 1980,1981; FA Trophy Winners 1978,1986; Bob Lord Trophy Winners 1981; N.P.L. Cup Winners 1970; N.P.L. Shield Winners 1980; Cheshire County League Winners 1966,1967; Cheshire County League Cup Winners 1951,1953,1964; Cheshire Senior Cup Winners 1905,1934,1967,1982; Manchester League Champions 1905; Cheshire Amateur Cup Winners 1904.

BATH CITY

Formed
1889

Chairman
R C Stock

Vice-Chairman
D Turner

Directors
I Prosser
L Kew
R C Twyford

Secretary
R C Twyford

Manager
Steve Millard

Commercial Manager:
Paul Cater

Programme Editor
Paul Cater

After two successive seasons when a comfortable twelfth position was realised, Bath were forced to endure a traumatic 1995/96 campaign which could so easily have ended in relegation. Scoring goals was City's biggest problem and only two clubs had a worse goals-for column and one of those was relegated Dagenham & Redbridge. There were few high points during the season, although skipper Nicky Brooks enjoyed a good campaign.

During the close season City's troubles mounted when first long-term tenants Bristol Rovers announced that they were returning to Bristol, thus losing Bath revenue of around £65,000 a year. Manager of five years, Tony Ricketts, resigned just three weeks before the start of the new season and Steve Millard, who had been the club's reserve team boss, stepped up to take on first-team duties. A number of City's more experienced players such as Adie Mings, Rob Cousins, Gary Smart and Jerry Gill departed, and with Millard having little or no money to spend on replacements, young players recently released by League clubs were brought in and will be aided by new 'veteran' player/coach Shaun Penny and new player/assistant-manager Richard Crowley.

With doubts still surrounding the future of the club and with such an inexperienced squad of players, the 1996/97 season doesn't look too rosy for the men from Twerton Park. **Steve Whitney**

Bath City F.C. 1996/97

Bath City

Match No.	Date		Comp.	Venue H/A	Opponents	Result	League Pos.	Goalscorers (Times if known)	Attendance
1	Aug	19	GMVC	A	Stevenage	Lost 0-2			1355
2		22	GMVC	A	Woking	Lost 0-2			1260
3		26	GMVC	H	Bromsgrove	Lost 0-1			510
4		28	GMVC	H	Dover	Won 2-1		Smart, Mings	439
5	Sep	2	GMVC	A	Macclesfield	Won 1-0		Spencer	1225
6		5	GMVC	A	Slough Town	Drew 1-1		Mings	980
7		9	GMVC	H	Southport	Won 4-0		Smart 2p, Mings, Birkby	584
8		12	GMVC	H	Welling	Drew 1-1		Cousins	458
9		16	GMVC	A	Kettering	Lost 0-3			1769
10		19	SCC	H	Farnborough	Lost 0-3			247
11		23	GMVC	A	Runcorn	Lost 0-1			590
12		30	GMVC	H	Stalybridge	Lost 0-4			580
13	Oct	3	SCC	A	Farnborough	Lost 0-3			374
14		7	GMVC	A	Altrincham	Won 2-1		Chiverton, Vernon	1057
15		10	GMVC	H	Woking	Lost 0-3			720
16		14	GMVC	H	Hednesford	Won 1-0		Birkby	661
17		21	FAC	A	Cinderford	Lost 2-3		Mings, Birkby	730
18		28	GMVC	H	Gateshead	Lost 0-1			481
19		31	GMVC	A	Welling	Lost 1-2		Birkby	412
20	Nov	4	GMVC	A	Halifax	Lost 1-3		Chiverton	811
21		11	GMVC	A	Morecambe	Lost 0-1			1007
22		14	SCC	H	Keynsham	Won 3-0		Chenoweth 2, Birkby p	197
23		18	GMVC	H	Northwich	Lost 0-3			417
24		25	GMVC	A	Bromsgrove	Lost 1-4		Vernon	796
25	Dec	2	FAC	A	Kidderminster	Won 2-1		Sugar, Chiverton	1883
26		9	GMVC	H	Kettering	Won 3-1		Withey 3	612
27		16	GMVC	A	Dover	Lost 0-1			826
28	Jan	1	GMVC	A	Farnborough	Drew 0-0			781
29		6	FAC	A	Northwich	Drew 2-2		Withey, Vernon	703
30		13	GMVC	H	Telford	Lost 0-3			517
31		21	FAT	H	Yeovil Town	Drew 1-1		Sugar	2225
32		23	FAT R	A	Yeovil Town	Won 3-2		Cousins 2, Vernon	2700
33	Feb	5	SPC	A	Bristol City	Lost 2-3*		Smart p, Withey	115
34		10	FAT	H	Hayes	Won 2-0		Withey 2	699
35		17	GMVC	A	Hednesford	Lost 1-2		Adcock p	1008
36		20	GMVC	H	Farnborough	Won 2-1		Vernon, Mings	290
37		24	GMVC	H	Halifax	Won 2-1		Withey, Mings	547
38	Mar	3	FAT	H	Bromsgrove Rovers	Drew 1-1		o.g.	1225
39		5	FAT R	A	Bromsgrove	Lost 1-2		Chiverton	1133
40		9	GMVC	H	Morecambe	Won 3-2		Adcock 2, Withey	511
41		16	GMVC	A	Gateshead	Lost 1-3		Adcock	582
42		25	GMVC	A	Dagenham & Redbridge	Won 1-0		Withey	602
43		30	GMVC	H	Runcorn	Won 3-0		o.g., Chiverton, Smart	503
44	Apr	3	GMVC	H	Slough	Won 3-1		Smart p, Mings 2	387
45		6	GMVC	A	Stalybridge	Lost 0-1			506
46		8	GMVC	H	Dagenham & Redbridge	Lost 0-2			541
47		13	GMVC	A	Southport	Lost 1-2		Withey	643
48		16	GMVC	H	Kidderminster	Drew 1-1		James	412
49		20	GMVC	H	Stevenage	Lost 1-2		Withey	806
50		27	GMVC	H	Altrincham	Drew 2-2		Scott, Withey	489
51		30	GMVC	H	Macclesfield	Drew 1-1		Cousins	361
52	May	4	GMVC	A	Telford	Lost 1-3		Scott	831

* After Extra Time

Bath City

1	2	3	4	5	6	7	8	9	10	11	12	14	Match No.
Mogg	Hedges	Walsh	Sugar	Crowley	Dicks	Saunders	Chenoweth	Mings	Smart	Spencer	Birkby	Ricketts	1
Mogg	Hedges	Dicks	Sugar	Crowley	Walsh	Saunders	Chenoweth	Mings	Smart	Spencer	Birkby	Ricketts	2
Mogg	Hedges	Dicks	Sugar	Crowley	Smart	Saunders	Chenoweth	Mings	Birkby	Spencer	Cousins	Vernon	3
Mogg	Hedges	Dicks	Sugar	Crowley	Smart	Saunders	Chenoweth	Mings	Birkby	Spencer	Vernon	Cousins	4
Mogg	Hedges	Dicks	Sugar	Walsh	Saunders	Cousins	Chenoweth	Mings	Birkby	Smart	Spencer	Ricketts	5
Mogg	Hedges	Dicks	Sugar	Vernon	Smart	Saunders	Chenoweth	Mings	Birkby	Cousins	Spencer	Ricketts	6
Mogg	Hedges	Dicks	Saunders	Crowley	Smart	Cousins	Chenoweth	Mings	Birkby	Vernon	Spencer	Graham	7
Mogg	Hedges	Dicks	Cousins	Crowley	Smart	Saunders	Chenoweth	Mings	Birkby	Vernon	Spencer	Walsh	8
Mogg	Hedges	Dicks	Cousins	Crowley	Smart	Saunders	Chenoweth	Mings	Spencer	Vernon	Hervin	Graham	9
Mogg	Hedges	Dicks	Cousins	Sugar	Walsh	Saunders	Chenoweth	Adcock	Birkby	Spencer	Lucas	Vernon	10
Mogg	Hedges	Dicks	Cousins	Sugar	Smart	Lucas	Chenoweth	Adcock	Spencer	Micciche	Chiverton	Vernon	11
Mogg	Hedges	Dicks	Cousins	Sugar	Smart	Lucas	Challender	Adcock	Birkby	Croft	Chiverton	Micciche	12
Mogg	Hedges	Dicks	Cousins	Micciche	Smart	Lucas	Saunders	Mings	Chiverton	Challender	Chenoweth	Adcock	13
Mogg	Hedges	Dicks	Cousins	Saunders	Smart	Micciche	Challender	Mings	Chiverton	Vernon	Lucas	Birkby	14
Mogg	Hedges	Dicks	Cousins	Micciche	Smart	Vernon	Saunders	Mings	Chiverton	Challender	Lucas	Chenoweth	15
Mogg	Hedges	Dicks	Cousins	Saunders	Smart	Micciche	Challender	Mings	Birkby	Adcock	Chiverton	Chenoweth	16
Mogg	Hedges	Dicks	Cousins	Saunders	Smart	Micciche	Challender	Mings	Birkby	Sugar	Chenoweth	Vernon	17
Mogg	Hedges	Dicks	Graham	Sugar	Smart	Micciche	Challender	Chiverton	Birkby	Cousins	Lucas	James	18
Mogg	Hedges	Dicks	Cousins	Saunders	Sugar	Smart	Micciche	Chiverton	Birkby	Graham	Adcock	James	19
Mogg	Hedges	Dicks	Cousins	Graham	Gill	James	Chenoweth	Chiverton	Birkby	Adcock	Lucas	Sugar	20
Mogg	Hedges	Dicks	Cousins	Graham	Chenoweth	James	Gill	Chiverton	Birkby	Adcock	Lucas	Sugar	21
Mogg	Gill	Hedges	Cousins	Graham	Sugar	James	Chenoweth	Chiverton	Birkby	Adcock	Lucas	Ricketts	22
Mogg	Gill	Dicks	Cousins	Sugar	Lucas	James	Chiverton	Adcock	Birkby	Smart	Vernon	Spencer	23
Mogg	Gill	Dicks	Cousins	Sugar	Lucas	James	Spencer	Chiverton	Birkby	Vernon	Smart	Ricketts	24
Mogg	Gill	Dicks	Cousins	Sugar	Hedges	James	Chiverton	Withey	Birkby	Smart	Adcock	Vernon	25
Mogg	Gill	Dicks	Cousins	Sugar	Hedges	James	Chiverton	Withey	Birkby	Smart	Saunders	Adcock	26
Mogg	Gill	Dicks	Cousins	Chiverton	Hedges	James	Brooks	Withey	Birkby	Smart	Saunders	Vernon	27
Mogg	Gill	Dicks	Cousins	Chiverton	Hedges	James	Brooks	Withey	Adcock	Saunders	Mings	Vernon	28
Mogg	Gill	Dicks	Cousins	Chiverton	Hedges	James	Brooks	Withey	Adcock	Saunders	Mings	Vernon	29
Mogg	Gill	Dicks	Cousins	Chiverton	Hedges	James	Brooks	Withey	Adcock	Saunders	Mings	Vernon	30
Mogg	Gill	Dicks	Cousins	Sugar	Mings	Hedges	Brooks	Withey	Adcock	Chiverton	Saunders	James	31
Mogg	Gill	Dicks	Cousins	Sugar	Mings	Hedges	Brooks	Withey	Adcock	Chiverton	Saunders	Vernon	32
Mogg	Gill	Dicks	Cousins	Sugar	Hedges	James	Smart	Withey	Adcock	Vernon	Chiverton	Saunders	33
Mogg	Gill	Dicks	Cousins	Saunders	Hedges	James	Chiverton	Withey	Adcock	Wigley	Vernon	Smart	34
Mogg	Gill	Dicks	Cousins	Sherwood	Saunders	James	Brooks	Withey	Adcock	Wigley	Smart	Vernon	35
Mogg	Gill	Dicks	Cousins	Sherwood	Saunders	Vernon	Brooks	Mings	Adcock	Smart	Hedges	Chiverton	36
Mogg	Gill	Dicks	Cousins	Sherwood	Sugar	Vernon	Chiverton	Withey	Mings	Wigley	Saunders	Smart	37
Mogg	Gill	Dicks	Cousins	Hedges	Sugar	Vernon	Brooks	Withey	Mings	Saunders	Chiverton	Smart	38
Mogg	Gill	Dicks	Cousins	Sugar	Saunders	Hedges	Chiverton	Withey	Mings	Smart	Adcock	Vernon	39
Mogg	Gill	Dicks	Cousins	Sherwood	Adcock	Hedges	Chiverton	Withey	Mings	Smart	James	Vernon	40
Mogg	Gill	Dicks	Cousins	Hedges	Chiverton	Smart	Brooks	Withey	Adcock	Lucas	James	Spencer	41
Mogg	James	Dicks	Cousins	Hedges	Chiverton	Smart	Brooks	Withey	Adcock	Sherwood	Lucas	Mings	42
Mogg	Gill	Dicks	Cousins	Sherwood	Chiverton	Smart	Brooks	Withey	Adcock	Scott	Lucas	Mings	43
Mogg	Gill	Dicks	Cousins	Sherwood	Chiverton	Smart	Brooks	Withey	Adcock	Scott	Ricketts	Mings	44
Mogg	Gill	Dicks	Cousins	Sherwood	Chiverton	Smart	Brooks	Withey	Adcock	Scott	James	Lucas	45
Mogg	Gill	Dicks	Cousins	Hedges	Chiverton	Smart	Brooks	Withey	Mings	Scott	James	Ricketts	46
Mogg	Gill	Dicks	Cousins	Sherwood	Hedges	Smart	James	Withey	Adcock	Scott	Mings	Ricketts	47
Mogg	Gill	Dicks	Cousins	Sherwood	Hedges	James	Brooks	Withey	Adcock	Scott	Mings	Chiverton	48
Mogg	Gill	Dicks	Cousins	Sherwood	Chiverton	James	Brooks	Withey	Adcock	Scott	Mings	Ricketts	49
Mogg	Gill	Dicks	Cousins	Sherwood	Chiverton	James	Brooks	Withey	Adcock	Scott	Mings	Smart	50
Mogg	Gill	Dicks	Cousins	Sherwood	Chiverton	James	Smart	Withey	Adcock	Scott	Mings	Crowley	51
Mogg	Gill	Dicks	Cousins	Sherwood	Chiverton	James	Brooks	Withey	Adcock	Scott	Lucas	Crowley	52

Hervin was an additional substitute in Match 52

STEVE MILLARD

Steve was appointed as manager just three weeks prior to the start of the 1996/96 season following the resignation of Tony Ricketts, who had been in charge at Twerton Park for five years.

A former Bath City player, Steve has also managed Glouceser City and Forest Green Rovers as well as being general manager of Clevedon Town recently and had been looking after City's reserve team prior to being handed the first-team post.

To help him in what look like being a very difficult season, Steve has enlisted the assistance of much-travelled striker Shaun Penny and crowd favourite Richard Crowley, who have been made player/coach and assistant/manager respectively.

Rob Cousins; Player's & Supporters Player of the Season 95-96.

Programme details:
36 pages for £1.20
Editor - Paul Cater.

Local Newspapers:
Bath Chronicle
Evening Post
Western Daily Press

Local Radio Stations:
Radio Bristol
GWR FM
Brunel

BATH CITY - PLAYING SQUAD 1996-97

Player	Honours	Birthplace and date	Transfer Fees	Previous Clubs
GOALKEEPERS				
David Mogg	ES, FAXI	Bristol 11/2/62		Bristol C, Alvidaberg (Swe), Abbotonians, Bath C, Cheltenham T, Gloucester C
DEFENDERS				
Grantley Dicks		Bristol 17/10/66		Clandown, Paulton Rovers
Richard Crowley	GSC, SSC	Bristol 28/12/59		Frome T, Bath C, Forest Green R, Cheltenham T, Bath C, Gloucester C
Jay Cleverly				West Bromwich Albion
Ian Hedges		Bristol 5/2/69	£7,500	Bristol Manor Farm, Gloucester C, AFC Bournemouth
Mark Madge	Bristol			Bristol City, Gloucester C, Mangotsfield U, Clevedon T
MIDFIELDERS				
Jimmy Fraser		Swindon 22/10/76		Portsmouth
Paul Tovey		Wokingham 5/12/73		Bristol R
Danny Hazlehurst		Southampton		Southampton
Jay Lucas		Bristol 9/6/76		Birmingham C
Nicky Brooks		Bristol 23/6/68		Bristol C, Barnstaple T, Mangotsfield Utd, Clevedon T
FORWARDS				
Michael Wyatt		Bristol 12/9/74		Bristol C, Bristol R
Mike Davis		Bristol 19/10/74		Yate T, Bristol R
Graham Withey		Bristol 12/6/66		Welton R, Bath, Bristol R, Coventry, Cardiff, Bath, Bristol C, Exeter, Bath, Yate,Clevedon
Shaun Penny	SLM	Bristol 24/9/57		Bris.C, Bris.R, KTP Kotkan (Fin), Bath C, Dorchester, Weymouth, FGR, Glocs, WSM

Departures during season:
Danny Baldwin (Chippenham T), Chris Honor (Slough T), Brian Croft (Hearts), Nick Wilson (Clevedon T), Greg Challender (Altrincham), Paul Chenoweth (Cheltenham T), Ben Graham (Released), Dean Birkby (Yeovil T), Nick Beaverstock (Blyth Spartans), Russell Wigley (Inter Cardiff), Mickey Spencer (Salisbury - Loan), Deion Vernon (Gloucester C).
Players on loan during season:
Andy Scott (Cardiff C).
Departures during close season: Paul Adcock (Torquay), Eston Chiverton (Cinderford T), Adie Mings (Gloucester C), Rob Cousins & Jerry Gill (Yeovil T), Neil Saunders (Tiverton T), Tony Ricketts & Jeff Sherwood (Brislington), Chris Sugar (Weston-S-M), Gary Smart (Mangotsfield U).

Twerton Park, Bath

ADDRESS: Twerton Park, Twerton, Bath Avon BA2 1DB.

TELEPHONE NUMBER: 01225 423087/313247 Fax: 01225 481391.

SIMPLE DIRECTIONS:
Twerton Park is situated on the A4/A36 Lower Bristol Road - on the Bristol side of Bath City Centre (Approx 2.5 miles). The area is serviced by J18 on the M4. From the centre of Bath the bus route is No.5 - Twerton High Street.

CAPACITY: 9,899 **SEATED:** 1,017 **COVERED TERRACING:** 4,800

RECORD ATTENDANCE:
18,020 v Brighton & Hove Albion, FA Cup.

CLUB SHOP:
Contact Mr P Cater or Mr K Sellick.

SOCIAL FACILITIES:
Several bars open all week and full service with menu on match-days catering for up to 250 people.

PREVIOUS GROUNDS:
The Belvoir Ground/ Lambridge - 1889-1932

Bath Fact File

Nickname: Romans

Club Sponsors:

Previous Leagues: Beazer Homes (Southern League)

Club colours: Black/white striped shirts, black shorts & black/white socks.

Change colours: All sky blue

Midweek home matchday: Tuesday

Record win:

Record defeat:

Record transfer fee: £15,000 for Micky Tanner from Bristol City.

Record transfer fee received: £80,000 for Jason Dodd from Southampton.

1995-96 Captain: Richard Crowley

1995-96 Top scorer: Paul Adcock

1995-96 Player of the Year: David Mogg

Club record goalscorer: Paul Randall

Record appearances:

Past players who progressed to the Football League: Alan Skirton (Arsenal), Tony Book (Plymouth Argyle, Manchester City), Kenny Allen (Bournemouth, Swindon Town), Peter Rogers (Exeter City), R Bourne (Torquay), Dave Wiffil (Manchester City), Stan Mortensen (Blackpool), Brian Wade (Swindon Town), Jeff Meacham (Bristol Rovers), Martin Hirst (Bristol City), Paul Bodin (Swindon), Graham Withey (Coventry), Jason Dodd (Southampton), Paul Adcock (Torquay).

Club Honours: Southern League Champions 59-60, 77-78; R-up 29-30, 32-33, 61-62, 89-90; Southern League Cup 78-79; Somerset Premier Cup 51-52, 52-53, 57-58, 59-60, 65-66, 67-68, 69-70, 77-78, 80-81, 81-82, 83-84, 84-85, 85-86, 88-89, 89-90, 93-94, 94-95; Anglo-Italian Cup Finalists 76-77, 77-78.

BROMSGROVE ROVERS

Formed:
1885

President:
Charles W Poole

Chairman:
Keith MacMaster

Football Secretary:
Brian Hewings

Manager:
Brian Kenning

Assistant Manager:
John Dyer

Physiotherapist:
Paul Sunners

Commercial Manager:
Rebecca O'Neill

Press Officer:

Once again the club made history. Bromsgrove's trophy cabinet found more silverware, a repeat of 94/95's cup double. The Victoria club needing to display yet more trophies. As in the previous season, Rovers retained the Worcestershire Senior Cup and the Vauxhall Conference League Cup in its new form, the Spalding Cup.

Under new leadership, Brian Kenning, who took over from the caretaker management team of John Dyer and Kevin Richardson, Bromsgrove achieved much in 1995/96. As well as retaining the two cups, Rovers went top of the Conference for the first time in their 110-year history. However, it lasted for just over a week as a 5-2 defeat at Welling ended a good start. Rovers league form was up and down, finally finishing up in eleventh place. The highlights of the league programme were few and far between. Mark Crisp had the individual performance, hitting four goals at home to Southport. Injuries played their part in keeping Rovers in mid-table and although Recky Carter scored 13 league goals he played in only 18 league fixtures. Defender Stewart Brighton played less than half a season and Stuart Randall, a promising defender, broke a leg in January.

Rovers lost the services of goalkeeper Alan Judge and international midfielder Steve Stott to Kettering, together with Steve Taylor, who was signed by Crystal Palace. Their replacements took time to settle but had a good season. Chris Taylor took over in goal and improved match by match, Darren Grocutt, the club's record signing, did well after a slow start and youngsters Richard Gardner and Nick Amos, the find of the season, promise much for the future.

Without any doubt the backbone of this successful side were defenders Craig Gaunt, Jimmy Skelding and skipper Kevin Richardson. However, the jewel in the crown is Adie Smith. Play anywhere-man Smith scooped all three player of the year awards.

The close season once again saw Rovers lose key players such as Recky

Back Row (L-R); Paul Sunners (Physio), Craig Gaunt, Lee Young, Nick Clarke, Paul Haywood, Neil Olden, Colin Radburn, Stewart Randall, Reckey Carter, Stewart Pinfield. Front Row; Brian Kenning (Mgr), Darren Grocutt, Andy Dale, Stuart Brighton, Kevin Richardson, Brendon Devery, Symon Burgher, Andy Powell, Mark Crisp, John Dyer (Asst Mgr).

Bromsgrove Rovers

Match No.	Date	Comp.	Venue H/A	Opponents	Result	League Pos.	Goalscorers (Times if known)	Attendance
1	Aug 19	GMVC		Gateshead	Won 3-1		Gaunt, Crisp 2	789
2	22	GMVC		Kettering Town	Drew 2-2		Gaunt, Carter	2006
3	26	GMVC		Bath City	Won 1-0		Dale	510
4	28	GMVC		Woking	Won 2-1		Carter, Crisp	1290
5	Sep 2	GMVC		Dover Athletic	Won 3-0		Smith, Carter, Crisp	1082
6	5	GMVC		Welling United	Lost 2-5		Skelding, Gaunt	602
7	9	GMVC		Altrincham	Lost 0-3			773
8	12	GMVC		Dagenham & Redbridge	Won 2-0		Skelding, Dale	728
9	16	GMVC		Stevenage boro	Drew 1-1		Crisp	1067
10	23	GMVC		Slough Town	Won 3-2		Gaunt, Crisp, og	931
11	26	GMVC		Telford United	Drew 0-0			742
12	30	GMVC		Runcorn	Won 2-0		Smith, Grocutt	973
13	Oct 7	GMVC		Macclesfield Town	Lost 1-2		Crisp	1137
14	14	GMVC		Farnborough Town	Lost 1-2		Smith	1145
15	21	FAC		Kettering Town	Drew 0-0			2427
16	24	FAC		Kettering Town	Drew 2-2		Skelding, Clarke	1426
17	28	GMVC		Morecambe	Lost 1-4		Hunt	955
18	30	FAC		Kettering	Won 2-1		Power, Grocutt	2283
19	Nov 4	GMVC		Stalybridge Celtic	Drew 1-1		Brighton	1033
20	11	FAC		Cinderford Town	Lost 1-2		Skelding	1850
21	18	GMVC		Farnborough Town	Lost 0-1			930
22	21	GMVC		Hednesford Town	Lost 1-4		Crisp	952
23	25	GMVC		Bath City	Won 4-1		Hunt 2, Carter, Amos	796
24	Dec 2	GMVC		Halifax Town	Drew 1-1		Skelding	843
25	5	SCC		Telford United	Won 3-1*		Amos, Grocutt, Crisp	548
26	9	GMVC		Stevenage Borough	Drew 3-3		Amos, Carter 2	1565
27	16	GMVC		Welling United	Drew 1-1		Gaunt	721
28	19	WSC		Moor Green	Won 5-0		Grocutt 2, Hunt, Carter 2	315
29	26	GMVC		Kidderminster Harr.	Won 2-1		Smith, Carter	4398
30	30	GMVC		Dagenham & Redbridge	Drew 2-2		Clarke, Carter	1020
31	Jan 1	GMVC		Kidderminster Harriers	Lost 0-1			4498
32	6	GMVC		Altrincham	Drew 0-0			852
33	13	GMVC		Runcorn	Drew 0-0			547
34	20	FAT		Bishop Aukland	Won 1-0		Carter	999
35	30	GMVC		Northwich Victoria	Drew 2-2		Skelding, Carter	630
36	Feb 3	GMVC		Woking	Drew 1-1		Smith	2481
37	10	FAT		Halifax Town	Won 1-0		Smith	883
38	17	GMVC		Macclesfield Town	Won 1-0		Carter	1481
39	24	GMVC		Dover Athletic	Won 2-0		Brighton, Marlowe	1011
40	27	SCC		Dover Athletic	Won 1-0		Skelding	464
41	Mar 3	FAT		Bath City	Drew 1-1		Brighton	1276
42	5	FAT		Bath City	Won 2-1		Amos, Carter	1133
43	9	GMVC		Southport	Won 2-1		Skelding, Hunt	894
44	12	GMVC		Telford United	Lost 0-2			746
45	16	GMVC		Hednesford Town	Lost 2-4		Dale, Carter	1119
46	19	SCC		Kettering Town	Won 2-0		Power, Amos	650
47	23	FAT		Northwich Victoria	Lost 0-1			1807
48	25	WSC		Solihull Borough	Drew 2-2		Brighton, Grocutt	183
49	30	GMVC		Slough Town	Drew 0-0			687
50	Apr 3	SCC		Kettering Town	Lost 1-2		Burgher	773
51	6	GMVC		Southport	Won 4-1		Crisp 4	729
52	8	GMVC		Stalybridge Celtic	Lost 1-2		Crisp	463
53	16	WSC		Solihull Borough	Won 3-1		Richardson, Carter 2	524
54	20	GMVC		Kettering Town	Won 3-2		Amos, Carter 2	824
55	22	WSC		Stourbridge	Lost 1-2		Amos	527
56	24	SCC		Macclesfield Town	Drew 1-1		og	547
57	27	GMVC		Gateshead	Lost 0-1			762
58	28	GMVC		Northwich Victoria	Drew 1-1		Grocutt	693
59	30	GMVC		Morecambe	Won 1-0		Hunt	626
60	May 4	GMVC		Halifax Town	Lost 0-1			887
61	6	SCC		Macclesfield Town	Won 3-1		Grocutt, Hunt, Carter	1341
62	9	WSC		Stourbridge	Won 3-1		Amos, Carter 2	750

* After Extra Time

Marlow was the third substitute used in the Second Leg of the Worcestershire Senior Cup Final. A Final that Rovers have won for the third consecutive year.

Bromsgrove Rovers

1	2	3	4	5	6	7	8	9	10	11	12	14	Match No.
Taylor	Skelding	Brighton	Richardson	Clarke	Gaunt	Smith	Grocutt	Dale	Radburn	Crisp	Power	Brain	1
Taylor	Skelding	Brighton	Richardson	Clarke	Gaunt	Smith	Grocutt	Dale	Radburn	Crisp	Brain	Power	2
Taylor	Skelding	Brighton	Richardson	Clarke	Gaunt	Smith	Grocutt	Dale	Carter	Crisp	Power	Brain	3
Taylor	Skelding	Brighton	Richardson	Clarke	Gaunt	Smith	Grocutt	Dale	Carter	Crisp	Power	Brain	4
Taylor	Skelding	Power	Richardson	Clarke	Gaunt	Smith	Whitehead	Dale	Carter	Crisp	Radburn	Brain	5
Taylor	Skelding	Power	Richardson	Clarke	Gaunt	Smith	Grocutt	Dale	Carter	Crisp	Radburn	Brain	6
Taylor	Skelding	Randall	Brain	Clarke	Gaunt	Smith	Power	Dale	Radburn	Crisp	Humphries	Dowling	7
Taylor	Skelding	Brighton	Richardson	Clarke	Gaunt	Crisp	Whitehouse	Dale	Brain	Hunt	Whitehead	Dowling	8
Taylor	Skelding	Randall	Richardson	Clarke	Gaunt	Smith	Grocutt	Dale	Brain	Crisp	Radburn	Glasser	9
Taylor	Skelding	Randall	Richardson	Clarke	Gaunt	Smith	Grocutt	Dale	Radburn	Crisp	Power	Brain	10
Taylor	Skelding	Randall	Richardson	Clarke	Gaunt	Smith	Grocutt	Dale	Burgher	Crisp	Radburn	Brighton	11
Taylor	Skelding	Randall	Richardson	Clarke	Gaunt	Smith	Grocutt	Dale	Crisp	Radburn	Glasser	Brain	12
Taylor	Skelding	Randall	Richardson	Clarke	Gaunt	Smith	Grocutt	Dale	Hunt	Crisp	Radburn	Glasser	13
Taylor	Skelding	Randall	Richardson	Clarke	Gaunt	Smith	Grocutt	Dale	Hunt	Crisp	Radburn	Power	14
Taylor	Skelding	Brighton	Richardson	Clarke	Gaunt	Smith	Grocutt	Dale	Radburn	Crisp	Randall	Young	15
Taylor	Skelding	Brighton	Richardson	Clarke	Gaunt	Smith	Grocutt	Dale	Radburn	Crisp	Randall	Burgher	16
Olden	Skelding	Brighton	Richardson	Clarke	Crisp	Smith	Grocutt	Dale	Hunt	Radburn	Power	Glasser	17
Taylor	Skelding	Power	Richardson	Clarke	Gaunt	Smith	Grocutt	Dale	Crisp	Burgher	Radburn	Dowling	18
Taylor	Skelding	Power	Richardson	Clarke	Randall	Smith	Grocutt	Hunt	Crisp	Glasser	Dale	Brighton	19
Taylor	Skelding	Brighton	Richardson	Randall	Dowling	Smith	Grocutt	Dale	Crisp	Radburn	Glasser	Power	20
Taylor	Skelding	Power	Smith	Dowling	Randall	Glasser	Crisp	Hunt	Carter	Amos	Dale	Young	21
Taylor	Skelding	Brighton	Smith	Gaunt	Randall	Burgher	Crisp	Hunt	Carter	Amos	Glasser	Dale	22
Taylor	Skelding	Randall	Smith	Clarke	Gaunt	Glasser	Crisp	Hunt	Carter	Amos	Young	Power	23
Taylor	Skelding	Power	Richardson	Clarke	Randall	Smith	Crisp	Hunt	Carter	Grocutt	Amos	Glasser	24
Taylor	Smith	Randall	Richardson	Clarke	Skelding	Amos	Burgher	Hunt	Carter	Grocutt	Power	Dale	25
Taylor	Randall	Power	Richardson	Clarke	Gaunt	Amos	Grocutt	Hunt	Carter	Crisp	Dowling	Glasser	26
Taylor	Smith	Power	Richardson	Randall	Gaunt	Grocutt	Amos	Hunt	Carter	Crisp	Dale	Young	27
Taylor	Smith	Power	Richardson	Grocutt	Gaunt	Amos	Burgher	Hunt	Carter	Crisp	Trowman	Young	28
Taylor	Skelding	Power	Richardson	Clarke	Randall	Smith	Grocutt	Hunt	Carter	Crisp	Amos	Dale	29
Taylor	Skelding	Randall	Richardson	Clarke	Gaunt	Smith	Grocutt	Hunt	Carter	Crisp	Amos	Dale	30
Taylor	Skelding	Randall	Richardson	Clarke	Gaunt	Glasser	Grocutt	Hunt	Carter	Crisp	Power	Dale	31
Taylor	Skelding	Randall	Richardson	Clarke	Gaunt	Smith	Glasser	Hunt	Carter	Crisp	Amos	Dale	32
Taylor	Skelding	Power	Richardson	Clarke	Gaunt	Smith	Crisp	Hunt	Carter	Amos	Dale	Glasser	33
Taylor	Skelding	Power	Richardson	Clarke	Gaunt	Smith	Crisp	Hunt	Carter	Amos	Dale	Glasser	34
Taylor	Skelding	Power	Richardson	Clarke	Gaunt	Smith	Amos	Hunt	Carter	Burgher	Dale	Glasser	35
Taylor	Skelding	Power	Richardson	Clarke	Gaunt	Smith	Amos	Dale	Crisp	Hunt	Brighton	Marlowe	36
Taylor	Skelding	Brighton	Richardson	Clarke	Gaunt	Smith	Amos	Hunt	Crisp	Grocutt	Power	Glasser	37
Taylor	Smith	Brighton	Richardson	Clarke	Gaunt	Carter	Amos	Hunt	Crisp	Grocutt	Power	Dale	38
Taylor	Smith	Brighton	Richardson	Clarke	Gaunt	Power	Amos	Hunt	Glasser	Grocutt	Dowling	Marlowe	39
Taylor	Skelding	Brighton	Richardson	Smith	Gaunt	Burgher	Amos	Hunt	Glasser	Grocutt	Power	Dale	40
Taylor	Skelding	Brighton	Richardson	Clarke	Smith	Burgher	Amos	Hunt	Carter	Grocutt	Glasser	Marlowe	41
Taylor	Skelding	Brighton	Richardson	Clarke	Smith	Burgher	Amos	Hunt	Carter	Grocutt	Power	Marlowe	42
Taylor	Skelding	Brighton	Richardson	Dowling	Smith	Crisp	Amos	Hunt	Dale	Grocutt	Marlowe	Power	43
Taylor	Skelding	Power	Richardson	Clarke	Gaunt	Smith	Amos	Burgher	Carter	Crisp	Marlowe	Hunt	44
Taylor	Skelding	Brighton	Richardson	Clarke	Gaunt	Smith	Dale	Hunt	Carter	Grocutt	Marlowe	Power	45
Taylor	Skelding	Power	Smith	Clarke	Gaunt	Amos	Crisp	Hunt	Carter	Grocutt	Marlowe	Burgher	46
Taylor	Skelding	Brighton	Smith	Clarke	Gaunt	Crisp	Amos	Dale	Carter	Grocutt	Gardner	Marlowe	47
Taylor	Skelding	Brighton	Richardson	Dowling	Gaunt	Smith	Grocutt	Crisp	Carter	Burgher	Marlowe	Dale	48
Taylor	Skelding	Brighton	Richardson	White	Smith	Marlowe	Crisp	Grocutt	Carter	Gardner	Dale	Young	49
Taylor	Skelding	Brighton	Richardson	White	Smith	Marlowe	Grocutt	Power	Carter	Burgher	Dowling	Dale	50
Taylor	Skelding	Brighton	Richardson	Smith	Gaunt	Marlowe	Grocutt	Dale	Crisp	Power	Young	White	51
Taylor	Skelding	Brighton	Richardson	Smith	Gaunt	Marlowe	Grocutt	Amos	Burgher	Crisp	Dale	Power	52
Taylor	Smith	Power	Richardson	Clarke	Gaunt	Burgher	Grocutt	Crisp	Carter	Amos	Trowman	Marlowe	53
Taylor	Smith	Brighton	Richardson	White	Clarke	Eades	Young	Amos	Carter	Crisp	Trowman	Gardner	54
Taylor	Trowman	Gardner	Richardson	Gaunt	Smith	Marlowe	Crisp	Dale	Burgher	Amos	Brighton	Grocutt	55
Taylor	Smith	Brighton	Richardson	Clarke	Gaunt	Burgher	Grocutt	Amos	Crisp	Gardner	Young	Dale	56
Taylor	Skelding	Brighton	Smith	Clarke	Gaunt	Trowman	Grocutt	Dale	Crisp	Amos	Gardner	Young	57
Olden	Skelding	Brighton	Richardson	Clarke	Gaunt	Marlowe	Grocutt	Amos	Crisp	Gardner	Hunt	Young	58
Taylor	Skelding	Brighton	Richardson	Clarke	Gaunt	Eades	Grocutt	Hunt	Crisp	Amos	Gardner	Marlowe	59
Taylor	Skelding	Brighton	Richardson	Clarke	Smith	Young	Amos	Hunt	Carter	Crisp	Gardner	Marlowe	60
Taylor	Smith	Gardner	Richardson	Clarke	Gaunt	Skelding	Grocutt	Hunt	Carter	Amos	Dale	Marlowe	61
Taylor	Skelding	Gardner	Richardson	Smith	Gaunt	Crisp	Grocutt	Hunt	Carter	Amos	Trowman	Dale	62

BRIAN KENNING

1995/96 was Brian's first as manager. He adapted well and led the team to retain both the Worcestershire Senior Cup and the Spalding Challenge Cup.

Bian had previously managed at Sutton Coldfield Town and had other managerial roles at Burton Albion and Kidderminster Harriers. As a player Brian was a midfielder for Worcester City, Alvechurch, Sutton Coldfield Town and Bromsgrove Rovers.

Brian's major task leading up to the 1996/97 season will be to find adequate replacements for the departed Craig Gaunt and Recky Carter and to build up a small squad and continue on his winning ways.

Brian Kenning Team Manager.

Adrian Smith; Player of the Year.

Programme details:
40 pages for £1.20

Any other club publications:
'Bored to Death' - Fanzine.

Local Newspapers:
Bromsgrove Advertiser
Bromsgrove Standard
Worcester Evening News

Local Radio Stations:
BBC Hereford & Worcester.
Radio Wyvern.

BROMSGROVE ROVERS - PLAYING SQUAD 1996-97

Player	Honours	Birthplace and date	Transfer Fees	Previous Clubs
GOALKEEPERS				
Chris Taylor		Birmingham		Bromsgrove R, Halesowen T, Evesham U, Moor Green, Solihull B
Matt Whitehead		Birmingham		Mile Oak, Bolehall, Tamworth, Worcester, Tamworth, Atherstone, Hinckley T, Tamworth
Neil Olden		Birmingham		Sutton Coldfield T
DEFENDERS				
Kevin Richardson	ESP, BHL FAXI	Walsall 22/11/62		Pelsall V, Sutton C, Stafford R, Worcester, Sutton C, Alvechurch, Hednesford T
Stewart Brighton	ESP, BHL, FAXI	Bromsgrove 3/10/66		Crewe Alexandra
Paul Wardle	BHL	Burton 1/2/70		Denaby U, Belper T, Bromsgrove R, Gresley R
Stuart Randall		Birmingham		Tamworth, Coleshill T, Redditch U, Sutton Coldfield T, Evesham U
Richard Knight		Burton 31/8/74		Walsall, Armitage, Leicester U
Nicky Clarke		Walsall 20/8/67		Wolverhampton W, Mansfield T, Bromsgrove R, Preston NE
Nick Dunphy		Birmingham 3/8/74		Rushall O, Sutton Coldfield, Hednesford, Peterborough, Cheltenham, Tamworth
Jimmy Skelding	BHL	Bilston 30/5/64		Bilston T, Wolves, Bromsgrove R, Burton Alb, Worcester C
Adrian Smith				Willenhall T Birmingham C.
MIDFIELDERS				
Darren Grocutt		Birmingham	£12,500	Northfield T, Moor Green, Evesham U, Burton Alb.
Mark Crisp	BHL	Birmingham		Smethwick, Redditch Utd, Bromsgrove R, Alvechurch, Bromsgrove R, Macclesfield T
Lee Young		Stourbridge 9/3/71		Dudley T, Lye T, Halesowen T, Dudley T, Stourbridge
FORWARDS				
Andy Dale		Birmingham		Birmingham C, Moor Green, Sutton Coldfield T, Dudley T
John Hunt		Birmingham		Paget Rangers, Sutton Coldfield T.
Andy Mainwaring		Wales		Cwmbran T

Departures during season:
Simon Brain (Evesham U), Neil Olden (Sutton Coldfield T - Loan), Paul Hayward (Nuneaton B), Colin Radburn (Hednesford T), Lee Young (Dudley T - Loan), Neil Glasser (Ilkeston T), Brendan Devery (Solihull B), Stuart Whitehead (Bolton W), Simon Brain (Evesham U).
Players on loan during season:
None.
Departures during close season: Recky Carter & Craig Gaunt (Kettering T), Andy Power (Worcester C), Symon Burgher & Chris Pearce (Moor Green), Fergus Dowling (Released).

Victoria Ground, Bromsgrove

ADDRESS:
Victoria Ground, Birmingham Road, Bromsgrove, Worcs, B61 0DR

TELEPHONE NUMBER:
Tel: 01527 876949 (Office + fax), 01527 878260 (Social Club). **Club Newsline:** 0891 88 44 96.

SIMPLE DIRECTIONS:
The Victoria Ground is situated on the north side of Bromsgrove on the Birmingham Road, which is off the A38 Bromsgrove by pass. The M5 and M42 join the A38 to the north of the town making it easy to get to the ground without having to go into town. The 144 Midland Red bus runs from New Street Station Birmingham and passes the ground.

CAPACITY: 4,423 **SEATED:** 394 **COVERED TERRACING:** 1,344

RECORD ATTENDANCE: 7,389 v Worcester City - 1957.

CLUB SHOP:
Sells all kinds of replica clothing & souvenirs. Contact Doug Bratt (01527 874997).

SOCIAL FACILITIES:
Victoria Club (01527 878260) - Serves hot & cold food. Big screen TV, pool table & darts. Open matchdays and week-day evenings.

PREVIOUS GROUNDS:
Old Station Road 1885-1887, Recreation Ground 1887-1889, Churchfields 1889-1891, Well Lane 1891-1910.

Bromsgrove Fact File

Nickname: Rovers or Greens

Club Sponsors: All Saints Masterfit (Bromsgrove).

Previous Leagues: Birmingham Combination 1910-1953, Birmingham/West Midlands League 1953-1973, Southern League (Northern Division) 1973-1979, Southern League (Midland Division) 1979-1986, Southern League (Premier Division) 1986-1992.

Club colours: Green & white stripes/black/green.

Change colours: All red.

Reserve team's league: Central Conference.

Midweek home matchday: Tuesday (7.45pm)

Record win: 11-0; v Hinckley Ath. 1970; v Halesowen Town 'A' 1939.

Record defeat: 0-12 v Aston Villa 'A' 1939.

Record transfer fee paid: £3,000 for Recky Carter (Solihull Borough) 93-94.

Record transfer fee received: Undisclosed for Scott Cooksey (Peterborough) December 1993.

1995/96 Captain: Kevin Richardson

1995/96 Top Scorer: Recky Carter - 22 goals (13 Lge + 9 Cup)

Club record goalscorer: Chris Hanks 238, 1983-84

Record appearances: Shaun O'Meara 763, 1975-94

Past players who progressed to the Football League: Mike McKenna (Northampton 1946), Ray Hartle (Bolton 1952), Angus McLean (Bury 1953), Alan Smith (A.Villa 1954), Mike Deakin (C Palace 1954), Brain Puster (Leicester 1958), Tom Smith (Sheff Utd 1978), Malcolm Goodman (Halifax 1979), Steve Smith (Walsall 1980), Gary Hackett (Shrewsbury 1983), Bill McGarry, Martyn O'Connor (C Palace 1992), Scott Cooksey (Peterborough 1993), Steve Taylor (Crystal Palace 1995).

Club Honours: Vauxhall Conference R-up 1992-93; Bob Lord Trophy 1994-95; Spalding Cup 1995/96; Southern League Premier Champions 1991-92; Southern League Prem. R-up 1986-87; Southern League Mid. Champions 1985-86; Bill Dellow Cup Winners 1985-86; Southern League Champions v Cup Winners Cup Winners 1992-93; Worcester Senior Cup Winners 1946-47, 1947-48, 1959-60, 1986-87, 1993-94, 1994/95; 1995/96; Birmingham Senior Cup Winners 1946-47; West Midlands League Champions 1960-61; Birmingham Combination Champions 1946-47.

DOVER ATHLETIC

Formed:
1983

Chairman:
Mr J T Husk

Football Secretary:
Mr J F Durrant

Manager
Joe O'Sullivan

Asst. Manager:
Dave Gulver

Physiotherapist:
Frank Brooks

Commercial Manager:
Jean Haves

Press Officer:
Mr J F Durrant

As stated in last year's review, very often a club's second season as a Vauxhall Conference club is the real test. Sometimes they adapt but in Dover's case it so nearly proved a test they couldn't handle. Peter Taylor, the former Tottenham Hotspur, Crystal Palace and England winger was charged with the task of guiding Dover to safety and he just managed to achieve that after taking over from John Ryan. Prolific scorer David Leworthy returned to form after an injury-ravaged campaign to score 25 goals but h lacked support and the sale of England midfielder Corey Browne didn't go down too well with supporters, but one or two of the younger players brought in by Taylor did quite well.

Then, during the close season, Peter Taylor was given an opportunity to return to top flight football and become the new full-time manager of the England under-21 team, joining the new regime under ex-Spurs team-mate Glen Hoddle. That left Dover seraching for their sixth new boss since their reformation in 1983. Their search ended when former Chelmsford City manager Joe O'Sullivan was handed his first chance to take charge of a team at Vauxhall Conference level. **Steve Whitney**

Dover Athletic FC:

Dover Athletic

Match No.	Date	Comp.	Venue H/A	Opponents	Result	League Pos.	Goalscorers (Times if known)	Attendance
1	Aug 10	EFC	A	Ashford Town	Lost 0-2			437
2	19	GMVC	A	Northwich Victoria	Won 2-1		Chambers, Leworthy	824
3	22	GMVC	H	Stevenage Borough	Lost 1-2		Leworthy	1157
4	26	GMVC	H	Hednesford Town	Lost 1-3		Strouts	866
5	28	GMVC	A	Bath City	Lost 1-2		Darlington	439
6	Sep 2	GMVC	A	Bromsgrove Rovers	Lost 0-3			1082
7	5	GMVC	H	Farnborough Town	Lost 1-3		Theodosiou	779
8	9	FAC	H	Bognor Regis Town	Lost 1-2		Leworthy	578
9	12	GMVC	A	Slough Town	Lost 2-3		Leworthy, Carruthers	846
10	16	GMVC	H	Macclesfield Town	Lost 2-3		Leworthy 2 (1p)	822
11	19	SC	A	Welling United	Won 2-1		Leworthy 2	409
12	26	GMVC	H	Slough Town	Lost 0-1			619
13	30	GMVC	A	Halifax Town	Lost 0-1			905
14	Oct 7	GMVC	A	Kidderminster Harriers	Drew 1-1		Leworthy	2259
15	10	SC	H	Welling United	Won 3-0		Restarick 2, Leworthy	664
16	14	GMVC	H	Runcorn	Won 4-2		Restarick, Strouts, Leworthy, Milton	1277
17	17	EFC	H	Folkestone Invicta	Lost 1-4		Daniels	534
18	21	GMVC	A	Gateshead	Drew 1-1		Hayes	512
19	28	GMVC	A	Altrincham	Drew 2-2		Lindsey, Leworthy	929
20	31	GMVC	H	Dagenham & Redbridge	Lost 0-1			1164
21	Nov 4	GMVC	H	Kidderminster Harriers	Won 2-1		Sowerby 2	1124
22	7	KSC	H	Ashford Town	Lost 1-2		Lewis	504
23	11	GMVC	A	Hednesford Town	Drew 2-2		Milton, Essex (og)	1147
24	18	GMVC	A	Morecambe	Lost 1-3		Lewis	1058
25	21	EFC	A	Folkestone Invicta	Lost 0-2			223
26	25	GMVC	H	Stalybridge Celtic	Lost 1-3		Hayes p	1069
27	28	SC	A	Farnborough Town	Won 3-1		Restarick, Sowerby, Hayes	320
28	Dec 2	GMVC	H	Kettering Town	Won 2-1		Sowerby 2	1045
29	9	GMVC	A	Dagenham & Redbridge	Lost 0-3			862
30	16	GMVC	H	Bath City	Won 1-0		Restarick	826
31	Jan 1	GMVC	A	Welling United	Lost 0-1			1006
32	6	GMVC	H	Telford United	Won 1-0		Daniels	1030
33	13	GMVC	A	Kettering Town	Drew 2-2		Lewis, Pilkington	1332
34	20	FAT	H	Cheltenham Town	Drew 2-2		Rogers, Darlington	904
35	23	FAT	A	Cheltenham Town	Drew 1-1*		Leworthy	640
36	31	FAT	H	Cheltenham Town	Won 1-0		Rogers	598
37	Feb 10	FAT	A	Boreham Wood	Lost 1-2		Restarick	506
38	13	GMVC	H	Woking	Won 4-3		Leworthy 4 (1p)	976
39	17	GMVC	A	Telford United	Lost 0-1			733
40	24	GMVC	H	Bromsgrove Rovers	Lost 0-2			1011
41	27	SC	H	Bromsgrove Rovers	Lost 0-1			464
42	28	EFC	H	Ashford Town	Lost 0-4			100
43	Mar 2	GMVC	H	Halifax Town	Won 3-2		Harris 2, Leworthy	895
44	4	GMVC	A	Stevenage Borough	Lost 2-3		Leworthy p, Harris	1062
45	9	GMVC	A	Runcorn	Won 3-1		Darlington, Leworthy, Harris	433
46	16	GMVC	H	Southport	Lost 0-1			1142
47	19	GMVC	A	Farnborough Town	Lost 2-3		Pilkington, Leworthy	416
48	23	GMVC	A	Woking	Lost 0-1			2438
49	26	GMVC	H	Welling United	Won 2-1		Milton, Leworthy	1001
50	30	GMVC	H	Morecambe	Lost 2-3		Leworthy, Lavelle (og)	1090
51	Apr 6	GMVC	H	Northwich Victoria	Lost 0-1			976
52	8	GMVC	A	Macclesfield Town	Won 1-0		Harris	1482
53	13	GMVC	H	Altrincham	Lost 1-4		Leworthy	1070
54	20	GMVC	A	Stalybridge Celtic	Lost 0-2			533
55	27	GMVC	A	Southport	Drew 0-0			849
56	May 4	GMVC	H	Gateshead	Drew 1-1		Leworthy	1103

* After Extra Time

Dover Athletic

1	2	3	4	5	6	7	8	9	10	11	12	14	Match No.
Ebbli	Budden	Embery	Strouts	Daniels	Theodosiou	Chambers	Ferney	Donn	Lawrence	Fox			1
Ebbli	Budden	Darlington	Chambers	Daniels	Walker	Strouts	Browne	Donn	Leworthy	Ferney	O'Brien	Lawrence	2
Ebbli	Budden	O'Brien	Chambers	Daniels	Walker	Strouts	Browne	Donn	Leworthy	Ferney	Lewis	Lawrence	3
Ebbli	Budden	Lawrence	Chambers	Daniels	Walker	Strouts	Browne	Donn	Leworthy	Ferney	O'Brien	Carruthers	4
Ebbli	Budden	Darlington	Theodosiou	Daniels	Walker	Strouts	Browne	Donn	Leworthy	O'Brien	Chambers	Carruthers	5
Ebbli	Budden	Chambers	Theodosiou	Daniels	Walker	Strouts	Browne	Donn	Lawrence	O'Brien	Ferney	Carruthers	6
Ebbli	Budden	Restarick	Theodosiou	Daniels	Walker	Lewis	Browne	Donn	Darlington	O'Brien	Milton	Chambers	7
Ebbli	Budden	Bond	Theodosiou	Daniels	O'Brien	Strouts	Lewis	Donn	Leworthy	Milton	Restarick	Chambers	8
Ebbli	Budden	Bond	Donn	Daniels	Restarick	Strouts	Browne	Darlington	Leworthy	Milton	Carruthers	Lewis	9
Ebbli	Budden	O'Brien	Strouts	Daniels	Walker	Restarick	Darlington	Donn	Leworthy	Milton	Chambers	Carruthers	10
Ebbli	Budden	Donn	Strouts	Daniels	Walker	Restarick	Darlington	Ferney	Leworthy	O'Brien	Chambers	Carruthers	11
Ebbli	Budden	Dalli	Foot	Donn	Walker	Restarick	Darlington	Rogers	Leworthy	O'Brien	Carruthers	Theodosiou	12
Ebbli	Donn	Dalli	Foot	Budden	Strouts	Restarick	Darlington	Ferney	Leworthy	Hayes	Rogers	Theodosiou	13
Ebbli	Budden	Donn	Strouts	Theodosiou	Foot	Restarick	Ferney	Rogers	Leworthy	Hayes	Southon	Milton	14
Ebbli	Foot	Donn	Campbell	Daniels	Ferney	Restarick	Milton	Rogers	Leworthy	Hayes	Jones	Southon	15
Ebbli	Donn	Campbell	Lindsay	Daniels	Strouts	Restarick	Milton	Rogers	Leworthy	Hayes	Pilkington	Sowerby	16
Ebbli	Pilkington	Donn	Lindsay	Daniels	Ferney	Restarick	Southon	Rogers	Sowerby	Taylor	Milton	Davies	17
Ebbli	Donn	Pilkington	Foot	Daniels	Lindsey	Strouts	Milton	Rogers	Leworthy	Hayes	Restarick	Sowerby	18
Ebbli	Foot	Pilkington	Budden	Daniels	Lindsey	Strouts	Donn	Rogers	Leworthy	Hayes	Restarick	Milton	19
Ebbli	Foot	Pilkington	Budden	Daniels	Lindsey	Strouts	Milton	Rogers	Leworthy	Hayes	Sowerby	Campbell	20
Ebbli	Foot	Pilkington	Budden	Daniels	Campbell	Lindsey	Milton	Rogers	Sowerby	Hayes	Restarick	Strouts	21
Davies	Foot	Pilkington	Donn	Theodosiou	Campbell	Lindsey	Milton	Rogers	Restarick	Lewis	Sowerby	Hayes	22
Ebbli	Foot	Pilkington	Budden	Daniels	Campbell	Lindsey	Milton	Rogers	Sowerby	Hayes	Lewis	Donn	23
Ebbli	Foot	Pilkington	Budden	Daniels	Campbell	Lindsey	Donn	Rogers	Lewis	Strouts	Theodosiou	O'Brien	24
Davies	Morgan	Lloyd	Husk	Morris	Binder	Jones	Chaston	Hancock	Laraman	O'Brien	Wilson	Sykes	25
Ebbli	Foot	Campbell	Budden	Daniels	Lewis	Lindsey	Milton	Rogers	Sowerby	Hayes	Donn	Jones	26
Ebbli	Donn	Pilkington	Lewis	Daniels	Strouts	Restarick	Milton	Rogers	Sowerby	Hayes	Jones	O'Brien	27
Ebbli	Budden	Campbell	Roget	Daniels	Strouts	Restarick	Milton	Lewis	Sowerby	Hayes	Pilkington	Darlington	28
Ebbli	Budden	Campbell	Roget	Daniels	Strouts	Restarick	Milton	Lewis	Sowerby	Hayes	Rogers	Darlington	29
Ebbli	Budden	Campbell	Roget	Daniels	Darlington	Restarick	Milton	Lewis	Sowerby	Hayes	Lindsey	Lawrence	30
Ebbli	Budden	Campbell	Roget	Daniels	Darlington	Restarick	Milton	Lewis	Rogers	Hayes	Pilkington	Lindsey	31
Ebbli	Lindsey	Pilkington	Campbell	Daniels	Darlington	Sowerby	Milton	Lewis	Rogers	Hayes	Strouts	Restarick	32
Ebbli	Lindsey	Pilkington	Campbell	Daniels	Darlington	Strouts	Budden	Lewis	Rogers	O'Brien	Donn	Restarick	33
Ebbli	Lindsey	Pilkington	Theodosiou	Daniels	Darlington	Budden	Milton	Lewis	Rogers	Hayes	Donn	Restarick	34
Ebbli	Lindsey	Pilkington	Campbell	Daniels	Budden	Darlington	Milton	Lewis	Rogers	Restarick	O'Brien	Leworthy	35
Ebbli	Lindsey	Pilkington	Campbell	Daniels	Budden	Darlington	Milton	Lewis	Rogers	Restarick	Donn	Leworthy	36
Ebbli	Lindsey	Pilkington	Campbell	Daniels	Budden	Darlington	Milton	Lewis	Rogers	Restarick	Donn	O'Brien	37
Ebbli	Budden	Pilkington	Campbell	Daniels	Lewis	Darlington	Milton	Rogers	Leworthy	Restarick	Donn	O'Brien	38
Ebbli	Budden	Pilkington	Campbell	Daniels	Lewis	Darlington	Milton	Rogers	Leworthy	Restarick	Donn	O'Brien	39
Ebbli	Budden	Pilkington	Campbell	Daniels	Lewis	Darlington	Lindsey	Rogers	Leworthy	O'Brien	Donn	Dixon	40
Ebbli	Budden	Pilkington	Campbell	Daniels	Donn	Strouts	Lindsey	Jones	Sowerby	O'Brien	Darlington	Dixon	41
Wilks	Morgan	McCabe	Wilson	Morris	Ferney	Chaston	Binder	Dixon	Laraman	Lloyd	Limbert	Hogg	42
Ebbli	Budden	Pilkington	Campbell	Daniels	Lewis	Darlington	Lindsey	Harris	Leworthy	Strouts	Donn	O'Brien	43
Ebbli	Donn	Pilkington	Campbell	Daniels	Lewis	Darlington	Lindsey	Harris	Leworthy	Strouts	O'Brien	Jones	44
Ebbli	Lindsey	Pilkington	Campbell	Mosely	Budden	Darlington	Milton	Harris	Leworthy	Strouts	Donn	O'Brien	45
Ebbli	Lindsey	Pilkington	Campbell	Mosely	Budden	Darlington	Milton	Harris	Leworthy	Strouts	Donn	O'Brien	46
Ebbli	Lindsey	Pilkington	Campbell	Mosely	Budden	Darlington	Milton	Harris	Leworthy	Strouts	Donn	O'Brien	47
Ebbli	Budden	Pilkington	Campbell	Daniels	Donn	Darlington	Lindsey	Harris	Leworthy	Strouts	Milton	Mitten	48
Mitten	Budden	Pilkington	Mosely	Daniels	Lewis	Darlington	Milton	Harris	Leworthy	Lindsey	Campbell	O'Brien	49
Mitten	Budden	Pilkington	Mosely	Daniels	Lewis	Strouts	Milton	O'Brien	Leworthy	Lindsey	Campbell	Harris	50
Ebbli	Budden	Pilkington	Campbell	Daniels	Lewis	Strouts	Milton	Harris	Leworthy	O'Brien	Jones	Darlington	51
Ebbli	Lindsey	Budden	Campbell	Daniels	Lewis	Donn	Milton	Harris	Leworthy	O'Brien	Jones	Darlington	52
Ebbli	Lindsey	Budden	Campbell	Daniels	Lewis	Strouts	Milton	Harris	Leworthy	O'Brien	Donn	Mosely	53
Mitten	Lindsey	Budden	Campbell	Daniels	Lewis	Strouts	Mosely	Harris	Leworthy	Donn	Pilkington	O'Brien	54
Mitten	Lindsey	Pilkington	Campbell	Daniels	Budden	Mosely	Lewis	Harris	Leworthy	Milton	Donn	Darlington	55
Mitten	Lindsey	Pilkington	Campbell	Daniels	Budden	Mosely	Milton	Harris	Leworthy	Lewis	Strouts	Darlington	56

JOE O'SULLIVAN

Joe was appointed as assistant-manager to Peter Taylor during the summer of 1996, having left his previous post as manager of Beazer Homes League Premier Division club Chelmsford City midway through the 1995/96 campaign. Then, just three weeks before the start of the new season, Taylor left The Crabble to take over as the new full-time manager of England's under 21 team under the new Glenn Hoddle regime and Joe was handed the chance to take charge of a team at Vauxhall Conference level for the first time.

As a player, Joe was a goalkeeper with Tilbury and a number of other Essex clubs. Since becoming a manager he has had two spells in charge at Chelmsford City, during one of which he signed Peter Taylor as a player, and has also had spells with Heybridge Swifts and Stambridge. Joe has also assisted John Still at both Dagenham and Maidstone United.

Joe has brought with him his long-serving number two, Dave Guiver, and together they will be relishing the opportunity of managing at the top level of the Pyramid.

Dover's John Budden in action in their match with Borehamwood. *Photo - Clive Butchins*

Programme details:
38 pages for £1.00
Editor - Chris Collings - 01304 822074

Any other club publications:
'Tales from the River End' - Fanzine

Local Newspapers:
Dover Express.
East Kent Mercury.

Local Radio Stations:
Radio Kent
Invicta FM
Coast AM

DOVER ATHLETIC - PLAYING SQUAD 1996-97

Player	Honours	Birthplace and date	Transfer Fees	Previous Clubs
GOALKEEPERS				
Charlie Mitten		Kent		Thamesmead T
Brian Horne	EY, Eu21	Billericay 5/10/67		Millwall, Portsmouth, Hartlepool U
DEFENDERS				
David Scott	SLP, SLS, E Univ.	Carlisle 15/4/67		Penrith, Hastings T, Canterbury C, Hastings T
Gerald Dobbs		Lambeth 24/1/71		Wimbledon
Graham Mansfield		Suffolk		Ipswich T, Chelmsford C
Scott Daniels		Benfleet 22/11/69		Colchester U, Exeter C
James Strouts	Army			Harrogate RA, Frickley A, Harrogate T, Sittingbourne
Stuart Munday		Newham 28/9/72		Brighton
Gary Stebbing	EY	Croydon 11/8/65		Cry Pal, Ostend (Belg), Maidstone, Kettering T, Dag & Red
MIDFIELDERS				
Iain O'Connell	SLP	Southend 9/10/70		Southend Utd
Udo Onwere		Hammersmith 9/11/71		Fulham, Lincoln C
Phil Barber		Tring 10/6/65		Aylesbury U, Crystal Palace, Millwall, Bristol C
Tim Dixon	SLP	Dover 31/12/65		Southampton, Waterford Utd
Scott Lindsey		Walsall 4/5/72		Scunthorpe, Goole, Stafford, Burton A, Tamworth, Sutton C, Bridlington, Gillingham
FORWARDS				
David Leworthy	ESP, FAY	Portsmouth 22/10/62	£50,000	Portsmouth, Fareham T, Spurs, Oxford U, Reading, Farnborough T
Russell Milton	ESP KS	London		Arsenal, Double Flower (HK), Instant Dict (HK)
Colin Sowerby	SLC	Essex 1/7/66		Tilbury, Aveley, Hendon, Southend, Orient, Dartfd, Redb F, Hendon, Erith, Purf't
Jermaine Darlington		London 11/4/74		Charlton Athletic
Liam Fox		Dover		From Youth Team
Ricky Reina		Kent		Gillingham, Folkestone Invicta, Sing Tao (HK)
Steve Lawrence		Gilbert & Elice Is		From Youth Team

Departures during season:
Tony Dixon (Margate), Corey Browne (Stevenage B), John Dalli (Released), Matt Carruthers (Ashford T), Paul Chambers (Folekstone I), Steve Lawrence (Margate - Loan), Andy Theodosiou & Steve Restarick (Crawley T - Loan), Martin Hayes (Cliftonville), David Walker (Gravesend), Tony Rogers (Crawley T).
Players on loan during season:
Danny Foot (Southend U), Lee Roget (Southend U).
Departures during close season: Nigel Donn & Paul O'Brien (Ashford T), Steve Mosely (Purfleet), Jason Bartlett, Effrem Ebbli, Cory Campbell, Junior Lewis & Martin Ferney (Released).

Crabble Athletic Ground, Dover Athletic

GROUND ADDRESS:
Crabble Athletic Ground, Lewisham Road, River, Dover, Kent. CT17 0JB.
TELEPHONE NUMBER: 01304 822373
SIMPLE DIRECTIONS:
Follow the A2 from Canterbury until you pass the Forte Posthouse Hotel on your left and approach a roundabout with MacDonald's drive-in restuarant and a petrol station at the roundabout on your left. Turn right signposted to Town Centre and go down the hill. At the mini-roundabout at the bottom turn left. At the next traffic lights turn right and follow the road under the railway bridge. The ground is up the hill on your left.
CAPACITY: 6,500 **SEATED:** 1,000 **COVERED TERRACING:** 4,900
RECORD ATTENDANCE:
4,035 v Bromsgrove Rovers, Beazer Homes League April 1992.
CLUB SHOP:
At the ground, open matchdays for general souvenirs, programmes, replica shirts (home & away) etc. Also at Worthington Street in the town, open daily. Contact Jean Haves 01304 240041.
SOCIAL FACILITIES:
Social Club open 7 days a week. Meals available.
Steward - Gavin Hughes 01304 822306.
PREVIOUS GROUNDS:
None

Dover Fact File

Nickname: Lilywhites

Club Sponsors: Daihatsu (UK) Ltd.
Previous Leagues: Kent League, Southern League.
Club colours: White shirts with black sleeves, black shorts and white socks.
Change colours: Yellow shirts, green shorts and yellow socks.
Reserve team league: Winstonlead Kent League Div.2.
Midweek home matchday: Tuesday
Record win: 7-0 v Weymouth 3rd April 1990.
Record defeat: 1-7 v Poole Town.
Record transfer fee: £50,000 for David Leworthy from Farnborough Town - Aug. 1993.
Record transfer fee received: £11,500 for Tony Rogers from Chelmsford City 1992.
1995-96 Captain: David Leworthy
1995-96 Top scorer: David Leworthy - 25 goals.
1995-96 Player of the Year: Dave Leworthy
Club record goalscorer: Lennie Lee - 160.
Record appearances: Jason Bartlett - 539.
Past players who progressed to the Football League: None

Club Honours: Beazer Homes League Premier Division Champions 1989/90, 1992/93; Beazer Homes League Southern Division Champions 1987/88; Beazer Homes League Championship Match Winners 1990 & 1993; Premier Inter League Cup Winners 1990/91; Southern League Cup Winners 1991/92; Kent Senior Cup Winners 1990/91, Runners-up 1993/4; Knight Floodlit Cup Winners 1987/88, 1988/89, Runners-up 1986/87

FARNBOROUGH TOWN

FARNBOROUGH TOWN F.C.

Formed: 1967

Chairman:
Tony Alper

President:
Maurice O'Brien

Football Secretary:
Terry Parr

Directors:
Brian Blewett
Charles Mortimore
Michael McCarthy
Gerry Darcey
John Davies
Alan Gillespie
Peter Gough
Terry Parr
Alan Spaven
Dennis Hayward
Jeffery Jeremiah

Manager:
Alan Taylor

Assistant Manager:
Ken Ballard

Coaches: M Savage, M Critchell D Beard

Physiotherapist:
A Morris C Cobb

Although the Hampshire club now have several Conference campaigns under theirbelts, this season will be the first time that the club has taken part in threeconsecutive seasons at this level. League standings of 14th and 10th in thelast two seasons was just what the club needed after several yo-yo years.

During the past season Farnborough forked out £12,500 to bring two highly-rated players to Cherrywood Road. Midfielder Phil Wingfield moved fromKingstonian to link up with David Harlow for a fee of £7,500 and then inFebruary Farnborough paid Worthing £5,000 for left-back Spencer Mintram. Theclub are hopeful that giving these players, along with Darren Robson, time tobed in will pay dividends in the coming season.

It was certainly another progressive season at Cherrywood Road with two youngdefenders coming through from the reserves to stake regular first-team spots,and there is a great future for Richard Williams and Jon Underwood, bothrewarded with contracts.

Farnborough enjoyed success in the FA Cup and after Trevor Senior's strikerat Griffin Park in the 1st Round, Farnborough found themselves live on Sky forthe replay for the second time in their short history - this bringing in muchwelcomed extra revenue.

Maybe the only disappointing time was in the FA Trophy where hopes of aWembley run were dashed when Boro went out in a close fought replay at SloughTown at a time of many injuries.

Farnborough though are rapidly getting a reputation for being a hard team tobeat and with a number of new players and the average age of the squad down,the club, who have revealed ambitious plans to bring the ground up to League requirements, can be confident of making further progress.

Vince Williams

Farnborough Town F.C. Main stand

Farnborough Town

Match No.	Date		Comp.	Venue H/A	Opponents	Result	League Pos.	Goalscorers (Times if known)	Attendance
1	Aug	19	GMVC	H	Kidderminster Harriers	Won 3-1	4	Boothe, Senior, Horton	840
2		21	GMVC	A	Dagenham & Redbridge	Drew 2-2	1	Boothe, Harlow	758
3		26	GMVC	A	Telford United	Lost 2-3	12	Boothe, Horton	809
4		28	GMVC	H	Kettering Town	Drew 1-1	13	Boothe	1037
5	Sep	2	GMVC	H	Northwich Victoria	Lost 0-1	16		808
6		5	GMVC	A	Dover Athletic	Won 3-1	12	Robson 2, Senior	779
7		9	FAC1Q	H	Dartford FC	Won 1-0		Harlow	602
8		16	GMVC	H	Stalybridge Celtic	Drew 1-1	16	Senior	707
9		19	SC1 1	A	Bath City	Won 3-0	-	Day, Boothe 2	257
10		23	FAC2Q	A	Fisher 93	Won 4-1	-	S Baker, Robson, Boothe 2	250
11		26	GMVC	H	Dagenham & Redbridge	Won 2-0	13	Coney, Boothe	494
12		30	GMVC	H	Macclesfield Town	Won 6-1	10	Boothe 3, Senior 2, Denny	740
13	Oct	3	SC1 2	H	Bath City	Won 3-2	-	Boothe 2, Denny	385
14		7	FAC3Q	H	Walton & Hersham	Won 3-2	-	Boothe 2, Senior	761
15		14	GMVC	A	Bromsgrove	Won 2-1	10	Boothe, Harlow	1145
16		21	FAC4Q	H	Yeovil Town	Won 2-1	-	Stemp, Boothe	1409
17		28	GMVC	H	Halifax Town	Drew 0-0	12		908
18		31	GMVC	A	Slough Town	Drew 1-1	10	Boothe	891
19	Nov	2	HSC2	H	New Street	Won 6-1	-	Steadman, Turkington, Juryeff 2, Unwin 2	186
20		4	GMVC	A	Southport	Lost 1-7	13	Day	819
21		11	FAC1	A	Brentford	Drew 1-1	-	Senior	4711
22		18	GMVC	H	Bromsgrove Rovers	Won 1-0	11	Boothe	930
23		22	FAC1R	H	Brentford	Lost 0-4	-		3581
24		25	GMVC	A	Macclesfield Town	Lost 0-1	14		1721
25		28	SC2 1	H	Dover Athletic	Lost 1-3	-	Boothe	320
26	Dec	2	GMVC	A	Northwich Victoria	Won 3-1	13	Underwood, Booth, Denny	687
27		9	GMVC	H	Hednesford Town	Lost 1-3	14	Gavin	716
28		12	GMVC	A	Welling United	Won 1-0	11	Robson	403
29		16	GMVC	A	Kettering Town	Won 2-0	9	S Baker, Boothe	1260
30		19	HSC3	H	DCA Basingstoke	Lost 1-4	-	Read	142
31	Jan	1	GMVC	H	Bath City	Drew 0-0	10		779
32		6	GMVC	H	Morecambe	Won 3-1	8	Boothe, Harlow, Gavin	729
33		8	GMVC	A	Stevenage Borough	Drew 0-0	8		1745
34		13	GMVC	A	Gateshead	Drew 1-1	8	Robson	881
35		20	FAT1	H	Slough Town	Drew 1-1	-	Gavin	856
36		23	FAT1R	A	Slough Town	Lost 3-4	-	Boothe, Harlow, Gavin	742
37	Feb	3	GMVC	H	Southport	Won 1-0	8	Robson	738
38		10	GMVC	A	Stalybridge Celtic	Drew 2-2	8	Boothe, Gavin	521
39		17	GMVC	A	Runcorn	Won 3-0	6	Boothe, Gavin, S Baker	429
40		20	GMVC	A	Bath City	Lost 1-2	6	Wingfield	290
41		24	GMVC	A	Altrincham	Drew 2-2	7	Boothe, Gavin	580
42	Mar	2	GMVC	H	Slough Town	Lost 0-1	7		1069
43		5	GMVC	H	Welling United	Lost 0-1	7		470
44		9	GMVC	A	Hednesford Town	Lost 1-4	8	Wingfield	1010
45		12	GMVC	H	Woking	Lost 0-2	8		1497
46		16	GMVC	H	Runcorn	Lost 0-1	9		619
47		19	GMVC	H	Dover Athletic	Won 3-2	8	Boothe, Gavin, S Baker	416
48		23	GMVC	A	Morecambe	Won 3-2	6	Underwood, Boothe, Gavin	868
49		30	GMVC	A	Halifax Town	Drew 0-0	7		697
50	Apr	6	GMVC	H	Gateshead	Lost 2-3	8	Gavin, Wingfield	625
51		8	GMVC	H	Altrincham	Drew 1-1	8	McAvoy	706
52		16	GMVC	A	Woking	Lost 1-2	9	Robson	3166
53		20	GMVC	H	Telford United	Won 2-1	8	Boothe, Wingfield	784
54		27	GMVC	A	Kidderminster Harriers	Drew 3-3	8	Harlow, Gavin, Wingfield	1559
55	May	4	GMVC	H	Stevenage Borough	Drew 2-2	10	Boothe, Baker S	1419

Farnborough Town

1	2	3	4	5	6	7	8	9	10	11	12	14	Match No.
MacKenzie	McAvoy	Stemp	Coney	K Baker	Robson	Boothe	Harlow	Senior	S Baker	Horton	Pratt	Denny	1
MacKenzie	McAvoy	Stemp	Coney	K Baker	Robson	Boothe	Harlow	Senior	S Baker	Horton	Denny	Pratt	2
MacKenzie	McAvoy	Stemp	Day	K Baker	Robson	Boothe	Harlow	Senior	S Baker	Horton	Coney	Denny	3
MacKenzie	Stemp	Pratt	Day	K Baker	Robson	Boothe	Harlow	Senior	S Baker	Horton	McAvoy	Denny	4
MacKenzie	Stemp	Pratt	Coney	Day	Robson	Boothe	Harlow	Senior	S Baker	Horton	McAvoy	Denny	5
Rowe	Stemp	K Baker	Coney	Day	Robson	Boothe	Harlow	Senior	S Baker	Horton	McAvoy	Denny	6
MacKenzie	Stemp	K Baker	Coney	Day	Robson	Boothe	Harlow	Senior	S Baker	McAvoy	Pratt	Denny	7
MacKenzie	Stemp	K Baker	Coney	Day	Robson	Boothe	Harlow	Senior	S Baker	Horton	Denny	McAvoy	8
MacKenzie	S Baker	Stemp	Coney	Day	Robson	Boothe	Harlow	Senior	Denny	McAvoy	K Baker	Horton	9
MacKenzie	S Baker	Stemp	Coney	Day	Robson	Boothe	Harlow	Senior	Denny	McAvoy	K Baker	Hayward	10
MacKenzie	S Baker	Stemp	Coney	Day	Robson	Boothe	Harlow	Juryeff	Denny	McAvoy	K Baker	Pratt	11
MacKenzie	S Baker	Stemp	Coney	Day	Robson	Boothe	Harlow	Senior	Denny	McAvoy	Pratt	K Baker	12
Rowe	Stemp	K Baker	Coney	Pratt	Robson	Boothe	Harlow	Senior	Denny	McAvoy	Hayward	Underwood	13
MacKenzie	S Baker	Stemp	Coney	Day	Robson	Boothe	Harlow	Senior	Denny	McAvoy	K Baker	Pratt	14
MacKenzie	S Baker	Stemp	Coney	Day	Robson	Boothe	Harlow	Senior	Denny	McAvoy	K Baker	Juryeff	15
MacKenzie	S Baker	Stemp	Coney	Day	Robson	Boothe	Harlow	Senior	Denny	K Baker	Juryeff	Turkington	16
MacKenzie	S Baker	Stemp	Coney	Day	Robson	Boothe	Harlow	Senior	Denny	K Baker	Juryeff	Turkington	17
MacKenzie	S Baker	Stemp	Coney	Day	Robson	Boothe	Harlow	Senior	Denny	K Baker	Juryeff	Turkington	18
Rowe	Steadman	Roberts	Underwood	Williams	Turkington	Watkinson	Hayward	Juryeff	Unwin	Reed	Bell	Johnson	19
MacKenzie	S Baker	Stemp	Coney	Day	Robson	Boothe	Harlow	Senior	Denny	K Baker	Juryeff	Turkington	20
MacKenzie	S Baker	Stemp	Coney	McAvoy	Robson	Boothe	Harlow	Senior	Denny	K Baker	Juryeff	Turkington	21
MacKenzie	S Baker	Stemp	Coney	Day	Robson	Boothe	Harlow	Juryeff	Denny	K Baker	McAvoy	Horton	22
MacKenzie	S Baker	Stemp	Coney	Day	Robson	Boothe	Harlow	Senior	Denny	K Baker	Juryeff	Horton	23
MacKenzie	S Baker	Stemp	Williams	McAvoy	Robson	Boothe	Harlow	Senior	Denny	K Baker	Underwood	Juryeff	24
MacKenzie	S Baker	Stemp	Williams	McAvoy	Robson	Boothe	Harlow	Senior	Denny	K Baker	Underwood	Juryeff	25
MacKenzie	S Baker	Stemp	Williams	Underwood	Robson	Boothe	Harlow	Horton	Denny	K Baker	Day	Hayward	26
MacKenzie	S Baker	Stemp	Williams	Horton	Robson	Boothe	Harlow	Gavin	Denny	K Baker	Underwood	Day	27
MacKenzie	S Baker	Stemp	Williams	Day	Robson	Boothe	Harlow	Gavin	Denny	K Baker	Horton	Underwood	28
MacKenzie	S Baker	Stemp	Williams	Day	Robson	Boothe	Harlow	Gavin	Underwood	K Baker	Hayward	Steadman	29
Rowe	Reed	Roberts	Underwood	Hooper	Steadman	Bell	Hayward	Unwin	Read	Jansen	Watkinson	Osborn	30
MacKenzie	Stemp	K Baker	Williams	Day	Robson	Boothe	Harlow	Gavin	S Baker	Wingfield	Underwood	Denny	31
MacKenzie	Stemp	K Baker	Williams	Day	Robson	Boothe	Harlow	Gavin	S Baker	Wingfield	Underwood	Denny	32
MacKenzie	Stemp	K Baker	Williams	Day	Robson	Boothe	Harlow	Gavin	S Baker	Wingfield	Underwood	Denny	33
MacKenzie	Underwood	K Baker	Williams	Day	Robson	Boothe	Harlow	Gavin	S Baker	Wingfield	Steadman	Denny	34
MacKenzie	Stemp	K Baker	Williams	Day	Robson	Boothe	Harlow	Gavin	S Baker	Denny	Underwood	Coney	35
MacKenzie	Stemp	K Baker	Williams	Underwood	Robson	Boothe	Harlow	Gavin	S Baker	Wingfield	McAvoy	Denny	36
MacKenzie	Stemp	K Baker	Williams	McAvoy	Robson	Boothe	Harlow	Gavin	Denny	Wingfield	Steadman	Reed	37
MacKenzie	Stemp	K Baker	Williams	Day	Robson	Boothe	Harlow	Gavin	McAvoy	Wingfield	Steadman	Denny	38
MacKenzie	Stemp	Denny	Williams	Day	Robson	Boothe	Harlow	Gavin	S Baker	Wingfield	Underwood	Reed	39
MacKenzie	Stemp	Mintram	Williams	Day	Robson	Boothe	Harlow	Gavin	S Baker	Wingfield	Underwood	Denny	40
MacKenzie	Underwood	Mintram	Denny	Day	Robson	Boothe	Harlow	Gavin	S Baker	Wingfield	McAvoy	Williams	41
MacKenzie	Stemp	Mintram	Underwood	Day	Robson	Boothe	Harlow	Gavin	S Baker	Wingfield	Williams	Denny	42
MacKenzie	Stemp	Underwood	Williams	Day	Robson	Boothe	Harlow	Gavin	S Baker	Wingfield	McAvoy	Denny	43
MacKenzie	Denny	Underwood	Williams	Day	Robson	Boothe	Harlow	Gavin	S Baker	Wingfield	McAvoy	Steadman	44
MacKenzie	Stemp	Underwood	McAvoy	Day	Robson	Boothe	Harlow	Gavin	S Baker	Wingfield	Williams	Denny	45
Rowe	Stemp	Underwood	McAvoy	Day	Robson	Boothe	Harlow	Gavin	S Baker	Wingfield	Williams	Denny	46
Rowe	Stemp	Underwood	McAvoy	Day	Robson	Boothe	Harlow	Gavin	S Baker	Wingfield	Williams	Denny	47
Rowe	Stemp	Underwood	McAvoy	Day	Denny	Boothe	Harlow	Gavin	S Baker	Wingfield	Steadman	Hayward	48
Rowe	Stemp	Underwood	McAvoy	Day	Robson	Boothe	Harlow	Gavin	S Baker	Wingfield	Denny	Steadman	49
MacKenzie	Stemp	Underwood	McAvoy	K Baker	Robson	Boothe	Harlow	Gavin	Denny	Wingfield	Steadman	Bell	50
MacKenzie	Stemp	Underwood	McAvoy	K Baker	Robson	Boothe	Harlow	Gavin	Denny	Wingfield	Steadman	Hayward	51
MacKenzie	Stemp	Underwood	McAvoy	Day	Robson	Boothe	Harlow	Gavin	K Baker	Wingfield	Denny	Hayward	52
MacKenzie	Stemp	Underwood	McAvoy	Day	Robson	Boothe	Harlow	Gavin	S Baker	Wingfield	Denny	K Baker	53
MacKenzie	Stemp	Underwood	McAvoy	Day	Robson	Boothe	Harlow	Gavin	S Baker	Wingfield	Denny	Steadman	54
MacKenzie	Stemp	Underwood	McAvoy	Day	Robson	Boothe	Harlow	Gavin	S Baker	Wingfield	Denny	Hayward	55

Farnborough Town

ALAN TAYLOR

In his playing days, Alan had a promising career with West Ham United and AFC Bournemouth before being forced out of the game by injury when he left the full time game.
After a short time at Hillingdon Borough he went to Craven Cottage where he served as Fulham's youth team coach for nine years. It was from Fulham that Alan joined Farnborough Town in 1986 and, apart from a brief spell as manager at Chesham United, he has been at Cherrywood Road ever since holding the position of assistant manager until the commencement of the 1993/94 season when he took over the top spot. Alan's first season at the helm was more than successful reaching the 1st Round Proper of the FA Cup, the Hampshire Senior Cup Final and guiding Boro to their second Beazer Homes Championship and back to the Conference. In the last two seasons Alan has steered the club to consolidation by finishing in respectable 14th and 10th positions.

Alan Taylor 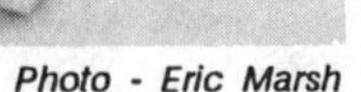 *Photo - Eric Marsh*

Dean Coney; Farnborough Town Captain

Programme details:
40 pages for £1
Editor - Ken Ballard

Any other club publications:
Simon Read's Haircut - Fanzine

Local Newspapers:
Faenborouigh News

Local Radio Stations:
B.B.C. Southern Counties

FARNBOROUGH TOWN - PLAYING SQUAD 1996-97

Player	Honours	Birthplace and date	Transfer Fees	Previous Clubs
GOALKEEPERS				
Stuart Mackenzie	FAV	Tooting 21/3/65	£3,250	Hounslow, Southall, Hounslow, Harrow B, Yeading
DEFENDERS				
Wayne Stemp	BHL	Epsom 9/9/70		Brighton, Woking, Staines T, Bognor Regis Town
Dean Coney	BHL	Dagenham 18/9/63		Fulham, QPR, Norwich City, Ernest Borel (HK)
Gordon McAvoy		Paisley 10/6/72		Queens Park, Kilmarnock, Bedfont
Keith Day		Aveley 29/11/62		Colchester U, Leyton Orient, Sittingbourne
Nicky Jansen		Hampshire		Southampton
Richard Williams		Surrey		Tottenham Hotspur
Spencer Mintram		Brighton	£5,000	Brighton, Lewes, Worthing
Jon Underwood		Surrey		From Youth Team
MIDFIELDERS				
Phil Wingfield		London	£7,500	Walton & Hersham, Kingstonian, Walton & Hersham, Hayes, Kingstonian
Steve Baker	BHL	Newcastle 2/12/61		Southampton, Leyton Orient, Aldershot
Phil Bell	HSC	Oslo (Nor) 8/6/74		From Youth Team
David Harlow		Epsom 2/11/67	£10,000	Fulham, Farnborough T, Kingstonian
Darren Robson		Woolwich 18/11/69		Petersfield, Andover, W'looville, Basingstoke, Gosport B, Southwick, Worthing
FORWARDS				
Chris Boothe	BHL	London		Hanwell Town
Danny Heywood		Hampshire		From Youth Team
Paul Harford		Chelmsford 21/10/74		Arsenal, Blackburn R
Richard Denny		London		Hanwell T
Pat Gavin		Hammersmith 5/6/67		Hanwell, Gillingham, Leicester, P'boro, Barnet, N'mpton, Wigan, Hayes, Aylesbury, Harrow

Departures during season:
Bradley Pratt (Chertsey T), Trevor Senior (Retired), Jamie Horton (Aldershot T).
Players on loan during season:
None.
Departures during close season: Keith Baker (Fleet T), Ian Juryeff (Havant T), Mark Turkington (Retired).

Cherrywood Road, Farnborough

ADDRESS:
John Roberts Ground, Cherrywood Road, Farnborough, Hampshire GU14 8UD.
TELEPHONE NUMBER: 01252 541469. **Club Newsline:** 0898 88 44 07.

SIMPLE DIRECTIONS:
M3 exit 4, A325 towards Farnborough, right into Prospect Avenue (club signposted), 2nd right into Cherrywood Rd, ground on right. 20-30 min walk from Farnborough Main, Farnborough North and Frimley BR stations. Whippet mini-bus route 19 passes ground.

CAPACITY: 4,900 **SEATED:** 561 **COVERED TERRACING:** 1,350

RECORD ATTENDANCE:
3,581 v Brighton 22/11/95 (FA Cup).

CLUB SHOP:
Boro' Leisurewear shop sells all types of club leisurewear and matchballs (contact Commercial Manager (01252 549328)). Supporters Club shop sells old progs, scarves, badges etc (contact Sandy Turnball).

SOCIAL FACILITIES:
Clubhouse open pub hours and matchdays. Hot pies, bar meals, crisps etc. Darts, pool, fruit machines & jukebox.

PREVIOUS GROUNDS:
Queens Road, Farnborough (1969-1976)

Farnborough Fact File

Nickname: The "Boro"

Colours: Yellow & blue/yellow/yellow
Change colours: Red & white/red/red
Previous Leagues: Surrey Senior 68-72/ Spartan 72-76/ Athenian 76-77/ Isthmian 77-89/ Alliance Premier (GMV Conference) 89-90 91-93/ Southern 90-91 93-94.
Midweek matchday: Tuesday
Reserve Team's League: Suburban League (Premier Division)
Best FA Cup season: 3rd Rd Proper replay 91-92 (lost 0-1 at West Ham United after 1-1 draw).
League Clubs defeated in FA Cup: Torquay United 91-92.
Record win: 11-0 v Chertsey Town (H), Spartan League 72-73.
Record defeat: 2-10 v Worplesdon (H), Surrey Senior League Division One 68-69.
Record Fee Paid: £10,000 to Kingstonian for David Harlow December 1994.
Record Fee Received: £50,000 from Dover Athletic for David Leworthy, August 1993.
Players progressing to Football League: Dennis Bailey (Crystal Palace & Birmingham City), Paul Mortimer (Charlton Athletic), Tommy Jones (Aberdeen & Swindon Town), Allan Cockram (Brentford), Paul Holsgrove (Millwall & Reading), Maik Taylor (Barnet).
Club Record Goalscorer (career): Simon Read 200, 1986-1994.
Club Record Goalscorer (season): Simon Read 53, 1988-89.
Club Record Appearances: Brian Broome 500, 1980-1994.
1995-96 Captain: Dean Coney.
1995-96 Player of the Year: Wayne Stemp
1995-96 Top scorer: Chris Boothe.

Honours: Southern Lg 90-91 93-94, Isthmian Lg R-up 88-89 (Div 1 84-85, Div 2 78-79), Athenian Lg Div 2 78-79, Spartan Lg 72-73 73-74 74-75 (Lg Cup 74-75), London Spartan Lg 75-76 (Lg Cup 75-76), Hants Snr Cup 74-75 81-82 83-84 85-86 90-91 (R-up 93-94), FA Trophy QF 92-93, FA Vase SF 75-76 76-77.

GATESHEAD

Formed:
1977

President:
J C Thomas

Vice Presidents:
Norman Lakey
Bill Gibson
John Lyon

Chairman:
John Gibson

Vice Chairman:
Peter Robinson

General Manager:
Mark Donnelly

Manager:
Colin Richardson

Coach:
George Cook

Physiotherapist:
Billy Thomson

Press Officer:
Andy Wilson

Match Secretary:
Arthur Waggott

Another excellent season for the north east club following on from seventh place in 1994/95. Colin Richardson continues to prove what a good manager he is and was even able to sell the Conference leading scorer Paul Dobson without any detrimental effect. That was due to the shrewd signing of Steve Harkus from Blyth Spartans. He came in and netted 19 league goals and attracted the attention of League clubs. The capture of former England semi-professional international midfielder Kenny Lowe was also a good move and there was interest for supporters in captures such as Liberian Delano Ketter and veteran goalkeepers Steve Sherwood and John Burridge.

This summer has seen Richardson busy again in the transfer market, bringing in some quality performers such as Paul Hague and Darren Foreman and the manager was even able to allow England midfielders Kenny Cramman and Mark Hine to move on.

The International Stadium could just see a serious championship challenge from Gateshead this season. **Steve Whitney**

Back Row (L/R): Billy Thompson (Physio), Kevin Eglon, Sam Kitchen, Paul Hague, Paul Thompson, Steve Sherwwod, Justin Robson, Nicky Peverall, Alan Dowson, Kenny Lowe, George Cook (Coach), Bob Howe (Kit). Front; Paul Prondlock, Darren Foreman, Gary Robinson, Derek Ord, Jeff Wrightson, John Watson, Steve Harkus, Andrew Hopwarth, Brian Rowe

Gateshead

Match No.	Date	Comp.	Venue H/A	Opponents	Result	League Pos.	Goalscorers (Times if known)	Attendance
1	Aug 19	GMVC	A	Bromsgrove Rovers	Lost 1-3	16	Thompson	789
2	23	GMVC	H	Stalybridge Celtic	Won 1-0	16	Thompson	524
3	26	GMVC	H	Macclesfield Town	Lost 0-1	17		650
4	28	GMVC	A	Altrincham	Drew 1-1	17	Trott	640
5	Sep 2	GMVC	H	Stevenage Borough	Drew 2-2	18	Proudlock 2	610
6	5	GMVC	A	Halifax Town	Lost 0-2	20		743
7	9	FAC1Q	H	Dunston FB	Won 3-2	-	Rowe, Ord, Thompson	492
8	13	GMVC	H	Runcorn	Won 1-0	18	Proudlock	375
9	16	GMVC	A	Telford United	Drew 0-0	18		750
10	20	GMVC	H	Halifax Town	Won 3-2	11	Marquis, Cramman, Thompson	559
11	23	FAC2Q	H	Barrow	Drew 2-2	-	Thompson 2	721
12	26	FAC2QR	A	Barrow	Lost 0-1	-		1908
13	30	GMVC	A	Woking	Lost 0-2	17		1939
14	Oct 7	GMVC	A	Welling United	Won 2-1	12	Thompson, Dobson	588
15	10	GMVC	A	Stalybridge Celtic	Won 2-0	10	Cramman, Harkus	480
16	14	GMVC	H	Dagenham & Redbridge	Won 2-0	7	Trott 2	587
17	21	GMVC	H	Dover Athletic	Drew 1-1	7	Cramman	512
18	28	GMVC	A	Bath City	Won 1-0	5	Ord	481
19	Nov 4	GMVC	H	Slough Town	Won 2-1	4	Harkus 2	642
20	11	GMVC	A	Dagenham & Redbridge	Won 4-0	3	Harkus, Trott 2, Proudlock	712
21	18	GMVC	H	Kettering Town	Won 1-0	4	Ord	712
22	25	GMVC	A	Southport	Lost 0-1	5		1008
23	Dec 2	GMVC	H	Hednesford Town	Lost 0-3	6		841
24	9	GMVC	H	Northwich Victoria	Drew 1-1	6	Cramman	612
25	16	GMVC	A	Macclesfield Town	Lost 0-1	8		1161
26	Jan 1	GMVC	A	Morecambe	Won 3-2	6	Harkus, Trott, Proudlock	1400
27	6	GMVC	A	Slough Town	Won 2-1	6	Harkus, Trott	768
28	10	SCC2	H	Halifax Town	Won 4-0	-	Lowe, Wrightson, Harkus, Proudlock	327
29	13	GMVC	H	Farnborough Town	Drew 1-1	7	Trott	881
30	20	FAT1	A	Kidderminster Harriers	Drew 0-0	-		1319
31	24	FAT1R	H	Kidderminster Harriers	Won 2-0	-	Cramman, Robson	383
32	31	GMVC	H	Morecambe	Won 3-0	5	Harkus 3	479
33	Feb 10	FAT2	A	Emley	Won 2-1	-	Cramman 2	668
34	17	GMVC	A	Stevenage Borough	Drew 1-1	7	Harkus	1364
35	24	GMVC	H	Telford United	Lost 1-2	9	Ord	813
36	27	GMVC	A	Runcorn	Drew 1-1	8	Watson	333
37	Mar 2	FAT3	A	Radcliffe Borough	Won 2-1	-	Kitchen, Thompson	716
38	5	SCC3	A	Southport	Lost 1-2	-	Thompson	315
39	9	GMVC	A	Kettering Town	Lost 0-1	9		1179
40	16	GMVC	H	Bath City	Won 3-1	7	Thompson 2, Proudlock	582
41	18	GMVC	A	Hednesford Town	Won 1-0	6	Cramman	1017
42	23	FAT4	A	Chorley	Lost 1-3	-	Proudlock	1136
43	27	GMVC	H	Altrincham	Lost 2-3	8	Cramman, Harkus	357
44	30	GMVC	H	Welling United	Drew 1-1	8	Ord	510
45	Apr 2	GMVC	A	Northwich Victoria	Won 2-1	6	Proudlock, Harkus	602
46	6	GMVC	A	Farnborough Town	Won 3-2	6	Harkus, Thompson, Lowe	625
47	8	GMVC	H	Kidderminster Harriers	Won 4-1	6	Ord, Harkus 2, Thompson	687
48	13	GMVC	H	Woking	Lost 0-1	6		919
49	20	GMVC	A	Kidderminster Harriers	Drew 1-1	6	Harkus	1509
50	24	GMVC	H	Southport	Drew 2-2	7	Harkus 2	469
51	27	GMVC	H	Bromsgrove Rovers	Won 1-0	6	Hine	762
52	May 4	GMVC	A	Dover Athletic	Drew 1-1	5	Harkus	1103

Gateshead

1	2	3	4	5	6	7	8	9	10	11	12	14	Match No.
Musgrave	Farrey	Dowson	Hine	Wrightson	Fowe	Ord	Dobson	Thompson	Cramman	Kitchen	Proudlock	Trott	1
Musgrave	Watson	Dowson	Hine	Wrightson	Farrey	Ord	Dobson	Thompson	Cramman	Rowe	Proudlock	Fell	2
Musgrave	Watson	Dowson	Hine	Wrightson	Farrey	Rowe	Dobson	Trott	Cramman	Kitchen	Proudlock	Thompson	3
Musgrave	Watson	Dowson	Hine	Wrightson	Rowe	Ord	Thompson	Trott	Cramman	Kitchen	Proudlock	Dobson	4
Musgrave	Watson	Dowson	Hine	Wrightson	Rowe	Ord	Thompson	Proudlock	Cramman	Kitchen	Farrey	Dobson	5
Musgrave	Watson	Dowson	Hine	Wrightson	Rowe	Ord	Thompson	Proudlock	Cramman	Kitchen	Farrey	Dobson	6
Musgrave	Watson	Dowson	Hine	Wrightson	Rowe	Ord	Thompson	Proudlock	Cramman	Kitchen	Farrey	Dobson	7
Musgrave	Watson	Dowson	Marquis	Wrightson	Rowe	Farrey	Thompson	Trott	Proudlock	Kitchen	Dobson	Ord	8
Musgrave	Watson	Dowson	Marquis	Wrightson	Rowe	Cramman	Thompson	Trott	Proudlock	Kitchen	Hine	Ord	9
Musgrave	Watson	Dowson	Marquis	Wrightson	Rowe	Cramman	Thompson	Trott	Proudlock	Kitchen	Hine	Dobson	10
Musgrave	Watson	Dowson	Hine	Wrightson	Rowe	Cramman	Thompson	Trott	Proudlock	Kitchen	Dobson	Ord	11
Musgrave	Watson	Dowson	Hine	Wrightson	Rowe	Cramman	Thompson	Trott	Proudlock	Ord	Dobson	Charlton	12
Musgrave	Watson	Ord	Hine	Wrightson	Rowe	Cramman	Thompson	Trott	Proudlock	Marquis	Dobson	Kitchen	13
Musgrave	Watson	Ord	Hine	Wrightson	Rowe	Cramman	Thompson	Trott	Proudlock	Marquis	Dobson	Kitchen	14
Musgrave	Watson	Ord	Hine	Wrightson	Kitchen	Cramman	Harkus	Trott	Proudlock	Marquis	Thompson	Dobson	15
Sherwood	Watson	Ord	Hine	Wrightson	Kitchen	Cramman	Harkus	Trott	Proudlock	Rowe	Thompson	Dowson	16
Sherwood	Watson	Ord	Hine	Wrightson	Kitchen	Cramman	Harkus	Trott	Proudlock	Rowe	Thompson	Dowson	17
Sherwood	Watson	Ord	Hine	Wrightson	Kitchen	Cramman	Harkus	Trott	Proudlock	Rowe	Thompson	Dowson	18
Sherwood	Watson	Ord	Hine	Wrightson	Kitchen	Cramman	Harkus	Trott	Proudlock	Rowe	Thompson	Dowson	19
Sherwood	Watson	Ord	Hine	Wrightson	Kitchen	Cramman	Harkus	Trott	Proudlock	Rowe	Thompson	Dowson	20
Sherwood	Watson	Ord	Hine	Wrightson	Kitchen	Cramman	Harkus	Trott	Proudlock	Rowe	Thompson	Dowson	21
Sherwood	Watson	Ord	Hine	Wrightson	Kitchen	Cramman	Harkus	Trott	Proudlock	Rowe	Thompson	Charlton	22
Sherwood	Watson	Ord	Hine	Parkinson	Kitchen	Cramman	Harkus	Thompson	Proudlock	Rowe	Dowson	Henderson	23
Sherwood	Watson	Ord	Hine	Wrightson	Kitchen	Cramman	Harkus	Trott	Robson	Rowe	Proudlock	Thompson	24
Sherwood	Watson	Ord	Robson	Wrightson	Kitchen	Cramman	Harkus	Trott	Proudlock	Rowe	Hine	Thompson	25
Sherwood	Watson	Ord	Robson	Wrightson	Kitchen	Cramman	Harkus	Trott	Proudlock	Rowe	Hine	Thompson	26
Sherwood	Watson	Ord	Hine	Wrightson	Kitchen	Cramman	Harkus	Trott	Proudlock	Rowe	Lowe	Dowson	27
Burridge	Watson	Ord	Lowe	Wrightson	Kitchen	Cramman	Harkus	Trott	Proudlock	Rowe	Hine	Thompson	28
Sherwood	Watson	Ord	Lowe	Wrightson	Kitchen	Cramman	Harkus	Trott	Proudlock	Rowe	Hine	Thompson	29
Sherwood	Watson	Ord	Lowe	Wrightson	Kitchen	Cramman	Harkus	Robson	Proudlock	Rowe	Trott	Thompson	30
Sherwood	Watson	Dowson	Lowe	Wrightson	Kitchen	Cramman	Harkus	Robson	Proudlock	Rowe	Trott	Thompson	31
Sherwood	Watson	Dowson	Lowe	Wrightson	Kitchen	Cramman	Harkus	Robson	Proudlock	Rowe	Trott	Thompson	32
Sherwood	Watson	Dowson	Lowe	Wrightson	Kitchen	Cramman	Harkus	Robson	Proudlock	Rowe	Trott	Thompson	33
Sherwood	Hine	Ord	Lowe	Wrightson	Kitchen	Cramman	Harkus	Robson	Proudlock	Rowe	Trott	Thompson	34
Sherwood	Hine	Ord	Lowe	Wrightson	Kitchen	Cramman	Trott	Robson	Proudlock	Rowe	Thompson	Scaife	35
Sherwood	Scaife	Ord	Hine	Wrightson	Kitchen	Thompson	Proudlock	Trott	Lowe	Rowe	Watson	Henderson	36
Sherwood	Watson	Ord	Proudlock	Wrightson	Kitchen	Cramman	Thompson	Robson	Lowe	Rowe	scaife	Farrey	37
Burridge	Watson	Ord	Proudlock	Wrightson	Kitchen	Cramman	Thompson	Thew	Lowe	Rowe	Charlton	Farrey	38
Sherwood	Thew	Ord	Hine	Wrightson	Kitchen	Thompson	Scaife	Robson	Lowe	Rowe	Farrey	Dowson	39
Sherwood	Watson	Ord	Hine	Wrightson	Kitchen	Cramman	Thompson	Proudlock	Lowe	Rowe	Dowson	Farrey	40
Sherwood	Farrey	Dowson	Hine	Wrightson	Kitchen	Cramman	Ketter	Robson	Lowe	Rowe	Ord	Proudlock	41
Sherwood	Thompson	Ord	Hine	Wrightson	Kitchen	Cramman	Harkus	Robson	Lowe	Rowe	Farrey	Watson	42
Sherwood	Watson	Ord	Hine	Wrightson	Kitchen	Cramman	Harkus	Robson	Proudlock	Rowe	Thompson	Farrey	43
Sherwood	Farrey	Ord	Lowe	Wrightson	Kitchen	Cramman	Harkus	Ketter	Proudlock	Rowe	Hine	Thompson	44
Sherwood	Farrey	Ord	Hine	Wrightson	Kitchen	Proudlock	Harkus	Thompson	Lowe	Thew	Watson	Ketter	45
Sherwood	Farrey	Ord	Hine	Wrightson	Kitchen	Proudlock	Harkus	Thompson	Lowe	Rowe	Thew	Ketter	46
Sherwood	Watson	Ord	Hine	Wrightson	Kitchen	Proudlock	Harkus	Thompson	Lowe	Rowe	Farrey	Thew	47
Sherwood	Watson	Ord	Farrey	Wrightson	Kitchen	Proudlock	Harkus	Thompson	Lowe	Rowe	Thew	Ketter	48
Sherwood	Farrey	Ord	Ketter	Wrightson	Thew	Proudlock	Watson	Thompson	Lowe	Rowe	Harkus	Trott	49
Sherwood	Watson	Ord	Hine	Wrightson	Kitchen	Proudlock	Harkus	Thompson	Lowe	Rowe	Ketter	Trott	50
Sherwood	Watson	Ord	Hine	Wrightson	Kitchen	Proudlock	Harkus	Trott	Lowe	Rowe	Farrey	Ketter	51
Sherwood	Watson	Ord	Hine	Wrightson	Kitchen	Proudlock	Harkus	Trott	Lowe	Rowe	Thew	Cramman	52

COLIN RICHARDSON

Colin Richardson became Gateshead's fourth manager in four years when he replaced former Northern Ireland international Tommy Cassidy in November 1993. He went on to guide the Tynesiders to eleventh position in his first season and in season 1994/95 finished seventh after occupying a top five position for most of the season.

The most successful manager in North East non-League football, he has won 25 trophies at the five clubs under his guidance; Ferryhill Athletic, Whickham, Blue Star, North Shields and Bridlington Town.

With both Whickham and Bridlington Town he won the FA Vase at Wembley. The Wearside League and Northern League Second Division titles were carried off during a nine year spell at Blue Star. During the 1990s, Colin won the Northern Counties (East) League at North Shields and the Northern Premier League Division One at Bridlington Town.

Now at 52, he is expecting further progress in his second full season of Conference management at Gateshead.

Programme details:
32 pages for £ 1.20
Editor - Andy Wilson (0191 4783883)

Any other club publications:
'A Different Corner' - Fanzine

Local Newspapers:
Gateshead Post
Newcastle Chronicle & Journal
Sunderland Echo

Local Radio Stations:
BBC Radio Newcastle
Metro FM

GATESHEAD - PLAYING SQUAD 1996-97

Player	Honours	Birthplace and date	Transfer Fees	Previous Clubs
GOALKEEPERS				
Steve Sherwood	Div 4	Selby 10/12/53		Chelsea, Watford, Grimsby T, Stalybridge C
DEFENDERS				
Justin Robson		Durham 29/4/63		Newcastle U, Gateshead, Newc.Blue Star, N.Shields, Bridlington T, Durham C, Gretna
Alan Dowson		Gateshead 17/6/70	£3,000	Millwall, Bradford C, Darlington, Slough T
John Watson		Newcastle 14/4/74		Newcastle U, Scunthorpe U
Ian Brady		Liverpool		Heswall, Bootle, Runcorn
David Kitchen		Rintein 11/6/67		Yorkshire M, Goole, Stafford, Goole, Frickley, Leyton O, Doncaster
Paul Hague		Shortley Bridge 16/9/72		Gillingham, Leyton Orient
MIDFIELDERS				
Jeff Wrightson	FAYC	Newcastle 18/5/68		Newcastle Utd, Preston NE
Derek Ord		Gateshead 18/1/63		N Shields, Blyth S, Gateshead, Chester LS, Spennymoor, B Auckland, Durham, Gretna
Kenny Lowe	ESP, FAT, GMVC, Div 2	Sedgefield 6/11/61		H'pool, Scarboro, G'head, Spearwood(Aust), Morecambe, Barrow, Barnet, Stoke, B'ham
Brian Rowe		Bromsgrove 24/10/71		Doncaster Rovers
Gary Robson	FL XI	Chester-Le-Street 6/7/65		WBA, Bradford City
FORWARDS				
Paul Thompson		Newcastle 17/4/73		Hartlepool U
Darren Foreman	ES	Southampton 12/2/68		Barnsley, Crewe Alex, Scarborough, IK Sirius (Switz), Hednesford T
Steve Harkus		Newcastle 18/2/68		Hebburn, South Shields, Blyth Spartans
Paul Proudlock		Washington 8/11/63		Sunderland, Birmingham C, Walsall, Carlisle Utd, Darlington

Departures during season:
Ian Taylor (Gainsborough T), Gavin Fell (Whitley Bay), Paul Dobson (B Auckland), Alan Lamb (New Zealand), Sean Musgrave (Released), Nick Scaife (Released).
Players on loan during season:
Paul Hague (Leyton O), Paul Marquis (Doncaster R)
Departures during close season: Kenny Cramman (Rushden & D), Mark Hine & Dean Trott (Stalybridge C), Mike Farrey (Blyth S), Delano Ketter (Malaysia).

International Stadium, Gateshead

ADDRESS:
International Stadium, Neilson Road, Gateshead, NE10 0EF
TELEPHOE NUMBER: 0191 4783883 **Fax:** 0191 4771315.

SIMPLE DIRECTIONS:
From the South follow A1(M) to Granada services (Birtley), take right hand fork off motorway marked A194 (Tyne Tunnel, South Shields) follow A194 to first roundabout, turn left - 3 miles. Turn right at traffic lights into Neilson Road.
BY RAIL to Newcastle Central Station, transfer to the Metro System and then to Gateshead Stadium.

CAPACITY: 11,750 **SEATED:** 11,750 **COVERED TERRACING:** 3,300

RECORD ATTENDANCE:
11,750 v Newcastle United (Pre-Season Friendly. 7th August 1995)

CLUB SHOP:
Yes, selling replica shirts, baseball caps, sweatshirts, badges, scarves, programmes, coffee mugs, pennants, fanzines, ski hats. Contact: Alan Donnelly (0191 4783883).

SOCIAL FACILITIES:
Bar inside Tyne & Wear stand open before, during and after matches. The Stadium Public House adjacent to ground.

PREVIOUS GROUNDS:
Redheugh Park - 1930-1971 (previous club)

Gateshead Fact File

Nickname: The Tynesiders

Club Sponsors: Cameron Hall Developments Ltd

Previous Leagues: Football League Division 3 North 1930-1958, Football Lge Div.4 1958-1960, Northern Counties League 1960-1962, North Regional League 1962-1968, Northern Premier League 1968-1970, Wearside League 1970-1971, Midland League 1971-1972, Northern Premier League 1973-1983, Alliance Premier League 1983-1985, Northern Premier League 1985-1986, Vauxhall Conference 1986-1987, Northern Premier League 1987-1990.

Club colours: Black & white halved shirts, black shorts and socks.

Change colours: All yellow.

Midweek home matchday: Wednesday

Record win: 8-0 v Netherfield, Northern Premier League.

Record defeat: 0-9 v Sutton United - 22/09/90 - GMVC.

Record transfer fee paid: £9,000 for Paul Cavell (Dagenham & Redbridge).

Record transfer fee received: For Kenny Cramman from Rushden & Diamonds

1995-96 Captain: Jeff Wrightson

1995-96 Top scorer: Steve Harkus - 19

1995-56 Player of the Year: Brian Rowe

Club record goalscorer: Bob Topping

Record appearances: Simon Smith - 450 - 1985-1994

Past players who progressed to the Football League: Osher Williams (Southampton, Stockport, Port Vale, Preston), John McGinley (Sunderland, Lincoln), Billy Askew (Hull City, Newcastle United), Lawrie Pearson (Hull City, Port Vale), Ian Johnson (Northampton Town), Ken Davies (Stockport).

Club Honours: Football League Division 3 North R-up 1931-32, 1949-50; FA Cup Quarter-Finalists 1952-53; Northern Premier League Champions 1982-83, 1985-86; Northern Premier League R-up 1989-90; Northern Premier League Cup Finalists 1989-90; Multipart Shield 1985-86.

HALIFAX TOWN

Formed:
1911

President:
S J Brown

Chairman:
J C Stockwell

Vice Chairman
C O Holland

Football Secretary:
Derek A Newiss

Manager:
John Carroll

Asst. Manager/Coach:
Billy Rodaway

Physiotherapist:
Alan Russell Cox

Commercial Director:
David Worthington

Halifax Town started season three in the Vauxhall Conference. This statement alone is testimony of the efforts put in by directors and supporters alike.

It was decided to move to a part-time squad supplemented by a number of full-time young professionals. This gave manager John Bird an opportunity to use his negotiating expertise in re-forming the team. Having lost the services of Dave Hanson, Colin Lambert, Alex Jones, Craig Boardman, Grant Leitch, Paul Fleming and David German, the manager's master stroke was the signing of midfield maestro Kieran O'Regan. Together with Jon Brown, Paul Stoneman, Michael Midwood and 'keeper Andy Woods, the nucleus was formed for season 1995/96. Simon Thompson was added to the squad and with loanee Chris Timons, the season commenced.

Meeting new boys Hednesford Town on the opening day and suffering a 3-0 reversal set the scene for a campaign of yo-yoing between top class and mediocre performances. Steve Prindiville moved to Dagenham & Redbridge and was followed by Simon Thompson and Gary Worthington. Newcomers from local league football, John Hendrick and Karl Cochrane, were added to the midfield force and Richard Annan took Prindiville's left-back position. Losing to Runcorn in the FA Cup and Bromsgrove in the FA Trophy brought and early end to the season. Losing heavily to Macclesfield and

Back Row (L-R); Noel Horner, William Griffiths, Damian Place, Gareth Hamlet, Michael Midwood, Mark Cameron, James Dougan, Andy Lee. Middle; Alan Russell-Cox (Physio), Billy Rodaway (Asst Mgr), Paul Kerr, Paul Stoneman, Mike Norbury, Michael Trotter, Larl Cochrane, Jon Brown, Gary Worthington, Gary Brooke, George Mulhall, Tommy Gildett. Front; Paul Mudd, Bobby Davison, Chris Horsfall, John Carroll, Andy Woods, Kieran O'Regan, Ian McInerney. Kneeling; Andy Hemingway, Paul Hand, Chris Newton

Photo - Halifax Evening Courier

Halifax Town

Match No.	Date	Comp.	Venue H/A	Opponents	Result	League Pos.	Goalscorers (Times if known)	Attendance
1	Aug 19	GMVC	A	Hednesford	Lost 0-3			1650
2	22	GMVC	H	Macclesfield	Won 1-0		Stoneman	1169
3	26	GMVC	H	Slough	Lost 1-2		Johnson	917
4	28	GMVC	A	Stalybridge	Lost 0-1			905
5	Sep 2	GMVC	H	Welling	Won 2-1		O'Regan, Johnson	766
6	5	GMVC	H	Gateshead	Won 2-1		Midwood, Beddard	743
7	9	GMVC	A	Woking	Lost 0-2			2065
8	12	GMVC	H	Northwich	Won 2-0		Stoneman, 1 og	829
9	16	GMVC	H	Kidderminster	Lost 0-2			1008
10	20	GMVC	A	Gateshead	Lost 2-3		Midwood, Worthington	559
11	23	GMVC	A	Altrincham	Lost 2-3		Trotter, 1 og	1085
12	26	GMVC	H	Morecambe	Drew 1-1		Midwood	910
13	30	GMVC	H	Dover	Won 1-0		Hendrick	905
14	Oct 7	GMVC	A	Runcorn	Won 1-0		Midwood	637
15	14	GMVC	H	Stevenage	Lost 2-3		Johnson, Brown	858
16	21	FAC4	A	Runcorn	Lost 1-2		Worthington	901
17	28	GMVC	A	Farnborough	Drew 0-0			908
18	Nov 4	GMVC	H	Bath City	Won 3-1		Cochrane, Midwood 2	811
19	11	GMVC	H	Kettering	Won 2-0		Worthington 2	929
20	18	GMVC	A	Dagenham	Drew 1-1		Midwood	701
21	25	GMVC	A	Welling United	Drew 0-0			666
22	Dec 2	FAC2	H	Bromsgrove	Drew 1-1		Worthington	843
23	5	CC	H	Ossett Town	Won 5-1		O'Regan, Johnson, Midwood 3	
24	9	GMVC	A	Slough	Won 3-2		Beddard 2, Midwood	862
25	16	GMVC	H	Runcorn	Lost 1-3		Johnson	834
26	Jan 1	GMVC	A	Southport	Drew 0-0			1318
27	6	GMVC	H	Dagenham & Redbridge	Won 3-0		O'Regan, Johnson, Cochrane	729
28	11	SPCC	A	Gateshead	Lost 0-4			327
29	13	GMVC	A	Stevenage	Lost 0-2			1841
30	20	FAT1	H	Southport	Won 2-1		Brown, Cochrane	966
31	Feb 3	GMVC	H	Hednesford	Lost 1-3		Brook	859
32	10	FAT2	H	Bromsgrove	Lost 0-1			887
33	17	GMVC	A	Northwich	Drew 1-1		Brook	879
34	24	GMVC	A	Bath City	Lost 1-2		Sansam	547
35	Mar 2	GMVC	A	Dover	Lost 2-3		Lee, Midwood	895
36	5	GMVC	H	Stalybridge	Lost 2-3		Trotter, O'Regan	509
37	9	GMVC	A	Macclesfield	Lost 0-7			1348
38	12	GMVC	A	Morecambe	Won 1-0		Cochrane	645
39	16	GMVC	H	Altrincham	Drew 1-1		Stoneman	755
40	18	GMVC	A	Kidderminster	Lost 1-6		Johnson	1168
41	26	GMVC	H	Southport	Drew 2-2		O'Regan, Horner	694
42	30	GMVC	H	Farnborough	Drew 0-0			691
43	Apr 6	GMVC	H	Telford	Drew 0-0			771
44	8	GMVC	A	Kettering	Won 2-1		Hendrick, Daws	1317
45	20	GMVC	A	Dover	Drew 1-1		Trotter	708
46	20	GMVC	H	Woking	Drew 2-2		Brook 2	1064
47	May 4	GMVC	A	Bromsgrove	Won 1-0		Midwood	887

Halifax Town

1	2	3	4	5	6	7	8	9	10	11	12	14	Match No.
Heyes	Thompson	Prindville	O'Regan	Stoneman	Timons	Horner	Johnson	Beddard	Worthington	Brown	Ludlow	Midwood	1
Woods	Thompson	Brown	Horner	Stoneman	Timons	O'Regan	Johnson	Midwood	Worthington	Beddard	Prindiville	Ludlow	2
Heyes	Thompson	Prindville	Trotter	Stoneman	Timons	O'Regan	Johnson	Midwood	Worthington	Brown	Beddard	Wilson	3
Heyes	Thompson	Prindville	Trotter	Stoneman	Timons	O'Regan	Wilson	Johnson	Worthington	Horner	Midwood	Beddard	4
Heyes	Timons	Prindville	Brown	Stoneman	Trotter	Thompson	O'Regan	Johnson	Worthington	Midwood	Beddard	Horner	5
Heyes	Timons	Prindville	Brown	Stoneman	Trotter	Thompson	O'Regan	Midwood	Wilson	Beddard	Ludlow	Hendrick	6
Heyes	Timons	Prindville	Brown	Stoneman	Trotter	Thompson	O'Regan	Midwood	Worthington	Beddard	Horner	Wilson	7
Heyes	Timons	Prindville	Brown	Stoneman	Trotter	Thompson	O'Regan	Midwood	Beddard	Constable	Ludlow	Worthington	8
Heyes	Timons	Prindville	Brown	Stoneman	Trotter	Thompson	O'Regan	Midwood	Beddard	Constable	Ludlow	Worthington	9
Heyes	Timons	Prindville	Brown	Stoneman	Trotter	Thompson	O'Regan	Midwood	Worthington	Constable	Horner	Beddard	10
Heyes	Timons	Prindville	Brown	Stoneman	Trotter	Thompson	O'Regan	Midwood	Worthington	Constable	Hendrick	Beddard	11
Heyes	Thompson	Prindville	Brown	Stoneman	Trotter	Hendrick	O'Regan	Midwood	Worthington	Graham	Timons	Horner	12
Heyes	Thompson	Prindville	Timons	Stoneman	Trotter	Brown	Broook	Midwood	Worthington	Hendrick	Hart	Horner	13
Heyes	Thompson	Prindville	Timons	Stoneman	Trotter	Brown	Johnson	Midwood	Brook	Hendrick	Horner	Murray	14
Heyes	Thompson	Prindville	Timons	Stoneman	Trotter	O'Regan	Johnson	Midwood	Worthington	Brown	Hendrick	Beddard	15
Woods	P Smith	Prindville	O'Regan	Brown	Trotter	Thompson	Johnson	Midwood	Worthington	Horner	Beddard	Hart	16
Woods	P Smith	Prindville	O'Regan	Trotter	Brown	Hendrick	Cochrane	Midwood	Worthington	Horner	Beddard	Johnson	17
Woods	Smith	Prindville	O'Regan	Trotter	Hendrick	Horner	Cochrane	Midwood	Worthington	Annan	Thompson	Johnson	18
Woods	Smith	Prindville	O'Regan	Stoneman	Trotter	Hendrick	Cochrane	Midwood	Worthington	Thompson	Johnson	Horner	19
Woods	Smith	Annan	O'Regan	Stoneman	Trotter	Hendrick	Cochrane	Midwood	Worthington	Thompson	Johnson	Horner	20
Woods	Smith	Annan	O'Regan	Stoneman	Trotter	Hendrick	Cochrane	Midwood	Worthington	Thompson	Beddard	Horner	21
Woods	P Smith	Annan	O'Regan	Stoneman	Trotter	Hendrick	Cochrane	Johnson	Worthington	Midwood	Brook	Thomson	22
Woods	P Smith	Annan	O'Regan	Stoneman	Trotter	Hendrick	Brown	Cochrane	Worthington	Johnson	Midwood	Thomson	23
Woods	P Smith	Annan	O'Regan	Stoneman	Trotter	Hendrick	Beddard	Midwood	Johnson	Brown	Cochrane	Griffiths	24
Woods	P Smith	Annan	O'Regan	Stoneman	Trotter	Hendrick	Beddard	Midwood	Johnson	Brown	Cochrane	Lee	25
Woods	P Smith	Annan	O'Regan	Stoneman	Brown	Hendrick	Scaife	Midwood	Johnson	Cochrane	Beddard	N Horner	26
Woods	P Smith	Annan	O'Regan	Stoneman	Brown	Hendrick	Scaife	Midwood	Johnson	Cochrane	Beddard	Horner	27
Woods	P Smith	Annan	O'Regan	Stoneman	Brown	Hendrick	Scaife	Midwood	Trotter	Cochrane	Beddard	Horner	28
Woods	P Smith	Annan	O'Regan	Stoneman	Trotter	Hendrick	Brown	Midwood	Johnson	Cochrane	Beddard	Horner	29
Buxton	Smith	Annan	O'Regan	Stoneman	Trotter	Hendrick	Brown	Midwood	Johnson	Cochrane	Beddard	Horner	30
Woods	Smith	Annan	O'Regan	Brown	Trotter	Hendrick	Benn	Midwood	Johnson	Cochrane	Beddard	Brook	31
Woods	Smith	Annan	O'Regan	Brown	Trotter	Hendrick	Beddard	Midwood	Brook	Cochrane	Benn	Horner	32
Woods	Smith	Brown	O'Regan	Stoneman	Trotter	Lee	Hendrick	Sansam	Brook	Annan	Horner	Heyes	33
Woods	Smith	Annan	O'Regan	Stoneman	Trotter	Lee	Hendrick	Sansam	Brook	Midwood	Horner	Heyes	34
Woods	Smith	Annan	O'Regan	Stoneman	Trotter	Lee	Hendrick	Sansam	Brook	Horner	Midwood	Cochrane	35
Woods	Smith	Annan	O'Regan	Stoneman	Trotter	Lee	Horner	Sansam	Midwood	Thornber	Brown	Cochrane	36
Woods	Smith	Annan	O'Regan	Stoneman	Trotter	Brown	Horner	Sansam	Midwood	Cochrane	Lee	Place	37
Heyes	Smith	Annan	O'Regan	Stoneman	Trotter	Brown	Horner	Brook	Midwood	Cochrane	Sansam	Lee	38
Heyes	Smith	Mudd	O'Regan	Stoneman	Trotter	Brown	Horner	Brook	Daws	Cochrane	Annan	Midwood	39
Heyes	Smith	Annan	O'Regan	Stoneman	Trotter	Brown	Mudd	Brook	Midwood	Cochrane	Horner	Johnson	40
Woods	Smith	Mudd	O'Regan	Stoneman	Brown	Horner	Hendrick	Trotter	Daws	Midwood	Johnson	Annan	41
Woods	Smith	Mudd	O'Regan	Stoneman	Brown	Horner	Hendrick	Trotter	Daws	Midwood	Brook	Annan	42
Woods	Smith	Mudd	O'Regan	Stoneman	Brown	Horner	Hendrick	Trotter	Daws	Midwood	Brook	Cochrane	43
Woods	Smith	Mudd	O'Regan	Stoneman	Brown	Horner	Hendrick	Trotter	Daws	Midwood	Brook	Cochrane	44
Woods	Smith	Annan	O'Regan	Stoneman	Brown	Horner	Hendrick	Trotter	Brook	Midwood	Johnson	Cochrane	45
Woods	Smith	Annan	O'Regan	Stoneman	Brown	Horner	Hendrick	Johnson	Brook	Midwood	Constable	Beddard	46
Woods	Smith	Annan	O'Regan	Stoneman	Brown	Horner	Hendrick	Midwood	Brook	Cochrane	Beddard	Griffiths	47

Halifax Town

JOHN CARROLL

John was appointed as manager in April 1996 following the resignation of John Bird. Carroll himself had lost his job at Runcorn earlier in the season after four years at the helm.

Aged 36, Carroll played for South Liverpool and Weymouth before joining Runcorn where he gained the reputation as one of best central defenders in the Vauxhall Conference. He made over 200 appearances for the Linnets and during his spell as manager he guided the club to two successive FA Trophy finals as well as fifth place in 1993/94.

Kieran O'Regan (Player of the Year) and John Hendrick in a match against Bromsgrove.

Programme details:
28 pages for £1.50
Editor - David Worthington (01422 353423)

Any other club publications:

Local Newspapers:
Halifax Courier
Yorkshire Post
Telegraph Argus

Local Radio Stations:
Pulse Radio
Radio Leeds

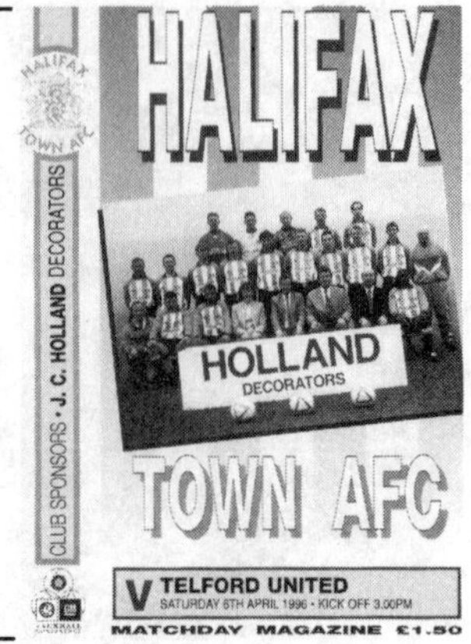

HALIFAX TOWN - PLAYING SQUAD 1996-97

Player	Honours	Birthplace and date	Transfer Fees	Previous Clubs
GOALKEEPERS				
Andrew Woods		Colchester 15/1/76		Oldham Athletic
Darren Heyes	EY	Swansea 11/1/67		Notts F, Scunthorpe, Wrexham, Shepshed, Shepshed, Tamworth, Shepshed, Rocester
DEFENDERS				
Paul Stoneman		Whitley Bay 26/2/73		Blackpool
Michael Trotter		Hartlepool 27/10/69		Middlesbrough, Darlington, Leicester C, Chesterfield
Paul Mudd	ES	Hull 13/11/70		Hull C, Scarborough, Scunthorpe, Lincoln C
Ian Harold		Liverpool 16/1/69		Newton, Runcorn, Stalybridge C, Altrincham, Barrow
Nathan Murray	ES, EY	South Shields 10/9/75		Newcastle U, Carlisle U
Andy Lee	ESP, FAT, NPL	Liverpool 4/7/62		Wrexham, Stafford, Camb U, Runcorn, Alty, Telford, Colne D, Witton, Runcorn
MIDFIELDERS				
Jonathan Brown		Barnsley 8/9/66		Denaby U, Exeter C
Noel Horner		Halifax 18/2/78		From YTS
Keiran O'Regan	Ei	Cork 9/11/63		Tramore Ath, Brighton, Swindon T, Huddersfield T, WBA
John Hendrick		Halifax		Liversedge
FORWARDS				
Michael Midwood		Burnley 19/4/76		Huddersfield T
Mike Norbury		Hemsworth 22/1/69		Ossett T, Scarboro, Bridlington, Camb.U, Preston, Doncaster, Guiseley, Stafford R
Bobby Davison	Div 2	South Shields 17/7/59		Seaham CW, Huddersfield, Halifax, Derby, Leeds, Leicester, Sheff.U, Rotherham
Gary Worthington	EY	Cleethorpes 10/11/66		Man.U, Huddersfield, Darlington, Wrexham, Wigan, Exeter, Halifax, Dag & Red
Karl Cochrane		Halifax 25/1/70		Brighouse T
Gary Brook	NCEL	Dewsbury 9/5/64		Ossett A, Frickley, Newport Co, S'boro, Blackpool, Frickley, Boston U

Departures during season:
Lee Wilson, Steve Prindiville, Gary Worthington, Deniol Graham & Simon Thompson (Dagenham & Red), Elliott Beddard (Emley - Loan), Nick Scaife (Gateshead).
Players on loan during season:
Chris Timons (Mansfield T), Tony Daws & Paul Mudd (Lincoln C).
Departures during close season: Richard Annan (Morecambe), Elliott Beddard, Simon Johnson, Glen Lee, Ian Hart, Shaun Constable, Christian Sansom & Paul Smith (Released).

The Shay, Halifax Town

OFFICE ADDRESS:
18 Prescott Street, Halifax, HX1 2LG.
TEL. NO. 01422 345543. **Fax:** 01422 349487.

GROUND ADDRESS: The Shay, Halifax, West Yorkshire HX1 2YS.
TEL. NO. 01422 330383 (Match days only).

SIMPLE DIRECTIONS:
From North: Take A629 to Halifax Town Centre. Take 2nd exit at roundabout into Broad Street and follow signs for Huddersfield (A629) into Skircoat Road. From South, East & West: Exit M62 junction 24 and follow Halifax (A629) signs to Town centre into Skircoat Road for ground.

CAPACITY: 5,149 **SEATED:** 1,878 **COVERED TERRACING:** 2,600

RECORD ATTENDANCE:
36,885 v Tottenham - 5th Round FA Cup - 14.02.53

CLUB SHOP:
Contact Dave Worthington on 01422 353423 for details.

SOCIAL FACILITIES:
No facilities on the ground.

Halifax Fact File

Nickname: The Shaymen

Club Sponsors: J C Holland Decorators

Previous Grounds: Sandhall Lane 1911-15, Exley 1919-21.

Previous Leagues: Yorkshire Combination 1911-12, Midland League 1912-21, Division 3 North 1921-58, Division 3 1958-63, 1969-76, 1992, Division 4 1963-69.

Club colours: Blue & white/white/white

Change colours: White & Violet/Violet/Violet

Reserve team league: Not in league this season

Midweek home matchday: Tuesday 7.45pm KO

Record win: 12-0 v West Vale Ramblers - 1st Qualifying Round FA Cup - 1913-14

Record defeat: 0-13 v Stockport County - Division 3 North - 1933-34

Record transfer fee: £50,000 for Ian Juryeff (Hereford United).

Record transfer fee received: £250,000 for Wayne Allison (Watford).

1995-96 **Captain:** Kieran O'Regan.

1995-96 **Top scorer:** Michael Midwood.

1995-96 **Player of the Year:** Keiran O'Regan.

Club record goalscorer: Albert Valentine

Record appearances: John Pickering

Past players who progressed to the Football League: N/A

Club Honours: Promoted to Division 3 1968-69

HAYES

Formed: 1909

President:
Les Lovering

Chairman:
Derek Goodall

Vice-Chairman
Trevor Griffith

Football Secretary:
John Price

Manager:
Terry Brown

Assistant Manager:
Willy Wordsworth

Physiotherapist:
Carl Ballard

General Manager:
Terry Brown

Press Officer:
Trevor Griffith

Manager Terry Brown made several changes to the squad that had finished the previous season. Significant signings included goalkeeper Russell Meara and Darron Wilkinson. The ground was also improved gradually as the knock-on effect from the sale of Les Ferdinand allowed Hayes to bring their home up to Conference standard.

The season began with a 1-0 win at Bromley, a great effort considering Meara was sent-off on his debut after only 35 minutes. A solid run followed but the turning point of the entire campaign came on December 19th with a 0-0 home draw with St.Albans City. Wins over Molesey, Bromley and Hendon established some momentum before the FA Trophy 1st round tie with Enfield. Victory over the then-league leaders was finally achieved at the fourth time of asking but the league campaign gathered pace as three away wins in a week came.

With just five league games to go, the time for team spirit and battling together had arrived. This was no more reflected then the game at Aylesbury.

Champions Hayes 95-96: *Photo - Mark Sandom*

Hayes

Match No.	Date	Comp.	Venue H/A	Opponents	Result	League Pos.	Goalscorers (Times if known)	Attendance
1	Aug 12	IFL		Bromley	Won 1-0		Cox	419
2	19	IFL		Dulwich Hamlet	Drew 2-2		Goodliffe, Randall	327
3	22	IFL		Hendon	Won 2-0		W Kelly, Driscoll	262
4	26	IFL		Sutton United	Drew 2-2		Pearce, Stevens	618
5	Sep 2	IFL		Molesey	Won 2-0		Goodliffe, Baker	318
6	5	GIC		Grays Athletic	Lost 0-1			109
7	9	FAC		Concord Rangers	Won 3-0		Baker, T Kelly, W Kelly p	150
8	16	IFL		Walton & Hersham	Won 2-0		Baker, Pearce	293
9	23	FAC		Baldock Town	Won 1-0		Kellman	390
10	30	IFL		Purfleet	Drew 0-0			181
11	Oct 3	IFL		Worthing	Won 2-0		T Kelly 2	240
12	7	FAC		Hendon	Won 3-0		Kellman, Randall 2	376
13	14	IFL		Enfield	Drew 1-1		Kellman	1023
14	21	FAC		Sudbury Wanderers	Won 4-0		Kellman 3, Pearce	420
15	24	IFL		Chertsey Town	Won 3-1		Kellman, T Kelly, Pearce	603
16	28	IFL		Yeading	Drew 0-0			437
17	31	IFL		Kingstonian	Lost 0-1			432
18	Nov 7	MSC		Cockfosters (at Hayes FC)	Won 3-2		Brady 2, Flitter	94
19	11	FAC1		Northampton Town	Lost 0-1			5389
20	13	CC		Purfleet	Lost 0-2			58
21	18	IFL		Hitchin Town	Drew 1-1		Pearce	303
22	21	IFL		Boreham Wood	Drew 0-0			308
23	25	FAT		Dorchester Town	Won 3-2		Pearce, T Kelly, Brady	515
24	Dec 2	IFL		Aylesbury United	Lost 0-1			393
25	9	IFL		Yeovil Town	Lost 0-3			2025
26	16	IFL		Carshalton Athletic	Lost 1-2		Baker	283
27	19	IFL		St Albans City	Drew 0-0			238
28	23	IFL		Molesey	Won 2-0		Haynes, T Kelly	200
29	Jan 2	IFL		Grays Athletic	Drew 3-3		Haynes, T Kelly, Hyatt	226
30	6	IFL		Bromley	Won 5-1		Haynes, Brady 2, Cox, Pearce	267
31	9	MSC		Kingsbury Town	Won 4-0		Cox, D Williams 2, Mee	77
32	13	IFL		Hendon	Won 3-1		Haynes 2, Pearce	347
33	20	FAT		Enfield	Drew 0-0			507
34	23	FAT		Enfield	Drew 2-2		Cox, Randall	436
35	29	FAT		Enfield	Drew 2-2		Cox, og	392
36	Feb 1	FAT		Enfield	Won 2-0		Goodliffe, Randall	369
37	3	IFL		Worthing	Won 3-0		D Williams, Haynes, Brady	305
38	10	FAT		Bath City	Lost 0-2			699
39	13	MSC		Feltham	Won 6-2		D Williams, Stevens, Flynn, Goodliffe p, Roberts, Carney	83
40	17	IFL		Walton & Hersham	Won 1-0		Haynes	302
41	20	IFL		Hitchin Town	Won 3-1		D Williams, Randall 2	164
42	24	IFL		Yeading	Won 1-0		W Kelly p	405
43	Mar 2	IFL		Kingstonian	Won 2-1		Cox, Pearce	431
44	5	IFL		Bishop's Stortford	Won 3-1		Pearce, Haynes, Hyatt	243
45	9	IFL		Enfield	Won 3-1		Baker, W Kelly p, Pearce	625
46	12	MSC		Harrow Borough	Won 2-1		Hyatt, W Kelly	194
47	16	IFL		St Albans City	Won 3-0		Stevens, Flynn, Brady	765
48	19	IFL		Dulwich Hamlet	Drew 1-1		W Kelly p	448
49	23	IFL		Bishop's Stortford	Won 2-1		G Williams, Stevens	472
50	26	IFL		Purfleet	Won 2-1		G Williams, Wilkinson	371
51	30	IFL		Chertsey Town	Won 4-0		Hyatt, Randall, Brady, Sugrue	505
52	Apr 6	IFL		Grays Athletic	Won 5-1		Cox 3 - 1p, G Williams, og	583
53	8	MSC F		Hampton (at Yeading FC)	Won 3-2		Stevens, W Kelly p, Goodliffe	713
54	13	IFL		Boreham Wood	Drew 1-1		Haynes	707
55	16	IFL		Sutton United	Drew 0-0			516
56	20	IFL		Aylesbury United	Won 3-1		Stevens, G Williams, Randall	809
57	23	IFL		Harrow Borough	Won 2-1		og, G Williams	716
58	27	IFL		Yeovil Town	Drew 1-1		G Williams	1537
59	May 1	IFL		Harrow Borough	Drew 1-1		Cox	1212
60	4	IFL		Carshalton Athletic	Won 3-0		G Williams 2, Haynes	1025

Hayes

1	2	3	4	5	6	7	8	9	10	11	12	14	Match No.
Meara	Hyatt	Flynn	W Kelly	Cox	Goodliffe	Driscoll	Kruszynski	Knight	Pearce	Wilkinson	Turner	Randall	1
Meara	Hyatt	Flynn	W Kelly	Cox	Goodliffe	Driscoll	Kruszynski	Knight	Pearce	Wilkinson	Turner	Randall	2
Meara	Hyatt	Flynn	W Kelly	Cox	Goodliffe	Driscoll	T Kelly	Knight	Randall	Wilkinson	Baker	Howard	3
Scrivens	Howard	Flynn	W Kelly	Cox	Goodliffe	Driscoll	Stevens	T Kelly	Pearce	Wilkinson	Baker	Knight	4
Scrivens	Hyatt	Flynn	W Kelly	Cox	Goodliffe	Baker	Stevens	T Kelly	Pearce	Wilkinson	Knight	Howard	5
Scrivens	Hyatt	Flynn	Howard	Cox	Goodliffe	Baker	Stevens	T Kelly	Knight	Wilkinson	Randall	Lazic	6
Meara	Howard	Flynn	W Kelly	Cox	Goodliffe	Baker	Hyatt	T Kelly	Pearce	Wilkinson	Randall	Lazic	7
Meara	Howard	Flynn	W Kelly	Cox	Denton	Baker	Kellman	T Kelly	Pearce	Wilkinson	Randall	Hyatt	8
Meara	Howard	Flynn	W Kelly	Cox	Denton	Baker	Kellman	T Kelly	Pearce	Wilkinson	Goodliffe	Randall	9
Meara	Goodliffe	Flynn	W Kelly	Cox	Denton	Baker	Kellman	T Kelly	Gavin	Wilkinson	Howard	Pearce	10
Meara	Pearce	Flynn	W Kelly	Cox	Denton	Baker	Kellman	T Kelly	Gavin	Wilkinson	Howard	Goodliffe	11
Meara	Randall	Flynn	W Kelly	Cox	Denton	Baker	Kellman	T Kelly	Pearce	Wilkinson	Howard	Goodliffe	12
Meara	Goodliffe	Randall	W Kelly	Cox	Denton	Baker	Kellman	T Kelly	Pearce	Wilkinson	Howard	Stevens	13
Meara	Goodliffe	Randall	W Kelly	Cox	Denton	Baker	Kellman	T Kelly	Pearce	Wilkinson	Howard	Stevens	14
Meara	Stevens	Randall	W Kelly	Cox	Denton	Baker	Kellman	T Kelly	Pearce	Wilkinson	Goodliffe	Brady	15
Meara	Stevens	Randall	W Kelly	Cox	Denton	Baker	Kellman	T Kelly	Pearce	Wilkinson	Howard	Goodliffe	16
Meara	Goodliffe	Brady	W Kelly	Cox	Denton	Baker	Kellman	T Kelly	Pearce	Wilkinson	Howard	Hyatt	17
Meara	Knight	Lazic	Waugh	Hedge	Hyatt	Flitter	Ellis	Sterling	Stevens	Brady	Mattis	Roberts	18
Scrivens	Wilkinson	Stevens	W Kelly	Cox	Denton	Baker	Kellman	T Kelly	Pearce	Goodliffe	Brady	Knight	19
Meara	Wilkinson	Stevens	W Kelly	Cox	Denton	Knight	Nartey	Hyatt	Pearce	Brady	Goodliffe	Baker	20
Meara	Wilkinson	Goodliffe	W Kelly	Cox	Denton	Hyatt	Quail	T Kelly	Pearce	Nartey	Kellman	Baker	21
Meara	Wilkinson	Goodliffe	W Kelly	Cox	Denton	Hyatt	Quail	T Kelly	Pearce	Brady	Kellman	Baker	22
Meara	Wilkinson	Goodliffe	W Kelly	Cox	Denton	Hyatt	Kellman	T Kelly	Pearce	Baker	Nartey	Quail	23
Meara	Wilkinson	Goodliffe	Brady	Cox	Denton	Hyatt	Quail	T Kelly	Pearce	Baker	Nartey	Kellman	24
Meara	Wilkinson	Randall	W Kelly	Goodliffe	Denton	Quail	Kellman	T Kelly	Pearce	D Williams	Nartey	Hedge	25
Scrivens	Wilkinson	Hedge	W Kelly	Goodliffe	Denton	Baker	D Williams	T Kelly	Pearce	Haynes	Brady	Kellman	26
Scrivens	Wilkinson	Flynn	W Kelly	Goodliffe	Brady	Baker	D Williams	T Kelly	Stevens	Haynes	Pearce	Denton	27
Scrivens	Wilkinson	Flynn	W Kelly	Cox	Goodliffe	Hyatt	Haynes	Brady	Pearce	T Kelly	Stevens	Denton	28
Scrivens	Wilkinson	Flynn	W Kelly	Cox	Goodliffe	Hyatt	Haynes	T Kelly	Pearce	Brady	D Williams	Denton	29
Meara	Wilkinson	Flynn	W Kelly	Cox	Goodliffe	Hyatt	Haynes	Stevens	Pearce	Brady	D Williams	Denton	30
Meara	Hedge	Flynn	Denton	Cox	Goodliffe	Baker	Randall	Nartey	D Williams	Brady	Roberts	Mee	31
Meara	Wilkinson	Flynn	W Kelly	Cox	Goodliffe	Hyatt	Haynes	Stevens	Pearce	Brady	Mee	Denton	32
Meara	Wilkinson	Flynn	W Kelly	Cox	Goodliffe	Hyatt	Mee	Stevens	Pearce	Brady	Baker	Randall	33
Meara	Wilkinson	Flynn	W Kelly	Cox	Goodliffe	Hyatt	Randall	Stevens	Pearce	Brady	Kellman	Baker	34
Meara	Wilkinson	Flynn	W Kelly	Cox	Goodliffe	Hyatt	Randall	Stevens	Pearce	Brady	Mee	Baker	35
Meara	Wilkinson	Flynn	W Kelly	Cox	Goodliffe	Hyatt	Randall	Stevens	Pearce	Brady	Mee	Baker	36
Meara	Smart	Flynn	W Kelly	Hyatt	Goodliffe	Baker	Haynes	Stevens	Randall	Wilkinson	Pearce	D Williams	37
Meara	Brady	Flynn	W Kelly	Cox	Goodliffe	Hyatt	Randall	Hedge	Pearce	Wilkinson	Mee	Baker	38
Meara	Smart	Flynn	Baker	Hedge	Goodliffe	Roberts	Mee	Stevens	D Williams	Wilkinson	Carney	Randall	39
Meara	Smart	Flynn	Randall	Cox	Goodliffe	Hyatt	Haynes	Stevens	Pearce	Wilkinson	Roberts	D Williams	40
Meara	Smart	Flynn	W Kelly	Cox	Goodliffe	Hyatt	Haynes	Stevens	D Williams	Wilkinson	Randall	Pearce	41
Meara	Smart	Flynn	W Kelly	Cox	Goodliffe	Randall	Haynes	Stevens	D Williams	Wilkinson	Pearce	Hyatt	42
Meara	Stevens	Flynn	W Kelly	Cox	Goodliffe	Hyatt	Haynes	Randall	Pearce	Wilkinson	Mee	Hedge	43
Meara	Smart	Flynn	W Kelly	Cox	Goodliffe	Hyatt	Haynes	Randall	Pearce	Wilkinson	Mee	Baker	44
Meara	Smart	Flynn	W Kelly	Cox	Goodliffe	Hyatt	Haynes	Randall	Pearce	Brady	Mee	Hedge	45
Meara	Baker	Sargent	W Kelly	Cox	Goodliffe	Hyatt	Mee	Randall	Stevens	Brady	Flynn	Hedge	46
Meara	Brady	Flynn	W Kelly	Cox	Goodliffe	Hyatt	Haynes	Stevens	Baker	Wilkinson	Randall	Mee	47
Meara	Brady	Flynn	W Kelly	Cox	Goodliffe	Hyatt	Haynes	G Williams	Stevens	Wilkinson	Sugrue	Baker	48
Meara	Brady	Flynn	W Kelly	Cox	Goodliffe	Hyatt	Haynes	G Williams	Sugrue	Wilkinson	Stevens	Baker	49
Meara	Sugrue	Flynn	W Kelly	Cox	Goodliffe	Hyatt	Haynes	G Williams	Brady	Wilkinson	Randall	Baker	50
Meara	Brady	Flynn	W Kelly	Cox	Goodliffe	Hyatt	Randall	G Williams	Sugrue	Wilkinson	Haynes	Baker	51
Meara	Brady	Flynn	W Kelly	Cox	Goodliffe	Haynes	Randall	G Williams	Stevens	Wilkinson	Baker	Nartey	52
Meara	Brady	Randall	W Kelly	Cox	Goodliffe	Stevens	Baker	Nartey	Pearce	Wilkinson	Hedge	Roberts	53
Meara	Sugrue	Flynn	W Kelly	Cox	Goodliffe	Hyatt	Randall	G Williams	Stevens	Wilkinson	Baker	Haynes	54
Meara	Brady	Flynn	W Kelly	Cox	Goodliffe	Hyatt	Sugrue	Haynes	Stevens	Wilkinson	Baker	Pearce	55
Meara	Sugrue	Flynn	W Kelly	Cox	Goodliffe	Hyatt	Stevens	G Williams	Brady	Wilkinson	Haynes	Randall	56
Meara	Brady	Flynn	W Kelly	Pearce	Goodliffe	Hyatt	Stevens	G Williams	Randall	Wilkinson	Haynes	Sugrue	57
Meara	Brady	Flynn	W Kelly	Cox	Goodliffe	Hyatt	Stevens	G Williams	Randall	Wilkinson	Haynes	Sugrue	58
Meara	Brady	Flynn	Sugrue	Cox	Goodliffe	Hyatt	Haynes	G Williams	Stevens	Wilkinson	Randall	Pearce	59
Meara	Brady	Flynn	Baker	Cox	Goodliffe	Hyatt	Randall	G Williams	Pearce	Wilkinson	Haynes	Sugrue	60

TERRY BROWN

Terry was born in Hillingdon in 1952 and made his debut for Hayes at the tender age of 18. He was a member of the successful 1972 FA Cup side that beat Bristol Rovers and drew with Reading. He moved to Slough Town shortly afterwards where he gained FA representative honours.

Terry returned to Churrch Road in the late 1970s for a season before joining Wokingham Town in a playing, and later, a coaching capacity. Working alongside Roy Merryweather, Wokingham finished 2nd in the Premier Division of the Isthmian League in 1989/90.

Terry took control at Hayes in November 1993, guiding the team to the respectability of 13th position. His first full season in charge saw a vast improvement as a best-ever finish of 3rd was achieved.

Last season was the most successful in the club's history as an FA Cup run to the first round was the forerunner to the capture of the Middlesex Senior Cup and the ICIS League title. The latter was sealed on the back of a superb 25-game unbeaten run that culminated in a 3-0 win at Carshalton on the last day, meaning that the league was won by a single goal from Enfield.

Hayes' Jon Brady rounds Carshalton's keeper Les Cleevely *Photo - Eric Marsh*

Programme details:
24 pages for £1.00
Editor - Robert Frape

Any other club publications:

Local Newspapers:
Hayes Gazette

Local Radio Stations:
Capital Radio

ICIS FOOTBALL LEAGUE PREMIER DIVISION.
SATURDAY 27TH APRIL 1996. Kick off 3.00 pm.
VS. YEOVIL TOWN F.C.

HAYES - PLAYING SQUAD 1996-97

Player	Honours	Birthplace and date	Transfer Fees	Previous Clubs
GOALKEEPERS				
Russell Meara	ILP	Hammersmith 12/7/74		Southampton, Brighton, Barnet, Aylesbury U, Wokingham T
DEFENDERS				
Warren Kelly	ILP	Watford 18/4/68		Hemel Hempstead, St.Albans C,
Jason Goodliffe	ILP	Hillingdon 7/3/74		Brentford
Lee Flynn	ILP	Hampstead 4/9/73		Boreham Wood, Romford, Hendon
Paul Watkins		Hillingdon 11/1/71		Harefield U
Andy Cox	ILP FAXI	Hemel Hempstead 1/5/69	£6,000	Chipperfield, Tring T, Berkhamsted T, St.Albans C
Nathan Bunce		Hillingdon 2/5/75	£2,000	Brentford, Yeading
Eddie Mee		West London 8/2/77		Southall Feltham & Hounslow
MIDFIELDERS				
Steve Baker	ILP	Hillingdon 31/5/74		Brentford, Brook House, Hayes, Southall, Yeading
Neal Stevens	ILP	Perivale 1/10/69		Mavericks, Brook House
Nick Roddis		Rotherham 18/2/73		Nottingham F, Boston FC, Boston U, Yeading
Darron Wilkinson	ILP	Reading 24/11/69		Wokingham T, Brighton, Kuitan (HK)
Freddie Hyatt	ILP	West London 18/1/68		Ruislip, Burnham, Wokingham T
Junior Lewis		Northwich Park 9/10/73		Brentford, Dover A
FORWARDS				
Jon Brady	ILP	Newcastle (Aust) 14/1/75		Adamstown Rosebuds (Aust), Swansea C, Brentford, Hayes, Mjolner (Nor)
Jimmy Sugrue	ILP	Hammersmith 1/1/74	£2,000	Fulham, Kingstonian, Aldershot T
Junior Haynes	ILP	Croydon 16/4/76		Tottenham H, Luton T, Barnet, Hendon
Ross Pickett		Hillingdon 10/2/75		Denham, Hayes, Slough T
Martin Randall	ILP	Pinner 3/3/73	£1,500	Northwood
Carl Bartley		Peckham 6/10/76		Fulham, Dulwich Hamlet
Gary Williams	ILP	Adelaide (Aust) 19/6/69	£1,000	Luton, Vauxhall M, Stevenage, Baldock T, Hitchin T

Departures during season:
Peter Scrivens (Cobham), Matt Howard (St.Albans C), Matt Flitter (Yeading), Jon Denton (Chertsey T), Tony Knight (Wealdstone), Paul Cooper (Yeading), Vladimir Lazic (Northwood), Tony Kelly (Hendon), Dave Kellman (Yeading), Simon Quail (Hendon), Mark Turner (Staines T), Detzi Kruszynski (Crawley T), Andy Driscoll (St.Albans C), Garry Smart (Slough T), Pat Gavin (Aylesbury U).
Players on loan during season:
None.
Departures during close season: David Pearce (Chertsey T).

Church Road, Hayes

ADDRESS: Townfield House, Church Road, Hayes, Middx UB3 2LE.

TELEPHONE NUMBER: 0181 573 2075. Fax: 0181 573 2075. **Club News:** 0891 884484. **Buzzline:** 0891 101922.

SIMPLE DIRECTIONS:
M25, M4, A312 (Hayes By-Pass), A4020 (Uxbridge Road), Church Road on left.

CAPACITY: 6,500 **SEATED:** 450 **COVERED TERRACING:** 2,000

RECORD ATTENDANCE:
15,370 v Bromley - FA Amateur Cup - 10.2.51.

CLUB SHOP:
Wide range of programmes, replica kits, souvenirs and books. Contact Lee Hermitage c/o Hayes FC.

SOCIAL FACILITIES:
Clubhouse open Sat. 12.00 - 3.00pm, 4.45 - 11.00pm. Sun. 12.00 - 3.00pm, 7.00 - 11.00pm. Midweek 7.00 - 11.00pm. Matchnights 6.30 - 11.00pm. Some cold snacks available.

Hayes Fact File

Nickname: The Missioners

Club Sponsors:

Previous Ground: Botwell Common.

Previous Leagues: Local leagues 09-14/ Gt Western Suburban 19-22, London 22-24, Spartan 24-30, Athenian 30-71.

Club colours: Red and White shirts, Black shorts, and black socks.

Change colours: Blue shirts, blue shorts, Blue socks.

Reserve team league: Suburban (North).

Midweek home matchday: Tuesday.

Record transfer fee: £6,000 to Hendon for Gary Keen - 1990.

Record transfer fee received: £30,000 from QPR for Les Ferdinand - 1987.

1995-96 Captain: Warren Kelly.

1995-96 Top scorer: Junior Haynes 10 goals.

1995-96 Player of the Year: Warren Kelly.

Club record goalscorer: Unknown.

Record appearances: Reg Leather - 701.

Past players who progressed to the Football League: Cyril Bacon (Orient 1946), Phil Nolan (Watford 1947), Dave Grommbridge (Orient 1951), Jimmy Bloomfield (Brentford 1952), Derek Neale & Les Champleover (Brighton 1956 & 57), Gordon Phillips (Brentford 1963), Robin Friday (Reading 1974), Les Smith (A Villa), Cyrille Regis (WBA 1977), Les Ferdinand (QPR 1987), Derek Payne (Barnet 1988), Paul Hyde (Wycombe 1991), Dean Hooper (Swindon 1995).

Club Honours: ICIS Lg Premier Div. 95-96, FA Amtr Cup R-up 30-31, Isthmian Lg R-up 78-79, 87-88, Athenian Lg 56-57, Spartan Lg 27-28, Gt Western Suburban Lg 20-24, London Snr Cup 31-32, 80-81, Middx Snr Cup 19-21, 25-26, 30-31, 35-36, 39-40, 49-50, 81-82, 95-96, London Charity Cup 60-61, Middx Charity Cup (15 times), Middx Premier Cup 87-88, 88-89, Suburban Lg (North) 88-89, 91-92.

HEDNESFORD TOWN

Formed: 1880

President:
Nigel Tinsley

Chairman:
Nick Smith

Vice-Chairman
John Baldwin

Secretary
Ritchie Murning

Commercial Manager
Terry Brumpton

Manager:
John Baldwin

Assistant Manager
John Allen

Physiotherapist:
Don Drakeley

Press Officer
Terry Brumpton

There has only been one better debut season, that by Bromsgrove Rovers in 1992/93, and Hednesford can be very pleased with their first campaign as a Conference club. Manager John Baldwin gave most of the squad which gained promotion the chance to play at the higher level and they responded marvellously. Striker Joe O'Connor ended up as the league's second top scorer and Gary Fitzpatrick attracted a host of League scouts with his performances from midfield. Even the sale of Dave Hanson to Leyton Orient for £50,000 didn't disrupt the side and that money gave Bladwin the scope to strenghten in the summer as the only outlay during the season was in bringing in the impressive Keith Russell from Atherstone United for a four-figure fee.

The close season has seen England midfielder Steve Taylor return to the Conference after an unhappy sojourn with Crystal Palace and the experienced Andy Comyn will, undoubtedly, strengthen the defence.

This season will ne the acid test for the Pitmen but I feel sure they are equipped to cope. **Steve Whitney**

Hednesford Town FC *Photo - Eric Marsh*

Hednesford Town

Match No.	Date	Comp.	Venue H/A	Opponents	Result	League Pos.	Goalscorers (Times if known)	Attendance
1	Aug 12	BHLCC	A	Hastings Town	Won 4-0	-	Devine, Hanson, O'Connor, Wright	356
2	19	GMVC	H	Halifax Town	Won 3-0	2	Essex, Lambert, Wright	1650
3	21	GMVC	A	Kidderminster H	Lost 1-3	3	O'Connor	1681
4	26	GMVC	A	Dover Athletic	Won 3-1	4	Essex, Devine, O'Connor	866
5	28	GMVC	H	Welling Utd	Drew 1-1	7	og	1732
6	Sep 2	GMVC	H	Woking	Won 2-1	3	Lambert, O'Connor	1711
7	4	GMVC	A	Dagenham	Won 2-1	2	Fitzpatrick, Hanson	837
8	9	FAC	H	Corby	Won 3-1	-	Essex, Wright, Street	732
9	11	GMVC	H	Telford United	Won 4-0	1	Carty, Hanson 2, O'Connor	2480
10	16	GMVC	A	Northwich Victoria	Won 2-0	1	O'Connor 2	1100
11	18	SC	A	Kidderminster H	Lost 1-4	-	Essex	1326
12	23	FAC	A	Tamworth	Won 2-1	-	Hackett, O'Connor	1138
13	25	SSC	H	Willenhall Town	Won 6-1	-	Carty, Street, Wright 2, O'Connor 2	583
14	30	GMVC	A	Slough Town	Won 2-0	3	Carty, O'Connor	971
15	Oct 2	SC	H	Kidderminster H	Won 2-0	-	O'Connor 2	1626
16	7	FAC	H	Solihull Borough	Drew 2-2	-	Devine, Wright	1013
17	11	FAC	A	Solihull Borough	Won 2-1	-	Essex, McNally	421
18	14	GMVC	A	Bath City	Lost 0-1	5		661
19	21	FAC	A	Canvey Island	Lost 0-2	-		537
20	28	GMVC	H	Southport	Won 2-1	4	Devine, Burr	1355
21	31	SSC	A	Armitage	Won 4-2	-	Carty, Lambert, Street, O'Connor	370
22	Nov 4	GMVC	H	Macclesfield Town	Lost 0-1	6		2019
23	11	GMVC	H	Dover Athletic	Drew 2-2	6	Street, O'Connor	1147
24	13	BSC	H	WBA	Lost 2-3	-	Carty, Jennings	1202
25	18	GMVC	A	Stalybridge Celtic	Won 1-0	5	Foreman	687
26	21	GMVC	A	Bromsgrove Rovers	Won 4-1	4	Fitzpatrick, Street, O'Connor 2	952
27	25	GMVC	H	Morecambe	Lost 1-2	4	Devine	1271
28	27	GMVC	H	Stalybridge Celtic	Lost 0-1	4		895
29	Dec 2	GMVC	A	Gateshead	Won 3-0	3	Foreman, O'Connor 2	841
30	9	GMVC	A	Farnborough Town	Won 3-1	3	Yates, Foreman, O'Connor	716
31	16	GMVC	H	Kidderminster	Lost 1-3	4	Foreman	1392
32	Jan 1	GMVC	A	Kettering Town	Lost 0-2	5		1712
33	6	GMVC	H	Runcorn	Won 2-0	4	Collins, Lambert	1008
34	13	GMVC	H	Northwich Victoria	Won 2-1	4	Yates, Lambert	1017
35	20	FAT	H	Northwich Victoria	Drew 1-1	-	McNally	935
36	23	FAT	A	Northwich Victoria	Lost 0-2	-		636
37	31	SSC	A	Paget Rangers	Lost 1-2	-	Carty	
38	Feb 3	GMVC	A	Halifax Town	Won 3-1	3	Devine, O'Connor, 1 og	839
39	10	GMVC	A	Southport	Drew 2-2	4	Lake, Carty p	811
40	17	GMVC	H	Bath City	Won 2-1	3	Essex, Lake	1006
41	24	GMVC	A	Stevenage Boro	Lost 0-1	5		1626
42	Mar 2	GMVC	A	Morecambe	Won 1-0	4	O'Connor	961
43	4	GMVC	H	Kettering Town	Won 1-0	3	Street	1049
44	9	GMVC	H	Farnborough	Won 4-1	3	McNally, Devine, Russell, O'Connor	1010
45	12	GMVC	A	Welling United	Drew 1-1	2	Russel p	400
46	16	GMVC	H	Bromsgrove Rovers	Won 4-2	2	Russell, O'Connor 2, Lake	1119
47	18	GMVC	H	Gateshead	Lost 0-1	2		1017
48	23	GMVC	A	Runcorn	Drew 2-2	2	Lambert	507
49	25	GMVC	H	Stevenage Borough	Won 2-1	2	Lambert, Russell	1651
50	30	GMVC	A	Woking	Lost 0-3	3		3194
51	Apr 2	GMVC	A	Telford United	Lost 1-2	3	Riddings	967
52	6	GMVC	H	Altrincham	Won 2-1	3	Essex, Ridings	1010
53	13	GMVC	H	Dagenham	Drew 0-0	3		946
54	20	GMVC	A	Altrincham	Lost 1-2	3	O'Connor	731
55	27	GMVC	H	Slough Town	Won 3-1	3	Simpson, O'Connor, Lake	1081
56	May 4	GMVC	A	Macclesfield Town	Drew 1-1	3		1246

Hednesford Town

1	2	3	4	5	6	7	8	9	10	11	12	14	Match No.
Cooksey	Yates	Collins	Simpson	Essex	Fitzpatrick	Devine	Street	Hanson	Lambert	O' Connor	Burr	Freeman	1
Cooksey	Yates	Collins	Simpson	Essex	Fitzpatrick	Street	Lambert	Hanson	Devine	O' Connor	Wright	Freeman	2
Cooksey	Yates	Collins	Simpson	Essex	Fitzpatrick	Street	Lambert	Hanson	Devine	O' Connor	Wright	Freeman	3
Cooksey	Yates	Collins	Simpson	Essex	Fitzpatrick	Street	Lambert	Hanson	Devine	O' Connor	Burr	Freeman	4
Cooksey	Yates	Collins	Simpson	Essex	Fitzpatrick	Street	Lambert	Hanson	Devine	Wright	Freeman	Burr	5
Cooksey	Fitzpatrick	Collins	Simpson	Essex	Carty	Devine	Lambert	Street	Hanson	O' Connor	Yates	Wright	6
Cooksey	Fitzpatrick	Collins	Simpson	Essex	Carty	Devine	Lambert	Street	Hanson	O' Connor	Yates	Wright	7
Cooksey	Yates	Collins	Devine	Essex	Carty	Fitzpatrick	Lambert	Wright	Hanson	Street	Burr	Hackett	8
Cooksey	Yates	Collins	Simpson	Essex	Carty	Fitzpatrick	Devine	Street	Hanson	O' Connor	Burr	Wright	9
Cooksey	Yates	Collins	Simpson	Essex	Carty	Fitzpatrick	Devine	Street	Hanson	O' Connor	Burr	Wright	10
Cooksey	Foster	Collins	Simpson	Essex	Carty	Devine	Wright	Street	Hanson	O' Connor	Yates	Burr	11
Cooksey	Yates	Collins	Simpson	Essex	Carty	Fitzpatrick	Hackett	Street	Hanson	O' Connor	Wright	Jennings	12
Cooksey	Harrold	Coates	Blewitt	Foster	Carty	Jennings	Hackett	Street	Wright	O' Connor	Hanson	Yates	13
Cooksey	Yates	Collins	Simpson	Essex	Carty	McNally	Devine	Street	Wright	O' Connor	Titterton	Jennings	14
Cooksey	Yates	Collins	Titterton	Essex	Carty	McNally	Devine	Street	Wright	O' Connor	Burr	Jennings	15
Cooksey	Yates	Collins	Titterton	Essex	Carty	McNally	Devine	Street	Wright	O' Connor	Burr	Jennings	16
Cooksey	Simpson	Collins	Titterton	Essex	Carty	McNally	Devine	Street	Wright	O' Connor	Lambert	Yates	17
Cooksey	Yates	Collins	Simpson	Essex	Carty	McNally	Devine	Street	Wright	O' Connor	Lambert	Jennings	18
Cooksey	Yates	Collins	Simpson	Essex	Carty	McNally	Lambert	Street	Burr	O' Connor	Devine	Wright	19
Cooksey	Yates	Titterton	Simpson	Essex	Carty	McNally	Devine	Street	Burr	Wright	Lambert	Collins	20
Williams	Harrold	Collins	Simpson	Blewitt	Carty	Jennings	Lambert	Street	Wright	O' Connor	Devine	Coates	21
Cooksey	Carty	Titterton	Simpson	Essex	Devine	McNally	Lambert	Street	Burr	O' Connor	Wright	Jennings	22
Cooksey	Yates	Collins	Simpson	Essex	Carty	Devine	Lambert	Street	Wright	O' Connor	Titterton	Burr	23
Cooksey	Yates	Collins	Simpson	Essex	Carty	Devine	Lambert	Street	Burr	O' Connor	Titterton	Wright	24
Cooksey	Fitzpatrick	Collins	Simpson	Essex	Carty	Devine	Lambert	Foreman	Street	O' Connor	Titterton	Wright	25
Cooksey	Fitzpatrick	Titterton	Collins	Essex	Carty	Devine	Lambert	Foreman	Street	O' Connor	Wright	Jennings	26
Cooksey	Fitzpatrick	Collins	Simpson	Essex	Carty	Devine	Lambert	Foreman	Street	O' Connor	Wright	Titterton	27
Cooksey	Carty	Collins	Simpson	Essex	Jennings	Devine	Fitzpatrick	Lambert	Foreman	O' Connor	Wright	Titterton	28
Cooksey	Yates	Collins	Simpson	Essex	Fitzpatrick	Devine	Street	Lambert	Foreman	O' Connor	Wright	Titterton	29
Cooksey	Yates	Collins	Simpson	Essex	Fitzpatrick	Devine	Street	Lambert	Foreman	O' Connor	Wright	Titterton	30
Cooksey	Yates	Collins	Simpson	Essex	Fitzpatrick	Devine	Street	Lambert	Foreman	O' Connor	Jennings	Wright	31
Cooksey	Yates	Collins	Simpson	Essex	Carty	Street	Fitzpatrick	Lambert	Foreman	O' Connor	Devine	Wright	32
Cooksey	Yates	Collins	Simpson	Fitzpatrick	McNally	Street	Devine	Lambert	Foreman	O' Connor	Wright	Carty	33
Cooksey	Yates	Collins	Simpson	Essex	McNally	Lake	Devine	Lambert	Street	O' Connor	Wright	Foreman	34
Cooksey	Yates	Collins	Fitzpatrick	Essex	McNally	Lake	Devine	Lambert	Street	O' Connor	Blewitt	Foreman	35
Cooksey	Yates	Collins	Fitzpatrick	Essex	McNally	Wright	Devine	Lambert	Street	O' Connor	Lake	Carty	36
Cooksey	Yates	Coates	Simpson	Essex	McNally	Carty	Fitzpatrick	Street	Foreman	O' Connor	Lake	Burr	37
Cooksey	Yates	Collins	Simpson	Essex	Carty	McNally	Fitzpatrick	Lambert	Devine	O' Connor	Street	Foreman	38
Cooksey	Yates	Collins	Simpson	Lake	Carty	McNally	Fitzpatrick	Lambert	Devine	O' Connor	Street	Foreman	39
Cooksey	Yates	Collins	Simpson	Essex	Lake	McNally	Fitzpatrick	Street	Foreman	O' Connor	Wright	Harnett	40
Williams	Fitzpatrick	Collins	Simpson	Essex	McNally	Carty	Lake	Street	Foreman	O' Connor	Devine	Harnett	41
Cooksey	McNally	Collins	Simpson	Essex	Carty	Fitzpatrick	Devine	Lambert	Russell	O' Connor	Street	Lake	42
Cooksey	McNally	Collins	Simpson	Essex	Carty	Fitzpatrick	Devine	Foreman	Russell	O' Connor	Street	Lake	43
Cooksey	Yates	Collins	Simpson	Essex	McNally	Fitzpatrick	Devine	Street	Russell	O' Connor	Foreman	Laek	44
Cooksey	Yates	Collins	Simpson	Essex	McNally	Fitzpatrick	Devine	Foreman	Russell	O' Connor	Wright	Lake	45
Cooksey	Yates	Collins	Simpson	Essex	Carty	McNally	Fitzpatrick	Wright	Russell	O' Connor	Lake	Foreman	46
Cooksey	Yates	Collins	Simpson	Essex	Carty	McNally	Fitzpatrick	Wright	Russell	O' Connor	Lake	Foreman	47
Cooksey	Yates	Collins	Simpson	Essex	Carty	Fitzpatrick	Devine	Lambert	McNally	O' Connor	Harnett	Lake	48
Cooksey	Yates	Collins	Simpson	Essex	Carty	Fitzpatrick	Devine	Lambert	Russell	O' Connor	Harnett	Lake	49
Cooksey	Yates	Fitzpatrick	Devine	Essex	Carty	Riddings	Pierce	Lambert	Russell	O'Connor	Harnett	Lake	50
Cooksey	Yates	Collins	Devine	Essex	Carty	Fitzpatrick	McNally	Lambert	Russell	O'Connor	Riddings	Pierce	51
Cooksey	Yates	Collins	Simpson	Essex	McNally	Ridings	Devine	Lambert	Russell	O' Connor	Pierce	Carty	52
Cooksey	Yates	McNally	Simpson	Essex	Fitzpatrick	Ridings	Devine	Lambert	Russell	O' Connor	Lake	Wright	53
Cooksey	Yates	Russell	Simpson	Essex	Ridings	Devine	McNally	Lake	Harnett	O' Connor	Pierce	Coates	54
Cooksey	Yates	Collins	Simpson	Essex	McNally	Fitzpatrick	Devine	Russell	Harnett	O'Connor	Lake	Wright	55
Cooksey	Yates	Collins	Simpson	Essex	McNally	Fitzpatrick	Devine	Russell	Wright	O'Connor	Lake	Harnett	56

Hednesford Town

JOHN BALDWIN

John originally played for Hednesford Town as a goalkeeper in the 1970s and returned to the club as manager midway through the 1989/90 season when the Pitmen were hovering just above the relegation zone of the Beazer Homes League Midland Division.
In the following seasons John led the club to promotion to the Beazer Premier Division plus the finals of the Staffs. Senior Cup, Birmingham Senior Cup and Welsh Cup when they narrowly lost to Cardfiff City at the National Stadium, Cardiff.
Last season John led Hednesford to the GM Vauxhall Conference thanks to their Beazer Premier Championship and in his dual role as vice-chairman was one of the driving forces behind the construction of the club's new stadium, Keys Park.
John originally cut his teeth as manager of Wolverhampton Sunday League sid Electricity and West Midlands League club Harrisons. During the day he runs his own accountancy business and his ambition is to see Hednesford Town promoted to the Football League.

Joe O'Connor (white shirt) Player of the Year:

Programme details:
40 pages for £1.20
Editor - Chris Southall

Other club publications:

Local Newspapers:
Express & Star
Chase Post, Cannock Mercury,
Lichfield Trader, The Chronicle

Local Radio Stations:
Radio WM, BRMB,
WABC, Beacon, Signal,
BBC Radio Stoke.

HEDNESFORD TOWN - PLAYING SQUAD 1996-97

Player	Honours	Birthplace and date	Transfer Fees	Previous Clubs
GOALKEEPERS				
Scott Cooksey	BHL, WSC	Birmingham 24/6/72		Derby Co, Shrewsbury T, Bromsgrove R, Peterborough U
Gavin Brant		Birmingham		Walsall
DEFENDERS				
Luke Yates	BHL	Birmingham 19/3/74		Nottingham F, Halesowen T, Sandwell B, Bilston T
Paul Edwards		Birkenhead 25/12/63		Altrincham, Crewe, Coventry, Wolves, WBA
John Cottrell		Birmingham		Wolves
Kevin Collins	FAT, BHL	Birmingham 21/7/64		Boldmere, Shrewsbury T, Stourbridge, Pelsall, Burton A, Kidderminster H, Rushall O
Wayne Simpson	BHL, FAXI	Newcastle 19/9/68		Port Vale, Stafford R
Steve Essex	BHL, FAXI	Walsall 2/10/60		Darlaston, Wolves U, Malvern T, Rushall O, Blakenall, Aylesbury U, Gresley R, Stafford R
Andy Comyn		Wakefield 2/8/68		Man.U, Alvechurch, Aston Villa, Derby, Plymouth, WBA
MIDFIELDERS				
Gary Fitzpatrick	BHL, Ei u-20	Birmingham 5/8/71		Leicester C, VS Rugby, Moor Green, Rannberg (Swe)
Steve Devine	BHL, WC, NIY	Strabane (NI) 11/12/64		Wolves, Derby Co, Hereford U, Corby T
Stuart Lake	BHL	Stone 15/10/75		Walsall
Bernard McNally	NI, WC	Shrewsbury 17/10/63		Shrewsbury T, WBA
Keith Russell		Birmingham	4-fig	Walsall, Tamworth, Atherstone U
Paul Carty	BHL	Birmingham 22/10/66		Everton, Nuneaton B, Bromsgrove R, Tamworth
Colin Lambert		Manchester 21/9/63		Flixton, Winsford U, Macclesfield T, Halifax T
FORWARDS				
Joe O'Connor	BHL	Wolverhampton 20/10/67		Lye T, Stafford R
Leighton Derry		Birmingham		Walsall
Tyrone Street	BHL	Birmingham 14/3/72		Blakenall, Cradley T, Willenhall T, Bilston T
Steve Taylor	ESP	Birmingham		Rushall O, Bromsgrove R, Crystal Palace
Dave Harnett		Birmingham		From Youth Team

Departures during season:
Keith Bertschin (Stafford R), Dave Hanson (Leyton O), Brendan Hackett (Rushden & D), Mark Freeman (Gloucester C), Richard Williams (Atherstone U), Andy Marlowe (Bromsgrove R), Dave Titterton (Burton A), Gareth Jennings (Stafford R - Loan), Colin Radburn (Sutton Coldfield T), Steve Burr (Macclesfield T), Darren Foreman (Barrow - Loan).
Players on loan during season:
Simon Pierce (Wolves), Dave Ridings (Crewe A), Gavin Brant (Walsall).

Keys Park, Hednesford

GROUND ADDRESS: Keys Park, Hednesford, Cannock, Staffordshire.
TEL. NO. 01543 422870

SIMPLE DIRECTIONS:
M6 J11 to Cannock, through traffic lights to island , 3rd exit, next island, 2nd exit onto Lichfield Rd. Next island 1st exit, next island straight on, next island 3rd exit, continue to mini-island. Keys Park is straight on (signposted from 2nd island.)

CAPACITY: 3,500 **SEATED:** 770 **COVERED TERRACING:** 1,000

RECORD ATTENDANCE:
10,000 v Walsall, FA Cup 1919-20

CLUB SHOP:
Yes

SOCIAL FACILITIES:
Dorchester Lounge Club - access via main entrance to stadium. Cold food and snacks

Hednesford Fact File

Nickname: The Pitmen

Club Sponsors: Bridgtown Doors

Previous Grounds: The Tins (behind Anglesey Hotel) until 1904, Cross Keys until 1995.

Previous Leagues: Walsall & District/ Birmingham Combination 08-15 45-53/ West Mids 19-39 53-72 74-84/ Midland Counties 72-74.

Club colours: White shirts & black & red trim, black shorts, white trim.

Change colours: Gold shirts, navy sleeves, navy shorts, gold trim.

Reserve team league: Central Conference League.

Midweek home matchday: Monday.

Record win: 12-1; v Birmingham City- Birmingham Wartime League Cup 40-41; v Redditch United, Birmingham Combination 52-53.

Record defeat: 0-15 v Burton , Birmingham Combination 24-25.

Record transfer fee: £12,000 for Steve Burr (Macclesfield Town 1991)

Record transfer fee received: £50,000 for Dave Hanson (Leyton Orient)

1995-96 Captain: Kevin Collins.

1995-96 Top scorer: Joe O'Connor.

1995-96 Player of the Year: Joe O'Connor.

Club record goalscorer: Dennis Cheney 61 (in one season)

Record appearances: Trevor Townsend 377

Past players who progressed to the Football League: Len Drake (Bristol Rovers 1957), David Noake (Luton 1959), Mike Turner (Swindon 1961), Trevor Senior (Portsmouth 1981), David West (Liverpool 1983), Mike Squire (Torquay 1984), Jeremy Judd (Torquay 1984), Anthony White (Bournemouth 1985) + Graham Roberts (Spurs, Chelsea, Rangers, England) who progressed via Weymouth.Darren Garner(Rotherham U,1995)

Club Honours: Beazer Homes League Premier Div. Winners 1994-95, Southern Lg R-up 79-80 (Div 1 (Sth) R-up 77-78, Lg Cup 86-87 (R-up 91-92), Western Lg 54-55 (R-up 60-61, Div 2 R-up 49-50), Dorset Snr Cup 50-51 60-61 67-68 68-69 71-72 94-95, Dorset Lg 37-38.

KETTERING TOWN

Formed:
1872

President:
S Chapman

Vice-President:
T F Bradley

Chairman:
P Mallinger

Vice-Chairman
P Oliver

Secretary/Press Officer:
G P Knowles

Manager:
Gary Johnson

Physiotherapist:
Tom Edwards

Commercial Manager:
Mr B Baker

It was a poor 1995/96 campaign for the Poppies, who suffered their worst finish for many seasons. The club's eight straight defeats was a record and there were some unprecedented scorelines, like the embarrasing 1-6 home defeat by Stalybridge Celtic on the final day of the season.

Kettering supporters were further angered by the record sale of Carl Alford to neighbours Rushden & Diamonds, following the earlier departures to Nene Park of England team-mates Steve Holden, Nick Ashby, Graham Benstead and Steve Stott.

There are some bright lights for the club however. A crop of promising young players have been signed on contract and manager Gary Johnson has also added a number of impressive new players for the new campaign, such as Steve Berry, Richard Nugent, Paul Harding and another duo from Bromsgrove Rovers, Recky Carter and Craig Gaunt.

Poppies fans have been long-suffering and deserve better fare than they have been getting recently. Now, with the added incentive of neighbours Rushden & Diamonds in the same league, nothing short of a promotion challenge will do. **Steve Whitney**

Action from Ketterings match with Slough. *Photo - Eric Marsh*

Kettering Town

Match No.	Date	Comp.	Venue H/A	Opponents	Result	League Pos.	Goalscorers (Times if known)	Attendance
1	Aug 19	GMVC		Altrincham	Won 3-1		Alford 2, Stringfellow	969
2	22	GMVC		Bromsgrove	Drew 2-2		Oxbrow, Alford	2006
3	26	GMVC		Runcorn	Won 4-0		Stott, Alford, Stringfellow 2	1583
4	28	GMVC		Farnborough	Drew 1-1		Scott	1037
5	Sep 2	GMVC		Southport	Drew 1-1		Pope	1944
6	4	GMVC		Kidderminster	Lost 0-1			1949
7	9	GMVC		Macclesfield	Drew 1-1		Stringfellow	1320
8	12	GMVC		Woking	Won 3-0		Oxbrow, Alford 2	1671
9	16	GMVC		Bath	Won 3-0		Pope, Alford, Stringfellow	1767
10	18	GMVC		Stevenage	Lost 1-5		Oxbrow	2033
11	23	GMVC		Stalybridge	Lost 2-3		Stott, Scott	627
12	30	GMVC		Telford	Won 4-3		Oxbrow, Pope, Alford, Scott	952
13	Oct 7	GMVC		Slough	Won 2-0		Alford, Scott	1902
14	14	GMVC		Morecambe	Lost 3-5		Stott, Alford, Scott	1098
15	21	FAC4Q		Bromsgrove	Drew 0-0			2427
16	24	FAC4QR		Bromsgrove	Drew 2-2		Alford, Scott	1426
17	28	GMVC		Runcorn	Lost 2-4		Hunter 2	569
18	30	FAC4QR		Bromsgrove	Lost 1-2		Alford	2283
19	Nov 4	GMVC		Dagenham	Won 2-0		Alford, Stringfellow	1616
20	11	GMVC		Halifax	Lost 0-2			929
21	14	GMVC		Welling	Lost 1-3		Scott	1232
22	18	GMVC		Gateshead	Drew 1-1		Alford	712
23	25	GMVC		Altrincham	Won 4-2		Alford 3, Scott	1369
24	28	SC2		Stevenage	Won 2-1		Harmon, Stringfellow	808
25	Dec 2	GMVC		Dover	Lost 1-2		Alford	1045
26	5	NSC2		Stewart & Lloyds	Won 2-1		Harmon, Alford	119
27	9	GMVC		Bath	Lost 1-3		Parsons	612
28	16	GMVC		Farnborough	Lost 0-2			1260
29	Jan 1	GMVC		Hednesford	Won 2-0		Alford, Haworth	1712
30	6	GMVC		Southport	Lost 1-6		Norman	916
31	9	GMVC		Northwich	Drew 2-2		Alford 2	912
32	13	GMVC		Dover	Drew 2-2		Pope, Haworth	1332
33	20	FAT1		St Albans City	Drew 1-1		Pope	1577
34	23	FAT1R		St Albans City	Won 3-2		Ibrahim, Pope, Alford	785
35	Feb 10	FAT2		Slough	Won 2-1		Gynn, Scott	1058
36	13	SC3		Slough	Won 2-0		Harmon, Pope	646
37	17	GMVC		Slough	Won 2-1		Nyamah, Alford	766
38	24	GMVC		Woking	Drew 1-1		Alford	2637
39	27	NSC SF		Rothwell Town	Lost 0-5			402
40	Mar 2	FAT2		Stevenage	Lost 0-3			2219
41	4	GMVC		Hednesford	Lost 0-1			1049
42	9	GMVC		Gateshead	Won 1-0		Alford	1179
43	16	GMVC		Macclesfield	Drew 2-2		Nyamah 2	1433
44	19	SC SF1		Bromsgrove	Lost 0-2			650
45	23	GMVC		Kidderminster	Won 2-0		Harmon, Mustafa	1376
46	Apr 4	SC SF2		Bromsgrove	Won 2-1		Mustafa, Gynn	773
47	6	GMVC		Dagenham	Won 2-1		Thomas, Crookes (og)	730
48	8	GMVC		Halifax	Lost 1-2		Benjamin	1317
49	13	GMVC		Morecambe	Lost 2-3		Oxbrow, Benjamin	1124
50	16	GMVC		Stevenage Borough	Lost 1-2		Mustafa	1414
51	20	GMVC		Bromsgrove Rovers	Lost 2-3		Benjamin, Dowling	824
52	23	GMVC		Welling	Lost 0-1			603
53	30	GMVC		Telford United	Lost 0-3			851
54	May 2	GMVC		Northwich Victoria	Lost 2-6		Pope 2	600
55	4	GMVC		Stalybridge	Lost 1-6		Dowling	962

Kettering Town

1	2	3	4	5	6	7	8	9	10	11	12	14	Match No.
Judge	Parsons	Nyamah	Holden	Oxbrow	Pope	Mustafa	Stott	Alford	Scott	Stringfellow	Saddington	March	1
Shoemake	Parsons	Nyamah	Holden	Oxbrow	Pope	Mustafa	Stott	Alford	Scott	Stringfellow	Saddington	March	2
Judge	Hunter	Nyamah	Holden	Oxbrow	Pope	Mustafa	Stott	Alford	Scott	Stringfellow	Saddington	March	3
Shoemake	Saddingto	Nyamah	Holden	Oxbrow	Pope	Mustafa	Stott	Arnold	Scott	Stringfellow	Parsons	Edwards	4
Judge	n	March	Holden	Oxbrow	Pope	Mustafa	Stott	Alford	Scott	Arnold	Stringfellow	Saddington	5
Judge	Hunter	March	Holden	Oxbrow	Pope	Mustafa	Stott	Alford	Arnold	Stringfellow	Saddington	Parsons	6
Judge	Hunter	March	Holden	Oxbrow	Pope	Mustafa	Stott	Alford	Scott	Stringfellow	Dowling	Parsons	7
Judge	Hunter	Nyamah	Holden	Oxbrow	Pope	Mustafa	Stott	Alford	Scott	Stringfellow	Arnold	Harmon	8
Judge	Hunter	Nyamah	Holden	Oxbrow	Pope	Mustafa	Stott	Alford	Scott	Stringfellow	Harmon	Arnold	9
Judge	Hunter	Nyamah	Holden	Oxbrow	Pope	Mustafa	Stott	Alford	Scott	Stringfellow	Harmon	Arnold	10
Judge	Hunter	Nyamah	Holden	Oxbrow	Pope	Arnold	Stott	Alford	Scott	Stringfellow	Harmon	March	11
Judge	Hunter	Nyamah	Holden	Oxbrow	Pope	Mustafa	Stott	Alford	Scott	Harmon	Arnold	Cox	12
Judge	Hunter	Nyamah	Cox	Oxbrow	Cullip	Mustafa	Stott	Alford	Scott	Pope	Stringfellow	March	13
Judge	Harmon	Nyamah	Cox	Oxbrow	Cullip	Mustafa	Stott	Alford	Scott	Pope	Stringfellow	Norman	14
Judge	Harmon	Nyamah	Norman	Oxbrow	Ibrahim	Stringfellow	Stott	Alford	Scott	Pope	March	Trigg	15
Judge	Harmon	Nyamah	March	Oxbrow	Ibrahim	Stringfellow	Stott	Alford	Scott	Pope	Trigg	Parsons	16
Judge	Harmon	Nyamah	Holden	Oxbrow	Cullip	Stringfellow	Stott	Alford	Scott	Pope	Harmon	McParland	17
Judge	Hunter	Nyamah	Holden	Ibrahim	Pope	Mustafa	Stott	Alford	Scott	Harmon	March	Stringfellow	18
Judge	Hunter	Norman	Holden	Oxbrow	Pope	Mustafa	Harmon	Alford	Scott	Nyamah	Stringfellow	McParland	19
Judge	Hunter	Norman	Holden	Ibrahim	Harmon	Mustafa	Stringfellow	Alford	Scott	Pope	McParland	March	20
Judge	Hunter	Norman	Holden	Rea	Pope	Mustafa	Harmon	Alford	Scott	Trigg	Ibrahim	Stringfellow	21
Judge	Hunter	Norman	Holden	Rea	Pope	Mustafa	Harmon	Alford	Scott	Stringfellow	Parsons	March	22
Judge	Hunter	Norman	Holden	Rea	Harmon	Mustafa	Stott	Alford	Nyamah	Stringfellow	Scott	March	23
Shoemake	Hunter	Nyamah	Rea	Norman	Harmon	Mustafa	March	Alford	Scott	Stringfellow	Edwards	Parsons	24
Judge	Hunter	Brownrigg	Rea	Norman	Harmon	Mustafa	Stott	Alford	Dowling	Stringfellow	Miles	March	25
Shoemake	Edwards	Norman	Brownrigg	Rea	Harmon	Stringfellow	Stott	Alford	Scott	Edwards	King	March	26
Judge	Holden	Norman	Brownrigg	Holden	Nyamah	Mustafa	Stott	Alford	Scott	Edwards	March	Parsons	27
Shoemake	Stringfellow	Norman	Holden	Brown	Pope	Harmon	Gynn	Alford	Haworth	Nyamah	Scott	Stringfellow	28
Shoemake	Rayment	Nyamah	Holden	Norman	Pope	Harmon	Gynn	Alford	Haworth	Scott	March	Millar	29
Judge	Rayment	Nyamah	Holden	Norman	Pope	Harmon	Gynn	Alford	Haworth	Scott	March	Ibrahim	30
Shoemake	Rayment	March	Norman	Ibrahim	Pope	Harmon	Nyamah	Alford	Haworth	Scott	Parsons	Miles	31
Judge	Cox	Nyamah	Brownrigg	Norman	Pope	Harmon	Fowler	Alford	Haworth	Scott	Ibrahim	Rayment	32
Judge	Cox	Harmon	Norman	Ibrahim	Pope	Fowler	Gynn	Alford	Scott	Trigg	March	Haworth	33
Judge	Cox	Harmon	Ibrahim	Norman	Pope	Fowler	Gynn	Alford	Scott	Trigg	March	Haworth	34
Judge	Harmon	Nyamah	Norman	Ibrahim	Cox	Fowler	Gynn	Pope	Scott	Haworth	March	Trigg	35
Shoemake	Rayment	March	Norman	Cox	Harmon	Fowler	Gynn	Nyamah	Pope	Haworth	Birch	Scott	36
Judge	Rayment	Nyamah	Norman	Cox	Harmon	Fowler	Gynn	Alford	Pope	Haworth	March	Scott	37
Judge	Cox	March	Norman	Rayment	Pope	Fowler	Gynn	Alford	Haworth	Nyamah	Scott	Oxbrow	38
Shoemake	Brown	Birch	King	Oxbrow	Miles	Trigg	Samyorke	Dowling	Scott	Thomas	Finn	Shaw	39
Judge	Harmon	March	Norman	Cox	Nyamah	Fowler	Gynn	Alford	Pope	Haworth	Scott	Oxbrow	40
Judge	Harmon	March	Norman	Cox	Nyamah	Fowler	Gynn	Alford	Pope	Haworth	Scott	Oxbrow	41
Judge	Harmon	Norman	Nyamah	Cox	Oxbrow	Fowler	Gynn	Alford	Heffernan	Pope	March	Scott	42
Judge	Harmon	March	Norman	Oxbrow	Nyamah	Mustafa	Gynn	Alford	Fowler	Heffernan	Ibrahim	Thomas	43
Judge	Harmon	March	Shanahan	Ibrahim	Nyamah	Mustafa	Gynn	Alford	Fowler	Heffernan	Scott	Thomas	44
Judge	Harmon	March	Norman	Oxbrow	Nyamah	Mustafa	Gynn	Alford	Fowler	Pope	Scott	Thomas	45
Judge	Harmon	March	Norman	Oxbrow	Pope	Mustafa	Gynn	Jones	Fowler	Thomas	King	Miles	46
Judge	Harmon	March	King	Oxbrow	Mustafa	Pope	Gynn	Scott	Fowler	Thomas	Benjamin	Jones	47
Judge	Harmon	March	Norman	King	Nyamah	Mustafa	Pope	Scott	Fowler	Thomas	Benjamin	Miles	48
Judge	Harmon	March	Norman	Oxbrow	Nyamah	Mustafa	Gynn	Pope	Fowler	Thomas	Scott	Benjamin	49
Shoemake	Thomas	March	Norman	Ibrahim	Nyamah	Mustafa	Benjamin	Scott	Fowler	Pope	King	Miles	50
Shoemake	Thomas	March	Norman	Oxbrow	Ibrahim	Mustafa	Nyamah	Benjamin	Fowler	Pope	Miles	King	51
Shoemake	Scott	March	Pope	Ibrahim	Nyamah	Mustafa	Gynn	Benjamin	Fowler	Thomas	King	Miles	52
Judge	King	March	Shanahan	Ibrahim	Nyamah	Mustafa	Gynn	Benjamin	Fowler	Scott	Dowling	Miles	53
Judge	King	March	Norman	Ibrahim	Nyamah	Mustafa	Pope	Benjamin	Fowler	Scott	Miles	Shanahan	54
Judge	Harmon	March	Norman	Ibrahim	Nyamah	Mustafa	Pope	Benjamin	Fowler	Scott	King	Miles	55

Kettering Town

GARY JOHNSON

Gary was appointed manager of Kettering Town in the summer of 1995, after a spell of scouting for Arsenal.

The ex-Watford midfielder spent three or so years in Sweden, playing in their 2nd Division (the first English player to play in Sweden). He then returned to run a soccer holiday business before joining Cambridge United in 1988 as reserve team manager. Gary then became assistant manager in 1990 when John Beck became manager, and finally took over the reins in May 1993.

During his time with Cambridge they reached the quarter finals of the F.A. Cup twice, won two consecutive promotions and reached the quarter finals of the Coca Cola Cup.

While at Cambridge Gary developed a successful youth policy which he is keen to continue at Kettering.

Recky Carter - Ketterings new striker from Bromsgrove *Photo - Martin Wray*

Programme details:
32 pages for £1.30
Editor:

Any other club publications:
Poppies at the Gates of Dawn (Fanzine)

Local Newspapers:
Evening Telegraph
Chronicle & Echo
Herald & Post
Citizen

Local Radio Stations:
Radio Northampton
Northants 96
KCBC

KETTERING TOWN - PLAYING SQUAD 1996-97

Player	Honours	Birthplace and date	Transfer Fees	Previous Clubs
GOALKEEPERS				
Alan Judge		Kingsbury 14/5/60	£3,000	Luton T, Reading, Oxford U, Hereford U, Bromsgrove R
Kevin Shoemake	SLP, FAXI	Chelmsford 28/1/65		Leyton O, Harlow, Chelmsford, Welling, P'boro U, Kettering T, Rush & D,
DEFENDERS				
Rob Marshall		Sussex		Stamco, Stevenage B, Watford
Kofi Nyamah		Islington 20/6/75		Cambridge U
Paul Miles		Haverhill 18/9/78		From Youth Team
Richard Nugent	GMVC, ILP	Birmingham 20/3/64		Royston, St'nage, Hitchin, Barnet, St.Albans, Barnet, Woking, St'nage, Yeovil
Eddie King		Haverhill 2/12/78		From Youth Team
Craig Gaunt	BLT	Sutton-in-Ashfield 31/3/73	£6,000	Arsenal, Scarborough, Bromsgrove R
Craig Norman		Perivale 21/3/75		Chelsea
Jamie March		Leicester 21/3/76		Leicester C, Friar Lane OB
MIDFIELDERS				
Paul Harding	FAT	Mitcham 6/3/64		Enfield, Barnet, Notts Co, Birmingham C, Cardiff C
Neil Pope		Cambridge 9/10/72	£2,000	Camb U, Peterborough U, Camb C, St.Neots T, Eynesbury R, Camb C
Russell Stock		Yarmouth 25/6/77		Cambridge U
Steve Berry	GMVC	Liverpool 4/4/63		Portsmouth, Sunderland, Swindon T, Northampton T, Instant Dict (HK)
Darren Harmon		Northampton 31/1/73		Northampton T
FORWARDS				
Luke Dowling		Kettering 9/9/78		From Youth Team
Leroy May	ESP	Wolverhampton 12/8/69	£15,000	Tividale, Hereford, Altrincham, Walsall, Stafford R, Kidderminster H
Lawrie Dudfield		Kettering 7/5/80		From Youth Team
Recky Carter	SLM, BLT SpC	Birmingham £20,000		Northfield, Faifield, Kidderminster, Worcester, Malvern, Solihull, Bromsgrove
Tony Lynch	GMVC	Paddington 20/1/66		Maidstone U, Brentford, Wealdstone, Barnet, Stevenage B, Yeovil T
Tarkan Mustapha		London 29/8/73		Clapton, Leyton Wimbledon

Departures during season:
Matt Edwards (Walton & Hersham), Mark Parsons (Hitchin T), Ian Arnold (Stalybridge C), Steve Stott (Rushden & D), Ian Stringfellow (Dag & Red), Junior Hunter (Hendon), Steve Holden (Rushden & D), Rob Haworth (Aylesbury U), Pat Rayment (Raunds T), Carl Alford (Rushden & D), Liam Heffernan (Corby T), Richard Brown (Stalybridge C), Paul Cox (Gresley R), David Jones (VS Rugby), Simon Trigg (Raunds T)
Players on loan during season:
Danny Cullip (Oxford U), Simon Rae (Birmingham C), Andy Brownrigg (Norwich C)
Departures during close season: Micky Gynn (King's Lynn), John Fowler (Camb.C), Ian Scott & Anton Thomas (Worcester C), Darren Oxbrow (Retired), Ian Benjamin (Chlemsford C).

Rockingham Road, Kettering

ADDRESS: Rockingham Road, Kettering, Northants, NN16 9AW.
TELEPHONE NUMBER: 01536 83028/410815 (Office). 01536 410962 (Social Club). **Fax:** 01536 412273.

SIMPLE DIRECTIONS:
M1 junction 15, A43 to Kettering use A14 and Kettering Northern by pass, turn right A6003, ground half a mile. From North M1 or M6 use junction 19 then A14 to Kettering. A1 use A14 at Huntingdon then as above. British Rail - Inter-City Midland - 50mins from London (St.Pancras), 20mins from Leicester.

CAPACITY: 6,100 **SEATED:** 1,800 **COVERED TERRACING:** 2,200

RECORD ATTENDANCE:
11,536 Kettering v Peterborough (pre-Taylor report).

CLUB SHOP:
Open before and after matches, and office staff will open on request on non-match days. Situated in front of main stand. Also Ken Burton's Sports in town centre.

SOCIAL FACILITIES:
Social Club (Poppies), Vice-Presidents Bar & Sponsor's Lounge.

PREVIOUS GROUNDS:
North Park / Green Lane.

Kettering Fact File

Nickname: Poppies

Club Sponsors: Fenner Power Transmission UK.

Previous Leagues: Southern League, Northants League, Midland League, Birmingham League, Central Alliance, United Counties League.

Club colours: Red & white shirts, red socks, red socks.

Change colours: White shirts, navy shorts, white socks.

Midweek home matchday: Tuesday

Record win: 16-0 v Higham YMCI (FA Cup 1909)

Record defeat: 0-13 v Mardy (Southern League Div. 2, 1911/12)

Record transfer fee paid: £25,000 to Macclesfield for Carl Alford, 1994.

Record transfer fee received: £150,000 from Newcastle United for Andy Hunt.

1995-96 Captain: Neil Pope

1995-96 Top scorer: Carl Alford

1995-96 Player of the Year: Darren Harmon

Club record goalscorer: Roy Clayton 171 (1972 - 1981)

Record appearances: Roger Ashby.

Past players who progressed to the Football League: Billy Kellock (Peterborough), Gary Wood (Notts Co.), Dave Longhurst (Nott'm Forest), Scott Endersby (Ipswich), Steve Fallon (Cambridge Utd), Andy Rogers (Plymouth), Martyn Foster (Northampton), Cohen Griffith (Cardiff City), Andy Hunt (Newcastle), Richard Brown (Blackburn Rovers).

Club Honours: Premier Inter League Cup winners; FA Trophy finalists; Alliance Premier League r-up (x3); Southern League Winners, County Cup Winners, Daventry Charity Cup Winners (x2); Northants Senior Cup (x25); Maunsell Cup Winners (x12).

KIDDERMINSTER HARRIERS

Formed:
1886

Chairman:
David L Reynolds

Vice-Chairman
Lionel Newton

Directors
Robert W Goodman
Graham R Lane
J Richard Painter
Colin C Youngjohns

Secretary
Roger Barlow

Manager:
Graham Allner

Asst Manager/Physio:
Jimmy Conway

Commercial Manager:
Mark Searl

It was a disappointing season for Harriers all round. At times it was a season that promised much but with manager Graham Allner unable to invest much during the campaign on bringing in new players due to the finance being injected in ground improvements, Harriers had to rely on much the same squad from the previous season.

Veteran strikers Paul Davies and Kim Casey proved yet again that they could score goals at the top of the non-League Pyramid and newboy Leroy May, when fit, looked a good buy from Stafford Rangers. England star Paul Webb was his usual consistent self whilst Lee Hughes emerged as an England sem-pro player with a good future and Harriers have a crop of promising youngsters coming through, with the likes of Mark Shepherd making it into the first-team ranks.

Allner worked hard during the close season and some quality players such as goalkeeper Fred Barber, defender Steve Prindiville, utility player Marcus Bignot and ex-Villa star Ian Olney have been brought in, thus giving Harriers one of the strongest squads they have ever possessed and another championship challenge looks on the cards. **Steve Whitney**

Kidderminster's Paul Webb, (centre playing the ball); Supporters Player of the Year 95-96

Kidderminster Harriers

Match No.	Date	Comp.	Venue H/A	Opponents	Result	League Pos.	Goalscorers (Times if known)	Attendance
1	Aug 19	GMVC	A	Farnborough Town	Lost 1-3	19	May	840
2	21	GMVC	H	Hednesford Town	Won 3-1	12	Casey, May, P Davies	1681
3	26	GMVC	H	Morecambe	Won 4-2	5	Deakin, Casey, P Davies 2	1702
4	28	GMVC	A	Slough Town	Lost 4-5	8	Yates 2, Casey, May	1092
5	Sep 2	GMVC	A	Altrincham	Drew 1-1	9	Deakin	881
6	4	GMVC	H	Kettering Town	Won 1-0	5	P Davies	1949
7	9	GMVC	H	Stalybridge Celtic	Won 3-0	1	Casey, May, P Davies	1962
8	12	GMVC	A	Macclesfield Town	Won 2-0	2	Hughes, Cartwright	1202
9	16	GMVC	A	Halifax Town	Won 2-0	2	Casey, May	1008
10	18	SCC1	H	Hednesford Town	Won 4-1		Brindley, Casey 2, May	1326
11	23	GMVC	H	Woking	Won 2-0	1	Casey, P Davies	2716
12	30	GMVC	A	Southport	Won 2-0	1	P Davies 2	1164
13	Oct 2	SCC1	A	Hednesford Town	Lost 0-2			1626
14	7	GMVC	H	Dover Athletic	Drew 1-1	1	Yates	2259
15	9	GMVC	H	Telford United	Won 2-0	1	May, P Davies	2433
16	14	GMVC	A	Northwich Victoria	Lost 2-5	1	Deakin, 1og	1106
17	21	GMVC	H	Altrincham	Drew 1-1	1	P Davies	2429
18	28	GMVC	A	Dagenham & Redbridge	Lost 2-4	2	Yates 2	756
19	Nov 4	GMVC	A	Dover Athletic	Lost 1-2	3	Yates	1124
20	11	FAC1	H	Sutton United	Drew 2-2		Webb, Hughes	2513
21	18	GMVC	H	Runcorn	Won 4-1	3	May 2, P Davies, Hughes	1879
22	21	FAC1R	A	Sutton United	Drew 1-1		Casey, lost on penalties	1804
23	25	GMVC	A	Woking	Drew 0-0	3		2264
24	28	SCC2	A	Macclesfield Town	Lost 1-4		Hughes	566
25	Dec 2	GMVC	H	Bath City	Lost 1-2	4	Casey	1833
26	9	GMVC	H	Southport	Lost 2-3	5	Webb, Casey	1664
27	16	GMVC	A	Hednesford Town	Won 3-1	5	May, P Davies, Dearlove	1392
28	18	WSC2	H	Dudley Town	Won 2-1		Dearlove, Shepherd	370
29	26	GMVC	A	Bromsgrove Rovers	Lost 1-2	5	May	4398
30	Jan 1	GMVC	H	Bromsgrove Rovers	Won 1-0	4	Yates	4481
31	6	GMVC	A	Stalybridge Celtic	Drew 2-2	5	Shepherd 2	605
32	13	GMVC	H	Macclesfield Town	Lost 0-4	6		2703
33	20	FAT1	H	Gateshead	Drew 0-0			1319
34	24	FAT1R	A	Gateshead	Lost 0-2			383
35	Feb 3	GMVC	H	Dagenham & Redbridge	Won 5-1	5	Willetts, Casey, Hughes 3	1439
36	10	GMVC	A	Runcorn	Won 1-0	5	Brindley	475
37	17	GMVC	A	Welling United	Drew 0-0	5		556
38	20	GMVC	A	Telford United	Drew 1-1	5	Hughes	918
39	24	GMVC	H	Slough Town	Won 4-3	3	Casey 2, P Davies, Hughes	1715
40	Mar 2	WSCSF	H	Stourbridge	Lost 1-2		P Davies	750
41	9	GMVC	H	Welling United	Won 3-0	4	Yates, Hughes, May	1685
42	16	GMVC	A	Stevenage Borough	Lost 1-4	5	Casey	2012
43	18	GMVC	H	Halifax Town	Won 6-1	4	Brindley, Casey 2, May, P Davies, Hughes	1168
44	23	GMVC	A	Kettering Town	Lost 0-2	5		1376
45	30	GMVC	H	Northwich Victoria	Won 2-1	5	Cartwright, Dearlove	1604
46	Apr 8	GMVC	A	Gateshead	Lost 1-4	5	Shepherd	687
47	16	GMVC	A	Bath City	Drew 1-1	5	Shepherd	412
48	20	GMVC	H	Gateshead	Drew 1-1	5	Hughes	1509
49	22	GMVC	H	Stevenage Borough	Lost 0-1	5		2060
50	27	GMVC	H	Farnborough Town	Drew 3-3	7	Willetts, Deakin, Hughes	1559
51	May 4	GMVC	A	Morecambe	Lost 1-3	7	May	1213

Kidderminster Harriers

1	2	3	4	5	6	7	8	9	10	11	12	14	Match No.
Rose	Hodson	Bancroft	Webb	Brindley	Yates	Deakin	Casey	May	P Davies	Eades	Powell	Dearlove	1
Rose	Hodson	Bancroft	Webb	Brindley	Yates	Deakin	Casey	May	P Davies	Cartwright	Eades	Dearlove	2
Rose	Hodson	Bancroft	Webb	Brindley	Yates	Deakin	Casey	May	P Davies	Cartwright	Eades	Dearlove	3
Rose	Hodson	Bancroft	Webb	Brindley	Yates	Deakin	Casey	May	P Davies	Cartwright	Eades	Dearlove	4
Steadman	Hodson	Bancroft	Webb	Brindley	Yates	Deakin	Casey	May	P Davies	Hughes	Eades	Dearlove	5
Steadman	Hodson	Bancroft	Webb	Brindley	Yates	Deakin	Casey	May	P Davies	Hughes	Eades	Dearlove	6
Steadman	Hodson	Bancroft	Webb	Brindley	Yates	Hughes	Casey	May	P Davies	Cartwright	Eades	Dearlove	7
Steadman	Hodson	Bancroft	Webb	Brindley	Yates	Hughes	Casey	May	P Davies	Cartwright	Eades	Dearlove	8
Steadman	Hodson	Bancroft	Webb	Brindley	Yates	Hughes	Casey	May	P Davies	Cartwright	Eades	Dearlove	9
Steadman	Hodson	Bancroft	Webb	Brindley	Yates	Hughes	Casey	May	P Davies	Cartwright	Eades	Dearlove	10
Steadman	Hodson	Bancroft	Webb	Brindley	Yates	Hughes	Casey	May	P Davies	Cartwright	Powell	Weir	11
Steadman	Hodson	Bancroft	Webb	Brindley	Yates	Hughes	Casey	May	P Davies	Cartwright	Eades	Powell	12
Steadman	Hodson	Bancroft	Webb	Brindley	Yates	Hughes	Shepherd	May	P Davies	Eades	Weir	Deakin	13
Steadman	Hodson	Webb	Weir	Brindley	Yates	Deakin	Casey	May	P Davies	Cartwright	Hughes	Eades	14
Steadman	Hodson	Webb	Weir	Brindley	Yates	Deakin	Casey	May	P Davies	Willetts	Cartwright	Hughes	15
Steadman	Hodson	Webb	Weir	Brindley	Yates	Deakin	Casey	May	P Davies	Willetts	Cartwright	Hughes	16
Steadman	Hodson	Webb	Weir	Brindley	Yates	Deakin	Casey	May	P Davies	Willetts	Eades	Shepherd	17
Steadman	Hodson	Webb	Weir	Brindley	Yates	Deakin	Casey	Hughes	P Davies	Willetts	Cartwright	Shepherd	18
Steadman	Hodson	Bancroft	Weir	Brindley	Yates	Hughes	Webb	May	P Davies	Cartwright	Eades	Dearlove	19
Steadman	Hodson	Bancroft	Weir	Brindley	Yates	Shepherd	Webb	May	P Davies	Hughes	Eades	Dearlove	20
Steadman	Hodson	Bancroft	Weir	Brindley	Yates	Shepherd	Webb	May	P Davies	Hughes	Dearlove	Casey	21
Steadman	Hodson	Bancroft	Weir	Brindley	Yates	Webb	Casey	May	P Davies	Hughes	Dearlove	Shepherd	22
Steadman	Hodson	Bancroft	Weir	Brindley	Yates	Webb	Casey	Dearlove	Willetts	Hughes	Cartwright	Deakin	23
Steadman	Cartwright	Willetts	Weir	Deakin	Yates	Webb	Casey	Dearlove	Shepherd	Hughes	Eades	P Davies	24
Steadman	Hodson	Bancroft	Webb	Brindley	Yates	Hughes	Casey	Shepherd	P Davies	Willetts	Dearlove	Eades	25
Steadman	Hodson	Bancroft	Weir	Brindley	Willetts	Webb	Casey	May	P Davies	Hughes	Dearlove	Shepherd	26
Steadman	Hodson	Bancroft	Webb	Brindley	Willetts	Robinson	Casey	May	P Davies	Hughes	Dearlove	Shepherd	27
Rose	Hodson	Willetts	Webb	Brindley	Dearlove	Robinson	Casey	May	P Davies	Hughes	Riley	Shepherd	28
Steadman	Hodson	Willetts	Webb	Brindley	Yates	Robinson	Casey	May	P Davies	Hughes	Bancroft	Deakin	29
Steadman	Hodson	Bancroft	Weir	Brindley	Yates	Robinson	Casey	May	P Davies	Hughes	Willetts	Deakin	30
Steadman	Hodson	Bancroft	Weir	Brindley	Yates	Robinson	Casey	Shepherd	P Davies	Hughes	Willetts	Deakin	31
Steadman	Hodson	Bancroft	Webb	Brindley	Yates	Deakin	Casey	Shepherd	P Davies	Robinson	Willetts	May	32
Steadman	Hodson	Bancroft	Weir	Brindley	Yates	Deakin	Casey	May	P Davies	Hughes	Willetts	Dearlove	33
Steadman	Hodson	Willetts	Dearlove	Brindley	Yates	Deakin	Casey	May	P Davies	Hughes	Weir	Bancroft	34
Steadman	Hodson	Willetts	Weir	Dearlove	Yates	Deakin	Casey	Cartwright	P Davies	Hughes	Bancroft	Shepherd	35
Steadman	Hodson	Willetts	Weir	Brindley	Yates	Deakin	Casey	Cartwright	P Davies	Hughes	Bancroft	Shepherd	36
Steadman	Hodson	Willetts	Weir	Brindley	Yates	Deakin	Dearlove	Cartwright	P Davies	Hughes	Shepherd	Casey	37
Steadman	Hodson	Willetts	Weir	Brindley	Yates	Deakin	Casey	Cartwright	P Davies	Hughes	Shepherd	Webb	38
Steadman	Hodson	Willetts	Weir	Brindley	Yates	Deakin	Casey	Webb	P Davies	Hughes	Dearlove	Shepherd	39
Rose	Hodson	Powell	Dearlove	Brindley	Yates	Deakin	Casey	Webb	P Davies	Hughes	Cartwright	Shepherd	40
Steadman	Hodson	Willetts	Weir	Brindley	Yates	Deakin	Casey	Webb	P Davies	Hughes	Cartwright	Shepherd	41
Steadman	Hodson	Willetts	Weir	Brindley	Yates	Cartwright	Casey	May	P Davies	Hughes	Dearlove	Shepherd	42
Steadman	Hodson	Willetts	Dearlove	Brindley	Yates	Cartwright	Casey	May	P Davies	Hughes	Purdie	Shepherd	43
Steadman	Hodson	Willetts	Dearlove	Brindley	Yates	Cartwright	Casey	May	P Davies	Hughes	Deakin	Shepherd	44
Steadman	Cartwright	Willetts	Dearlove	Brindley	Yates	Deakin	Casey	May	P Davies	Webb	Daniel	Shepherd	45
Steadman	Cartwright	Willetts	Dearlove	Brindley	Yates	Deakin	Casey	Webb	P Davies	Hughes	Hodson	Shepherd	46
Steadman	Hodson	Willetts	Webb	Brindley	Yates	Deakin	Cartwright	Shepherd	P Davies	Hughes	Dearlove	Casey	47
Steadman	Hodson	Willetts	Webb	Brindley	Yates	Deakin	Cartwright	May	Shepherd	Hughes	Dearlove	P Davies	48
Steadman	Hodson	Willetts	Webb	Brindley	Yates	Deakin	Casey	May	Shepherd	Hughes	Dearlove	P Davies	49
Steadman	Hodson	Willetts	Dearlove	Webb	Yates	Deakin	Casey	May	Shepherd	Hughes	Powell	P Davies	50
Steadman	Hodson	Willetts	Webb	Dearlove	Yates	Deakin	Cartwright	May	P Davies	Hughes	Powell	Casey	51

Kidderminster Harriers

GRAHAM ALLNER

Graham Allner joined Kidderminster Harriers as manager in October 1983. Formerly assistant manager at Cheltenham Town, he had won the Southern League championship when manager of the now defunct AP Leamington.

Graham's playing days began at Walsall where he gained England Youth honours. He then moved into non-League football where he played at Worcester City, Stafford Rangers and Alvechurch.

1993-94 was, without doubt, Graham's most successful as a manager, steering Kidderminster to the GM Vauxhall Conference championship and through to the last sixteen of the FA Cup.

During his time at Aggborough, Graham has encouraged youth through their YT programme and many of his young players have come through to the first team.

Harriers Lee Hughes shields the ball from Morecambe's Paul West. *Photo - Alan Watson*

Programme details:
40 pages for £1.30.
Editor - Mark Searl

Any other club publications:

Local Newspapers:
Kidderminster Shuttle/Times
Kidderminster Chronicle
Evening Mail, Express & Star
Worcester Evening News

Local Radio Stations:
BBC Hereford & Worcester
Radio Wyvern
Beacon Radio, BRMB

KIDDERMINSTER HARRIERS - PLAYING SQUAD 1996-97

Player	Honours	Birthplace and date	Transfer Fees	Previous Clubs
GOALKEEPERS				
Kevin Rose	GMVC	Evesham 23/11/60		Ledbury T, Lincoln C, Ledbury T, Hereford, Bolton W, Rochdale
Fred Barber	FLXI	Ferryhill 26/8/63		Darlington, Everton, Walsall, Peterborough, Luton T, Birmingham C
DEFENDERS				
Kevin Willetts	FAXI, Middx Wanderer	Gloucester 15/8/62		Sharpness, Cheltenham T, Forest Green R, Gloucester C, Weston-Super-Mare
Chris Brindley	GMVC, FAT, FAXI	Stoke 5/7/69	£20,000	Hednesford T, Wolves, Telford United
Steve Prindiville		Harlow 26/12/68		Leicester C, Chesterfield, Mansfield, Doncaster, Wycombe, Halifax, Dag & Red
Simeon Hodson	ESP, GMVC	Lincoln 5/3/66		Notts Co, Charlton, Lincoln, Newport Co, WBA, Doncaster, Kidderminster, Mansfield
Martin Weir	GMVC, FAXI, Middx Wand.	Birmingham 4/7/68		Birmingham City
MIDFIELDERS				
Neil Cartwright	GMVC	Stourbridge 20/2/71		West Bromwich Albion
John Deakin	GMVC	Sheffield 29/9/66		Barnsley, Doncaster, Grimsby, Frickley A, Shepshed, Birmingham, Carlisle, Wycombe
Marcus Bignot		Birmingham 28/8/74	£10,000	Birmingham C, Telford U
Mark Yates		Birmingham 24/1/70		Birmingham C, Burnley, Doncaster R
FORWARDS				
Paul Davies	ESP, GMVC, FAT, FAXI	Kidderminster 9/10/60		Cardiff C, Trowbridge T, SC Hercules (Holl)
Kim Casey	ESP, FAT, GMVC	Birmingham 3/3/61		Sutton C, Leamington, Gloucester, K'minster, Cheltenham, Wycombe, Solihull
Lee Hughes	ESP	Birmingham 22/5/76		From Youth Team
James McCue		Glasgow 29/6/75	£5,000	WBA, Partick Thistle
Ian Olney	E u-21	Luton 17/12/69		Aston Villa, Oldham Ath
Neil Doherty	FAT, NPL FAXI	Barrow 21/2/69		Watford, Barrow, Birmingham C

Departures during season:
Gary Eades (Retired), Paul Bancroft (Shephed Dynamo), Jay Powell (Bridgnorth T - Loan), Jon Purdie (Telford U), Delwyn Humphreys (Northwich V).
Players on loan during season:
Steve Robinson (Birmingham C).
Departures during close season: Paul Grainger (Stafford R), Jay Powell (Bridgnorth T).

Aggborough, Kidderminster Harriers

ADDRESS: Aggborough Staduim, Hoo Road, Kidderminster, DY10 1NB.

TELEPHONE NUMBER: 01562 823931 (Ground). 01562 823931 (Social Club). **Fax:** 01562 827329.

SIMPLE DIRECTIONS:
From North - exit M5 at junction 3, follow A456 to Kidderminster and on reaching the town at first traffic lights turn left into Chester Road. At next traffic lights turn right into Comberton Road, continue past station and Hoo Road is on the left halfway down the hill. From the South & West - exit M5 at junction 6. Follow A449 to Kidderminster. At first roundabout (Adjacent to railway viaduct) turn right into Chester Road and first left into Hoo Road. From London direction via M42 then follow M5 north to junction 4 (Lydiate Ash). Exit motorway turn left and follow A491 towards Stourbridge. At Hagley roundabout turn left and follow A456 to Kidderminster as above.

CAPACITY: 6,290 **SEATED:** 1,100 **COVERED TERRACING:** 4,690

RECORD ATTENDANCE:
9,155 - Hereford United - FA Cup 1st Round Proper 27.11.48.

CLUB SHOP:
Open Monday to Friday 9am-5pm, plus 1st XI match days.

SOCIAL FACILITIES:
Executive Club and Vice Presidents lounge bar for members, officials & players. Social & supporters club (3 bars) open to visiting supporters before & after the match, temporary admission fee 50p. Hot & cold food available.

Kidderminster Fact File

Nickname: Harriers

Previous Grounds: None

Previous Leagues: Birmingham League 1889-1890, 1891-1939, 1947-1948, 1960-1962, Midland League 1890-1891, Southern League 1939-1945 (Abandoned - World War II), 1948-1960, 1972-1983, Birmingham Combination 1945-1947, West Midlands League 1962-1972.

Club colours: Red & white

Change colours: Yellow & blue

Reserve team league: Midland Combination Reserve Division

Midweek home matchday: Mondays 7.45pm.

Record win: 25-0 v Hereford (H) - 12.10.1889 - Birmingham Senior Cup 1st Rnd.

Record defeat: 0-13 v Darwen (A) - 24.01.1891 - FA Cup 1st Rnd Proper.

Record transfer fee: £20,000 for Chris Brindley from Telford - 1992

Record transfer fee received: £60,000 each for Paul Jones from Wolves - 1991 & Steve Lilwall from W.B.A - 1992.

1995-96 Captain: Simeon Hodson

1995-96 Top scorer: Kim Casey

1995-96 Player of the Year: Paul Webb

Club record goalscorer: Peter Wassall 432 - 1963-1974

Record appearances: Brendan Wassall 686 - 1962-1974

Past players who progressed to the Football League: Too numerous to list.

Club Honours: GMV Conference Champions 1994; FA Trophy Winners 1987, Runners-up 1991, 1995; Welsh FA Cup finalists 1986, 1989; Southern League Cup 1980; Worcester Senior Cup (19); Birmingham Senior Cup (7); Staffordshire Senior Cup (4); West Midland League Champions (6), Runners-up (3); Southern Premier Runners-up (1); West Midland League Cup winners (7); Keys Cup winners (7); Border Counties Floodlit League Champions (3), Camkin Floodlit Cup Winners (3); Bass County Vase Winners (1); Conference Fair Play Trophy (3).

MACCLESFIELD TOWN

Formed: 1874

Chairman:
A Jones

Football Secretary:
Colin Garlick

Directors:
R Higginbotham
J Brooks
A Masheder
B Lingard
R Curran
A Cash

Manager:
Sammy McIlroy
Assistant Manager:
Gil Prescot

Physiotherapist:
Eric Campbell

Press Officer:
Colin Garlick

Although disappointed to lose their championship crown to Stevenage Borough, Macclesfield still enjoyed a very successful season. For the majority of the campaign the Silkmen led a determined defence of their title but, in the end they had to be satisfied with fourth place. Perhaps cup games had an influence on league performances. However, winning the FA Umbro Trophy for the second time in their history will have been a great consolation, although they did lose out to Bromsgrove Rovers in the Spalding Cup final.

Manager Sammy McIlroy, who rejected overtures for his services from League clubs to stay at Moss Rose, built on his title-winning squad and certainly winger Tony Hemmings, defenders Darren Tinson and Mark Gardiner and England goalkeeper Ryan Price added substantially to the strength in depth. During the close season further signings have been made

Back Row (L-R) C Edey, D Norman, M Gardiner, D Tinson, K Hulme, S Payne, S Hutchinson. Middle; D Lyons, S Tobin, M Beadshaw, R Price, N Sorvel, S Burr, M Coates. Front Row; G Prescott (Asst Mgr), T Hemmings, P Power, S McIlroy (Mgr), N Howarth, P Cavell, E Campbell (Physio).

Macclesfield Town

Match No.	Date	Comp.	Venue H/A	Opponents	Result	League Pos.	Goalscorers (Times if known)	Attendance
1	Aug 19	GMVC		Woking	Won 3-2	9	Lyons, Coates, Marginson	1370
2	22	GMVC		Halifax Town	Lost 0-1	13		1169
3	26	GMVC		Gateshead	Won 1-0	10	Power	650
4	28	GMVC		Dagenham & Redbridge	Won 3-1	2	Bradshaw 2, McDonald p	1172
5	Sep 2	GMVC		Bath City	Lost 0-1	7		1225
6	5	GMVC		Morecambe	Won 4-2	4	Lyons, Cavell 2, Power	1413
7	9	GMVC		Kettering Town	Drew 1-1	3	Cavell	1322
8	12	GMVC		Kidderminster Harriers	Lost 0-2	6		1202
9	16	GMVC		Dover Athletic	Won 3-2	5	Cavell 2, Power	822
10	19	CH SH		Woking	Won 3-2	5	Lyons, Coates 2	636
11	23	GMVC		Southport	Won 3-1	4	Sorvel, Cavell, Power	1282
12	26	SSC1		Pelsall V	Drew 1-1	4	Coates	228
13	30	GMVC		Farnborough Town	Lost 1-6	6	Coates	740
14	Oct 3	SSC1R		Pelsall V	Won 1-0	6	Coates	152
15	7	GMVC		Bromsgrove Rovers	Won 2-1	5	Lyons, Cavell	1137
16	10	GMVC		Morecambe	Won 2-0	2	Sorvel, Coates	1034
17	14	GMVC		Slough Town	Drew 2-2	2	Howarth, Cavell	1007
18	21	FAC4Q		Northwich Victoria	Lost 0-1	3		1707
19	24	GMVC		Runcorn	Drew 0-0	3		600
20	28	GMVC		Welling United	Won 2-1	3	Bradshaw, Coates	988
21	31	GMVC		Stalybridge Celtic	Won 2-1	1	Sorvel, Cavell	884
22	Nov 4	GMVC		Hednesford Town	Won 1-0	1	Coates	2019
23	11	GMVC		Stalybridge Celtic	Won 1-0	1	Lyons p	1457
24	18	GMVC		Altrincham	Won 4-0	1	Lyons 2, Coates 2	1648
25	21	CSC2		Vauxhall GM	Won 4-0	1	Sorvel, Lyons 2-1p, Coates	161
26	25	GMVC		Farnborough Town	Won 1-0	1	Sorvel	1721
27	28	SCC2		Kidderminster Harriers	Won 4-1	1	Lyons p, Cavell, Coates 2	566
28	Dec 2	GMVC		Stevenage Borough	Lost 0-4	1		2021
29	5	SSC2		Boldmere St M	Won 5-2	1	Payne, Lyons, Gardiner, Hutchinson 2	124
30	16	GMVC		Gateshead	Won 1-0	1	Howarth	1161
31	Jan 6	GMVC		Stevenage Borough	Drew 0-0	1		2126
32	9	SSC3		Bilston Town	Lost 1-2	1	Power	298
33	13	GMVC		Kidderminster Harriers	Won 4-0	1	Gardiner, Power 3	2703
34	20	FAT1		Runcorn	Won 1-0	1	Power	1401
35	30	GMVC		Altrincham	Lost 2-3	1	Power, Hemmings	1301
36	Feb 10	FAT2		Purfleet	Won 2-1	1	Bradshaw, Payne	1003
37	13	GMVC		Telford United	Won 1-0	1	Lyons	866
38	17	GMVC		Bromsgrove Rovers	Lost 0-1	2		1481
39	24	GMVC		Runcorn	Won 1-0	2	Hutchinson	1410
40	26	CSC SF1		Hyde United	Lost 1-2	2	Lyons p	716
41	Mar 2	FAT3		Sudbury Town	Won 1-0	2	Coates	1140
42	5	SCC3		Morecambe	Won 4-1	2	Payne, Hulme 2, Hemmings	625
43	9	GMVC		Halifax Town	Won 7-0	2	Payne, Hulme 2, Power 2, Hemmings, Lyons p	1348
44	12	CSCSF2		Hyde United	Drew 1-1	3	Hemmings	707
45	16	GMVC		Kettering Town	Drew 2-2	3	Wood, Power	1433
46	19	SCCSF1		Southport	Drew 4-4	3	Sorvel, Power, Hemmings, og	561
47	23	FAT4		Gresley R	Won 2-0	4	Bradshaw, Power	1727
48	26	GMVC		Northwich Victoria	Drew 0-0	4		1117
49	30	GMVC		Telford United	Won 2-1	4	Coates 2	1015
50	Apr 3	SCCSF2		Southport	Won 2-1	4	Coates, Power	510
51	6	GMVC		Woking	Lost 2-3	4	Power 2	4583
52	8	GMVC		Dover Athletic	Lost 0-1	4		1482
53	13	FATSF1		Chorley	Won 3-1	4	Coates, Power, og	2260
54	16	GMVC		Northwich Victoria	Won 2-1	4	Tinson, Wood	936
55	20	FATSF2		Chorley	Drew 1-1	4	Sorvel	3048
56	22	GMVC		Southport	Lost 1-2	4	Lyons	736
57	24	SCC F		Bromsgrove Rovers	Drew 1-1	4	Coates	547
58	27	GMVC		Dagenham & Redbridge	Lost 0-3	4		660
59	28	GMVC		Welling United	Won 2-1	4	Hulme, Wood	558
60	30	GMVC		Bath City	Drew 1-1	4	Hulme	361
61	May 2	GMVC		Slough Town	Drew 1-1	4	Coates	591
62	4	GMVC		Hednesford Town	Drew 1-1	4	Coates	1236
63	6	SCC F2		Bromsgrove Rovers	Lost 1-3	4	Sorvel p	1341
64	19	FAT F		Northwich Victoria	Won 3-1	4	Payne, Hemmings, og	8672

Macclesfield Town

1	2	3	4	5	6	7	8	9	10	11	12	14	Match No.
Williams	Locke	Bradshaw	Payne	Howarth	Sorvel	Lyons	McDonald	Coates	Power	Marginson	Tobin	Cavell	1
Williams	Locke	Bradshaw	Payne	Howarth	Sorvel	Lyons	McDonald	Coates	Power	Marginson	Tobin	Cavell	2
Williams	Locke	Bradshaw	Payne	Howarth	Sorvel	Lyons	McDonald	Cavell	Power	Marginson	Tobin	Coates	3
Williams	German	Bradshaw	Payne	Howarth	Sorvel	Lyons	McDonald	Cavell	Power	Marginson	Locke	Coates	4
Williams	German	Bradshaw	Middlemass	Howarth	Sorvel	Lyons	McDonald	Cavell	Power	Marginson	Locke	Coates	5
Williams	German	Bradshaw	Payne	Middlemass	Sorvel	Lyons	McDonald	Cavell	Power	Marginson	Locke	Coates	6
Williams	German	Bradshaw	Payne	Howarth	Sorvel	Lyons	McDonald	Cavell	Power	Marginson	Evans	Coates	7
Williams	German	Bradshaw	Payne	Howarth	Sorvel	Lyons	McDonald	Cavell	Coates	Clark	Marginson	Tobin	8
Williams	German	Bradshaw	Payne	Howarth	Sorvel	Lyons	McDonald	Cavell	Power	Marginson	Evans	Coates	9
Williams	Middlemass	Bradshaw	Payne	Howarth	Sorvel	Lyons	McDonald	Cavell	Power	Marginson	Locke	Coates	10
Williams	Locke	Bradshaw	Payne	Howarth	Sorvel	Lyons	McDonald	Cavell	Power	Clark	Marginson	Coates	11
Williams	Locke	Bradshaw	Payne	Middlemass	Clark	Lyons	McDonald	Cavell	Coates	Marginson	Sorvel	Howarth	12
Williams	Locke	Bradshaw	Payne	Howarth	Sorvel	Lyons	Clark	Cavell	Coates	Tobin	German	Marginson	13
Williams	German	Locke	Payne	Howarth	Sorvel	Lyons	McDonald	Cavell	Coates	Marginson	Bradshaw	Tobin	14
Morgan	German	Locke	Payne	Howarth	Sorvel	Lyons	McDonald	Cavell	Coates	Marginson	Bradshaw	Tobin	15
Morgan	German	Locke	Payne	Howarth	Sorvel	Lyons	McDonald	Cavell	Coates	Marginson	Bradshaw	Tobin	16
Morgan	German	Locke	Payne	Howarth	Sorvel	Lyons	McDonald	Cavell	Coates	Marginson	Edey	Monk	17
Williams	Edey	Locke	Payne	Howarth	Sorvel	Lyons	McDonald	Cavell	Coates	Marginson	Monk	German	18
Morgan	German	Bradshaw	Payne	Howarth	Edey	Lyons	Gardiner	Cavell	Coates	Sorvel	Monk	Locke	19
Morgan	German	Bradshaw	Payne	Howarth	Edey	Lyons	Gardiner	Cavell	Coates	Sorvel	Monk	Locke	20
Morgan	Edey	Bradshaw	Payne	Howarth	Sorvel	Lyons	Gardiner	Cavell	Coates	Hemmings	Monk	Locke	21
Price	Edey	Bradshaw	Payne	Howarth	Sorvel	Lyons	Gardiner	Cavell	Coates	Hemmings	Marginson	Locke	22
Price	Edey	Bradshaw	Payne	Howarth	Sorvel	Lyons	Gardiner	Cavell	Coates	Hemmings	Locke	Clark	23
Price	Edey	Bradshaw	Payne	Howarth	Sorvel	Lyons	Gardiner	Cavell	Coates	Hemmings	Locke	Marginson	24
Price	Locke	Bradshaw	Edey	Howarth	Sorvel	Lyons	Gardiner	Hutchinson	Coates	Marginson	German	Brown	25
Price	Edey	Bradshaw	Payne	Howarth	Sorvel	Lyons	Gardiner	Cavell	Coates	Hemmings	Locke	Marginson	26
Price	Edey	Bradshaw	Payne	Howarth	Sorvel	Lyons	Gardiner	Cavell	Coates	Hemmings	Hutchinson	German	27
Price	Edey	Bradshaw	Payne	Howarth	Sorvel	Lyons	Gardiner	Cavell	Coates	Hemmings	Hutchinson	German	28
Price	Edey	Bradshaw	Payne	Howarth	Sorvel	Lyons	Gardiner	Cavell	Hutchinson	Clark	Locke	German	29
Price	Edey	Bradshaw	Payne	Howarth	Sorvel	Lyons	Gardiner	Coates	Power	Hemmings	Locke	Cavell	30
Price	Edey	Bradshaw	Payne	Howarth	Sorvel	Hutchinson	Gardiner	Hulme	Power	Hemmings	Locke	Lyons	31
Price	Edey	Bradshaw	Payne	Howarth	Sorvel	Hutchinson	Gardiner	Cavell	Power	Hemmings	Locke	Lyons	32
Price	Edey	Bradshaw	Payne	Howarth	Sorvel	Lyons	Gardiner	Hulme	Power	Hemmings	Locke	Hutchinson	33
Price	Edey	Bradshaw	Payne	Howarth	Sorvel	Lyons	Gardiner	Hulme	Power	Hemmings	Locke	Hutchinson	34
Price	Edey	Bradshaw	Payne	Howarth	Sorvel	Lyons	Gardiner	Hulme	Power	Hemmings	Locke	Hutchinson	35
Price	Locke	Bradshaw	Payne	Edey	Sorvel	Lyons	Gardiner	Hulme	Power	Hemmings	Coates	Hutchinson	36
Morgan	Locke	Bradshaw	Payne	Edey	Sorvel	Lyons	Wood	Hulme	Power	Hemmings	Gardiner	Hutchinson	37
Morgan	Tinson	Bradshaw	Payne	Howarth	Sorvel	Lyons	Wood	Hulme	Power	Hemmings	Edey	Hutchinson	38
Morgan	Tinson	Bradshaw	Payne	Howarth	Sorvel	Hutchinson	Wood	Coates	Power	Hemmings	Lyons	Gardiner	39
Morgan	Edey	Bradshaw	Payne	Howarth	Gardiner	Hutchinson	Wood	Coates	Hulme	Hemmings	Sorvel	Lyons	40
Price	Edey	Bradshaw	Payne	Howarth	Sorvel	Hutchinson	Wood	Coates	Power	Hemmings	Cavell	Gardiner	41
Price	Edey	Bradshaw	Payne	Howarth	Sorvel	Wood	Hulme	Coates	Power	Hemmings	Cavell	Gardiner	42
Price	Tinson	Bradshaw	Payne	Howarth	Sorvel	Wood	Hulme	Coates	Power	Hemmings	Edey	Lyons	43
Price	Edey	Bradshaw	Payne	Howarth	Sorvel	Lyons	Gardiner	Cavell	Power	Hemmings	Wood	Hutchinson	44
Price	Tinson	Bradshaw	Payne	Howarth	Sorvel	Wood	Hulme	Coates	Power	Hemmings	Norman	Hutchinson	45
Price	Norman	Bradshaw	Payne	Edey	Sorvel	Wood	Gardiner	Cavell	Power	Hemmings	Lyons	Hutchinson	46
Price	Edey	Bradshaw	Payne	Howarth	Sorvel	Wood	Hulme	Coates	Power	Hemmings	Cavell	Hutchinson	47
Price	Tinson	Bradshaw	Payne	Howarth	Sorvel	Wood	Hulme	Coates	Power	Hemmings	Edey	Hutchinson	48
Price	Tinson	Gardiner	Edey	Howarth	Sorvel	Wood	Hutchinson	Coates	Cavell	Hemmings	Lyons	Norman	49
Price	Edey	Gardiner	Payne	Howarth	Sorvel	Wood	Hulme	Coates	Power	Hemmings	Cavell	Lyons	50
Price	Tinson	Gardiner	Payne	Howarth	Sorvel	Wood	Hulme	Coates	Power	Hemmings	Lyons	Edey	51
Price	Edey	Gardiner	Payne	Tinson	Sorvel	Wood	Hulme	Coates	Power	Hemmings	Lyons	Cavell	52
Price	Edey	Gardiner	Payne	Howarth	Sorvel	Lyons	Hulme	Coates	Power	Hemmings	Cavell	Wood	53
Price	Edey	Gardiner	Tinson	Howarth	Sorvel	Lyons	Hulme	Wood	Cavell	Hemmings	Burr	Hutchinson	54
Price	Edey	Gardiner	Payne	Howarth	Sorvel	Wood	Hulme	Coates	Power	Hemmings	Lyons	Hutchinson	55
Price	Tinson	Edey	Payne	Howarth	Sorvel	Lyons	Wood	Cavell	Burr	Hemmings	Norman	Tobin	56
Price	Edey	Gardiner	Payne	Howarth	Sorvel	Lyons	Wood	Cavell	Coates	Hemmings	Norman	Tobin	57
Price	Edey	Gardiner	Payne	Tinson	Sorvel	Hutchinson	Hulme	Coates	Cavell	Hemmings	Burr	Wood	58
Price	Tinson	Gardiner	Payne	Howarth	Sorvel	Lyons	Hulme	Wood	Burr	Hemmings	Norman	Tobin	59
Price	Edey	Gardiner	Payne	Howarth	Sorvel	Tinson	Hulme	Cavell	Burr	Hemmings	Norman	Coates	60
Price	Edey	Gardiner	Tinson	Howarth	Sorvel	Lyons	Hulme	Coates	Wood	Hemmings	Cavell	Tobin	61
Price	Tinson	Bradshaw	Payne	Howarth	Sorvel	Lyons	Hulme	Coates	Wood	Hemmings	Cavell	Tobin	62
Price	Norman	Bradshaw	Payne	Edey	Sorvel	Gardiner	Hulme	Coates	Wood	Hemmings	Lyons	Tobin	63
Price	Edey	Gardiner	Payne	Howarth	Sorvel	Lyons	Wood	Coates	Power	Hemmings	Hulme	Bradshaw	64

Macclesfield Town

SAMMY McILROY

The last of the 'Busby Babes', Sammy followed in the footsteps of the legendary George Best when he moved from his native Belfast to join Manchester United as a raw teenager in the late sixties. He became an established member of the highly successful and exciting United side built by Tommy Docherty. In all he made 418 appearances for United, the highlight being the 1977 FA Cup Final success over Liverpool.

In 1982 he moved to Stoke City where he played 144 times before heading back to Manchester to join United's deadly rivals, City. His time at Maine Road was curtailed when he accepted an offer to join Bury, then managed by Martin Dobson, whom he was to succeed at Northwich Victoria. He then took up a post as player-coach with Preston, but a severe knee injury virtually ended his playing days.

In July 1991, he was appointed as manager at Northwich Victoria. Coming into the job cold with virtually no experience of the non-league scene, everyone at the club was delighted with his and his team's performance. Happily his own injuries recovered sufficiently for him to make a welcome, and most effective, comeback as a player with the Vics towards the end of the season. The experience of playing in a green shirt again no doubt brought back memories of his 78 appearances in an emerald shirt for his country, Northern Ireland.

Sammy left Northwich Victoria in 1992 and became manager of Ashton United for short spell before joining Macclesfield Town for the start of the 1993-94 season. In his first season he won the Drinkwise Cup (Bob Lord Trophy) as well as the Staffordshire Senior Cup. Sammy's second season in charge saw him bring the Vauxhall Conference Championship to the Moss Rose and his third brought further success with the FA Umbro Trophy now settled in the trophy cabinet.

Sammy McIlroy with the FA Umbro Trophy
Photo John Rooney

Programme details:
36 pages for £1
Editor - Alan Cash

Any other club publications:
Silk Yarns (Fanzine)

Local Newspapers:
Macclesfield Express
Manchester Evening News
Manchester Evening News Pink

Local Radio Stations:
GMR (BBC)
BBC Radio Stoke
Piccadilly Radio
Signal Radio

MACCLESFIELD TOWN - PLAYING SQUAD 1996-97

Player	Honours	Birthplace and date	Transfer Fees	Previous Clubs
GOALKEEPERS				
Ryan Price	ESP, FAT FAXI	Wolverhampton 13/3/70	5-fig	Bolton W, Stafford R, Birmingham C
DEFENDERS				
Steve Payne	GMVC, FAT	Castleford 1/8/75		Huddersfield T
Neil Howarth	ESP, GMVC FAT, BLT	Bolton 15/11/71		Burnley
Darren Tinson		Birmingham 15/11/69	5-fig	Connah's Quay Nomads, Colwyn Bay, Northwich V
Cec Edey	FAT	Manchester		Lancaster C, Chorley, Lancaster C, Morecambe, Winsford U, Witton A
Mark Gardiner	FAT	Cirencester 25/12/66		Swindon T, Torquay U, Crewe A, Frederikstad (Swe)
Mark Bradshaw	GMVC	Ashton 7/9/69	£5,000	Blackpool, Stafford R
Neil Matthews	NI u-21, Div 3	Manchester 3/12/67		Blackpool, Cardiff C, Songdal, Cardiff C, Rochdale
MIDFIELDERS				
Neil Sorvel	GMVC, FAT BLT	Widnes 2/3/73		Crewe Alexandra
Kevin Hulme	FAT	Farnworth 2/12/67		Radcliffe B, Bury, Doncaster R, Lincoln C
John Askey	ESP, GMVC NPL, CSC	Stoke 4/11/64		Port Vale, Milton Utd
Steve Wood	GMVC, FAT, BLT	Manchester 23/6/63		Chadderton, Mossley, Droylsden, Stalybridge C
Neil Mitchell	ES	Lytham 7/11/74		Blackpool
Aidan Brodigan		Manchester		Congleton T
Gary Evans		Welshpool 20/12/69		Llansantffraid
FORWARDS				
Phil Power	GMVC, FAT, BLT	Salford 25/7/66	Player/ Exchange	Northwich V, Witton A, Crewe, Horwich, Chorley, Barrow, Stalybridge C
Steve Circuit		Sheffield		Sheffield U, Stafford R, Halifax T, Boston U
Carwyn Williams		Pwllheli 21/10/74		Crewe A, Northwich V
Tony Hemmings	FAT	Burton 21/9/67		Rocester, Northwich V, Wycombe W
Marc Coates	FAT	Swansea 10/10/72		Swansea C, Merthyr Tydfil, Yeovil T

Departures during season:
Ian Monk (Morecambe), Scott Middlemass (Chorley), Steve Tobin (Hyde U - Loan), Karl Williams (Curzon Ashton), Martin McDonald (Southport), Martin Clark (Albion R), Stuart Locke (Flixton - Loan), Karl Marginson (Ashton U - Loan), David German (Winsford U - Loan), David Norman (Llansantffraid - Loan).
Players on loan during season:
Phil Morgan (Stoke C).
Departures during close season: George Shepherd (Altrincham), Paul Cavell (Purfleet), Karl Marginson (Chorley), David German (Winsford U), David Norman (Barry T), Simon Hutchinson (Released), Stuart Locke (Leek T), Steve Tobin (Flixton).

Moss Rose, Macclesfield

ADDRESS:
Moss Rose, London Road, Macclesfield, Cheshire SK10 3JH.

TELEPHONE NUMBER: 01625 264686 (Commercial Office), 01625 424324 (Social Club).
Club Call: 0891 88 44 82.

SIMPLE DIRECTIONS:
Approximately 1 mile south of the Town Centre on the A523 (Leek Road). British Rail Macclesfield approximately 1.5 miles, regular bus service on Match day. Ample unrestricted parking around the ground.

CAPACITY: 6,112 **SEATED:** 1,072 **COVERED TERRACING:** 3,000

RECORD ATTENDANCE:
9,003 v Winsford United - Cheshire Senior Cup 2nd Round 04.02.48.

CLUB SHOP:
Open Monday - Friday 10.00 to 4.00 and on match days. Contact Andy Ridgway on 0625 423099 for more details.

SOCIAL FACILITIES:
The Blues Club - open match days and functions.

PREVIOUS GROUNDS:
None

Macclesfield Fact File

Nickname: Silkmen

Club Sponsors: Zeneca Pharmaceutical

Previous Leagues: Manchester League, Cheshire League, Northern Premier League.

Club colours: Blue & white

Change colours: All white.

Reserve team league: North West Alliance League

Midweek home matchday: Tuesday (7.45pm)

Record win: 15-0 v Chester St.Marys - Cheshire Senior Cup 2nd Round 16.02.1886.

Record defeat: 13-1 v Tranmere Rovers Reserves 03.05.1929.

Record transfer fee: £10,000 to Birmingham City for Ryan Price - 1995.

Record transfer fee received: £40,000 for Mike Lake from Sheffield United - 1988.

1995-96 Captain: Neil Howarth.

1995-96 Top scorer: Marc Coates.

1995-96 Supporters' Player of the Year: Steve Payne.

1994-95 Players' Player of the Year: Steve Payne

Club record goalscorer: Albert Valentine 84 - 1933-34.

Record appearances: Keith Goalen - 1957-1970.

Past players who progressed to the Football League: Numerous, but latest: Steve Farrelly (Rotherham United) and Stuart Bimson (Bury) 94/95.

Club Honours: Conference Champions 94-95; FA Trophy Winners 1970, 1996, Runners-up 1989, 1986; Bord Lord Trophy winners 1994, Runners-up 1996; NPL Challenge Cup 1986; Presidents Cup 1986; Cheshire Senior Cup 1890, 1891, 1894, 1896, 1911, 1930, 1935, 1951, 1952, 1954, 1960, 1964, 1969, 1971, 1973, 1983; Cheshire County League 1932, 1933, 1953, 1961, 1964, 1968; Staffs Senior Cup Winners 93-94; Championship Shield 1996.

MORECAMBE

Formed:
1920

President
Jim Bowen

Chairman
Ken Parker

Vice-Chairman
Graham Hodgson

Directors:
David Robinson
Peter McGuigan
Dickie Danson
David Derham
Rod Taylor

Football Secretary
Neil Marsdin

Manager
Jim Harvey
Assistant Manager
Tony Hesketh

Physiotherapist
David Edge

Commercial Manager
Peter Howard

The 1995/96, Morecambe's first season in the highest echelon of non-League football, can be likened to a ride, 20 miles down the coastline, on the Pepsi Max Big One at Blackpool Pleasure Beach. On the one hand there were some massive highs, conversely there were some disappointing lows.

The season started promisingly with over 1600 watching the Shrimps gain their first Conference points beating Telford 2-0, further success followed as Runcorn were beaten the following midweek to elevate Morecambe to the top of the table after only two games. The harsh reality of higher league status was evident during a run of five defeats, which was to prove the pattern for the season, a good run followed by a bad one.

Scoring goals wasn't something the newboys found hard, and many exciting games took place. Christmas approached with Morecambe on one of the seasonal highs, six games unbeaten leaving the club in seventh place at the turn of the year.

January and early February proved unproductive for the seasiders, as defeats by Gateshead (twice), Farnborough, Emley and Woking left the club under half way in the league and out of the FA Trophy. One of the season highs was during February when Altrincham visited the much-improved Christie Park and were handed a crushing 7-0 defeat. The form continued to fluctuate and it was only during the last month of the season that some consistency was achieved. Late March, April and May saw only one defeat in nine games with the Shrimps taking four points off would-be champions Stevenage, and closing a highly satisfactory first season beating Kidderminster 3-1.

The club captured the ATS Lancashire Trophy, beating Bamber Bridge at Preston, although other cups only brought disappointment. With good management both on and off the field, Morecambe are looking to make steady progress this coming season and build on the solid foundation laid during 1995/96. Lawrence Bland

Back Row (L-R); J Norman, S Drummond, P Comstive, G Johnstone, A Banks, S Hodgson, J McCluskie, R Armstrong. Middle; D Danson, D Edge, B Lavelle, A Livingstone, M Ceroalo, G Dullaghan, M Lambert, W Maddock, J Udall, M Lingwood. Front Row; M Knowles, J Coleman, P Rushton, P Tomlinson, J Harvey, A Grimshaw, I Cain, P Burns, P Withers.
Photo - Darren Andrews.

Morecambe

Match No.	Date	Comp.	Venue H/A	Opponents	Result	League Pos.	Goalscorers (Times if known)	Attendance
1	Aug 19	GMVC	H	Telford	Won 2-0		Burns, Cain	1532
2	22	GMVC	H	Runcorn	Won 3-1		Burns 2, McCluskie	1452
3	26	GMVC	A	Kidderminster	Lost 2-4		Coleman, Cain	1702
4	28	GMVC	A	Northwich Victoria	Lost 1-2		Coleman	903
5	Sep 2	GMVC	H	SloughTown	Lost 1-2		Cain	1120
6	5	GMVC	H	Macclesfield	Lost 2-4		Coleman, Ceraolo	1459
7	9	FACQ1	H	Sheffield	Won 7-0		Burns, Coleman 2, Ceraolo 3, og	469
8	12	GMVC	A	Altrincham	Lost 0-3			752
9	16	GMVC	A	Dagenham	Drew 2-2		Burns, og	838
10	19	SPAL	H	Stalybridge	Won 4-1		Knowles, Coleman, Ceraolo, Norman	604
11	23	FAC2Q	A	Worksop	Won 3-2		Coleman, McCluskie, og	529
12	26	GMVC	A	Halifax	Drew 1-1		Norman	917
13	30	GMVC	H	Welling	Won 1-0		Coleman	976
14	Oct 7	FACQ3	H	Gainsboro'	Won 6-2		Grimshaw, Norman, Coleman 4	807
15	10	GMVC	A	Macclesfield	Lost 0-2			957
16	14	GMVC	H	Kettering Town	Won 5-3		Coleman 3, Norman, Cain	1095
17	21	FACQ4	A	Witton	Lost 2-3		Burns, Knowles	931
18	28	GMVC	H	Bromsgrove	Won 4-1		McCluskie, Cain, Norman,	965
19	Nov 4	GMVC	A	Woking	Lost 0-3		Ceraolo	2679
20	7	SPAL	A	Stalybridge	Lost 2-5		McCluskie, Ceraolo	467
21	11	GMVC	H	Bath City	Won 1-0		Burns	1007
22	18	GMVC	H	Dover Athletic	Won 3-0		Tomlinson, Coleman, McCluskie	1058
23	25	GMVC	A	Hednesford	Won 2-1		Burns, Knowles	1273
24	Dec 2	GMVC	H	Southport	Won 4-3		Coleman, McCluskie, Monk 2	1745
25	5	SPAL	H	Altrincham	Won 6-4		Comstive, Coleman, McCluskie 3, Cain	546
26	9	GMVC	A	Telford	Drew 2-2		Comstive, Coleman	724
27	16	GMVC	H	Stalybridge	Won 2-0		Grimshaw, Ceraolo	1143
28	Jan 1	GMVC	H	Gateshead	Lost 2-3		McCluskie 2	1400
29	6	GMVC	A	Farnborough	Lost 1-3		McCluskie	729
30	13	GMVC	H	Woking	Lost 4-5		Dullaghan, Knowles, Coleman, Monk	1312
31	16	ATS	H	Leigh	Won 2-0		Ceraolo, Monk	262
32	20	FAT1	H	Emley	Drew 2-2		McCluskie, Cain	650
33	23	FAT1	A	Emley	Lost 1-3		McCluskie	412
34	31	GMVC	A	Gateshead	Lost 0-3			480
35	Feb 10	GMVC	H	Dagenham	Drew 2-2		Monk 2	789
36	13	ATS	H	Radcliffe	Won 3-0		Burns, Monk, Norman	318
37	17	GMVC	H	Altrincham	Won 7-0		Burns, Monk, Norman 3, Ceraolo 2	983
38	20	GMVC	H	Northwich Victoria	Drew 2-2		Armstrong, Cain	932
39	24	GMVC	A	Stalybridge	Won 2-0		Coleman, Cain	504
40	27	ATS	H	Southport	Won 2-1		Burns, Coleman	910
41	Mar 2	GMVC	H	Hednesford	Lost 0-1			961
42	5	SPAL	H	Macclesfield	Lost 1-4		McCluskie	625
43	9	GMVC	A	Bath City	Lost 2-3		Cain, Norman	511
44	12	GMVC	H	Halifax	Lost 0-1			648
45	16	GMVC	A	Welling	Lost 0-1			508
46	23	GMVC	H	Farnborough	Lost 2-3		West, Ceraolo	748
47	30	GMVC	A	Dover Athletic	Won 3-2		Ceraolo 2, Cain	1090
48	Apr 6	GMVC	H	Stevenage	Won 1-0		Ceraolo	1247
49	8	GMVC	A	Runcorn	Won 3-1			694
50	13	GMVC	A	Kettering	Won 3-2		Jackson, McCluskie, Norman	1104
51	16	GMVC	A	Southport	Drew 1-1		Jackson	764
52	20	GMVC	A	Slough	Drew 1-1		McCluskie	826
53	24	ATS	H	Bambel Bridge	Won 1-0		Jackson	1786
54	27	GMVC	A	Stevenage	Drew 1-1		Ceraolo	2574
55	30	GMVC	A	Bromsgrove	Lost 0-1			562
56	May 4	GMVC	H	Kidderminster	Won 3-1		Monk, Ceraolo, McCluskie	1213

Morecambe

1	2	3	4	5	6	7	8	9	10	11	12	14	Match No.
Johnstone	Burns	Lavelle	Tomlinson	Rushton	Maddock	Knowles	Comstive	Coleman	Withers	Cain	McCluskie	Norman	1
Johnstone	Burns	Lavelle	Tomlinson	Rushton	Maddock	Knowles	Comstive	Coleman	McCluskie	Cain	Withers	Norman	2
Johnstone	Burns	Lavelle	Tomlinson	Rushton	Maddock	Knowles	Comstive	Coleman	McCluskie	Cain	Withers	Drummond	3
Johnstone	Burns	Lavelle	Rushton	Hughes	Maddock	Harvey	Grimshaw	Coleman	McCluskie	Cain	Knowles	Comstive	4
Johnstone	Burns	Lavelle	Rushton	Hughes	Maddock	Knowles	Grimshaw	Coleman	McCluskie	Cain	Withers	Comstive	5
Johnstone	Burns	Lavelle	Tomlinson	Grimshaw	Hughes	Knowles	Comstive	Coleman	Withers	Cain	Ceraolo	Norman	6
Johnstone	Burns	Lavelle	Tomlinson	Grimshaw	Hughes	Knowles	Comstive	Coleman	Ceraolo	Cain	Withers	Norman	7
Johnstone	Burns	Lavelle	Tomlinson	Rushton	Hughes	Knowles	Comstive	Coleman	Maddock	Cain	Ceraolo	McCluskie	8
Johnstone	Burns	Rushton	Tomlinson	Grimshaw	Hughes	Knowles	Comstive	Coleman	McCluskie	Cain	Ceraolo	Norman	9
Johnstone	Burns	Rushton	Grimshaw	Hodgson	Maddock	Knowles	Comstive	Coleman	Ceraolo	Norman	McCluskie	Drummond	10
Banks	Burns	Rushton	Grimshaw	Maddock	Hughes	Knowles	Comstive	Coleman	Ceraolo	Cain	McCluskie	Norman	11
Banks	Burns	Rushton	Grimshaw	Maddock	Hughes	Knowles	Comstive	McCluskie	Ceraolo	Norman	Coleman	Harvey	12
Banks	Burns	Rushton	Grimshaw	Maddock	Hughes	Norman	Comstive	Coleman	Ceraolo	Cain	McCluskie	Tomlinson	13
Banks	Burns	Rushton	Grimshaw	Maddock	Hughes	Norman	Comstive	Coleman	Ceraolo	Cain	McCluskie	Tomlinson	14
Banks	Burns	Rushton	Tomlinson	Hughes	Maddock	Knowles	Grimshaw	Coleman	Ceraolo	Norman	Comstive	Taylor	15
Banks	Burns	Tomlinson	Maddock	Hughes	Grimshaw	Ceraolo	Comstive	Coleman	Norman	Cain	Knowles	Drummond	16
Banks	Burns	Taylor	Tomlinson	Hughes	Grimshaw	Ceraolo	Comstive	Coleman	Norman	Cain	Knowles	McCluskie	17
Banks	Burns	Stimpson	Tomlinson	Hughes	Horrigan	Knowles	Comstive	Coleman	McCluskie	Cain	Norman	Maddock	18
Banks	Burns	Stimpson	Tomlinson	Hughes	Horrigan	Knowles	Comstive	Coleman	McCluskie	Cain	Norman	Maddock	19
Banks	Burns	Stimpson	Maddock	Hughes	Horrigan	Knowles	Norman	Coleman	McCluskie	Cain	Rushton	Grimshaw	20
Johnstone	Burns	Rushton	Tomlinson	Hughes	Grimshaw	Knowles	Comstive	Coleman	McCluskie	Cain	Maddock	Stimpson	21
Johnstone	Burns	Rushton	Tomlinson	Hughes	Grimshaw	Knowles	Comstive	Coleman	McCluskie	Monk	Maddock	Cain	22
Johnstone	Burns	Rushton	Tomlinson	Hughes	Grimshaw	Knowles	Comstive	Coleman	McCluskie	Monk	Maddock	Norman	23
Johnstone	Burns	Rushton	Tomlinson	Hughes	Grimshaw	Knowles	Comstive	Coleman	McCluskie	Monk	Maddock	Norman	24
Johnstone	Burns	Rushton	Tomlinson	Hughes	Grimshaw	Knowles	Comstive	Coleman	McCluskie	Cain	Maddock	Horrigan	25
Johnstone	Burns	Rushton	Tomlinson	Hughes	Grimshaw	Knowles	Comstive	Coleman	McCluskie	Monk	Dullaghan	Cain	26
Johnstone	Burns	Rushton	Tomlinson	Dullaghan	Grimshaw	Knowles	Comstive	Coleman	McCluskie	Monk	Horrigan	Cain	27
Johnstone	Burns	Rushton	Tomlinson	Dullaghan	Grimshaw	Knowles	Comstive	Coleman	McCluskie	Monk	Horrigan	Cain	28
Johnstone	Knowles	Lavelle	Tomlinson	Hughes	Grimshaw	Horrigan	Comstive	Coleman	McCluskie	Monk	Dullaghan	Cain	29
Banks	Burns	Hughes	Tomlinson	Dullaghan	Grimshaw	Knowles	Cain	Coleman	McCluskie	Monk	Horrigan	Comstive	30
Banks	Burns	Lavelle	Tomlinson	Dullaghan	Hughes	Knowles	Horrigan	Coleman	McCluskie	Cain	Ceraolo	Monk	31
Banks	Burns	Rushton	Hughes	Dullaghan	Grimshaw	Knowles	Comstive	Coleman	McCluskie	Monk	Norman	Cain	32
Banks	Burns	Armstrong	Rushton	Dullaghan	Grimshaw	Norman	Comstive	Coleman	McCluskie	Ceraolo	Horrigan	Hodgson	33
Banks	Burns	Lavelle	West	Armstrong	Rushton	Monk	Comstive	Coleman	Foley	Cain	McCluskie	Dullaghan	34
McIlhargey	Burns	Armstrong	Rushton	Hughes	Lavelle	Monk	Foley	Drummond	McCluskie	Cain	Knowles	Norman	35
McIlhargey	Burns	Armstrong	Rushton	Lavelle	Grimshaw	Monk	Foley	McCluskie	Norman	Cain	Ceraolo	Dullaghan	36
McIlhargey	Burns	Armstrong	Rushton	Lavelle	Grimshaw	Monk	Foley	Norman	Ceraolo	Cain	McCluskie	Comstive	37
Johnstone	Burns	Armstrong	Rushton	Lavelle	Grimshaw	Monk	Foley	Norman	Ceraolo	Cain	McCluskie	Comstive	38
Johnstone	Burns	Armstrong	Rushton	Lavelle	Grimshaw	Monk	Foley	Coleman	Norman	Cain	McCluskie	Comstive	39
Johnstone	Burns	Armstrong	Dullaghan	Lavelle	Grimshaw	Foley	Comstive	Coleman	McCluskie	Cain	Knowles	Monk	40
Johnstone	Burns	Knowles	Dullaghan	Lavelle	Grimshaw	Monk	Foley	Coleman	Norman	Cain	McCluskie	Comstive	41
Banks	Burns	Armstrong	Dullaghan	Lavelle	Grimshaw	Foley	Comstive	Coleman	McCluskie	Knowles	Norman	Sang	42
McIlhargey	Burns	Armstrong	Dullaghan	Lavelle	Sang	Foley	Comstive	Coleman	McCluskie	Cain	Norman	Hughes	43
McIlhargey	Burns	Armstrong	Dullaghan	Lavelle	Sang	Monk	Knowles	Ceraolo	Norman	Cain	Comstive	Tomlinson	44
McIlhargey	Burns	Armstrong	Tomlinson	Hughes	Grimshaw	Monk	Sang	Ceraolo	Norman	Cain	McCluskie	Knowles	45
McIlhargey	West	Lavelle	Tomlinson	Dullaghan	Grimshaw	Monk	Knowles	Ceraolo	Norman	Cain	Hughes	Sang	46
McIlhargey	Burns	Lavelle	Tomlinson	Hughes	Grimshaw	Monk	West	Ceraolo	McCluskie	Cain	Knowles	Norman	47
McIlhargey	Burns	Lavelle	Tomlinson	Hughes	West	Monk	Grimshaw	Ceraolo	McCluskie	Jackson	Knowles	Norman	48
McIlhargey	Burns	Armstrong	Tomlinson	Hughes	West	Monk	Grimshaw	Knowles	McCluskie	Lavelle	Norman	Livingstone	49
McIlhargey	Burns	Armstrong	Tomlinson	Hughes	West	Monk	Grimshaw	Jackson	McCluskie	Cain	Norman	Knowles	50
McIlhargey	Burns	Lavelle	Tomlinson	Hughes	West	Monk	Grimshaw	Jackson	McCluskie	Cain	Norman	Knowles	51
McIlhargey	Burns	Lavelle	West	Hughes	Sang	Cain	Grimshaw	Jackson	McCluskie	Norman	Monk	Knowles	52
McIlhargey	Burns	Lavelle	Tomlinson	Hughes	Grimshaw	Monk	Knowles	Jackson	McCluskie	Cain	Sang	Ceraolo	53
McIlhargey	Burns	Armstrong	Lavelle	Hughes	Sang	Monk	Knowles	Jackson	Ceraolo	Cain	Norman	McCluskie	54
McIlhargey	Burns	Armstrong	Lavelle	Hughes	Sang	Monk	Knowles	Norman	Ceraolo	Cain	McCluskie	Grimshaw	55
McIlhargey	West	Armstrong	Lavelle	Hughes	Sang	Monk	Knowles	Norman	Ceraolo	Rushton	McCluskie	Grimshaw	56

Morecambe

JIM HARVEY

Jim's playing career began with his home town club Glenavon, Northern Ireland, until in 1977 Arsenal paid a substantial amount for "Gentleman Jim". Opportunities were limited at Highbury so Jim joined Hereford on a permanent basis. He spent six happy years at Edgar Street, until in 1987 after a short stop at Bristol City and Wrexham, Tranmere Rovers made what was most likely their most important signing, by bringing the softly spoken Harvey to Prenton Park. Success followed success, with promotion achieved from the 4th division to the then 2nd, Mercantile Trophy glory at Wembley, and possibly Jim's finest hour as a player, receiving the Leyland Daf Trophy at Wembley after leading his side to victory over Bristol Rovers. After a season at Crewe, Jim joined the Shrimps as assistant to Leighton James in January 1994, taking over as player-manager in June of the same year. The Irishman made an enormous impact at Christie Park, and it was soon apparent that success as a manager would not elude him for long - Morecambe had been a club dormant for too long and Jim proved to be the catalyst. Promotion to the Conference was was gained at the first attempt, but ultimately the manager's and the club's ambitions are for League football at Christie Park.

James Harvey

Ian Monk; Players & Supporters, Player of the Year

Programme details:
40 pages for £1.00.
Editor - Neil Marsdin

Any other club publications:
Corpus Christie (fanzine)
"Going Up?" (part fanzine)

Local Newspapers:
Morecambe Visitor
Morecambe Guardian
Lancashire Evening Post
The Citizen

Local Radio Stations:
Radio Lancashire
Red Rose Radio
Bay Radio

MORECAMBE - PLAYING SQUAD 1996-97

Player	Honours	Birthplace and date	Transfer Fees	Previous Clubs
GOALKEEPERS				
Steve McIlhargey		Glasgow 10/12/62		Blantyre Celtic, Walsall, Blackpool
Andy Banks		Preston 21/4/76		Preston NE, Bury
Glen Johnstone		Preston 5/6/67	£5,000	Lancaster C, Preston NE, Lancaster C
DEFENDERS				
Paul Burns		Liverpool 1/10/67		Grimsby, Burscough, Prescot, Caernarfon, Altrincham, Accrington Stanley
Paul Rushton		Chester 25/1/74		Crewe A
Dave McKearney		Crosby 20/6/68		Prescot, Bolton W, Northwich V, Crewe A, Wigan, Chorley
Paul West		Birmingham 22/6/72		Alcester T, Port Vale, Bradford C, Wigan A
Richard Annan		Leeds 4/12/68		Leeds, Doncaster, Guiseley, Crewe, Farsley C, Guiseley, Halifax T
Steve Hodgson		Kendal 28/8/76		From Youth Team
Ben Lavelle		Blackburn 12/8/63		Bury, Preston, Fleetwood, Blackpool R, Fleetwood, Morecambe, Ashton U
Tony Hughes	EY	Liverpool 3/10/73		Crewe A
MIDFIELDERS				
Michael Knowles	BC	Morecambe 3/3/74		From Youth Team
Stuart Drummond	BC	Preston 11/12/75		From Youth Team
David Leaver	ULP	Preston		Leyland Daf, Bamber Bridge
Andy Grimshaw	NPL	Bacup 30/3/64		Rossendale U, Manchester U, Bury, Colne D, Witton A
John Norman		Birkenhead 26/6/71		Tranmere R, Bury, Heswall, Mold A
FORWARDS				
Jim McCluskie	NPL XI	Rawtenstall 29/9/66		Rochdale, Mossley, Hyde U, Witton A, Accrington Stanley
Mark Ceraolo		Birkenhead 10/11/75		Crewe Alexadra
Justin Jackson		Nottingham 26/6/75		Bolton W, Ayr U, Penrith, Ilkeston T
Ian Monk	GMVC	Burnley 39/6/68		Clitheroe, Ashton U, Macclesfield T
David Miller		Burnley 8/1/64		Burnley, Tranmere R, Colne D, Preston, Carlisle U, Stockport, Wigan
Ian Cain	NPL XI	Blackpool 10/11/64		Wren R, Fleetwood T

Departures during season:
Phil Hodgson (Netherfield), Ben Lavelle (Ashton U), Wayne Maddock (Bamber B), Ian Horrigan (Altrincham), Garry Dullaghan & John Coleman (Lancaster C), Steve Foley (Released), Paul Comstive (Chorley).
Players on loan during season:
None.

Christie Park, Morecambe

ADDRESS:
Christie Park, Lancaster Road, Morecambe, Lancashire LA4 5TJ

TELEPHONE NUMBERS:
01524 411797 Fax: 01524 411797

SIMPLE DIRECTIONS:
From south leave M6 motorway at junction 34. Follow signs for Morecambe through Lancaster, on A589, go straight across the first 2 roundabouts, and at the third (with the Shrimp pub on your left), follow the signs for Town Centre - Christie Park is approx. 600 metres on your left.

CAPACITY: 6,000 **SEATED:** 2,000 **COVERED TERRACING:** 1,000

RECORD ATTENDANCE: 9,324 v Weymouth FA Cup 4.1.62

CLUB SHOP:
On ground and open on matchdays, also commercial office open Monday to Friday 9.00 - 5.00 selling the same goods.

SOCIAL FACILITIES:
J B's open normal licensing hours.

PREVIOUS GROUNDS:
Woodhill Lane 1920-25, shared with cricket club who still play there.

Morecambe Fact File

Nickname: The Shrimps

Club sponsor: Able Projects

Previous Leagues: Lancs Combination 1920-68, Northern Premier 1968-1995.

Club colours: Red & white striped shirts, black shorts, red & white socks.

Change colours: Dark & light purple shirts, purple shorts, purple & yellow socks.

Midweek home matchday: Tuesdays, 7.45pm kick-off.

Record win: 16-0 v Rossendale Utd, Lancs Combination Sept 1967 (Arnold Timmins scored 8)

Record defeat: 0-7 v Darwen, November 7th 1953

Record transfer fee paid: £7,500 to Fleetwood for Ian Cain, 1988

Record transfer fee received: £6,000 from Colne Dynamoes for Barrie Stimpson.

95-96 Captain: Paul Burns

95-96 P.o.Y.: Paul Tomlinson

95-96 Top scorer: John Coleman 20.

Club Record Scorer: Keith Borrowdale 289 goals 1956-68, 78-79 Lancashire Combination.
John Coleman 130 goals 1990-1995 (Northern Premier League)

Club Record Appearances: Steve Done 523 + 7 sub. (1968-78)

Past players who progressed to the Football League: Fred Blondel & Malcolm Darling (Bury 1946 & 78), Herbert Harrison (Accrington 1947), Gordon Milne (Preston 1956), Ray Charnley (Blackpool 1957), Geoff Slack (Stockport 1958), Ron Mitchell (Leeds 1958), Derek Armstrong (Carlisle 1961), Alan Taylor (Rochdale 1973), John Coates (Southport via Burscough & Skelmersdale 1975), Keith Galley (Southport 1975), Brian Thompson (West Ham 1977), David Eyres (Blackpool), Kenny Lowe (Barnet via Barrow), Steve Gardner (Bradford City), Dave Lancaster (Chesterfield).

Club Honours: FA Trophy 73-74 (QF 93-94), Northern Premier Lg Presidents Cup 91-92, NPL Runners-up 94-95, Lancs Combination(5) 24-25 61-63 66-68 (R-up 25-26, Lg Cup 26-27 45-46 64-65 66-68), Lancs Jnr Cup (now ATS Tphy)(8) 25-27 61-63 68-69 85-87 92-93, 95-96; Lancs Snr Cup 67-68, Lancs Lg Div 2 83-84.

NORTHWICH VICTORIA

Formed: 1874

Chairman
Rod J Stich

Vice Chairman
Dave Stone

President & Football Secretary:
Derek Nuttall

Company Secretary:
Graham Fenton

Other Directors
A Stich (Chief Exec.)
Rod Stich
Colin Adshead
Roger Stubbs
Graham Cookson
Dave Edgeley

Manager:
Mark Hancock

Coach:
Tommy Martin

Physiotherapist:
Phil Lea

Northwich enjoyed their best season since 1984/85 and showed their fighting spirit with a tremendous effort in the FA Umbro Trophy final against neighbours Macclesfield Town.

Although the Vics finished in 8th in the Vauxhall Conference, but for some inconsistency, a much higher placing could have been achieved. Northwich gained some outstanding results, such as a 5-2 Drill Field thrashing of Kidderminster Harriers, a 5-1 win at Stalybridge Celtic and a 6-2 hammering of Kettering Town in the penultimate game of the season but, on the other hand, they also suffered a 1-5 defeat at Stevenage Borough and a 1-2 home reverse against Welling United on the last day of the campaign.

Manager Brian Kettle did an excellent job in his first season in charge and made some shrewd signings like England forward Delwyn Humphreys, defender Derek Ward and young striker Lee Steele, who looks a good prospect. However, following the Trophy final, Kettle departed in somewhat acrimonious terms and, despite the club receiving applications from a number of well-known names, they turned to Mark Hancock, the former central defender who had been in charge of the club's reserve side, as the new man in charge. **Steve Whitney**

Back Row (L-R); W Simpson, M Jones, D Vicary, L Steele, R Sweeney. Middle; P Lea (Phy), C Duffy, P Tait, G Oghani, T Ball, D Greygoose, D Burgess, S Walters, G Abel, T Martin (Coach). Front; I Cooke, C Williams, B Butler, B Kettle (Mgr), J Wiliams, D Humphries, D Ward. Photo - Northwich Guardian

Northwich Victoria

Match No.	Date	Comp.	Venue H/A	Opponents	Result	League Pos.	Goalscorers (Times if known)	Attendance
1	Aug 19	GMVC	H	Dover Athletic	Lost 1-2		Vicary	824
2	22	GMVC	A	Southport	Drew 2-2		Clayton, McAuley	1542
3	26	GMVC	A	Welling United	Drew 1-1		Butler	538
4	28	GMVC	H	Morecambe	Won 2-1		McAuley, Clayton	941
5	Sep 2	GMVC	A	Farnborough Town	Won 1-0		Duffy	808
6	5	GMVC	H	Stalybridge Celtic	Won 1-0		Walters	816
7	9	FAC1Q	H	Burscough	Won 5-0		Walters, Butler, Williams 2, Clayton	655
8	12	GMVC	A	Halifax Town	Lost 0-2			829
9	16	GMVC	H	Hednesford Town	Lost 0-2			1100
10	19	SC1	A	Telford United	Won 2-1		Walters, Cooke	512
11	23	FAC2Q	A	Lincoln United	Won 4-1		Butler, Cooke, Williams, Vicary	354
12	26	CSC	H	Runcorn	Won 3-1		Cooke, Williams, Walters	502
13	30	GMVC	A	Dagenham	Won 3-0		Butler, Williams, Vicary	646
14	Oct 3	SC2	H	Telford United	Lost 0-3			514
15	7	FAC3Q	H	Eastwood Town	Drew 0-0			742
16	10	FAC3QR	A	Eastwood Town	Won 2-1		Vicary 2	642
17	14	GMVC	H	Kidderminster Harriers	Won 5-2		Williams 4, Clayton	1106
18	21	FAC4Q	A	Macclesfield Town	Won 1-0		Duffy	1707
19	28	GMVC	A	Stevenage Borough	Lost 1-5		Simpson	1645
20	31	GMVC	H	Southport	Lost 1-2		Williams	724
21	Nov 4	GMVC	H	Runcorn	Won 4-3		Walters 2, Williams, Cooke	1007
22	11	FAC1	H	Scunthorpe United	Lost 1-3		Cooke	2685
23	18	GMVC	A	Bath City	Won 3-0		Walters, Williams, Butler	417
24	21	CSC2	A	Witton Albion	Lost 0-2			1006
25	25	GMVC	A	Slough Town	Drew 1-1		Vicary	703
26	Dec 2	GMVC	H	Farnborough Town	Lost 1-3		Clayton	687
27	9	GMVC	A	Gateshead	Drew 1-1		Vicary	612
28	16	GMVC	H	Stevenage Borough	Lost 1-3		Oghani	673
29	19	GMVC	H	Telford United	Won 2-0		Butler 2	503
30	26	GMVC	H	Altrincham	Won 2-1		Butler 2	1278
31	Jan 1	GMVC	A	Altrincham	Won 4-3		Ward 2, Butler, Cooke	1076
32	6	GMVC	H	Bath City	Drew 2-2		Butler, Cooke	708
33	9	GMVC	A	Kettering Town	Drew 2-2		Williams, Vicary	912
34	13	GMVC	A	Hednesford Town	Lost 1-2		Cooke	1017
35	20	FAT1	A	Hednesford Town	Drew 1-1		Vicary	935
36	23	FAT1R	H	Hednesford Town	Won 2-0		Walters, Cooke	636
37	30	GMVC	H	Bromsgrove Rovers	Drew 2-2		Butler, Williams	609
38	Feb 10	FAT2	A	Wembley	Won 2-0		Butler, Cooke	268
39	17	GMVC	H	Halifax Town	Drew 1-1		Jones	879
40	20	GMVC	A	Morecambe	Drew 2-2		Cooke, Vicary	830
41	24	GMVC	H	Dagenham	Won 1-0		Butler	727
42	27	MCCSF	A	Witton Albion	Lost 2-3		Walters, Cooke	667
43	Mar 2	FAT3	A	Merthyr Tydfil	Drew 1-1		Abel	528
44	5	FAT3R	H	Merthyr Tydfil	Drew 2-2		Butler, Vicary	833
45	9	GMVC	A	Telford United	Lost 0-1			712
46	11	FAT3R2	H	Merthyr Tydfil	Won 3-0		Butler 2, Humphreys	765
47	16	GMVC	H	Slough Town	Lost 0-3			634
48	23	FAT QF	A	Bromsgrove Rovers	Won 1-0		Cooke	1807
49	26	GMVC	A	Macclesfield Town	Drew 0-0			1117
50	30	GMVC	A	Kidderminster Harriers	Lost 1-2		Williams	1604
51	Apr 2	GMVC	H	Gateshead	Lost 1-2		Butler	602
52	6	GMVC	A	Dover Athletic	Won 1-0		Williams	976
53	13	FATSF1	A	Hyde United	Won 2-1		Cooke, Humphreys	2253
54	16	GMVC	H	Macclesfield Town	Lost 1-2		Vicary	936
55	20	FATSF1	H	Hyde United	Won 1-0		Abel	2809
56	23	GMVC	A	Runcorn	Won 4-3		Williams 2, Butler, Steele	653
57	25	GMVC	A	Stalybridge Celtic	Won 5-1		Williams, Butler, Steele 3	
58	27	GMVC	H	Woking	Won 3-0		Steele	842
59	28	GMVC	A	Bromsgrove	Drew 1-1		Tait	693
60	30	GMVC	A	Woking	Drew 0-0			1771
61	May 2	GMVC	H	Kettering	Won 6-2		Walters 2, Williams 2, Vicary 2	632
62	4	GMVC	H	Welling United	Lost 1-2		Cooke	875

Northwich Victoria

1	2	3	4	5	6	7	8	9	10	11	12	14	Match No.
Greygoose	Hilton	Jones	Burgess	Abel	Simpson	Williams	Butler	Cooke	Clayton	Vicary	Hughes	Cooper	1
Greygoose	Hilton	Simpson	Tinson	Abel	Walters	Burgess	Butler	Cooke	Clayton	Vicary	McAuley	Jones	2
Greygoose	Burgess	Simpson	Tinson	Abel	Walters	Williams	Butler	Cooke	Clayton	Vicary	Jones	McAuley	3
Greygoose	Burgess	Jones	Tinson	Abel	Walters	McAuley	Butler	Cooke	Clayton	Vicary	Oghani	Simpson	4
Greygoose	Burgess	Jones	Tinson	Simpson	Walters	McAuley	Butler	Cooke	Clayton	Duffy	Williams	Oghani	5
Newall	Burgess	Jones	Tinson	Simpson	Walters	McAuley	Butler	Cooke	Clayton	Duffy	Williams	Oghani	6
Ball	Burgess	Jones	Tinson	Simpson	Walters	McAuley	Butler	Williams	Clayton	Duffy	Vicary	Oghani	7
Newall	Burgess	Jones	Tinson	Simpson	Walters	Duffy	Butler	Humphreys	Clayton	Vicary	McAuley	Oghani	8
Greygoose	Burgess	Jones	Tinson	Simpson	Walters	Duffy	Butler	Humphreys	Williams	Vicary	McAuley	Hughes	9
Greygoose	Simpson	Jones	Tinson	Abel	Walters	McAuley	Butler	Humphreys	Cooke	Vicary	Williams	Hughes	10
Greygoose	Simpson	Jones	Tinson	Abel	Walters	McAuley	Butler	Cooke	Williams	Vicary	Burgess	Hughes	11
Greygoose	Burgess	Simpson	Hughes	Abel	Duffy	McAuley	Butler	Cooke	Williams	Vicary	Clayton	Walters	12
Greygoose	Simpson	Jones	Tinson	Abel	Walters	McAuley	Butler	Cooke	Williams	Vicary	Hughes	Burgess	13
Greygoose	Simpson	Jones	Tinson	Abel	Walters	McAuley	Butler	Cooke	Williams	Vicary	Hughes	Burgess	14
Greygoose	Simpson	Jones	Tinson	Abel	Walters	McAuley	Butler	Cooke	Williams	Vicary	Clayton	Duffy	15
Greygoose	Simpson	Jones	Tinson	Abel	Walters	Burgess	Butler	Williams	Clayton	Vicary	McAuley	Duffy	16
Greygoose	Burgess	Jones	Tinson	Abel	Walters	Sunderland	Duffy	Williams	Clayton	Vicary	Butler	Hughes	17
Greygoose	Simpson	Jones	Tinson	Abel	Walters	Duffy	Butler	Williams	Clayton	Vicary	Burgess	McAuley	18
Greygoose	Simpson	Jones	Tinson	Abel	Walters	Sunderland	Butler	Williams	Clayton	Duffy	McAuley	Burgess	19
Greygoose	Simpson	Jones	Tinson	Abel	Walters	Sunderland	Butler	Williams	Clayton	Duffy	McAuley	Burgess	20
Greygoose	Simpson	Jones	Tinson	Burgess	Walters	Williams	Butler	Cooke	Clayton	Duffy	McAuley	Holden	21
Greygoose	Burgess	Jones	Tinson	Simpson	Walters	Williams	Butler	Cooke	Clayton	Duffy	McAuley	Vicary	22
Greygoose	Simpson	Jones	Tinson	Burgess	Walters	Williams	Butler	Cooke	Holden	Vicary	McAuley	Clayton	23
Greygoose	Simpson	Duffy	Tinson	Burgess	Walters	Williams	Butler	Cooke	Holden	Vicary	McAuley	Clayton	24
Greygoose	Ward	Duffy	Tinson	Burgess	Walters	Williams	Butler	Cooke	Clayton	Vicary	McAuley	Logan	25
Greygoose	Ward	Jones	Tinson	Burgess	Walters	Williams	Butler	Cooke	Edwards	Vicary	Clayton	Oghani	26
Greygoose	Ward	Jones	Tinson	Burgess	Duffy	Williams	Butler	Cooke	Clayton	Vicary	Abel	Oghani	27
Greygoose	Ward	Duffy	Tinson	Jones	Edwards	Williams	Butler	Humphreys	Clayton	Vicary	Oghani	Wilkinson	28
Greygoose	Hilton	Duffy	Tinson	Cooke	Williams	Ward	Butler	Cumusky	Humphreys	Vicary	Oghani	Wilkinson	29
Greygoose	Hilton	Duffy	Tinson	Burgess	Walters	Ward	Butler	Humphreys	Cooke	Vicary	Williams	Jones	30
Greygoose	Hilton	Duffy	Tinson	Burgess	Walters	Ward	Butler	Cooke	Humphreys	Vicary	Williams	Oghani	31
Greygoose	Burgess	Duffy	Tinson	Abel	Walters	Ward	Butler	Cooke	Humphreys	Vicary	Williams	Simpson	32
Greygoose	Hilton	Duffy	Tinson	Burgess	Simpson	Ward	Butler	Cooke	Williams	Vicary	Oghani	Jones	33
Greygoose	Hilton	Duffy	Tinson	Burgess	Jones	Ward	Butler	Cooke	Williams	Vicary	Oghani	Simpson	34
Greygoose	Burgess	Duffy	Tinson	Jones	Walters	Ward	Cooke	Williams	Vicary	Simpson	Hilton	Oghani	35
Greygoose	Burgess	Duffy	Tinson	Jones	Walters	Ward	Humphreys	Cooke	Williams	Vicary	Simpson	Oghani	36
Greygoose	Burgess	Duffy	Tinson	Jones	Walters	Ward	Butler	Cooke	Williams	Vicary	Simpson	Hilton	37
Greygoose	Burgess	Jones	Tinson	Duffy	Walters	Simpson	Butler	Cooke	Williams	Vicary	Ward	Oghani	38
Greygoose	Duffy	Jones	Burgess	Abel	Simpson	Ward	Butler	Cooke	Humphreys	Vicary	Williams	Oghani	39
Greygoose	Duffy	Jones	Burgess	Abel	Simpson	Ward	Butler	Cooke	Williams	Vicary	Oghani	Logan	40
Greygoose	Ward	Jones	Burgess	Abel	Walters	Simpson	Butler	Cooke	Duffy	Vicary	Williams	Sweeney	41
Ball	Ward	Ogden	Sweeney	Logan	Walters	Williams	Simpson	Oghani	Cooke	Duffy	Patterson	Carthy	42
Greygoose	Ward	Jones	Burgess	Abel	Walters	Simpson	Butler	Cooke	Humphreys	Vicary	Duffy	Williams	43
Greygoose	Ward	Jones	Abel	Burgess	Walters	Simpson	Butler	Cooke	Humphreys	Vicary	Duffy	Williams	44
Greygoose	Ward	Ogden	Jones	Burgess	Sweeney	Duffy	Butler	Cooke	Williams	Vicary	Oghani	Patterson	45
Greygoose	Simpson	Duffy	Burgess	Abel	Walters	Ward	Butler	Cooke	Humphreys	Vicary	Williams	Oghani	46
Greygoose	Simpson	Duffy	Burgess	Abel	Ogden	Ward	Butler	Williams	Humphreys	Vicary	Oghani	Sweeney	47
Greygoose	Ward	Duffy	Burgess	Abel	Simpson	Williams	Butler	Cooke	Humphreys	Vicary	Oghani	Sweeney	48
Greygoose	Ward	Duffy	Burgess	Abel	Simpson	Sweeney	Butler	Williams	Oghani	Vicary	Carthy	Logan	49
Greygoose	Ward	Duffy	Burgess	Abel	Simpson	Williams	Butler	Cooke	Humphreys	Vicary	Tait	Steele	50
Greygoose	Ward	Duffy	Burgess	Abel	Simpson	Williams	Butler	Cooke	Tait	Vicary	Steele	Oghani	51
Greygoose	Ward	Duffy	Burgess	Abel	Simpson	Williams	Butler	Cooke	Tait	Vicary	Sweeney	Oghani	52
Greygoose	Ward	Duffy	Burgess	Abel	Simpson	Williams	Butler	Cooke	Humphreys	Vicary	Tait	Steele	53
Greygoose	Ward	Duffy	Burgess	Simpson	Walters	Williams	Sweeney	Steele	Tait	Vicary	Butler	Harwood	54
Ball	Ward	Duff	Burgess	Abel	Walters	Simpson	Butler	Cooke	Humphreys	Vicary	Williams	Tait	55
Ball	Ward	Sweeney	Burgess	Abel	Walters	Williams	Butler	Steele	Tait	Vicary	Oghani	Duffy	56
Ball	Ward	Duffy	Burgess	Cooke	Walters	Williams	Butler	Tait	Steele	Vicary	Oghani	Sweeney	57
Ball	Ward	Duffy	Burgess	Abel	Walters	Williams	Butler	Cooke	Steele	Vicary	Tait	Oghani	58
Ball	Ward	Duffy	Burgess	Abel	Walters	Williams	Butler	Tait	Steele	Cooke	Oghani	Humphreys	59
Ball	Ward	Tait	Sweeney	Cooke	Duffy	Williams	Steele	Oghani	Humphreys	Vicary	Carty	Simpson	60
Greygoose	Ward	Tait	Burgess	Cooke	Walters	Williams	Butler	Steele	Humphreys	Vicary	Simpson	Oghani	61
Greygoose	Simpson	Duffy	Burgess	Abel	Walters	Williams	Butler	Cooke	Steele	Vicary	Ward	Humphreys	62

Northwich Victoria

MARK HANCOCK

Born in Ellesmere Port on September 30th, 1960, Mark began playing for works side Van Leer. A strong, dominant and fearless centre-half, he resisted calls to play semi-professional football for some time but was finally persuaded to join Telford United. Several successful seasons at the Bucks Head followed before 'Hanks' left Shropshire for mid-Cheshire after being signed by then Vics boss Cliff Roberts in 1990.

After 182 games for the Greens, Mark's playing career was sadly curtailed by injury. It was probably fitting however, that his last act in a Green shirt was to hoist aloft a trophy after Vics landed the 1994 Mid-Cheshire Senior Cup.

Vics were keen to keep Mark at the club and when the reserve team management duo of Nigel Deeley and Jimmy Evans left the club for Congleton Town in August 1995, he was appointed manager of Vics' second string.

He made an immediate impression, commanding respect from young and senior players alike, and when Brian Kettle left the club following the FA Trophy final, hancock saw off a list of well-known applicants to earn the Drill Field post.

Delwyn Humphreys of Northwich in action. *Photo - Northwich Chronicle*

Programme details:
32 pages for £1.20
Editor - William Hughes

Any other club publications:
Northwich Victoria 1996 Yearbook
by Wm. Hughes £3.00
Not in the Same League £1 (Fanzine)

Local Newspapers:
Northwich Guardian (Wednesday) 01606 43333
Northwich Chronicle (Wednesday) 01606 42272
Daily Post
Manchester Evening News Pink (Saturday evenings)

Local Radio Stations:
GMR (BBC Manchester)
Piccadilly Radio, Signal Radio

NORTHWICH VICTORIA - PLAYING SQUAD 1996-97

Player	Honours	Birthplace and date	Transfer Fees	Previous Clubs
GOALKEEPERS				
Dean Greygoose	EY	Thetford 18/12/64		Camb.Utd, Leyton Orient, Crystal Palace, Crewe Alexandra, Holywell T
DEFENDERS				
Dave Burgess		Liverpool 20/1/60		Tranmere R, Grimsby T, Blackpool, Carlisle U
Derek Ward		Birkenhead 17/5/72		Bury, Southport
Wayne Fairclough		Nottingham 27/4/68		Notts Co, Mansfield, Chesterfield
Wes Simpson		Winsford 29/3/77		Crewe Alexandra
MIDFIELDERS				
Chris Duffy		Manchester 31/10/73		Crewe Alexandra, Wigan Ath.
Jason Gallagher		Liverpool 25/3/72		Marine, Ternia (Belg), Witton Alb.
Shane Reddish		Bolsover 20/9/69		Mansfield T, Doncaster R, Carlisle U, Hartlepool U
Steve Walters	EY	Plymouth 9/1/72		Crewe Alexandra
Eddie Bishop		Liverpool 28/11/62		Winsford U, Northwich V, Altrincham, Runcorn, Tranmere R, Chester C
FORWARDS				
Delwyn Humphreys	ESP, GMVC FAT, SSC	Shrewsbury 13/2/65	£10,000	Newtown, Bridgnorth T, Kidderminster H
Paul Tait		Newcastle 24/10/74		Everton, Wigan Athletic, Runcorn
Lee Steele		Liverpool		Bootle
Darren Vicary		Liverpool		Cammell Lairds
Ian Cooke		Bebington 1/11/73		Cammell Lairds

Departures during season:
Jeff Parker (Barrow), Lee Cooper (Knowsley U), Neil Hardy (Altrincham), Rob Radcliffe (Macclesfield T), Rob Hilton (Tetley Walker), George Oghani (Guiseley - Loan), Charlie Boyd (Congleton T - Loan), Steve Holden (Released), Hugh McAuley (Skelmersdale U), Darren Tinson (Macclesfield T), Charlie Boyd (Winsford U), Paul Clayton (Released), Graeme Hughes (Released), Neil Ogden (Released).
Players on loan during season:
Jon Sunderland (Blackpool), Mike Edwards (Tranmere R).
Departures during close season: George Oghani (Released), Brian Butler (Southport), Mark Jones (Hyde U), Graham Abel (Chorley), Carwyn Williams (Macclesfield T).

Drill Field, Northwich Victoria

ADDRESS:
The Drill Field, Drill Field Road, Northwich, Cheshire. CW9 5HN.

TELEPHONE NUMBERS:
01606 41450. Fax: 01606 330577. Internet address: http://www.u-net.com/~sandiway/home.htm. **Club Newsline:** 0891 12 27 13

SIMPLE DIRECTIONS:
Leave M6 at Junc.19 and follow A556 towards Chester. At second roundabout (approx. 6 miles), turn right onto A533. Ground on right 1.5 miles behind Volunteer Public House.

CAPACITY: 14,000 (currently limited to 3,500) **SEATED:** 660 **COVERED TERRACING:** 2,000

RECORD ATTENDANCE:
11,290 v Witton Albion, Cheshire League, Good Friday 1949.

CLUB SHOP:
Located inside ground. Open match days. Manager: Andy Dakin.

SOCIAL FACILITIES:
Large social club with members lounge and seperate function room - both available for hire Tel: 0606 43120. Food available on matchdays with prior notice. Bass beers, Pool, Darts, TV.

PREVIOUS GROUNDS: None

Northwich Fact File

Nickname: The Vics

Club Sponsors: Harvey's Tyres.

Previous Leagues: The Combination 1890-1892, Football League Div.2 1892-94, The Combination 1894-1898, The Cheshire League 1898-1900, Manchester League 1900-12, Lancashire 1912-19, Cheshire County League 1919-68, Northern Premier League 1968-79.

Club colours: Green & white shirts, green shorts and white socks.

Change colours: Navy & red stripes, navy shorts, navy sock.

Midweek home matchday: Monday.

Record transfer fee: £10,000 to Hyde United for Malcolm O'Connor - August 1988 and to Kidderminster Harriers for Delwyn Humphreys - September 1995.

Record transfer fee received: £50,000 from Chester City for Neil Morton - October 1990.

Club record goalscorer: Peter Burns 160 - 1955-65.

Record appearances: 970 by Ken Jones 1969-85.

Past players who progressed to the Football League: To numerous to list.

Club Honours: Welsh Cup Runners-up 1881/82,1888-89; FA Trophy Winners 1983/84, Runners-up 1982/83 & 1995/96; Bob Lord Trophy Winners 1979/80, 92/93; Northern Premier League Runners-up 1976/77; Northern Premier League Cup Winners 1972/73, Runners-up 1978/79; Cheshire County League Champions 1956/57, Runners-up 1924/25, 47/48; Cheshire County League Cup Winners 1925/35; Manchester League Champions 1902/03, Runners-up 1900/01, 03/04, 07/08, 08/09, 11/12; The Combination Runners-up 1890/91; Cheshire Senior Cup Winners 1880-81, 81/82, 82/83, 83/84, 84/85, 85/86, 1928/29, 36/37, 49/50, 54/55, 71/72, 76/77, 78/79, 83/84, 93/94. Runners-up 1891/92, 96/97, 1905/06, 08/09, 47/48, 50/51, 63/64, 1965/66, 69/70, 70/71, 77/78, 85/86; Staffordshire Senior Cup Winners 1978/79, 79/80, 89/90, Runners-up 1986/87, 90/91; Cheshire Amateur Cup Winners 1901/02, Runners-up 1898/99, 02/93, Northwich Senior Cup Winners 1948/49, 58/59, 59/60, 63/64, 64/65, 65/66, 67/68, 68/69, 69/70, 71/72, 74/75, Runners-up 1953/54, 54/55, 55/56, 57/58, 60/61, 61/62.1972/73; Mid Cheshire Senior Cup Winners 1984/85, 85/86, 87/88, 89/90, Runners-up 1982/83, 83/84, 90/91, 92/93; North-West Floodlit League Winners 1966/67, 75/76; Cheshire League Lancashire Combination Inter-League Cup Winners 1961/62; Guardian Charity Shield Winners 1985/86, 86/87, 87/88.

RUSHDEN & DIAMONDS

Formed 1992

President
D Attley

Chairman
W M Griggs

Managing Director
M G Darnell

Football Secretary
David Joyce

Manager
Roger Ashby
Assistant Manager
Billy Jeffrey
Coach
Paul Richardson

Physiotherapist
Peter Bronwn

Press Officer
David Joyce

The story of Rushden & Diamonds FC is almost a fairystory, and their short, rapid rise since being formed just four years ago, now sees them performing at the top of non-League's Pyramid. Who would have thought that when they were still a Southern League Midland Division outfit in 1994. However, backed by the Griggs Group, Diamonds have gone through the Premier Division after a season of stabilising when they finished in fifth place, and now possess absolutely superb facilities which would grace any league.

It almost seemed inevitable that Diamonds would win the Premier Division last season. Manager Roger Ashby was able to go out and sign quality players such as England semi-professional internationals Graham Benstead and Nick Ashby from neighbours Kettering Town and they were followed later in the campaign by fellow internationals Steve Holden, Steve Stott and, for a non-League record fee of £85,000, striker Carl Alford. Equally important signings during the summer of 1995 were defender Al James Hannigan, striker Kevin Wilkin and winger Brendan Hackett.

It was expected that opposition would mainly come from Gloucester City and Cheltenham Town, but it was Halesowen Town who pushed Diamonds really hard in the end, and a dip in form around Christmasn time caused some concern at Nene Park. But, the signing of Alford, who netted seven goals in ten games, helped Diamonds to take the title with Halesowen having to make do with the runners-up spot.

More work has been done in the last close season to make Nene Park even better, with a new stand being built which will take its all-seater capacity to beyond 10,000. Roger Ashby was able to strengthen his squad by signing two more internationals in Mark Tucker and Kenny Cramman, although it would be a surprise if they went straight through the Conference to the League at the first attempt, it seems almost inevitable that it will happen sooner or later. Steve Whitney

Back Row (L-R); Andy Kirkup, Al James Hannigan, Brendan Hackett, Steve Stott, Terry Wilson, Glen Fuff, Tim Wooding, Steve Lilwall. Centre; Peter Brown (Physio), Paul Richardson (Coach), Darren Collins, Steve Holden, Nick Ashby, Martin Davies, Graham Benstead, Kevin Wilkin, Andy Furnell, Mark Tucker, Billy Jeffrey (Asst Mgr), Kenny Mist (Res Mgr). Front; Kenny Cramman, Carl Alford, Neil Smith, Roger Ashby (Mgr), Gary Butterworth, Ian King, Andy Peaks.

Photo - Peter Barnes

Rushden & Diamonds

Match No.	Date		Comp.	Venue H/A	Opponents	Result	League Pos.	Goalscorers (Times if known)	Attendance
1	Aug	19	BHL	H	Salisbury	Won 3-0		Wilkin, Kirkup, Collins	1532
2		21	BHL	A	Chelmsford	Won 2-1		Spooner, Watkins	1003
3		26	BHL	H	Crawley	Won 3-1		Butterworth, Watkins 2	1611
4		28	BHL	A	Burton	Lost 2-4		Watkins, Collins	901
5	Sep	2	BHL	A	Hastings	Won 1-0		Watkins	552
6		5	BHL	H	VS Rugby	Won 6-1		Ashby, Wilkin, Watkins 3, Bailey	1624
7		9	FAC	H	Grantham	Won 4-1		Collins 3, Wilkin	1681
8		16	BHL	A	Worcester	Drew 0-0			960
9		19	BHL	H	Chelmsford	Won 2-1		og, Collins	1747
10		23	FAC	H	Eastwood Han	Won 1-0		Collins	1652
11		30	BHL	A	Cheltenham	Won 2-0		Kirkup, Collins	1122
12	Oct	7	FAC	A	Sandwell	Won 6-1		Wilkin 4, Collins 2	250
13		14	BHL	A	Gresley	Won 3-0		Hannigan, Collins, Butterworth	808
14		21	FAC	A	Purfleet	Drew 1-1		Hannigan	794
15		24	FAC	H	Purfleet	Won 3-1		Watkins, Collins, Wilkin	2850
16		28	BHL	A	Merthyr	Won 3-0		Collins, Kirkup, Watkins	464
17	Nov	1	DMC	H	Kings Lynn	Won 1-0		Collins	1098
18		4	BHL	H	Stafford	Won 5-1		Wooding, Watkins, Wilkin 2, Hackett	2078
19		7	SC	H	Long Buckby	Won 4-0		Nuttell 2, Watkins, Kirkup	574
20		11	FAC	H	Cardiff	Lost 1-3		Hannigan	4214
21		15	BHL	A	VS Rugby	Won 3-1		Wilkin 3	741
22		18	BHL	A	Gravesend	Won 3-1		Wilkin, Collins, Smith	658
23		21	BHL	H	Burton	Won 2-0		Wilkin, Collins	1651
24		25	BHL	H	Atherstone	Won 7-3		Collins 4, Hackett, Hannigan, Ashby	2231
25		28	BHL	H	Baldock	Won 3-0		Collins, Kirkup, Wilkin	1922
26	Dec	2	BHL	A	Crawley	Drew 2-2		Wooding, Collins	1118
27		5	DMC	A	Kings Lynn	Lost 0-2			432
28		9	BHL	A	Dorchester	Drew 1-1		Wilkin	684
29		12	BHL	H	Gloucester	Won 3-2		Kirkup, Collins 2	1666
30		16	BHL	H	Hastings	Drew 1-1		Watkins	1946
31		23	BHL	H	Ilkeston	Won 3-0		Wilkin, Hackett, Watkins	2312
32	Jan	13	BHL	A	Atherstone	Won 3-1		Wilkin, Collins 2	605
33		20	FAT	H	Purfleet	Lost 0-1			1906
34		30	SC	H	Raunds	Won 1-0		Collins	904
35	Feb	3	BHL	H	Worcester	Won 1-0		Collins	2197
36		10	BHL	H	Gravesend	Lost 2-3		Watkins, Collins	1841
37		13	BHL	A	Baldock	Won 3-0		Stott, Collins 2	854
38		17	BHL	H	Cheltenham	Won 4-1		Watkins, Kirkup 2, Wilkin	2472
39		24	BHL	A	Newport	Drew 1-1		Ashby	1170
40	Mar	5	BHL	H	Sudbury	Won 3-1		Collins, Hackett, Kirkup	1409
41		16	BHL	A	Cambridge	Won 2-0		Collins, Hannigan	750
42		19	BHL	A	Halesowen	Drew 0-0			1725
43		23	BHL	A	Ilkeston	Drew 1-1		Hackett	1009
44		26	SC	A	Rothwell	Lost 0-1			511
45		30	BHL	H	Halesowen	Lost 1-2		Alford	3481
46	Apr	4	BHL	H	Dorchester	Lost 0-1			1823
47		6	BHL	H	Cambridge	Won 2-1		Collins, Alford	2135
48		8	BHL	A	Sudbury	Lost 1-4		Alford	918
49		13	BHL	H	Newport	Won 3-0		Collins, Alford, Ashby	2914
50		16	BHL	H	Gresley	Won 2-1		Collins, Alford	2250
51		20	BHL	A	Gloucester	Lost 1-2		Collins	1226
52		24	BHL	A	Salisbury	Won 2-0		Collins, Kirkup	596
53		27	BHL	A	Stafford	Won 4-0		Kirkup 2, Alford, Hackett	1160
54	May	4	BHL	H	Merthyr	Won 3-2		Butterworth, Collins, Alford	4664

Rushden & Diamonds

1	2	3	4	5	6	7	8	9	10	11	12	14	Match No.
Benstead	Reed	Ashby	Lilwall	Creaser	Hannigan	Kirkup	Butterworth	Wilkin	Smith	Collins	Spooner	Watkins	1
Benstead	Reed	Ashby	Lilwall	Creaser	Hannigan	Spooner	Butterworth	Wilkin	Smith	Collins	Kirkup	Watkins	2
Benstead	Reed	Ashby	Smith	Creaser	Hannigan	Kirkup	Butterworth	Wilkin	Watkins	Collins	Bailey	Spooner	3
Benstead	Reed	Ashby	Smith	Creaser	Hannigan	Spooner	Butterworth	Wilkin	Watkins	Collins	Kirkup	Wooding	4
Benstead	Wooding	Ashby	Peaks	Creaser	Spooner	Kirkup	Butterworth	Smith	Watkins	Collins	Wilkin	Nuttell	5
Benstead	Wooding	Ashby	Peaks	Creaser	Smith	Wilkin	Butterworth	Bailey	Watkins	Collins	Spooner	Nuttell	6
Benstead	Wooding	Ashby	Peaks	Creaser	Smith	Wilkin	Butterworth	Kirkup	Watkins	Collins	Spooner	Hannigan	7
Benstead	Wooding	Ashby	Peaks	Creaser	Hannigan	Wilkin	Butterworth	Smith	Watkins	Collins	Kirkup	Bailey	8
Benstead	Wooding	Ashby	Peaks	Hannigan	Smith	Wilkin	Butterworth	Nuttell	Watkins	Collins	Kirkup	Bailey	9
Benstead	Wooding	Ashby	Peaks	Hannigan	Smith	Wilkin	Butterworth	Nuttell	Watkins	Collins	Kirkup	Bailey	10
Benstead	Wooding	Ashby	Peaks	Smith	Hannigan	Kirkup	Butterworth	Collins	Watkins	Hackett	Wilkin	Nuttell	11
Benstead	Wooding	Ashby	Peaks	Smith	Hannigan	Kirkup	Butterworth	Collins	Wilkin	Lilwall	Bailey	Creaser	12
Benstead	Wooding	Ashby	Peaks	Smith	Hannigan	Kirkup	Butterworth	Collins	Wilkin	Hackett	Lilwall	Watkins	13
Benstead	Wooding	Ashby	Peaks	Smith	Hannigan	Kirkup	Butterworth	Wilkin	Collins	Lilwall	Nuttell	Watkins	14
Benstead	Wooding	Ashby	Peaks	Smith	Hannigan	Kirkup	Butterworth	Wilkin	Collins	Watkins	Nuttell	Lilwall	15
Benstead	Wooding	Ashby	Peaks	Smith	Hannigan	Kirkup	Butterworth	Collins	Wilkin	Hackett	Lilwall	Watkins	16
Benstead	Wooding	Ashby	Peaks	Smith	Creaser	Collins	Lilwall	Nuttell	Watkins	Hackett	Bailey	Capone	17
Benstead	Wooding	Ashby	Peaks	Smith	Hannigan	Kirkup	Butterworth	Wilkin	Watkins	Hackett	Nuttell	Lilwall	18
Benstead	Hannigan	Lilwall	Creaser	Smith	Spooner	Kirkup	Butterworth	Nuttell	Watkins	Collins	Wilkin	Bailey	19
Benstead	Wooding	Ashby	Peaks	Smith	Hannigan	Kirkup	Butterworth	Nuttell	Nuttell	Collins	Watkins	Spooner	20
Benstead	Wooding	Ashby	Peaks	Smith	Hannigan	Kirkup	Butterworth	Collins	Wilkin	Hackett	Nuttell	Watkins	21
Benstead	Wooding	Ashby	Peaks	Smith	Hannigan	Kirkup	Butterworth	Collins	Wilkin	Hackett	Nuttell	Watkins	22
Benstead	Wooding	Ashby	Peaks	Smith	Hannigan	Kirkup	Butterworth	Collins	Wilkin	Hackett	Nuttell	Watkins	23
Benstead	Wooding	Ashby	Peaks	Smith	Hannigan	Kirkup	Butterworth	Collins	Wilkin	Hackett	Nuttell	Watkins	24
Benstead	Wooding	Ashby	Peaks	Smith	Hannigan	Kirkup	Butterworth	Collins	Wilkin	Hackett	Nuttell	Watkins	25
Benstead	Wooding	Ashby	Creaser	Smith	Hannigan	Kirkup	Butterworth	Collins	Wilkin	Hackett	Watkins	Lilwall	26
Lomas	Wooding	Ashby	Creaser	Smith	Hannigan	Lilwall	Spooner	Bailey	Watkins	Hackett	Wilkin	Collins	27
Benstead	Wooding	Ashby	Peaks	Smith	Hannigan	Kirkup	Butterworth	Collins	Wilkin	Hackett	Watkins	Creaser	28
Benstead	Wooding	Ashby	Peaks	Smith	Hannigan	Kirkup	Butterworth	Collins	Wilkin	Hackett	Watkins	Creaser	29
Benstead	Wooding	Ashby	Peaks	Smith	Stott	Kirkup	Butterworth	Collins	Wilkin	King	Watkins	Spooner	30
Benstead	Peaks	Ashby	Creaser	Smith	Stott	Kirkup	Butterworth	Collins	Wilkin	Hackett	Watkins	Spooner	31
Benstead	Peaks	Ashby	Hannigan	Smith	Stott	Kirkup	Butterworth	Collins	Wilkin	Hackett	Nuttell	Spooner	32
Benstead	Peaks	Ashby	Hannigan	Smith	Stott	Kirkup	Butterworth	Collins	Wilkin	Hackett	Nuttell	Spooner	33
Benstead	Wooding	Ashby	Peaks	Smith	Spooner	Kirkup	Butterworth	Collins	Wilkin	Hackett	Watkins	Bailey	34
Benstead	Peaks	Ashby	Holden	Smith	Stott	Kirkup	Butterworth	Collins	Watkins	King	Wilkin	Spooner	35
Benstead	Peaks	Ashby	Holden	Smith	Stott	Kirkup	Butterworth	Collins	Watkins	King	Wilkin	Spooner	36
Benstead	Peaks	Ashby	Holden	Smith	Stott	Kirkup	Butterworth	Collins	Watkins	Hackett	Wilkin	Spooner	37
Benstead	Peaks	Ashby	Holden	Smith	Stott	Kirkup	Butterworth	Collins	Watkins	Hackett	Wilkin	Spooner	38
Benstead	Peaks	Ashby	Holden	Smith	Stott	Kirkup	Butterworth	Collins	Taylor	Hackett	Watkins	Wooding	39
Benstead	Wooding	Ashby	Holden	Smith	Spooner	Kirkup	Butterworth	Collins	Watkins	Hackett	Peaks	Johnson	40
Benstead	Wooding	Ashby	Holden	Smith	Hannigan	Kirkup	Butterworth	Collins	Taylor	Hackett	Spooner	Watkins	41
Benstead	Wooding	Ashby	Holden	Smith	Hannigan	Kirkup	Butterworth	Collins	Taylor	Hackett	Stott	Watkins	42
Benstead	Wooding	Ashby	Holden	Smith	Hannigan	Kirkup	Butterworth	Collins	Taylor	Hackett	Stott	Watkins	43
Benstead	Wooding	Ashby	Peaks	Smith	Hannigan	Kirkup	Spooner	Collins	Wilkin	Hackett	Watkins	Bailey	44
Benstead	Wooding	Ashby	Holden	Stott	Hannigan	Kirkup	Butterworth	Collins	Taylor	Hackett	Peaks	Holmes	45
Lomas	Wooding	Ashby	Peaks	Stott	Hannigan	Wilkin	Butterworth	Collins	Alford	Holmes	Spooner	Watkins	46
Lomas	Wooding	Ashby	Peaks	Stott	Hannigan	Kirkup	Butterworth	Collins	Alford	Hackett	Spooner	Holmes	47
Lomas	Wooding	Ashby	Peaks	Spooner	Hannigan	Kirkup	Butterworth	Collins	Alford	Hackett	Stott	Lilwall	48
Benstead	Peaks	Ashby	Holden	Spooner	Stott	Kirkup	Butterworth	Collins	Alford	Hackett	Watts	Bailey	49
Benstead	Peaks	Ashby	Holden	Spooner	Stott	Kirkup	Butterworth	Collins	Alford	Hackett	Hannigan	Bailey	50
Benstead	Peaks	Ashby	Holden	Spooner	Stott	Kirkup	Butterworth	Collins	Alford	Hackett	Hannigan	Holmes	51
Benstead	Peaks	Ashby	Hannigan	Spooner	Stott	Kirkup	Butterworth	Collins	Alford	Hackett	Watkins	King	52
Benstead	Peaks	Lilwall	Hannigan	Spooner	Stott	Kirkup	Butterworth	Collins	Alford	Hackett	Holden	Watkins	53
Benstead	Peaks	Lilwall	Holden	Stott	Hannigan	Kirkup	Butterworth	Collins	Alford	Hackett	King	Holmes	54

Rushden & Diamonds

ROGER ASHBY

Roger, who began his playign career at Northampton Town, made over 500 appearances for Kettering Town where he made the number two shirt his own. He played under a number of managers at Rockingham Road, most notably Ron Atkinson and Mick Jones, for whom he played at Wembley in the FA Trophy final in 1979, losing to Stafford Rangers.

He commenced his managerial career at Irthlingborough Diamonds where he led them to many successes including an FA Vase semi-final. After a brief sojourn at Wolverton in the Isthmian League he moved to Rushden Town where he revived their fortunes and led them to promotion from the Southern League Midland Division. Unfortunately, ground standards meant a swift exit from the Premier Division after one year.

1992 saw the merger between Irthlingborough Diamonds and Rushden Town and Roger was the obvious choice to manage the newly-formed Rushden & Diamonds FC. The rest is history.

Rushden & Diamonds leading scorer and Player of the Year; Darren Collins

Programme details:
48 pages for £1.30
Editors - Ted Carroll & Dave Joyce

Any other club publications:

Local Newspapers:
Northants Evening Telegraph
Chronicle & Echo
Citizen
Herald & Post

Local Radio Stations:
Radio Northampton
KCBC
Northants 96
Radio Diamonds

RUSHDEN & DIAMONDS - PLAYING SQUAD 1996-97

Player	Honours	Birthplace and date	Transfer Fees	Previous Clubs
GOALKEEPERS				
Martin Davies		Swansea 28/6/74	£6,000	Coventry C, Cambridge U
Graham Benstead	ESP, EY, BHP	Aldershot 20/8/63		QPR, Norwich C, Sheffield U, Brentford, Kettering T
DEFENDERS				
Steve Holden	ESP, BHP	Luton 4/9/72		Leicester C, Carlisle U, Kettering T
Nick Ashby	ESP, BHP	Northampton 29/12/70	£14,000	Nottingham F, Rushden T, Aylesbury U, Kettering T
Jim Rodwell	BHP		£40,000	Darlington, Sabam(Malaya), Bury, Boston, Boston U, B'worth, H'ford, N'ton, H'owen
Tim Wooding	BHP	Wellingborough 5/7/73		Norwich C, AFC Bournemouth
Mark Tucker	ESP, FAT,	Woking 27/4/72	£35,000	Fulham, Woking
Al-James Hannigan	BHP	London 26/1/71	£5,000	Arsenal, Barnet, Harwich & Parkeston, Harlow T, Marlow, Enfield
Andy Peaks	BHP, BHM	Northampton 25/11/70		Northampton T
MIDFIELDERS				
Gary Butterworth	BHP	Peterborough 8/9/69	£20,000	Peterborough U, Dagenham & Redbridge
Steve Lilwall	BHP	Birmingham 15/2/70		Moor Green, Kidderminster H, WBA
Steve Stott	ESP, BHP	Leeds 3/2/65	£30,000	Alvechurch, Bromsgrove R, Kettering T
Kenny Cramman	ESP	Gateshead 17/8/65	£40,000	Hartlepool, Bishop Auckland, Gateshead
Neil Smith	BHP	Cradley 29/12/70	£11,000	Shrewsbury T, Redditch U, Lincoln C,
Brendan Hackett		Wolverhampton 2/3/66		Bilston, Redditch, Stourbridge, Dudley, Worcester, Gloucester, Telford, Hednesford
FORWARDS				
Carl Alford	ESP	Denton 11/2/72	£85,000	Rochdale, Stockport, Burnley, Witton A, Macclesfield T, Kettering T
Darren Collins	ESP, BHP	Winchester 24/5/67	£20,000	Petersfield U, Northampton T, Aylesbury U, Enfield
Andy Furnell		Peterborough 13/2/77		Peterborough U
Kevin Wilkin		Cambridge 1/10/67		Histon, Cambridge C, Northampton T
Ian King	BHP	Rugby 23/12/74		Aston Villa, WBA, VS Rugby, Stoke C
Richard Bailey		Kettering 29/10/74		From Youth Team
Andy Kirkup	BHP, BHM	Hartlepool 17/10/64		Rushden T, Wellingborough T, Rushden T

Departures during season:
Glyn Creaser (Dagenham & R), Dave Johnson & Dale Watkins (Gliucester C), Graham Reed (Dagenham & R), Mickey Nuttell (Burton A), Kevin Brock, Steve Spooner, Andy Lomas (Released).
Players on loan during season:
Steve Taylor (Crystal Palace).

Nene Park, Irthlingborough

ADDRESS: Nene Park, Station Road, Irthlingborough, Northants (01933 652000).

TELEPHONE NUMBER: 01933 652000. Fax: 01933 650418. **Newsline:** 0891 12 29 25.

SIMPLE DIRECTIONS:
South from M1 exit 15, A45 bypassing Northampton until A6 - 1st exit North - ground approx 400 yards right. North & West from A14 exit A6 South (Bedford), follow A6 for approx 6 miles, ground on left. East from A14 exit A45 (Northampton) follow A45 for approx 4 miles to A6 - 3rd exit North - ground approx 400 yards on right.

CAPACITY: 3,900 (until Dec.1996) then 6,000. **SEATED:** 2,000 (until Dec.1996) then 4,500. **COVERED:** 4,000

RECORD ATTENDANCE:
4,664 v Merthyr Tydfil - Southern League Premier Div. May 1996.

CLUB SHOP:
Sells programmes, replica shirts, scarves, hats etc. Contact Bernard Lake (01933 652000, extn.2263).

SOCIAL FACILITIES:
Lounge facilities. Open all day, every day. Full restaurant facilities.

Rushden & D. Fact File

Nickname: Diamonds

Club Sponsors: Whitworths Ltd

Previous Grounds: Rushden Town: Hayden Road, Rushden (pre-1992).

Previous Leagues: Rushden Town: Midland 1894-1901/ Utd Co's 01-04, 19-56, 61-83, Central Alliance 61-83. Irthlingborough Diamonds: Rushden Yth/Rushden & Dist/Kettering Am. Rushden & Diamonds: Southern League 92-96.

Club colours: White (Red & Blue trim) shirts, Blue shorts, white socks.

Change colours: Blue & White striped shirts, Blue shorts, Blue socks.

Reserve team league: Capital League (midweek), Endsleigh Insurance Midland Football Comb.

Midweek home matchday: Tuesday.

Record win: 7-0 v Redditch Utd (H), Southern League Midland Div. 7/5/94.

Record defeat: 0-4 v Leicester Utd (A), Southern League Midland Div. 92/93.

Record transfer fee: £85,000 to Kettering Town for Carl Alford - 1996.

1995-96 Captain: Neil Smith

1995-96 Top scorer: Darren Collins 39 goals.

1995-96 Player of the Year: Darren Collins.

Club record goalscorer: Darren Collins 67.

Record appearances: Andy Peaks - 129.

Past players who progressed to the Football League: From Rushden Town: Gordon Inwood (WBA 1949), Robert Peacock (Northampton 1957). From Irthlingborough Diamonds: Scott Endersby (Ipswich), Steve Brown & Dave Johnson (Northampton),

Club Honours: As Rushden Town: Southern Lg Midland Div R-up 88-89, Utd Co's Lg 02-03, 26-27, 29-30, 31-32, 34-38, 63-64, 72-73, R-up twelve times, Lg Cup 33-35, 36-38, 46-47, Northants Snr Cup 25-28, 29-31, 34-35, 36-37, 57-58, 77-78, FA Vase QF 89-90. As Irthlingborough Diamonds: Utd Co's Lg 70-71, 76-77, 78-79, 82-83, KO Cup 78-79, 80-81, Northants Snr Cup 80-81. **As Rushden & Diamonds:** Southern Lg Premier Div 95-96, Southern Lg Midland Div 94-95, Northants Snr Cup 94-95, Daventry Charity Cup 92-93, Campri Leisurewear Cup 92-93, FA Trophy S/F 94-95.

SLOUGH TOWN

Formed:
1890

Chairman
A A Thorne

Vice-Chairman
B A Thorne

Chief Executive
Bob Breen

Secretary
David Stanley

Manager
Brian McDermott

Player/Coach
Gary Micklewhite

Physiotherapist
Kevin McGoldrick

Press Officer:
David Stanley

An eventual finishing position of seventeenth could have been infinitely worse for Slough. It looked as though the Rebels would lose their Conference place straight away as they slid to the foot of the table, and their form eventually cost manager Dave Russell his job. However, Football in the Community officer, Brian McDermott, did a great job after replacing the ex-Marlow boss and, although results tailed off a little towards the end of the season, enough points were acrued to secure their Conference status.

Veteran striker Mark West showed that he had lost nothing of his predatory instincts with 28 goals and, although Cliff Hercules had a slightly disappointing time of it, he did provide many chances for West.

The close season saw McDermott recruit some quality players, including former QPR and Derby star Gary Micklewhite as his new player/coach, and with Gary Abbott, signed from Enfield, Slough possess a very experienced and potent attacking force and could provide Rebels supporters with a season to remember. **Steve Whitney**

Back Row (L-R): Brian McDermott (Mgr), Simon Stapleton, Steve Bateman, Robert Paris, Jamie Jackson, Paul Wilkerson, Gary Blackford, Cliff Hercules, Gary Abbott, Dave Brown (Asst Mgr). Middle; Bryon Walton, Garry Smith, Danny Bolt, Mark Fiore, Mark West, Gary Micklewhite, Andy Clement.
Front; Gavin Mernagh, Grant Eaton, Gary McGinnis.

Slough Town

Match No.	Date	Comp.	Venue H/A	Opponents	Result	League Pos.	Goalscorers (Times if known)	Attendance
1	Aug 19	GMVC		Southport	Lost 2-5		West 25, Blackman 41	942
2	22	GMVC		Welling	Won 3-0		Baron 13, Bushay 38,40	747
3	26	GMVC		Halifax	Won 2-1		Baron 56, 90	917
4	28	GMVC		Kidderminster Harriers	Won 5-4		West 17, Blackman 27, 49, Lay, 60,68	1092
5	Sep 2	GMVC		Morecambe	Won 2-1		Blackman 33, Picket 55	1120
6	5	GMVC		Bath City	Drew 1-1		West 16	980
7	9	GMVC		Runcorn	Lost 3-4		Fiore 35, West 49, 75	480
8	12	GMVC		Dover Athletic	Won 3-2		Bushay 46, West 49, 65	846
9	16	GMVC		Altrincham	Lost 1-2		Blackman	991
10	18	SC1		Dagenham & Redbridge	Won 3-0		Pickett 26, Bushay 47, Blackman 56	403
11	23	GMVC		Bromsgrove Rovers	Lost 2-3		West 15 p, Bushay 58	931
12	26	GMVC		Dover	Won 1-0		og	619
13	30	GMVC		Hednesford	Lost 0-2			971
14	Oct 3	SC2		Dagenham & Redbridge	Won 3-0		Bushay, West 2	456
15	7	GMVC		Kettering	Lost 0-2			1902
16	14	GMVC		Macclesfield	Drew 2-2		West 38 p, 80	1007
17	21	FACQ4		Yeading	Won 2-0		Bushay 43, 71	473
18	28	GMVC		Telford	Lost 0-2			808
19	31	GMVC		Farnborough	Drew 1-1		West 83	891
20	Nov 4	GMVC		Gateshead	Lost 1-2		West 30	642
21	11	FAC1		Plymouth Argyle	Lost 0-2			3030
22	18	GMVC		Woking	Lost 2-3		Bushay 17, Baron 63	1659
23	20	GMVC		Dagenham & Redbridge	Won 3-1		Catlin 24, 45, 60	712
24	25	GMVC		Northwich Victoria	Drew 1-1		West 15	703
25	Dec 2	GMVC		Stalybridge	Won 1-0		Hercules 52	558
26	9	GMVC		Halifax	Lost 2-3		Hercules 45, Catlin 55	862
27	16	SC		Woking	Won 3-0		West 6, 86, Hercules 54	774
28	Jan 1	GMVC		Stevenage	Lost 1-3		West 77	2123
29	6	GMVC		Gateshead	Lost 1-2		Hercules 41	768
30	13	GMVC		Altrincham	Lost 0-1		West 65 p	648
31	20	FAT1		Farnborough	Drew 1-1		West 93	856
32	23	FAT1R		Farnborough	Won 4-3		West 17 p, 58, Baron 64, 71	742
33	30	B&BSC		Reading	Lost 2-3		West 15, 52	525
34	Feb 3	GMVC		Telford	Lost 1-2		Hercules 9	682
35	10	FAT2		Kettering	Lost 1-2		Pickett 31	1058
36	13	SC		Kettering	Lost 0-2			646
37	17	GMVC		Kettering	Lost 1-2		Pickett 18	766
38	24	GMVC		Kidderminster	Lost 3-4		West, Harvey, Bushay	1715
39	Mar 2	GMVC		Farnborough	Won 1-0		Hercules	1069
40	9	GMVC		Dagenham & Redbridge	Won 5-0		Bushay 1, West 33 p, 50, Bateman 62, Catlin 64	912
41	12	GMVC		Stevenage Borough	Lost 2-6		Hercules 34, West 45	1126
42	16	GMVC		Northwich	Won 3-0		Fiore 6, Clement 78, 85	634
43	19	GMVC		Woking	Lost 0-3			1911
44	23	GMVC		Stalybridge	Won 2-1		West 46, Blackman 85	748
45	30	GMVC		Bromsgrove Rovers	Drew 0-0			687
46	Apr 3	GMVC		Bath City	Lost 1-3		Bushay 3	397
47	8	GMVC		Southport	Lost 0-2			677
48	13	GMVC		Welling United	Drew 0-0			785
49	20	GMVC		Morecambe	Drew 1-1		Hercules 46	882
50	27	GMVC		Hednesford Town	Lost 1-3		West 43	1031
51	May 2	GMVC		Macclesfield Town	Drew 1-1		Smart 60	591
52	4	GMVC		Runcorn	Lost 0-1			835

Slough Town

1	2	3	4	5	6	7	8	9	10	11	12	14	Match No.
Preddie	Clement	Fiore	Harvey	Baron	Bressington	Lee	Pye	West	Bushay	Blackman	Bateman	Pickett	1
Preddie	Clement	Fiore	Harvey	Baron	Bressington	Lee	Pye	West	Bushay	Blackman	Bateman	Pickett	2
Preddie	Clement	Fiore	Harvey	Baron	Connor	Lee	Pye	West	Bushay	Blackman	Bateman	Pickett	3
Preddie	Clement	Fiore	Harvey	Baron	Catlin	Lee	Pye	West	Lay	Blackman	Bateman	Pickett	4
Preddie	Clement	Fiore	Harvey	Baron	Catlin	Lay	Pye	West	Pickett	Blackman	Bateman	Connor	5
Preddie	Clement	Fiore	Harvey	Bressington	Catlin	Lay	Pye	West	Bushay	Blackman	Connor	Pickett	6
Preddie	Clement	Fiore	Harvey	Baron	Catlin	Lay	Pye	West	Bushay	Blackman	Lee	Pickett	7
Bunting	Clement	Fiore	Harvey	Baron	Catlin	Lee	Pye	West	Bushay	Blackman	Bateman	Pickett	8
Bunting	Clement	Fiore	Harvey	Baron	Catlin	Lee	Pye	West	Bushay	Blackman	Lay	Pickett	9
Bunting	Clement	Fiore	Harvey	Baron	Catlin	Lee	Pye	West	Pickett	Blackman	Bushay	Connor	10
Bunting	Rake	Fiore	Harvey	Baron	Catlin	Lee	Bushay	West	Pickett	Blackman	Bateman	Connor	11
Preddie	Rake	Fiore	Harvey	Baron	Catlin	Lee	Bressington	West	Bushay	Blackman	Connor	Pickett	12
Preddie	Rake	Fiore	Harvey	Baron	Catlin	Lee	Bressington	West	Bushay	Blackman	Stone	Pickett	13
Frame	Rake	Honor	Paris	Baron	Catlin	Lee	Pye	West	Bushay	Stone	Blackman	Pickett	14
Lomas	Honor	Paris	Bressington	Baron	Catlin	Stone	Pye	West	Rake	Blackman	Lee	Bushay	15
Preddie	Honor	Blackman	Paris	Baron	Catlin	Clement	Pye	West	Bushay	Rake	Lee	Pickett	16
Preddie	Honor	Fiore	Paris	Baron	Catlin	Clement	Pye	West	Bushay	Rake	Blackman	Lee	17
Preddie	Fiore	Clement	Paris	Baron	Catlin	Rake	Pye	West	Bushay	Lee	Blackman	Harvey	18
Preddie	Honor	Clement	Paris	Baron	Harvey	Blackman	Pye	West	Bushay	Fiore	Lee	Catlin	19
Preddie	Honor	Clement	Paris	Baron	Catlin	Harvey	Pye	West	Bushay	Blackman	Lee	Pickett	20
Preddie	Honor	Clement	Paris	Baron	Harvey	Catlin	Bushay	West	Pickett	Fiore	Lee	Blackman	21
Preddie	Honor	Lee	Paris	Baron	Catlin	Fiore	Pye	West	Bushay	Blackman	Harvey	Pickett	22
Preddie	Honor	Lee	Paris	Baron	Blackman	Catlin	Pye	West	Bushay	Fiore	Harvey	Rake	23
Preddie	Honor	Lee	Paris	Baron	Catlin	Blackman	Pye	West	Bushay	Fiore	Harvey	Pickett	24
Bunting	Honor	Lee	Paris	Baron	Catlin	Clement	Pye	West	Hercules	Fiore	Harvey	Bushay	25
Bunting	Clement	Lee	Paris	Baron	Catlin	Rake	Pye	West	Hercules	Fiore	Harvey	Bushay	26
Bunting	Rake	Lee	Paris	Baron	Catlin	Clement	Pye	West	Hercules	Fiore	Harvey	Preddie	27
Bunting	Rake	Lee	Paris	Baron	Catlin	Clement	Pye	West	Hercules	Fiore	Harvey	Honor	28
Bunting	Honor	Lee	Paris	Baron	Catlin	Clement	Pye	West	Hercules	Fiore	Harvey	Bushay	29
Moussaddik	Honor	Lee	Paris	Baron	Catlin	Clement	Bushay	West	Hercules	Fiore	Harvey	Pye	30
Moussaddik	Blackman	Lee	Paris	Baron	Catlin	Clement	Pye	West	Bushay	Fiore	Bateman	Pickett	31
Moussaddik	Rake	Lee	Paris	Baron	Catlin	Clement	Pye	West	Bushay	Fiore	Bateman	Pickett	32
Moussaddik	Harvey	Lee	Paris	Baron	Bateman	Clement	Bushay	West	Hercules	Fiore	Blackman	Pickett	33
Moussaddik	Harvey	Lee	Paris	Baron	Bateman	Rake	Bushay	West	Hercules	Fiore	Blackman	Pickett	34
Moussaddik	Clement	Lee	Paris	Baron	Catlin	Blackman	Bushay	West	Harvey	Fiore	Pickett	Bateman	35
Moussaddik	McVie	Bateman	Paris	Baron	Blackman	Clement	Pickett	West	Bushay	Fiore	Dalli	Horner	36
Moussaddik	Clement	Lee	Paris	Baron	Bateman	Blackman	Bushay	West	Pickett	Fiore	Rake	Dalli	37
Miles	Harvey	Lee	Paris	Bateman	Clement	Bushay	Rake	West	McVie	Fiore	McDermott	Pickett	38
Miles	Lee	Sansom	Paris	Bateman	Catlin	Clement	Rake	West	Hercules	Fiore	Harvey	McDermott	39
Miles	Lee	Sansom	Paris	Bateman	Catlin	Rake	Bushay	West	Harvey	Fiore	Horner	McDermott	40
Miles	Lee	Sansom	Paris	Bateman	Catlin	Hercules	Bushay	West	Harvey	Fiore	Rake	Blackman	41
Miles	Harvey	Sansom	Paris	Bateman	Catlin	Clement	Rake	West	Hercules	Fiore	Lee	Bushay	42
Miles	Harvey	Sansom	Paris	Bateman	Clement	Catlin	Blackman	West	Hercules	Fiore	Rake	Lee	43
Miles	Harvey	Lee	Smart	Bateman	Catlin	Clement	Pickett	West	Gray	Fiore	McDermott	Blackman	44
Miles	Harvey	Smith	Smart	Bateman	Catlin	Clement	Gray	West	Hercules	Fiore	Lee	Pickett	45
Miles	Smart	Gray	Bateman	Harvey	Catlin	Clement	Bushay	West	Hercules	Fiore	Blackman	Pickett	46
Miles	Smart	Lee	Harvey	Bateman	Catlin	Pickett	Bushay	West	Hercules	Fiore	Gray	Blackman	47
Miles	Lee	Sansom	Harvey	Bateman	Catlin	Clement	Bushay	West	Hercules	Fiore	Pickett	Gray	48
Miles	Smart	Nolan	Harvey	Bateman	Catlin	Gray	Lee	West	Hercules	Fiore	Pickett	Eaton	49
Miles	Smart	Nolan	Harvey	Bateman	Catlin	Pickett	Lee	West	Hercules	Fiore	Blackman	Wicks	50
Miles	Smart	Nolan	Harvey	Bateman	Catlin	McDermott	Lee	West	Pickett	Fiore	Gray	Wicks	51
													52

Slough Town

BRIAN McDERMOTT

Brian was appointed as manager mid-way through the 1995/96 season following the departure of Dave Russell. It was an appointment from withing the Wexham Park ranks as he had already been with the club for a year as Football in the Community Officer.

Born in Slough, Brian's playing career began with Arsenal, where he progressed through to make 61 first-team appearances for the Gunners before joining Oxford United in 1984. Spells with Cardiff City and Exeter City followed and after a total of around 200 League games, Brian moved into the semi-professional game with Yeovil Town. He then moved out to play in Hong Kong with the South China club before returning to play for Marlow and then Stamco (now St.Leonards Stamcroft) in the Sussex County League alongside a number of other former League stars, including ex-Arsenal team-mate Steve Gatting.

Now 35, the former England Youth international winger is embarking on his first full season as manager of the Rebels and has enlisted the help of another experienced former professional in Gary Micklewhite as playr/coach.

Brian McDermott

Mark West Player of the Year & Top Scorer
Photo - Dave West

Programme details:
36 pages for £1.50
Editor - David Stanley.

Any other club publications:
Rebels without a Clue (fanzine)

Local Newspapers:
Slough Observer
Slough Express

Local Radio Stations:
Thames Valley FM
Star FM

SLOUGH TOWN - PLAYING SQUAD 1996-97

Player	Honours	Birthplace and date	Transfer Fees	Previous Clubs
GOALKEEPERS				
Paul Wilkerson		Hertford 11/12/74		Watford
DEFENDERS				
Steve Bateman	ILP, FAYC	Berkhamsted 22/4/65		Everton, Chesham U, Harrow B
Danny Bolt		Wandsworth 5/2/76		Fulham
Gary Blackford	ILP	Redhill 25/9/68		Whyteleafe, Croydon, Fisher A, Barnet, Dag & Red, Enfield
Gary Smart		Totnes 29/4/64		Wokingham T, Oxford U, Stevenage B, Hayes
Gary McGinnis	Su21	Dundee 21/10/63		Celtic, Dundee U, St.Johnstone, Happy Valley (HK)
Andy Clement	FAT	Cardiff 12/11/67		Wimbledon, Plymouth A, Woking
Grant Eton		Slough		From Youth Team
MIDFIELDERS				
Mark Pye	ILP	Hammersmith 29/2/68	£5,500	West Ham U, North Greenford U, Harrow B, Enfield
Simon Stapleton	ESP, GMVC, FAT, ILP	Oxford 10/12/68		Portsmouth, Bristol R, Wycombe W
Mark Fiore		Southwark 18/11/69		Wimbledon, Plymouth A
Gary Micklewhite	Div 2	Southwark 21/3/61		Manchester U, QPR, Derby Co, Gillingham
Andy Gray		Southampton 25/10/73		Reading, Leyton Orient
FORWARDS				
Mark West	ESP, FAT	High Wycombe 16/2/66		West Ham U, Reading, Wycombe W
Byron Walton		London 2/4/65		Millwall, Aylesbury, Hayes, Wokingham, Wycombe, Windsor, Chesham, Chertsey
Gary Abbott	ESP, ILP	Catford 7/11/64		Welling U, Barnet, Enfield, Welling U, Enfield
Gavin Mernagh		Slough 11/6/78		Queens Park Rangers
Cliff Hercules	FAXI, ILP	Aylesbury 16/8/63	£10,000	Oving, Aylesbury U

Departures during season:
Andy Sayer (Enfield), Ross Pickett (Chesham U - Loan), Steve Bateman (Berkhamsted T - Loan), Trevor Baron (Woking), Graham Bressington (Released), Delroy Preddie (Walton & Hersham - Loan), Alan Paris (Stevenage B).

Players on loan during season:
Andy Lomas (Rushden & D), Ben Miles (Swansea C).

Departures during close season: Garfield Blackman, Ansil Bushay, Brian Lee, Barry Rake, Delroy Preddie (Walton & Hersham), Ross Pickett (Hayes), Lee Harvey (Yeovil T).

Wexham Park Stadium, Slough

ADDRESS: Wexham Park Stadium, Wexham Road, Slough, Berkshire. SL2 5QR.
TELEPHONE NUMBER: 01753 523358 Fax: 01753 516956.

GROUND DIRECTIONS:
From North: M25 J16 East London M40 J1 - South A412 through Iver Heath to George Green. 2nd set lights turn right by George PH, George Green. Church Lane 1 mile to end, then small roundabout, turn left, ground 1/4 mile on right.
From East: M25 J15/M4 J5 to A4 West to Co-Op Superstore on right, A412 North (Uxbridge), dual carriageway to 4th set lights. Church Lane, then as from North.
From South: If M25 then as from East. From Windsor A355 under M4 J6 to A4, turn right, pass Brunel Bus station on left, Tesco Superstore, also on left, then first left, Wexham Road, signposted Wexham Park Hospital, ground just over 1 mile on left. From West: If M4 J6 then as from South.

CAPACITY: 5,000 **SEATED:** 450 **COVERED TERRACING:** 1,890

RECORD ATTENDANCE: 8,000 - Schoolboys u15 Final Slough v Liverpool - 1976

CLUB SHOP: Contact John Linlow (0753 571710).

PREVIOUS GROUNDS: Dolphin Playing Fields & Stadium, Chalvey Road Sports Ground, York Road Maidenhead 1920, Centre Sports Ground 1936-42.

SOCIAL FACILITIES: Rebels bar & Lounge bar open weekdays 7pm-11pm, weekends lunchtime/evenings. Banqueting hall for all types of functions. 25 bay golf driving range.

Slough Town Fact File

Nickname: The Rebels

Club Sponsor: The Cable Corporation

Previous Leagues: Southern Alliance 1892-93/ Berks & Bucks 1901-05/ Gt Western Suburban 1906-19/ Spartan 1920-39/ Herts & Middx 1940-45/ Corinthian 1946-63/ Athenian 1963-73/ Isthmian 1973-90, 94-95/ Alliance Prem. (GMVC) 90-94.

Club colours: Amber shirts, navy blue shorts, amber socks

Change colours: All white

Midweek home matchday: Tuesdays

Record win: 17-0 v Railway Clearing House - 1921-22.

Record defeat: 1-11 v Chesham Town 1909/10.

Record transfer fee: £18,000 for Colin Fielder from Farnborough - 1991

Record transfer fee received: £22,000 from Wycombe Wanderers for Steve Thompson **Record goalscorer:** Terry Norris 84 - 1925/26

Record appearances: Terry Reardon 458 - 1964/81

1995-96 Captain: Andy Clement

1995-96 Top scorer: Mark West

1995-96 Player of the Year: Mark West

1995-96 Supporters' Player of the Year: Mark West

Past players who progressed to the Football League: Bill McConnell, Peter Angell, Dennis Edwards, Ralph Miller, John Delaney, Paul Barron, Dave Kemp, Roy Davies, Mickey Droy, Eric Young, Alan Paris, Tony Dennis.

Honours: FA Amateur Cup R-up 72-73; Great Western Suburban League R-up 19-20: Spartan League R-up 20-21 21-22 31-32 32-33 38-39; Herts & Middx League R-up 43-44; Corinthian League 50-51 (R-up 45-46 46-47 57-58); Athenian League 67-68 71-72 72-73 (R-up 68-69, Div 1 64-65, Memorial Shield 64-65 71-72 72-73); Isthmian League 80-81 89-90 R-up 94-95, (Div 2 R-up 73-74), League Shield 80-81 89-90 (R-up 94-95); Berks & Bucks Senior Cup(9) 02-03 19-20 23-24 35-36 54-55 70-72 76-77 80-81.

SOUTHPORT

Formed:
1881

President:
Jack Carr

Chairman:
Charles Clapham

Football Secretary:
Roy Morris

Manager:
Steve Joel

Assistant Manager
Peter Davenport

Physiotherapist:
Mark Thompson

Press Officer:
Roy Morris

The 1995/96 season began with a degree of high hopes for Southport following the unbeaten eight game run-in under new manager Billy Ayre at the end of the previous season. Former Manchester United, Nottingham Forest and England star Peter Davenport signed on the opening day of the season and a Steve Haw hat-trick and a brace of Dave Gamble penalties lifted the club to a 5-2 win at Slough - it was to be the only time that the team topped the table all season. A number of seasoned professionals were brought in by Ayre, including exBlackpool winger Bryan Griffiths and former York forward Ian Blackstone, but the latter was dogged by injury and only made 12 starts all season.

By the end of October the club had sunk to 18th place in the table and had bowed out of the FA Cup at Telford at the first attempt. A surge in mid-season lifted the Sandgrounders to the top six and it was in that position that they finally finished. Another big disappointment saw the 'Port fall at the first hurdle in the FA Trophy, going down 2-1 at Halifax. The club won its first game in the Spalding Cup but bowed out at Macclesfield in the semi-final, despite holding the lead for an hour after drawing the first-leg 4-4 at Haigh Avenue.

The average age of the side was into the early thirties and it was clear that some new, younger blood needed to be introduced and in the closing stages of the season, some of the tremendously promising youngsters from the club's treble-winning youth side broke through into the first-team. Most impressive in this area were goalkeeper Stephen Howard and centre-half Chris Blakeman, without doubt names for the future. The other big find was prolific marksman Andy Whittaker, who netted a superb return of 25 goals in just 38 starts.

No sooner had the season ended that news filtered through of Billy Ayre's resignation to move to Swansea City as assistant to Jan Molby and within two weeks, assistant manager of the last four years, Steve Joel, was appointed as the new manager.

Southport FC: *Photo - Southport Visitor*

Southport

Match No.	Date	Comp.	Venue H/A	Opponents	Result	League Pos.	Goalscorers (Times if known)	Attendance
1	Jul 22	MC	H	Burnley	Won 1-0		Gamble	1372
2	29	MC	A	Wigan Athletic	Lost 2-4		Penman, Griffiths	1468
3	Aug 19	GMVC	A	Slough Town	Won 5-2	1	Haw 3, Gamble 2p	942
4	22	GMVC	H	Northwich Victoria	Drew 2-2	3	Whittaker, Blackstone	1542
5	26	GMVC	H	Stevenage Borough	Lost 0-1	11		1179
6	28	GMVC	A	Runcorn	Drew 1-1	12	Gamble	708
7	Sep 2	GMVC	A	Kettering Town	Drew 1-1	11	Whittaker	1944
8	5	GMVC	H	Altrincham	Lost 1-2	17	Ward	1127
9	9	GMVC	A	Bath City	Lost 0-4	18		584
10	12	GMVC	A	Stalybridge Celtic	Won 4-1	14	Davenport, Gamble, Griffiths 2	496
11	16	GMVC	H	Welling United	Won 2-0	9	Davenport, Griffiths	915
12	19	GMVC	H	Runcorn	Drew 1-1	9	Griffiths	1004
13	23	GMVC	A	Macclesfield Town	Lost 1-3	11	Gamble	1282
14	30	GMVC	H	Kidderminster Harriers	Lost 0-2	15		1164
15	Oct 14	GMVC	H	Telford United	Won 3-2	16	Clark, Haw, Davenport	812
16	21	FAC4Q	A	Telford United	Lost 0-3			898
17	28	GMVC	A	Hednesford Town	Lost 1-2	18	Farley	1355
18	31	GMVC	A	Northwich Victoria	Won 2-1	13	Davenport 2	724
19	Nov 4	GMVC	H	Farnborough Town	Won 7-1	10	Horner, Whittaker 2, Davenport, Gamble, Griffiths, og	819
20	18	GMVC	A	Stevenage Borough	Won 3-1	9	Dove, Whittaker, og	1785
21	25	GMVC	H	Gateshead	Won 1-0	8	Haw	1008
22	28	SCC2	A	Runcorn	Won 5-1		Haw 2, Davenport 2, Griffiths	401
23	Dec 2	GMVC	A	Morecambe	Lost 3-4	11	Fuller, Davenport, Gamble p	1750
24	9	GMVC	A	Kidderminster Harriers	Won 3-2	8	Farley, Haw, Davenport	1664
25	16	GMVC	H	Dagenham & Redbridge	Won 2-1	6	Farley, Whittaker	904
26	Jan 1	GMVC	H	Halifax Town	Drew 0-0	7		1318
27	6	GMVC	H	Kettering Town	Won 6-1	7	Whittaker 3, Davenport, Blackstone 2	916
28	13	GMVC	A	Dagenham & Redbridge	Won 2-1	5	Whittaker, Davenport	964
29	16	ATS2	H	Marine	Won 1-0		Whittaker	513
30	20	FAT1	A	Halifax Town	Lost 1-2		Whittaker	966
31	30	LSC2	H	Everton	Drew 3-3		Whittaker 3	416
32	Feb 3	GMVC	A	Farnborough Town	Lost 0-1	7		738
33	10	GMVC	H	Hednesford Town	Drew 2-2	7	Whittaker, Griffiths	811
34	12	LSC2R	H	Everton	Lost 0-2			298
35	14	ATS3	H	Barrow	Won 3-1		Whittaker, Gamble p, og	321
36	17	GMVC	H	Woking	Drew 2-2	8	McDonald, Whittaker	1074
37	24	GMVC	A	Welling United	Won 1-0	6	Davenport	600
38	27	ATS SF	A	Morecambe	Lost 1-2		Griffiths	910
39	Mar 2	GMVC	A	Altrincham	Drew 1-1	6	McDonald	851
40	5	SCC QF	H	Gateshead	Won 2-1		Whittaker, Haw	315
41	9	GMVC	H	Bromsgrove Rovers	Lost 1-2	7	Haw	894
42	16	GMVC	A	Dover Athletic	Won 1-0	6	Whittaker	1142
43	19	SCC SF1	H	Macclesfield Town	Drew 4-4		Whittaker, Davenport 2, Cunningham	561
44	23	GMVC	A	Telford United	Lost 1-2	8	McDonald p	758
45	26	GMVC	A	Halifax Town	Drew 2-2	7	Whittaker, Davenport	694
46	30	GMVC	H	Stalybridge Celtic	Won 5-3	6	McDonald p, Whittaker, Mitchell, Haw	704
47	Apr 3	SCC SF2	A	Macclesfield Town	Lost 1-2		Whittaker	510
48	6	GMVC	A	Bromsgrove Rovers	Lost 1-4	7	Davenport	729
49	8	GMVC	H	Slough Town	Won 2-0	7	Mitchell 2	677
50	13	GMVC	H	Bath City	Won 2-1	7	Dove, Goulding	643
51	16	GMVC	H	Morecambe	Drew 1-1	6	Fuller	729
52	22	GMVC	H	Macclesfield Town	Won 2-1	5	Lodge, Mitchell	736
53	24	GMVC	A	Gateshead	Drew 2-2	5	Clark, Whittaker	469
54	27	GMVC	H	Dover Athletic	Drew 0-0	5		849
55	May 4	GMVC	A	Woking	Lost 0-4	6		2543

Southport

1	2	3	4	5	6	7	8	9	10	11	12	14	Match No.
McKenna	Fuller	Thomas	Dove	Goulding	Lodge	Clark	Cunningham	Penman	Gamble	Griffiths	Ward	Challender	1
McKenna	Farley	Fuller	Dove	Goulding	Lodge	Clark	Cunningham	Penman	Gamble	Griffiths	Haw	Blackhurst	2
McKenna	Clark	Thomas	Dove	Goulding	Lodge	Blackhurst	Whittaker	Haw	Gamble	Griffiths	Davenport	Blackstone	3
McKenna	Clark	Thomas	Dove	Goulding	Lodge	Blackhurst	Whittaker	Haw	Gamble	Griffiths	Davenport	Blackstone	4
McKenna	Clark	Thomas	Dove	Goulding	Lodge	Blackhurst	Whittaker	Haw	Gamble	Cunningham	Davenport	Blackstone	5
McKenna	Clark	Fuller	Dove	Goulding	Lodge	Blackhurst	Whittaker	Haw	Gamble	Cunningham	Davenport	Ward	6
McKenna	Clark	Fuller	Cochran	Goulding	Lodge	Ward	Whittaker	Haw	Gamble	Challender	Davenport	Thomas	7
McKenna	Clark	Fuller	Dove	Goulding	Lodge	Ward	Whittaker	Haw	Gamble	Challender	Davenport	Thomas	8
McKenna	Clark	Fuller	Dove	Goulding	Lodge	Ward	Whittaker	Davenport	Gamble	Griffiths	Challender	Thomas	9
McKenna	Clark	Thomas	Dove	Goulding	Lodge	Farley	Cunningham	Davenport	Gamble	Griffiths	Haw	Whittaker	10
McKenna	Clark	Thomas	Dove	Goulding	Lodge	Farley	Cunningham	Davenport	Gamble	Griffiths	Haw	Whittaker	11
McKenna	Clark	Cavanagh	Dove	Goulding	Lodge	Farley	Cunningham	Davenport	Gamble	Griffiths	Haw	Whittaker	12
McKenna	Clark	Fuller	Dove	Goulding	Lodge	Farley	Cunningham	Davenport	Gamble	Griffiths	Haw	Whittaker	13
McKenna	Clark	Fuller	Dove	Goulding	Lodge	Farley	Cunningham	Davenport	Gamble	Griffiths	Haw	Whittaker	14
McKenna	Clark	Fuller	Dove	Goulding	Lodge	Kelly	Haw	Davenport	Gamble	Griffiths	Ward	Cavanagh	15
McKenna	Clark	Fuller	Dove	Goulding	Lodge	Ward	Haw	Davenport	Gamble	Griffiths	Whittaker	Cavanagh	16
McKenna	Clark	Farley	Dove	Goulding	Lodge	Horner	Haw	Davenport	Gamble	Griffiths	Whittaker	Cavanagh	17
McKenna	Clark	Farley	Dove	Goulding	Lodge	Horner	Whittaker	Davenport	Gamble	Griffiths	Haw	Cavanagh	18
McKenna	Clark	Farley	Dove	Goulding	McDonald	Horner	Whittaker	Davenport	Gamble	Griffiths	Fuller	Cavanagh	19
McKenna	Clark	Farley	Dove	Goulding	Fuller	Horner	Whittaker	Davenport	Gamble	Griffiths	Haw	Cavanagh	20
McKenna	Clark	Farley	Dove	Goulding	McDonald	Horner	Haw	Davenport	Gamble	Griffiths	Fuller	Cavanagh	21
McKenna	Fuller	Farley	Dove	Goulding	McDonald	Horner	Haw	Davenport	Gamble	Griffiths	Blackstone	Cavanagh	22
McKenna	Clark	Farley	Dove	Goulding	Fuller	Horner	Haw	Davenport	Gamble	Griffiths	Blackstone	Whittaker	23
McKenna	Clark	Farley	Dove	Goulding	Fuller	Horner	Haw	Davenport	Gamble	Griffiths	Blackstone	Whittaker	24
McKenna	Fuller	Farley	Dove	Goulding	McDonald	Horner	Haw	Davenport	Gamble	Griffiths	Blackstone	Whittaker	25
McKenna	fuller	Farley	Cochran	Goulding	Lodge	Horner	McDonald	Davenport	Blackstone	Griffiths	Whittaker	Thomas	26
McKenna	Farley	Thomas	Dove	Goulding	Lodge	Horner	Whittaker	Davenport	Gamble	Blackstone	Griffiths	Clark	27
McKenna	Farley	Thomas	Dove	Goulding	Lodge	Horner	Whittaker	Davenport	Gamble	Blackstone	McDonald	Haw	28
McKenna	Farley	Thomas	Dove	Goulding	Lodge	Horner	Whittaker	Davenport	McDonald	Blackstone	Clark	Gamble	29
McKenna	Clark	Farley	Dove	Goulding	Lodge	McDonald	Whittaker	Davenport	Gamble	Blackstone	Haw	Griffiths	30
McKenna	Clark	Farley	Dove	Goulding	Lodge	McDonald	Whittaker	Davenport	Gamble	Haw	Cunningham	Fuller	31
McKenna	Fuller	Farley	Dove	Goulding	Lodge	McDonald	Whittaker	Davenport	Gamble	Griffiths	Cunningham	Clark	32
McKenna	Fuller	Farley	Dove	Goulding	Lodge	McDonald	Whittaker	Davenport	Gamble	Blackstone	Cunningham	Clark	33
Croasdale	Fuller	Clark	Dove	Cochran	Lodge	McDonald	Whittaker	Haw	Cunningham	Blackstone	Farley	Griffiths	34
McKenna	Clark	Farley	Dove	Goulding	Cochran	McDonald	Whittaker	Davenport	Gamble	Griffiths	Blackstone	Cavanagh	35
McKenna	Fuller	Farley	Dove	Goulding	Cochran	McDonald	Whittaker	Davenport	Lodge	Blackstone	Haw	Gamble	36
McKenna	Fuller	Farley	Dove	Goulding	Cochran	McDonald	Whittaker	Davenport	Lodge	Blackstone	Haw	Gamble	37
McKenna	Fuller	Farley	Dove	Lodge	Cochran	McDonald	Whittaker	Davenport	Gamble	Blackstone	Haw	Griffiths	38
McKenna	Fuller	Farley	Dove	Lodge	Cochran	McDonald	Whittaker	Davenport	Griffiths	Blackstone	Haw	Cunningham	39
McKenna	Fuller	Farley	Dove	Lodge	Cochran	McDonald	Whittaker	Haw	Griffiths	Clark	Cavanagh	Cunningham	40
McKenna	Fuller	Farley	Dove	Lodge	Cochran	McDonald	Whittaker	Haw	Gamble	Griffiths	Cavanagh	Cunningham	41
McKenna	Cochran	Farley	Dove	Goulding	Lodge	McDonald	Whittaker	Davenport	Cunningham	Haw	Fuller	Gamble	42
McKenna	Cochran	Clark	Dove	Goulding	Lodge	McDonald	Whittaker	Davenport	Cunningham	Haw	Gamble	Griffiths	43
Croasdale	Cochran	Fuller	Dove	Goulding	Lodge	McDonald	Whittaker	Haw	Cunningham	Griffiths	Gamble	Clark	44
Croasdale	Clark	Fuller	Dove	Goulding	Lodge	McDonald	Whittaker	Davenport	Gamble	Haw	Cochran	Cunningham	45
McKenna	Clark	Fuller	Dove	Cochran	Lodge	McDonald	Whittaker	Davenport	Mitchell	Haw	Gamble	Griffiths	46
McKenna	Clark	Fuller	Dove	Goulding	Lodge	McDonald	Whittaker	Davenport	Mitchell	Haw	Gamble	Cochran	47
McKenna	Cochran	Fuller	Dove	Goulding	Lodge	McDonald	Whittaker	Davenport	Mitchell	Griffiths	Gamble	Blakeman	48
Croasdale	Clark	Cochran	Dove	Goulding	Lodge	McDonald	Whittaker	Davenport	Gamble	Mitchell	Haw	Griffiths	49
Croasdale	Clark	Cochran	Dove	Goulding	Lodge	Haw	Whittaker	Davenport	Gamble	Mitchell	Fuller	Griffiths	50
Howard	Clark	Fuller	Cochran	Goulding	Lodge	McDonald	Whittaker	Davenport	Blakeman	Mitchell	Gamble	Griffiths	51
Croasdale	Clark	Fuller	Dove	Goulding	Lodge	McDonald	Haw	Davenport	Cochran	Mitchell	Gamble	Griffiths	52
Croasdale	Clark	Farley	Dove	Goulding	Lodge	Cochran	Whittaker	Davenport	Gamble	Mitchell	Haw	Ashton	53
Croasdale	Clark	Farley	Dove	Goulding	Lodge	McDonald	Whittaker	Davenport	Cochran	Mitchell	Gamble	Griffiths	54
Croasdale	Clark	Fuller	Dove	Goulding	Lodge	Cochran	Whittaker	Davenport	Gamble	Farley	Haw	Cavanagh	55

Southport

STEVE JOEL

Steve was signed by then manager Brian Kettle in the early 1990s, although he quickly hung up his boots to become Brian's assistant. He played a big part in the NPL title season in 1992/93 and following Brian's departure towards the end of the 94/95 season, Steve, who played a Football League match for Southport back in 1977, continued in the assistant manager's role under Billy Ayre. When Ayre departed for Swansea at the end of last term, Steve was the supporters' choice for the job and chairman Charles Clapham agreed and appointed Steve as the new manager with the potential of lifting the club back into the Football League once more.

Steve Joel (left) with assistant Peter Davenport.

Programme details:
36 pages for £1.20
Editor - Derek Hitchcock (01704 579458)
Assistant Editor - Martin Hagan

Local Newspapers:
Southport Visiter
Southport Advertiser
The Champion

Local Radio Stations:
Radio Merseyside
Red Rose
Radio City
Radio Lancashire

SOUTHPORT - PLAYING SQUAD 1996-97

Player	Honours	Birthplace and date	Transfer Fees	Previous Clubs
GOALKEEPERS				
Billy Stewart		Liverpool 1/1/65		Liverpool, Wigan A, Chester C, Northampton T, Chester C
Peter Croasdale		Blackpool 1/1//77		Blackpool
DEFENDERS				
Derek Goulding	GMVC, NPL, NPLC, SSC	Liverpool 6/5/63		Altrincham, Bangor C, Stafford R, Oswestry T, Bangor C, Chorley
Leroy Dove	NPL, FAXI LSC	Manchester 27/4/63		Prestwich H, Droylsden, Buxton
Stuart Cochran		Glasgow 7/3/72		From University
Chris Blakeman		Southport 3/6/78		From Youth Team
Phil Horner		Leeds 10/11/68		Leicester C, Halifax T, Blackpool
Alex Jones		Blackburn 27/11/64		Oldham, Preston, Carlisle, Rochdale, Motherwell, Rochdale, Halifax, Stalybridge
Lee Anderson		Bury 4/10/73		Bury, Altrincham
Martin Clark		Accrington 12/9/70		Accrington Stanley, Crewe A
MIDFIELDERS				
Andy Farley		Preston 18/12/74		From Youth Team
Dave Carroll		Blackpool 25/9/76		Blackpool
Brian Butler	ESP, BLT,	Salford 4/7/66		Blackpool, Stockport Co, Halifax T, Northwich V
David Gamble	NPL	Liverpool 23/3/71		Grimsby T, Altrincham
FORWARDS				
Andy Whittaker		Preston 29/1/68	4-fig	Bamber Bridge, Netherfield, Barrow
Francis Powell		Burnley 17/6/77		Burnley, Rochdale
Peter Davenport	EI	Birkenhead 24/3/61		Cammell Laird, Nottingham F, Manchester Middlesbrough, Sunderland, Airdrie
Rod McDonald		London 20/3/67		Sth.Liverpool, Colne D, Walsall, Partick Thistle
Bryan Griffiths		Prescot 26/1/65		St.Helens T, Wigan Ath, Blackpool, Telford U

Departures during season:
Greg Challender (Bath C), Jon Penman & Jimmy Blackhurst (Marine), Derek Ward (Northwich V), Mark Kelly (Curzon Ashton), Brian Pritchard (Witton A).
Players on loan during season:
Phil Horner (Blackpool).
Departures during close season: Martin McDonald (Doncaster), Ian Blackstone, Steve Haw & Gary Thomas (Chorley), Paul Lodge & Dave Fuller (Bangor C), John McKenna (Ashton U), Andy Cavanagh (Marine), Harvey Cunningham (Released).

Haig Avenue, Southport

ADDRESS:
Haig Avenue, Southport, Merseyside. PR9 7DR.

TELEPHONE NUMBER:
Ground: 01704 533422 Ticket Office: 01704 530182 Fax: 01704 533422. **Club Newsline:** 0891 44 68 36

SIMPLE DIRECTIONS:
Signposted from all entrances to town.

CAPACITY: 6,012 **SEATED:** 1,880 **COVERED TERRACING:** 1,100

RECORD ATTENDANCE:
20,000 v Newcastle United - FA Cup - 1932

CLUB SHOP:
Scarves, replica kits, programmes and various other souvenirs for sale. Contact D Hitchcock, c/o Southport F.C.

SOCIAL FACILITIES:
Open 7.30-11.00 every night and match days. (Tel: 01704 530182).

Southport Fact File

Nickname: The Sandgrounders

Club Sponsors: Apollo Leisure

Previous Grounds: Ash Lane

Previous Leagues: Northern Premier League, Football League, Lancashire Combination

Club colours: Old Gold & black

Change colours: White & black

Midweek home matchday: Tuesday

Record win: 8-1 v Nelson - 01.01.31.

Record defeat: 0-11 v Oldham - 26.12.62

Record transfer fee: £20,000 for Martin McDonald from Macclesfield Town - 1995.

Record transfer fee received: £25,000 from Rochdale for Steve Whitehall - 1991

1995-96 Captain: Paul Lodge.

1995-96 Top scorer: Andy Whittaker.

1995-96 Player of the Year: Peter Davenport.

Club record goalscorer: Alan Spence 98

Record appearances: Arthur Peat 401 - 1962-72

Club Honours: Football League Division Four Champions 1972/73 (Runners-up 1966/67); Northern Premier League Champions 1992/93 (League Cup Winners 1990/91, League Shield 1993/94); Third Division North Section Cup Winners 1937/38; Liverpool Senior Cup Winners 1930/31, 1931/32, 1943/44, 1957/58 (shared), 1963/64 (shared), 1974/75, 1990/91, 1992/93 (Runners-up 1993/94); Lancashire Senior Cup Winners 1904/05; Lancashire Junior Cup (now ATS Challenge Trophy) Winners 1919/20, 1992/93 (Runners-up 1993/94).

STALYBRIDGE CELTIC

Formed:
1909

President:
Joe Jackson

Chairman:
Peter Barnes

Vice Chairman
Derek Wolsterholme

Football Secretary:
Martyn Torr

Manager:

Assistant Manager:
Dave Denby

Physiotherapist:
Dave Pover

Commercial Manager:
Martyn Torr

Press Officer:
Martyn Torr

It was an inconsistent 1995/96 season for Stalybridge but they were never in danger of ending their tenure in the Vauxhall Conference. Scoring goals was a problem for Celtic, despite having the likes of Brendan Burke and Ian Arnold, signed from Kettering Town for £10,000 midway through the season, on their books, but perhaps the addition of Gateshead's Dean Trott during the close season will help in that department. However, they will have to do without the services of manager Peter Wragg, who stepped down in early September after a three-year return spell. That ended an eleven-year term of management in the Conference for the former Halifax Town and Macclesfield Town boss, and the experienced ex-Sheffield United, Rochdale and Southport midfielder, David Frain, was handed the job on a caretaker capacity.

Stalybridge have worked hard on making their Bower Fold stadium almost ready for grading as suitable for the Football League, and it would be a shame if they found themselves back in the UniBond League after all that.

Stalybridge Celtic FC 1996/97. (L-R) - Back Row: Dave Pover (physio), Simon Heaton, Craig Powell, Ian Arnold, Greg Chellender, Harvey Willetts, Mark Powell, David Frain, Dave Denby (asst.man). Middle: Steve O'Shaughnessy, Dean Trott, Steve Charles, Peter Wragg (ex-manager), Brenan Burke, Steve Jones, Craig Boardman. Front: Mark Hine, Jamie Bates, Darren Vine, Lee Coathup.

Stalybridge Celtic

Match No.	Date	Comp.	Venue H/A	Opponents	Result	League Pos.	Goalscorers (Times if known)	Attendance
1	Aug 19	GMVC	H	Dagenham & Redbridge	Won 2-1		Shaw, Burke	547
2	23	GMVC	A	Gateshead	Lost 0-1			524
3	26	GMVC	A	Woking	Lost 1-2		Jones A	1613
4	28	GMVC	H	Halifax Town	Won 1-0		Wheeler	905
5	30	FA Y C	H	Southport	Lost 0-4			110
6	Sep 2	GMVC	H	Telford United	Drew 2-2		Jones A, Burke	619
7	5	GMVC	A	Northwich Victoria	Lost 0-1			816
8	9	GMVC	A	Kidderminster Harriers	Lost 0-3			1962
9	12	GMVC	H	Southport	Lost 1-4		Ryan	496
10	16	GMVC	A	Farnborough Town	Drew 1-1		Higginbotham	707
11	19	SC1	A	Morecambe	Lost 1-4		Higginbotham	605
12	23	GMVC	H	Kettering Town	Won 3-2		Burke, Wheeler, og	627
13	30	GMVC	A	Bath City	Won 4-0		Higginbotham, Jones S, Wheeler, Ryan	580
14	Oct 3	CSC1	A	Congleton Town	Won 6-2		Jones S, Burke 2, Wheeler, Higginbotham, Ellis	280
15	10	GMVC	H	Gateshead	Lost 0-2			480
16	14	GMVC	H	Welling United	Won 2-1		Frain, Wheeler	605
17	21	FAC4Q	H	Colwyn Bay	Drew 2-2		Burke, Wheeler	617
18	24	FAC4QR	A	Colwyn Bay	Lost 0-3			613
19	28	GMVC	H	Woking	Lost 2-4		Arnold, Goodacre	754
20	31	GMVC	H	Macclesfield Town	Lost 1-2		Burke	884
21	Nov 4	GMVC	A	Bromsgrove Rovers	Drew 1-1		Arnold	1033
22	7	SC1	H	Morecambe	Won 5-2		Burke 2, Goodacre, Ryan 2	454
23	11	GMVC	A	Macclesfield Town	Lost 0-1			1457
24	18	GMVC	H	Hednesford Town	Lost 0-1			687
25	21	CSC2	H	Hyde United	Lost 0-3			614
26	25	GMVC	A	Dover Athletic	Won 3-1		O'Shaughnessy, Goodacre, Ryan	1069
27	27	GMVC	A	Hednesford Town	Won 1-0		Burke	895
28	Dec 2	GMVC	H	Slough Town	Lost 0-1			558
29	9	GMVC	H	Altrincham	Won 1-0		Goodacre	653
30	16	GMVC	A	Morecambe	Lost 0-2			1123
31	Jan 6	GMVC	H	Kidderminster Harriers	Drew 2-2		Arnold 2	605
32	13	GMVC	A	Welling United	Drew 1-1		Frain	626
33	20	FAT1	H	Gresley Rovers	Drew 1-1		Goodacre	638
34	23	FAT1R	A	Gresley Rovers	Lost 0-1			603
35	Feb 10	GMVC	H	Farnborough Town	Drew 2-2		Burke, Ellison	521
36	17	GMVC	A	Dagenham & Redbridge	Lost 1-4		Ellis	706
37	24	GMVC	H	Morecambe	Lost 0-2			585
38	Mar 2	GMVC	A	Telford United	Won 1-0		Goodacre	783
39	5	GMVC	A	Halifax Town	Won 3-2		Goodacre 2, Jones S	509
40	9	GMVC	H	Stevenage Borough	Lost 2-5		Burke, Goodacre	834
41	19	GMVC	H	Runcorn	Won 2-0		Burke, Jones S	478
42	23	GMVC	A	Slough Town	Lost 1-2		Jones S	748
43	30	GMVC	A	Southport	Lost 3-5		Coathup, O'Shaughnessy, Powell	704
44	Apr 6	GMVC	H	Bath City	Won 1-0		Powell	506
45	8	GMVC	H	Bromsgrove Rovers	Won 2-1		Burke, Goodacre	463
46	13	GMVC	A	Stevenage Borough	Drew 2-2		Burke, Powell	1767
47	16	GMVC	A	Runcorn	Won 1-0		Burke	352
48	20	GMVC	H	Dover Athletic	Won 2-0		Coathup, Goodacre	533
49	23	GMVC	A	Altrincham	Lost 0-1			608
50	25	GMVC	H	Northwich Victoria	Lost 1-3		Jones S	514
51	May 4	GMVC	A	Kettering Town	Won 6-1		Burke, Goodacre 2, Arnold 2, og	962

Stalybridge Celtic

1	2	3	4	5	6	7	8	9	10	11	12	14	Match No.
Sherwood	Jones S	Coathup	Frain	Jones A	Hall	Shaw	Higginbotham	Bauress	Burke	Ryan	Wheeler	Goodacre	1
Sherwood	Jones S	Coathup	Frain	Jones A	Hall	Shaw	Higginbotham	Bauress	Burke	Ryan	Wheeler	Goodacre	2
Sherwood	Jones S	Coathup	Frain	Jones A	Hall	Shaw	Higginbotham	Bauress	Burke	Ryan	Wheeler	Goodacre	3
Sherwood	Jones S	Coathup	Frain	Jones A	Hall	Shaw	Higginbotham	Bauress	Burke	Ryan	Wheeler	O'Shaughnessy	4
Dudley	Wright	McClure	Morris	Towell	Edkins	Bergin	Tanner	Barkin	Slater	Cowen	Morris	Taylor	5
Sherwood	Jones S	Coathup	Megson	Jones A	Hall	Shaw	Higginbotham	Bauress	Burke	Ryan	Wheeler	Patterson	6
Sherwood	Megson	Coathup	Jones S	Jones A	Hall	Shaw	Bauress	O'Shaughnessy	Burke	Ryan	Wheeler	Patterson	7
Sherwood	Jones S	Coathup	Frain	Jones A	Hall	Megson	Bauress	Pearson	Burke	Ryan	Wheeler	Higginbotham	8
Sherwood	Jones S	Coathup	Frain	Patterson	Hall	Megson	Bauress	Pearson	Burke	Ryan	Wheeler	Higginbotham	9
Sherwood	Megson	Coathup	Frain	Jones A	Hall	Shaw	Bauress	Pearson	Burke	Ryan	Wheeler	Higginbotham	10
Sherwood	Megson	Coathup	Ellis	Jones A	Hall	Shaw	Wheeler	Pearson	Higginbotham	Ryan	Patterson	Burke	11
Quy	Megson	Coathup	Frain	Jones A	Hall	Burke	Higginbotham	Jones S	Wheeler	Ryan	Shaw	Patterson	12
Quy	Megson	Coathup	Frain	Jones A	Hall	Burke	Higginbotham	Jones S	Wheeler	Ryan	Shaw	Pearson	13
Sherwood	Shaw	Coathup	Frain	Jones S	Hall	Burke	Bauress	Wheeler	Higginbotham	Ellis	Ryan	Pearson	14
Quy	Megson	Coathup	Frain	Jones S	Hall	Burke	Bauress	Wheeler	Higginbotham	Ryan	Shaw	Goodacre	15
Quy	Edmonds	Coathup	O'Shaughnessy	Patterson	Bauress	Burke	Frain	Wheeler	Higginbotham	Ellis	Megson	Goodacre	16
Willetts	Edmonds	Coathup	O'Shaughnessy	Jones A	Bauress	Burke	Frain	Wheeler	Higginbotham	Ellis	Megson	Goodacre	17
Willetts	Shaw	Coathup	O'Shaughnessy	Jones A	Hall	Burke	Bauress	Wheeler	Goodacre	Frain	Ellis	Edmonds	18
Willetts	Edmonds	Coathup	O'Shaughnessy	Jones A	Megson	Burke	Arnold	Frain	Goodacre	Ryan	Ellis	Higginbotham	19
Willetts	Edmonds	Coathup	O'Shaughnessy	Jones A	Megson	Burke	Arnold	Frain	Goodacre	Ryan	Ellis	Wheeler	20
Willetts	O'Shaughnessy	Coathup	Bauress	Jones A	Hall	Burke	Goodacre	Jones S	Arnold	Ryan	Ellis	Wheeler	21
Willetts	Edmonds	Ellis	O'Shaughnessy	Jones A	Bauress	Burke	Goodacre	Wheeler	Arnold	Ryan	Coathup	Shaw	22
Willetts	O'Shaughnessy	Coathup	Hall	Jones A	Bauress	Burke	Goodacre	Wheeler	Arnold	Ryan	Edmonds	Shaw	23
Willetts	Bauress	Hall	O'Shaughnessy	Jones A	Ellis	Burke	Goodacre	Wheeler	Arnold	Ryan	Frain	Shaw	24
Willetts	O'Shaughnessy	Coathup	Bauress	Jones A	Hall	Burke	Frain	Wheeler	Arnold	Ryan	Goodacre	Patterson	25
Nicholls	O'Shaughnessy	Coathup	Bauress	Jones A	Hall	Burke	Goodacre	Frain	Arnold	Ryan	Edmonds	Higginbotham	26
Willetts	O'Shaughnessy	Coathup	Bauress	Jones A	Hall	Burke	Goodacre	Frain	Arnold	Ryan	Edmonds	Higginbotham	27
Willetts	O'Shaughnessy	Coathup	Bauress	Jones A	Hall	Higginbotham	Goodacre	Frain	Arnold	Ryan	Edmonds	Wheeler	28
Willetts	Edmonds	Coathup	O'Shaughnessy	Jones A	Hall	Burke	Frain	Goodacre	Arnold	Ellis	Ryan	Higginbotham	29
Willetts	Edmonds	Coathup	O'Shaughnessy	Jones A	Hall	Burke	Frain	Bauress	Arnold	Ryan	Goodacre	Wheeler	30
Willetts	Edmonds	Coathup	O'Shaughnessy	Jones A	Hall	Burke	Frain	Ellis	Arnold	Ryan	Goodacre	Jones S	31
Willetts	O'Shaughnessy	Coathup	Frain	Jones A	Hall	Burke	Goodacre	Jones S	Arnold	Ellis	Higginbotham	Edmonds	32
Willetts	O'Shaughnessy	Coathup	Frain	Jones A	Hall	Burke	Goodacre	Jones S	Arnold	Ellis	Higginbotham	Edmonds	33
Willetts	O'Shaughnessy	Coathup	Ryan	Jones A	Hall	Burke	Higginbotham	Jones S	Arnold	Ellis	Goodacre	Edmonds	34
Willetts	Jones S	Coathup	Frain	Jones A	O'Shaughnessy	Burke	Ellison	Ellis	Arnold	Ryan	Goodacre	Hall	35
Willetts	Jones S	Coathup	Frain	Jones A	O'Shaughnessy	Burke	Ellison	Ellis	Arnold	Ryan	Goodacre	Hall	36
Willetts	Jones S	Coathup	Frain	Hall	O'Shaughnessy	Burke	Ellison	Ellis	Arnold	Ryan	Goodacre	Edmonds	37
Willetts	Edmonds	Coathup	Frain	Hall	O'Shaughnessy	Burke	Goodacre	Jones S	Arnold	Ellis	Megson	Ellison	38
Willetts	Edmonds	Coathup	Frain	Hall	O'Shaughnessy	Burke	Goodacre	Jones S	Arnold	Ellis	Megson	Ellison	39
Willetts	Edmonds	Coathup	Jones S	Jones A	Hall	Burke	Goodacre	Frain	Arnold	Ellis	Megson	Ryan	40
Willetts	Edmonds	Coathup	Frain	Booth	Hall	Burke	Goodacre	Jones S	Arnold	Ellis	Megson	Challender	41
Willetts	Edmonds	Challender	Frain	Hall	O'Shaughnessy	Burke	Goodacre	Jones S	Arnold	Megson	Wilson	Powell	42
Dixon	Edmonds	Coathup	O'Shaughnessy	Hall	Challender	Burke	Megson	Frain	Arnold	Wilson	Goodacre	Pearson	43
Willetts	Megson	Coathup	Brown	O'Shaughnessy	Hall	Burke	Goodacre	Jones S	Arnold	Powell	Challender	Pearson	44
Willetts	Megson	Coathup	Brown	O'Shaughnessy	Hall	Burke	Goodacre	Jones S	Arnold	Pearson	Challender	Edmonds	45
Willetts	Megson	Coathup	Brown	O'Shaughnessy	Hall	Burke	Powell	Jones S	Arnold	Challender	Goodacre	Wilson	46
Willetts	Megson	Coathup	Brown	O'Shaughnessy	Hall	Burke	Goodacre	Jones S	Arnold	Pearson	Challender	Frain	47
Willetts	Megson	Coathup	Brown	O'Shaughnessy	Hall	Burke	Goodacre	Jones S	Arnold	Pearson	Challender	Frain	48
Willetts	Megson	Coathup	Brown	O'Shaughnessy	Hall	Pearson	Goodacre	Jones S	Burke	Challender	Powell	Frain	49
Willetts	Megson	Coathup	Frain	O'Shaughnessy	Hall	Burke	Powell	Jones S	Arnold	Challender	Edmonds	Goodacre	50
Willetts	Megson	Coathup	Frain	O'Shaughnessy	Hall	Burke	Goodacre	Jones S	Arnold	Challender	Pearson	Powell	51

Stalybridge Celtic

Action from Celtics pre-season match with Witton Albion

DAVID FRAIN

David Frain is one of Stalybridge Celtic's most experienced players, so when manager Peter Wragg decided to resign at the beginning of September, just seven games into the new season, the club turned to the 34-year-old to take charge of team affairs, initially on a temporary basis.

Born in Sheffield, David eventually signed for Sheffield United following a spell in local football. He made 44 first-team appearances for the Blades before joining Rochdale in 1988. After just one season at Spotland, David was then signed by Stockport County for a fee of £50,000. He was not only captain of County butn he also made four Wembley appearances during his six year spell at Edgeley Park. He joined Celtic in April 1995.

Programme details:
40 pages for £1.20
Editor - Nick Shaw (0161 633 1117)

Any other club publications:
None

Local Newspapers:
Manchester Evening News
Manchester Evening News Pink (Saturday evenings)

Local Radio Stations:
GMR (BBC Manchester)
Piccadilly Radio, Signal Radio

STALYBRIDGE CELTIC - PLAYING SQUAD 1996-97

Player	Honours	Birthplace and date	Transfer Fees	Previous Clubs
GOALKEEPERS				
Harvey Willetts		Manchester		Leeds U, Cape Cod Crusaders
DEFENDERS				
Ian Patterson		Chatham 4/4/73		Sunderland, Burnley, Wigan Ath
Jamie Bates		Manchester		Maine Road, Runcorn
Lee Coathup		Singapore 2/5/67		Everton, Newtown, Vauxhall GM, Stalybridge C, Witton Alb
David Hall		Manchester 19/10/73		Oldham Ath, Halifax T
Greg Challender		Rochdale 5/2/73		Mossley, Oldham Ath, Preston, Southport, Bath C, Altrincham
Steve O'Shaughnessy	WY	Wrexham 13/10/67		Leeds U, Bradford C, Rochdale, Exeter C, Darlington, Stalybridge C, Barry T
MIDFIELDERS				
David Frain		Sheffield 11/10/62		Sheffield U, Rochdale, Stockport Co
Steve Charles	ES	Sheffield 10/5/60		Sheffield U, Wrexham, Mansfield T, Scarborough
Mark Hine	ESP, GMVC Div 4	Middlesbrough 18/5/64		Grimsby, Darlington, Doncaster, Peterborough, Gateshead
Steve Jones		Stoke	£3.250	Stoke C, Stafford R, Esatwood Hanley, Leek T
FORWARDS				
Brendan Burke		Manchester 13/10/70	£12,000	Manchester U, Mossley, Witton Alb
Dean Trott		Barnsley 13/5/67		Ossett A, Frickley A, Boston U, Northampton, Gateshead
Darren Vine		Sheffield 22/12/76		Sheffield U
Craig Powell		Doncaster 10/6/77		Sheffield U
Sam Goodacre		Sheffield 1/12/70		Sheffield W, Scunthorpe U
Ian Arnold	ESP	Durham 4/7/72	£15,000	Middlesbrough, Carlisle U, Kettering T

Departures during season:
Mark Ogley (Leek T), Stewart Anderson (Accrington Stanley), Ian Patterson (Leigh RMI - Loan), Sam Goodacre (Gainsborough T - Loan), Neil Edmonds (Leigh RMI - Loan), Steve Sherwood (Gateshead), John Pearson (Chorley), Nigel Shaw (Nuneaton B), Gary Bauress (Released), Paul Wheeler (Leigh RMI), Alex Jones (Chorley - Loan).
Players on loan during season:
Andy Quy (Derby Co), Ken Dixon (Wrexham), Gary Pearson & Craig Powell (Sheffield U).
Departures during close season: Alex Jones (Southport), John Ryan & Kevin Megson (Released), Neil Edmonds (Chorley), Richard Brown & Neil Ellis (America).

Bower Fold, Stalybridge Celtic

ADDRESS:
Bower Fold, Mottram Road, Stalybridge, Cheshire SK15 2RT.

TELEPHONE NUMBER:
0161 338 2828 Fax: 0161 338 8256 Mobile: 0860 841765.

SIMPLE DIRECTIONS:
M6 to A556 to M63 to M67; end of Motorway through roundabout to traffic lights, left; left at end into Molltram Road, up hill, down hill into Stalybridge, ground on left next to Hare & Hounds pub.

CAPACITY: 6,000 **SEATED:** 407 **COVERED TERRACING:** 1,300

RECORD ATTENDANCE:
9,753 v WBA - FA Cup replay - 1922-23

CLUB SHOP:
Contact Martyn Torr for details (0161 338 2828)

SOCIAL FACILITIES:
Clubhouse open matchdays and evenings during the week. Food available on matchdays.

PREVIOUS GROUNDS:
None

Stalybridge Fact File

Nickname: Celtic

Club Sponsors: Hickson Manro Ltd

Previous Leagues: Lancashire Combination 1911-12, Central Lge 1912-21, Football Lge 1921-23, Cheshire Co. Lge 1923-1982, North West Co's 1982-87, Northern Prem. Lge 1987-92.

Club colours: Blue shirts with white sleeves, blue shorts, blue socks.

Change colours: Black & white stripes/black & white trim.

Midweek home matchday: Tuesday

Record win: 16-2 twice; v Manchester NE 1/5/26; v Nantwich 22/10/32

Record defeat: 0-6 v Northwich Victoria

Record transfer fee paid: To Kettering Town for Ian Arnold 1995

Record transfer fee received: £3,000 for Martin Filson from Halifax Town

1996-97 Captain: Brendan Burke

1995-96 Top scorer: Brendan Burke

1995-96 Player of the Year: Brendan Burke

Club record goalscorer (in a season): Chris Camden 45, 1991-92

Record appearances: Kevin Booth 354

Past players who progressed to the Football League: Too numerous to list.

Honours: Northern Premier Lg Prem Div 91-92, NPL R-up 90-91 (Div.1 R-up 87-88); Cheshire Cnty Lg 79-80 (R-up 77-78), Lg Cup 21-22 (R-up 46-47,81-82); Challenge Shield 77-78 (runners-up 79-80), Reserves Div R-up 81-82), NW Co's Lg 83-84, 86-87 (Lge Cup R-up 83-84), Champions v Cup Winners Trophy 83-84, Lancs Comb Div 2 11-12; Cheshire Snr Cup 52-53 (R-up 54-55, 80-81; Manchester Snr Cup 22-23 (Intermediate Cup 57-58, 68-69 (R-up 56-57, 67-68, 69-70)); Challenge Shield 54-55, (Junior Cup 62-63), Lancs Floodlit Cup 88-89 (R-up 89-90); Reporter Cup R-up 74-75; Edward Case Cup 77-78.

STEVENAGE BOROUGH

Formed
1976

President
Rod Resker

Chairman
Victor Green

Club Secretary
Janice Hutchings

Manager
Paul Fairclough

Coach
Paul Peterson/
Noel Blackwell

Physiotherapist
Ray Lainchbury

Commercial Manager
Clive Abrey

Stevenage set their stall out in 1994/95 by finishing in fifth place in what was their first season at the top of the non-League Pyramid and then followed that up by winning the title by a whopping eight point margin.

There were success stories all over the field for manager Paul Fairclough's side. Striker Barry Hayles ended up as the league's top scorer with 34 goals, Mark Smith and Efetobor Sodje in defence, the now departed Steve Berry and Corey Browne in midfield and Dave Venables in attack and Hayles, Smith and Venables were all selected for the England semi-professional side as a tribute to their success. Fairclough further strengthened his squad by adding Neil Trebble and Alan Paris towards the end of the season.

Although obviously disappointed not to attain promotion, even after a long and costly court battle, it does look as though Borough are going to be contenders again this season and now that their Broadhall Way stadium is fully ready to stage League football there is nothing stopping them from making the step up. **Steve Whitney**

Back Row (L-R); Brian Hierons (Res Phy), Miguel Luque (Res Mgr), Bill Bannister (Res Asst Mgr), Efetobor Sodje, Des Gallagher, Nicholas Grime, Neil Trebble, Dave Venables, Richard Wilmot, Corey Browne, Eric Richards (Kit), Robbie Scott (Scout). Middle; Shaun Stevens, Matthew Vier, Mike Bignall, Paul Peterson (Asst Mgr), Paul Fairclough (Mgr), Noel Blackwell (Coach), Kenny Webster, Dominic Grime, Barry Hayles. Front; Alan Paris, Mark Smith, Neil Catlin, Scott Cretton, Stuart Beevor, Gary Crawshaw, Paul Barrowcliff, Rob Mutchell, John Ugbah.

Stevenage Borough

Match No.	Date	Comp.	Venue H/A	Opponents	Result	League Pos.	Goalscorers (Times if known)	Attendance
1	Aug 15	HCC2	H	Hitchin Town	Won 3-0		Sodje, Marshall, og	818
2	19	GMVC	H	Bath City	Won 2-0	8	Nugent, Lynch	1355
3	22	GMVC	A	Dover Athletic	Won 2-1	2	Lynch, Hayles	1157
4	26	GMVC	A	Southport	Won 1-0	1	Marshall	1179
5	28	GMVC	H	Telford United	Lost 0-1	3		2023
6	Sep 2	GMVC	A	Gateshead	Drew 2-2	4	Nugent, Hayles	610
7	5	GMVC	A	Woking	Lost 1-4	8	Venables	1864
8	9	FAC1Q	H	Brook House	Drew 0-0			814
9	12	FAC1QR	A	Brook House	Won 5-1		Nugent, Barrowcliff 2, Marshall, Beevor	167
10	16	GMVC	A	Bromsgrove Rovers	Drew 1-1	11	Barrowcliff	1067
11	18	GMVC	H	Kettering Town	Won 5-1	8	Smith, Barrowcliff, Crawshaw, Browne, Marshall	2033
12	23	FAC2Q	A	Uxbridge	Won 1-0		Marshall	460
13	30	GMVC	H	Altrincham	Drew 1-1	11	Smith	1615
14	Oct 7	FAC3Q	H	Staines Town	Won 2-0		Crawshaw, Lynch	1176
15	14	GMVC	A	Halifax Town	Won 3-2	11	Sodje, Smith, Lynch	858
16	21	FAC4Q	A	Aylesbury United	Won 3-1		Browne, Crawshaw 2	1480
17	23	GMVC	H	Welling United	Won 4-1	8	Webster, Barrowcliff, Browne, Hayles	1903
18	28	GMVC	H	Northwich Victoria	Won 5-1	6	Smith, Browne, Crawshaw 2, Hayles	1645
19	Nov 4	GMVC	A	Telford United	Won 3-1	5	Sodje, Browne, Crawshaw	883
20	11	FAC1	A	Hereford United	Lost 1-2		Crawshaw	3321
21	18	GMVC	H	Southport	Lost 1-3	6	Venables	1785
22	25	GMVC	A	Runcorn	Won 8-0	6	Smith, Venables 2, Browne, Berry, Hayles 3	442
23	28	SC2	A	Kettering Town	Lost 1-2*		Bates	808
24	Dec 2	GMVC	H	Macclesfield Town	Won 4-0	5	Sodje, Berry, Lynch, Hayles	2021
25	4	HSC2	H	Watford	Drew 0-0			
26	9	GMVC	H	Bromsgrove Rovers	Won 3-0	4	Barrowcliff, Lynch, Hayles	1565
27	11	GMVC	A	Dagenham & Redbridge	Won 2-1	4	Webster, Hayles	767
28	16	GMVC	A	Northwich Victoria	Won 3-1	2	Browne, Hayles 2	673
29	Jan 1	GMVC	H	Slough Town	Won 3-1	2	Browne, Lynch, Marshall	2123
30	3	HSC2R	A	Watford	Lost 3-4		Cretton, Marshall, Haag	
31	6	GMVC	A	Macclesfield Town	Drew 0-0	2		2126
32	8	GMVC	H	Farnborough Town	Drew 0-0	2		1745
33	13	GMVC	H	Halifax Town	Won 2-0	2	Venables 2	1841
34	20	FAT1	H	Dagenham & Redbridge	Won 3-2		Venables, Marshall, Hayles	1388
35	Feb 3	GMVC	H	Runcorn	Won 4-1	2	Lynch, Hayles 3	1432
36	10	FAT2	H	Burton Albion	Won 2-1		Venables, Hayles	1362
37	13	GMVC	A	Welling United	Won 3-0	2	Lynch 2, Hayles	572
38	17	GMVC	H	Gateshead	Drew 1-1	1	Browne	1364
39	24	GMVC	H	Hednesford Town	Won 1-0	1	Hayles	1626
40	Mar 2	FAT3	H	Kettering Town	Won 3-0		Smith, Hayles 2	2219
41	4	GMVC	H	Dover Athletic	Won 3-2	1	Hayles 2, Marshall	1062
42	9	GMVC	A	Stalybridge Celtic	Won 5-2	1	Venables, Browne, Hayles 3	843
43	12	GMVC	A	Slough Town	Won 6-2	1	Webster, Barrowcliff, Venables, Browne 2, Hayles	1126
44	16	GMVC	H	Kidderminster Harriers	Won 4-1	1	Smith, Browne 2, Hayles	2012
45	23	FAT QF	A	Hyde United	Lost 2-3		Venables, Hayles	2012
46	25	GMVC	A	Hednesford Town	Lost 1-2	1	Venables	1651
47	30	GMVC	A	Altrincham	Won 2-0	1	Webster, Browne	838
48	Apr 6	GMVC	A	Morecambe	Lost 0-1	1		1227
49	8	GMVC	H	Woking	Won 4-0	1	Sodje, Venables, Trebble, Hayles	3976
50	13	GMVC	H	Stalybridge Celtic	Drew 2-2	1	Beevor, Hayles	1767
51	16	GMVC	A	Kettering Town	Won 2-1	1	Hayles 2	1414
52	20	GMVC	A	Bath City	Won 2-1	1	Beevor, Hayles	806
53	22	GMVC	A	Kidderminster Harriers	Won 1-0	1	Trebble	2060
54	27	GMVC	H	Morecambe	Drew 1-1	1	Browne	2556
55	29	GMVC	H	Dagenham & Redbridge	Won 1-0	1	Barrowcliff	2379
56	May 4	GMVC	A	Farnborough Town	Drew 2-2	1	Mutchell, og	1413

* After Extra Time

Stevenage Borough

1	2	3	4	5	6	7	8	9	10	11	12	14	Match No.
Gallagher	Webster	Smith	Sodje	Nugent	Simpson	Venables	Berry	Crawshaw	Lynch	Marshall	Hayles	Barrowcliff	1
Gallagher	Webster	Smith	Sodje	Nugent	Simpson	Venables	Berry	Crawshaw	Lynch	Hayles	Marshall	Beevor	2
Gallagher	Webster	Smith	Sodje	Nugent	Simpson	Venables	Berry	Crawshaw	Lynch	Hayles	Marshall	Barrowcliff	3
Gallagher	Webster	Smith	Sodje	Nugent	Simpson	Venables	Berry	Crawshaw	Lynch	Marshall	Beevor	Barrowcliff	4
Gallagher	Webster	Smith	Sodje	Nugent	Simpson	Venables	Berry	Marshall	Lynch	Hayles	Barrowcliff	Beevor	5
Gallagher	Webster	Mutchell	Sodje	Nugent	Simpson	Venables	Berry	Crawshaw	Smith	Hayles	Marshall	Barrowcliff	6
Gallagher	Webster	Mutchell	Sodje	Nugent	Simpson	Smith	Berry	Crawshaw	Lynch	Hayles	Venables	Barrowcliff	7
Wilmot	Webster	Mutchell	Sodje	Nugent	Simpson	Smith	Berry	Venables	Lynch	Hayles	Crawshaw	Barrowcliff	8
Wilmot	Webster	Mutchell	Sodje	Nugent	Barrowcliff	Smith	Berry	Marshall	Lynch	Hayles	Beevor	Crawshaw	9
Gallagher	Webster	Mutchell	Smith	Nugent	Barrowcliff	Browne	Berry	Marshall	Lynch	Hayles	Sodje	Crawshaw	10
Gallagher	Webster	Mutchell	Sodje	Smith	Barrowcliff	Simpson	Berry	Crawshaw	Lynch	Browne	Marshall	Beevor	11
Gallagher	Cretton	Mutchell	Sodje	Smith	Barrowcliff	Simpson	Berry	Crawshaw	Marshall	Hayles	Nugent	Beevor	12
Gallagher	Smith	Mutchell	Sodje	Nugent	Barrowcliff	Simpson	Beevor	Crawshaw	Lynch	Marshall	D Grime	Bates	13
Wilmot	Cretton	Mutchell	Smith	Nugent	Barrowcliff	Simpson	Beevor	Crawshaw	Lynch	Marshall	Hayles	Grime	14
Wilmot	Webster	Mutchell	Sodje	Smith	Barrowcliff	Simpson	Browne	Crawshaw	Lynch	Hayles	Marshall	Beevor	15
Gallagher	Webster	Mutchell	Sodje	Smith	Barrowcliff	Simpson	Browne	Crawshaw	Lynch	Hayles	Marshall	Nugent	16
Gallagher	Webster	Mutchell	Sodje	Smith	Barrowcliff	Simpson	Browne	Crawshaw	Lynch	Hayles	Marshall	Nugent	17
Gallagher	Webster	Mutchell	Sodje	Smith	Barrowcliff	Beevor	Browne	Crawshaw	Lynch	Hayles	Marshall	Nugent	18
Gallagher	Webster	Mutchell	Sodje	Nugent	Barrowcliff	Beevor	Browne	Crawshaw	Lynch	Hayles	Marshall	Venables	19
Gallagher	Webster	Mutchell	Sodje	Nugent	Barrowcliff	Beevor	Browne	Crawshaw	Lynch	Hayles	Berry	Venables	20
Gallagher	Webster	Mutchell	Sodje	Nugent	Barrowcliff	Beevor	Browne	Venables	Berry	Hayles	Lynch	Marshall	21
Wilmot	Webster	Mutchell	Sodje	Smith	Barrowcliff	Venables	Browne	Berry	Lynch	Hayles	Marshall	Beevor	22
Gallagher	Gonzague	Cretton	Wedlock	Smith	Beeke	Beevor	Phillips	Bates	Lynch	Marshall	D Grime	N Grime	23
Wilmot	Webster	Mutchell	Sodje	Smith	Barrowcliff	Venables	Browne	Berry	Lynch	Hayles	Bates	Beeke	24
Gallagher	D Grime	N Grime	Cretton	Gonzague	Beeke	Hoy	Beevor	Berry	Phillips	Wedlock	Keepence	Huggins	25
Wilmot	Webster	Mutchell	Sodje	Smith	Barrowcliff	Venables	Browne	Berry	Lynch	Hayles	Cretton	Beeke	26
Wilmot	Webster	N Grime	Sodje	Smith	Barrowcliff	Venables	Browne	Berry	Lynch	Hayles	Haag	Beeke	27
Wilmot	Webster	Mutchell	Sodje	Smith	Barrowcliff	Venables	Browne	Haag	Lynch	Hayles	Bates	Beeke	28
Wilmot	Webster	Mutchell	Cretton	Smith	Barrowcliff	Venables	Browne	Berry	Lynch	Crawshaw	Bates	Marshall	29
Gallagher	D Grime	Wedlock	Gonzague	Cretton	Beeke	Marshall	Beevor	Venables	Keepence	Bates	Huggins	Coughlin	30
Wilmot	Webster	Mutchell	Sodje	Smith	Barrowcliff	Venables	Browne	Berry	Lynch	Hayles	Bates	Beeke	31
Wilmot	Webster	Mutchell	Sodje	Smith	Barrowcliff	Berry	Browne	Berry	Lynch	Hayles	Cretton	Marshall	32
Wilmot	Webster	Mutchell	Sodje	Smith	Barrowcliff	Venables	Browne	Berry	Beeke	Hayles	Vier	Bates	33
Wilmot	Webster	Mutchell	Sodje	Smith	Barrowcliff	Venables	Marshall	Berry	Lynch	Hayles	Beeke	Cretton	34
Wilmot	Cretton	Mutchell	Sodje	Smith	Barrowcliff	Venables	Marshall	Berry	Lynch	Hayles	Beeke	Beevor	35
Wilmot	Cretton	Mutchell	Sodje	Smith	Barrowcliff	Venables	Marshall	Berry	Lynch	Hayles	Browne	Beevor	36
Wilmot	Webster	Mutchell	Sodje	Cretton	Barrowcliff	Venables	Marshall	Berry	Lynch	Hayles	Browne	Beevor	37
Wilmot	Webster	Mutchell	Cretton	Smith	Barrowcliff	Venables	Browne	Berry	Lynch	Hayles	Marshall	Beevor	38
Wilmot	Webster	Mutchell	Sodje	Smith	Barrowcliff	Venables	Browne	Berry	Lynch	Hayles	Marshall	Cretton	39
Wilmot	Webster	Mutchell	Sodje	Smith	Barrowcliff	Venables	Browne	Berry	Lynch	Hayles	Marshall	Cretton	40
Wilmot	Webster	Mutchell	Sodje	Smith	Barrowcliff	Venables	Browne	Berry	Lynch	Hayles	Marshall	Cretton	41
Gallagher	Webster	Mutchell	Sodje	Smith	Barrowcliff	Venables	Browne	Berry	Marshall	Hayles	Vier	Beevor	42
Wilmot	Webster	Mutchell	Sodje	Smith	Barrowcliff	Venables	Browne	Berry	Marshall	Hayles	Cretton	Beevor	43
Wilmot	Webster	Mutchell	Sodje	Smith	Barrowcliff	Venables	Browne	Berry	Marshall	Hayles	Cretton	Beevor	44
Wilmot	Webster	Mutchell	Sodje	Smith	Barrowcliff	Venables	Browne	Berry	Marshall	Hayles	Cretton	Beevor	45
Gallagher	Webster	Mutchell	Sodje	Smith	Barrowcliff	Venables	Browne	Berry	Beevor	Hayles	Cretton	Marshall	46
Gallagher	Webster	Mutchell	Paris	Smith	Barrowcliff	Venables	Browne	Berry	Beevor	Hayles	Trebble	Crawshaw	47
Gallagher	Webster	Mutchell	Howell	Smith	Barrowcliff	Venables	Browne	Berry	Beevor	Hayles	Trebble	Crawshaw	48
Gallagher	Cretton	Mutchell	Sodje	Smith	Barrowcliff	Venables	Trebble	Berry	Beevor	Hayles	Crawshaw	Marshall	49
Gallagher	Cretton	Mutchell	Sodje	Smith	Barrowcliff	Venables	Trebble	Berry	Beevor	Hayles	Browne	Howell	50
Gallagher	Webster	Mutchell	Sodje	Smith	Barrowcliff	Venables	Browne	Berry	Beevor	Hayles	Paris	Marshall	51
Gallagher	Webster	Mutchell	Sodje	Smith	Barrowcliff	Venables	Browne	Berry	Beevor	Hayles	Paris	Marshall	52
Gallagher	Webster	Paris	Sodje	Smith	Barrowcliff	Venables	Browne	Berry	Beevor	Hayles	Crawshaw	Howell	53
Gallagher	Webster	Paris	Sodje	Smith	Barrowcliff	Venables	Browne	Berry	Trebble	Hayles	Beevor	Mutchell	54
Wilmot	Webster	Mutchell	Sodje	Smith	Barrowcliff	Paris	Browne	Berry	Beevor	Hayles	Venables	Crawshaw	55
Wilmot	Webster	Mutchell	Sodje	Smith	Barrowcliff	Paris	Browne	Berry	Beevor	Hayles	Venables	Crawshaw	56

PAUL FAIRCLOUGH

Possibly the most successful manager in non-League football, in five seasons in charge Paul Fairclough has led the Stevenage Borough side from the obscurity of the Isthmian League Division 2 North to the threshold of the Endsleigh League, as they are already a force to be reckoned with in the Vauxhall Conference.

Embarking on the second year of a five year contract, three championship successes have established Paul as one of the most respected bosses at this level.

Fairclough, who hails from Liverpool and is an Everton fanatic, is very ambitious to see Borough through to the ultimate goal of league football.

As a player, Fairclough was a member of Harlow Town's famous 1979-80 FA Cup squad which reached the Fourth Round Proper - he scored the winning goal in the First Round clash with Leytonstone-Ilford. Among other clubs, he also played for St Albans and Hertford.

His first taste of management came at Hertford Town when he succeeded Tony Woodrow at the start of the 1986-87 season. After four seasons in charge he had led them to their first County Cup success for 23 years and to third in Division Two North of the Isthmian League. At the start of 1990-91 he replaced Brian Williams at Stevenage, and the rest is history.

Paul Fairclough *Photo - Eric Marsh*

Paul Barrowcliff; Player of the Year

Programme details:
32 pages for £1.20
Editor - Simon Mortimer (01585 188600)

Any other club publications:
The Borough Yearbook £2.00
Gitts is Up. 50p (Fanzine)

Local Newspapers:
Stevenage Gazette
Comet
Herald
Stevenage Mercury

Local Radio Stations:
Chiltern Radio
BBC Three Counties Radio

STEVENAGE BOROUGH - PLAYING SQUAD 1996-97

Player	Honours	Birthplace and date	Transfer Fees	Previous Clubs
GOALKEEPERS				
Des Gallagher	GMVC, ILP	Luton 23/1/62		Watford, Eaton Bray Utd, Stevenage Borough, Dunstable
Richard Wilmot	GMVC	Matlock 29/8/69		Hitchin T, Halifax T, Hitchin T
DEFENDERS				
Mark Smith	ESP, GMVC, ILP	Luton		Hitchin T, Letchworth GC, Hitchin T, Woking, Hitchin T
John Ugbah		Nigeria 12/8/72		Faweh, Fisher'93, Carshalton A
Efetobor Sodje	GMVC	Greenwich 5/10/72		Delta Steel Pioneer (Nigeria)
Shaun Stevens		Chertsey 8/3/76		Wycombe W
Kenny Webster	GMVC	Hammersmith 2/3/73		Arsenal, Peterborough U
Robert Mutchell	GMVC	Solihull 3/1/74		Oxford U, Barnet, Telford U
Alan Paris		Slough 15/8/64		Slough T, Watford, Peterborough U, Leicester C, Notts Co, Slough T
MIDFIELDERS				
Corey Browne	ESP, GMVC	Edmonton 2/7/70	4-fig	Kingsbury T, Fulham, Haringey B, Exeter C, Wealdstone, Dover A
Stuart Beevor	GMVC	Welwyn Garden City 23/4/75		Stevenage B, Hatfield T
Neil Catlin		Amersham 15/9/72		Marlow, Thame, Flackwell, Marlow, Maidenhead U, Marlow, Slough T
Paul Barrowcliff	GMVC	London		Hendon, Ruislip M, Hayes, Harrow, Kingstonian, Wycombe, Sutton U, Aylesbury
FORWARDS				
Barry Hayles	ESP, GMVC	London 17/5/72		Willesden Hawkeye
David Venables	ESP, GMVC ILP	Horsham 6/11/67		Eastbourne United, Crawley Town, Wealdstone
Mike Bignall		Liverpool		Wrexham, Runcorn
Gary Crawshaw	GMVC, ILP	Reading 4/2/71		Luton Town, Wycombe Wanderers, Staines Town, Hendon
Neil Trebble		Hitchin 16/2/69		Stevenage B, Scunthorpe U, Preston NE, Scarborough

Departures during season:
Phil Simpson (Barnet), Adam Parker (Hitchin T), Richard Nugent (Yeovil T), Marvin Bates (Molesey - Loan), Tony Lynch (Yeovil T).
Players on loan during season:
Corey Browne (Dover A).
Departures during close season: Steve Berry (Kettering T), Shaun Marshall (Enfield).

Broadhall Way, Stevenage

ADDRESS:
Stevenage Stadium, Broadhall Way, Stevenage, Herts SG2 8TH (01438 743322).

TELEPHONE NUMBER: 01438 743322 Fax: 01438 743666.

SIMPLE DIRECTIONS:
Stevenage South exit off A1(M) - ground on right at second roundabout. Spectators are however advised to go straight on at this roundabout and park in the Showground opposite the stadium. The stadium is one mile from Stevenage BR station. Buses SB4 and SB5.

CAPACITY: 3,700 **SEATED:** 488 **COVERED TERRACING:** 2,000

RECORD ATTENDANCE:
3,976 v Woking, GM Vauxhall Conference 8/4/96.

CLUB SHOP:
Yes, selling programmes, scarves and other club merchandise. Contact Bob Davies c/o the Club.

SOCIAL FACILITIES:
Tel.: 01438 367059. Clubhouse at ground open Monday to Friday 7 - 11pm, Saturday noon - 2.00 & 4.30 - 11pm, Sunday: All day from noon.

PREVIOUS GROUNDS:
King George V Playing Field 1976-80.

Stevenage Fact File

Nickname: Boro'

Reserve Team's League: Essex & Herts Border Combination & Capital League.

Previous Leagues: Chiltern Youth 76-79/ Wallspan South Combination 79-80/ United Counties 80-84/ Isthmian 84-94.

Club colours: White & Red striped shirts, white with red trim shorts & white with red trim socks.

Change colours: Blue and yellow shirts, yellow shorts, yellow socks.

Midweek home matchday: Monday

Record win: 11-1 v British Timken Athletic (H), United Counties League Div.1, 1980-81.

Record defeat: 0-7 v Southwick (H), Isthmian League Div. 1, 1987-88.

Record transfer fee paid: Undisclosed.

Record transfer fee received: Undisclosed.

1995-96 Captain: Steve Berry.

1995-96 Top scorer: Barry Hayles.

1995-96 Player of the Year: Paul Barrowcliff.

Club record goalscorer: Barry Hayles.

Record appearances: Martin Gittings.

Past players who progressed to the Football League: Richard Wilmot & Neil Trebble (Scunthorpe Utd) 1993, Simon Clark (Peterborough United) 1994, Leo Fortune West (Gillingham) 1995, Phil Simpson (Barnet) 1995.

Honours: GM Vauxhall Conference 95-96, Isthmian Lge Prem 93-94, Div 1 91-92, Div 2 (North) 85-86 90-91; Utd Counties Lg Div 1 80-81 (Div 1 Cup 80-81), Herts Snr Cup R-up 85-86, 93/94; Herts Charity Cup R-up 93-94, Herts Charity Shield R-up 83-84, Herts Charity Cup R-up 93/94; Televised Sports Snr Floodlit Cup 89-90, Eastern Professional F'llt Cup Group winners 81-82 85-86 86-87 88-89 90-91 91-92, South Co's Comb. Cup 91-92; Essex & Herts Border Comb.(Reserves) 94/95, Essex & Herts (Western Div) 95-96.

TELFORD UNITED

Formed: 1876

President:
G E Smith

Chairman:
A H Esp

Football Secretary:
M J Ferriday

Player-Manager:
Wayne Clarke

Assistant Manager:
Brian Caswell

Physiotherapist:
Paul Heath

Press Officer:
Robert Cave

A very good second half of the season saw Telford move away from being a relegation candidate to the security of a mid-table position.

It took time for player-manager Wayne Clarke to acclimatise to the rigours of the Vauxhall Conference, having spent all his previous career in the Football League, but he did well and made some good signings.

Telford produced some excellent football during the 1995/96 season and, despite the financial contraints which has forced the sale of their Buck's Head ground and the departure of the highly-rated Marcus Bignot to Kidderminster Harriers for £10,000, Clarke new-look squad, which includes a number of young players released from League clubs, could well surprise a few this season. **Steve Whitney**

Back Row (L-R); Mark Turner, Brian Caswell, Steve Eccleston, Brett Wilcox, Brian Gray, Derek Dudley, Darren Simkin, Nigel Niblett, Steve Foster, Chris Harrison, Mark Keorney. Front; Lee Fowler, Kevin Ashley, Justin Ellitts, Brian Taylor, Wayne Clarke, Tony Esp, Lee Robinson, Tim Langford, Jan Purdie.

Telford United

Match No.	Date	Comp.	Venue H/A	Opponents	Result	League Pos.	Goalscorers (Times if known)	Attendance
1	Aug 19	GMVC	A	Morecambe	Lost 0-2			1532
2	22	GMVC	H	Altrincham	Won 2-0		Myers, Clarke	820
3	26	GMVC	H	Farnborough	Won 3-2		Bignot, Myers, Clarke	808
4	28	GMVC	A	Stevenage	Won 1-0		Langford	2003
5	Sep 2	GMVC	A	Stalybridge	Drew 2-2		Myers, Clarke	619
6	5	GMVC	H	Runcorn	Lost 1-2		Gray	1008
7	9	FACQ1	H	Shifnal	Won 4-0		Myers 2, Bignot, Gray	837
8	11	GMVC	A	Hednesford	Lost 0-4			2480
9	16	GMVC	H	Gateshead	Drew 0-0			750
10	19	SC1	H	Northwich	Lost 1-2		Wilcox	540
11	23	FACQ2	A	Raunds Town	Won 2-1		Clarke, Langford	244
12	26	GMVC	H	Bromsgrove	Drew 0-0			745
13	30	GMVC	H	Kettering	Lost 3-4		Myers 2, Clarke	952
14	Oct 3	SC2	A	Northwich	Won 3-0		Crookes, Myers, Clarke	514
15	7	FACQ3	H	Halesowen	Won 4-1		Fowler, Myers, Clarke, Langford	904
16	9	GMVC	A	Kidderminster	Lost 0-2			2433
17	14	GMVC	A	Southport	Lost 2-3		Gray 2	812
18	21	FACQ4	H	Southport	Won 3-0		Myers, Langford 2	898
19	28	GMVC	H	Slough	Won 2-0		Myers, Fereday	808
20	Nov 4	GMVC	H	Stevenage	Lost 1-3		Bignot	883
21	11	FACR1	H	Witton Albion	Won 2-1		Foster, Langford	1277
22	18	GMVC	A	Welling	Lost 1-3		Langford	613
23	25	GMVC	H	Dagenham	Drew 0-0			711
24	Dec 2	FACR2	H	Notts County	Lost 0-2			2831
25	5	SRC	A	Bromsgrove	Lost 1-3		Clarke	583
26	9	GMVC	H	Morecambe	Drew 2-2		Simkin, Robinson	728
27	16	GMVC	A	Altrincham	Lost 0-1			633
28	19	GMVC	A	Northwich	Lost 0-2			503
29	Jan 6	GMVC	A	Dover	Lost 0-1			1030
30	13	GMVC	A	Bath	Won 3-0		Myers 3	517
31	20	FATR1	A	Burton Albion	Lost 1-3		Gray	950
32	Feb 3	GMVC	A	Slough	Won 2-1		Clarke, Turner	682
33	10	GMVC	A	Woking	Lost 1-5		Langford	2384
34	13	GMVC	A	Macclesfield	Lost 0-1			866
35	17	GMVC	H	Dover	Won 1-0			733
36	20	GMVC	H	Kidderminster	Drew 1-1		Gray	918
37	24	GMVC	A	Gateshead	Won 2-1		Robinson, Langford	813
38	Mar 2	GMVC	H	Stalybridge	Lost 0-1			783
39	9	GMVC	H	Northwich	Won 1-0		Langford	712
40	12	GMVC	A	Bromsgrove	Won 2-0		Niblett, Gray	746
41	16	GMVC	A	Dagenham	Drew 1-1		Niblett	668
42	23	GMVC	H	Southport	Won 2-0		Gray 2	758
43	26	GMVC	H	Woking	Lost 1-2		Adams	736
44	30	GMVC	H	Macclesfield	Lost 1-2		Purdie	1015
45	Apr 2	GMVC	H	Hednesford	Won 2-1		Wilcox, Turner	967
46	6	GMVC	A	Halifax	Drew 0-0			771
47	8	GMVC	H	Welling	Drew 0-0			782
48	13	GMVC	H	Halifax	Drew 1-1		Eccleston	708
49	20	GMVC	A	Farnborough	Lost 1-2		Adams	784
50	27	GMVC	A	Runcorn	Won 3-2		Purdie, Gray, Turner	401
51	30	GMVC	A	Kettering	Won 3-0		Gray 2, Adams	851
52	May 4	GMVC	H	Bath	Won 3-1		Niblett, Bignot, Adams	831

Telford United

1	2	3	4	5	6	7	8	9	10	11	12	14	Match No.
Goodwin	Davidson	Mutchell	Wilcox	Foster	Crookes	Myers	Clarke	Gray	Bignot	Kearney	Moore	Ellitts	1
Goodwin	Bignot	Mutchell	Wilcox	Foster	Crookes	Myers	Clarke	Gray	Ellitts	Kearney	Moore	Gardiner	2
Goodwin	Bignot	Mutchell	Wilcox	Foster	Crookes	Myers	Clarke	Gray	Ellitts	Langford	Moore	Gardiner	3
Goodwin	Davidson	Mutchell	Wilcox	Foster	Crookes	Myers	Clarke	Gray	Langford	Bignot	Ellitts	Gardiner	4
Goodwin	Bignot	Davidson	Wilcox	Foster	Crookes	Myers	Clarke	Gray	Langford	Kearney	Ellitts	Gardiner	5
Goodwin	Bignot	Davidson	Wilcox	Foster	Crookes	Myers	Clarke	Gray	Ellitts	Kearney	Langford	Fowler	6
Goodwin	Davidson	Fowler	Wilcox	Foster	Niblett	Myers	Bignot	Gray	Langford	Kearney	Crookes	Ellitts	7
Goodwin	Davidson	Fowler	Wilcox	Foster	Niblett	Myers	Clarke	Gray	Bignot	Kearney	Crookes	Langford	8
Goodwin	Davidson	Fowler	Wilcox	Robinson	Crookes	Myers	Clarke	Gray	Bignot	Kearney	Langford	Ellitts	9
Straney	Kearney	Fowler	Wilcox	Robinson	Crookes	Myers	Bignot	Gray	Langford	Ellitts	Gardiner	Clarke	10
Goodwin	Gardiner	Fowler	Wilcox	Foster	Kearney	Myers	Clarke	Gray	Langford	Bignot	Ellitts	Crookes	11
Straney	Gardiner	Fowler	Ramsey	Foster	Kearney	Myers	Clarke	Gray	Langford	Bignot	Robinson	Ellitts	12
Straney	Gardiner	Fowler	Ramsey	Foster	Kearney	Myers	Clarke	Gray	Bignot	Fereday	Crookes	Langford	13
Goodwin	Fereday	Fowler	Crookes	Foster	Kearney	Myers	Clarke	Gray	Bignot	Langford	Ellitts	Gardiner	14
Goodwin	Crookes	Fowler	Kearney	Foster	Niblett	Myers	Clarke	Gray	Bignot	Robinson	Langford	Gardiner	15
Goodwin	Fereday	Niblett	Crookes	Foster	Kearney	Myers	Bignot	Gray	Langford	Ellitts	Robinson	Gardiner	16
Goodwin	Fereday	Fowler	Simkin	Foster	Niblett	Myers	Clarke	Gray	Bignot	Kearney	Ellitts	Gardiner	17
Goodwin	Gardiner	Fowler	Ramsey	Foster	Niblett	Myers	Langford	Gray	Bignot	Kearney	Clarke	Ellitts	18
Goodwin	Simkin	Fowler	Ramsey	Foster	Niblett	Myers	Langford	Gray	Bignot	Fereday	Clarke	Ellitts	19
Goodwin	Simkin	Fowler	Ellitts	Foster	Niblett	Myers	Langford	Gray	Bignot	Fereday	clarke	Robinson	20
Goodwin	Gardiner	Fowler	Ramsey	Foster	Niblett	Myers	Clarke	Gray	Bignot	Robinson	Ellitts	Langford	21
Goodwin	Simkin	Fowler	Kearney	Foster	Niblett	Myers	Langford	Ellitts	Bignot	Robinson	Clarke	Gardiner	22
Goodwin	Bignot	Fowler	Wilcox	Simkin	Kearney	Myers	Clarke	Gray	Langford	Adams	Gardiner	Niblett	23
Goodwin	Gardiner	Fowler	Wilcox	Niblett	Kearney	Myers	Clarke	Langford	Bignot	Adams	Gray	Robinson	24
Goodwin	Bignot	Fowler	Wilcox	Simkin	Kearney	Myers	Clarke	Gray	Ellitts	Adams	Niblett	Robinson	25
Germaine	Gardiner	Adams	Wilcox	Fowler	Simkin	Myers	Clarke	Gray	Bignot	Robinson	Kearney	Ellitts	26
Germaine	Bignot	Adams	Wilcox	Simkin	Kearney	Myers	Clarke	Gray	Turner	Robinson	Gardiner	Foster	27
Germaine	Gardiner	Adams	Kearney	Foster	Simkin	Myers	Bignot	Gray	Turner	Robinson	Ellitts	Caswell	28
Germaine	Bignot	Kearney	Eccleston	Foster	Niblett	Myers	Adams	Gray	Turner	Robinson	Wassell	Clarke	29
Germaine	Bignot	Wassell	Eccleston	Foster	Kearney	Myers	Adams	Gray	Turner	Robinson	Gardiner	Clarke	30
Hughes	Foster	Wassell	Robinson	Kearney	Niblett	Myers	Ellitts	Gray	Turner	Adams	Gardiner	Langford	31
Germaine	Bignot	Adams	Robinson	Eccleston	Niblett	Farrington	Clarke	Gray	Turner	Langford	Caswell	Gardiner	32
Germaine	Wilcox	Adams	Kearney	Eccleston	Niblett	Robinson	Farrington	Gray	Turner	Langford	Clarke	Gardiner	33
Hughes	Wilcox	Kearney	Robinson	Foster	Niblett	Myers	Eccleston	Gray	Turner	Adams	Langford	Ellitts	34
Germaine	Warner	Fowler	Kearney	Foster	Niblett	Myers	Robinson	Gray	Turner	Adams	Wilcox	Langford	35
Germaine	Warner	Fowler	Kearney	Foster	Niblett	Myers	Robinson	Gray	Turner	Adams	Wilcox	Langford	36
Germaine	Warner	Fowler	Robinson	Foster	Kearney	Myers	Langford	Gray	Turner	Adams	Clarke	Ellitts	37
Hughes	Warner	Fowler	Kearney	Foster	Niblett	Myers	Langford	Gray	Turner	Adams	Ellitts	Gardiner	38
Hughes	Eccleston	Warner	Robinson	Foster	Niblett	Myers	Langford	Gray	Turner	Adams	Ellitts	Gardiner	39
Hughes	Eccleston	Warner	Robinson	Foster	Niblett	Myers	Langford	Gray	Turner	Adams	Ellitts	Gardiner	40
Dudley	Eccleston	Warner	Robinson	Foster	Niblett	Wilcox	Langford	Gray	Turner	Adams	Ellitts	Gardiner	41
Hughes	Eccleston	Kearney	Robinson	Foster	Niblett	Warner	Langford	Gray	Turner	Adams	Fowler	Wilcox	42
Hughes	Eccleston	Fowler	Wilcox	Foster	Niblett	Warner	Langford	Gray	Turner	Adams	Myers	Kearney	43
Hughes	Eccleston	Fowler	Wilcox	Foster	Niblett	Warner	Langford	Gray	Turner	Adams	Kearney	Myers	44
Hughes	Eccleston	Fowler	Wilcox	Foster	Kearney	Myers	Langford	Gray	Turner	Adams	Bignot	Purdie	45
Hughes	Eccleston	Fowler	Wilcox	Foster	Kearney	Myers	Langford	Gray	Turner	Adams	Bignot	Purdie	46
Hughes	Bignot	Fowler	Wilcox	Foster	Kearney	Myers	Purdie	Gray	Turner	Adams	Eccleston	Robinson	47
Hughes	Bignot	Kearney	Eccleston	Foster	Niblett	Myers	Langford	Gray	Turner	Adams	Purdie	Clarke	48
Huges	Bignot	Kearney	Wilcox	Foster	Niblett	Myers	Purdie	Gray	Turner	Adams	Fowler	Clarke	49
Hughes	Eccleston	Kearney	Wilcox	Foster	Niblett	Bignot	Purdie	Gray	Turner	Adams	Fowler	Robinson	50
Hughes	Eccleston	Fowler	Wilcox	Foster	Niblett	Bignot	Purdie	Gray	Turner	Adams	Kearney	Robinson	51
Hughes	Eccleston	Fowler	Wilcox	Foster	Niblett	Bignot	Purdie	Gray	Turner	Adams	Myers	Kearney	52

Telford United

WAYNE CLARKE

Following the departure of George Foster, Wayne Clarke was appointed as player-manager. This is Wayne's first managerial appointment and with a squad full of very young players he will have his work cut out to maintain Telford's status as a Vauxhall Conference club.

One thing is certain and that is that he should manage to contribute plenty of goals. He started his playing career as an apprentice at Wolverhampton Wanderers for whom he made well over 150 appearances before starting his wandering. He then moved to Birmingham City in 1984, making over 100 appearances for them before his 'big move' to Everton. He was with Everton for just over two years before moving to Leicester City for six months and then to Manchester City. Although he was there for over two years he had three loan spells with Shrewsbury, Stoke City and Wolves during that time. At the age of 31 he was given a free transfer from City to Walsall where he had a very successful season scoring 21 goals in 39 league games. His final move, prior to joining Telford, was to Shrewsbury Town.

Morecambe's keeper Glen Johnstone takes the ball in the air following a Telford free kick during the first half of the GMVC fixture at Christie Park. *Photo - Martin Wray*

Programme details:
32 pages for £1
Editor - R Sheridan

Any other club publications:

Local Newspapers:
Shropshire Star
Telford Journal

Local Radio Stations:
BBC Radio Shropshire
Beacon Radio

TELFORD UNITED - PLAYING SQUAD 1996-97

Player	Honours	Birthplace and date	Transfer Fees	Previous Clubs
GOALKEEPERS				
Ken Hughes		Barmouth 9/1/66		Crystal Palace, Shrewsbury Town, Wrexham, Telford U, Hinckley T
Derek Dudley		Birmingham 2/2/70	£1,000	A Villa, Sutton Coldfield T, Stourbridge, Worcester C, VS Rugby, WBA, Halesowen
DEFENDERS				
Nigel Niblett	SLC, BSC, MFC, FAXI	Stratford 12/8/67	4-fig	Snitterfield Sports, Stratford T, VS Rugby
Steve Foster		Mansfield 3/12/74		Mansfield T
Lee Fowler		Nottingham 26/1/69		Stoke C, Preston NE, Doncaster R, Halifax T
Darren Simkin		Walsall 24/3/70		Blakenall, Wolves, Shrewsbury
Kevin Ashley		Birmingham 31/12/68		Birmingham C, Wolves, Peterborough U
MIDFIELDERS				
Brett Wilcox		Sutton Coldfield 27/12/68		Kidderminster H, Bridgnorth T, Shifnal T
Mark Kearney		Ormskirk 12/6/62		Everton, Mansfield T, Bury
Lee Martin		Birmingham		Shrewsbury T
Martyn Naylor		Birmingham 2/8/77		Hereford U
Lee Robinson		Wythenshawe 23/11/73		Burnley
Mark Turner		Bebbington 4/10/72		Wolves, Northampton T
Steve Eccleston		Birmingham 17/1/67		Welshpool, Bridgnorth T, Tamworth, Atherstone U, Hednesford T, Bridgnorth T
FORWARDS				
Wayne Clarke	ES, EY	Wolverhampton 28/2/61		Wolves, Birmingham C, Everton, Leicester Man.City, Walsall, Shrewsbury T
Justin Ellits		Wolverhampton 3/10/76		Wolves
Jon Purdie	ES, FAXI, GMVC, FAT	Corby 22/2/67		Arsenal, Wolves, Oxford U, Brentford, Shrewsbury T, Worcester C, Kidderminster
Tim Langford	GMVC	Kingswinford 12/9/65		Halesowen T, Telford U Wycombe W
Damon Russell		Wales 10/4/67		Congleton T, Welshpool
Brian Gray		Birmingham 25/11/72		Birmingham C, Bromsgrove R

Departures during season:
Lee Wilson (Halifax T), Paul Straney (Glenavon), Jon Davidson (Dag & Red), Dominic Crookes (Dag & Red), Paul Ramsey (Torquay U), Wayne Fereday (Released), Kim Wassall (Finland).
Players on loan during season:
Darren Simkin (Shrewsbury), Gary Germaine (WBA), Michael Warner (Northampton)
Departures during close season: Marcus Bignot (Kidderminster H), Martin Myers (Solihull B), Nick Goodwin (Released).

Bucks Head, Telford United

ADDRESS: Bucks Head Ground, Watling Street, Wellington, Telford, Shropshire TF1 2NJ.

TELEPHONE NUMBER: 01952 223838. Fax: 01952 246431.

SIMPLE DIRECTIONS:
M54 Junction 6, A518 to B5061 (Watling Street). Ground is on several bus routes.

CAPACITY: 4,600 **SEATED:** 1,200 **COVERED TERRACING:** 1,500

RECORD ATTENDANCE:
13,000 v Shrewsbury Town - Birmingham League - 1936.

CLUB SHOP:
Contact Shirley Finnigan on 0952 223838 for details.

SOCIAL FACILITIES:
Social club adjacent to ground - open matchdays and selected other hours.

PREVIOUS GROUNDS:
None

Telford Fact File

Nickname: Lilywhites

Club Sponsors: Eastern Generation.

Previous Leagues: Southern League, Cheshire League, Birmingham League.

Previous Grounds: None

Previous Name: Wellington Town (prior to 1969).

Club colours: White shirts, blue shorts, blue socks.

Change colours: Blue shirts, blue shorts and blue socks.

Midweek home matchday: Tuesday

Record win: Undisclosed

Record defeat: Undisclosed

Record transfer fee: £10,000 to Northwich Victoria for Paul Mayman.

Record transfer fee received: £50,000 from Scarborough for Stephen Norris.

1995-96 Captain: Marcus Bignot.

1995-96 Top scorer: Brian Gray.

1995-96 Player of the Year: Brett Wilcox.

Club record goalscorer:

Past Players who progressed to the Football League: A.Walker (Lincoln City), G.French (Luton Town), K.McKenna (Tranmere Rovers), S.Norris (Scarborough), David Pritchard (Bristol Rovers) 1994, Sean Parrish (Doncaster Rovers) 1994.

Club Honours: Birmingham League 1920-21, 1934-35, 1935-36; Cheshire League 1945-46, 1946-47, 1951-52; Edward Case Cup 1952-53, 1954-55; Welsh Cup 1901-02, 1905-06, 1939-40; Birmingham Senior Cup 1946-47; Walsall Senior Cup 1946-47; Birmingham League Challenge Cup 1946-47; Shropshire Senior Cup (30); Southern League Cup 1970-71; Midland Floodlit Cup 1970-71; Midland Floodlit Cup 1970-71, 1982-83, 1988-89, Runnser-up 1969-70, 1987-88.

WELLING UNITED

Formed:
1963

President:
E.Brackstone

Chairman:
P.Websdale

Vice Chairman
S.Pain

Football Secretary:
Barrie Hobbins

Manager:
Kevin Hales

Assistant Manager
Ray Burgess

Coach:
Kevin Hales

Physiotherapist:
Peter Green

Commercial Manager:
S Wells

Press Officer:
Paul Carter

The 1995/96 season is not one that the club will look back upon with fond memories. For the first part of the campaign the Wings were strong relegation candidates and their cup form was once more disastrous. Fortunately the club were able to introduce new faces into the squad, with England semi-pro international midfielder Derek Brown and former Cambridge United and England Youth international striker Ollie Morah being particularly influential as results gradually improved.

The relegation zone, after such a poor start, was never very far away, and although it was a case of survival once more, it certainly wasn't the best of times to introduce yet one more of the club's youth products in Richard Dimmock, who netted his first goal for the senior outfit in March just prior to his 17th birthday. Striker Paul Gorman was unable to recover the sort of form that he was showing prior to sustaining a broken leg, whilst the loss of the talented wingers Steve Finnan and Steve Barnes to Birmingham City weakened the squad still further. However, the fees received helped greatly to balance the books in a season when home gates dipped to their lowest.

Several clubs in similar situations to Welling with regard to low gates, have found it impossible to sustain Conference football, but with commercial activities revamped in the close season, the continuation of the club's YT scheme and manager Kevin Hales now fully aware of the needs at Conference level, the Wings are looking to do more than just survive. **Barrie Hobbins**

Welling's Derek Brown (R) & Dagenham's Dominic Crookes. *Photo - K Gillard*

Welling United

Match No.	Date	Comp.	Venue H/A	Opponents	Result	League Pos.	Goalscorers (Times if known)	Attendance
1	Aug 19	GMVC	A	Runcorn	Won 3-1		Gamble 2, Farley	410
2	22	GMVC	H	Slough Town	Lost 0-3			747
3	26	GMVC	H	Northwich Victoria	Drew 1-1		Berry	538
4	28	GMVC	A	Hednesford	Drew 1-1		og	1732
5	Sep 2	GMVC	A	Halifax	Lost 1-2		Copley	766
6	5	GMVC	H	Bromsgrove Rovers	Won 5-2		Henry, Barnes 3, Wordsworth	602
7	9	FAC	H	Wick	Won 2-0		Farley, Sykes	547
8	12	GMVC	A	Bath City	Drew 1-1		Farley	458
9	16	GMVC	A	Southport	Lost 0-2			915
10	19	SC1	H	Dover	Lost 1-2		O'Keefe	409
11	23	FAC	H	Bromley	Drew 2-2		Brown, Gorman	722
12	26	FAC	A	Bromley	Drew 3-3		Watts, Appiah, Barnes	451
13	30	GMVC	A	Morecambe	Lost 0-1			857
14	Oct 2	FAC	H	Bromley	Lost 1-2		Copley	701
15	7	GMVC	H	Gateshead	Lost 1-2		Morah	588
16	10	SC2	A	Dover Athletic	Lost 0-3			664
17	14	GMVC	A	Stalybridge Celtic	Lost 1-2		Morah p	605
18	17	KSC	H	Deal Town	Won 1-0		Appiah	157
19	21	GMVC	H	Woking	Lost 1-2		Morah p	1066
20	23	GMVC	A	Stevenage	Lost 1-4		Morah	1731
21	28	GMVC	A	Macclesfield Town	Lost 1-2		Morah	988
22	31	GMVC	H	Bath City	Won 2-1		Morah p, Henry	403
23	Nov 4	GMVC	H	Altrincham	Drew 1-1		Henry	623
24	14	GMVC	A	Kettering Town	Won 3-1		Wordsworth, Rutherford, Brown	1232
25	18	GMVC	H	Telford United	Won 3-1		Henry, Brown,og	613
26	21	LSC	H	Southall	Won 12-0		Wordsworth 2, Morah 5, Henry 4, Gorman	101
27	25	GMVC	H	Halifax	Drew 0-0			666
28	Dec 2	GMVC	A	Dagenham	Drew 1-1		Morah	805
29	12	GMVC	H	Farnborough	Lost 0-1			403
30	16	GMVC	A	Bromsgrove Rovers	Drew 1-1		Copley	721
31	Jan 1	GMVC	H	Dover Athletic	Won 1-0		Wordsworth	1006
32	9	KSC	H	Ashford Town	Lost 2-3		Morah, Watts	202
33	13	GMVC	H	Stalybridge Celtic	Drew 1-1		Gorman	626
34	20	FAT1	A	Rothwell Town	Drew 2-2		Tierling, Morah p	238
35	Feb 1	FATR	H	Rothwell Town	Won 2-0		Tierling, Morah	312
36	3	GMVC	A	Altrincham	Lost 0-1			762
37	10	GMVC	A	Hyde United	Lost 1-4		Henry	680
38	13	GMVC	H	Stevenage	Lost 0-3			572
39	15	LCC	A	Tooting & Mitcham	Lost 1-2		Sykes	
40	17	GMVC	H	Kidderminster Harriers	Drew 0-0			556
41	24	GMVC	H	Southport	Lost 0-1			600
42	Mar 2	GMVC	AS	Woking	Lost 2-3		Hanson 2	2286
43	5	GMVC	A	Farnborough	Won 1-0		Morah	470
44	9	GMVC	A	Kidderminster Harriers	Lost 0-3			1685
45	12	GMVC	H	Hednesford Town	Drew 1-1		Farley	400
46	16	GMVC	H	Morecambe	Won 1-0		Dimmock	501
47	23	GMVC	H	Dagenham & Redbridge	Drew 0-0			623
48	26	GMVC	A	Dover Athletic	Lost 1-2		Hanson	1001
49	30	GMVC	A	Gateshead	Drew 1-1		Rutherford	510
50	Apr 6	GMVC	H	Runcorn	Drew 1-1		Morah	616
51	8	GMVC	A	Telford	Drew 0-0			782
52	13	GMVC	A	Slough Town	Drew 0-0			785
53	23	GMVC	H	Kettering Town	Won 1-0		Morah	603
54	28	GMVC	H	Macclesfield	Lost 1-2		Gardner	558
55	May 4	GMVC	A	Northwich Victoria	Won 2-1		Abel (og), Morah	875

Welling United

1	2	3	4	5	6	7	8	9	10	11	12	14	Match No.
Harris	Gritt	Horton	Watts	Copley	Berry	Wordsworth	Rutherford	Gamble	Farley	Barnes	Smith	Sykes	1
Harris	Gritt	Horton	Watts	Copley	Berry	Wordsworth	Rutherford	Gamble	Farley	Barnes	Smith	Sykes	2
Harris	Brown	Horton	Watts	Copley	Berry	Wordsworth	Rutherford	Gamble	Sykes	Barnes	Smith	Farley	3
Harris	Brown	Horton	Watts	Copley	Berry	Wordsworth	Rutherford	Sykes	Farley	Barnes	Smith	Ash	4
Harris	Brown	Horton	Watts	Copley	Berry	Wordsworth	Rutherford	Sykes	Farley	Barnes	Smith	Ash	5
Wastell	Brown	Horton	Watts	Copley	Berry	Wordsworth	Rutherford	Henry	Farley	Barnes	Smith	Appiah	6
Wastell	Brown	Horton	Watts	Copley	Berry	Wordsworth	Rutherford	Smith	Farley	Barnes	Sykes	Appiah	7
Wastell	Brown	Horton	Watts	Copley	Berry	Wordsworth	Rutherford	Henry	Farley	Barnes	Smith	Sykes	8
Wastell	Brown	Horton	Watts	Copley	Berry	Wordsworth	Rutherford	Appiah	Farley	Barnes	Smith	Sykes	9
Harris	Brown	Horton	Barrett	Ash	Smith	Wordsworth	O'Keefe	Sykes	Farley	Barnes	Gorman	Berry	10
Wastell	Brown	Horton	Watts	Copley	Berry	Wordsworth	Rutherford	Sykes	Farley	Barnes	Smith	Gorman	11
Wastell	Brown	Horton	Watts	Copley	Berry	Wordsworth	Rutherford	Appiah	Farley	Barnes	Smith	Gorman	12
Wastell	Brown	Horton	Watts	Copley	Berry	Smith	Rutherford	Morah	Farley	Barnes	Gorman	Sykes	13
Wastell	Ash	Horton	Watts	Copley	Berry	Smith	Rutherford	Gorman	Farley	Barnes	Sykes	Brown	14
Wastell	Brown	Horton	Watts	Copley	Berry	Smith	Rutherford	Morah	Gorman	Barnes	Farley	Sykes	15
Harris	Brown	Horton	Watts	Copley	Berry	Gorman	Rutherford	Morah	Farley	Ash	Smith	Sykes	16
Wastell	Brown	Horton	Watts	Copley	Berry	Ash	Rutherford	Morah	May	Sykes	Smith	Farley	17
Harris	Brown	Horton	Watts	Copley	Berry	Wordsworth	Rutherford	Morah	Appiah	Tierling	Farley	Sykes	18
Harris	Brown	Horton	Watts	Copley	Berry	Wordsworth	Rutherford	Morah	Appiah	Tierling	Farley	Henry	19
Harris	Tierling	Horton	Watts	Copley	Berry	Wordsworth	Rutherford	Morah	Farley	Appiah	Ash	Smith	20
Harris	Ash	Horton	Tierling	Copley	Berry	Wordsworth	Rutherford	Morah	Farley	Henry	Sykes	Smith	21
Harris	Tierling	Horton	Ash	Copley	Berry	Wordsworth	Rutherford	Morah	Henry	Farley	Sykes	Smith	22
Harris	Ash	Horton	Tierling	Copley	Berry	Wordsworth	Rutherford	Morah	Henry	Farley	Smith	Sykes	23
Harris	Ash	Horton	Tierling	Copley	Berry	Wordsworth	Rutherford	Morah	Henry	Brown	Watts	Farley	24
Harris	Ash	Horton	Tierling	Copley	Berry	Wordsworth	Rutherford	Morah	Henry	Brown	Watts	Farley	25
Harris	Ash	Horton	Farley	Copley	Berry	Wordsworth	Rutherford	Morah	Henry	Brown	Watts	Smith	26
Harris	Ash	Horton	Tierling	Copley	Berry	Wordsworth	Rutherford	Morah	Henry	Brown	Farley	Watts	27
Harris	Ash	Horton	Tierling	Copley	Berry	Wordsworth	Watts	Morah	Henry	Farley	Gorman	Smith	28
Harris	Ash	Horton	Tierling	Copley	Berry	Wordsworth	Rutherford	Morah	Henry	Brown	Watts	Farley	29
Harris	Ash	Horton	Tierling	Copley	Berry	Wordsworth	Rutherford	Morah	Henry	Brown	Watts	Farley	30
Harris	Farley	Horton	Tierling	Copley	Berry	Wordsworth	Rutherford	Morah	Henry	Brown	Watts	Smith	31
Harris	Farley	Horton	Tierling	Copley	Berry	Wordsworth	Rutherford	Morah	Henry	Brown	Watts	Ash	32
Harris	Ash	Horton	Tierling	Copley	Berry	Wordsworth	Rutherford	Morah	Gorman	Farley	Watts	Brown	33
Harris	Ash	Horton	Tierling	Copley	Berry	Wordsworth	Rutherford	Morah	Gorman	Brown	Farley	Watts	34
Harris	Farley	Horton	Tierling	Copley	Berry	Wordsworth	Rutherford	Morah	Henry	Brown	Gorman	Watts	35
Harris	Farley	Horton	Tierling	Copley	Berry	Wordsworth	Watts	Morah	Henry	Brown	Gorman	Smith	36
Harris	Farley	Horton	Tierling	Copley	Berry	Wordsworth	Watts	Morah	Henry	Brown	Gorman	Smith	37
Wastell	Farley	Horton	Tierling	Copley	Berry	Watts	Rutherford	Morah	Henry	Brown	Ash	Gorman	38
Wastell	Ash	Farley	Coatham	Berry	Smith	Hulance	Brown	Gorman	O'Keefe	Sykes	Hopper	Brown	39
Harris	Farley	Horton	Tierling	Copley	Berry	Watts	Brown	Morah	Hanson	Ash	Gorman	Smith	40
Harris	Farley	Horton	Tierling	Copley	Berry	Watts	Brown	Hanson	Morah	Ash	Gorman	Smith	41
Harris	Brown	Horton	Tierling	Copley	Berry	Watts	Brown	Morah	Hanson	Farley	Smith	Ash	42
Harris	Brown	Horton	Tierling	Copley	Berry	Farley	Rutherford	Morah	Hanson	Brown	Watts	Ash	43
Harris	Brown	Horton	Tierling	Copley	Berry	Farley	Rutherford	Morah	Hanson	Smith	Dimmock	Ash	44
Harris	Brown	Horton	Tierling	Copley	Berry	Farley	Rutherford	Morah	Hanson	Brown	Watts	Ash	45
Harris	Brown	Horton	Tierling	Copley	Berry	Farley	Rutherford	Morah	Dimmock	Brown	Ash	Watts	46
Harris	Brown	Horton	Tierling	Copley	Ash	Farley	Rutherford	Morah	Hanson	Brown	Watts	Dimmock	47
Harris	Brown	Horton	Watts	Copley	Berry	Farley	Rutherford	Morah	Hanson	Brown	Ash	Dimmock	48
Harris	Ash	Horton	Watts	Copley	Berry	Farley	Rutherford	Morah	Hanson	Brown	Smith	Dimmock	49
Harris	Ash	Horton	Watts	Copley	Berry	Farley	Rutherford	Morah	Hanson	Brown	Dimmock	Smith	50
Harris	Ash	Horton	Watts	Copley	Berry	Farley	Rutherford	Morah	Dimmock	Brown	Sykes	Smith	51
Harris	Ash	Horton	Watts	Copley	Berry	Farley	Smith	Morah	Hanson	Brown	Dimmock	Sykes	52
Harris	Ash	Horton	Watts	Brown	Berry	Hales	Smith	Morah	Hanson	Brown	Sykes	Dimmock	53
Harris	Ash	Horton	Watts	Copley	Berry	Farley	Rutherford	Morah	Smith	Brown	Sykes	Hales	54
Harris	Brown	Horton	Watts	Copley	Berry	Farley	Rutherford	Morah	Dimmock	Brown	Sykes	Smith	55

KEVIN HALES

Three hundred Football League appearances for Chelsea and Leyton Orient counted for little as Kevin Hales was thrust into the managerial seat shortly before the opening of the 1995/96 Conference campaign. With little time to put into operation his own plans, he had little alternative but to go largely with the squad of players he inherited, and early results showed the problems he faced. Gradually he overcame the difficulties of poor early season results in league and cup, and by mid-season there was renewed hope for a team that at one stage looked doomed. During the second half of the campaign his side became difficult to beat, and whilst there was never too much hope of real success, at least a platform was being built for the future by the manager.

With that first difficult year under his belt, Kevin, whilst unable to compete with the major clubs in the Conference tarnsfer market, will be looking forward with more optimism to the 1996/97 season.

Kevin Hales

Kidderminster keeper Darren Steadman saves bravely at the feet of Welling's Ollie Moram

Programme details:
32 pages for £1.20
Editor - Paul Carter

Any other club publications:
'Winning isn't Everything' (Fanzine)

Local Newspapers:
Kentish Times
Bexleyheath & Welling Mercury

Local Radio Stations:
Radio Kent
Radio Invicta
R.T.M.

WELLING UNITED - PLAYING SQUAD 1996-97

Player	Honours	Birthplace and date	Transfer Fees	Previous Clubs
GOALKEEPERS				
James Wastell		Carshalton 4/10/77		Chipstead
DEFENDERS				
Duncan Horton	GMVC	Maidstone 18/2/67		Maidstone U, Barnet, Wycombe W
Wayne Brown	FAXI	Waterloo 19/1/70		From Youth Team
Paul Copley		Dartford 13/8/70		Slade Green, Crockenhill
Robin Trott		Orpington 17/8/74		Gillingham
MIDFIELDERS				
Mike Rutherford		Woolwich 6/6/72		QPR
Danny Smith		London 7/9/75		From YTS
Kevin Hales		Dartford 13/1/61		Chelsea, Leyton Orient
John Farley		Greenwich 18/2/73		Lewisham Elms
Lewis Watts		Maidstone 14/9/74		Gravesend & Northfleet, Fisher'93
Derek Brown	ESP, FAT, FAXI	London 8/8/63	4-fig	Wembley, Hendon, Wembley, Hendon, Woking, Walton & Hersham
FORWARDS				
Barry Lakin		Dartford 19/9/73		Leyton Orient
Richard Dimmock		Woolwich 27/3/79		Charlton A
Sam Appiah		Ghana 14/4/75		Charlton Athletic
Ollie Morah	ES, EY, FAYC	Islington 3/9/72		Tottenham H, Swindon T, Sutton U, Cambridge U

Departures during season:
Murray Jones (Hong Kong), Steve Barnes (Birmingham C), Steve Gritt (Tooting & Mitcham U), Paul Gorman (Fisher'93), Dean Wordsworth (Bromley), Liburd Henry (Bromley), Paul Sykes (Folkestone - Loan).
Players on loan during season:
Dave Hanson (Leyton Orient), Ollie Morah (Cambridge U).
Departures during close season: Lee Tierling, Andy Harris & Gwynne Berry (Sutton U), Christian Barrett, Bradley Gamble, Jason Ash (Released).

Park View Road, Welling

ADDRESS:
Park View Road Ground, Welling, Kent DA16 1SY.

TELEPHONE NUMBER: 0181 301 1196. Fax: 0811 301 5676.
Welling Wingsline: 0891 80 06 54.

SIMPLE DIRECTIONS:
M25, then A2 towards London. Take Welling turn-off, ground 1 mile. By rail to Welling station (BR) - ground 3/4 mile.

CAPACITY: 5,500 **SEATED:** 500 **COVERED TERRACING:** 1,500

RECORD ATTENDANCE:
4,100 v Gillingham, FA Cup

CLUB SHOP:
On sale programmes (League & non-League), scarves, mugs, caps, hats, badges, replica kits and Conference merchandise - matchday manager Peter Mason.

SOCIAL FACILITIES:
Clubhouse open on match days

PREVIOUS GROUNDS:
Butterfly Lane, Eltham - 1963/78

Welling Fact File

Nickname: The Wings

Club Sponsors:

Previous Leagues: Eltham & District League 1963/71, London Spartan League 1971/77, Athenian League 1977/79, Southern League 1979/86.

Club colours: Red shirts, red shorts, white socks.

Change colours: White & blue shirst, white shorts, blue socks.

Midweek home matchday: Tuesday

Record win: 7-1

Record defeat: 0-7

Record transfer fee paid: £30,000 for Gary Abbott from Enfield

Record transfer fee received: £70,000 from Birmingham City for Steve Finnan. 1995.

1995-96 Captain: Mike Rutherford.

1995-96 Top scorer: Ollie Morah.

1995-96 Player of the Year: Duncan Horton.

Club record goalscorer: John Bartley - 533

Record appearances: Nigel Ransom - 1,066 & Ray Burgess - 1,044.

Past players who progressed to the Football League: Paul Barron (Plymouth, Arsenal, Stoke, WBA, C. Palace, QPR), Andy Townsend (Southampton, Norwich, Chelsea), Ian Thompson (AFC Bournemouth), John Bartley (Millwall), Dave Smith (Gillingham, Bristol City), Murray Jones (C. Palace, Bristol City, Exeter City), Kevin Shoemaker (Peterborough), Tony Agana (Watford, Sheffield Utd), Duncan Horton (Barnet), Mark Hone (Southend), Steve Finnan & Steve Barnes (Birmingham City).

Club Honours: London Spartan League 1978; Southern League Premier Division 1985/86; Kent Senior Cup 1985/86; London Senior Cup 1989/90; London Challange Cup 1991/92, Runners-up 1993/94.

WOKING

Formed
1889

President
L A Gosden MBE

Chairman
P J Ledger

Vice Chairman
J Davies

Football Secretary
P J Ledger

Manager
Geoff Chapple

Asst. Man./Coach
Colin Lippiatt

Physiotherapist
Barry Kimber

Press Officer
Terry Molloy

Comm Projects Manager
Philip Shorter

Commercial Assistant
Rosemary Hurl

Woking - Runners-Up Again

By finishing runners-up for the second successive season, Woking became the first side to register three consecutive top three Conferemve finishes. The season started with a run of five away defeats, contrasting sharply with a truly magnificent home record. Manager Geoff Chapple kept faith with the majority of the side that had served the club so well the previous season. He did however introduce ex-Manchester City defender Nick Reid and Carl Hoddle, brother of new England supremo Glenn. Neither player saw the season out at Kingfield.

The FA Cup threw up yet another meeting with Barnet and again the Cards won through after a replay. Old adversaries Enfield were beaten after another replay and the side did themselves proud, despite going down 2-0 in the Third Round at Swindon. After the FA Trophy highlights of the previous two seasons it was a great disappointment to go out at the first hurdle at Carshalton. There were grumblings about the state of the pitch, but having two players sent off certainly did not help matters.

Geoff Chapple signed ex-Wycombe midfielder Steve Thompson. His partnership with player of the year Andy Ellis was the key to many of the victories. Former Kettering full-back Junior Hunter burst on to the scene with an amazing four-goal debut at Morecambe and only injury and suspension prevented him from challenging Clive Walker and Darran Hay as leading scorer.

In the Conference Woking clung on to second place, never quite catching long-time leaders Stevenage and in the end being convincingly beaten to the title. Nevertheless, they completed the season with an unbeaten home record and their highest ever points total in the Conference. For good measure the Surrey Senior Cup was won with a rather low key 2-0 victory over Tooting & Mitcham.

Off the pitch, the club opened its magnificent new stand. Built with the assistance of Woking Borough Council, the stand, along with other improvements, ensured that Kingfield met the criteria for the Football League. The end of the season saw the club lose perhaps the best defender in the Conference, Mark Tucker. He was snapped up by Rushden & Diamonds for a fee of £45,000 - a record sale for the Kingfield club. Paul Beard

Action between Woking v Macclesfield

Woking

Match No.	Date		Comp.	Venue H/A	Opponents	Result	League Pos.	Goalscorers (Times if known)	Attendance
1	Aug	19	GMVC		Macclesfield Town	Lost 2-3	12	Steele 2	1370
2		22	GMVC		Bath City	Won 2-0	9	Steele, Hay	1708
3		26	GMVC		Stalybridge Celtic	Won 2-1	8	Wye, Brown	1613
4		28	GMVC		Bromsgrove Rovers	Lost 1-2	10	Ellis	1290
5	Sep	2	GMVC		Hednesford Town	Lost 1-2	13	Walker	1711
6		5	GMVC		Stevenage Borough	Won 4-1	10	Reid, Peters, Hay, Walker	1864
7		9	GMVC		Halifax Town	Won 2-0	6	Walker, Steele	2065
8		12	GMVC		Kettering	Lost 0-3	7		1671
9		16	GMVC		Runcorn	Won 2-1	7	Fielder, Hay	1620
10		19	CS		Macclesfield	Lost 2-3	8	Hay 2	636
11		23	GMVC		Kidderminster Harriers	Lost 0-2	8		2716
12		30	GMVC		Gateshead	Won 2-0	8	Steele, Hay	1939
13	Oct	10	GMVC		Bath City	Won 3-0	6	Ellis, Walker 2	720
14		14	GMVC		Altrincham	Won 2-0	3	Hay, Walker	2081
15		21	GMVC		Welling United	Won 2-1	2	Brown, Steele	1066
16		28	GMVC		Stalybridge Celtic	Won 4-2	1	Ellis, Walker 3	754
17	Nov	4	GMVC		Morecambe	Won 3-0	2	Steele 2, Hay	2679
18		11	FAC1R		Barnet	Drew 2-2	2	Steele, Hay	3034
19		18	GMVC		Slough Town	Won 3-2	2	Steele, Walker 2	1659
20		21	FAC1R		Barnet	Won 2-1	2	Steele, Hay	3535
21		25	GMVC		Kidderminster Harriers	Drew 0-0	2		2264
22	Dec	2	FAC2		Enfield	Drew 1-1	2	Walker	3477
23		9	GMVC		Runcorn	Won 3-2	2	Fielder, Ellis, Hay	707
24		12	FAC2R		Enfield	Won 2-1	2	Hay 2	2253
25		16	SC		Slough	Lost 0-3	3		774
26		26	GMVC		Dagenham & Redbridge	Drew 2-2	2	Hay, og	2874
27	Jan	1	GMVC		Dagenham & Redgridge	Drew 0-0	3		1358
28		6	FAC3		Swindon Town	Lost 0-2	3		10322
29		13	GMVC		Morecambe	Won 5-4	3	Thompson, Hunter 4	1312
30		15	SSC1		Epsom & Ewell	Won 6-0	3	Tucker, Wye 2, Steele, Walker 2	593
31		20	FAT1		Carshalton Athletic	Lost 1-3	3	Steele	1485
32		23	SSC2		Molesey	Won 8-1	3	Rainbow, Thompson, Ellis, Steele, Hunter 3, Hay	443
33	Feb	3	GMVC		Bromsgrove Rovers	Drew 1-1	4	Ellis	2481
34		8	SSC SF		Crystal Palace	Drew 0-0	4		595
35		10	GMVC		Telford United	Won 5-1	3	Wanless, Steele, Hunter 3	2384
36		13	GMVC		Dover Athletic	Lost 3-4	3	Hunter 2, Hay	976
37		17	GMVC		Southport	Drew 2-2	4	Hunter, Walker	1074
38		24	GMVC		Kettering Town	Drew 1-1	4	Hunter	2637
39	Mar	2	GMVC		Welling United	Won 3-2	3	Crumplin, Steele, Hay	2286
40		9	GMVC		Altrincham	Lost 0-2	5		971
41		12	GMVC		Farnborough Town	Won 2-0	4	Walker 2	1497
42		16	SSC SF		Crystal Palace	Won 4-1	4	Baron, Ellis, Steele, Hay	1063
43		19	GMVC		Slough Town	Won 3-0	4	Ellis, Hay, og	1911
44		23	GMVC		Dover Athletic	Won 1-0	3	Fielder	2494
45		26	GMVC		Telford United	Won 2-1	3	Girdler, Hay	736
46		30	GMVC		Hednesford Town	Won 3-0	2	Ellis, Walker 2	3194
47	Apr	6	GMVC		Macclesfield Town	Won 3-2	2	Hunter, Adams 2	4583
48		8	GMVC		Stevenage	Lost 0-4	2		3976
49		13	GMVC		Gateshead	Won 1-0	2	Hay	919
50		16	GMVC		Farnborough Town	Won 2-1	2	Adams, og	3166
51		20	GMVC		Halifax Town	Drew 2-2	2	Walker, Baron	1064
52		23	SSC F		Tooting & M. United	Won 2-0	2	Walker 2	1007
53		27	GMVC		Northwich Victoria	Lost 0-3	2		842
54		30	GMVC		Northwich Victoria	Drew 0-0	2		1771
55	May	4	GMVC		Southport	Won 4-0	2	Hay, Crumplin, Steele, Walker	2544

Woking

1	2	3	4	5	6	7	8	9	10	11	12	14	Match No.
Batty	Alexander	Wye	Fielder	Brown	Crumplin	Hoddle	Ellis	Steele	Hay	Walker	Henry	Reid	1
Batty	Tucker	Wye	Fielder	Brown	Crumplin	Hoddle	Ellis	Steele	Hay	Henry	Girdler	Tierling	2
Batty	Tucker	Wye	Fielder	Brown	Crumplin	Hoddle	Ellis	Henry	Hay	Walker	Reid	Girdler	3
Batty	Tucker	Tierling	Fielder	Brown	Crumplin	Reid	Ellis	Alexander	Hay	Walker			4
Batty	Tucker	Tierling	Fielder	Brown	Crumplin	Reid	Ellis	Omigie	Hay	Walker	Peters	Girdler	5
Batty	Tucker	Wye	Fielder	Brown	Crumplin	Reid	Ellis	Peters	Hay	Walker	Omigie	Girdler	6
Batty	Tucker	Wye	Fielder	Brown	Crumplin	Reid	Ellis	Peters	Hay	Walker	Steele		7
Batty	Tucker	Tierling	Fielder	Brown	Crumplin	Reid	Ellis	Steele	Hay	Walker	Omigie		8
Batty	Tucker	Wye	Fielder	Brown	Crumplin	Reid	Ellis	Steele	Hay	Walker	Omigie		9
Batty	Tierling	Wye	Fielder	Brown	Crumplin	Reid	Ellis	Steele	Hay	Omigie	Peters	Timothy	10
Batty	Tucker	Wye	Fielder	Brown	Crumplin	Reid	Ellis	Steele	Hay	Omigie	Peters	Timothy	11
Batty	Tucker	Timothy	Fielder	Brown	Reid	Hoddle	Ellis	Steele	Hay	Omigie	Peters	Tierling	12
Batty	Tucker	Timothy	Fielder	Brown	Crumplin	Reid	Ellis	Steele	Hay	Walker			13
Batty	Tucker	Timothy	Fielder	Brown	Crumplin	Reid	Ellis	Steele	Hay	Walker	Peters		14
Batty	Tucker	Timothy	Fielder	Brown	Crumplin	Reid	Ellis	Steele	Hay	Thompson			15
Batty	Tucker	Timothy	Fielder	Brown	Crumplin	Thompson	Ellis	Steele	Hay	Walker	Reid		16
Batty	Tucker	Timothy	Fielder	Brown	Crumplin	Thompson	Ellis	Steele	Hay	Walker			17
Batty	Tucker	Timothy	Fielder	Brown	Crumplin	Thompson	Ellis	Steele	Hay	Walker	Wye		18
Batty	Tucker	Wye	Fielder	Brown	Timothy	Thompson	Ellis	Steele	Hay	Walker			19
Batty	Tucker	Wye	Fielder	Brown	Timothy	Thompson	Ellis	Steele	Hay	Walker	Alexander		20
Batty	Tucker	Wye	Fielder	Brown	Timothy	Thompson	Ellis	Steele	Dowe	Walker	Girdler		21
Batty	Tucker	Wye	Fielder	Brown	Crumplin	Thompson	Ellis	Timothy	Hay	Walker			22
Batty	Tucker	Wye	Fielder	Brown	Crumplin	Thompson	Ellis	Steele	Hay	Walker	Dowe	Alexander	23
Batty	Tucker	Wye	Fielder	Brown	Timothy	Thompson	Ellis	Steele	Hay	Dowe			24
Batty	Tucker	Wye	Fielder	Brown	Timothy	Thompson	Ellis	Steele	Hay	Dowe	Alexander	Girdler	25
Gregory	Tucker	Wye	Fielder	Timothy	Crumplin	Thompson	Ellis	Steele	Hay	Walker			26
Batty	Tucker	Wye	Fielder	Brown	Crumplin	Thompson	Ellis	Steele	Hay	Walker			27
Batty	Tucker	Wye	Fielder	Brown	Crumplin	Thompson	Ellis	Steele	Hay	Walker			28
Batty	Tucker	Wye	Fielder	Brown	Crumplin	Thompson	Ellis	Steele	Hunter	Walker	Hay	Dowe	29
Gregory	Tucker	Wye	Fielder	Brown	Crumplin	Thompson	Timothy	Steele	Dowe	Walker	Rainbow	Girdler	30
Batty	Tucker	Wye	Fielder	Timothy	Crumplin	Thompson	Codner	Steele	Hunter	Walker	Hay		31
Batty	Rainbow	Wye	Fielder	Timothy	Crumplin	Thompson	Ellis	Steele	Hunter	Walker	Gregory	Hay	32
Batty	Wanless	Timothy	Fielder	Brown	Codner	Thompson	Ellis	Steele	Hay	Gordon			33
Batty	Alexander	Timothy	Fielder	Brown	Codner	Thompson	Ellis	Steele	Hay	Girdler	Lansdown		34
Batty	Wanless	Wye	Fielder	Brown	Timothy	Thompson	Ellis	Steele	Hay	Hunter	Codner	Girdler	35
Batty	Wanless	Timothy	Fielder	Brown	Codner	Thompson	Ellis	Steele	Hunter	Walker	Girdler	Hay	36
Batty	Wanless	Wye	Fielder	Brown	Crumplin	Thompson	Ellis	Steele	Hunter	Walker	Hay		37
Batty	Wanless	Wye	Fielder	Brown	Crumplin	Thompson	Ellis	Steele	Hunter	Walker	Hay		38
Batty	Baron	Wye	Fielder	Brown	Crumplin	Thompson	Ellis	Steele	Hunter	Walker	Hay		39
Batty	Baron	Wye	Fielder	Brown	Crumplin	Thompson	Ellis	Hay	Hunter	Walker	Steele		40
Batty	Baron	Wye	Fielder	Brown	Crumplin	Thompson	Ellis	Steele	Hunter	Walker	Hay		41
Batty	Tucker	Timothy	Fielder	Brown	Crumplin	Baron	Ellis	Steele	Hay	Walker	Girdler		42
Batty	Tucker	Wye	Fielder	Brown	Crumplin	Thompson	Ellis	Steele	Hay	Walker			43
Batty	Tucker	Wye	Fielder	Brown	Crumplin	Thompson	Ellis	Steele	Hay	Walker			44
Gregory	Tucker	Girdler	Fielder	Brown	Crumplin	Baron	Ellis	Steele	Hay	Walker			45
Batty	Tucker	Girdler	Fielder	Brown	Crumplin	Baron	Ellis	Steele	Hay	Walker	Hunter	Adams	46
Batty	Tucker	Girdler	Fielder	Brown	Crumplin	Baron	Ellis	Steele	Hunter	Walker	Timothy	Adams	47
Batty	Tucker	Timothy	Fielder	Brown	Crumplin	Baron	Ellis	Steele	Hay	Walker	Hunter	Thompson	48
Batty	Tucker	Wye	Fielder	Brown	Crumplin	Thompson	Ellis	Steele	Adams	Walker	Hay		49
Batty	Tucker	Wye	Fielder	Brown	Crumplin	Thompson	Ellis	Steele	Adams	Hunter	Walker	Hay	50
Batty	Tucker	Wye	Fielder	Brown	Crumplin	Thompson	Ellis	Steele	Adams	Walker	Timothy	Hay	51
Batty	Tucker	Wye	Baron	Brown	Crumplin	Thompson	Ellis	Steele	Hay	Walker	Timothy	Kilner	52
Batty	Tucker	Wye	Fielder	Baron	Crumplin	Thompson	Ellis	Steele	Adams	Walker			53
Batty	Tucker	Wye	Fielder	Baron	Crumplin	Timothy	Ellis	Steele	Hay	Walker			54
Batty	Tucker	Wye	Fielder	Baron	Crumplin	Thompson	Ellis	Steele	Hay	Walker	Timothy	Baron	55

Woking

GEOFF CHAPPLE

Chapple became manager of Woking in September 1984 and his first game in charge was against Clapton. Only 87 supporters witnessed the landmark event. This was the first victory of the season and despite relegation at the end of the campaign, the Chapple years were underway.

Chapple had joined Aldershot from school but did not break into the first-team. He appeared for Woking, Guildford City and Windsor & Eton, breaking a leg with the Berkshire outfit before becoming their manager in 1980. Moving to Kingfield to take over a club that was then in Division One of the Isthmian League, in 1984 he has led the club to the most successful period in its history. His side achieved promotion back to Division One in the 86/87 season and into the Premier Division in 1990. Promotion to the Conference was secured at the end of the 1991/92 campaign and the honours continued to come the way of Woking.

Runcorn were beaten 2-1 in the FA Trophy final of 1994 and Kidderminster Harriers were victims of the sane scoreline twelve months later, these victories giving Chapple and the club their finest moments for some time. The 1995/95 season saw Chapple granted a testimonial season and the appearance of a full strength West Ham team drew a large and appreciative crowd to Kingfield to honour the man who has overseen the astonishing rise of the Cards.

Geoff Chapple

Andy Ellis; Player of the Season Photo: Paul Dennis

Programme details:
40 pages for £1.20
Editor - Paul Beard

Any other club publications:
"The Cardinal" (Published quarterly) £1.00.

Local Newspapers:
Woking News/Mail
Surrey Advertiser
Woking Herald

Local Radio Stations:
BBC Southern Counties Radio

WOKING - PLAYING SQUAD 1996-97

Player	Honours	Birthplace and date	Transfer Fees	Previous Clubs
GOALKEEPERS				
Laurence Batty	ESP, FAT, ILP	Westminster 15/2/64		Maidenhead Utd, Fulham, Brentford, Farense (Port)
DEFENDERS				
Steve Wood	Div 2, Div 3	Bracknell 2/2/63		Reading, Millwall, Southampton, Oxford U
Kevan Brown	ESP, Div 3, FAT	Andover 2/1/66		Southampton, Brighton, Aldershot
Terry Howard	Eu-19	Stepney 26/2/66		Chelsea, Leyton Orient, Wycombe W
Lloyd Wye	FAT, ILP, NZL, FAXI	Wokingham 14/5/67		Southampton, Woking, Wanganui Athletic (NZ)
MIDFIELDERS				
Andy Ellis	FAT, WSP	Cardiff		Barry T, Inter Cardiff, Barry T
Scott Steele	FAT, SS	Motherwell 19/9/71		Airdrie
Stuart Girdler		London		Fulham
Tom Jones	ESP, Div 2	Aldershot 7/10/64		Chelsea, Farnborough T, Weymouth, Aberdeen, Swindon, Reading
Robin Taylor	British Students	Leicester		Camb.C, Hinckley T, Kettering, P'Boro, Kettering, Port Vale, Dag & Red
Aiden Kilner		London		From Youth Team
Steve Thompson	ESP, GMVC, FAT, ILP	Plymouth 12/1/63		Bristol C, Torquay U, Saltash U, Slough T, Wycombe W
FORWARDS				
Clive Walker	ES, FAT	Oxford 26/5/57		Chelsea, Sunderland, QPR, Fulham, Brighton
Simon Garner		Boston 23/11/59		Blackburn R, WBA, Wycombe W
Darron Hay	FAT	Hitchin 17/12/69		Biggleswade T, Cambridge U
Junior Hunter		Lambeth 1/2/75		Cambridge U, Kettering T, Hendon

Departures during season:
Liburd Henry (Dag & Red), Lee Tierling (Welling U), Carl Hoddle (Enfield), Nicky Reid (Bury), Tim Alexander (Dag & Red), Julian Dowe (Hyde U), Robert Codner (Ilkeston T), Richard Newbery (Wokingham T).
T), Paul Haylock (Sittingbourne).
Players on loan during season:
Joe Omigie (Brentford), Paul Wanless (Lincoln C), Neville Gordon (Reading), Darren Adams (Cardiff C).
Departures during close season: John Crumplin (Crawley T), Mark Tucker (Rushden & D), Trevor Baron (Walton & Hersham).

Kingfield Sports Ground, Woking

GROUND ADDRESS:
Kingfield Sports Ground, Kingfield, Woking, Surrey. GU22 9AA.
TELEPHONE NUMBER: 01483 772470

SIMPLE DIRECTIONS:
M25 J10 or 11, signposted from outskirts of Town. Ground 1 mile. Woking B.R.Station & buses from Woking.

CAPACITY: 6,000 **SEATED:** 2,500 **COVERED TERRACING:** 1,400

RECORD ATTENDANCE:
6,000 v Swansea, FA Cup - 1978/79

CLUB SHOP:
Phone 01483 772470 for details.

SOCIAL FACILITIES:
Clubhouse open on matchdays. Food available.

PREVIOUS GROUNDS:
Wheatsheaf, Ivy Lane (pre 1923)

Woking Fact File

Nickname: The Cards

Club Sponsors: Woking Borough Council
Previous Leagues: Isthmian 1991/92
Club colours: Red/white halves & black shorts
Change colours: Yellow and Navy
Reserve team's league: Capital League
Midweek home matchday: Tuesday 7.45pm.
Record win: 17-4 v Farnham, 1912-13.
Record defeat: 0-16 v New Crusaders, 1905-06.
Record transfer fee: Undisclosed for Darran Hay (Cambridge Utd.) - 1995
Record transfer fee received: £45,000 from Rushden & Diamonds for Mark Tucker, May 1996. 1995
1995/96 Captain: Kevan Brown
1995/96 Top scorer: Clive Walker 23
1995/96 Player of the Year: Andy Ellis
Club record goalscorer: C Mortimore 331, 1953-65
Record appearances: B Finn 564, 1962-74
Past players who progressed to the Football League: Ray Elliott (M'wall 1946), Charlie Mortimore (A'shot 1949), Robert Edwards (Chelsea 1951), Ron Newman (Portsmouth 1955), Mervyn Gill (Southampton 1956), John Mortimore (Chelsea 1951), Reg Stratton (Fulham 1959), George Harris (Newport 1961), Norman Cashmore (A'shot 1963), Alan Morton (C.Palce 1967), William Holmes (Millwall 1970), Richard Forbes (Exeter 1979), Kevin Rattray (Gillingham 1995).

Honours: FA Trophy 93-94, 94-95; FA Amateur Cup 57-58; GM Vauxhall Conference R-up 94-95, 95-96; Isthmian League R-up 56-57, Lge AC Delco Cup 90-91, Div.1 R-up 89-90, Div.2 South 86-87, Reserve Section (2); West Surrey Lge (4), London Senior Cup R-up 82-83; Surrey Senior Cup 12-13, 26-27, 55-56, 56-57, 71-72, 90-91, 93-94, 95-96; Surrey Senior Shield (9); Surrey Premier Cup (2); Surrey Invitation Cup 66-67; Surrey Intermediate Cup (2); Channel Islands Victory Cup (2); Suburban Lge (2), Lge Cup (2); Diadora Premier Division 91-92; Isthmian League Charity Shield 91-92, 92-93; Vauxhall Championship Shield 94-95, R-up 95-96.

NORTHERN PREMIER LEAGUE

President: N White, Esq.
Chairman: K Marsden, Esq.
Vice-Chairman: K F Brown Esq.
Secretary/Treasure: R D Bayley, Esq.
22 Woburn Drive, Hale, Altrincham, Cheshire WA15 8LZ
(061 980 7007 - Fax: 061 980 7007)

Few would have been able to forecast that Bamber Bridge would go on to win the Premier Division title in their first season after winning promotion as runners-up to Blyth Spartans in 1995. Brig were playing in the Preston & District League just five years previous to that, which is really quite some achievement. Sadly for the UniBond League, Bamber Bridge's title success came to early for them in terms of their ground being ready for the next step up, the Vauxhall Conference, and runners-up Boston United unfortunately also missed out due to an administrative error, leaving the league without any promotee.

At the other end of the table it was goodbye to the Premier Division, at least for the time being, for Matlock Town and Droylsden, the latter having only just escaped in 1994/95. Replacing them are Lancaster City and Alfreton Town, both having narrowly missed out the previous season. Just behind them, in third place, were Lincoln United, who enjoyed an excellent first campaign as a UniBond League club after gaining promotion from the Northern Counties East League. Sadly, after a couple of years of constant battle against financial struggle, Fleetwood Town were forced to close. That, combined with the fact that no Northern League club were eligible for promotion, gave Harrogate Town a lifeline.

This season the league welcomes Runcorn back into the fold after a long sojourn in the Conference, plus Stocksbridge Park Steels, runners-up in the Northern Counties East, and Flixton, champions of the North West Counties League.

The league enjoyed an excellent run in the FA Umbro Trophy with both Chorley and Hyde United reaching the semi-final stage. Unfortunately, both clubs came up against north-west Vauxhall Conference sides Macclesfield Town and Northwich Victoria and, despite valiant efforts, went out on aggregate scores.

Finally, I should like to pay tribute to league secretary Duncan Bayley, who has been rewarded for all his hard work by being elected on to the FA Council. Duncan topped a poll in which he stood against Everton vice-chairman Sir Philip Carter, Crewe Alexandra's David Rawlinson and Conference chairman Bill King, and joins UniBond League chairman Ken Marsden, who has been an FA Council member since 1991. Shortly after being elected, Duncan was appointed on to two committee's, the FA Challenge Vase and the Rules Revision Committee. This gives the league representation on both of the semi-professional game's major knockout competitions as Ken Marsden already serves on the FA Trophy commitee. Steve Whitney.

Bamber Bridge celebrating after winning the Premier Championship

Photo - Keith Clayton

Boston United's Greg Fee in action, chased by Hyde United's Julian Dowe

Photo - Colin Stevens

PREMIER DIVISION FINAL LEAGUE TABLE 1995/96

		P	W	D	L	F	A	Pts
1.	Bamber Bridge	42	20	16	6	81	49	76
2.	Boston United	42	23	6	13	86	59	75
3.	Hyde United	42	21	11	10	86	51	74
4.	Barrow	42	20	13	9	69	42	73
5.	Gainsborough Trinity	42	20	13	9	60	41	73
6.	Blyth Spartans	42	17	13	12	75	61	64
7.	Accrington Stanley	42	17	14	11	62	54	*62
8.	Emley	42	17	10	15	57	53	61
9.	Spennymoor Utd	42	14	18	10	67	61	60
10.	Guiseley	42	15	14	13	62	57	59
11.	Bishop Auckland	42	16	11	15	60	55	59
12.	Marine	42	15	14	13	59	54	59
13.	Witton Albion	42	17	8	17	60	62	59
14.	Chorley	42	14	9	19	67	74	*48
15.	Knowsley United	42	14	6	22	61	89	48
16.	Winsford United	42	10	16	16	56	79	46
17.	Leek Town	42	10	15	17	52	55	45
18.	Colwyn Bay	42	8	21	13	43	57	45
19.	Frickley Athletic	42	11	14	17	63	87	*44
20.	Buxton	42	9	11	22	43	72	38
21.	Droylsden	42	10	8	24	58	100	38
22.	Matlock Town	42	8	11	23	71	86	35

** 3 points deducted for breach of Rules*

RESULTS CHART 1995-96

HOME TEAM		1	2	3	4	5	6	7	8	9	10	11	12	13	14	15	16	17	18	19	20	21	22
1.	Accrington S	*	1-2	1-1	2-1	1-2	0-2	1-0	7-3	3-1	0-2	0-0	2-1	2-1	0-1	1-1	4-2	0-0	0-0	2-1	0-0	1-2	1-2
2.	Bamber Bridge	1-1	*	2-2	0-2	3-0	1-2	2-0	2-0	5-0	3-2	0-1	2-3	1-1	3-1	3-3	2-2	0-0	4-4	4-1	2-0	2-0	1-1
3.	Barrow	0-3	0-2	*	0-0	2-1	2-0	1-0	6-2	1-1	3-3	0-0	1-1	0-1	0-2	2-1	7-0	1-0	2-0	3-1	1-1	1-1	3-0
4.	Bishop Auck	2-2	1-1	1-2	*	3-0	1-3	1-1	3-1	1-0	3-2	1-0	3-1	1-1	2-2	1-1	1-2	1-1	0-1	2-3	1-2	1-0	1-2
5.	Blyth Spartans	2-2	1-1	1-2	6-0	*	0-3	1-1	3-2	2-0	2-1	0-0	1-1	0-0	3-3	5-1	4-1	2-1	2-2	3-0	3-1	3-2	2-0
6.	Boston Utd	4-0	0-3	2-1	1-0	1-0	*	9-3	2-1	0-0	0-1	1-1	1-3	1-2	4-3	0-3	4-2	2-2	0-1	1-0	4-1	2-2	1-2
7.	Buxton	0-1	1-2	0-0	1-2	2-1	0-3	*	5-2	0-1	0-3	1-2	1-0	1-2	0-0	0-1	3-2	1-2	1-3	3-1	1-1	1-3	0-4
8.	Chorley	0-0	0-0	2-3	2-0	1-4	0-2	2-1	*	1-1	6-0	1-0	1-1	0-6	1-0	1-1	1-0	3-1	1-1	3-2	0-3	1-1	4-0
9.	Colwyn Bay	1-2	1-1	0-1	1-3	0-0	3-1	1-1	1-1	*	0-0	1-0	1-3	0-0	0-0	1-3	0-0	0-0	0-0	3-3	2-3	1-1	1-1
10.	Droylesden	1-2	1-2	0-4	1-4	2-2	2-5	1-3	0-6	0-1	*	3-0	2-2	1-2	1-2	0-2	5-1	2-1	2-1	3-0	1-1	1-1	2-1
11.	Emley	1-3	1-1	1-2	1-1	1-3	2-0	2-1	0-3	4-1	4-0	*	5-2	1-0	2-0	1-0	1-3	0-1	2-0	3-2	0-2	1-1	1-0
12.	Frickley Ath	4-1	0-5	0-0	0-3	1-2	1-2	0-2	1-0	1-1	4-5	2-1	*	3-0	2-2	3-0	4-3	1-1	1-1	1-4	2-3	3-3	1-1
13.	Gainsborough	1-1	1-3	2-0	1-0	4-0	2-1	2-2	1-0	2-2	7-1	0-3	0-2	*	0-2	1-1	2-1	1-0	1-0	2-2	0-1	0-0	1-0
14.	Guiseley	1-3	4-0	1-3	2-0	1-1	4-2	1-0	0-3	1-0	3-0	1-1	3-0	1-3	*	0-1	1-1	3-1	2-4	4-2	2-2	1-1	0-1
15.	Hyde Utd	0-0	2-3	0-0	3-1	4-1	2-4	7-0	3-1	5-1	1-1	7-2	4-1	1-2	1-1	*	5-0	3-2	4-0	1-1	3-2	0-1	1-0
16.	Knowsley Utd	1-0	2-2	0-2	1-2	1-0	2-4	2-0	1-2	1-3	2-0	1-3	1-2	2-3	1-1	2-1	*	3-1	2-1	1-0	2-0	4-1	2-2
17.	Leek Town	2-2	2-3	2-0	0-1	1-3	2-2	0-0	2-1	1-1	4-0	2-2	1-1	0-0	1-1	0-1	2-0	*	0-1	4-2	0-2	5-1	2-1
18.	Marine	1-2	0-0	1-2	2-2	0-0	0-4	1-1	3-2	1-1	6-1	0-1	1-1	3-0	0-1	4-0	2-1	2-1	*	1-0	2-1	3-1	2-1
19.	Matlock Town	2-0	0-1	0-4	1-1	3-3	0-2	0-1	2-2	1-4	2-2	1-1	6-0	0-2	3-0	1-3	8-0	0-1	3-3	*	1-1	1-1	5-2
20.	Spennymoor U	3-4	4-2	1-1	1-0	2-1	2-3	0-0	0-2	0-0	2-0	2-0	2-2	1-1	0-0	0-1	1-4	4-2	2-2	1-1	*	3-3	3-1
21.	Winsford Utd	2-2	1-4	4-3	0-4	2-4	1-0	1-1	2-1	1-3	3-2	0-4	4-1	1-1	1-2	1-4	0-1	0-0	1-0	3-1	2-2	*	2-1
22.	Witton Alb	0-2	0-0	1-0	1-2	2-1	1-1	1-3	2-1	2-3	2-1	3-1	5-0	0-2	3-2	1-1	2-1	2-1	2-0	3-2	2-2	2-0	*

Lancaster City's Peter Borrowdale leaves Whitley Bay's Paul Greenwood behind

Photo - Alan Watson

Gretna's Marc Irwin outjumps a Curzon Ashton defender to head towards the goal

Photo - Alan Watson

DIVISION ONE FINAL LEAGUE TABLE 1995/96

Division One		P	W	D	L	F	A	Pts
1.	Lancaster City	40	24	11	5	79	38	83
2.	Alfreton Town	40	23	9	8	79	47	78
3.	Lincoln United	40	22	7	11	80	56	73
4.	Curzon Ashton	40	20	7	13	73	53	67
5.	Farsley Celtic	40	19	9	12	66	61	66
6.	Radcliffe Borough	40	17	13	10	70	48	64
7.	Eastwood Town	40	18	9	13	60	47	63
8.	Whitley Bay	40	18	8	14	72	62	62
9.	Ashton United	40	19	7	14	73	65	*60
10.	Atherton L R	40	15	12	13	60	61	57
11.	Worksop Town	40	16	8	16	84	90	56
12.	Gretna	40	13	13	14	75	65	52
13.	Warrington Town	40	13	10	17	75	72	49
14.	Leigh	40	14	7	19	53	59	49
15.	Netherfield	40	13	10	17	64	73	49
16.	Workington	40	11	12	17	50	62	45
17.	Bradford Park Ave	40	9	14	17	57	72	41
18.	Congleton Town	40	11	11	18	36	59	*41
19.	Gt Harwood Town	40	9	7	24	44	78	*33
20.	Fleetwood	40	7	10	23	41	81	31
21.	Harrogate Town	40	7	10	23	54	96	31

** Ashton United 4 points deducted*
Congleton Town 3 points deducted
Gt Harwood Town 1 point deducted
For Breach of Rules

RESULTS CHART 1995-96

HOME TEAM	1	2	3	4	5	6	7	8	9	10	11	12	13	14	15	16	17	18	19	20	21
1. Alfreton Town	*	3-0	1-2	3-2	2-1	3-2	2-2	2-3	1-0	4-1	4-0	2-0	1-6	1-0	2-1	4-1	1-0	5-1	2-3	2-1	2-2
2. Ashton United	2-1	*	2-1	0-1	2-0	1-4	2-1	2-1	3-0	1-2	2-1	1-4	1-1	3-2	1-1	5-0	1-1	3-1	2-3	3-1	1-2
3. Atherton	0-0	1-2	*	3-1	2-1	2-2	2-1	1-1	1-0	2-2	1-1	0-2	2-1	3-1	0-1	2-4	1-1	2-1	2-1	0-0	1-4
4. Bradford P Ave	1-1	0-1	2-2	*	0-0	2-3	2-2	1-1	2-2	1-3	2-2	1-1	0-3	3-1	2-3	0-2	2-2	1-0	2-3	3-0	4-4
5. Congleton Town	0-1	3-0	4-1	1-2	*	1-1	1-1	0-1	1-0	0-0	0-1	2-1	1-1	1-0	0-2	1-1	1-4	0-4	2-1	0-0	0-2
6. Curzon Ashton	0-1	4-2	2-3	0-1	0-0	*	0-0	1-0	1-1	4-1	2-2	2-1	0-3	2-1	1-2	2-1	1-2	2-1	1-3	3-0	3-0
7. Eastwood Town	2-0	2-1	1-0	0-1	3-0	2-3	*	1-2	3-0	1-0	3-1	1-1	1-2	1-0	4-2	1-0	2-1	2-1	0-2	2-1	2-3
8. Farsley Celtic	1-0	2-4	3-3	3-3	0-2	1-1	2-1	*	0-2	1-0	0-2	2-2	2-1	2-1	2-1	3-1	4-1	1-0	1-0	3-0	2-2
9. Fleetwood	0-2	0-1	2-2	3-2	0-2	1-2	2-2	1-3	*	1-2	2-1	1-2	2-1	0-4	1-1	1-2	1-0	0-1	0-0	1-1	1-4
10. Gt Harwood Tn	1-3	2-3	2-0	1-3	1-2	3-4	1-0	3-0	2-1	*	1-1	2-3	1-1	0-2	0-1	0-2	0-4	0-5	2-0	1-0	1-2
11. Gretna	0-0	3-2	0-0	1-1	2-1	0-2	0-2	7-1	7-1	0-2	*	4-1	2-3	3-1	3-3	1-4	1-0	1-3	1-3	1-1	6-0
12. Harrogate Town	0-3	0-4	3-1	1-2	1-1	2-4	1-3	1-6	2-2	3-2	0-5	*	2-2	1-2	2-5	4-6	2-2	1-3	2-3	0-3	3-2
13. Lancaster City	1-1	2-0	1-0	1-0	3-0	2-1	2-2	1-2	0-1	4-1	1-0	2-1	*	5-2	2-0	2-2	3-1	4-2	3-1	2-1	3-1
14. Leigh RMI	1-1	1-4	3-1	1-0	1-1	1-0	1-0	0-0	2-0	3-1	1-3	2-0	0-1	*	2-0	1-4	1-1	2-2	0-1	4-2	1-1
15. Lincoln United	0-2	2-1	2-0	5-2	1-1	1-4	2-0	0-0	2-2	3-1	2-0	5-0	1-3	3-1	*	4-0	2-1	1-0	4-3	4-0	4-1
16. Netherfield	4-4	1-1	2-4	0-0	3-0	1-0	1-4	1-3	0-3	3-1	2-2	0-0	2-2	1-0	0-0	*	0-2	0-1	1-2	1-1	0-2
17. Radcliffe Boro	1-3	1-1	4-2	3-0	1-2	2-1	1-1	2-0	3-2	2-0	1-1	1-0	0-0	3-1	3-1	1-2	*	3-1	1-0	4-1	5-1
18. Warrington Tn	2-2	2-2	1-2	1-1	4-1	0-2	2-0	5-1	3-3	1-1	3-4	2-2	1-1	0-1	4-2	3-6	1-1	*	2-1	2-3	3-2
19. Whitley Bay	0-5	5-1	1-0	2-1	1-2	3-2	0-0	5-2	6-0	1-1	1-1	1-1	0-1	3-1	2-0	2-1	1-1	2-1	*	1-2	3-3
20. Workington	1-2	2-2	0-1	3-2	2-0	0-1	1-2	2-1	3-0	0-0	2-2	2-0	0-0	0-3	1-2	1-0	1-1	2-2	1-0	*	6-2
21. Worksop Town	2-0	1-3	1-3	4-1	6-0	0-3	1-2	1-0	4-1	3-2	4-2	2-1	0-2	1-1	2-4	3-2	2-2	2-3	6-2	2-2	*

UNIBOND LEAGUE CUP COMPETITION 95-96.

First Round;

Alfreton Town	v	Lincoln United	4-0
Blyth Spartans	v	Gretna	2-1
Bradford Park Avenue	v	Farsley Celtic	2-0
Congleton Town	v	Worksop Town	1-3
Curzon Ashton	v	Eastwood Town	1-2
Lancaster City	v	Fleetwood	4-2
Leigh	v	Great Harwood Town	6-4
Radcliffe Borough	v	Droylsden	0-3
Warrington Town	v	Ashton United	1-2
Whitley Bay	v	Harrogate Town	1-2
Workington	v	Netherfield	3-2

Second Round;

Atherton LR	v	Winsford United	3-2
Barrow	v	Accrington Stanley	3-4
Colwyn Bay	v	Droylsden	3-1
Eastwood Town	v	Alfreton Town	3-2
Frickley Athletic	v	Bradford Park Avenue	1-1, 3-1
Guiseley	v	Blyth Spartans	1-0
Harrogate Town	v	Emley	0-2
Hyde United	v	Ashton United	3-1
Lancaster City	v	Knowsley United	2-0
Leek Town	v	Buxton	1-0
Leigh	v	Witton Albion	2-2, 0-3
Marine	v	Chorley	0-0, 4-2
Matlock Town	v	Gainsborough Trinity	0-1
Spennymoor United	v	Bishop Auckland	2-2, 3-1
Workington	v	Bamber Bridge	0-1
Worksop Town	v	Boston United	0-5

Third Round;

Atherton LR	v	Witton Albion	2-5
Bamber Bridge	v	Lancaster City	0-1
Boston United	v	Guiseley	3-2
Colwyn Bay	v	Accrington Stanley	2-3
Gainsborough Trinity	v	Frickley Athletic	4-1
Hyde United	v	Marine	5-3
Leek Town	v	Eastwood Town	4-3
Spennymoor United	v	Emley	5-0

Fourth Round;

Accrington Stanley	v	**Leek Town**	0-0, 1-3
Boston United	v	Spennymoor United	3-0
Gainsborough Trinity	v	Witton Albion	3-2
Hyde United	v	Lancaster City	5-1

Semi-Finals;

Gainsborough Trinity	v	**Hyde United**		0-2
Hyde United	v	Gainsborough Trinity	1-0	3-0 (agg)
Boston United	v	**Leek Town**		1-2
Leek Town	v	Boston United	2-0	4-1 (agg)

Final; Hyde United v Leek Town 1-1 (aet), 7-6 penalties

UNIFILLA FIRST DIVISION CUP 95-96

First Round;

Atherton LR	v	Congleton Town		3-1
Farsely Celtic	v	Eastwood Town		2-1
Leigh	v	Curzon Ashton		0-1
Lincoln United	v	Bradford Park Avenue		2-0
Workington	v	Fleetwood		2-2, 3-0
		Second Round;		
Curzon Ashton	v	Ashton United		1-1, 0-2
Farsley Celtic	v	**Lancaster City**		1-1, 1-3
Gretna	v	Whitley Bay		1-2
Lincoln United	v	Alfreton Town		1-4
Radcliffe Borough	v	Great Harwood Town		0-1
Warrington Town	v	**Atherton LR**		0-1
Workington	v	Netherfield		4-2
Worksop Town	v	Harrogate Town		5-1
		Third Round;		
Alfreton Town	v	Ashton United		3-0
Great Harwood Town	v	Worksop Town		1-1, 2-1
Lancaster City	v	Whitley Bay		2-1
Workington	v	**Atherton LR**		2-3
		Semi-Finals;		
Alfreton Town	v	**Atherton LR**		0-4
Atherton LR	v	Alfreton Town	1-2	5-2 (agg)
Lancaster City	v	Great Harwood Town		4-1
Great Harwood Town	v	**Lancaster City**	0-2	1-6 (agg)

Final; Atherton LR v Lancaster City 0-1

UNIBOND LEAGUE PRESIDENTS CUP 95-96

First Round;

Ashton United	v	Buxton		0-1
Bamber Bridge	v	Warrington Town		4-1
Boston United	v	Alfreton Town		2-2, 4-0
Guiseley	v	Blyth Spartans		4-0
Hyde United	v	Leek Town		2-2, 2-0
Marine	v	Witton Albion		2-0
Radcliffe Borough	v	Spennymoor United		3-2
Worksop Town	v	Gainsborough Trinity		3-1
		Second Round;		
Buxton	v	**Guiseley**		1-1, 1-3
Boston United	v	**Worksop Town**		0-2
Marine	v	Hyde United		0-3
Radcliffe Borough	v	Bamber Bridge		0-0, 1-2
		Semi-Finals;		
Hyde United	v	**Guiseley**		0-2
Guiseley	v	Hyde United	1-1	3-1 (agg)
Worksop Town	v	Bamber Bridge		1-0
Bamber Bridge	v	**Worksop Town**	2-2	2-3 (agg)
		Final;		
Guiseley	**v**	**Worksop Town**		**0-1**
Worksop Town	**v**	**Guiseley**	**3-1**	**4-1 (agg)**

1968 ACCRINGTON STANLEY Reds

Back Row (L-R); Jim Coffey (Coach), Stan Allan (Mgr), G Hughes, O Parrillon, G Walsh, R Mulloy, A Burns, D Quick, P Mellor, J McNally, P Beck, Phil Leather (Kit). Front Row; D Thornton, T McKenna, B Ormerod, M Rawstron, S Anderson, C Molloy, B Welch. *Photo - T R Slinger*

Chairman: Eric Whalley. **President:** J C Prescott/ J Hudson.
Secretary: Philip Terry, 8 Princess Street, Colne, Lancs BB8 9AN (01286 866768).
Manager: Stan Allen. **Asst Manager:** **Osteopath:** Martin Dixon D.O. M.G.O.
Coach: Jimmy Coffey. **Press Officer:** Philip Terry **Commercial Advisor:** John de Maine
Ground: Crown Ground, off Livingstone Road, Accrington (01254 383235).
Directions: Arriving on A680 from Clayton-le-Moors Livingstone Road is on left 50 yds past Crown Hotel. From M62/M66, through town centre on A680 - Livingstone Road 500 yds on right after Victoria Hospital. One and a half miles from Accrington (BR).
Capacity: 4,000 **Cover:** 1,650 **Seats:** 700 **Floodlights:** Yes **Metal Badges:** Yes
Club Shop: Yes, selling replica kits, sweaters, t-shirts, videos, photos etc. Contact John De Maine
Colours: Red/white/red **Change colours:** All royal blue
Previous Leagues: Lancs Combination 70-78/ Cheshire County 78-82/ North West Counties 82-87.
Midweek home matchday: Wednesday **Reserve Team's League:** North West Alliance.
Youth League: Lancs Youth Floodlit League. **Sponsors:** Hollands Pies, Baxenden.
Record Attendance: 2,096 v Fleetwood Town, FA Cup 4th Qualifying Rd 27/10/90 *(10,081 v Crewe Alexandra, F.A. Cup Second Round Proper 5/12/92 - played at Ewood Park, Blackburn).*
Best FA Cup season: Second Rd Proper 92-93 (lost 1-6 at home to Crewe Alexandra).
League clubs defeated in FA Cup: None.
Record win: 9-0 v Ashton Town, Lancashire Combination 75-76.
Record defeat: 1-9 v Runcorn (A), FA Cup 2nd Qual Rd replay 85-86.
Record Fees - Paid: £2,250 for Bernie Hughes (Droylsen 90-91).
Received: £10,000 for Martin Clark (Crewe A. 92-93).
Players progressing to Football League: David Hargreaves (Blackburn Rovers 1977), Ian Blackstone (York City), Gus Wilson (Crewe), Glen Johnstone (Preston), Darren Lyons (Bury), Martin Clark (Crewe 92-93), Mark Wright (Wigan 93-94).
Clubhouse: Open two nights and matchdays. Private functions. Well stocked tea sar in ground.
Club Record Scorer: David Hargreaves 318
Club Record Appearances: Chris Grimshaw 352.
95-96 Captain: Stewart Anderson
95-96 P.o.Y.: Darren Quick.
95-96 Top scorer: Jihn McInally.
Local Press: Accrington Observer (01254 871444), Lancashire Evening Telegraph (01254 63588).
Local Radio Stations: Radio Lancashire, Red Rose Radio.
Newsline: 0891 227 343.
Honours: N West Counties Lg R-up 86-87, Cheshire County Lg Div 2 80-81 (R-up 79-80), Lancs Comb 73-74 77-78 (R-up 71-72 75-76, Lg Cup 71-72 72-73 73-74 76-77), George Watson Trophy 71-72 73-74 74-75, John Duckworth Trophy 85-86, Lancs Junior Cup (now ATS Trophy) R-up 85-86, FA Trophy 1st Rd 72-73 78-79 92-93, Lancs under-18 Yth Cup 89-90. N.W.All Div Cup 94-95, Anglo-Barbados Cup 1995.

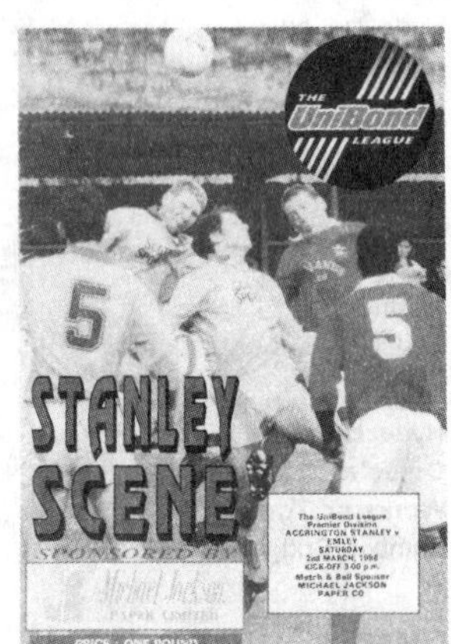

PROGRAMME DETAILS
Pages: 32 **Price:** £1
Editor: Secretary/David Ellis.
(01282 866768 - David Ellis)

ACCRINGTON STANLEY'S 1995-96 CAMPAIGN

DATE		OPPONENTS	COMP	RESULT		GATE	GOALSCORERS
Aug 19	A	Leek Town	UL	D	2-2	367	McNally, Welch
23	H	Knowsley United	UL	W	4-2	472	McNally, Welch, Rogerson, Rawstron
26	H	Winsford United	UL	L	1-2	475	Anderson
28	A	Barrow	UL	W	3-0	1485	Rogerson, Rawstron, Anderson
Sept 2	A	Colwyn Bay	UL	W	2-1	415	Rawston, Welch
6	H	Spennymoor United	UL	D	0-0	461	
9	H	Ossett Town	FAC	W	2-1	429	Anderson, Ormerod
12	A	Witton Albion	UL	W	2-0	525	McNally 2
16	H	Buxton	UL	W	1-0	549	McNally
19	A	Spennymoor United	UL	W	4-3	327	Thornton 2, Quick, Anderson
23	H	Bradford P.A.	FAC	L	1-2	553	Grimshaw
30	A	Boston United	UL	L	0-4	851	
Oct 4	H	Blyth Spartans	UL	L	1-2	446	Thornton
7	H	Boston United	UL	L	0-2	484	
14	H	Bradford P.A.	FAT	D	2-2	415	Welch, Thornton
17	A	Bradford P.A.	FAT R	W	3-2	258	Welch 2, Walsh
21	H	Droylsden	UL	L	0-2	472	
24	A	Barrow	ULC	W	4-3	932	McNally 2, Rogerson, Welch
28	H	Matlock Town	UL	W	2-1	384	Rawstron, Shaughnessy
Nov 4	A	Atherstone United	FAT	W	3-1	422	McNally, Mellor, Shaughnessy
8	H	Chorley	UL	W	7-3	483	Welch 2, McNally 2, Quick, Walsh, Shaughnessy
11	H	Guiseley	UL	L	0-1	602	
18	A	Bishop Auckland	UL	D	2-2	179	Shaughnessy, Anderson
25	H	Gresley Rovers	UL	L	2-3	542	Shaughnessy 2
Dec 2	H	Hyde United	UL	D	1-1	464	Shaughnessy
5	A	Colwyn Bay	ULC	W	3-2	263	Hughes 2, Welch
9	A	Gainsborough Town	UL	D	1-1	499	Walsh
13	H	Barrow	UL	D	1-1	447	McNally
16	H	Witton Albion	UL	L	1-2	409	Walsh
19	A	Marine	UL	W	2-1	342	Quick,Thornton
Jan 1	H	Marine	UL	D	0-0	622	
6	A	Hyde United	UL	D	0-0	512	
13	H	Leek Town	UL	D	0-0	421	
17	H	Radcliffe Borough	ATS	D	1-1	276	Quick
20	A	Frickley Athletic	UL	L	1-1	154	Quick
23	A	Radcliffe Borough	ATS R	L	1-2	156	Quick
Feb 3	H	Bishop Auckland	UL	W	2-1	415	Rogerson 2
13	A	Leek Town	ULC	D	0-0	117	
17	H	Gainsborough Town	UL	W	2-1	404	McKenna, McNally
24	A	Blyth Spartans	UL	D	2-2	541	McNally 2
28	H	Leek Town	ULC R	L	1-3	201	McNally
Mar 2	H	Emley	UL	D	0-0	361	
9	A	Buxton	UL	W	1-0	217	Hughes
16	A	Droylsden	UL	W	2-1	180	Thornton 2
19	A	Knowsley United	UL	L	0-1	45	
23	H	Frickley Athletic	UL	W	2-1	348	Thornton, Welch
26	A	Bamber Bridge	UL	D	1-1	512	Welch
30	A	Emley	UL	W	3-1	268	Anderson, Thornton, Welch
Apr 6	A	Winsford United	UL	D	2-2	168	Quick (P), Hughes
8	H	Bamber Bridge	UL	L	1-2	760	Thornton
13	A	Matlock Town	UL	L	0-2	308	
20	H	Colwyn Bay	UL	W	3-1	565	Walsh, McNally, Ormerod
23	A	Chorley	UL	D	0-0	355	
27	A	Guiseley	UL	W	3-1	507	Ormerod 2, Thornton

ACCRINGTON STANLEY PLAYING SQUAD 1996-97

Goalkeepers: Rob Mulloy (Nelson, Crosshills, Colne Dynamoes)

Defenders: Ollie Parillon (Barrow, Morecambe, Horwich RMI, Leyland Motors), **Les Thompson** (Burnley, Maidstone U, Hull), **Peter Mellor** (Witton A, Droylsden, Barrow, Radcliffe B, Hyde U), **Chris Molloy** (Leigh RMI, Hyde U, Mossley, Altrincham, St.Helens T, Witton A, York), **Mark Rawstron** (Great Harwood T, Rossendale U, Great Harwood T, Bacup B, Rossendale U, Whitworth Valley, Bacup B, Burnley (A)), **Iain McLellan** (Hyde U, Curzon Ashton, Radcliffe B, Flixton, Irlam T, Bacup B, Northwich V, Altrincham), **Andy Burns** (Wythenshawe Am), **Neil Edmonds** (Stalybridge C, East Bengal (Ind), Stalybridge C, Chorley, Rochdale, Oldham), **Mike Duxbury** (South China (HK), Bradford C, Blackburn, Manchester U)

Midfielders: Darren Thornton (Droylsden, Hyde U, Baildon Ath, Salt GSOB), **Brian Welch** (Barrow, Burnley, Hebburn), **Darren Quick** (Salford C, Blackpool (T)), **John McNally** (Morecambe, Vauxhall GM), **Stewart Anderson** (Stalybridge C, Morecambe, Witton A, Colne Dynamoes, Chadderton), **Ged Walsh** (Great Harwood T, Bacup B, Rossendale U, Bacup B), **Andy Robinson** (Great Harwood T, Haslingden, Buxton, Glossop, Rossendale U, Helmshore U), **Rodger Wilkins** (Great Harwood T), **Tony Briffa** (Leigh RMI, Curzon Ashton, Salford C)

Forwards: Brett Ormroyd (Blackburn (T)), **Paul Hargreaves** (Padiham), **Paul Moulden** (Rochdale, Birmingham, Oldham, AFC Bournemouth, Manchester C), **Paul Rushby** (Mitchell & Shackleton), **Stuart Taylor** (Guiseley, Thackley, Eccleshill U)

Formed: 1959

ALFRETON TOWN

The Reds

Alfreton Town FC. Back Row (L/R): Lee Coombes, Paul Mitchell (Joint Manager), Phil Stafford, Jason Maybury, Bob Dawes, Paul Norton, Kerry Spray, Lee Hirst, Neil Pickering, Andy Glenister, Danny Hague(Joint Manager), John Peach. Front Row: Arran Brady, Paul Eshelby, Craug Weston, John Megson, Kevin Haigh, Matt Walsh, John McFadzean, Steve Johnson, Tim Atkinson.

Chairman: Sean Egan **Vice Chairman:** Dave Gregory.
Secretary: Roger Taylor, 9 Priory Rd, Alfreton, Derbyshire DE55 7JT (01773 835121).
Joint Managers: Danny Hague/ Paul Mitchel. **Physio:** Steve Howson.
Press Officer: Chris Tacey (01773 511012). **Commercial Manager:** Alan Cleaver.
Ground: Town Ground, North Street, Alfreton, Derbyshire(01773 830277).
Directions: M1 junction 28 and follow A38 towards Derby for 1 mile, left onto B600, right at main road to town centre and after half a mile turn left down North Street - ground on right. Half mile from Alfreton & Mansfield Parkway (BR) station. Buses 242 & 243 from both Derby and Mansfield.
Capacity: 5,000 **Cover:** 1,000 **Seats:** 300 **Floodlights:** Yes **Metal Badges:** Yes
Club Shop: Yes, selling programmes (English & Scottish Lge + non-Lge), club badges, pens, key rings, ties, sewn-on badges. Contact Mr Brian Thorpe, 13 Oakland Str., Alfreton, Derbyshire (01773 836251).
Colours: Red & white/white/white. **Change colours:** Yellow (green trim)/green/yellow.
Previous Leagues: Cent All *21-25* 59-61/ Midland (Counties) *25-27* 61-82/ Nth Counties (E) 82-87.
Midweek home matchday: Wednesday **Reserve League:** No Reserves.
Sponsors: Alfreton Town council. **Record Attendance:** 5,023 v Matlock Town, Central Alliance 1960.
Best FA Cup season: 1st Rd 3rd replay 69-70. Also 1st Rd 73-74.
League clubs defeated in FA Cup: Lincoln 24-25, but none since club's reformation in 1959.
Record win: 15-0 v Loughborough,Midland League.69-70.
Record Defeat:2-9 v Worksop61, 0-8 v Bridlington 1992.
Record Fees - Paid: £1,000 for R Mountain (Matlock)
Received: £2,500 for R Greenough (Chester City).
Players progressing to Football League: M Wright (68), A Kowalski (73), Tony Henson (81), Ricky Greenhough (85), Philip Greaves (86) (All Chesterfield), A Woodward (Grimsby Tn 70), A Taylor (Chelsea 72), Keith Smith (Exeter City 89).
Clubhouse: Clubhouse on ground for members. Hot & cold food & drinks available on ground. Supporters Clubs just outside ground open 11am-4pm matchdays and 7-11pm at night.
Record Scorer: J Harrison 303. **Record Appearances:** J Harrison 560.
95-96 Captain: L.Hirst/P.Stafford. **95-96 Top Scorer:** Phil Stafford 32.
95-96 P.o.Ys: Phil Stafford & Craig Weston.
Local Newspapers: Derbyshire Times, Derby Evening Telegraph, Nottingham Evening, Ripley/Heanor News, Mansfield Chad.
Local Radio Stations: Radio Derby.
Honours: FA Trophy 1st Rd Proper 94-95, Northern Counties (E) Lg 84-85 (Lg Cup 84-85), Midland (Count) Lg 69-70 73-74 76-77 (R-up 71-72 80-81 81-82, Lg Cup 71-72 72-73 73-74), Derbyshire Sen Cup 60-61 69-70 72-73 73-74 81-82,94-95, (R-up; 1962-63, 64-65, 77-78, 79-80, 84-85, 87-88, 92-93.) Divl Cup (N) 64-65, Evans Halshaw Floodlit Cup 87-88,95-96, Cent All Lg. R-Up 63-64, Unibond Lge Div 1 R-Up 1995-96.

PROGRAMME DETAILS:
Pages: 32 **Price:** 70p
Editor: Chris Tacey
(01773 511012)

ALFRETON TOWN'S 1995-96 CAMPAIGN

DATE		OPPONENTS	COMP	RESULT		GATE	GOALSCORERS
Aug 19	H	Warrington Town	UL	W	5-1	203	Maybury, Weston, Eshelby, McFadzean, Haigh
22	A	Lincoln United	UL	W	2-0	237	Maybury,Stafford
26	A	Radcliffe Boro (Prelim)	FAC	L	2-3#	118	McFadzean, og
28	H	Workshop	UL	D	2-2	418	Stafford, Dawes
Sept 2	H	Atherton L.R.	UL	L	1-2	230	Dawes
5	A	Harrogate Town	UL	W	3-0	270	Johnson, Stafford, Megson
9	A	Gretna	UL	D	0-0	97	
13	H	Harrogate Town	UL	W	2-0	182	Stafford
16	A	Leigh RMI	UL	D	1-1	176	Stafford
19	A	Eastwood Town	UL	L	0-2	290	
27	H	Lincoln United	ULC	W	4-0	135	Pickering, Maybury,Hirst, Eshelby
Oct 4	H	Curson Ashton	UL	W	3-2	181	Haigh, Stafford, McFadzean
7	H	Fleetwood	UL	W	1-0	213	Maybury
11	A	Bradford Park Avenue	UL	D	1-1	183	McFadzean
14	H	Congleton Town	FAT	W	5-0	202	Hirst,TIbenham 2,Walsh, Stafford
18	H	Lincoln United	UL	W	2-1	201	Stafford, McFadzean
21	H	Farsley Celtic	UL	L	0-1	164	
24	A	Eastwind Town	ULC	L	2-3†	261	Stafford, og
28	H	Ashton United	UL	W	3-0	235	McFadzean, Maybury,Johnson
Nov 4	H	Dudley Town	FAT	D	2-2	260	Hirst, Johnson
8	A	Dudley Town	FAT R	L	0-2	183	
11	A	Lancaster City	UL	D	1-1	214	Stafford
18	H	Great Harwood Town	UL	W	4-1	224	Stafford, Dawes, Johnson, Waller
22	H	Ashfield United	EHF	D	2-2	109	Eshelby, Askey
25	A	Congleton Town	UL	W	1-0	144	Waller
Dec 2	H	Radcliffe Borough	UL	W	1-0	183	Johnson
9	H	Farsley Celtic	UL	L	2-3	184	Johnson 2
12	A	Lincoln United	UFC	W	4-1	76	Stafford 2, McFadzean, Dawes
16	H	Whitley Bay	UL	L	2-3	171	McFadzean, Stafford
20	H	Heanor Town	DSC	W	9-1	135	Johnson, Eshelny 3,Stafford, McFadzean 2, Askey, Walsh
Jan 6	A	Workington	UL	W	2-1	230	Johnson, Stafford
10	H	Boston United	UPC	D	2-2	188	McFadzean, Stafford
13	H	Lancaster City	UL	L	1-6	333	Johnson
17	H	Ilkeston Town	EHF	W	7-1	163	Stafford 6, Tibenham
20	A	Warrington Town	UL	D	2-2	110	Pickering, Stafford
Feb 3	H	Gretna	UL	W	4-0	195	Pickering 2, Rinkcavage, Stafford
10	A	Workshop	UBI	L	0-2	467	
14	H	Ashton United	UFC	W	3-0	126	Stafford 2, Walsh
17	A	Radcliffe Borough	UL	W	3-1	202	Pickering 2, Cheetham
24	H	Congleton Town	UL	W	2-1	181	Eshelby 2
27	A	Belper Town	DSC	L	3-4	404	Pickering 2, Stafford
Mar 2	A	Atherton LR	UL	D	0-0	126	
6	A	Boston United	UPC	L	0-4	325	
9	H	Leigh RMI	UL	W	1-0	140	Cotton
11	A	Ilkeston Twon	EHF	W	2-0	103	Eshelby, McFadzean
16	A	Fleetwood	UL	W	2-0	55	Wston, Hirst
20	H	Atherton LR	UFC	L	0-4	130	
23	A	Ashton United	UL	L	1-2	192	McFadzean
26	A	Atherton LR	UFC	W	2-1	123	Walsh, Dawes
30	A	Great Harwood Town	UL	W	3-1	90	Walsh,Staffor, Eshelby
Apr 3	A	Ashfield United	EHF	W	6-2	65	Cheetham 2, Walsh 2, Stafford, Tibenham
6	A	Curzon Ashton	UL	W	1-0	129	Eshelby
8	H	Eastwood Town	UL	D	2-2	305	Eshelby, Stafford
10	A	Belper Town	EHF	W	4-1*	223	Dawes 2, Eshelby, og
13	H	Workington	UL	W	2-1	204	Haigh, Walsh
17	H	Netherfield	UL	W	4-1	171	Haigh, Stafford 2, Eshelby
20	A	Whitley Bay	UL	W	5-0	187	Dawes 2, Stafford 2, Maybury
27	H	Bradford Park Avenue	UL	W	3-2	364	Stafford 3
May 1	A	Holbeach United	EHFCF	W	4-0	223	Walsh, Cheetham 2, McFadzean
4	A	Netherfield	UL	D	4-4	188	Dawes 2, Stafford, Eshelby

Own goals scored by #D. Bean (Radcliffe Borough) †G.Bush (Eastwood Town) *G.Rigg (Belper Town)
Key: UL = UniBond League First Division; ULC = UniBond League Cup; UFC = UniFilla First Division Cup; UPC = UniBond President's Cup; FAC = FA Cup; FAT = FA Trophy; EHF = Evans Halshaw Floodlit Competition; DSC = Derbyshire Senior Cup.

ALFRETON TOWN PLAYING SQUAD 1996-97

Goalkeepers: Phil Yeomans (Kiveton Park, Denaby U)
Defenders: Tim Atkinson (Rotherham, Sheffield U (T)), **Neil Pickering** (Worksop T, Sutton T, Crookes), **Lee Hirst** (Coventry, Scarborough), **David Cutts** (Matlock T, Boston U, Glapwell), **Andy Glenister** (Matlock T, Rossington Main, Scarborough), **Jason Maybury** (Sheffield Aurora, Worksop T, Frickley Ath, Crookes, Goole T, Hull (A)), **Darren Schofield** (Denaby U, Alfreton T)
Midfielders: Caine Cheetham (Matlock T, Hatfield Main), **Matthew Walsh** (Leek T, Alfreton T, Stafford R, Bradford C, Swansea), **Craig Weston** (Belper T, Gresley R, Grantham T, Belper T, Burton A), **Scott Elliot** (Gresley R, Long Eaton U), **Ian Askey** (Sheffield Aurora), Marcus Wood (Matlock T, Rotherham (T))
Forwards: Phil Stafford (Ashfield U, Sheffield Aurora, Sutton T, Frickley Ath, Denaby U, Sheffield, Goole T, Gainsborough T), **Paul Eshelby** (Scarborough, Exeter, Endcliffe U), **John McFadzean** (Sheffield Aurora, Sheffield, Denaby U, Rotherham), **Andy Tibbenham** (Stocksbridge PS, Exeter, Denaby U), **Peter Cotton** (Worksop T, Parkgate, Hallam, Goole T, Hallam)

Founded: 1952

BAMBER BRIDGE

Bamber Bridge FC: Back Row (L-R); Jason Kerfoot, Stuart Barton, Steve Senior, Steve Berryman, Dave Leaver. Middle; Wayne Maddock, Mark Milligan, David Eaves, {aul Allen, Nigel Greenwood, Mark Edwards, Damian Corcoran, Steve O'Neil, Steve Denny. Front; Mel Gainer, Phil Chadwick, Darren Brown, Tony Greenwood, Jez Baldwin, Phil Entwhistle, Shaun McHugh, Stuart Pheonix, Dave Dunderdale.

President: Harold Hargreaves **Chairman:** D Allan **Vice Chairman:** H Milburn.
Secretary & Press Officer: D G Spencer, 11 Tennyson Place, Walton-le-Dale, Preston, Lancs PR5 4TT (011772 34355).
Commercial Manager: Nigel Webster.
Manager: Mick Holgate. **Asst Manager:** Mel Gainer. **Physio:** A Jones
Ground: Irongate, Brownedge Road, Bamber Bridge, Preston, Lancs. Tel Nos: Club Office 01772-909690; Social Club 01772-909695; Fax No. 01772-909691. 627387).
Directions: M6 Junct 29, A6 (Bamber Bridge Bypass) towards Walton-le-Dale, to r'bout, A6 London Road to next r'bout, 3rd exit signed Bamber Bridge (Brownedge Road) and first right. Ground 100 yds at end of road on left. Just over a mile from Bamber Bridge (BR).
Seats: 250 **Cover:** 800 **Capacity:** 2,500 **Floodlights:** Yes **Metal badges:** Yes.
Club Shop: Yes - a Supporters Club caravan on ground. Sells hats, cups, scarves, key rings, badges etc plus large selection of programmes. Contact Russ Rigby (01772 909690)
Colours: White/black/white. **Change:** Red/Black/Red.
Midweek Matches: Tuesday **Sponsors:** Baxi Partnership
Record Win: 8-0 v Curzon Ashton N.W.Co. 94-95
Reserve Teams League: North West Alliance.
Previous Leagues: Preston & District 52-90/ North West Counties 90-93.
Previous Ground: King George V Ground, Higher Walton 1952-86.
Best FA Vase season: Semi Final 91-92 (lost 0-2 on agg to Wimborne Tn).
Best FA Cup season: Second Qualifying Round 92-93 (lost 0-4 at home to Spennymoor United).
Record Attendance: 2,300 v Czech Republic, Pre-Euro 96 Friendly.
Clubhouse: On ground, open all day Saturday matchdays, every evening and Sunday lunchtimes. Refreshment cabin on ground serves hot & cold drinks, pies, sandwiches crisps etc during matches.
Record Transfer Fee Paid: £10,000 to Horwich R.M.I.for Mark Edwards.
Record Transfer Fee Recieved: £15,000 from Wigan Athletic for Tony Back.1995.
95-96 Captain: Jez Baldwin. **95-96 P.o.Y.:** Jez Baldwin.
95-96 Top scorer: Dave Leaver.
Hons: FA Vase SF 91-92, Nth West Co's Lge R-up 92-93 (Div 2 91-92, F'lit Cup R-up 91-92), Preston & Dist Lge(4) 80-81 85-87 89-90 (R-up 78-79 82-83 84-85), Guildhall Cup 78-79 80-81 84-85 89-90 (R-up 77-78 79-80 87-88), Lancs Amtr Shield 81-82 (R-up 80-81 89-90), Lancastrian Brigade Cup 76-77 89-90 90-91. A.T.S.Lancs Trophy Winners 94-95, R-Up 95-96, Unibond Challenge Cup Winners 94-95, Unibond 1st Div R-Up.94-95. Unibond Northern Prem Div Champions 95-96.

PROGRAMME DETAILS:
Pages: TBA **Price:** £1.
Editor: Dave Rowland.
(01772 465659)

BAMBER BRIDGE'S 1995-96 CAMPAIGN

DATE		OPPONENTS	COMP	RESULT		GATE	GOALSCORERS
Aug 12	A	Marine	UL Shield	D	2-2	354	Mayers, McCrea
19	H	Matlock T.	UL	W	4-1	376	Senior, Byrne, Edwards, Corcoran
22	A	Marine	UL	D	0-0	298	
26	A	Buxton	UL	W	2-1	406	Byrne, Allen
28	A	Chorley	UL	W	2-0	754	McHugh, Leaver
Sept 2	A	Witton Albion	UL	D	0-0	623	
5	H	Colwyn Bay	UL	W	5-0	511	Edwards 3, Senior, Greenwood
9	H	Heanor T.	FAC	W	4-1	453	Greenwood 2, Senior, Byrne
12	A	Barrow	UL	W	2-0	1520	Allen, Byrne
16	A	Gainsborough T.	UL	W	3-1	396	Allen 2, Byrne
19	H	Winsford U.	UL	W	2-0	655	McHugh, Byrne
23	H	Mossley	FAC	L	0-2	583	
30	H	Hyde U.	UL	D	3-3	571	Mayers 2, Senior
Oct 3	H	Barrow	UL	D	2-2	1238	Brown, Leaver
7	A	Leek T.	UL	W	3-2	293	Leaver 2, Mayers
10	A	Chorley	UL	D	0-0	975	
14	H	Boston U.	UL	L	1-2	681	O'Neill
17	A	Knowsley U.	UL	D	2-2	94	Mayers, O'Neill
21	A	Hyde U.	UL	W	3-2	569	Mayers, Burton, Leaver
24	A	Workington	ULC	W	1-0	194	Mayers
28	H	Emley	UL	L	0-1	519	
Nov 4	H	Blyth Spartans	UL	W	3-0	464	Leaver 2, Edwards
6	A	Winsford U.	UL	W	4-1	202	Leaver 2, Baldwin, Senior
11	A	Frickley A.	UL	W	5-0	152	Leaver 2, Greenwood 2, Edwards
18	H	Buxton	UL	W	2-0	495	Greenwood 2
21	H	Warrington T.	PC	W	4-1	496	O'Neill 3, Eaves
25	A	Burton Alb.	FAT	D	3-3	964	Leaver 3
28	H	Burton Alb.	FATR	L	2-3	502	Allen, Edwards
Dec 2	A	Boston U.	UL	W	3-0	1423	Allen, O'Neill, Leaver
5	H	Lancaster C.	CC	L	0-1	349	
9	H	Droylsden	UL	W	3-2	358	McHugh, Eaves, Senior
16	A	Guiseley	UL	L	0-4	550	
Jan 6	H	Gainsborough T.	UL	D	1-1	531	Maddock
13	A	Blyth Spartans	UL	D	1-1	576	Edwards
16	H	Lancaster C.	ATS	W	4-3	380	Maddock, Edwards, McHugh, og
20	H	Leek T.	UL	D	0-0	424	
Feb 3	H	Knowsley U.	UL	D	2-2	451	Chadwick 2
12	H	Daisy Hill	ATS	W	3-1	290	Eaves 2, Allen
17	A	Matlock T.	UL	W	1-0	326	Maddock
20	H	Radcliffe B.	PC	D	0-0	302	
24	H	Guiseley	UL	W	3-1	601	Leaver 2, Chadwick
27	A	Radcliffe B.	PC	W	2-1	226	Maddock, Chadwick
Mar 2	A	Bishop Auckland	UL	D	1-1	184	Chadwick
9	A	Emley	UL	D	1-1	264	Chadwick
12	H	Chorley	ATSSF	W	3-0	542	Maddock, Edwards, O'Neill
23	H	Marine	UL	D	4-4	608	Milligan, Maddock, Allen, O'Neill
26	H	Accrington S.	UL	D	1-1	512	Senior
30	H	Bishop Auckland	UL	L	0-2	363	
Apr 2	A	Worksop T.	PCSF	L	0-1	410	
6	A	Colwyn Bay	UL	D	1-1	405	Leaver
8	A	Accrington S.	UL	W	2-1	760	Leaver, Edwards
10	H	Worksop T.	PCSF	D	2-2	430	Maddock, Edwards
13	H	Spennymoor U.	UL	W	2-0	388	Maddock, Leaver
20	A	Droylsden	UL	W	2-1	237	Edwards, O'Neill
24	N	Morecambe	ATSF	L	0-1	1708	
27	H	Frickley A.	UL	L	2-3	466	Edwards, O'Neill
30	A	Spennymoor U.	UL	L	2-4	288	Eaves, og
May 4	H	Witton Alb.	UL	D	1-1	589	Leaver

BAMBER BRIDGE PLAYING SQUAD 1996-97

Goalkeepers: Steve Berryman (Leyland Daf, Altrincham, Preston, Barnet, Cambridge U, Exeter, Hartlepool)
Defenders: Stuart Phoenix (Leigh RMI, St.Helens T, Wigan), **Jez Baldwin** (Fleetwood T, Bamber Bridge, Leyland Celtic), **Mark Milligan** (Youth team), **Darren Brown** (Great Harwood T, Preston), **Denis Hill** (Clitheroe, Great Harwood T), **Gordon Dugdale** (Burnley (T)), **Paul Taylor** (Bury)
Midfielders: David Eaves (Morecambe, Preston), **Jason Kerfoot** (Netherfield, Preston), **Ged Byrne** (Winsford U, Witton A, Winsford U, Maine Road, Winsford U, Maine Road, Salford C), **Neil Spencer** (Atherton LR, Bamber B), **Damian Corcoran** (Preston), **Ryo Takahashi** (Maine Road), **Darren Royle** (Altrincham)
Forwards: Mark Edwards (Horwich RMI, Ashton U, Stalybridge C, Horwich RMI, Witton A, Chorley, Horwich RMI, St.Helens T), **Steve O'Neill** (Altrincham, Bootle, Marine), **Wayne Maddock** (Morecambe, Barrow, Netherfield, Marine, BAC Preston, Leyland Motors), **David Ward** (Blackpool), **Mick Doherty** (Runcorn, Knowsley U, Altrincham, Marine, Macclesfield T, Farnborough T, Runcorn, Yeovil T, Maidstone U, Weymouth, Reading, Basingstoke T)

BARROW

Founded: 1901 Nickname: Bluebirds

Back Row; V Pepper (Physio), J Doolan, N Morton, J Parker. Middle; T Ford, S Humphreys, I Leeming, C Speak, M Deegan, A Green, L O'Keefe, J McGuire, F Ventre. Front; P Smith, A McDonald, S Vaughan (Chr), M Walsh (Mgr), D McKenna, A Hoskins, G Hennegan.

Chairman: Stephen Vaughan. **President:** W A McCullough.
Secretary: Pat Brewer, c/o The Club (below)(01229 820346 or (H) 01229 828913)
Manager: Mike Walsh. **Press Officer:** Phil Yelland,83 Camus Avenue,Edinburgh EH10 6QY(0131 445 1010)
Ground: Holker Street Ground, Wilkie Rd, Barrow-in-Furness, Cumbria LA14 5UH (01229 820346/823839). Commercial Office: (at ground) 01229 823061 - Manager Mrs Linda Barker.
Directions: M6 to junction 36, A590 to Barrow, enter Barrow on Park Road and after about 2 miles turn left into Wilkie Rd - ground on right.B.R.1/4 mile .
Capacity: 3,500 **Cover:** 1,200 **Seats:** 1000+. **Floodlights:** Yes
Club Shop: Yes Contact: Linda Barker. **Metal Badges:** Yes
Colours: Blue & White Hoops/Blue/Blue & white hoops. **Change colours:** Green white trim/Green/Green.
Prev Lgs: Lancs Comb 01-21/Football Lge 21-72/N Prem 72-79 83-84 86-89/GMVC 79-83 84-86 89-92.
Midweek home matchday: Tuesday **Previous Grounds:** The Strawberry & Little Park, Roose.
Reserve League: Furness Premier Lge. **Record Attendance:** 6,002 v Enfield, FA Trophy Semi-Final, Apr 88.
Best FA Cup season: Third Round Proper on nine occasions including once as a non-League club (90-91, lost 0-1 at Bolton Wanderers).
Record defeat: 1-10 v Hartlepools Utd, Football Lge Div 4, 1959.
Record win: 12-0 v Cleator, FA Cup 1920.
Record Fees - Paid: £9,000 for Andy Whittaker (Ashton Utd, July 94).
Received: £40,000 for Kenny Lowe (Barnet, Jan 91).
Players progressing to Football League: I McDonald, N McDonald, J Laisby, B Diamond, F Gamble, B Knowles, G Skivington, P Byron, L Edwards, K Lowe, M Dobie, T Rigby, N Doherty.
Clubhouse: Barrow Sports & Leisure centre next to ground (01229 823839). Open matchdays and Functions only. Snack bars on grd.
Club Record Goalscorer: Colin Cowperthwaite 282 (Dec '77-Dec '92)
Club Record Appearances: Colin Cowperthwaite 704
95-96 Captain: Jeff Parker **95-96 P.o.Y.:** Jeff Parker.
95-96 Top scorer: Mark Dobie and Neil Martin.
Sponsors: R.T.James & Stephen Vaughan Promotions.
Local Press: North West Evening Mail (01229 821835), Barrow & West Cumberland Advertiser (01229 832032).
Local Radio Stations: BBC Radio Furness, BBC Radio Cumbria, Red Rose, Bay Radio. **Barrow A.F.C. Hotline:** 0891 88 44 38.
Honours: FA Trophy 89-90 (SF 87-88), Nth Prem Lge 83-84 88-89 (Lge Cup R-up 87-88, Lge Shield 84-85), Bord Lord Trophy R-up 90-91, Cumbrian Cup 82-83 83-84 (R-up 84-85), Lancs Floodlit Cup R-up 86-87, Lancs Sen Cup 54-55 (R-up 51-52 65-66 66-67 69-70), Lancs Challenge Trophy 80-81 (R-up 81-82 84-85), Lancs Comb 20-21 (R-up 13-14, Div 2 R-up 04-05 10-11).

PROGRAMME DETAILS:
Pages: 24 **Price:** £1
Editor: D Gardner
(01229 834348)

BARROW'S 1995-96 CAMPAIGN

DATE		OPPONENTS	COMP	RESULT		GATE	GOALSCORERS
Aug 19	H	Knowsley United	UL	W	7-0	1124	Dobie 3, Morton, Hoskin, Todhunter, Brown
22	A	Chorley	UL	W	3-2	591	Parker, Todhunter, Hoskin
26	H	Colwyn Bay	UL	D	1-1	1311	Morton
28	H	Accrington Stanley	UL	L	0-3	1483	
Sept 2	A	Emley	UL	L	0-3	386	Dobie, Hoskin
5	A	Marine	UL	W	2-1	510	J. Kennedy, Dobie
9	H	Consett	FAC	W	3-0	1029	J. Kennedy, Dobie, Brown
12	H	Bamber Bridge	UL	W	3-0	1520	
16	A	Matlock T	UL	W	4-0	406	Smith 2, Brown, Humphries
19	H	Chorley	UL	W	6-2	1513	Smith 3, Morton 2, Brown
23	A	Gateshead	FAC	D	2-2	721	Parker, Dobie
26	H	Gateshead	FAC R	W	1-0	1908	Hoskin
30	H	Frickley A.	UL	D	1-1	1287	Todhunter
Oct 3	A	Bamber Bridge	UL	D	2-2	1238	Dobie, Hoskin
7	H	Durham C	FAC	D	1-1	1413	Dobie
11	A	Durham C	FAC R	W	1-0	764	Todhunter
14	H	Hinckley T	FAT	W	3-0	1119	Dobie, Morton
17	H	Witton Alb	UL	W	3-0	1420	Morton 3
21	A	Winsford United	FAC	W	3-0	714	Parker, Brown, Hoskin
24	H	Accrington Stanley	ULC	L	3-4	932	Morton 2, Smith
28	H	Hyde United	UL	W	2-1	1174	Morton, OG
Nov 4	H	Winsford United	FAT	L	0-1	1222	
11	H	Nuneaton B	FAC	W	2-1	2869	Dobie, Morton
18	H	Spennymoor United	UL	D	1-1	1176	Parker
22	A	Droylsden	UL	W	4-0	118	Parker, Smith, Dobie, Morton
25	A	Knowsley United	UL	W	2-0	145	Smith, Dobie
28	H	Fleetwood T	LCT	W	3-1	506	Todhunter, Morton, Hoskin
Dec 2	H	Wigan Athletic	FAC	L	0-4	3500	
9	H	Boston United	UL	W	2-0	1092	Speak, Hoskin
13	A	Accrington Stanley	UL	D	1-1	447	Dobie
16	A	Frickley Athletic	UL	D	0-0	146	
26	H	Blyth Spartans	UL	W	2-1	1665	Morton, Smith
Jan 1	A	Hyde United	UL	D	0-0	736	
6	A	Leek Town	UL	L	0-2	324	
9	A	Colwyn Bay	UL	W	1-0	271	Kenny
13	H	Guiseley	UL	L	0-2	1466	
16	A	Holker OB	LCT	W	2-1	700	Kenny (p), Smith
20	H	Droylsden	UL	D	3-3	1023	Smith 2, McDonald
30	H	Bishop Auckland	UL	D	0-0	982	
Feb 3	H	Emley	UL	D	0-0	1182	
14	A	Southport	LCT	L	1-3	321	Harold
17	A	Bishop Auckland	UL	W	2-1	251	Green 2
24	H	Gainsborough T	UL	L	0-1	1216	
Mar 2	A	Witton Alb	UL	L	0-1	591	
9	H	Leek T	UL	W	1-0	1077	Grimes
16	A	Spennymoor United	UL	D	1-1	245	Humphries
23	A	Gainsborough T	UL	L	0-1	414	
25	A	Winsford United	UL	L	3-4	170	Foreman 2, Green
30	H	Winsford United	UL	D	1-1	953	Green
Apr 6	H	Marine	UL	W	2-0	981	Green, Brown
8	A	Blyth Spartans	UL	W	2-1	544	Humphries, Foreman
13	A	Guisley	UL	W	3-1	380	Humphries, Foreman, Parker
20	H	Buxton	UL	W	1-0	1093	Foreman
23	A	Buxton	UL	D	0-0	351	
27	A	Boston United	UL	L	1-2	781	Foreman
May 4	H	Matlock T	UL	W	3-1	1139	Green, McKenna, Hoskin

BARROW PLAYING SQUAD 1996-97

Goalkeepers: Mark Deegan (Bangor C, Oxford U, Holywell T, Droylsden, Everton, Liverpool (T))
Defenders: Alan McDonald (Chorley, Southport, Altrincham, Witton A, Southport, Gen. Chemicals, St.Helens T), **Darren Oliver** (Altrincham, Rochdale, Bolton), **Jeff Parker** (Northwich V, Brunei Darussalam, Northwich V, Crewe, Everton), **John McGuire** (Everton), **Fran Ventre** (Skelmersdale U, Burscough, Caernarfon T, Skelmersdale U, Morecambe, Knowsley U, Vauxhall GM), **Mark Jackson** (Netherfield, Vickers SC), **David McKenna** (Burscough)
Midfielders: Stuart Humphries (Atherton LR, Ellesmere Port, St.Helens T), **Jimmy Brown** (Witton A, Runcorn, Morecambe, Vauxhall GM, Bootle), **Lee Chambers** (Workington, Millom, Barrow), **Ashley Hoskin** (Accrington Stanley, Burnley Bank Hall, Wrexham, Burnley), **Tony Ford** (Scunthorpe, Grimsby, WBA, Stoke, Grimsby), **John Doolan** (Wigan, Knowsley U), **Gerard Hennigan** (Everton)
Forwards: Neil Morton (Altrincham, Wigan, Chester, Northwich V, Crewe), **Peter Smith** (Great Harwood T, BAC Preston, Barrow), **Andy Green** (Altrincham, Knowsley U, Morecambe, Macclesfield T, Binche (Belg), South Liverpool, Bootle), **Chris Speak** (Blackpool), **Lee O'Keefe** (Holker OB, Workington)

Formed: 1886

BISHOP AUCKLAND

Bishops

Chorley's keeper Simon Marsh does well to thwart Paul Dobson, Bishop Auckland's star goalscorer last season. *Photo - Alan Watson*

Chairman: S Newcomb **Vice-Chairman:** C Backhouse **President:** B.T.Newton
Secretary: Tony Duffy, 8 Ennerdale Grove, West Auckland, Co.Durham. DL14 9LN. (01388 833410)
Manager: Tony Lee **Asst Mgr:** Tony Boylan **Press Officer:** Secretary
Physio: Dave Nesbitt. **Commercial Managers:** Bill Stephenson and Brian Collinson
Ground: Kingsway, Bishop Auckland, County Durham (01388 603686).
Directions: A1 to Scotch Corner (or M6 to Barnard Castle) then follow signs to Bishop Auckland. Ground in town centre (rear of Newgate Str). Half mile from station.
Capacity: 3,500 **Cover:** 2,000 **Seats:** 600 **Shop:** Yes **Metal Badges:** £3.00
Colours: Sky & Navy blue **Change colours:** Red & white. **Sponsors:** E Bac Ltd
Previous Leagues: N East Counties 1889-90/ Northern Alliance 1890-91/ Northern 1893-1988.
Midweek home matchday: Wednesday. **Reserve Team:** None.
Record Attendance: 17,000 v Coventry, FA Cup 2nd Rd 6/12/52.
Record win: 13-0 **Record defeat:** 1-7.
Best FA Cup season: 4th Rd 54-55 (lost 1-3 at home to York City).
Record Fees - Paid: £2,000 **Received:** £9,000 for David Laws.
Players progressing to Football League: B Paisley (Liverpool), F Richardson & S O'Connell (Chelsea 46 & 54), R Hardisty & K Williamson (Darlimgton 46 & 52), W Shergold (Newport 47), N Smith (Fulham 48), R Steel & K Murray (Darlington 50), A Adey (Doncaster 50), F Palmer & A Stalker (Gateshead 51 & 58), A Sewell (Bradford City 54), G Barker (Southend 54), J Major (Hull 55), H Sharratt (Oldham 56), F McKenna (Leeds 56), J Barnwell (Arsenal 56), D Lewis (Accrington Stanley 57), C Cresswell (Carlisle 58), WBradley (Man Utd), L Brown (Northampton), P Baker (Southampton), M Gooding (Rotherham), K Nobbs & A Toman (Hartlepool), P Hinds (Dundee Utd).
Clubhouse: Open every lunchtime and evening noon-4 & 7-11pm, and Saturday matchdays noon-4 & 5-6 & 7-11pm. Large bar, pool, juke box. Also snack bar within grounds sells hot & cold pies & drinks.
Club Record Appearances: Bob Hardisty
95-96 Captain: Kevin Todd. **95-96 P.o.Y.:** Micky Waller.
95-96 Top scorer: Paul Dobson
Local Newspapers: Northern Echo, Evening Gazette, N'castle Journal.
Local Radio Stations: Radio Cleveland, Radio Tees.
Honours: FA Amateur Cup(10) 1895-96, 1899-1900 13-14 20-22 34-35 38-39 54-56 57-58 (R-up(8) 01-02 05-06 10-11 14-15 45-46 49-51 53-54), FA Trophy QF 78-79 88-89, Northern Lg(19) 1898-99 1900-02 08-10 11-12 20-21 30-31 38-39 46-47 49-52 53-56 66-67 84-86 (R-up(16) 03-04 05-06 14-15 19-20 21-23 36-38 39-40 47-49 52-53 60-61 72-73 78-79 86-87, Lg Cup(7) 49-51 53-55 59-60 66-67 75-76), D'ham Chall Cup 1891-92 98-99 1930-31 38-39 51-52 55-56 61-62 66-67 84-85 85-86 87-88, HFS Loans Lg Div 1 R-up 88-89. Plus tournaments in Isle of Man, Spain, Portugal etc.

PROGRAMME DETAILS:
Pages: 28 **Price:** £1.
Editor: Peter Craig
(01388 609016)

BISHOP AUCKLAND'S 1995-96 CAMPAIGN

DATE		OPPONENTS	COMP	RESULT		GATE	GOALSCORERS
Aug 17	A	Buxton	UL	W	2-1	203	Norton, Adams
21	H	Hyde U.	UL	D	1-1	229	Hyde
26	A	Boston U.	UL	L	0-1	1015	
28	A	Emley	UL	D	1-1	400	Adams
Sept 2	A	Chorley	UL	L	0-2	324	
4	H	Blyth Spartans	UL	W	3-0	559	Hyde, Robinson 2
9	H	Harrogate	FAC1Q	W	2-1	156	Robinson 2
12	A	Blyth Spartans	UL	L	0-6	571	
16	H	Winsford U.	UL	W	1-0	185	Farrell (og)
23	H	Tow Law T.	FAC2Q	W	2-1	311	Lubb, McKinlay
25	H	Frickley A.	UL	W	3-1	133	Issacs, Robinson, Adams
30	A	Leek T.	UL	W	1-0	321	West
Oct 2	H	Guiseley	UL	D	2-2	249	Hyde 2
7	H	Lancaster C.	FAC3Q	L	0-1	298	
9	A	Guiseley	UL	L	0-2	544	
14	H	Marine	UL	L	0-1	203	
16	H	Buxton	UL	D	1-1	113	Hampton
21	A	Matlock T.	UL	D	1-1	229	Hyde
23	H	Spennymoor U.	ULC	D	2-2	521	Norton, Carter
28	A	Droylsden	UL	W	4-1	193	Carter 2, Todd, Jewson
29	H	Colwyn Bay	UL	W	1-0	124	Jewson
31	A	ESM Winning	DSC	W	3-2	93	Waller, Fletcher 2
Nov 4	H	Witton A.	UL	L	1-2	208	Waller
6	A	Spennymoor	ULC	L	1-3	521	Millner
11	H	Matlock T.	UC	L	2-3	112	Fletcher, Sinclair
18	H	Accrington S.	UL	D	2-2	179	Dobson 2
25	H	Witton A.	FAT	D	2-2	239	Dobson 2
28	A	Witton A.	FAT R	D	0-0	451	
Dec 2	A	Gainsborough T.	UL	L	0-1	318	
5	H	Witton A.	FAT R2	W	3-1	222	Dobson, Banks, Todd
9	H	Knowsley	UL	L	1-2	122	Jewson
13	A	West Auckland	DSC	W	5-1	50	Carter, Dobson 3, Sinclair
16	A	Hyde U.	UL	L	1-3	424	Banks
Jan 6	H	Droylesden	UL	W	3-2	15-	Millner 2
120	H	Murton	DSC	W	2-0	75	Waller 2
13	A	Witton A.	UL	W	2-1	510	Dobson, Millner
20	A	Bromsgrove R.	FAT	L	0-1	999	
30	A	Barrow	UL	D	0-0	982	
Feb 3	A	Accrington S.	UL	L	1-2	415	Millner
10	H	Leek T.	UL	D	1-1	173	Bayles
17	H	Barrow	UL	L	1-2	251	Dobson
24	A	Colwyn Bay	UL	W	3-1	348	Lobb 2, Dixon
26	H	Spennymoor U.	UL	L	1-2	346	Hyde
Mar 2	H	Bamber Bridge	UL	D	1-1	184	Dobson
5	A	Frickley A.	UL	W	3-0	103	Dobson, Fletcher, Yates (og)
9	H	Gainsborough T.	UL	D	1-1	163	Carter
16	A	Winsford U.	UL	W	4-0	120	Dobson 3, Carter
23	H	Boston U.	UL	L	1-3	163	Carter
30	A	Bamber Bridge	UL	W	2-0	363	Milner, Dobson
Apr 6	H	Chorley	UL	W	3-1	190	Milner, Bayles, Carter
8	A	Spennymoor	UL	L	0-1	416	
13	H	Emley	UL	W	1-0	173	Dobson
27	A	Knowsley	UL	W	2-1	44	Milner, Dixon
May 4	A	Marine	UL	D	2-2	478	Waller 2

BISHOP AUCKLAND PLAYING SQUAD 1996-97

Goalkeepers: Simon Bishop (Northallerton T, Whitby T, Guisborough T, Newcastle U)
Defenders: Steve West (Youth team), **Mark Foster** (Willington, B Auckland, Ferryhill Ath, Shildon), **David McKinlay** (Bradford C, Middlesbrough), **David Lobb** (Hartlepool T, Peterlee Newtown), **Michael Waller** (Northallerton T, B Auckland, Northallerton T, South Bank, Middlesbrough), **Nick Scaife** (Gateshead, Halifax T, York, Whitby T), **Chris Lynch** (Hartlepool)
Midfielders: Andy Dixon (Hartlepool), **Paul Norton** (Middlesbrough), **George Adams** (Shildon), **Jade Sinclair** (Youth team), **Andrew Banks** (Billingham Syn., Ipswich), **Steve Carter** (Jarrow Roofing, B Auckland, Durham C, Scarborough, Durham C, Northallerton T, N Shields, Scarborough, Manchester U)
Forwards: Paul Dobson (Gateshead, Darlington, Lincoln, Scarborough, Doncaster, Torquay, Horden CW, Hartlepool, Newcastle U), **Gary Hyde** (Whitby T, Scunthorpe, Leicester C, Darlington), **David Robinson** (Gateshead, Blackpool, Reading, Newcastle U), **John Milner** (Seaham RS, Newcastle U), **Stuart Jewson** (Tow Law T, Inglewood Falcons (Aust), Middlesbrough), **Andrew Fletcher** (Spennymoor U, Billingham Syn., Hartlepool, Scarborough, Middlesbrough), **Nick Peverell** (Hartlepool, Middlesbrough), **Jon Bolam** (Chester-le-Street)

Formed: 1899

BLYTH SPARTANS

Spartans

Blyth Spartan FC:

Chairman (acting): John Bradhead
Secretary: Bob Cotterill, 34 Solingen Estate, Blyth, Northumberland NE24 3ER (01670 361057).
Manager: Peter Harrison **Assistant Manager:** Dereck Bell **Press Officer:** Ken Teasdale
Ground: Croft Park, Blyth, Northumberland. (01670) 354818
Directions: Through Tyne tunnel heading north on A19, take Cramlington turn, follow signs for Newsham/Blyth. Right fork at railway gates in Newsham, down Plessey Rd, ground can be seen on left behind chip shop and before Masons Arms. Buses X24, X25, X26, X1 from Newcastle.
Seats: 300 **Cover:** 1,000 **Capacity:** 6,000 **Floodlights:** Yes
Colours: Green & white stripes **Change colours:** Yellow or all purple.
Previous leagues: Northumberland 01-07/ Northern Alliance 07-13/ 46-47/ North Eastern 13-14 19-39 47-58 62-64/ Northern Combination 45-46/ Midland 58-60/ Northern Counties 60-62/ Northern 62-94.
Sponsors: Federation Brewery.
Souvenir Shop: Yes, selling hats, pennants, programmes etc. Contact: Kevin Little (01670 362168) or Stan Watson (01912-739138)
Record transfer fee received: £30,000 for Les Mutrie (Hull City) 1979.
Midweek Matches: Tuesday
Best FA Trophy season: Quarter-Final replay 79-80 82-83.
Best FA Amateur Cup season: Semi-Final 71-72.
Best FA Cup season: 5th Rd replay 77-78 (lost to Wrexham).
Competition Proper on 46 occasions.
League Clubs defeated in FA Cup: Ashington, Gillingham 22-23/ Crewe Alexandra, Stockport County 71-72/ Chesterfield, Stoke City 77-78, Bury 95-96.
Players progressing to Football League: William McGlen (Manchester United 1946), Joe Roddom (Chesterfield 1948), Henry Mills (Huddersfield 1948), John Allison (Reading 1949), James Kelly (Watford 1949), Robert Millard (Reading 1949), Jim Kerr (Lincoln 1952), James Milner (Burnley 1952), John Hogg (Portsmouth 1954), John Allison (Chesterfield 1955), John Inglis (Gateshead 1957), John Longland (Hartlepool 1958), Alan Shoulder (Newcastle) 1979, Les Mutrie (Hull City) 1979, Steve Carney (Newcastle) 1980, Craig Liddle (Middlesbrough) 1994.
Clubhouse: Open every night plus Saturday & Sunday lunch & matchdays. Available for wedding functions. Pies & sandwiches available.
Local Newspapers: Newcastle Journal & Evening Chronicle.
95-96 Captain: Stephen Pyle. **95-96 Top Scorer:** Stephen Pyle.
95-96 Player of the Year: Steve Raffell.
Hons: Nth Lg(10) 72-73 74-76 79-84 86-88 (R-up 71-72 73-74 77-78 84-85 94-95, Lg Cup(5) 72-73 77-79 81-82 91-92), Nth Eastern Lg 35-36 (R-up 22-23, Lg Cup 49-50 54-55), Northumberland Lg 03-04, Northern All. 08-09 12-13 (R-up 46-47), Northumberland Snr Cup(19) 13-15 31-32 33-37 51-52 54-55 58-59 62-63 71-72 73-75 77-78 80-82 84-85 94-95. Unibond 1st Div Champions and Lge Cup 94-95. Shields Gazette Cup 95-96.

PROGRAMME DETAILS:
Pages: 64 **Price:** 80p
Editor: Brian Grey.
(011912 745305)

BLYTH SPARTAN'S 1995-96 CAMPAIGN

DATE		OPPONENTS	COMP	RESULT		GATE	GOALSCORERS
Aug 19	A	Gainsborough Trinity	UL	L	0-4	445	
22	H	Spennymoor Utd	UL	W	3-1	626	Pyle, Ditchburn, Harkus
26	H	Leek Town	UL	W	2-1	510	Ditchburn, Harkus
28	A	Spennymoor Utd	UL	L	1-2	503	Hays
Sept 2	H	Matlock	UL	W	3-0	498	Harkus 2, Ditchburn
4	A	Bishop Auckland	UL	L	0-3	599	
9	H	Garforth Town	FAC 1	W	6-0	498	Pyle 2, Harkus 2, Bond, Johnson
12	H	Bishop Auckland	UL	W	6-0	571	Harkus 3, Johnson, Bond, Cooper
16	A	Droylsden	UL	D	2-2	183	Harkus, Cooper
19	H	Guiseley	UL	D	3-3	577	Harkus 2, Bond
23	A	Billingham Synthonia	FAC 2	W	2-0	246	Harkus, Bond
26	H	Gretna	UCC 1	W	2-1	432	Harkus, Hays
30	H	Buxton	UL	D	1-1	574	Hays
Oct 4	A	Accrington Stanley	UL	W	2-1	416	Bond, Adams
7	H	Bedlington Terriers	FAC 3	W	3-1	130	Harkus 2, Ditchburn
10	H	Frickley Athletic	UL	D	1-1	553	Milroy
14	A	Witton Albion	UL	L	1-2	500	Ditchburn
17	A	Frickley Athletic	UL	W	2-1	130	McDonald, Gamble
21	H	Guiseley	FAC 4	W	2-0	773	Ditchburn, Pyle
23	A	Guiseley	UCC 2	L	0-1	465	
28	A	Boston Utd	UL	L	0-1	1019	
Nov 4	A	Bamber Bridge	UL	L	0-3	464	
11	A	Bury	FAC 1	W	2-0	1076	Bond, Ditchburn
18	A	Knowsley Utd	UL	L	0-1	87	
21	A	Emley	UL	W	3-1	193	Walker, Moat, Raffell
25	H	Gretna	FAT 3	W	3-2	453	McDonald 3
27	A	Chorley	LPC 1	L	0-4	256	
Dec 2	A	Stockport County	FAC 2	L	0-2	5683	
9	H	Chorley	UL	W	3-2	387	Pyle 3
16	A	Matlock Town	UL	D	3-3	319	Curry, Proctor, Walker
26	A	Barrow	UL	L	1-2	1668	Bond
Jan 6	A	Marine	UL	D	0-0	394	
13	H	Bamber Bridge	UL	D	1-1	576	Moat
20	A	Ashton United	FAT 1	W	3-1	244	Bond 2, Pyle
Feb 3	H	Colwyn Bay	UL	W	2-0	338	Bond, Young
10	H	Gresley Rovers	FAT 2	L	1-2	626	Young
17	A	Leek Town	UL	W	3-1	251	Young, Moat, Pyle
24	H	Accrington Stanley	UL	D	2-2	541	Pyle, Bond
Mar 2	A	Winsford United	UL	W	4-2	162	Bond, Pyle, Walker, Young
9	H	Witton Albion	UL	W	2-0	497	Young, Bond
12	H	Emley	UL	D	0-0	310	
16	A	Chorley	UL	W	4-1	304	Nicholls 3, Bean
23	H	Winsford United	UL	W	3-2	435	Walker, Young, Pyle
10	H	Gainsborough Trinity	UL	D	0-0	443	
Apr 2	H	Droylsden	UL	W	2-1	445	Pyle, Young
6	A	Guiseley	UL	D	1-1	348	Young
8	H	Barrow	UL	L	1-2	544	Bond
13	A	Baxton	UL	L	1-2	198	Nicholls
16	H	Marine	UL	D	2-2	336	Young 2
20	H	Knowsley United	UL	W	4-1	379	Moat 2, Bond 2
22	H	Hyde United	UL	W	5-1	396	Raffell 2, Bond, Young, Adams
27	A	Colwyn Bay	UL	D	0-0	315	
28	A	Hyde United	UL	L	1-4	386	Bond
May 4	H	Boston United	UL	L	0-3	441	

BLYTH SPARTANS PLAYING SQUAD 1996-97

Goalkeepers: Paul O'Connor (Bedworth U, Seaham RS, Hinckley T, Nuneaton B, Leicester C), **John Burridge** (Queen of the South, Northampton, Witton A, Grimsby, Darlington, Notts Co, Manchester C, Falkirk, Dumbarton, Newcastle U, Aberdeen, Lincoln, Scarborough, Newcastle U, Southampton, Sheffield U, Wolves, QPR, Crystal Palace, Aston Villa, Blackpool, Workington)

Defenders: Michael Bean (Hebburn), **Gary Hays** (Gateshead, Northampton), **Anthony Cole** (Berwick R, Gateshead, St. Johnstone, Middlesbrough), **Danny Hall** (Manchester U), **Steve Raffell** (Bedlington Terriers, Blyth Spartans, Boston U, Doncaster), **Graham Curry** (Northallerton T), **Bruce Halliday** (Dunston Fed., Gateshead, Apia (Aust), Bath C, Hereford, Bristol C, Bury, Newcastle U)

Midfielders: Tony Cosgrove (Middlesbrough), **John Gamble** (Fleetwood T, Bishop Auckland, Seaham RS, Newcastle Blue Star, Queen of the South), **Darren Nicholls** (Hebburn, Gateshead, Blyth Spartans), **Derek Bell** (Whitley Bay, Berwick R, Bishop Auckland, Bridlington T, Gateshead, North Shields, Gateshead, Newcastle U), **Peter Kirkham** (Darlington, Newcastle U), **Michael Farrey** (Gateshead, Chester-le-Street, Whickham)

Forwards: Steve Pyle (Gateshead, North Shields, Blyth Spartans, Kumu (Fin), Torquay, Cambridge U), **Richie Bond** (Bishop Auckland, Carlisle, Blackpool, Blyth Spartans), **Stuart Young** (Scunthorpe, Scarborough, Northampton, Hull, Arsenal), **Willie Moat** (Whitley Bay, Hebburn, Gretna, Brandon U, Swalwell), **Damian Henderson** (Hartlepool, Scunthorpe, Scarborough, Leeds)

Founded: 1934

BOSTON UNITED

The Pilgrims

Boston United F.C. 1995-96. Back Row: Gerald Starling(Physio), Gary Brook(Now Halifax T),Steve Chambers, Gregg Fee, Martin Bunce, Simon Grayson (now Ilkeston Town), Paul Bastock, Mark Smith,(now with Gainsborough T), Martin Hardy, Simon Mills (now Matlock T), Peter Manning (Kit Asst). Front Row: Chris James, Daren Munton, Steve Circuit, Mel Sterland (Player-Mgr), Paul Casey, Ronnie Reid (Asst Mgr), Andy Gray, Phil Brown, Steve Appleby. Photo courtesy of A & K Markham (Boston).

President: Mr A E Bell **Chairman (acting)** S.Burgess **Vice-Chairman (acting)** B.James
Secretary: John Blackwell, 14-16 Spain Place, Boston, Lincs PE26 6HN (0205 364406(club office)).
Manager: Gregg Fee **Asst Manager:** Chris Cook **Commercial Manager:** Secretary.
Ground: York Street, Boston, Lincs (0205 364406-office, 365524/5-matchday no., 354063-fax).
Directions: A1 to A17 Sleaford-Boston, over rail crossing, bear right at Eagle pub to lights over haven Bridge, thru lights opposite B & Q, right into York Street. Ground just off town centre.
Capacity: 8,771 **Cover:** 8,771 **Seats:** 1,826 **Floodlights:** Yes **Metal Badges:** Yes
Club Shop: Yes, but at club office (as secretary's address, above) not ground.
Colours: Amber/black/amber **Change colours:** All blue or white & green.
Previous Leagues: Midland 21-58 62-64/ Southern 58-61/ Central Alliance 61-62/ United Counties 65-66/ West Midlands (Regional) 66-68/ Northern Premier 68-79/ Alliance Premier (Conference) 79-93.
Previous Grounds: None. **Previous Names:** Boston Town/ Boston Swifts.
Midweek matchday: Wednesday **Reserve League:** Lincolnshire League.
Sponsors: Batemans Brewery.
Record Attendance: 10,086 v Corby Town, floodlight inauguration 1955.
Best FA Cup season: Third Rd Proper replay 73-74 (lost 1-6 at home to Derby County after 0-0 draw).
League clubs defeated in FA Cup: Derby 55-56, Southport 70-71, Hartlepool 71-72, Crewe 82-83.
Record win: 14-0 v Spilsby Town, Grace Swan Cup, 1992-93.
Record Fees - Paid: £14,000 for Micky Nuttell (Wycombe Wanderers).
Received: £25,000 for Gary Jones (Southend United, 1993).
Players progressing to Football League: Jim Smith (Colchester), Steve Thompson (Lincoln), Brendon Phillips (Mansfield), Gordon Simmonite (Blackpool), Simon Garner (Blackburm), John Froggatt & Bobby Svarc (Colchester), David Gilbert, Neil Grayson, Jamie Pascoe, Robbie Curtis, Dean Trott (Northampton), Tim Dalton (Bradford City), Gary Jones (Southend).
Clubhouse: (0205 362967) Open every day except Tuesday. Live entertainment Saturday, pool, darts, dominoes, Sunday football teams.
Club Record Scorer: Jimmy Rayner 55, 66-67.
Club Record Appearances: Billy Howells, 500+.
95-96 Captain: **95-96 P.o.Y.:**
95-96 Top scorer: **Newsline:** 0898 121 539.
Honours: FA Trophy R-up 84-85, Northern Prem Lg 72-73 73-74 76-77 77-78 (R-up 71-72, Lg Cup 73-74 75-76 (R-up 77-78), Challenge Shield 73-74 74-75 76-77 77-78), Lincs Snr Cup 34-35 36-36 37-38 45-46 49-50 54-55 55-56 76-77 78-79 85-86 87-88 88-89, E Anglian Cup 60-61, Central All 61-62 (Lg Cup 61-62), Utd Counties Lg 65-66 (Lg Cup 65-66), W Mids (Reg) Lg 66-67 67-68, Eastern Professional Floodlit Cup 71-72 (R-up 76-77), Non-League Champion of Champions Cup 72-73 73-74 76-77 77-78, Midland Lg R-up 55-56, Lincs Lg (res) R-up 81-82 82-83. Unibond Prem Lge R-Up 95-96.

PROGRAMME DETAILS:
Pages: 44 **Price:** £1
Editor: Secretary

BOSTON UNITED'S 1995-96 CAMPAIGN

DATE		OPPONENTS	COMP	RESULT		GATE	GOALSCORERS
Aug19	H	Witton Albion	UL	L	1-2	1167	Brook
22	A	Emley	UL	L	0-2	331	
26	H	Bishop Auckland	UL	W	1-0	1015	Cook
29	A	Matlock T	UL	W	2-0	507	Varadi, Fee (p)
Sept 2	A	Droylsden	UL	W	5-2	198	Brook 2, Brown 2, Hardy
6	H	Frickley A	UL	L	1-3	870	Brown
9	H	Wisbech T	FAC	L	1-2	983	Gray
11	A	Guiseley	UL	L	2-4	504	Cook, Circuit
16	H	Hyde United	UL	L	0-3	716	
20	H	Buxton	UL	W	9-3	608	
23	H	Droylsden	UL	L	0-1	706	
26	A	Buxton	UL	W	3-0	210	Grayson 2, Circuit
30	H	Accrington Stanley	UL	W	4-0	851	Grayson, Gray, Brown, Hardy
Oct 3	A	Frickley A	UL	W	2-1	194	Brown 2
7	A	Accrington Stanley	UL	W	2-0	484	Grayson, Fee
11	H	Emley	UL	D	1-1	820	Circuit
14	A	Bamber Bridge	UL	W	2-1	681	Fee (p), Brown
18	H	Leek Town	UL	D	2-2	944	Cook, Baines
21	A	Chorley	UL	W	2-0	331	Gray, Circuit
24	A	Worksop T	ULC	W	5-0	483	Brown 2, Gray 2, Price
28	H	Blyth Spartans	UL	W	1-0	1019	Brown
Nov 4	A	Marine	UL	W	4-0	707	Brown 2, Cook 2
11	A	Winsford United	UL	L	0-1	181	
18	H	Matlock Town	UL	W	1-0	1008	Brown
25	A	Leek Town	FAT	D	0-0	370	
29	H	Leek Town	FAT R	W	2-0	819	Fee (2p)
Dec 2	H	Bamber Bridge	UL	L	0-3	1423	
6	H	Grimsby T	LSCF	L	1-4	353	Melson
9	A	Barrow	UL	L	0-2	1092	
16	H	Marine	UL	L	0-1	720	
19	A	Guiseley	ULC	D	1-1	250	Nuttell
Jan 1	H	Gainsborough T	UL	L	1-2	1176	Cook
6	A	Knowsley U	UL	W	4-2	42	Cook 2, Phillips 2
10	A	Alfreton T	PC	D	2-2	188	Fee 2 (1p)
13	H	Colwyn Bay	UL	D	0-0	639	
20	H	Chorley	FAT	D	1-1	808	Brown
23	A	Chorley	FAT R	L	1-2	294	Cook
Feb 3	H	Chorley	UL	W	2-1	609	Cook, Gray
10	H	Spennymoor U	UL	W	4-1	648	Chambers, Fee (p), Cook, Gray
17	A	Colwyn Bay	UL	L	1-3	277	James
24	H	Winsford U	UL	D	2-2	611	Cook, Grayson
28	H	Guiseley	ULC	W	3-2	268	Grayson, Cook, Brown
Mar 2	H	Spennymoor U	ULC	W	3-0	424	Cook, Brown, Gray
6	H	Afreton T	UL	W	4-0	328	Grayson 2, Brown, Fee (p)
9	A	Spennymoor U	UL	W	3-2	237	Cook 2, Fee (p)
16	H	Knowsley U	UL	W	4-2	618	Cook 2, Grayson, Fee
20	H	Worksop T	PC	L	0-2	331	
23	A	Bishop Auckland	UL	W	3-1	163	Brown, Price, Cook
27	H	Leek T	ULC	L	1-2	345	Circuit
30	A	Witton Alb	UL	D	1-1	469	James
Apr 2	H	Leek T	ULV	L	0-2	165	
6	A	Hyde U	UL	W	4-2	604	Brown 2, Price, Munton
13	A	Gainsborough T	UL	L	1-2	854	Munton
23	A	Leek T	UL	D	2-2	188	Gray, OG
27	H	Barrow	UL	W	2-1	781	Circuit, Brown
May 2	H	Guiseley	UL	W	4-3	587	Brown 2, Hardy, Munton
4	A	Blyth Spartans	UL	W	3-0	411	Munton 2, Mason

BOSTON UNITED PLAYING SQUAD 1996-97

Goalkeepers: Paul Bastock (Kettering T, Cambridge U, Coventry C)
Defenders: Greg Fee (Mansfield, Sheffield Wed., Boston U, Kettering T, Bradford C), **Gareth Price** (Ashfield U, Kettering T, Bury, Mansfield), **Paul Casey** (Lincoln C, Boston U, Sheffield U), **Martin Hardy** (Matlock T, Boston U, Worksop T, Notts Co), **Richard Mason** (Sheff.Wed (T)), **Chris Withe** (Shrewsbury, Mansfield, Bury, Notts Co, Bradford C, Newcastle)
Midfielders: Steve Appleby (Bourne T, Boston U, Bourne T, Kettering T, Bourne T), **Steve Chambers** (Mansfield, Sheffield Wed.(A)), **Danny Marshall** (Chesterfield), **Andy Gray** (Local football)
Forwards: Phil Brown (Kettering T, Lincoln C, Stockport, Chesterfield), **Chris Cook** (Boston, Boston U, King's Lynn, Altrincham, Boston U), **Neil Timby** (Boston, Bourne T), **Terry Maddigan** (Local football), **Simon Armstrong** (Skegness T), **Carl Smaller** (Boston T), **Steve Williams** (Peterborough, Lincoln), **Leroy Chambers** (Chester, Sheffield Wed)

Formed: 1877

BUXTON

The Bucks

It can get a little bleak in the 'Peak District' but the Buxton players are used to the conditions.

Chairman: Les Waterfall. **Vice Chairman:** S Dakin.
Secretary/Press Officer: David Belfield, 20 Hereford Road, Buxton, Derbyshire SK17 8PG. Tel. 01298 26033 (Home), 01298 811390 (Bus), Fax 01298 811387.
Manager: David Vaughan **Asst Manager:** **Physio:** K Perrins
Ground: The Silverlands, Buxton, Derbyshire (01298 24733).
Directions: 200 yards of Buxton Market Place, opposite County Police HQ. Half mile from Buxton (BR).
Capacity: 4,000 **Cover:** 2,500 **Seats:** 490 **Floodlights:** Yes
Club Shop: Contact David Hughes (01298 70902).
Colours: All white. **Change colours:** All yellow (blue trim). **Sponsors:** Josiah Tetley.
Midweek home matchday: Tuesday **Record Attendance:** 6,000 v Barrow, FA Cup 1st rd 51-52.
Previous Leagues: The Combination 1891-99/ North Derbyshire/ E Cheshire/ Manchester 1907-32/ Cheshire County 32-73.
Best FA Cup season: 3rd Rd 51-52. Also 2nd Rd 58-59, 1st Rd 62-63.
League clubs defeated in FA Cup: Aldershot 51-52.
Best FA Trophy season: Quarter Finals 70-71 71-72.
Record Fees - Paid: £5,000 for Gary Walker (Hyde United, 1989)
Received: £16,500 for Ally Pickering (Rotherham, 1989).
Players progressing to Football League: Peter Robinson (Notts Co 1950), John Higgins (Bolton 1950), Maurice Brooks (Stockport 1951), Ray Parker (Bradford City 1951), Fred Marlow (Grimsby 1951), Ian Greaves (Man Utd 1953), John Brindley (Chesterfield 1953), Les Ferriday (Walsall 1954), John Good (Tranmere 1955), Jimmy Anders (Bradford PA 1956), William Haydock (Man City 1959), Anthony Parkes (Blackburn 1970), Andy Proudlove (Sheffield Wednesday 1975), Graham Collier (York City 1978), Harry Charlton (Darlington 1979), Ally Pickering (Rotherham 1990).
Clubhouse: (01298 23197). Open nightly + Sunday lunchtimes. Tetleys beers, no hot food.
Club Record Goalscorer: Dave Herbert
Club Record Appearances: Mick Davis.
95-96 Captain: Wayne Goodison. **95-96 P.o.Y.:** Jason Maxwell.
95-96 Top scorer: Jason Maxwell.
Local Newspapers: Buxton Advertiser (01298 22118/22119), Matlock Mercury (Matlock 2432/3).
Local Radio Stations: Radio Derby.
Honours: Northern Premier Lg Cup 90-91 (Presidents Cup R-up 81-82), Cheshire County 72-73 (R-up 46-47 62-63, Lg Cup 56-57 57-58 68-69), Manchester Lg 31-32 (R-up 04-05 28-29 29-30 30-31, Lg Cup 25-26 26-27), Derbyshire Senior Cup 38-39 44-45 45-46 56-57 59-60 71-72.

PROGRAMME DETAILS:
Pages: 36 **Price:** 60p
Editor: Andy Sellors
(01484 718907)

BUXTON'S 1995-96 CAMPAIGN

DATE		OPPONENTS	COMP	RESULT		GATE	GOALSCORERS
Aug 19	H	Bishop Auckland	UL	L	1-2	248	Bancroft
23	A	Droylsden	UL	W	3-1	206	Bancroft, Lee 2
26	H	Bamber Bridge	UL	L	1-2	298	Maxwell
28	A	Gainsborough Town	UL	D	2-2	555	Hwywood, Lee
Sep 2	H	Spennymoor United	UL	D	1-1	244	Lee
5	H	Witton Albion	UL	L	0-4	350	
9	A	Eastwood Town	FAC1Q	L	1-2	229	Maxwell
16	A	Accrington Stanley	UL	L	0-1	549	
20	A	Boston United	UL	L	3-9	608	Maxwell 2, Wilson
26	H	Boston United	UL	L	0-3	210	
30	A	Blyth Spartans	UL	D	1-1	574	Bancroft
Oct 3	H	Droylsden	UL	L	0-3	203	
7	H	Knowsley United	UL	W	3-2	194	Holmes, Maxwell, Bainbridge
10	A	Leek Town	UL	D	0-0	310	
14	H	Hyde United	UL	L	0-1	350	
16	A	Bishop Auckland	UL	D	1-1	113	Maxwell
21	A	Frickley Athletic	UL	W	2-0	105	Maxwell, Holmes
28	H	Marine	UL	L	1-3	237	Hopkinson
Nov 4	A	Guiseley	UL	L	0-1	431	
11	A	Knowsley United	UL	L	0-2	43	
18	A	Bamber Bridge	UL	L	0-2	495	
21	H	Leek Town	UL	L	1-2	304	Holmes
25	A	Matlock Town	FAT3Q	L	0-1	516	
Dec 2	H	Winsford United	UL	L	1-3	165	Maxwell
9	A	Hyde United	UL	L	0-7	394	
?	A	Colwyn Bay	UL	D	1-1	257	Cunningham
16	A	Spennymoor United	UL	D	0-0	217	
Jan H	3	Frickley Athletic	UL	W	1-0	188	Damus
?	A	Winsford United	UL	D	1-1	159	Maxwell
Feb 13	A	Gresley Rovers	DSC	L	0-2	401	
17	A	Chorley	UL	L	1-2	327	Blackwood
24	H	Emley	UL	L	1-2	201	Bancroft
Mar 2	A	Marine	UL	D	1-1	346	Brown
9	H	Accrington Stanley	UL	L	0-1	217	
16	A	Emley	UL	L	1-2	173	Lowe
19	H	Guiseley	ULPC	L	1-3	97	Bainbridge
30	H	Colwyn Bay	UL	L	0-1	160	
Apr 1	H	Matlock Town	UL	W	3-1	336	Johnson 2, Lowe
6	A	Matlock Town	UL	W	1-0	418	Fox
8	h	Gainsborough Town	UL	L	1-2	234	Johnson
13	H	Blyth Spartans	UL	W	2-1	198	Maxwell, Johnson (pen)
20	A	Barrow	UL	L	0-1	1093	
23	h	Barrow	UL	D	0-0	351	
27	A	Witton Albion	UL	W	3-1	419	Blackwood, Bancroft, Johnson
30	H	Guiseley	UL	D	0-0	322	
May 4	H	Chorley	UL	W	5-2	437	Maxwell 2, Blackwood 2, Bancroft

BUXTON PLAYING SQUAD 1996-97

Goalkeepers: Jon Godwin (Grantham T, Sheffield U (T)), **John Morrell** (Chinley)

Defenders: Tim Ryan (Scunthorpe), **Wayne Goodison** (Accrington Stanley, Hyde U, Rochdale, Crewe, Barnsley), **Neil Broadhurst** (Derby), **Paul Green** (Rotherham), **Lee Machin** (Local football), **Dave Bainbridge** (Leek T, Stalybridge C, Buxton, Biggin R), **Robert Brown** (Winsford U, Buxton, Irlam T)

Midfielders: Richard Taylor (Matlock T, Frecheville, Scarborough), **Steve Johnson** (Matlock T, Alfreton T, Buxton, Matlock T), **Jason Tee** (Sheffield FC, Sheffield U), **Chris Martin** (Dove Holes), **Mark Heywood** (Local football), **Darren Holmes** (Sheffield Wed.), **Jamie Evans** (Matlock T, Grantham T, Sheffield U)

Forwards: Mark Hopkinson (Bridlington T, Sheffield Aurora), **Stacy Reed** (Matlock T, Sheffield Aurora), **Peter Lee** (Local football), **Alan Pannett** (Droylsden, Mossley, Winsford U, Curzon Ashton), **Carl Holmes** (Dove Holes, Buxton, Stockport), **Daniel Jacks** (Sheffield Wed.), **Mark Wilson** (Derby, Manchester U), **Dave Brocklehurst** (Staveley MW, Eastwood T, Sheffield U (T))

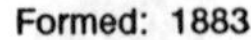

CHORLEY

Formed: 1883 The Magpies

Back Row (L-R): A Thorpe, S Hook, A Critchley, S Marsh, T Doyle, P Flemming, D McKearney, B Ross.
Front Row: G Leitch, L Trundle, M Wright, D Emerson, K Mayers, J Pearson.

Chairman: Jack Kirkland **Vice Chairman:** Dennis Benson. **President:** Dr P J Wren.
Secretary/Press Officer: Mick Wearmouth, 6 Avondalr Road, Chorley, Lancs. PR72ED (01257 271395).
Manager: Dave Sutton. **Asst Manager:** Steve Doyle. **Commercial Manager:** Ernie Howe.
Ground: Victory Park, Duke Street, Chorley, Lancs (01257 263406).
Directions: M61 jct 6, A6 to Chorley, going past Yarrow Bridge Hotel on Bolton Rd turn left at 1st lights into Pilling Lane, 1st right into Ashley Str., ground 2nd left. From M6; jct 27, follow signs to Chorley, left at lights, continue for two and a half miles on A49, right onto B5251, on entering Chorley turn right into Duke Street 200yds after Plough Hotel. Quarter mile from Chorley (BR).
Capacity: 9,000 **Cover:** 4,000 **Seats:** 900 **Floodlights:** Yes **Shop:** Yes.
Colours: White & black stripes/black/black & white **Change colours:** Yellow/Black.
Previous Leagues: Lancs Alliance 1890-94/ Lancs 94-1903/ Lancs Comb. 03-68 69-70/ Northern Premier 68-69 70-72 82-88/ Cheshire County 72-82/ GMV Conference 88-90.
Previous Grounds: Dole Lane 1883-1901/ Rangletts Park 01-05/ St George's Park 05-20.
Midweek matchday: Tuesday **Reserve League:** Alliance League.
Sponsors: Coloroll. **Record Gate:** 9,679 v Darwen, 1931-32.
Best FA Cup year: 2nd Rd 86-87 (lost in replay at Preston), 90-91 (lost at Shrewsbury).
Best F.A.Trophy year: Semi-Final 1995-96.
Record Fees - Paid: Undisclosed fee tp Marine for Brian Ross 1995.
Received: £22,500 for Paul Mariner (Plymouth, 1973).
Players progressing to Football League: Charles Ashcroft (Liverpool 1946), William Healey (Arsenal 1949), Stan Howard (Huddersfield 1952), Derek Hogg (Leicester 1952), William Norcross (Southport 1959), Micky Walsh (Blackpool 1971), Paul Mariner (Plymouth 1973), Graham Barrow (Wigan 1976), Steve Galliers (Wimbledon 1977), Kevin Tully (Bury 1980), Geoff Twentyman (Preston 1983), Gary Buckley (Bury 1984), Chris Hunter (Preston 1984).
Clubhouse: (01257 275662). Open every evening. Entertainment at weekends. Snacks available.
Club Record Goalscorer: Peter Watson.
95-96 Captain: Dean Emerson. **95-96 P.o.Y.:**
95-96 Top scorer: Brian Ross.
Local Newspapers: Lancs Evening Post, Chorley Guardian.
Local Radio Stations: Radio Lancs, Red Rose.
Honours: Northern Premier Lg 87-88, Cheshire Co. Lg 75-76 76-77 81-82, Lancs Comb. 19-20 22-23 27-28 28-29 32-33 33-34 45-46 59-60 60-61 63-64 (R-up 21-22 26-27 48-49 62-63 64-65 65-66, Lg Cup 24-25 58-59 62-63), Lancs Lg 1896-97 98-99, Lancs Alliance 1892-93 (R-up 94-95), Lancs Jnr Cup 1894-95 1908-09 23-24 39-40 45-46 57-58 58-59 60-61 63-64 64-65 75-76 79-80 81-82 82-83, FA Tphy QF (replay) 76-77.

PROGRAMME DETAILS:
Pages: 32 **Price:**£1.
Editor: Alan Robinson

CHORLEY'S 1995-96 CAMPAIGN

DATE		OPPONENTS	COMP	RESULT		GATE	GOALSCORERS
Aug 19	A	Frickley A.	UL	L	0-1	164	
22	H	Barrow	UL	L	2-3	591	Jardine, McDonald
26	H	Guiseley	UL	W	1-0	329	McDonald
28	A	Bamber Bridge	UL	L	0-2	754	
Sept 2	H	Bishop Auckland	UL	W	2-0	324	McDonald, Ross
5	A	Knowsley U.	UL	W	2-0	182	McKearney, Leitch
9	H	Farsley Celtic	FAC	D	2-2	215	A. McDonald, T. McDonald
13	A	Farsley Celtic	FAC R	W	2-1	221	A. McDonald, Ross
16	A	Colwyn Bay	UL	D	1-1	386	McKearney
19	A	Barrow	UL	L	2-6	1513	McKearney, Green
23	H	Colwyn Bay	FAC	L	1-2	234	Leitch
26	H	Knowsley U.	UL	W	1-0	184	T. McDonald
30	A	Spennymoor U.	UL	D	2-2	326	T. McDonald 2
Oct 4	A	Witton Alb.	UL	L	1-2	583	Ross
7	H	Witton Alb.	UL	W	4-0	332	T. McDonald 2, McKearney, A. McDonald
10	H	Bamber Bridge	UL	D	0-0	975	
14	A	Atherton LR	FAT	W	2-1	298	Leitch, Critchley
21	H	Boston U.	UL	L	0-2	331	
24	H	Marine	ULC	D	0-0	262	
28	A	Leek T.	UL	L	0-2	256	
31	A	Marine	ULC	L	2-4	173	T. McDonald, Ross
Nov 4	A	Eastwood T.	FAT	W	1-0	231	T. McDonald
8	A	Accrington S.	UL	L	3-7	483	Emerson, Ross, Pearson
11	H	Gainsborough T.	UL	L	0-6	130	
18	A	Droylsden	UL	W	6-0	285	Ross 5, Trundel
21	H	Marine	UL	D	1-1	221	McKearney (p)
25	H	Winsford U.	FAT	W	3-1	297	Mayers 2, Leitch
Dec 2	H	Droylesden	UL	W	6-0	242	Ross2, McKearney, Wright, Leitch, Trundle
9	A	Blyth Spartans	UL	L	2-3	387	Ross, Hook
16	H	Winsford U.	UL	D	1-1	221	Ross
26	A	Guiseley	UL	W	3-0	552	Mayers, Ross, Trundle
Jan 9	A	Emley	UL	W	3-0	241	Ross 2, McKearney
13	H	Spennymoor U.	UL	L	0-3	278	
16	A	Atherton LR	ATS	W	2-1	168	Ellerby 2
20	A	Boston U.	FAT	D	1-1	808	Hook
23	H	Boston U.	FAT R	W	2-1	296	Ross, Trundle
Feb 3	A	Boston U.	UL	L	1-2	609	Emerson
13	H	Gainsborough T.	FAT	W	2-0	425	Ross 2
17	H	Buxton	UL	W	2-1	327	Hook, Trundle
24	A	Marine	UL	L	1-2	401	Mayers
26	A	Clitheroe	ATS	W	3-2	420	Worttington, Ross, og
Mar 2	A	Boreham Wood	FAT	D	1-1	525	Leitch
5	H	Boreham Wood	FAT R	W	4-3	833	Mayers 2, Ross, Hook
9	A	Hyde U.	UL	L	1-3	603	Ross
12	A	Bamber Bridge	ATS	L	0-3	542	
16	H	Blyth Spartans	UL	L	1-4	304	Ross
19	H	Frickley A.	UL	D	1-1	218	Wright
23	H	Gateshead	FAT	W	3-1	1136	Ross, Mayers, Trundle
30	H	Leek T.	UL	W	3-1	326	Ross 2, McKearney
Apr 1	A	Winsford U.	UL	W	2-0	188	Trundle 2
6	A	Bishop Auckland	UL	L	1-3	190	Ross
8	H	Colwyn Bay	UL	D	1-1	288	Hook
13	A	Macclesfield T.	FAT S/F	L	1-3	2260	Hook
15	H	Matlock T.	UL	W	3-2	181	Hook 2, Worttington
20	H	Macclesfield T.	FAT S/F	D	1-1	3048	Ross
23	H	Accrington S.	UL	D	0-0	355	
25	A	Gainsborough T.	UL	L	0-1	479	
27	H	Emley	UL	W	1-0	321	Ross
29	A	Matlock T.	UL	L	3-4	374	Hook 2, Ross
30	H	Hyde U.	UL	D	1-1	348	og
May 4	A	Buxton	UL	L	2-5	437	McKearney, Hook

CHORLEY PLAYING SQUAD 1996-97

Goalkeepers: Simon Marsh (Hyde U, Blackpool (T)), **Chris Clarke** (Rochdale, Bolton)

Defenders: Paul Fleming (Halifax T, Mansfield, Halifax T), **Adam Critchley** (Preston), **Mark Wright** (Wigan, Huddersfield, Everton), **Andy Thorpe** (Buxton, Witton Alb, Melbourne (Aust), Stockport, Tranmere, Stockport), **Steve Hook** (Bury, Goole T, Halifax T), **Tony Ward** (Marine, Chorley, Wigan, Everton), **Shaun McHugh** (Bamber B, Fleetwood T, Clitheroe, Chorley, Barrow, Feniscowles, Ipswich (T)), **Graham Abel** (Northwich V, Crewe, Chester, Runcorn, Northwich V), **Darren Zoldan** (Ossett T, Ossett A, Ossett T, Belper T, Gainsborough T, Worsbrough Bridge MW, Woolley MW)

Midfielders: Dean Emerson (Preston, Stockport, Hartlepool, Coventry, Rotherham, Stockport), **Grant Leitch** (Altrincham, Halifax T, Blackpool), **Steve Doyle** (Rochdale, Hull, Sunderland, Huddersfield, Preston), **Kenny Mayers** (Bamber Bridge, Horwich RMI), **Paul Comstive** (Morecambe, Southport, Chester, Bolton, Burnley, Wrexham, Wigan, Blackburn), **Neil Dunford** (Rochdale), **Andy Westwell** (Horwich RMI, Leyland Motors), **Gary Thomas** (Southport, Witton A, Winsford U), **Jimmy Proctor** (Rochdale)

Forwards: Brian Ross (Marine, Chorley, Winsford U, Northwich V, Rochdale, Manchester U (A)), **Dave Cockram** (Altrincham, Mold Alex, Bury, Caernarfon T, Poulton V), **John Pearson** (Ashfield U, Stalybridge C, Merthyr Tydfil, Cardiff, Carlisle, Barnsley, Leeds, Charlton, Sheffield Wed.), **Lee Trundle** (Burscough, St.Dominics), **Karl Marginson** (Macclesfield T, Rotherham, Ashton U, Droylsden, Curzon Ashton, Blackpool, Stockport (T)), **Ian Blackstone** (Southport, Scarborough, York, Harrogate RA), **Steve Haw** (Southport, Marine)

Formed: 1885

COLWYN BAY

'Bay' or 'Seagulls'

Colwyn Bay FC.

Chairman: Mr G Owens **Vice Chairman:** Mr J A Humphreys
Secretary/Press Officer: Mr A J Banks, 15 Smith Avenue, Old Colwyn, Clwyd LL29 8BE (01492 516941).
Manager: Bryn Jones **Assistant Manager:** Dave Brett. **Physio:** John Carmichael.
Ground: Llanelian Road, Old Colwyn, Clywd, N.Wales. (01492 516554)
Directions: M55 North Wales Coast - approaching Colwyn Bay take 1st exit signposted Old Colwyn, left at bottom slip road, straight over r'bout into Llanelian Rd - ground half mile on right. 2 miles from Colwyn Bar BR station.
Capacity: 2,500 **Seats:** 250 **Cover:** 700 **Floodlights:** Yes **Metal Badges:** Yes
Club Shop: Yes (contact:A.Holden.01492 534287) **Sponsors:** Deakin Electrical
Colours: Maroon withwide blue stripes,maroon/maroon. **Change colours:** White/Red/Red.
Previous Grounds: Eiras Park 1930-82/ Llanelian Road 82-92/ Northwich Victoria FC 92-93/ Ellesmere Port Stadium 94-95 *(two years in exile due to dispute with FAW over the League of Wales).*
Previous Leagues: Nth Wales Coast 01-21 33-35/ Welsh National 21-30/ Nth Wales Comb. 30-31/ Welsh Lg (Nth) 45-84/ North West Counties 84-91.
Midweek home matchday: Tuesday **Reserve Team:** None.
Record Attendance: 5,000 (at Eiras Park) v Borough United, 1964.
Best FA Cup season: Second Round Proper 95-96.
League clubs defeated in FA Cup: None.
Clubhouse: Open before and after matches. Usual club food (pies etc).
95-96 Captain: Peter Donnelly
95-96 P.o.Y.: Graham Roberts
95-96 Top scorer: Graham Roberts 30
Local Newspapers: North Wales Weekly News, North Wales Pioneer.
Honours: Northern Premier Lg Div 1 91-92 (Div 1 Cup 91-92), North West Counties Lg R-up 90-91 (Div 3 R-up 83-84, Lg Cup 88-89, Floodlit Cup 90-91), Welsh Cup SF 91-92, Welsh National Lg R-up 27-28 29-30, Nth Wales Comb. 30-31, Welsh Lg Nth 64-65 82-83 83-84 (R-up 35-36 45-46 63-64, Lg Cup 27-28), Alves Cup 63-64, Cookson Cup 73-74 79-80 80-81 81-82 83-84, Barritt Cup 79-80 81-82 83-84, Nth Wales Coast Chal. Cup 30-31 31-32 81-82 82-83 83-84 95-96, Nth Wales Coast Jnr Cup 1898-99.

PROGRAMME DETAILS:
Pages: 28 **Price:** 80p
Editor: M Richardson

COLWYN BAY'S 1995-96 CAMPAIGN

DATE		OPPONENTS	COMP	RESULT		GATE	GOALSCORERS
Aug 19	H	Marine	UL	D	0-0	403	
22	A	Witton Alb.	UL	W	3-2	621	Roberts 3
26	A	Barrow	UL	D	1-1	1311	Roberts
28	H	Knowsley U.	UL	D	0-0	396	
Sept 2	H	Accrington S.	UL	L	1-2	415	Drury
5	A	Bamber Bridge	UL	L	0-5	511	
9	A	Rossendale U.	FACT	W	4-1	102	Donnelly 2, Rigby, Roberts
12	H	Hyde U.	UL	L	1-3	338	Roberts
16	H	Chorley	UL	D	1-1	386	Mann
20	A	Knowsley	UL	W	3-1	68	Nicholas, Donnelly, og
23	A	Chorley	FAC	W	2-1	234	Donnelly, Rigby
26	H	Witton Alb.	UL	D	1-1	323	Mann
30	H	Emley	UL	W	1-0	295	Drury
Oct 7	A	Hyde U.	FAC	W	2-1	414	Roberts, Donnelly
10	H	Winsford U.	UL	D	1-1	276	Drury
14	A	Guiseley	UL	L	0-1	463	
16	A	Hyde U.	UL	L	1-5	286	Morgan
21	A	Stalybridge C.	FAC	D	2-2	617	Nicholas 2
24	H	Stalybridge C.	FAC R	W	3-0	613	Donnelly 2, Roberts
28	A	Spennymoor U.	UL	D	0-0	339	
29	A	Bishop Auckland	UL	L	0-1	124	
Nov 4	H	Droylsden	ULC	W	3-1	280	Donnelly 2, Dulson
11	A	Spennymoor U.	FAC	W	1-0	824	Nicholas
18	A	Pwllheli	NWC	W	7-1	123	Drury 2, Roberts
25	H	Guiseley	UL	D	0-0	374	
Dec 2	A	Blackpool	FAC	L	0-2	4581	
5	H	Accrington S.	ULC	L	2-3	263	Harley, Donnelly
9	A	Look T.	UL	D	1-1	186	Morgan
16	H	Buxton	UL	D	1-1	257	Nicholas
Jan 3	H	Prestatyn	NWC	W	3-0	173	Nicholas, Drury, Dulson
6	H	Frickley A.	UL	L	1-3	229	Rigby
9	H	Barrow	UL	L	0-1	271	
13	A	Boston U.	UL	D	0-0	639	
20	H	Altrincham	FAT	D	3-3	596	Donnelly 2, Roberts
23	A	Altrincham	FAT R	L	0-2	525	
Feb 3	A	Blyth Spartans	UL	L	0-2	338	
10	H	Droylsden	UL	D	0-0	283	
17	H	Boston U.	UL	W	3-1	277	Roberts, Donnelly, Dulson
24	H	Bishop Auckland	UL	L	1-3	348	Roberts
28	H	Droylesden	UL	W	1-0	229	Roberts
Mar 2	H	Leek T.	UL	D	0-0	257	
9	A	Matlock T.	UL	W	4-1	336	Donnelly 3, Nicholas
16	H	Matlock T.	UL	D	3-3	251	Nicholas 2, Roberts
23	H	Spennymoor U.	UL	L	2-3	280	Roberts, Donnelly
26	H	Bangor C.	NWC	W	4-0	541	Roberts 2, Drury, Donnelly
30	A	Buxton	UL	W	1-0	160	Roberts
Apr 2	A	Marine	UL	D	1-1	311	Roberts
6	H	Bamber Bridge	UL	D	1-1	408	McQuillan
8	A	Chorley	UL	D	1-1	288	Donnelly
10	H	Cemaes Bay	NWC	W	3-0	319	Roberts 2, Nicholas
13	A	Frickley A.	UL	D	1-1	115	Roberts
16	H	Gainsborough T.	UL	D	0-0	246	
20	A	Accrington S.	UL	L	1-3	535	Drury
23	A	Emley	UL	L	1-4	112	Roberts
27	H	Blyth Spartans	UL	D	0-0	315	
30	A	Gainsborough T.	UL	D	2-2	464	Roberts, Donnelly
May 2	N	Rhydymwyn	NWC S/F	W	3-0	235	Roberts 2, Donnelly
15	N	Porthmadog	NWCF	W	2-1	625	Woods, Roberts

COLWYN BAY PLAYING SQUAD 1996-97

Goalkeepers: Richie Roberts (Christleton), **Lee Williams** (Knowsley U, Colwyn Bay, Winsford U, Rhyl, Knowsley U, Colwyn Bay, Bethesda U, Birmingham, Bolton)

Defenders: Gary McGosh (Local football), **Paul Nelson** (Bangor C, Rhyl, Caernarfon T), **Mark Price** (Connah's Quay N), **Mark Woods** (Pieksamaki (Fin), Colwyn Bay, Flint T, United Services), **Steve Mann** (Caernarfon T, Mold Alex, Newtown, Upton T, Connah's Quay N), **Matt McQuillan** (Conwy U), **Neil Rigby** (Caernarfon T, Colwyn Bay, Holywell T, Southport, Vauxhall GM, Marine, Chester, Tranmere, Everton (A)), **Dave Fuller** (Southport, Witton A, Bangor C, Gainsborough T, Bangor C), **Glen Graham** (Flint Town U, Mostyn, Holywell T)

Midfielders: Graham Roberts (Macclesfield T, Colwyn Bay, Flint T, Mold Alex, British Steel), **Lee Harley** (Flint T), **Mark Uprichard** (Youth Team), **Les Armor** (Caernarfon T, Stalybridge C, Bangor C, Rhyl, Colwyn Bay), **Dave Brett** (Chester, Colwyn Bay), **Matthew Wild** (Christleton, Knowsley U)

Forwards: Peter Donnelly (Northwich V, Colwyn Bay, Rhyl, Oswestry T, Chester), **Alan Nicholas** (Hyde U, Bangor C, Rhyl, Llay RBL, Malpas, Everton), **Gareth Drury** (Vauxhall GM, Knowsley U, Marine), **Craig Dulson** (Stalybridge C), **Jason McKinlay** (Droylsden, Congleton T, Macclesfield T)

Formed: 1903

EMLEY

Emley pictured before Ray Dennis's 750th appearance for the club. Ray is seen being congratulated by manager Ronnie Glavin with the team. Back row (L-R); N Wood , R Hurst, P Viner, N Lacey, P David, D Graham, M Sugden, D Brook (Physio), R Hopley. Front Row: I Banks, S Whitehead, R Tonks, M Wilson, M Reynolds (partly hidden!), S Nicholson, S Constable. Photo: Huddersfield Daily Examiner.

Chairman: Peter Matthews. **President:** Peter Maude **Manager:** Ronnie Glavin.
Secretary: Richard Poulain, 3, Stone Acre Heights, Meltham, Huddersfield. (01484 851492)
Physio: Daryl Brook. **Coach:** Ian Banks. **Press Officer:** Alan Blackman (01924 403959).
Ground: Emley Welfare Sports Ground, Emley, Huddersfield (01924 848398. Office: 840087).
Directions: Follow Huddersfield signs from M1 junction 38, left onto A636 at r'bout, then right after about three quarters of a mile for Emley.
Seven miles from Huddersfield (BR) station - buses to Emley Cross.
Capacity: 3,000 **Cover:** 1,000 **Seats:** 250 **Floodlights:** Yes **Metal Badges:** Yes.
Club Shop: Yes.Contact Mrs Linda Sykes (01484 656406)
Previous Leagues: Huddersfield/ Yorkshire 69-82/ Northern Counties East 82-89.
Colours: Maroon and Blue/Blue/Maroon. **Change:** All yellow.
Midweek matchday: Monday. **Reserve League:** Nth Co's (E) Res Div.
Record Attendance: 5,134 v Barking, Amateur Cup Third Round Proper 1/2/69. *9,035 v Bolton Wanderers, FA Cup 1st Rd Proper 17/11/92.*
Best FA Cup season: First Round Proper 91-92 (lost 0-3 at home to Bolton Wanderers in a match played at Huddersfield).
Record Fee Received: £10,000 for John Francis (Sheffield United, 88).
Players progressing to Football League: A Sweeney (Hartlepool Utd 79), G Cooper (Huddersfield Tn 84), J Francis (Sheffield Utd 88), S Smith (Crewe Alexandra 1992), C Alcide (Lincoln City 95)
Clubhouse: (01924 848398). Members' social club open five nights a week and Saturday & Sunday. Bingo, discos, occasional caberet.
Club Record Goalscorer: Mick Pamment 305
Club Record Appearances: Ray Dennis 751.
95-96 Captain: Ian Banks. **95-96 P.o.Y.:** Paul David.
95-96 Top scorer: Paul Viner 13.
Local Newspapers: Huddersfield Examiner (01484 430000), Huddersfield & District Chronicle.
Local Radio Stations: Radio Leeds, Radio Sheffield.
Honours: FA Vase R-up 87-88 (SF 86-87), FA Trophy 4th Rd 90-91, FA Amateur Cup 3rd Rd replay 69-70, Northern Prem Lg Div 1 R-up 90-91, Northern Counties E Lg(2) 87-89 (R-up 85-86), Yorkshire Lg 75-76 77-78 79-80 81-82 (R-up(5) 72-74 76-77 78-79 80-81, Lg Cup 69-70 78-79 81-82, Div 2 R-up 69-70, Sheffield & Hallamshire Senior Cup 75-76 79-80 80-81 83-84 88-89 90-91 91-92, Huddersfield Challenge Cup 82-83 83-84 85-86, Huddersfield Lg(4) 65-69.

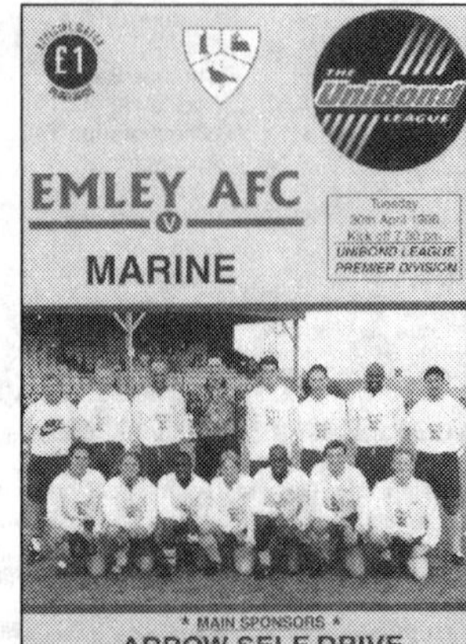

PROGRAMME DETAILS:
Pages: 34 **Price:** 80p
Editor: Alan Blackman
(01924 403959)

EMLEY'S 1995-96 CAMPAIGN

DATE		OPPONENTS	COMP	RESULT		GATE	GOALSCORERS
Aug 19	A	Winsford U	UL	W	4-0	222	Banks, Butterfield, Wilson G
22	H	Boston U	UL	W	2-0	361	Chapman, og
26	A	Marine	UL	W	1-0	378	Wilson M
28	H	Bishop Auckland	UL	D	1-1	400	Jones
Sept 2	H	Barrow	UL	L	1-2	386	Chapman
5	A	Matlock T	UL	L	1-1	374	Butterfield
9	H	Thackley	FAC	H	6-0	186	Butterfield 3, Alcide, Chapman, Wilson M
12	A	Spennymoor U	UL	L	0-2	239	
16	H	Witton Alb	UL	W	1-0	314	Chapman
19	H	Hyde U	UL	W	1-0	215	Chapman
23	H	Winsford U	FAC	D	1-1	252	Alcide
25	A	Winsford U	FAC R	L	1-2	248	Viner
30	A	Colwyn Bay	UL	L	0-1	295	
Oct 3	H	Spennymoor U	UL	L	0-2	210	
7	H	Matlock T	UL	W	3-2	167	Banks, Viner, Middleton
11	A	Boston U	UL	D	1-1	575	Viner
14	H	Leek Town	UL	L	0-1	225	
17	H	Gainsborough Trinity	UL	W	1-0	225	Viner
21	A	Leek Town	UL	D	2-2	293	David, Constable
24	A	Harrogate Town	UL	W	2-0	203	Viner, Constable
28	A	Bamber Bridge	UL	W	1-0	519	Chapman
Nov 4	H	Racing Club Warwick	FAC	W	2-1	225	Chapman, Constable
7	H	Worksop Town	SSC	W	2-1	175	Tonks, Viner
11	H	Droylsden	UL	W	4-0	196	Viner 2, Chapman, og
18	A	Witton Alb	UL	L	1-3	387	Banks
21	H	Blyth Spartans	UL	L	1-3	193	Alcide
25	H	Great Harwood	FAT	W	3-1	224	Peltier, Viner, Reynolds
Dec 2	H	Guiseley	UL	W	2-0	362	Lacey, Viner
5	A	Spennymoor U	UL	L	0-5	158	
9	A	Frenchville C A	UL	L	0-1	106	
16	A	Knowsley U	UL	W	3-1	56	McLean 2, Banks
26	H	Frickley Ath	UL	W	5-2	314	Lacey, McLean, Graham, Constable, Viner
Jan 9	H	Chorley	UL	L	0-3	241	
13	H	Knowsley U	UL	L	1-3	186	McLean
20	A	Morecambe	FAT	D	2-2	656	Banks, Graham
23	H	Morecambe	FAT R	W	3-1	412	David 2, McLean
3	A	Barrow	UL	D	0-0	1182	
10	H	Gateshead	FAT	L	1-2	668	Banks
17	H	Winsford U	UL	D	1-1	196	Graham
24	A	Buxton	UL	W	2-1	201	Banks, Graham
Mar 2	A	Accrington Stanley	UL	D	0-0	361	
9	H	Bamber Bridge	H	D	1-1	264	Graham
12	A	Blyth Spartans	A	D	0-0	310	
16	H	Buxton	UL	W	2-1	173	Lacey, McLean
19	A	Gainsborough Trinity	UL	W	3-0	378	Viner 2, David
30	H	Accrington Stanley	UL	L	1-3	268	Banks
Apr 3	A	Hyde U	UL	L	2-7	333	Graham, Constable
8	A	Frickley Athletic	UL	L	1-2	218	Graham
13	A	Bishop Auckland	UL	L	0-1	173	
15	A	Guiseley	UL	D	1-1	365	Graham
23	H	Colwyn Bay	UL	W	4-1	185	Graham 2, David, Reynolds
27	A	Chorley	UL	L	0-1	321	
30	H	Marine	UL	W	2-0	164	Graham 2
May 4	A	Droylsden	UL	L	0-3		

EMLEY PLAYING SQUAD 1996-97

Goalkeepers: John Hawkes (Thackley)

Defenders: Floyd Peltier (Farsley C, Accrington Stanley, Redditch U, Coventry Sporting, Nuneaton B, Bedworth U, Coventry Sporting), **Steve Ball** (Farsley C, Cork C, Darlington, Leeds), **Neil Lacey** (Frickley A, Gateshead, Frickley A, Goole T, Hatfield Main), **Steve Nicholson** (Farsley C, Leeds (T)), **Richard Hopley** (Local football), **Mark Sugden** (Eccleshill U), **Scott Whitehead** (Frickley A, Huddersfield), **Dave Edmondson** (Harrogate RA, Harrogate T), **Lawrie Madden** (Chesterfield, Darlington, Wolves, Sheffield Wed., Millwall, Charlton, Mansfield, Arsenal)

Midfielders: Paul David (Bradley R), **Robert Tonks** (Local football), **Mark Fella** (Tadcaster Alb), **Ian Banks** (Darlington, Rotherham, Barnsley, WBA, Bradford C, Huddersfield, Leicester C, Barnsley), **Mark Wilson** (Bradford PA, Farsley C, Shepshed Alb, Frickley A, Huddersfield, Rotherham), **Wayne Scargill** (Bradford C, Frickley A, Worsbrough Bridge MW), **Warren Saxton** (Hull), **Mike Thompson** (Frickley A, Ashfield U, Frickley A, Goole T, Scunthorpe (T)), **James O'Donnell** (Hatfield Main)

Forwards: Charlie McLean (Largs Thistle, Hamilton Acc., Celtic), **Deniol Graham** (Dag & Red, Halifax T, Barnsley, Manchester U), **Dave Middleton** (Worsbrough Bridge MW), **Simon Jones** (Local football), **Paul Viner** (Bradford PA, Eccleshill U, Guiseley, Torquay), **Michael Reynolds** (Local football), **Carey Williams** (Denaby U, Rotherham, Denaby U, Brunsmere A), **Chris Shaw** (Ossett T, Pontefract Coll., South Shields, Langley Park)

1866 # FRICKLEY ATHLETIC
The Blues

The refurbished main stand at Frickley Athletic's ground.

Chairman: Mike Twiby
Secretary/Treasurer: D.Fisher, 31 Vickers Ave., South Elmsall WF9 3LW. (01977 643316)
Manager: Mark Dempsey. **Physio:** J.Cox. **Fin Secretary:** D Fisher.
Ground: Westfield Lane, South Elmsall, Pontefract (01977 642460).
Directions: Follow signs for South Elmsall from A1 and A638. Left at Superdrug warehouse, right at T junction and immediately left up Westfield Lane. Left into Oxford Road (opposite Westfield Hotel) - ground at bottom on right. Two miles from South Elmsall (BR).
Capacity: 6,000 **Cover:** 2,500 **Seats:** 800 **Floodlights:** Yes **Club Shop:** Yes.
Colours: All blue **Change colours:** Yellow & black.
Previous Leagues: Sheffield/ Yorkshire 22-24/ Midland Counties 24-33 34-60 70-76/ Cheshire County 60-70/ Northern Premier 76-80/ GMV Conference (Alliance Premier) 80-87.
Midweek home matchday: Tuesday **Sponsors:** Berwin & Berwin.
Record Attendance: 6,500 v Rotherham United, FA Cup First Round 1971.
Previous Name: Frickley Colliery Athletic. **Best FA Trophy season:** Quarter-Finals 84-85.
Best FA Cup season: 3rd Rd 1985-86 (lost 1-3 at home to Rotherham). 2nd Rd 84-85 (0-1 at Darlington). 1st Rd 36-37 57-58 63-64 71-72 73-74 83-84 86-87 88-89.
League clubs defeated in FA Cup: Hartlepool United 85-86.
Record Fees - Paid: £1,800
Received: £12,500 for Paul Shirtliff (Boston Utd).
Players progressing to Football League: Dennis Smith & Jack Brownsword (Hull 1946), Stan Scrimshaw (Halifax 1947), William Callaghan (Aldershot 1949), Leo Dickens 1950), John Ashley & Graham Caulfield (York 1950 & 67), Ron Barritt (Leeds 1951), John Pickup (Bradford PA 1955), Tom Hymers & Arthur Ashmore & Stewart Gray (Doncaster 1958 & 66 & 78), Colin Roberts (Bradford City 1959), Derek Downing (Middlesbrough 1965), Graham Reed & Russell Wilcox (Northampton 1985 & 86), Will Foley (Swansea 1986), Gary Brook (Newport 1987), Wayne Scargill (Bradford City 94-95),Andy Hayward (Rotherham Utd.). **Clubhouse:** Harlequin Club outside ground. TV, pool, other facilties.
Club Record Scorer: K Whiteley
Top Scorer 95-96: Scott Armstrong.
Player of the Year 95-96: Gary Hatto.
Local Newspapers: S Yorks Times (0977 642214), Hemsworth & S Elmsall Express (0977 640107).
Local Radio Stations: Radio Sheffield, Radio Hallam, Radio Leeds.
Honours: Alliance Premier Lg R-up 85-86, Midland Counties Lg R-up 72-73 (Lg Cup 75-76), Yorkshire Lg R-up 23-24, Sheffield & Hallamshire Senior Cup 27-28 56-57 60-61 62-63 66-67 78-79 85-86 87-88 89-90, Sheffield Association Lg 20-21 (R-up 11-12).

PROGRAMME DETAILS:
Pages: 40 **Price:** 70p
Editor: D Fisher

FRICKLEY ATHLETIC'S 1995-96 CAMPAIGN

DATE		OPPONENTS	COMP	RES		GATE	GOALSCORERS
Aug 19	H	Chorley	UL	W	1-0	164	Duffy
23	H	Gainsborough Trinity	UL	W	3-0	252	Fuller, Wells, Rayson
26	A	Witton Albion	UL	L	0-5	529	
28	A	Guiseley	UL	L	0-3	623	
Sept 2	H	Marine	UL	D	1-1	179	Wells
6	A	Boston United	UL	W	3-1	870	Canwing, Dempsey, Rayson
9	H	Prescot AFC	FACIQ	D	0-0	160	
12	A	Prescot AFC	FACIQR	D	2-2	60	Armstrong, Hatto
16	A	Leek Town	UL	D	1-1	262	Thompson
18	A	Prescot AFC	FACIQR	W	1-0	50	
23	H	Eastwood Town	FAC2Q	L	2-4	201	Hatto, Thorpe
25	A	Bishop Auckland	UL	L	1-3	153	Whitehurst
30	A	Barrow	UL	D	1-1	1,287	Fuller
Oct 2	H	Boston United	UL	L	1-2	194	Hatto
7	H	Droylsden	UL	L	4-5	105	Armstrong, Thompson, Wells, Hatto
10	A	Blyth Spartans	UL	D	1-1	553	Thompson
14	A	Stourbridge	FAT1Q	W	2-1	126	Thorpe, Armstrong
17	H	Blyth Spartans	UL	L	1-2	150	Armstrong
21	H	Buxton	UL	L	0-2	105	
25	A	Bradford PA	ULC	D	1-1	184	Wells
28	A	Knowsley	UL	W	2-1	140	Thompson, Armstrong
31	H	Bradford PA	ULC	W	3-1	112	Dickenson, Hatto, Rayson
Nov 4	A	Great Harwood	FAT2P	L	2-3	105	Wells, Rayson
11	H	Bamber Bridge	UL	L	0-5	152	
18	A	Marine	UL	D	1-1	366	Hatto
25	A	Droylsden	UL	D	2-2	88	Rayson 2
Dec 2	H	Witton Albion	UL	D	1-1	145	Dempsey
9	A	Wetherby Town	SHSC	W	3-1	150	Armstrong 2, Dickenson
12	H	Matlock Town	UL	L	1-4	116	Rubinson
16	H	Barrow	UL	D	0-0	146	
19	A	Gainsborough Trinity	UL	L	1-4	368	Dempsey
26	A	Emley	UL	L	2-5	314	Dickenson, Armstrong
Jan 6	A	Colwyn Bay	UL	W	3-1	229	Rayson 2, Thorpe
9	H	Stocksbridge PS	S+HC	D	2-2	151	Dempsey, Thorpe
13	A	Buxton	UL	L	0-1	188	
17	A	Stocksbridge PS	S+HC	L	0-2	150	
20	H	Accrington Stanley	UL	W	4-1	154	Armstrong 2, Yates, Dickenson
Feb 3	A	Spennymoor United	UL	D	2-2	245	Rayson 2
10	H	Winsford United	UL	D	3-3	112	Armstrong, Duffy, Dempsey
17	A	Hyde United	UL	L	1-4	485	Thompson
24	H	Hyde United	UL	W	3-0	176	Yates, Duffy
27	A	Matlock	UL	L	0-6	245	
Mar 5	H	Bishop Auckland	UL	L	0-3	103	
9	A	Winsford United	UL	L	1-4	128	Thorpe
19	A	Chorley	UL	D	1-1	218	Armstrong
23	A	Accrington Stanley	UL	L	1-2	348	Dickenson
30	H	Knowsley United	UL	W	4-3	100	Hatto, Stubbs 2, Hancock
Apr 6	A	Gainsborough Trinity	UL	W	2-0	448	Armstrong, Hatto
8	H	Emley	UL	W	2-1	218	Duffy 2
13	H	Colwyn Bay	UL	D	1-1	115	Kelly
17	H	Guiseley	UL	D	2-2	147	hatto, Thorpe
20	H	Leek Town	UL	D	1-1	122	Thorpe
23	H	Spennymoor United	UL	L	2-3	109	Hatto,Taylor
27	A	Bamber Bridge	UL	W	3-2	466	Dempsey 3

FRICKLEY ATHLETIC PLAYING SQUAD 1996-97

Goalkeepers: Ian Taylor (Gateshead, Bridlington T, Scarborough, Carlisle, Bridlington T, Hatfield Main), **Derek Craven** (Priory Arms)
Defenders: Gary Hatto (Ossett T, Frickley A, Doncaster, Huddersfield), **Glyn Yates** (Maltby MW, Gainsborough T, Boston U, Maltby MW), **Peter Heaney** (Matlock T, Frickley A, Denaby U, Buxton, Frickley A, Ossett T, Goole T), **Paul Taylor** (Local football), **Gary Barnsley** (Buxton, Sheffield, Frickley A)
Midfielders: Chad Colley (Buxton), Justin Dickinson (Tickhill), **Chris Hilton** (Rotherham), **Karl Mann** (Immingham T), **Mark Dempsey** (Buxton, Altrincham, Macclesfield T, Rotherham, Sheffield U, Manchester U), **Mark Hancock** (Wharncliffe Arms, Grimethorpe MW)
Forwards: Simon Fuller (Ossett T, Bradford C), **Gary Duffy** (Rotherham), **Miles Thorpe** (Parkgate, Worsbrough Bridge MW), **Viv Rayson** (Staveley, Belper T, Borrowash V, Chesterfield), **Scott Armstrong** (Huddersfield (T)), **Adie Wells** (Staveley, Matlock T, Staveley)

Formed: 1873

GAINSBOROUGH TRINITY

Back Row(L-R); Ernie Moss (Mgr), S Dunphy, K Riley, J Maxwell, M Smith, G Ingham, G Morrow, P Ellender, A Williams, G Warboys, C Timins. Front; Phil Tingay (Asst Mgr), W Travers (Asst Phy), M Nicholson, M Matthews, G Humphries, S Price, N Tilly, E Beaumont (Physio), P Brown (Scout).

Chairman: John Davis. **President:** Ken Marsden.
Sec.: Frank Nicholson, 9 North Street, Morton, Gainsborough, Lincs DN21 3AS. Tel. 01427 615239.
Manager: Ernie Moss. **Asst Manager:** Phil Tingay.
Physio: Ernie Beaumont. **Commercial Director:** Tim Hanson. **Press Officer:** Basil Godley.
Ground: The Northolme, Gainsborough, Lincs DN21 2QW (01427 613295 - office or 01427 615625 - club).
Directions: The Northolme is situated near the town centre 250 yards from the Magistrates Court and the Post Office. Two miles from Lea Road (BR).
Capacity: 7,500 **Cover:** 5,000 **Seats:** 238 **Floodlights:** Yes **Metal Badges:** Yes
Club Shop: Yes, contact Nigel Tasker on 01522 542014.
Colours: Blue Shirts, White Shorts, Blue Socks. **Change colours:** White/Black/Black.
Sponsors: National Power, West Burton.
Previous Leagues: Mid.Counties 1889-96, 12-60, 61-68, Football Lge 1896-1912, Cent Alliance 60-61.
Midweek home matchday: Tuesday.
Record Attendance: 9,760 v Scunthorpe Utd. Midland Lge. 1948.
Best FA Cup season: 3rd Rd 1886-87, 1st Rd on 33 occasions.
Best FA Trophy season: 2nd Rd, 2nd replay 86-87.
Record Fee Paid: £3,000 for Stuart Lowe (Buxton 89-90).
Record Fee Received: £30,000 for Tony James (Lincoln 1988).
Record win: 7-0 v Fleetwood Town and Great Harwood Town.
Record defeat: 2-7 v Hyde Utd.
Players progressing to Football League: Since 1980 - Stewart Evans (Sheffield Utd 1980), Tony James, Ian Bowling & John Schofield (Lincoln 1988), Dave Redfern (Stockport 1991), Richard Logan (Huddersfield 1993), Glenn Humphries (Hull City).
Clubhouse: Executive 'Club on the Park' (01427 615625) open nightly and Saturday matchday lunchtimes. Restaurant facilities.
95-96 Captain: Colin Bishop. **95-96 Supporters' P.o.Y.:** Paul Ellender.
95-96 Top scorer: Gary Evans.
Local Newspapers: Gainsborough News, Lincolnshire Echo.
Local Radio Stations: BBC Radio Lincs.
Honours: Northern Premier Lg Cup 81-82 (R-up 71-72), Midland Co's Lg 1890-91, 1927-28, 48-49, 66-67 (R-up 1891-92, 95-96, 1913-14, 28-29), Lincs Snr Cup (15) 1889-90, 92-93, 94-95, 97-98, 1903-05, 06-07, 10-11, 46-49, 50-51, 57-59, 63-64.

PROGRAMME DETAILS:
Pages: 32 **Price:** £1
Editor: Basil Godley
(01427 611612)

GAINSBOROUGH TRINITY'S 1995-96 CAMPAIGN

DATE		OPPONENTS	COMP	RESULT		GATE	GOALSCORERS
Aug 19	H	Blyth Spartans	LGE	W	4-0	445	Evans, Bishop, Castledine, Matthews
23	A	Frickley Ath	LGE	L	0-3	252	
26	A	Hyde Utd.	LGE	W	2-1	319	Kabia, Castledine
28	H	Buxton	LGE	D	2-2	555	Matthews, Bishop
Sept 2	A	Winsford Utd.	LGE	D	1-1	222	Matthews
5	H	Guiseley	LGE	K0-2		570	
9	H	Arnold Town	FAC1Q	W	2-0	385	Womble, Ellender
13	A	Droylsden	LGE	W	2-1	94	Matthews 2
16	H	Bamber Bridge	LGE	L	1-3	389	Matthews
23	H	Nantwich Town	FAC2Q	W	5-0	375	Kabia3, Bishop, Evans
30	A	Knowsley Utd	LGE	A	3-2	74	Goodacres Kabia, og
Oct 3	H	Matlock Town	LGE	D	2-2	510	Stiles, og
7	A	Morecambe	FAC3Q	L	2-6	807	Kabia 2
10	A	Matlock Town	LGE	W	2-0	410	Matthews, Evans
14	H	Spennymoor U.	LGE	L	0-1	417	
17	A	Emley	LGE	L	0-1	225	
21	H	Knowsley Utd	LGE	W	2-1	369	Snodin, Evans
24	A	Matlock Town	LC 2	W	1-0	292	Moore
28	A	Witton Albion	LGE	W	2-0	455	Smith, Evans
31	H	Hyde Utd.	LGE	D	0-0	423	
Nov 4	H	Leek Town	LGE	W	1-0	416	Beech
7	A	Leek Town	LGE	D	0-0	228	
11	A	Chorley	LGE	W	6-0	285	Evans 3, Snodin, Kabia, Smith
25	A	Ilkeston Town	FAT 3Q	W	5-0	626	Evans 3, Snodin, Smith
28	A	Worksop Town	PC 1	L	1-3	500	Evans
Dec 2	H	Bishop Auckland	LGE	W	1-0	378	Morrow
9	H	Accrington S.	LGE	D	1-1	499	Ellender
16	A	Spennymoor U.	LGE	D	1-1	242	Morrow
19	H	Frickley Ath.	LC 3	W	4-1	368	Morrow 2, Smith, Stiles
Jan 1	A	Boston Utd.	LGE	W	2-1	1176	Morow, Snodin
6	A	Bamber Bridge	LCE	D	1-1	531	Smith
13	H	Marine	LGE	W	1-0	494	Morrow
20	H	Nuneaton Boro	FAT 1	W	4-1	867	Snodin 3, Morrow
Feb 3	H	Winsford Utd.	LGE	D	0-0	464	
13	A	Chorley	FAT 2	L	0-2	425	
17	A	Accrington S.	LGE	L	1-2	404	Hardwick
24	A	Barrow	LGE	W	1-0	1216	Moore
Mar 2	H	Droylsden	LGE	W	7-1	406	Evans 2, Snodin 2, Smith, Bishop 2
5	H	Witton Albion	LC QF	W	3-2	420	Ellender, Evans 2
9	A	Bishop Auckland	LGE	D	2-2	163	N. Matthews
16	A	Marine	LGE	L	0-3	335	
19	H	Emley	LGE	L	0-3	378	
23	H	Barrow	LGE	W	2-0	414	Riley 2
26	H	Hyde Utd.	LCS F1	L	0-2	440	
30	A	Blyth Spartans	LGE	D	0-0	443	
Apr 1	A	Hyde Utd.	LCS F2	L	0-1	368	
8	A	Buxton	LGE	W	2-1	234	Ellender, Bishop
13	H	Boston United	LGE	W	2-1	854	Smith, Ellender
16	A	Colwyn Bay	LGE	D	0-0	246	
20	H	Witton Albion	LGE	W	1-0	404	Snodin
25	H	Chorley	LGE	W	1-0	479	Morrow
30	H	Colwyn Bay	LGE	D	2-2	464	Stiles, Lanigan
May 4	A	Guiseley	LGE	W	3-1	260	Morrow, Evans, Bishop

GAINSBOROUGH TRINITY PLAYING SQUAD 1996-97

Goalkeepers: Gary Ingham (Boston U, Maltby MW, Bridlington T, Goole T, Shepshed Charterhouse, Gainsborough T, Rotherham)
Defenders: Chris James (Boston U, Worksop T, Bridlington T, Scarborough, Worksop T, Sheffield FC), **Glen Humphries** (Hull, Gainsborough T, Scunthorpe, Bristol C, Doncaster), **Neil Beech** (Sheffield U (T)), **Chris Timons** (Mansfield, Clipstone MW), **Steve Price** (Oldham), **Paul Ellender** (Lincoln Moorlands, Scunthorpe)
Midfielders: John Stiles (Doncaster, Leeds, Vancouver Whitecaps (Can)), **Colin Bishop** (Bridlington T, Frickley A), **Richard Cooper** (Yeovil T, Weymouth, Exeter, Lincoln, Sheffield U), **Glyn Snodin** (Carlisle, Barnsley, Hearts, Rotherham, Leeds, Sheffield Wed., Doncaster), **Jamie Hardwick** (Grantham T, Boston U, Clipstone Welfare, Lincoln (T)), **Jason Maxwell** (Buxton, Grantham T, Appleby Frodingham, Scunthorpe (T))
Forwards: Mark Smith (Boston U, Scunthorpe, Grimsby, Huddersfield, Rochdale, Kettering T, Scunthorpe, Gainsborough T, Worksop T, Sheffield U), **Grant Morrow** (Boston U, Colchester, Doncaster, Rowntree Mackintosh), **Mick Matthews** (Kuitan (HK), Kitchee (HK), Boston U, Hull, Scarborough, Stockport, Scarborough, Halifax T, Scunthorpe, Wolves), **Max Nicholson** (Torquay, Scunthorpe, Hereford, Doncaster), **Nick Tilly** (Matlock T, Belper T, Matlock T, Sheffield FC, Matlock T, Crookes)

GUISELEY

Formed: 1909

Back Row (L-R); John Rhodes (Physio), Marc Ledingham, Gavin Haigh, Simon Portrey, Paul Bottomley, Lee Adamson, Steve Dickinson, Paul Stevenson, Gavin Warboys, Colin Hogarth, Steve Richards (Mgr). Front: Elliot Beddard, Neil Grayson, Ben Davey, Matt Edeson, Matt Flanagan, Peter Atkinson, Greg Abbott, Des Hazel.

Chairman: Gary Douglas **President:** David Brotherton.
Sec.: P Rogerson, 8 Viewlands Cres, Chevin End, Menston, Ilkley, W Yorks LS29 6BH (01943 879236).
Manager: Steve Richards. **Asst Manager:** Greg Abbott.
Physio: John Rhodes **Commercial Manager:** John Holmes. **Press Officer:** Secretary
Ground: Nethermoor, Otley Road, Guiseley, Leeds LS20 8BT (0943 873223).
Directions: Via M1 to M62 junction 28, follow Leeds road to Leeds ring-road to junction of A65 at Horsforth. At r-about turn left onto A65 through Rawdon to Guiseley centre. Ground quarter of a mile past traffic lights, on the right, entrance on A65 opposite Silver Cross factory. Additional car parking available off Ings Crescent. Five mins walk from Guiseley (BR/Metro) station.
Capacity: 3,000 **Cover:** 1,040 **Seats:** 427 **Floodlights:** Yes **Metal Badges:** Yes
Club Shop: Yes, selling programmes, various items of clothing, key rings, badges, mugs etc. Phone Jonathan Spinks on 01943 878160.
Colours: White,blue sleeves/blue/white.
Change colours: Yellow/Navy
Sponsors: Laser Care Clinics Ltd.
Previous Leagues: West Riding Co. Amtr/ West Yorks/ Yorkshire 68-82/ Northern Co's (East) 82-91.
Midweek home matchday: Tuesday.
Reserves' League: Northern Co's (E) Res Div.
Record Attendance: 2,486 v Bridlington Town, FA Vase Semi Final 1st Leg 89-90.
Best FA Cup season: First Round Proper 1994-95 (lost 1-4 at Valley Parade).
Players progressing to Football League: Keith Walwyn (York City), Frank Harrison (Halifax Town), Dean Walling (Carlisle United), Richard Annan (Crewe Alexandra).
Clubhouse: (01943 872872) Open before and after all games (closes 11pm). Snack bar within ground open before and during matches.
95-96 Captain: Steve Richards. **95-96 P.o.Y.:** Richard Hepworth.
95-96 Top scorer: Stuart Taylor.
Local Newspapers: Yorkshire Evening Post, Bradford Telegraph & Argus, Airedale & Wharfdale Observer, Wharfe Valley Times.
Honours: FA Vase 90-91 (R-up 91-92, SF 89-90), FA Trophy SF 94-95, Northern Premier Lg Div 1 94-95 (Presidents Cup 94-95, Div 1 Cup 92-93), Northern Counties (East) Lg 90-91 (Lg Cup 90-91), West Riding County Cup(5 inc 94-95), Yorkshire Lg R-up 79-80 81-82 (Lg Cup 79-80).

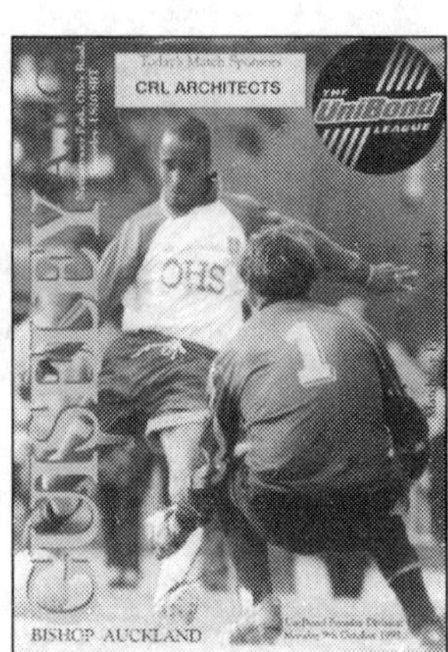

PROGRAMME DETAILS:
Pages: 40 **Price:** £1
Editor: Les Wood
(01532 509181)

GUISELEY'S 1995-96 CAMPAIGN

DATE		OPPONENTS	COMP	RESULT		GATE	GOALSCORERS
Aug 19	A	Droylsden	UL	W	2-1	254	James 2
21	H	Matlock Town	UL	W	4-2	355	Colville 2, Annan, Brockie
26	A	Chorley	UL	L	0-1	329	
28	H	Frickley Athletic	UL	W	3-0	623	Brockie (pen), Colville, Edeson
Sept 2	H	Leek Town	UL	W	3-1	606	Brockie 2,(2 pens), Roberts
5	A	Gainsborough Town	UL	W	2-0	570	Cook, Chards
9	H	Leigh RMI	FAC1Q	W	3-0	484	Roberts, Annan, Horsfield
11	H	Boston United	UL	W	4-2	504	Flanagan, James, Bottomley, M.Cook
16	A	Knowsley United	UL	D	1-1	152	Flannagan
19	A	Blyth Spartans	UL	D	3-3	577	James, Horsfield 2
23	H	Leek Town	FAC2Q	W	4-0		
25	H	Spennymoor United	UL	D	2-2	452	Flannagan, Roberts
30	A	Witton Albion	UL	L	2-3	616	Roberts, Brockie (pen)
Oct 2	A	Bishop Auckland	UL	D	2-2	249	Brockie 2 (pen)
7	H	Mossley	FACQ3	W	6-1	608	Brockie, Richards, Horsfield, James, Roberts, Edeson
9	H	Bishop Auckland	UL	W	2-0	544	Robets, Edeson
14	H	Colwyn Bay	UL	W	1-0	463	Brockie
17	A	Spennymoor United	UL	D	0-0	509	
21	A	Blyth Spartans	FAC4Q	L	0-2	775	
28	H	Winsford United	UL	D	1-1	300	Roberts
Nov 4	H	Buxton	UL	W	1-0	431	Roberts
11	A	Accrington Stanley	UL	W	1-0	602	James
18	H	Hyde United	UL	L	0-1	453	
21	A	Matlock Town	UL	L	0-3	330	
25	A	Colwyn Bay	UL	D	0-0	374	
27	H	Blyth Spartans	ULPC	W	4-0	256	Hepworth, Taylor 3 (pen)
Dec 2	A	Emley	UL	L	0-2	362	
4	H	Hatfield Main	ERSC	D	3-3	161	Brockie (pen), Taylor, Cook
9	A	Marine	UL	W	1-0	414	Cook
12	A	Hatfield Main	ERSC	W	2-0	72	Brockie 3 (pen), Roberts
16	H	Bamber Bridge	UL	W	4-0	550	Heald 4, Taylor 3
19	H	Boston United	ULCC	D	1-1	250	Taylor
26	H	Chorley	UL	L	0-3	552	
Jan 6	H	Witton Albion	UL	L	0-1	360	
13	A	Barrow	UL	W	2-0	1466	Flanagans, Norbury
20	A	Stafford Rangers	FAT1	D	1-1	689	Norbury
22	H	Stafford Rangers	FAT1r	W	2-1	365	Norbury 2
Feb 10	H	Accrington Stanley	FAT2	W	4-0	690	Norbury 2, Cook, Brockie
13	A	Thackley	WRSC	W	2-1	200*	Norbury, Brockie (pen)
17	H	Knowsley United	UL	D	1-1	450	Norbury
24	A	Bamber Bridge	UL	L	1-3	601	Roberts
28	A	Boston United	ULCC	L	2-3	268	James, Taylor
Mar 2	H	Gresley Rovers	FAT3	L	1-2	790	Norbury
4	H	Buxton	ULPC	D	1-1	126	Taylor
6	A	Harrogate Railway Ath'	ULPC	W	3-1	180	Norbury 3 (pen)
9	H	Marine	UL	L	2-4	380	Taylor, Atkinson
16	A	Leek Town	UL	D	1-1	222	Taylor
19	A	Buxton	ULPC	W	1-3	97	Cook, James, Flanagan
23	H	Droylsden	UL	W	3-0	249	Taylor, James, Tunmlliffe
26	A	Hyde United	ULPC	W	2-0	241	James 2
30	H	Hyde United	ULPC+	D	1-1	307	Hepworth
Apr ^	H	Blyth Spartans	UL	D	1-1	348	James
13	H	Barrow	UL	L	1-3	380	Flanagan
15	H	Emley	UL	D	1-1	204	Roberts (pen)
17	A	Frickley Athletic	UL	D	2-2	147	James, Roberts
20	A	Winsford United	UL	W	2-1	137	Taylor, Mathews
22	H	Worksop Town	ULPCF1	L	0-1	470	
24	A	Hyde United	UL	D	1-1	204	James
27	H	Accrington Stanley	UL	L	1-3	507	Mathews
30	A	Buxton	UL	D	0-0	322	
May 2	A	Boston United	UL	L	3-4	587	Taylor 3
4	H	Gainsborough Town	UL	L	1-3	200	Roberts (pen)

*After Extra Time + Won on penalties

GUISELEY PLAYING SQUAD 1996-97

Goalkeepers: Steve Dickinson (Bradford C)

Defenders: Steve Richards (Doncaster, Halifax T, Scarborough, Cambridge U, Lincoln, Gainsborough T, York, Hull), **Peter Atkinson** (Otley T), **Phil Joyce** (Whitby T), **Paul Bottomley** (Bridlington T, Guiseley, Garforth T), **Paul Stevenson** (Bridlington T, Farsley C, Blackpool, Farsley C, Harrogate T, Farsley C), **Colin Hogarth** (Lancaster C, Guiseley, Harrogate T, Guiseley, Otley T, Thackley), **Paul Kendall** (Macclesfield T, Halifax T, Scarborough, Halifax T), **Gavin Haigh** (Hull), **Jimmy Graham** (Hull, Rochdale, Bradford C)

Midfielders: Lee Thew (Scarborough, Doncaster), **Andrew Hudson** (Pickering T, Scarborough), **Matthew Flannagan** (Local football), **Chris Lee** (Hull, Scarborough, Rochdale, Bradford C), **Simon Portrey** (Ipswich), **Jamie Robshaw** (Rotherham), **Greg Abbott** (Hull, Guiseley, Halifax, Bradford C, Coventry), **Paul Mattison** (Darlington, North Ferriby U)

Forwards: Neil Matthews (Gainsborough T, Dag & Red, Lincoln, Stockport, Halifax T, Grimsby), **Matty Edeson** (Hull), **Elliott Beddard** (Halifax T, Middlesbrough, Farsley Celtic), **Des Hazel** (Chesterfield, Rotherham, Sheffield Wed)

Formed: 1919

HYDE UNITED

The Tigers

Hyde United 1995-96: Back Row (L/R): G.Clowes (physio), P.Cox, J.Donnelly, I. McClellan, M. Booth, A.Willliams, T.Camilleri, A.Gill, W.Garton, C.Little, J.Donnelly, T.Megram. Front Row: D. Nolan, V.Owen, T.Carroll, G.Kimmins, G Switzer, M.McKenzie (Manager), G.Wilson, D Pybus, G.Henshaw, D Esdaille, D. O'Brien, Callaghan, D Thornton, B Dodd (Trainer). *Photo - John Newton.*

Chairman: W.Paterson. **Vice Chairman:** A Slater
Secretary: Alan Slater, 83 King Edward Road, Hyde, Cheshire SK14 5JJ (0161 368 3687).
Manager: Mike McKenzie **Physio:** G.Clowes. **Coach:** Billy Garton.
Press Officer: Secretary **Commercial Manager:** Brian Slater.
Ground: Tameside Stadium, Ewen Fields, Walker Lane, Hyde SK14 5PL (0161 368 1031).
Directions: On entering Hyde follow signs for Tameside Leisure Park - in Walker Lane take 2nd car park entrance nr Leisure Pool, follow road around to the stadium. Quarter of a mile from Newton (BR).
Capacity: 4,000 **Cover:** 2,000 **Seats:** 400 **Floodlights:** Yes **Metal Badges:** Yes
Colours: Red/white/black **Change colours:** Blue&White/Blue/Blue. **Club Sponsors:** TMI Metals.
Club Shop: Yes. Replica shirts, scarves, sports shirts, baseball caps, bronx hats, badges. Contact either Joan Slater (0161 368 3687)
Previous Leagues: Lancashire & Cheshire 19-21/ Manchester 21-30/ Cheshire County 30-68 70-82/ Northern Premier 68-70.
Midweek home matchday: Monday **Record Attendance:** 9,500 v Nelson, FA Cup 1952.
Best F.A. Cup season: 1st Rd 54-55 (v Workington), 83-84 (v Burnley),94-95 v Darlington.
Record Fee Paid: £8,000 for Jim McCluskie (Mossley, 1989).
Record Fee Received: £50.000 for Colin Little (Crewe Alexandra) 1995.
Record Defeat: (as Hyde F.C.) 0-26 v Preston North End, F.A. Cup.
Players progressing to Football League: Charles McClelland & John Webber & Patrick Barry (B'burn 1946 & 47 & 48), L Battrick (Manc. City 1968), Jack Hilton (Wrexham 1950), David Teece (Hull 1952), Ray Calderbank & William Bell & Neil Colbourne (R'dale 1953 & 74 & 80), Jeff Johnson (Stockport 1976), David Constantine & Donald Graham (Bury 1979), George Oghani (Bolton 1983), Kevin Glendon (Burnley 1983), Peter Coyne (Swindon 1984), Colin Little (Crewe Alexandra 1995)
Clubhouse: (0161 368 1621). Open most nights, full facilities, 150 seats. Stewards: Lil & Doug.
Club Record Scorer: P O'Brien 247
Club Record Appearances: S Johnson 623.
95-96 Captain: G.Wilson. **95-96 Top scorer:** T.Carroll 37.
95-96 Players' P.o.Y.: Ged Kimmins. **Supporters' P.o.Y.:** G. Wilson.
Local Newspapers: North Cheshire Herald (0161 303 1910) & Hyde Reporter (0161 368 3595).
Local Radio Stations: GMR, Picadilly.
Honours: FA Trophy SF 88-89,94-95, 95-96, Premier Inter-Lge Cup R-up(2) 88-90, NPL R-up(2) 87-89 (Lg Cup 85-86 88-89 95-96 (R-up 83-84 94-95), Chal. Shield R-up 86-87 90-91), Cheshire Co. Lg(3) 54-56 81-82 (Lg Cup 33-34 52-53 54-55 72-73 81-82, Lg Chal. Shield(2) 80-82 Manchester Lg(5) 20-23 28-29 29-30 (Lg (Gilgryst) Cup(4) 27-29 49-50 70-71), Cheshire Snr Cup 45-46 62-63 69-70 80-81 89-90, Manchester Prem. Cup 93-94, 94-95, 95-96 , Senior Cup 74-75, Int Cup 55-56 56-57(jt), Junior Cup 21-22 68-69, Lancs & Cheshire F'lit Cup(2) 54-56, Ashton Chal. Cup(6) 30-34 39-40 47-48, Hyde Chal Cup(2) 27-29, Reporter Cup(3) 72-74 75-76, Gavin Nicholson Mem Trophy 79-80, Lancs F'lit Trophy(2) 86-88, Edward Case Cup(4) 56-8 59-60 80-81.

PROGRAMME DETAILS
Pages: 32 **Price:** £1.
Editor: M Dring

HYDE UNITED'S 1995-96 CAMPAIGN

DATE		OPPONENTS	COMP	RESULT		GATE	GOALSCORERS
Aug 19	A	Spennymoor U.	UL	W	1-0	321	Little
21	A	Bishop Auckland	UL	D	1-1	228	Nolan
26	H	Gainsborough T.	UL	L	1-2	319	Little
28	A	Droylesden	UL	W	2-0	286	Owen, Carroll
Sept 2	A	Knowsley U.	UL	L	1-2	72	Kimmins
4	H	Winsford U.	UL	L	0-1	274	
9	H	Winterton R.	FAC	W	6-0	240	Kimmins 2, Nolan 2, Carroll, Esdaille
12	A	Colwyn Bay	UL	W	3-1	338	Kimmins 3
16	A	Boston U.	UL	W	3-0	716	Kimmins 2, Little
19	A	Emley	UL	L	0-1	215	
23	A	Denaby U.	FAC	W	2-1	185	Little, Bolan
30	A	Bamber Bridge	UL	D	3-3	571	Kimmins 2, Little
Oct 2	A	Winsford U.	CSC	W	4-1	213	Little 2, Carroll, Nolan
7	H	Colwyn Bay	FAC	L	1-2	414	Kimmins
9	H	Knowsley U.	UL	W	5-0	249	Little 2, Carroll, Owen, Kimmins
14	A	Buxton	UL	W	1-0	350	Carroll
16	H	Colwyn Bay	UL	W	5-1	286	Little 2, Carroll, Kimmins, Gallagher
21	H	Bamber Bridge	UC	L	2.3-	569	Kimmins, Nolan
23	H	Ashton U.	ULC	W	3-1	446	Tobin, Little, Nolan
28	A	Barrow	UL	L	1-2	1174	Little
31	A	Gainsborough T	UL	D	0-0	423	
Nov 4	H	Spennymoor U.	UL	W	3-2	462	Kimmins, Tobin, Nolan
11	H	Leek T.	UL	W	3-2	441	Carroll, Nolan, Owen
18	A	Guiseley	UL	W	1-0	415	Tobin
21	A	Stalybridge C.	CSC	W	3-0	614	Nolan 3
25	H	Marine	UL	W	4-0	561	Switzer, Little, Carroll, Nolan
Dec 2	A	Accrington S.	UL	D	1-1	464	Little
9	H	Buxton	UL	W	7-0	394	Kimmins 2, Little 2, Nolan 2, Carroll
11	H	Marine	ULC	W	5-3	330	Kimmins2, Carroll 2, Little
16	H	Bishop Auckland	UL	W	3-1	424	Carroll 2, Owen
Jan 1	H	Barrow	UL	D	0-0	736	
6	H	Accrington S.	UL	D	0-0	512	
9	A	Keek T.	PC	D	2-2	140	Little, Esdaille
13	A	Winsford U.	UL	W	4-1	261	Little 2, Carroll, Nolan
20	A	Marine	FAT	D	0-0	467	
24	H	Marine	FAT R	D	0-0	416	
Feb 1	H	Marine	FAT R	W	3-0	375	Carroll, Nolan, og
3	A	Matlock T.	UL	W	3-1	415	Kimmins, Dowe, Nolan
10	H	Welling U.	FAT	W	4-1	680	Kimmins 4
13	A	Marine Road	MSC	W	2-1	220	Esdaille, Carroll
17	H	Frickley A.	UL	W	4-1	485	Carroll 3, Garton
22	H	Leek T.	PCR	W	2-0	285	Carroll 2
24	A	Frickley A.	UL	L	0-3	176	
26	H	Macclesfield T.	CSC	W	2-1	716	Carroll, Nolan
Mar 2	H	Carshalton A.	FAT	W	3-2	854	Kimmins, Owen, Carroll
5	A	Marine	PC	W	3-0	142	Nolan 2, Murphy
7	H	Lancaster C.	ULC	W	5-1	231	Kimmins 2, Varden 2, Nolan
9	H	Chorley	UL	W	3-1	603	Varden 2, Murphy
12	A	Macclesfield T.	CSC	D	1-1	707	Varden
16	A	Witton Albion	UL	D	1-1	638	Carroll
19	H	Radcliffe B.	MSC	W	2-0	320	Kimmins, Carroll
23	H	Stevenage B.	FAT	W	3-2	2012	Kimmins, Carroll, Nolan
26	A	Gainsborough T.	ULC	W	2-0	440	Kimmins, Nolan
28	H	Guiseley	PC	L	0-2	241	
30	A	Guiseley	PC	D	101	307	Carroll
Apr 1	H	Gainsborough T	ULC	W	1-0	368	Carroll
3	H	Emley	UL	W	7-2	333	Carroll 2, Varden 2, Evans, Nolan, Kimmins
6	H	Boston U.	UL	L	2-4	604	Carroll, Murphy
8	H	Matlock T.	UL	D	1-1	508	Carroll
10	A	Marine	UL	L	0-4	333	
13	H	Northwich V.	FAT S/F	L	1-2	2253	Varden
15	H	Witton Albion	UL	W	1-0	367	Carroll
20	A	Northwich V.	FAT S/F	L	0-1	2809	
22	A	Blyth Spartans	UL	L	1-5	396	Evans
24	H	Guiseley	UL	D	1-1	264	Carroll
26	H	Droylsden	UL	D	1-1	491	Carroll
28	H	Blyth Spartans	UL	W	4-1	396	Carroll 2, Nolan, Switzer
30	A	Chorley	UL	D	1-1	348	Evans
May 3	A	Leek T.	ULC F	D	1-1	501	(penalties) og
4	A	Leek T.	UL	W	1-0	213	Donnelly
6	A	Witton Albion	CS CF	L	1-3	768	Evans
7	A	Curzon Ashton	MP Cf	D	2-2	390	(penalties) Henshaw, Esdaille

HYDE UNITED PLAYING SQUAD 1996-97

Goalkeepers: Gary Walker (Witton A, Stafford R, Buxton, Radcliffe B, Buxton, Hyde U, Manchester C, Stockport, Ashton U)
Defenders: Billy Garton (Witton Alb, Salford C, Manchester U), **Gus Wilson** (Crewe, Runcorn, Accrington Stanley, Droylsden, Flixton, Northwich V), **George Switzer** (Darlington, Manchester U), **Paul Cox** (Altrincham), **Darren Esdaille** (Knowsley U), **Derek Hall** (Rochdale, Hereford, Halifax T, Southend, Swindon, Torquay, Coventry), **Mark Jones** (Northwich V, Southport, Preston)
Midfielders: Vince Brockie (Guiseley, Goole T, Doncaster, Leeds), **Val Owen** (Local football), **Jason Donnelly** (Winsford U, Maine Road, Trafford), **Jason Gallagher** (Caernarfon T, Witton Alb, Marine, Ternie (Belg), Newton), **Dave Nolan** (Barrow, Chester, Bromborough Pool, Prescot)
Forwards: Ged Kimmins (Salford C), **Tony Carroll** (Bamber Bridge, Radcliffe B), **Paul Varden** (Winsford U, Maine Road, Atherton Coll., Maine Road), **Lutel James** (Guiseley, Selby T, Guiseley, Yorkshire Am), **Julian Dowe** (Woking, Ayr U, Wigan), **Nigel Evans** (Droylsden), **Jimmy Cameron** (Flixton, Halifax T, Winsford U, Runcorn, Winsford U, Acc.Stanley, Buxton, Maine Road)

Formed: 1984

KNOWSLEY UNITED

The Reds

Knowsley United's ground. *Photo - Mal Keenan*

Chairman: P G Orr **President:** The Mayor of Knowsley.
Secretary Ken O'Brien, 153 Church Road, Litherland, Merseyside L21 7LS. Tel. 0151 4743808. Fax 0151 4743808 or 0151 4808077.
Manager: P J Orr **Coach:** R Willingham **Physio:** L Blasberry
Press Officer: As secretary. **Commercial Manager:** D Johnstone.
Ground: Alt Park, Endmoor Road, Huyton, Merseyside L36 3LV (0151 480 2529).
Directions: M62 junc 6 onto M57. Leave at junc 2 (Prescot), onto Liverpool Rd at r'bout, 3rd right at 3rd set of lights into Seth Powell Way. From Jct 3 (Huyton), go straight across r-about onto Huyton link road (Seth Powell Way) and turn right at lights. Buses 10, 10a, 8, 210 to Page Moss. Nearest station is Huyton 2 miles away - bus from station to Page Moss.
Capacity: 9,000 **Cover:** 3,500 **Seats:** 350 **Floodlights:** Yes **Club Shop:** No.
Colours: Red & black stripes/Black/Black. **Change:** Yellow & black hoops. **Sponsors:** Rogersons (Builders).
Previous Name: Kirkby Town (pre-1988) **Previous Leagues:** North West Counties 84-91.
Previous Grounds: Simonswood Lane, Kirkby 84-86/ Kirkby Sports Centre 86-88.
Midweek matchday: Wednesday. **Reserve Team's League:** Liverpool Co. Comb.
Women's Team League: F.A. National League, Premier Division.
Record Attendance: 900 v Everton, Liverpool Senior Cup, 1984.
Best FA Cup season: 1st Rd Proper 93-94 (lost 1-4 v Carlisle Utd).
Best FA Trophy season: 1st Qual. Rd 2nd replay 93-94 (lost 0-3 at Matlock Tn).
Record win: 10-1 v Flixton **Record defeat:** 1-7 v Colwyn Bay.
Record Fee Paid Received: £5,000 for Paddy Wilson (Stalybridge Celtic 1996).
Players progressing to Football League: Phil Daly (Wigan), Mike Marsh (Liverpool), Rodney McDonald (Walsall), Steve Farrelly (Chester City).
Clubhouse: Lounge, 2 Function Suites, Sponsors Box, Directors Room. Clubhouse open normal licensing hours - filled rolls available.
Refreshment bar in ground sells pies, rolls, chips, tea, coffee oxo etc.
Club Record Goalscorer: Jimmy Bell, 50.
95-96 **Captain:** Robbie Gaffney.
95-96 **P.o.Y.:** Paddy Wilson.
95-96 **Top scorer:** Paddy Wilson 20.
Local Press: Liverpool Daily Post/Liverpool Echo (051 227 2000), Knowsley Challenger (051 548 0710).
Local Radio Stations: Radio Merseyside (051 708 5500), Radio City.
Hons: FA Vase 5th Rd 90-91 91-92, Northern Premier Lg Div 1 R-up 92-93, North West Counties Lg 90-91 (R-up 88-89 89-90, Div 2 85-86, Div 3 84-85, Raab Karcher Cup 89-90, Champions v Cup Winners Trophy 89-90).

PROGRAMME DETAILS:
Pages: 32 **Price:** 70p
Editor: J.Pinick.
(0772 749 768)

KNOWSLEY UNITED'S 1995-96 CAMPAIGN

DATE		OPPONENTS	COMP	RESULT		GATE	GOALSCORERS
Aug 19	A	Barrow	UL	L	0-1	1124	
23	A	Accrington Stanley	UL	L	2-4	472	Cooper, Jones
26	A	Matlock Town	UL	L	0-8	258	
28	A	Colwyn Bay	UL	D	0-0	396	
Sept 2	H	Hyde United	UL	W	2-1	72	Rowlands, Goldbourne
6	H	Chorley	UL	L	1-2	152	Edwards
9	H	Bradford Park Avenue	FAC1Q	D	0-0	74	
13	A	Bradford Park Avenue	FAC1Qr	L	2-3	158	Rowlands 2
16	H	Guiseley	UL	D	1-1	112	Wilson
20	H	Colwyn Bay	UL	L	1-3	68+	Jones
23	A	Witton Albion	UL	L	0-2	436	
26	A	Chorley	UL	L	0-1	184	
30	H	Gainsborough Town	UL	L	2-3	74	Wilson, Harland
Oct 3	A	Marine	UL	L	1-2	342	Wilson
7	A	Buxton	UL	L	2-3	194	Wilson 2
9	A	Hyde United	UL	L	0-5	249	
14	H	Moor Green	FAT 1Q	W	3-2	78	Wilson 2, Jones
17	H	Bamber Bridge	UL	D	2-2	94	Jones, Barton
21	A	Gainsborough Town	UL	L	1-2	369	Jones
28	H	Frickley Athletic	UL	L	1-2	140	Brown
Nov 4	A	Nuneaton Borough	FAT2Q	L	2-3	1017	Wilson 2
8	A	Spennymoor United	UL	W	4-1		
11	H	Buxton	UL	W	2-0	43	Johnston, Williams
18	H	Blyth Spartans	UL	W	1-0	87	Clarke
25	H	Barrow	UL	L	0-2	145	
27	A	Winsford United	UL	W	1-0	111	Wilson
Dec 9	A	Bishop Auckland	UL	W	2-1	122	Wilson, Jones
12	H	Skelmersdale United	LSC	W	2-0	48	Barton, Johnston
16	H	Emley	UL	L	1-3	56	Wilson
Jan 6	H	Boston United	UL	L	2-4	42	Wilson 2
13	A	Emley	UL	W	3-1	186	Wilson 2, Esdaille
20	H	Spennymoor United	UL	W	2-0	42	Kinney, Wilde
23	H	Winsford United	UL	W	4-1	44	Harland 2, Wilde 2
30	H	Bootle	LSC	W	4-0	38	Tyrrell, Kinney, Harland 2
Feb 3	A	Bamber Bridge	UL	D	2-2	451	Wilde, Stephens
17	A	Guiseley	UL	D	1-1	450	Wilson
24	H	Leek Town	UL	W	3-1	33	Wilde, Jones, Williams (pen)
Mar 2	H	Matlock Town	UL	W	1-0	145	Cowlerton
9	A	Droylsden	UL	L	1-5	125	Wilde
16	A	Boston United	UL	L	2-4	618	Kinney, Wilde
19	H	Accrington Stanley	UL	W	1-0	42	Famy
23	H	Witton Albion	UL	D	2-2	112	Congleton, Parker
30	A	Frickley Athletic	UL	L	3-4	100	Wilde, Birchau, Tyrell
Apr 2	H	Everton	LSC	L	0-2	204	
8	H	Droylsden	UL	W	2-0	66	Wilde, Williams (pen)
13	A	Leek Town	UL	L	0-2	177	
20	A	Blyth Spartans	UL	L	1-4	379	Johnston
25	H	Marine	UL	W	2-1	129	Barton, Jones
27	H	Bishop Auckland	UL	L	1-2	44	Barton

KNOWSLEY UNITED PLAYING SQUAD 1996-97

Goalkeepers: Ian Haigh (Bangor C, Caernarfon T)

Defenders: Kevin Lewis (Southport), **Dave O'Brien** (Hyde U, Knowsley U, Southport, Marine, Everton (T)), **Mick Stevens** (Skelmersdale U, Bootle, Warrington T, Hyde U), **Eddie Johnston** (Accrington Stanley, Bangor C, South Liverpool), **Robbie Gaffney** (Skelmersdale U, Knowsley U, Morecambe, South Liverpool, Runcorn, Carlisle), **Lee Royle** (Formby), **Paul Smith** (Mold Alex), **Mike Halliday** (Flixton, Ashton U, Southport, Winsford U, Witton Alb, Leek T, Chorley, Buxton, Stalybridge C, Mossley, Buxton, Stalybridge C, Irlam T, Buxton, Stalybridge C, Irlam T, Buxton, Prestwich Heys, Witton Alb, Mossley, Stockport, Manchester U (A))

Midfielders: Phil Whelan (Sutton U, Crystal Palace), **Lee Congerton** (Weymouth, Knowsley U, Rhyl, Newtown, Crewe (T)), **Joe Barton** (Warrington T, Northwich V), **Mick Arnold** (Local football), **Mark Wakefield** (Morecambe, Aston Villa (T)), **Tony Miller** (Bootle)

Forwards: Alan Tyrrell (Bamber Bridge, Leek T, Chorley, Bridlington T, Knowsley U, Wrexham), **Dave Siddell** (Local football), **Mick Jones** (Skelmersdale U), **Tony Clarke** (Local football), **Ronnie Gouldbourne** (Liverpool (T))

LANCASTER CITY

1902 Dolly Blues

Lancster City's 1995-96: Back row (L-R): Paul Byron, Andy Newell, Steve Trainor, Mark Thornley, Andy Moran. Middle Row: Dave May (Coach), Brian Curwen, Stuart Diggle, Graham Yeo, Steve Hartley, Jimmy Bell, Barrie Stimpson, Steve Horrocks, Mick Hoyle (Ass. Mgr). Front Row: Stuart Gelling, Mark Shirley, Martin Eatough, Alan Tinsley (Mgr), Dave Sharples, Dennis Hill, Jay Flannery. Photo - Alan Watson.

Chairman: John Bagguley **Vice-Chairman:** K Lancaster. **President:** M Woodhouse.
Secretary: Barry Newsham, 104 Willow Lane, Forest Park, Lancaster LA1 5QF (01524 35774).
Manager: Alan Tinsley **Coach:** John Coleman **Physio:** D McKevitt/F Charlton/D Hughes
Commercial Mgr: Mike Hoyle. **Press Officer:** M Hoyle (c/o the club).
Ground: Giant Axe, West Road, Lancaster LA1 5PE (01524 382238 Office).
Directions: M6 junc 33, follow into city, left at lights immediately after Waterstones bookshop, 2nd right, pass railway station on right, follow road down hill, ground 1st right. 5 mins walk from both bus & rail stations.
Capacity: 2,500 **Cover:** 800. **Seats:** 300 **Floodlights:** Yes **Metal Badges:** Yes
Club Shop: Yes - now inside ground, selling metal badges, pennants, programmes and other souvenirs etc. Contact Dave Crawford at club.
Colours: Blue/white/blue **Change colours:** Red/black **Sponsors:** Thwaites Breweles
Previous Leagues: Lancs Combination 05-70/ Northern Premier 70-82/ North West Counties 82-87.
Midweek matchday: Tuesday. **Reserve League:** North Western Alliance.
Previous Names: Lancaster Town **Previous Ground:** Quay Meadow 05-06 (club's 1st 2 games only!)
Record Attendance: 7,500 v Carlisle, FA Cup 1936.
Best FA Cup season: 2nd Rd 46-47 (01-4 v Gateshead) 72-73 (1-2 v Notts County).
League Clubs defeated in FA Cup: Barrow, Stockport County 21-22.
Record win: 8-0 v Leyland Motors (A), 83-84.
Record defeat: 0-10 v Matlock T, NPL Division One, 73-74.
Players progressing to Football League: John McNamee (Workington 1975), Brendan O'Callaghan (Stoke City), Ian Stevens (Stockport County 1986), Glenn Johnstone (Preston North End 1993), Martin Clark & Wayne Collins (Crewe Alexandra), Gus Wilson (Crewe Alexandra).
Club Fanzines: The Mad Axeman, Bambula Azzurri.
Clubhouse: "The Dolly Blue Tavern" just outside the ground. Two bars,hot and cold food available. Also a new tea bar inside ground serving food and drinks.
Club Record Appearances: Edgar J Parkinson.
95-96 Captain: Martin Eatough.
95-96 Top Scorer: Stuart Diggle 32. **95-96 P.O.Y:** Mark Thornley
Local Newspapers: Lancaster Guardian, Morcambe Visitor, Lancashire Evening Post and Lancaster Citizen.
Local Radio Stations: Red Rose, Radio Lancashire and Bay Radio.
Honours: Northern Premier Lg Cup R-up 79-80 (Div 1 Cup R-up 90-91), Lancs Combination 21-22 29-30 34-35 35-36 (R-up 19-20 22-23 27-28 51-52, Lg Cup 21-22, Div 2 R-up 14-15), Lancs Junior Cup (ATS Challenge Trophy) 27-28 28-29 30-31 33-34 51-52 74-75 (R-up 06-07 08-09 19-20 26-27), FA Vase 2nd Rd 86-87 90-91, FA Trophy 3rd Rd 74-75 75-76, Lancs Yth (under 18) Cup 87-88 88-89 (R-up 86-87 89-90), President's Cup 1994-95. Unibond 1st Div Champs 95-96, Lge Cup 95-96.

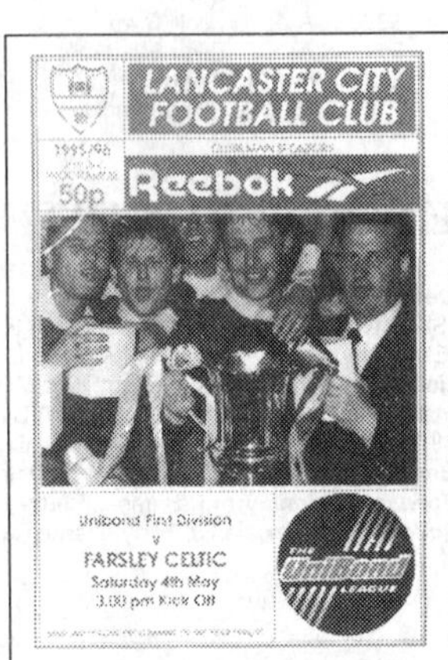

PROGRAMME DETAILS:
Pages: 32 **Price:** 50p
Editor: Colin Dyer
(c/o the club)

LANCASTER CITY'S 1995-96 CAMPAIGN

DATE		OPPONENTS	COMP	RESULT		GATE	GOALSCORERS
Aug 19	A	Bradford P.A.	UL	W	3-0	241	Diggle 2, Yeo
22	H	Gretna	UL	W	1-0	218	Bell
26	H	Congleton T.	UL	W	3-0	198	Key, Diggle, Shirley
Sept 2	H	Ashton U.	UL	W	2-0	226	Diggle, Gelling
5	A	Workington	UL	D	0-0	320	
9	H	Pickering T.	FAC	W	2-1	208	Yeo 2
12	H	Workington	UL	W	2-1	246	Yeo, Bell
16	A	Lincoln U.	UL	W	3-1	209	Bell 2
19	A	Fleetwood T.	UL	L	1-2	250	Bell
23	H	Peterlee	FAC	W	3-0	217	Diggle 2, Yeo
26	H	Fleetwood T.	LCC	W	4-2	154	Diggle 3, Gelling
30	A	Farsley Celtic	UL	L	1-2	162	Shirley
Oct 3	H	Liegh RMI	UL	W	5-2	202	Key 2, Borrowdale 2, Diggle
7	A	Bishop Auckland	FAC	W	1-0	298	Diggle
10	A	Gretna	UL	W	3-2	135	Borrowdale 2, Eatough
14	H	Solihull B.	FAT	W	3-0	173	Gelling, Trainor, Bell
17	H	Great Harwood	UL	W	4-1	205	Gelling 2, Yeo, Diggle
21	A	Spennymoor U.	FAC	L	0-1	621	
24	H	Knowsley U.	LCC	W	2-0	143	Byron, Diggle
28	A	Stherton LR	UL	L	1-2	177	Trainor
31	H	Fleetwood T.	UL	L	0-1	220	
Nov 4	A	Curzon Ashton	FAT	D	1-1	278	Shirley
7	H	Curzon Ashton	FAT R	W	3-0	206	Bell 2, Shirley
11	H	Alfreton T.	UL	D	1-1	214	Key
18	A	Whitley Bay	UL	W	1-0	136	Diggle
20	A	Great Harwood	UL	D	1-1	135	Borrowdale
25	A	Ashton U.	FAT	D	1-1	229	Flannery
28	H	Ashton U.	FAT R	L	0-2	228	
Dec 2	A	Ashton U.	UL	D	1.1-	203	Borrowdale
5	A	Bamber Bridge	LCC	W	1-0	349	Diggle
9	H	Bradford P.A.	UL	W	1-0	278	Borrowdale
12	H	Farsley Celtic	DIC	D	1-1	115	Bell
16	A	Eastwood T.	UL	W	2-1	120	Trainor, Shirley
Jan 6	H	Curzon Ashton	UL	W	2-1	201	Diggle, Shirley
10	A	Farsley Celtic	DIC R	W	3-1	99	Shirley 2, Key
13	A	Alfreton T.	UL	W	6-1	333	Borrowdale 2, Shirley 2, Bell, Key
16	A	Bamber Bridge	ATS	L	3-4	380	Byron, Diggle, Shirley
20	H	Harrogate T.	UL	W	2-1	2-7	Borrowdale, Diggle
Feb 3	H	Worksop T.	UL	W	3-1	264	Diggle 3
10	H	Atherton LR	UL	W	1-0	176	Diggle
13	A	Warrington T.	UL	D	1-1	76	Diggle
17	A	Congleton T.	UL	D	1-1	162	Byron
20	H	Whitley Bay	DIC	W	2-1	139	Byron
24	A	Worksop T.	UL	W	2-0	452	Borrowdale, Shirley
Mar 2	H	Netherfield	UL	D	2-2	231	Borrowdale, Flannery
7	A	Hyde U.	LCC	L	1-5	231	Diggle
9	A	Harrogate T.	UL	D	2-2	219	Diggle, Borrowdale
13	A	Leigh RMI	UL	W	1-0	151	Coleman
16	H	Whitley Bay	UL	W	3-1	243	Coleman, Byron, Borrowdale
19	H	Great Harwood	DIC	W	4-1	188	Diggle 3, Shirley
23	H	Lincoln U.	UL	W	2-0	508	Diggle 2
25	A	Great Harwood	DIC	W	2-0	116	Gelling, Trainor
30	A	Radcliffe B.	UL	D	0-0	321	
Apr 6	H	Warrington T.	UL	W	4-1	330	Shirley 2, Coleman, Borrowdale
8	A	Netherfield	UL	D	2-2	238	Diggle, Gelling
13	H	Eastwood T.	UL	D	2-2	303	Coleman 2
20	A	Curzon Ashton	UL	W	3-0	197	Coleman 3
23	N	Atherton LR	Dic F	W	1-0	436	Coleman
27	H	Radcliffe B.	UL	W	3-1	503	Coleman 2,Trainor
May 4	H	Farsley Celtic	UL	L	1-2	383	Coleman

LANCASTER CITY PLAYING SQUAD 1996-97

Goalkeepers: Mark Thornley (Morecambe, Fleetwood T, Matlock T, Stafford R, Alfreton T, Sutton T, Belper T, Alfreton T)

Defenders: Tony Key (Leek T, Eastwood Hanley, Stoke (T)), **Jay Flannery** (Southport, Bamber Bridge), **Paul Byron** (Accrington Stanley, Morecambe, Bamber Bridge, Morecambe, Bamber Bridge, Fleetwood T, Southport, Hartlepool, Blackburn, Sunderland), **Brian Curwen** (Wyre Villa), **Gary Dullaghan** (Morecambe, Rhyl, Oswestry T, Witton Alb, Ford Motors, South Liverpool), **Barrie Stimpson** (Morecambe, Barrow, Lancaster C, Barrow, Colne D, Morecambe, Gateshead, Hartlepool, Chesterfield, Hartlepool), **Steve Hartley** (Blackpool R), **Robbie Armstrong** (Morecambe), **Steve McNeilis** (Witton A, Colne D, Northwich V, Burscough, Formby), **Carl MacAuley** (Witton A, Vauxhall GM, Prescot Cables, Bromborough Pool), **Paul Tomlinson** (Morecambe, Mossley, Burscough)

Midfielders: Steve Horrocks (Morecambe), **Stuart Gelling** (Fleetwood T, Knowsley U, Liverpool (T)), **Dave Sharples** (Great Harwood T, Darwen, Morecambe, Accrington Stanley, Clitheroe, Chorley, Clitheroe, Padiham, Blackburn)

Forwards: John Coleman (Morecambe, Witton Alb, Rhyl, Macclesfield T, Runcorn, Souhtport, Marine, Burscough, Kirkby T), **Mark Shirley** (Ashton U, Caernarfon T, Netherley RBL, Nottingham F (T)), **Stuart Diggle** (Fleetwood T, Blackpool R, Southport, Blackpool Mech., Halifax T, Blackpool), **Peter Borrowdale** (Morecambe, Blackpool Mech., Netherfield)

LEEK TOWN

Formed: 1952 | The Blues

Back Row (L-R); G Heath (Pres), Stuart Leicester, K Birchg-Machin (Physio), Stuart Locke, Mick Bates, Steve Gillford, John Diskin, Tony Bullock, Martin Filson, Steve Soley, Matt Beeby, Mark Ogley, Dave Bancroft, Phil Wilson (Mgr), Mike Cope (V Chr). Front; R Halton (Dir), P Moran (Dir), Justin Parker, Nick Harland, Lindin Davies (Chair), F Ball (Sponsor), Garry Bauress, Nigel Shaw, W France (Dir), C France (Dir).

President: Mr G Heath **Chairman:** Mr L.Davis.
Secretary: Michael Rowley, 62 London Rd, Chesterton, Newcastle, Staffs ST5 7DY (01782 562890).
Manager: Phil Wilson. **Asst Manager:** P Ward **Physio:** K.Birch-Machin.
Coach: **Commercial Manager:** Rod Buxton. **Press Officer:** Mike Cope
Ground: Harrison Park, Macclesfield Road, Leek ST13 8LD (01538 399278. Fax;- 01538 399826).
Directions: Opposite Courtaults chemical works on A523 Macclesfield to Buxton road half a mile out of Leek heading towards Macclesfield.
Capacity: 3,600 **Cover:** 3,300 **Seats:** 625 **Floodlights:** Yes **Metal Badges:** Yes
Club Shop: Yes - contact club on 0538 399278.
Colours: All Blue. **Change colours:** All Yellow. **Sponsors:** Britannia/F Ball & Co Ltd
Previous Leagues: Staffs County/ Manchester 51-54 57-73/ West Mids (B'ham) 54-56/ Cheshire County 73-82/ North West Counties 82-87/ Northern Premier 87-94.The Beazer League 94-95
Previous Names: Abbey Green Rovers/ Leek Lowe Hamil. **Midweek home matchday:** Tuesday
Record Attendance: 5,312 v Macclesfield Town, F.A. Cup Second Qualifying Round 73-74.
Best FA Cup season: 2nd Rd 90-91 (lost 0-4 at Chester after 1-1)
League clubs defeated in FA Cup: Scarborough 90-91.
Record Fees - Paid: £2,000 for Simon Snow (Sutton Town)
Received: £3,250 Steve Jones (Stalybridge)
Players progressing to Football League: Geoff Crosby (Stockport 1952), Bill Summerscales & Mark Bright & Martyn Smith (Port Vale 1970 & 81 & 84), Paul Edwards (Crewe 1989).
Clubhouse: (01538 383734). Open nightly + weekend lunchtimes.
Club Record Goalscorer: Dave Suttons 144.
Club Record Appearances: Gary Pearce 447.
Local Newspapers: Leek Post & Times (01538 399599), Evening Sentinel (01782 289800).
Local Radio Stations: Radio Stoke, Signal Radio.**Newsline:** 0891 122727.
95-96 Captain: Alan Somerville
95-96 Top Scorer: Darren Twigg 19 **95-96 P.o.Y.:** Tony Bullock
Honours: FA Trophy R-up 89-90 (QF 85-86); Northern Premier Lg R-up 93-94 (Div 1 89-90, Div 1 Cup R-up 88-89, Presidents Cup R-up 93-94, Lg Shield 90-91); North West Co's Lg Cup 84-85 (Charity Shield 84-85); Cheshire County Lg 74-75 (Challenge Shield 74-75); Manchester Lg 51-52 71-72 72-73 (Lg Cup 72-73); Staffs Snr Cup R-up 54-55 81-82 95-96, Jnr Cup 51-52 70-71 (R-up 47-48 48-49 49-50)); Staffs Co. Lg 50-51 69-70 70-71 73-74 (R-up 47-48 49-50, Lg Cup 70-71 73-74); Leek Post Charity Shield 46-47; Leek Cup 47-48 52-53 70-71 71-72 (R-up 46-47); May Bank Cup 47-48 50-51 71-72; Hanley Cup 48-49 70-71 (R-up 49-5); Mid Cheshire Lg Div 2 87-88 (Div 2 Cup 87-88); Evans Halshaw Floodlit Cup Winners 93-94 94-95; Doc Martens(Southern Lg) Cup Finalists 94-95; Unibond Lge Chall Cup R-up 95-96

PROGRAMME DETAILS:
Pages: 36 **Price:** £1
Editor: Mike Cope

LEEK TOWN'S 1995-96 CAMPAIGN

DATE		OPPONENTS	COMP	RESULT		GATE	GOALSCORERS
Aug 19	H	Accrington Stanley	UL	D	2-2	367	Washington, Sutton
21	A	Winsford United	UL	D	0-0	268	
26	A	Blyth Spartans	UL	L	1-2	510	Sutton
28	H	Witton Albion	UL	W	2-1	471	Wheaton (pen), ?
Sept 2	A	Gresley Rovers	UL	L	1-3	606	Twigg
5	H	Droylsden	UL	W	4-0	221	Wheaton, Soley 2, Twigg (pen)
9	H	Clitheroe	FAC1Q	D	1-1	202	Twigg
11	A	Clitheroe	FAC1Qr	D	2-2	237*	Otley, Rilot
16	H	Frickley Athletic	UL	D	1-1	262	Soley
23	A	Guiseley	FAC2Q	L	0-4		
26	A	Matlock Town	UL	W	1-0	328	Wheaton
30	H	Bishop Auckland	UL	L	0-1	231	
Oct 2	H	Stoke City	SSC1	W	3-2	132	Soley, Twigg (pen), Brown
7	H	Bamber Bridge	UL	L	2-3	293	Soley, Twigg (pen)
10	H	Buxton	UL	D	0-0	310	
14	A	Emley	UL	W	1-0	225	Somerville
18	A	Boston United	UL	D	2-2	944	Fisher, Twigg
21	H	Emley	UL	D	2-2	293	Twigg 2
28	H	Chorley	UL	W	2-0	256	Diskin, Twigg
Nov 4	A	Gainsborough Trinity	UL	L	0-1	416	
7	H	Gainsborough Trinity	UL	D	0-0		
11	A	Hyde United	UL	L	2-3	441	Sutton2
14	A	Rocester	SSC2	W	3-2	112	Leicester, Diskin, Sutton
18	H	Winsford United	UL	W	5-1	220	Giblin, Sutton, Leicester, Wheaton 2 (pen)
21	A	Buxton	UL	W	2-1	304	Sutton, Wheaton
25	H	Boston United	FAC3Q	D	0-0	370	
29	A	Boston United	FAC3Qr	L	0-2	819	
Dec 2	A	Spennymoor United	UL	L	2-4	232	Twigg 2
5	H	Eastwood Town	ULCC	W	4-3	67	Wheaton 2, Somerville, Soley
9	H	Colwyn Bay	UL	D	1-1	186	Wheaton
16	A	Droylsden	UL	L	1-2	124	Leicester
Jan 1	A	Witton Albion	UL	L	1-2	607	Wheaton
6	H	Barrow	UL	W	2-0	324	Soley, Wheaton
9	H	Hyde United	ULPC	D	2-2	140	Soley 2
13	A	Accrington Stanley	UL	D	0-0	421	
16	H	Halesowen Harriers	BSC	W	3-2	97	Soley 2, Filson
20	A	Bamber Bridge	UL	D	0-0	424	
Feb 10	A	Bishops Auckland	UL	D	1-1	177	Soley (pen)
3	H	Accrington Stanley	ULCC	D	0-0	117	
17	H	Blyth Spartans	UL	L	1-3	251	Bauress
22	A	Hyde United	OLPC	L	0-2	285	
24	A	Knowsley United	UL	L	1-3	33	Twigg
28	A	Accrington Stanley	ULCC	W	3-1	201	Twigg 2, Giblin
Mar 2	A	Colwyn Bay	UL	D	0-0	257	
9	A	Barrow	UL	L	0-1	1077	
16	H	Guiseley	UL	D	1-1	222	Giblin
19	A	Bilston Town	SSC	W	1-0	34	Wheaton
23	H	Matlock	UL	W	4-2	250	Leicester, Soley 2, Twigg
27	A	Boston United	ULCC	W	2-1	345	Twigg, Wheaton
30	A	Chorley	UL	L	1-3	326	Twigg
Apr 1	H	Boston United	ULCC	W	2-1	165	Sutton, Leicester
6	H	Spennymoor United	UL	L	0-2	212	
8	A	Marine	UL	L	1-2	349	Batho
13	H	Knowsley United	UL	W	2-0	177	Bates, Batho
16	A	Newcastle Town	SSC.F1	L	0-1	221	
20	A	Frickley Athletic	UL	D	1-1	122	Batho
23	H	Boston United	UL	D	2-2	188	Twigg (pen), Filson
27	H	Marine	UL	L	0-1	229	
29	H	Newcastle Town	SSC.F1	W	4-2	204	Twigg 2, Soley, Bauress
May 3	N	Hyde United	ULCC	D	1-1	•	Filson
4	H	Hyde United	UL	L	0-1	213	

*After extra time
•Lost 6-7 on pens at Burnden Park

LEEK TOWN PLAYING SQUAD 1996-97

Goalkeepers: Tony Bullock (Northwich V, Barnton), Simon Pay (Nantwich T)
Defenders: John Diskin (Nantwich T), **Mark Ogley** (Stalybridge C, Altrincham, York, Aldershot, Carlisle, Burnley), **Gary Bauress** (Stalybridge C, Ashton U, Stalybridge C, Tranmere, Everton), **Martin Filson** (Caernarfon T, Dag & Red, Halifax T, Stalybridge C, Rhyl, Blackpool, Wrexham, Tranmere), **Justin Parker** (Crewe), **Stuart Locke** (Macclesfield T, Stalybridge C, Northwich V, Crewe, Manchester C)
Midfielders: Matthew Beeby (Leek CSOB, Macclesfield T, Port Vale (T)), **Mick Bates** (Eastwood Hanley, Port Vale, Arsenal (A)), **Nigel Shaw** (Nuneaton B, Stalybridge C, Altrincham, Runcorn, Macclesfield T, Congleton T, Nantwich T, Stoke), **Richard Carter** (Stoke), **Nick Harland** (Caernarfon T, Knowsley U, Tranmere (T)), **Steve Soley** (Warrington T, Avon A)
Forwards: Ian Wheaton (Eastwood Hanley, Nantwich T, Crewe, Manchester C), **Stuart Leicester** (Ashton U, Witton A, Stalybridge C, Macclesfield T, Stalybridge C, Irlam T), **Marc Hawkes** (Stoke), **Dave Bancroft** (Buxton, Hyde U, Leek T, Witton A, Stockport), **Mark Massey** (Newcastle T, Kidsgrove A, Redgate Clayton)

MARINE

Formed: 1894 | The Mariners

Marine's Brendan Grant slides in their first goal, past Bamber Bridge's keeper Steve Berryman.
Photo - Rob Ruddock

Chairman: Tom Culshaw **President:** David Bryant.
Secretary: John Wildman, 4 Ashbourne Avenue, Blundellsands, Liverpool L23 8TX (0151 924 5248).
Manager: Roly Howard **Asst Mgr/Coach:** Roger Patience **Physio:** John Bradshaw
Press Officer: David Wotherspoon **Commercial Manager:** T.B.A.
Ground: Rossett Park, College Road, Crosby, Liverpool (0151 924 1743).
Directions: College Road is off main Liverpool-Southport road (A565) in Crosby. Ground ten minutes walk from Crosby & Blundellsands (Mersey Rail). Bus No. 92.
Capacity: 2,500 **Cover:** 1,900 **Seats:** 400 **Floodlights:** 210 lux **Metal Badges:** Yes.
Club Shop: Yes, selling replica kit, baseball caps, polo shirts, scarves, mugs, pens/pencils, bookmarks, car stickers, combs, tax disc holders.(Dave Rannard 01514 749848)
Colours: White/black/black **Change:** Yellow/green/green **Midweek matchday:** Tuesday
Sponsors: Murphys Irish Stout. **Reserve Team's League:** Lancashire League Division One.
Previous Lges: I Zingari/ Liverpool Co. Comb./ Lancs Combination 35-39 46-69/ Cheshire County 69-79.
Previous Name: Waterloo Melville **Previous Ground:** Waterloo Park 1894-1903.
Record win: 14-2 v Rossendale United (A), Cheshire County League 25/2/78.
Record defeat: 1-7 v Dulwich Hamlet, FA Amateur Cup final at West Ham United, 1932.
Record Gate: 4,000 v Nigeria, Friendly 49.
Best FA Cup year: 3rd Rd 92-93 (lost 1-3 at Crewe Alexandra).
Record Fee Paid: £6,000 for Jon Penman (Southport October 1995).
Record Fee Received: £16,000 for Brian Ross(Chorley 1995).
Players progressing to Football League: J Veacock, A Sharrock, S Brooks (Southport 47 & 73 & 77), S Parker (Accrington 48), H Conner (Stoke 53), A Jones (Leeds 60), G Williams (Preston 72), J Lacy (Fulham & Spurs), P Beesly (Sheffield Utd), M Kearney (Everton 81), A Finlay (Shrewsbury 81), P Cook (Norwich), P Edwards (Crewe & Coventry), I Nolan (Tranmere), J McAteer (Liverpool).
Clubhouse: Open daily. Concert Hall (250 seats), Members Lounge (100 seats).
Club Record Goalscorer: Paul Meachin 200
Club Record Appearances: Peter Smith 952
95-96 Captain: **95-96 Top Scorer:** Jim Blackhurst
95-96 Player of the Year:
Local Press: Crosby Herald, Liverpool Echo, Daily Post
Local Radio Stations: BBC, Radio Merseyside, Radio City.
Hons: FA Amtr Cup R-up 31-32 (SF 46-47), FA Trophy SF 83-84 91-92, Northern Prem Lg 94-95 (R-up 85-86 91-92, Lg Cup 84-85 91-92 (R-up 80-81 85-86), Presidents Cup R-up 83-84 86-87), Cheshire Co. Lg 73-74 75-76 77-78 (R-up 72-73), Lancs Comb. R-up 46-47 (Lg Cup 46-47 63-64 68-69), Liverpool Comb. 27-28 30-31 33-34 34-35 (Lg Cup 30-31), Lancs Tphy 87-88 90-91, Lancs Jnr Cup 78-79, Lancs Amtr Cup 21-22 25-26 30-31 31-32 32-33, Liverpool Snr Cup 78-79 84-85 87-88 89-90 94-95, Liverpool Non-Lge Cup 68-69 75-76 76-77, Liverpool Chal. Cup 42-43 44-45 71-72.

PROGRAMME DETAILS:
Pages: 24 **Price:** 80p
Editor: David Wotherspoon

MARINE'S 1995-96 CAMPAIGN

DATE		OPPONENTS	COMP	RES		GATE	GOALSCORERS
Aug 12	N	Bamber Bridge	ULS	D	2-2	354	Grant, Watson
19	A	Colwyn Bay	UL	D	0-0	403	
22	H	Bamber Bridge	UL	D	0-0	406	
26	H	Emley	UL	L	0-1	380	
28	A	Winsford United	UL	L	0-1	210	
Sep 2	A	Frickley Athletic	UL	D	1-1	179	Ward
6	H	Barrow	UL	L	1-2	510	Blackhurst
9	H	Louth United	FAC 1Q	W	4-0	290	McNally, Grant, Gantrey (pen), Atkinson
16	H	Spennymoor United	UL	W	2-1	431	Pewman, Rowlands
19	H	Droylsden	U/L	W	6-1	340	Rowlands 2, Blackhurst 2, Baines, Watson
23	A	Newcastle Town	FAC 2Q	W	1-0	310	Blackhurst
36	H	Matlock Town	UL	W	1-0	420	Blackhurst
Oct 3	H	Knowsley United	UL	W	2-1	342	Blackhurst, Wards
7	H	Ilkeston Town	FAC 3Q	D	0-0	499	
14	A	Bishop Auckland	UL	W	1-0	203	Blackhurst
21	H	Bradford Park Ave	FAC 4Q	W	2-0	626	Grant, Blackhurst
24	A	Chorley	ULC	D	0-0	262	
28	A	Buxton	UL	W	3-1	237	Pewman, Blackhurst 2
31	H	Chorley	ULC	W	4-2	173	Blackhurst, Withers, Ward, Grant
Nov 4	H	Boston United	UL	L	0-4	707	
11	A	Shrewsbury Town	FAC 1	L	2-11	2845	Pewman, Rowlands
18	H	Frickley Athletic	UL	D	1-1	366	Grant (pen)
21	A	Chorley	UL	D	1-1	221	Grant
25	A	Hyde United	UL	L	0-4	561	
Dec 2	A	Matlock Town	UL	D	3-3	295	Murray, McNally, Blackhurst
9	H	Guiseley	UL	L	0-1	414	
11	A	Hyde United	ULC	L	3-5	330	Murray, Rowlands, Blackhurst
16	A	Boston United	UL	W	1-0	720	Withers
19	H	Accrington Stanley	UL	L	1-2	324	Blackhurst
Jan 1	A	Accrington Stanley	UL	D	0-0	622	
6	H	Blyth Spartans	UL	D	0-0	394	
9	H	Witton Albion	UL	W	2-0	254	Gantrey, Withers
20	H	Hyde United	FAT 1	D	0-0	467	
22	A	Hyde United	FAT 1r	D	0-0	416	
Feb 1	A	Hyde United	FAT 1r	L	0-3	374	
10	A	Witton Albion	UL	L	0-2	457	
13	H	St Helen's Town	LSC	W	1-0	138	McNally
17	H	Witton Albion	UL	W	2-0	453	Blackhurst, McNally
24	H	Chorley	UL	W	2-1	401	Blackhurst (pen), Pewman
Mar 2	H	Buxton	UL	D	1-1	346	Draper
5	H	Hyde United	ULPC	L	0-3	142	
9	A	Guiseley	UL	W	4-2	380	Brewman, Hogarth, Blackhurst, Pewman
16	H	Gainsborough Trinity	UL	W	3-0	335	Prostor, McNally, Blackhurst (pen)
23	A	Bamber Bridge	UL	D	4-4	606	Rowlands 2, Lunden, Ward
25	H	Tranmere Rovers	LSC	L	1-4	273	Pewman
30	A	Droylsden	UL	L	1-2	162	Blackhurst
Apr 2	H	Colwyn Bay	UL	D	1-1	311	Blackhurst
6	A	Barrow	UL	L	0-2	981	
8	H	Leek Town	UL	W	2-1	349	Ward, Rowlands
10	H	Hyde United	UL	W	4-0	333	Pewman, Rowlands, Blackhurst 2 (pen)
16	A	Blyth Spartans	UL	D	2-2	367	Rowlans, Ward
20	A	Spennymoor United	UL	D	2-2	255	Blackhurst, Rowlands
23	H	Winsford United	UL	W	3-1	336	Pewman 2, Draper
25	A	Knowsley United	UL	L	1-2	129	McNally
27	A	Leek Town	UL	W	1-0	229	Pewman
30	A	Emley	UL	l	0-2	164	
May 4	H	Bishops Auckland	UL	D	2-2	475	McNally, Rowlands

MARINE PLAYING SQUAD 1996-97

Goalkeepers: Kevin O'Brien (Sth Liverpool, Chorley, Runcorn, Burscough, Rhyl, Maghull, Everton)
Defenders: Andy Rooney (Barrow, Marine, Altrincham, Runcorn, Crewe, Everton), **Andy Draper** (Local football), **Sean Lundon** (Runcorn, Bath C, Chester, Everton), **Ray Moss** (Youth team), **Ian Baines** (Southport, Knowsley U, Rhyl, Knowsley U, Southport, Kirkby T), **Ian Renshaw** (Youth team), **Keith Proctor** (Youth team)
Midfielders: Jon Gautrey (Southport, Bolton), **Eddie Murray** (Altrincham, Tranmere, Stork, Maghull), **Paul McNally** (Warrington T, Southport, Stalybridge C, Runcorn, Oswestry T), **Mark Brennan** (Ashton U, Chorley, Southport, Morecambe, Sth Liverpool, Bootle, Sth Liverpool), **Andy Cavanagh** (Southport), **Graham Rowlands** (Coastal (USA), Southport, Formby, Southport, Preston)
Forwards: Jimmy Blackhurst (Southport, Sth Liverpool, Marine), **Robbie Cowley** (Witton A, Burscough, Morecambe, Caernarfon T, Bootle), **Mick McDonough** (Burscough, Witton A, Burscough, Everton (T))

RUNCORN

Formed: 1918 | The Linnets

Back Row (L-R); Paul Robertson, Colin Taylor, Neil Doherty, Peter Bywe, Mark Morris, John Igglesden, Carl Ruffer, Ian McInerney, Mike Smith. Middle; Mike Bignall, Aidan Warder, Graham Hill, Graham Parsons, Alan Finley, Ray Curtis, Peter Ellis, Ian Brady, Jamie Bates. Front; Geoff Hughes (Physio), Lee Clowes, Billy Rodway (Asst Mgr), John Carroll (Mgr), Gary Anderson, Mick Doherty, Terry Bratt (Kit).

Chairman: Dr David Robertson **Vice Chairman:** Tony Bamber
Secretary: Graham Ost, 120 Warrington Road, Penketh, Warrington, Cheshire WA5 2JZ. Tel. 01925 722540 (Home), Tel/Fax 01928 560076 (Business), Mobile 0378 378595.
Manager: Derek Brownbill **Assistant Manager:** Alan Blair **Physio:** G Hughes
Ground: Canal Street, Wivern Place, Runcorn, Cheshire WA7 1RZ. Tel. 01928 560076. Fax 01928 560076.
Directions: From South: Leave M56 (junct 11). Follow A56 to Warrington for 1.5 miles. Turn left at roundabout onto A558 signposted Liverpool for 3 miles. Take left hand slipway sign posted Football Ground. From North: Leave M62 (junct 7). Travel via Widnes and over Runcorn bridge. Follow signs for Northwich for 1 mile. Take left hand slipway sign posted Football Ground.
Capacity: 4,600 **Cover:** 1,200 **Seats:** 441 **Floodlights:** Yes **Metal Badges:** Yes
Colours: Yellow Shirts, Green Shorts, Yellow socks.
Previous Leagues: Lancashire Combination/ Cheshire County Lg/ Northern Premier Lg/ Alliance Premier/ GM Vauxhall Conference.
Club Shop: Yes, selling usual club memorabilia. Contact Phil Wainwright. Tel. 01928 560075.
Midweek home matchday: Tuesday
Record Attendance: 10,111 v Preston - FA Cup 1938-39.
Record win: 11-0 v Congelton.
Record defeat: 0-8 v South Shields.
Record Fees - Paid: £17,000 for Simon Rudge from Hyde United.
Received: £80,000 for Ian Woan from Nottingham Forest.
Players progressing to Football League: Mark McCarrick, Eddie Bishop, Jim Cumbes, Graham Abel, Barry Knowles, Mark Jones, Don Page, David Pugh, Ian Woan, Gary Brabin, Paul Robertson, Mike Smith.
Clubhouse: Open on matchedays.Light snacks available.
Club Record Goalscorer: Alan Ryan.
95-96 P.o.Y.: **95-96 Top scorer:** Mike Bignall.
Local Newspapers: Runcorn Weekley News, Liverpool Echo, Runcorn World, Manchester Evening News.
Local Radio Stations: Radio Merseyside, GMR.
Honours: Lancs Jnr Cup 1918-19; Cheshire Lg 1919-20, 36-37, 38-39, 39-40, 62-63; Cheshire Snr Cup 24-25, 35-36, 61-62, 64-65, 67-68, 73-74, 74-75, 84-85, 85-86, 86-87, 87-88, 88-89, R-up 93-94; Cheshire County Bowl 37-38; Northern Premier Lg 75-76, 80-81; NPL Chall Cup 74-75, 79-80, 80-81; NPL Challenge Shield 80-81, 81-82; Alliance Premier Lg 81-82, Gola Lg Championship Shield 82-83, 85-86; Bob Lord Trophy 82-83, 84-85, R-up 91-92. FA Trophy R-up 85-86, 92-93, 93-94.

PROGRAMME DETAILS:
Pages: 32 **Price:** £ 1.20
Editor:

RUNCORN'S 1995-96 CAMPAIGN

DATE		OPPONENTS	COMP	RES		GATE	GOALSCORERS
Aug 19	H	Welling United	GMVC	L	1-3	410	Finley
22	A	Morecambe	GMVC	L	1-3	1,425	Warder
26	A	Kettering	GMVC	L	0-4	1,582	
28	H	Southport	GMVC	D	1-1	708	N. Doherty
Sept 2	H	Dagenham & Redbridge	GMVC	W	2-0	461	Bignall 2
6	A	Telford United	GMVC	W	2-1	1,008	Bignall 2
9	H	Slough Town	GMVC	W	4-3	460	Robertson, N. Doherty, Taylor, Bignell
13	A	Gateshead	GMVC	L	0-1	375	
16	A	Woking	GMVC	L	1-2	1,620	Taylor
19	A	Southport	GMVC	D	1-1	1,004	Taylor
23	H	Bath City	GMVC	W	1-0	518	N. Doherty
26	A	Northwich Victoria	CSC	L	1-3	502	N. Doherty
30	A	Bromsgrove Rovers	GMVC	L	0-2	973	
Oct 7	H	Halifax Town	GMVC	L	0-1	637	
14	A	Dover Athletic	GMVC	L	2-4	1,277	Bignall, Smith
21	H	Halifax Town	FAC	W	2-1	801	Taylor, Bignall
24	H	Macclesfield	GMVC	D	0-0	600	
28	H	Kettering	GMVC	W	4-2	569	Bates, Farrington 2, Clowes
Nov 4	A	Northwich Victoria	GMVC	L	3-4	1,007	Taylor, Bignall 2
11	H	Wigan Athletic	FAC	D	1-1	2,844	Bignall
18	A	Kidderminster Harriers	GMVC	L	1-4	1,879	Farrington
21	A	Wigan Athletic	FAC	L	2-4	3,224	Ruffer, Smith
25	H	Stevenage Borough	GMVC	L	0-8	442	
28	H	Southport	SCC	L	1-5	401	Smith
Dec 2	A	Altrincham	GMVC	D	2-2	707	N. Doherty, Bignall
9	H	Woking	GMVC	L	2-3	707	Bignall 2
16	A	Halifax Town	GMVC	W	3-1	834	Eyre, Bignall 2
Jan 6	A	Hednesford Town	GMVC	L	0-2	1,008	
13	H	Bromsgrove Rovers	GMVC	D	0-0	547	
20	A	Macclesfield	FAT	L	0-1	1,401	
Feb 3	A	Stevenage Borough	GMVC	L	1-4	1,432	Taylor
10	H	Kidderminster Harriers	GMVC	L	0-1	475	
17	H	Farnborough Town	GMVC	L	0-3	429	
20	H	Gateshead	GMVC	Ab	0-2	318	
24	A	Macclesfield	GMVC	L	0-1	1,410	
27	H	Gateshead	GMVC	D	1-1	333	Bignall
Mar 5	H	Altrincham	GMVC	L	0-1	607	
9	H	Dover Athletic	GMVC	L	1-3	433	Bignall
16	A	Farnborough Town	GMVC	W	1-0	619	Taylor
19	A	Stalybridge Celtic	GMVC	L	0-2		
23	H	Hednesford Town	GMVC	D	2-2	507	Taylor, Eyre
30	A	Bath City	GMVC	L	0-3	503	
Apr 6	A	Welling United	GMVC	D	1-1		Taylor
8	H	Morecambe	GMVC	L	1-3	681	Eyre
16	H	Stalybridge Celtic	GMVC	L	0-1	352	
20	A	Dagenham & Redbridge	GMVC	W	3-2	755	Allen, Thomas, Clowes
23	H	Northwich Victoria	GMVC	L	3-4	653	Allen, Ruffer, Eyre (p)
27	H	Telford United	GMVC	L	2-3	401	Taylor, Clowes
May 4	A	Slough Town	GMVC	W	1-0	835	Allen

RUNCORN PLAYING SQUAD 1996-97

Goalkeepers: Alan Thomson (Partick T)

Defenders: Neil Williams (Curzon Ashton, Warrington T, Eagle Sports), **Mark Ashton** (Curzon Ashton, Warrington T, Mossley, Castleton Gab, Mossley), **Peter Ellis** (Knowsley U), **Alan Finley** (Stockport, Shrewsbury, Marine), **Danny Kent** (Mossley, Leigh RMI, Chorley, Bury (T)), **Neil Boardman** (Warrington T), **Carl Ruffer** (Everton)

Midfielders: Aidan Warder (Curzon Ashton, Runcorn, Warrington T, Sth Liverpool), **Gary Randles** (Curzon Ashton, Warrington T, Cosmo (USA), Warrington T, Avon A), **Ian Callaghan** (Curzon Ashton, Warrington T, Droylsden, Hyde U, Northwich V, Bolton), **Neil Cook** (Curzon Ashton, Warrington T, Altrincham, Warrington T, Monks Sports, Bolton), **Danny Glass** (Warrington T), **Kevin Langley** (Bangor C, Witton A, Wigan, Birmingham, Manchester C, Everton, Wigan)

Forwards: Terry Nestor (Curzon Ashton, Warrington T, Liverpool), **Chris Lee** (Curzon Ashton, Warrington T, Chorley, Knowsley U, Ford Motors), **Phil Chadwick** (Bamber B, Atherton Coll, Glossop, Hyde U, Droylsden), **Paul Heavey** (Curzon Ashton, Warrington T, Preston, Netherfield), **Gavin McDonald** (Trafford, Atherton LR, Warrington T, Irlam T, Chesterfield), **Joey Dunn** (Atherton LR, Curzon Ashton, Warrington T, Caernarfon T, Warrington T, Marine, Burscough, Altrincham, Formby, Sth Liverpool, Earle), **Karl Thomas** (Bangor C, Witton A, Runcorn, Witton A, Colne D, Sth Liverpool, Ellesmere Pt)

SPENNYMOOR UNITED

1904 The Moors

Spennymoor United AFC:

Chairman: Barry Hindmarsh. **Vice Chairman:** J Norman **President:** Mr T Beaumont, MA
Secretary: J Nutt, 41 Warwick Cl, Grange Est, Spennymoor, Cty Durham DL16 6UU (01388 812179).
Manager: Matty Pearson **Asst Manager:** Dave Barton **Physio:** Alan Jackson
Commercial Mgr: Des Beamson **Press Officer:** Gary Nunn (01388 810831).
Ground: Brewery Field, Durham Road, Spennymoor, County Durham DL16 6JN (01388 811934).
Directions: A1(M), A167, A688, straight on at mini-r'bout, 3rd exit at next large r'bout (St Andrews church opposite), pass Asda on left, straight on at junction, pass Salvin Arms (Durham Rd), ground 200 yds on left. Nearest rail station Durham - buses from there.
Seats: 300 **Cover:** 2,000 **Capacity:** 7,500 **Floodlights:** Yes **Club Shop:** Yes
Club colours: Black & white stripes/black/white. **Change colours:** All red **Midweek matches:** Tuesday
Sponsors: Home: Rothmans (Spennymoor). Away: Welland Medical (Leicester)
Previous Leagues: Northern 05-08 60-90/ North Eastern 08-37 38-58/ Wearside 37-38/ Midland Counties 58-60/ Northern Counties (East) 90-93.
Previous Ground: Wood Vue 1901-1904.
Record Gate: 7,202 v Bishop Auckland, Durham County Challenge Cup 30/3/57.
Local Press: Northern Echo/ The Journal.
Best FA Cup season: 3rd Rd 36-37 (lost 1-7 at West Bromwich Albion).
Best FA Trophy season: Semi Final 77-78.
Record win: 19-0 v Eden Colliery, North Eastern Lge 6/2/37.
Record defeat: 0-16 v Sunderland 'A', Durham Snr Cup 4/1/02 (Half-time: 0-10).
Players progressing to Football League: Over fifty, including: H Hubbick (Burnley 25), T Dawson (Charlton 39), T Flockett (Charlton 49), J Smallwood (Chesterfield 49), J Oakes (Aldershot 54), J Adams (Luton Town 53), A Moore (Chesterfield), M Heathcote (Sunderland 87), J Ainsley (Hartlepool, 94).
Record transfer fee paid: £2,500 for Dean Gibb (Seaham Red Star, 1991).
Record Transfer Fee Received: £20,000 for Michael Heathcote (Sunderland, 1988).
Clubhouse: (01388 814100) Open nightly 7-11pm, Sat noon-11pm, Sun noon-2 & 7-10.30pm. Bar snacks available. Private functions. Well stocked tea bar in ground.
Club Record Scorer: Dougie Humble 200+
Club Record Appearances: Ken Banks 600+
95-96 Captain: Brian Healy.
95-96 P.o.Y.: Wes Saunders. **95-96 Top scorer:** Andrew Shaw.
Hons: Northern Premier Lg Cup 93-94 (Div 1 R-up 93-94), Northern Lg(6) 67-68 71-72 73-74 76-79 (R-up(3) 74-75 79-81, Lg Cup(5) 65-66 67-68 79-81 86-87, Turney Wylde Cup 80-81, J R Cleator Cup 80-81 86-87), Northern Counties (East) Lg 92-93 (Lg Cup 92-93), Durham Challenge Cup (13); Durham Benevolent Bowl (6); North Eastern Lg(4) 09-10 44-46 56-57 (Lg Cup 28-29); FA Trophy SF 77-78.

PROGRAMME DETAILS:
Pages: 32 **Price:** 80p
Editor: Gary Nunn
(01388 814100)

SPENNYMOOR UNITED 1995-96 CAMPAIGN

DATE		OPPONENTS	COMP	RES		GATE	GOALSCORERS
Aug 19	H	Hyde United	UL	L	0-1	321	
22	A	Blyth Spartans	UL	L	1-3	836	O'Hara
28	H	Droylsden	UL	W	2-0	263	Suddick, Goodrick
28	H	Blyth Spartans	UL	W	2-1	503	Shaw, Skedd
Sept 2	A	Buxton	UL	D	1-1	244	Healy
6	A	Accrington Stanley	UL	D	0-0	461	
9	H	Glasshoughton W.	FAC	W	1-0	247	Healy
12	H	Emley	UL	W	2-0	239	Suddick 2
16	A	Marine	UL	L	1-2	431	Veart
19	H	Accrington Stanley	UL	W	3-1	327	Skedd 2, Healy
23	A	Workington	FAC	W	4-2	487	Skedd, Healy, Shaw, Veart
25	A	Guiseley	UL	D	2-2	452	Veart, Goodrick
30	H	Chorley	UL	D	2-2	326	og, Healy
Oct 3	A	Emley	UL	W	2-0	210	Shaw, Ludlow
7	H	Billingham Town	FAC	W	6-1	337	Healy 2, Cowell, Alderson, Goodrick, Veart
10	H	Witton Albion	UL	W	3-1	357	Healy, Ludlow, Shaw
14	A	Gainsborough Trinity	UL	W	1-0	417	Healy (p)
17	H	Guiseley	UL	D	0-0	509	
21	H	Lancaster City	FAC	W	1-0	621	Gorman
23	A	Bishop Auckland	ULC	D	2-2	521	Saunders, Healy
28	H	Colwyn Bay	UL	D	0-0	339	
31	H	Birtley Town	DSC	W	3-2	208	Alderson 2, Cowell
Nov 4	A	Hyde United	UL	L	2-3	462	Ludlow, Healy
8	H	Knowsley United	UL	L	1-4	276	Healy (p)
18	A	Barrow	UL	D	1-1	1,176	Veart
21	A	South Shields	DSC	W	3-0	183	Ludlow 2, Healy (p)
25	H	Nuneaton Borough	FAT	L	0-2	486	
Dec 2	H	Leek Town	UL	W	4-2	232	Alderson, Veart, Ludlow, Osbourne
5	H	Emley	ULC	W	5-0	158	Alderson, Veart (p), Ludlow, Osbourne 2
9	A	Witton Albion	UL	D	2-2	374	Alderson, Ainsley
16	H	Gainsborough Trinity	UL	D	1-1	243	Ainsley
Jan 6	H	Buxton	UL	D	0-0	217	
9	H	Tow Law Town	DSC	W	2-0	273	Alderson, Osbourne
13	A	Chorley	UL	W	3-0	278	Veart, O'Hara, Osbourne
20	A	Knowsley United	UL	L	0-2	42	
Feb 3	H	Frickley Athletic	UL	D	2-2	245	Healy, Ainsley
10	A	Boston United	UL	L	1-4	648	Alderson
17	A	Droylsden	UL	D	1-1	172	Shaw
24	H	Matlock Town	UL	D	1-1	242	Skedd
26	A	Bishop Auckland	UL	W	2-1	346	Purvis, Shaw
Mar 2	A	Boston United	ULC	L	0-3	424	
9	H	Boston United	UL	L	2-3	237	Alderson, Innes
16	H	Barrow	UL	D	1-1	245	Alderson
19	A	Dunston Fed.	DSC	W	1-0	190	Shaw
23	A	Colwyn Bay	UL	W	3-2	280	Alderson 2, Cowell
30	A	Matlock Town	UL	D	1-1	283	Alderson
Apr 6	A	Leek Town	UL	W	2-0	212	Innes, og
8	H	Bishop Auckland	UL	W	1-0	416	Shaw
13	A	Bamber Bridge	UL	L	0-2	388	
20	H	Marine	UL	D	2-2	255	Innes, Osbourne
23	A	Frickley Athletic	UL	W	3-2	109	Skedd, Alderson, Healy
27	H	Winsford United	UL	D	3-3	215	Healy 2, Shaw
30	H	Bamber Bridge	UL	W	4-2	288	Healy, Ainsley, Cowell, Shaw
May 4	A	Winsford United	UL	D	2-2	110	Osbourne, Coatsworth

SPENNYMOOR UNITED PLAYING SQUAD 1996-97

Goalkeepers: Adrian Swan (Billingham T)

Defenders: Wes Saunders (Torquay, Dundee, Carlisle, Newcastle), **Ronnie Robinson** (Scarborough, Huddersfield, Exeter, Peterborough, Rotherham, WBA, Doncaster, Leeds, Vaux SC, Ipswich), **Gary O'Hara** (Port Vale, Leeds (T)), **Richie Watson** (Billingham T, B Auckland, Billingham T, Whitley Bay, Billingham T), **Gary Coatsworth** (Leicester C, Darlington, Barnsley), **Ralph Petitjean** (B Auckland, Spennymoor U, Ferryhill A), **Andy Purvis** (Blackpool)

Midfielders: Lee Innes (Darlington), **Brian Healy** (Gateshead, B Auckland, Billingham T, West Auckland T), **Mark Elliott** (Darlington), **Tony Skedd** (Hartlepool), **Gary Cowell** (Ferryhill A), **Jason Ainsley** (Hartlepool, Spennymoor U, B Auckland, Spennymoor U, Guisborough T), **Craig Veart** (Gateshead, Ferryhill A, Middlesbrough). **Kevin Todd** (B Auckland, Berwick R, Whitley Bay, Newcastle Blue Star, Darlington, Newcastle U, Ryhope CA)

Forwards: Steve Osbourne (Chester-le-Street), **Ritchie Alderson** (Youth team), **Andy Shaw** (Whitley Bay, B Auckland, Crook T), **Keith Gorman** (B Auckland, Ferryhill A, Brandon U, Darlington, Ipswich)

Founded: 1883

WINSFORD UNITED

Blues

Winsford's keeper Robinson comes out to save against Witton's Morley with Winsford's Edwards shadowing.
Photo - Keith Clayton

Chairman: M.Morgan. **Vice Chairman:** D.Cotterill. **President:** A Bayliss
Secretary: Peter Warburton, 3 Maisey Avenue, Winsford, Cheshire CW7 3DU (01606 554295).
Manager: John Bingham. **Asst Manager:** John Imrie.
Ground: Barton Stadium, Wharton, Winsford, Cheshire CW7 3EU (01606 593021).
Directions: From north; M6 junction 19, A556 towards Northwich to Davenham, then A5018 to Winsford. From south; M6 junction 18, A54 through Middlewich to Winsford. Ground quarter mile off main road in Wharton area of town. 1 mile from Winsford (BR).
Capacity: 6,000 **Cover:** 5,000 **Seats:** 250 **Floodlights:** Yes **Club Shop:** Yes
Colours: Blue/white/blue. **Change colours:** Maroon/white/white.
Sponsors: Dickson Motors Ltd, Winsford (Ford).
Previous Name: Over Wanderers (prior to 1914). **Previous Leagues:** The Combination 02-04/ Cheshire County 19-40 47-82/ North West Counties 82-87.
Midweek home matchday: Monday. **Record Attendance:** 7,000 v Witton Albion 1947.
Best F.A. Cup season: 2nd Rd 1887-88. Also 1st Rd 1975-76 1991-92.
League clubs defeated in F.A. Cup: None.
Record Fees - Paid: Nil
Received: £6,000 for Neville Southall from Bury.
Players progressing to Football League: William Foulkes (Chester 1948), Cliff Marsh (Leeds 1948), Bennett Nicol (Rochdale 1949), Eric Johnson (Coventry 1952), Walter Hughes (Liverpool 1954), Reg Lewis (Luton 1954), William Heggie (Accrington 1955), Joe Richardson (Birmingham City 1959), John Abbott (Crewe Alexandra 961), Robert Walters (Shrewsbury 1962), Phil Mullington (Rochdale 1978), Neville Southall (Bury 1980), Mark Came (Bolton Wanderers 1984), Dave Bamber (Blackpool), Bob Sutton (West Ham United), J Richardson (Sheffield United), Stanley Wood (West Bromwich Albion), R Pearce (Luton Town).
Clubhouse: Mon-Sat 8-11pm, Sun 8-10.30pm
Club Record Goalscorer: Graham Smith 66
Club Record Apps: Edward Harrop 400.
95-96 P.o.Y.:
95-96 Top scorer: Jock Russell.
Local Newspapers: Winsford Chronicle, Winsford Guardian.
Local Radio Stations: Signal, Piccadilly.
Honours: Northern Premier Lg R-up 92-93 (Div 1 R-up 91-92, Lg Cup 92-93, Presidents Cup 92-93, Div 1 Cup SF 89-90), Cheshire County Lg 20-21 76-77 (R-up 74-75 79-80, Lg Cup 49-50 55-56 59-60 76-77 78-79 79-80 80-81 (R-up 36-37 68-69 77-78)), Cheshire Senior Cup 58-59 79-80 92-93, Mid-Cheshire Snr Cup 90-91 92-93 (R-up 88-89), Cheshire Amateur Cup 00-01 02-03, Lancs Comb/Cheshire County Inter-Lg Cup 62-63, FA Trophy QF 77-78.

PROGRAMME DETAILS:
Pages: 24 **Price:** 80p
Editor: A Maylor

WINSFORD UNITED'S 1995-96 CAMPAIGN

DATE		OPPONENTS	COMP	RES		GATE	GOALSCORERS
Aug 19	H	Emley	UL	L	0-4	222	
21	H	Leek Town	UL	D	0-0	208	
26	A	Accrington Stanley	UL	W	2-1	475	T. Bishop (p), V. Bishop
28	H	Marine	UL	W	1-0	210	Russell
Sept 2	H	Gainsborough Trinity	UL	D	1-1	222	Farrelly
4	A	Hyde United	UL	W	1-0	274	Edwards
9	H	Borrowash Victoria	FAC	W	1-0	206	T. Bishop
16	A	Bishop Auckland	UL	L	0-1	185	
19	A	Bamber Bridge	UL	L	0-2	655	
23	A	Emley	FAC	D	1-1	252	Edwards
25	H	Emley	FAC	W	2-1	248	McIlroy, Edwards
30	A	Droylsden	UL	D	1-1	217	Talbot
Oct 2	H	Hyde United	CSC	L	1-4	213	Edwards
7	H	Hinckley Athletic	FAC	W	3-2	236	O'Loughlin, Russell, T. Bishop
10	A	Colwyn Bay	UL	D	1-1	276	Russell
14	H	Paget Rangers	FAT	D	1-1	183	T. Bishop
18	A	Paget Rangers	FAT	W	2-0	124	McCarrick, V. Bishop
21	H	Barrow	FAC	L	0-4	714	
24	A	Atherton LR	ULC	L	2-3	82	Russell, V. Bishop
28	A	Guiseley	UL	D	1-1	360	Talbot
Nov 4	A	Barrow	FAT	W	1-0	1,222	Russell
6	H	Bamber Bridge	UL	L	1-4	202	Russell
11	H	Boston United	UL	W	1-0	183	Farrelly
18	A	Leek Town	UL	L	1-5	220	Edwards
20	H	Colwyn Bay	UL	L	1-3	123	V. Bishop
25	A	Chorley	FAT	L	1-3	297	T. Bishop
27	H	Knowlsey United	UL	L	0-1	111	
Dec 2	A	Buxton	UL	W	3-1	165	Dicken, Russell, Farrelly
9	H	Matlock Town	UL	W	3-1	127	Blundell, Russell 2
16	A	Chorley	UL	D	1-1	221	O'Loughlin
Jan 6	A	Matlock Town	UL	D	1-1	325	Farrelly
13	H	Hyde United	UL	L	1-4	261	Farrelly
20	H	Buxton	UL	D	1-1	159	McCarrick
23	A	Knowsley United	UL	L	1-4	44	V. Bishop
Feb 3	A	Gainsborough Trinity	UL	D	0-0	404	
10	A	Frickley Athletic	UL	D	3-3	112	Russell, Talbot, T. Bishop
17	A	Emley	UL	D	1-1	196	Russell
24	A	Boston United	UL	D	2-2	611	Farrelly, Talbot
Mr 2	H	Blyth Spartans	UL	L	2-4	162	Danskin, Russell (p)
9	H	Frickley Athletic	UL	W	4-1	128	Farrelly, O'Loughlin, Russell, Danskin
16	H	Bishop Auckland	UL	L	0-4	120	
23	A	Blyth Spartans	UL	L	2-3	405	Russell, Farrelly
25	H	Barrow	UL	W	4-3	170	Russell 3 (1p), Farrelly
30	A	Barrow	UL	D	1-1	953	Russell
Apr 1	H	Chorley	UL	L	0-2	188	
6	H	Accrington Stanley	UL	D	2-2	168	Bishop, German
8	A	Witton Albion	UL	L	0-2	513	
13	H	Droylsden	UL	W	3-2	150	Farrelly, Russell 2
20	H	Guiseley	UL	L	1-2	137	Dicken
23	A	Marine	UL	L	1-3	336	Russell
27	A	Spennymoor United	UL	D	3-3	215	O'Loughlin, Danskin, Talbot
29	H	Witton Albion	UL	W	2-1	160	German, V. Bishop (p)
May 4	H	Spennymoor United	UL	D	2-2	110	Farrelly, Russell

WINSFORD UNITED PLAYING SQUAD 1996-97

Goalkeepers: Phil Robinson (Stalybridge C, Huddersfield), **Jamie McVey** (Witton A)
Defenders: Mark Came (Exeter, Chester, Bolton, Winsford U), **Dan Leeming** (Northwich V, Stafford R, Everton), **Gary Talbot** (Wilmslow A, Rhyl), **Steve Baines** (Burscough, Caernarfon T, Droylsden, Knowsley U, Southport, Newton), **Elfyn Edwards** (Southport, Halifax T, Macclesfield T, Altrincham, Runcorn, Tranmere, Wrexham), **Mark McCarrick** (Marine, Bangor C, Northwich V, Tranmere, Runcorn, Crewe, Lincoln, Birmingham, Witton A), **Danny Goodall** (Blackburn)
Midfielders: Colin O'Loughlin (Witton A, Winsford U, Cheadle T, Flixton, Maine Road), **Jason Danskin** (Northwich V, Witton A, Mansfield, Everton), **Kevin Coyne** (Port Vale), **David German** (Macclesfield T, Halifax T), **Jon Hill** (Stalybridge C, Witton A, Preston, Rochdale, Crewe), **Paul Newton** (Flixton, Witton A, Winsford U, Radcliffe B, Cheadle T, Stockport, Flixton, Manchester C), **Paul Allen** (Bamber B, Buxton, Leek T, Stalybridge C, Fleetwood T, Buxton, Fleetwood T, Southport, Preston, Southport, Preston, Bolton)
Forwards: Darryl Dickin (Congleton T, Grove U), **Phil Farrelly** (Witton A), **Jock Russell** (Trafford, Bury, Winsford U, Nth Trafford, Barrow, Nth Trafford, Broadheath Central, Manchester C), **Steve Hockenhull** (St.Helens T, Tetley Walker, St.Helens T), **Darren Lyons** (Macclesfield T, Southport, Bury, Ashton U, Mossley, Leek T, Macclesfield T, Droylsden, Rhyl, Oldham), **Lee Raby** (Local football)

WITTON ALBION

Formed: 1887 | The Albion

Witton Albion FC: Back Row (L-R); T Clarke, S Brenchley, N Whalley, D Whyte, T Rodwell, M Wilde, B Pritchard. Front L Watson, C Rose, A Fahy, P Jones, D Morley *Photo: Keith Clayton.*

President: T Stelfox **Manager:** Ray Ranson. **Chairman:** D.J.Lloyd.
Secretary: David Leather, 34 Grosvenor Ave., Hartford, Northwich, Cheshire (01606 76488).
Coaches: Russ Perkins. **Physio:** Mike Carrick. **Commercial Mgr:** Jackie Birks
Ground: Wincham Park, Chapel St, Wincham, Northwich (Tel/Fax: 01606 43008) **Directions:** M6 junc 19. A556 towards Northwich, after 3 miles turn onto A559 at beginning of dual carriageway, after 3/4 mile turn left opposite Black Greyhound Inn, grd 1/2 mile on left immediately after crossing Canal Bridge.
Capacity: 4,500 **Seated:** 650 **Cover:** 2,300 **Floodlights:** Yes. **Club Shop:** Yes.
Colours: Red & white stripes **Change colours:** Blue and White.
Record Attendance: 3,940 v Kidderminster Harriers - FA Trophy Semi-Final.
Midweek matchday: Tuesday
Reserve League: None.
Record win: 6-0 v Stafford Rangers - 1992/93
Record defeat: 0-5 v Welling United (H), GMV Conference 12/3/94.
Record transfer fee: £10,000 (twice) for Karl Thomas from Colne Dynamoes and for Jim McCluskie from Hyde United both 1990.
Record fee received: £11,500 for Peter Henderson from Chester City.
Previous Grounds: Central Ground, Witton Street, Northwich.
Club Sponsors: L.M.P.
Previous Leagues: Lancs Comb./ Cheshire County/ Northern Premier/ GMV Conference 91-94.
Past players who progressed to the Football League: P Henderson (Chester City), Chris Nicholl (ex-Southampton manager), Phil Powell (Crewe), Neil Parsley & Mike Whitlow (Leeds).
Social Facilities: Concert room and Vice-Presidents room open matchdays, Tuesday, Thursday, Friday and Sunday evenings. Food available for private functions.
95-96 Captain: Neil Whalley.
95-96 Top Scorer: Liam Watson. **95-96 P.o.Y:** Colin Rose.
Club record goalscorer: Frank Fidler 122
Record appearances: John Goryl 652
Honours: Northern Prem Lge 90-91; Cheshire County Lge 48-49 49-50 53-54 (R-up 50-51), Lge Cup 53-54 75-76; Cheshire County Sen Cup (7); FA Trophy R-up 91-92 (SF 90-91 92-93).

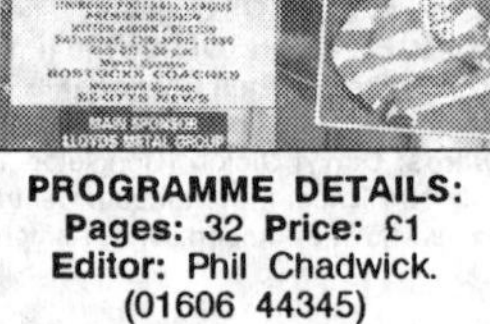

PROGRAMME DETAILS:
Pages: 32 **Price:** £1
Editor: Phil Chadwick.
(01606 44345)

WITTON ALBION'S 1995-96 CAMPAIGN

DATE		OPPONENTS	COMP	RESULT		GATE	GOALSCORERS
Aug 19	A	Boston U.	UL	W	2-1	1167	Thomas, Cowley
22	H	Colwyn Bay	UL	L	2-3	621	Camdon 2
26	H	Frickley Ath.	UL	W	5-0	529	Rose 2, Camdon, Thomas, Byrne
28	A	Leek Town	UL	L	1-2	471	Thomas
Sept 2	H	Bamber Bridge	UL	D	0-0	623	
5	A	Buxton	UL	W	4-0	350	Stannard, Rose, Thomas, Cowley
12	H	Accrington S.	UL	L	0-2	525	
16	A	Emley	UL	L	0-1	314	
19	H	Matlock T.	UL	W	3-2	439	Thomas 3
23	H	Knowsley	UL	W	2-1	436	Thomas, Camden
29	A	Colwyn Bay	UL	D	1-1	323	Rose
30	H	Guiseley	UL	W	3-2	615	Rodwell, Thomas, Camden
Oct 4	H	Chorley	UL	W	2-1	583	Thomas, Camden
7	A	Chorley	UL	L	0-4	332	
10	A	Spennymoor U.	UL	L	1-3	357	Thomas
14	H	Blyth Spartans	UL	W	2-1	502	Camden 2
17	A	Barrow	UL	L	0-3	1490	
21	H	Morecambe	FAC 4Q	W	3-2	931	Watson 2, Cowley
24	H	Leigh RMI	ULC	D	2-2	305	Camden 2
28	H	Gainsborough T.	UL	L	0-2	455	
Nov 1	A	Leigh RMI	ULC	W	3-0	72	Macauley, Watson, Pritchard
4	A	Bishop Auckland	UL	W	2-1	208	McNeilis, Watson
11	A	Telford U.	FAC 1	L	1-2	1277	Watson
18	H	Emley	UL	W	3-1	439	McNeilis, Cowley, Watson
21	H	Northwich Vic.	CSC	W	2-0	1006	McCauley, Cowley
25	A	Bishop Auckland	FAT 3	D	0-0	239	
28	H	Bishop Auckland	FAT 3R	L	0-0	461	Watson (pen)
Dec 4	A	Bishop Auckland	FAT 3R2	L	1-3	222	Watson
9	H	Spennymoor U.	UL	D	2-2	374	Watson 2
16	A	Accrington S.	UL	W	2-1	409	Pritchard, Brenchley
19	A	Atherton Lab. R.	ULC	W	5-2	183	Watson 5, Jones
Jan 1	H	Leek T.	UL	W	2-1	607	Horsfield, Watson
6	A	Guiseley	UL	W	1-0	360	Taylor
9	A	Marine	PC	L	0-2	254	
13	H	Bishop Auckland	UL	L	1-2	510	Brenchley
Feb 10	H	Marine	UL	W	2-0	457	Whalley, Watson
17	A	Marine	UL	L	1-2	453	Taylor
20	H	Altrincham	CSC	D	1-1	460	Watson (pen)
24	H	Droylsden	UL	W	2-1	399	McNeilis, Horsfield
27	H	Northwich Vic.	MCC	W	3-2	680	Cowley 2,Horsfield
Mar 2	H	Barrow	UL	W	1-0	591	McNeilis
5	A	Gainsborough T.	ULC	L	2-3	420	Watson2
9	H	Blyth Spartans	UL	L	0-2	497	
12	A	Altrincham	CSC	W	2-1	481	McDonald 2
16	H	Hyde U.	UL	D	1-1	628	Watson
19	A	Matlock T.	UL	L	2-5	232	Whalley, Horsfield
23	A	Knowsley	UL	A	2-2	112	McDonald, Watson (pen)
30	H	Boston U.	UL	D	1-1	469	Watson
Apr 6	A	Droylsden	UL	L	1-2	167	Horsfield
8	H	Winsford U.	UL	W	2-0	513	Watson 2
15	A	Hyde U.	UL	L	0-1	367	
20	A	Gainsborough T.	UL	L	0-1	404	
27	H	Buxton	UL	L	1-3	419	Watson
29	A	Winsford U.	UL	L	1-2	160	McDonald
May 1	A	Winsford U.	MCC	W	2-1	180	Watson 2
4	A	Bamber Bridge	UL	D	1-1	589	Watson
6	N	Hyde United	CSC	W	3-1	780	Stanard 2, Watson (pen)

WITTON ALBION PLAYING SQUAD 1996-97

Goalkeepers: Tim Clarke (Shrewsbury, Huddersfield, Coventry, Halesowen T)

Defenders: Ray Ransom (Reading, Manchester C, Newcastle, Birmingham, Manchester C), **Brian Pritchard** (Southport), **Colin Caton** (Colwyn Bay, Rhyl), **Andy Taylor** (Buxton, Rotherham), **Mark Sharrock** (Burscough, Marine, Everton (T)), **Andy Milne** (Manchester C (T)), **Neil Parsley** (Exeter, WBA, Huddersfield, Leeds, Witton A), **Trevor Matthewson** (Bury, Preston, Birmingham, Lincoln, Stockport, Newport Co, Sheffield Wed)

Midfielders: Colin Rose (Crewe), **Tony Rodwell** (Scarborough, Blackpool, Colne D, Runcorn, Buxton, Southport), **Alan Fahy** (Knowsley U, Caernarfon T, Ashton U, Waterloo Dock, Knowsley U, Bury), **Neil Whalley** (Altrincham, Preston, Warrington T), **Phil Jones** (Warrington T, Wigan, Everton), **Scott Brenchley** (Chester)

Forwards: Tony McDonald (Chorley, Horwich RMI, Radcliffe B), **Geoff Horsfield** (Guiseley, Halifax T, Scarborough, Worsborough Bridge MW), **Liam Watson** (Marine, Preston, Warrington T, Burscough, Maghull), **Dominic Morley** (Liverpool), **Mark Wilde** (Knowsley U, Bootle), **Matthew Helme** (Skelmersdale U, Burscough, Warrington T, Fleetwood T, Burscough)

ASHTON UNITED

Formed: 1878 | Robins

Ashton United's Darren Twigg in action, tracked by Tayport's Dave Riley during their International Challenge
Photo - Colin Stevens

Chairman: T.N.Styring. **Vice Chairman:** Mrs A Cummings **President:** Sid Sykes.
Secretary: Mrs C Slater, 1 Crossway Rd, Sneyd Green, Stoke-on-Trent, ST6 2ND. 01782 858280 (H)
Manager: Phil Staley. **Asst Manager:** Steve Waywell **Physio:** Ronnie Fox
Press Officer: T Liverside **Commercial Manager:** TBA
Ground: Surrey Street, Hurst Cross, Ashton-u-Lyne OL6 8DY (0161 339 4158, Fax-0161 652 6413)
Directions: M62 jct 20, A627(M) to Oldham, keep in righthand lane, take Ashton sign after 2 miles passing Belgrade Hotel, take A627 at next island, keep in left lane and take slip road signed Ashton-under-Lyme, at island follow Stalybridge/Park Road sign, go strght ahead 3 miles to grd at Hurst Cross. BR to Charles Street (Ashton), or Stalybridge. Buses 331, 332, 337, 408 (Ashton-Stalybridge)
Seats: 250 **Cover:** 750 **Capacity:** 4,500 **Floodlights:** Yes
Club Shop: Yes - contact Mr K Lee (0161 330 9800).
Cols: Red & white halves/black/red **Change colours:** Blue/white/blue.
Record Attendance: 11,000 v Halifax Town, FA Cup First Round 1952.
Midweek matches: Monday. **Club Sponsors:** Coral Travel.
Prevs Name: Hurst 1878-1947 **Prevs Ground:** Rose Hill 1878-1912.
Previous Leagues: Manchester/ Lancs Combination 12-23 48-64 66-68/ Midland 64-66, Cheshire Co. 23-48 68-82/ North West Counties 82-92.
Record Transfer Fees - Paid: £9,000 for Andy Whittaker (Netherfield, 1994).
Received: £15,000 for Karl Marginson (Rotherham, March 1993).
Best FA Cup season: 1st Rd replay 55-56 (lost 1-6 at Southort)
Players progressing to Football League: A Ball (Blackpool, Everton, Arsenal & England), J Mahoney (Stoke City & Wales), B Daniels (Manchester City), R Jones (Rotherham Utd), A Arrowsmith (Liverpool), N Stiffle (Crystal Palace & Bournemouth), K Marginson (Rotherham).
Clubhouse: Open 11am-11pm. Refreshment bar open matchdays.
95-96 Captain:
95-96 Top Scorer: Jimmy Bell 19. **95-96 P.o.Y.:**
Club Record Scorer: Mark Edwards, 37.
Club Record Appearances: Micky Boyle, 462.
Hons: Northern Premier League Division 1 Cup 94-95, Manchester Senior Cup 1884-85 13-14 75-76 77-78, Manchester League 11-12, Lancs Comb. Div 2 60-61 (League Cup 62-63), Manchester Prem. Cup 79-80 82-83 92-93, North West Counties League 91-92 (Challenge Cup 91-92, Div 2 87-88, Floodlit League 90-91, Challenge Shield 92-93), Manchester Challenge Shield 35-36 38-39 49-50 53-54 (R-up 34-35 39-40), Manchester Intermediate Cup 58-59 62-63 65-66 (R-up 60-61 64-65), Manchester Jnr Cup(4) 1894-95 10-12 32-33.

PROGRAMME DETAILS:
Pages: 46 **Price:** 70p
Editor: Debbie Quaile

1954 **ATHERTON LABURNUM ROVERS** 'L.R.'

The impressive new stand at Atherton LR's Crilly Park. *Photo - Colin Stevens*

President: Pat Mulcahy **Chairman:** Derek Halliwell. **Vice Chairman/Treasuer:** A Grundy
Secretary: Steve Hartle, 32 Greensmith Way, Westhoughton, Bolton BL5 3DR (01942 840906).
Manager: Dave Morris **Assistant Manager:** Peter Lee **Coach:** Gerry Luczka.
Ground: Crilly Park, Spa Road, Atherton, Greater Manchester (01942 883950).
Directions: M61 to Jct 5, follow signs for Westhoughton, left onto A6, right onto A579 (Newbrook Rd/Bolton Rd) over the railway bridge, right into Upton Rd passing Atherton Central Station, left into Springfield Rd and left again into Hillside Rd into Spa Rd and ground.
Seats: 250 **Cover:** 3 sections **Capacity:** 3,000 **Floodlights:** Yes
Club Shop: Yes, selling programmes etc. Contact Mrs C Pottinger 01942 875304.
Record Gate: 1,856 v Aldershot Town, FA Vase Quarter-Final replay 5/3/94.
Colours: Yellow/blue/blue **Change colours:** Royal/yellow/yellow.
Previous leagues: Bolton Combination/ Cheshire County 80-82/ North West Counties 82-94.
Reserve Team's League: North West Alliance.
Club Sponsors: Norweb (Retail).
Previous Name: Laburnum Rovers 54-79
Previous Grounds: Laburnum Road 54-56/ Hagfold 56-66.
Best FA Cup season: Second Qualifying Round replay 90-91 (lost 0-4 at Bangor City after 0-0 draw).
Best FA Vase season: Semi-Final replay 94-95 (lost 1-2 to Diss Town).
Best FA Trophy season: 1995/96.
Clubhouse: Open normal licensing hours.
Midweek Matches: Tuesday
Players progressing to Football League: Barry Butler (Chester).
Local Newspapers: Bolton Evening News, Manchester Evening News, Leigh Reporter.
Club Record Scorer: Sean Parker
Club record appearances: Jim Evans.
Captain 95-96: Jim Evans.
Top Scorer 95-96: Joey Dunn.
Player of the Year 94-95: Joey Dunn.
Honours:: North West Counties Lg 92-93 94-95 (Champions Cup 92-93), FA Vase Semi-Finalists 94-95.

PROGRAMME DETAILS:
Pages: 48 **Price:** 70p
Editor: Peter Jones
(0942 883950)

Formed: 1878

BRADFORD PARK AVENUE

Avenue

Bradford Park Avenue are back in Bradford at last and are now playing at The Horsfall Stadium, Bradford. Photo - R Sims

Chairman: Mike Firth. **President:** Charlie Atkinson.

Secretary: Alan Hirst, 24 Quarryfields, Mirfield, West Yorks WF14 0NT. Tel. 0192480349 (Home), 01924 474477 (Bus).

Manager: **Asst Manager:** Dave Heeley

Physio: Ray Killick. **Press Officer:** T R Clapham. **Commercial Manager:** Garry Sawyer

Ground: Horsfall Stadium, Cemetery Road, Bradford, West Yorks ND6 2NG.

Directions: M62 Jct 26. Go along M606 to the end. At the roundabout go along the A6036 (signposted Halifax) and pass Odsal Stadium on left hand side. At next roundabout take the 3rd exit A6036 (Halifax), in approx. 1 mile turn left down Cemetery Road (by Kings Head Pub). Ground 150 yards on left.

Seats: 1,300 **Cover:** 2,000. **Capacity:** 5,000 **Floodlights:** Yes **Reformed:** 1988

Record Gate: 1,740 v Leeds Utd, pre-season 1989 (at Batley).

Colours: Green/White Shirts, White Shorts, Green/White socks.

Change colours: Amber/red/black.

Midweek Matches: Wednesday.

Nickname: Avenue

Club Shop: Yes - contact G Sawyer (01274 607780).

Previous Leagues: West Riding County Amtr 88-89, Central Mids 89-90.N.W.Counties90-95.

Prev. Grounds: Manningham Mills, Bradford 88-89/ Bramley R.L.F.C., McLaren Field, Bramley, Leeds 89-93, Batley 93-96.

Record win: 6-0 v Penrith (A) 92-93

Record defeat: 0-6 v Gainsborough Town (A) 89-90.

Club record scorer: Darren Wardman 85.

Club record appearances: Peter Edmondson 176.

Captain 95-96: Tony Pearson

Top Scorer 95-96: Milton Brown.

P.o.Y. 95-96: Mark Price.

Best FA Cup year: Second Qual. Rd 92-93 (01-2 at Accrington)

Hons: West Riding Snr Cup 90-91,N.W.Lg Champions 94-95,N.W.Carling Challenge trophy 94-95.

PROGRAMME DETAILS:
Pages: 36 **Price:** £1.00
Editor: Tim Clapham

Formed: 1901

CONGLETON TOWN

Humbugs/Bears

Congleton Town Squad

Chairman: Paul Marshall.
Secretary and Press Officer: David Wilcock, 4,Maxwell Rd., Congleton, Cheshire. CW12 3HY.(H) 01260 276347 or (W) 01260 270275.
Manager: Nigel Deeley. **Physio:** Gary Yeo. **Press Officer:** Carolyne Slater.
Ground: Booth Street Ground, Crescent Road, Congleton, Cheshire (0260 274460).
Directions: On approach to Congleton via Clayton bypass take second right after fire station, into Booth Street. Two miles from Congleton (BR).
Capacity: 5,000 **Cover:** 1,200 **Seats:** 250 **Floodlights:** Yes
Club Shop: Yes.Contact: Robert Fletcher.
Colours: White & black flashes/black/black & white **Change colours:** All red.
Previous Leagues: Crewe & Dist/ North Staffs/ Macclesfield/ Cheshire 20-39 46-65 78-82/ Mid Cheshire 68-78/ North West Counties 82-87.
Previous Name: Congleton Hornets *(prior to 1901).*
Midweek home matchday: Tuesday.
Record Attendance: 7,000 v Macclesfield, League 53-54.
Best FA Trophy season: 3rd Qualifying Rd 89-90 90-91
Best FA Vase season: 4th Rd 76-77 80-81.
Best FA Cup season: 1st Rd 89-90 (lost 0-2 at Crewe).
League clubs defeated in FA Cup: None.
Record Fees - Paid: None
Received: £5,000 for D Frost (Leeds).
Players progressing to Football League: Ron Broad (Crewe 1955), Jack Mycock (Shrewsbury 1958), Steve Davies (Port Vale 1987), L Hamlet (Leeds), Jimmy Quinn (West Ham, N Ireland), Ian Brightwell (Man City).
Clubhouse: Open match days only.
Club Record Goalscorer: Mick Biddle (150+)
Club Record Appearances: Ray Clack (600+)
95-96 Captain: Paul Cuddy.
95-96 P.o.Y.: Richard Bland. **95-96 Top Scorer:** Joey Roberts.
Local Newspapers: Congleton Chronicle (0260 273737), Staffs Evening Sentinel (0782 289800).
Local Radio Stations: Radio Stoke, Signal.
Honours: North West Counties Lge R-up 85-86; Cheshire County Lge R-up 20-21 21-22 (Div 2 81-82); Mid Cheshire Lge 73-74 75-76 77-78 (R-up 69-70 71-72 76-77, Lge Cup 71-72), Cheshire Senior Cup 20-21 37-38.

PROGRAMME DETAILS:
Pages: 48 **Price:** 60p.
Editor: Paul Marshall.

CURZON ASHTON

Formed: 1963 — Curzon

Curzon Ashton's Gary Randles beats Gretna's Dean Wilkinson. *Photo Alan Watson*

Chairman: Harry Galloway **Chief Executive:** Harry Twamley. **President:** Peter Mayo.
Secretary: Alun Jones, 36 Forrest Road, Denton, Manchester M34 1RL (0161 336 8004).
Manager: Terry McLean. **Assistant Manager:**
Physio: Malcolm Liptrot. **Press Officer:** Barry Thorpe
Ground: National Park, Katherine Street, Ashton-under-Lyne OL7 6DA (0161 330 6033).
Directions: Behind Ashton police station off Manchester Rd (A635), Ashton-under-Lyne, one and a half miles from Ashton-under-Lyne (BR).
Capacity: 5,000 **Cover:** 450 **Seats:** 350 **Floodlights:** Yes **Nickname:** Curzon.
Club Shop: Yes. Contact: Roy Howe (0161 2208345).
Colours: All Blue. **Change colours:** Yellow/green/yellow.
Sponsors: Byford Computer Services/ P M Communications.
Kit Sponsors: Coral Travel **Away Kit Sponsor:** P.D.A.International.
Previous Lges: Manchester Amtr/ Manchester (until 1978)/ Cheshire Co. 78-82/ North West Co's 82-87.
Midweek home matchday: Tuesday. **Record Gate:** 1,826 v Stamford, FA Vase SF 1980.
Best FA Cup season: Third Qualifying Round replay 89-90 (lost 1-3 at Mossley after 1-1 draw).
Record win: 7-0 v Ashton United. **Record defeat:** 0-8 v Bamber Bridge.
Record Transfer Fees
Paid: £1,000 for Garry Stewart (Witton Albion, 1993)
Received: £3,000 for Keith Evans (Ashton Utd.).
Players progressing to Football League: Gordon Taylor (Bolton 1962), Steve Wigley (Nottm Forest 1981), Malcolm O'Connor (Rochdale 1983), Eric Nixon (Man. City 1983).
Clubhouse: Open every night. Food on matchdays. Function room for private hire. Also, five-a-side astro pitch available for hire every day.
Club Record Goalscorer: Alan Sykes
Club Record Appearances: Alan Sykes 620.
95-96 Captain: Gary Finley. **95-96 P.o.Y.:** Malcolm O'Connor.
95-96 Top scorer: Malcolm O'Connor.
Local Newspapers: Ashton Reporter, 0161 303 1910.
Local Radio Stations: Manchester Radio, Piccadilly.
Honours: FA Vase SF 79-80, Cheshire County League Div 2 R-up 78-79 (Reserve Div 81-82), Manchester League 77-78 (R-up 74-75 75-76, League Cup 77-78 (R-up 74-75 75-76), Murray Shield R-up 75-76, Reserve Div 74-75 75-76 76-77 77-78), Manchester Amateur League 63-64 65-66 (R-up 64-65 79-80(Res) 80-81(Res)), Manchester Premier Cup 81-82 83-84 85-86 86-87 89-90, Manchester Intermediate Cup 71-72 72-73 73-74 (R-up 70-71), Manchester Amateur Cup R-up 63-64, Ashton Challenge Cup 64-65 67-68, Philips F'lit Cup R-ups 77-78, FA Trophy 2nd Qualifying Rd 82-83 84-85, North West Counties Reserve Div 82-83 84-85 (R-up 83-84, League Cup 84-85 (R-up 83-84 85-86)), Northern Combination Supplemently Cup 87-88 88-89, South East Lancs League Shield R-up 84-85.

PROGRAMME DETAILS:
Pages: 16 **Price:** 50p
Editor: Barry Thorpe

DROYLSDEN

Formed: 1892

The Bloods

Droylsden's Dave Ashton closely marking Trevor Jones of Stocksbridge Park Steels. Photo - Colin Stevens

Chairman: David Pace
Secretary: Bernard King, 22 Hart Street, Droylsden, Manchester M43 7AW. Tel. 0161 2855232 (Home), Fax 0161 3701426.
Manager: Tommy Lawson. **Asst Manager:** Alan Blair.
Ground: The Butchers Arms Ground, Market Street, Droylsden, Manchester (0161 370 1426).
Directions: 4 miles east of Manchester via A662 Ashton New Road, behind Butchers Arms Hotel.
Capacity: 3,500 **Cover:** 2,000 **Seats:** 500 **Shop:** Yes **Metal Badges:** Yes.
Colours: Red/white/red **Change colours:** Green/white/green.
Prevs Leagues: Manchester/ Lancs Com 36-39 50-68/ Cheshire County 39-50 68-82/ NW Counties 82-87.
Midweek matchday: Wednesday. **Reserve Team:** None.
Sponsors: Alpha Court Windows/ Hastings Taxis.
Record Attendance: 4,250 v Grimsby, FA Cup 1st rd 1976.
Best FA Cup season: 2nd Rd 78-79.
League clubs defeated in FA Cup: Rochdale 78-79.
Record transfer fees received: £11,000 for Tony Naylor (Crewe).
Record win: 13-2 v Lucas Sports Club.
Players progressing to Football League: Albert Butterworth & F Letchford (Blackpool 1931), William Davies & Maurice Randall (Crewe 1947), William Mellor (Accrington 1950), Geoff Tonge (Bury 1960), David Campbell (WBA 1962), Kevin Randall (Bury 1965), Peter Litchfield (Preston 1979), Tony Naylor (Crewe 1990).
Clubhouse: Pub hours except atchdays. Pool and darts.
Club Record Scorer: E Gillibrand 78 (1931-32)
95-96 Captain:
95-96 P.o.Y.: Nigel Evans.
95-96 Top scorer: Nigel Evans.
Local Newspapers: Droylsden Reporter (0161 303 1910), Advertiser.
Local Radio Stations: BBC Manchester.
Honours: Northern Prem League Division 1 Runners-up 89-90 (Division 1 Cup 87-88), NW Counties League Division 2 86-87, Cheshire County League Runners-up 39-40 45-46 (League Cup 77-78 (Runners-up 76-77)), Lancs Comb Division 2 Runners-up 55-56 58-59 62-63, Manchester League 30-31 32-33 (League Cup 23-24 33-34), Manchester Premier Cup 80-81 (Runners-up 83-84 90-91 93-94), Manchester Senior Cup 72-73 75-76 78-79 (Runners-up 72-73 75-76 78-79), Manchester Intermediate Cup 59-60 64-65 69-70, Manchester Challenge Shield 46-47.

PROGRAMME DETAILS:
Pages: 20 **Price:** 80p
Editor: John Schofield

Formed: 1953

EASTWOOD TOWN

The Badgers

Back Row (L-R): Adrian Hall, John Knapper, Carl Flint, Mark Place, Richard Parkin, Scott Downer, Asa Ingall, Richard Mellon, Martin Connelly. Front Row: Kieran Heath, Lee Marshall, Kris Hoy, Martyn Chadbourne, Shaun Browne, Jamie Roberts, John Jaynes, Jamie Marshall, Simon Johnson.

Chairman: George Belshaw **Vice Chairman:** Richard James **President:**
Sec./Press Off.: Paddy Farrell, 7 Primrose Rise, Newthorpe, Notts NG16 2BB (Tel/Fax: 01773 715500).
Manager: Bryan Chambers **Reserves' Mgr:** Paul McFarland **Physio:** Derek Myatt.
Ground: Coronation Park, Eastwood, Notts (01773 715823).
Directions: From North - M1 junction 27 then follow Heanor signs via Brinsley to lights in Eastwood. Turn left then first right after Fire Station - ground entrance on Chenton Street. Nearest rail station is Langley Mill. Buses every 10 mins (R11, R12 or R13) from Victoria Centre, Nottingham.
Capacity: 5,500 **Cover:** 1,150 **Seats:** 200 **Floodlights:** Yes **Metal Badges:** Yes
Club Shop: Yes, selling programmes, mugs, scarves, badges etc. Contact R.K. Storer (0115 938 5239).
Colours: Black & white stripes/black/black **Change Colours:** Jellow/Blue/Yellow.
Previous Leagues: Notts Alliance 53-61/ Central Alliance 61-67/ East Midlands 67-71/ Midland Counties 71-82/ Northern Counties (East) 82-87.
Prevs Names: None **Prevs Ground:** Coronation Park 1953-65 **Midweek matchday:** Tuesday
Best F.A. Cup season: Final Qualifying Rd replay 75-76 (lost 0-1 at Wycombe Wanderers).
Record Attendance: 2,723 v Enfield, FA Amateur Cup, February 1965.
Record win: 26-0 **Record defeat:** 1-7.
Record Fees - Paid: £500 for Jamie Kay, Gainsborough Trinity 90-91.
Received: £72,500 for Richard Liburd (Middlesbrough 92-93).
Players progressing to Football League: John Butlet (Notts County 1957), Tony Woodcock (Nottm Forest), Paul Richardson (Derby), Alan Buckley, Steve Buckley (Luton), Richard Liburd (Middlesbrough 92-93), Martin Bullock (Barnsley 94-95).
Clubhouse: Large social club open daily - normal licensing hours (Sat 11am-11pm, midweek matches 6.30-11pm). Hot & cold food available.
Steward: Mr Peter Leadwood.
Club Record Goalscorer: Martin Wright
Club Record Appearances: Arthur Rowley, over 800 1st team games, but not a single booking, 1955-76.
95-96 Captain: Everton Marsh.
95-96 P.o.Y.: Mark Place **95-96 Top scorer:** Neil Illman.
Sponsors: Tricon Automotive.
Local Newspapers: Eastwood Advertiser (01773 713563), Nottingham Evening Post (01602 482000), Derby Telegraph (01332 291111).
Local Radio Stations: Radio Nottingham, Radio Trent.
Honours: Nth Counties (East) Lg R-up 82-83 84-85, Mid Counties Lg 75-76 (R-up 74-75 77-78, Lg Cup 77-78 79-80), Central Alliance 63-64 (R-up 64-65), Notts Alliance 56-57 (R-up [6], Lg Cup 55-56), E Midlands Lg R-up 68-69, Notts Sen Cup [9] (R-up 57-58 63-64 65-66), Evans Halshaw Floodlit Cup R-up 89-90 94-95, Notts Interm Cup 86-87, Ripley Hospital Charity Cup(6) 76-81, FA Trophy 1st Rd 78-79, FA Amateur Cup 3rd Rd replay 67-68.

PROGRAMME DETAILS:
Pages: 24 **Price:** 50p
Editor: P.Farrell.

Formed: 1908

FARSLEY CELTIC

Villagers

Farsley Celtic 1995-96; Back Row (L-R): Denis Metcalfe (Mgr), Ian McCreadie (physio), Steve Learoyd, Calvin Allen, Ben Carrington, Phil Sharpe, Wayne Baker, Nathan Dury, John McClelland, Alun Jones (Res Mgr). Front Row: Jason Day, Nigel Thompson, Richard Smith, Paul Cawthorne, Robbie Whellans, Richard Walker and Clive Freeman *Photo: Yorkshire Evening Post.*

Chairman: John E Palmer **Vice Chairman:** Paul Robinson.
Secretary: Mrs Margaret Lobley, 29 Spring Bank Road, Farsley, Leeds, West Yorks LS28 5LS (01132 575675).
Manager: M.Haresign **Coach:** J.Macay. **Physio:** Ian McGready **Press Officer:** D.Metcalf.
Ground: Throstle Nest, Newlands, Farsley, Pudsey, Leeds LS28 5BE (01532 561517).
Directions: From North East: A1 south to Wetherby, A58 to Leeds, at 1st island (approx 8 miles) take 3rd exit (A6120 ring-rd), follow Bradford signs to 12th r'bout (approx 12 miles) - 1st exit (B6157 Stanningley). From M62 jct 26, M606 (Bradford) to r'bout, 4th exit (A6177) passing Rooley pub on left, continue on Rooley Lane - Sticker Lane passing Morrisons store on left to lights (approx 3 miles) - right onto A647 (Leeds) to 2nd r'bout, 2nd exit (B6157 Stanningley). Continue 800yds passing Police & Fire Stations on left. Turn left down New Street at Tradex warehouse before turning right into Newlands. Ground at bottom of road. 1 mile from New Pudsey (BR).
Capacity: 4,000 **Cover:** 1,000 **Seats:** 430 **Floodlights:** Yes **Metal Badges:** Yes.
Club Shop: Yes. League and non-League programmes and magazines. Club badges, scarves, ties, sweaters, training suits, polo and T-shirts. Various souvenirs and photographs. Contact Brian Falkingham (01132 550749) at 27 Rycroft Court, Leeds LS13 4PE.
Colours: Sky & navy/navy/navy **Change colours:** All white.
Previous Grounds: Red Lane/ Calverley Lane, Farsley (prior to 1948).
Prev. Lges: West Riding County Amateur/ Leeds Red Triangle/ Yorkshire 49-82/ Northern Counties (East) 82-87.
Midweek home matchday: Wednesday
Reserve Team's League: Northern Counties (E) Reserve Div.
Record Attendance: 11,000 (at Elland Road) v Tranmere Rovers, FA Cup 1st Rd 1974.
Best FA Cup season: 1st Rd 74-75 (see above). Lost 0-2.
League clubs defeated in FA Cup: None.
Best FA Amateur Cup season: Third Round, 34-35.
Players progressing to Football League: Barry Smith (Leeds 1951), Paul Madeley (Leeds 1962), William Roberts (Rochdale 1988), Stuart McCall (Bradford City, Everton, Scotland).
Clubhouse: Lounge, games room and committee room open every evening and Friday and weekend lunchtimes. New multi-purpose Leisure Centre available evenings and afternoons.
95-96 Captain: Nigel Smith.
95-96 P.o.Y.: R.Whellans. **95-96 Top scorer:** R.Whellans.
Local Newspapers: Yorkshire Evening Post, Telegraph & Argus, Pudsey Times.
Local Radio Stations: Radio Leeds, Radio Aire, Radio Pennine.
Honours: FA Vase QF 87-88, West Riding County Cup 57-58 59-60 66-67 70-71 83-84 87-88 95-96, Yorkshire League 59-60 68-69 (R-up 57-58 58-59 70-71 71-72, Div 2 51-52, League Cup 62-63 63-64 66-67).

PROGRAMME DETAILS:
Pages: 26 **Price:** 60p
Editor: John Williams.

FLIXTON

Formed: 1960

Valley Roaders

Newly promoted Flixton's impressive 'home' at Valley Road.

Chairman: A Edge **Vice Chairman:** **President:** F H Eadie
Sec./Press Off.: John Fradley, 3 Hawthorn Road, Stretford, Manchester M32 8WE, (0161 865 0418)
Manager: Dalton Steele **Asst Manager:** Steve Smythe **Physio:** Dave Stevens
Ground: Valley Road, Flixton, Manchester M31 2RQ (0161 748 2903).
Directions: M63 Jct 3, B5214 (signed Urmston), follow Trafford General Hosp. signs, at 4th r'bout take 3rd exit (Woodbridge Rd), ground at top. One and a quarter miles from Flixton BR station (trains from Manchester Oxford Rd) - turn right out of station onto Flixton Rd, left after quarter mile into Woodsend Rd, at r'bout after quarter mile take 2nd exit into Woodbridge Rd - ground at top. Take any bus from Manchester Picadilly bus station to Flixton and alight at Flixton Red Lion.
Capacity: 2,000 **Cover:** 650 **Seats:** 250 **Floodlights:** Yes **Club Shop:** No
Colours: Sky blue & white stripes/blue/blue **Change Colours:** All red.
Previous Leagues: South Manchester & Wythenshawe 60-63/ Lanc & Cheshire 63-73/ Manchester 73-86.
Midweek home matchday: Tuesday **Record Attendance:** 1,543 v Brigg Town FA Vase Semi-Final 95-96
Best F.A. Cup season: 1st Qualifying Rd replay 91-92 (lost 1-2 at Mossley after 1-1 draw.
Best FA Vase season: Semi-final 1995-96
Record win: 10-2 Iriam 94-95
Record defeat: 1-10 v Knowsley Utd 90-91
Clubhouse: Open daily 12pm-11pm. Snacks available most evenings.
Club Record Goalscorer: John Mitchell
Club Record Appearances: John Mitchell/ Stan Matthews
95-96 Captain: Kojo Taylor.
95-96 P.o.Y.: Sean McWilliams **95-96 Top scorer:** Jimmy Clarke
Hons: N.W.Co Div I Champions and Cup Winners 95-96; NW Co's Lg Div 2 Winners 94-95; Lg.Cup Winners 94-95, R-up 87-88 (Div 3 R-up 86-87, Div 3 Cup SF 86-87, Res. Chal. Cup 87-88 90-91 (R-up 88-89 89-90 91-92 92-93), Res. Div East 89-90, Res. Div Sth 92-93); Manc. Lg R-up 78-79 81-82 85-86 (Div 1 77-78, Div 2(res) 82-83 85-86; Open Tphy 80-81; Lancs Amtr Cup 79-80 (R-up 80-81); Manc. Chal. Tphy 83-84 (R-up(2) 84-86); Manc. Prem. Cup R-up 86-87 91-92; Manc. Amtr Cup R-up 88-89.

PROGRAMME DETAILS:
Pages: 36 **Price:** 50p
Editor: Secretary.

1978 **# GREAT HARWOOD TOWN** Robins

Great Harwood Town's 'Showground'.

Chairman: William Holden.
Secretary: Roy Smith, 56 Gladstone St., Gt.Harwood.Blackburn.BB6 7NH.(01254 877908)
Manager: Martin Eatough. **Asst Manager:** Dave Sargent. **Coach:**
Press Officer: K Lambert **Commercial Manager:** Mark Smith.
Ground: The Showground, Wood Street, Great Harwood, Lancs (01254 883913).
Directions: M66 from Manchester to Haslingden exit, A680 through Baxenden, Accrington to Clayton-le-Moors, left at the Hyndburn Bridge Hotel into Hyndburn Road and right into Wood Street to ground. Or M6 jct 31, Clitheroe/Skipton road to Trafalgar Hotel, A677 to Blackburn, left at Moat House Hotel and follow ring-road to M65 junction, A678 to Rishton, left at lights (B6536) to Gt Harwood, right at Town Gate into Queen Str., follow signs for Lomax Square, left into Park Rd, right into Balfour Street to ground. 3 miles from Rishton (BR), 6 miles from Blackburn (BR). Various buses from Heyes Lane & Park Road to Blackburn & Accrington.
Seats: 200 **Cover:** 700 **Capacity:** 2,500 **Floodlights:** Yes
Colours: All red **Change colours:** All blue.
Club Shop: Yes, selling programmes, badges, key rings, shirts. Contact:Jean Smith(c/o club).
Reserve Team: West Lancs Lge **Record Gate:** 5,397 v Manchester Utd, 1980
Midweek Matches: Monday. **Club Sponsors:** None at present.
Previous Name: Great Harwood Wellington.
Previous Leagues: West Lancashire/ Lancs Combination 79-82/ North West Counties 82-92.
Previous Ground: Park adjacent to the Showground until demise of Great Harwood FC in 1978.
Record win: 7-0 v Farsley Celtic (H), NPL Division One 1992-93.
Record defeat: 0-6 v Spennymoor United (H), NPL Division One, 1994-95.
Best FA Cup season: 1st Qualifying Round replay 92-93 (lost 1-2 at home to Atherton LR after 1-1 draw).
Best FA Vase season: Quarter Finals 90-91 (lost 1-2 at Littlehampton Town).
Clubhouse: Yes - The Sportsman just outside ground. Normal licensing hours. Full bar facilities. Squash courts and gym. Hot & cold snacks and drinks on matchdays from tea bar within ground.
95-96 Captain:
95-96 Top Scorer:
95-96 Player of the Year: Ian Lang. **Hons:** North West Counties League R-up 91-92 (Div 2 90-91, Lamot Pils Tphy 89-90 (R-up 90-91), Tennents Floodlit Trophy 91-92), Lancs ATS Challenge Trophy 91-92 (R-up 90-91).

PROGRAMME DETAILS:
Pages: 20 **Price:** 20p
Editor: G.Snowden.

GRETNA

1946 Black & whites

Gretna FC: Back Row (L-R); Billy Bentley, Shane Bird, Les Armstrong, Tony Monaghan, Gavin Armstrong, Derek Townsley, Marc Irwin, Jason Jones, John Thompson. Front; Dean Wuilkinson, Derek Walsh, Craig Potts, Andy Walker, Gary Forbes, Mike McCartney (Player/Mgr), Craig Watson (Mascot).

Photo - Alan Watson

Chairman: Brian Fulton **President:** Thomas Kerr.
Secretary: Ron MacGregor, Brackenhurst, Lochmaben, Lockerbie, Scotland. DG11 1QA (01387 811820).
Physio: William Bentley **Manager:** Michael McCartney
Ground: Raydale Park, Dominion Rd., Gretna, Dumfriesshire (01461 337602).
Directions: 8 miles north of Carlisle on A74. Take slip road to Gretna over border bridge, left at Crossways Inn for Township along Annan Rd for quarter of a mile, left into Dominion Rd, ground on right. Buses leave Carlisle on the half hour. Also trains from Carlisle.
Seats: 385 **Cover:** 800 **Capacity:** 2,200 **Floodlights:** Yes
Club Shop: Yes, contact Alan Watson on 01387 251550.
Club colours: Black & white hoops/black/black & white **Change colours:** All blue.
Previous Leagues: Dumfriesshire Amateur 47-47/ Carlisle & District 47-51/ Cumberland 51-52/ Northern 83-92.
Midweek Matches: Tuesday
Record Gate: 2,307 v Rochdale, F.A. Cup First Round Proper, 16/11/92.
Midweek matchday: Tuesday
Previous Ground: Station Park 1946-47.
Club Sponsors: Gables Hotel.
Record win: 13-0 **Record defeat:** 1-5.
Best season in FA Trophy: Third Round 90-91.
Best season in FA Cup: 1st Round Proper 1991-92 (lost 1-3 in replay at Rochdale).
Players progressing to Football League: John Hamilton (Hartlepool United) 1982, Russell Black & Don Peattie (Sheffield United) 1984, Mark Dobie (Cambridge United).
Clubhouse: Bar, lounge, TV room, concert room. Cooked meals available. Open every day. Late bar at weekends.
Club record scorer: Denis Smith
Club record appearances: William Cross.
95-96 Captain:
95-96 Top Scorer: Andy Walker.
95-96 P.o.Y.: Derek Townsley.
Local Newspapers: Cumberland News
Honours: Northern Lg 90-91 91-92 (Lg Cup 90-91), Cumberland Senior Cup (9), JR Cleator Cup 89-90 90-91 91-92, Craven Cup 91-92, Carlisle & Dist. Lg (28)(Charity Shield(25), Lg Cup(20), Benevolent Cup(15)).

PROGRAMME DETAILS:
Pages: 28 **Price:** 80p
Editor: R.MacGregor.
(01387 811820)

Formed: 1919

HARROGATE TOWN

Harrogate keeper Andy McWilliam saves from Gretna's Andy Walker (on ground).

Photo - Alan Watson.

Chairman: George Dunnington **President:** C Margolis.
Secretary: Roy Dalby, 123a Dene Park, Harrogate, North Yorkshire HG1 4JX (01423 567973).
General Manager: Alan Smith **Coach:** Mick Doig.
Youth Development Coach: Malcolm Richardson.
Ground: Wetherby Road, Harrogate. (01423 883671 (880675-press)).
Directions: From Leeds turn right at traffic lights (Appleyard's) into Hookstone Road, continue to Woodlands Hotel (traffic lights) turn left into Wetherby Road, ground on the right. From Harrogate (BR), turn left and left again, cross road (Odeon Cinema), proceed for about 400yds to main road, cross over to The Stray (open land) using footpath which leads to Wetherby Rd, ground 200yds on left.
Capacity: 3,800 **Cover:** 600 **Seats:** 450 **Floodlights:** Yes **Metal Badges:** Yes
Club Shop: Yes, selling scarves, ties, pens shirts and other common souvenirs.
Colours: Yellow/black/yellow **Change colours:** All blue.
Previous Names: Harrogate FC 26-34/ Harrogate Hotspurs 36-50.
Previous Ground: Starbeck Lane 1919-20.
Previous Leagues: Yorkshire 20-21 22-31 51-82/ Midland 21-22/ Northern 31-32/ Harrogate & District 36-46/ West Yorkshire 46-51/ Northern Counties (East) 82-87.
Midweek home matchday: Tuesday
Reserve Team's Lge: Northern Co's (East) Reserve Div.
Club Sponsors: Crystal Motors.
Record Attendance: 3,208 v Starbeck LNER (now Harrogate R.A.), Whitworth Cup final 1948.
Best FA Vase season: 4th Round 89-90.
Best FA Cup season: 3rd Qualifying Rd 94-95 (lost 0-3 at Bishop Auckland).
League clubs defeated in FA Cup: None.
Record win: 9-1 v Winsford
Record defeat: 0-7; v Hyde Utd & v Lancaster City.
Players progressing to Football League: Tony Ingham (Leeds) 1947, Stewart Ferebee (York City 1979), Tim Hotte (Halifax Town 1985), Andy Watson (Halifax Town 1988),Ian Blackstone York City 1995)
Clubhouse: On ground, open Tuesday, Thursday and every other Wednesday in addition to every matchday. Sandwiches available.
95-96 Captain: Gary Lormor.
95-96 P.o.Y.: Gary Lormor.
95-96 Top scorer: Rick Greenough.
Local Newspapers: Yorkshire Post, Harrogate Herald Advertiser.
Local Radio Stations: Radio Leeds, Radio York, local hospital radio.
Honours: Northern Premier League Division 1 Cup 89-90, Northern Counties (East) Division 1 (Nth) R-up 84-85 (Reserve Division 85-86, Reserve Division Cup 86-87), Yorkshire League Division 1 26-27 (Division 2 81-82, Division 3 R-up 71-72 80-81), West Riding County Cup 62-63 72-73 85-86, West Riding Challenge Cup 24-25 26-27.

PROGRAMME DETAILS:
Pages: 32 **Price:** 60p
Editor: R Chambers/ T Moseley

Formed: 1896

LEIGH RMI

Railwaymen

Leigh's Chris Shaw in action against Congleton *Photo - Bolton Evening News*

Chairman: Chris Healey. **President:** G H Fisher.
Secretary: Alan Robinson, 55,Janice Drive, Fulwood, Preston, Lancs. PR2 9TY.(01772 719266).
Manager: Steve Waywell. **Asst Manager/Coach:** Kevin Booth. **Press Officer:** P O'Berg
Ground: Hilton Park, Kirkhall Lane, Leigh. WN7 1RN.
Capacity: 8000. **Cover:** 4,000. **Seats:** 2,000. **Floodlights:** Yes. **Club Shop:** Not Yet.
Colours: Red & white stripes/black/white.
Change colours: Yellow & black/white/white.
Previous Name: Horwich R.M.I. FC.
Midweek home matchday: Tuesday.
Previous Leagues: Lancs Alliance 1891-97/ Lancs 1897-1900/ Lancs Combination 17-18 19-39 46-68/ Cheshire County 68-82/ North West Counties 82-83.
Reserve Team's League: Preston and District Football League.
Sponsors: Dunhall Financial Services **Record Gate:** 4,500.
Best FA Cup season: 1st Rd 28-29 82-83.
Record Fee Received: £5,000 for Tony McDonald (Chorley).
Players progressing to Football League: H Lea, D Holland, J Cunliffe (Stockport 58 & 59 & 60), F Wignall (Everton 58), G Cooper (Rochdale 73), T Caldwell (Bolton 83), R Redshaw (Wigan 84), T Ellis (Oldham 86).
Clubhouse: Yes.
Local Newspapers: Bolton Evening News (Bolton 52345).
Local Radio Stations: Radio Lancs, Red Rose Radio, G.M.R.
95-96 Captain: **95-96 P.o.y.:**
95-96 Top Scorer:
Club Record Appearances:
Club Record Goalscorer:
Honours: FA Trophy QF 90-91, Premier Inter League (GMAC) Cup 87-88, Cheshire County Lg 78-79 (Challenge Shield 78-79), Lancs Combination 57-58 (R-up 29-30 55-56 66-67, Lg Cup 28-29 53-54 56-57 65-66, Div 2 R-up 48-49 50-51), West Lancs Lg 10-11 11-12, Lancs Junior Cup 24-25 29-30 (R-up 53-54 57-58 62-63 82-83), Lancs Floodlit Trophy 84-85 (R-up 83-84), Lancs FA Cup 84-85.

PROGRAMME DETAILS:
Pages: 32 **Price:** 80p
Editor: Garry Culshaw

1938

LINCOLN UNITED

United

Lincoln United:

President: A Simpson **Chairman:** K Roe **Vice Chairman:** Maurice Bull.
Secretary/Press Officer: Keith Weaver, 22 Grainsby Close, Lincoln LN6 7QF (01522 531832).
Manager: Gary Goddard **Asst Manager:** Gerard Creane **Coach:** John Wilkinson.
Physio: Anthony Adams **Commercial Manager:** Roy Parnham.
Ground: Ashby Avenue, Hartsholme, Lincoln (01522 690674).
Directions: From Newark A46 onto Lincoln relief road (A446), right at 2nd r'bout for Birchwood (Skellingthorpe Rd), go for 1 mile passing lake and Country Park, 1st right 10yds after 30mph sign into Ashby Ave., ground entrance 200 yds, opposite Old Peoples home. 3 miles from Lincoln Central (BR).
Capacity: 2,714. **Seats:** 400. **Covered:** 1,084. **Floodlights:** Yes **Club Shop:** Yes
Colours: All white **Change Colours:** Red/Black.
Clubhouse: Open every day normal licensing hours. Matchday snack bar - hot & cold food & drinks.
Prev. Lges: Lincs 45-48 60-67/ Lincoln 48-60/ Yorks 67-82/ Northern Co's East 82-86/ Central Mids 82-92.
Prev. Grounds: Skew Bridge (1940's)/ Co-op Spts Ground (til mid-60's)/ Hartsholme Cricket Grnd (til '82).
Previous Name: Lincoln Amateurs (until an ex-prof signed in 54).
Record Gate: 2,000 v Crook Town, FA Amat Cup 1st Rd Prop 68.
Best FA Cup season: 1st Rd Proper 91-92 (lost 0-7 at Huddersfield Town).
Club Sponsors: Hykeham Forum Supplies/ City Tyre Experts.
Midweek matchday: Tuesday **Reserve League:** Lincolnshire.
Record win: 12-0 v Pontefract Colls 95..
Record defeat: 0-7 v Huddersfield T FA Cup 1st Rd Proper 91
Record transfer fee paid: £250 for Dean Dye (Sutton Town 90)
Record transfer fee received: £3,000 for Dean Dye (Charlton Ath 91).
95-96 Captain: Darren Bye.
95-96 Top Scorer:
95-96 P.o.Y.:
Record scorer: Terry Nelson 189
Record appearances: Brian Davies 439.
Local Newspapers: Lincolnshire Echo, Lincoln Standard.
Hons: Northern Co's (E) Lg Div 1 92-93 (Div 1 Sth 82-83, Div 2 85-86, Presidents Cup 94-95); Yorks Lg 70-71 73-74 (Lg Cup 70-71); Lincs Lg 63-64; Lincs Snr 'A' Cup 72-73 85-86 (R-up 91-92 94-95, 'B' Cup 63-64 70-71); Central Mids Lg 91-92 (Wakefield Cup 90-91); Evans Halshaw Floodlit Cup R-up 92-93; Lincs I'mediate Cup(7) 67-73 80-81; N.Co.East Prem Div.Champions 94-95; Blankney Hunt Inter Lge 95-96, Cup 95-96.

PROGRAMME DETAILS:
Pages: 40 **Price:** 50p
Editor: John Wilkinson

Formed: 1885

MATLOCK TOWN

The Gladiators

Matlock defend resolutely at their picturesque Causeway Lane Ground against Bamber Bridge.
Photo - Rob Ruddock

Chairman: Donald T Carr
Secretary: K F Brown, 'Barncroft', 1 Malvern Gardens, Matlock DE4 3JH (01629 584231).
Manager: Imre Varadi. **Physio:**
Press Officer: G M Tomlinson. **Commercial Manager:** Mrs S Tomlinson.
Ground: Causeway Lane, Matlock, Derbyshire (01629 583866).
Directions: On A615, 500 yds from town centre and Matlock (BR).
Capacity: 7,500 **Cover:** 2,000 **Seats:** 240 **Floodlights:** Yes
Club Shop: Yes. Contact: Sue Tomlinson (01629 583866)
Colours: All Royal blue. **Change colours:** All yellow.
Sponsors: Westons of Wirksworth/ Panasonic.
Previous Ground: Hall Leys (last century).
Previous Leagues: Midland Counties 1894-96 1961-69/ Matlock & District/ Derbys Senior/ Central Alliance 24-25 47-61/ Central Combination 34-35/ Chesterfield & District 46-47.
Midweek home matchday: Tuesday
Record Attendance: 5,123 v Burton Albion, FA Trophy 1975.
Best FA Cup season: 3rd Rd 76-77. Also 1st Rd 1885-86 86-87 86-87 87-88 1959-60 74-75 75-76 89-90.
League clubs defeated in FA Cup: Mansfield Town 76-77.
Record Fees - Paid: £300 for Mick Chambers (Grantham)
Received: £10,000 for Ian Helliwell (York).
Players progressing to Football League: Keith Haines (Leeds 1959), Wayne Biggins (Burnley 1984), Darren Bradshaw (Chesterfield 1987), Les McJannet (Scarborough 1987), Ian Helliwell (York 1987).
Clubhouse: Gladiators Social Club, on ground, open six nights per week.
Local Newspapers: Matlock Mercury, Derbyshire Times.
Local Radio Stations: Radio Derby.
95-96 Captain:
95-96 P.o.Y.:
95-96 Top Scorer:
Honours: FA Trophy 74-75, Northern Premier League Runners-up 83-84 (League Cup 77-78, Shield 78-79), Midland Counties League 61-62 68-69, Central Alliance (North) 59-60 60-61 (Runners-up 61-62 62-63, Division 1 Cup Runners-up 61-62, Division 2 59-60, Division 2 Cup 59-60 60-61), Derbyshire Senior Cup 74-75 76-77 77-78 80-81 83-84 84-85 91-92 (Runners-up 60-61 72-73 73-74 75-76 80-81 81-82 82-83 89-90 93-94), Derbshire Divisional Cup (North) 61-62 (Runners-up 62-63), Evans Halshaw Floodlit Cup 88-89, Anglo-Italian Non-League Cup 1979.

PROGRAMME DETAILS:
Pages: 32 **Price:** 70p
Editor: I.Richardson.

NETHERFIELD

Formed: 1920 | The Field

Back Row (L-R): B Richardson (Asst Mgr), D Emmett, P Renwick, M Brown, T Wood, P Hodgson, D Burrows, G Cumberbatch, S Edmuondson (Mgr). Front Row: C Short, J Howard, G Yeo, S McCullough (Capt), P Gibson, L Blamire, I Aplin.

Chairman: Ian Needham **President:** Ty Power.
Match Secretary: Craig Campbell, 34 High Sparrowmire, Kendal Cumbria LA9 5PD (01539 725557).
Manager: Steve Edmondson. **Asst Manager:** Bruce Richardson.
Physio: TBA **Press Officer:** Peter Savage (01539 726488).
Ground: Parkside Road, Kendal, Cumbria (01539 727472).
Directions: M6 junction 36, follow signs for Kendal (South), right at lights, left at r-bout to 'K' Village - Parkside Rd on right opposite factory main offices - ground 400 yds. One and a half miles from Oxenholme (BR) station - bus service to 'K' village.
Capacity: 2,490. **Cover:** 1,000 **Seats:** 250 **Floodlights:** Yes **Club Shop:** No.
Colours: Black & white/black/white. **Change colours:** Yellow/blue/yellow **Sponsors:** 'K' shoes
Previous Leagues: Westmorland/ North Lancs/ Lancs Combination 45-68/ Northern Premier 68-83/ North West Counties 83-87.
Midweek home matchday: Tuesday **Reserve Team's League:** North West Alliance.
Record Attendance: 5,184 v Grimsby Town, FA Cup 1st Rd 1955.
Record win: 11-0 v Great Harwood 22/3/47.
Record defeat: 0-10 v Stalybridge Celtic 1/9/84.
Record transfer fee paid: Undisclosed for Tom Brownlee (Bradford City, 1966).
Record transfer fee received: £10,250 for Andy Milner (Man.City 1995).
Best FA Vase season: 3rd Rd 89-90
Best FA Trophy season: 2nd Rd 80-81.
Best FA Cup season: 2nd Rd replay 63-64 (lost 1-4 at Chesterfield after 1-1 draw), 2nd Rd 49-50, 1st Rd 45-46 48-49 52-53 54-55 55-56 64-65.
Players progressing to Football League: John Laidlaw (Carlisle 46), Louis Cardwell (Crewe 47), Herbert Keen (Barrow 53), Alec Aston (Preston 55), Horace Langstreth (Torquay 56), John Simpson (Lincoln 57), Dennis Rogers (Accrington 59), Tom Brownlee (Bradford City 65), Peter McDonnell (Bury 73), Keith Silken (Workington 73), Roger Wicks (Darlington 81), Andy Milner (Man City).
Clubhouse: The Park, open all matchdays. Pies & pasties available.
Club Record Goalscorer: Tom Brownlee
95-96 Captain: Steve McCullough
95-96 P.o.Y.: Steve McCullough **95-96 Top scorers:** Steve Watt.
Local Press: Westmorland Gazette (01539 720555), Lancaster Evening Post.
Local Radio Stations: Radio Cumbria, Red Rose.
Hons: Lancs Comb. 48-49 64-65 (R-up 45-46 53-54 61-62 63-64, Lg Cup 55-56 60-61), Westmorland Snr Cup(12) 24-25 31-33 35-36 46-48 63-64 65-66 71-72 86-87 89-89 90-91.

PROGRAMME DETAILS:
Pages: 36 **Price:** 80p
Editor: P Savage
(01539 726488)

1949 # RADCLIFFE BOROUGH Boro'

Radcliffe Borough FC 1995-96. *Photo - Andrew Chitty*

Chairman: Bernard Manning Jnr **President:** A A Swarbrick.
Directors: B.Manning Jnr., R.Doyle, G.E.Fielding, K.Glendon and D.Murgatroyd.
Company Sec: G E Fielding, 93 Callender St, Ramsbottom, Bury, Lancs BL0 9DU (01706 825299).
Football Club Sec: David Murgatroyd, 62,Croston Rd., Lostock Hall, Preston, PR5 5LA.(0161-724-8346)
Manager: Kevin Glendon **Asst Manager/Coach:** Jimmy Golder **Physio:** Roy Davies
Press Officer: M Collins **Commercial Co-ordinator:** David Johnston (01772-495306).
Ground: Stainton Park, Pilkington Road, Radcliffe, Lancs M26 0PE (0161 724 5937-club), (0161-724-8346 Office) and FAX 0161 723 3178. 9197).
Directions: M62 junction 17 - follow signs for Whitefield and Bury then A665 to Radcliffe. Through town centre, turn right into Unsworth Street (opposite Turf Hotel), ground half mile on left, Colshaw Close Easy. Half a mile from Radcliffe (BR).
Capacity: 3,000 **Cover:** 1,000 **Seats:** 350 **Floodlights:** Yes
Club Shop: Yes - contact Ryan Davies at ground.(0161-724-5937).
Colours: Blue/blue/white. **Change colours:** All white.
Sponsors: Comet Copiers. **Prevs Ground:** Bright Street 1949-70.
Previous Leagues: South East Lancs/ Manchester 53-63/ Lancs Combination 63-71/ Cheshire County 71-82/ North West Counties 82-87.
Midweek matchday: Tuesday **Reserve Team:** None.
Record Attendance: 1,468 v Caernarvon Town, North West Counties League 1983.
Best FA Trophy season: Third Round v Gateshead 1995-96.
Best FA Cup season: Second Qualifying Rounds replay 75-76 (lost 1-4 at Rossendale United after 2-2 draw).
Record Fees - Paid: £5,000 for Gary Walker (Buxton, 1991)
Received: £5,000 for Kevin Hulme (Bury, 1989).
Players progressing to Football League: Jim Hayman (Bury 1950), Ian Wood (Oldham Athletic 1965), Robert Hutchinson (Rochdale 1974), Gary Hawarth (Rochdale 1984), Kevin Hulme (Bury 1989).
Clubhouse: (0161 724 5937). 'The Borough'- public house on ground. No food available.
Club Record Goalscorer: Gary Haworth
Club Record Appearances: Chris Lilley.
95-96 Captain: Simon Whittle.
95-96 P.o.Y.: Andy Johnson. **95-96 Top scorer:** Ian Lunt 29.
Local Newspapers: Radcliffe Times, Bolton Evening News, Manchester Evening News.
Local Radio Stations: Grt Manchester Radio (GMR), Piccadilly.
Honours: N W Counties Lg 84-85 (Div 2 82-83), Lancs Comb Lg Cup 69-70), Manchester Lg R-up 55-56 (Lg Cup 58-59(joint)).

PROGRAMME DETAILS:
Pages: 28 **Price:** *60p*
Editor: *David Johnson.*

STOCKSBRIDGE PARK STEELS

1986 Steels

Stocksbridge Park Steels FC: Back Row (L-R); Brad Elam, Richard Holmshaw, Dave Griffiths, Andy Carney, Gavan Walker, Bob Spotswood, Paul Sykes, Steve Shutt, Geoff Littlewood (Physio). Front; Simon Howe, Shaun Joyce, Trevor Jones, Trevor Gough (asst Mgr), Mick Horne (Mgr), Craig Chadburn, Simon Maples, John Tesh, Ian Swallow.

President: C D Sedgwick **Chairman:** A Bethel **Vice-Chairman:** M Grimmer.
Secretary: Michael Grimmer, 48 Hole House Lane, Stocksbridge, Sheffield S30 5BP (0114 2886470).
Manager: Mick Horne **Asst Manager:** Trevor Gough.
Physio/Press Officer: Geoff Littlewood (0114 2463328).
Commercial Manager: Andrew Horsley (0114 2883867).
Ground: Bracken Moor Lane, Stocksbridge, Sheffield (0114 2742 882045).
Directions: M1 jct 35a from south, 36 from north, A616 to Stocksbridge (A6102 from Sheffield – on arriving at Stocksbridge turn left into Nanny Hill under the Clock Tower and continue up the hill for about 500 yds - ground on left.
Seats: 450 **Cover:** 700 **Capacity:** 3,500 **Floodlights:** Yes
Colours: Yellow/blue **Change colours:** All blue
Midweek matches: Tuesday **Sponsors:** St Christophers **Metal badges:** £2
Prev. Ground: Stonemoor 49-51 52-53
Record Gate: 2,000 v Sheffield Wed., Floodlight opening Oct '91.
Reserves' Lge: Beefeater County Senior.
Prev. Names: Stocksbridge Works, Oxley Park; clubs merged in 1986.
Previous Leagues: Sheffield Amateur/ Sheffield Association/ Yorkshire 49-82.
Club Shop: No, but badges, mugs and scarves on sale.
Players progressing to Football League: Peter Eustace (Sheffield Wednesday) 1960 *(from Stocksbridge Works)*, Lee Mills (Wolverhampton Wanderers) 1992.
Record fee received: £15,000 for Lee Mills (Wolves, 1992).
Local newpapers: Sheffield Trader, Green'un, The Star
Clubhouse: Open seven days (lunchtime & evenings). No food, but separate food bar open for matches.
95-96 Captain: Trevor Jones. **95-96 Top Scorer:** Trevor Jones.
Hons: Northern Co's East Lg 94-95, R-up 95-96, (Div 1 91-92, Lg Cup SF 92-93, Presidents Cup SF 91-92), Sheffield & Hallamshire Snr Cup 51-52 92-93 (SF 94-95), Yorks Lg 51-52 54-55 55-56 56-57 57-58 61-62 62-63 (R-up 60-61, Div 2 50-51 64-65, Div 3 70-71 74-75 (R-up 78-79), Lg Cup 61-62).

PROGRAMME DETAILS:
Pages: 28 **Price:** 80p
Editor: E O'Sullivan
(0114 2884218)

1949 WARRINGTON TOWN The Town

Warrington's Neil Boardman tangles with Gretna's Derek Townsley. *Photo - Alan Watson*

Chairman: Steve Plant. **Vice Chairman:** M P McShane **President:** R Smith.
Secretary: Ian Dick, c/o Club. 01614 995317 (Bus)
Manager: Alan Lord. **Asst Manager:** Dave Entwhistle.
Coach: Gary Bradley. **Press Officer:** Colin Serjent **Physio:** Lynda Roberts.
Ground: Cantilever Park, Common Lane, Latchford, Warrington WA4 2RS (01925 653044 grd).
Directions: M6 junction 20, then A50 towards Warrington. After 2 miles turn left immediately after swing bridge into Station Road, ground 600yds on left.
Capacity: 2,000 **Cover:** 650 **Seats:** 350 **Floodlights:** Yes **Club Shop:** Yes
Colours: Yellow/blue/yellow **Change colours:** All purple. **Sponsors:** TBA.
Prevs Name: Stockton Heath 1949-62. **Prevs Ground:** London Road,Stockton Lane and Loushers Lane.
Prevs Lge: Warrington & Dist. 49-52/ Mid-Cheshire 52-78/ Cheshire Co. 78-82/ Nth West Co's 82-90.
Record Attendance: 2,600 v Halesowen Town, FA Vase Semi Final 1st leg 85-86.
Best FA Trophy season: Quarter-Finalists 92-93 (lost 1-2 at Sutton United).
Best FA Cup season: 4th Qualifying Rd 94-95 (replay with Hyde Utd.)
Best FA Vase season: Finalists 86-87 (lost 2-3 to St Helens Town).
Midweek matchday: Tuesday **Reserve League:** Mid-Cheshire.
Record win: 14-0 v Crosfields (H), Depot Cup 1951-52.
Record defeat: 0-10 v Eastwood, Mid-Cheshire Challenge Cup 67-68.
Record transfer fee paid: £2,000; for Paul McNally (Southport) 1992; for Darren Schofield (Mossley) 1993.
Record transfer fee received: £60,000 for L Watson (Preston N E) 92-93
Players progressing to Football League: S Morris (Chester 51), J Green, J Bramhall (Tranmere 58 76), R Hunt (Liverpool 59), J Richards (Wolves), M Leonard (Everton, Stockport, Bradford City), N Whalley & L Watson (Preston N E) 92-93.
Clubhouse: Weekdays 1pm-11pm, Sat. noon-11pm, Sun. 12-3pm, 7pm-10.30pm. Lounge, concert room & Sports room. Rooms for hire for all occasions. Pools, darts, dominoes & indoor bowls. Bar food on matchdays.
Club Record Goalscorer: Steve Hughes 167.
95-96 Captain: Mike Edwards. **95-96 Top Scorer:** Billy O'Callaghan.
Supporters, Managers and Players P.of Y. 95-96: Billy O'Callaghan.
Local Newspapers: Warrington Guardian (0925 33033), Warrington Mercury, Manchester Evening News, Liverpool Post & Echo.
Local Radio Stations: Radio Merseyside, Radio Manchester (GMR).
Honours: FA Vase R-up 86-87 (SF 85-86), FA Trophy QF 92-93, N West Count Lg 89-90 (Lg Cup 85-86 87-88 88-89 (R-up 89-90), Div 2 R-up 86-87, Div 3 R-up 82-83, Res Div W 89-90), Mid-Cheshire Lg 60-61 (R-up 57-58, Lg Cup 54-55 55-56); Altrincham Amat Cup 54-55.

80p
The UniBond League
The Town
Unibond League Division One Season 1995/96
WARRINGTON TOWN v Atherton LR
Tuesday, 5th September Kick off 7:30pm

PROGRAMME DETAILS:
Pages: 36 **Price:** 50p
Editor. Garry Clarke

WHITLEY BAY

Formed: 1897 The Bay

Whitley Bay's keeper Terry Burke struggling on a cross against Gretna.

Photo - Alan Watson

Chairman: Michael Robinson. **Vice Chairman:** Peter Siddle. **President:** J Hedworth.
Secretary: Ian Fitz-gerald, 116 Claremont Road, Whitley Bay, Tyne And Wear, NE26 3TX (0191 2520419).
Manager: Ken Parker. **Asst Manager:** Paddy Lowery. **Coach:**
Ground: Hillheads Park, Hillheads Road, Whitley Bay, Tyne & Wear (0191 251 3680).
Directions: 1 mile from bus station - leave St Pauls Church southward, turn right at r-about, grd 3rd left at rear of ice rink. Whitley Bay or Monkseaton metro stations, both 1 mile.
Capacity: 4,500 **Cover:** 650 **Seats:** 450 **Floodlights:** Yes **Metal Badges:** Yes
Club Shop: Yes, selling programmes, club scarves, hats etc. Contact David McCall (0191 252 6546).
Colours: Blue & white stripes/blue/white **Change colours:** All yellow
Previous Leagues: Tyneside 09-10/ Northern Alliance 50-55/ North Eastern 55-58/ Northern 58-88.
Previous Name: Whitley Bay Athletic 1950-58.
Midweek home matchday: Tuesday. **Record Gate:** 7,301 v Hendon, FA Amateur Cup 1965.
Record Win: 12-0 v Shildon 1961
Record Defeat: 1-8 v Bishop Auckland 1979.
Record Fee Paid: £500
Best FA Cup season: 3rd Rd 89-90 (lost 0-1 at Rochdale). 2nd Rd 90-91 (lost 0-1 at home to Barrow).
League clubs defeated in F.A. Cup: Scarborough, Preston N E 89-90.
Players progressing to Football League: William Dodd (Burnley 1956), William Younger (Nottm Forest 1957), Ron Brown (Blackpool 1965), John Ritchie (Port Vale 1965), John Brodie & Aiden McCaffery (Carlisle 1967 & 88), Mike Spelman (Wolves 1969), Tony Harrison (Southport 1977), Mark Miller (Gillingham 1981), Garry Haire (Bradford City 1983), Stewart Ferebee (Darlington 1987).
Clubhouse: Open every night except Wednesday & Sunday 7-11pm. Bar and concert room. Darts, pool, 5-a-side courts.
Club Record Goalscorer: Billy Wright 307
Club Record Appearances: Bill Chater 640.
95-96 Captain: Phil Coxall.
95-96 P.O.Y.: Ian MCkenzie. **95-96 Top scorer:** Andy Blower.
Local Newspapers: The News, Guardian, Herald & Post.
Local Radio: Radio Newcastle, Metro.
Honours: FA Amateur Cup SF 65-66 68-69, FA Trophy 3rd Rd 86-87, Northern Premier Lg Div 1 90-91 (Div 1 Cup 88-89 90-91), Northern Lg 64-65 65-66 (R-up 59-60 66-67 68-69 69-70, Lg Cup 64-65 70-71 (R-up 67-68)), Northern Alliance 52-53 53-54 (Lg Cup 52-53 53-54), Northumberland Senior Cup 52-53 60-61 63-64 64-65 67-68 68-69 69-70 70-71 72-73 86-87 (R-up 53-54 54-55 55-56 65-66 76-77 85-86 90-91).

OFFICIAL MATCHDAY PROGRAMME OF WHITLEY BAY F.C.

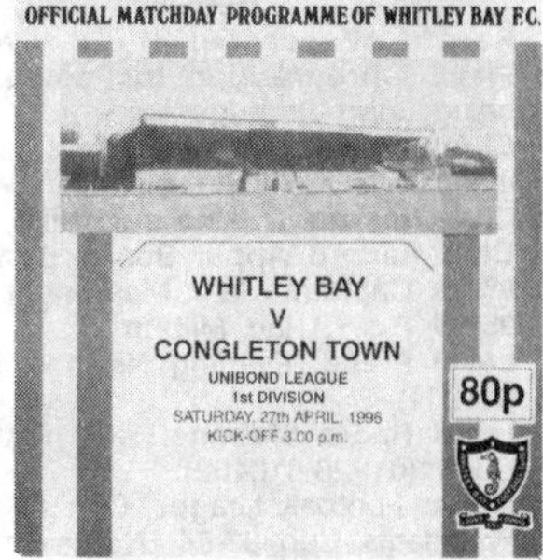

PROGRAMME DETAILS:
Pages: 24 **Price:** 75p
Editor: Lynn Bone
(0191 262 6234)

WORKINGTON

1884 (reformed 1921) Reds

Workington A.F.C. 95-96: Back row (L-R): Ian Williamson, Gary Messenger, John Holliday, Lee Copeland, Ian Milburn, Martin Henderson, Graham Emerson. Front: Kevin Rowntree, Garry Wright, George Corrie, Simon Parry, Nigel Dustin, David Taylor, Darren Wilson.

Chairman: Jackie Donald **President:** Eric Fisher.
Secretary: Tom Robson, 12 Derwent Bank, Seaton, Workington CA14 1EE (01900 65566).
Manager: Wayne Harrison. **Asst Manager:** Keith Hunton.
Press Officer: Steve Durham (01946 61380) **Physio:** Reg Cartner.
Ground: Borough Park, Workington, Cumbria CA14 2DT (01900 602871).
Directions: A66 into town, right at 'T' junction, follow A596 for three quarters of a mile - ground is then visible and signposted. Ground is to north of town centre quarter of a mile from Workington (BR) station and half mile from bus station in town centre.
Capacity: 2,500 **Cover:** 800 **Seats:** 300 **Floodlights:** Yes **Metal Badges:** Yes
Club Shop: Yes, selling programmes, badges, magazines, pennants, photographs, replica kit, T-shirts. Contact Keith Lister (01900 812867).
Colours: Red/white/red. **Change colours:** Jade & Navr Quarters/Jade/Jade & Navy.
Midweek home matchday: Tuesday **Reserve Team's League:** West Cumberland.
Previous Leagues: Cumberland Association 1890-94/ Cumberland Snr 94-1901 03-04/ Lancs Lge 1901-03/ Lancs Combination 04-10/ North Eastern 10-11 21-51/ Football League 51-77.
Previous Grounds: Various 1884-1921/ Lonsdale Park 21-37.
Best FA Cup season: 4th Rd, 1933-34. Competition Proper on 53 other occasions.
Best FA Trophy season: 1st Round replay 77-78.
Record win: 17-1 v Cockermouth Crusaders, Cumberland Sen Lge 1901.
Record loss: 0-9 v Chorley (A), NPL Prem. Division, 10/11/87.
Record Fees - Paid: £6,000 for Ken Chisholm (Sunderland, 1956).
Received: £33,000 for Ian McDonald (Liverpool, 1974).
Record Attendance: 21,000 v Manchester Utd, FA Cup 3rd Rd 4/1/58.
Players progressing to Football League: Numerous, the best known being John Burridge.
Clubhouse: Open matchdays and for private functions. Food on matchdays restricted menu.
Club Record Goalscorer: Billy Charlton 193
Club Record Apps: Bobby Brown 419
95-96 Captain: Gary Messenger/John Holliday.
95-96 P.o.Y.: Ian Milburn. **95-96 Top Scorer:** Martin Henderson 21.
Local Press: Evening News & Star, Times & Star (John Walsh 0900 601234).
Local Radio Stations: BBC Radio Cumbria (01228 592444) C.F.M.(01228-810400)
Hons: Football League Cup QF 63-64 64-65; Northern Prem Lge Presidents Cup 83-84; North Eastern Lge R-up 38-39 (Lge Cup 34-35 36-37 (R-up 37-38)); Cumberland County Cup [21], (R-up [13]).

PROGRAMME DETAILS:
Pages: 28 **Price:** 60p
Editor: Steve Durham (01946 61380)

Formed: 1861

WORKSOP TOWN

The Tigers

Worksop Town 1995-96 with the Unibond League Presidents Cup. Back row (L-R): Tony Morris, Tony Starkey, Terry Harris, Darren Brookes, Jamie Holmshaw, Mark Rookyard, David Mc Nicholas, Kerry Clark, Nigel Dobson. Front: Gary Lockwood, Lee Howard, Linden Whitehead, Tommy Spencer (Mgr), Danny Campbell, Gary Thorpe, Danny Scott, Gary Marrow (Asst Mgr).

Chairman: Rick Knowles. **Vice Chairman:** John Shuker. **Company Sec:**Mel Bradley.
Football Secretary: Keith Illett,2 Mount Avenue,Worksop,Notts (01909 487934)
Press Officer: Mel Bradley **Manager:** Tommy Spencer **Physio:** Gary Marrow.
Commercial Manager: Kevin Barratt.
Ground: Babbage Way, off Sandy Lane, Worksop, Notts S80 1UJ (0909 501911).
Directions: M1 jct 31 (from north) jct 30 (from south), follow Worksop signs, join A57 and follow signs for Sandy Lane Industrial Estate - ground on left. 5 mins walk from station.
Capacity: 2,500 **Cover:** 1,000 **Seats:** 360 **Floodlights:** Yes. **Metal Badges:** Yes.
Club Shop: The Tigershop selling badges, scarves, magazines, programmes. 30 page catalogue from Steve Jarvis, 10 Wood End Drive, Ravenshead, Notts NG15 9EJ.
Colours: Amber/black **Change colours:** Blue/white.
Previous Grounds: Netherton Road/ Bridge Meadow/ Central Avenue (prior to 1989)/ The Northolme (Gainsborough Trinity F.C.) (shared) 89-92.
Previous Leagues: Midland (Counties) 00-30 49-60 61-68 69-74/ Sheffield Ass 1898-99 31-33/ Cent Comb 33-35/ Yorkshire 35-39/ Cent All 47-49 60-61/ Nth Prem 68-69.
Sponsors: O.T.H. Engineers, Eyres of Worksop and Norwood Fisheries.
Midweek matchday: Tuesday. **Reserve League:** Sheffield County Sen
Record Attendance: 1,503 v Sheffield United, friendly.
Record win: 20-0 v Staveley, 1/9/1894 **Record defeat:** 1-11 v Hull City Reserves, 55-56.
Best FA Trophy season: 2nd Rd replay 73-74.
Best FA Cup year: Last 64. **Record Fees - Paid:** None.
Received: £10,000 for Martin Hardy (Boston U. 1987).
Players progressing to Football League: J Brown (Sheff Wed & England), G Dale (Chesterfield 48), A Daley (Doncaster 50), K Wood (Grimsby 51), H Jarvis (Notts County 51), B Taylor (Leeds 51), Stan Rhodes, D Gratton, A Hodgkinson, J Harrison (Sheffield Utd 51 & 52 & 53 67), S Lloyd & P Marshall (Scunthorpe 54), A Rhodes (QPR 54), R Moore (Rotherham 55), H Mosby (Crewe 56), L Moore (Derby 57), H Bowery (Nottm Forest 75), T Moore (Rochdale 84), S Adams (Scarborough 87), D Moss (Doncaster 93).
Clubhouse: Tigers Club. Normal lic hours. Pool, quiz nights, disco etc.
Club Record Goalscorer: Kenny Clark, 287.
Club Record appearances: Kenny Clark 347.
95-96 Captain: Linden Whitehead.
95-96 P.o.Y.: Darren Brookes. **95-96 Top scorer:** Kenny Clark 37.
Local Press: Worksop Guardian (500500), Worksop Star (486335), Nottingham Football Post (0602 475221).
Local Radio Stations: Radio Sheffield, Radio Hallam, Radio Lincoln.
Hons: Northern Prem. Lg Presidents Cup 85-86 95-96; Midland Co's Lg 21-22 65-66 72-73 (R-up 62-63 66-67 73-74); Sheffield Assoc Lg 1898-99, Sheffield & Hallamshire Snr Cup (8); Mansfield Charity Cup 22-23.

PROGRAMME DETAILS:
Pages: 28-32 **Price:** 50p
Editor: Mel Bradley
(01909 500491/500500)

NORTH WEST COUNTIES Division One Ten Year Records

	86/7	87/8	88/9	89/0	90/1	91/2	92/3	93/4	94/5	95/6
Accrington Stanley	2	-	-	-	-	-	-	-	-	-
Ashton United	-	-	17	9	3	1	-	-	-	-
Atherton Laburnam Rovers	-	17	14	14	18	11	1	1	-	-
Bacup Borough	-	-	-	-	14	14	15	20	22	-
Bamber Bridge	-	-	-	-	-	-	2	-	-	-
Blackpool Mechanics	-	-	-	-	-	-	22	-	-	-
Blackpool Rovers	-	-	-	-	-	4	12	8	7	17
Bootle	5	13	9	11	13	18	-	6	19	6
Bradford Park Avenue	-	-	-	-	-	17	6	15	1	-
Burscough	12	10	10	17	-	-	10	3	8	5
Chadderton	-	-	-	18	-	-	3	19	11	16
Clitheroe	3	3	12	5	15	9	7	9	2	7
Colne Dynamoes	-	1	-	-	-	-	-	-	-	-
Colwyn Bay	-	4	4	3	2	-	-	-	-	-
Congleton Town	11	-	-	-	-	-	-	-	-	-
Curzon Ashton	19	-	-	-	-	-	-	-	-	-
Darwen	-	7	5	6	16	10	17	16	17	19
Eastwood Hanley	14	-	-	-	4	3	18	5	13	14
Ellesmere Port & Neston	-	6	11	-	-	-	-	-	-	-
Fleetwood Town	8	-	-	-	-	-	-	-	-	-
Flixton	-	-	7	12	7	8	11	22	-	1
Formby	-	14	18	-	-	-	-	-	-	-
Glossop North End	20	18	-	-	-	-	16	17	6	12
Great Harwood Town	-	-	-	-	-	2	-	-	-	-
Holker Old Boys	-	-	-	-	-	-	-	-	14	11
Irlam Town	18	-	-	-	-	-	-	-	-	-
Kidsgrove Athletic	-	-	-	-	-	-	20	10	15	13
Knowsley United	4	9	2	2	1	-	-	-	-	-
Leek Town	16	-	-	-	-	-	-	-	-	-
Leyland Motors	13	11	8	13	12	-	-	-	-	-
Maine Road	-	-	-	-	9	16	19	13	12	15
Mossley	-	-	-	-	-	-	-	-	-	4
Nantwich Town	-	-	-	7	11	12	13	4	16	9
Netherfield	17	-	-	-	-	-	-	-	-	-
Newcastle Town	-	-	-	-	-	-	5	14	5	2
Penrith	9	-	-	-	17	6	14	7	10	18
Prescot AFC	-	12	15	10	6	5	4	12	9	10
Radcliffe Borough	15	-	-	-	-	-	-	-	-	-
Rossendale United	10	2	1	-	-	-	-	2	18	21
St Helens Town	6	5	3	8	8	15	8	11	3	8
Salford City	-	15	16	16	19	-	9	18	21	20
Skelmersdale United	-	16	13	15	10	7	21	21	20	22
Stalybridge Celtic	1	-	-	-	-	-	-	-	-	-
Trafford	-	-	-	-	-	-	-	-	4	3
Vauxhall GM	-	-	-	4	5	13	-	-	-	-
Warrington Town	-	8	6	1	-	-	-	-	-	-
Winsford United	7	-	-	-	-	-	-	-	-	-
No of clubs competing	20	18	18	18	19	18	22	22	22	22

NORTH WEST COUNTIES LEAGUE

FEEDER TO:
NORTHERN PREMIER LEAGUE

FOUNDED: 1982

President: Canon J R Smith, MA

Chairman: J E Hinchliffe. **Treasurer:** K H Dean

Secretary: M Darby, 87 Hillary Road, Hyde, Cheshire SK14 4EB (0161 368 6243).

The 1995/96 season has had the usual hard luck stories, the 'if only' stories, and of course the performances which have brought a smile to the faces of at least some supporters of clubs in the North West Counties league.

So first the congratulations; to Flixton and Vauxhall GM champions of Division One and Division Two respectively. Both will be playing their football at a higher level next season. Congratulations too to Atherton Collieries who finished as runners up in the Second Division and will receive the Leagues Grading Committee recommendation for promotion at the Annual General Meeting in June.

Burscough also deserve our congratulations on winning the League Challenge Cup defeating Flixton at Gigg Lane by 1-0 just 48 hours after they went down at Valley Road 2-0.

Congratulations also to Clitheroe and Newcastle Town, both did the League proud in outside cup competitions. Clitheroe and Newcastle's cup exploits have been outstanding this season. In all they played thirty five cup ties, finishing as runners up in the Staffordshire Senior Cup and the Walsall Senior Cup, both after extra time, the Walsall after penalties. They lifted the Leagues Floodlit Trophy defeating Mossley at Altrincham and just for good measure finished as runners up in Division One.

Ramsbottom United in their first season defeated Cheadle Town in the Second Division Cup, a notable achievement, in deed all the new clubs have been a credit to the League.

To the clubs who finished at the wrong end of their respective Divisions, better luck next season. Both Bacup Borough and Squires Gate passed the first hurdle when they met the Grading Committee requirements, as did the three clubs who will be applying for membership at the Annual General Meeting, Colne, Garswood United and Leek CSOB.

Champions Flixton also enjoyed a great FA Vase run to the Semi-Final. On the way they recorded a supurb 3-0 victory over favourites Canvey Island and here we see Paul Dixon powering in a header, in front of the clubs impressive Club House with balcony and terraces. Photo - Colin Stevens

Finally so many thank yous. To Paul Cowburn for his endless supply of statistics, it is impossible to ask Paul the wrong question about NWCL clubs. To Irene Davies for all her efforts, it was Irene who produced the Newsletter until the end of March and to Frank Clayton for his forbearance since then.

NORTH WEST COUNTIES FINAL LEAGUE TABLES 1995/96

Div One

		P	W	D	L	F	A	Pts
1.	Flixton	42	28	8	6	85	30	92
2.	Newcastle Tn	42	26	7	9	88	42	85
3.	Trafford	42	26	5	11	89	45	83
4.	Mossley	42	24	8	10	87	59	80
5.	Burscough	42	23	8	11	77	40	77
6.	Bootle	42	23	5	14	74	55	74
7.	Clitheroe	42	20	12	10	63	44	72
8.	St Helens Tn	42	19	13	10	71	53	70
9.	Nantwich Tn	42	20	7	15	64	59	67
10.	Prescot C	42	17	11	14	70	66	62
11.	Holker O B	42	19	4	19	77	72	61
12.	Glossop N E	42	15	15	12	55	48	60
13.	Kidsgrove A	42	15	9	18	61	64	54
14.	Eastwood H	42	12	15	15	60	57	51
15.	Maine Rd	42	12	14	16	60	71	50
16.	Chadderton	42	14	8	20	52	69	50
17.	Blackpool R	42	11	9	22	49	74	42
18.	Penrith	42	9	12	21	57	69	39
19.	Darwen	42	9	10	23	57	77	37
20.	Salford C	42	10	5	27	49	93	35
21.	Rossendale U	42	6	10	26	32	114	28
22.	Skelmersdale	42	5	3	34	45	121	18

Div Two

		P	W	D	L	F	A	Pts
1.	Vauxhall GM	34	28	4	2	112	25	88
2.	Atherton C	34	25	5	4	90	43	80
3.	Tetley Walk	34	22	7	5	75	35	73
4.	Castleton G	34	19	5	10	77	52	62
5.	Nelson	34	17	9	8	78	55	60
6.	Cheadle Tn	34	17	5	12	67	49	56
7.	Haslingden	34	15	9	10	69	45	54
8.	Maghull	34	16	3	15	55	42	51
9.	Oldham Tn	34	14	8	12	75	74	50
10.	Middlewich A	34	12	7	15	45	74	43
11.	Daisy Hill	34	12	4	18	46	66	40
12.	Ramsbottom	34	11	6	17	60	65	39
13.	Formby	34	10	7	17	59	76	37
14.	Stantondale	34	11	4	19	47	75	37
15.	Blackpool M	34	8	8	18	56	74	32
16.	Ashton Tn	34	8	3	23	53	102	27
17.	Squires Gate	34	5	7	22	37	82	22
18.	Bacup Boro	34	4	3	27	35	102	15

NORTH WEST COUNTIES DIV ONE RESULTS CHART 1995-96

HOME TEAM	1	2	3	4	5	6	7	8	9	10	11	12	13	14	15	16	17	18	19	20	21	22
1. Blackpool	*	1-4	1-0	2-1	1-3	1-1	2-2	1-2	0-3	3-1	2-1	1-1	2-3	0-2	0-2	1-0	2-2	1-1	1-1	3-0	1-2	0-1
2. Bootle	0-1	*	0-2	2-0	1-1	3-2	3-2	2-3	1-3	3-1	1-1	4-3	2-1	1-0	1-0	1-0	0-0	8-1	2-0	4-3	3-1	0-3
3. Burscough	4-2	3-1	*	2-0	2-0	2-2	2-2	0-1	2-3	5-1	2-0	2-0	1-0	2-1	1-2	3-1	2-2	6-0	0-2	1-0	3-0	1-1
4. Chadderton	0-1	0-1	0-4	*	4-2	3-2	0-0	2-3	0-1	1-2	3-2	1-1	0-0	2-2	0-1	1-1	2-0	1-0	1-0	1-0	5-1	1-5
5. Clitheroe	1-0	2-0	1-3	2-0	*	2-0	0-1	1-0	0-0	4-0	1-1	3-3	1-0	3-1	0-0	1-1	3-2	5-0	1-1	4-1	2-0	2-1
6. Darwen	0-0	2-3	3-1	1-1	1-2	*	1-2	0-0	1-1	3-0	0-2	1-0	4-4	2-2	1-2	2-3	1-2	3-0	0-0	2-1	3-2	2-3
7. Eastwood H	1-0	0-3	1-0	0-1	2-2	1-0	*	1-1	1-1	3-0	1-1	2-1	0-1	1-1	1-2	1-1	0-0	7-0	1-1	2-3	0-2	2-1
8. Flixton	2-0	2-0	2-0	4-0	1-0	1-0	4-0	*	3-0	5-0	3-1	2-0	1-2	2-1	3-3	4-0	2-2	5-0	1-0	3-1	3-0	1-0
9. Glossop N E	1-1	0-0	1-1	4-3	0-2	3-1	0-0	0-2	*	0-1	4-2	1-1	2-0	1-0	4-2	0-2	0-0	3-2	0-2	1-3	3-0	0-1
10. Holker O B	4-2	2-0	1-3	4-1	1-2	1-1	4-3	1-1	1-1	*	5-1	1-1	3-0	6-0	1-4	4-2	0-2	4-0	5-1	5-1	4-0	0-2
11. Kidgrove Ath	0-2	3-1	0-1	1-3	2-0	1-1	1-1	0-5	0-0	1-0	*	1-0	0-1	1-1	1-0	1-0	0-1	2-0	1-2	3-0	3-0	6-1
12. Maine Road	3-0	1-0	2-2	3-0	0-1	0-0	0-3	1-3	1-1	0-2	1-1	*	2-4	2-1	1-2	1-0	2-2	3-0	2-2	1-1	5-2	0-4
13. Mossley	3-2	1-3	1-0	0-0	4-0	5-0	3-2	1-1	0-4	2-1	4-2	3-0	*	2-1	2-1	1-0	1-1	3-0	0-3	3-2	5-1	0-4
14. Nantwich Tn	3-1	2-0	0-2	1-0	1-0	2-0	1-0	1-0	1-2	2-1	5-1	0-2	2-4	*	3-2	2-1	2-1	3-0	1-1	0-2	1-0	3-1
15. Newcastle T	1-0	1-4	0-0	3-0	3-1	2-1	2-1	0-1	2-0	2-0	4-2	7-0	2-2	2-1	*	2-0	4-2	4-0	0-0	2-1	4-1	2-1
16. Penrith	1-2	1-1	1-2	1-0	0-0	3-1	2-2	2-1	1-1	0-1	2-3	1-1	2-2	3-3	0-3	*	1-1	1-1	0-1	4-1	5-2	1-3
17. Prescot AFC	3-1	1-0	2-0	5-1	2-1	3-0	1-0	2-0	3-2	3-1	0-3	1-3	1-3	2-3	0-2	2-4	*	0-0	4-1	6-1	1-1	3-2
18. Rossendale	3-3	0-1	1-1	0-4	2-2	1-4	1-1	1-3	1-2	0-2	0-3	2-2	1-8	0-1	1-1	1-0	1-2	*	1-1	1-0	3-2	0-3
19. St Helens T	1-1	1-2	1-0	4-4	0-2	3-1	1-4	0-0	1-0	2-0	3-1	0-2	2-0	2-1	1-1	4-3	4-1	7-0	*	5-1	2-1	1-1
20. Salford City	3-1	0-2	0-7	0-1	2-2	1-3	0-4	1-1	2-2	1-3	1-1	2-0	0-4	1-2	1-0	3-1	4-1	1-2	1-2	*	1-0	0-1
21. Skelmersdale	3-1	1-5	0-1	0-2	0-1	2-3	3-1	1-2	0-0	2-3	1-3	3-5	1-2	3-3	0-8	1-2	3-1	1-2	0-4	0-2	*	1-7
22. Trafford	4-1	3-1	0-1	1-2	0-0	3-0	4-1	2-1	1-0	2-0	1-0	1-1	2-2	0-1	2-1	2-1	3-2	0-2	6-1	2-0	4-1	*

ATHERTON COLLIERIES

Chairman: A P Delooze **Vice Chairman:** W Shaw **President:** J Fielding
Secretary/Press Officer: C Neill, 40 Winmarleigh Gdns, Pennington, Leigh (0942 679255/886600).
Manager: Steve Walton **Asst Manager:** I Lamb **Coach:** R Hough
Physio: Trevor Ball **Commercial Manager:** D Pratano.
Ground: Alder House, Alder Street, Atherton, Gt Manchester (0942 884649).
Directions: M61 Jct 5, follow sign for Westhoughton, left onto A6, right onto A579 (Newbrook Rd/Bolton Rd) into Atherton. *(From M61 jct 4, left, right onto A6 after 80yds, left down Newbrook Rd at 1st lights).* At lights next to Atherton town hall turn left into High Str., 2nd left into Alder St. to ground. Quarter mile from Atherton Central (BR).
Seats: 300 **Cover:** 1,000 **Capacity:** 2,500 **Floodlights:** Yes **Founded:** 1916
Cols: Black & white stripes/black/black. **Change colours:** All red. **Nickname:** Colls
Reserves' Lge: CNWCL Res Div **Record Gate:** 3,300 in Lancs Combination, 1920's
Midweek Matches: Tuesday **Club Sponsors:** L & I Eaton
Club Shop: Yes, selling replica shirts, programmes, enamel badges, key-rings. Contact Secretary.
Programme: 40 pages, 50p **Editor:** Secretary *(CNWCL Div 2 Programme of the Year, 93-94)*
Previous Lges: Bolton Comb. 20-50 52-71, Lancs Comb. 50-52 71-78, Cheshire Co. 78-82.
Players progressing to Football League: J Parkinson (Wigan), Russell Beardsmore (Manchester Utd).
Clubhouse: Open Mon-Fri 7-11pm, Sat 11am-11pm, Sun noon-3 & 7-10.30pm. Hot & cold food on matchdays.
Captain 93-94: S Wallace **P.O.Y.:** D Owen **Top Scorer 93-94:** K Daley.
Hons: NW Co's. Lg Div 3 86-87, Bridge Shield 85-86, Lancs Jnr Shield 19-20 22-23 41-42 45-46 56-57 64-65.

BLACKPOOL (Wren) ROVERS

Chairman: J Nolan **Manager:** John Dodd
Secretary: Paul Kimberley, 34 Priory Gate, South Shore, Blackpool, Lancs FY4 2QE (01253 349853)
Ground: Bruce Park, School Road, Marton, Blackpool, Lancs, (01253 760570)
Directions: M6 to M55, leave junc 4, left onto A583, sharp right at 1st lights (Whitehill Rd), follow signs for Airport. Ground approx 1.5 miles on right. 6 miles from Blackpool North BR station.
Seats: 250 **Cover:** 750 **Capacity:** 1,000 **Floodlights:** Yes **Club Shop:** No.
Programme: 20 pages, 20p **Editor:** P Kimberley
Colours: All red **Change colours:** All blue
Sponsors: **Nickname:** **Founded:** 1936
Midweek matchday: Tuesday **Reserve League:**
Record Attendance: 1,011 v Manchester City, floodligyht opener Oct 1991
Previous leagues: Blackpool Amt. West Lancs, Lancs Comb 72-82
Previous Name: Wren Rovers
Clubhouse: Open matchdays
95-96 Captain: **95-96 Top Scorer:**
Hons: W Lancs Lg 69-70 70-71, (Lge Cup 2); Lancs FA Shield 69-70 70-71; Lancs Comb 78-79 80-81, (R-up 77-78), Lge Cup 78-79; Bridge Shield 76-77.

BOOTLE

Chairman: Frank Doran. **Manager:** Steve Smith
Secretary/Press Officer: Paul Carr, 58 Orchard Hey, Old Roan, Bootle, Merseyside L30 8RY (0151 474 0153).
Ground: Bucks Park, Northern Perimeter Road, Netherton, Bootle, Merseyside L30 7PT (0151 526 1850).
Directions: End of M57 & M58 follow signs to Bootle/All Docks. Turn right at next lights by Police station. Entrance 150 yds on right. Old Roan statiom 300yds. Bus 55 (150yds from grd), 302 341 345 350 (350yds).
Seats: 400 **Cover:** 1,400 **Capacity:** 5,000 **Floodlights:** Yes **Club Shop:**Yes.
Programme: 32 pages, 50p **Editor:** Secretary
Colours: All blue **Change colours:** Yellow/black/black
Sponsors: Samsung Lift Trucks **Nickname:** Bucks **Founded:** 1953
Midweek matchday: Tuesday **Reserve League:** Liverpool Co. Combination.
Record Attendance: 750 v Carshalton Athletic, FA Trophy 2nd Rd 31/1/81.
Previous leagues: Liverpool Shipping, Liverpool County Comb., Lancs Comb. 74-78, Cheshire Co. 78-82.
Players progressing to Football League: Graeme Worsley (Shrewsbury Town 1989).
Clubhouse: Yes. Normal pub hours. Darts & pool.
95-96 Captain: Billy Loughlin **95-96 Top Scorer:** Lee Steele 22
Players of the Year(4 awards of equal status): Lee Steele (2), John King, Billy Loughlin
Club record appearances: Peter Cumiskey (almost 400).
Hons: North West Counties League Div 2 Runners-up 92-93 (Floodlit Trophy 93-94), Liverpool Challenge Cup 64-65 75-76 78-79, Liverpool Amtr Cup 65-66 67-68 73-74, Lancs Amtr Cup 69-70, Liverpool County Combination 64-65 65-66 67-68 68-69 69-70 70-71 71-72 72-73 73-74, George Mahon Cup 66-67 67-68 68-69 69-70 72-73 73-74, Lancs Combination 75-76 76-77 (League Cup 75-76), Cheshire County League Div 2 78-79.

BURSCOUGH

Chairman: Frank Parr **Vice Chairman:** Stuart Heaps **President:** John Mawdsley
Secretary: Stan Strickland, 109 Redgate, Ormskirk, Lancs L39 3NW (01695 574722).
Manager: John Davison **Asst Manager:** Peter King. **Physio:** Rod Cottam
Ground: Victoria Park, Mart Lane, Burscough, Ormskirk, Lancs L40 0SD (01704 893237).
Directions: M6 Jct 27, follow signs thru Parbold A5209, right into Junction Lane (signed Burscough & Martin Mere) to lights, right onto A59 from Ormskirk to Burscough Village, 2nd left over canal bridge into Mart Lane to ground. Half a mile from Burscough Bridge BR station (Wigan-Southport line). Slightly further from Burscough Junction (Ormskirk-Preston line).
Seats: 220 **Cover:** 1,000 **Capacity:** 3,000 **Floodlights:** Yes **Club Shop:** No
Programme: 36 pages, 50p **Editor:** Mark Parr (01704 896243) **Press Officer:**
Colours: Green/white/green. **Change colours:** White/blue/blue
Sponsors: Crown Computer Products. **Founded:** 1946 **Nickname:** Linnets
Midweek Matches: Tuesday
Record Attendance: 4,798 v Wigan Athletic,F.A.Cup 3rd Qual.Rd.1950-51.
Previous Leagues: Liverpool County Comb. 46-53, Lancs Comb. 53-70, Cheshire Co. 70-82.
Best FA Cup season: 1st Rd 59-60 77-78 79-80 80-81.
Players progressing to Football League: L Bimpson (Liverpool 53), B Parker (Liverpool 54), B Pilson (Stoke 54), A Green (Huddersfield), K Waterhouse (Preston), K Spencer (Everton), F Gamble (Derby 80), T Rigby (Bury), S Teale (Aston Villa), L Watson (Preston), K Formby (Rochdale 94), G Martindale (Bolton 94),A Russell (Rochdale 94)
Clubhouse: 'Barons Club' (privately owned, access from outside ground). Mon-Thurs 7-11pm, Fri 4-11pm, Sat 1-11pm, Sun noon-3 & 7-10.30pm. No food. John Smiths & Websters beers.
95-96 Captain: Ged Nolan. **95-96 Top Scorer**: Terry McPhillips **95-96 P.o.Y.:** Andy Howard.
Club Record Appearances: **Club Record Goalscorer:** Johnny Vincent 60 53-54
Hons: Cheshire County League R-up 70-71 (League Cup 74-75 (R-up 73-74)), Liverpool Snr Non-League Cup 55-56, 71-72, Lancs Combination 55-56 69-70,Lancs Comb.Div 2 53-54, Lancs Jnr Cup 47-48 49-50 66-67, Nth West Co's League 82-83 (League Cup 92-93 95-96(R-up 91-92), Challenge Shield 82-83 95-96), George Mahon Cup 47-48, Liverpool County Combination 49-50 (Div 2 53-54), Liverpool Challenge Cup 47-48 50-51,54-55. Liverpool Snr Cup R-up 92-93, Bill Tyrer Memorial Trophy 1990.Lord Wavertree Cup Winners 67-68. .gap 5

CHADDERTON

Chairman: Harry Mayall **Vice Chairman:** Marshall Parker. **President:** Derek Glynn
Secretary: R Manton, 24 Whitegate Lane, Chadderton, Oldham, Lancs OL9 8LS, (0161 620 0368)
Manager: Mick McKay. **Asst Manager:** TBA **Physio:** Roy Houghton
Ground: Andrew Street, Chadderton, Oldham, Lancs (0161 624 9733).
Directions: M62 Jct 20, A627(M) to Oldham. Motorway then becomes dual carriageway. Turn left at first major traffic lights A669 (Middleton Road), then first left opposite 'Harlequin' P.H. into Burnley Street - Andrew Street 2nd left. 1 mile from Oldham Werneth (BR), buses 458 & 459 (Oldham-Manchester) stop at the Harlequin.
Seats: 200 **Cover:** 700 **Capacity:** 2,500 **Floodlights:** Yes **Club Shop:** No
Programme: 28-32 pages **Editor:** Secretary **Press Officer:** Secretary
Colours: Red/White/Red. **Change colours:** White/Blue/White.
Sponsors: Royton Metals,Nationwide Building Society and Asda. **Nickname:** Chaddy **Founded:** 1947
Midweek Matches: Tuesday. **Reserves' Lge:** Carling NWCL Reserve Division.
Record Attendance: 1,500 v Guinness Exports 1969 & 1,257 v Oldham Athletic, pre-season friendly 1991.
Previous Leagues: Oldham Amateur, Manchester Amateur, Manchester 64-80, Lancs Comb. 80-82
Players progressing to Football League: D Platt (Crewe, Aston Villa, Bari, Juventus, Sampdoria,Arsenal), J Pemberton (Crewe, Crystal Palace, Sheffield Utd, Leeds), G Bell (Oldham, Preston), P Hilton (Bury, West Ham), D Graham (Bury).
Clubhouse: Matchdays only. Hot & cold snack during & after games
95-96 Captain: Steve Gartside. **95-96 P.o.Y.:** **95-96 Top Scorer:**
Club Record Appearances: Billy Elwell 750+ (64-90). **Club Record Goalscorer:**
Honours: Oldham Amat Lg Cup 54-55, Manchester Amat Lg 62-63 (North Div 55-56), Manchester Prem Cup R-up 82-83 (Challenge Tphy 71-72, R-up 72-73), Manchester Lg Div 1 66-67 (Div 2 64-65), Gilgryst Cup. 69-70, Murray Shield 65-66, Lancs Comb. Cup R-up 81-82, Alfred Pettit & Hulme Celtic Cup 61-62, Nth West Co's F/lit Tphy R-up 92-93 (Res Div 85-86, R-up 90-91), Res Cup 91-92 (R-up 90-91)), Manchester Yth Cup 59-60 (R-up 60-61).

CLITHEROE

Formed: 1877. The Blues

Chairman: S Rush **President:** Jer Aspinall
Secretary/Press Officer: Colin Wilson, 4 Moss Street, Clitheroe, Lancs BB7 1DP (01200 24370).
Mgr: Denis Underwood/Gary Butcher **Coach:** **Physio:** Keith Lord.
Ground: Shawbridge, Clitheroe, Lancs (01200 23344).
Directions: M6 jct 31, A59 to Clitheroe (17 miles), at 4th r'bout continue for half a mile and turn left at Pendle Road.Ground one mile.just before Bridge
Inn' on the right. 11 miles from Blackburn BR station

Seats: 300 **Cover:** 1200 **Capacity:** 2,000 **Floodlights:** Yes **Club Shop:**Yes.
Programme: 12 pages, 60p **Editor:** Ian Rimmer **Press Officer:**
Colours: Blue & white stripes/blue **Change colours:** Red/Navy.
Midweek home matchday: Monday **Reserves' Lge:** N.W.C.L.
Record Attendance: 2,000 v Mangotsfield, FA Vase Semi/F 95-96.
Previous Lges: Blackburn & Dist./Lancs Comb. 03-04 05-10 25-82.
Players progressing to Football League: Ray Woods (Leeds 1950), Chris Sims (Blackburn 1960), Lee Rogerson (Wigan Ath).
Clubhouse: Open during matches. Snacks available.
95-96 Captain: Simon Westwell **95-96 Top Scorer:** Jon Riley 12 **95-96 P.o.Y.:** Carlo Nash
Club Record Goalscorer: Don Francis **Club Record Appearances:** Lindsey Wallace.
Hons: Lancs Comb. 79-80 (Lg Cup 34-35), Lancs Challenge Tphy 1892-93 1984-85, NW Co's Lg 85-86 (Div 2 84-85, Div 3 83-84, Div 1 Fair Play Award 94-95), East Lancs Floodlit Trophy 94-95.

Burscough AFC: Back Row (L-R); Andy Diggle, Darren Saint, Phil Snow, Tommy Knox, Ray Birch, Chris Stanton. Middle Row; Rod Cottam (Physio), Andy Matthews, Dave Oxton, Lee Bedson, Calvin Wade, Paul Blasbery, Stephen Jackson, Stuart Whittle, Neil Hanson, Peter King (Asst Mgr). Front Row; Mick McDonough, Paul Dawson, John Davison (Mgr), Dave Roberts, Andy Howard.

Mossley AFC: Back R (L-R); Bernie Hughes, Mike Turner, Paul Uttley, Rod Bates, Mark Thomas, Wayne Joynes, Mark Murray, Mark Walsh, Kevan Keelan (Mgr), Peter Cole. Front R; Lee Cuncliffe, Carl Conlon, Tim Crane, AlexHurst (mas), Chris Lomas, Steven Beswick (mas), Matthew Holt, Peter Withers, Andy Baines.

DARWEN

President: E Devlin **Chairwoman:** Mrs K.Marah.
Secretary: Lynn Atkinson, 58 Harwood Str., Darwen, Lancs BB3 1PD (01254 761755).
Manager: Ian McGarry **Asst Manager:** Brian Gardner **Physio:** Mick Sharples
Ground: Anchor Ground, Anchor Road, Darwen, Lancs (01254 705627).
Directions: A666 Blackburn/Bolton road, 1 mile north of Darwen town centre, turn right at Anchor Hotel, ground 100 yds on left. One and a half miles from Darwen (BR), bus 51 to Anchor Hotel.
Seats: 250 **Cover:** 2,000 **Capacity:** 4,000 **Floodlights:** Yes **Founded:** 1875
Previous Ground: Barley Bank. **Record Gate:** 9,000 v Luton, FA Cup 1909
Colours: Red & white/white/red **Change colours:** All blue
Prev. Lges: Football Alliance 1889-91, Football Lg 91-99, Lancs Lg 99-03, Lancs Comb. 03-75, Ches. Co. 75-82.
Programme: 20 pages, 20p **Programme Editor:** D.Marah. **Club Shop:** No
Sponsors: Prince Moran **Reserve Team's League:** North West Alliance.
Clubhouse: Matchday only. **Best FA Cup season:** Semi Finals
Midweek Matches: Tuesday. **Local Newspapers:** Darwen Advertiser, Lancs Eve. Tele.
Captain 94-95: Mark Walsh. **P.o.Y. 94-95:** Mark Walsh. **Top Scorer 94-95:** Mark Walsh.
Hons: NW Co's Lg 82-83 (Res. Div Cup 94-95), Lancs Lg 01-02, Lancs Comb. 30-31 31-32 72-73 74-75 (Lg Cup 29-30 30-31 74-75, Lancs Jnr Cup 72-73, George Watson Tphy 72-73, Lancs FA Yth Cup 74-75, Lancs F'lit Tphy 89-90.

EASTWOOD HANLEY

Chairman: Les Wagg **Vice Chairman:** Geoff Eccleston **President:** Gerald Littlehales
Secretary: John L Reid, 2 Northam Rd, Sneyd Green, Stoke-on-Trent, Staffs ST1 6DA (01782 279062).
Manager: Jimmy Wallace **Coach:** Chris Hagen **Physio:** Graham Plant
Ground: Lyme Valley Stadium, Newcastle-u-Lyme, Staffordshire. (Sharing with Newcastle Town FC).
Directions: M6 jct 15, A500 for Stoke, left at r'bout A519 for Newcastle, right at 2nd r'bout into Stafford Ave., 1st left into Tittensor Road to ground. 3 miles from Stoke-on-Trent (BR).
Seats: 300 **Cover:** 1,000 **Capacity:** 4,000 **Floodlights:** Yes **Club Shop:** No
Programme: 32 pages, 60p **Editor:** Fiona Reid **Press Officer:** John Reid.
Colours: All blue **Change Colours:** White/black/white **Nickname:** Blues.
Midweek home matchday: Tuesday **Reserve team:** None. **Founded:** 1946
Record Attendance: 5,000 v Stoke City (Brooks Bros Testimonial) 1978
Previous Leagues: Mid-Cheshire, Manchester, West Midlands (Regional) 68-78, Cheshire County 78-82, North West Counties Lg 82-87, Northern Premier 87-90.
Players progressing to League: Melia Alecksic (Spurs), Maurice Doyle (QPR).
Clubhouse: Open matchdays. Refrestment bar open matchdays.
95-96 Top Scorer: **95-96 Captain:** **95-96 P.o.Y.:**
Club Record scorer: A Tunstall 84 (63-64) **Club Record appearances:** Mick Astley, 1968-78.
Honours: Manc. Lg Gilgryst Cup 67-68, Staffs Snr Cup 85-86, Staffs FA Vase 81-82.

GLOSSOP NORTH END

Chairman: P Heginbotham **President:** C T Boak
Secretary: P Hammond, 15 Longmoor Road, Simmondley, Glossop, Derbys SK13 9NH (0457 863852).
Manager: Ged Coyne **Asst Manager:** Tommy Martin **Physio:** TBA
Ground: Arthur Goldthorpe Stadium, Surrey Street, Glossop, Derbys (0457 855469).
Directions: A57 (Manchester-Sheffield) to Glossop town centre, turn into Shrewsbury Street, follow to top of the hill, left at T-junction for ground. 700 yds from Glossop (BR). Buses 236 & 237 from Manchester.
Seats: 209 **Cover:** 509 **Capacity:** 2,374 **Floodlights:** Yes **Club Shop:** Yes
Programme: 32 pages, 40p **Editor:** Mr P Heginbotham (0161 439 8982) **Press Officer:** Secretary.
Colours: Blue & white stripes/blue/red **Change colours:** All gold.
Sponsor: Davis Blank Furniss Solicitors **Nickname:** Hillmen. **Founded:** 1886
Midweek Matches: Tuesday **Reserve's League:** North Western Alliance.
Record Attendance: 10,736 v Preston North End, FA Cup 1913/14
Previous Leagues: Midland 1896-98/ Football Lge 1898-1915/ Manchester Lge 15-56 66-78/ Lancs Combination 56-66/ Cheshire County 78-82.
Players progressing to Football League: Jimmy Rollands (Rochdale), Ray Redshaw (Wigan Athletic).
Clubhouse: Licensed bar. Hot & cold drinks and pies etc on matchdays.
95-96 Captain: **95-96 Top Scorer:** Neil Brown **95-96 P.o.Y.:** Steve Morgan.
Honours: Nth West Co's Lg Lamot Pils Trophy 90-91, Manchester Lg 27-28 (Gilgryst Cup 22-23 29-30 34-35 74-75), Football Lg Div 2 R-up 1898-99, FA Amateur Cup QF 08-09.

HOLKER OLD BOYS

President: R Brady **Chairman:** Ron Moffatt **Vice Chairman:** Ray Sharp.
Secretary: Allan Wilson, 56 Fairfield Lane, Barrow-in-Furness, Cumbria LA13 9AL (0229 822983).
Manager: Des Johnson **Asst Manager:** Jim Capstick **Coach:** Jim Ballantyne.
Physio: Mark Hetherington **Comm. Manager:** Ged Woods **Press Officer:** John Taylor
Ground: Rakesmoor Lane, Howcoat, Barrow-in-Furness, Cumbria (0229 828176).
Directions: M6 Jct 36, A590 to Barrow-in-Furness, on entering Barrow, continue across r'bout, 2nd right (Dalton Lane) to top of road, right into Rakesmoor Lane, ground on right.
Seats: 220 **Cover:** 500 **Capacity:** 2,500 **Floodlights:** Yes **Founded:** 1936
Colours: Green/white **Change colours:** Blue/red **Nickname:** Cobs.
Midweek Matches: Wednesdays **Club Sponsors::** Kitchen Design Studio.
Previous Leagues: North Western/ Furness Premier/ West Lancs 70-91.
Previous Grounds: None.
Programme: 8 pages, 30p **Rec. Gate:** 400 v Emlyn Hughes All Stars **Club Shop:** No.
Record win: 12-0 **Record defeat:** 1-8 v Newcastle T. (H) 91-92.
Clubhouse: Weekdays 8-11pm, Sat noon-11pm, Sunday normal licensing hours. Pies & peas on matchdays.
Top Scorer 93-94: Mike Ballantyne **Captain & P.o.Y. 93-94:** Mike Ballantyne
Club record scorer: Dave Conlin **Hons:** W Lancs Lg 86-87, Lancs Junior Shield 88-89 90-91.

KIDSGROVE ATHLETIC

Chairman: D Stringer **Manager:** Peter Ward.
Secretary: Dave Stringer,66 Chatterley Drive,Kidsgrove,Stoke-on-Trent,ST7 $Il. Trent (01782 784582).
Coach: Jack Heath. **Physio:** Arthur Duckworth.
Press Officer: Dave Stringer. **Commercial Manager:** Peter Ward.
Ground: Clough Hall, Hollinwood Road, Kidsgrove, Stoke-on-Trent, Staffs (01782 782412).
Directions: M6 Jct 16, A500 towards Stoke, 2nd junction onto A34 towards Manchester, turn right at 1st set of lights into Cedar Ave., 2nd right into Lower Ash Rd., and 3rd left into Hollinwood Road to ground. British Rail Kidsgrove(5mins)
Seats: 250 **Cover:** 600 **Capacity:** 4,500 **Floodlights:** Yes **Formed:** 1952
Colours: Blue 7 White/white/blue & white **Change Colours:** White/blue/blue.
Record Gate: 538 **Clubhouse:** Yes
Midweek Home Matches: Wednesday
Prev. Leagues: Staffs Co./ Mid Cheshire (pre-1991).
Hons: Mid Cheshire Lg 70-71 78-79 86-87 87-88 (R-up 68-69 85-86, Lg Cup 67-68 69-70 85-86 (R-up 84-85 86-87)), Staffs Co. FA Vase 78-79 88-89, Sentinel Cup 66-67 76-77 84-85 (R-up 58-59 78-79 79-80 83-84), Leek Cup 84-85, Hanley Cup 65-66.

MAINE ROAD

Chairman: Mr R Meredith **President:** Mr F G Thompson.
Secretary: Mr K Hunter, 157 Aston Ave., Fallowfield, Manchester M14 7HN (0161 226 9937).
Manager: Mr D Barber **Asst Manager:** C Nicholson **Physio:** A Adamajtis.
Ground: Manch. Co. FA Grnd, Brantingham Rd., Chorlton-cum-Hardy, Manchester M21 1TG (0161 862 9619).
Directions: M63 Jct 7, A56 towards City Centre, right onto A5145, onto A6010 to Chorlton, through lights (ignore pedestrian lights), left at next lights into Withington Rd, left into Brantingham Rd, ground 400 yds on left. Manchester A-Z ref. 100/6B. 2 miles from Stretford (Metrolink(tram)), 3 miles from Piccadilly and Victoria (BR). Buses 85 100 102 103 168 188 260 261 275
Seats: 200 **Cover:** 700 **Capacity:** 2,000 **Floodlights:** Yes **Club Shop:** No
Programme: 48 pages, 50p **Editor:** Mr R Price (0161 442 7269) **Press Officer:** P Ramsden
Colours: All blue **Change Colours:** All yellow
Sponsors: Surface Engineers **Nickname:** Blues
Founded: 1955
Midweek matchday: Tuesday **Reserves League:** NW Co's Lge Reserve Division.
Record Attendance: 875 v Altrincham, FA Cup 2nd Qual. Rd 29/9/90.
Best FA Cup year: 2nd Qual. 2nd replay 92-93.
Best FA Vase year: 4th Rd 94-95.
Previous Leagues: Rusholme Sunday 55-66/ Manchester Amtr Sunday 66-72/ Manchester 72-87.
Clubhouse: Before/during/after games. Refreshment bar sells hot & cold drinks, pies, crisps, confectionary.
95-96 Captain: Ian Walker. **95-96 Top scorer:** Antoni Adamajtis **95-96 P.o.Y.:** Mark Flowers.
Club Record Goalscorer: John Wright 140 **Club Record Appearances:** Robin Gibson 382.
Honours: Manc. Prem. Lg(4) 82-86 (R-up 86-87, Div 1 73-74, Div 2 72-73, Gilgryst Cup(2) 82-84 (R-up(2) 85-87), Murray Shield(2) 72-74), Manc. Prem. Cup 87-88 (Chal. Cup(4) 82-83 84-87, I'mediate Cup(2) 75-77, Amtr Cup 72-73), NW Co's Lg Div 2 89-90 (R-up 88-89).

MOSSLEY

Formed: 1903 **Nickname:** Lilywhites
Chairman: Frank Whelan. **President:**
Secretary: Andrew Fenna,254 Fairfied Rd.,Droylsden,Manchester M43 6AN((0161 370 0508).
Manager: Kevan Keelan. **Coach:** N/A **Physio:** John Cunliffe.
Ground: Seel Park, Market Street, Mossley, Ashton-under-Lyme (01457 832369).
Directions: From north; M62 Junc 20, A627M/A627 to Ashton-U-Lyne, A670 to Mossley- ground in town centre. From south; M56, M63, M66, M67 to end, then A57/A6018 to Stalybridge on reaching Stalybridge follow A635 to Mossley. Local station Mossley BR. Buses 153 from Manchester, 343 from Oldham, 350 from Ashton.
Capacity: 4,500 **Cover:** 1,500 **Seats:** 200 **Floodlights:** Yes **Club Shop:** Yes
Programme: 28 Pages 50p **Editor:** Mike Smith
Colours: White/black/black **Change colours:** Yellow/green/green.
Midweek home matchday: Tuesday
Record Attendance: 7,000 v Stalybridge, 1950.
Best FA Cup season: 2nd Rd replay 49-50. Also 2nd Rd 80-81, 1st Rd 69-70 77-78 78-79 79-80 81-82 83-84.
Previous Leagues: Ashton/ South East Lancs/ Lancs Combination 18-19/ Cheshire County 19-72.
Players progressing to Football League: John Wright (Blackpool 1946), Tom Bell & Albert Wadsworth (Oldham 1946 & 49), Albert Lomas (Rochdale 1950), Arthur Tyrer (Leeds 1946), Eric Williams (Halifax 1951), John Willis (A Villa 1958), Mike Eckershall (Torquay 1959), Alan Roberts (Bradford PA 1969), Gary Pierce (Huddersfield 1971), Eamon O'Keefe (Everton 1979), David Young (Wigan 1983).
Clubhouse: Open nights and matchdays.
95-96 Captain: Bernie Hughes **95-96 Top Scorer:** Bernie Hughes **95-96 P.o.Y.:** Wayne Joyngs
Honours: FA Trophy Runners-up 79-80, Northern Premier League 78-79 79-80 (Runners-up 80-81 81-82 82-83, League Cup 78-79 88-89 (Runners-up 75-76 81-82), Challenge Shield 88-89 (Runners-up 78-79 79-80 80-81 81-82)), Cheshire County League Runners-up 19-20 69-70 (League Cup 20-21 60-61), Manchester Premier Cup 88-89 90-91, Manchester Intermediate Cup 60-61 66-67 67-68 (Runners-up 58-59 63-64 70-71 78-79), Manchester Challenge Shield 14-15 33-34 37-38 48-49 (Runners-up 36-37 38-39 50-51), Reporter Floodlit Cup 74-75 88-89, North West Floodlit Cup Runners-up 76-77 95-96.

NANTWICH TOWN

Chairman: R Tilley **Vice Chairman:** P Temmen **President:** J Davies
Secretary: A J Birtwistle, 26 Kinloch Close, Crewe. (01270 258751)
Manager: Clive Jackson. **Asst Manager:** John Brydon. **Physio:** Keith Leigh.
Ground: Jackson Avenue, off London Road, Nantwich, Cheshire (01270 624098).
Directions: M6 Jct 16, A500 for Nantwich (about 8 miles), continue on A52 over railway crossing (London Rd), first right into Jackson Avenue. From Chester take A51. 3 miles from Crewe (BR).
Seats: 150 **Cover:** 555 **Capacity:** 1,500 **Floodlights:** Yes **Club Shop:** Yes
Programme: 18 pages, 65 **Editor:** Che Kerrin (01270 624098).
Colours: Black/white **Change colours:** All green.
Club Sponsors: Jim Barrie Plant Hire **Founded:** 1894 **Nickname:** Dabbers
Reserves' League: Refuge Assurance **Midweek matchday:** Tuesday.
Record Attendance: 2,750 v Altrincham, Cheshire Senior Cup 66-67.
Previous Leagues: Shropshire & Dist./ The Combination 1892-94 1(0111-10/ Lancs Comb. 12-15/ Cheshire Combination 19-38/ Manchester/ Mid-Cheshire/ Cheshire County 68-82.
Clubhouse: Every night except Sunday 8pm-11pm. Hot pies available.
95-96 Captain: Frank Boon. **95-96 P.o.Y.:** B.Ellershaw. **95-96 Top scorer:**
Club Record Goalscorer: Gerry Duffy, 42 in 61-62. **Club Record Appearances:**
Hons: Cheshire Co. Lg 80-81 (R-up 00-01), Ches. Snr Cup 32-33 75-76 (R-up 1898-99 13-14 29-30), Ches. Jnr Cup 1895-96 (R-up 18(011-91 96-97), Manc. Lg R-up 66-67 (Gilgryst Cup R-up 67-68), Crewe & Dist Cup 97-98 98-99 01-02 61-62 (R-up 1889-(011 (011-91 04-05 51-52 60-61), The Combination R-up 02-03, Crewe Amtr Comb. 46-47, Shropshire & Dist Lg R-up 1891-92, Mid Ches. Lg 63-64 (R-up 61-62 64-65, Lg Cup 61-62 63-64 (R-up 64-65)), Ches. Amtr Cup 63-64 (R-up 61-62), Ches. Jnr Cup 1895-96 (R-up (011-91 96-97), Mid Ches. Cup 48-49. Carling N.W. Co.Lg.Cup 94-95,Res Lg Cup R-Up 94-95, Refuge Assurance Lg 94-95.

NEWCASTLE TOWN

Chairman: J W Walker **Vice-Chairman:** K G Walshaw **President:** K H Walshaw.
Secretary: John F Cotton, 293 Weston Road, Weston Coyney, Stoke-on-Trent, Staffs ST3 6HA (0782 333445).
Manager: Glyn Chamberlain **Asst Manager:** Trevor Brissett **Physio:** Colin Spencer
Ground: 'Lyme Valley Parkway Stadium', Lilleshall Road, Clayton, Newcastle-under-Lyne, Staffs (01782 662351).
Directions: M6 jct 15, A500 for Stoke, left at r'bout A519 for Newcastle, right at 2nd r'bout into Stafford Ave., 1st left into Tittensor Road to ground. 3 miles from Stoke-on-Trent (BR).

Club Shop: Yes **Seats:** 300 **Cover:** 1,000 **Capacity:** 4,000 **Floodlights:** Yes
Programme: 40 pages, 50p **Editor:** Peter Tindall (01260 28093) **Press Officer:** Ray Tatton.
Colours: Royal/royal/red **Change colours:** All yellow
Club Sponsors: A.N.C.Ltd **Nickname:** Castle. **Founded:** 1986
Midweek Matches: Tuesday **Reserve Team:** Lycett's Burshlem & Newcastle Dist Lge
Record Attendance: 3,586 v Stoke City, friendly August 1991. *Competitive: 577 v Gresley Rovers, FA Vase 4th Rd 18/1/92. Parkway Clayton: 2,620 v Stoke City, 1964.*
Previous Lges: Hanley & Dist. Sunday/ North Staffs Sunday/ Potteries & Dist. Sunday/ Newcastle/ Staffs Co./ Mid Cheshire.
Players progressing to Football League: Carl Beeston, Graham Shaw, Paul Ware, Dave Ritchie, Darren Hope, Shaun Wade.
Clubhouse: Open Saturday matchdays noon-7.30pm and midweek 5-11pm. Hot & cold food always available.
95-96 Captain: Andy Holmes **95-96 Top Scorer:** John Burndred 39 **95-96 P.o.Y.:** Wayne Johnson
Record Scorer: Shaun Wade 80 (NWCL only) **Record appearances:** Philip Butler 249 (NWCL only).
Hons: Nth West Co's Lg Div 2 R-up 91-92 95-96; (Floodlit Tphy 92-93 95-96, Lamot Pils Tphy 91-92), FA Vase 5th Rd 91-92, Mid Cheshire Lg 85-86 (R-up 86-87, Div 2 82-83 90-91(res), Lg Cup 84-85), Walsall Snr Cup 93-94 (R-up 95-96), Newcastle Mayor's Charity Cup 89-90, Staffs FA Vase R-up 92-93(res), Midland Sunday Cup 85-86 86-87 (R-up 84-85 87-88), Potteries & Dist Sunday Lg 84-85 85-86 (Lg Cup 84-85 85-86), Staffs Sunday Cup 79-80 (R-up 86-87), Leek Cup 87-88, Sentinel Sunday Cup 84-85, Sentinel u-18 Shield 86-87 (R-up 93-94), Staffs Snr Cup R-up 95-96; Staffs Yth u-18 Cup 88-89 92-93 93-94 (R-up 86-87, u-16 86-87), Wirral programme award (for NWCL) 88-89 91-92 92-93 93-94 95-96 (Div 2 87-88 88-89 90-91 91-92); N Staffs M/W F/Light Lge 94-95.

Newcastle Town FC.

Maine Road FC: Back Row (L-R): R Meredith (Chr), S Savage, C Simms, A Hogan, A Cain, A Gray, B Fleet, B Maher, A Adamajtis, A Adamajtis (Physio). Front Row; C Nicholson (Asst Mgr), G Woods, P Wadsworth, P Varden, D Swindells, T Crane, I Walker, J Smith.

PENRITH

Chairman: D Johnson **Vice Chairman:** M Robson **Secretary:** D Johnson
Manager: Geoff Byers **Physio:** Les Cornwell.
Ground: Southend Road Ground, Penrith, Cumbria (01768 863212).
Directions: M6 Jct 40, onto dual carriageway to Appleby & Scotch Corner, turn off at next r'bout approx 1/2 mile to Penrith, follow A6 into town, take 1st left for grd. 3/4 a mile from Penrith (BR).
Seats: 200 **Cover:** 1,000 **Capacity:** 4,000 **Floodlights:** Yes **Club Shop:** No
Programme: 24 pages, 50p **Editor/Press Officer:** J Bell (01768 63898)
Colours: Blue/white/blue **Change colours:** All yellow
Sponsors: Cumbrian Industries Ltd **Nickname:** Blues. **Founded:** 1894
Midweek Matches: Wednesday **Reserve team:** None
Record Attendance: 4,000 v West Auckland, 1961. **Best FA Cup season:** 2nd Rd 81-82
Previous leagues: Carlisle & Dist., Northern 48-82, NW Co's 82-87, Northern Prem. 87-90
Players progressing to Football League: K Sawyers, G Fell, G Mossop (all Carlisle).
Clubhouse: Open Thurs-Fri 9.30pm-2am, Sat 2-6pm & 9.30pm-2am, Wed match nights 6.30-10.30pm.
95-96 Captain: Martin Kirkby **95-96 P.o.Y.:** Martin Kirkby **95-96 Top Scorer:** Jeff Henderson
Club Record Goalscorer: C Short **Club Record Appearances:** Ray Thornton.
Hons: Northern Lg R-up 61-62, NW Co's Lg R-up 83-84, NW Co's F/Light Trophy 95-96, Cumberland Snr Cup 60-61 61-62 62-63 63-64 64-65 65-66 70-71 72-73 74-75 80-81.

PRESCOT A.F.C.

President: Mr B F Taylor **Chairman:** Ted Mercer **Vice Chairman:** Arthur Creegan
Secretary: Mr G H Hayward, 38 Central Ave., Prescot, Merseyside L34 1NB (051 430 6762).
Manager: Joe Gibiliru **Asst Manager:** Lee Madin
Commercial Manager: John Richards (0744 57613).
Ground: 'Sandra Park', Hope Street, Prescot, Knowsley, Merseyside (051 430 0507).
Directions: M62 Jct 7, A57 to Prescot town centre (3 miles), right into Hope Street. Three quarters of a mile from Prescot (BR). Buses 10, 10A, 10C from Liverpool & Wigan.
Seats: 400 **Cover:** 2,000 **Capacity:** 8,000 **Floodlights:** Yes **Founded:** 1884
Record Gate: 8,122 v Ashton National, 1932 **Metal Badges:** Yes.
Colours: Gold/black/black **Change colours:** All red **Nickname:** Tigers.
Previous Names: Prescot Athletic/ Prescot Cables 46-65 80-90/ Prescot Town 65-80.
Previous Leagues: Liverpool Co. Comb./ Lancs Comb. 1897-98 18-20 27-33 36-67/ Ches. Co. 33-36 78-82/ Lancs Lg 01-02/ Mid Cheshire 67-78.
Programme: 30 pages, 40p **Editor:** S Richards **Club Shop:** No
Midweek Matches: Tuesday **Best FA Cup season:** 2nd Rd 57-58 59-60
Clubhouse: Refreshment bar, open matchdays/evenings for hot & cold refreshments.
Hons: Lancs Comb. 56-57 (Lg Cup 47-48), Ches. Co. Lg 78-79, Mid Ches. Lg 76-77, L'pool Non-League Cup(4) 51-53 58-59 60-61, L'pool Chal. Cup(6) 27-30 48-49 61-62 77-78, Lancs Int. Cup 1895-96, George Mahon Cup 23-24 25-27 36-37, Lord Wavertree Cup 65-66.

ROSSENDALE UNITED

Chairman: J Feber **Vice-Chairman:** **President:**
Secretary/Press Officer: Brian Melia
Manager: Mickey Graham **Coach:** John Hughes **Physio:** B Melia
Ground: Dark Lane, Staghills Road, Newchurch, Rossendale, Lancs BB4 7UA (01706 215119).
Directions: M66 Junc 18, M66 north following signs for Burnley, then A682 to Rawstenstall, keep left around r'bout past library until Bishop Blaize pub, right into Newchurch Road (past market), after a mile turn right into Staghills Road - through estate to ground (half mile). Buses 32 or 33 from Rawtenstall (to Todmorden, Edgenride or Burnley) stop at ground.
Capacity: 2,500 **Cover:** Yes **Seats:** 500 **Floodlights:** Yes **Club Shop:** T.B.A.
Programme: Yes **Editor:** Bill Howarth. **Press Officer:** B Melia
Colours: Blue & white/white/blue **Change colours:** Yellow (blue sleeves)/blue/yellow
Sponsors: T.B.A. **Nickname:** Rossy **Founded:** 1898
Midweek matchday: Wednesday **Reserve League:** Carling NWCL Reserve Division.
Record Attendance: 12,000 v Bolton Wanderers FA Cup 2nd Rd.
Best FA Cup season: 2nd Rd 71-72 (1-4 v Bolton at Bury FC)
Best FA Trophy/Vase Season: Vase 5th Rd 86-87 88-89; Tphy 2nd Rd 81-82.
Previous Leagues: North East Lancs Comb./ Lancs Comb. 1898-99 1901-70/ Central Lancs 1899-1901/ Cheshire County 70-82/ North West Counties 82-89/ Northern Premier 89-93.
Players progressing to Football League: Tommy Lawton, Geoff Smith (Bradford City 1952), Edmund Hartley & William O'Loughton (Oldham 1956 & 60), Colin Blunt (Burnley 1964), Fred Eyre (Bradford PA 1969), Dave O'Neill (Huddersfield), Carl Parker (Rochdale 1992).
Clubhouse: Evenings & matchdays. Hot snacks. Snooker room. Pool, darts, satellite TV, concert room.
95-96 Captain: **95-96 P.o.Y.:** **95-96 Top scorer:**
Club Record Goalscorer: Bob Scott **Club Record Appearances:** Johnny Clarke 770, 1947-65.
Honours: North West Counties Lg 88-89 (R-up 87-88 93-94, Div 2 R-up 85-86, Lg Cup 93-94, Champions Trophy R-up 93-94), Lancs Comb 26-27 (R-up 54-55, Lg Cup 28-29, Div 2 56-57), Cheshire County Lg 70-71 (R-up 71-72 73-74, Lg Cup 73-74), Lancs Junior Cup (ATS Challenge Tphy) 11-12 72-73 (R-up 27-28), Central Lancs Lg 1900, Lancs Floodlit Cup 70-71 71-72 73-74, Carling Chall Cup 93-94

St HELENS TOWN

President: Mr J Jones. **Chairman/Press Officer:** J Barrett
Secretary: W J Noctor, 95 Sutton Park Drive, Marshalls Cross, St Helens WA9 3TR (01744 816182).
Manager: James McBride **Asst Manager:** Bob Howard **Coach:** John Neary
Ground: Houghton Road, Sutton, St Helens, Merseyside (01744 812721).
Directions: M62 Jct 7, at r'bout take 5th exit (St Helens linkroad, A570) for 3 miles, at 3rd r'bout take exit for Sutton, at next r'bout take 1st exit,
follow road to right, down Robins Lane, straight on to Station Rd, at crossroads (station on right) straight across into Leonard Street, right at t-junction, ground on right. Buses 121, 122, 5D, 41, 6 to St Helens Junction.
Seats: 200 **Cover:** 550 **Capacity:** 4,400 **Floodlights:** Yes **Club Shop:** Yes
Programme: 24 pages, 50p **Editor:** John McKiernan (01744 815726)
Colours: Blue/white/blue **Change colours:** All yellow
Nickname: 'Town' **Founded:** 1901
Midweek Matches: Wednesday **Reserve League:**
Record Attendance: 4,000 v Manchester City, Bert Trautmann transfer match, April 1950.
Previous Leagues: Lancs Comb. 03-14 49-75/ Liverpool County Comb 49-74/ Cheshire County 74-82.
Players progressing to Football League: Bert Trautmann, John Connelly, John Quinn, Mike Davock, Billy Foulkes, Dave Bamber, Bryan Griffiths, Mark Leonard, Joe Paladino.
Clubhouse: Weekdays 8-11pm, Saturday matchdays 2-6.30pm.
95-96 P.o.Y.: **95-96 Captain:** **95-96 Top Scorer:**
Club Record Goalscorer: **Club Record Appearances:** Alan Wellens.
Honours: FA Vase 86-87, North West Counties Lg Cup R-up 94-95 (Res Div Champions 94-95 R-Up.94-95), George Mahon Cup 49-50, Lancs Comb. 71-72 (Div 2 50-51, Lg Cup R-up 70-71), Liverpool Snr Cup R-up 76-77, Lancs Jnr Cup R-up 66-67, Bass Charrington Cup 72-73, St Helens Comb. Hosp. Cup Winners & R-up.

SALFORD CITY

Chairman: Harold Brearley **Manager:** Syd Whyte. **Asst Manager:**
Secretary: Trevor D Cartwright, 22 St Austells, Swinton, Manchester M27 4JH (061 736 6359).
Press Officer: Ged Carter **Commercial Manager:** Mike Hilditch.
Ground: Moor Lane, Kersal, Salford, Manchester (061 792 6287).
Directions: M62 jct 17, A56 Bury New Road to Manchester, continue thro' 4 sets of lights, right into Moor Lane, 1st left into Neville Road to ground. 4 miles from Manchester Victoria (BR). Buses 96, 139, 94, 95 to Moor Lane.
Seats: 260 **Cover:** 600 **Capacity:** 8,000 **Floodlights:** Yes **Founded:** 1940
Midweek Matches: Tuesday **Record Attendance:** 3,000 v Whickham FA Vase 1981
Colours: Tangerine/black/black **Change colours:** Blue & white stripes/blue/blue.
Prev. Names: Salford Central 40-63/ Salford Amateurs 1963 until merger with Anson Villa/ Salford FC.
Previous Ground: Crescent, Salford **Previous Leagues:** Manchester 63-80/ Cheshire Co. 80-82.
Programme: 24 pages, 50p **Programme Editor:** Secretary **Nickname:** Ammies.
Clubhouse: Open matchdays only. Hot snacks.
Captain 94-95: **Top Scorer 94-95:** **P.o.Y. 94-95:**
Hons: Lancashire Amateur Cup 72-73 74-75 76-77, Manchester Senior Cup(4) 73-77, Manchester Challenge Cup(3) 73-76, Manchester Lg(4) 74-77 78-79 (Div 1 68-69, Open Tphy 75-76, Murray Shield 68-69), Manchester I'mediate Cup. *As Anson Villa: Manchester Lg Div 2 62-63 (Open Tphy 77-78(res)).*

TRAFFORD

Chairman: J Ackerley **Vice-Chairman:** D Brown **President:** K Illinworth
Secretary: Graham Foxall, 62 Grosvenor Road, Urmston M41 5AQ (0161 746 9726)
Manager: David Law **Asst Manager:** John Ferguson **Coach:** Dave Higgs
Ground: Shawe View, Pennybridge Lane, Flixton, Urmston, Manchester M41 5DL (0161 747 1727)
Directions: M63 jct 4, B5158 towards Urmston, 1st exit at island, rht into Moorside Rd at next lights,2nd exit at next island, sharp left at next lights, 1st right into Pennybridge Lane (next to Bird in Hand Pub), car park 100yds left.
Seats: 284 **Cover:** 732 **Capacity:** 2,500 **Floodlights:** Yes **Club Shop:** No
Programme: 24 pages, 50p **Editor:** David Murray (0161 775 7509)
Colours: All White **Change colours:** All Red
Sponsors: Quicks Motor Group **Nickname:** **Founded:** 1990
Midweek Matchday: Tuesday **Reserve League:** NW Co's Res Div
Record Attendance: 433 v Flixton (NWCL 5-3-96)
Previous Leagues: Mid Cheshire 90-92
Players progressing to Football League: Anthony Vaughan (Ipswich)
Clubhouse: Yes

95-96 Top Scorer: **95-96 Captain:** **95-96 P.o.Y.:**
Club Record Goalscorer: Colin Small 70 **Club Record Appearances:** Peter Jones 201
Honours: North West Co's Lge Lamont Pils Trophy 93-94, Div 2 R-up 93-94; Mid Cheshire Lg Div 2 R-up 90-91; NWCL Chall Cup R-up 95-96; Manchester Cup R-up 95-96.

VAUXHALL MOTORS

Chairman: Tony Woodley 0151 348 1143 (H) 0171 828 7788 (B)
Secretary: Steve McInerney, 12 Merton Rd, Great Sutton, South Wirral L66 2SW 0151 356 0941 (H) 0385 343633 (B mobile)
Ground: Vauxhall Sports Ground, Rivacre Road, Hooton, Ellesmere Port, South Wirrall. Tel. 0151 327 2115.
Directions: M53 junction 5, take A41 to Chester, on reaching the first set of traffic lights turn left into Hooton Green, Left at the T-junction, right at the next T-junction into Rivacre Road, ground is 250 yards on the right.
Colours: White/white/white. **Club Sponsors:** James Edwards **Founded:** 1963
Record Attendance: 1,500 v English F.A. XI, 1987. **Floodlights:** Yes
Previous Leagues: North West Counties League, West Cheshire League (to 1995)
Honours: B.N.W.C.F.L. 2nd Division Champions 1988-89; Raab Karcher Challenge Cup Winners 1990-91.

Daisy Hill; Back Row (L-R); Jimmy Hulton (Mgr), Keith Daley, Gareth Webster, Danny Mills, Rob Marsden, Colin Smith, Graham Morris, Phil Donlan, Chris Williams, Tony Riley (Asst Mgr). Front Row; Neil Barlow, John Groves, Shaun Lilley, Phil Collier, Gary Crosby, Jason Jones

Maghull FC: Back Row (L-R); Frank O'Brien, George Phoenix, Steve Vickers, Paul Jackson, Lee Lawson, Tony Rolfe, Mark Vickers, Joe Doyle. Front Row; Ian Hodgson, John King, Gary Rimmer, John McInnes, Mark Vogul, Gary Shepherd, Ritchie Hughes (Asst Mgr).

ASHTON TOWN

President: W Pomfrett **Chairman:** G Messer
Secretary: C G Ashcroft, 8 Mason Close, Ashton-in-Makerfield, Wigan WN4 8SD (0942 717565).
Manager: Norman Hickson
Ground: Edge Green Street, Ashton-in-Makerfield, Wigan WN4 8SY (0942 719168).
Directions: M6 Jct 23, A49 to Ashton-in-M. Right at lights onto A58 towards Bolton. After 3/4 mile turn right at 'Rams Head' P.H. into Golbourne Rd. After 200 yds right into Edge Green Str. Ground at end.
Record Gate: 600 v Accrington Stanley 76-77 **Floodlights:** No **Founded:** 1965
Colours: Red with white pin stripe/red/red **Change colours:** All sky blue
Best FA Vase season: Prelim. Rd 84-85
Previous Leagues: Warrington, Lancs Comb. 03-11 71-78, Ches. Co. 78-82.
Midweek Matches: Tuesday **Hons:** Warrington Lg Guardian Cup.

BACUP BOROUGH

President: W Shufflebottom **Chairman:** W Heywood **Vice Chairman:** D Whatmough
Secretary: F Manning, 10 Warwick Street, Haslingden, Rossendale, Lancs BB4 5LR (0706 221886).
Manager: TBA **Asst Manager:** TBA **Commercial Mgr:**
Ground: West View, Cowtoot Lane, Blackthorn, Bacup, Lancashire (0706 878655).
Directions: From M62, M66 onto A681 through Rawtenstall to Bacup centre, left onto A671 towards Burnley, after approx 300 yds right (immed. before the Irwell Inn) climbing Cooper Street, right into Blackthorn Lane then first left into Cowtoot Lane to ground.
Seats: 500 **Cover:** 1,000 **Capacity:** 3,000 **Floodlights:** Yes **Founded:** 1875
Colours: Black & white stripes/black/black **Change colours:** All red
Previous league: Lancs Comb. 03-82. **Midweek Matches:** Tuesday.
Previous Name: Bacup FC. **Previous Grounds:** None
Programme: 12 pages, 30p **Editor:** D Whatmough (0706 875041) **Club Shop:** Not yet
Club Sponsors: Hoover Ltd **Record Gate:** 4,980 v Nelson 1947 **Nickname:** The Boro
Clubhouse: Open matchdays and private functions (for which buffets can be provided). Pies and sandwiches on matchdays.
Captain 93-94: **P.o.Y. 93-94:** **Club record scorer:** Jimmy Clarke
Hons: Lancs Jnr Cup 10-11 (R-up 22-23 74-75), Lancs Comb. 46-47 (Lg Cup R-up 46-47 80-81, NW Co's Lg Div 2 R-up 89-90.

BLACKPOOL MECHANICS

Chairman: Thomas Baldwin **Vice Chairman:** John Sanderson **President:** Peter Sutton
Sec./Press Off./Physio: William Singleton, 'Circular Quay', 36 Colwyn Ave., Blackpool FY4 4EU (01253 768105).
Manager: Jim Betmead **Asst Manager:** Gary Collings. **Physio:** Alan Gamble
Coach: Billy Singleton. **Commercial Manager:** Andrew Sneddon.
Ground: Back Common Edge Rd, Blackpool, Lancs (01253 761721).
Directions: M6 to M55, follow Airport signs. Left at r'bout along A583 (Preston New Rd) to lights, right into Whitehill Rd, becomes School Road, to lights. Straight over main road & follow signs for Blackpool Mechanics F.C. to ground. Rail to Blackpool North - then bus 11c from Talbot Road bus station (next to rail station) and alight at Shovels Hotel, Common Edge Rd.
Seats: 250 **Cover:** 1,700 **Capacity:** 2,000 **Floodlights:** Yes **Founded:** 1947
Club colours: Yellow & Green. **Change colours:** All blue **Nickname:** Mechs
Programme: 10 pages, 50p [illegible] **Editor:** Andrew Sneddon(01253 729962) **Metal Badges:** Yes
Midweek home matchda[illegible] **Club Sponsors:** Yates Wine Lodge, Talbot Rd, Blackpool.
Club Shop: Yes, Man[illegible]ddon (01253 729962). Ties, sweaters, old programmes, m[illegible]
Prev. Ground: St[illegible] **Record Gate:** 1,200 v Morecambe, Lancs Comb, August 1968
Previous Leagu[illegible]kpool & Fylde Combination, West Lancs, Lancs Comb. 62-68.
Clubhouse: Match days, training nights. Dancehall. Matchday food: pie & peas, hot dogs, hamburgers, hot pot.
Captain, Top Scorer & P.o.Y. 93-94:
Hons: Lancs Comb. R-up 74-75 (Bridge Shield 72-73, George Watson Tphy 75-76), NW Co's. Lg Div 3 85-86, W Lancs Lg 60-61 62-63 (R-up 59-60), Fylde & Dist Lg 53-54 56-57 (R-up(3) 54-56 57-58, Div 2 50-51, Lg Cup 52-53 57-58 (R-up 55-56 58-59)), Bannister Cup 52-53 56-57 (R-up(3) 55-56 57-59), Evening KO Cup 61-62, B'pool & Dist Amtr Lg Brackwell Cup R-up(2) 57-59, Lancs Jnr Shield 57-58 60-61 (R-up 54-55), Richardson Cup(2) 60-62, B'pool Co-op Medal 54-55 60-61. Nederlands Cuttrale Sportsbond Festival: Den Haag Cup R-up 53-54, Dordrecht R-up 55-56, Rotterdam R-up 59-60.

CASTLETON GABRIELS

Chairman: T E Butterworth **Vice Chairman:** R Butterworth.
Secretary: David Lord, 34 Fairway, Castleton, Rochdale OL11 3BU (01706 522719).
Manager/Coach:: Peter Freakes. **Assistant Manager:** Dave Jones.
Coach: Neil Mills **Press Officer:** Peter Wilson(01616 249602.
Ground: Butterworth Park, Chadwick Lane, off Heywood Rd., Castleton, Rochdale (01706 527103).
Directions: M62 Jct 20, A6272M to r'bout. Left towards Castleton (A664 Edinburgh Way) to next r'bout, keeping Tesco Superstore to the left, take 1st exit to next r'bout, take 2nd exit into Manchester Rd (A664), after just under mile turn right at 'Top House' P.H. into Heywood Rd., to end & ground on right.
Seats: 250 **Cover:** 500 **Capacity:** 1,500 **Floodlights:** Yes **Founded:** 1924
Cols: Blue & white stripes/blue/blue. **Change colours:** Red/white/red. **Nickname:** Gabs.
Prev. Name: St Gabriels (pre-1960s) **Previous Ground:** Park pitches/ Springfield Pk 1960s-81.
Previous Leagues: Rochdale Sunday Schools 24-84/ Manchester 84-89.
Record Gate: 640 v Rochdale, pre-season friendly 1991. Competitive: 450 v Bamber Bridge 86-87, Lancs Shield
Programme: 28 pages, 50p **Editor:** Pter Wilson(01616 249602) **Club Shop:** No.
Club Sponsors: Dale Mill **Reserve Team's League:** N.W.Co.Res.Division.
Record win: 8-0 v Squires Gate (H) N.W.Co.Div 2 3/12/94.
Record defeat: 1-10 v Blackpool Mechanics(A) N.W.Co.Div 2 1/4/95.
Players progressing to Football League: Dean Stokes (Port Vale) 1992.
Clubhouse: Open seven nights a night and all day Saturday. Pie & peas and sandwiches available matchdays (pie & peas only at Reserve matches).
Midweek home matchday: Tuesday **Club record scorer for a Season:** Tony Diamond 17.
Capt. 94-95: Tony McCombe. **P.o.Y. 94-95:** Tony McCombe. **Top Scorer 93-94:** Tony Diamond .
Hons: Manc. Lg 86-87 (Murray Shield 86-87), Nth West Co's Lg Cup SF 91-92.

CHEADLE TOWN

President: Freddie Pye **Chairman:** Chris Davies **Vice-Chairman:** Clive Williams
Secretary: Susan Burton, 2 Lavington Ave., Cheadle, Stockport, Cheshire SK8 2HH (0161 491 0823).
Manager: Peter Blundell. **Physio:** John Hornbuckle
Ground: Park Road Stadium, Park Road, Cheadle, Cheshire SK8 2AN (0161 428 2510).
Directions: M63 Jct 11, follow signs towards Cheadle, Park Road half mile on left. 1 mile from Gatley (BR), buses from Stockport.
Seats: 300 **Cover:** 300 **Capacity:** 2,500 **Floodlights:** Yes **Club Shop:** No
Programme: 20 pages, 50p. **Editor:** Stuart Crawford **Press Officer:** Chris Davies (0161 428 2510).
Colours: White/Navy/Navy. **Change colours:** All blue. **Founded:** 1961
Midweek Matches: Tuesday **Reserves' Lge:** NW Counties Lge
Record Gate: 1,500 v Stockport County, August 1994.
Previous Lges: Manc. (pre 1987).
Players progressing to Football League: Ashley Ward (Crewe), Steve Bushell (York).
Clubhouse: Open every night. Food available.
95-96 Captain: Martin Randles **95-96 P.o.Y.:** **95-96** [illegible]**rer:**
Club record scorer: Peter Tilley **Club record appe**[illegible] McArdle
Hons: Manchester Lg Div 1 79-80 (R-up 80-81 81-82), Manches[illegible] Manchester Challenge Cup R-up(3) 79-82, Derbys Cup 80-81 (R-up 81-82).

COLNE

Chairman: D Blacklock (01282 696340)
Secretary: Jean Moore, 5 Haverholt Close, Colne, BB8 9SN [illegible]
Ground: Colne Dynamoes Stadium, Holt House, Colne, Lancs, [illegible]
Directions: Enter Colne from M65 to roundabout, 1st left on to Harrison [illegible] [illegible]undabout at top of hill, follow road to ground.
Colours: All red
Formed: 1996 **Floodlights:** Yes
Midweek Matchday: Wednesday

DAISY HILL

Chairman: Mark Ford
Secretary: Bob Naylor, 8 Bailey Fold, Westhoughton, Bolton, Lancs BL5 3AH (0942 813720).
Manager: Jimmy Hulton. **Asst Mgr:** Tony Riley **Physio:** Gary Bradley
Ground: New Sirs, St James Street, Westhoughton, Bolton, Lancs (0942 818544).
Directions: M61 Jct 5, A58 (Snydale Way/Park Road) for 1.5 miles, left into Leigh Road (B5235) for 1 mile, right into village then left. Straight forward between Church and School into St James Street. Ground 250 yds on the left. Half mile from Daisy Hill (BR).

Club Shop: No **Seats:** 200 **Cover:** 250 **Capacity:** 2,000 **Floodlights:** No
Programme: 38 pages 50p **Editor:** **Press Officer:** John Bullen (01942 874719)
Colours: All royal blue. **Change:** Red & black stripes/black/black
Founded: 1894 **Reformed:** 1951
Midweek Matches: Tuesday **Reserves' Lge** CNWL Res Div.
Record Attendance: 2,000 v Horwich RMI, Westhoughton Charity Cup final May 1980.
Previous Leagues: Westhoughton/ Bolton Comb./ Lancs Combination. 78-82.
Players progressing to Football League: Barry Butler (Chester City via Atherton LR).
Clubhouse: Open normal licensing hours during any football activity. Snacks on matchdays.
95-96 Captain: **95-96:Top Scorer:** **95-96 P.o.Y.:** Ford.
Club Record scorer/appearances: Alan Roscoe, 300 goals. 450 games.
Hons: Bolton Comb. 62-63 72-73 75-76 77-78 (Lg Cup(4) 59-60 61-62 71-73), Lancs Shield 61-62 71-72 86-87.

FORMBY

Chairman: Chris Welsh
Secretary: B G Prescott, 5 Abbotts Way, Formby, Merseyside L37 6DR (01704 879857).
Managers: Peter Hennerty + Mike Scott. **Assistant Manager:** John Foster.
Coach: Billy Buck **Physio:** Keith Johnson
Commercial Manager/ Press Officer: Paul Lawler (01704 878409).
Ground: Brows Lane, Formby, Merseyside (01704 833505)
Directions: A565 Liverpool-Southport, turn for Formby at lights opposite Di-it-All DIY into Altcar Rd, fork left at junction to r'bout (opposite Blundell Arms Hotel), take 2nd exit then sharp left into Duke Street, 1st right into Elbow Lane, ground entrance 50yds on left. Half a mile from Formby (BR), buses from Formby & Southport stations.
Seats: 200 **Cover:** 500 **Capacity:** 2,000 **Floodlights:** No **Founded:** 1919
Midweek Matches: Wednesday. **Record Gate:** 2,500 v Oldham, FA Cup 1st Rd 24/11/73
Colours: Yellow/blue/yellow **Change:** White/navy/navy. **Nickname:** Squirrels
Programme: 36 pages, 50p **Editor:** Paul Lawler,13 Sefton Rd.,Formby.L37 2JG.
Club Shop: Yes, stocking programmes, enamel badges and other souvenirs. Contact Paul Lawler (01704 878409).
Best FA Cup season: 1st Rd 73-74 (lost 0-2 at home to Oldham Athletic).
Club Sponsors: Classic Lifts.
Previous Leagues: Liverpool Co. Comb. 19-68/ Lancs Comb. 68-71, Ches. Co. 71-72.
Reserve team: None
Record win: 11-1 v Earle (H) 18/10/52
Record defeat: 0-10 v Irlam Town (H) 18/1/86.
Record transfer fee paid: Unknown **Received:** £1,000 for Geoff Twentyman (Chorley).
Clubhouse: Social club and offices sadly destroyed in fire in September 1990, and as yet unreplaced. However, matchday refreshment bar stocks hot food & drinks.
Top Scorer 94-95: Colin Beck 15. **Captain & P.o.Y. 94-95:** Dave Walbank.
Hons: Liverpool Co. Comb. 48-49 (R-up 51-52 52-53 64-65, George Mahon Cup 64-65 67-68 (R-up 55-56 56-57), Liverpool Senior Cup 77-78 (R-up 84-85, Challenge Cup 52-53 63-64 67-68 (R-up 64-65), Amtr Cup(3) 29-30 47-49), Lancs Amtr Cup 34-35
Lamot Pils Trophy 94-95.

GARSWOOD UNITED

Chairman: R Jones
Secretary: John Anelay, 128 Victoria Road, Garswood, Nr Wigan WN4 0RE (01942 519231)
Ground: Simms Lane End, Garswood Road, Garswood, Nr Wigan (01744 892258)
Directions: A580 towards Liverpool. Turn right into A58, Liverpool Road, turn left into Garswood Road, signed Garswood 3/4 mile, follow road bearing left at triangle up to crossroads, straight ahead, ground 100 yards on left
Colours: Blue & white/blue/blue
Founded: 1967
Floodlights: No
Previous Leagues: Mid Cheshire, Liverpool County Comb, Warrington & Dist, St Helens Comb.
Honours: Griffiths Trophy 70-71; Worral Cup 71-72; Burtonwood Cup 72-73; Chadwick Cup 73-74; Ford Cup 74-75; Dodds Shield, Guardian Cup, Jubilee Cup 76-77; Liverpool Comb Div 2, Lord Wavertree Cup 78-79; Liverpool Jun Cup 79-80; Mid Cheshire Div 2 Cup 88-89; Lge Div 2 89-90; Whitbread Amt Cup, Mid Cheshire Div 1, Parker Cup, Wigan Cup 94-95; Mid Cheshire Div 1, Liverpool Chall Cup, Wigan Cup 95-96

HASLINGDEN

Chairman: Brian Horsbrough **Manager:** Steve Parry
Secretary: Len Chenery, 83 Belgrave Road, Darwen, BB8 2SF (01254 704518)
Ground: Ewood Bridge, Manchester Rd, Haslingden, Lancs (01706 217814).
Directions: From South: M66 Blackburn/Clitheroe exit, left at r'bout past Woolpack Hotel, sharp left at bottom of hill - ground 100yds on right. From North; M6 Jct 31, A59 to Blackburn, take ring-road at Moat House Hotel and follow signs to M65, leave M65 at jct 8 and follow signs for Bury, follow dual-c'way for about 5 miles and leave at Todmorden exit, right at lights, straight across r'bout by Woolpack Hotel, then follow as above.
Seats: **Cover:** **Capacity:** 1,500 **Floodlights:** Yes **Founded:** 1969
Colours: Tangerine/black/black **Record Gate:** 551 v Blackburn, August 1993.
Midweek Matches: Tuesdays **Previous Leagues:** West Lancashire (pre-1993)
Hons: North West Co's Lg Div 2 93-94, West Lancs Lg Div 2 80-81 (R-up 92-93, Presidents Cup 71-72 80-81 92-93).

LEEK C.S.O.B. FC

Chairman: K J Hill
Secretary: Stan Lockett, 5 Fitzherbert Close, Swynnerton, Stone, Staffs ST15 0PQ, (01782 796551)
Ground: Harrison Park, Macclesfield Road, Leek, Staffs, (01538 383734)
Directions: M6 south Junc 17, A534 to Congleton - follow signs for Leek (A54), carry on until junction with A523, turn right on to A523, this road is direct to Leek, ground is 8 miles, on right just into Leek.
Colours: Red & white/white/red
Founded: 1945
Floodlights: Yes
Midweek Matchday: Wednesday
Previous Leagues: Leek & Moorland Lge, Staffs County North, Refuge Midland Lge.
Honours: Refuge Midland Lge 95-96. Lge Cup 95-96 94-95; Leek Cup 95-96 94-95; Midland Ref Charity Shield 95-96; Sportsline Chall Cup 95-96.

MAGHULL

Chairman: Les Jacques **Vice Chairman:** G Fisher **President:** M Latham.
Secretary: Danny Sherlock, 14 Alexander Drive, Lydiate, Merseyside L31 2NJ (0151 526 2306).
Manager: Frank O'Brien **Coach:** Ritchie Hughes. **Physio:** Fred Smith.
Ground: Old Hall Field, Hall Lane, Maghull, Merseyside (0151 526 7320).
Directions: M57 or M58 to end (Switch Island), A59 towards Preston (Northway) to lights at Hall Lane, turn right following signs for Maghull Station. Ground 200 yds on the left. Half mile from Maghull (Merseyrail).
Seats: None **Cover:** 75 **Capacity:** 500 **Floodlights:** No **Club Shop:** No.
Programme: 40 pages, 50p **Editor/Press Officer:** Andy Boyd (0151 526 2715).
Colours: Blue & red stripes **Change colours:** All yellow
Sponsors: John McCabe, Butchers **Founded:** 1921
Midweek Matches: Tuesday **Reserves' League:** Liverpool County Comb.
Record Attendance: 500 v Marine, L'pool Chal. Cup 1982/83
Previous Leagues: Liverpool Co. Comb./ Lancs Comb. 72-78/ Cheshire Co. 78-82.
Clubhouse: Fully licenced clubhouse & lounge open matchdays and midweek. Hot & cold food available.
95-96 Captain: John McInnes. **95-96 Top Scorer:** Mark Vickers. **95-96 P.O.Y.:**
Club Record Goalscorer: Bobby Prince **Club Record Appearances:** Bobby Prince.
Hons: Liverpool Co. Amtr Cup 34-35 58-59, Liverpool Co. Chal. Cup 79-80 80-81 85-86 94-95, Lancs FA Amtr Cup 49-50, Lancs Comb. Cup 77-78, Liverpool Co. Comb. 66-67, North West Co's Lg Div 2 92-93 (Res. Div Cup R-up 94-95).

MIDDLEWICH ATHLETIC

Chairman: J McAteer
Secretary: Bryan Longley, 16 Northway, Holmes Chapel, Cheshire CW4 7EF (01477 537310)
Ground: Seddon Street, Middlewich (01606 835842)
Directions: M6 junc 18, A54 Middlewich to traffic lights, forward to end of dual carriageway, right into Pepper Street/Webbs Lane, second left Seddon Street, ground on right
Colours: Red & white/red/red
Founded: 1988
Floodlights: No
Midweek Matchday: Wednesday
Previous Leagues: Crewe & Dist, Mid Cheshire Lge.
Honours: Crewe & Dist Prem Lge 89-90; Crewe FA Dist Cup 89-90; Mid Cheshire Dist FA Sat Cup 93-94 95-96.

NELSON

Chairman: Ken Broom. **Vice-Chairman:** A Barnes.
Secretary: C R King, 1 Grange Ave, Barrowford, Nelson, Lancashire BB9 6AN (01282 695578)
Manager: Nigel Coates. **Assistant Manager:** P Rigby.
Ground: Victoria Park, Lomesway, Nelson, Lancs (01282 613820).
Directions: M65 jct 13, 1st left (A6068), 2nd left (B6249 for Nelson), 2nd right sign Lomeshaye Vill to grd.
Capacity: **Seats:** 60 **Cover:** 200 **Floodlights:** No **Club Shop:**
Programme: **Editor:** **Nickname:** Blues
Colours: Blue & white stripes **Change colours:** White/red
Midweek matchday: Wednesday **Reserve League:** North West Co's Reserve Div.
Previous Leagues: Lancashire 1889-98 1900-01/ Football League 1898-1900/ Lancs Comb 01-16 46-82/ N W Counties 82-88/ W Lancs 88-92. **Clubhouse:** Bar open matchdays
Honours: Lancs Lg 1895-96 (R-up 97-98), Lancs Comb. 1949-50 51-52 (R-up 47-48 50-51 60-61, Lg Cip 49-50 50-51 59-60, Bridge Shield 75-76, George Watson Tphy 78-79, Lancs Jnr Cup 07-08 54-55, FA Cup 2nd Rd Proper 30-31(replay) 50-51 (1st Rd 32-33 51-52 53-54).

OLDHAM TOWN

Chairman: Ken Hughes **Manager:** Paul Dale
Secretary: Graham Shuttleworth, 42 Southgate Road, Chadderton, Oldham OL9 9PT
Ground: Whitebank Stadium, Whitebank Rd, Hollins, Oldham, Lancs OL8 3JH (061 624 2689).
Directions: M62 jct 18, M66 to Heaton Pk, right on to A576, left at 2nd lights on to A6104, follow Victoria Ave. on to Hollinwood Ave. under bridge to T-junction, right/ 1st left at Roxy Cinema, follow Hollins Rd for 1.5 miles to Fire Station, left on to Elm Rd & follow to next left, Whitebank Rd on left.
Seats: 25 **Cover:** Yes **Capacity:** 1,000 **Floodlights:** Yes **Founded:** 1964
Programme: 16 pages, 50p **Editor:** Secretary
Colours: Blue/white/blue. **Change Colours:** **Midweek Matches:** Tuesday
Record Attendance: 325 v Flixton, NWCL Div 2 Championship decider May 95
Clubhouse: Open evenings and matchdays. **Previous Leagues:** Manch. Amtr/ Lancashire Comb. 81-82.

RAMSBOTTOM UNITED

Chairman: H Williams (01706 822799)
Secretary: John Maher, 75 Ramsbottom Road, Hawkshaw, Bury BL8 4JS. (01204 852742)
Ground: Riverside Ground, Acre Bottom, Ramsbottom.
Directions: M66 (North) to junction 1, take A56 towards Ramsbottom. After 1 mile turn left down Bury New Road. Turn left after Trinity paper Mill along the road running parallel with the East Lancs Railway.
Colours: Blue with white trim/blue/blue **Formed:** 1966 **Floodlights:** No
Previous Leagues: Bury Amateur League, Bolton Combination, Manchester League.
Honours: Bolton Comb. Div 1 Champ 72-73; Bolton Comb. Prem Div. 76-77, 86-87; Manchester Lge Div 1 Cham 90-91; Cup 90-91; Gilgryst Cup 94-95.

SKELMERSDALE UNITED

Chairman: D Tomlinson **Vice Chairman:** T Garner.
Secretary: Ken Hilton, 58 Higgins Lane, Burscough, Ormskirk, Lancs L40 7SD (01704 894504).
Manager: Barry Hedley **Asst Manager:** Ged Parr **Physio:** Ronnie Taylor
Ground: White Moss Park, White Moss Road, Skelmersdale, Lancs (01695 722123).
Directions: M58 Jct 3, at 2nd r'bout take 3rd exit towards Skelmersdale, continue for approx 1 mile, ground on the right. 4 miles from Ormskirk (BR).
Seats: 250 **Cover:** 1,000 **Capacity:** 10,000 **Floodlights:** Yes **Club Shop:** No
Programme: 20 pages, 50p **Editor:** Team effort **Press Officer:** Secretary
Colours: Blue/white/blue. **Change colours:** Yellow/black/yellow
Sponsors: Tamcos Training **Nickname:** Skemmers **Founded:** 1882
Midweek Matches: Wednesday **Record Attendance:** 7,500 v Slough FA Amat Cup 67
Best FA Cup year: 1st Rd 67-68 (0-2 at Scunthorpe), 68-69 (0-2 at Chesterfield), 71-72 (0-4 at Tranmere).
Previous Leagues: Liverpool County Combination, Lancashire Combination 1891-93 03-07 21-24 55-68 76-78, Cheshire County 68-71 78-82, Northern Premier 71-76.
Clubhouse: None, but matchday food bar sells hot drinks, soup, hot pies & pasties etc.
Hons: FA Amateur Cup 70-71 (R-up 66-67), Ches. Co. Lg(2) 68-70 (Jubilee Cup 69-70), Liverpool Co. Comb 10, Lancs Comb Div 2 55-56, Liverpool Challenge Cup 8, Lancs Amat Shield 07-08, George Mahon 5, Lancs F'lit Cup 69-70, Lancs Jnr Cup(3), Ashworth Cup 70-71, Barassi Anglo-Italian Cup 70-71, Liverpool Non-Lge Cup(2), North West Co's Lg Cup R-up 82-83.

SQUIRES GATE

Chairman: Brian Hammond **Vice President:** Brian Addison.
Secretary: John Maguire, 2 Squires Court, Cairn Grove, Blackpool, Lancs FY4.
Manager: Paul Arnold **Assistant Manager:** John Chippendale.
Ground: School Road, Marton, Blackpool, Lancs (0253 798584).
Directions: M6 to M55 jct 4, left onto A583, right at 1st lights (Whitehall Rd) follow signs for airport. Ground approx. one and a half miles on right.
Seats: 2 rows **Cover:** One side **Capacity:** **Floodlights:** No **Formed:** 1948
Colours: All royal **Midweek Matches:** Tuesday **Prog.:** 20 pages **Clubhouse:** Yes
Prev. Lges: W. Lancs (pre-1991) **Hons:** W. Lancs Lg Div 2 80-81 (Richardson Cup 86-87).

STANTONDALE

President: Ken Wood **Chairman:** Roy Grundy **Vice-Chairman:** Mike Shiels
Secretary: Alan James Hardaker, 89 Park Lane, Netherton, Merseyside. L30 1QB. (0151 521 6313)
Mgr/Press Off.: Tommy Lawson **Asst Manager:** Garry Britton **Coach:** Eric Warren
Ground: Leisure Time Club, Orrell Lane, Bootle, Merseyside L20 (0151 525 2115).
Directions: M57 then M58 to the end at Switch Island, follow signs to Bootle and Docks (A5063) Dunnings Bridge Road to roundabout, left into Netherton Way, take left hand lane at traffic lights into Orrell Lane, ground on left next to M.F.I.
Colours: Green/green/green. **Midweek home matchdays:** Tuesday **Floodlights:** No
Colours: All green **Change colours:** **Founded:** 1986
Sponsors: Charlotte Sports **Previous League:** Liverpool County Combination (pre-1992).
Programme: 28 pages, 50p **Editor:** Garry Britton (0695 23199). **Clubhouse:** Yes.
Honours: North West Co's Lg Lamot Pils Cup 92-93, Liverpool County Comb. 90-91 (Div 2 87-88, George Mahon Cup R-up 90-91), Liverpool Jnr Cup 90-91 (R-up 88-89), Liverpool Challenge Cup 91-92, McEwans Lager Cup 91-92, Lord Wavertree Cup R-up 87-88.

TETLEY WALKER

President: J Sixsmith **Chairman:** R Fisher **Secretary:** B Gleave, 8 Cossack Ave., Orford, Warrington, Cheshire WA2 9PB (01925 659559).
Manager Ray Fisher. **Asst.Manager:**
Physio: P Cowell **Press Officer:** B McLaughlin.
Ground: Tetley Walker Club, Long Lane, Orford, Warrington, Cheshire WA2 9PB (01925 634904).
Ground: From M62 follow signs to Warrington town centre on A49. After about one and a half miles turn left at 2nd r'bout (next to Coachmans pub), ground about 500yds on left. Rail to Warrington Central station then taxi - fare about £2 from station to ground.
Capacity: **Seats:** 40 **Cover:** 150 **Floodlights:** No **Founded:** 1974
Midweek matches: Tuesday **Reserves' Lge:** Warrington & D. **Nickname:** Walkers
Colours: White/red **Change Cols:** Maroon & sky stripes **Club Shop:** Not yet.
Programme: Average 10 pages **Programme Editor:** Mr P Cowell (01925 573063).
Previous League: Warrington & District 1974-94.
Previous Grounds: None **Clubhouse:** Open noon-midnight. Food includes sandwiches & pies.
Record win: 10-1 v Grappenhall Sports (A), Guardian Cup 1992-93.
Record appearances: Ray Arnold **Top Scorer 93-94:** Tony Plant, 36.
Captain 94-95: **Player of the Year 94-95:**
Hons: Warrington & Dist. Lg 86-87 93-94 (R-up 85-86 92-93); Guardian Cup 84-85 85-86 93-94 (R-up 86-87).

MANCHESTER FOOTBALL LEAGUE

President: A Booth

Vice-Presidents: G S Sinclair, W P D Haig

Vice-Chairman: M Magor

Secretary: F Fitzpatrick, 102 Victoria Road, Stretford, Manchester M32 0AD (0161 865 2726)

FINAL LEAGUE TABLES 1995/96

Premier Div	P	W	D	L	F	A	Pts
1. Little Hulton	30	22	4	4	78	37	70
2. Springhead	30	18	7	5	61	36	61
3. Abbey Hey	30	19	3	8	62	38	60
4. Highfield U	30	17	5	8	59	39	56
5. B.I.C.C.	30	14	10	60	60	43	52
6. Wythenshawe	30	16	4	10	50	33	52
7. Woodley	30	12	8	10	49	41	44
8. M Shackleton	30	11	10	9	55	48	43
9. Wythenshawe	30	12	7	11	50	44	43
10. E Manchester	30	10	12	8	54	51	42
11. Atherton Tn	30	12	50	13	54	53	41
12. Dukinfield Tn	30	9	6	15	39	58	33
13. Stockport Ge	30	5	5	20	45	74	20
14. Monton Amt	30	5	5	20	37	73	20
15. Prestwich Hy	30	4	7	19	37	75	19
16. Sacred Heart	30	3	4	23	34	81	13

Div One	P	W	D	L	F	A	Pts
1. Stand Ath	26	18	5	3	83	25	59
2. Elton Fold	26	15	5	6	75	38	50
3. M/chester R	26	14	3	9	77	58	45
4. Breightmet U	26	12	9	5	59	42	45
5. Pennington	26	11	8	7	50	52	41
6. Whitworth V	26	11	7	8	68	66	40
7. Hollinwood	26	10	8	8	55	47	38
8. Old Aths.	26	9	7	10	52	46	34
9. Ashton Ath	26	7	9	10	37	48	30
10. Whalley Ran	26	8	5	13	58	83	29
11. Coldhurst	26	7	6	13	53	79	27
12. Milton	26	6	7	13	51	66	25
13. New Mills	26	6	6	14	54	85	24
14. G M Police	26	2	7	17	33	70	13

SEASON 1995-96: CHAMPIONS/RUNNERS-UP/PROMOTIONS/RELEGATIONS RE-ELECTIONS/RESIGNATIONS/NEW CLUBS/CUP SUCCESSES

	Premier	Div 1	Div 2	Div 3
CHAMPIONS:	Liitle Hulton Utd	Stand Athletic	East Manchester Res	Hollinwood Res
Runners Up:	Springhead	Elton Fold	M. Shackleton Res	BICC Res
PROMOTED:		Stand Athletic Elton Fold		Hollinwood Res BICC Res
RELAGTED:	Prestwich Heys Sacred Heart			
Re-ELECTION:		New Mills G.M.P.		Pennington Res Coldhurst Utd Res
RESIGNED:			L Hulton Utd Res	
NEW CLUBS:		Gamesley Tottington Utd Willows		Gamesley Res Tottington Utd Res Willows Res

MANCHESTER LEAGUE PREMIER DIVISION CLUBS 1995-96

ABBEY HEY

Secretary: Mr G Lester, 6 Newhaven Ave., Higher Openshaw, Manchester M11 1HU.
Colours: Green & white/white/green **Ground:** Goredale Avenue, Gorton (0161 231 7147).
Directions: A57 towards Hyde, right into Woodland Avenue approx one & a half miles past Belle Vue junction, right again into Ryder Brow Rd, 1st left after bridge into Goredale Ave.

ATHERTON TOWN

Secretary: G Butler, 43 Hope Fold Ave., Atherton, Lancs M29 0BW (01942 870326).
Colours: All royal **Ground:** Howe Bridge Spts Centre, Howe Bridge, Atherton (01942 870403).
Directions: A579 Atherton to Leigh road - Sports Centre on left approx one & a half miles from Atherton.

B.I.C.C.

Secretary: L. Stone, 51 Coppieridge Drive, Crumpsall,Manchester M8 4PB (01161 740 6621)
Colours: Blue & black/black/blue **Ground:** Blackley New Road, Blackley.
Directions: Follow Rochdale Rd A664 from Manchester. Turn left at Brackley into Old Market St, then fork right into Blackley New Rd, ground 330yards on left. (01161 740 9151)

DUKINFIELD TOWN

Secretary: L Walton, 280 Yew Tree Lane, Dukinfield, Cheshire SK16 5DN (0161 338 6108).
Colours: Yellow/blue/yellow **Ground:** Blocksages Birch Lane, Dukinfield.
Directions: To Ashton along by-pass, right at 2nd island into Dewsnap Lane, left into Birch Lane, ground 100yds on lefy behind public baths and Colliers garage.

EAST MANCHESTER

Secretary: D Wilkinson, 76 Sandy Lane, Dukinfield, Cheshire SK16 5NL (0161 330 4450).
Colours: Sky/navy/blue **Ground:** G.M.T. Tranport Ground, Mount Rd, Gorton (0161 224 1176).
Directions: A57 from Manchester or Hyde to Belle Vue junction, turn into Mount Rd, ground 1 mile on left after Mellands Field.

HIGHFIELD UNITED

Secretary: J Flynn, 58 Springside Rd, Bury BL9 5JQ (0161 764 9986).
Colours: Red/white/red **Ground:** Bridge Hall Lane, Bury (0161 797 2282).
Directions: A58 from Bury centre towards Heywood, at M66 junction pass under motorway and Bridge Hall Lane is first left - ground 200yds on left.

LITTLE HULTON UNITED

Secretary: Mrs E Blood, 4 Cloudstock Grove, Little Hulton, Worsley M28 6DR (0161 790 8925).
Colours: All royal **Change colours:** Sky & white stripes/white/white.
Ground: Avon Close, off Worsley Avenue, Little Hulton.
Directions: A6 from Manchester, two miles after Walkden turn left towards Tyldesley into Armitage Lane, left at Welcome pub after half mile into Madamswood Lane, 2nd right into Worsley Ave., 2nd right is Avon Close. Or, M61 jct 4, A6 towards Manchester, right into Armitage Lane and follow as above.

MITCHELL SHACKLETON

Secretary: C L Flynn, 3 Adelaide Str., Swinton, Manchester M27 3JW (0161 794 7953).
Colours: Green & white hoops/white/green **Change colours:** All maroon.
Ground: Salteye Park, Peel Green, Eccles (0161 788 8373).
Directions: Leave M63 at Peel Green r'bout (jct 2), take A57 Liverpool Road towards Irlam, ground entrance half mile on left behind Kara Cafew opposite Barton airport. Or, follow A57 from Manchester via Salford & Eccles, then follow Irlam signs.

PRESTWICH HEYS

Secretary: M Johnston, 23 Fairways, Horwich, Bolton BL6 5QA (01204 692086).
Colours: Red & white stripes/black/red **Ground:** Sandgate Rd, Prestwich (0161 773 8888).
Directions: Follow Old Bury Rd (A665) from Manchester to Prestwich, right into Heywood Rd, 3rd left into Mount Rd/Sandgate Rd - ground on right.

SACRED HEART

Secretary: K D Devlin, 61 Buersil Ave., Balderstone, Rochdale, Lancs OL16 4TR (01706 313309).
Colours: Red/red/red & black **Ground:** Fox Park, Belfield Mill Lane, Rochdale.
Directions: M62 jct 21, follow Rochdale signs, right at 2nd lights into Albert Royds St, grd half mile on right.

SPRINGHEAD

Secretary: K Gibson, 1 Little Oak Close, Lees, Oldham OL4 3LW (0161 627 3760).
Colours: Red/white/red **Ground:** St John Str., Lees, Oldham (0161 627 0260).
Directions: From Oldham (Mumps r'bout) follow A669 towards Lees for approx one & a half miles, left at St John Str., grounds 500yds on right.

STOCKPORT GEORGIANS

Secretary: M Kennedy, 45 Shakespeare Rd, Bredbury, Stockport SK6 2HS (0161 494 5210).
Colours: Blue & white/blue/white **Ground:** Cromley Rd, Woodsmoor (0161 483 6581).
Directions: Follow Stockport-Hazel Grove Rd (A6), right into Woodsmoor Lane at Davenport Theatre, 1st left into Moorland Rd, left at Flowery Field for Cromley Rd.

WOODLEY SPORTS

Secretary: D Dawson, 19 Woodstock Rd, Woodley, Stockport SK6 1QP (0161 236 9177).
Colours: Orange/white/orange **Ground:** Lambeth Grove, off Mill Lane, Woodley (0161 494 6429).
Directions: A560 from Stockport towards Woodley, left into Mill Str./Mill Lane at St Marks Church, Woodley, then 2nd right into Lambeth Grove.

WYTHENSHAWE AMATEURS

Secretary: S R Hall, 14 Southpark Rd, Gatley, Cheadle, Cheshire SK8 4AN (0161 428 6074).
Colours: Blue & white stripes/blue/blue **Ground:** Longley Lane, Northenden (0161 998 7268).
Directions: Princess Parkway from Manchester to Post House hotel, via Palatine Rd & Moor End Rd to Longley Lane - ground entrance opposite Overwood Rd.

WYTHENSHAWE TOWN

Secretary: P Whiles, 29 Lorna Rd, Cheadle Hulme SK8 5BJ (0161 485 7380).
Colours: All royal **Ground:** Ericstan Park, Timpson Rd, Baguley, Manchester (0161 998 5076).
Directions: Princess Parkway from Manchester, right into Altrincham Rd (A560), left into Southmoor Rd and 1st right into Timpson Rd - ground at end.

MANCHESTER LEAGUE DIVISION ONE CLUBS 1995-96

ASHTON ATHLETIC

Secretary: S Halliwell, 20 Kings Rd, Golborne, Warrington WA3 3PJ (01942 270778).
Colours: All green **Ground:** Brocstedes Park, Brocstedes Rd, North Ashton, Wigan (01942 716360).
Directions: A580 or M6 to Haydock Island, A49 to Ashton (Bryn Cross), left at lights onto Downall Green Rd, over M6, 2nd right, 2nd right is Brocstedes Rd.

BREIGHTMET UNITED

Secretary: P G Lee, 37 Meadow Close, Little Lever, Bolton BL3 1LJ (01204 792280).
Colours: White/black/red **Ground:** Moss Park, Back Bury Rd, Breightmet, Bolton (01204 33930).
Directions: From Manchester follow A56 Bury road, at Whitefield take A665 towards Radcliffe, at Radcliffe proceed to Bolton Rd/Countess Lane and Radcliffe Moor Rd to A58 junction, left towards Bolton - ground half mile situated behind Coopers Egg Packing station.

COLDHURST UNITED

Secretary: Mr B Jackson, 526 Higginshaw Lane, Royton, Oldham OL2 6HW.
Colours: Blue & white/blue/blue **Ground:** Crompton Cricket Club, Glebe Str., Shaw (01706 847421).
Directions: From Manchester via Oldham road (A62) and Broadway/Shaw Rd (A663) to 'Big Lamp' r'bout near Shaw, by-pass Shaw centre, left into Salt Str., right into Glebe Street.

ELTON FOLD

Secretary: Guy Mallinson 14 Lonsdale St Bury BL8 2QD (Bury 797 7090)
Colours: Blue & black/black/black **Ground:** Bolton Rd Sports Club, Bolton Rd, Bury
Directions: A58 from Bury to Bolton. 1 mile from Bury pass Wellington Pub on right 200 yards turn left into Connaught St. Halfway down turn right in between houses into car park

GREATER MANCHESTER POLICE

Secretary: P Davidson, 2 Oakwood, Sale M33 5RH (0161 962 2327).
Colours: Green & white/white/green **Ground:** Hough End Police Club (0161 856 1798).
Directions: Princess Parkway from central Manchester, right at Mauldeth Rd West, grd entrance half mile left.

HOLLINWOOD

Secretary: K Evans, 20 Meadow Rise, High Crompton, Shaw, Oldham OL2 7QG (01706 840987).
Colours: All blue **Ground:** Lime Lane, Hollinwood (0161 681 3385).
Directions: Oldham Road (A62) from Manchester to Roxy Cinema, right into Hollins Rd, 1st right into Albert Street, left at junction with Roman Road, 1st right into Lime Lane for quarter mile.

MANCHESTER ROYAL

Secretary: Mr A Royle, 34 Tennison Rd, Chedle SK8 2AR.
Colours: Red (black trim)/black/red (black trim) **Ground:** Barnes Hospital, Cheadle.
Directions: From Manchester, hospital entrance is on the left of Kingsway just after M63 jct 10. Keep left within hospital grounds, pitch is adjacent to motorway.

MILTON

Secretary: Mr R Curzon, 56 Abbey Crescent, Heywood OL10 4UG.
Cols: Green & yel. stripes/black/yel. **Grnd:** Athletic Stadium, Springfield Pk, off Bolton Rd, Rochdale.
Directions: From Manchester via Middleton (A664) to Hollins, A6046 towards Heywood then A58 towards Rochdale - Park on left after one and a half miles. Or, M62 jct 20 then follow Heywood signs (A58) - Park on right after one and a half miles.

MONTON AMATEURS

Secretary: T Lee, 28 Wheatley Rd, Swinton, Manchester M27 3RW (0161 793 8033).
Colours: All royal **Ground:** As Mitchell Shackleton (above).

NEW MILLS

Secretary: A Bowers, 5 Digland Villas, New Mills SK12 4HS (01663 744932).
Colours: Amber/black/black **Ground:** Church Lanw, New Mills (01663 747435).
Directions: A6 to Swan Hotel, left into Albion Rd, continue to Church Rd, left into Church Lane.

OLD ALTRINCHAMIANS

Secretary: K Ingham, 27 Oakleigh Ave., Timperley, Altrincham, Cheshire WA15 6QT (0161 962 6496).
Colours: Black & white stripes/black/black **Ground:** Crossford Bridge P.F., Meadows Rd, Sale.
Directions: From Manchester via Stretford (A56), under M63, left at lights into Dane Rd, 1st left into Meadows Rd, ground entrance at end.

PENNINGTON

Secretary: K J Mullineaux, 271 Devonshire Rd, Atherton, Manchester M29 9QB (01942 879769).
Colours: Royal & white stripes/white/blue **Ground:** Jubilee Park, Leigh Rd, Atherton (01942 894703).
Directions: From Manchester follow East Lancs Rd towards Liverpool, right at Greyhound hotel towards Leigh, in Leigh take Atherton Rd (A579), ground on left after about one & a half miles before G.M.T. offices.

STAND ATHLETIC

Secretary: T H Edwards, 3 Burndale Drive, Unsworth, Bury BL9 8EN (0161 766 3432).
Colours: All maroon **Ground:** Elms Playing Fields, George Street, Whitefield.
Directions: From Manc. city centre proceed via Bury New Rd (A56) to Whitefield. George St. is on right just before Fire Station. Car park & changing facilities are at Whitefield Community Centre in Green Lane, off George Str.

WHALLEY RANGE

Secretary: R Lapsley, 8 Withnell Rd, Burnage, Manchester M191GHN (0161 432 6158).
Colours: Black & red stripes/black/black (red tops) **Ground:** King's Rd, Chorlton (0161 881 2618).
Directions: Princess Parkway from Manchester, right at Wilbraham Rd, left at Withington Rd South, King's Rd is 1st right, ground entrance opposite Daventry Rd.

WHITWORTH VALLEY

Secretary: A Riley, 31 John Street, Whitworth, Rochdale OL12 8BT (01706 852619).
Colours: All royal **Ground:** Rawstron Str., Whitworth (01706 853030).
Directions: Bacup road (A671) from Rochdale, after just over 2 miles turn left at Whitworth centre into Tonge Lane then 3rd right left into Crown Park Way.

GREEN INSULATION MID-CHESHIRE FOOTBALL LEAGUE

Founded: 1948

President: W Salt. **League Secretary:** E.B. Davies

34 Ryebank Road, Firswood, Manchester M16 0FP (0161 881 5732)

The 1995-96 season of the Mid-Cheshire League saw both divisions run with 16 teams. Cheadle Heath Nomads and Warrington Town Res were promoted, Bollington Athletic were relegated, the knock on effect was their reserve side were expelled from Division Two.

The Inter-League fixture with West Cheshire League was played on the 4th October and the league did well to level the score after trailing 3-1. Mid-season saw Garswood United top the table, it seemed nothing would stop them winning the Division One title, this they did having led from the 1st league table until crowned as champions. Barnton had a tremendous finish to the season giving them a deserved Runner-up spot. Grove United had two league wins over Garswood but they and Bramhall failed to last the pace.

The 2nd Division title went to Bollington Athletic determined to regain their previous season's Division One position. They had shared the leadership with Zeneca and Pilkington throughout the season, Zeneca took runners-up spot despite loosing their last two fixtures, goal difference edging them over Alsager.

In the Division One Cup Bramhall beat both of last seasons finalists in the first two rounds, and then lost the semi-final against Rylands. Chorlton Town were the other finalist and it was they that took an early lead, which was enough to land them the trophy. The Division Two Cup saw neighbours Bollington Athletic and Zeneca dispute the final, a late goal seeing Zeneca home, a great acheivement considering that they finished 2nd from bottom in the league the previous season.

Garswood United M.C.F.L. Division One Champions 95-96, Liverpool FA Challenge Cup and Wigan Senior Cup winners. Now moving to N.W.C.F.L. for 96-97 season.

FINAL LEAGUE TABLES 1995/96

Div One		P	W	D	L	F	A	Pts
1.	Garswood U	30	24	4	2	89	25	76
2.	Barnton	30	21	4	5	96	37	67
3.	Grove Utd	30	20	3	7	65	35	63
4.	Bramhall	30	16	6	8	83	42	54
5.	Knutsford	30	13	7	10	69	48	46
6.	Linotype	30	12	9	9	56	47	45
7.	Chorlton Tn	30	11	10	9	53	52	43
8.	Warrington T	30	9	12	9	60	43	39
9.	Wilmslow Alb	30	11	6	13	46	52	39
10.	Rylands	30	9	7	14	42	68	34
11.	Broadheath C	30	8	9	13	38	59	33
12.	Cheadle Hth	30	9	5	16	46	64	32
13.	Poynton	30	7	7	16	39	57	28
14.	Whitchurch A	30	6	9	15	30	57	27
15.	Malpas	30	6	8	16	35	98	26
16.	The Beeches	30	3	4	23	35	98	13

Div Two		P	W	D	L	F	A	Pts
1.	Bollington A	30	23	4	3	89	25	73
2.	Zeneca	30	21	4	5	78	37	67
3.	Alsager	30	21	4	5	62	27	67
4.	Pilkington	30	19	4	7	77	39	61
5.	Littlemoor	30	18	2	10	75	48	56
6.	Lostock Gr	30	17	5	8	72	44	56
7.	Chester Nom	30	14	7	9	66	54	49
8.	Poynton Res	30	10	7	13	53	52	37
9.	Garswood R	30	11	3	16	48	76	36
10.	Beeches Res	30	11	2	17	43	72	35
11.	Linotype Res	30	9	7	14	60	58	34
12.	Chorlton T R	30	9	5	16	55	64	32
13.	Grove U R	30	9	3	18	37	68	30
14.	W/church R	30	5	7	18	39	72	22
15.	Styal	30	4	7	19	55	79	19
16.	Rylands Res	30	2	3	25	24	110	9

DIVISION ONE LEAGUE CUP

First Round:

Chorlton Town	v	Broadheath Cen	3-2
Cheadle H N	v	Malpas	6-1
Rylands	v	Whitchurch A	1-1,2-0
The Beeches	v	Grove Utd	0-2
Bramhall	v	Garswood Utd	2-0
Wilmslow Alb	v	Linotype	0-3
Warrington R	v	Poynton	1-1,1-1,4-3p
Knutsford	v	Barnton	2-1

Second Round:

Chorlton Tn	v	Cheadle H N	2-1
Knutsford	v	Grove Utd	2-1
Rylands	v	Warrington R	1-0
Bramhall	v	Linotype	3-2

Semi-Finals

Bramhall	v	Rylands	1-2
Knutsford	v	Chorlton T	1-3

Cup Final: Chorlton Town 1, Rylands 0.

DIV ONE RESULTS CHART 1995-96

HOME TEAM	1	2	3	4	5	6	7	8	9	10	11	12	13	14	15	16
1. Barnton	*	3-0	5-1	8-1	3-3	0-4	3-1	2-1	5-1	6-0	4-0	4-2	1-1	0-2	3-1	5-2
2. Bramhall	2-5	*	2-2	1-2	3-0	3-4	1-1	0-1	2-2	9-1	2-0	8-0	1-1	4-1	3-3	3-1
3. Broadheath	1-1	0-3	*	3-2	2-2	0-1	1-3	1-5	2-2	3-1	1-1	3-1	0-2	0-0	2-1	2-0
4. Cheadle Hth Nom	1-2	1-4	0-1	*	2-0	0-2	0-1	0-1	1-2	1-0	0-2	4-2	4-2	2-2	3-0	2-2
5. Chorlton Tn	1-3	2-5	2-1	3-4	*	4-4	2-0	1-1	3-1	0-3	2-4	0-1	4-3	2-2	1-0	2-1
6. Garswood Utd	2-1	4-1	4-0	3-1	2-2	*	1-2	2-0	0-0	5-1	1-1	3-0	5-0	3-1	7-0	3-0
7. Grove Utd	2-1	0-2	1-0	3-1	2-1	1-0	*	2-0	1-2	5-0	2-0	4-2	3-1	1-3	2-1	2-3
8. Knutsford	0-1	0-3	3-0	6-3	2-2	1-2	2-7	*	1-1	14-0	2-1	1-2	3-2	2-1	1-1	3-1
9. Linotype	4-1	2-2	4-0	1-3	1-3	1-2	1-2	3-2	*	4-2	1-1	3-1	3-2	3-3	1-1	0-1
10. Malpas	1-9	0-6	1-2	1-1	0-0	1-2	2-2	2-2	0-7	*	1-0	2-3	2-1	0-3	1-0	0-3
11. Poynton	1-4	1-4	2-2	3-5	0-0	0-5	0-4	1-2	2-0	3-3	*	1-2	5-1	1-0	0-3	1-2
12. Rylands	1-1	1-2	1-4	1-1	0-0	0-5	1-1	0-1	3-0	1-1	1-2	*	5-4	1-5	2-2	0-2
13. The Beeches	0-5	1-5	4-2	1-0	0-5	2-4	1-3	1-1	0-2	1-4	0-5	1-3	*	0-4	1-1	1-3
14. Warrington T	1-2	0-2	1-1	6-1	1-2	0-1	2-1	4-0	1-1	3-3	1-1	0-1	7-1	*	1-1	3-0
15. Whitchurch A	0-4	1-0	3-0	1-0	0-1	0-5	1-3	1-7	0-2	1-1	1-0	2-3	4-0	1-1	*	0-0
16. Wilmslow Alb	1-5	1-0	1-1	1-1	2-3	1-2	0-1	5-3	0-1	1-2	1-0	1-1	5-1	4-4	1-0	*

DIV TWO RESULTS CHART 1995-96

HOME TEAM	1	2	3	4	5	6	7	8	9	10	11	12	13	14	15	16
1. Afc Zeneca	*	1-2	3-2	2-0	3-2	2-1	4-1	3-1	3-5	2-2	1-2	1-1	2-0	2-1	1-1	4-2
2. Alsager	0-1	*	1-1	7-1	1-0	4-0	1-0	1-1	2-1	1-0	3-0	0-1	2-1	3-2	3-0	3-1
3. Bollington A	1-2	2-1	*	1-1	1-0	10-1	2-0	3-1	1-2	1-0	3-0	3-0	2-1	6-1	5-0	5-1
4. Chester Nomads	1-5	1-2	1-1	*	1-1	2-1	4-0	4-1	3-2	2-1	2-3	4-1	10-2	4-2	5-0	1-1
5. Chorlton Tn Res	1-4	2-4	1-2	3-1	*	1-2	5-2	1-4	3-1	2-4	0-6	1-2	1-1	3-2	3-1	2-2
6. Garswood Utd Res	0-2	2-2	0-4	0-2	3-4	*	4-2	3-3	0-4	0-3	0-3	1-0	2-0	3-3	2-0	2-0
7. Grove Utd Res	1-1	0-3	0-1	2-3	3-1	1-3	*	4-1	1-3	2-3	1-1	1-1	0-2	3-2	3-1	2-1
8. Linotype Res	1-3	1-4	0-3	5-0	0-1	3-0	5-0	*	2-3	1-4	2-2	1-1	1-3	2-2	2-1	1-1
9. Littlemoor	2-1	1-2	1-4	2-2	1-0	4-0	6-0	0-1	*	2-2	3-2	3-1	5-1	2-0	2-3	4-0
10. Lostock Gral	0-3	1-3	2-2	1-1	1-0	8-3	4-1	2-0	0-2	*	5-1	4-1	5-0	3-2	2-0	3-2
11. Pilkington	3-2	1-0	1-2	2-1	4-1	2-1	2-1	3-0	2-1	2-1	*	1-2	9-0	2-2	7-0	5-1
12. Poyntyon Res	2-4	0-0	2-6	1-2	0-0	1-2	0-1	4-2	1-3	1-3	1-1	*	3-0	0-0	5-0	4-0
13. Rylands Res	0-5	0-3	0-7	1-2	1-4	0-4	1-3	0-1	0-2	2-2	0-8	1-6	*	1-4	1-2	1-1
14. Styal	1-2	2-4	0-2	1-1	2-1	1-3	3-1	2-3	5-6	0-1	1-3	2-6	6-3	*	0-2	1-1
15. The Beeches Res	1-4	3-0	2-4	2-0	1-6	2-1	0-1	0-4	3-0	0-3	2-0	5-2	4-1	1-1	*	4-2
16. Whitchurch Al Res	0-5	0-1	0-2	2-4	3-3	3-4	0-1	0-0	3-2	1-0	0-1	0-3	4-0	5-4	2-0	*

DIVISION ONE CLUBS 1994-95

BARNTON

Secretary: Peter Stanley, 10 Westfield Grove, Barnton, Nr Northwich, Cheshire CW8 4QB (01606 782305).
Ground: Townfield, Townfield Lane, Barnton.
Colours: Black & white stripes/black/black **Change Colours:** Amber/black/amber.

(THE) BEECHES

Secretary: David Corrigan, 7 Burrows Avenue, Haydock, St Helens WA11 0DE (01744 572273).
Ground: Beechams Social Club, Sutton Rd, St Helens (01744 25906).
Colours: All blue **Change Colours:** Claret & blue/claret/claret

BOLLINGTON ATHLETIC

Secretary: Anthony Holmes, 79 Parkgate Rd, Macclesfield, Cheshire SK11 7SZ (01625 615044).
Ground: Recreation Ground, Bollington.
Colours: Jade & silver/silver **Change Colours:** Tangerine/black.

BRAMHALL

Secretary: Bernard Johnson, 25 Bean Leach Rd, Hazel Grove SK7 4LD (0161 456 2542).
Ground: Lumb Lane, Bramhall.
Colours: Red/black/black **Change Colours:** Yellow/blue/blue (All blue:Res)

BROADHEATH CENTRAL

Secretary: David Murphy, 10 Green Drive, Timperley, Altrincham WA15 6JW (0161 980 1925).
Ground: Viaduct Rd, Broadheath, Altrincham.
Colours: Black & red stripes/black/black **Change Colours:** All blue.

CHORLTON TOWN

Secretary: Jim Calderbank, 9 Trafford Drive, Timperley, Altrincham WA15 6ET (0161 969 1156).
Ground: Longford Stadium, Longford Park.
Cols: Black & red stripes/white/white (Blue & black stripes/black/black:Res) **Change Colours:** All white.

GARSWOOD UNITED

Secretary: John Richards, 359 Elephant Lane, Chatto Heath, St Helens WA9 5HF (01744 851569).
Ground: Simms Lane Ends, Garswood Road, Garswood, Nr Wigan (0744 892258).
Colours: Blue & white stripes/blue/blue **Change Colours:** All red.

GROVE UNITED

Secretary: Mark Boothby, 68 Deneside Cres., Hazel Grove, Cheshire SK7 4NU (0161 456 7610).
Ground: Half Moon Lane, Alfreton Rd, Offerto/ Lisburne Lane, Stockport.
Colours: Red/black/black **Change Colours:** All blue.

KNUTSFORD

Secretary: Michael Binnie, The Bungalow, 145 Manchester Rd, Wilmslow SK9 2JN (01625 537909).
Ground: Manchester Road, Knutsford.
Colours: Red/white (All blue:Res) **Change Colours:** All blue (White or red:Res)

LINOTYPE

Secretary: Graham Fothergill, 11 St Marys Rd, Sale, Cheshire M33 1SB (0161 969 4999).
Ground: British Airways Club, Clay Lane, Timperley, Altrincham (0161 980 7354).
corner.
Colours: White/black/red **Change Colours:** Red & black/black/black.

MALPAS

Secretary: Bernard Lloyd, 15 Springfield Avenue, Malpas, Cheshire SY14 8QD (01948 860812).
Ground: Malpas & District Sports Club, Oxheys, Wrexham Rd, Malpas, Cheshire (01948 860662).
Colours: Red/blue/red **Change Colours:** All blue.

MIDDLEWICH ATHLETIC

Secretary: Brian Longley, 16 Northway, Holmes Chapel CW4 7EF (01477 373310).
Ground: Seddon Street, Middlewich
Colours: Red/white/red **Change Colours:** All blue.

POYNTON

Secretary: Paul Burch, 24 Brooklands Avenue, Poynton, Cheshire SK12 1HZ (01625 871205).
Ground: London Rd North, Poynton (01625 875765).
Colours: Red/black/black **Change Colours:** White & blue/blue/blue.

RYLANDS

Secretary: Ian Finchett, 31 Elizabeth Drive, Padgate, Warrington WA1 4JQ (01925 816911).
Ground: Gorsey Lane, Warrington (01925 35700).
Colours: Maroon & grey/maroon/grey **Change Colours:** All yellow.

WHITCHURCH ALPORT

Secretary: Andrew Mitchell, 8 Mill Cottages, Grindley Brook, Whitchurch, Salop SY13 4QH (01948 6150).
Ground: Yockings Park, Whitchurch, Shropshire.
Colours: Red & white stripes/black/black **Change:** Yellow/green/yellow.

WILMSLOW ALBION

Secretary: John Smith, 3 Holly Farm House, Isherwood Rd, Carrington, Urmston M31 4BH.
Ground: Oakwood Farm, Styal Rd, Styal, Wilmslow (01625 535823).
Colours: Yellow/blue/yellow **Change Colours:** All blue.

CARLSBERG WEST CHESHIRE LEAGUE

President: K Halsall
Treasurer: R Prescott
Hon. Secretary: L Bullock, 8 Cambridge Road, Bromborough, Wirral, L62 7JA (0151 334 3545)

For the third consecutive year one club claimed both Divisional titles with Poulton Victoria topping a tremendous campaign when their reserve side defeated West Kirby 2-1 to lift the West Cheshire Bowl. Vics Division One side opened with 9 straight wins and never looked in danger of slipping up, eventually finshing 6 points clear of Heswall having lost only twice in the process. The second division title was decided on the last day with Vics just pipping Capenhurst Reserves by one point after the Ellesmere Port side had won their last 11 games.

Mersey Royal are proud holders of the Pyke Cup having overcome Heswall 2-1 in extra time after the sides had drawn 0-0 at the 1st time of asking. Royal had overcome favorities Poulton Victoria in the semi-finals while Merseyside Police also went out at the last 4 stage. Unfortunately Royals season was to end on a tragic note when secretary Billy Morris collapsed and died shortly after receiving a long service award for over 30 years unselfishly given to football.

In recent years the West Cheshire league has made the Cheshire Amateur Cup virtually their own and this season 2 member clubs, Christleton & Ashville, were making their first appearance in the final. After a memorable encounter which finished 3-3 after extra time it was Christleton who lifted the trophy thanks to a 4-2 penalty shoot out success.

Christleton also retained the Chester Senior Cup, General Chemicals reversed the result of the previous seasons Runcorn Senior Cup Final when overcoming Mond Rangers while Heswall made sure of some silverware with a single goal victory over Cammell Laird in the Wirral Senior Cup, completing a double for the club as their 2nd string were Amateur Cup winners.

On the national scene the Merseyside Police team brought honour to themselves and the league by winning the Police National Cup with a 2-0 final victory over ICIS side Metropolitan Police at West Hams ground, while a side of ex West Cheshire players representing Manor Athletic over40's won the Umbro Veterans trophy.

The League representative side lost out 3-1 in the final of the Sportslines Inter League Cup to the Refuge Assurance Midland League having enjoyed a 6-0 success over the Central Midland League at the previous stage. The annual contest with the Green Insulation Mid Cheshire League produced a trilling 3-3 draw while in a game to celebrate the Centanary of the Zingari League, West Cheshire edged home 2-1.

Poulton Victoria won the George Law Cup, awarded to the club doing the most to enhance the reputation of the League, while Ashvilles fine discipline and administration record was rewarded with them becoming Carlsberg Club of the year. Both clubs also received financial recompense.

At the Leagues AGM New Brighton gained admittance with Merseyside Police Reserves deciding not to seek re-election. A major constitutional change will take place at the start of next season when a Division exclusively for Reserve sides will be set in place leaving the way for two Divisions for the remaining clubs plus any suitable applicants

Ray Condliffe

PYKE CUP:

Round One:

Bromborough P	v	Merseyside Police	3-5	Mond Rangers	v	Heswall	1-4
Shell	v	Poulton Victoria	0-4	Ashville	v	Capenhurst	4-2
Christleton	v	Newton	1-0	Moreton	v	Vauxhall Motors	4-1
Cammell Laird	v	Mersey Royal	0-1	Stork	v	Gen Chemicals	2-2,3-0

Round Two:

Poulton Victoria	v	Stork	5-2	Christleton	v	Heswall	0-1
Ashville	v	Mersey Royal	1-1,2-2,0-4	Moreton	v	Merseyside Police	1-1,0-1

Semi-Finals:

Heswall	v	Merseyside Police	1-0	Poulton Victoria	v	Mersey Royal	0-2

Final: **Mersey Royal, Heswall, 0-0** (Aet), **2-1** (Aet).

FINAL LEAGUE TABLES 1995/96

Div One	P	W	D	L	F	A	Pts
1. Poulton Vic	30	22	6	2	91	25	50
2. Heswall	30	17	10	3	77	38	44
3. Cammell Ld	30	17	9	4	82	37	43
4. M/side Pol	30	14	9	7	61	42	37
5. Christleton	30	13	9	8	48	41	35
6. Mersey Royal	30	8	15	7	44	48	31
7. Vauxhall Mot	30	11	9	10	64	69	31
8. Capenhurst	30	8	14	8	52	50	30
9. Ashville	30	10	7	13	51	63	27
10. Bromb/gh P	30	9	6	15	36	44	24
11. Newton	30	8	8	14	52	71	24
12. G Chemicals	30	8	7	15	53	62	23
13. Moreton	30	8	7	15	47	61	23
14. Stork	30	8	5	17	44	71	21
15. Mond Rang	30	7	7	16	39	68	21
16. Shell	30	5	6	19	41	92	16

Div Two	P	W	D	L	F	A	Pts
1. Poulton R	34	25	4	5	113	37	54
2. Capenhurst R	34	23	7	4	93	40	53
3. Upton A A	34	20	8	6	85	40	48
4. Heswall R	34	20	8	6	81	38	48
5. Castrol Soc	34	16	9	9	72	53	41
6. West Kirby	34	17	6	11	61	49	40
7. Vauxhall R	34	15	8	11	81	63	38
8. Christleton R	34	14	9	11	73	59	37
9. Willaston	34	12	11	11	59	52	35
10. B/boro P R	34	12	8	14	61	80	32
11. Shell Res	34	12	6	16	64	83	30
12. Ashville Res	34	10	7	17	67	73	27
13. Mersey Ry R	34	11	5	18	64	73	27
14. Cammell L R	34	11	5	18	72	84	27
15. Stork Res	34	9	4	21	50	87	22
16. Manor Ath	34	7	8	19	68	104	22
17. Blacon Yth C	34	8	4	22	48	86	20
18. M/side P R	34	5	1	28	56	167	11

WEST CHESHIRE LEAGUE BOWL

First Round:

Heswall v Capenhurst 4-2
Vauxhall Mot v Stork 3-2

Second Round:

Upton Ath As v Castrol Soc 1-2
Christleton v Merseyside Pol 10-2
Mersey Royal v Bromborough P 2-4
Blacon Yth C v Heswall 2-5
Manor Ath v West Kirby 1-3
Shell v V/Hall *(Disq)* 0-2
Poulton Vic v Willaston 2-0
Cammell Laird v Ashville 4-2

Third Round:

West Kirby v Cammell Laird 2-1
Heswall v Poulton V 1-1,0-1
B/borough P v Christleton 0-1
Castrol Soc v Shell 7-0

Semi-Finals

West Kirby v Christleton 1-1,1-0
Castrol Soc v Poulton V 2-3

Final: Poulton Victoria 2, West Kirby 1

CASTLEMAINE XXXX Competition:

Divisional Winners = Semi-Finalists.

Semi-Finals:

Gen Chemicals v Christleton 3-2
Castrol Soc v Ashville 5-4

Final: General Chemicals 6, Castrol Social 5.

BILL WRIGHT MEMORIAL TROPHY:

Semi-Finals:

Vauxhall Motors v Christleton 2-3
Mond Rangers v Poulton Vic 2-1

Final: Christleton 0, Mond Rangers 0,
(Trophy to be held jointly by both clubs 6 months each).

CLUB DIRECTORY

ASHVILLE FC

Secretary: Eddie Parker, 48A Upton Road, Claughton Village, Birkenhead, Wirral, Merseyside, L41 0DF (0151 653 2297).
Ground: Villa Park, Cross Lane, Wallasey Village, Wallasey, (0151 638 2127)
Sponsor: Clinitex Potterton **Formed:** 1949 **Colours:** White/black/black

BLACON YOUTH CLUB FC

Secretary: Colin Lawson, 54 Adelaide Road, Blacon, Chester, Cheshire, (01244 375508)
Ground: Cairns Crescent Playing Fields, Cairns Crescent, Blacon, Chester.
Sponsor: Acorn Glass **Formed:** 1964 **Colours:** Black & white/black/black

BROMBOROUGH POOL FC

Secretary: Trevor Patterson, 102 Princes Boulevard, Higher Bebington, Wirral L63 5LP (0151 645 1642)
Ground: Bromborough Pool Village, The Green, South View Road, Bromborough Pool.
Sponsor: Ocean Software **Formed:** 1884 **Colours:** All Blue

CAMMELL LAIRD FC

Secretary: Ray Steele, 46 Croft Ave, Bromborough, Wirral L62 2BR (0151 334 8998) **Ground:** Kirklands, St Peters Road, Rock Ferry, Birkenhead (0151 645 5991)
Sponsor: Met Arc **Formed:** 1900 **Colours:** All blue

CAPENHURST FC

Secretary: Martin Williams, 157 Hope Farm Road, Great Sutton, South Wirral L66 2TJ (0151 339 8935)
Ground: Capenhurst Sports Ground, Capenhurst Lane, Capenhurst (0151 339 4101)
Sponsor: Atlantic Comm/Deeglass **Formed:** 1952 **Colours:** Claret & sky/claret/claret & sky

CASTROL SOCIAL FC

Secretary: Dave Bebbington,490 Overpool Road, Whitby, Ellermere Port, South Wirral L66 2JJ (0151 357 1979)
Ground: Castrol Sports & Social Club, Chester Road, Whitby, Ellermere Port (0151 355 1730)
Sponsor: Castrol/ Peninsula Restaurant **Formed:** 1954 **Colours:** Blue & white/black/black

CHRISTLETON FC

Secretary: Ken Price, 35 Canadian Ave, Hoole, Chester, Cheshire CH2 3HQ (01244 313513)
Ground: Little Heath, Christleton (01244 332153)
Sponsor: Manweb. **Formed:** 1966 **Colours:** Red/black/red

GENERAL CHEMICALS FC

Secretary: Vincent O'Brien, 1 Marindale Grove, Runcorn, Cheshire WA7 2TU (01928 577810)
Ground: Pavilions Club, SDandy Lane, Weston Point, Runcorn (01928 590508)
Sponsor: Lamburns Bistro **Formed:** 1958 **Colours:** White & navy/navy/navy

HESWALL

Secretary: Jake Horan, 13 Reedville Road, Bebington, Wirral L63 2HS (0151 644 0459)
Ground: Gayton Park, Brimstage Road, Heswall, Wirral, (0151 342 8172)
Sponsor: Pyramids Shopping Centre **Formed:** 1891 **Colours:** Yellow/blue/yellow

MANOR ATHLETIC

Secretary: Stewart Galtress, 3 Centurion Close, Meols, Wirral L47 7BZ (0151 632 3211)
Ground: Unilever Sports Ground, Bromborough
Sponsor: Vavoline Oil Co **Formed:** 1968 **Colours:** White/black/red

MERSEY ROYAL

Secretary: Dave Lawson, 7 Mount Park, Higher Bebington, Wirral L63 %rd (0151 608 2261)
Ground: Unilver Sports Ground, Bromborough
Sponsor: N S Glazier **Formed:** 1946 **Colours:** Black & white/black/black

MERSEYSIDE POLICE

Secretary: George Todd, 14 Crowther Street, St Helens, Merseyside WA10 4NH (01744 755845)
Ground: Police Club, Fairfield, Prescot Road, Liverpool L7 0JD (0151 228 2352)
Sponsor: Davies Loss Adjuster **Formed:** 1885 **Colours:** Green/black/black

MOND RANGERS

Secretary: Beverley Crilly, 26 Perrin Ave, Weston Point, Runcorn, Cheshire WA7 4BJ (01928 575938
Ground: Pavilions Club, Sandy Lane, Weston Point, Runcorn (01928 590508)
Sponsor: **Formed:** 1967 **Colours:** Blue & navy/navy/navy

MORETON FC

Secretary: Jeff Lloyd, 46 Burrell Drive, Moreton, Wirral L46 0TQ (0151 677 9840)
Ground: Elm Grove, Hoylake
Sponsor: Tilney & Co **Formed:** 1900 **Colours:** Red/navy/navy

NEW BRIGHTON

Secretary: Russell Holmes, 10 Rudgrave Square, Wallasey, Wirral L44 0EL (0151 638 9506)
Ground: Hsarrison Drive, Wallasey Village, Wallasey
Sponsor: George Major Skip Hire **Formed:** 1993 **Colours:** Blue & white//blue/white

NEWTON F C

Secretary: Alan Dabner, 41 St David Road, Claughton, Birkenhead L43 8SW (0151 653 2151)
Ground: Millcroft, Frankby Road, Greasby, Wirral (0151 677 8382)
Sponsor: Cory Bothers Shipping Ltd **Formed:** 1933 **Colours:** All Yellow

POULTON VICTORIA

Secretary: Harry Deery, 15 Dorset Drive, Irby, Wirral L61 8SX (0151 648 2903)
Ground: Victoria Park, Rankin Street, Wallasey (0151 638 3559)
Sponsor: Carlsberg **Formed:** 1935 **Colours:** All Royal Blue

SHELL FC

Secretary: Joseph Davies, 35 Glencoe Road, Great Sutton, South Wirral L66 4NA (0151 339 0652)
Ground: Chester Road, Whitby, Ellermere Port, South Wirral (0151 200 7080) .
Sponsor: Portion Controls Ltd **Formed:** 1924 **Colours:** Yellow & red/red/yellow

STORK FC

Secretary: Steve Carter, 7 Elm Road, Bebington, Wirral L63 8PF (0151 645 6697)
Ground: Unilever Sports Ground, Bromborough
Sponsor: The Village Leisure Hotel **Formed:** 1920 **Colours:** All green

UPTON ATHLETIC

Secretary: Bary Gaulton, 24 St Marks Crescent, Whitby, Ellermere Port L66 2XD (0151 339 1504)
Ground: Cheshire County Council Sports & Social Club, Plas Newton Lane, Chester (01244 318367)
Sponsor: **Formed:** 1964 **Colours:** All white

VAUXHALL MOTORS

Secretary: Carole Paisey, 26 South Road, West Kirby, Wirral L48 3HQ (0151 625 6936)
Ground: Vauxhall Sports Ground, Rivacre Road, Hooton, Ellesmere Port (0151 328 1114)
Sponsor: James Edwards/Lookers **Formed:** 1963 **Colours:** All Sky

WEST KIRBY

Secretary: John Gossage, 40 Milton Road, West Kirby, Wirral L48 5ES (0151 625 5221)
Ground: Masrine Park, Greenbank Road, West Kirby (0151 625 7734)
Sponsor: Don Walker Insurance **Formed:** 1895 **Colours:** White/black/white

WILLASTON

Secretary: Peter Lloyd Armstrong, 22 Deeside, Whitby, Ellesmere Port, South Wirral L65 6RQ (0151 200 2068)
Ground: Johnston Recreation Ground, Neston Road, Willaston, South Wirral
Sponsor: The Pollard Inn **Formed:** 1962 **Colours:** Yellow & royal/royal/royal

NORTHERN COUNTIES (EAST) LEAGUE

FEEDER TO:
NORTHERN PREMIER LEAGUE

FOUNDED: 1982
(Amalgamation of Yorkshire League (founded 1920) and the Midland League (founded 1889))

President: H F Catt.

Chairman: C Morris.

Vice Chairman: T Dixon.

Hon. Secretary: B Wood, 6 Restmore Ave., Guiseley, Leeds LS20 9DG (01943 874558)

The promotion/demotion system between our League and the Unibond League operated for the first time in many years when Goole Town took the place of the promoted Lincoln United. Indeed, it has operated only twice in the 14 years of our existence, the previous occasion being the relegation of Ashfield United then known as Sutton Town. It is pleasing to report the rapid rise of our ex-club Lincoln United who played at Central Midlands League level not so long ago before embarking on a successful campaign in our Divisions.

Predictions of Premier Div. success inevitably involved the leading teams from the previous season - Arnold Tn, Stocksbridge PS and Belper Tn amongst others - and it was the Derbyshire club which led the Div. for a lengthy spell during the middle part of the season with North Ferriby United also in contention. John Reid's Hatfield Main entered the fray as promoted champions of Div. 1 and very few would have believed possible the success Main achieved particularly in their excellent run of victories since their last defeat in mid-January. That consistency brought its reward in a thrilling battle for honours at the end of the season. Victory by 3-1 in their last match meant that the Doncaster club were the new Prem. Div. champions.

Hatfield Main FC; Back Row (L-R); John Reed (Mgr), Phil Watkin, Gary Kay, Steve Codd (Capt), Dave Redfern, Fraser Foster, Jason Miller, Nigel Downing, Paul Cygan, Khn Kirk (Asst Mgr). Front Row; Jay Horne, Eddie Lloyden, Gary Margetts, James O'Donnell, Gary Hurlestone, Shaun Lanaghan, Alan Irwin, Martin Turner. Mascots: Michael Head, Jonathan Margetts, Rachel Reed.

Additional interest revolved round the runners-up spot and its influence on the possible promotion candidates to the Unibond League bearing in mind Hatfield Main's ground not being of the required standard. Stocksbridge PS had failed to make the grade as Prem. Div. champions two season ago and were vying with Belper Town for the vital promotion position. In the end Town's last match 1-0 defeated at Ossett Town meant that the Steelmen took runners-up positions and with it a chance for promotion which they have now achieved after resolving the problem of a fence on the cricket side of their ground.

Pontefract Colls. were at a low ebb at the end of the 1994\95 season when they were demoted to Div. 1 but rallied successfully during this campaign to feature as one of the leading sides. The continued link with the Central Midlands League brought in new comers, Borrowash Victoria, as a promoted club and based on past evidence of that league's candidates it was expected that they too, would be prominent. However, the main challengers were Garforth Town, Yorkshire Amat. Selby Town and Hall Road Rgrs. with the latter dropping out towards the season's end and what a climax to the championship race it eventually proved. The magic point total was 63 with four clubs capable of reaching it and two of them playing each other on the final Saturday - Selby Town v Yorkshire Amat. The result was in doubt until the last ten minutes of the game when Town scored and secured the Div. 1 championship from Pontefract Colls on goal difference with Garforth Town and Yorkshire Amat. in 3rd and 4th positions. Propping up the Div. for the second season were Parkgate and Brodsworth MW and, indeed, it is the third successive occasion when the Miners will have to seek re-election. One major problem for the Div. was the demise of Immingham Town at the end of November when the club folded after a troublesome period with us. The League Table had to be adjusted, the club's officials and players were suspended by Lincs. CFA and the matter is still rumbling on involving time and effort by your officers which could be put to better use.

The League Cup competition often provides some surprises but results were largely predictable when Prem. Div. sides faced lower Div. opposition. Ossett Albion defeated leading Prem. Div. contenders North Ferriby United and Stocksbridge PS in previous rounds and it was expected that they might continue this trend when meeting Ashfield United in the Final at Belper Town. However, United proved far too strong on the evening when the Albion goalkeeper had a 'nightmare' game and a remarkable 8-2 scoreline (incl. a Mark Thompson hat-trick) provided a victory for the Notts club.

The President's Cup Final was two-legged between Brigg Town and Belper Town and the competition suffered from difficulties in earlier rounds when some matches had to be postponed. Brigg's involvement in the FA Carlsberg Vase (highlighted later) also affected their interest in the competition and both legs resulted in 2-0 wins for Belper Town which was some consolation for the Derbyshire side's failure to take Prem. Div. honours.

A new competition was organised this season - the Wilkinson Sword Trophy for Div. 1 clubs only - when Pontefract Colls. proved too strong for Louth United in the Final matches. A 2-1 away win at Louth meant that the Colls. had a goal in hand for their home leg and a 4-0 win gave them the Sword on a 6-1 aggregate.

In outside competitions there can be no doubt about the outstanding achievement of one of our clubs - the accolades go to Brigg Town as FA Carlsberg Vase winners when, in their 10th match in the competition, they achieved every non-League club's dream by taking the trophy at Wembley in a poised and accomplished win against Clitheroe by 3-0 before a 7340 crowd.

The prospect of a Wembley final had obviously boosted interest both in the north Lincolnshire area as well as in the town itself where it was rumoured that at least half the population were due to travel to London to cheer on their heroes. Plenty of black and white favours were evident on Wembley Way as the fleet of coaches, mini-buses and cars flooded to the Stadium in the welcome sunshine creating that never-to-be-forgotten carnival atmosphere. Two goals by Carl Stead and a deflected shot by Simon Roach was enough to bring victory in a great advert for non-League soccer at our level.

The traditional Wembley scenes of elation followed and it was a superb way for captain Dave McLean and manager Frank Clayton to crown their successes with the club by climbing those famous steps to receive the Vase from the Carlsberg representative flanked by senior FA officials. Everyone at the club who contributed to the triumph, from chairman- Dave Crowder, secretary - Bob Taylor, asst. manager - John Kay, gen. man. - Harry Williams and all the players and backroom staff and helpers can be proud of the club's achievement and all at the NCE offer their congratulations.

Finally, just a few facts. Town conceded only two goals in their Vase run and earned £10,350 in Carlsberg sponsorship cash. The NCE League has produced four Vase Finalists since 1988 and two winners - Brigg Town and Guiseley. Let's hope that Brigg's success is repeated next season.

Our link with the Unibond League means that Harrogate Town should be re-joining the League as the demoted club whilst Stocksbridge PS move up with the League's best wishes for future success. Promotion from Div. 1 to the Prem. Div. for both Selby Town and Pontefract Colls. is dependent on the two clubs agreeing to provide a minimum grading standard and a similar provision is applied to the promotion candidate from the Central Midlands League (Glapwell FC) to Div. 1. In the Res. Div. Hatfield Main Res. have dropped out whilst there are two new applicants - North Ferriby Utd Res. and Selby Town Res. The exact position will be resolved at the AGM.

Future entry to FA competitions now seems to be dependent on adequate floodlighting and the League has had to embark on a survey on behalf of all clubs, the results of which must be sent to the FA by 1.1.97. Already, though, entry to next season's FA Cup is likely to be restricted to those clubs which can prove a minimum 120 lux system the spread of light not being a factor at this stage.

BARRY WOOD - Sec\Treas.

NORTHERN COUNTIES EAST FINAL LEAGUE TABLES 1995-96

Prem Div	P	W	D	L	F	A	Pts
1. Hatfield Main	38	22	9	7	77	45	75
2. Stockbridge PS	38	21	10	7	59	36	73
3. N Ferriby Utd	38	21	9	8	78	33	72
4. Belper Town	38	20	10	8	66	39	70
5. Thackley	38	20	9	9	60	40	69
6. Denaby Utd	38	19	5	14	63	56	62
7. Brigg Town	38	17	8	13	65	50	59
8. Ashfield Utd	38	17	5	16	56	50	56
9. Liversedge	38	16	7	15	52	49	55
10. Ossett Albion	38	13	12	13	56	55	51
11. Armthorpe Wel	38	13	11	14	53	47	50
12. Pickering Tn	38	14	5	19	73	88	47
13. Arnold Tn	38	13	7	18	51	57	46
14. Ossett Tn	38	12	9	17	48	61	45
15. Goole Tn	38	13	8	17	53	74	43*
16. Hucknall Tn	38	12	6	20	52	67	42
17. Hallam	38	11	7	20	41	68	40
18. G/houghton W	38	10	9	19	47	62	39
19. Maltby MW	38	11	5	22	58	83	38
20. Sheffield	38	6	7	25	46	94	25

Div One	P	W	D	L	F	A	Pts
1. Selby Tn	30	19	6	5	79	34	63
2. Pontefract C	30	19	6	5	76	33	63
3. Garforth Tn	30	18	7	5	63	27	61
4. Yorkshire Am	30	18	6	6	51	30	60
5. Hall Road Rg	30	17	5	8	65	34	56
6. Eccleshill Utd	30	18	1	11	74	53	55
7. Borrowash Vic	30	13	5	12	59	46	44
8. Harrogate Rl	30	12	5	13	48	52	41
9. Winterton Rg	30	11	6	13	44	51	39
10. Rossington M	30	10	7	13	43	55	37
11. Worsbrough B	30	9	5	16	48	60	32
12. Louth Utd	30	8	7	15	54	66	31
13. Blidworth W	30	9	3	18	47	83	30
14. Tadcaster A	30	6	5	19	25	61	23
15. Parkgate	30	6	4	20	36	81	22
16. Brodsworth MW	30	2	12	16	23	69	18

* Premier Division, Goole Town had 4 points deducted

PREMIER DIV RESULTS CHART 1995-96

HOME TEAM	1	2	3	4	5	6	7	8	9	10	11	12	13	14	15	16	17	18	19	20
1. Armthorpe Welfare	*	3-0	1-0	5-3	0-1	0-2	1-0	0-0	3-0	0-0	1-2	1-3	5-1	0-3	1-1	3-4	2-1	3-1	1-1	2-2
2. Arnold Town	0-1	*	1-3	0-3	1-2	0-2	3-0	4-1	0-0	0-4	2-0	3-0	1-0	0-2	2-2	2-1	4-1	3-1	1-1	2-0
3. Ashfield United	2-1	2-1	*	0-1	3-1	4-2	2-0	2-1	0-1	0-0	3-1	0-1	7-0	0-0	3-2	2-0	3-0	5-2	0-1	1-3
4. Belper Town	1-1	0-0	0-0	*	1-1	1-0	2-0	2-3	3-1	2-0	4-1	0-0	1-1	2-1	0-1	3-1	3-1	4-0	1-0	0-0
5. Brigg Town	2-0	3-1	4-0	3-0	*	2-2	1-1	1-4	0-2	1-4	1-3	3-0	3-0	0-0	1-2	1-2	4-3	3-0	5-0	1-1
6. Denaby United	0-0	1-0	0-1	2-1	4-2	*	7-3	1-0	4-0	2-1	3-0	1-3	3-1	1-0	1-7	0-0	2-1	1-0	0-1	2-0
7. Glasshoughton Wel	2-1	2-2	1-2	1-2	0-1	3-4	*	0-1	4-1	2-4	2-0	0-0	2-1	1-1	3-1	3-0	1-2	1-3	0-0	2-3
8. Goole Town	0-4	1-6	2-1	2-3	2-1	1-0	0-1	*	1-1	2-4	3-1	3-2	2-2	1-1	2-4	1-0	1-5	2-3	1-2	0-0
9. Hallam	3-2	2-0	1-2	1-2	1-1	1-1	2-0	3-1	*	1-4	0-3	0-1	0-2	0-0	2-3	1-5	2-1	2-1	2-0	1-2
10. Hatfield Main	3-2	0-0	2-0	1-1	1-1	3-1	4-1	1-1	0-0	*	3-1	2-0	3-2	2-0	3-1	1-0	3-1	6-3	0-3	1-0
11. Hucknall Town	1-2	0-3	1-1	1-3	0-2	3-1	0-0	1-0	1-3	1-0	*	1-1	2-1	2-3	0-1	2-2	4-1	3-0	2-1	2-4
12. Liversedge	0-0	0-2	0-1	0-2	0-1	3-1	1-1	8-1	1-0	0-2	0-0	*	5-2	0-1	0-2	2-1	6-2	1-1	1-2	2-3
13. Maltby Miners Welfare	0-2	2-0	2-0	1-3	4-2	0-2	4-3	3-3	2-1	3-0	4-3	0-1	*	4-1	3-1	3-1	1-3	2-3	0-1	0-1
14. North Ferriby United	2-0	5-0	7-2	0-0	0-3	3-2	1-0	1-2	4-3	1-2	4-0	4-0	2-0	*	1-0	1-1	3-1	4-0	0-1	2-1
15. Ossett Albion	2-2	1-0	2-1	0-3	1-1	3-0	0-0	0-0	1-0	0-0	2-2	0-2	3-0	1-3	*	2-2	0-2	3-1	1-3	0-0
16. Ossett Town	1-1	3-1	1-0	1-0	2-0	1-3	0-0	0-1	2-2	1-7	2-1	0-2	2-2	0-4	3-2	*	0-0	4-1	0-1	0-1
17. Pickering Town	1-1	2-2	4-2	1-5	2-4	2-1	4-3	2-0	7-0	5-1	1-12	2-3	3-2	0-6	2-1	1-0	*	2-0	1-6	0-2
18. Sheffield	0-1	1-2	0-0	4-1	1-0	1-1	0-1	1-4	0-1	3-3	1-5	1-2	4-2	0-6	2-2	0-1	3-3	*	1-2	1-2
19. Stocksbridge Park Stl	1-0	4-2	2-1	1-0	2-0	2-0	0-1	2-3	2-0	2-0	1-0	3-0	1-1	0-0	0-0	3-4	3-3	0-0	*	3-3
20. Thackley	1-0	1-0	1-0	3-3	0-2	2-3	1-2	1-0	2-0	1-2	1-0	0-1	3-0	1-1	4-1	1-0	2-0	6-2	1-1	*

LEADING GOALSCORERS 1995-96 Season: Premier Division;

M A Tennison	North Ferriby Utd	34.	G Hurlestone	Hatfield Main	26.
J MacDermott	Pickering Town	24.	D B France	North Ferriby Utd	21.
T Jones	Stocksbridge PS	21.	J Balmer	Ossett Albion	18.
D Lancaster	Maltby MW	16.	M Taplin	Belper Town	16
S Taylor	Thackley	15	J A Tesh	Stocksbridge PS	15
M Thompson	Ashfield United	15.			

Division One:

G J Cygan	Pontefract Coll	39.	C A Hodgson	Selby Town	29.
S Daykin	Garforth Town	24	D G Kearns	Pontefract Coll	24
A Nesovic	Eccleshill Utd	18.	R Beardshaw	Yorkshire Amt	17.
R Jackson	Hall Rd Rangers	17.	P Flaherty	Garforth Town	16.
M Brock	Pontefract Coll	16.	C Winfarrah	Louth United	15.

DIV ONE RESULTS CHART 1995-96

HOME TEAM	1	2	3	4	5	6	7	8	9	10	11	12	13	14	15	16
1. Blidworth Welfare	*	1-3	1-1	2-3	2-3	2-3	0-2	3-2	1-1	1-6	1-4	4-2	3-1	2-0	1-4	0-1
2. Borrowash Victoria	2-0	*	4-2	3-6	0-0	0-1	2-5	4-1	2-0	1-1	0-1	1-1	8-1	1-2	2-1	0-0
3. Brodsworth Welfare	2-3	0-2	*	2-1	0-4	0-3	0-0	1-1	1-1	1-2	1-2	0-4	0-1	0-4	0-0	1-1
4. Eccleshill United	5-1	1-0	4-1	*	4-1	1-0	2-3	5-3	2-1	0-2	5-3	3-4	3-1	3-1	1-0	2-5
5. Garforth Town	3-1	4-0	6-0	2-0	*	0-0	3-0	2-0	2-0	0-0	2-0	4-0	1-0	1-2	3-1	0-2
6. Hall Road Rangers	3-0	1-2	7-0	2-1	0-2	*	1-1	2-1	4-0	2-0	0-0	1-2	3-0	1-1	3-0	2-4
7. Harrogate Rail Ath	3-4	2-1	2-0	1-0	2-2	3-4	*	0-2	3-2	0-3	0-3	0-4	4-1	0-2	0-2	3-4
8. Louth Utd	4-0	3-2	2-2	0-4	0-3	1-4	0-0	*	9-1	1-1	0-1	2-3	0-0	4-1	2-2	1-1
9. Parkgate	2-3	2-6	1-1	1-6	2-1	1-7	2-1	1-2	*	1-3	2-1	0-4	2-2	1-2	3-1	0-1
10. Pontefract Colls	7-3	3-2	1-1	4-0	0-2	2-0	3-0	2-4	4-1	*	6-0	4-2	4-2	2-4	2-1	2-0
11. Rossington Main	1-0	1-3	0-2	2-4	1-1	1-2	1-3	2-3	3-2	0-4	*	1-1	2-0	1-1	4-1	2-4
12. Selby Town	7-0	2-1	0-0	1-1	3-1	3-0	1-1	6-1	4-1	0-2	1-1	*	4-0	1-2	4-1	1-0
13. Tadcaster Albion	3-0	1-4	2-2	1-4	1-2	0-3	1-3	1-0	0-2	0-0	1-1	0-1	*	1-0	1-0	3-0
14. Winterton Rangers	1-3	2-1	1-1	0-1	4-4	1-2	1-4	5-3	1-0	2-2	1-2	0-2	1-0	*	1-3	0-0
15. Worsbrough B M W	3-4	1-1	8-1	4-1	1-3	3-3	0-2	3-1	1-2	1-4	1-1	0-7	2-0	2-1	*	0-2
16. Yorkshire Amtrs	1-1	0-1	1-0	2-1	1-1	2-1	1-0	4-1	3-1	1-0	3-1	2-4	2-0	3-0	0-1	*

LEAGUE CUP 1995-96:

Round 1;

Eccleshill Utd	v	Yorkshire Amt	2-1	Harrogate Rail	v	Rossington M	2-0
Louth United	v	Brodsworth MW	4-1	Tadcaster Alb	v	Winterton Rang	0-1
Worsbrough Brdg		Garforth Town	2-1				

Round 2;

Arnold Town	v	Parkgate	5-2	Belper Town	v	Pontefract Coll	2-0
Denaby United	v	Glasshoughton	2-3	Goole Town	v	Maltby MW	2-2,2-1
Hall Rd Rang	v	Eccleshill Utd	3-1	Harrogate Rail	v	Immingham T	w/o HR
Hucknall Tn	v	Pickering Tn	1-2	Liversedge	v	Brigg Town	2-4
Louth United	v	Stocksbridge PS	0-5	N Ferriby Utd	v	Armthorpe Wel	5-3
Ossett Town	v	Borrowash Vic	2-2,0-1	Selby Town	v	Hallam	0-0,4-2
Sheffield	v	Ossett Albion	1-3	Thackley	v	Hatfield Main	3-0
Winterton Rang	v	Ashfield Utd	1-3	Worsbrough Bge	v	Blidworth Wel	3-1

Round 3;

Ashfield Utd	v	Borrowash Vic	0-0,5-2	Belper Tn	v	Worsbrough Brdg	4-1
Brigg Town	v	Pickering Tn	3-1	Goole Town	v	Arnold Town	0-1
Harrogate Rail	v	N Ferriby Utd	1-4	Selby Town	v	Ossett Alb	0-1
Stocksbridge	v	Hall Rd Rangers	5-1	Thackley	v	Glasshoughton	2-1

Round 4;

Belper Town	v	Brigg Town	1-0	N Ferriby Utd	v	Ossett Alb	3-3,0-1
Stocksbridge	v	Arnold Tn	3-0	Thackley	v	Ashfield Utd	0-2

Semi-Finals;

Ashfield Utd	v	Belper Tn	2-0	Stocksbridge PS	v	Ossett Alb	1-2

Final: Ashfield United v Ossett Albion 8-2.

PRESIDENTS CUP 1995-96: Semi-Finals;

Belper Town	v	Selby Town	3-1	Denaby United	v	Brigg Town	0-2

Final; Brigg Town 0, 0; Belper Town 2, 2; (Belper Tn won 4-0 on agg)

WILKINSON SWORD TROPHY 1995-96: Semi-Finals;

Pontefract Coll	v	Eccleshill Utd	4-3	Worsbrough B	v	Louth United	0-2

Final: Louth United 1, 0; Pontefract Collieries 2, 4; (Pontefract won 6-1 on agg)

RESERVE DIVISION CUP 1995-96: Semi-Final;

Farsley Celtic R	v	Hall Rd Ran R	3-2	Tadcaster A R	v	Thackley R	0-2

Final; Farsley Celtic Reserves 1, Thackley Reserves 0.

ARMTHORPE WELFARE

Chairman: Alan Bell **Vice Chairman:** James Houston
Secretary: Maureen Cottam, 'Roydean', Whiphill Lane, Armthorpe, Doncaster DN3 3JP (01302 832514).
Manager: Carl Leighton **Asst Manager:** John McKeown **Coach:** Steve Taylor.
Physio: Joey Johnson **Comm. Manager:** Peter Camm **Press Officer:** Sharon Morgan.
Ground: Welfare Ground, Church Str., Armthorpe (01302 833674-Welfare, 0302 831247-Club No.).
Directions: M18 junc 4, A630, left at r'bout then proceed to next r'bout and turn right. Ground 400yds on left behind Plough Inn. Two and a half miles from Doncaster (BR). Buses A2, A3 & 181 pass ground.
Seats: 200 **Cover:** 400 **Capacity:** 2,500 **Floodlights:** Yes **Nickname:** Wellie.
Midweek matches: Tuesday **Record Att.:** 2,000 v Doncaster R., Charity match 85-86
Colours: White/navy/white **Change colours:** Navy/white/navy **Club Shop:** No.
Programme: 24 pages **Editor:** Miss Sharon Morgan (01302 834475).
Previous League: Doncaster Senior **Club Sponsors:** Houston Transport.
Clubhouse: No. Wheatsheaf Hotel used after matches.
Captain 94-95: **Top Scorer 94-95:** **P.o.Y. 94-95:**
Club record scorer: Martin Johnson **Club record appearances:** Gary Leighton.
Club honours: Northern Co's East Lg R-up 87-88 (Lg Cup R-up 91-92, Div 1 R-up 83-84, East Central Div 1 84-85); Doncaster & Dist. Lg 82-83 (Div 1 81-82, Div 2 79-80, Div 3 78-79; Lg Cup 79-80 80-81 81-82 82-83; Challenge Cup 82-83); West Riding Chall. Cup 81-82 82-83; Goole & Thorne Dist. Cup 82-83

ARNOLD TOWN

President: Alan Croome **Chairman:** David Law. **Vice-Chairman:** T.B.A.
Secretary: Steve Shout, 11 Newholme Drive, Wilford, Nottm NG11 7FR (0115 9815390).
Manager: Iain McCulloch **Asst Manager:** Bill Brindley **Physio:** John Scott.
Ground: King George V Recreation Ground, Gedling Rd, Arnold, Notts (01159 9263660).
Directions: From Nth M1 jct 26, B6004 (Stockhill Lane) 3 miles to A60 (White Hart pub on left), right at A60, immediate left (St Albans Rd), thru lights by Sainsburys, left at rear of Sainsburys, ground on right adjacent to market. From A1(M)/A614/A60 to lights (White Hart on right), 1st left thru lights, St Albans Rd then as above.
Capacity: 3,400 **Seats:** 150 **Cover:** 950 **Floodlights:** Yes **Club Shop:** Yes
Programme: 44 pages, 50p **Editor:** Melvyn Draycott **Press Officer:** Andrew Walker (0115 9229749).
Colours: Yellow and Blue stripes/blue/yellow. **Change Colours:** All white (blue trim)
Founded: 1989 **Nickname:** Eagles **Sponsors:** Mapperley Sports/Neartone Ltd/Terry Cooper Services Ltd
Midweek matches: Tuesday **Reserves' Lge:** Beauvale Midland Reg. All. **Supporters' Club:** Yes.
Record Attendance: 3,390; Arnold FC v Bristol Rovers, FA Cup 1st Rd, 9/12/67.
Previous Leagues: Central Midlands 89-93.
Player progressing to Football League: Devon White.(Lincoln C 85), Chris Freestone Middlesbrough 94.)
Clubhouse: Licensed bar open matchdays & training night. Hot/cold drinks/food on matchdays.
95-96 Captain: Peter Fletcher. **95-96 Top Scorer:**Simon Osborne 19.
95-96 Players' P.o.Y.: Kris Maddison **95-96 Supporters P.o.Y.:** Neil Waters
95-96 Managers P.o.Y.: Pete Catling
Club Record scorer: Peter Fletcher 98 **Club Record appearances:** Neil Waters 229
Honours (as Arnold FC + Arnold Town FC): Central Mids Lg 92-93 (R-up 88-89, Lg Cup 87-88 (R-up 90-91), Floodlit Cup 89-90); Northern Co's East Lg 85-86 (R-up 83-84,94-95, Div 1 94-95); Notts Snr Cup 60-61 64-65 65-66 68-69 70-71 92-93 95-96,(R-up 69-70 75-76 76-77 84-85); FA Cup 1st Rd replay 77-78; Central Alliance 62-63; FA Tphy 2nd Rd replay 71-72; Midland Co's Lg R-up 70-71 75-76 (Lg Cup 74-75 (R-up 80-81)). President's Cup 94-95.

ASHFIELD UNITED

President: Frank Haynes MP **Chairman:** Roy Gregory. **Vice-Chairman:**
Secretary: Frank Grainger, Hawthorn Cottage, New Street, South Normanton DE55 2BS (01773 510066).
Manager: Bud Evans **Asst Manager:** Dave Moxon **Coach:** Darrel Bailey
Physio: Ken Peck **Press Officer:** Peter Bough **Comm. Mgr:** Secretary.
Ground: Lowmoor Road, Kirkby-in-Ashfield, Notts (01623 752181).
Directions: M1 jct 28, A38 towards Mansfield, at 4th lights turn right onto B6021 (s.p. Kirkby-in-Ashfield). After half mile turn right at lights into Lowmoor Rd immediately after crossing railway lines. Ground half mile on left next to Lowmoor Inn. Nearest rail station is Alfreton & Mansfield Parkway - 3 miles.
Seats: 250 **Cover:** 500 **Capacity:** 8,000 **Floodlights:** Yes **Founded:** 1885.
Club Shop: Yes (contact Peter Bough).
Prev. Name: Sutton Town 1885-1992 **Midweek matches:** Wednesday **Nickname:** Snipes
Club colours: Claret & blue **Change colours:** All white
Programme: 60 pages, 60p **Editor:** Peter Bough
Sponsors: Home Brewery Co. **Reserve League:** Midlands Regional Alliance.
Previous leagues: Notts & District, Notts & Derbys, Midland Comb., Derbys Senior, Central Comb., Notts Alliance, Central Alliance, Midland League, NE Counties, Northern Premier.
Record attendance: 1,562 v Leeds United, floodlight opening, 1980.
Captain 94-95: **Player of the Year 94-95:**
Honours: Notts Snr Cup 08-09 12-13 13-14 23-24 55-56 57-58 59-60 61-62 62-63 63-64 67-68 69-70 71-72 72-73 73-74 74-75 76-77; Notts & Dist Lg 05-06 06-07; Derby Snr Lg 30-31 31-32 32-33; Central Alliance 50-51; Northern Co. East Lg R-up 91-92 (Lg Cup 85-86); Mansfield Charity Cup 1892-93 05-06 23-24; Sutton Charity Cup 29-30 30-31 31-32; Byron Cup 30-31 31-32; FA Cup 2nd Rnd 1933-34

BELPER TOWN

President: Alan Benfield **Chairman:** Phil Varney **Manager:** Martin Rowe.
Secretary: David Laughlin, Lorne Cottage, 1 Top Hagg Lane, Fritchley, Derbys DE5 2HJ (01773 856556).
Asst Manager: Mick Williamson **Press Officer:** D R Laughlin/S Wilton
Ground: Christ Church Meadow, Bridge Street, Belper (01773 825549).
Directions: From M1 North, Jnct. 28 onto A38 towards Derby, turn off at A610 (s.p. Ripley/Nottingham), then 4 exit at roundabout towards Ambergate. At junction with A6 (Hurt Arms Hotel) left to Belper. Ground on right past traffic lights. 400 yards from Belper (BR).
Seats: 200 **Cover:** 1,500 **Capacity:** 6,000 **Floodlights:** Yes **Year formed:** 1883
Colours: Gold/black/black. **Change colours:** Sky & white **Nickname:** Nailers
Midweek matches: Tuesday **Programme:** 24 pages, 40p, **Editor:** David Laughlin.
Rec. Gate: 3,600 v Ilkeston, 1951 **Prev. Lges:** Central Alliance 57-61/ Midland Co's 61-82
Clubhouse details: Bar (Tetley and Castlemaine). Hot & cold food.
Prev. Ground: Acorn Ground (pre-1951) **Local newspapers:** Derby Evening Telegraph, Belper News
Captain: Mark Townsend.
Honours: Midland Counties Lg 79-80, Central Alliance League 1958-59, N. Counties East League 1984-85, Derbys Snr Cup 58-59 60-61 62-63 79-80, FA Cup 1st Round Proper 1887-88 (4th Qual. Rnd 1964-65), FA Vase 5th Rd 94-95.

BRIGG TOWN

President: G Thompson **Chairman:** David Crowder. **Manager:** Ralph Clayton
Secretary: R B Taylor, 'Highfield House', Barton Rd, Wrawby, Brigg, South Humbs DN20 8SH (01652 652284).
Coach: John Kaye **Commercial Manager:** H Williams
Ground: The Hawthorns, Hawthorn Avenue, Brigg (01652 652767).
Directions: From M180 Scunthorpe East, A18 through Brigg leaving on Wrawby Rd, left into East Parade/Woodbine Ave, follow houses on right into Hawthorn Ave. One mile from Brigg (BR).
Seats: 250 **Cover:** 2 Stands **Capacity:** 2,500 **Floodlights:** Yes **Year formed:** 1864
Colours: Black & white stripes/black/black **Change colours:** White/red
Programme: 16 pages **Editor:** John Martin (01652 654526) **Nickname:** Zebras
Previous Leagues: Lindsey/ Lincs 48-76/ Midland Counties 76-82
Previous Grounds: Manor House Convent, Station Rd (pre 1939); Brocklesby Ox 1939-59
Rec. Gate: 2,000 v Boston U. 1953 (at Brocklesby Ox).
Clubhouse: Licensed club open matchdays
Honours: Northern Co's East Lg Presidents Cup R-up 91-92 92-93, Lincs Lg 49-50 53-54 73-74 75-76 (Div 1 68-69 69-70 70-71 71-72, Lg Cup 49-50 65-66 68-69 69-70 72-73); Mids Co's Lg 77-78 (Lg Cup 77-78), Lincs 'A' Snr Cup 75-76 76-77 94-95, Lincs 'B' Snr Cup 54-55 56-57 66-67 68-69 84-85; Presidents Cup R-up 91-92 92-93 94-95 95-96; FA Vase 95-96.

DENABY UNITED

Chairman: Brian Beckett **Vice Chairman:** David Hough **President:** Alan Wilson
Secretary: Mrs B Norton, 8 Ravenscarr Close, Denaby Main, Doncaster, DN12 4HJ (01709 867606)
Manager: David Lloyd **Asst Manager:** Dennis Hobson **Physio:** John Carver
Ground: Tickhill Square, Denaby Main, Doncaster (01709 864042).
Directions: From Conisbrough take first left in Denaby along Wadworth St. From Mexborough take first right after Reresby Arms, left on to Bolton St. then left on to Wheatley Street. Rail to Conisbrough.
Seats: 250 **Cover:** 350 **Capacity:** 6,000 **Floodlights:** Yes **Club Shop:** Yes
Programme: 64 pages 60p **Editor:** David Green (01709 862319) **Press Officer:**
Colours: Red with white stripe,black/black. **Change colours:** White/blue/blue
Sponsors: various **Nickname:** None. **Formed:** 1895
Midweek matches: Wednesday **Reserves' League:** Beefeater Cty Sen Prem Div.
Record attendance: 5,200 v Southport FA Cup 1st Rnd Proper 1927
Previous Leagues: Sheffield Ass 1900-02 15-18 19-20 40-45/ Midland 02-13 20-40 45-60 61-65/ Doncaster & District 18-19/ Central Alliance 60-61/ Yorks 65-82.
Players progressing to Football League: Jack Barker (Derby & England), Keith Burkinshaw (Liverpool 1953), Andy Barnsley (Rotherham 1985), Chris Beaumont (Rochdale 1988), Jonathan Brown (Exeter 1990).
Clubhouse: None.
95-96 Captain: Craig Thompson **95-96 Top Scorer:** **95-96 P.O.Y.:** Gary Lynam
Honours: Yorks Lg R-up 67-68 (Div 2 R-up 66-67, Div 3 R-up 81-82, Lg Cup 71-72); Northern Counties East Div 1 South R-up 83-84; Midland Lg R-up 07-08; Sheffield & Hallamshire Snr Cup 32-33 35-36 86-87; Thorn EMI Floodlight Competition R-up 83-84; Sheffield Association Lg 40-41; Mexborough Montague Cup 14-15.

Belper Town: *Photo - James Bell*

Selby Town:

Ossett Albion:

GLASSHOUGHTON WELFARE

President: R Rooker **Chairman:** Mr G Day
Secretary: E Jones, 'Marrica', Westfields Ave., Cutsyke, Castleford W10 5JJ (01977 556257).
Manager: Mr Wayne Day **Asst Manager/Coach:** Mr M Ripley.
Ground: Glasshoughton Welfare, Leeds Rd, Glasshoughton, Castleford (01977 518981).
Directions: M62 junct. 31 or 32 towards Castleford. From exit 32 the road comes into Glasshoughton. From exit 31 turn right at 2nd roundabout at Whitwood Tech. College. Ground is on left in Leeds Road. Car park on ground. 1 mile from Castleford (BR).
Club colours: Blue and White stripes/blue/blue. **Change colours:** All yellow
Seats: None **Covered:** 250 **Capacity:** 2,000 **Floodlights:** Yes **Founded:** 1964
Record Attendance: 300 v Bradford City - Floodlight opening 1990
Previous Name: Anson Sports 1964-76 **Previous Ground:** Saville Park 1964-76
Previous League: West Yorkshire **Clubhouse:** Bar & refreshment facilities.
Programme: 20 pages, 20p **Editor:** Nigel Lee (01977 516615)

HALLAM

Chairman: A Scanlan **Vice Chairman:** P Fuller **President:** A Cooper.
Secretary: G L Holland, 34 Standon Cres., Sheffield S9 1PP (0114-2490428)
Manager: K Johnson. **Asst Manager:** **Physio:** A Jackson
Ground: Sandygate, Sandygate Road, Crosspool, Sheffield S10 (0114-2309484)
Directions: A57 Sheffield to Glossop Rd, left at Crosspool shopping area signed 'Lodge Moor' on to Sandygate Rd. Ground half mile on left opposite Plough Inn. 51 bus from Crucible Theatre.
Seats: 100. **Cover:** 200 **Capacity:** 1,000 **Floodlights:** Yes **Club Shop:** Yes
Programme: Yes 30p **Editor:** Mark Radford (0114-2497287.**Press Officer:** M Radford
Colours: Blue/white/blue **Change colours:** All red
Sponsors: Umbro,Bank of Scotland,S.Peace&Son. **Nickname:** Countrymen **Formed:** 1860
Midweek Matches: Wednesday **Reserve League:**
Record Attendance: 2,000 v Hendon, FA Amtr Cup 3rd Rd 1959. (13,855 v Dulwich at Hillsborough, FA Amtr Cup 1955).
Previous leagues: Yorks 52-82.
Players progressing to Football League: Sean Connelly to Stockport County, 1992-93.
Clubhouse: Licensed bar and meals in Plough Inn opposite. Hot & cold snacks in ground for matches.
95-96 Captain: J Hunter **95-96 Top Scorer:** P Quixall 9 **95-96 P.o.Y.:** S Mason/G Slack
Club Record Goalscorer: A Stainrod 46 **Club Record Appearances:** P Ellis 500+.
Honours: Northern Counties (East) Lg Div 1 R-up 90-91 94-95, Yorkshire Lg Div 2 60-61 (R-up 56-57), Sheffield & Hallamshire Snr Cup 50-51 61-62 64-65 67-68.

HATFIELD MAIN

President: G Bailey **Chairman:** A Jones **Vice Chairman:** B Keenan
Secretary: Mr Bruce Hatton, 92 Ingram Rd, Dunscroft, Doncaster, Sth Yorks DN7 4JE (01302 841648).
Manager: John Reed **Asst Manager:** John Kirk **Coach:** Steve Codd.
Physio: Tommy Kirk. **Commercial Manager:** Barry Speakman.
Ground: Dunscroft Welfare Ground, Dunscroft, Doncaster, Sth Yorks (01302 841326).
Directions: From Doncaster (A18) Scunthorpe Rd to Dunsville, left at Flarepath Hotel down Broadway. Ground half mile on right. Half mile from Stamforth & Hatfield (BR). Buses every fifteen minutes from Doncaster.
Seats: 200. **Cover:** 600 **Capacity:** 4,000 **Floodlights:** Yes **Founded:** 1936.
Programme: 25 pages, 50p **Editor:** Tony Ingram (01302 842795) **Club Shop:** No.
Colours: All white **Change:** Red & white stripes/red/red **Nickname:** The Main
Previous League: Yorkshire 55-82.
Clubhouse: Full licensing hrs. Hot/cold drinks/snacks.
Record Gate: 1,000 v Leeds, A Jones testimonial. Competitive: 750 v Bishop Auckland, FA Amtr Cup
Midweek home matchday: Tuesday **Reserve Team's League:** Northern Co.EastRes.Div.
Club Sponsors: K Greenall.
Players progresing to Football League: Mark Atkins (Scunthorpe, Blackburn), Mark Hall (York).
Captain 94-95: Steve Codd. **Top Scorer 94-95:** Gary Hurlstone.15.
P.o.Y. 94-95: Gary Hurslone. **Club record appearances:** Lal Dutt.
Honours: Northern Counties East Division One Champions 95-96.

HUCKNALL TOWN

Chairman: John Coleman **Vice-Chairman:** John Beharall **President:** Andy Stewart
Secretary: Brian Scothern, 95 Brookfield Ave., Shortwood Estate, Hucknall, Notts NG15 6FF (0115 956 3151)
Manager: John Ramshaw **Assistant Manager:** **Physio:** Ken Burton.
Ground: Watnall Road, Hucknall, Notts NG15 7LP (0115 956 1253)
Directions: M1 jct 27, A608 to lights, right onto A611 to Hucknall, right at r'bout (new by-pass), over next r'bout, right at next r'bout into Watnall Rd - grd on right. From M1 jct 26 follow Nottm signs to lights on island, left onto A610, right at Three Ponds Pub onto B600 towards Watnall, 200 yds past Queens Head turn right signed Hucknall, follow over motorway and past Rolls Royce - ground on left. Nearest station Hucknall
Capacity: 3,000 **Seats:** 240 **Cover:** 1,100 **Floodlights:** Yes **Club Shop:** Yes
Programme: 72 pages, 50p **Editor:** Simon Matters.
Colours: Yellow/black/black **Change colours:** All Red.
Sponsors: Doff-Portland **Nickname:** The Town. **Founded:** 1945.
Midweek matches: Tuesday **Reserve League:** Midlands Regional Alliance.
Record Attandance: 1,305 v Macclesfield, FA Cup 2nd Qual 26/9/92.
Previous Leagues: Bulwell & Dist. 46-59 60-65/ Central Alliance 59-60/ Notts Spartan 65-70/ Notts Alliance 70-89/ Central Midlands 89-92.
Clubhouse: Every night and weekend lunchtimes
95-96 Captain: John Allcock **95-96 P.O.Y.:** John Allcock **95-96 Top Scorer:** Paul Tomlinson
Club Record Goalscorer:
Club Record Appearances: Ted Mullane
Hons: Northern Counties (East) Lg Div 1 R-up 92-93 (Lg Cup 93-94); Central Mids Lg(2) 89-91 (R-up 91-92, Lg Cup(3) 89-92); Notts All.Sen (4) 76-78 87-89, Div 1 Div 1 72-73 80-81 86-87 Div 2 70-71; Intermediate Cup 72-73 78-81 84-84; Lge Cup 78-79; Notts Snr Cup 84-85 90-91 (R-up 83-84 85-86 87-88 89-90); FA Vase QF 85-86.

LIVERSEDGE

Chairman: Bob Gawthorpe **Manager:** Paul Murphy **Asst Mgr:** Tony Passmore
Secretary/Press Officer: Michael Balmforth, 5 Victoria Rd., Gomersal, Cleckheaton BD19 4RG (01274 862123).
Ground: Clayborn Ground, Quaker Lane, Hightown Rd, Cleckheaton, West Yorks (01274 862108).
Directions: M62 jct 26, A638 into Cleckheaton, right at lights on corner of Memorial Park, through next lights & under railway bridge, 1st left (Hightown Rd) and Quaker Lane is approx quarter mile on left and leads to ground. From M1 jct 40, A638 thru Dewsbury and Heckmondwike to Cleckheaton, left at Memorial Park lights then as above. Buses 218 & 220 (Leeds-Huddersfield) pass top of Quaker Lane.
Seats: 250 **Cover:** 750 **Capacity:** 2,000 **Floodlights:** Yes **Club Shop:** No
Programme: 28 pages, 50p **Editor:** Secretary
Colours: All Blue **Change colours:** All Red
Sponsors: Sondico **Nickname:** Sedge **Founded:** 1910
Midweek Matches: Tuesday **Reserves League:** NCEL Res. Div.
Previous Leagues: Spen Valley/ West Riding County Amateur 22-72/ Yorkshire 72-82.
Players progressing to Football League: Garry Briggs (Oxford), Martin Hirst (Bristol City).
Clubhouse: Matchdays, Tues, Thursday. Pool, TV. Pies + crisps
95-96 Captain: **95-96 P.o.Y.:** **95-96 Top Scorer:**
Honours: West Riding Co. Chal. Cup 48-49 51-52 69-70; West Riding County Cup 89-90; North Counties East Lg Div 1 R-up 89-90 (Div 2 R-up 88-89); West Riding Co. Amtr Lg(6) 23-24 25-27 64-66 68-69 (Lg Cup 57-58 64-65).

MALTBY MAIN

Chairman: G McCormick **Vice Chairman:** M Richardson **President:** H Henson
Secretary: Nick Dunhill, Conrad Drive, Maltby, Rotherham, Sth Yorks S66 8RS (01709 815676).
Manager: Dave McCarthy **Asst Manager:** **Physio:** Frank Cutler
Ground: Muglet Lane, Maltby (01709 812462 (match days)).
Directions: Exit M18 at junct 1 with A631. Two miles into Maltby, right at traffic lights at Queens Hotel corner on to B6427 Muglet Lane. Ground 3/4 mile on left. Bus 101 from Rotherham stops at ground. Bus 287 from Sheffield to Queens Hotel, then follow as above.
Seats: 150e **Cover:** 300 **Capacity:** 2,000 **Floodlights:** Yes **Club Shop:** No
Programme: 12 pages, 50p **Editor:** Nick Dunhill (01709 815676) **Press Officer:** Secretary
Colours: White/black/white **Change colours:** Yellow/blue/yellow
Sponsors: Jack Green Sports,RJB Mining. **Nickname:** Miners
Formed: Maltby Main 1916 disbanded 67, Miners Welfare formed 70, name change 96-97.
Midweek matchday: Tues. **Reserve League:** None
Record Attendance: 1,500 v Sheffield Wed., friendly June 91-92. Competitive: 940 v Thackley, Yorks Lg Cup 77-78.
Previous leagues: Sheffield Co. Snr/ Yorks 73-82.
Players progressing to Football League: Michael Williams (Sheffield Wednesday) 1991-92.
Clubhouse: No
95-96 Captain: Russ Evans. **95-96 Top Scorer:** Darren Lancaster**95-96 P.O.Y.:**
Honours: Sheffield & Hallamshire Snr Cup 77-78, Northern Counties East Lg Presidents Cup 92-93 (SF 90-91), Mexborough Montague Cup 76-77 80-81 90-91, Yorks Lg R-up 77-78, Sheffield Wharncliffe Cup 80-81.

NORTH FERRIBY UNITED

President: Jeff Frank **Chairman:** Les Hare **Vice Chairman:** Brian Sievewright
Secretary: Stephen Tather, 16 Peasholme, Heads Lane, Hessle, E Yorks HU13 0NY (01482 642046).
Manager: Tim Hotte. **Asst Mgr:** Brian France. **Coach/Physio:** Colin Wilson
Ground: Grange Lane, Church Road, North Ferriby HU14 3AA (01482 634601).
Directions: Leeds-Hull road A63 or M62, N Ferriby is 8 miles west of Hull. Into N Ferriby, thru village past the Duke of Cumberland Hotel, right down Church Rd, grd 1/2 mile left. 1 mile N Ferriby (BR).
Seats: 250 **Cover:** 1,000 **Capacity:** 5,000 **Floodlights:** Yes **Club Shop:** No
Programme: 32 pages, 50p **Editor:** Jeff Frank (01482 633387). **Press Officer:** Roy Wallis
Colours: Green/white **Change colours:** Black/white stripe/black
Sponsors: Dransfield Developments **Nickname:** United **Founded:** 1934.
Midweek matcheday: Tuesday **Reserves League:** N Counties East Res Div
Record Attendance: 1,800 v Tamworth, FA Vase Semi-Final, 1989
Previous leagues: East Riding Church/ East Riding Amateur/ Yorks 69-82.
Players progressing to Football League: T Hotte (Hull) 88, I Ironside (Halifax) 88, D France, D Windass & M Matthews (Hull) 91.
Clubhouse details: Bar, lounge, TV, pool - open every night
95-96 Captain: Steve Brentano. **95-96 P.o.Y.:** Michael Heath. **95-96 Top Scorer:** Mark Tennison 43
Club Record Goalscorer: Mark Tennison **Club Record Appearances:** Richard Woomble, 1974-94.
Honours: FA Vase SF 88-89 (QF 89-90, 5th Rd 87-88); Yorkshire Lg R-up 75-76 (Lg Cup 74-75, Div 2 70-71), Northern Co's East Div 1 85-86 (Lg Cup R-up) 90-91, Presidents Cup 90-91, Div 1 (North), R-up 82-83; East Riding Snr Cup 70-71 76-77 77-78 78-79 90-91; East Riding Church Lg 37-38.

North Ferriby United: Back Row (L-R); D Wilson, B France (Asst Mgr), D France, D Hall, J Walsmsley, B Heath, M Heath, G Deverson, B McNeil, M Tennison, M Brock (physio). Front Row; T Hotte (Pl/Mgr), J Deacey, K Harrison, S Milner, S Brentano, A Smith.

OSSETT ALBION

President: Miss Helen Worth **Chairman:** N A Wigglesworth **Vice-Chairman:** S B Garside.
Secretary: David Chambers, 109 South Parade, Ossett, West Yorks WF5 0EB (01924 276004).
Manager: Jimmy Martin **Coach:** Peter Eaton. **Physio:** John Hirst
Ground: Dimple Wells, Ossett (01924 273618-club, 0924 280450-ground (matchday only)).
Directions: M1 jct 40. Take Wakefield road, right at Post House Hotel down Queens Drive. At end right then second left down Southdale Rd. At end right, then first left down Dimple Wells (cars only). Four miles from both Wakefield and Dewsbury BR stations. Buses 116 and 117.
Seats: 200 **Cover:** 500 **Capacity:** 3,000 **Floodlights:** Yes **Founded:** 1944
Reserves' Lge: NCEL Res Div **Midweek matches:** Tuesday **Nickname:** Albion
Cols: Old gold & black stripes/black/gold **Change colours:** All white **Sponsors:** Arco.
Programme: 44 pages, 50p **Editor:** N Wigglesworth (01924 275630).
Club Shop: Yes, selling lapel badges, pennants, programmes etc. Contact chairman.
Previous Ground: Fearn House **Record Gate:** 1,200 v Leeds Utd, floodlight opening 1986.
Previous Lges: Heavy Woollen Area 44-49/ West Riding Co. Amtr 49-50/ West Yorks 50-57/ Yorks 57-82.
Clubhouse: 3 bars + function room, open 7 days per week - catering available.
Players progressing to Football League: Gary Brook (Newport, Scarborough, Blackpool) 1987, Ian Ironside (Barnsley, Middlesbrough, Scarborough) 1980.
Club record appearances: Peter Eaton - 800+ in 22 years. **Club record scorer:** John Balmer.
Hons: Yorks Lg 74-75 (R-up 59-60 61-62, Lg Cup 75-76, 76-77, Div 2 78-79, 80-81 (R-up 58-59)); Northern Co. East Div 1 86-87 (Lg Cup 83-84); West Yorks Lg 53-54 55-56 (Div 2 52-53, Lg Cup 52-53); West Riding County Cup 64-65 65-66 67-68; Wheatley Cup 56-57 58-59

OSSETT TOWN

Chairman: Graham Firth **Vice Chairman:** Bruce Saul. **President:** Paul Jervis.
Secretary: Frank Lloyd, 27 Park Close, Mapplewell, Barnsley S75 6BY (01226 382415).
Manager: Trevor Best **Asst Manager:** Paul Murphy **Coach:** Steve Carter
Ground: Ingfield, Prospect Road, Ossett, Wakefield WF5 8AN (01924 272960).
Directions: M1 jct 40, B6129 to Ossett, left into Dale St, left at lights opposite bus station on ring rd, grd on left. Nearest stations Dewsbury or Wakefield Westgate - both 3 miles. Buses 116, 117, 126 and 127 from Wakefield, buses 116, 126 and 127 from Dewsbury, buses 117, 118 or 216 from Leeds.
Seats: 360 **Cover:** 650 **Capacity:** 4,000 **Floodlights:** Yes **Club Shop:** No
Programme: 12 pages, 50p **Editor:** Tony Timlin **Press Officer:** Bruce Saul
Colours: All red **Change colours:** All sky
Sponsors: Action Stations **Founded:** 1936
Midweek matches: Tuesday **Reserve Team's League:** Northern Co's Lge Res Div.
Record Attendance: 2,600 v Manchester Utd, friendly 1988
Previous Leagues: Leeds 36-39/ Yorkshire 45-82.
Players progressing to Football League: A Kendall, R Liversedge, G Chapman (Bradford City) 49,56,88; D Blackburn (Swansea) 57, S Lowe (Barnsley) 83, M Norbury (Scarborough) 89, M Williams (Sheffield Wed) 90, D Trott (Northampton).
Clubhouse details: Open Fri & Sun lunctimes, all day Sat and every evening. Hand-pulled bitter. Pie & peas, chips, soup from tea bar.
95-96 Captain: **95-96 P.o.Y.:** **95-96 Top Scorer:** Ricardo Gabbiadini 14
Club Record Scorer: Don Scarlett. **Club Record Appeances:** Frank Lloyd.
Hons: West Riding County Cup 58-59 81-82, West Riding Sen Cup 47-48, Northern Co's Lg Cup 89-90 (Div 2 88-89, Reserve Div 88-89, Reserve Cup 87-88 88-89).

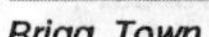

Brigg Town

North Ferriby v Arnold Town *Photo - F W Lee*

PICKERING TOWN

President: S P Boak **Chairman:** A.Dunning. **Vice Chairman:** T.B.A.
Secretary/Press Officer: A.Brenkley, 32,The Chase,Norton,Malton,N.Yorks.YO17 9AS North Yorks YO18 8NN (01751 473348).
Manager: Nigel Tate **Assistant Manager/Physio:** Michael Hudson
Coach: Robbie Goodwill. **Commercial Manager:** T.B.A.
Ground: Recreation Club, Mill Lane (off Malton Rd), Pickering, North Yorkshire (01751 473317).
Directions: A169 from Malton, 1st left past Police Station and B.P. garage into Mill Lane, ground 300yds on right.
Seats: 100 **Cover:** 500 **Capacity:** 2,000 **Floodlights:** Yes **Founded:** 1888
Midweek home matches: Tuesday **Club Sponsors:** Flamingoland **Nickname:** Pikes
Programme: 32 pages, 50p **Programme Editor:** Alma Page. **Club Shop:** Not yet
Colours: Royal/white/royal **Change colours:** Amber/Black/Amber
Reserves' Lge: York & Dist. **Record Gate:** 1,412 v Notts County, friendly, August 1991.
Previous leagues: Beckett/ York & District/ Scarborough & District/ Yorkshire 72-82.
Clubhouse: Open 1.30pm for Saturday games, 6pm for midweek games. Various beers. Food available from Football Club Kitchen at half-time and after games.
Players progressing to Football League: Chris Short (Scarborough & Notts Co.)
Craig Short(Scarborough,Notts Co,DerbyCo,Everton.) **Local Press:** Pickering Gazette & Herald, Yorkshire Evening Press, Mercury, Scarborough Evening News.
Captain 94-95: **P.o.Y. 94-95:** **Top Scorer 94-95:**
Hons: Northern Co's East Lg R-up 92-93 (Div 2 1987-88, Div 1 R-up 91-92), Yorks Lg Div 3 73-74, North Riding Snr Cup R-up 93-94 94-95, North Riding County Cup 90-91.

PONTEFRACT COLLIERIES

President: J Betts **Chairman:** M Norman. **Vice Chairman:** A Dean.
Secretary: Alan Slater, 1 Northland View, Pontefract, West Yorks WFS 1HS (01977 600966)
Manager: Jim Kenyon. **Asst Mgr:** Frank Maclachlan. **Physio:** Alan Dean.
Ground: Skinner Lane, Pontefract, West Yorkshire (01977 600818)
Directions: M62 jct 32 towards Pontefract. Left at traffic lights opposite Racecourse entrance (travelling through Pontefract follow Racecourse/Leeds signs to traffic lights and turn right) - ground past Territorial Army unit. 1 mile from Monkhill (BR). All Leeds and Castleford buses stop near ground.
Seats: 300 **Cover:** 400 **Capacity:** 1,200 **Floodlights:** Yes **Club Shop:** No
Programme: 16 pages, 50p. **Editor/Press Officer:** Alan Dean (01977 796091).
Colours: Blue & Black/Black/Black. **Change Colours:** White/blue/blue
Sponsors: John Betts Quality Used Cars **Nickname:** Colls **Founded:** 1958
Midweek Matches: Tuesday **Reserve League:** Northern Co's (East) Reserve Div.
Record Attendance: 1,000 v Hull City – floodlight opening 1985.
Previous Leagues: West Yorkshire 58-79/ Yorkshire 79-82.
Players progressing to Football League: David Penney to Derby County, 1985.
Clubhouse: Fully licensed. Hot & cold snacks. Open one and a half hours before any game, and after games with hours to suit demand.
95-96 Captain: Dean Helliwell **95-96 P.o.Y.:** Neil Jackson. **95-96 Top Scorer:** Gary Cygan.
Club Record Scorer: Gary Cygan **Club Record Appearances:** John Brown
Hons: Northern Co's East Lg Div 1 83-84 95-96 (Div 2 R-up 82-83); Floodlit Comp 87-88 88-89; Yorks Lg Div 3 81-82; West Riding Co. Cup R-up 87-88 90-91; Embleton Cup 82-83 86-87 95-96; Castleford FA Cup 82-83 86-87,94-95; Wilkinson Sword 95-96

SELBY TOWN

Chairman: J Vause **General Mgr:** B Wilkes **President:** Stan Henry
Secretary: Mr J A Storey, Cobblecroft, Hardenshaw Lane, Camblesforth, York YO8 8JA.
Manager: B Walker/ T Carter **Asst Manager:** J Storey **Coach:** B Walker.
Ground: Flaxley Road Ground, Richard Street, Selby, North Yorkshire YO8 0BN.
Directions: From Leeds, left at main traffic lights in Selby down Scott Rd. then 1st left into Richard St. From Doncaster go straight across main traffic lights into Scott Road then 1st left. From York right at main traffic lights into Scott Rd, and 1st left. 1 mile from Selby (BR).
Seats: 220 **Cover:** 350 **Capacity:** 5,000 **Floodlights:** Yes **Club Shop:**
Programme: 30 pages, 50p **Editor:** M Fairweather (01757 705376).
Colours: All white **Change colours:** All yellow
Sponsors: Hazlewood Preserves **Nickname:** The Robins **Founded:** 1911
Midweek Matches: Wednesday
Record attendance: 7,000 v Bradford Park Avenue (FA Cup 1st Rnd 1953-54)
Best FA Cup performance: Second Round Proper 1954-55
Best FA Vase performance: Preliminary Round 1989-90

Players progressing to Football League: Numerous
Previous League: Yorkshire (1920-82)
Clubhouse: Bar at ground open first and second team matchdays
95-96 Captain: **95-96 P.o.Y.:** **95-96 Top Scorer:**
Honours: Yorkshire Lg 32-33 34-35 35-36 52-53 53-54 (R-up 24-25 25-26 27-28 28-29 30-31 31-32 50-51 55-56, Div 3 R-up 74-75, Lg Cup 37-38 53-54 54-55 62-63); Northern Co. East Div 1 95-96, Div 2 R-up 89-90; West Riding Snr Cup 37-38; West Riding Co Cup 27-28 48-49; West Riding Chall. Cup 34-35 35-36

SHEFFIELD

Chairman: Alan Methley **Vice Chairman:** Paul Wilder. **President:** John Green
Secretary: Stephen Hall, 24 Crofton Ave., Sheffield S6 1WF (01142 344553).
Manager: Kenny Johnson **Asst Manager:** Andy Morley **Coach:** Andy Jackson
Press Officer: Alan Methley **Commercial Manager:** John Green.
Ground: Sheffield Sports Stadium, Penistone Rd, Owlerton Green, Sheffield (01142 343074).
Directions: Close to Sheffield Wednesday FC.
Seats: **Cover:** **Capacity:** **Floodlights:** Yes **Founded:** 1856.
Colours: Red with black trim/black/black **Change colours:** All blue. **Nickname:** The Club.
Programme: Average 16 pages, 50p **Editor:** B Willis (01142 392423). **Club Shop:** No.
Previous league: Yorks 49-82 **Club Sponsors:** Daily Star **Reserve Team:** No.
Previous grounds: Abbeydale Park, Dore (1956-1989)/ Sheffield Amateur Sports Club, Hillsborough Park 1989-91/ Sheffield International (Don Valley) Stadium 1991-94.
Clubhouse: No. **Record Gate:** 2,000 v Barton Rovers, FA Vase SF 76-77.
Midweek matchday: Wednesday **Player progressing to Football Lge:** Richard Peacock, Hull 94-95.
Captain 95-96: **Top Scorer 95-96:** **P.o.Y. 95-96:**
Hons: FA Amateur Cup 03-04, FA Vase R-up 76-77, Northern Co's East Lg Cup 94-95 (Div 1 88-89 90-91), Yorkshire Lg Div 2 76-77.

THACKLEY

President: **Chairman:** John Myers **Manager/Coach:** Mick Wood.
Secretary: Stewart Willingham, 3 Kirklands Close, Baildon, Shipley, West Yorks BD17 6HN (01274 598589).
Asst Manager: Mick Driver. **Physio:** John Waller.
Treasurer: Paul Clark **Press Officer:** Jamie Scott (01274 611520).
Ground: Dennyfield, Ainsbury Avenue, Thackley, Bradford (01274 615571).
Directions: On main Leeds/Keighley A657 road, turn off at Thackley corner which is 2 miles from Shipley traffic lights and 1 mile from Greengates lights. Ainsbury Avenue bears to the right 200yds down the hill. Ground is 200yds along Ainsbury Avenue on the right. 3 miles from Bradford Interchange (BR), one and a half miles from Shipley (BR). Buses to Thackley corner (400 yds).
Seats: 100 **Cover:** 300 **Capacity:** 3,000 **Floodlights:** Yes **Founded:** 1930.
Colours: Red & white/white/red **Change colours:** All white
Midweek matches: Tuesday
Programme: 20 pages, 50p **Editor:** Secretary
Club Shop: Yes. Programmes, souvenirs. Metal badges available - £2.50 + s.a.e. Contact Jamie Scott (01274 61152).
Previous leagues: Bradford Amateur, W. Riding County Amateur, W. Yorks, Yorks 67-82.
Record Att.: 1,500 v Leeds Utd 1983 **Previous name:** Thackley Wesleyians 1930-39.
Sponsors: Diamond International Shipping.
Best FA Vase year: 5th Rd 80-81 (01-2 v Whickham).
Players progressing to Football League: Tony Brown (Leeds, Doncaster, Scunthorpe, Rochdale), Ian Ormondroyd (Bradford City, Aston Villa, Derby, Leicester).
Clubhouse details: Hot & cold snacks on matchdays. Open Tues-Sunday evenings, matchdays and weekend lunchtimes. Boardroom, committee room, dancefloor, darts, pool, gaming machines.
Local Press: Bradford Telegraph & Argus, Bradford Str, Aire Valley Target.
Captain 95-96: **Top Scorer 95-96:**
Honours: Northern Co's (East) Lg R-up 94-95 (Lg Cup R-up 94-95), Yorks Lg Div 2 73-74, West Yorks Lg 66-67, West Riding Co. Amtr Lg 57-58 58-59 59-60, West Riding Co. Cup 73-74 74-75, West Riding Co. Chal. Cup 63-64 66-67,(R-Up 94-95); Bradford & Dist. Snr Cup(11) 38-39 49-50 55-56 57-60 65-67 78-79 87-88.94-95.

NORTHERN COUNTIES (East) Premier Division Nine Year Records

	87/8	88/9	89/0	90/1	91/2	92/3	93/4	94/5	95/6
Armthorpe Welfare	2	11	7	9	13	19	10	8	11
Arnold Town	-	-	-	-	-	-	-	2	13
Ashfield United	-	-	8	12	2	11	18	5	8
Belper Town	16	10	12	13	11	13	15	4	4
Bridlington Town	4	3	1	-	-	-	-	-	-
Bridlington Trinity	13	16	4	-	-	-	-	-	-
Brigg Town	15	14	10	5	8	6	5	11	7
Denaby United	3	6	3	15	3	7	13	14	6
Eccleshill United	-	-	-	-	17	9	19	-	-
Emley	1	1	-	-	-	-	-	-	-
Glasshoughton Welfare	-	-	-	-	19	18	12	16	18
Grimethorpe Miners Welfare	9	15	17	-	-	-	-	-	-
Guiseley	7	5	11	1	-	-	-	-	-
Hallam	10	12	14	-	-	-	-	17	17
Harrogate Railway Athletic	12	8	5	7	18	20	-	-	-
Hatfield Main	11	2	2	-	-	-	-	-	1
Hucknall Town	-	-	-	-	-	-	14	15	16
Lincoln United	-	-	-	-	-	-	3	1	-
Liversedge	-	-	-	-	14	14	11	19	9
Long Eaton United	14	13	-	-	-	-	-	-	-
Maltby Miners Welfare	-	-	-	6	7	4	7	13	19
North Ferriby United	6	4	6	4	4	3	9	7	3
North Shields	-	-	2	2	1	-	-	-	-
Ossett Albion	17	17	16	14	10	8	8	10	10
Ossett Town	-	-	-	8	12	12	16	12	14
Pickering Town	-	-	-	-	-	2	6	6	12
Pontefract Collieries	8	7	13	16	16	17	17	20	-
Sheffield	-	-	9	-	6	15	4	18	20
Spennymoor United	-	-	-	3	5	1	-	-	-
Stocksbridge Park Steels	-	-	-	-	-	16	1	3	2
Thackley	5	9	15	11	9	5	2	9	5
Winterton Rangers	-	-	-	10	15	10	20	-	-
No of Clubs Competing	17	17	18	16	19	20	20	20	20

Arnold Town keeper Waters saves at the feet of Stocksbridge Park Steel's John Tesh. Photo - Peter Hague.

BLIDWORTH WELFARE

President: Ray Hilton **Chairman:** Neil Bettison. **Vice-Chairman:** TBA
Secretary: Bill Deakin, 220 Brick Kiln Lane, Mansfield, Notts NG19 6LR (01623 29033).
Manager: Andy Brown **Asst Manager:** John Miller **Coach:** Shaun Hird.
Comm. Manager: Chris Jukes **Press Officer:** Pete Craggs, 21 Pecks Hill, Mansfield.
Ground: Welfare Ground, Mansfield Rd, Blidworth, Mansfield (01623 793361).
Directions: On B6020, Rainworth side of Blidworth. From M1 jct 27 take A608 to Kirby and Annesley Woodhouse, at lights follow A611 to Kirby then take B6020 through Ravenshead to Blidworth - thru village and ground at top of hill on right. From A1 follow A614 and A617 to Rainworth, left at lights then 1st right on to B6020 to Blidworth - ground on left at top of hill. Served by Mansfield-Nottingham buses.
Capacity: 3,000 **Seats:** 200 **Cover:** 700 **Floodlights:** Yes **Reformed:** 1980.
Programme: 32 pages, 50p **Editor:** Pete Craggs **Club Shop:** No.
Colours: All green **Change colours:** All yellow **Nickname:** Hawks
Midweek home matchdays: Wednesday **Record Gate:** 400 v Shirebrook Colliery, league 89-90.
Previous Grounds: None. **Prev. Lges:** Notts All. 80-82/ NCEL 82-86/ Centrals Mids 86-94.
Record win: 6-0 v Harworth Colliery Institute (H), League Cup 91-92.
Record defeat: 0-11 v Sheffield Aurora (A), Central Midlands League 90-91.
Clubhouse: Welfare Social Club built 199. Normal matchday hours.
Club record scorer: Andy Locker **Club record appearances:** Dave Colley.
Honours: None to date.

BORROWASH VICTORIA

Chairman: Ian Anderson **Vice Chairman:** Peter Erwin.
Sec./Press Officer: Ian Collins, 30 Margreave Road, Chaddesden, Derby DE21 6JD (01332 678016).
Manager/Coach: Peter McGurk **Asst Manager:** Graham Walker **Physio:** Stewart Worthington
Ground: Asterdale Club, Borrowash Road, Spondon, Derby (01332 668656).
Directions: M1 jct 25, A52 towards Derby, 3rd left off by-pass into Borrowash Rd, ground 400 yds on left. 2 miles from Spondon (BR). Nottingham to Derby buses pass nearby.
Capacity: 5,000 **Seats:** No **Covered:** 500 **Floodlights:** Yes **Founded:** 1911
Midweek matches: Tuesday **Prev. Grnd:** Dean Drive, B'wash 11-84
Colours: Red/white/black **Change Colours:**Yellow/Sky Blue/Yellow.
Nickname: Vics. **Reformed:** 1963.
Programme: 16 pages, 50p **Editor:** Secretary.
Club Shop: No, but club ties, pens, badges (home & away), T Shirts, sweatshirts, pencils and key rings are available - contact secretary.
Record Gate: 2,000 v Nottingham Forest, floodlight opening 22/10/85.
Prev. Lges: Derby Sunday School & Welfare 52-57/ Derby Comb./ Midland 79-82/ Northern Co's East.
Club Sponsors: Derwent Print. **Clubhouse:** Normal pub hours. Hot & cold food.
Record win: 11-1 **Record defeat:** 3-8
Club record scorer: Paul Acklam **Club record appearances:** Neil Kellogg.
Captain 94-95: Richard Harris. **P.O.Y. 94-95:** Kevin Harrigan. **Top Scorer 94-95:** Donald Wilkinson.
Hons: Northern Co's East Lg Div 1 Sth 83-84 (R-up 84-85, Div 2 Sth R-up 82-83), Derby Comb. 77-78 (R-up(10) 65-66 68-74 75-77 78-79, Lg Cup 68-69 75-76 (R-up 63-64 66-67), Midland Co's Lg Div 80-81 (Div 1 Cup 80-81), Derbys Snr Cup R-up 90-91, Derbys Div. Cup 73-74 (R-up 70-71 72-73), Central Midlands Lg B E Webbe Cup R-up 88-89 (Reserves Cup 94-95), FA Cup 3rd Qual. Rd 91-92.

BRODSWORTH WELFARE

Chairman: Barry Hogg **Press Officer:** Mr J Mounsey
Secretary: Daphne K.Hogg, 109a Tenter Balk Lane, Adwick-le-Street, Doncaster Dn6 7EE (01302 723644)
Manager: Neil Harle **Asst Manager:** **Physio:** J Bedford.
Ground: Welfare Ground, Woodlands, Nr. Doncaster (01302 728380).
Directions: Adjacent to the old Great North Rd (A638), 3 miles north of Doncaster at Woodlands. Ground entrance approx 30 yds into Welfare Rd. Left turn into Car Park. Regular bus service from North Bridge Bus Station, Doncaster.
Seats: No **Cover:** 250 **Capacity:** 3,000 **Floodlights:** No **Founded:** 1912
Colours: Green and Yellow stripes/green/green. **Change colours:** TBA
Club Shop: No **Nickname:** Brody
Previous Name: Brodsworth Main **Previous Leagues:** Doncaster Snr/ Sheffield/ Yorks.
Midweek home matchday: Tuesday **Programme:** 8 pages, compiled by committee.
Record fee paid: Nil **Record fee received:** From Wolves for Barry Stobart, 1960.
Clubhouse: No. Matchday drinks and snacks at Foresters Arms Hotel, off Doncaster Rd in Woodlands.
Captain 94-95: **Top scorer 94-95:**
Hons: Yorks Lg 24-25, Donc. & Dist. Lg 84-85 (Lg Cup 85-86, Div 2 78-79, Div 2 Cup 78-79), Sheffield Jnr Cup 83-84, Mexborough Montagu Cup 91-92 92-93.

ECCLESHILL UNITED

Chairman: Keith Firth **President:**
Secretary: Lewis N Dixon, 61 Mount St., Eccleshill, Bradford BD2 2JN (01274 638053).
Manager: Barry Gallagher **Physio:** Gordon McGlynn **Press Officer:** Bill Rawlings (01274 635753).
Ground: Plumpton Park, Kingsway, Wrose, Bradford BD2 1PN (01274 615739).
Directions: M62 jct 26 onto M606, right on Bradford Ring Road A6177, left onto A650 for Bradford at 2nd r'bout. A650 Bradford Inner Ring Road onto Canal Rd, branch right opposite Woodheads Builders Merchants into Kings Rd, fork right after 30mph sign to junction with Wrose Rd, across junction - continuation of Kings Rd, 1st left onto Kingsway - ground 200 yds on roght. 2 miles from Bradford (BR). Buses 686 or 687 for Wrose.
Seats: 225 **Cover:** 225 **Capacity:** 2,225 **Floodlights:** Yes **Year Reformed:** 1948
Midweek matches: Wednesday **Reserves' Lge:** NCE Res. Div. **Nickname:** Eagles
Colours: Blue & white stripes/blue/blue. **Change colours:** All yellow
Programme: 24-28 pages, 50p **Programme Editor:** Raymond Maule (01274 662428).
Previous Ground: Myers Lane **Record Gate:** 600 v Bradford City 90-91.
Previous Lges: Bradford Amateur/ West Riding County Amateur. **Previous Name:** Eccleshill FC
Record win: 7-1 v Yorkshire Main (H), Northern Counties (East) League Division Two 86-87.
Record defeat: 0-6 v Rossington Main (A), Northern Counties League Cup 2nd Rd 92-93, & v Great Harwood Town (A), FA Cup Preliminary Rd 91-92.
Club Shop: Yes, selling pennants, enamel badges, old programmes, mugs etc. Contact Roy Maule Snr, 25 Third Avenue, Bradford Moor, Bradford (01274 662428).
Players progressing to Football League: Terry Dolan (Huddersfield, Bradford PA, Bradford City).
Clubhouse: Open normal licensing hours. Bar, lounge, games room, kitchen (hot & cold snacks).
Captain 94-95: **Top Scorer 94-95:**
Club record scorer: Paul Viner. **Club record appearances:** Paul Viner.
Local newspapers: Bradford Telegraph & Argus, Bradford Star Free Press.
Honours: Northern Counties East Div 2 R-up 86-87 (Reserve Div 86-87 89-90 (R-up 87-88 94-95)); Bradford Amtr Lg Cup 61-62; Bradford & Dist. Snr Cup 84-85; Bradford & Dist. FA Snr Cup 85-86; West Riding County Amateur Lg 76-77

GARFORTH TOWN

President: Norman Hebbron **Chairman:** Stephen Hayle.
Secretary: Paul Bracewell, 24 Coupland Rd, Garforth, Leeds LS25 1AD (0113 2863314).
Manager/Coach: Dave Parker. **Asst Manager:** Phil Thompson **Physio:** Jack Coup
Ground: Brierlands Lane, Aberford Road, Garforth, Leeds (0113 2864083).
Directions: From South/East/North, A642 from A1 to Garforth, ground one and a half miles on left over brow of hill. From South West, M62 jct 30, A642 to Garforth (A63 to Garforth from Leeds), thru Garforth on A642, ground on right 1 mile on from lights just past new housing developement and Indian restaurant. Buses 18 & 83 from Leeds, alight at East Garforth Post Office - ground 500yds on right walking away from Garforth. By rail to Garforth (Leeds-York) line - cross over bridge to Safeways side and ground just under 1 mile down road.
Seats: None **Cover:** 250 **Capacity:** 2,000 **Floodlights:** Yes. **Club Shop:** Yes
Programme: 28 pages, 50p **Editor:** K Strangeway (01532 866500) **Press Officer:** Secretary
Colours: Red/black/red **Change colours:** Blue& White Halves/Blue/Blue.
Sponsors: Aagrah Indian Restaurants. **Nickname:** The Miners **Founded:** 1965
Midweek matches: Tuesday **Record Attendance:** 817 v Leeds, friendly 1987
Previous leagues: Leeds Sunday Combination/ West Yorks/ Yorks 78-82.
Clubhouse: Open matchdays & training nights.
95-96 Captain: Darren Hamer **95-96 P.O.Y.:** Brendan Ormsby **95-96 Top Scorer:** Steve Daykin 22
Club Record Goalscorer: Vinnie Archer **Club Record Appearances:** Philip Matthews (82-93).
Honours: FA Vase QF 85-86; Northern Co's East Lg Div 2 R-up 85-86; Yorks Lg Div 3 R-up 79-80; Barkston Ash Snr Cup 80-81 84-85 85-86 86-87 92-93 94-95.

GLAPWELL

Secretary: Steven Brown, 2 Carter Lane West, Shirebrook, Mansfield NG20 8NA (0623 743661).
Manager: Dave Waller
Ground: Hall Corner, Park Ave., Glapwell, Chesterfield, Derbyshire (0623 812213).
Directions: A617 towards Mansfield from M1 jct 29, left at Young Vanish Inn after 2 miles, ground 100yds on right. From Mansfield on A617, right at Glapwell crossroads after 5 miles, ground 100 yds on right.
Colours: Black & white stripes/black/black **Change colours:** Red/black/black.
Floodlights: Yes **Midweek home matches:** Wednesday
Programme: 16 pages, 30p **Editor:** Brian Caton.
Top Scorers 93-94: David Waller 28, Andrew Womble 11, Willie Gamble 10.
Hons: Central Midlands Lg 93-94 (Floodlit Cup 93-94), Derbyshire Senior Cup SF 93-94.

Ossett Town: Back Row(L-R); Keith Cooper (Physio), Simon Wilkins, Chris Shaw, Simon O'Hara, Karl Lenaghan, Paul Teasdale, Paul Arkle, Paul Cawthorn, Wayne Day (ex Mgr), Frank Lloyd (Sec). Front Row; Phil Thompson, David Dodd, Steve Worsfold, Darren Zoldan, Gareth Dodd, Matthew Crowther.

Hatfield Main's Nigel Downing heads home in the final minutes to make the score 3-1, aginst Denaby, for the NCE Premier Championship
Photo - G Whittington

Sheffield FC: Back Row (L-R); Wally Chambers, Mark Wilson, Fraser Foster, Tom Evans, Gregg Pearson, Russell Ingram, Nicky Legdon, Darren Spooner. Front Row; James Rixon, Lee Andrews, Andy Hibbert, Martin Thompson, Wayne Pickering, Matthew Hall.

HALL ROAD RANGERS

Chairman: R Smailes **Vice Chairman:** **President:**
Secretary: Peter Smurthwaite, 52 Bricknell Avenue,Hull HU5 4JT (01482 441421)
Manager: Pete Smith **Asst Mgr:** Peter Smurthwaite **Coach:** Pete Smith
Ground: Dene Park, Dene Close, Beverley Rd, Dunswell, Nr Hull (01482 850101).
Directions: M62 to A63, turn left before Humber Bridge onto A164 to Beverley, after approx 5 miles turn right onto A1079. In 2 miles turn left at large roundabout to ground 20 yards on right.
Seats: 50 **Cover:** 750 **Capacity:** 1,200 **Floodlights:** Yes **Club Shop:** Yes
Programme: 36 pages, 50p **Editor/Press Officer:** Brendon Smurthwaite (01482 441421)
Colours: Blue & white hoops/blue/blue **Change colours:** Green & white hoops
Sponsor: **Nickname:** Rangers. **Founded:** 1959.
Midweek Matches: Wednesday **Reserve League:** NCEL Res Div.
Record Attendance: 400 v Manchester City August 93
Previous Leagues: East Riding/ Yorks 68-82.
Players progressing to Football League: Gerry Ingram (Blackpool, Sheff Wed).
Clubhouse: Open all week for drinks and snacks. Bar snacks. Snooker, pool, darts.
95-96 Captain: Paul Osbourne **95-96 Top Scorer:** Roy Jackson **95-96 P.o.Y.:** Roy Jackson
Club Record Scorer: G James **Club Record Appearances:** G James.
Hons: Northern Co's East Lg Div 2 90-91, Yorks Lg Div 3 72-73 79-80, E Riding Snr Cup 72-73 93-94.

HARROGATE RAILWAY ATHLETIC

President: J Robinson **Chairman:** M.Gray. **Secretary:** W D Oldfield, 80 Stonefall Ave., Harrogate, Nth Yorks HG2 7NP (01423 888941).
Manager: G Shepherd **Coach:** P Williamson **Physio:** J Tope
Press Officer/Programme Ed.: C Dinsdale (01423 521815) **Commercial Mgr:** G.Shepherd(01423 883273).
Ground: Station View, Starbeck, Harrogate (01423 885539).
Directions: A59 Harrogate to Knaresborough road. After approx 1.5 miles turn left just before railway level crossing. Ground is 150 yds up the lane. Adjacent to Starbeck (BR). Served by any Harrogate to Knareborough bus.
Seats: None **Cover:** 600 **Capacity:** 3,000 **Floodlights:** Yes **Founded:** 1935
Colours: Red & Green Halves/Red/Red. **Change:** White & blue hoops **Nickname:** The Rail
Midweek home matchday: Wednesday **Rec. Gate:** 1,400; 1962 FA Amtr Cup **Sponsors:** T.B.A.
Club Shop: Yes, selling programmes, pennants, badges etc. Contact K Dinsdale (01423 521815).
Previous leagues: West Yorkshire/ Harrogate District/ Yorkshire 55-73 80-82.
Clubhouse: Games, TV room, lounge, open normal public house hours every day. Hot food.
Top Scorer 94-95: A.Everitt. **Captain 94-95:** A.Davies.
Hons: Northern Co's (East) Lg Cup 86-87 **Local Press:** Yorkshire Post, Harrogate Herald & Advertiser.

LOUTH UNITED

Chairman: G Horton. **Vice-Chairman:** Andrew Sylvester **President:** Dave Fairburn
Secretary/Press Officer: Albany Jordan, 20d Upgate, Louth, Lincs.(01507 600694)
Manager: Steve Newby. **Coaches::** Nigel Fanthorpe/D Cole. **Physio:** Kenny Vincent.
Ground: Park Avenue, Louth, Lincs (01507 607351).
Directions: A16 To Louth Market Place, exit via Eastgate/Eastfield Rd, to Fire Station turn right into Park Avenue
Capacity: 2,500 **Seats:** None **Cover:** 400 **Floodlights:** Yes **Club Shop:** No
Programme: 50p **Editor/Press Officer:** Albany Jordan
Colours: Royal blue/ white **Change Colours:** Red & black stripes
Sponsors: Foxhall Plant Hire. **Nickname:** The Lions **Founded:** 1947
Midweek matches: Tuesday **Reserves League:** Lincolnshire
Record Attendance: 2,500 **Previous Leagues:** Lincs 47-75 82-88/ Central Midlands 88-93.
Players progressing to Football League: Terry Donovan (Grimsby), Paul Bartlett (Derby), Brian Klug (Ipswich), Glen Cockerill (Lincoln, Watford, Southampton), Peter Rawcliffe & Peter Green (Grimsby), Martin Chalk (Derby).
Clubhouse: Weekdays 6.30-11.45pm, Sat noon-11.45pm. Full bar facilities. Snacks: filled rolls, crisps etc.
95-96 Top Scorer: **95-96 Captain:** **95-96 P.o.Y.:**
Club Record Goalscorer: Peter Rawcliffe 39 **Club Record Appearances:** Gary Smith 476.
Honours: Lincs Lg Prem 72-73 85-86 86-87 (Div 1 57-58 66-67 67-68; Lg Challenge Cup 73-74 86-87; Lg Charity Cup 55-56 56-57 67-68; Central Mids Lg Cup R-up 92-93; Wakefield F'lit Cup R-up 91-92; Lincs Snr 'A' Cup 77-78.

PARKGATE

President: T L Dabbs **Chairman:** A T Dudill **Vice Chairman:** Les Taylor.
Secretary: Bruce Bickerdike, 2 Cardew Close, Rawmarsh, Rotherham S62 6LB (01709 522305 Fax:01709 528583).
Manager: Gary Gillatt. **Asst Manager:** Alan Smith. **Physio:** Peter Wakefield.
Press Officer: Bruce Bickerdike (01709 522305).
Ground: Roundwood Sports Complex, Green Lane, Rawmarsh, Rotherham (01709 523471).
Directions: From Rotherham A633 to Rawmarsh. From Doncaster A630 to Conisbrough, then A6023 through Swinton to Rawmarsh. Ground at Green Lane – right from Rotherham, left from Conisbrough at the Crown Inn. Ground 800yds on right
Seats: 300 **Cover:** 300 **Capacity:** 1,000 **Floodlights:** Yes **Founded:** 1969
Colours: White/black/white **Change colours:** All sky. **Nickname:** The Gate or The Steelmen.
Midweek matches: Tuesday **Club Sponsors:** British Steel.
Programme: 20 pages, 50p **Editor:** Bruce Bickerdike (01709 522305) **Club Shop:** No.
Previous Grounds: None **Previous Name:** BSC Parkgate (until mid-eighties)/ RES Parkgate (pre-1994).
Previous leagues: Rotherham Association/ Whitbread County Senior/ Yorkshire 74-82
Record attendance: v Worksop 1982
Clubhouse: Licensed bar, 2 lounges, including dance floor. Open until 12 - 2.30 7-11p.Meals available lunchtime Mon-Sat.
Local Newspapers: Star/ Green'Un/ Rotherham Advertiser/ Sth Yorks Times/ Dearne Valley Weekender.
95-96 P.o.Y.: **95-96 Captain:** **95-96 Top Scorer:**

ROSSINGTON MAIN

Chairman: Mr S Tagg
Secretary: Gerald Parsons, 15 Seaton Gardens, Rossington, Doncaster DN11 0XA, (01302 867542)
Managers: D Ridley & L Ostle **Physio:** J White
Ground: Oxford Street, Rossington, Doncaster (01302 865524).
Directions: Enter Rossington and go over the railway crossings. Pass the Welfare Club on right, Oxford Street is next right - ground is at bottom. 8 miles from Doncaster (BR).
Seats: 200 **Cover:** 500 **Capacity:** 2,000 **Floodlights:** Yes **Club Shop:** Unknown
Programme: Yes, 50p **Editor:** Mr S Tagg. **Press Officer:**
Colours: All white **Change colours:** Blue & black
Sponsor: RJB Mining **Founded:** 1925 **Nickname:** The Colliery
Midweek matches: Wednesday **Reserve League:** Beefeater County Sen
Record attendance: 864 v Leeds United 8/91.
Previous Leagues: Doncaster Sen, Yorkshire Lge, Sheffield County Sen, Cent Mids.
Players progressing to Football League: Jim Harkin (Shrewsbury, Mansfield, Doncaster Rov),Shaw Bothers (WBA, Doncaster), Joe Leiversly (Arsenal), Dennis Leiversly/Ken Hardwicke/Brian Makepease/Jack Teasdale/Gary Jones (Doncaster), Ronnie Spence (York City), Reg Brian (Blackpool), Bob Forest/Brian Taylor (Leeds Utd), Malcolm Webster (Arsenal/Southend/Cambridge).
Clubhouse: Evenings & matchdays, Sandwiches, rolls, satillite TV, pool.
95-96 Captain: L Ostle **95-96 Top Scorer:** S Rowland **95-96 P.o.Y.:** S Barrass
Club Record Goalscorer: Mark Illman **Club Record Appearances:** Darren Phipps
Honours: Sen Lge 44-45, Cup 44-45, CMFL Prem Lge 84-85, Cup 83-84 84-85, DDSAL Shield 90-91 R-up 89-90.

TADCASTER ALBION

Chairman: Mike Burnett **President:** Lord Edward Stourton. **Manager:** Ken Payne.
Secretary: Mrs A J Burnett, 6 Beech Grove House, Ouston Lane, Tadcaster LS24 8DP (01937 832802).
Ground: The Park, Ings Lane, Tadcaster.(01937 832844) **Directions:** From West Riding and South Yorks, turn right off A659 at John Smith's Brewery Clock. From East Riding turn left off A659 after passing over river bridge and pelican crossing (New Street).
Colours: Scarlet and Navy Halves,Navy,Navy. **Change colours:** White/black/black
Programme: 20 pages. **Programme Editor:** As Secretary

WINTERTON RANGERS

President: J W Hiles **Chairman:** D Waterfall **Vice Chairman:** A Smith
Secretary/Press Officer: G Spencer, 2 Dale Park Ave., Winterton, Scunthorpe, Sth Humbs DN15 9UY (01724 732039).
Manager: Peter Daniel **Asst Manager/Coach:** Dave Robinson.
Ground: West Street, Winterton, Scunthorpe, South Humberside (01724 732628).
Directions: From Scunthorpe take A1077 Barton-on-Humber road for 5 miles. On entering Winterton take second right (Eastgate), third left (Northlands Road) and first right (West Street). Ground 200yds on left
Seats: 200 **Covered:** 200 **Capacity:** 3,000 **Floodlights:** Yes **Founded:** 1930
Colours: White/navy/white **Change colours:** All red **Nickname:** Rangers
Midweek home matches: Wednesday **Sponsors:** Ledgerwood Motors **Club Shop:** No.
Programme: 28-36 pages, 50p **Programme Editor:** M Fowler (01724 732628).
Previous Grounds: Watery Lane 1930-48. **Best FA Vase year:** QF 76-77
Best FA Cup year: 4th Qualifying Rd replay 76-77 (lost 2-3 at Droylsden after 3-3 draw).
Previous League: Scunthorpe & Dist. 45-65/ Lincs 65-70/ Yorkshire 70-82.
Record attendance: 1,200 v Sheffield Utd – Official opening of floodlights, October 1978.
Record transfer fee received: £5,000 for Henry Smith (Leeds United, 1979).
Clubhouse: Open matchdays & evenings Mon-Sat, hot & cold food available on matchdays. Pool and snooker rooms.
Local Press: Scunthorpe Evening Telegraph
Players progressing to Football League: Henry Smith (Leeds, Hearts), Keith Walwyn (Chesterfield, York, Carlisle), Rick Greenhough (Chester, York)
Captain 94-95: **P.o.Y. 94-95:** **Top Scorer 94-95:**
Hons: Lincs Jnr Cup 47-48 61-62; Lincs Snr 'B' Cup 69-70; Yorks Lg 71-72 76-77 78-79 (Lg Cup 80-81); Northern Co's East Lg Div 2 89-90; S'thorpe Lg & Cup many times; Philips National F'light 6-aside 76-77.

WORSBROUGH BRIDGE M.W. & ATHLETIC

Chairman: Mr J Wright **Press Officer:** Mr A Wright (01226 243418).
Secretary: D Smith, 18 Shield Avenue, Worsbrough Bridge, Barnsley, S. Yorks S70 5BQ (01226 243418).
Manager: K Paddon **Asst Manager:**
Ground: Park Road, Worsbrough Bridge, Barnsley (01226 284452).
Directions: On the A61 Barnsley-Sheffield road two miles south of Barnsley, 2 miles from M1 jnt 36 opposite Blackburns Bridge. Two and a half miles from Barnsley (BR). Yorkshire Traction run buses every 10 mins thru Worsbrough Bridge.
Seats: 175 **Cover:** 175 **Capacity:** 2,000 **Floodlights:** Due **Founded:** 1921
Colours: All red **Change colours:** Yellow/blue **Reformed:** 1947
Record attendance: 2,300 v Blyth Spartans, FA Amateur Cup 1971
Previous Leagues: Barnsley 52-61/ County Snr 62-70/ Yorks 71-82. **Prog:** 20 pages, 20p
Hons: Northern Co's East Lg Div 1 R-up 90-91 (Div 3 R-up 85-86), Sheffield Snr Cup R-up 72-73, County Snr Lg 65-66 69-70 (R-up 62-63, Lg Cup 65-66), Barnsley Lg 52-53 58-59 59-60 (Lg Cup 56-57 58-59 (R-up 53-54)), Beckett Cup 57-58.

YORKSHIRE AMATEUR

Chairman: William Ellis **President:** Rayner Barker
Secretary: Brian Whaley, 50 Moseley Wood Walk, Leeds LS16 7HG (01132 679806).
Manager: Kevin Smith **Coach:** Dave Holmes **Physio:** Terry Davies
Ground: Bracken Edge, Sycamore Avenue, Leeds LS8 4DZ (01132 624093).
Directions: From South M1 to Leeds, then A58 Wetherby Road to Fforde Green Hotel, left at lights and proceed to Sycamore Ave. (on right). From East A1 to Boot & Shoe Inn then to Shaftesbury Hotel, turn right into Harehills Lane, then to Sycamore Avenue. Two and a half miles from Leeds (BR). Buses 2, 3 & 20 from Briggate to Harehills Ave.
Seats: 200 **Cover:** 160 **Capacity:** 1,550 **Floodlights:** Yes **Club Shop:** Yes
Programme: 12 pages, 50p **Editor:** Chas Sharman (01132 938894). **Press Officer:**
Colours: White/blue/red **Change colours:** All red
Sponsors: Bridge Electrical **Nickname:** Ammers. **Founded:** 1919.
Midweek Matches: Tuesday **Reserve League:**
Record Attendance: 4,000 v Wimbledon, FA Amateur Cup QF 1932.
Previous League: Yorks 20-24 30-82.
Players progressing to Football League: Gary Strodder & Stuart Naylor (WBA), Peter Swan (Leeds), Brian Deane (Doncaster, Sheffield United, Leeds).
Clubhouse: Bar, tea bar, games, lounge. Every night 8.30-11pm, Sat m/days 12-11pm, Sun lunch 12-3pm.
95-96 Captain: Steve Templeton **95-96 Top Scorer:** Richard Beardshaw **95-96 P.o.Y.:** Mick Whaley
Honours: FA Amtr Cup SF 31-32, West Riding Co. Cup(3), Yorks Lg 31-32 (Div 2 58-59 (R-up 52-53 71-72), Div 3 77-78, Lg Cup 32-33), Leeds & Dist. Snr Cup.

REDFERNS INTERNATIONAL REMOVERS CENTRAL MIDLANDS LEAGUE

FEEDER TO:
Northern Counties East League

Chairman & General Secretary:

F A Harwood. 103 Vestry Road, Oakwood, Derby. DE21 2BN (01332 832372).

Public Relations Officer: S Wilton, 57 Main Road, Smalley, Derby, DE7 6DS. (01332 880199)

Oakham United became Supreme Division champions and promptly folded because of restrictions with their ground, shared with cricket, prevented promotion. The Sutton-in-Ashfield side led the way almost from the first day of the season. They hardly suffered a hic-up and finally won the title by seven points.

However, it wasn't as cut and dried as it might seem. Glapwell chased them all the way, and at one time were favourites, and reigning champions Heanor Town were always in with a shout despite suffering from a management and player walk-out in December. Bill Fossey was brought in as manager and assembled a squad which might have become runners-up had they not dropped five home points out of their last six.

Glapwell passed the ground grading test and become the seventh club promoted under the Northern Pyramid agreement from the Central Midlands League to the Northern Counties East League.

The Supreme Division also lost Kiveton Park, who folded after 112 years. Very sad this, because many people tried hard to keep the club afloat but they were beaten in the end by apathy and vandalism. Rossington were demoted due to their three year Supreme Division trial period without floodlights having evaporated, and they too almost went out of existence. However, secretary Ian Wilson and manager Gary Mountford found all their players willing to stay, and with such loyalty, there has to be success.

Elswhere in the Supreme Division, there were success stories for Kimberley Town and Long Eaton United, who both had tremendous second halves to the season and enjoyed their best campaigns for some time. There were also successful baptisms in the top flight for promoted clubs Case Sports and Mickleover Sports.

The top four clubs in the Premier Division were offered promotion, subject to ground grading. Only champions and League Cup winners Killamarsh Juniors failed to beat the set deadline. Dunkirk, Graham Street Primary, who enjoyed a remarkable first year back in the game, and Nuthall were all promoted.

It proved to be a bitterley disappointing finale for Killamarsh, who won their division by five points and became only the second Premier Division team in history to lift the League Cup when they beat Supreme Division Sandiacre Town at Mansfield Town's Field Mill ground.

The League's Sportsmanship Award went to Sheepbridge, who finished bottom in their first season but never let their heads fall. They promoted the League with great credit dispite taking a few pastings, but they will come out of it a much better club.

Harworth Colliery Institute won the Wakefield Floodlit Cup beating Gedling Town in the two-legged final. This was reward for the hard work put in by manager Alan Needham. However, their league season was to him a disappointment.

The League welcomes two new clubs - Holbrook FC a completely new club and no relation to past clubs of similiar name - and Grimethorpe Miners Welfare from the Beefeater County Senior League.

For the new season the League also welcomes three new sponsors. Redfernn International Removers will sponsor the league, with Travis Perkins the Supreme Division and Sign Masters the Premier Division. Wakefield Trophy World continue as sponsors of the Wakefield Floodlit Cup.

Chairman/General Secretary Frank Harwood and Treasurer Tony Baugh begin their 26th season with the league, and it is a season which promises to be one of the most competitive for many a long time.

A number of clubs have ambitions of promotion within the Northern Pyramid System, including Gedling Town, Staveley Miners Welfare, Kimberley Town, Heanor Town, Dunkirk and Long Eaton United. Staveley, who have done a considerable amount of work on their Inkersall Road ground, were disappointed to miss out last season, and will be pulling out all the stops this time.

The League continues to support the Northern Pyramid in every possible way.

Stam Wilton; Press & Public Relations Officer.

Action from the match between South Normanton Athletic (yellow) and Rossington (blue).
Photo - Martin Wray

Glapwell attack the Oakham United goal. *Photo - Martin Wray*

FINAL LEAGUE TABLES 1995/96

Supreme Div		P	W	D	L	F	A	Pts
1.	Oakham Utd	32	22	4	6	71	37	70
2.	Glapwell	32	19	6	7	51	31	63
3.	Heanor Town	32	19	5	8	70	41	62
4.	Kimberley Tn	32	17	6	9	70	56	57
5.	Staveley MW	32	16	8	8	52	43	56
6.	Long Eaton U	32	16	4	12	69	52	52
7.	S Normanton A	32	14	7	11	47	40	49
8.	Case Sport	32	14	7	11	52	51	49
9.	Gedling Town	32	13	8	11	57	42	47
10.	Sandiacre Tn	32	11	7	14	52	58	40
11.	Harworth Col I	32	12	3	17	55	76	39
12.	Mickleover Sp	32	12	2	18	55	63	38
13.	Rossington	32	10	7	15	49	59	37
14.	Kiverton Park	32	9	5	18	40	61	32
15.	Nettleham	32	5	13	14	34	55	28
16.	Shirebrook Tn	32	8	2	22	47	75	26
17.	Thorne Coll	32	6	4	22	26	57	22

Prem Div		P	W	D	L	F	A	Pts
1.	Killamarsh Jun	34	26	3	5	110	46	81
2.	Dunkirk	34	23	7	4	130	34	76
3.	Graham St Pr	34	20	7	7	67	36	67
4.	Nuthall	34	18	12	4	74	36	66
5.	Clipstone Wel	34	18	4	12	83	51	58
6.	Sneiton	34	18	4	12	87	63	58
7.	Radford	34	16	8	10	69	51	56
8.	Askern Wel	34	17	4	13	78	65	55
9.	Shardlow St J	34	15	8	11	66	59	53
10.	Hemsworth	34	15	5	14	62	59	50
11.	Sheffield H Un	34	13	5	16	65	72	44
12.	Mexboro Ath	34	10	9	15	64	76	39
13.	Derby R R	34	11	5	18	62	78	38
14.	Collingham	34	10	6	18	60	75	36
15.	Stanton Ilkest.	34	10	5	19	54	79	35
16.	Mickleover RBA	34	9	4	21	42	86	31
17.	Blackwell MW	34	2	8	24	44	125	14
18.	Sheepbridge	34	2	2	30	34	162	8

SUPREME DIVISION RESULTS CHART 1995-96

HOME TEAM	1	2	3	4	5	6	7	8	9	10	11	12	13	14	15	16	17
1. Case Sports	*	4-2	1-1	2-2	1-1	1-2	1-3	3-2	0-1	2-0	3-1	3-0	0-2	4-3	0-4	1-2	1-0
2. Gedling Town	1-2	*	1-1	4-0	0-2	1-1	3-0	1-0	4-1	3-3	1-2	2-1	5-0	4-1	0-4	1-2	2-2
3. Glapwell	1-0	1-0	*	2-3	0-2	1-1	1-0	1-1	0-2	1-0	1-1	1-0	1-0	4-0	2-0	5-2	2-0
4. Harworth Coll Inst	0-2	3-2	1-3	*	6-2	4-1	0-2	1-2	3-4	1-0	3-1	2-1	2-0	4-0	0-0	3-1	0-1
5. Heanor Town	2-0	0-1	2-0	4-1	*	2-3	4-0	1-3	5-2	1-2	2-0	4-3	3-1	4-0	1-0	2-3	1-0
6. Kimberley Town	2-3	3-1	3-0	4-1	2-2	*	4-2	3-1	3-0	3-1	2-6	1-1	3-1	6-3	2-3	1-2	3-2
7. Kiverton Park	0-2	3-1	1-3	1-1	3-3	2-1	*	1-4	1-0	0-0	1-2	2-1	3-2	1-3	4-0	1-4	0-2
8. Long Eaton Utd	3-3	0-2	0-2	5-3	1-0	7-1	1-2	*	0-1	1-1	1-2	4-2	3-2	2-1	1-2	4-1	4-1
9. Mickleover Spt	2-0	0-4	0-2	7-0	2-3	0-3	2-1	1-2	*	5-1	0-1	3-0	0-1	4-6	5-0	0-5	0-1
10. Nettleham	1-1	0-0	2-2	2-1	0-1	0-0	1-1	0-4	2-2	*	1-5	2-2	1-3	2-1	1-5	2-3	3-0
11. Oakham United	3-0	3-1	2-0	8-2	3-2	3-0	2-0	3-4	1-1	0-0	*	3-2	1-0	3-2	3-2	1-1	3-0
12. Rossington	1-1	1-1	0-2	7-1	2-7	2-3	3-2	1-0	3-1	1-0	0-2	*	1-1	3-1	1-3	1-0	2-1
13. Sandiacre Town	2-5	2-2	2-3	2-1	0-0	2-3	3-0	5-3	4-2	2-2	1-2	2-2	*	3-2	0-2	1-1	3-1
14. Shirebrook Town	2-4	2-0	1-3	1-0	0-1	0-2	2-1	2-3	3-1	1-1	1-0	4-3	0-1	*	1-1	1-2	0-1
15. S Normanton Ath	4-0	1-3	0-1	0-2	2-2	0-0	1-1	1-0	2-0	1-0	0-2	0-1	2-3	3-1	*	4-2	0-0
16. Staveley M W	1-1	2-2	2-1	3-1	0-3	1-0	1-0	0-0	1-3	2-1	3-1	0-0	1-0	1-0	1-1	*	4-0
17. Thorne Colliery	0-1	0-1	1-3	2-3	0-1	1-4	3-1	2-3	1-3	0-2	0-1	0-1	1-1	3-2	0-2	0-0	*

PREMIER DIVISION RESULTS CHART 1995-96

HOME TEAM	1	2	3	4	5	6	7	8	9	10	11	12	13	14	15	16	17	18
1. Askern Welfare	*	7-0	2-3	2-2	6-1	2-1	1-4	2-1	1-2	1-1	5-2	1-2	4-1	1-0	4-0	4-2	5-1	2-0
2. Blackwell M W	2-4	*	1-6	4-3	1-1	1-8	2-7	2-4	1-7	0-3	3-0	0-1	1-1	2-3	3-3	2-2	0-4	3-3
3. Clipatone Wel	0-1	5-0	*	2-0	0-2	1-0	0-1	1-1	1-4	2-2	2-0	3-1	2-0	4-1	11-1	0-3	1-3	4-2
4. Collingham	2-1	6-0	0-1	*	5-5	2-6	1-3	3-2	0-0	1-2	4-1	2-3	2-3	2-2	6-1	1-3	1-3	3-1
5. Derby Rolls Royce	0-3	5-3	1-3	0-2	*	2-7	3-1	2-1	1-3	0-1	4-1	0-0	1-1	0-2	7-1	4-1	2-4	5-2
6. Dunkirk	6-1	6-0	4-1	8-1	6-1	*	2-1	3-2	1-2	7-0	1-0	1-1	5-3	4-1	11-0	2-1	1-0	6-0
7. Graham Street Prim	3-0	4-0	1-0	0-0	1-0	1-1	*	2-1	1-2	1-0	3-1	0-0	5-2	3-1	3-1	2-1	3-0	1-0
8. Hemsworth Town	2-1	4-3	4-3	1-1	0-1	3-2	3-1	*	4-3	2-2	1-2	2-1	2-1	0-4	6-0	0-1	4-2	0-1
9. Killamarsh	2-0	4-1	3-0	5-0	6-2	1-6	1-1	1-2	*	1-0	7-1	3-5	2-1	4-2	11-0	5-1	5-2	5-3
10. Mexborough Ath	3-3	3-1	1-1	3-4	0-2	0-0	4-0	1-2	0-3	*	2-4	0-4	1-3	1-2	6-3	5-4	2-1	4-2
11. Mickleover R B L	4-1	3-1	1-4	2-0	2-1	0-6	1-2	0-2	2-0	2-2	*	2-2	1-4	3-2	1-2	0-4	0-4	0-0
12. Nuthall	1-1	3-2	1-0	4-0	3-2	0-0	1-1	2-1	1-1	3-0	3-0	*	0-2	6-0	3-0	2-1	1-1	0-3
13. Radford	0-2	0-0	2-0	2-1	1-1	0-3	3-0	3-0	1-3	0-0	4-0	0-0	*	2-1	5-2	4-0	4-2	3-0
14. Shardlow St James	4-1	2-1	1-3	0-2	3-1	1-1	1-1	0-0	2-3	2-2	2-1	2-2	2-2	*	4-0	3-2	1-0	2-1
15. Sheepbridge	2-3	2-2	1-10	2-0	0-1	1-8	0-4	2-3	1-3	0-9	0-1	1-8	1-2	0-6	*	1-2	3-5	1-2
16. Sheffield Hallam Uni	5-2	3-0	2-4	0-3	3-1	2-2	0-0	1-1	0-4	4-2	3-1	1-6	2-1	3-3	2-0	*	0-1	4-2
17. Sneiton	4-1	6-0	2-2	2-0	3-2	2-2	3-2	2-1	1-3	6-0	4-2	2-3	3-3	1-3	6-1	2-1	*	3-1
18. Stanton Ilkeston	2-3	2-2	2-3	1-0	2-1	0-3	0-4	3-0	1-3	5-2	1-1	1-1	2-5	0-1	4-1	2-1	3-2	*

CENTRAL MIDLANDS LEAGUE CUP 1995-96

Preliminary Round;

Nuthall v Nettleham 1-1, 0-1
Oakham United v Gedling Town 0-0, 4-0
South Normanton Athletic v Mickleover Sports 1-3

First Round;

Blackwell Miners Welfare v Kimberley Town 1-1, 1-3
Case Sports v Derby Rolls Royce 2-1
Clipstone Welfare v Oakham United 0-2
Dunkirk v Long Eaton United 0-0, 3-4
Glapwell v Thorne Colliery 1-3
Graham Street Prims v Shirebrook Town 1-4
Killamarsh Juniors v Mickleover Sports 2-1
Mexborough Athletic v Nettleham 0-2
Mickleover R B A v Collingham 3-4
Radford v Heanor Town 0-4
Rossington v Kiveton Park 3-3, 4-0
Sandiacre Town v Staanton Ilkeston 8-1
Shardlow St James v Hemsworth Town 0-1
Sheepbridge v Askern Welfare 1-2
Sheffield Hallam Uni v Harworth Colliery Inst. 5-3
Sneiton v Staveley Miners Welfare 1-1, 1-5

Second Round;

Askern Welfare v Nettleham 3-2
Killamarsh Juniors v Kimberley Town 4-3
Long Eaton United v Heanor Town 8-2
Rossington v Hemsworth Town 1-1, 7-2
Shirebrook Town v Sheffield Hallam Univ. 5-5, 1-2
Staveley Miners Welfare v Case Sports 1-2
Collingham v Sandiacre Town 2-2, 0-3
Thorne Colliery v Oakham United 1-3

Third Round;

Askern Welfare v Rossington 1-5
Killamarsh Juniors v Case Sports 5-1
Long Eaton United v Sandiacre Town 3-3, 0-3
Oakham United v Sheffield Hallam Univ 1-3

Semi-Finals;

Rossington v Sandiacre Town 1-2
Killamarsh Juniors v Sheffield Hallam Uni 4-3

FINAL;

Killamarsh Juniors v Sandiacre Town 3-0

WAKEFIELD FLOODLIT CUP 1995-96

Group A;

Oakham United v Hemsworth Town 1-0
Nuthall v Hemsworth Town 1-0
Oakham United v Stanton Ilkeston 6-1
Hemsworth Town v Oakham United 0-2
Nuthall v Oakham United 0-2
Oakham United v Nuthall 0-1
Stanton Ilkeston v Hemsworth Town 0-1
Nuthall v Stanton Ilkeston 2-0
Hemsworth Town v Nuthall 2-0
Stanton Ilkeston v Nuthall 0-3
Stanton Ilkeston v Oakham United 1-3
Hemsworth Town v Stanton Ilkeston 3-1

	P	W	D	L	F	A	Pts
Oakham United	6	5	1	1	14	3	15
Nuthall	6	4	0	2	7	4	12
Hemsworth Town	6	3	0	3	6	5	9
Stanton Ilkeston	6	0	0	6	3	18	0

Group B;

Nettleham v Shirebrook Town 1-4
Nettleham v Gedling Town 1-3
Gedling Town v Nettleham 4-1
Gedling Town v Shirebrook Town 2-1
Shirebrook Town v Gedling Town 3-2
Shirebrook Town v Nettleham 4-0

	P	W	D	L	F	A	Pts
Shirebrook Town	4	3	0	1	12	5	9
Gedling Town	4	3	0	1	11	6	9
Nettleham	4	0	0	4	3	15	0

Group C;

Collingham v Staveley Miners Welfare 0-3
Heanor Town v Staveley Miners Welfare 2-2
Collingham v Heanor Town 3-5
Staveley Miners Welfare v Heanor Town 0-3
Staveley Miners Welfare v Collingham 2-1
Heanor Town v Collingham 1-4

	P	W	D	L	F	A	Pts
Heanor Town	4	2	1	1	11	9	7
Staveley Miners Welfare	4	2	1	1	7	6	7
Collingham	4	1	0	3	8	11	3

Group D;

Harworth Coll Inst v Kimberley Tn 1-4
Glapwell v Harworth Coll Inst. 5-2
Kimberley Town v Harworth Coll Inst 0-3
Glapwell v Kimberley Town 3-1
Harworth Coll Inst v Glapwell 5-3
Kimberley Town v Glapwell 0-0

	P	W	D	L	F	A	Pts
Glapwell	4	2	1	1	11	8	7
Harworth Colliery Institue	4	2	0	2	11	15	6
Kimberley Town	4	1	1	2	5	7	4

Second Round	First Leg	Second Leg	Aggr Score
Harworth Coll Inst v Oakham Utd	1-1	3-2	4-3
Staveley Miners Welfare v Shirebrook Town	2-1	0-3	2-4
Gedling Town v Heanor Town	1-0	3-3	4-3
Nuthall v Glapwell	0-1	1-2	1-3
Semi-Finals			
Shirebrook Town v Harworth Colliery Institute	0-3	3-3	3-6
Glapwell v Gedling Town	0-0	1-2	1-2
Final;			
Harworth Colliery Institute v Gedling Town	3-1	3-3	6-4

KEN MARSLAND TROPHY 1995-96

Group One;

Gedling Town v Long Eaton United	5-0	Gedling Town v Nuthall	5-1
Gedling Town v Shardlow St James	2-2	Gedling Town v Sneiton	6-1
Long Eaton United v Gedling Town	1-6	Long Eaton United v Nuthall	2-3
Long Eaton Utd v Shardlow St James	1-2	Long Eaton United v Sneiton	1-3
Nuthall v Gedling Town	1-3	Nuthall v Long Eaton United	3-0
Nuthall v Shardlow St James	3-0	Nuthall v Sneiton	1-1
Shardlow St James v Gedling Town	2-2	Shardlow St James v Long Eaton Utd	4-1
Shardlow St James v Nuthall	3-2	Shardlow St James v Sneiton	3-0
Sneiton v Gedling Town	0-3	Sneiton v Long Eaton Utd	4-1
Sneiton v Nuthall	7-1	Sneiton v Shardlow St James	3-6

	P	*W*	*D*	*L*	*F*	*A*	*Pts*
Gedling Town	8	6	2	0	33	8	18
Shardlow St James	8	5	3	1	25	11	16
Sneiton	8	3	1	4	19	22	10
Nuthall	8	3	1	4	15	21	10
Long Eaton United	8	0	0	8	7	30	0

Group Two;

Clipstone Welfare v Glapwell	1-3	Clipstone Welfare v Kimberley Town	1-6
Clipstone Welfare v Rossington	2-2	Clipstone Welfare v Sandiacre Town	4-1
Glapwell v Clipstone Welfare	1-0	Glapwell v Kimberley Town	1-2
Glapwell v Rossington	3-0	Glapwell v Sandiacre Town	3-0
Kimberley Town v Clipstone Welfare	0-2	Kimberley Town c Glapwell	6-3
Kimberley Town v Rossington	2-1	Kimberley Town v Sandiacre Town	2-0
Rossington v Clipstone Welfare	4-3	Rossington v Glapwell	4-3
Rossington v Kimberley Town	0-3	Rossington v Sandiacre Town	3-2
Sandiacre Town v Clipstone Welfare	0-2	Sandiacre Town v Glapwell	2-1
Sandiacre Town v Kimberley Town	1-5	Sandiacre Town v Rosington	1-5

	P	*W*	*D*	*L*	*F*	*A*	*Pts*
Kimberley Town	8	7	0	1	26	10	21
Rossington	8	4	1	3	19	19	13
Glapwell	8	4	0	4	17	15	12
Clipstone Welfare	8	3	1	4	15	17	10
Sandiacre Town	8	1	0	7	7	25	3

Group Three;

Borrowash Victoria v Radford	3-0	Borrowash Victoria v Shirebrook Town	3-1
Borrowash Victoria v St Normanton Ath	1-1	Borrowash Victoria v Stanton Ilkeston	3-3
Radford v Borrowash Victoria	3-1	Radford v Shirebrook Town	3-1
Radford v Sth Normanton Ath	2-2	Radford v Stanton Ilkeston	2-3
Shirebrook Town v Borrowash Victoria	3-3	Shirebrook Town v Radford	2-1
Shirebrook Town v Sth Normantn Ath	0-2	Shirebrook Town v Stanton Ilkeston	3-1
Sth Normanton Ath v Borrowash Victoria	2-0	Sth Normanton Ath v Radford	6-3
Sth Normanton Ath v Shirebrook Town	2-0	Sth Normanton Ath v Stanton Ilkeston	1-1
Stanton Ilkeston v Borrowash Victoria	2-2	Stanton Ilkeston v Radford	5-1
Stanton Ilkeston v Shirebrook Town	1-2	Stanton Ilkeston v Sth Normanton Ath	1-2

	P	*W*	*D*	*L*	*F*	*A*	*Pts*
South Normanton Athletic	8	5	3	0	18	8	18
Borrowash Victoria	8	2	4	2	16	15	10
Shirebrook Town	8	3	1	4	16	16	10
Stanton Ilkeston	8	2	3	3	17	16	9
Radford	8	2	1	5	15	23	7

Group Four;

Dunkirk v Heanor Town	4-3	Dunkirk v Mickleover R B L	6-0
Dunkirk v Staveley Miners Welfare	2-1	Heanor Town v Dunkirk	2-4
Heanor Town v Mickleover RBL	6-0	Heanor Town v Staveley Miners Welfare	3-3
Mickleover RBL v Dunkirk	3-2	Mickleover RBL v Heanor Town	0-3
Mickleover RBL v Staveley Miners Welfare	1-2	Staveley Miners Welfare v Dunkirk	5-3
Staveley Miners Welfare v Heanor Town	2-0	Staveley Miners Welfare v Mickleover RBL	1-1

	P	*W*	*D*	*L*	*F*	*A*	*Pts*
Dunkirk	6	4	0	2	21	14	12
Staveley Miners Welfare	6	3	2	1	14	10	11
Heanor Town	6	2	1	3	17	13	7
Mickleover RBL	6	1	1	4	5	20	4

Semi-Finals;

Dunkirk V Gedling Town	2-5 (Aet)	Sth Normanton Ath v Kimberley Town	3-2 (Aet)

Final; Gedling Town 1, South Normanton Athletic 1, (after extra time)
Gedling Town won 8-7 on penalties.

SUPREME DIVISION CLUBS 1994-95

CASE SPORTS

Secretary: D W Henderson, 18 King George's Road, New Rossington, Doncaster, South Yorkshire DN11 0PR (01302 865027).
Ground & Directions: Cantley Park,Doncaster.Jct 3 off M18 to White Rose Way,follow signs to Racecourse.Right at racecourse roundabout toBawtry Rd (A638).Pass Doncaster Rovers and leasure cebtre on right.Left into Cantly lans at Cantly traffiv lights.200 yds left intoAscot Avenue.Ground entrance opposite Beechers Brooke public house.Ground at end of drive.
Colours: All white.
Change Colours: Red/black/red.

DUNKIRK

Secretary: Mr John G Peck, 5 Thistledown Rd, Clifton, Nottm NG11 9DP (0602 842147).
Ground & Directions: The Ron Steel Sports Ground, Trentside Farm, Clifton Bridge, Nottingham (0602 850803). Ring Road - Clifton Bridge (North End), Industrial Estate, Lenton Lane.
Colours: Red/Black
Hons: Notts Alliance Div 1 84-85 (Div 2 82-83, Lg Cup R-up 84-85), Notts I'mediate Cup 83-84.

GEDLING TOWN

Chairman: R A Ash **President:** P M Robinson.
Secretary: Paul Dobson, 26 Chevin Gardens, Top Valley Estate, Nottingham NG5 9ES (01159 274790)
Manager: Dave Sands/ Cameron Holroyd **Physio:** Pete Tyas
Ground: 'Riverside Ground', rear Ferry Boat Inn, Stoke Inn, Stoke Bardolph, Gedling, Nottm (01159 402145)
Directions: From Notts County F.C., A612 towards Southwell for 2 miles to Burton Joyce, Station Rd, then Stoke Lane. Ground rear of Ferry Boat Inn.
Capacity: 2,000 **Seats:** None **Cover:** 500 **Floodlights:** Yes **Club Shop:** No.
Programme: 32 pages, 50p **Editor:** Paul Dodson **Press Officer:**
Colours: Red/black/red **Change colours:** Yellow/blue/yellow
Sponsors: **Founded:** 1989. **Nickname:** None.
Midweek home matchday: Wednesday **Reserve League:**
Record Attendance: 250 v Arnold Town, Wakefield Floodlit Trophy 1992-93.
Previous Leagues: Notts Amateur.
Clubhouse: Matchdays only. Hot & cold food. Licensed bar.
95-96 Captain: **95-96 Top Scorer:** Mark Daly 12 **95-96 P.o.Y.:**
Club Record Goalscorer: Darren Terry **Club Record Appearances:** G Watson.
Honours: Central Mids Lg Div 1 90-91 (Premier Div R-up 91-92, Wakefield Floodlit Trophy 92-93, Ken Marsland Cup(Res.) 93-94), Notts Amtr Lg 89-90 (Snr Cup R-up 89-90).

GRAHAM STREET PRIM.

Secretary: David Wright, 6 Athol Close, Sinfin Moor, Derby DE24 9L2
Manager: S Wooding & D Tice
Ground: Carriage & Wagon Welfare Club, Longbridge Lane, off Ascot Drive, Derby (01332 571376)
Directions: M1 Junc 25, take A52 to Derby, turn left onto A5111 ring road, Raynesway. Take left at next island Ascot Drive and first right into Longbridge Lane
Colours: All red **Change Colours:** All blue
Midweek Night: Wednesday **Floodlights:** No

HARWORTH COLLIERY INSTITUTE

Chairman: Paul Wilson **Vice-Chairman:** N/A **President:** Bert Fielding.
Secretary: Tom Brogan, 30 Lindsey Road, Harworth, Doncaster, Sth Yorks DN11 8QH (01302 750132).
Manager: Alan Needham **Asst Manager:** Terry Griffin **Physio:** David Butler.
Commercial Mgr: Steve Tucker **Press Officer:** Mark Hickling (01302 744569)
Ground: Recreation Ground, Scrooby Rd, Bircotes, Doncaster (01302 750614).
Directions: Off A1(M) at Blyth, head towards Bawtry for approx 2 miles, take third left, ground in village at top of hill on left. Or, from Doncaster to Bawtry then head for A1(M) and turn left after caravan site - ground at top of hill.
Capacity: 2,000 **Seats:** None **Cover:** 500 **Founded:** 1931 **Floodlights:** Yes
Colours: Amber and Black/Black/Amber **Change Colours:** All Red **Nickname:** Reds.
Programme: 44 pages, 40p **Editor:** Steve Owen (01302 750322). **Club Shop:** No.
Midweek matches: Wednesday **Reserve Team's League:** Gainsborough & District.
Previous Grounds: None **Record Gate:** 350 v Congleton, FA Cup 1st Qual. Rd 1988.
Previous Lges: Doncaster Senior/ Sheffield County Senior/ Yorkshire 46-50 77-82/ Northern Co's (East).
Players progressing to Football League: Billy Griffin (Sheffield Wednesday) 1957, Graham Cawthorne (Grimsby Town) 1979), Lee Butler (Lincoln City) 1986.
Clubhouse: Open most night, Sat afternoon & evening & Sun lunchtime. Sandwiches available. Matchdays & Sunday lunchtimes. Darts, pool, food
95-96 Captain: **Club record appearances:** Robert Needham.

95-96 P.o.Y.: **95-96 Top Scorer:**
Hons: Wharncliffe Charity Cup 62-63 74-75, Central Midlands League 87-88 (Runners-up 86-87, Challenge Cup 86-87 87-88, F'lit Cup 91-92 (Runners-up 89-90)), Sheffield Senior League 64-65 74-75, Sheffield & Hallamshire Senior Cup SF 87-88

HEANOR TOWN

Secretary: Keith Costello, 45 Stainsby Avenue, Heanor, Derbyshire DE75 7EL (01773 719446).
Manager: Bobby Sykes
Ground: The Town Ground, Mayfield Avenue, Heanor (01773 713742/715815).
Directions: North: M1 (J27), A608. South: M1 (J26), A610-A608
Capacity: 3,500 **Seats:** 200 **Cover:** 800 **Founded:** 1883 **Floodlights:** Yes
Programme: 20 pages, 30p **Programme Editor:** Secretary **Clubhouse:** Yes
Midweek matches: Wednesday **Record Gate:** 6,411 v Carlisle, FA Cup 1958.
Colours: White/black/blue **Change Colours:** Red and White stripes/Red/Red.
Previous Name: Heanor Athletic **95-96 Top Scorer:**
Previous League: Midland Co's 1894-97 98-1900 26-28 61-72 74-82/ Central Alliance 21-25 47-61/ West Midlands (Regional) 72-74/ Northern Co's League East 82-86.
Hons: Central Midlands League Cup 94-95 (Runners-up 86-87 92-93, B E Webbe Removals Cup 88-89), West Midlands Reg. League Runners-up 72-73; Midland Co's League Runners-up 65-66 67-68; Derbys Senior Cup(9) 1892-94 1946-47 65-69 70-71 78-79; FA Cup 1st Rd 58-59 63-64.

KIMBERLEY TOWN

Chairman: George Giddens **Vice Chairman:** Reg Izzard **President:** R J Penney.
Secretary: Stewart Brown, 14 Brendon Drive, Kimberley, Nottingham NG16 2J2 (01159 383542).
Manager: Julian Garmston **Asst Manager:** Brian Harrison
Press Officer: Gary Jayes **Commercial Manager:** Carl Parkin.
Ground: Stag Ground, Nottingham Road, Kimberley (01159 382788).
Directions: Through Nuthall from M1 jct 26 to Kimberley, ground entrance 150 yds after Stag Inn. 6 miles from Nottingham (BR). Trent Buses R11, R12, R13, 357 & 358 all stop outside ground.
Seats: None **Cover:** 150 **Capacity:** 2,500 **Floodlights:** Yes **Founded:** 1948
Colours: Blue/white/blue **Change colours:** White/black/white **Nickname:** Stags.
Previous Grounds: None **Prev. Name:** Kimberley YMCA, 1948-56.
Reserves' Lge: CML Res Div 1 **Record Gate:** 1,122 v Eastwood, Midland Co's Lg April 76.
Previous Leagues: Notts Amateur 48-55/ Central Alliance 55-66/ East Midlands 66-71/ Midland Counties 71-80/ Northern Counties (East) 80-86.
Programme: 20 pages, 20p **Programme Editor:** TBA **Club Shop:** No.
Midweek home matchday: Tuesday **Clubhouse:** Matchdays and evenings, snacks available.
Record win: 8-1 (opponents not known) **Record defeat:** 1-9 v Bridlington Trinity (H), NCEL 4/5/81.
Record transfer fee paid: Nil **Received:** £2,000 for Andy Hill (Derby, Sept '81).
95-96 Captain: **95-96 Top Scorer:** **95-96 P.o.Y.:**
Club record scorer: Graham Cutts **Club record appearances:** Dennis Froggatt.
Hons: Notts Amateur Lg Div 1 54-55, Central Alliance Div 2 R-up 57-58.

LONG EATON UNITED

Chairman: J C Fairley **Vice Chairman:** B.Webster.
Secretary: David Hampson, 4 Airedale Close, Long Eaton, Nottingham. NG10 3HW (01115-9726342.
Manager: Neil Lovell/Martin Dick **Physio:** Les Fountain
Ground: Grange Park, Station Road, Long Eaton, Nottingham (01602 735700).
Directions: From Nottingham, A52 to r'bout by 'Bardills Garden Centre', left onto B6003 to t-junction & lights.Turn right and take left into Station Rd.The entrance is opposite the Speedway Stadium car park. M1 Jnc 25 take A52 towards Nottingham and Bardills Garden Centre is on the nest island. 2 miles from Long Eaton (BR).
Seats: None **Cover:** 500 **Capacity:** 5,000 **Floodlights:** No **Club Shop:** No.
Programme: 16-20 pages, 50p **Editor:** **Press Officer:** Mick Raven (01115-939-3947)
Colours: Blue & black/black/black **Change:** Yellow/green/black.
Sponsors: M C Builders **Nickname:** Blues. **Founded:** 1956
Midweek matchday: Tuesday
Record Attendance: 2,000 1973 FA Cup.
Previous Leagues: Central Alliance 59-61/ Midland Co's 61-82/ Northern Co's East 82-89.
Clubhouse: Open matchdays one hour either side of kick-off. Hot & cold drinks, confectionery, sausage rolls, burgers etc.
95-96 Captain: **95-96 Top Scorer:** Paul Acklam 22. **95-96 P.o.Y.:**
Club Record Scorer: Gary Weston 32, Graham Walker 32.
Club Record Appearances:
Honours: Derbys Snr Cup 64-65 75-76, Midland Co's Lg R-up 76-77, Central Alliance Div South 58-59, Northern Co's (East) Div 1 South 84-85.

MICKLEOVER SPORTS

Secretary: Derek Hewitt, 1 Milton Close, Mickleover, Derbyshire DE3 5QN (01332 515295).
Ground: Mickleover Sports Ground, Station Rd, Mickleover, Derby (01332 521167).
Midweek matchdays: Tuesday **Colours:** Red & black stripes/black/red.
Programme: 28 pages **Programme Editor:** Tony Shaw **Floodlights:** No.
95-96 Captain: **95-96 P.o.Y.:** **95-96 Top Scorers:**

NETTLEHAM

Secretary: John Wilson, 21 Chaucer Drive, Lincoln LN2 4LN (01522 530566).
Manager: Ian Musson **Ground:** Mulsanne Park, Field Close, Nettleham (01522 750007).
Directions: A46 approx. 3 miles north of Lincoln, right at Brown Cow Pub, proceed past Church 2nd turning on right.
Colours: Blue & White Stripes/Blue/White. **Change Colours:** Red (white trim)/red/red **Floodlights:** Yes.
Midweek home matches: Tuesday **Programme:** 48 pages, 50p (Editor: Colin Benton).
95-96 Captain: **95-96 P.o.Y.:** **95-96 Top Scorer:**
Hons: Central Mids Lg Premier Division Cup R-up 87-88, Village Tphy, Nursing Cup, Kelly Read Cup, Blankney Hunt Cup, Lincoln & Dist. Amtr Cup R-up, Joe Miller Tphy(2).

NUTHALL

President: Bill Smith **Chairman:** A Farmer **Vice Chairman:** R Naylor.
Secretary: Tony Benniston, 117 Broad Lane, Brinsley, Nottm NG16 5BU (0773 712350).
Manager/Coach: G Webster **Asst Mgr:** M Cook **Physio:** A Gunn.
Press Officer: K Robinson **Commercial Manager:** J Heading.
Ground & Directions: Basil Russell Playing Fields, Maple Drive, Nuthall, Nottingham (0602 384765). M1 jct 26/ A610 southbound left southbound, right northbound.
Seats: None **Cover:** 50 **Floodlights:** No **Founded:** 1976 **Nickname:** Larks
Colours: Sky/navy/sky **Change colours:** All yellow.
Previous Grounds: None **Previous Leagues:** East Midlands Regional.
Programme: 30 pages, 50p **Editor:** Mr P Taylor (0602 507071) **Club Shop:** No.
Clubhouse: Open matchdays. Food & drinks from one hour prior to kick-off.
Club record scorer: J Paxton **Club record appearances:** L Wild.

SANDIACRE TOWN

Chairman: John Ellis. **President:** None
Secretary: Mel Williams, 38 Pasture Road, Stapleford NG9 8GL (0115 939 2415)
Manager: Geoff Barrowcliffe **Asst Manager:** **Physio:** Kevin Knowles
Ground: St Giles Park, Stanton Road, Sandiacre, Nottingham NG10 5EP (0115 939 2880).
Directions: M1 jct 25, follow signs to Sandiacre passing Post House Hotel on right, straight over crossroads into Rushy Lane and towards Stanton Rd.,, 1st right after 1000yds into Stanton Rd, ground at bottom after another 1000yds. Trent buses from Nottingham to Derby alighting at Sandiacre Market Place - from traffic lights go along Town Street (canal on your right) eventually past Comet (on right) then left into Church Street, follow to Stanton Road and ground is 200yds on right (total distance half mile).
Seats: None **Cover:** 250 **Capacity:** 2,000 **Floodlights:** Yes **Club Shop:** No.
Programme: 44 pages, 50p **Editor:** Secretary **Press Officer:** Mel Williams.
Colours: Red/navy/red **Change colours:** All sky
Sponsors: Webster Bros.& J.T.D.Autos. **Founded:** 1978 **Nickname:** Saints.
Midweek matchday: Tuesday **Reserves' League:** CML Res. Div.
Clubhouse: Members club open 8-11pm Daily. Sunday lunchtimes & from 3.45pm on Saturday match days. Hot & cold drinks and light refreshments available.
95-96 Top Scorer: Gary Briscoe 20 **95-96 Captain:** Ged Le Blond. **95-96 P.o.Y:**
Club Record Goalscorer: Ged Le Bond. 151. **Club Record Appearances:**
Honours: Central Mids Lg Premier Div 92-93 (Lg Cup 92-93), Midlands Regional Alliance R-up 91-92, Central Mids Lge Cup R-up 95-96.

Glapwell FC; before CML match at Oakham United

Photo - Martin Wray

South Normanton FC; before match against Rossington

Photo - Martin Wray

SHIREBROOK TOWN

Chairman: Mr T Rowbottom
Secretary: Mr S P Wall, 26 Carter Lane West, Shirebrook, Mansfield, Notts NG20 8NA (01623 747638).
Manager: Neil Moore **Assistant Manager:** Graham Charlesworth.
Ground: BRSA Ground, Langwith Rd, Mansfield (01623 742535).
Directions: M1 jct 29, A617 to Mansfield, 2.5 miles, B6407 Shirebrook, through town to Langwith Rd. Bus 81 from Chesterfield or 23 from Mansfield.
Capacity: 2,000 **Seats:** None **Cover:** 400 **Floodlights:** Yes **Clubhouse:** No.
Programme: 14 pages, 25p **Editor/Press Officer:** G Harworth (01623 748375)
Colours: Red & black stripes/black/red **Change Colours:** White & Blue.
Sponsors: Topline Windows **Nickname:** **Founded:** 1985
Midweek matches: Tuesday **Clubhouse:**
Record Attendance: 2,200 v Mansfield, floodlight opening 10/10/91
95-96 Captain: G Tennant **95-96 Top Scorer:** C Tansley **95-96 P.o.Y.:** C Dickens.
Club Record Goalscorer: S Hill **Club Record Appearances:** P Hayes 165, 1985-89.
Honours: Central Midlands League Reserve Prem Div 94-95 95-96.

SOUTH NORMANTON ATHLETIC

Chairman: Robert Ravenhall **Vice Chairman:** Jim Wright **President:** Monsieur A Thibaudeau.
Secretary: D Meredith.
Manager: Andrew Farbey **Coach:** Chris Lee **Physio:** Terry Ball
Ground: South Normanton Miners Welfare Ground, Lees Lane, South Normanton, Derby (01773 581491).
Directions: B6019 from from M1 exit 28, right after 1 mile (in South Normanton) at Mobil garage into Market Street, after quarter mile turn left immediately after The Clock pub into Lees Lane, ground at bottom. Half hour's walk from Alfreton & Mansfield Parkway BR station.
Capacity: 2,000 **Seats:** 50 **Cover:** 800 **Floodlights:** No **Club Shop:** Yes
Programme: Yes 50p **Editor/Press Officer:** Andrew Meredith
Colours: Yellow/blue/blue **Change colours:** White/red/red
Sponsors: Oldershaws Transport **Nickname:** **Founded:** 1980
Midweek matchdays: Wednesday
Record Attendance: 409 v Heanor Town, Central Midlands League Cup Second Rd 1/1/94.
Previous Leagues: Alfreton & District Sunday 80-87/ Mansfield Sunday 87-90.
Clubhouse: Open matchdays 11am-11pm and Wednesdays 6.30-11pm. Matchday refreshments from tea bar include pie & peas, soups etc, (01773 581491)
Club Record Goalscorer: Peter Green 31 **Club Record Appearances:** Dave Vallance 132 (Sat only), Mick Kane 286 (overall)
Honours: Central Mids Lg Prem Div R-up 93-94, Alfreton & Dist. Sunday Lg 86-87 (Div 2 83-84, Div 3 R-up 80-81, Suppl. Shield 84-85, W L Screen Bowl 86-87), Mansfield Sunday Lg Prem. Div Cup 88-89 (Div 1 R-up 87-88).

STAVELEY MINERS WELFARE

Chairman: Henry Ireson **Vice-Chairman:** Phil White.
Secretary: John Wilmot, 12 Winster Rd, Staveley, Chesterfield, Derbyshire S43 3HZ (01246 476875).
Manager: David Tromans **Asst Manager:** David Pugh **Physio:** Dominic Gage/Neil Gilliver
Ground: Inkersall Road, Staveley, Chesterfield, Derbyshire (01246 471441).
Directions: M1 jct 30, follow A619 Chesterfield - Staveley is 3 miles from jct 30. Turn left at GK Garage in Staveley town centre into Inkersall Rd - ground 200yds on right at side of Speedwell Rooms. Frequent buses (47, 70, 72, 75, 77) from Chesterfield stop in Staveley town centre - 3 mins walk to ground.
Capacity: 5,000 **Cover:** 200 **Seats:** 200 **Floodlights:** Yes **Founded:** 1989
Cols: Blue & black halves/black/black **Change cols:** Yellow/blue/yellow **N'name:** The Welfare
Midweek home matches: Wednesday. **Prev. Lgs:** Chesterfield & D. Amtr 89-91/ County Snr 91-93.
Programme: 16 pages, 30p **Editor:** Tony Barnes (01246 474448).
Sponsors: Autoworld Garage **Record Gate:** 280 v Stocksbridge, Sheffield Snr Cup 22/1/94.
Reserve Team's League: Central Midlands Lge Reserve Div.
Club Shop: Yes. Sells numerous programmes. Contact Craig Cousins (01246 475068).
Clubhouse: The Staveley Miners Welfare, 500yds from ground, is open before and after games.
Club record scorer: Paul Nicholls **Club record appearances:** Shane Turner.
95-96 Captain: **95-96 Top Scorer:** **95-96 P.o.Y.:**
Hons: County Snr Lg Div 2 92-93 (Div 3 91-92), Chesterfield & D. Amtr Lg R-up 89-90 90-91 (Byron (Lge) Cup 89-90 (R-up 90-91)).

THORNE COLLIERY

Secretary: Glyn Jones, Democratic Club & Institute, Southfield Rd, Thorne, Doncaster DN8 5NS (0405 816329).
Ground: Miners Welfare Ground, Southfield Rd, Thorne, Doncaster.(01374 996474)
Colours: Green & White/Green/Green. **Change Colours:** Blue & White/Blue/Blue.
Prev. Lge: Doncaster Snr (pre-1993) **Floodlights:** No.
Programme Editor: Secretary **Midweek home matchday:** Wednesday

PREMIER DIVISION CLUBS 1994-95

ASKERN MINERS WELFARE

Secretary: Miss Lynn Sudworth, Holly Croft, Main St., Stillington, York YO6 1JU (01347 810038)
Ground: Askern Welfare, Doncaster Road, Askern, Doncaster (01302 700957).
Directions: A1/A639 Pontefract. Follow sign for Askern/Campsall. At T-junction right. Left at Anne Arms, right at Supersave, ground on right.
Floodlights: No **Colours:** White (black trim)/black/black
Programme: 20 pages, 50p **Editor:** Ron Poundall.

BLACKWELL MINERS WELFARE

Secretary: Julian Riley, 22 Glinton Ave., Blackwell, Alfreton, Derbys DE55 5HD (01773 862411).
Manager: Michael Hopkinson **Asst Mgr/Coach:** Phil Burnham **Physio:** Eric Eyley.
Ground & Directions: Welfare Ground, Primrose Hill, Blackwell, Derbyshire DE55 5JE. (01773 811295). A38 towards Mansfield from M1 jct 38, left onto B6406 after half a mile, left after a mile, ground on left.
Cols: Red & white stripes/red/red **Change colours:** All silver grey. **Club Shop:** No.
Programme: 28 pages, 50p **Editor:** Secretary
Honours: Central Mids Lg Senior Div 84-85 (Central Div R-up 85-86, Senior Div Cup 84-85, Div 1 Cup 87-88), Derbyshire Jnr Cup 77-78 82-83 83-84 (R-up 76-77), Derbyshire Divisional Cup 85-86.

CLIPSTONE WELFARE

Secretary: Barry Clarke, 40 Church Road, Clipstone, Mansfield, NG21 9DG (01623 640829).
Manager: Carl Hanson.
Ground & Directions: Clipstone Lido Ground (01632 655674). B6030 from Mansfield, on left entering Clipstone.
Colours: Blue & White stripes/black/red. **Previous League:** Notts Alliance (pre-1994).
Hons: Notts Snr Cup 85-86 94-95, Notts Alliance 72-73 73-74 74-75 92-93 94-95 (Lg Cup 72-73 73-74 74-75 94-95 (R-up 92-93)), Notts I'mediate Cup 55-56.

COLLINGHAM

Secretary: Mr G Williams, 47 Dukes End, Collingham, Newark, Nottinghamshire NG23 7LD (01636 892189 H, 01636 893175 B)
Manager: Paul Hyde (01777 228156) **Ground:** Collingham FC, Station Road, Collingham, Newark, Notts.
Directions: Take A46 Newark to Lincoln road (Newark bypass). Turn left into Collingham on the A1133 road. In village turn right at traffic lights. Ground 100 yards on left.
Colours: Amber & black/black/black **Change Colours:** Blue & white/blue/blue

DERBY ROLLS ROYCE

Secretary: Mr A Burns, 67 Field Rise Littleover, Derby DE23 7DF (01332 767332)
Manager: Trevor Hammond **Ground:** Rolls Royce Rec. Society, Moor Lane, Derby (01332 249167).
Directions: Derby ringroad, Osmaston Park Road, Moor Lane; ground adjacent to Swimming Baths.
Cols: Blue/white/blue **Change:** Black & white stripes/black/black
Programme: 8-12 pages, 50p **Editor:** Paul McCracken.
Hons: Central Mids Lg Ken Marsland Cup(Res.) R-up 94-95.

GRIMETHORPE MINERS WELFARE

Secretary: Arthur Gill, 7 Duke Street, Grimethorpe, Barnsley, Yorks S72 7NJ (01226 712863)
Ground: Grimethorpe Miners Welfare, Cemetery Road, Grimethorpe.
Directions: A1M to A635 Hickleton to Thurnscoe, turn right to Houghton, At Robin Hood, turn left to Grimethorpe M1 junc 36. A628 to Shafton traffic lights, turn right to Grimethorpe.
Colours: All blue **Change Colours:** All red

HEMSWORTH TOWN

Secretary: Mike Pickering, 1 Sycamore Road, Hemsworth, Nr Pontefract, West Yorks WF9 4PD (01977 613974)
Manager: Sammy Waugh (01977 615722)
Ground: Hemsworth Town FC, Sports Complex, Kirby Road, Hemsworth
Directions: M1 to M18 to A1M.North to A638 Wakefield Road, 3miles turn off left.Signposted Langwaite Grange Ind Est (Netto). 2 miles on join B6422 Hemsworth. 2 miles further on in Hemsworth, ground 400 yards on left after Fina garage
Colours: All nvay blue **Change Colours:** White/navy/navy

HOLBROOK

Secretary: Peter Begent, 22 Grasmere Close, Stapenhill, Burton on Trent, Staffs DE15 9DS (01283 540583)
Ground: The Welfare Ground, Shaw Lane, Holbrook, Derbyshire
Directions: From A38 take B6179 for Kilburn, turn left at lights for Belper. 1 mile on left at Bulls Head for Holbrook. 2 miles on turn right at Venture garage into Shaws Lane.
Colours: Blue & White/blue/blue & white **Change Colours:** Yellow/black/black

KILLAMARSH JUNIORS

Secretary: Philip Bright, 17 Marrison Drive, Killamarsh, Sheffield S31 8HF (0114 2482763)
Manager: Steven Fleetwood (01909 773607)
Ground: Killamarsh Juniors Athletic Club & Institute, 284 Sheffield Road, Killamarsh. Sheffield 31 (0114 2484390)
Directions: M1 junc 31. Take A57 towards Sheffield follow signs for Rother Valley Park to Killamarsh.
Colours: All white **Change Colours:** All green

MEXBOROUGH ATHLETIC (OAKHOUSE)

Secretary: Nev Wheeler, 15 Holmshore Drive, Sheffield, South Yorkshire S13 8UJ (01142 694142).
Ground: Mexborough Athletic Club, Hampden Rd, Mexborough (01709 586479).
Directions: Just off A6023 Conisborough-Mexborough road opposite Police Station. Half mile from Mexborough BR station.
Colours: Red and Navy/black/black.

MICKLEOVER ROYAL BRITISH LEGION

Secretary: Ray Taylor, 15 Inglwood Avenue, Mickleover, Derby DE3 5RT (01332 515047).
Manager: Ray Barker **Assistant Manager:** Dave Mann.
Ground: Mickleover RBL, Ypres Lodge, Western Road, Mickleover (01332 513548).
Colours: All royal blue **Midweek home matchday:** Tuesday **Founded:** 1945 **Nickname:** Legionnaires.
Programme: 36 pages, 30p **Editor:** Michael Mouse Snr.
Hons: Centrals Mids Lg Premier Div 89-90 90-91 (R-up 88-89, Lg Cup 88-89 89-90, Reserve Lg Cup 82-83 (R-up 88-89 92-93), Res Div 1 Cup R-up 88-89), East Mids Lg 80-81, Derbys Divisional Cup South 80-81.

RADFORD

Secretary: Malcolm Goodwin (0115 978 1587) **Manager:** Terry Lack
Ground: Radford Road, Radford, Nottm (0602 423250).
Directions: A610 Alfreton Road, left just into Bobbersmill Road, ground at top on right.
Cols: Claret & blue/blue/blue **Change:** White/black/black **Floodlights:** No
Programme: 16 pages, 30p (Editor: Secretary). **Hons:** Derbys Prem. Lg Div 1 R-up 84-85.

ROSSINGTON

Sec./Press Off.: Ian Wilson, The Wickets, 3 Hollin Close, Rossington, Doncaster DN11 0XX (01302 867221).
Manager: Gary Mountford. **Physio:** G Murden. **Commercial Mgr:** G Shaw.
Ground: Welfare Ground, West End Lane, Rossington, Doncaster (01302 868272).
Directions: From: M18 jct 1, A631 to Bawtry via Maltby/Tickhill, 1 mile out of Tickhill take B6463 to Rossington. In Rossington take road to colliery, over level crossing, ground on right after Sports Centre. 6 miles from Doncaster (BR)
Colours: White/navy/white. **Change colours:** Blue+Black/black/blue. **Club Shop:** No.
Programme: 40+ pages, £1 with entry **Editor:** Secretary
Hons: Central Mids Lg Div 1 87-88 (Prem Div R-up 92-93, Div 1 Cup R-up 86-87 87-88, Res. Div 1 Cup 87-88, Res Div 1 R-up 94-95, Res. Div 2 Champs Cup R-up 86-87), Doncaster Snr Lg Div 2 R-up 85-86 (Div 1 Cup R-up 85-86), Sheffield & Hallamshire Jnr Shield 83-84, Bentley Lg 77-78 78-79 (Lg Shield 74-75 78-79).

SHARDLOW St JAMES

Secretary: S R Symcox, 22 West End Drive, Shardlow, Derby DE7 2GY (01332 792733).
Manager: M Spooner **Asst Manager:** Ray Foulds **Physio:** Richard Foulds
Ground: The Wharf, Shardlow, Derby.
Directions: A6 Derby/Leicester, 6 miles out of Derby at Shardlow take next left after Shardlow church (on right), ground 100yds on left.
Colours: Sky/navy/sk **Club Sponsor:** Mr D Irving. **Nickname:** Saints

SHEFFIELD HALLAM UNIVERSITY

Secretary: Stephen Wright, 198 Home Lane, Mainsbridge, Sheffield S6 (0378 481483)
Ground: Aurora Sports & Social Club, Bawtry Rd, Brinsworth, Rotherham
Directions: M1 junc 34, take A631 Bawtry Rd, ground 1 mile on right.
Colours: Red/white/blue **Change Colours:** Blue/blue/white

SHEEPBRIDGE

Secretary: A Staniforth, 11 Grasmere Close, Newbold Chesterfield, Derbyshire S41 8EG (01246 205541)
Manager: David Barnes (01246 277465)
Ground: GKN Sports Ground, Newbold Road, Chesterfield, (01246 234282)
Directions: When reaching Chesterfield use bypass and on reaching island with Tesco store follow signs for Newbold. Ground on the Newbold Road.
Colours: All blue **Midweek home matchday:** Wednesday

SNEINTON

Secretary: Paul Shelton, 28 Freda Gloss, Gedling, Nottingham NG4 4GP (0115 9877527)
Manager: Gary Saxby (01623 810643)
Ground: Stoke Lane Gedling, Nottingham
Directions: A612 Nottingham to Southwell Road. Stoke Lane is situated off A612 between Gedling & Burton Joyce (signed Stoke Bardolph). Ground 200 yards on left over level crossing
Colours: Blue & black/black/white **Midweek Night:** Tuesday

STANTON (ILKESTON)

Secretary: Steven Hurst, 32 Bennett Str., Long Eaton, Nottingham NG10 4RA (0602 730229).
Manager: Martin Cooper.
Ground & Directions: Hallam Fields Sports Ground, Stanton Club, Hallam Fields, Nr Ilkeston, Derbys (0602 323244). From South, M1 (J25) to Nottm, 1st r-about turn left. From North, M1 (J26), Ilkeston, through to to Hallam Fields.
Cols: Blue & white stripes/blue/blue **Change Colours:** Yellow/black/blue
Programme: 28 pages, 50p **Editor:** Graham Barksby.
Hons: Central Mids Lg Prem. Div 85-86 86-87 (Prem. Div Cup 85-86).

NOTTS FOOTBALL ALLIANCE

ESTABLISHED: 1894
President: R J Leafe
Chairman: A Wright. **Vice Chairman:** Bryn Richards
Secretary: Godfrey Stafford,
7 The Rushes, Gotham, Nottingham NG11 0HY (0115 9830576)

FINAL LEAGUE TABLE 1995/96

Senior Division	P	W	D	L	F	A	Pts
1. Rainworth M W	30	19	8	3	83	40	65
2. Boots Athletic	30	20	4	6	75	41	64
3. Pelican FC	30	19	5	6	74	39	62
4. Hucknall Rolls Royce	30	17	4	9	63	37	55
5. Greenwood Meadows	30	16	3	11	46	51	51
6. John Player	30	14	5	11	54	42	47
7. Notts Police	30	13	5	12	59	47	44
8. Keyworth United	30	11	10	9	46	46	43
9. Cotgrave C W	30	11	4	15	46	56	37
10. Ruddington United	30	10	5	15	59	79	35
11. Thoresby C W	30	9	7	14	39	46	34
12. Welbeck C W	30	10	3	17	42	58	33
13. Southwell City	30	10	3	17	39	58	33
14. Wollaton	30	8	6	16	40	65	30
15. Basford United	30	8	3	19	41	60	27
16. G P T	30	6	3	21	43	84	21

NOTTS ALLIANCE SENIOR DIVISION 1996-97

AWSWORTH VILLA

Secretary: Keith Slaney, 24 Attewell Road, Awsworth, Nottm NG16 2SY (0602 302514).
Ground: Attewell Road, Awsworth. **Colours:** Red & white & black/black

BOOTS ATHLETIC

Secretary: Ian Whitehead, 21 Rosthwaite Close, West Bridgford, Nottingham NG2 6RA (01159 812830).
Ground: Lady Bay, West Bridgford, Nottingham (01159 822392). **Colours:** White/black.
Hons: Notts Alliance Div 1 91-92 (Lg Cup 91-92), Notts Snr Cup R-up 93-94, Notts Inter R-up 91-92.

COTGRAVE COLLIERY WELFARE

Secretary: Kevin Whitehead, 51 Cross Hill, Cotgrave, Nottinham. (0115 9894043)
Ground: Cotgrave Miners Welfare. **Colours:** Yellow/black.

GREENWOOD MEADOWS

Secretary: Brian Hall, 35 Sullivan Close, Marmion Estate, Nottingham NG3 2HX (0115 958 2459)
Ground: Lenton Lane, Clifton Bridge, Nottm (01159 630134). **Colours:** Green & White/green/green

HUCKNALL ROLLS ROYCE WELFARE

Secretary: Adrian Ward, 7 Redwood Court, Hucknall, Nottm (01159 538491).
Ground: Sports and Social Club, Entrance Watnall Road (01159 635724).
Colours: All Blue. **Hons:** Notts I'mediate Cup 92-93

JOHN PLAYER

Secretary: Ron Walton, 27 St Margarets Ave., Aspley Lane, Nottm NG8 5GD (01159 292027).
Ground: Aspley Lane, Nottm (01159 292027)
Colours: Yellow & navy/navy
Hons: Notts Alliance 21-22 22-23 23-24 24-25 25-26 26-27 67-68 68-69 69-70 85-86 89-90 (Div 1 93-94).

KEYWORTH UNITED

Secretary: M Simpson, 25 Waddington Drive, Wilford Hill, West Bridgford, Nottm NG2 7GT (0602 232921).
Ground: Platt Lane, Keyworth (0607 375998). **Colours:** Green/black

NOTTINGHAMSHIRE POLICE

Secretary: John Beeston, 17 Alandene Ave, Watnall, Nottingham NG16 1HH (0115 938 2110)
Ground: Force Training School, Epperstone Manor, Notts.
Colours: White/navy.
Hons: Notts Snr R-up 91-92, Notts All. Div 1 & Lge Snr Cup R-up 85-86, PAAN Nat. K-O Comp 63-64.

OLLERTON TOWN

Secretary: Jack Graham 73 Petersmith Drive, New Ollerton, Mansfield, Notts NG22 9SD (01623 863127)
Ground: Walesby Lane, New Ollerton, Notts
Colours: Red & black/black

PELICAN

Secretary: Dave Eastwood, 42 Chetwin Road, Bilborough, Nottm NG8 4HN (01159 138345).
Ground: John Pearson Spts Ground, Lenton Lane, Nottm (01159 868255)
Colours: All Blue. **Hons:** Notts Alliance Lg Cup 90-91 (R-up 91-92 93-94).

RAINWORTH MINERS WELFARE

Secretary: Alan Wright, 10 Faraday Road, Mansfield NG18 4ES (01632 24379).
Ground: Kirklington Road, Rainworth.
Directions: On A617 Mansfield - Newark Road. **Colours:** All White
Hons: Notts Alliance 77-78 78-79 79-80 80-81 81-82 82-83 (R-up 93-94, Lg Cup 81-82), Notts Snr Cup 80-81 81-82 (R-up 82-83 92-93), FA Vase R-up 82-82, Thorn EMI F'lit Cup R-up 82-83 83-84 84-85.

RUDDINGTON UNITED

Secretary: John Fisk, 3 Savages Road, Ruddington, Nottm NG11 6EW (01159 842552).
Ground & Directions: The Elms Park Ground, Loughborough Road, Ruddington (01159 844976. On A60 Nottm to Loughborough, 5 miles out of Nottingham.
Colours: Red & blue stripes/blue. **Honours:** Notts Comb. Lg 79-80 (Lg Cup 70-71 76-77 80-81).

SOUTHWELL CITY

Secretary: P K Johnson, 63 The Ropewalk, Southwell, Notts NG25 0AL (0636 814386).
Ground: War Memorial Ground, Southwell (0636 4386) **Colours:** Black & white stripes/black

THORESBY COLLIERY WELFARE

Secretary: Brian Wathall, 29 First Ave., Edwinstowe, Nr Mansfield NG21 9NZ (01636 812594).
Ground: Thoresby Colliery, Fourth Avenue, Edwinstowe, Nr Mansfield. **Colours:** Blue/white.

WELBECK COLLIERY

Secretary: Mr Ron Turner, 75 Hamilton Drive, Warsop, Mansfield, Notts NG20 0EY (01623 847738).
Ground: Welbeck Colliery Pit (0623 842611). **Colours:** Black & yellow/black.
Hons: Notts Alliance Div 2 93-94 (Intermediate Cup 93-94), Chesterfield & District Lg 92-93.

WOLLATON

Secretary: Andrew Moon, 150 Wollaton Vale, Wollaton, Nottm NG8 2PL (01159 281215).
Ground: Wollaton Sports Club, Wollaton Village, Nottm (01159 289748).
Colours: Sky/maroon **Hons:** Notts All. Div 1 R-up 92-93 (Div 2 91-92 (I'mediate Cup R-up 91-92)).

FINAL LEAGUE TABLES 1995/96

Div One	P	W	D	L	F	A	Pts
1. Ollerton Town	30	19	7	4	66	28	64
2. Awsworth Villa	30	16	7	7	71	52	55
3. City & Sherwood	30	15	4	11	51	44	49
4. Abacus	30	14	6	10	46	43	48
5. Retford United	30	12	10	8	43	40	46
6. Linby CW	30	11	10	9	49	50	43
7. Boots Ath Res	30	10	11	9	65	63	41
8. Teversal Grange	30	10	11	9	56	54	41
9. Rainsworth MWR	30	11	7	12	72	63	40
10. Bilsthorpe CW	30	11	6	13	58	68	39
11. Bestwood MW	30	11	5	14	53	58	38
12. Gedling MW	30	8	11	11	46	48	35
13. W'ton Simpsons	30	9	8	13	63	70	35
14. Clifton	30	9	4	17	51	72	31
15. Pelican Res	30	7	8	15	54	65	29
16. Radcliffe Oly	30	4	11	15	39	65	23

Div Two	P	W	D	L	F	A	Pts
1. Beeston Town	30	23	4	3	92	41	73
2. Attenborough	30	22	4	4	82	42	70
3. Carlton DC	30	21	4	5	105	33	67
4. Wollaton Res	30	19	4	7	69	50	61
5. Kimberley MW	30	15	6	9	68	55	51
6. Southwell C R	30	15	3	12	77	54	48
7. Ruddington UR	30	14	4	12	61	69	46
8. John Player R	30	12	7	11	61	54	43
9. East Lake Ath	30	11	6	13	47	56	39
10. Calverton Tn	30	11	4	15	63	61	37
11. Grnw'd Meadows	30	10	5	15	53	64	35
12. Basford Utd	30	8	3	19	56	75	27
13. W'ton Simpsons	30	8	2	20	48	99	26
14. Thoresby CWR	30	7	4	19	53	97	25
15. Hucknall RR R	30	6	4	20	48	77	22
16. GPT Res	30	4	4	22	39	95	16

NOTTS ALLIANCE DIVISION ONE CLUBS 1996-97

ABACUS

Secretary: Mr Stephen Bingley, 6 Brisbane Close, Mansfield Woodhouse NG19 8QZ (0623 23072).
Ground: Sherwood Colliery Sports Ground, Debdale Lane, Mansfield Woodhouse, Notts.
Colours: Black & white stripes.

ATTENBOROUGH

Secretary: Terry Allen, 3 Firth Close, Arnold, Nottingham NG5 8RU (0602 200698).
Ground & Directions: The Village Green, The Strand, Attenborough, Beeston, Nottingham. Midway between Beeston & Long Eaton on A6005 - adjacent to Nature Reserve (via Attenborough Lane).
Colours: All blue **Change cols:** White/black/black.

BASFORD UNITED

Secretary: Paul Dobson, 26 Chevin Gardens, Top Valley, Nottm NG5 9ES (01159 274790
Ground: Greenwich Ave, Sports Ground, Bagnall Road, Basford, Nottm (01159 423918).
Directions: M1 (J26) follow signs 'A610 Nottingham' then 'B6004 Arnold' into Mill Street.
Colours: Yellow/black **Hons:** Notts Snr Cup 46-47 87-88, Notts Alliance Div 1 R-up 71-72 84-85 93-94.

BEESTON TOWN

Secretary: Andy Meakin, 26 Redland Drive, Chilwell, Nottingham NG9 5LE (0115 967 7520
Ground: University Ground, Nottingham **Colours:** Red & black/black

BESTWOOD MINERS WELFARE

Secretary: Mrs Alana Jackson, 9 Derwent Drive, Hucknall, Nottm NG15 6DS (0602 630189).
Ground: Bestwood Workshops, Park Rd, Bestwood (0602 273711) **Colours:** White/blue.

BILSTHORPE COLLIERY WELFARE

Secretary: Mr Les Lee, 42 Chapel Lane, Ravenshead, Mansfield NG15 9DA (0623 794442).
Ground: Bilsthorpe CW Ground, Eakring Road, Bilsthorpe. **Colours:** White/navy/navy.

CITY & SHERWOOD HOSPITALS

Secretary: Mr Alan Bird, 72 Bilborough Rd, Nottm NG8 4DW (0602 285507).
Ground: COD Military Ground, Chilwell (0602 254811). **Colours:** All Royal blue

CLIFTON

Secretary: Keith Elliott, 61 Greencroft, Clifton Est., Nottm NG11 8GT (0602 215401).
Ground: Green Lane, Clifton Est., Nottm (0602 844903). **Colours:** All white

GEDLING COLLIERY WELFARE

Secretary: Mrs Maureen Chambers, 8 Fraser Road, Carlton, Nottm NG4 1NJ (0602 612994).
Ground: Gedling Colliery Welfare, Plains Road, Mapperley (0602 266300) **Colours:** Yellow/blue

G.P.T.

Secretary: Roger Marshall, Sports Office, GPT, Beeston, Nottm NG9 1LA (01159 433669)
Ground: Trent Vale Rd, Beeston, Nottm (01159 258695). **Colours:** Black & Blue stripes/Black.
Hons: Notts Alliance 66-67 91-92 (R-up 92-93, Lg Cup 92-93).

LINBY COLLIERY MINERS WELFARE

Secretary: D G Dickens, 4 Old Mill Close, Bestwood, Nottingham, NG6 8TA (0602 276598).
Ground: Church Lane, Linby **Colours:** Red/White

RETFORD UNITED

Secretary: Jeff Lamb, 18 Northumbria Drive, Retford, Notts, DN22 7PR (0602 705833).
Ground: Oaklands Lane (Off London Road), Retford. **Colours:** Black & white stripes/black

TEVERSAL GRANGE

Secretary: Kevin Newton, 8 Vere Ave., Sutton in Ashfield, Notts NG17 2ES (0623 511402).
Ground: Carnarvon Street, Sutton in Ashfield. **Colours:** Red & black hoops/red/red.

WORTHINGTON SIMPSONS

Secretary: Alan Toule, 54 Elterwater Drive, Gamston, Nottingham NG2 6PX (0602 810258).
Ground: Lowfields, off Hawton Lane, New Baldeton, Newark, Notts (0636 702672).
Colours: Maroon/sky **Hons:** Notts Alliance Lg Cup (Intermediate Cup(res) 92-93 (R-up 93-94)).

This Division also includes the Reserve sides of: Boots Athletic, Rainworth MW.

NOTTS ALLIANCE DIVISION TWO 1996-97

CALVERTON TOWN

Secretary: Derek Voce, 20 Ashdale Road, Arnold, Nottingham NG5 8BH (0115 926 0120)
Ground: William Lee Memorial Park, Park Road East, Calverton, Nottingham **Colours:** White/black

CARLTON DC

Secretary: Robert Huckerby, 30 Vernon Ave, Carlton, Nottingham NG4 3FX (0115 955 9120)
Ground: Carlton Hill Recreation Ground, Carlton, Nottingham **Colours:** Black & blue/black

EAST LEAKE ATHLETIC

Secretary: Andrew Fletcher, 35 Manor Farm Meadow, East Leake, Loughborough, Leics, LE12 6LL (01509 852087)
Ground: Costock Road, East Leake, Loughborough, Leics **Colours:** Maroon & blue/maroon

KIMBERLEY MINERS WELFARE

Secretary: Graham Rowley, 47 Noel Street, Kimberley, Nottingham NG16 2NF (0115 938 9151)
Ground: Didby Street, Kimberley, Nottingham **Colours:** Black & red/black

MAGDALA AMATEURS

Secretary: Alan Gilmour, 9 Adbolton Grove, West Bridgford, Nottingham NG2 5AR (0115 982 1071)
Ground: Civil Service Sports Ground, Wilford Lane, W Bridgford. **Colours:** Maroon & Sky/sky/sky

RADCLIFFE OLYMPIC

Secretary: C Johnson, 2 The Firs, Holme Pierrepoint, Nottingham NG12 2LT (0115 933 3791)
Ground: Wharf Lane, Radcliffe-on-Trent, Nottingham **Colours:** Blue/red

This League also contains the reserve sides of:

Basford United: Greenwood Meadows: Hucknall Rolls Royce: John Player FC: Pelican FC: Ruddington United: Southwell City: Thoresby Welfare: Wollaton FC: Worthington Simpsons:

EVERARDS BREWERY LEICESTERSHIRE SENIOR LEAGUE

FOUNDED: 1896

President: J M Elsom **Chairman:** P Henwood

Hon. Secretary: David Jamieson, 48 King George Road, Loughborough, Leics LE11 2PA (01509 267912)

St Andrews capped another fine season bt kaking the Premier League title for the second time in three seasons, by a clear 4 pints. For the first six weeks Ibstock Welfare occupied the top spot, losing only one game in the first six and that was to St Andrews. From this point on, the Saints took over the top position, but were closely followed by Oadby Town and this is how it remained for the rest of the season. To Oadby's credit they were close on the heels of St Andrews, but they dropped vital points inthe final weeks of the season, drawing with Anstey Nomads and losing to Friar Lane OB. However they had the consolation of being the Premier Division top scorers with 122 goals.

St Andrews also finished runners-up in the Westerby Challenge Cup Final, losing to a very strong Leicester City side by 2 goals in a very close game, but had the consolation of beating Friar Lane OB in the final of the Everards Beacon Bitter Senior League Cup Final.

Birstall United were a little disappointing finishing in third place, but never seriously challenged the top two. But nevertheless they did have some consolation in beating Oadby Town in the leicestershire Senior Cup Final by 1-0 in extra time, this being their first Senior Cup Final win, having been runners-up twice before. Friar Lane OB who finished fourth didn't start off too well, winning only one of their first five games, but from the beginning of November until the end of the season they were never out of the top four. Newly promoted Kirby Muxloe fully justified this, finishing in fifth place and could be well satisfied with their season.

At the other end of the table North Kilworth finished at the bottom, a position they held from the end of January, taking only one point from their last 17 games. Aylestone Park OB who were newly promoted finished in the other relegation spot but not without a very hard fight. Only two points separated three clubs, Thringstone finshed one point better than Aylestone and Newfoundpool two points better. Both Highfield Rangers and Downes Sports were also sweating up to the last couple of weeks.

In division one Quorn walked away with the honours, going through the season unbeaten in the League and winning 33 of their 36 League games. A truly wonderful performance. A great tribute not only to the players, but also to Stuart Turner and the backroom boys, who have worked so hard over the past years providing a first class stadium and a first class team to go with it. They will be a great asset to the Premier Division especially having scored the most goals, 134 and conceded the least, 17, in the two divisions.Division One also suffered a great disappointment by the resignation of Hillcroft FC. They played their last game on March 2nd and all their results were deleted.

Anstey Nomads FC: *Photo - Martin Wray*

Narborough and Littlethorpe finished in the runners-up spot being hotly pursued at times by Leicestershire Constabulary and Coalville Town. Fosse Imps had a very satisfactory season finishing fifth, six places higher than last season. Stoney Stanton, newcomers to the League, can feel well satisfied with their first season gaining 43 points from 36 games and steering well clear of trouble. Houghton who finished in the bottom place had a terrible run from December 2nd, having gained only 10 points in their last 26 games, 3 of which were deducted. Earl Shilton Albion and Harborough both struggled thoughout the season, but Syston St Peters who applied for re-election last season did much better and finished comfortably mid-table.

FINAL LEAGUE TABLES 1995/96

Premier Div	*P*	*W*	*D*	*L*	*F*	*A*	*Pts*
1. St Andrews	34	28	3	3	95	28	87
2. Oadby Town	34	27	2	5	122	40	83
3. Birstall Utd	34	21	7	6	60	37	70
4. Friar Lane OB	34	20	5	9	68	37	65
5. Kirby Muxloe	34	16	8	10	55	48	56
6. Ibstock Wel	34	17	3	14	58	60	54
7. Burbage OB	34	15	7	12	62	64	52
8. Barrow Tn	34	15	6	13	80	77	51
9. Anstey Nomads	34	14	7	13	88	71	49
10. Holwell Spts	34	14	5	15	74	59	47
11. Cottesmore Am	34	12	4	18	62	84	40
12. Asfordby Am	34	11	6	17	44	61	39
13. Highfield Rang	34	9	8	17	47	64	35
14. Downes Spts	34	10	4	20	54	79	34
15. Newfoundpool	34	9	5	20	45	75	32
16. Thringstone MW	34	8	7	19	40	69	31
17. Aylestone Pk	34	8	6	20	48	76	30
18. N Kilworth	34	3	5	26	38	111	14

Div One	*P*	*W*	*D*	*L*	*F*	*A*	*Pts*
1. Quorn	36	33	3	0	134	17	102
2. Narborough	36	23	4	9	93	53	73
3. Leics Const	36	21	7	8	83	50	70
4. Coalville	36	21	4	11	91	56	67
5. Fosse Imps	36	18	9	9	75	58	63
6. Sileby Town	36	16	7	13	74	60	55
7. Saffron Dynamo	36	16	4	16	67	68	52
8. Anstey Town	36	13	10	13	48	49	49
9. Lough Dynamo	36	13	8	15	78	74	47
10. Blaby Whetsone	36	12	9	15	43	59	45
11. Syston St P	36	12	8	16	57	73	44
12. Utd Collieries	36	14	2	20	71	90	44
13. Stoney Stanton	36	12	7	17	63	57	43
14. Huncote S&S	36	13	4	19	56	70	43
15. Lutterworth Tn	36	12	6	18	45	77	42
16. Bardon Hill	36	9	12	15	46	72	39
17. E Shilton Alb	36	8	8	20	66	97	32
18. Harborough Tn	36	8	5	23	50	93	29
19. Houghton Rang	36	7	5	24	37	104	*23

* *3pts deducted; Hillcroft expunged*

Ibstock Welfare's Randal Carpenter clears the danger despite the intentions of two Highfield Rangers players.
Photo - Ray Pruden

CLUB DIRECTORY 1996-97

ANSTEY NOMADS **Colours:** Red & white stripes/white/red
Secretary: Andy Coleman, 14 Church Lane, Anstey, Leicester LE7 7AF (01533 363191).
Ground: Cropston Road, Anstey, Leicester (01533 364868).

ANSTEY TOWN **Colours:** All blue
Secretary: G Ford, 99 Hollow Rd, Anstey, Leics LE7 7FR (0533 364170).
Ground: Leicester Road, Thurcaston (0533 368231)

ASFORDBY AMATEURS **Colours:** Green/black/black
Secretary: Richard Smith, 17 Cheviot Drive, Shepshed, Leics LE12 9ED (01509 502857).
Ground: Hoby Road Sports Ground, Asfordby, Melton Mowbray (01664 434545).

AYLESTONE PARK OLD BOYS **Colours:** Red & white/white/red
Secretary: Brendon Tyrrell, 8 Melbourne Close, Kibworth, Beauchamp, Leicester LE8 0JP (0533 793136).
Ground: Dorset Avenue, Fairfield Estate, Wigston, Leics (0533 775307)

BARDON HILL **Colours:** Yellow & green/green/yellow
Secretary: Adrian Bishop, 138 Bradgate Drive, Coalville, Leics LE67 4HG (0530 815560).
Ground: Bardon Close, Coalville, Leicester (0530 815560).

BARROW TOWN **Colours:** Red & black/black/red
Secretary: Nick J Freeman, 1 Beacon Drive, Loughborough, Leics LE11 2BD (01509 212853).
Ground: Riverside Park, Barrow Road, Quorn, Leics (01509 620650).

BIRSTALL UNITED **Colours:** White/navy/white
Secretary: Bob Garrard, 58 Halstead Rd, Mountsorrel, Leicester LE12 7HF (0533 376886).
Ground: Meadow Lane, Birstall (671230)

BLABY & WHETSTONE ATHLETIC **Colours:** All blue
Secretary: Mrs S C Morris, 10 Winchester Road, Blaby, Leics LE8 3HJ (0533 773208).
Ground: Blaby & Whetstone Boys Club, Warwick Road, Whetstone (0533 864852).

BURBAGE OLD BOYS **Colours:** Blue/white/royal
Secretary: Mrs S Taylor, 8 Brockhurst Avenue, Burbage, Leics LE10 2HG (0455 633916).
Ground: Britannia Rd, Burbage, Leics (0455 890413).

COALVILLE **Colours:** White & black/black/black.
Secretary: Robert Brooks, 17 Ashland Drive, Coalville, Leics LE67 3NH (01530 833269).
Ground: Ravenslea Estate, Ravenstone, Leics.

COTTESMORE AMATEURS **Colours:** Green/black/green.
Secretary: K Nimmons, 17 Redwing Close, Oakham, Rutland LE15 6DA (0572 724582).
Ground: Rogues Park, Main Street, Cottesmore, Rutland (0572 813486).

DOWNES SPORTS **Colours:** Tangerine/black/tangerine
Secretary: Stuart Millidge, 25 Elizabeth Rd, Hinckley, Leics LE10 0QY (0455 635808).
Ground: Leicester Rd, Hinckley *(adjacent Hinckley Town FC)*

EARL SHILTON ALBION **Colours:** Green & white/green/white
Secretary: Adrian Knight, 19 Waverly Rd, Blaby, Leics LE8 3HH (0533 785042).
Ground: Stoneycroft Park, New Street, Earl Shilton, Leics (0455 844277).

FOSSE IMPS **Colours:** Red/white/black
Secretary: Ivan V Colbourne, 55 Harrowgate Drive, Birstall, Leics LE4 3GQ (0533 671424).
Ground: Co-op Ground, Birstall Rd, Leicester (0533 674059)

FRIAR LANE OLD BOYS **Colours:** Black & white stripes/black/black
Secretary: J Knibbs, 75 Brighton Avenue, Wigston Fields, Leicester LE18 1JB (0533 888928).
Ground: Knighton Lane East, Leicester (0533 833629).

HARBOROUGH TOWN IMPERIAL **Colours:** Red & black stripes/black/black
Secretary: Gary Waterfield, 4 Lindsey Gdns, Market Harborough, Leics LE16 9JF (0858 431620).
Ground: Imperial Park, Northampton Road Sports Ground, Market Harborough, Leics.

HIGHFIELD RANGERS **Colours:** Yellow/black/yellow
Secretary: Maurice Christian, 18 Blanklyn Avenue, Leicester LE5 5FA (0533 734002).
Ground: 443 Gleneagles Ave., Rushey Mead, Leicester (0533 660009)

HOLWELL SPORTS **Colours:** Green & gold/green/green & gold
Secretary: Mrs Margaret Hutton, 25 Welby Rd, Asfordby Hill, Melton Mowbray LE14 3RB (0664 812151).
Ground: Welby Road, Asfordby Hill, Melton Mowbray, Leics (0664 812663)

HOUGHTON RANGERS **Colours:** Blue/white/white
Secretary: J P Silver, 'Red Roofs', 41 Main St., Houghton-on-the-Hill, Leics LE7 9GE (0533 433951).
Ground: Weir Lane, Houghton-on-the-Hill, Leics (0533 419551).

HUNCOTE SPORTS & SOCIAL **Colours:** All blue.
Secretary: D Russell, 72 Sycamore Way, Littlethorpe, Leics LE9 5HU (0533 841952).
Ground: Enderby Lane, Thurlaston, Leics (0455 888430).

IBSTOCK WELFARE **Colours:** All red.
Secretary: R A Wilkinson, 6 Valley Rd, Ibstock, Leicester LE67 6NY (0530 260744).
Ground: The Welfare, Leicester Road, Ibstock (0530 260656).

KIRBY MUXLOE S.C. **Colours:** All blue.
Secretary: R Pallett, 184 Blackbird Road, Leicester LE4 0AF (0533 626020).
Ground: Ratby Lane, Kirby Muxloe (0533 393201)

LEICESTERSHIRE CONSTABULARY **Colours:** Yellow/green/green
Secretary: Mrs Judith Leacy, 6 Lena Drive, Groby, Leicester LE6 0FJ (0530 243110).
Ground: Police HQ, St Johns, Enderby (0533 482198).

LOUGHBOROUGH DYNAMO **Colours:** Gold/black/gold.
Secretary: Max Hutchinson, 3 Wythburn Close, Loughborough, Leics LE11 3SZ (0509 266092).
Ground: Nanpanton Sport Ground, Loughborough (0509 612144).

LUTTERWORTH TOWN **Colours:** White/navy/navy
Secretary: Kevin Zupp, 14 Swiftway, Lutterworth, Leics LE17 4PB (0455 550358).
Ground: Hall Lane, Bitteswell, Lutterworth, Leics (0455 554046)

NARBOROUGH & LITTLETHORPE **Colours:** All blue
Secretary: Ronald Bexley, 53 Trinity Rd, St Johns, Narborough, Leics LE9 5BW (0533 862818).
Ground: Leicester Road, Narborough (Near M1 bridge) (0533 751855).

NEWFOUNDPOOL W.M.C. **Colours:** Green & yellow stripes/green/green & yellow.
Secretary: Reg Molloy, 110 Wand Street, Leicester LE4 5BU (0533 665051).
Ground: Meadow Lane, Birstall (0533 673965).

NORTH KILWORTH **Colours:** Blue & white halves/white/blue
Secretary: R Bell, 3 High Street, North Kilworth, Lutterworth, Leics LE17 6ET (0858 464048)(Steve Bell).
Ground: Rugby Road, North Kilworth, Lutterworth, Leics (0858 880890).

OADBY TOWN **Colours:** Red/white/black
Secretary: D P Collins, 26 Hill Way, Oadby, Leics LE2 5YG (0533 713557).
Ground: Invicta Park, Wigston Road, Oadby, Leics (0533 715728)

QUORN **Colours:** Red/white/red
Secretary: W L Caunt, 64 Wood Lane, Quorn, Leics LE12 8DB (0509 414213).
Ground: Farley Way, Quorn, Leics (0533 620490).

SAFFRON DYNAMO **Colours:** Red & black stripes/black/black
Secretary: Bob King, 14 Bramley Close, Broughton Astley, Leicester LE9 6QU (0455 284270).
Ground: Cambridge Road, Whetstone

SILEBY TOWN **Colours:** All blue.
Secretary: G Clarke, 123 Highgate Road, Sileby, Leics LE12 7PW (01509 813503).
Ground: Memorial Park, Seagrave Road, Sileby, Leics (01509 816104)

St ANDREWS SOCIAL CLUB **Colours:** Black & white/black/red
Secretary: Martin Wilson, 3 Ainsdale Rd, Western Park, Leicester LE3 0UD (0533 858227).
Ground: Canal Street, Old Aylestone, Leicester (0533 839298).

STONEY STANTON **Colours:** Blue & black/black/black
Secretary: Brian Chapman, 54 Bold Avenue, Stony Stanton, Leicester LE9 4DN (01455 274295)
Ground: Highfields Farm, Huncote Road, Stoney Stanton

SYSTON St PETERS **Colours:** Red & black stripes/black/black
Secretary: Denis Stringer,15 Unicorn St.,Thurmaston, Leicester (01162 698037)
Ground: Memorial Ground, Necton Street, Syston, Leics (01162 698110).

THRINGSTONE MINERS WELFARE **Colours:** Gold/black/gold.
Secretary: Paul A Nelson, 30 Bardon Rd, Coalville, Leics (0530 838694).
Ground: Homestead Road, Thringstone (0530 223367).

UNITED COLLIERIES **Colours:** Sky blue/navy/navy.
Secretary: John Meason, 29 Standard Hill, Coalville, Leics LE67 3HN (01530 810941).
Ground: 1 Terrace Rd, Ellistown, Coalville.(01530 230159)

FEDERATION BREWERY NORTHERN LEAGUE

FEEDER TO:
NORTHERN PREMIER LEAGUE

FOUNDED: 1889
(The World's Second Oldest League)

President: Arthur Clark

Chairman: Mike Amos.

Hon.Secretary: A Golightly, 85 Park Road North, Chester-le-Street, Co. Durham DH3 3SA (0191 388 2056)

An era ended on June 1 when Arthur Clark, the man with more blazers than Harrods, stood down as the Leagues chairman after 21 years. Arthur's 50 year involvement with the League had also embraced long spells as secretary of Crook and Whitley Bay, outstanding service recognised at a dinner on April 19th at which Graham Kelly was principle speaker. Arthur was only the fourth chairman since 1896.

Young Kelly, it might be added, used part of his speech to announce that he'd brought his boots to the North-East and was 'available'. That Sunday morning the FA chief executive turned out at centre forward for an unaffiliated team on a virtual sheep field at Ushaw Moor, first putting up the nets and last getting the beers in. Though he failed to score, Graham gave the impression of a man who thinks about the game. Pity about his pace.

The team, which included incoming Tow Law Town chairman John Flynn, are still anxious for another word in the chief executive's ear, however. He didn't pay his subs.

Arthur, at any rate, now becomes League President in succession to the Rt. Hon Ernest Armstrong, former deputy Speaker of the House of Commons and Stanley United bone cruncher, who hosted in a red and white striped marquee - Stanley's colours, and Sunderland's - the annual meeting at which he retired. Arthur continues as a member of the FA Council, and its international committe.

It had all begun 12 months earlier, of course, with the obligatory round of ground inspections. Though the management committee had tried to be as elastic as a Marks and Spencer knicker department, finally it was felt that Hebburn had culpably failed to meet every deadline, and they were relegated, reluctantly, from the first division.

Durham City's impressive new ground had had deadline problems, too, but was finally up and away. South Shields, who joined the second division on promotion from the Vaux Wearside League, handsomely met the grading criteria. John Rundle, passionate chairman and effective owner, is reckoned to have put around £400,000 into the club. The non-league scene, happily, still has its benefactors, too.

For the first time both first and second division FBNL clubs entered the FA Vase and left it without making much impression. None got past the last 32, a real (though doubtless temporary!) embarrassment to the League that in Amateur Cup days seemed to be at Wembley every season. Endless theories (some would say excuses) have been aired, none convincingly. If only on the grounds that we could hardly do worse, we shall do better - very much better - in 1996-97

League competition, particularly the first division, proved more dramatic than for many seasons. Durham, anxious for promotion through the Pyramid, seemed to have had the championship in their pockets until a nervous run at the end brought only two points from the four games going into the season's final match - at reigning champions Tow Law.

Were City to have won they'd still have been champions, a draw would have secured second place and likely promotion - since none of the other contending teams had sought the move. Billingham Synthonia, born again Bedlington Terriers and, mathematically, the Lawyers all had a final day chance of the title.

City took the lead but lost to two goals in a minute. Wins for both Synthonia and Terriers gave them first and second places, the latter on goal difference above Durham and Tow Law. Utterly engrossing stuff, and rather more compelling (in truth) than issues at the foot of the table, where the three relegated clubs had long been adrift.

Long standing members Ferryhill Athletic, bottom and without a win all season, have been allowed a further season's ground sharing at Brandon but have promised plans for a new ground. Eppleton CW and Peterlee Newtown also approached Christmas needing a sackful of points, and found them little easier to come by thereafter.

In the second division, the newcomers from South Shields had long seemed championship favorites but were overhauled by a marvellous late run by Morpeth Town, second season members. Morpeth's standing this season will be further enhanced by the opening of a luxurious clubhouse at the out-of-town Craik Park ground. Easington Colliery secured the third promotion spot, after a long tussle with their neighbours Shotton.

Whitby Town won the LCL Pils League Cup, thanks to the 60th goal of the season from Paul Pitman, known everywhere as Yakka for reasons that may be obscure to those outside the North-East. (Translations on request). The prolific Yakka was also the league's player of the year for the second successive season.

Easter saw the fifth and final Groundhopper's weekend, almost an institution although the anious organiser found certain irony in the fact that after shepherding the cream of non-league football enthusiasts around 41 Northern League grounds in five years, the one with which they hopelessly and irredeemably fell in love was the one 'outsider' - Stanley United of the Vaux Wearside League. Mind, he loves it, too.

A marvellous last weekend - piper, presentations, the lot - was marred only for Henk van der Sluis, a regular visitor from Holland who was obliged to spend ten days in Durham hospital because of diabetic problems. Though his English is perfect, Henk hasn't quite the hang of Geordie.
"Why, aa's sorry to see thoo's bad, son" observed an elderly pit yakka in the next bed.
"i am not a bad person" said Henk, as if he hadn't enough to worry about. And he missed Stanley United.

Though the Groundhoppers weekends now cease, the Federation Brewery's sponsorship, happily continues. We are also grateful to JustSport, a Newcastle based sportswear company, whose generous backing makes possible our Team of the Month and fair play awards. Evenwood Town won both fair play and good conduct awards, though there was talk of disciplinary action on the day they ran out of pies even before the match kick off. Atkinson Stairs of Newton Aycliffe sponsor the programme competition, won by Durham City; the Groundhoppers sponsored the Unsung Hero Awards, won by Shildon tea ladies Edith Aisbitt and Joan Clarkson, with over 70 years kettle boiling between them.

It applies equally, no doubt, to every other league in our fraternity, but we are lucky to have such selfless, dedicated people to keep the game alive, and well, in this corner of England.

Tony Golightly, greyer by the minute, continues as League secretary; Ted Ilderton and Steve Rock in their posts as referees' and registrations secretary. The new League chairman - or Chair, as FA correspondence worryingly insists - looks forward to a season of peace and progress and to an FBNL team or two at Wembley, but is far too unassuming to say another word.

Mike Amos:

Whitby Town: after winning the Federartion Brewery L.C.L. Pils League Cup 95-96

FEDERATION BREWERY NORTHERN LEAGUE
FINAL LEAGUE TABLES 1995/96

Div One		P	W	D	L	F	A	Pts
1.	Billingham Syn	38	24	8	6	78	34	80
2.	Bedlington Ter	38	22	12	4	90	37	78
3.	Durhan City	38	24	6	8	85	35	78
4.	Tow Law Town	38	23	9	6	82	43	78
5.	Whitby Town	38	21	7	10	100	59	70
6.	Guisborough T	38	20	8	10	80	54	68
7.	Dunston Fed	38	20	8	10	75	52	68
8.	West Auckland	38	19	5	14	66	57	62
9.	Crook Town	38	17	9	12	59	41	60
10.	Consett	38	17	7	14	76	64	58
11.	Stockton	38	16	8	14	88	71	56
12.	Shildon	38	16	2	19	74	74	51
13.	Seaham R S	38	13	11	14	62	66	50
14.	Murton	38	12	11	15	57	53	47
15.	RTM Newcastle	38	13	7	18	38	58	46
16.	Chester Le St	38	11	9	18	72	78	42
17.	Whickham	38	11	8	19	43	77	41
18.	Peterlee Newtn	38	5	4	29	40	96	19
19.	Eppleton	38	2	3	33	26	153	9
20.	Ferryhill Ath	38	0	5	33	27	146	5

Div Two		P	W	D	L	F	A	Pts
1.	Morpeth Town	36	27	5	4	94	40	86
2.	South Shields	36	25	4	7	89	34	79
3.	Easington Coll	36	23	7	6	86	40	76
4.	Shotton Com/d	36	22	7	7	74	42	73
5.	Northallerton	36	19	9	8	70	43	66
6.	Ashington	36	18	9	9	66	48	63
7.	Billingham T	36	18	6	12	72	51	60
8.	Evenwood Tn	36	16	8	12	83	61	56
9.	Prudhoe Town	36	17	4	15	75	69	55
10.	Brandon Utd	36	16	6	14	59	55	54
11.	Esh Winning	36	13	7	16	80	75	46
12.	Hebburn	36	13	5	18	50	58	44
13.	Washington	36	14	4	18	71	74	*43
14.	Willington	36	11	8	17	53	75	41
15.	Horden C W	36	12	3	21	65	75	39
16.	Alnwick Town	36	10	6	20	47	65	36
17.	Ryhope C A	36	6	5	25	40	83	23
18.	Norton	36	6	5	25	54	122	#17
19.	Darlington C S	36	0	4	32	34	152	4

* Washington 3 points deducted
# Norton 6 points deducted

DIV ONE RESULTS CHART 1995-96

HOME TEAM	1	2	3	4	5	6	7	8	9	10	11	12	13	14	15	16	17	18	19	20
1. Bedlington Terriers	*	3-1	1-0	2-1	4-2	2-2	3-2	10-0	1-1	1-1	1-1	3-1	3-0	9-2	4-2	0-2	1-1	1-0	2-1	0-1
2. Billingham Synthonia	0-0	*	3-1	3-0	5-0	4-0	1-0	3-0	3-0	2-2	4-1	3-0	1-1	0-4	3-0	2-1	1-1	2-0	2-0	1-0
3. Chester Le St. Town	2-3	0-1	*	1-2	0-2	2-2	1-1	5-2	5-1	1-1	3-2	1-0	2-2	1-3	2-0	0-0	1-3	4-3	2-2	2-1
4. Consett	1-2	3-0	2-1	*	0-3	5-3	0-0	5-0	1-1	0-1	1-0	3-0	1-1	3-0	0-2	2-4	1-1	3-1	3-2	1-3
5. Crook Town	0-0	1-1	2-0	0-1	*	0-0	1-0	2-0	2-0	1-2	3-1	5-1	1-0	1-0	4-0	0-0	0-0	1-3	2-0	0-1
6. Dunston Fed. Brewery	1-1	1-3	3-0	2-1	2-3	*	1-0	1-0	7-1	3-2	1-1	7-0	1-0	3-3	0-5	1-0	0-0	2-3	4-0	1-2
7. Durham City	2-1	3-1	4-1	5-0	3-2	2-1	*	7-0	4-1	3-0	3-1	5-0	1-0	2-0	1-0	1-1	2-3	0-2	0-1	1-1
8. Eppleton Coll Welfare	1-3	1-3	0-6	2-7	1-74	0-4	2-6	*	1-1	0-10	1-3	0-5	0-5	0-4	0-2	1-4	1-1	1-2	0-0	0-5
9. Ferryhill Athletic	1-4	0-4	2-9	2-4	0-4	1-2	0-2	1-3	*	0-6	3-3	1-5	0-8	0-1	1-7	1-8	1-4	0-3	0-4	0-5
10. Guisborough Town	1-1	3-3	4-0	1-4	1-0	0-1	2-1	7-0	2-1	*	1-0	0-3	4-2	1-1	4-2	2-0	1-0	0-1	2-0	0-1
11. Murton	0-3	1-3	6-0	1-3	0-0	0-1	0-0	3-0	3-0	0-0	*	2-0	1-2	1-1	0-2	2-0	2-2	3-0	1-0	2-1
12. Peterlee Newtown	1-3	0-3	2-3	2-1	1-2	0-2	1-3	1-2	3-2	0-2	1-3	*	1-2	1-1	1-3	1-1	0-4	0-4	0-2	0-5
13. RTM Newcastle	0-0	0-0	2-1	0-0	1-2	0-3	1-3	3-0	4-0	1-4	0-2	2-0	*	5-1	5-1	3-0	1-3	0-4	1-2	1-2
14. Seaham Red Star	0-0	0-2	1-1	2-1	2-0	1-3	0-3	4-0	1-1	1-2	3-0	2-1	5-3	*	2-2	1-1	1-4	1-2	1-0	4-2
15. Shildon	1-3	1-1	3-2	2-5	4-2	2-4	0-2	6-3	2-0	4-1	1-1	3-2	3-2	2-1	*	0-1	3-1	1-0	1-2	2-3
16. Stockton	3-2	1-2	4-2	6-2	2-0	2-1	0-3	3-1	7-2	4-5	2-2	3-2	0-5	2-2	3-2	*	1-2	2-3	1-1	2-4
17. Tow Law Town	0-0	0-1	2-1	2-2	1-0	5-1	2-1	2-0	4-0	3-0	1-4	1-0	3-2	4-3	3-0	4-2	*	4-0	4-0	2-4
18. W. Auckland Town	0-3	2-1	1-1	1-3	0-0	0-1	3-5	3-1	3-1	1-2	2-1	3-0	1-0	1-1	2-0	4-2	1-3	*	2-2	1-2
19. Whickham	1-6	1-4	2-2	2-1	0-4	0-2	0-1	4-1	1-0	3-3	3-2	1-1	2-2	0-1	1-0	0-7	0-1	3-2	*	0-3
20. Whitby Town	1-4	2-1	3-6	3-3	3-3	1-1	1-2	8-1	6-0	5-0	1-1	3-3	0-1	2-1	1-4	3-6	4-1	1-1	6-0	*

FEDERATION BREWERY DIV TWO RESULTS CHART 1995-96

HOME TEAM	1	2	3	4	5	6	7	8	9	10	11	12	13	14	15	16	17	18	19	20
1. Alnwick Town	*	3-2	1-2	1-2	0-0	0-0	2-1	0-0	0-0	2-0	2-3	0-2	3-1	0-0	3-1	0-1	0-2	1-4	3-3	
2. Ashington	3-2	*	2-2	1-0	3-0	5-1	5-0	1-1	2-2	3-2	0-2	2-2	2-0	0-1	2-1	5-2	2-0	0-5	3-0	
3. Billingham Town	2-0	3-0	*	1-0	3-1	1-3	2-2	4-0	2-3	2-0	0-2	1-2	5-1	6-0	2-2	1-0	1-0	3-1	1-2	
4. Brandon Town	1-2	2-2	1-1	*	3-1	0-1	0-3	1-1	0-3	3-1	2-3	0-1	1-0	5-2	3-1	1-2	1-3	3-2	1-2	
5. Darlington Cle. Soc	1-5	1-2	0-3	1-2	*	0-2	1-2	1-2	1-1	2-3	0-5	0-4	3-3	3-6	3-6	2-2	0-4	2-5	2-5	
6. Easington Colliery	4-1	0-0	3-1	0-0	10-0	*	2-1	4-0	2-0	3-2	0-0	3-2	4-3	2-1	4-1	1-1	2-1	3-2	4-0	
7. Esh Winning	4-1	1-2	3-1	2-2	4-2	0-4	*	1-2	1-0	6-2	3-5	1-6	11-0	1-2	1-0	2-3	1-3	1-1	4-2	
8. Evenwood Town	5-0	2-2	4-0	6-1	4-2	3-3	2-1	*	2-0	1-2	3-5	2-0	4-0	2-0	3-1	2-6	1-2	5-2	0-0	
9. Hebburn	3-2	0-1	1-1	1-2	5-0	0-5	1-1	1-2	*	4-2	2-0	0-1	4-1	1-6	3-0	2-0	0-2	1-2	2-1	
10. Horden Colliery Wel	2-1	0-1	0-3	1-4	8-0	3-2	2-3	3-1	0-2	*	1-3	1-2	3-3	0-1	3-0	0-3	1-4	2-1	7-1	
11. Morpeth Town	2-1	1-0	5-2	1-3	7-0	3-1	2-2	2-1	1-0	3-2	*	4-1	8-0	5-0	4-1	1-1	4-2	3-0	1-1	
12. Northallerton	4-0	2-1	3-1	2-0	6-0	1-1	4-4	1-1	1-2	3-2	1-1	*	1-0	1-1	3-0	0-0	0-1	3-2	1-0	
13. Norton & Stockton	1-2	2-3	0-4	1-3	4-2	0-6	1-3	4-2	2-0	2-2	1-3	1-1	*	4-2	1-1	1-2	3-4	0-3	3-2	
14. Prudhoe Town	0-4	3-2	1-4	1-3	10-0	1-2	4-2	0-4	1-0	2-2	0-3	0-0	3-2	*	4-0	2-1	0-2	3-1	3-1	
15. Ryhope Comm Assc	2-1	0-2	1-2	0-1	5-0	0-1	0-3	2-2	2-3	0-3	1-5	1-3	1-5	0-3	*	3-0	1-1	0-2	0-0	
16. Shotton Comrades	3-0	2-1	2-2	2-1	5-1	3-0	2-1	2-0	6-1	0-1	2-1	2-1	2-1	3-0	3-0	*	1-1	1-0	0-2	
17. South Shields	2-1	2-2	1-2	1-1	7-0	2-1	2-0	4-0	2-0	3-1	2-0	2-0	10-1	1-0	3-0	1-3	*	1-2	6-1	
18. Washington	1-3	1-2	2-1	1-4	4-1	1-2	2-1	2-0	2-1	0-1	1-2	4-0	4-2	1-6	1-4	4-4	1-3	*	3-3	
19. Willington	1-0	0-0	2-0	1-2	2-1	1-0	3-3	1-3	2-1	1-0	1-4	2-4	8-0	1-6	0-2	0-2	0-2	1-1	*	

FEDERATION BREWERY L.C.L. Pils LEAGUE CUP 1995-96

First Round:

West Auckland v **Dunston Fed.**	0-4	RTM Newcastle v Stockton	3-1
Peterlee v Chester-Le-Street	1-0	Ashington v Evenwood	3-4
Willington v Billingham Town	1-3	Hebburn v Crook Town	0-1
Durham City v Horden C W	6-0	Shotton v Norton	1-2
Whitby Town v Prudhoe Town	3-1	Tow Law Town v Morpeth Town	4-1
Consett v Darlington C S	9-1	Guisborough v Murton	2-1
Brandon United v Eppleton CW	1-2	Whickham v Seaham Red Star	1-2
South Shields v Billingham Syn	* 1-1	Alnwick v Shildon	1-0

Second Round:

Dunston Fed v RTM Newcastle	1-0	Peterlee v Evenwood	1-3
Billingham Town v Crook Town	2-1	Durham City v Norton	6-0
Whitby Town v Tow Law Town	5-2	Consett v Guisborough	2-1
Eppleton C W v Seaham Red Star	2-3	South Shields v Alnwick	7-1

Quarter Finals:

Dunston Fed v Evenwood	2-1	Billingham Town v Durham City	0-6
Whitby Town v Consett	2-1	Seaham Red Star v South Shields	1-2

Semi-Finals;

Dunston Fed v Durham City	#2-4	**Whitby Town** v Consett	8-5

Final;

Dunston Federation 0, **Whitby Town** 1

* match won on penalties; # Durham City eliminated due to playing ineligible player.

DIVISION ONE CLUBS 1996-97

BEDLINGTON TERRIERS

Chairman: David Perry. **Press Officer:** Eric Young (01670 829196)
Secretary: Eric Young, 6 Millbank Place, Bedlington, Northumberland NE22 5AT (01670 829196).
Manager: Keith Perry **Assistant Manager:** Steven Locker.
Coach: Tony Lowery **Physio:** John Nicholson.
Ground: Welfare Park, Park Rd., Bedlington, Northumberland (01670 825485).
Directions: Into Bedlington, left at 'Northumberland Arms' on Front St, 2nd right, grd on right
Seats:150 **Cover:** 200 **Capacity:** 1,500 **Floodlights:** Yes **Year Formed:** 1949
Midweek Matches: Wednesday **Previous Lgs:** Northern Alliance. **Programme:** 40 pages, 50p
Colours: Red/black **Change colours:** All blue **Souvenir Shop:** No
Clubhouse: Open every evening, 11-11pm Sat. & Sun lunch. Pool, darts etc.
Record win: 9-0 v Ashington (A), Northumberland Senior Cup 94-95.
Record Attendance: 1,013 v Blyth Spartans, Northern Lg 85-86.
Previous Names: Bedlington Mechanics 49-53/ Colliery Welfare 53-56/ Mechanics 56-61/ Bedlington United 61-65/ Bedlington Colliery 65-68/ Bedlington Town 68-74.
95-96 Captain: **Club record scorer:** Ian Donaldson.
Hons: Northern League Div 2 94-95 (R-up 84-85), Northern Alliance 66-67 (R-up 67-68 69-70 71-72, Lg Cup 57-58 66-67 69-70 81-82.

BILLINGHAM SYNTHONIA

Chairman: Don Beattie. **Vice Chairman:** Peter Lax **President:** Harry Davies.
Secretary: Graham Craggs, 2 Ribble Close, Billingham, Cleveland TS22 5NT (01642 535856).
Manager: Stuart Coleby **Physio:** Tommy Cushley. **Coach:** Lenny Gunn
Ground: The Stadium, Central Avenue, Billingham, Cleveland (01642 552358).Prees Box(01642 532348).
Directions: Turn off A19 onto A1027 signposted Billingham, Norton (this applies from either north or south), continue straigh on along Central Avenue, ground on left opposite office block. By rail; ground 1 mile along Cowpen Lane from Billingham (BR).
Seats: 370 **Cover:** 370 **Capacity:** 1,970 **Floodlights:** Yes **Club Shop:** No.
Programme: 12 pages (+ads), 50p **Editor:** Nigel Atkinson (01642 342469) **Press Officer:** Secretary
Club colours: Green/white/green. **Change colours:** All blue
Nickname: Synners **Club Sponsors:** T.B.A. **Founded:** 1923
Midweek Matches: Wednesday **Previous League:** Teesside (1923-War).
Record Attendance: 4,200 v Bishop Auck. 6/9/58.
Best FA Trophy season: Quarter-final replay 93-94 (lost 1-2 after 1-1 draw at Woking).
Best FA Cup season: 1st Rd 48-49 51-52 56-57 57-58 87-88 89-90.
Players progressing to Football League: Peter Atkinson & Ken Harrison (Hull 1947), Ernie Wardle & John Murray (M'boro 1948 & 49), Richard Mulvaney (Blackburn 1964), Mike Hodgson (Hartlepool 1964), David Hockaday (Blackpool 1975), Terry Gaffney (Hartlepool 1977), Aidan Davidson (Notts County 1988).
Clubhouse: 200yds across car park. Normal club hours.
95-96 Captain: Tommy Connor. **95-96 Top Scorer:** Michael Ward. **95-96 P.O.Y.:** David O'Gorman
Club record scorer: Tony Hetherington **Club record appearances:** Andy Harbron.
Honours: Northern Lg 56-57 88-89 89-90 95-96, R-up 49-50 50-51 51-52, Lg Cup 51-52 87-88 89-90, Div 2 86-87, Teesside Lg 36-37 (Lg Cup 34-35 38-39), Durham Challenge Cup 88-89 90-91, North Riding Snr Cup 66-67 71-72, North Riding Amateur Cup 38-39 56-57 62-63 63-64, FA Amateur Cup 4th Rd 48-49, FA Trophy QF replay 94-95.

CHESTER-LE-STREET TOWN

Chairman: John Tomlinson **Vice Chairman:** Jack Thornback **President:** John Holden.
Secretary: Melvin Atkinson, 1 St Marys Close, Chester-le-Street, Co Durham DH2 3EG (0191 388 3664).
Manager: Peter Mulcaster **Asst Mgr/Coach:** Joe Burlison. **Physio:** Joe Burlison.
Commercial Manager: Paul Days **Press Officer:** Jack Thornback (0191 3883554).
Ground: Moor Park, Chester Moor, Chester-le Street, County Durham (0191 3883363).
Directions: Ground lies approx 2 miles south of town on A167 (C.-le-S. to Durham road). Regular buses from C.-le-S. and Durham pass ground. Railway station 2 miles distant in town centre.
Seats: 200 **Cover:** 600 **Capacity:** 2,000 **Floodlights:** Yes **Founded:** 1972
Midweek Matches: Tuesday **Shop:** No, but old programmes available from editor.
Cols: Blue & white hoops/white/white **Change colours:** All yellow.
Programme: 32 pages, 30p **Editor:** Press Officer **Nickname:** Cestrians
Clubhouse: Open matchdays, Wed/Thurs 7-10.30pm, Sun 12-2pm, midweek matches 6.30-10.30pm.
Previous Leagues: Newcastle City Amtr 72-75/ Washington 75/ Wearside 77-83.
Record Gate: 473 v Barrow, FA Cup 83-84 (3,000 for Sunderland v Newcastle, Bradford appeal match 1985).
Players progressing to Football League: Dave Atkinson (Sunderland 1986), Peter Ward (Huddersfield 1987).
Club record scorer: Colin Howey, 50 **Club record appearances:** Brian Wray, 148.
Hons: Northern Lg Div 2 83-84, Wearside Lg 80-81 (R-up 82-83), Monkwearmouth Cup 80-81 81-82, FA Vase 4th Rd 91-92, Washington Lg, Durham Minor Cup, Washington AM Cup.

CONSETT

Chairman: Dave Struthers. **Vice Chairman:** I Hamilton. **President:** D McVickers
Secretary: Peter McClean, 11 Cohort Close, Ebchester, Consett, Co. Durham DH8 0PG (01207 562712).
Manager: Colin Carr **Physio:** Joe Darroch **Press Officer:** Ian Hamilton (01207 509366)
Ground: Belle Vue Park, Ashdale Road, Consett, County Durham (01207 503788)
Directions: Quarter of mile north of town centre - along Medomsley Rd, left down Ashdale Rd, ground 100m yards on left. Follow signs for Sports Centre and Baths.
Seats: 400 **Cover:** 1,000 **Capacity:** 4,000 **Floodlights:** Yes **Founded:** 1899
Colours: Red with white trim/black/red **Change colours:** Sky blue/dark blue/sky blue
Previous Leagues: Northern Alliance 19-26 35-37/ North Eastern 26-35 37-58 62-64/ Midland 58-60/ Northern Counties 60-62/ Wearside 64-70.
Programme: 16 pages, 30p **Programme Editor:** Colin French **Souvenir Shop:** No
Record Gate: 7,000 v Sunderland Reserves, first match at Belle Vue, 1950. **Nickname:** Steelmen
Best FA Cup season: 1st Rd 58-59 (lost 0-5 at Doncaster Rovers).
Players progressing to Football League: Tommy Lumley (Charlton), Alan Ellison (Reading), Laurie Cunningham (Barnsley), Jimmy Moir (Carlisle), Jackie Boyd (West Bromwich Albion).
Clubhouse: Matchdays, and evenings on request. Darts & pool. **Midweek Matches:** Wednesday
Hons: North Eastern Lg 39-40 (Div 2 26-27, Lg Cup 50-51(jt) 53-54), Durham Challenge 5, (R-up 2), Northern Lg R-up 76-77 (Div 2 88-89, Lg Cup 78-79 80-81), Northern Counties Lg 61-62, Sunderland Shipowners Cup 67-68, Monkwearmouth Charity Cup 67-68, Wearside Lg R-up 68-69 69-70, FA Trophy 2nd Rd 78-79.

CROOK TOWN

Chairman: Wilf Dobinson **Vice-Chairman:** Bob Emerson **President:** Sir Tom Cowie O.B.E.
Secretary: Alan Stewart, The Wardens Flat, 47 Grasmere Grove, Crook, Co Durham DL15 8NX (01388 763425)
Manager: Alan Shoulder **Physio:** Alan Stokeld **Coach:** John Parnaby
Ground: Millfield Ground, West Road, Crook, County Durham (01388 762959).
Directions: 400 yds west of town centre on Wolsingham Road (A689). Nearest BR station is Bishop Auckland (5 miles). Buses 1A & 1B from Bishop Auckland or X46 & X47 from Durham.
Seats: 400 **Cover:** 300 **Capacity:** 3,500 **Floodlights:** Yes **Club Shop:** Yes
Programme: Yes **Editor:** Secretary **Press Officer:** Secretary
Colours: Amber/black/amber **Change colours:** All White
Sponsors: Vaux Breweries **Formed:** 1889 **Nickname:** Black & Ambers
Midweek Matches: Wednesday **Reserve Team's League:** None
Record Attendance: 17,500 v Walton & Hersham, FA Amateur Cup quarter-final 24/02/52.
Best FA Trophy season: 3rd Rd 76-77. **Best FA Vase season:** 2nd Rd 94-95, 95-96
Best FA Cup season: 3rd Rd (v Leicester) 31-32. 2nd Rd(4), 1sr Rd.(10).
Previos Leagues: Auckland & District 1894-96/ Northern 1896-28 29-30/ Durham Central 28-29/ North Eastern 30-36/ Wartime Durham Central League 40-41/ Durham Cen 41-45.
Players progressing to Football League: Since 1960; F Clark (Newcastle 62), K Bowron (Berwick 63), A Coates (Q.o.t.S 63), P Garbutt (Carlisle 64), R Snowball (Darlington 64), W Hepplewhite (Carlisle 65), C Neal (Darlington 67), D Attlee (Seattle Sounders 75), T Turnbull (Hartlepool 76), G Whetter (Darlington 86).
Clubhouse: Lic Bar open matchdays. Hot & Cold Food available from Shop
95-96 Captain: Michael Vasey. **95-96 Top Scorer:** Wayne Edgcumbe 17 **95-96 P.o.Y.:** W Edgcumbe.
Club Record Scorer: Ronnie Thompson 118, 52-62 **Club Record appearances:** Jimmy McMillan 505, 51-68
Honours: FA Amtr Cup 00-01 53-54 58-59 61-62 63-64 (SF 48-49 57-58 59-60), Northern Lg 5, (R-up 4), Lg Cup 3, (R-up 4). Durham Challenge Cup 26-27 31-32 54-55 59-60, Durham Benevolent Bowl 5.

DUNSTON FEDERATION BREWERY

Chairman: Malcolm James. **Vice-Chairman:** Fred Fowles **President:** Norman Rippon.
Secretary: Bill Montague, 12 Dundee Close, Chapel House, Newcastle-upon-Tyne NE5 1JJ (0191 2672250).
Manager: Peter Quigley **Asst Manager:** Steve Kendal **Physio:** Glen Martin.
Press Officer: Ian McPherson (01914 205583) **Commercial Secretary:** Malcolm James.
Ground: Federation Park, Wellington Road, Dunston, Gateshead (0191 493 2935).
Directions: Dunston/Whickham exit off A1(M), ground 400 yds north along Dunston Rd on left. 1 mile from Dunston or Metrocentre stations. Buses from Gateshead & Metrocentre stop outside ground.
Seats: 80 **Cover:** 200 **Capacity:** 2,000 **Floodlights:** Yes **Founded:** 1975
Colours: All blue (white trim) **Change:** Green/white. **Nickname:** The Fed
Programme: 28 pages, 30p **Editor:** Ian McPherson (0191 420 5583) **Souvenir Shop:** No
Record Attendance: 1,550 - Sunderland Shipowners Cup Final 1/4/88.
Best F.A. Vase season: Quarter-Finals 92-93 (lost 0-2 at Gresley Rovers).
Best F.A. Cup season: 3rd Qualifying Rd 92-93 (lost 0-3 to Northallerton Town).
Sponsors: Federation Brewery **Clubhouse:** Matchdays only. Hot & cold snacks, darts, pool.
Midweek home matchday: Tuesday **Reserve team:** None.
Club record scorer: Paul King **Club record appearances:** Paul Dixon.
Hons: Northern Lg Div 2 92-93, Northern Amtr Lg 77-78 (R-up 2), Lg Cup 77-78 78-79 (R-up 75-76), Lg Shield 78-79 79-80), Wearside Lg 88-89 89-90 (R-up 90-91, Lg Cup 90-91), Northern Comb. 86-87 (R-up 3), Lg Cup 83-84 86-87 (R-up 3), Sunderland Shipowners Cup 87-88, Durham County Tphy 81-82 (R-up 2), Minor Cup 79-80 (R-up 78-79)), Gateshead Charity Cup 77-78 80-81, Heddon Homes Cup 80-81.

Durham's Justin Robson finds himself crowded out by two Chester-Le-Street defenders, in Durham's 4-1 victory

Photo - Alan Watson

Crook Town FC:

DURHAM CITY

Chairman: John Lindsey **Vice Chairman:** A Thompson **President:** G Newton.
Secretary: Brian Last, 5 Belle Vue Road, Ashbrooke, Sunderland SR2 7SQ (01915 229181)
Manager: B Cruddas **Asst Manager/Coach:** T Harrison
Physio: Joanne Dowson **Commercial Manager:** D Willis. **Press Officer:** Secretary.
Ground: TBA (to groundshare at Chester-le-Street Town at start of 94-95 season).
Colours: Yellow/blue/blue **Change colours:** Red/black/red. **Reformed:** 1949.
Programme: 30 pages **Editor:** Dave Asberry (0191 386 6469) **Shop:** No
Clubhouse details: Mon - Fri 7-11pm & Sat 12-6 & 7-11pm (closed Sunday). **Nickname:** City
Previous Leagues: Victory 18-19/ N Eastern 19-21 28-38/ Football Lge 21-28/ Wearside 38-39 50-51.
Best FA Cup season: 2nd Rd 25-26 57-58 (Also 1st Rd 27-28 55-56).
Players progressing to Football League: Harry Houlahan (Newcastle 51), Derek Clark (Lincoln 51), Leo Dale & David Adamson (Doncaster 54/70), Stan Johnstone (Gateshead 54), Dennis Coughlan (Barnsley 57), John Wile (Sunderland 66), Brian Taylor (Coventry 68), Paul Malcolm (Rochdale 84).
Midweek Matches: Wednesday.
Club Sponsors: Key Windows **Club record appearances:** Joe Raine, 552.
Hons: Northern Lg 94-95 (R-up 70-71, Div 2 R-up 30-31 91-92), FA Vase QF 87-88, Durham Benevolent Bowl 55-56, FA Amtr Cup 2nd Rd rep. 57-58, FA Tphy 1st Rd 83-84, Durham Challenge Cup R-up(2).

EASINGTON COLLIERY

Chairman: F Wellburn **Vice-Chairman:** Charlie Dodds.
Secretary: Alan Purvis, 12 Wald Crescent, Jarrow, Tyne & Wear, NE32 4SH (0191 489 6930)
Manager: Lol Jones **Asst Mgr/Coach:** Chris Gofton
Ground: Easington Colliery Welfare Ground, CW Park, Easington, Co Durham. (0191 527 3047)
Directions: A19 Easington turn-off, B1284 thru Easington till Black Diamond PH (next to zebra crossing), turn right for ground.
Seats: 175 **Cover:** 475 **Capacity:** 2,450 **Floodlights:** Yes **Club Shop:** No
Programme: Yes **Editor:** Tommy Goodrum **Press Officer:** Alan Purvis
Colours: White & green stripes/green/green **Change colours:** Yellow/black/yellow
Sponsors: None. **Nickname:** The Colliery. **Founded:** 1913
Midweek Matches: Tuesday **Reserves:** None.
Record Attendance: 4,500 v Tranmere Rovers, FA Cup 1st Round 1955.
Previous Leagues: Wearside 13-37 39-64 73-88.
Best FA Cup season: 1st Round Proper 1955-56.
Players progressing to Football League: Ron Greener (Newcastle 1951), Frank Wayman (Darlington 1957), John Langridge (Hartlepool 1982).
Clubhouse details: Normal licensing hours. Pies, soup and sandwiches available.
95-96 Captain **95-96 P.o.Y.:** **95-96 Top Scorer:**
Club record scorer: D Howard **Club record appearances:** D Howard.
Honours: Northern Lg Div 2 R-up 85-86, Wearside League 29-30 31-32 32-33 47-48 48-49 (R-up 28-29 46-47 73-74, Lg Cup 32-33 45-46 61-62), Monkwearmouth Cup 30-31 47-48 75-76, Sunderland Shipowners Cup 74-75 79-80, FA Trophy 2nd Qualifying Rd replay 88-89, FA Vase 4th Rd replay 82-83.

GUISBOROUGH TOWN

Chairman: Ron Ball **Vice Chairman:** Keith Watson **President:** Vacant
Secretary: Keith Smeltzer, 55 Thames Ave., Guisborough, Cleveland TS14 8AR (01287 638993).
Manager: Alan Robinson. **Asst Manager:** Bob Dewhirst **Physio:** Betty Cushley
Ground: King George V Ground, Howlbeck Rd, Guisborough, Cleveland (01287 636925).
Directions: From west: bear left at 2nd set of lights, left into Howlbeck Rd after quarter mile, ground at end. Buses from Middlesbrough.
Seats: 150 **Cover:** 400 **Capacity:** 3,500 **Floodlights:** Yes **Club Shop:** Yes
Programme: 32 pages, 40p **Editor:** B Thompson(011281 633633). **Press Officer:** J Newton.(01287 636914)
Colours: Red & white stripes/Black/Red. **Change colours:** Yellow
Club Sponsors: Bells Stores. **Nickname:** Priorymen **Founded:** 1973.
Midweek home matchday: Wednesday **Reserve Team's League:** Teesside Strongarm.
Record Gate: 3,112 v Hungerford, FA Vase SF, 1980 *(at Middlesbrough FC - 5,990 v Bury, FA Cup 1st Rd 1988).*
Best FA Cup season: First Round Proper 1988-89 (lost 0-1 to Bury).
Previous Leagues: Middlesbrough & District/ South Bank/ Northern Alliance 77-80/ Midland Counties 80-82/ Northern Counties (East) 82-85.
Players progressing to Football League: Frank Harrison (Middlesbrough 1982), Mark Foster (Leicester 1983).
Clubhouse: Evenings & weekends. Darts & pool. Hot & cold snacks and drinks from kitchen on matchdays.
95-96 Captain: **95-96 P.o.Y.:** **95-96 Top Scorer:**
Club Record Goalscorer: Mark Davis 551 **Club Record Appearances:** Mark Davis 323.
Honours: FA Vase R-up 79-80, Northern Lg Cup 87-88 (Div 2 R-up 86-87), Northern Alliance 79-80 (R-up 78-79, Lg Cup 78-79), North Riding Senior Cup 89-90 90-91 91-92 92-93 94-95, FA Trophy 1st Rd replay 90-91.

MORPETH TOWN

Chairman: Ken Beattie. Tel.: 01670 515271 (H), 01670 520565 (B).
Secretary: Joe Hobin, 23 Princes Gardens, Malvins Close, Blyth, Northumberland. NE24 5HJ. (01670 360820).
Press Officer: Secretary
Ground: Craik Park, Morpeth Common, Morpeth, Northumberland. (01670 513785).
Directions: Morpeth is signed off the A1 onto A197. Take the B6524, right at Mitford sign, then right after about a mile into the ground, next to Morpeth Common.
Colours: Yellow & black/black/yellow. **Change colours:** All red with white trim.
Previous Leagues: Northern Alliance. (pre 1994). **Previous Ground:** Storey Park, Morpeth. (pre 1992).
Honours: Northern Alliance 83-84, 93-94 (R-up 37-38, 65-66, 73-74, 81-82, 84-85); Challenge Cup Winners 38-39, 85-86, 93-94 (R-up 36-37, 62-63, 73-74).

MURTON

Chairman: Tom Torrence **Vice Chairman:** J Hudson **President:** John Hellens.
Secretary: J C Gardner, 74 Winds Lonnen, Murton, County Durham SR7 9TG (0191 526 3449).
Manager: Jeff Cranson **Asst Mgr:** Brian Burlinson **Coach:** Richie Madden.
Physio: Vince Symmonds **Press Officer:** James Hudson (01915 260283) **Commercial Mgr:** T Carr.
Ground: Recreation Park, Church Lane, Murton, County Durham (0191 517 0814).
Directions: Exit A19 onto B1285 heading west into Murton - Church Lane on left opposite church.
Seats: 100 **Cover:** 320 **Capacity:** 3,500 **Floodlights:** Yes **Founded:** 1904
Colours: White (red trim) **Change colours:** Red/black/red **Nickname:** Gnashers
Previous Grounds: Fatton Pasture 04-28.
Previous Names: Murton Red Star 04-28/ Murton Colliery Welfare 28-88.
Previous Leagues: Wearside 13-46 51-88/ North East Counties 46-51.
Past players progressing to Football League: Numerous.
Programme: 12 pages, 30p **Programme Editor:** Stuart Upperton **Club Shop:** No.
Club Sponsors: John Hellyns **Midweek home matchday:** Wednesday
Record Gate: 3,500 v Spennymoor Utd, Durham Challenge Cup 1951.
Record win: 17-1 v Thornley **Record defeat:** 0-14 v South Shields (H).
Clubhouse: 'The International' 300 yards from ground on B1285. Normal pub hours. Restaurant upstairs. Function room for 100. Open plan downstairs with horse shoe bar. Matchday snacks at ground.
95-96 Captain: **95-96 Top Scorer:** **95-96 P.o.Y.:**
Club record scorer: **Club record appearances:** Robert Welch 500 (1962-78).
Hons: Northern Lg Div 2 89-90, Wearside Lg 28-29 36-37 59-60 (Lg Cup 58-59 70-71), Sunderland Shipowners Cup 59-60 69-70 70-71, Monkwearmouth Charity Cup 21-22 28-29 34-35 35-36 63-64 70-71 87-88, Durham Chall. Cup 92-93, Durham Jnr Cup 50-51.

R.T.M. NEWCASTLE

Chairman: Tom Brown **Vice-Chairman:** Brian Mordue.
Sec: Jim Anderson, 7 Whitbeck Rd, Statyford, Newcastle-upon-Tyne NE5 2XA (0191 274 3941 H, 6606 B).
Manager/Coach: Rob Atkin **Asst Manager:** T Mitchell **Physio:** Paul Winspur
Ground: Wheatsheaf Sports Ground, Woolsington, Newcastle-upon-Tyne. NE13 8DF. (0191 286 0425).
Directions: From central station follow airport signs for 7 miles - ground next to Wheatsheaf Hotel on left, approximately 800yds before airport. Callerton Parkway metro station is 400yds from ground.
Seats: 300 **Cover:** 300 **Capacity:** 2,000 **Floodlights:** Yes **Club Shop:** Yes
Programme: 12 pages, 30p **Editor:** Brian Mordue (0191 267 9698). **Press Officer:** Secretary.
Colours: Blue/white/blue **Change colours:** Yellow & black stripes/black/yellow
Sponsors: RTM **Nickname:** 'Star' **Founded:** 1930
Midweek home matchday: Monday **Reserve League:** None.
Record Attendance: 1,800 v Almondsbury Greenway, FA Vase SF 77-78.
Best FA Cup season: 1st Rd 84-85 (lost 0-2 at York C.).
Best FA Trophy season: Qtr-finals 88-89 (lost 1-4 at home to Telford Utd)
Previous Leagues: Newcastle Business Houses 32-38/ North East Amateur/ Tyneside Amateur/ Northern Combination/ Wearside 75-85.
Players progressing to Football League: Ian Crumplin & Tony Robinson (Hartlepool 1976 & 1986), Barry Dunn (Darlington 1979), Ian McInerney (Huddersfield Town 1988).
Clubhouse: Matchdays only. Hotdogs, soup, sandwiches available.
Club Record Appearances & Record Goalscorer: Ian Crumplin.
Honours: FA Vase 77-78 (SF 81-82), FA Trophy QF 88-89, Northern Lg R-up 87-88 (Lg Cup 85-86 (R-up(1)), Div 2 85-86), Wearside Lg 73-74 75-76 82-83 83-84 84-85 (R-up 74-75 77-78 79-80, Lg Cup 76-77 79-80 80-81 82-83 83-84, Sunderland Shipowners Cup 82-83 84-85, Monkwearmouth Charity Cup 74-75 79-80 82-83 88-89, Northern Comb. 62-63 68-69 (Lg Cup 66-67 71-72), Northumberland Snr Cup 76-77 82-83 85-86 87-88 (R-up 74-75 78-79 80-81, Minor Cup 64-65), J R Cleator Cup 86-87.

SEAHAM RED STAR

Chairman: Bryan C Mayhew **Vice Chairman:** Reg Atkinson **President:** Michael English.
Secretary: John McBeth, 29 Frederick Street, Seaham, County Durham SR7 7HX (0191 581 5712).
Manager: Chris Copeland **Asst Manager:** Paul Walker.
Physio: Allan Jackson **Press Officer:** John Campbell (0191 581 4308).
Ground: Seaham Town Park, Stockton Road, Seaham, County Durham (0191 581 2540).
Directions: From Tyne Tunnel: A19 Teeside approx 8 miles; B1404 Seaham slip road, left at top of slip road. Right at traffic lights & first left past school into ground.
Seats: 60 **Cover:** 200 **Capacity:** 4,000 **Floodlights:** Yes **Formed:** 1973
Colours: Red & white stripes/red/red **Change colours:** All blue **Nickname:** The Star
Previous Leagues: Sunday football/ Houghton & District 73-74/ Northern Alliance 74-79/ Wearside 79-83.
Programme: 20 pages **Editor:** David Copeland (0191 581 8514) **Club Shop:** No.
Clubhouse details: New clubhouse. Mon-Sat 11am-11pm, Sun 12-2, 7-10.30pm. Large function room, snooker, pool, Restuarant & Bars.
Record Attendance: 1,500 v Guisborough, Wearside Lg/ v Sunderland, floodlight opener 1979.
Players progressing to Football League: Bobby Davison (Huddersfield 1980), Nigel Gleghorn (Ipswich 1985), Billy Stubbs (Nottm Forest 1987), Paul Nixon (Bristol Rovers (1989), Mick Smith (Hartlepool).
Midweek home matchday: Wednesday **Reserve team's League:** Banks Youth League.
95-96 Captain: **95-96 Top Scorer:** **95-96 P.o.Y.:**
Club record scorer: Tom Henderson **Club record appearances:** Michael Whitfield.
Hons: Northern Lg Cup 92-93, Phillips F'lit Tphy 78-79, Durham Chal. Cup 79-80, Wearside Lg 81-82 (Lg Cup 81-82, Div 2 R-up 87-88, Monkwearmouth Charity Cup R-up 79-80), FA Vase 5th Rd 78-79, FA Tphy 2nd Rd 89-90.

SHILDON

Chairman: Bill Aisbitt **Vice Chairman:** George Elliott **President:** John Atkinson.
Secretary: Mike Armitage, 22 Hambleton Ct, Byerley Park, Newton Aycliffe, Co. Durham DL5 7HR (01325 316322).
Manager: Ray Gowan **Asst Manager:** **Physio:** Jimmy Smalls
Ground: Dean Street, Shildon, County Durham (01388 773877).
Directions: In the town centre 1 mile BR station & 300yds from Darlington-B/ Auckland bus stop.
Seats: 400 **Cover:** 500 **Capacity:** 4,000 **Floodlights:** Yes **Club Shop:** No
Programme: 48 pages, 40p **Editor:** Neil Bennett (01325 332310) **Press Officer:** Secretary
Colours: All red **Change colours:** All blue.
Sponsors: Atkinsons Stairs **Nickname:** Railwaymen. **Founded:** 1890
Midweek Matches: Wednesday
Record Attendance: 13,000 - Leeholme v Perkinsville, schoolboys game, 1920s. For Shildon game; 11,000 Shildon v Ferryhill Athletic, Durham Senior Cup 1922.
Best FA Cup season: 2nd Rd 36-37. Also 1st Rd 27-28 29-30 34-35 36-37 55-56 59-60 61-62.
Previous Leagues: Auckland & District 1892-96/ Wearside 96-97/ North Eastern 07-32.
Players progressing to Football League: Ken Whitfield (Wolves 1947), James Smith (Chelsea 1951), Mike Peacock & Philip Shute (Darlington 1960 & 84), Kevin Stonehouse (Blackburn 1979).
Clubhouse: Open every evening 7.30-11pm (open earlier on matchnights), 1pm onwards on Satruday matchdays. Bar, pool & darts.
95-96 Captain: Bryan Liddle **95-96 P.o.Y.:** Tony Evans **95-96 Top Scorer:** Nigel Bolton 32
Club Record Appearances: Bryan Dale **Club Record Goalscorer:** Jack Downing, 61 (1936-37).
Honours: Northern Lg 33-34 34-35 35-36 36-37 39-40 (R-up 32-33 38-39, Lg Cup 33-34 34-35 37-38 38-39 39-40 52-53), Durham Challenge Cup 07-08 25-26 71-72, Durham Amateur Cup 01-02 02-03, Durham Benevelopment Bowl 24-25, FA Trophy 3rd Qualifying Rd 74-75, FA Amateur Cup 4th Rd 58-59, FA Vase 1st Rd 86-87.

SOUTH SHIELDS

Chairman: John Rundle **Vice Chairman:** George Scott **President:** Dick Butler.
Secretary/Press Officer: David Fall, 50 Basil Way, South Shields NE34 8UD (0191 536 6809).
Manager: Peter Feenan **Physio:** John Watson **Comm. Mgr:** M McGuire
Ground: Filtrona Park, Shaftesbury Avenue, Simonside Industrial Estate, South Shields NE34 9PH.(01914 279839)
Directions: From A1(M) take A194(M) to South Shields, A194 town centre road for 5 miles, ignore A1300 (Sunderland & coast) and turn left at next lights beside Co-op store into Simonside Ind. Est. (Shaftesbury Ave.), ground at bottom on right.
Seats: None **Cover:** 200 **Capacity:** 2,000 **Floodlights:** Yes **Founded:** 1974
Colours: Claret/blue/white/white **Change:** Black/white **Nickname:** Mariners
Prev. Lge: Northern Alliance 74-76. **Prev. Ground:** Jack Clarke Park 74-92.
Record Attendance: 1,400 v Hartlepool Town, Sunderland Shipowners Cup final 3/5/93.
Programme: 20p **Programme Editor:** Steve Leonard **Club Shop:** Yes.
Midweek home matchday: Wednesday **Reserve team:** None.
Clubhouse: Two function suites, club kitchen.
95-96 Captain: **95-96 Top Scorer:** **95-96 P.o.Y.:**
Honours: FA Vase QF 75-76, Northern Alliance 74-75 75-76, Wearside Lg 76-77 92-93 (Monkwearmouth Charity Cup 86-87 (R-up 94-95), Lg Cup R-up 82-83 83-84 94-95, Shipowners Cup 92-93 (R-up 83-84)), Durham Chal. Cup 76-77.

Whitby's Paul Pitman gets goal No 5 of the day against Eppleton *Photo - N Thaler*

Shildon's Dean Street Ground

Eppleton's Dean Moon hooks the ball past Murton's Ian Evans *Photo - Alan Watson*

STOCKTON

Chairman: David Scott.
Secretary/Commercial Manager: Peter Morris,20 Wheatear Lane,Ingleby Barwick,Stockton-on-Tees ,Cleveland TS17 0TB(01642 760779)
Manager: Alan Robinson **Asst Mgr:** Michael Watson. **Coach:** Peter May.
Ground: Teesdale Park, Acklam Road, Thornaby, Stockton-on-Tees TS17 8TZ (01642 606803).
Directions: A19 to Thornaby turn off, ground half mile on right. One mile from Thornaby BR station. Any Stockton-Middlesbrough bus - stop at Acklam Rd, Thornaby.
Seats: 150. **Cover:** 350. **Capacity:** 5,000 **Floodlights:** Yes **Year Formed:** 1980
Club colours: Red & black stripes/black/red **Change colours:** All sky.
Previous Leagues: Stockton & District 80-81/ Wearside 81-85.
Reserves' Lge: Teesside **Previous Names:** Stockton Cricket Club 65-80.
Previous Grounds: Grangefield Youth & Community Centre, Stockton 80-82/ Tilery Sports Centre 82-83.
Programme: 24 pages, 30p **Programme Editor:** Alan Reddy(01642 585625) **Souvenir Shop:** No.
Midweek Matches: Tuesday. **Local Newspapers:** Northern Echo, Evening Gazette.
Clubhouse: 150+ seater social club with concert room, pool/games room and bar. Open every night and Sunday lunchtimes and all day Saturday. Sandwiches available in bar, canteen in ground sells pies, burgers, soup, drinks etc.
Best FA Cup season: 4th Qual. Rd replay 92-93 (lost 1-2 at home to Blyth after 1-1 draw).
Record Attendance: 3,000 v Middlebrough, pre-season friendly August 1986.
Club Sponsors: T.B.A. **Record win:** 11-0 v Horden C.W.(H) Buchanan Cup 94-95.
95-96 Captain: **95-96 P.o.Y.:** **Club record appearances:** Michael Watson.
Hons: Northern Lg Div 2 87-88 91-92, Nth Riding Co. Cup 85-86, FA Vase 2nd Rd, FA Tphy 1st Rd.Inaugral winners of Craven Cup(Northern Div 2 clubs)94-95.

TOW LAW TOWN

Chairman: Harry Hodgson
Secretary/Press Officer: Bernard Fairbairn, 3 Coppice Walk, Mowden Park, Darlington, County Durham DL3 9DP (01325 350743).
Manager: Stuart Leeming **Assistant Manager:** Terry Kirkbride.
Ground: Ironworks Road, Tow Law, Bishop Auckland (01388 731443).
Directions: Just of High Street in Tow Law town centre.
Founded: 1890 **Seats:** 200 **Cover:** 300 **Capacity:** 6,000 **Floodlights:** Due
Colours: Black & white stripes/black/black & white **Change colours:** Red & white
Previous leagues: None **Programme:** Yes. **Club Shop:** Yes
Clubhouse: Every evening 8.30 -10.30. **Record Gate:** 5,500 v Mansfield Town, FA Cup 1967.
Best F.A. Cup season: 2nd Rd replay 67-68. Also Competition Proper 68-69 84-85 89-90.
Midweek Matches: Tuesday **Nickname:** Lawyers.
Players progressing to Football League: Reuben Cook & Ralph Guthrie (Arsenal 1951 & 53), Gordon Hughes & Terry Melling & Chris Waddle (Newcastle 1956 & 65 & 80), Eric Johnstone & Kevin Dixon (Carlisle 1963 & 83), Keith Adamson (Barnsley 1966), Tom Henderson (Bradford PA 1969), Vincent Chapman (Huddersfield 1988).
Hons: Rothmans National Cup 1977, Northern Lg 23-24 24-25 Federation Brewery Northern League Champions 94-95, (R-up 28-29 88-89, Lg Cup 73-74, Rothmans Overseas Cup 76-77), Durham Chal. Cup 1895-96, Durham Amtr Cup 1892-93, FA Amtr Cup 3rd Rd rep. 70-71, FA Tphy 2nd Rd rep. 82-83.

WEST AUCKLAND TOWN

Chairman: Mr Norman Ayton
Sec/Press Officer: A Bayles, 11 Edith Terrace, West Auckland, Co.Durham. DL14 9JT (011388 833783).
Manager: Alan Gates **Ass.Manager:**Roger Wicks **Coach:**Eric Gates
Commercial Manager: Dave Buckingham
Ground: Darlington Road,West Auckland,Co.Durham(011388 834403)
Directions: Leaving West Auckland take A68-ground on right before leaving village.Bus route via Bishop Auckland fron Newcastle or Darlington.
Founded: 1892 **Seats:** 250 **Cover:** 250 **Capacity:** 3,000 **Floodlights:** Yes
Midweek Matches: Tuesday **Previous Names:** St Helens Utd(1919 only),West Auck Town.
Colours: Amber+black pin stripe/black/black **Change Colours:**All White **Nickname:**West
Sponsors: Tenwick Transport,Hathaway Roofing,Southend Builders.
Previous League: Auckland & District **Club Shop:** No
Clubhouse: On ground reception room for visiting officials and snack bar selling teas, coffees, soup, pies, etc.
Record Gate: 6,000 v Dulwich Hamlet, FA Amateur Cup 58-59.
Best F.A. Cup season: First Round 58-59,61-62.
League Clubs defeated in F.A. Cup: None **Record Victory:** 11-0 in Durham County Cup
95-96 P.o.Y.: **95-96 Top Scorer:** **95-96 Captain:**
Hons: F.A.Amateur Cup Finalists 60-61 (QF 59-60) Northern League Champions 59-60,60-61Div 290-91,Lg Cup 59-60,62-639r-UP;48-49,61-62,63-64) Durham Challenge Cup 63-64 Durham Benevolent Bowl 62-63 Best F.A.Trophy 3rd Rd.77-78 Sir Thomas Lipton Trophy 'First World Cup'(as featured in a television play 'The Captains Tale'1909,+1911

WHICKHAM

Chairman: Bob Ferriday **Manager:** Billy Hodgson **Press Officer:** Secretary
Secretary: Mr M A McIntyre, 43 Duckpool Lane, Whickham, Newcastle upon Tyne, Tyne & Wear NE16 4TE (0191 488 4644).
Ground: Glebe Ground, Rectory Lane, Whickham (0191 488 3054).
Directions: A692 (Consett) from A69. Left at r'bout signed Consett/Whickham. Up hill, right at mini-r'bout. Continue along & turn left into Rectory Lane (by Lloyds Bank) for 500 yds, clubhouse on right.
Seats: 100 **Cover:** Yes **Capacity:** 4,000 **Floodlights:** Due **Founded:** 1944
Colours: Black & white stripes/black/black & white hoops. **Change colours:** All white
Prevs Lgs: Derwent Valley -55/ Northern Comb. 55-57 59-74/ Tyneside Amtr 57-59/ Wearside 74-88.
Programme: 20p **Midweek Matches:** Wednesday **Souvenir Shop:** No
Clubhouse: Mon-Fri. 12-3 & 7-11, Sat.11-11, Sun. 12-2, 7.30-11
Record Gate: 3,165 v Windsor & Eton, F.A. Vase SF 1981.
Prev. Ground: Rectory Rec. Field **Best F.A. Cup season:** 1st Qual. 89-90 (01-1 at Nth Shields)
Players progressing to Football League: Nigel Walker (Newcastle 1977), David Norton (Hartlepool 1981), Mike Carroll (Chesterfield 1981).
Honours: FA Vase 80-81, Wearside Lg 77-78 87-88 (R-up 80-81 84-85, Lg Cup 86-87, Monkwearmouth Charity Cup 76-77, Sunderland Shipowners Cup 77-78 80-81), Northern Comb 3, (Lg Cup 60-61 73-74).

WHITBY TOWN

Chairman: G Manser **President:** Brooks Mileson.
Secretary: Charles T Woodward, 6 Westlands Avenue, Whitby, North Yorks YO21 3DZ (01947 602312).
Manager: Harry Dunn **Asst Manager:** Steve Harland **Physio:** I Jackson.
Ground: Turnbull Ground, Upgang Lane, Whitby, North Yorks (01947 604847).
Directions: Take A174 road from town centre. Ground on offside travelling towards Sandsend.
Seats: 200 **Cover:** 400 **Capacity:** 4,000 **Floodlights:** Yes **Club Shop:** Yes
Programme: 22 pages, 40p **Editor:** G Manser (01947 83382) **Press Officer:** Secretary
Colours: All royal blue **Change colours:** All white
Sponsors: Arnott Insurance **Nickname:** Seasiders. **Founded:** 1926
Previous Lges: None **Midweek Matches:** Wednesday
Record Attendance: 4,000 v Scarborough, North Riding Snr Cup 18/4/65
Best F.A. Cup season: 2nd Rd 83-84 (01-1 at Wigan).
Players progressing to Football League: Malcolm Poskett (Hartlepool, Brighton, Watford, Sammy Kemp (Huddersfield), Jimmy Mulvaney (Hartlepool, Barrow, Stockport), Bobby Veart (Hartlepool), Derek Hampton & Trevor Smith & John Linacre & Phil Linacre (Hartlepool), Mark Hine (Grimsby).
Clubhouse: Mon-Fri 7-11pm, Sat 12-11pm, Sun 12-2 & 7-10.30.
95-96 Captain: David Logan. **95-96 Top Scorer:** Paul Pitman 60 **95-96 P.o.Y.:**
Club Record Goalscorer: Paul Pitman **Club Record Appearances:** Derek Hampton.
Honours: FA Amateur Cup R-up 64-65, FA Trophy QF 83-84, Northern Lg 92-93 (R-up 27-28 63-64 67-68 81-82 82-83, Lg Cup 28-29 63-64 69-70 76-77 84-85 95-96), Rothmans National Cup 75-76 77-78), Nth Riding Snr Cup 64-65 67-68 82-83 89-90, N Riding Bene Cup 92-93, J R Cleator Cup 84-85 92-93, Mickey Skinner Trophy 83-84 84-85 87-88 88-89 90-91.

Whitby's Graham Robinson (No 9) is tackled by Eppleton Colliery Welfare's No 6 *Photo - Mr N Thaler*

FEDERATION BREWERY NORTHERN LEAGUE

Div One Ten Year Records

	86/7	87/8	88/9	89/0	90/1	91/2	92/3	93/4	94/5	95/6
Alnwick Town	-	-	-	8	19	-	-	-	-	-
Bedlington Terriers	20	-	-	-	-	-	-	-	4	2
Billingham Synthonia	-	3	1	1	4	5	2	10	2	1
Billingham Town	-	-	5	19	-	-	-	-	-	-
Bishops Auckland	2	6	-	-	-	-	-	-	-	-
Blyth Spartans	1	1	9	9	3	6	4	2	-	-
Brandon United	12	10	7	18	17	15	15	19	-	-
Chester-le-Street Town	16	18	19	-	-	-	9	17	16	16
Consett	13	20	-	6	5	9	10	12	9	10
Crook Town	17	17	20	-	-	-	-	-	-	9
Dunston Federation Brewery	-	-	-	-	-	-	-	11	8	7
Durham City	-	-	14	17	20	-	6	1	7	3
Easington Colliery	10	15	13	20	-	17	18	-	-	-
Eppleton Colliery Welfare	-	-	-	-	-	-	-	16	18	19
Ferryhill Athletic	18	14	8	13	8	16	17	13	17	20
Gretna	7	7	3	2	1	1	-	-	-	-
Guisborough Town	-	5	4	7	2	4	3	5	6	6
Hartlepool United Reserves	15	-	-	-	-	-	-	-	-	-
Hebburn	-	-	-	-	-	-	16	15	11	-
Langley Park	-	-	-	-	-	19	-	-	-	-
Murton	-	-	-	-	13	2	8	8	15	14
Newcastle Blue Star	4	2	6	4	10	13	13	14	-	-
Northallerton Town	-	-	-	-	9	8	11	6	19	-
North Shields	6	9	18	-	-	-	-	-	-	-
Peterlee Newtown	19	-	-	-	16	12	19	-	14	18
Prudhoe Town	-	-	-	-	-	-	-	-	20	-
RTM Newcastle	-	-	-	-	-	-	-	-	5	15
Ryhope Community Assoc	14	19	-	-	-	-	-	-	-	-
Seaham Red Star	-	-	16	10	11	11	5	3	13	13
Shildon	-	12	17	14	14	18	-	9	10	12
South Bank	8	16	15	16	12	7	20	-	-	-
Spennymoor United	3	1	11	11	-	-	-	-	-	-
Stockton	-	-	10	5	18	-	7	20	-	11
Tow Law Town	9	8	2	3	7	10	14	7	1	4
West Auckland Town	-	-	-	-	-	14	12	18	12	8
Whickham	-	-	-	15	15	20	-	-	-	17
Whitby Town	11	13	12	12	6	3	1	4	3	5
Whitley Bay	5	4	-	-	-	-	-	-	-	-
No of Clubs Competing	20	20	20	20	20	20	20	20	20	20

Billingham Town's Harry Andrews kicks the ball away from the advancing Ashington striker Garth Watkins
Photo - Ray Pruden

DIVISION TWO CLUBS 1996-97

ALNWICK TOWN

Chairman: John Common **Press Officer:** Secretary
Secretary: R Miller, 1 Beech Grove,Alnwick,Northumberland (01665 603162)
Manager: D Clark **Assistant Manager:** Dave Williamson.
Ground: St James' Park, Alnwick, Northumberland (01665 603162).
Directions: 35 miles north of Newcastle on A1, take the slip road to Alnwick, then first left. At roundabout turn left, ground is then on your left.
Seats: 100 **Cover:** 200 **Capacity:** 2,500 **Floodlights:** Yes **Founded:** 1879
Colours: Black & white/black/black **Change colours:** All yellow
Programme: 20 pages, 25p **Prevs Lgs:** Northern All 35-39 46-64 64-82.
Best FA Cup season: 3rd Qual. Rd 51-52 (3-4 at Blyth), 57-58 (4-6 at Easington Colliery).
Honours: Northern Lg Div 2 R-up 88-89, Northern All 9, (R-up 4), Lg Cup 5, Subsidiary Cup 80-81), Durham Central Lg Cup 64-65, N/land Benevolent Bowl 86-87, N/land SNR Cup R-up 61-62, N/land Amtr Cup 71-72, FA Trophy 3rd Qual Rd 90-91.

ASHINGTON

Chairman: T.Brash. **Joint Predidents:** Sir Bobby Charlton and Jackie Charlton OBE
Secretary: Alan Hayton 21 Chillingham Cres, Ashington, N/thumberland NE63 8BQ.
Manager: Keith Grant. **Asst.Manager:** Colin Stocks. **Physio:**Brian Hogg
Ground: Portland Park, Ashington NE63 9XG . **Directions:** 200 yds north at traffic lights in centre of town.
Seats: 350 **Cover:** 2,200 **Capacity:** 4,000 **Floodlights:** Yes **Club Shop:** No
Programme: Yes, 50p **Editor:** A.Marchett (01670 854585) **Press Officer:** Brian Bennett (01670 856606)
Club colours: Black & white stripes/black/black **Change colours:** Yellow with black trim.
Midweek Matches: Tuesday. **Sponsors:** Furst Renault Garage. **Formed:** 1883
Nickname: The Colliers. **Best F.A. Cup season:** 3rd Rd 26-27.
Previous Leagues: Northern Alliance 1892-93 1902-14 69-70/ Football League/ North Eastern 14-21 29-58 62-64/ Midland 58-60/ Northern Counties 60-62/ Wearside 64-65/ Northern Premier 68-69.
Clubhouse: Open normal licensing hours in evenings & from 11.0 a.m. on Tuesdays (market days)
95-96 Captain: Dave Metthews **95-96 P.o.Y.:** Dave Matthews **95-96 Top Scorer:** Gary Caldow.
Honours: FA Amateur Cup SF 73-74, Northumberland Snr 9, Northumberland Chall Bowl 6, Midland Lg 58-59, North Eastern Lg Cup 33-34(jt with Sunderland Reserves) 39-40, Northern Alliance 13-14, (R-up 05-06 10-11 11-12)

BILLINGHAM TOWN

Chairman: Mr.P.Martin. **Hon.President:** Mr.F.Cook M.P. **President:** Mr G.A.Maxwell.
Sec/Press Off: T Donnelly, 36 Cumberland Cres, Billingham, Cleveland TS23 1AY (01642 555332).
Manager: Trevor Arnold **Assistant Manager:** Joe Roddy
Ground: Bedford Terrace, Billingham, Cleveland. (01642 560043)
Directions: Leave A19 on A1027 (signed Billingham). Turn left at 3rd roundabout, over bridge 1st left, then 1st left again to ground.
Seats: 250 **Cover:** 750 **Capacity:** 3,000 **Floodlights:** Yes **Founded:** 1967
Colours: Blue and White Quarters/Blue/Blue. **Change colours:** All red
Programme: 28 pages, 50p. **Editor:** Alex Matthews (01642 586570)
Clubhouse: Open matchdays. Hot & cold food. **Midweek Matches:** Tuesday
Reserves' Lge: Teesside **Nickname:** The Social.
Best FA Cup season: 1st Round Proper 1955-56.
Record scorer: Paul Rowntree 100 **Record appearances:** Darren Marsh, 250 in Northern League.
Honours: Durham Amateur Cup 76-77 77-78, Teesside Lg 77-78 81-82, Nth Riding Snr Cup R-up 76-77 81-82, Stockton & Dist. Lg(3).

BRANDON UNITED

Chairman: Neil Scott **Vice Chairman:** Joe Cutmore. **President:** Terry Jacques
Secretary: Brian Richardson, 108 Braunespath Estate, New Brancepeth, Durham DH7 7JF (0191 373 1304).
Manager: John Carey **Asst Mgr:** Roli Bell **Physio:** Bev Dougherty
Ground: Welfare Ground, rear of Commercial Street, Brandon, Durham (0191 378 2957).
Directions: A690 - 3 miles west of Durham City. Buses 49 & 49A from Durham.
Seats:200 **Cover:** 300 **Capacity:** 3,000 **Floodlights:** Yes **Club Shop:** No
Programme: 40 pages, 30p. **Editor:** Keith Nellis (0191 378 0704)
Colours: All red **Change colours:** All blue.
Club Sponsors: Shildon Sawmills. **Nickname:** United **Founded:** 1968.
Midweek Matches: Wednesday **Best FA Cup season:** 1st Rd replay 88-89
Previous Lges: Durham & Dist. Sunday 68-77/ Northern All. 77-80/ Northern Amtr 80-81/ Wearside 81-83.
Clubhouse: Open every day, lunch & evening. Pool & juke box. Entertainment at weekends.
95-96 Captain: **95-96 Top Scorer:** Stuart Salvin **95-96 P.o.Y.:** Darren Brewis
Club Record Goalscorer: Tommy Holden **Club Record Appearances:** Derek Charlton.
Honours: FA Sunday Cup 75-76, FA Vase QF 82-83 83-84, Northern Lg Div 2 84-85 (Lg Cup R-up 1), N/thern All.(2) (R-up 1), Lg Cup 2, (R-up 1), Sunderland Shipowners Cup 81-82, FA Tphy 3rd Qual. Rd 87-88 89-90.

DARLINGTON CLEVELAND SOCIAL

Secretary: B Pickering, (01325 461907)
Ground: Neasham Road, Darlington
Darlington have resigned from the League and has ceased to exist.

EPPLETON COLLIERY WELFARE

Chairman: Ralph Lawson **Vice Chairman:** Mr R D Tate **President:** Mr F Hartis.
Secretary: A.Tate, 2 Fletcher Terrace, Newbottle, Houghton-le-Spring, Tyne & Wear. (01191 5943927)
Manager: Ian Gaunt. **Asst Manager:** Hartey Maddison. **Physio:** Ted Collinson.
Ground: Eppleton Welfare Park, Park View, Hetton-le-Hole, Tyne & Wear (0191 5261048).
Directions: Situated behind Front Street Post Office & directly behind Hetton swimming baths, Hetton-le-Hole on A182. Buses 194, 535, 231, X5, X94 in Front Street. 8 miles from Durham BR statio; buses 154 and 254 from Durham.
Seats:250. **Cover:** 500 **Capacity:** 2,500 **Floodlights:** Yes **Founded:** 1929.
Colours: White (blue/black trim)/blue/blue **Change:** Yellow/green/yellow.
Record Attendance: 2,300 v Emlyn Hughes All-Stars, July 1992. Competitive: 1,250 - Monkwearmouth Charity Cup Final 1987-88.
Previous Leagues: Wearside 51-65 74-92/ Houghton & District 65-74.
Programme: 16 pages, 20p **Editor:** Fred Berry (0191 584 2452) **Nickname:** Welfare
Club Shop: Yes contact David Gardiner (0191 526 5543).
Club Sponsors: T.B.A. **Midweek home matchday:** Wednesday
Clubhouse: Bar & lounge on ground. Normal opening hours. Whitbread beers.
Hons: Northern Lg Div 2 R-up 92-93, Wearside Lg 90-91 91-92 (Lg Cup 74-75 78-79 87-88, Sunderland Shipowners Cup 47-48 85-86 90-91 (R-up 91-92), Monkwearmouth Charity Charity Cup 89-90 90-91 91-92), Durham Challenge Cup 89-90.

ESH WINNING

Chairman: Allan Morton **Vice Chairman:** Billy Hall **President:** Jack Lumsden
Secretary: Mr R Hinds, 158 Norburn Park, Witton Gilbert, Co. Durham DH7 6SQ (0191 371 0204).
Manager: T.B.A. **Physio:** T.B.A.
Ground: West Terrace, Waterhouses, Durham (0191 373 3872).
Directions: Durham to Ushaw Moor, to Esh Winning; ground 1 mile further at Waterhouses.
Seats: 160 **Cover:** 160 **Capacity:** 3,500 **Floodlights:** Yes **Club Shop:** No
Programme: 20 pages, 50p **Editor/Press Officer:** Ian Fish (0191 3730641)
Colours: Green & yellow halves/black/black. **Change colours:** Purple & Black.
Club Sponsors: Renault Trucks (North East). **Formed:** 1967 **Nickname:** 'Esh'
Midweek Matches: Tuesday **Record Gate:** 900 v Liverpool Fantail, FA Sunday Cup 1982.
Best FA Cup season: 2nd Qualifying Rd 90-91 (lost 1-3 at home to Spennymoor).
Best FA Vase season: 2nd Round 83-84.
Prev. Lges: Durham & Dist Sunday/ Northern Alliance 81-82.
Clubhouse: Open daily. Snacks served
95-96 Top Scorer: Paul Ward 31 **95-96 Captain:** **95-96 P.O.Y.:** Paul Ward.
Club Record Goalscorer: Paul Ward 31 **Club Record Appearances:** Paul Hewitson 40.
Honours: Durham & District Sunday Lg 78-79 79-80, Durham County Sunday Cup R-up 78-79, Staffieri Cup 74-75, Guards Cup 72-73, North Durham Youth Lg 94-95, Auckland Yth Lge 94-95.

EVENWOOD TOWN

Chairman: **President:** N Colegrove.
Secretary: Jim Coates, 19 Wellgarth, Evenwood, Bishop Auckland, Co Durham DL14 9QU (01388 833035).
Manager: Dr Graeme Forster. **Press Officer:** David Dowson (01388 832163)
Ground: Welfare Ground, Stones End, Evenwood, County Durham (01388 832281).
Directions: In village centre by Sports & Social club in Stones Rd.
Seats: 32 **Cover:** 200 **Capacity:** 3,500 **Floodlights:** Yes **Founded:** 1890
Sponsors: C A Roofing **Midweek Matches:** Wednesday **Programme:** None
Club colours: All blue **Change:** Red & white/white/red & white
Nickname: The Wood. **Clubhouse:** Open lunch & evening every day.
Best FA Cup season: 1st Rd 1936. **Record Gate:** 9,000 v Bishop Auckland, FA Amtr Cup 1931.
Previous Leagues: Barnard Castle & District 1894-95/ Auckland & District 1894-96 1903-04 08-23 28-31/ Wear Valley 1896-99 1904-06 24-25/ Gauntlett Valley 06-07/ South Durham 27-28.
Hons: Northern Lg 48-49 69-70 70-71 (Lg Cup 35-36), Durham Challenge Cup 69-70.

Willington's Malcom Foster speeds away from Shotton's Karl White. *Photo - Alan Watson*

Brandon's keeper Chris Flear does well to parry a close range shot from Northallerton
Photo - Alan Watson

FERRYHILL ATHLETIC

Chairman: B Campbell **Vice Chairman:** W Walker **President:** Forster.
Secretary: Eric Burton, 12 West End Villas,Crook, Co.Durham. DL15 9FF (01388 762026)
Manager: P Mulcaster **Asst Manager:** M Crowe **Coach:** G Hartley.
Press Officer: Secretary **Physio:** V Chapman/ M Mulcaster.
Ground: Darlington Road, Ferryhill, County Durham (01740 651937).
Directions: Grd on A167 Darlington-Durham rd, on left coming from south. Buses 722 & 723
Seats: 400 **Cover:** 400 **Capacity:** 6,000 **Floodlights:** Yes **Founded:** 1921.
Colours: Amber & black/black/amber & black **Change colours:** Red & white/white/white.
Midweek Matches: Tuesday **Previous Leagues:** Palatine 21-23. **Nickname:** Latics.
Record Attendance: 13,000 v Bishop Auckland, FA Amateur Cup.
Previous Name: Dean Bank Villa. **Best F.A. Cup season:** 1st Rd 35-36 53-54.
Programme: TBA **Midweek home matchday:** Tuesday **Club Shop:** No.
Clubhouse: Opens 7pm Mon-Fri, 7pm Sat (1pm matchdays), Sun 12-3 & 7pm Sundays.
Honours: Northern Lg 37-38 47-48 57-58 (R-up 23-24), Durham Challenge Cup 23-24 70-71, Durham Benevolent Cup 53-54 56-57 61-62, Durham Amateur Cup 21-22, FA Amateur Cup 4th Rd 25-26 63-64, FA Trophy 2nd Qualifying Rd replay 81-82 89-90 90-91.

HEBBURN

Chairman: Bill Laffy **Vice-Chairman:** Brian Lowe.
Secretary: Tom Derrick, 63 Staneway, Felling, Gateshead, NE10 8LS. (0191 442 1563)
Manager: Tony Robinson **Assistant Manager:** Dennis Mella **Physio:**
Ground: Hebburn Sports & Social, Club Ground, South Drive, Hebburn (0191 483 5101).
Directions: On the main road through the town about 1 mile from railway station. Hebburn lies on the Metroline - excellent bus service from Heworth Metro.
Seats: 153. **Cover:** 420. **Capacity:** 2,000 **Floodlights:** Yes **Club Shop:** No
Programme: 24 pages, 30p **Editor:** Steve Newton. **Press Officer:** Alan Armstrong (0191 430 0078).
Colours: Yellow & black trim/sky blue/white. **Change colours:** All red
Nickname: Hornets. **Founded:** 1912 **Midweek Matches:** Wednesday
Record Attendance: 503 v Darwen, FA Cup Preliminary Round replay 7/9/91.
Best FA Vase season: 2nd Rd 91-92. **Best FA Cup season:** 2nd Qual Rd 89-90
Previous Leagues: Jarrow & Dist. Jnr 12-14/ South Shields Comb. 19-22/ Tyneside Comb. 22-27/ Tyneside 27-39/ Northern Comb. 41-44 45-59/ North Eastern 44-45 59-60/ Wearside 60-89.
Clubhouse: Open 7-11pm weekdays, Sat 11am-1pm, Sun noon-2.30pm. Pool, darts etc.
Club Record Goalscorer: Keith Carter **Club Record Appearances:**
Honours: Shields Gazette Cup 91-92, Wearside Lg 66-67 (Monk/th Charity Cup 68-69), Durham Chall Cup 42-43 91-92, Nth Comb. 43-44.

HORDEN COLLIERY WELFARE

Chairman: J McCoy **Press Officer:** Karl Henson (01915 842479)
Secretary: Robert Wood, 29 Morpeth Str., Horden, Peterlee, County Durham SR8 4BE (0191 586 8802).
Ground: Welfare Park Ground, Park Road, Horden, Peterlee, County Durham (0191 518 0248)
Directions: A19 to Peterlee, signposted from there.
Seats: 300 **Cover:** 400 **Capacity:** 4,500 **Floodlights:** Yes **Reformed:** 1980
Midweek Matches: Tuesday **Programme:** 10 pages, 20p **Nickname:** Colliers
Colours: Red (white trim)/red/red **Change colours:** Blue/black/blue
Clubhouse: Normal licensing hours. Hot & cold snacks, darts, pool.
Previous Lges: Wearside 07-35 63-75/ N. Eastern 35-58 62-64/ Midland (Co's) 58-60/ Nthern Cos 60-62.
Best FA Cup year: 2nd Rd 38-39 (2-3 at home to Newport Co.).
Previous Names: Horden Athletic. **Record Attendance:** 8,000 - FA Cup 1937.
Hons: Durham Chall Cup 4, Durham Benevolent Cup 33-34, Wearside Lg 10, (Lg Cup 33-34 49-50, Monk/th Charity Cup 5, Sunderland Ship Cup 65-66 72-73), N Eastern Lg 37-38 63-64

JARROW ROOFING BOLDON C.A.

Chairman: Richard McLoughlin. **Press Officer/Treasurer:** Rose McLoughlin.
Secretary/Manager: Richard McLoughlin, 8 Kitchener Terrace, Jarrow NE32 5PU (0191 4899825).
Coach: Paul Bayson **Physio:** Fred Corner.
Ground: Adjacent to Boldon CA
Seats: 150 **Cover:** 800 **Capacity:** 3,500 **Floodlights:** Yes **Club Shop:**Yes
Programme: 20 pages, free with entry **Editor:** Brian Marshall (0191 455 1190)
Colours: Blue & red **Change colours:** Claret & blue
Sponsors: Jarrow Roofing Co. **Nickname:** Roofing. **Founded:** 1987.
Midweek matchday: Tuesday **Record Attendance:** 500 v South Shields
Previous Leagues: Mid-Tyne/ Tyneside Amtr 88-91.
Clubhouse: Open nights & weekend lunch. Food available
95-96 Captain: Vincent Brand . **95-96 Top Scorer:** Paul Thompson **95-96 P.o.Y.:** Vincent Brand
Club Record Appearances: Mick Haley **Club Record Goalscorer:**
Hons: Wearside Lg Div 2 R-up 91-92 95-96; Sunderland Shipowners Cup R-up 93-94, 94-95; Tyneside Amtr Lg R-up 90-91, Chal. Shield 90-91 (R-up 89-90); Bill Dixon Cup 90-91; Mid-Tyne Lg 87-88; Fred Giles Cup R-up 87-88; Gateshead Charity Cup SF 90-91; Monkwearmouth Cup 94-95.

NORTHALLERTON

Chairman: Philip Terry. **Vice Chairman:** Ian Bolland **President:** Dennis Cope
Secretary: David Watson,c/o Club.
Manager/Coach: Archie Stevens **Physio:** John Murray
Ground: Ainderby Rd, Romanby, Northallerton, North Yorks (01609 772418).
Directions: Leave A1 at Leeming Bar (A684) follow signs to Northallerton, approaching town take B1333 signed Romanby - ground 250yds on left.
Seats: 150 **Cover:** 500 **Capacity:** 3,000 **Floodlights:** Yes **Founded:** 1893
Colours: Yellow & Black/black/yellow & black.**Change:** Yellow/blue/yellow. **Nickname:** Town
Previous Leagues: Allertonshire (now defunct)/ Vale of Mowbray (defunct)/ Ripon & Dist./ Teesside/ North Yorks (defunct)/ Darlington & Dist./ Harrogate & Dist.
Programme: 16 pages, 50p **Editor:** TBA **Club Shop:** Yes
Record Gate: 671 v Farnborough, FA Tphy 3rd Rd 93. **Midweek matchday:** Wednesday
Best FA Cup year: 4th Qual. Rd 92-93. **Best FA Trophy year:** 3rd Rd 92-93
Clubhouse: Mon-Fri 7.30-11pm, Sat noon-7.30pm, Sun 12-2 & 7.30-10.30pm.
Club record scorer: John Woods **Club record appearances:** Lee Wasden.
Hons: Northern Lg Cup 93-94 (Div 2 R-up 89-90), N Riding Snr Cup R-up 83-84, Harrogate & Dist. Lg, Richmond Cup, Bedale Cup, Millbank Cup, Orde Powlett Cup, Harrogate Invit Cup, Alverton Trophy.

NORTON & STOCKTON ANCIENTS

Chairman: Richard Scott **President:** Dennis Swales.
Secretary: Steve Clarkson, 4 South Way, Norton, Stockton-on-Tees, Cleveland TS20 2TQ (01642 534524)
Press Officer: Eric Laverick (01642 531168)
Ground: Station Road, Norton, Stockton-on-Tees, Cleveland (01642 530203).
Directions: Norton village 2 miles from Stockton centre, turn into Station Road on outskirts of village.
Seats: 200 **Cover:** Yes **Capacity:** 2,000 **Floodlights:** No **Year Formed:** 1959
Midweek Matches: Wednesday
Cols: Amber (black trim)/black/amber **Change colours:** White with amber trim
Nickname: Ancients **Previous Name:** Norton & Stockton Cricket Club Trust.
Programme: 12 pages with entry **Programme Editor:** Richard Scott
Clubhouse details: Full bar facilities, 150 yds from ground.
Previous Leagues: Teesside (pre-1982). **Record Attendance:** 1,430 v Middlesbrough, Friendly 1988.
Best F.A. Cup season: First Qualifying Rd(4) 88-89 90-93. **Hons:** Northern Lg Cup 81-82.

PETERLEE NEWTOWN

President: David Brown **Chairman:** Ian Ripley **Vice-Chairman:** Bill Burnett.
Press Off/Sec: Danny Cassidy, 23 Melbury Str., Seaham, County Durham SR7 7NF (0191 581 4591).
Manager: Tommy Smith **Asst Manager:** Eddie Freeman **Physio:** Ron Lamdrel.
Ground: Eden Lane, Peterlee, County Durham (0191 586 3004).
Directions: From town centre Fire Station, turn left into Edenhill Rd, then right into Robson Ave. Left at the next junction and ground is on the right.
Seats: 50 **Cover:** 200 **Capacity:** 6,000 **Floodlights:** Yes **Formed:** 1976
Colours: Sky/navy/sky **Change colours:** Yellow/black/yellow **Club Shop:** No.
Programme: 10 pages, 30p **Programme Editor:** Secretary
Sponsors: Artix Ltd **Previous Lges:** Northern Alliance 76-79/ Wearside 79-82.
Clubhouse: Open normal licensing hours. Sandwiches etc available.
Nickame: Newtowners. **Rec. Gate:** 2,350 v Northern, Hillsborough Fund match 1989.
Midweek Matches: Wednesday. **Best FA Cup season:** 4th Qual. Rd 85-86
Club record scorer: Keith Fairless **Club record appearances:** Keith Bendelow.
Honours: Northern Lg Div 2 82-83, North Eastern F'lit League, 4th Qual Rd FA Cup

PRUDHOE TOWN

Chairman: Alex Waters
Secretary: Brian Tulip, 12 Orchard Close, Prudhoe NE42 5LP (01661 833169).
Manager: Terry Hunter **Asst Manager:** Kenny Barton **Physio:** Ernie Goodfellow
Ground: Kimberley Park, Broomhouse Road, Prudhoe, Northumberland NE42 5EH (Tel/Fax: 01661 835900).
Directions: Approach Prudhoe along A695, turn right at 'Falcon' Inn, 200 yds down Eastwood Rd., turn left into Broomhouse Rd., ground on right.
Seats: 150 **Cover:** Yes **Capacity:** 5,000 **Floodlights:** Yes **Founded:** 1959
Colours: Purple and Jade/Jade/Purple. **Change:** White & blue/navy/sky.
Programme: 8 pages, 20p **Editor:** J Smith **Nickname:** Citizens
Midweek Matches: Wednesday **Clubhouse:** Open every evening plus Sat/Sun lunchtimes
Prev. Lges: Hexham & Dist 59-69/ Newcastle & Dist 69-71/ Nthn Comb./ Nthn Amtr/ Nthn All. 84-88.
Sponsors: Swinton Insurance **Record Gate:** 2,500 v Blyth, Northumberland Snr Cup 1981.
Hons: Newcastle & Dist. Lg 69-70 70-71 (Lg Cup 69-70, Charity Shield 69-70 70-71), Northern Comb. 79-80, Northerm Amtr Lg 71-72, Clayton Charity Cup 68-69, N/land Minor Cup 78-79, N/land Benevolent Bowl 79-80, Heddon Homes Charity Cup 81-82.

RYHOPE COMMUNITY ASSOCIATION

Chairman: D Lawson **Vice Chairman:** R Baines **President:** A Clark.
Secretary: R F Lewins, 7 Belsay Gdns, St Gabriels Est., Sunderland, Tyne & Wear SR4 7SZ (091 528 8358).
Manager: John Oliver **Asst Mgr:** Mick Clark **Coach:** Ralph Wright
Ground: Meadow Park, Ryhope, Sunderland (091 523 6555).
Directions: From Sunderland follow signs for A19 south, grd adj to Cherry Knowle Hosp in Ryhope.
Seats: 150 **Cover:** 200 **Capacity:** 2,000 **Floodlights:** Yes **Founded:** 1960
Midweek Matches: Tuesday **Record Gate:** 2,000 v Newcastle, friendly 1982.
Colours: Red & white stripes **Change colours:** All blue **Nickname:** Ryes.
Programme: 40 pages, 50p **Editor:** D Lawson (091 567 799) **Club Shop:** No.
Sponsors: Lawson Freight **Clubhouse:** Open matchdays. Hot dogs, burgers, beverages.
Previous Leagues: Seaham & District/ Houghton & District/ Northern Alliance 78-82.
Record appearances: Paul Carr **Club Record scorer & Top Scorer 94-95:**
Hons: Northern Alliance Lg Cup 80-81, Northern Lg Div 2 83-84, Banks Yth League & Cup double 92-93.

SHOTTON COMRADES

Chairman: J Maddison **Vice Chairman:** T.Robindon. **President:** G Taylor.
Secretary/Press Officer: W Banks, 6 Syston Close, Chilton Moor, Fencehouses, Houghton-le-Spring, Tyne & Wear DH4 6TB (0191 385 5361).
Manager: B.Huntingdon. **Asst Manager:** **Physio:** W.Banks.
Ground: Shotton Recreational Ground, Station Road, Shotton Colliery, Co. Durham (0191 526 2859).
Directions: A19 Peterlee to Shotton, right at War Mem. t-junction, follow rnd 800yds, grd on rght.
Seats: 80 **Cover:** 400 **Capacity:** 1,700 **Floodlights:** No **Formed:** 1973
Colours: Black & white halves/black/black **Change colours:** All orange.
Club Sponsors: T.B.A. **Midweek home matches:** Wednesday **Nickname:** Coms
Programme: 12 pages, 20p **Programme Editor:** Mr E A Jones **Club Shop:** No
Previous Leagues: Peterlee Sunday 74-76/ Houghton & District 76-80/ Northern Alliance 80-83.
Record Attendance: 1,726 v Dennis Waterman XI. **Best F.A. Cup season:** 2nd Qualifying Rd 85-86
Clubhouse: No. **Reserves' Lge:** Banks u-19 Yth
Record scorer: Keith Willets 50 **Record appearances:** J Cudlip.
Hons: Houghton & District Lg 78-79 (Lg Cup(2)), Northern Alliance Lg Cup SF, Hetton Charity Cup 78-79, FA Vase 1st Rd 86-87 90-91, Northern Lg.Div 2 Cup R-Up. 94-95.

WASHINGTON

Chairman: Derek Armstrong **Press Officer:** John Kinross (0191 438 4513).
Secretary: George Abbott, 14 Grosvenor Street, Southwick, Sunderland SR5 2DG (0191 549 1384).
Ground: Albany Park, Spout Lane, Concord, Washington (0191 417 7779).
Directions: Ground situated behind the cinema opposite bus station.
Seats: 25 **Cover:** Yes **Capacity:** 3,000 **Floodlights:** No **Founded:** 1949
Colours: All red **Change colours:** All blue
Record Gate: 3,800 v Bradford Park Avenue, FA Cup 1970. **Midweek Matches:** Wednesday
Programme: 8 pages, 10p **Editor:** Mr Bull (0191 4164618) **Club Shop:** No
Clubhouse: Open normal licensing hours, with live entertainment, pool etc. **Nickname:** Mechanics

WILLINGTON

Chairman: Desmond Ayre **Vice-Chairman:** Bob Nichols **President:** Don Warner
Secretary/Press Officer: Bob Nichols, 34 Stephenson Cres., Willington, Co. Durham DL15 0EG (01388-745297)
Manager: Malcolm Smith **Player/Asst.Mgr:** K Stonehouse **Physio:** Ceiran Gallagher.
Ground: Hall Lane, Hall Lane Estate, Willington, County Durham (01388 746221).
Directions: Willington A690 7 miles west of Durham City & 2 miles east of Crook. Off main through road at 'The Black Horse Tavern' corner turn off Commercial St, then into Hall Lane after 100yds.
Seats: 350 **Cover:** 400 **Capacity:** 2,680. **Floodlights:** Yes **Club shop:**
Programme: 20 pages, 30p **Editor:** T.B.A.
Colours: Blue & white stripes/blue/blue **Change colours:** Yellow/green/yellow.
Sponsor: **Nickname:** Blue & Whites **Founded:** 1906.
Midweek Matches: Wednesday **Youth League:** Auckland & district League.
Record Attendance: 10,000 v Bromley, FA Amateur Cup 2nd Rd 24/1/53.
Best FA Cup season: 1st Rd replay 73-74 (lost 1-6 at Blackburn after 0-0 draw).
Previous Leagues: Auckland & Dist. 1906-11.
Clubhouse: Open evenings 7-11pm at Saturday matchdays 1-11pm. Bar facilities. Tea shop on matchdays.
95-96 Captain: Richard Hall. **95-96 Top Scorer:** Alan Tolley 14 **95-96 P.o.Y.:** R Hall/K Stonehouse
Club Record Goalscorer: J 'Boxer' Taylor 55-69. **Club Record Appearances:** S Rutherford 47-61.
Honours: FA Amateur Cup 49-50 (R-up 38-39, SF 27-28), Northern League 13-14 25-26 29-30 (R-up 12-13 57-58 75-76, League Cup 24-25 25-26 27-28 56-57 30-31 31-32 48-49 74-75), FA Trophy 3rd Rd 75-76, Durham Benevolent Cup 48-49 50-51 57-58.

FEDERATION BREWERY NORTHERN LEAGUE

Div Two Ten Year Records

	86/7	87/8	88/9	89/0	90/1	91/2	92/3	93/4	94/5	95/6
Alnwick Town	7	6	2	-	-	9	9	15	17	16
Ashington	10	15	5	13	12	12	8	17	7	6
Bedlington Terriers	-	7	7	9	11	19	17	1	-	-
Billingham Synthonia	1	-	-	-	-	-	-	-	-	-
Billingham Town	4	4	-	-	5	7	4	6	5	7
Brandon United	-	-	-	-	-	-	-	-	4	10
Chester-le-Street Town	-	-	-	5	16	3	-	-	-	-
Consett	-	-	1	-	-	-	-	-	-	-
Crook Town	-	-	-	6	13	8	18	7	2	-
Darlington Cleveland Soc	16	14	16	12	10	18	11	9	18	19
Dunston Federation Brewery	-	-	-	-	-	5	1	-	-	-
Durham City	13	3	-	-	-	2	-	-	-	-
Easington Colliery	-	-	-	-	3	-	-	5	10	3
Eppleton Colliery Welfare	-	-	-	-	-	-	2	-	-	-
Esh Winning	17	5	15	20	7	11	13	12	13	11
Evenwood Town	14	16	17	7	6	17	6	4	8	8
Guisborough Town	2	-	-	-	-	-	-	-	-	-
Hartlepool Town	-	-	-	-	-	-	-	-	6	-
Hebburn	-	-	-	15	4	4	-	-	-	12
Horden Colliery Welfare	18	11	8	16	19	15	19	19	19	15
Langley Park Welfare	19	12	13	4	2	-	20	13	20	-
Morpeth Town	-	-	-	-	-	-	-	-	14	1
Murton	-	-	11	1	-	-	-	-	-	-
Northallerton Town	12	9	9	2	-	-	-	-	-	5
Norton & Stockton Ancients	8	10	14	18	9	13	12	8	16	18
Peterlee Newtown	-	8	6	3	-	-	-	2	-	-
Prudhoe Town	-	-	4	8	8	6	5	3	-	9
Ryhope Community Assoc.	-	-	10	11	14	10	10	18	15	17
Seaham Red Star	9	2	-	-	-	-	-	-	-	-
Shildon	3	-	-	-	-	-	3	-	-	-
Shotton Comrades	15	18	20	17	15	14	14	14	12	4
South Shields	-	-	-	-	-	-	-	-	-	2
Stockton	6	1	-	-	-	1	-	-	3	-
Washington	-	-	18	10	17	16	15	11	9	13
West Auckland Town	5	17	12	19	1	-	-	-	-	-
Whickham	-	-	3	-	-	-	7	10	1	-
Willington	11	13	19	14	18	20	16	16	11	14
No of Clubs Competing	19	18	20	20	19	20	20	19	20	19

NORTHERN ALLIANCE PREMIER DIV LGE CHAMPIONS & CHALLENGE CUP WINNERS

Seaton Delaval Amateurs: Back Row (L-R); Ken Scott (Mgr), Colin Burr, Jim Muses, Mick Bell, Ian Archbold, Dave Malone, Dave Walton, Bill Hays (Coach). Front Row; Mark Binney, Rob Arkless, Graham Forbes, Paul Leavey, Simon Williams, Brian Atkinson, Graham Smith, Mark Watson (Mascot).

Haltwhistle come close against Gillford Park

Photo - Alan Watson

Carlisle's Gary Milne shoots for goal as West Allotment Celtic's Keith Woods closes in.

Photo - Alan Watson

NORTHERN ALLIANCE

Founded: 1890
Feeder To: Federation Brewery Northern Alliance
President: Sir John Hall, **Chairman:** G F Dobbins
Press Officer: Bill Gardner, 12 Coronation Road, Sunniside, Newcastle upon Tyne, NE16 5NR (0191 488 3422).

A Third Title for Delaval.

Seaton Delaval, champions in 1990 and again in 1993, clinched a third Premier Division title after seeing off the challenge of Cumbrian rivals Carlisle City and Gillford Park and defending champions Benfield Park.

Delaval wenr on to complete a notable double by beating Benfield 2-1 in the Premier Division Challenge Cup Final at Whitley Bay's Hillhead Ground.

Sadly after many years in charge, Seaton Delaval's manager Ken Scott decided to resign after his team's double triumph but he was later installed as Vice-Chairman of the League.

Thanks largely to the goal-scoring exploits of their student striker Andy Morrell, Gosforth Bohemians claimed the First Division title at the expense of runners-up Walker Ledwood who were only promoted at the end of the previous season.

Bohemians' team boss Rob Alkin, who saved the hundred-year-old club from possible extinction, is unfortunately not leading his successful side into the Premier Division. He has decided instead to manage RTM Newcastle in the Northern League.

In their very first Northern Alliance season Walbottle Masons were the Second Division Champions. The Masons also earned promotion alongside Heddon Institute who are set to have their second spell in Division One.

Amble Town were 4-0 victors against West Allotment Celtic to retain the Northern Alliance League Cup and the League also tasted success in the Northumberland County competitions.

The Senior Benevolent Bowl was won by Ponteland United and the County Minor Cup was claimed by Walker Ledwood.

Bill Gardner; Press Officer.

FINAL LEAGUE TABLES 1995/96

Premier Div	P	W	D	L	F	A	Pts
1. Seaton Delaval	32	23	4	5	97	39	73
2. Carlisle City	32	19	10	3	85	23	67
3. Gillford Park	32	20	6	6	62	23	66
4. Benfield Park	32	21	3	8	73	41	66
5. M/brough Ath	32	17	7	8	79	37	58
6. W Allotment C	32	18	4	10	79	49	58
7. Ponteland Utd	32	15	7	10	73	39	52
8. Amble Town	32	15	6	11	81	58	51
9. Haltwhistle CP	32	14	5	13	52	58	47
10. Walker Central	32	13	5	14	59	62	44
11. St Columbas	32	12	7	13	56	55	43
12. Westerhope	32	13	4	15	58	68	43
13. Winlaton	32	9	9	14	59	56	36
14. Blyth Seahorse	32	7	2	23	32	86	*20
15. Spittal Rovers	32	5	6	21	27	71	*18
16. Longbenton	32	4	1	26	29	156	13
17. Ht Stanninton	32	3	2	26	34	114	11

* Points deducted

Div One	P	W	D	L	F	A	Pts
1. Gosforth Boh	30	25	3	2	100	28	78
2. Walker Led	30	21	5	4	73	33	68
3. Newbiggin CW	30	20	4	6	84	41	64
4. Ryton	30	18	3	9	82	47	57
5. Orwin	30	17	4	9	83	50	55
6. Percy Main A	30	15	5	10	75	55	50
7. Forest Hall	30	14	5	11	75	62	47
8. Shankhouse	30	14	5	11	78	70	47
9. H/b Reyrolle	30	13	5	12	68	49	44
10. Swalwell	30	13	3	14	61	58	42
11. Dudley Welfare	30	10	5	15	67	79	35
12. Ashington Ht P	30	9	4	17	56	79	31
13. Proctor Gamble	30	7	4	19	42	81	25
14. Hexham Swin	30	7	3	20	37	63	24
15. Wark	30	3	4	23	36	110	13
16. Wylam	30	3	0	27	26	138	9

Top Scorers:
Andy Morrell (Gosforth Bohemians) 35
Peter Jennings (Shankhouse) 35

Top Scorers:
Dave Walton (Seaton Delaval) 30
Jimmy Moses (Seaton Delaval) 30

NORTHERN ALLIANCE PREMIER DIV RESULTS CHART 1995-96

HOME TEAM	1	2	3	4	5	6	7	8	9	10	11	12	13	14	15	16	17
1. Amble Town	*	6-2	3-3	1-3	1-2	6-0	11-0	1-7	2-0	3-0	0-0	3-4	4-3	3-0	2-1	3-2	5-3
2. Blyth Seahorse	1-3	*	2-2	1-2	0-1	1-0	2-0	1-4	0-3	2-1	0-3	0-6	1-3	0-3	3-1	1-3	2-0
3. Carlisle City	4-1	0-0	*	0-0	2-0	3-0	13-0	0-0	0-2	3-1	0-0	6-0	6-0	1-0	1-2	4-2	5-1
4. Gillford Park	1-0	3-1	1-0	*	2-0	6-2	2-0	1-2	0-1	3-2	3-1	3-0	4-0	0-1	2-1	0-0	2-0
5. Haltwhistle	2-0	2-1	1-2	1-0	*	3-0	4-2	0-3	4-2	0-0	2-1	2-5	2-0	0-0	2-4	1-0	0-0
6. Heaton Stannington	0-8	1-4	1-5	0-4	1-0	*	6-1	0-2	3-6	2-7	0-5	1-9	1-1	0-3	0-3	1-3	1-1
7. Longbenton	0-2	4-0	1-9	0-5	0-5	0-6	*	0-7	0-7	1-7	3-2	1-7	1-0	1-7	0-8	1-4	1-3
8. Middlesbrough A	1-1	7-0	1-1	4-0	4-1	6-1	4-0	*	0-4	0-1	3-0	0-1	2-0	1-3	1-2	3-0	1-1
9. Benfield Park	4-2	1-0	0-0	0-0	5-2	3-2	4-0	4-1	*	3-1	0-2	1-3	4-0	3-2	0-3	4-1	4-2
10. St Columbas	0-0	3-2	0-3	2-2	1-1	2-0	2-0	1-2	0-2	*	3-2	1-3	1-1	7-2	0-1	1-1	2-3
11. Ponteland United	3-1	7-2	1-1	0-0	1-2	3-2	6-0	3-1	1-1	2-3	*	0-1	3-1	6-2	6-1	2-0	1-1
12. Seaton Delaval	4-1	4-0	0-0	2-0	2-1	7-0	4-0	2-1	3-0	4-1	1-2	*	0-0	2-2	6-0	2-3	2-2
13. Spittal Rovers	1-4	1-0	0-2	1-2	1-2	2-1	2-5	0-0	1-2	0-1	1-1	0-5	*	0-3	0-3	0-1	0-3
14. Walker Central	2-3	1-0	0-2	0-4	6-3	1-0	0-0	2-0	0-2	5-0	1-2	0-1	1-3	*	0-2	2-1	2-1
15. West Allotment Cel	4-0	1-2	1-2	0-0	6-2	4-0	7-2	1-2	4-0	0-0	0-6	0-3	2-2	7-1	*	3-0	2-2
16. Westerhope	1-1	3-1	2-3	0-5	4-2	2-1	4-3	5-5	0-1	1-3	2-1	6-1	3-1	1-3	1-2	*	2-0
17. Winlaton	0-0	7-0	0-2	0-2	2-2	3-1	6-1	0-2	2-0	1-2	1-0	1-3	1-2	4-4	1-3	7-0	*

LEAGUE CUP 1995-96

First Round: (Premier Division Exempt)

Dudley Welfare v Otterburn	3-1	Swalwell v Walbottle Masons	2-1
Highfields United v Hexham B C	2-1	Wylam v Forest Hall	1-3
Wallington v Wark	1-2	Rutherford v Heddon Institute	3-0
Ryton v Northbank	1-2	Newbiggin C W v Aydon Forest	0-1
Shilbottle C W v Ashington Hirst	1-2	Orwin V Marden Athletic	5-1
Shankhouse v Newcastle Telecom	1-2	Hebburn Reyrolle v Newcastle Uni	2-2, 3-1
Monkseaton KOSA v Gosforth Boh	1-3	Proctor & Gamble v Walker Ledwood	2-5
Hexham Swinton v Percy Main	1-1, 1-1, 5-6p		

Second Round;

Aydon Forst v Dudley Welfare	0-3	Blyth Seahorse v Forst Hall	0-3
Carlisle City v Walker Ledwood	2-1	Gillford Park v Amble Town	1-2
Gosforth Bohemians v Newcastle Telecom	2-1	Heaton Stannington v Ponteland Utd	0-2
Spittall Rovers v Seaton Delaval	1-3	Percy Main v Highfields United	1-2
Longbenton v Northbank	2-5	Middlesbrough A v Haltwhistle C P	1-2
Orwin v Benfield Park	2-4	Hebburn Reyrolle v Swalwell	3-0
Rutherford v Wark	8-0	St Columbas v Winlaton	2-1
West Allotment Celtic v Walker Central	2-0	Westerhope v Ashington Hirst	3-1

Third Round;

Carlisle City v West Allotment Celtic	1-2	St Columbas v Haltwhistle C P	2-2, 3-2
Highfields United v Benfield Park	1-4	Rutherford v Hebburn Reyrolle	1-0
Amble Town v Westerhope	6-1	Dudley Welfare v Seaton Delaval	6-6, 1-4
Ponteland United v Gosforth Bohemians	2-3	Forest Hall v Northbank	2-1

Fourth Round;

Benfield Park v St Columbas	2-3	Forest Hall v Seaton Delaval	0-2
Amble Town v Gosforth Bohemians	1-0	Rutherford v West Allotment Celtic	0-1

Semi-Finals;

Amble Town v St Columbas	4-3	West Allotment Celtic v Seaton Delaval	2-1

Final; (at Heaton Stannington FC)

Amble Town v West Allotment Celtic 4-0

PREMIER DIVISION CLUBS 1996-97

AMBLE TOWN

Chairman/Press Officer: R Prouse **Manager/Coach:** R Gibbard.
Secretary: R Falkous, 30 George Street, Amble, Morpeth, Northumberland NE65 0DW (01665 711041).
Ground: Amble Running Track Ground, Amble. **Directions:** From Ashington or Morpeth; north on A1068 entering Amble after industrial est. on right, 100yds past zebra crossing turn left before Masons Arms, follow as if you are going out of Amble. At new Hassal Housing estate on right, turn left into Coquet High School car park. Pitch adjacent.
Colours: Tangerine/black **Change colours:** All blue.

CARLISLE CITY

Chairman: J Ewbank **Manager:** W Armstrong.
Secretary: D Ivison, 40 Skiddaw Road, Carlisle CA2 5OS (01228 31654).
Ground: The Sheepmount Sports Complex, Carlisle (01228 26569).
Directions: B6264 Brampton-Carlisle road & follow Workington signs, dual-c'way down hill (Carlisle Castle on right), where road intersects double back on yourself and take turning left just before castle, follow down hill keeping left until ground.
Colours: Sky & navy **Change colours:** White/red

CARLISLE GILLFORD PARK

Chairman: R Wilson **Manager/Coach:** R Rutherford/M Herring.
Secretary: B Allen, 10 Rudchester Close, Sandsfield Park, Carlisle (01228 26113).
Ground: Gillford Park, Carlisle (01228 26649).
Directions: A69 to Rose Hill r'bout, straight over & 2nd left into Eastern Way, 1 mile to lights, left, 1st right Petrill Bank Rd, right at bridge, ground 200yds up this road.
Colours: All red **Change colours:** White/black.

GOSFORTH BOHEMIAN

Chairman/Press Officer: J Bell (0191 266 1522) **Manager/Coach:** M Cave
Secretary: B Dale, 118 Newton Road, High Heaton, Newcastle-upon-Tyne NE7 7HN (0191 281 1403)
Ground: Benson Park, Brunton Park Estate, Gosforth
Directions: Turn off Great North Road after passing Three Mile Garage into Polwarth Dr. 2nd left into Layfield Rd, 1st right into South Ridge. grd 50 yards left (concealed ent between houses)
Colours: Red & white **Change colours:** Old Gold

HALTWHISTLE CROWN PAINTS

Chairman: J Jackson **Manager/Coach:** A Batey.
Secretary: R Skeet, 14 Westgate, Haltwhistle, Northumberland NE49 9AF (01434 320703).
Ground: Bardon Mill Sports Ground, Bardon Mill, Northumberland
Directions: A69 to Bardon Hill 1st right under bridge, ground on the left
Colours: Blue & white/blue **Change colours:** Black & white/black

HARTLEPOOL UNITED

Chairman: H Hornsey **Manager/Coach:** K Houchen
Secretary: S Bagnall 19 Wolsingham Road, Gosforth, Newcastle upon Tyne (0191 2843889)
Ground: Victoria Park, Clarence Road, Hartlepool, Cleveland (01429 222077). **Directions:** From Newcastle A19 south, turn off to A179 Hartlepool, follow signs for Marina into Clarence Rd.
Colours: Sky & White **Change colours:** Red with white trim

LEMINGTON UNITED SOCIAL

Chairman: R M Alsop **Manager:** S Armstrong
Secretary: A Findlay, 14 Tewkesbury Road, West Denton Park, Newcastle, NE15 8UU (0191 267 6493).
Ground: Cowgate New Tavern Sports Ground, Ponteland Rd, Cowgate, Newcastle-upon-Tyne.
Directions: Kenton turn off A1, over Kenton r'bout & next 2 r'bouts, ground on right before garage and behind Co-op dairy.
Colours: Red & black/black **Change colours:** White & navy/white

MIDDLESBROUGH

Chairman: S Gibson **Manager:** B Robson
Secretary: Ms K Nelson, Cellnet Riverside Stadium, Middlesbrough (01642 207003).
Ground: Norton & Stockton Ancients FC, Station Road, Norton, Stockton-on-Tees (01642 530203).
Directions: A19 to Billingham and Norton slip road, right towards Norton to r'bout, take Carlton exit then 1st left into Station Rd, ground at end on left.
Colours: Red/white **Change colours:** All Blue

NEWCASTLE BENFIELD PARK

Chairman: J Rowe **Manager:** T Sword/ D McDonald.
Secretary: G J Martin, 2 The Fold, Eastfield Est., Walker, Newcastle-upon-Tyne NE6 4XL (0191 263 5237).
Ground: Benfield Park, Benfield Rd, Newcastle-upon-Tyne.
Directions: From Newcastle towards coast take 2nd exit after Corner House pub lights, right into Benfield Rd, ground on left opp. Walkergate Hosp. & adjacent to school.
Colours: White/blue **Change colours:** Black & white stripes/black.

NORTH SHIELDS St COLUMBAS

Chairman: N Hooper **Manager/Coach:** J Wall.
Secretary: A J Baird, 23 Balkwell Ave., North Shields, Tyne & Wear NE29 7JN (0191 258 0833).
Ground: Purvis Park, St John's Green, Percy Main, North Shields.
Directions: From Tyne Tunnel take N Sdields road past Duke Of Wellington, after 1/2 mile take 2nd left, ground on right.
Colours: All white **Change colours:** Sky/black

PONTELAND UNITED

Chairman: F W Smith **Manager:** B Wardrobe/S Baxter
Secretary: L McMahon, 1 Wardle Drive, Annitsford, Cramlingham NE23 7DB (0191 250 0463).
Ground: Ponteland Leisure Centre, Ponteland (01661 25441).
Directions: Left at lights entering Ponteland from N'castle, ground 100m on left adjacent to Leisure Centre.
Colours: Black & white stripes/black **Change colours:** All white.

SEATON DELAVAL AMATEURS

Chairman: T Ashburn **Manager/Coach:** I Watts
Secretary: V Donnelly, 6 Hollymount Square, Bedlington (01670 829464).
Ground: Wheatridge Park, Seaton Delaval.
Directions: A189 from Newcastle, at Annitsford r'bout A190 to Seaton Delaval, left at r'bout entering village, ground 450yds on right next to Deal Garage and behind Market Garden. 3 miles from Cramlington BR station. Bus 363 from Newcastle passes ground.
Colours: All Blue **Change colours:** White/red

SPITTAL ROVERS

Chairman: B Young **Manager/Coach:** B Cordery
Secretary: G Burn, 7 Sea Road, Spittal, Berwick-on-Tweed TD15 1RN (01289 306049).
Ground: Newfields, Berwick-on-Tweed.
Directions: From south take Berwick by-pass to 3rd r'bout. Safeway Store on right - pitch reached by taking 2nd left on r'bout.
Colours: Black & white stripes/black **Change colours:** White/navy

WALKER CENTRAL

Chairman: R T McClellan **Manager/Coach:** A Bell.
Secretary: Mr B Mulroy, 31 Dalton Cres., Byker Wall, Newcastle-upon-Tyne NE6 2DA (0191 265 7803).
Ground: Monkchester Recreation Ground, Walker, Newcastle.
Directions: From City: Shields Rd to Union Rd, to Welbeck Rd, right into Monkchester Rd, left into pitch (between houses) opposite Norbury Grove.
Club colours: Blue & yellow/blue **Change colours:** All Yellow

WALKER LEDWOOD FOSSE

Chairman: W A Callanan **Manager/Coach:** T Lunn.
Secretary: K Slade, 59 Moorland Cres., Walkergate, Newcastle-upon-Tyne NE6 4AT (0191 276 1519)
Ground: Miller's Dene, Walkergate, Newcastle-upon-Tyne.
Directions: Miller's Dene Fosseway from Newcastle, travel through Byker to the r'bout at the top of Shields Rd, turn right & continue to next r'bout, left at B & Q store & continue down Fosseway. The ground is the second one down the Fosseway past Fire Station on left.
Colours: All white **Change colours:** Green & black/black

WEST ALLOTMENT CELTIC

Chairman: J Mather **Manager/Coach:** J Kiddie.
Secretary: J T Jackson, 4 Rosewood Crescent, Seaton Sluice, Whitley Bay NE26 4BL (0191 237 0416).
Ground: Hillheads Park, Whitley Bay
Directions: From Newcastle take A1058 to Tynemouth Baths, turn left roundabout on A192 to Foxhunters Pub. Turn right follow A191 to Ice Rink on right, ground beside.
Colours: Black & white stripes/black **Change colours:** Red/blue.

WINLATON HALLGARTH

Chairman: R Young **Manager/Coach:** K Rides/S Breen.
Secretary: G S Batey, 6 Wylam View, Winlaton, Tyne & Wear NE21 4RJ (0191 414 7970).
Ground: Shibdon Park, Shibdon Road, Blaydon-on-Tyne, Tyne & Wear.
Directions: From north, over A1 Tyne Bridge to 1st slip road, take Swalwell and Consett road to r'bout, right, Blaydon Baths car park and ground 400yds on right.
Colours: Yellow & black/black **Change colours:** Purple/green.

VAUX
WEARSIDE LEAGUE

FOUNDED: 1892

FEEDER TO:
FEDERATION BREWERY NORTHERN LEAGUE

President: J C Thomas **Chairman:** P J Maquire

Hon. Secretary & Treasurer: Bill Robson
12 Deneside, Howden-le-Wear, Crook, Co. Durham DL15 8JR

The Promotion of Jarrow Roofing, via the Pyramid, was tempered by the League being reduced to one division for the coming season. Following the loss of Wingate before a ball had been kicked, and the resignation of Murton International in mid season, the league was faced with the resignations of Chilton Moor, Northallerton Ainderby and Sunderland SC Fulwellat the AGM to leave a membership of nineteen teams for the 1996-97 season.
It is hoped that will only be a temporary setback with moves already being in place to restore the League to two divisions in 1997-98 season. With the five remaining clubs in Division Two having been included in the revised line up of Division One for this coming season teams have been made fully aware of the current requirements to bring their grounds up to the standard needed for membership of the Pyramid to be maintained.

On the domestic front Jarrow Roofing, having been found guility of playing an unregistered player towards the end of the season found themselves pipped for the Championship by Marske United. However with the latters ground failing to come up to the standard called for by the deadline set by the F.B.N.L. Roofing were rewarded for the hard work put in on their ground and facilities during the season by gaining promotion via the runners up position.

The domestic Cup scene was dominated by Marske United who became the first team since Blue Star in 1982-83 to capture all three trophies. Their comfortable win in the League Cup over Whitehaven Amateurs being followed up by wins over Nissan, after a replay, in the Monkwearmouth Cup and an extra time victory over Annfield Plain in the Shipowners Cup. The cup competitions again saw clubs from Division Two enjoying good runs with pride of place going to Whitehaven Amateurs who followed up their losing finalists place in the League Cup with a semi-final placing in the Sunderland Shipowners Cup. Whitehaven, after a spell of end of season nerves, finally clinched the divisional title with Stanley United ending up in the runners up spot. Stanley United achieved some consolation by taking the Division Two Knockout Cup with an easy 4-1 win over Northallerton Ainderby.

It was to prove to be a poor season in County Cups for clubs from the League with only North Shields Athletic achieving any success when the reached the semi-final stage of the Northumberland Senior Bowl.

W Robson

Stanley United's Steve Thompson makes a well timed tackle on South Bank's Chris Watson

Photo - Alan Watson

FINAL LEAGUE TABLES 1995/96

Division One	*P*	*W*	*D*	*L*	*F*	*A*	*Pt*
1. Marske United	30	22	3	5	97	29	69
2. Jarrow Roofing	30	22	4	4	93	40	67*
3. Birtley Town	30	15	6	9	61	49	51
4. South Tyneside United	30	15	9	6	41	32	51*
5. Ryhope C W	30	14	8	8	53	31	50
6. Windscale	30	16	7	10	69	54	46
7. Kennek Roker	30	12	5	13	56	55	41
8. Nissan	30	11	7	12	44	40	40
9. Annfield Plain	30	12	4	14	50	47	40
10. Boldon C A	30	12	6	12	59	50	39*
11. Wolviston	30	10	4	16	48	60	34
12. Cleadon S C	30	8	9	13	43	60	33
13. Jarrow	30	10	3	17	41	71	33
14. Hartlepool BWOB	30	11	2	17	46	66	32*
15. North Shields Athletic	30	7	5	18	34	74	26
16. S C Fulwell	30	5	0	25	36	116	15
Division Two							
1. Whitehaven Ams	18	12	1	5	54	27	37
2. Stanley United	18	10	1	7	56	25	31
3. Harton & Westoe C W	18	8	3	7	39	34	27
4. Washington Glebe	18	8	2	8	39	30	26
5. Chilton Manor	18	6	3	9	22	47	21
6. Northallerton Aind	18	6	3	9	22	48	21
7. Southbank	18	4	5	9	15	36	17

** Three points deducted*

DIVISION ONE RESULTS CHART 1995-96

HOME TEAM	**1**	**2**	**3**	**4**	**5**	**6**	**7**	**8**	**9**	**10**	**11**	**12**	**13**	**14**	**15**	**16**
1. Annfield Plain	*	1-2	2-0	1-0	7-0	2-3	4-0	2-1	1-2	1-2	3-0	3-2	0-3	0-1	4-3	1-4
2. Birtley Town	2-0	*	2-2	4-0	3-1	5-4	1-4	0-2	0-0	3-0	3-0	2-0	0-2	3-2	5-3	3-2
3. Boldon C A	2-1	2-3	*	2-3	1-2	2-1	1-3	6-1	0-0	1-2	2-0	3-1	0-2	2-1	2-2	6-1
4. Hartlepool BWOB	2-2	1-2	0-4	*	2-1	1-6	0-4	2-1	2-1	0-3	1-0	1-0	0-1	2-4	1-3	6-2
5. Jarrow	2-1	1-0	3-1	4-0	*	3-4	0-4	0-1	1-1	2-2	2-3	1-4	0-4	2-1	4-2	2-1
6. Jarrow Roofing	3-1	3-2	3-3	2-0	4-3	*	3-1	3-1	5-0	0-0	5-0	2-1	1-2	2-0	5-2	2-2
7. Marske United	3-0	4-0	4-0	3-2	8-1	0-2	*	8-0	3-0	2-0	10-0	1-1	2-2	1-2	3-1	3-0
8. N Shields Athletic	1-3	1-2	1-5	0-1	1-3	0-4	1-4	*	2-1	2-0	2-4	2-4	0-1	1-1	2-2	1-4
9. Cleadon S C	2-2	1-1	0-0	1-1	1-0	0-5	2-4	0-2	*	5-0	2-4	3-1	2-5	1-5	2-1	1-0
10. S Tyneside United	0-0	2-2	4-0	1-0	2-0	0-3	2-1	1-1	2-0	*	3-1	1-0	1-1	2-1	1-1	2-1
11. S C Fulwell	0-3	3-2	2-4	1-9	1-0	2-7	1-4	4-5	2-8	0-3	*	2-3	0-6	1-4	0-6	2-5
12. Kennek Roker	1-2	2-0	1-4	4-3	3-2	2-3	1-6	5-0	6-0	0-0	1-0	*	1-0	1-1	0-0	4-3
13. Ryhope C W	0-0	1-1	2-2	1-2	0-3	0-0	0-1	0-1	4-3	0-1	6-1	0-1	*	3-1	4-3	0-0
14. Nissan	2-1	1-5	0-1	0-1	0-0	1-2	0-3	0-0	1-1	0-0	3-1	4-1	1-1	*	1-0	4-0
15. Windscale	3-0	1-1	1-0	5-2	5-0	4-3	1-1	1-1	0-3	4-3	2-0	4-3	3-1	2-0	*	0-2
16. Wolviston	1-2	3-1	2-1	3-1	4-2	0-3	1-2	3-0	0-0	0-1	2-1	2-2	0-1	0-2	0-4	*

DIVISION TWO CUP 1995-96

First Round;

Stanley United v Chilton Moor	5-1	Chilton Moor v Stanley United	1-0
Southbank v Harton & Westoe	2-2	Harton & Westoe v Southbank	1-2
Washington Glebe v Whitehaven Ams	1-1	Whitehaven Ams v Washington Glebe	4-1

Semi-Finals;

Northallerton Aind v Southbank	2-0	Southbank v Northallerton Aind	3-2
Whitehaven Ams v Stanley Utd	3-0	Stanley United v Whitehaven Ams	5-1

Final; Stanley United v Northallerton Aind 4-1

LEAGUE CUP 1995-96

First Round;

Wolviston v Kennek Roker	2-4	Stanley United v Jarrow Roofing	2-5
Jarrow v Harton & Westoe C W	2-1	Birtley Town vNorth Shields Ath	1-1, 2-0
Chilton Moor v Whitehaven Amt	1-2	Boldon C A v S Tynesdide Utd	0-0, 0-5
Washington Glebe v Cleadon S C	2-1	Northallerton Aind v Windscale	1-4
Murton Inter v S C Fulwell	1-0		

Second Round;

Jarrow Roofing v Southbank	3-2	Marske United v Murton Inter	6-1
Ryhope C W v Nissan	4-3	Hartlepool BWOB v Jarrow	2-1
South Tyneside Utd v Annfield Plain	1-0	Whitehaven Ams v Kennek Roker	3-2
Windscale v Birtley Town	3-0	Washington Glebe	Bye

Third Round;

Washington Glebe v Whitehaven Ams	1-3	Ryhope C W v S Tyneside Utd	4-1
Windscale v Marske United	1-2	Hartlepool BWOB v Jarrow Roofing	2-4

Semi-Finals;

Marske United v Jarrow Roofing	3-1	Whitehaven Ams v Ryhope C W	2-2, 2-1

Final; Marske United v Whitehaven Ams 4-0

MONKWEARMOUTH CHARITY CUP 1995-96

First Round;

Chilton Moor v Windscale	2-6	Murton Inter v Annfield Plain	1-5
Marske United v North Shields Ath	4-0	Birtley Town v Southbank	4-0
Jarrow v Whitehaven Ams	2-1	S Tyneside Utd v Northallerton Aind	5-0
Boldon C A v S C Fulwell	5-1	Washington Glebe v Cleadon S C	1-0

Second Round;

Birtley Town v Washington Glebe	4-5	Hartlepool BWOB v Jarrow	2-4
Stanley United v Wolviston	2-4	Nissan v Ryhope C W	2-1
Harton & Westoe v Jarrow Roofing	2-5	Annfield Plain v S Tyneside Utd	0-1
Kennek Roker v Windscale	3-2	Boldon C A v Marske United	0-5

Third Round;

Jarrow Roofing v S Tyneside Utd	4-0	Wolviston v Jarrow	6-4
Nissan v Washington Glebe	4-1	Kennek Roker v Marske United	1-3

Semi-Finals;

Marske United v Jarrow Roofing	2-1	Wolviston v Nissan	1-4

Final; Marske United v Nissan 3-3, 1-0

SUNDERLAND SHIPOWNERS CUP 1995-96

First Round;

Northallerton Aind v Cleadon S C	4-1	Harton & Westoe v S C Fulwell	3-4
Hartlepool BWOB v Jarrow	6-3	Windscale v Whitehaven Ams	0-1
Birtley Town v Chilton Moor	6-3	Southbank v Boldon C A	0-7
South Tyneside v Ryhope C W	2-0	Washington Glebe v Annfield Plain	0-2

Second Round;

Annfield Plain v Boldon C A	3-0	Jarrow Roofing v North Shields Ath	5-1
Nissan v Whitehaven Ams	0-1	S C Fulwell v Birtley Town	3-5
Murton Inter v Kennek Roker	2-7	Hartlepool BWOB v S Tyneside Utd	1-5
Wolviston v Stanley United	3-2	Marske United v Northallerton Aind	7-1

Third Round;

Whitehaven Ams v Wolviston	5-3	Birtley Town v Annfield Plain	3-6
Jarrow Roofing v Marske United	1-3	Kennek Roker v S Tyneside Utd	2-1

Semi-Finals;

Marske United v Kennek Roker	3-0	Annfield Plain v Whitehaven Ams	5-3

Final: Marske United v Annfield Plain 3-2 (aet)

DIVISION ONE CLUBS 1995-96

ANNFIELD PLAIN

Chairman: Frank Ross **Press Officer:**
Secretary: M Lawson, 24 Northgate, Anfield Plain, Stanley, Co. Durham DH9 7UY (01207 235879).
Manager: D Longstaff **Ground:** Derwent Park, Annfield Plain.
Directions: On A693 road to Consett, 200 yds west of junction with A6067. Ground behind new housing estate. 6 miles from Durham (BR). Buses from Sunderland, Newcastle & Durham.
Seats: 20 **Cover:** 200 **Capacity:** 6,000 **Floodlights:** No **Founded:** 1890.
Colours: Claret/white/claret **Change colours:** All blue.
Programme: 16 pages, 20p **Hons:** Wearside Lg 84-85 (Monkwearmouth Charity Cup 92-93), FA Cup 1st Rd 26-27 28-29 64-65.

BIRTLEY TOWN

Chairman: J Heslington **Vice-Chairman:** J Grainger. **Manager:** Barry Fleming
Secretary: Kevin McConnell, 8 Leyburn Place, Birtley, (0191 4100495)
Asst Manager: David Smith **Coach:** Malcolm Thompson **Commercial Manager:** Ray Stafford.
Ground: Birtley Sports Complex. **Directions:** (From Durham) Off A1(M) signpsted for Chester-le-Street, take 2nd turn off r-bout signed Birtley, take last turn off next r-bout (still signed Birtley), after one and a half miles take 1st left after AEI Cables - ground at rear of sports complex.
Seats: None **Cover:** None **Capacity:** **Floodlights:** No. **Founded:** 1890
Cols: Green & white stripes/white/white **Change colours:** Yellow/blue/red. **Reformed:** 1986
Midweek home matches: Wednesday **Club Sponsors:** C & C Coachworks **Club Shop:** No
Reserves' Lge: None **Clubhouse:** Matchdays only. Not licensed.
Programme: 32 pages, 25p **Programme Editor:** D Smith, 25 Penshaw View, Birtley.
Record appearances: Barry Fleming **Hons:** Wearside Lg 45-46 (Lg Cup 35-36), Northern Alliance 23-24 (R-up 13-14).

BOLDON COMMUNITY ASSOCIATION

Chairman: R A O Shepherd. **Vice Chairman:** G Smith **President:** A Brewster.
Sec./Press Off./Commercial Mgr: George Pollard, 126 Horsley Hill Road, South Shields (0191 4546821).
Manager: Bill Newham **Asst Manager:** P Quinn **Coach:** Tommy Frazer.
Ground: Boldon Community Association, New Road, Boldon Colliery.
Directions: A19 to junc A184 Sunderland/Newcastle. Follow signs to Boldon Asda stores, then to North Road Social Club (SHACK). Ground behind. 800 yds from East Boldon (BR). Buses 533, 531, 319, 528.
Seats: 100 **Cover:** 400 **Capacity:** 3,500 **Floodlights:** No **Founded:** 1892.
Colours: Green & yellow/black **Change:** Red/black/red **Programme:** No.
Nickname: Villa. **Clubhouse:** Matchdays only. Bar snacks
Club Sponsors: Tyne Dock Engineering Co., South Shields. **Midweek matchday:** Mon or Wed
Hons: Wearside Lg 3, (Lg Cup 3), M/mouth Char Cup 2, Shipowners Cup 6.

HARTLEPOOL BOYS WELFARE OLD BOYS

Chairman: Ken Handisides **Press Officer/Treasurer:** George Lester (01429 275327).
Secretary: Phillip Jordan, 473 Catcote Road, Hartlepool TS25 2RA (01429 870015)
Manager: Jimmy Costello **Asst Manager:** Wilf Constantine **Physio:** Tony Metcalfe.
Ground: Grayfields Enclosure, Jesmond Road, Hartlepool.
Directions: Leave A19 on A179 signed Hartlepool, right for Throston Grange at 1st r'bout, left at 1st lights into Jesmond Road, ground 400yds on left.
Seats: None **Cover:** No **Capacity:** **Floodlights:** No **Founded:** 1952.
Colours: All white **Change colours:** Light blue/navy/black **Nickname:** None.
Programme: 10 pages, 50p **Programme Editor:** Secretary **Club Shop:** No.
Midweek home matchday: Monday **Clubhouse:** No.
Hons: FA Vase 3rd Rd, Wearside Lg Div 2 92-93, Hartlepool Church Lg(2)(Lg Cup(3)), Hartlepool Mem. Shield, Durham Amat Cup 2, Hartlepool & Dist. Lg(3)(Lg Cup(3)), Teesside Lg 73-74 85-86 (R-up 3).

JARROW

Chairman: Thomas Ridley **Treasurer:** Gavin Bainbridge.
Secretary/Press Officer: Calum McAuley, 109 Bamburgh Avenue, South Shields (0191 4555924).
Ground: Perth Green Community Centre. **Directions:** From A19 or A1(M) follow drections to South Shields, right onto John Reid Road. First slip road onto Brockley Whinns Estate, follow road past Red Hackle pub, third left left onto Inverness Road, then right into Perth Green Community Centre.
Colours: All blue **Change:** All yellow **Founded:** 1980.
Hons: Sth Tyne Lg & Lg Cup, Washington Lg R-up 89-90 (Lg Cup 90-91, Aged Peoples Tphy R-up 90-91), Gateshead Charity Cup 90-91, Durham Tphy R-up 90-91.

MARSKE UNITED

Chairman/Press Off.: John Hodgson **Vice Chairman:** John Corner. **President:** Raymond Jarvis
Secretary: Ian Rowe, 19 High Row, Loftus, Saltburn, Cleveland. TS13 4SA (01287 643440)
Manager: Alan Marples **Coach:** Charlie Bell **Physio:** Barry Schollay
Ground: Mount Pleasant, Mount Pleasant Ave., Marske-by-Sea, Redcar (01642 471091).
Directions: From A19 take A174 exit marked Yarm, Teesport, Redcar, Whitby and head east towards Teesport and Redcar, continue on A174 and enter Marske by A1040 or A1084. In town square right into Southfield Road, and right again to ground. 300 yds from Marske BR station
Seats: 100. **Cover:** 150. **Capacity:** 3,000 **Floodlights:** No **Club Shop:** Yes
Programme: 32 pages 30p **Editor:** John Hodgson (01642 484006).
Colours: Yellow/blue/white **Change:** Blue/white/yellow

Founded: 1956. **Sponsors:** Arnott Insurance **Nickname:** The Seasiders.
Midweek matchday: Wednesday **Reserve League:** Teesside Alliance.
Clubhouse: Open every night and weekend lunchtimes. Food served after all games.
Club Record Goalscorer: Chris Morgan 212 **Club Record Appearances:** John Hodgson.
Honours: N Riding Sen Cup 94-95; N Riding County Cup 84-85; Teesside Lg 80-81 84-85; Wearside Lg 95-96, (R-up 2), Lg Cup 3; M/mouth Charity Cup 93-94 95-96; Sunderland Ship. Cup 95-96.

NORTH SHIELDS

Chairman: Alan Matthews. **Manager:** Bob Weir. **Coach:** Wilf Keilty.
Secretary: Dave Thompson, 38 Barnstable Road, North Shields, (0191 2590249)
Ground: Ralph Gardner Park, West Percy Rd., N.Shields, Tyne & Wear,NE29 OES
Directions: A19 northbound through Tyne Tunnel.Take first slip round to first roundabout and take third exit and over next roundabout.Take third exit again at next roundabout into Waterville Road.Over another roundabout and second left into\silkey's Lane. First right into West Percy Road and ground is on right.
Capacity: 2,000 **Seats:** No **Cover:** **Floodlights:** No **Club Shop:** No
Programme: 64 pages, 50p **Editor:** Ken Green (0378 055469) **Press Officer:** Secretary
Colours: All red **Change colours:** Blue/black strips
Sponsors: Wilkinson Stores **Nickname:** New Robins **Founded:** 1896 **Clubhouse:** None
95-96 Captain: **95-96 Top Scorer:** Graeme McDonald **95-96 P.o.Y.:** Graeme McDonald
Club Record Scorer: Tommy Cole (244 30-39) **Club Record Appearances:** Ron Tatum 560
Hons: Nthn Cnt E, Champ/Cup/Presidents Cup 91-92. FA Amt Cup 68-69, N Lge 68-69.

SOUTH BANK

Chairman: Peter Livingstone **Treasurer:** Paul Watson
Secretary: David L Di Marco, Mannion Park Broadway, Trunk Road, Grangetownm Middlesbrough TS6 7RS (01642 826514)
Ground: Mannion Park, The Broadway, Trunk Road, Grangetown
Directions: There are three main routes leading to the club; A66 Middlesbrough bypass. A1085 Redcar Trunk Road and A174 Parkway signpost for Wilton I.C.I. west gate roundabout. Entrance is 200 metres from roundabout heading towards Grangetown
Colours: Red & white/red/red & white **Change colours:** All blue

---

SOUTH SHIELDS CLEADON SOCIAL CLUB

Chairman: Gordon Ferries **Vice-Chairman/Press Off./Manager:** David Wood (091 4554607).
Secretary: Mr Charlie Appleby, 49 Tynedale Rd, South Shields (091 454 5724).
Asst Manager: Steve Duguid **Commercial Manager:** Joan Wood
Coach: Andy Wilkinson **Ground:** Jack Clarke Park, South Shields.
Directions: Enter South Shields on A194 to r'bout taking you on to A1300 John Reid Rd. 2nd left at 3rd r'bout into King George Rd then Sunderland Road, right at lights into Grosvenor Rd then then left into Horsly Hill Rd. Ground on right behind indoor bowls centre. 3/4 mile from Chichester Metro station.
Capacity: 400 **Seats:** 25 **Cover:** 75 **Floodlights:** No **Founded:** Early 60s
Colours: Amber/black/black **Change:** All maroon **Club Shop:** No
Midweek home matches: Wednesday **Sponsors:** Cleadon & Dist. Soc. Club **Nickname:** The Club
Clubhouse: Cleadon Social Club, Fulwell Avenue, South Shields. Normal pub hours except Saturday.
Hons: Wearside Lg Div 2 90-91, Shields & Dist. Lg, Washington Lg 77-78 84-85

SOUTH SHIELDS HARTON & WESTOE

Chairman: Ronald Wightman **President:**
Secretary/Treasurer: Graham Bass, 76 Stanhope Road, South Shields NE33 4BS (0191 4544798)
Ground: Harton Colliery Welfare.
Directions: A1M at Whitemare Pool take A194 to South Shields for 2 1/2 miles. At third roundabout turn right onto A1300. At 2nd roundabout turn left onto Boldon Lane. Ground 50 yards on right
Colours: Blue & white/blue/blue **Change colours:** All red

SOUTH TYNESIDE UNITED

Secretary: Martin Lynn, 261 Sunderland Road, South Shields NE34 8AL (0191 4555145)
Chairman: Barry Raper **Treasurer:** Susan Raper.
Ground: Monkton Stadium, Dene Terrace, Jarrow. **Directions:** From A1 north straight onto Jarrow slip road, then left into York Ave, take 6th left into Dene Terrace. ground on left
Colours: Yellow & blue/blue/yellow **Change colours:** Green & white/black/green & white

---

STANLEY UNITED

President: A Westgarth **Vice-President:** B Waiting.
Secretary: J V Kirkup, 9 Brookes Rise, Regents Green, Langley, Durham DH7 8XY (0191 3780921)
Physio: J Burn. **Asst Manager/Coach:** K Finnegan
Ground: High Road, Stanley, near Crook (nicknamed Hill Top Ground).
Directions: Teeside on A689 to Bishop Auckland and onto Crook, turn left at Market Place then 1st right for Tow Law to Billy Row and Stanley, right at top of bank then 1st left, grd 250 yards on left.
Seats: None **Cover:** 300 **Capacity:** 3,000 **Floodlights:** No **Founded:** 1890.
Colours: Red & white stripes/black/red **Change colours:** Sky/navy/navy **Nickname:** The Nops
Programme: Yes, new for 94-95 **Programme Editor:** Vince Kirkup (Tel Nos above).
Sponsors: Company Cars Direct **Clubhouse:** Open matchdays. **Club Shop:** No
Major Honours: Northern Lg 3, R-up 62-63), Lg Cup 3, FA Cup 1st Rd 53-54, FA Amtr Cup SF 19-20.

SUNDERLAND KENNEK ROKER

Chairman: J Broadbent **Press Officer:** Secretary **Treasurer:** Les Dodd.
Secretary: Adrian Forster, 42 Sunnybrow, Silksworth, Sunderland (0191 521 4007)
Ground: Silksworth Welfare Park
Directions: Behind Lord Seaham Public House. Blind Lane Silsworth
Colours: Red & white stripes/black/black **Change:** Sky/navy/navy.
Hons: Wearside Lg Cup 91-92 (Shipowners Cup 89-90 (R-up 80-81), M/mouth Charity Cup R-up 80-81).

SUNDERLAND RYHOPE C W

Chairman: David Lawson **Press Officer:** Secretary
Secretary: Bob Lewins, 7 Belsay Gardens,St.Gabriels Estate,Sunderland. SR4 7SZ (01915 141725)
Ground: Ryhope Recreation Park, Ryhope Street, Ryhope, Sunderland (0191 521 2843).
Directions: Take A19 (3 miles south of Sunderland centre) to Ryhope village, at Village Green turn into Evelyn Terrace/Ryhope Street and carry on up bank past Presto's for 600 yds - ground appears on left. 3 miles from Sunderland Central (BR), bus every 10 minutes from Sunderland centre.
Seats: No **Cover:** No **Capacity:** 1,000 **Floodlights:** Yes **Founded:** 1988.
Colours: Red and White stripes/Black/Red **Change colours:** All Blue
Honours: Wearside Lg 4, (Lg Cup 2), Durham Challenge Cup 77-78, M/mouth Charity Cup 3, Sunderland Shipowners Cup 2.

WASHINGTON GLEBE

Chairman: **Press Officer:** Secretary **Treasurer:** Graham Thirlaway
Secretary: Robert Robson, 24 Talbot Close, Glebe, Washington NE38 7RH (091 4151893).
Ground: Washington Glebe Welfare.
Directions: A1 them A19, A1231 into Washington, 3rd exit road (signed Gateshead A195), turn for District 9 at r'bout, right for Washington Village at next r'bout, right at 1st T-jnct., pitch 200 yds on right.
Colours: Blue & white **Change colours:** All red.

WASHINGTON NISSAN

Chairman: A Hill **Treasurer:** Tom Dixon **Press Officer:** Secretary
Secretary: Harry English, 159 Alston Crescent, Seaburn Dene, Sunderland SR6 8NF (091 5487194)
Manager: Stan Fenwick **Assistant Manager:** Keith Robertson.**Coach:** Darren Ward
Ground: Nissan Spts Complex.
Directions: North along A1 (M) use A690 (sign post Sunderland) connect with A19, north on A19, after passing the A1231 turn off, plant on the left. Past plant & follow signs 'Nissan Offices'.
Colours: Red & black/black/black **Change colours:** Yellow & blue/blue/blue **Founded:** 1988
Clubhouse: Open Mon-Fri 5-11pm, Sat 11am-11pm, Sun noon-3 & 7-10.30pm
Hons: Wearside Lg Div 1 93-94 (Lg Cup R-up 91-92, Div 2 Cup 92-93 93-94), Nissan European Tphy 3.

WHITEHAVEN AMATEURS

Chairman: S Hocking **Press Officer:** Secretary
Secretary: Harry Upton 14 Foxhouses Road, Whitehaven CA28 8AF (01946 61750)
Manager: Ian Green **Assistant Manager:** Ian Atkins.
Ground: Whitehaven County Ground, Coach Road, Whitehaven
Directions: Barrow on A595, ignore branch to town centre at B.P. garage turn right at t/lights on A5094. 1/2 mile turn left at Esso garage into Coach Rd. Narrow lane ent immed after l/ crossing to grd behind Rugby Lge Stadium.
Colours: Yellow/blue/blue **Change colours:** White/red/red
Honours: Cumberland Cup 90-91, County League 87-88 88-89, Wearside Lg Div 2 Cup R-up 93-94.

WINDSCALE

Chairman: R Napier **Press Officer:** Secretary **Treasurer:** A Barwise
Secretary: Geoff Turrell, 65 Leathwaite, Loop Road South, Whitehaven, Cumbria CA28 7UG (01936 62229)
Ground: Falcon Field, Egremont. **Directions:** A66 to Bridgefoot. A595 Barrow, bottom of hill approaching Egremont take 3rd turn off island (signed) Smithfield/Gillfoot, grd in housing estate
Colours: All navy **Change:** White/red/red
Hons: Furness Snr Cup 85-86 **Founded:** 1950

WOLVISTON

Chairman: Eddie Poole **Vice Chairman:** Derek Stockton **President:** Bob Smith
Sec./Press Officer: Keith Simpson, 14 Lodore Grove, Acklam, Middlesbrough TS5 8PB (01642 823734).
Manager: John Johnson **Asst Manager:** Kevin Smith **Coach:** Alan Lucas
Ground: Metcalfe Way, Wynyard Road, Wolviston, Billingham, Cleveland TS22 5NE.
Directions: On Wynyard Road between Thorpe Thewles & Wolviston. A19 onto A689 into Wolviston village, take Wynyard Road heading towards Thorpe Thewles, grd left before Sir John Halls Estate.
Seats: None **Cover:** 200 **Capacity:** 2,000 **Floodlights:** No **Founded:** 1910
Colours: Royal/white/royal **Change:** Red/red/white **Nickname:** Wolves
Programme: 8 pages, 20p **Editor:** Secretary or Ben Foreman (01642 550352).
Sponsors: R.C.I. Industrial Cleaners **Rec. Gate:** 500 v Middlesbrough 27/7/93 **Club Shop:** No.
Clubhouse: Licensed bar. Hot & cold meals. Open 11am-11pm on matchdays.
Hons: Wearside Lg Div 2 89-90 (Lg Cup R-up 92-93), Teesside Lg R-up 84-85 (R T Raine Cup 86-87), Durham FA Trophy R-up 89-90, Stockton & District Lg 3, (Lg Cup 3), Lg Charity Cup 79-80).

Dr MARTENS FOOTBALL LEAGUE

President: G E Templeman

Chairman: D S R Gillard

Hon. Secretary: D J Strudwick,
11 Welland Close, Durrington, Worthing,
West Sussex BN13 3NR (01903 267788)

Diamonds are a Griggs best friend. After just four years since the merger of Rushden Town and Irthlingborough Diamonds the consolidated club, Rushden & Diamonds FC, chaired by Max Griggs, are the champions of the Beazer Homes (Southern Football) League.

Rushden & Diamonds after winning the League Championship

After finishing fifth in the 1994\5 season Rushden & Diamonds FC, the pre-season favourite for the title, lost just one of its opening eight matches. On 23rd September, Diamonds moved to the top of the table and did not surrender its lead once. Having led the marathon for 34 weeks of the 39 week season, establishing a lead on occasions of 15 points, having an average Home League attendance of 2168 (a gate of 4664 attended the final home match of the season), clearly the Southern Football League will be providing another outstanding candidate to non-Football League's elite to the GM Vauxhall Conference.

Don't believe for one moment, however, that Rushden & Diamonds had life all their own way. The nucleus of the chasing pack contained Cheltenham Town, Gloucester City and Halesowen Town. Given the opportunity, all four were capable of promotion to the Football Conference and all four sustained positions within the top six of the table from 28th October. In such a competitive division, this is a record to be proud of.

By the second week of February however, it looked as though only Halesowen Town would be in a position to take advantage of any disaster that might befall Rushden. But having moved four points clear of Gloucester, Halesowen were still ten points adrift of the top. Undeterred by the enormity of the task (Halesowen trailed Rushden 18 points on the 2nd December) the Yeltz continued to collect points at a rate that in many other seasons would have been good enough to lift the Shield.

Aided by the Diamonds losing four of their last 10 matches, Halesowen, who were only defeated twice in their final 34 outings, took Rushden to the wire. With Halesowen winning at Newport AFC on the final day of the season, Diamonds needed at least a point from their home encounter with Merthyr Tydfil. After racing into a 3-0 lead, Rushden allowed the jitters to set in before passing the winning post 3-2 and two league points ahead of Halesowen. Celebrations at the finest football stadium outside of the Football League went on long into the night.
Having cut Diamonds' Kohinoor size lead and having come so close and yet so far from the title, Halesowen Town, (who were not beaten by Rushden during the season) can be consoled that the club attained its highest ever position in football. The League table does not lie, but Halesowen lost two fewer matches than Rushden and their 92 point tally would have been sufficient to win the Championship on four out of the last five occasions.
Gloucester, who finished third, and Cheltenham, who were fourth, maintained their amazingly consistent records. Despite the close proximity of these two big clubs, competition remains fierce and success high on the agenda. Surely their day will come. They will have to watch out for another 'new kid on the block', however, in Gresley Rovers. The Moatment attained their highest ever position in the Premier Division and are building a reputation for good football as quickly as they are building a new stadium.
In the Southern Division, Waterlooville failed in the final furlong, as they did last year. Newport I.O.W. once again proved to be a difficult side to beat and maintained their steady improvement in the League whilst, at the same time, appearing in the F.A. Cup First Round for the second consecutive season. Braintree also continued improving its League form and would have done so more emphatically had it not had three points deducted for fielding an ineligible player. Their 93 League goals confirms the club's serious attempt at promotion to the Premier Division and the broadening of the club's development that this inevitably entails. But it wasn't to be, Braintree finished fifth in the table and have resigned from the League preferring to play more local football.
Had it not been for Weymouth's 6 defeats in their first 10 matches, the Terras would have joined Waterlooville, Newport I.O.W. and Havant Town in enhancing the 'western' challenge for the title. Weymouth ended up in sixth position and Havant Town in seventh, following the deduction of six points for fielding an ineligible player. Instead, the honours were left to Kent. Sittingbourne creamed the awards and will regain the Premier Division status that was lost only last year. Ashford Town finished in the runners-up spot and regain the Premier Division status that the 'Nuts and Bolts' lost in 1992. After some barren years in the 'Garden of England', that have seen the loss to the Southern League of Canterbury City, Chatham Town, Dartford, Folkestone, Hythe Town and Sheppey United, the resurgence of these two clubs, coupled with the resurrection and promotion of Dartford has, I am sure, buoyed up the Kentish men and the Men of Kent. This point is emphasised by Sittingbourne's winning of the Merit Cup for the most League goals, 102. It is the Brickies second victory in this category in four years.
Sleeping giants were also stirred in the Midland section. With the exception of King's Lynn, the main challenge for the title came from the very heart of the Midlands, Bedworth United relived some former glory days and their challenge lasted until the final week of the campaign despite losing a point for fielding an ineligible player. Moor Green's fourth place underlines the consistent strength of the Hall Green Club. The vibrant thrust of freshmen Paget Rangers earned the club new esteem before achieving a credible 5th place. But what of Tamworth? With the Lamb's ability to attract big crowds, Tamworth on a roll would be a threat in any Division. Lying in second place and three points clear of their nearest rivals (and with two games in hand!) at the end of February, Tamworth looked to be the most serious threat to Nuneaton's lead. Then the rot set in. Eleven defeats and just four wins from their remaining 15 matches, sheared off the Lambs' chances. Tamworth ended the season in sixth position.
Despite a couple of stutters and the penalty of a two point deduction, King's Lynn lasted the pace better and finished second, three points above Bedworth, Nuneaton ran out worthy Champions by nine points and completed a League and cup double by defeating Baldock Town 5-2 on aggregate over two legs. Can such a successful 'double' season, then provide the foundation for the fulfilment of all the potential that Nuneaton so often promise but so frequently fail to produce. Borough's last visit to the Premier only lasted one season. This was preceded by a highly successful sojourn in the Conference which was ended by an ignominious relegation to the Premier Division and, twelve months later, a further relegation to the Midland section. Nuneaton, once again has the platform to recapture some of its former glory.
Certainly the 'Boro restored a lot of its previous 'street cred' with the convincing Dr. Martens Cup triumph. Before Moor Green were eventually beaten in a tight semi-final, Nuneaton had already dispatched Buckingham Town and Premier Division opposition in the shape of V.S. Rugby, Atherstone United and Gresley Rovers. Baldock's route to the final came by way of victories over Bury Town, King's Lynn, Crawley Town and a semi-final victory over Salisbury City. The semi-Final success was earned by way of the 'away goals' rule. Baldock's goal at Salisbury was the only strike in 180 minutes of closely fought play.
In the final, Nuneaton Borough looked exceptionally strong and quick in the first leg at Baldock. The League's joint leading goal scorer, Robert Straw, looked particularly effective in a 3-1 win and scored twice, himself, Nick Andersen had already opened the scoring for Nuneaton, Baldock concluded the evening's goals with a penalty converted by Andrew Wallace. Without Straw in the second leg, Nuneaton didn't look quite the same team. Baldock took full advantage and soon pulled a goal back when Darren Fenton fired home. Within a minute, though, the usually reliable Paul Bowgett conceded a penalty and Borough's two goal lead from the first leg was restored by Ian Drewitt. Another goal towards the end by Anthony Simpson underlined Nuneaton's superiority and left Baldock with Premier Division survival on their minds four days later.
Nuneaton were one of thirteen Beazer Homes League clubs in the Fourth Qualifying Round of the FA Cup. This number may be three less than last year but considering only three clubs were exempt until this stage of the competition, thirteen is nontheless a good representation. Remarkably, eight teams won through to the First Round Proper, two more than last year. Eight clubs at this stage represented more than any other non-Football League competition except for the Football Conference who had 10 representatives. (But it must be remembered that the Football Conference received eight exemptions to the 4th Qualifying Round and two to the First Round Proper). Unfortunately for the Beazer Homes League, six clubs fell at this hurdle. Nuneaton lost by the odd goal in 3 at Barrow; Burton Albion went out gallantly at Bradford 4-3 despite being 2-0 and 3-1 down; Rushden & Diamonds, perhaps surprisingly, lost at home 3-1 to Cardiff; Newport IOW and Ashford Town both took their opposition to replays before going out 2-1 and 1-0 to Enfield and Bognor Regis Town respectively, and Dorchester Town crashed 9-1 at Oxford United despite holding the score to 2-1 at half-time. There were, though, two incredible results to shout about, and shout loudly, too. In front of over 3000 fans, Gravesend & Northfleet overturned Football League

opposition in Colchester United. And Cinderford Town, Beazer Homes League newcomers who had never gone beyond the Second Qualifying Round before, defeated Football Conference club Bromsgrove Rovers. (Bath City, also from the Football Conference, had been Cinderford's victim in the previous round). So with two clubs in the 2nd Round of the F.A. Cup, the draw from Lancaster Gate was eagerly awaited. Under the guidance of Chief Executive, Graham Kelly, Cinderford and Gravesend were paired together!

It was, of course, bitter sweet news, but both clubs felt they had a realistic chance of victory and a place in the Third Round along with the Premiership clubs. After a 1-1 draw on a murky December day in the Forest of Dean, the clubs were advised of the fate that awaited the winner, in new style glitzy, but tasteful, presentation in London W2. A home tie against Aston Villa was to be the reward. In the replay, Gravesend demonstrated their League superiority by defeating Cinterford 3-0.

Space prevents me from describing the quality and success of the day to it's full extent. Aston Villa looked after everyone to a degree beyond expectations and Gravesend and Northfleet were magnificent. After going behind to a Mark Draper goal after just two minutes, a combination of good defence, good fortune and some potent attacking play of their own enabled the 'Fleet' to hold the scoreline until Savo Milosevic volleyed home in the first minute of the second half. And not even a third goal from Tommy Johnson in the 72nd minute could suppress the courage of Gravesend. The club covered itself with glory. Chairman Lionel Ball was the last to leave the Grandstand. Filled with pride, he watched every player leave the pitch and nearly every spectator safely depart from the terraces before reliving his club's greatest day in the company of the generous Villa Chairman, Doug Ellis.

In the F.A. Trophy, hopes were justifiably high when seven Beazer Homes League clubs reached the Second Round Proper, the last 32 in the competition. Unfortunately, four clubs were drawn against one another. Sudbury Town succeeded at the expense of Gloucester City whilst Merthyr Tydfil knocked out Dudley Town, Newport AFC lost at Carshalton Athletic, 2-1 and Burton Albion lost by the same score at Stevenage Borough, the eventual winners of the Football Conference. Gresley Rovers made up a trio of Beazer League clubs in the Third Round of the competition by accounting for Blyth Spartans, 2-1.

Gresley then repeated this scoreline with an excellent performance at Guisely. Eventual finalists, Northwich Victoria, relieved Merthyr Tydfil of its position in the tournament, but only after three attempts, 1-1, 2-2 & 3-0. Sudbury Town's assault on the Trophy was ended by the eventual winners, Macclesfield Town, by the only goal of the game. Gresley Rovers' reward for reaching the Quarter Final of the competition for the first time in the club's history was a home tie with Macclesfield. The Silkmen curtailed the former F.A. Vase winner's interest in the competition with a sound 2-0 win.

Well, for every winner there is a loser. In welcoming the winners of promotion from the Feeder Leagues to the Southern Football League, Cirencester Town, Dartford, Raunds Town, Shepshed Dynamo and St. Leonards Stamcroft, the League must say a sad farewell to the relegated clubs, Bridgnorth Town, Bury Town and Poole Town. I hope you will regain your former status quickly. The relegation of Poole Town also signals the departure of Barry Hughes from the Management Committee. Mr. Hughes must relinquish his position as a result of Poole Town's demotion. Thank you for your four years service, Barry.

Rushden & Diamonds move to the Football Conference with everyone's good wishes and confidence that this progressive club will make a significant impact in its new sphere.

Only two clubs, therefore, will be relegated from the Football Conference. Runcorn and Dagenham & Redbridge will be placed in the Northern Premier League and the Isthmian League, respectively. Dover Athletic, who would have returned to the Southern League had there been a third club promoted, avoid relegation.

The fact that the relegated clubs are not geographically commensurate with the promoted clubs, and the fact that it has not proved possible to redress the situation by relocating a club (in accordance with the National Joint Liaison Committee's 'Movement of Clubs' document, as in previous years) has regurgitated thoughts of restructuring the Pyramid of Football. But the lifeblood of the Pyramid is the ability to have a fluid promotion and relegation of clubs between Leagues at the end of each season. The Pyramid of Football will stagnate and cease to exist without this exchange of clubs. Surely, therefore, the first problem to be addressed is why it is that clubs are not being promoted.

The Southern Football League has a good and vibrant working relationship with its Feeder Competitions. Thirteen clubs have been promoted to the Southern Football League in the last four years. Since the promotion link with the Alliance League (now the Football Conference) was established in 1978, the Southern Football League has never failed to have a club promoted. So far, fifteen clubs have now been elevated to Football Conference status. Furthermore, with only two exceptions, the promoted club has been the champion club. This after initially supplying more clubs to aid the formation of the Alliance League than any other competition. What's more, the Southern Football League remains the best supported League outside the football Conference. The top 70 best supported non-Football League clubs comprises the 22 Football Conference teams, 12 Isthmian teams, 10 Northern Premier teams and 26 Southern Football League teams.

If there is to be a restructuring of the Pyramid of Football it must be motivated by objectives that are guided by the best interest of clubs and football in general. A resturcture must not dilute or beark down the obvious strengths that currently exist within the structure simply to cover the weaknesses that presently prevail elsewhere.

And talking of strengths, for the last nine years the Southern Football League has enjoyed the fantastic backing of one of the country's leading house builders, Beazer Homes. during the last few months, though, it has not proved possible to agree a new term. The size of my regret at not renewing the contract with Beazer Homes is, however, exceeded by my thanks to the company's chief executive, Dennis Webb, and his organisation for the huge contribution to the competition. It is now with considerable excitement and anticipation that, on behalf of the League, I am looking forward to a new era of sponsorship with the R. Griggs Group Ltd., whose brand name Dr. Martens will be carried by the League, the League Cup and their peripheral awards for the next four years. Thank you once again, Beazer Homes. Welcome Dr. Martens.

In thanking the League's sponsors, I must also include Spalding Sports Ltd., for providing all the clubs with their match balls during the season. I look forward to two further years of working together.

As I compile this, my fourteenth Annual Report, I am looking forward to compiling the Fixture List and getting started on the 1996\97 DR. MARTENS FOOTBALL LEAGUE season.

DENNIS STRUDWICK.

PREMIER DIVISION TEN YEAR RECORDS

	86/7	87/8	88/9	89/0	90/1	91/2	92/3	93/4	94/5	95/6
Alvechurch	8	7	14	21	-	-	-	-	-	-
Ashford Town	-	12	18	19	-	-	-	-	-	-
Atherstone United	-	-	-	6	15	13	15	4	15	17
Aylesbury United	3	1	-	-	-	-	-	-	-	-
Baldock Town	-	-	-	-	-	-	-	-	-	18
Bashley	-	-	-	-	10	4	9	21	-	-
Basingstoke Town	16	-	-	-	-	-	-	-	-	-
Bath City	-	-	9	2	-	-	-	-	-	-
Bedworth United	12	14	22	-	-	-	-	-	-	-
Bromsgrove Rovers	2	4	10	10	5	1	-	-	-	-
Burton Albion	-	16	8	4	7	10	8	11	3	16
Cambridge City	6	3	5	8	3	5	14	17	9	19
Chelmsford City	5	19	-	18	18	18	12	6	15	12
Cheltenham Town	-	-	-	-	-	-	2	2	2	3
Corby Town	9	10	16	20	-	14	3	9	22	-
Crawley Town	13	6	12	15	19	17	=6	5	11	9
Dartford	4	2	2	3	13	6	-	-	-	-
Dorchester Town	-	11	13	14	11	11	18	18	6	13
Dover Athletic	-	-	6	1	4	2	1	-	-	-
Dudley Town	21	-	-	-	-	-	-	-	-	-
Fareham Town	14	9	19	-	-	-	-	-	-	-
Farnborough Town	-	-	-	-	1	-	-	1	-	-
Fisher Athletic	1	-	-	-	-	21	-	-	-	-
Folkestone	22	-	-	-	-	-	-	-	-	-
Gloucester City	-	-	-	9	2	12	13	10	4	4
Gosport Borough	18	15	7	22	-	-	-	-	-	-
Gravesnd & Northfleet	-	-	-	7	21	22	-	-	14	11
Gresley Rovers	-	-	-	-	-	-	-	14	8	5
Halesowen Town	-	-	-	-	8	8	10	3	13	2
Hastings Town	-	-	-	-	-	-	16	12	12	8
Hednesford Town	-	-	-	-	-	-	4	13	1	-
Ilkeston Town	-	-	-	-	-	-	-	-	-	20
King's Lynn	20	-	-	-	-	-	-	-	-	-
Leek Town	-	-	-	-	-	-	-	-	7	-
Leicester United	-	8	20	-	-	-	-	-	-	-
Merthyr Tydfil	-	-	1	-	-	-	-	-	-	7
Moor Green	-	-	15	11	16	9	19	19	-	-
Newport A F C	-	-	-	-	-	-	-	-	-	14
Nuneaton Borough	-	21		-	-	-	-	22	-	-
Poole Town	-	-	-	-	17	20	-	-	-	-
Redditch United	7	18	21	-	-	-	-	-	-	-
Rushden Town	-	-	-	-	14	-	-	-	-	-
Rushden & Diamonds	-	-	-	-	-	-	-	-	5	1
Salisbury	19	-	-	-	-	-	-	-	-	15
Shepshed Charterhouse	11	13	-	-	-	-	-	-	-	-
Sittingbourne	-	-	-	-	-	-	-	8	20	-
Solihull Borough	-	-	-	-	-	-	=6	6	19	-
Stafford Rangers	-	-	-	-	-	-	-	-	-	21
Sudbury Town	-	-	-	-	-	-	-	-	18	10
Trowbridge Town	-	-	-	-	-	7	5	7	21	-
V.S. Rugby	-	17	3	5	9	3	20	-	17	22
Waterlooville	-	-	17	16	20	15	11	20	-	-
Wealdstone	-	-	11	12	12	19	-	-	-	-
Weymouth	-	-	-	17	22	-	21	-	-	-
Willenhall Town	15	20	-	-	-	-	-	-	-	-
Witney Town	17	22	-	-	-	-	-	-	-	-
Worcester City	10	5	4	13	6	16	17	15	10	6
No of Clubs Competing	22	22	22	22	22	22	21	22	22	22

FINAL LEAGUE TABLES 1995/96

Division One		*P*	*W*	*D*	*L*	*F*	*A*	*Pts*
1.	Rushden & Diamonds	42	29	7	6	99	41	94
2.	Halesowen Town	42	27	11	4	70	36	92
3.	Cheltenham Town	42	21	11	10	76	57	74
4.	Gloucester City	42	21	8	13	65	47	71
5.	Gresley Rovers	42	20	10	12	70	58	70
6.	Worcester City	42	19	12	11	61	43	60
7.	Merthyr Tydfil	42	19	6	17	67	59	63
8.	Hastings Town	42	16	13	13	68	56	61
9.	Crawley Town	42	15	13	14	57	56	58
10.	Sudbury Town	42	15	10	17	69	71	55
11.	Gravesend & N	42	15	10	17	60	62	55
12.	Chelmsford City	42	13	16	13	46	53	55
13.	Dorchester Town	42	15	8	19	62	57	53
14.	Newport AFC	42	13	13	16	53	59	52
15.	Salisbury City	42	14	10	18	57	69	52
16.	Burton Albion	42	13	12	17	55	56	51
17.	Atherstone Utd	42	12	12	18	58	75	48
18.	Baldock Town	42	11	14	17	51	56	47
19.	Cambridge City	42	12	10	20	56	68	46
20.	Ilkeston Town	42	11	10	21	53	87	43
21.	Stafford Rangers	42	11	4	27	58	90	37
22.	V S Rugby	42	5	10	27	37	92	25

LEADING GOALSCORERS LEAGUE & CUP:

D Collins	Rushden & Diamonds	31	J Smith	Cheltenham Town	27
J Eaton	Cheltenham Town	24	I Brown	Sudbury Town	23
P Evans	Merthyr Tydfil	23	E Wright	Halesowen Town	23
S Cuggy	Hastings Town	21	M Munday	Gravesend & Northfleet	20
D Taylor	Ilkeston Town	18	D Webley	Newport AFC	18
S Norris	Worcester City	17	O Pickard	Dorchester Town	17

PREMIER DIV RESULTS CHART 1995-96

HOME TEAM	**1**	**2**	**3**	**4**	**5**	**6**	**7**	**8**	**9**	**10**	**11**	**12**	**13**	**14**	**15**	**16**	**17**	**18**	**19**	**20**	**21**	**22**
1. Atherstone U	*	2-2	0-3	2-2	1-2	1-2	2-1	3-4	2-1	2-0	1-2	0-1	1-0	3-3	0-2	0-0	1-3	3-1	2-2	0-0	4-1	1-1
2. Baldock Town	1-1	*	1-1	0-0	2-1	1-1	0-0	2-1	0-1	2-2	0-1	0-2	1-3	1-1	1-1	1-2	0-3	4-2	5-0	1-3	2-0	0-1
3. Burton Albn	2-2	1-0	*	0-0	1-1	3-2	2-1	1-0	1-0	1-2	1-1	1-1	1-1	1-2	1-3	0-1	4-2	0-1	5-1	2-3	0-0	2-0
4. Cambridge C	3-1	0-0	3-2	*	0-0	1-2	1-2	1-2	0-4	2-1	2-3	0-1	0-3	2-3	1-2	0-1	0-2	1-3	2-0	1-0	4-1	4-2
5. Chelmsford C	1-1	0-2	0-0	0-0	*	3-3	0-0	2-2	1-1	6-1	1-2	1-0	0-3	1-0	1-4	0-0	1-2	0-0	1-0	2-1	3-0	1-0
6. Cheltenham T	1-1	3-1	1-0	2-3	2-1	*	1-1	3-0	0-0	0-0	2-0	2-0	1-2	4-0	1-0	2-0	0-2	3-3	4-0	1-1	4-0	1-3
7. Crawley Town	0-1	1-2	1-1	3-3	3-2	4-1	*	1-1	0-0	1-0	2-0	1-3	3-2	1-0	1-0	0-0	2-2	2-0	2-1	2-2	3-1	1-3
8. Dorchester T	0-1	1-2	2-1	1-2	1-1	4-0	3-1	*	0-1	2-2	2-1	0-0	1-4	3-0	7-1	0-3	1-1	0-2	4-2	2-0	4-0	1-2
9. Gloucester C	0-2	3-1	2-1	3-1	5-0	0-3	1-1	1-0	*	3-1	1-2	0-2	0-2	3-1	3-1	1-1	2-1	2-0	3-2	1-0	1-1	2-1
10. Gravesend	2-1	1-1	1-2	2-0	0-1	1-0	3-1	4-1	0-0	*	1-1	0-1	4-0	3-1	1-0	4-0	1-3	1-1	0-3	3-3	2-0	0-1
11. Gresley Rov	1-0	3-0	2-1	2-2	0-2	0-2	1-0	0-2	1-0	3-1	*	1-1	1-1	2-3	3-1	1-3	0-3	2-2	1-1	5-2	4-0	1-0
12. Halesowen Tn	5-4	1-0	1-1	2-1	3-0	0-1	2-0	1-0	2-1	2-1	1-1	*	0-1	3-2	2-1	3-1	0-0	2-0	2-2	3-3	0-0	3-0
13. Hastings Tn	5-0	2-2	0-3	3-1	2-3	4-1	0-1	1-1	2-0	1-3	2-4	0-2	*	2-1	2-1	1-1	0-1	6-2	0-2	2-1	2-2	0-0
14. Ilkeston Tn	1-1	3-2	1-0	2-2	1-1	1-4	1-4	1-0	1-2	1-1	0-0	1-3	1-0	*	0-1	1-1	1-1	2-1	1-3	4-2	1-1	2-3
15. Merthyr Tyd	4-0	1-0	4-3	2-1	0-1	0-1	1-1	3-1	1-0	2-2	2-1	0-2	1-1	10-1	*	0-1	0-3	1-0	3-1	2-1	2-3	0-1
16. Newport AFC	1-2	1-1	0-1	1-2	1-2	2-3	1-1	3-2	1-0	0-1	0-1	1-2	1-1	2-3	0-0	*	1-1	1-1	2-1	5-1	5-2	1-1
17. Rushden & D	7-3	3-0	2-0	2-1	2-1	4-1	3-1	0-1	3-2	2-3	2-1	1-2	1-1	3-0	3-2	3-0	*	3-0	5-1	3-1	6-1	1-0
18. Salisbury City	2-0	1-2	2-0	1-0	0-0	3-3	2-1	1-0	3-3	2-0	1-4	2-3	3-4	0-2	0-0	1-3	0-2	*	2-1	3-0	1-0	3-1
19. Stafford Rang	1-4	0-1	2-3	2-4	3-0	0-1	3-0	0-3	3-4	1-0	3-5	1-0	1-1	1-0	1-2	6-1	0-4	2-1	*	0-1	1-2	0-2
20. Sudbury Town	0-1	2-1	3-0	1-1	2-0	3-4	1-2	2-1	0-2	5-3	3-1	1-2	0-0	1-0	1-2	3-1	4-1	3-3	3-1	*	3-2	0-0
21. VS Rugby	3-0	0-6	3-1	0-1	2-2	1-1	1-4	0-0	1-2	0-1	1-2	0-1	1-1	4-0	1-2	1-3	1-3	0-1	0-3	0-2	*	0-0
22. Worcester C	1-0	0-0	1-1	2-1	0-0	1-2	2-0	0-1	1-3	3-1	3-3	0-1	1-0	4-3	4-2	2-0	0-0	2-0	4-0	1-1	4-0	*

The Dr. MARTEN'S CUP 1995-96

Preliminary Round

Solihull Borough	v	Redditch United	2-4, 1-2,	(3-6ag)
Merthyr Tydfil	v	Cinderford Town	4-3, 4-1,	(8-4ag)

First Round Two Legs:

Nuneaton Borough	v	V.S. Rugby	4-2, 2-1,	(6-3ag)
Atherstone United	v	Tamworth	4-3, 3-2,	(7-5ag)
Buckingham	v	Braintree Town	1-0, 0-0,	(1-0ag)
Cambridge City	v	Sudbury Town	1-1, 3-1,	(4-2ag)
Weston Super Mare	v	Cheltenham Town	1-3, 2-4,	(3-7ag)
Witney Town	v	Gloucester City	1-0, 0-3,	(1-3ag)
Leicester United	v	Paget Rangers	0-3, 3-5,	(3-8ag)
Burton Albion	v	Gresley Rovers	0-2, 2-1,	(2-3ag)
Halesowen Town	v	Worcester City	0-2, 1-4,	(1-6ag)
Stourbridge	v	Dudley Town	4-2, 4-4,	(8-6ag)
Grantham Town	v	Ilkeston Town	0-3, 2-2,	(2-5ag)
Hinckley Town	v	Bedworth United	1-0,1-0,	(2-0ag)
Redditch United	v	Evesham United	0-0, 2-3,	(2-3ag)
Bilston Town	v	Sutton Coldfield	3-0, 3-3,	(6-3ag)
Stafford Rangers	v	Bridgnorth Town	0-2, 2-3,	(2-5ag)
R C Warwick	v	Moor Green	1-4, 0-4,	(1-8ag)
Baldock Town	v	Bury Town	1-1, 2-0,	(3-1ag)
Sittingbourne	v	Margate	0-1, 1-3,	(1-4ag)
Corby Town	v	Rothwell Town	0-1, 2-2,	(2-3ag)
Kings Lynn	v	Rushden & Diamonds	2-0, 0-1,	(2-1ag)
Gravesend & Northfleet	v	Chelmsford City	0-1, 3-1,	(3-2ag)
Crawley Town	v	Hastings Town	2-1, 1-1,	(3-2ag)
Tonbridge Angels	v	Ashford Town	1-1, 5-3,	(6-4ag)
Fisher 93	v	Erith & Belvedere	2-0, 4-0,	(6-0ag)
Forest Green Rovers	v	Clevedon Town	3-1, 2-1,	(5-2ag)
Newport AFC	v	Merthyr Tydfil	1-1, 2-1,	(3-2ag)
Waterlooville	v	Newport I O W	3-1, 0-1,	(3-2ag)
Fareham Town	v	Fleet Town	0-2, 2-2,	(2-4ag)
Trowbridge Town	v	Yate Town	0-2, 4-1,	(4-3ag)
Bashley	v	Weymouth	0-0, 3-0,	(3-0ag)
Dorchester Town	v	Havant Town	1-0, 1-0,	(2-0ag)
Poole Town	v	Salisbury City	0-6, 0-5,	(0-11ag)

Second Round;

Nuneaton Borough	v	Atherstone United	3-1
Buckingham Town	v	Cambridge City	1-0
Cheltenham Town	v	Gloucester City	4-0
Paget Rangers	v	Gresley Rovers	2-3
Worcester City	v	Stourbridge	3-0
Ilkeston Town	v	Hinckley Town	2-3
Evesham United	v	Bilston Town	2-2, 2-5
Bridgnorth Town	v	Moor Green	0-0, 1-2
Baldock Town	v	Margate	1-0
Rothwell Town	v	Kings Lynn	0-1
Gravesend & Northfleet	v	Crawley Town	1-2
Tonbridge Angels	v	Fisher 93	3-0
Forest Green Rovers	v	Newport AFC	2-4
Waterlooville	v	Fleet Town	4-0
Trowbridge Town	v	Bashley	1-1, 2-1
Dorchester Town	v	Salisbury City	1-2

Third Round;

Nuneaton Borough	v	Buckingham Town	3-1	
Cheltenham Town	v	Gresley Rovers	3-3, 2-2.	
		Gresley Rovers win on away goals rule		
Worcester City	v	Hinckley Town	2-3	
Bilston Town	v	Moor Green	1-3	
Baldock Town	v	Kings Lynn	2-0	
Crawley Town	v	Tonbridge Angels	3-0	
Newport AFC	v	Waterlooville	1-0	
Trowbridge Town	v	Salisbury City	1-1, 1-2	

Fourth Round;

Nuneaton Borough	v	Gresley Rovers	4-1	
Hinckley Town	v	Moor Green	0-4	
Baldock Town	v	Crawley Town	2-2, 1-1	
Baldock Town win on away goals rule				
Newport AFC	v	Salisbury City	1-2	

Semi-Finals Two Legs;

Nuneaton Borough	v	Moor Green	2-0, 1-1	(3-1agg)
Baldock Town	v	Salisbury City	0-0, 1-1	(1-1ag)
Baldock Town win on away goal rule				

Final Two Legs;

Nuneaton Borough	v	**Baldock Town**	**3-1, 2-1**	**(5-2agg)**

Champions Nuneaton Borough

Formed: 1930

ASHFORD TOWN

Nuts & Bolts

Ashford Town FC: Back Row (L-R); Andy Pearson, Andy Morris, Dave Arter, Stuart White. Middle; Ian Heathcote (Comm Mgr), George Sergent (Physio), Dave Collinson, Carlton Wynter, Adrian Lemoine, Maurice Munden, Jason Wheeler, Tommy Warrilow, Scott McRobert, Dave Williams (Asst Mgr), Roger West (V Chr). Front: Peter McRobert. Mark Stanton, Ernie Warren (Chr), Neil Cugley (Mgr), Peter Barton (MD), Jeff Ross, Darren Light. Kneeling; Mark Williams (Mascot).

Chairman: Ernie Warren **Vice Chairman:** Roger West **President:** Ashley M Batt.
Secretary/Press Officer: A Lancaster, 128 Kingsnorth Rd, Ashford, Kent TN23 2HY (01233 621325).
Manager: Neil Cugley **Asst Manager:** Dave Williams **Coach:** Nigel Donn
Commercial Manager: Ian Heathcote, (01233 611838) **Physio:** George Sargeant
Ground: The Homelands, Ashford Road, Kingsnorth, Ashford, Kent TN26 1NJ (01233 611838).
Directions: M20 jct 10, follow A2070 signs towards Brenzett & Lydd airport, dual carriageway to junction of old A2070, ground one mile on left through village of Kingsnorth. 4 miles south of Ashford
Capacity: 3,200 **Cover:** 1,250 **Seats:** 500 **Floodlights:** Yes **Metal Badges:** Yes
Club Shop: Yes, selling old prog, pennants, scarves, etc. Contact Alan Bird (01233 662680)
Colours: Green/white/white **Change colours:** White/green/green
Previous Leagues: Kent 30-59. **Previous Ground:** Essella Park, Essella Rd 30-87.
Midweek home matchday: Tuesday **Reserve Team's League:** No Reserve team for 1996-97.
Record Attendance: 6,525 (at Essella Park, previous ground), v Crystal Palace, FA Cup 1st Rd 1959. 3,363 (at current ground), v Fulham FA Cup 1st Round 1994
Best FA Cup season: 2nd Rd 61-62 (lost 0-3 at home to QPR), 66-67 (0-5 at Swindon). Also 1st Rd 7 times.
League clubs defeated in FA Cup: None.
Previous Names: Ashford United/ Ashford Railway/ Ashford F.C.
Record Fees - Paid: £7,000 for J Ross & D Arter (Sittingbourne, March 1994) £2,000 for Tim Hulme (Hythe Town, August 1988)
Received: £25,000 for Jeff Ross & Dave Arter (Hythe Tn, 90). *Individually: £20,000 for Lee McRobert (Sittingbourne, 93).*
Record win: 10-1 v Bury Town, February 1964.
Record defeat: 0-8 v Crawley Town, November 1964.
Players progressing to Football League: Ollie Norris (R'dale 1961), Howard Moore (Coventry 1966), Tony Godden (WBA 1975), Lee McRobert (Millwall 1994)
Clubhouse: Open matchdays and for special functions. Licensed bar, function room. Limited food available; sandwiches, sausage & chips, pie & chips etc.
Club Record Goalscorer: Dave Arter 197
Club Record Appearances: Paul McRobert 761
95-96 Captain: Carlton Wynter **95-96 P.o.Y.:** Andy Pearson
95-96 Top scorer: Dave Arter 32
95-96 Clubman o.Y: Frank Dobson
Local Newspapers (+Tel.Nos.): Kentish Express (01233 623232)
Local Radio Stations: Radio Kent, Invicta Radio
Honours: FA Trophy SF 72-73, Southern Lg Southern Div R-up 86-87 95-96, Kent Lg 48-49 (R-up 31-32, Lg Cup 38-39), Kent Senior Cup 58-59 62-63 92-93 95-96

PROGRAMME DETAILS:
Pages: 32 **Price:** £ 1.00
Editor: Elaine Orsbourne

ASHFORD TOWN'S 1995-96 CAMPAIGN

DATE		OPPONENTS	COMP	RESULT		GATE	GOALSCORERS
Aug 3	A	Folkestone	EFC	D	1-1	156	Light
10	H	Dover A.	EFC	W	2-0	437	Arter, Stanton
19	H	Poole Town	BHL	W	1-0	433	Arter
22	H	Sittingbourne	BHL	D	0-0	891	
26	A	Bashley	BHL	L	0-2	242	
28	A	Braintree T.	BHL	D	1-1	251	Griffiths
Sept 2	H	Havant T.	BHL	D	1-1	405	Griffiths
5	A	Margate	BHL	W	1-0	380	Stanton
9	H	Tonbridge	FAC	W	2-0	732	Stanton, Griffiths
16	H	Newport IOW	BHL	W	4-2	412	Stanton 2, Allon, Arter
20	A	Sittingbourne	BHL	L	0-4	947	
23	H	Hastings Town	FAC	W	3-1	966	Allon, Stanton, Ross
30	H	Trowbridge T.	BHL	W	1-0	490	Stanton
Oct 4	A	Tonbridge	DMC	L	3-5	408	Arter 2, Stanton
7	A	Tooting & Mitcham	FAC	W	1-0	540	Wynter
14	H	Sudbury Town	FAT	L	0-2	569	
21	H	Aldershot Town	FAC	W	2-0		Warrilow, Arter
24	H	Braintree T.	BHL	W	7-1	436	Arter 3, Carruthers 2, Lemoine, Wheeler
28	H	Cinderford T.	BHL	W	4-0	564	Warrilow, Arter, Wynter, Stanton
31	H	Tonbridge	DMC	D	1-1	440	Wynter
Nov 4	H	Weston-super-Mare	BHL	D	2-2	515	Arter 2
7	A	Dover A.	KSC	W	2-1	505	Stanton, Carruthers
11	A	Bognor Regis	FAC	D	1-1	2200	Allon
14	H	Margate	BHL	W	2-0	499	Arter 2
18	H	Yate T.	BHL	W	4-2	554	Arter 2, Carruthers, og
21	H	Bognor Regis	FACR	L	0-1	2542	
25	A	Fisher	BHL	D	0-0	290	
Dec 2	A	Newport IOW	BHL	L	1-2	341	Stanton
9	H	Bashley	BHL	L	1-4	405	Stanton
16	A	Fleet Town	BHL	L	2-3	117	Arter, Allon
Jan 1	A	Erith & Belvedere	BHL	W	3-2	162	Carruthers 2, Ross
6	A	Havant T.	BHL	L	1-2	168	Arter
9	A	Wlling U.	KSC	W	3-2	462	Allon, Ross, Arter
13	A	Weston-super-Mare	GHCL	D	1-1	249	Arter
16	H	Folkestone	EFC	W	2-1	156	Warrilow, Wheeler
20	H	Fareham T.	BHL	W	3-1	126	Arter 2, Carruthers
30	H	Canterbury C.	FNT	W	3-0	141	Arter 2, Ross
Feb 3	A	Yate T.	BHL	W	1-0	114	Morris
10	H	Waterlooville	BHL	W	3-2	395	Wynter, Stanton, og
17	H	Fisher	BHL	W	1-0	489	Allon
28	A	Dover A.	EFC	W	4-0	109	Allon 3, Chambers
Mar 2	A	Poole T.	BHL	W	4-0	122	White, Wheeler, Arter, Ross
9	A	Trowbridge T.	BHL	D	1-1	346	White
12	H	Gillingham	KSC	W	3-1	439	Ross 2, Arter
16	H	Witney T.	BHL	W	2-0	423	Morris (P), Wynter
20	A	Forest Green R.	BHL	W	3-2	131	Morris (P), Wynter, Ross
23	H	Clevedon T.	BHL	W	2-1	457	Arter, Carruthers
30	A	Weymouth	BHL	W	2-0	766	Warrilow, Wynter
Apr 2	H	Forest Green R.	BHL	W	3-0	441	Arter, Carruthers, Allon
6	H	Erith & Belvedere	BHL	W	2-0	558	Arter, Ross
8	A	Tonbridge	BHL	L	1-2	761	Arter
10	H	Bishop's Stortford	EFC	L	0-2	253	
13	A	Cinderford T.	BHL	W	1-0	245	Arter
16	H	Weymouth	BHL	W	1-0	587	Warrilow
18	A	Witney T.	BHL	W	2-1	112	Warrilow 2
20	H	Fleet T.	BHL	W	1-0	711	Pearson
23	A	Clevedon T.	BHL	L	2-4	157	Chambers, Arter
27	H	Fareham T.	BHL	W	2-1	688	Arter, Allon
30	H	Tonbridge	BHL	D	1-1	1036	Pearson
May 4	A	Waterlooville	BHL	D	1-1	266	Chambers
6	N	Charlton A.	KSCF	W	3-0	1200	Arter, Allon, Carruthers

ASHFORD TOWN PLAYING SQUAD 1996-97

Goalkeepers: Maurice Munden (Sing Tao (HK), Dover Ath, Welling U, Folkestone T, Charlton), **Joe Radford** (Canterbury C, Hythe T, Canterbury C, Margate, Dover A, Gillingham)

Defenders: Tommy Warrilow (Gravesend, Sittingbourne, Hythe T, Crawley T, Torquay, Kuopio Elo (Fin), Adelaide C (Aust), Canterbury C, Gravesend, Tonbridge, Millwall), **Andy Morris** (Folkestone), **Andy Pearson** (Folkestone, Chatham T, Maidstone U), **Adrian Lemoine** (Hythe T, Ashford T, Chelmsford C, Barking, Welling U, Maidstone U), **Andy Allon** (Margate, Hythe T, Folkestone, Ashford T, Folkestone, Dover, Folkestone), **Nigel Donn** (Dover A, Maidstone U, Leyton O, Gillingham)

Midfielders: Stuart White (Welling U, Brighton, Gillingham, Charlton), **Carlton Wynter** (Hastings T, Sittingbourne, Ashford T, Hastings T, Ashford T, Bromley Green), **Mark Stanton** (Hythe T), **Matt Carruthers** (Dover Ath), **Jason Wheeler** (Herne Bay, Ashford T, Hythe T, Crawley T, Maidstone U), **Paul Chambers** (Folkestone Invicta, Dover Ath, Folkestone Invicta)

Forwards: Jeff Ross (Sittingbourne, Hythe T, Ashford T, Gravesend, Tonbridge, Herne Bay, Welling U, Ashford T), **Tony Reynolds** (Gravesend, Welling U, Maidstone U, Ashford T, Folkestone), **Scott McRobert** (Youth team), **Paul O'Brien** (Dover A), **Nicky Dent** (Sing Tao (HK), Ashford T, Dover A, Poole T, Yeovil T, Bristol C, Bristol Manor Farm)

1979 # ATHERSTONE UNITED The Adders

Back Row (L-R):Ron Bradbury (Mgr), Keith Russell (Hednesford), Lee Harriman (Barwell), Craig Knight, Barry Rumble, Lee Spencer, Ade Gregory, Robbie Ellison, Bobby Parker, Steve Jackson, Rod Brown (Kit). Front Row: Bob Stockley, Liegh Everitt, Richard Wade, Robin Judd, Mark Rauole, Dean Albrighton, Rob Burke.

Chairman: S.Holland. **Vice Chairman:** L.Spencer. **President:** C Culwick
Secretary: Neil Dykes, 18 Greendale Close, Atherstone, Warwickshire CV9 1PR, (01827 714326)
Manager: R Bradbury. **Asst Manager:** R Stockley. **Physio:** S Welch.
Press Officer: T.B.A. **Commercial Manager:** M Steebleton**Ground:** Sheepy Road, Atherstone, Warks CV9 1HG (01827 717829)
Directions: Half mile north of town centre on B4116 Twycross/Ashby road.
Capacity: 3,500 **Cover:** 1,000 **Seats:** 373 **Floodlights:** Yes **Metal Badges:** Yes
Club Shop: Yes. Programmes, magazines, souvenirs etc. Contact Simon Gilbert (01827 718583)
Colours: Red & white **Change colours:** Yellow & blue
Club Sponsors: T.B.A. **Previous Leagues:** West Midlands 1979-87
Midweek home matchday: Tuesday
Reserve's Lge: Midland Comb. Reserve Div.
Record Attendance: 2,873 v V.S. Rugby, F.A. Cup 1st Round Proper 1987-88
Record win: 12-2 v Tipton Town (H), West Midlands (Regional) League Premier Division 86-87.
Record defeat: 1-7 v Rushden & Diamonds, Beazer League Premier Division 94-95.
Best F.A. Cup season: 2nd Rd Proper 1990-91 (lost 0-1 at Crewe Alexandra)
Record Fee Paid: £4,500 to Gloucester City for Gary Bradder, 1989.
Record Fee Received: £40,000 for Andy Rammell from Manchester United, September 1989.
Past Players who have progressed into The Football League: Andy Rammell (Manchester United).
Clubhouse: Normal hours, all usual facilities.
Record Goalscorer: Alan Bourton
Record Appearances: Lee Spencer
95-96 Captain: Steve Jackson.
95-96 P.o.Y.: Richard Williams.
95-96 Top scorer: Keith Russell.
Local Newspapers: Tamworth Herald (01827 60741), Evening News (01203 353534), Atherstone Herald, Coventry Telegraph (01203 382251).
Local Radio Stations: Mercia Sound, CWR.
Honours: Southern Lg Midland Div 88-89, West Mids Lg 81-82 86-87 (Lg Cup 81-82, Premier Div Cup 86-87, Div 2 Cup (Reserves) 86-87), Walsall Snr Cup 83-84, Midland Comb. Reserve Division 87-88, Birmingham Snr Cup R-up 89-90, FA Tphy 1st Rd 88-89 91-92.

PROGRAMME DETAILS:
Pages: 28 **Price:** 70p
Editor: Phil Bellinger

ATHERSTONE UNITED'S 1995-96 CAMPAIGN

DATE		OPPONENTS	COMP	RESULT		GATE	GOALSCORERS
Aug 19	A	Dorchester Town	BHL	W	1-0	604	Judd
22	H	Ilkeston Town	BHL	D	3-3		Judd, Wright (P), Knight
26	H	Gravesend & Northfleet	BHL	W	2-0	286	Russell, Wright
28	A	Stafford Rangers	BHL	W	4-1	522	Ellison, Campbell, Read, Tomlinson
Sept 2	H	Chelmsford City	BHL	L	1-2	303	Judge
5	A	Gresley Rovers	BHL	L	0-1	702	
9	H	Armitage	FAC 1Q	D	2-2	258	Read 2
12	A	Armitage	FAC 1R	D	3-3	229	Russell, Donovan 2
16	H	Cheltenham T.	BHL	L	1-2	402	Randall
18	A	Armitage	FAC 2R	L	4-5	275	Randall, C. Knight, Judd, Donovan
30	H	Baldock Town	BHL	D	2-2	235	Russell (P), Albrighton
Oct 3	H	Tamworth	DMT 1L	W	4-3	423	Tomlinson, Albrighton, Russell, Ellison
7	A	Cambridge C.	BHL	L	1-3	191	Wade
14	H	Lincoln Utd.	FAC 1Q	W	2-1	278	Ellison 2
17	A	Gornall	BSC	D	0-0	101	
21	H	Sudbury Town	BHL	D	0-0	234	
24	H	Stafford Rangers	BHL	D	2-2	263	Russell 2 (1 P)
28	A	Halesowen Town	BHL	L	4-5	694	Albrighton, Russell 2, Randall
31	A	Tamworth	DMT 2L	W	3-2	617	Ellison 2, Judd
Nov 2	H	Gornal Athletic	BSC R	W	4-2	120	Albrighton 2, Campbell, Parker
4	H	Accrington S.	FAT 2Q	L	1-3	422	Knight
11	A	Chelmsford City	BHL	D	1-1	789	Judd
14	H	Gresley Rovers	BHL	L	1-2	454	Parker
18	H	Dorchester T.	BHL	L	3-4	222	Russell, Ellison, Albrighton
20	H	Coventry City	BSC	L	0-3	246	
25	A	Rushden & Diamonds	BHL	L	3-7	2231	Russell, Judd, Albrighton
Dec 2	A	Salisbury City	BHL	L	0-2	533	
9	H	Crawley Town	BHL	W	2-1	244	M. Albrighton, Hart
12	H	Nuneaton Borough	DMT	L	1-3	467	Russell
23	A	Gloucester City	BHL	W	2-1	615	Ellison, Russell
Jan 6	A	Baldock Town	BHL	D	1-1	251	Judd
13	H	Rushden & Diamonds	BHL	L	1-3	605	Russell (P)
20	A	Hastings Town	BHL	L	0-5	407	
23	H	Gornal Athletic	MFC	W	5-0	78	Judd 2, D. Albrighton 3
Feb 3	A	Cheltenham Town	BHL	D	1-1	516	Russell
10	A	Worcester City	BHL	L	0-1	588	
17	A	Gravesend & Northfleet	BHL	L	1-2	511	Russell
24	H	Salisbury City	BHL	W	3-1	244	Russell 2 (1P), Albrighton
27	H	Merthyr Tydfil	BHL	L	0-2	229	
Mar 2	H	Newport AFC	BHL	L	0-0	328	
5	A	Gornall Athletic	MFC	L	1-3	40	Higgs
9	A	VS Rugby	BHL	L	0-3	620	
12	H	Burton Albion	BHL	l	0-3	278	
16	H	Halesowen Town	BHL	L	0-1	339	
19	A	Ilkeston Town	BHL	D	1-1	377	Ellison
23	H	Gloucester City	BHL	W	2-1	284	Bennett, Speedie
26	H	VS Rugby	BHL	W	4-1	334	Ellison, Speedie, Blair, Higgs
30	A	Merthyr Tydfil	BHL	L	0-4	402	
Apr 6	H	Worcester City	BHL	D	1-1	326	Greenman (og)
8	A	Burton Albion	BHL	D	2-2	538	Judd, Bennett
13	H	Hastings Town	BHL	W	1-0	301	Speedie
20	A	Sudbury Town	BHL	W	1-0	390	Osman (og)
27	A	Crawley Town	BHL	W	1-0	732	Speedie
May 4	H	Cambridge City	BHL	D	2-2	865	Albrighton, Ellison

ATHERSTONE UNITED PLAYING SQUAD 1996-97

Goalkeepers: Richard Williams (Hednesford T, Atherstone U, Birmingham C)

Defenders: Craig Knight (Telford U, Atherstone U, Rushall O), **Leigh Everitt** (Nuneaton B), **Lee Middleton** (Camb.U, Swindon, Coventry C), **Mark Allbrighton** (Nuneaton B), **Steve Woodfine** (Bedworth U, Nuneaton B), **Malcolm Randle** (Bedworth U, Hurley DM), **Barry Rumble** (Walsall)

Midfielders: Scott Blair (Stoke C), **David Hart** (Nuneaton B), **Robin Judd** (Solihull B, Atherstone U, Redditch U, Mile Oak R, Kidderminster H, Birmingham C), **Bobby Parker** (Bedworth U, Atherstone U, Bedworth U, Sutton C, Alvechurch, Tamworth, Atherstone U, Nuneaton B), **Robert Higgs** (Solihull B), **Matt Owen** (VS Rugby, Atherstone U)

Forwards: Sven Sinden (Hinckley T, Hinckley A, Barrow T), **Dave Bennett** (Hinckley Ath, Nuneaton B, Swindon, Sheff.Wed, Coventry, Cardiff, Man.City), **Robbie Ellison** (Hednesford T, Atherstone U, Tamworth, Mile Oak R), **Darren Dickson** (VS Rugby, Hinckley Ath, Tamworth, Coventry (T)), **Dean Allbrighton** (Bolehall S, Bedworth U)

BALDOCK TOWN

Formed: 1889

Reds

Baldock Town FC, Back Row (L-R); Brian Stein, Mick Small, Danny Power, Dean Mann, Matt Barnaby, Lee Graves, Darren Fenton. Front; Danny Howell, Grant Wedlock, Mark Phillips, Ray Kilby, Marcelle Bruce, Matthew Woolgar, Richard Chattoe.

Joint Chairmen: Mike Watson-Challis, R Childerstone
Secretary: C T Hammond, 2 Elmwood Court, High Str., Baldock, Herts SG7 6AY (01462 894253).
Manager/Commercial: Brian Stein **Coach:** Dave Moseley **Physio:** Fred Day.
Press Officer: David Hammond (01462 892797)
Ground: Norton Road, Baldock, Herts SG7 5AU (01462 895449).
Directions: Off A1(M) at Letchworth/Baldock sign, left to 3rd island, A505 to Baldock, Norton Road is left off A505, left past Orange Tree pub, ground on right after railway bridge. From North or East turn left into town, Hitchin Street, right into Norton then proceed as above. From Baldock station (Kings Cross to Royston line) - left down Ickneild Way and right into Norton Road.
Capacity: 3,000 **Cover:** 1,250 **Seats:** 250 **Club Shop:** No **Metal Badges:** Yes
Colours: Red/white/red **Change colours:** All White.
Supporters Club: Phil Rosendale (01462 896314)
Prevs Lges: S Midlands 25-39 47-54 63-83/ Parthenon 54-59/ London 59-63/ Utd Counties 83-87.
Previous Ground: Bakers Close (until 1982).
Midweek home matchday: Wednesday **Reserve Team's League:** No reserve team.
Record Attendance: 1,200 v Arsenal, floodlight opening 1984.
Best F.A. Cup season: 4th Qualifying Round replay (lost 0-1 at Halesowen Town after 1-1 draw) 91-92.
Record Fees - Paid: £2,000; for Colin Hull (Bishop's Stortford); for Glen Russell (Braintree 1993)
Received: £30,000 for Kevin Phillips (Watford F.C.).
Players progressing to Football League: Ian Dowie (Luton & West Ham), Alan Stewart (Portsmouth), Kevan Phillips (Watford).
Clubhouse: Members' bar and seperate function room. Food available.
Club Record Goalscorer: Unknown.
Club Record Apps: Keith (Paddy) Stanton 550
95-96 Captain: **95-96 P.o.Y.:**
95-96 Top scorer:
Local Newspapers: Comet, Gazette, Herald.
Local Radio: Radio Bedfordshire, Chiltern.
Hons: FA Tphy 2nd Qual. Rd 90-91, FA Vase 5th Rd 83-84, United Counties Lg R-up 83-84 86-87, South Mids Lg 27-28 65-66 67-68 69-70 (R-up 53-54 82-83, Lg Cup 65-66 69-70, Div 1 49-50, Reserve Div 1 66-67), Herts Charity Cup 91-92 94-95, Herts Charity Shield 57-58 69-70, Wallspan Floodlit Cup 85-86, Hinchingbrooke Cup 86-87, TSI Floodlit Cup 88-89, Woolwich Equitable Buliding Society Cup 83-84, Herts Intermediate Cup 86-87. Sth League Runners Up 94-95. Sth Leag Cup Dr Martens 95-96

PROGRAMME DETAILS:
Pages: 48 **Price:** £1
Editor: TBA

BALDOCK TOWN'S 1995-96 CAMPAIGN

DATE		OPPONENTS	COMP	RESULT		GATE	GOALSCORERS
Aug 19	A	Merthyr Tydfil	BHL	L	0-1	453	
22	H	VS Rugby	BHL	W	2-0	352	Cook, Kamara
26	H	Dorchester Town	BHL	W	2-1	281	Cook, Howells
28	A	Hastings Town	BHL	D	2-2	527	Cook, Debnam
Sept 2	H	Gresley Rovers	BHL	L	0-1	277	
4	A	Chelmsford City	BHL	W	2-0	902	Cook, Russell
16	H	Crawley Town	BHL	D	0-0	401	
20	A	VS Rugby	BHL	W	6-0	322	Guile 3, Russell 2, Cook
30	A	Atherstone United	BHL	D	2-2	235	Cook 2
Oct 3	A	Bury Town	DDMC 1	W	2-0	140	Woolgar, Bates
7	H	Stafford Rangers	BHL	W	5-0	289	Guile 2, Russell, Fenton, Debnam
21	A	Ilkeston Town	BHL	L	2-3	485	Howells 2
24	H	Hastings Town	BHL	L	1-3	189	Chaftoe
28	A	Sudbury Town	BHL	L	1-2	405	Chaftoe
31	H	Bury Town	DMC	D	1-1	110	Howells
Nov 14	H	Chelmsford City	BHL	W	2-1	231	Wallace 2
18	A	Gloucester City	BHL	L	1-3	584	Russell
25	H	Merthyr Tydfil	BHL	D	1-1	237	Wallace
28	A	Rushden & Diamonds	BHL	L	0-3	1922	
Dec 2	A	Dorchester Town	BHL	W	2-1	560	Debnam, Cook
9	A	Cheltenham Town	BHL	L	1-3	751	Wallace
13	H	Margate	DMC 2	W	1-0	81	Wallace (P)
16	H	Ilkeston Town	BHL	D	1-1	238	Haag
23	A	Salisbury City	BHL	W	2-1	351	Wallace 2
Jan 1	A	Cambridge City	BHL	D	0-0	352	
6	H	Atherstone United	BHL	D	1-1	258	Fenton
9	H	King's Lynn	DMC 3	W	2-0	275	Fenton,Russell
13	A	Burton Albion	BHL	L	0-1	611	
20	H	Gravesend & N'fleet	BHL	D	2-2	360	Russell, Wallace
30	A	Crawley Town	DMC 4	D	2-2	2437	Cook, Russell
Feb 3	A	Stafford Rangers	BHL	W	1-0	511	Fenton
13	H	Rushden & Diamonds	BHL	L	0-3	853	
17	A	Crawley Town	BHL	W	2-1	546	Wallace 2
24	H	Cheltenham Town	BHL	D	1-1	283	Wallace
27	H	Crawley Town	DMC 4R	D	1-1	187	Wallace
Mar 6	H	Worcester City	BHL	L	0-1	220	
9	A	Gresley Rovers	BHL	L	0-3	657	
12	H	Halesowen Town	BHL	L	0-2	163	
16	H	Newport AFC	BHL	L	1-2	357	Haag
19	H	Watford	HSC SF	L	1-2	187	Wallace
23	H	Salisbury City	BHL	W	4-2	280	Woolger, Wallace, Cullum, Russell
27	H	Cambridge City	BHL	D	0-0	222	
30	A	Worcester City	BHL	D	0-0	555	
Apr 4	H	Salisbury City	DMC SF	D	0-0	104	
6	H	Sudbury Town	BHL	L	1-3	382	Bruce
8	A	Gravesend & N'fleet	BHL	D	1-1	525	Debnam
10	A	Salisbury City	DMC SF	D	1-1	357	Russell
13	H	Gloucester City	BHL	L	0-1	261	
17	A	Nuneaton Boro	SLC 1L	L	1-3	469	Wallace (P)
20	A	Newport AFC	BHL	D	1-1	724	Bruce
27	A	Halesowen Town	BHL	L	0-1	1053	
30	H	Nuneaton Boro	SLC 2L	L	1-2	1248	Fenton
May 4	H	Burton Albion	BHL	D	1-1	442	Howell

BALDOCK TOWN PLAYING SQUAD 1996-97

Goalkeepers: Jimmy Jones (Fisher`93, Southend, Brighton)

Defenders: Laurence Cullum (Cambridge C, Histon), **Lee Graves** (Gravesend, Brentford (T)), **Marcelle Bruce** (Colchester, Tottenham H), **Richard Chattoe** (Weston-S-M, Bristol R), **Keith Stanton** (Arlesey T, Pirton), **Danny Power** (Luton), **Matt Barnaby** (B Stortford, Stevenage B)

Midfielders: Stuart Endacott (Hemel Hempstead, Barton R, Wootton BC, Barton R), **Matthew Woolgar** (Luton (T)), **Ray Kilby** (Hatfield T), **Grant Wedlock** (Stevenage B)

Forwards: Brian Stein (Boreham Wood, Enfield, St.Albans C, Stevenage B, Barnet, Luton, Caen (FR), Luton, Edgware T), **Danny Howells** (Letchworth GC), **Darren Fenton** (Cobh Ramblers), **Mike Small** (Stevenage B, West Ham, Brighton, PAOK Salonika, Go Ahead Eagles, Peterborough, Standard Liege, Luton), **Gary Roberts** (B Stortford, Hitchin T, Braintree T, Camb.C, Baldock T, Berkhamsted T, Baldock T, MK Borough, Stevenage B, Baldock T, Stevenage B, Hitchin T, St.Albans C, Maidstone U, Barnet, Brentford, Wembley)

BURTON ALBION

Formed: 1950 — Brewers

Back Row (L-R): Matt Brown (Physio), Steve Brown, Mark Wood, Darren Stride, Darren Acton, Brian Donnelly, Andy Trigwell, Paul Gretton, Simon George, Dave Hadley, John Newman (Asst Mgr). Front Row: Martin Devaney, Matt Freeman, Jon Williams, Alan Davies, John Barton (Mgr), Simon Redfern, Matt Simpson, Karl Payne, Andy Pepper, Jason Rhodes.

Chairman: B.Robinson **Vice Chairman:**
Secretary: Tony A Kirkland, 40 Hurst Drive, Stretton, Burton-on-Trent DE13 0ED (01283 536510.
Manager: John Barton **Assistant Manager:** John Newman **Physio:** Matt Brown
Press Officer: David Twigg (01283 562013) **Commercial Mgr:** G Tate.
Ground: Eton Park, Princess Way, Burton-on-Trent DE14 2RU (01283 565938)
Directions: From south - M1 jct 22, A50 (Ashby) follow to Burton over Trent bridge, thru 3 sets of lights, right at mini-r'bout (Derby Turn Pub), left at next island - ground on left: From M42 - A38 (Lichfield), follow signs for Burton, take 2nd turn for Burton (A5121), right at island - ground on left: From M6 north - jct 15 and follow A50 for Stoke and Uttoxeter, follow A50 signs to Burton, ob reaching Burton continue under bypass, left into Shakespeare Rd after canal bridge (opposite Navigation Inn), ground at end.
Capacity: 4,500 **Cover:** 2,500 **Seats:** 300 **Club Shop:** Yes **Metal Badges:** Yes
Colours: Yellow with black trim. **Change colours:** All White. **Sponsors:** B.I. Industries.
Previous Leagues: West Midlands 1950-58/ Southern 58-79/ Northern Premier 79-87
Midweek matchday: Tuesday **Previous Ground:** Wellington Street 50-57.
Record Attendance: 5,860 v Weymouth, Southern Lg Cup Final 2nd leg, 1964 *(22,500 v Leicester City, F.A. Cup 3rd Rd 1984 - played at Derby County F.C.).*
Best F.A. Cup season: 3rd Rd Proper 55-56/ 84-85. 1st Rd 9 times
Record Fees - Paid: £21,000 to for R Jones and J Pearson (Kidderminster).
Received: £60,000 for Darren Carr (C Palace 89).
Past players progressing to Football League: Ray Russell (Shrewsbury 54), David Neville (Rochdale 55), Derek Middleton (York 58), Tom McGlennon (Barrow 59), Les Green & Tony Parry & Stan Aston (Hartlepool 65/66), George Hunter (Lincoln 65), David Jones (Newport 68), Richie Barker & Jeff Bourne & Tony Bailey (Derby 67/69/70), Maitland Pollock & Steve Buckley (Luton 74), Peter Ward (Brighton 75), Tony Moore (Sheffield Utd 79), Carl Swan & Gary Clayton (Doncaster 80 & 86), Richard Jobson (Watford 82), Paul Haycock (Rotherham 86), Alan Kamara (Scarborough 87), Paul Groves (Leicester City 88), Steve Cotterill & John Gayle (Wimbledon 89), Darren Carr (Crystal Palace 89), Darren Smith & Darren Roberts (Wolves 90 & 92).
Clubhouse: 'The Football Tavern' - open normal pub hours. Full hot & cold menu.**Steward:** Brian Finch
Club Record Goalscorer: Ritchie Barker, 157
Club Record Appearances: Phil Annable, 567
95-96 Captain: **95-96 P.o.Y.:** Matthew Smith.
95-96 Top scorer: Jason Rhodes.
Local Newspaper: Burton Daily Mail (01283 43311).
Local Radio: Radio Derby.
Honours: Sth Lg Cup 63-64 (R-up 88-89, Div 1 (Nth) R-up 71-72 73-74), Nth Prem Lg Challenge Cup 82-83 (R-up 86-87, Presidents Cup R-up 85-86 (SF 86-87), Birmingham Snr Cup 53-54 70-71 (R-up 86-87), FA Trophy R-up 86-87 (SF 74-75), GMAC Cup SF 86-87, Bass Charity Vase 81-82 85-86, Bass Challenge Cup 84-85, Wt Mids Lg R-up 53-54, Staffs Sen Cup 55-56.

PROGRAMME DETAILS:
Pages: 48 Price: £1
Editor: David Twigg
(01283 562013)

BURTON ALBION'S 1995-96 CAMPAIGN

DATE		OPPONENTS	COMP	RESULT		GATE	GOALSCORERS
Aug 19	H	Hastings Town		D	1-1		Devaney
22	A	Cambridge City		L	2-3		Redfern, Rhodes (pen)
26	A	Sudbury Town		L	0-3		
28	H	Rushden & Diamonds		W	4-2		Devaney 2, Rhodes 2
Sept 2	H	Crawley Town		W	2-1		Rhodes, Redfern
5	A	Stafford Rangers		W	3-2		Rhodes 2, Devaney
16	A	Gloucester City		L	1-2		Stride
19	H	Cambridge City		D	0-0		
30	A	Worcester City		D	1-1		Rhodes
Oct 14	A	Merthyr Tydfil		L	3-4		Gretton, Stride, Rookyard
17	H	VS Rugby		D	0-0		
28	A	Gravesend & Northfleet		W	2-1		Redfern, Devaney
Nov 4	A	Hastings Town		W	3-0		Stride 2, Gretton
14	H	Stafford Rangers		W	5-1		Devaney, Redfern, Keast, Davies, Stride
18	H	Worcester City		W	2-0		Stride, Rhodes (pen)
21	A	Rushden & Diamonds		L	0-2		
Dec 2	A	Newport AFC		W	1-0		Rhodes
9	A	VS Rugby		L	1-3		Devaney
16	H	Merthyr Tydfil		L	1-3		Keast
19	H	Salisbury City		L	0-1		
23	H	Chelmsford City		D	1-1		Devaney
Jan 1	H	Gresley Rovers		D	1-1		Redfern
6	A	Crawley Town		D	1-1		Rhodes (pen)
13	H	Baldock Town		W	1-0		Payne
Feb 3	H	Sudbury Town		L	2-3		Keast, Donnelly
17	A	Salisbury City		L	0-2		
24	H	Gloucester City		W	1-0		Davies
27	H	Dorchester Town		W	1-0		Stride
Mar 2	H	Halesowen Town		D	1-1		Rhodes (pen)
9	A	Cheltenham Town		L	0-1		
12	A	Atherstone United		W	3-0		Nuttell, Stride, Devaney
16	A	Gresley Rovers		L	1-2		Redfern
23	A	Chelmsford City		D	0-0		
30	H	Ilkeston Town		L	1-2		Stride
Apr 6	A	Halesowen Town		D	1-1		Payne
8	H	Atherstone United		D	2-2		Nuttell, Devaney
13	A	Dorcester Town		L	1-2		Gretton
16	A	Ilkeston Town		L	0-1		
20	H	Cheltenham Town		W	3-2		Redfern, Keast, Rhodes (pen)
23	H	Gravesend & Northfleet		L	1-2		Nuttell
27	H	Newport AFC		L	0-1		
May 4	A	Baldock Town		D	1-1		Stride

BURTON ALBION PLAYING SQUAD 1996-97

Goalkeepers: Darren Acton (Telford U)

Defenders: Matthew Smith (Cork C, Plymouth, Derby), **Allan Davies** (Manchester C (T)), **Richard Smith** (Nottingham F (T)), **David Titterton** (Hednesford T, Wycombe W, Hereford, Coventry), **David Benton** (Worcester C, Kidderminster H, Birmingham), **Les Hornby** (VS Rugby, Yeovil T, Rothwell T, Desborough T, Spalding U, Desborough T, Northampton), **Charlie Palmer** (Walsall, Notts Co, Hull, Derby, Watford)

Midfielders: Dougie Keast (Rushden & D, Corby T, Kettering T, Shepshed Chart., Hibernian), **Simon Redfern** (Local football), **Karl Payne** (Chesterfield), **Darren Stride** (Youth team), **Steve Spooner** (Rushden & D, Chesterfield, Blackpool, Mansfield, Rotherham, York, Hereford, Chesterfield, Halifax, Derby)

Forwards: Mickey Nuttell (Rushden & D, Dag & Red, Kettering T, Boston U, Wycombe W, Cheltenham T, Peterborough), **Martin Devaney** (Gresley R, Leek T, Tamworth, Gresley R, Hanford, Ilkeston T), **Dave Hadley** (Kidderminster H, Moor Green, Mile Oak R, Tamworth), **Emeka Efiofor** (Youth team), **Micky Cotter** (Gravesend, Dover Ath, Erith & Belvedere, Welling U)

Formed: 1908

CAMBRIDGE CITY

Lilywhites

Cambridge City's keeper Kevin Murray foils Baldock's Danny Howells attack.

Chairman: Dennis Rolph **President:** Sir Neil Westbrook, CBE MA FRICS
Secretary: Stuart Hamilton, 55 Crowhill, Godmanchester, Huntingdon, Cambs (01480 412266).
Manager: Steve Fallon **Asst Manager:** Michael Cook **Physio:** John Aves, Collin Pettit
Press Officer: Secretary **General Manager:** W E Leivers
Ground: City Ground, Milton Road, Cambridge CB4 1UY (0223 357973)
Directions: 50 yards on left from start of A1309, Cambridge to Ely Rd. 30 mins walk Cambridge BR
Capacity: 5,000 **Cover:** 1,400 **Seats:** 400 **Floodlights:** Yes **Metal Badges:** Yes
Club Shop: Yes, selling programmes, club history, badges, scarves, pennants, replica shirts etc. Contact Neil Harvey (01223 235991).
Colours: White/black/white **Change colours:** All sky
Club Sponsors: Lancer UK **Previous Name:** Cambridge Town 1908-51.
Previous Leagues: Bury & Dist. 08-13 19-20/ East Anglian 08-10/ Southern Olympian 11-14/ Southern Amateur 1913-35/ Spartan 35-50/ Athenian 50-58.
Midweek matchday: Tuesday **Reserve Team's League:** Jewson Eastern Counties.
Record Attendance: 12,058 v Leytonstone, FA Amateur Cup 1st Rd, 1949-50.
Best FA Cup season: 1st Rd; v Ashford 66, v Swindon 46, v Walthamstow Ave. 48, v Hereford 93.
Record Fee Paid: £7,000 for Andy Beattie (Barnet, 1991).
Record Fee Received: £15,500 for Kevin Wilkin (Northampton Tn 91)
Players progressing to Football League: Ken Wright (West Ham 46), Antonio Gallego (Norwich 47), Alf Stokes (Watford 61), Derek Weddle (Middlesbrough 61), Dave Hicksen (Bury 62), Bryan Harvey (Blackpool 62), Robert Whitehead (Darlington 62), George Cummins (Hull 62), Reg Pearce & Dom Genovese (Peterborough 63 & 88), Alan Banks (Exeter 63), Tom Carroll (Ipswich 66), Roy Jones (Swindon), Winston Dubose (Oldham).
Clubhouse: 11am-11pm Mon-Sat, 12-3pm & 7pm-10.30pm Sun. Bingo, Dances, Pool, Stag nights, Darts.
Club Record Scorer: Gary Grogan
Club Record Appearances: Mal Keenan
95-96 Captain: **95-96 Top Scorer:**
95-96 Players' P.o.Y.: **95-96 Supporters' P.o.Y.:**
Local Press: Cambridge Evening News 35877
Local Radio: BBC Radio Cambridge
Honours: Southern Lg 62-63 (R-up 70-71, Southern Div 85-86, Div 1 R-up 69-70, Champ Cup 62-63), E Anglian Cup 30-31 35-36 42-43 43-44 45-46 47-48 59-60 64-65 75-76, Eastern Prof Floodlit Lg 65-66 72-73, Cambs Prof Cup 60-61 61-62 62-63 70-71 72-73 74-75, Cambs Invitation Cup 50-51 76-77 78-79 85-86 88-89 89-90 92-93, Spartan Lg 47-48 48-49 (R-up 49-50, Eastern Div Champs 45-46), Southern Amat Lg 20-21 27-28 28-29 30-31 31-32, Bury & Dist. Lg 09-10 10-11 12-13 19-20, E Anglian Lg 09-10 39-40 40-41 41-42 42-43 44-45, AFA Snr Cup 30-31 46-47 47-48(shared) 48-49 49-50, AFA Invitation Cup 50-51, Hunts Prem Cup 62-63 64-65, Suffolk Sen Cup 09-10, FA Trophy 2nd Rd 86-87 87-88, FA Amat Cup SF 27-28, Addenbrookes Hosp Cup 87-88, The Munns Youth Cup 82-83 83-84 84-85, Chiltern Youth Lge Cup R-up 75-76, South Mids Lg Youth Trophy 82-83, Robinson Cup 87-88 89-90, Jim Digney 89-90, Essex & Herts Youth Lg 89-90.

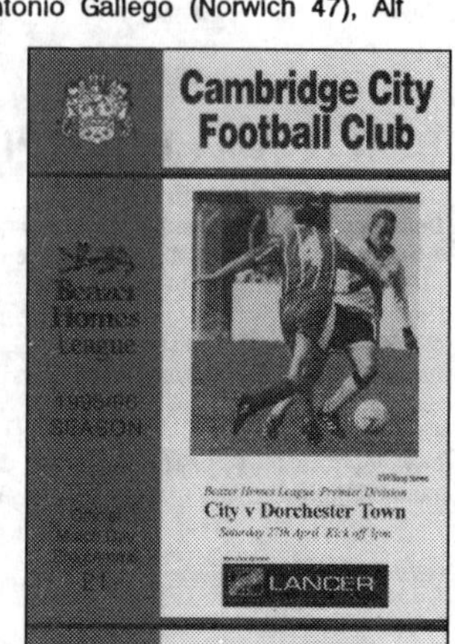

PROGRAMME DETAILS:
Pages: 20 **Price:** £1.00
Editor: David Crane
(0223 233057)

CAMBRIDGE CITY'S 1995-96 CAMPAIGN

DATE		OPPONENTS	COMP	RESULT		GATE	GOALSCORERS
Aug 19	A	Stafford Rangers	BHL	W	4-2	550	Harrington, Flack, Coe 2
22	H	Burton Albion	BHL	W	3-2	331	Cambridge, Pincher, Flack
26	H	Gloucester City	BHL	L	0-4	342	
28	A	VS Rugby	BHL	W	1-0	338	Coe
Sept 2	H	Newport AFC	BHL	L	0-1	495	
5	A	Gravesend & N'fleet	BHL	L	0-2	471	
9	H	Canvey Island	FAC	L	2-3	268	Ryan, Coe
16	H	Merthyr Tydfil	BHL	L	1-2	257	Harrington
19	A	Burton Albion	BHL	D	0-0	764	
30	A	Hastings Town	BHL	L	1-3	411	Coe
Oct 3	H	Sudbury Town	DMC 1R	D	1-1	180	Cambridge
7	H	Atherstone United	BHL	W	3-1	191	Pincher 2, Flack
10	H	Histon	EAC 1R	W	6-1	107	Pincher, Saddington, Ryan 2, Cambridge
14	H	Cheltenham Town	BHL	L	1-2	289	Ryan
21	A	Worcester City	BHL	L	1-2	825	McLean
24	H	VS Rugby	BHL	W	4-1	233	McLean 2, Coe 2
28	H	Ilkeston Town	BHL	L	2-3	276	Coe
31	A	Sudbury Town	DMC 1R	W	3-1	226	Cambridge, Tovey, Coe
Nov 4	A	Cheltenham Town	BHL	W	3-2	764	Tovey 2
14	H	Gravesend & N'fleet	BHL	W	2-1	272	Rowler, McLean
18	H	Stafford Rangers	BHL	W	2-0	257	Hercock, McLean
25	H	Hendon	FAT 3Q	W	2-0	234	Tovey, Pincher
Dec 2	A	Chelmsford City	BHL	D	0-0	853	
5	A	Buckingham Town	DMC 2R	L	0-1	56	
9	A	Gloucester City	BHL	L	1-3	666	Lockhart
12	H	Sudbury Town	BHL	W	1-0	141	McIntosh (og)
19	A	Warboys Town	EAC 2R	W	4-2	95	Harrington 2, McLean, Lockhart
Jan 1	H	Baldock Town	BHL	D	0-0	341	
6	A	Ilkeston Town	BHL	D	2-2	435	Tovey 2
9	A	Mildenhall Town	CIC	L	1-2	110	Harrington
13	H	Halesowen Town	BHL	L	0-1	409	
20	H	Boreham Wood	FAT 1P	L	1-2	234	Lockhart
23	A	Crawley Town	BHL	D	3-3	343	Retallick, Gawthrop, Cambridge
Feb 3	A	Merthyr Tydfil	BHL	L	1-2	239	Harrington
10	H	Salisbury City	BHL	L	1-3		McLean
27	A	Sudbury Town	BHL	D	1-1	279	Harrington
Mar 2	A	Salisbury City	BHL	L	0-1	272	
5	H	Hastings Town	BHL	L	0-3	139	
9	A	Newport AFC	BHL	W	2-1	828	Pincher, Cambridge
12	A	Dorchester Town	BHL	W	2-1	300	Pincher, Coe
16	H	Rushden & Diamonds	BHL	L	0-2	750	
19	A	Potton United	EAC	W	2-0	70	Cambridge, Coe
27	A	Baldock Town	BHL	D	0-0	222	
30	H	Crawley Town	BHL	L	1-2	218	Cambridge
Apr 4	A	Concord Rangers	EAC	L	0-1	80	
6	A	Rushden & Diamonds	BHL	L	1-2	2135	Cambridge
8	H	Chelmsford City	BHL	D	0-0	341	
13	A	Halesowen Town	BHL	L	1-2	952	Fallon
20	H	Worcester City	BHL	W	4-2	243	Williams 2, Lockhard, Dolby
25	A	Gresley Rovers	BHL	D	2-2	483	Fallon, Coe
27	H	Dorchester Town	BHL	L	1-2	256	Coe
30	H	Gresley Rovers	BHL	L	2-3	303	Cambridge, Lockhart
May 4	A	Atherstone United	BHL	D	2-2	865	Beattie, Williams

CAMBRIDGE CITY PLAYING SQUAD 1996-97

Goalkeepers: Kevin Murray (Saffron Walden T, Cambridge C), **Barry Piggott** (Royston T, Cambridge C)
Defenders: Andy Beattie (Hendon, Cambridge C, Barnet, Maidstone U, Barnet, Cambridge U), **Dave Hercock** (Boston T, Lincoln C (T)), **James Saddington** (Kettering T, Millwall, Cambridge C, Newmarket T), **Steve Gawthrop** (Youth team), **Graham Retallick** (Corby T, Peterborough), **Steve Hubbard** (Bury T, Haverhill R, Sudbury T, Cambridge C, Chelmsford C, Sudbury T, Saffron Walden T, Haverhill R, Sudbury T), **Andy Jeffrey** (Camb.U, Camb.C, Leicester C)
Midfielders: Andy Pincher (Cambridge U (T)), **Adrian Cambridge** (Foxton, Cambridge C, Foxton), **Wayne Goddard** (Soham Town R, Rushden & D, Cambridge C, Histon), **Keith Lockhart** (Sudbury T, Cambridge C, Hartlepool, Wolves, Cambridge U), **Chris Tovey** (Great Shelford, Cambridge C, Royston T, Cambridge C, Royston T, Letchworth GC), **Mike Cook** (Corby T, Wycombe W, Cambridge U, Coventry), **John McLean** (Eynesbury R, Newmarket T, Cambridge C, Histon, Whitby T, Northallerton T), **John Fowler** (Kettering T, Camb.U)
Forwards: Paul Coe (Rushden & D, Cambridge C, Sudbury T, Newmarket T), **Gavin Dolby** (King's Lynn, Ipswich), **Ian Cambridge** (Foxton), **Colin Sinclair** (Newmarket T, Cambridge U)

Formed: 1938 **CHELMSFORD CITY** City

Back Row (L-R); Chris Heasman, Neal Docking, Graham Mansfield, Darren Morrell, Robert Bird, Craig Davidson, Steve Mosely, Glyn Roberts. Middle; Joe O'Sullivan (Mgr), Paul Smith (Physio), Bobby Mayes, Tony Rogers, John Keeley, Lee Ballard, Mark Keen, Mark Bellingham, Ian Butcher (Kit), Dave Guiver (Asst Mgr). Front; Mark Kane, Barry Hudson, Trevor Wright (Chr), Robbie Garvey, Ray Taylor, Dean Ketley (Sponsor), Lee Hunter, Paul Watts. Photo - The Essex Chronicle.

Chairman: Trevor Wright (01245 356840 H, 0850 468403 Mob)
Secretary: David Gore C/o Club. **Manager;** Roy McDonough **Asst Manager:** Paul Roberts
Ground: The Stadium, New Writtle Street, Chelmsford CM2 0RP (01245 353052).
Directions: A1016 (Chelmsford) exit off A12, follow Colchester signs to 3rd r'bout, left (B1007, New London Rd), left at 2nd lights (signed County Cricket Ground), grd 100 yds right. Residents only parking New Writtle St, A public car park next to grd (£1.30). 5 mins Chelmsford (BR) station.
Capacity: 2,850 (Police limit) **Seats:** 1,296 **Cover:** 1,700 **Metal Badges:** Yes
Club Shop: Yes, selling progs, badges, scarves, mugs etc. Contact Helen Williams/R Wigley via club.
Colours: Red/red/red **Change colours:** **Sponsors:** Britvic UK
Midweek home games: Tuesday **Reserve Team's League:** Essex & Herts Border Comb.
Previous Name: None (Brentwood Town were incorporated in 1968).
Previous Leagues: None **Record Gate:** 16,807 v Colchester, Southern League 10/9/49.
Best FA Cup season: 4th Rd Proper, 1938-39 (v Birmingham City). 1st Rd Proper on 25 occasions.
Record win: 10-3 v Billericay Town (H), Essex Senior Cup, 4/1/93.
Record defeat: 2-10 v Barking (A), FA Trophy, 11/11/78.
Record Fee Paid: £10,000 for Tony Rogers (Dover Athletic, 1992).
Received: £20,000 from Ian Brown (Bristol City, 1993).
Players progressing to Football League: G Merton (Watford 48), G Adams (Orient 49), W O'Neill (Burnley 49), B Farley & S McClellan (Spurs 49), O Hold (Everton 50), R Marden (Arsenal 50), C McCormack (Barnsley 50), L Dicker (Spurs 51), D Sexton (Luton 51), W Bellet & R Mason & A Nicholas (Orient 61 & 63 & 65), R Gladwin (Norwich 66), B King (Millwall 67), P Collins (Spurs 68), J O'Mara (Bradford City 74), N Spink (Aston 77), M Dziadulewicz (Wimbledon 79), M Cawston (Southend 84), P Coleman (Exeter 84), J Keeley & A Owers (Brighton 86 & 87), I Brown (Bristol C 93).
Clubhouse: Open matchdays & evening except Sunday (open Sunday lunchtimes). Pool, darts, satellite TV. Available for hire. Snacks served.
Club Record Goalscorer: Tony Butcher, 287 (1957-71).
Club Record Appearances: Derek Tiffin, 550 (1950-63).
Captain 95-96: **Top Scorer 95-96:**
Player of the Year 95-96:
Local Newspapers: Essex Chronicle (01245 262421), Chelmsford Weekly News (01245 493444), East Anglian Daily Times (01473 230023).
Local Radio Stations: Essex Radio/Breeze AM, BBC Essex.
Hons: Southern Lg 45-46 67-68 71-72 (R-up 48-49 60-61 63-64 65-66, Southern Div 88-89, Lg Cup 45-46 59-60 (R-up 60-61), Merit Cup 71-72, Southern Lg War-Time (East) 39-40), Essex Prof Cup 5; Essex Snr Cup 85-86 88-89 92-93, Non-League Champs Chall Cup 71-72, E Anglian Cup 48-49, Eastern Co's Lg(3) 46-49 (Lg Cup 59-60), Eastern Floodlit Comp 6; (Cup 72-73 74-75), Metropolitan Lg 67-68 (Lg Professional Cup 67-68, Autumn Shield 70-71), Essex Snr Lg Cup 84-85 (Harry Fisher Memorial Tphy 88-89).

PROGRAMME DETAILS:
Pages: 32 **Price:** £1.20
Editor: Trevor Smith
(01245 353052)

CHELMSFORD CITY'S 1995-96 CAMPAIGN

DATE		OPPONENTS	COMP	RESULT		GATE	GOALSCORERS
Aug 19	A	Gloucester City	BHL	L	0-5	764	
12	H	Rushden & Diamonds	BHL	L	1-2	1003	Garvey
26	H	Ilkeston Town	BHL	W	1-0	827	Garvey
28	A	Crawley Town	BHL	L	2-3	1146	Garvey, Mayes
Sept 2	A	Atherstone United	BHL	W	2-1	303	Keen, Bellingham
4	H	Baldock Town	BHL	L	0-2	902	
9	H	Collier Row	FAC1Q	W	1-0	991	Docking
16	A	Gresley Rovers	BHL	W	2-0	545	Garvey, Docking
19	A	Rushden & Diamonds	BHL	L	1-0	1747	Bellingham
23	A	Holbeach United	FAC2Q	D	0-0	350	
25	H	Holbeach United	FAC2Q	W	3-1	858	Keen, Bellingham 2
30	H	Halesowen Town	BHLPD	W	1-0	1185	Bellingham
Oct 3	A	Gravesend & Northfleet	DMC1	L	1-3	386	Bird
7	H	Billericay Town	FAC3Q	D	1-1	2074	Davidson
10	A	Billericay Town	FAC3Q	L	1-2	1704	Hudson
14	A	VS Rugby	BHL	D	2-2	454	Watts, Bellingham
21	H	Gloucester City	BHL	D	1-1	804	Garvey
23	H	Crawley Town	BHL	D	0-0	1149	
28	A	Dorcester Town	BHL	D	1-1	714	Greene
Nov 4	H	Gresley Rovers	BHL	L	1-2	947	Heasman
11	H	Atherstone United	BHL	D	1-1	789	Keen
14	A	Baldock Town	BHL	L	1-2	287	Bellingham
18	A	Newport AFC	BHL	W	2-1	896	Garvey, Bellingham
20	H	Gravesend & Northfleet	DMC1	W	1-0	534	Garvey
25	H	Yeading	FAT3Q	W	2-1	828	Kane, Garvey
Dec 2	H	Cambridge City	BHL	D	0-0	853	
4	H	Tilbury	ESC2	W	3-0	309	Kane, Garvey 2
9	A	Merthyr Tydfil	BHL	W	1-0	409	Keen
12	A	Sawbridgeworth Town	EFCQG	W	6-1	44	Davidson, Rutter 2, Heasman
16	H	Sudbury Town	BHL	W	2-1	776	Hunter, Mansfield
23	A	Burton Albion	BHL	D	1-1	652	Keen
Jan 1	A	Hastings Town	BHL	W	3-2	616	Mayes 2 Mosley
6	A	Cheltenham Town	BHL	L	1-2	788	Mayes
9	A	Braintree Town	ESC3	L	2-3	305	Keen, Davidson
13	H	Stafford Rangers	BHL	W	1-0	990	Roberts
15	H	Sawbridgeworth Town	EFC QF	D	0-0	237	
20	H	Newport AFC	FAT1	L	0-1	1,121	
Feb 12	H	Gravesend & Northfleet	BHL	W	6-1	618	Mansfield, Garvey 2 Mayes, Davidson, og
14	A	St. Albans City	EFC QF	W	2-0	82	Garvey, Bellingham
17	A	Worcester City	BHL	D	0-0	743	
24	A	Sudbury Town	BHLPD	L	0-2	604	
27	A	Witham Town	ETT2	L	1-2	139	Docking
Mar 2	H	Worcester City	BHLPD	W	1-0	710	Garvey
4	H	Dorcester Town	BHLPD	D	2-2	552	Keen, Garvey
6	H	St. Albans City	EFCQG	D	3-3	91	Hudson, Scott, Guiver
9	A	Halesowen Town	BHLPD	L	0-3	693	
11	H	Salisbury City	BHLPD	D	0-0	556	
16	H	Cheltenham Town	BHLPD	D	3-3	713	Keen 2, Lock
23	H	Burton Albion	BHLPD	D	0-0	755	
30	A	Salisbury City	BHLPD	D	0-0	355	
31	H	Newport AFC	BHLPD	D	0-0	804	
Apr 6	H	Hastings Town	BHLPD	L	0-3	648	
8	A	Cambridge City	BHLPD	D	0-0	341	
11	A	Clacton Town	ERCQF	L	1-2	104	Guiver
123	H	Merthyr Tydfil	BHLPD	L	1-4	715	Garvey
20	A	Stafford Rangers	BHLPD	L	0-3	460	
23	A	Ilkeston Town	BHLPD	D	1-1	592	Docking
27	A	Gravesend & Northfleet	BHLPD	W	1-0	670	Docking
May 4	H	VS Rugby	BHLPD	W	3-0	722	Scott, Docking 3, Mansfield

CHELMSFORD CITY PLAYING SQUAD 1996-97

Goalkeepers: Lee Ballard (Great Wakering R, Stambridge), **Ron Fearon** (Leyton O, Southend, Ipswich, Leyton O, Ipswich, Sutton U, Reading, QPR)

Defenders: Lee Hunter (Hendon, Wivenhoe T, Wigan, Colchester), **Paul Watts** (Dag & Red, Barking), **Ray Taylor** (Youth team), **Darren Morrell** (Youth team), **Robert Bird** (Youth team), **Paul Roberts** (Fisher`93, Purfleet, Enfield, Chesham U, Colchester, Fisher Ath, Southend, Leyt & Ilf, Exeter, Aldershot, Southend, Swindon, Brentford, Millwall), **John Devine** (Braintree T), **Gary Bellamy** (Leyton O, Wolves, Chesterfield), **Christian Hyslop** (Hendon, Colchester, Southend)

Midfielders: Mark Kane (Hendon, Enfield, Chelmsford C, Barking, Tampa Bay (USA), Barking, Woodford T, Walthamstow Ave, Woodford T, Leyton O), **Robbie Garvey** (Hendon, Redbridge F, Dartford, Grays A, Billericay T, Purfleet), **Neal Docking** (Saffron Walden T), **Jean Dalli** (Slough T, Dover A, Colchester), **Jason Cook** (Heybridge S, Dag & Red, Braintree T, Colchester, Southend, Tottenham), **Tony Cook** (Colchester)

Forwards: Roy McDonough (Heybridge S, Canvey Is, Dag & Red, Braintree T, Colchester, Southend, Cambridge U, Exeter, Southend, Colchester, Chelsea, Walsall, Birmingham), **Bobby Mayes** (Sudbury T, Dag & Red, Wivenhoe T, Kettering T, Bury T, Ipswich, FC Boon (Belg), West Ham), **Danny Scott** (Canvey Is), **Ian Benjamin** (Kettering T, Bury T, Wigan, Brentford, Luton, Southend, Exeter, Chester, Camb.U, Northampton, Peterborough, Notts Co, WBA, Sheffield U)

1892 **CHELTENHAM TOWN** Robins

CHELTENHAM TOWN

Cheltenham Town 96-97: Back Row (L-R); John Atkinson (Physio), Chris Robinson (Mgr), Bob Bloomer, Scott Starr, Kevin Malao, Mark Freeman, Darren Wright, David Elsey, Chris Price (Asst Mgr). Middle Row; Mark Bellingham, Paul Chenoweth, Jimmy Wring, Chris Banks, Andy Hughes, Jimmy Smith, Phil Serjeant, Wally Attwood (Kit). Front Row; Dean Clarke, Steve Benton, Martin Boyle, Jason Eaton.

Chairman: Arthur Hayward **Press Officer:** Arthur Hayward **Comm Mgr:** P G Cook.
Secretary: Reg Woodward, 3 Harveys Lane, Winchcombe, Glos GL54 5QS (01242 602261).
Manager: Chris Robinson. **Coach:** Chris Price **Physio:** John Atkinson
Ground: Whaddon Road, Cheltenham, Gloucestershire GL52 5NA (01242 513397).
Directions: M5 jct 10, A4019 through Cheltenham centre and join B4632 Prestbury Road. Whaddon Rd turning on right. Grd 1 mile town centre & 2 miles Cheltenham (BR).
Capacity: 5,000 **Cover:** 4,000 **Seats:** 1,000 **Floodlights:** Yes **Metal Badges:** Yes
Club Shop: Yes, selling souvenirs of all descriptions.
Colours: Red/white/black **Change colours:** Blue/white **Sponsors:** Empress Car Sales.
Midweek matches: Tuesday **Reserve's Lge:** Endsleigh Insurance Cen Conf
Previous Leagues: Birmingham Combination/ Birmingham Lge/ Southern 35-85/ GMV Conf 85-92.
Record Attendance: 8,326 v Reading, FA Cup 1st Rd 56-57.
Best F.A. Cup season: 3rd Rd Proper 33-34 (lost 1-2 at Blackpool).
League clubs defeated in F.A. Cup: Carlisle United 33-34.
Record Fee Paid: £20,000 to Kidderminster Harriers (Kim Casey)
Received: £60,000(initial) from Southampton for Christer Warren. **Players progressing to Football League:** Paul Tester (Shrewsbury), Brett Angell (Derby), Keith Knight (Reading), Peter Shearer (Bournemouth), Simon Brain (Hereford), Chris Burns (Portsmouth), Christer Warren (Southampton), Steve Jones (Swansea).
Clubhouse: Open every evening. 3 bars; clubroom, lounge, Robin's Nest. Open before and after Saturday matches. Nest & clubroom Available for private hire.
Club Record Scorer: Dave Lewis 290 (1970-83)
Club Record Apps: Roger Thorndale 701 (58-76)
95-96 Captain: Mark Freeman **95-96 P.o.Y.:** Jason Eaton.
95-96 Top scorer: Jimmy Smith
Local Newspapers: Echo/ Western Daily Press.
Local Radio Stations: Radio Glos/Cheltenham Radio
Hons: Southern Lg 84-85 (R-up 92-93 94-95, Midland Div 82-83, Lg Cup 57-58 (R-up 68-69 84-85), Championship Shield 58-59, Merit Cup 84-85), Nth Glos. Snr Professional Cup(30), Midland Floodlit Cup 85-86 86-87 87-88.

PROGRAMME DETAILS:
Pages: 24 **Price:** £1
Editor: Paul Godfrey
(01242 517554)

CHELTENHAM TOWN'S 1995-96 CAMPAIGN

DATE		OPPONENTS	COMP	RESULT		GATE	GOALSCORERS
Aug 19	A	Crawley Town	BHL	L	1-4	917	Tucker
22	H	Dorchester Town	BHL	W	3-0	642	Howells, Tucker, Smith
26	H	VS Rugby	BHL	W	4-0	730	Tucker, Howells Eston, Smith
28	A	Halesowen Town	BHL	W	1-0	843	Eaton
Sept 2	A	Worcester City	BHL	W	2-1	1212	Licata
5	H	Ilkeston Town	BHL	W	4-0	788	Wring, Tucker, Eaton, Howell
9	H	Yate Town	BHL	W	5-0	659	Tucker, Smith 2, Howell, Boyle
16	A	Atherstone United	BHL	W	2-1	402	Smith 2
19	A	Dorchester Town	BHL	L	0-4	639	
23	A	Forest Green Rovers	FAC	L	0-3	544	
30	H	Rushden & Diamonds	BHL	L	0-2	1122	
Oct 3	A	Weston-super-Mare	DMC	W	2-1	195	Eaton
7	H	Gresley Rovers	BHL	W	2-0	607	Smith 2
14	A	Cambridge City	BHL	W	2-1	235	Smith 2
17	H	Weston-super-Mare	DMC	W	4-2	211	Jones, Licata, Smith 2
24	H	Halesowen Town	BHL	D	2-2	534	Wring, Eaton
28	A	Salisbury City	BHL	D	3-3	547	Eaton, Smith, Wright
Nov 1	H	Yate Town	GSC	W	2-0	131	Smith, Howell
4	H	Cambridge City	BHL	L	2-3	764	Wright, Smith
11	H	Newport AFC	BHL	W	2-0	1092	Smith, Wring
14	A	Ilkeston Town	BHL	W	4-1	758	Howells, Eaton 2, Smith
18	A	Sudbury Town	BHL	W	4-3	349	Banks, Wright, Eaton 2
25	H	Crawley Town	BHL	D	1-1	715	Eaton
Dec 2	A	Gresley Rovers	BHL	W	2-0	662	Eaton, Smith
5	H	Gloucester City	DMC	W	4-0	551	Chenoweth, Smith 2
9	H	Baldock Town	BHL	H	3-1	751	Eaton, Smith, Wring
16	H	Worcester City	BHL	H	1-3	1010	Chenoweth
23	A	Hasting Town	BHL	L	1-4	523	Smith
Jan 6	H	Chelmsford City	BHL	W	2-1	738	Wright, Eaton
9	H	Gresley Rovers	DMC	D	3-3	308	Banks, Wring, Smith
13	H	Gravesend & Northfleet	BHL	L	0-1	834	
20	A	Dover Athletic	FAT	D	2-2	908	Wright 2
23	H	Dover Athletic	FAT	D	1-1	640	Banks
31	A	Dover Athletic	FAT	A	0-1	598	
Feb 3	H	Atherstone United	BHL	D	1-1	516	Eaton
17	A	Rushden & Diamonds	BHL	L	1-4	2472	Elsey
24	A	Baldock Town	BHL	D	1-1	236	Wring
27	H	Gloucester City	BHL	D	0-0	1010	
Mar 2	H	Gravesend & Northfleet	BHL	D	0-0	549	
5	A	Gresley Rovers	DMC	D	2-2	407	Smith, Dunphy
9	H	Burton Albion	BHL	W	1-0	608	Freeman
16	A	Chelmsford City	BHL	D	3-3	713	Wright, Eaton, Smith
18	A	Newport AFC	BHL	W	3-2	646	Wring, Smith 2
23	H	Hasting Town	BHL	L	1-2	603	Eaton
26	A	Merthyr Tydfil	BHL	W	1-0	277	Eaton
30	A	Stafford Rangers	BHL	W	1-0	654	Eaton
Apr 2	H	Gloucester City	GSC	D	0-0	432	
6	H	Merthyr Tydfil	BHL	W	1-0	603	Wring
8	A	Gloucester City	BHL	W	3-0	1523	Elsey, Eaton 2
13	H	Sudbury Town	BHL	D	1-1	602	Chenoweth
16	H	Stafford Rangers	BHL	W	4-0	425	Banks, Smith 2, Chenoweth
20	A	Burton Albion	BHL	L	2-3	532	Banks, Eaton
27	A	VS Rugby	BHL	D	1-1	291	Wright
May 4	H	Salisbury City	BHL	D	3-3	548	Wright, Eaton 2, Smith

CHELTENHAM TOWN PLAYING SQUAD 1996-97

Goalkeepers: Kevin Maloy (Weston-S-M, Taunton T, Blackpool, Exeter, Taunton), **Scott Starr** (Canberra Cosmos (Aust))
Defenders: Lee Howells (Brisbane C (Aust), Bristol R), **Steve Benton** (Clevedon T, Bristol C (T)), **Bob Bloomer** (Bristol R, Chesterfield), **Chris Banks** (Bath C, Exeter, Port Vale), **Mark Freeman** (Gloucester C, Hednesford T, Willenhall T, Bilston T, Wolves, Bilston T), **Dave Elsey** (Fairford T, Weston-S-M, Gloucester C, Swindon), **Darren Wright** (Atherstone U, Willenhall T, Worcester C, Wrexham, Wolves), **Dean Clarke** (Hereford), **Phil Serjeant** (Bristol R (T))
Midfielders: Paul Chenoweth (Bath C, Bristol R), **Jimmy Wring** (Mangotsfield U, Bath C, Bristol R (T)), **Gary Wotton** (Weston-S-M, Liskeard Ath, Dorchester T, Yeovil T, Reading, Plymouth), **Danny Donovan** (Rushall O, Pelsall V, Atherstone U, Chasetown, Atherstone, Walsall (T)), **Andy Hughes** (Fairford T, Swindon, Wolves, Chelsea), **Jamie Victory** (AFC Bournemouth, West Ham)
Forwards: Jimmy Smith (Salisbury C, Torquay), **Jason Eaton** (Gloucester C, Bristol C, Bristol R, Trowbridge T), **Martin Boyle** (Bath C, Mangotsfield U, Trowbridge T, Bristol R), **Steve Campbell** (Atherstone U, Redditch U, Knowle), **Mark Bellingham** (Chelmsford C, Great Wakering R, Stambridge)

Formed: 1896

CRAWLEY TOWN

Red Devils

Crawley Town FC: Back Row (L-R); Russel Milton, Alan Lester, Paul Adam, Mario Otero, Gavin Geddes, Mark Pullen, Ian Chatfield, Leighton Allen, Mark Ford, John Mackie, Danny Foot, Tony Vessey, John Crumplin, Terry Graves (Coach), Gary Brown (Asst Mgr). Middle; Viv Jeffery, Spencer Mears, Dominic Shepherd, Raphael Meade, Dave Haining (Mgr), Steve Restarick, Andy Driscoll, Sean Edwards, Graham Haper. Front; Clinton Moore, James Ashcroft, Paul Potrac. *Photo - Andrew Chitty.*

Chairman: John Maggs **President:** K Symons
Secretary: Stan Markham, 105 Winchester Road, Tilgate, Crawley RH10 5HH (01293 522371).
Player/Manager: Colin Pates. **Asst Manager:** Vic Akers. **Commercial Mgr:** Andy Bell.
Coach: Colin Pates. **Physio:** Vic Akers.
Ground: Town Mead, Ifield Avenue, West Green, Crawley (01293 410000).
Directions: M23 exit 10, A264 for Horsham, left at 2nd island, over mini r-about, right at next island into Ifield Avenue and ground 150 yards on right behind fire station. 10 mins walk from Crawley (BR).
Capacity: 4,750 **Cover:** 1,800 **Seats:** 400 **Floodlights:** Yes **Metal Badges:** Yes.
Club Shop: Yes, selling programmes, metal badges, hats, scarves, mugs, replica kits. Contact Ian Hands.
Colours: Red/red/white **Change cols:** All Blue. **Sponsors:** TBA
Previous Grounds: Malthouse Farm 1896-1914 38-39/ Victoria Hall + Rectory Fields 18-38/ Yetmans Field 45-52.
Previous Leagues: Sussex County 1951-56/ Metropolitan 56-63
Reserves' Lge: Suburban (Capital Lge also entered for 94-95, but the first team will play these fixtures).
Midweek matchday: Tuesday **Record Gate:** 4,104 v Barnet, FA Cup 2nd Round 4/12/93.
Best FA Trophy season: 2nd Rd 85-86 87-88.
Best FA Cup season: 3rd Rd Proper 91-92 (lost 0-5 at Brighton).
League Clubs defeated in FA Cup: Northampton Town 91-92.
Record win: 10-0 v Chichester United, Sussex County League Division Two 17/12/55.
Record defeat: 0-10 v Dartford (H), Mid-Surrey Prof. Floodlit Lge 8/4/75.
Record Fee Paid: £5,000 for David Thompson (Wokingham, May 1992)
Record Received: £50,000 for Craig Whitington (Scarborough 1993).
Players progressing to Football League: Ray Keeley (Mansfield 1968), Graham Brown (Mansfield 1969), Andy Ansah (Brentford 1987 (now Southend)), Craig Whitington (Scarborough 1993).
Clubhouse: Weekdays noon-3 & 6-11pm, Sat noon-11pm, Sun noon-3 & 7-10.30pm. Snacks available.
Club Record Goalscorer: Phil Basey 108.(1968-72).
Club Record Apps: John Maggs 652.(1963-73).
95-96 Captain: **95-96 P.o.Y.:**
95-96 Top scorer:
Local Newspapers: Crawley Observer (01293 526929), Crawley News (01293 526474).
Local Radio Stations: Radio Mercury, BBC Radio Sussex,Southern Counties Radio.
Hons: Sussex Snr Cup(2) 89-91 (R-up 58-59), Sussex Intermediate Cup 26-27, Sussex Prof. Cup 69-70 (beat Brighton 1-0 in final), Southern Lg Southern Div R-up 83-84 (Merit Cup 70-71), Sussex Floodlit Cup(3) 90-93, Sussex Lg Div 2 R-up 55-56, Gilbert Rice Floodlit Cup 79-80 83-84, Southern Co's Comb. Floodlit Cup 85-86, Metropolitan Lg Chal. Cup 58-59, Mid-Sussex Snr 02-03, Montgomery Cup 25-26.

PROGRAMME DETAILS:
Pages: 40 **Price:** £1
Editor: Ian Hands

CRAWLEY TOWN'S 1995-96 CAMPAIGN

DATE		OPPONENTS	COMP	RESULT		GATE	GOALSCORERS
Aug 19	H	Cheltenham Town	BHL	W	4-1		
22	A	Sudbury Town	BHL	W	2-1	370	Sakala, Dineen
26	A	Rushden & Diamonds	BHL	L	1-3	1,661	Sakala
28	H	Chelmsford City	BHL	W	3-2	1,146	Meade, Jeffery, Geddes
Sept 2	A	Burton Albion	BHL	L	1-2	950	Speedie
5	H	Salisbury City	BHL	W	2-0	722	Meade 2
16	A	Baldock Town	BHL	D	0-0	401	
19	H	Sudbury Town	BHL	D	2-2	822	Meade, Nockler (p)
23	H	Worcester City	BHL	L	1-3	1,004	Speedie
30	A	Dorchester Town	BHL	L	1-3	709	Speedie
Oct 3	H	Hastings Town	DMC	D	1-1	425	Speedie
7	H	Gloucester City	BHL	D	0-0	855	
14	A	Barton Rovers	FAT	W	3-1	331	Speedie, Meade, og
23	A	Chelmsford City	BHL	D	0-0	1,149	
28	H	Newport AFC	BHL	D	0-0	853	
31	A	Hastings Town	DMC	W	2-1	328	Meade, Geddes
Nov 4	H	Bashley	FAT	L	0-1	609	
11	A	Worcester City	BHL	L	0-2	887	
18	H	Ilkeston Town	BHL	W	1-0	618	Clark
22	A	Lancing	SSC	W	4-0	160	Speedie 2, og, Sakala
25	A	Cheltenham Town	BHL	D	1-1	715	Speedie
Dec 2	H	Rushden & Diamonds	BHL	D	2-2	1,118	Hudson, Speedie
9	A	Atherstone United	BHL	L	1-2	244	
19	A	Gravesend & N'fleet	DMC	W	2-1	189	Meade 2
26	H	Hastings Town	BHL	W	3-2	757	Sakala, Meade, Ford
Jan 1	A	Gravesend & N'fleet	BHL	L	1-3	633	Lester
6	H	Burton Albion	BHL	D	1-1	657	Meade
10	A	Selsey	SSC	W	3-1	250	Meade 2, Sakala
13	A	Newport AFC	BHL	D	1-1	827	Meade
16	H	Tonbridge	DMC	W	3-0	289	Shepstone, Speedie, Sakala
20	A	Salisbury City	BHL	L	1-2	272	Smith
23	H	Cambridge City	BHL	D	3-3	343	Meade 2, Sakala
29	H	Baldock Town	DMC	D	2-2*	237	Meade, Speedie
Feb 3	A	Gloucester City	BHL	D	1-1	606	Speedie
5	A	Worthing	SSC	W	4-1	314	Meade, Jeffery, Hudson, og
10	A	Halesowen Town	BHL	L	0-2	681	
17	H	Baldock Town	BHL	L	1-2	546	Hudson
24	A	Stafford Rangers	BHL	L	0-3	679	
27	A	Baldock Town	DMC	D	1-1	107	Ford
Mar 9	A	Ilkeston Town	BHL	W	4-1	547	Restarick, Meade, Theodosiou 2
12	H	Wick	SSC	W	4-1	236	Meade 2, Restarick, Ford
23	H	VS Rugby	BHL	W	3-1	671	Restarick 2, Kruszywski
26	H	Gresley Rovers	BHL	W	2-0	437	Rogers, Restarick
30	A	Cambridge City	BHL	W	2-1	218	Geddes, Restarick
Apr 1	H	Dorchester Town	BHL	D	1-1	607	Restarick
6	H	Gravesend & N'fleet	BHL	W	1-0	843	Geddes
8	A	Hastings Town	BHL	W	1-0	713	Geddes
13	H	Stafford Rangers	BHL	W	2-1	740	Rogers, Restarick
16	H	Merthyr Tydfil	BHL	W	1-0	534	Meade
20	A	Merthyr Tydfil	BHL	D	1-1	404	Geddes
24	A	VS Rugby	BHL	W	4-1	220	Restarick 2, Geddes, Sakala
27	H	Atherstone United	BHL	L	0-1	732	
29	H	Halesowen Town	BHL	L	1-3	802	Theodosiou
May 4	A	Gresley Rovers	BHL	L	0-1	611	

* Baldock Town won on away goals

CRAWLEY TOWN PLAYING SQUAD 1996-97

Goalkeepers: Ian Chatfield (Dorking, Hayes, Chelsea (T), Redhill)

Defenders: John Mackie (Arsenal (T)), Lee McCauley (Brighton), **Tommy Ford** (Youth team), **Micky Turner** (Peterborough, Portsmouth), **John Crumplin** (Woking, Brighton, Bognor Regis T), **Tony Vessey** (Worthing, Steyning, Vasalund (Swe), Brighton)

Midfielders: Viv Jeffrey (Banstead Ath), **Paul Adam** (Molesey, Sutton U), **Mark Ford** (Sutton U), **Billy Hudson** (Wealdstone, Crewe, Tottenham H (T)), **Rob Goddard** (Brentford), **Andy Driscoll** (Hendon, St.Albans C, Hayes, St.Albans C, Hayes, Chertsey T, Papatoetoe (NZ), Yeading, Brentford), **Danny Smith** (Brighton)

Forwards: Raphael Meade (Brighton, Plymouth, Odense (Den), Ipswich, Luton, Dundee U, Sporting Lisbon (Port), Arsenal), **Landy Salaka** (Brighton, Chelsea (T)), **Gavin Geddes** (Brighton, Wick, Shoreham, Lewes), **Tony Rogers** (Dover Ath, Chelmsford C, Dover Ath, Maidstone U, Barking, Dartford, Tilbury, Leyt & Ilf, Basildon U), **Steve Restarick** (Dover A, Chelmsford C, Colchester U), **John Byrne** (Brighton, Oxford U, Millwall, Sunderland, Brighton, Le Havre (Fr), QPR, York)

Formed: 1880

DORCHESTER TOWN

The Magpies

Back Row (L-R); Darren Reeks, Craig Taylor, Paul Thorpe, Darren Tallow, James Reeve, Paul Wilkinson. Centre; Brain Benjafield (Asst Mgr), Peter Watts, Toby Redwood, Tommy Killick, Dave Lovell, Paul Gadsby, Steve Richardson, Ken Veysey, Marcus Crocker. Middle: Matthew Turner, Paul Watts, Geoff Dine (Physio), Peter Peavoy (Kit). Front; Andy Gater, Martyn Sullivan, Neil Coates,Stuart Morgan (Mgr), Owen Pickard, Mark Lisk, Russell Coughlin. *Photo - E Wastin*

Chairman: P J Aiken **Vice Chairman:** C E Clark **President:** J Pitfield
Secretary: Albert Miller, 29 Shaston Crescent, Dorchester DT1 2EB (01305 264843)
Manager: Stuart Morgan **Physio:** Geoff Dine **Comm Mgr:** Keith Kellaway (01305 262451).
Ground: Avenue Stadium, Weymouth Avenue, Dorchester DT1 2RY (01305 262451).
Directions: At junction of southern bypass (A35) and Weymouth road (A354).
Capacity: 7,210 **Cover:** 4,000 **Seats:** 710 **Floodlights:** Yes **Metal Badges:** Yes
Club Shop: Yes, selling replica shirts, badges, mugs, etc.
Colours: Black & white stripes/black/black **Change colours:** All sky/white/sky blue.
Previous Leagues: Dorset/ Western 1947-72. **Sponsors:** Wool & Bovington Motors.
Previous Grounds: Council Recreation Ground, Weymouth Avenue 1880-1929/ The Avenue Ground, Weymouth Avenue 29-90.
Record Attendance: 4,000 v Chelsea, official ground opening 1990. Competitive: 3,027 v Weymouth, Southern Lge Prem Div 92.
Best FA Cup season: 2nd Rd Replay 81-82 (lost 1-2 to A.F.C. Bournemouth after 1-1 draw). 2nd Rd 54-55 57-58, 1st Rd on seven occasions;
Best F.A.Trophy season: 3rd Rd replay 71-72.
Midweek games: Tuesday **Reserve Lge:** Dorset Comb
Record win: 7-0 v Canterbury (A), Southern Lge Southern Div 86-87.
Record defeat: 0-6 on four occasions: v Kettering 7/4/79, Cambridge City 2/9/89, Bath City 6/2/90.
Record Fees: Paid: £12,000 for Chris Townsend (Gloucester City, 1990)
Received: £35,000 for Trevor Senior (Portsmouth, 1981)
Players progressing to The Football League: Len Drake (Bristol Rovers 1957), David Noake (Luton 1959), Mike Turner (Swindon 1961), Trevor Senior (Portsmouth 1981), David West (Liverpool 1983), Mike Squire (Torquay 1984), Jeremy Judd (Torquay 1984), Anthony White (Bournemouth 1985) + Graham Roberts (Spurs, Chelsea, Rangers, England) who progressed via Weymouth.Darren Garner(Rotherham U,1995) **Clubhouse:** Dorchester Lounge Club - access via main entrance to stadium. Cold food and snacks
Club Record Goalscorer: Dennis Cheney 61 (in one season)
Club Record Appearances: Trevor Townsend 377.
95-96 Captain: **95-96 P.o.Y.:**
95-96 Top scorer:
Local Press: Dorset Evening Echo, Western Gazette, Western Daily Press.
Local Radio Stations: Two Counties Radio, Wessex FM .
Newsline (Magpies Hotline): 0839 664412.
Hons: Southern Lg R-up 79-80 (Div 1 (Sth) R-up 77-78, Lg Cup 86-87 (R-up 91-92), Western Lg 54-55 (R-up 60-61, Div 2 R-up 49-50), Dorset Snr Cup 50-51 60-61 67-68 68-69 71-72 94-95, Dorset Lg 37-38.

PROGRAMME DETAILS:
Pages: 32 **Price:** 80p
Editor: David Martin
(011305 264740)

DORCHESTER TOWN'S 1995-96 CAMPAIGN

DATE		OPPONENTS	COMP	RESULT		GATE	GOALSCORERS
Aug 19	H	Atherstone	BHL	L	0-1	604	
22	A	Cheltenham	BHL	L	0-3	624	
26	A	Baldock	BHL	L	1-2	281	Pickard
28	H	Newport AFC	BHL	L	0-3	944	
Sept 2	A	Ilkeston	BHL	L	0-1	545	
3	H	Merthyr Tydfil	BHL	W	7-1	502	Wilkinson, Richardson, Killick Pickard 3,Gater
9	H	Wimborne	FAC	D	2-2	764	Killick, Reeve
12	A	Wimborne	FAC	W	2-0	604	Pickard 2
16	A	Hastings	BHL	D	1-1	466	Pickard
19	H	Cheltenham	BHL	W	4-0	689	Kiloour, Richardson, Killick 2
23	H	Basingstoke	FAC	W	2-0	609	Pickard 2
30	H	Crawley	BHL	W	3-1	709	Richardson, Killick, Pickard
Oct 3	H	Havant	DMC	W	1-0	309	Killick
7	A	Weymouth	FAC	W	3-2	2527	Pickard 3
14	A	Stafford	BHL	W	3-0	382	Kiloour, Wilkinson, Pickard
21	A	Sittingbourne	FAC	W	2-1	1232	Pickard, Evans
25	A	Newport AFC	BHL	L	2-3	1077	Wilkinson, Killick
28	H	Chelmsford	BHL	D	1-1	714	Pickard
31	A	Havant	DMC	W	1-0	72	?
Nov 4	H	Stur Newton	DSC	W	10-1	308	Tallon, Wilkinson, Taylor, Killick, Pickard 5, Reeve
11	A	Oxford United	FAC	L	1-9	3819	Killick
14	A	Merthyr Tydfil	BHL	L	1-3	222	Evans
18	A	Atherstone	BHL	W	4-3	222	Richardson, Taylor, Pickard 2
25	H	Hayes	FAT	L	2-3	515	Killick, Pickard
28	A	Weymouth	DSC	W	2-0	937	Pickard 2
Dec 2	H	Baldock Town	BHL	L	1-2	540	Killick
6	A	Salisbury	DMC	L	1-2	145	Taylor
9	H	Rushden & Diamonds	BHL	D	1-1	684	Pickard
16	A	Halesowen	BHL	L	0-1	534	
26	H	Salisbury	BHL	L	0-2	1032	
30	H	Gravesend & N'fleet	BHL	D	2-2	607	Reeve, Pickard
Jan 6	H	Hastings	BHL	L	1-4	510	Killick
13	A	Sudbury	BHL	L	1-2	344	Reeve
Feb 10	H	VS Rugby	BHL	W	4-0	660	Wilkinson, Richardson, Killick, Pickard
17	A	Gresley	BHL	W	2-0	640	Pickard, Cooper
24	H	Ilkeston	BHL	H	3-0	755	Tallon 2, Evans
27	A	Burton	BHL	L	0-1	458	
Mar 2	H	Bournemouth SP	DSC	D	0-0	272	
4	A	Chelmsford	BHL	D	2-2	552	Fallon, Reeve
9	A	Bournemouth SP	DSC	D	2-2	283	Sullivan, Reeve
12	H	Cambridge	BHL	L	1-2	300	Morgan
16	A	Bournemouth SP	DSC	W	1-0	200	Pickard
19	H	Sudbury	BHL	W	2-0	480	Richardson, Killick
23	H	Worcester	BHL	L	1-2	705	Pickard
26	H	Halesowen	BHL	D	0-0	454	
30	A	Gravesend & N'fleet	BHL	L	1-4	427	Wilkinson
Apr 1	A	Crawley	BHL	D	1-1	601	Killick
4	A	Rushden & Diamonds	BHL	W	1-0	1023	Killick
6	H	Gloucester	BHL	L	0-1	770	
8	A	Salisbury	BHL	L	0-1	422	
13	H	Burton	BHL	W	2-1	647	Richardson, Pickard
15	A	Worcester	BHL	W	1-0	543	Wilkinson
16	?	St. Pauls, JSEY	DSC	W	3-1	362	Evans, Pickard 2
20	A	VS Rugby	BHL	D	0-0	277	
23	A	Gresley	BHL	W	2-1	536	Fallon, Pickard
27	A	Cambridge	BHL	W	2-1	256	Killick, Pickard
30	A	Gloucester	BHL	L	0-1	523	
May 4	H	Stafford	BHL	W	4-2	688	Killick, Sullivan, Richardson, og

DORCHESTER TOWN PLAYING SQUAD 1996-97

Goalkeepers: Kenny Veysey (Oxford U, Torquay, Arsenal), **Tony Oliver** (Bournemouth FC, Weymouth, Brentford, Portsmouth)
Defenders: Neil Coates (Yeovil T, Dorchester T, Yeovil T, AFC Bournemouth, Watford), **Scott Morgan** (Brentford, AFC Bournemouth (T)), **Toby Redwood** (Exeter), **Mark Sullivan** (Plymouth), **Paul Thorpe** (Trowbridge T, Dorchester T, Yeovil T, Torquay, Bristol C, Newport Co), **Mark Lisk** (Bashley, AFC Lymington, Eastleigh)
Midfielders: Steve Richardson (Poole T, Wimborne T, Ferryhill Ath, Hartlepool), **Jamie Reeve** (Hereford, AFC Bournemouth), **Craig Taylor** (Bath C, Plymouth), **Paul Smith** (Truro C), **Rob Taylor** (Local football), **Andy Gater** (Christchurch), **Russell Coughlin** (Torquay, Exeter, Swansea, Blackpool, Plymouth, Carlisle, Blackburn, Manchester C)
Forwards: Tommy Killick (Wimborne T, Bashley, Wimborne T, Swanage, Poole T), **Paul Wilkinson** (Bashley, Wokingham T, Reading (T)), **Chris Evans** (Weymouth), **Owen Pickard** (Hereford, Plymouth), **Marcus Crocker** (Torquay, Plymouth)

Formed: 1889

GLOUCESTER CITY

The Tigers

Action from Gloucester City's Meadow Park.

Chairman: Keith Gardner **Vice-Chairman:** Michael Tuck.
President: R F Etheridge **Chief Executive:** Keith Gardner.
Secretary: Ken Turner, 24 Ladysmith Road, Cheltenham, GL52 5LQ (01242 522514).
Manager: John Murphy **Asst Manager:** Bob Baird **Coach:** Brian Hughes.
Press Officer: J Mills (01452 728663) **Physios:** B & A Tandy **Comm Dir:** A Hindmarsh.
Ground: Meadow Park, Sudmeadow Road, Hempsted, Gloucester GL2 6HS (01452 523883. Commercial Office: 0452 421400).
Directions: From North: A40 then then A4301 towards City Centre & Historic Docks, right into Severn Road over swingbridge, right into Llanthony Road/Hempsted Lane, 2nd right into Sudmeadow Road, ground 50yds on left.
Capacity: 5,000 **Cover:** 2,000 **Seats:** 560 **Club Shop:** Yes **Metal Badges:** Yes
Colours: Yellow & Black/Black/Black. **Change colours:** Red & White/White/Red
Midweek games: Tuesday **Sponsors:** Hartland Motors.
Previous Leagus: Bristol & Dist. (now Western) 1893-96/ Gloucester & Dist. 97-1907/ Nth Glos. 07-10/ Glos. Nth Snr 20-34/ Birmingham Comb. 1935-39.
Previous Grounds: Longlevens 1935-1965/ Horton Road 65-86.
Previous Name: Gloucester Y.M.C.A.
Record Attendance: 3,952 v Arsenal, July 87)
Best FA Cup season: 2nd Rd 89-90
Best FA Trophy season: 3rd Rd 90-91.
Record Transfer Fee: Paid: £25,000 S Fergusson (Worcester City)
Received: £25,000 Ian Hedges (AFC Bournemouth, 1990)
Players progressing to The Football League: George Beattie & David Pugsley (Newport County 50 & 53), John Boyd & Robert Etheridge & Charlie Cook (Bristol City 50/56/57), David Jones (Leeds Utd 54), Mike Johnson (Fulham 58), William Teague & Rod Thomas (Swindon 61 & 64), John Layton (Hereford 74), Ian Main (Exeter 78), Mike Bruton (Newport 79), Mel Gwinnett (Bradford City 84), Steve Talboys (Wimbledon 91).
Clubhouse: Meadow Park Sports & Social Club at entrance to ground. Normal licensing hours. Hot & cold food available.
Club Record Goalscorer: Reg Weaver, 250
Club Record Apps: Stan Myers & Frank Tredgett in 1950s
95-96 Captain: **95-96 P.o.Y.:**
95-96 Top scorer:
Local Press: Gloucester Citizen, Western Daily Press
Local Radio Stations: Severn Sound, BBC Radio Gloucestershire
Hons: Southern Lg R-up 90-91 (Lg Cup 55-56 (R-up 81-82), Midland Div 88-89), Glos Nth Snr Lg 33-34, Glos Snr Prof. Cup 37-38 49-58 65-66 68-69 70-71 74-75 78-79 79-80 81-82 82-83 83-84 90-91 92-93 (R-up 94-95, Snr Amtr Cup (Nth) 31-32).

PROGRAMME DETAILS:
Pages: 44 **Price:** £1
Editor: Helen Lodge/ Debbie Dembny

GLOUCESTER CITY'S 1995-96 CAMPAIGN

DATE		OPPONENTS	COMP	RESULT		GATE	GOALSCORERS
Aug 19	H	Chelmsford City	BHL	W	5-0	764	Rouse, Knight, Adebowale, Hallam, Holmes
23	A	Newport AFC	BHL	L	0-1	1524	
26	A	Cambridge City	BHL	W	4-0	342	Adeboweale, Hallam, Holmes, Portway
28	H	Salisbury City	BHL	W	2-0	1576	Kemp, Portway
Sep 2	H	Gravesend & N'Fleet	BHL	W	3-1	891	Knight, Holmes 2
5	A	Halesowen Town	BHL	L	1-2	678	Knight
9	H	Bristol Manor Farm	FAC	W	8-0	514	Portway 2, Rouse, Knight, Adebowale, Webb, Warner, Adams
16	H	Burton Albion	BHL	W	2-1	867	Adebowale, Holmes
19	H	Newport AFC	BHL	D	1-1	1412	Knight
23	H	Cinderford Town	FAC	L	0-1	921	
30	A	Sudbury Town	BHL	W	2-0	421	Knight, Holmes
Oct 7	A	Crawley Town	BHL	D	0-0	855	
14	H	Worcester City	BHL	W	2-1	1285	Adebowale, Hallam
21	A	Chelmsford City	BHL	D	1-1	804	Milsom
25	A	Salisbury City	BHL	D	3-3	583	Phillips, Milsom 2
28	H	Hastings Town	BHL	L	0-2	712	
Nov 4	A	Ilkeston Town	BHL	W	2-1	751	Kemp, Phillips
11	A	Stafford Rangers	BHL	W	4-3	543	Webb, Milsom, Holmes, Phillips
14	H	Halesowen Town	BHL	L	0-2	578	
18	H	Baldock Town	BHL	W	3-1	584	Milsom 2, Holmes
25	H	Aldershot Town	FAT	W	5-1	1041	Holmes 2, Webb, Milsom, Adebowale
Dec 2	A	Worcester City	BHL	W	3-1	1109	Hallam, Webb, og
9	H	Cambridge City	BHL	W	3-1	666	Phillips 2, Knight
12	A	Rushden & Diamonds	BHL	L	2-3	1666	Milsom, Adebowale
23	H	Atherstone United	BHL	L	1-2	615	Knight
Jan 6	A	VS Rugby	BHL	W	2-1	446	Rouse, Hallam
13	H	Merthyr Tydfil	BHL	W	3-1	781	Webb, Hallam 2
21	H	Staines Town	FAT	W	5-0	748	Hallam 2, Knight, Phillips Portway
Feb 3	H	Crawley Town	BHL	D	1-1	606	Hallam
15	A	Sudbury Town	FAT	L	1-3	262	Hallam
24	A	Burton Albion	BHL	L	0-1	672	
27	A	Cheltenham Town	BHL	D	0-0	1010	
Mar 2	H	VS Rugby	BHL	D	1-1	509	Holmes
9	A	Merthyr Tydfil	BHL	L	0-1	456	
12	H	Stafford Rangers	BHL	W	3-2	435	Webb, Adebowale, Milsom
16	H	Sudbury Town	BHL	W	1-0	509	Webb
19	A	Gresley Rovers	BHL	L	0-1	511	
23	A	Atherstone United	BHL	L	1-2	284	Milsom
26	A	Gravesend & N'fleet	BHL	D	0-0	383	
30	H	Gresley Rovers	BHL	L	1-2	613	Holloway
Apr 6	A	Dorchester Town	BHL	W	1-0	770	Black
8	H	Cheltenham Town	BHL	L	0-3	1523	
13	A	Baldock Town	BHL	W	1-0	261	Black
20	H	Rushden & Diamonds	BHL	H	2-1	1226	Mardenborough, Milsom
27	H	Ilkeston Town	BHL	W	3-1	607	Kemp, Howell, Holloway
30	H	Dorchester Town	BHL	W	1-0	523	Black
May 4	A	Hastings Town	BHL	L	0-2	504	

GLOUCESTER CITY PLAYING SQUAD 1996-97

Goalkeepers: David Coles (Yeovil T, Fulham, Aldershot, Brighton, Crystal Palace, HJK Helsinki (Fin), Aldershot), **Chris Hamblin** (Swindon), **Shane Cook** (Cheltenham T, Swindon (T))

Defenders: Neil Reeves (Clevedon T, Trowbridge T, Bath C, Trowbridge T, Bristol R), **Don O'Riordan** (Dorchester T, Torquay, Notts Co, Grimsby, Middlesbrough, Carlisle, Preston, Tulsa Roughnecks (USA), Derby), **Gary Kemp** (Almondsbury Picksons), **Dave Johnson** (Rushden & D, Northampton, Irthlingborough D, Kettering T), **Gary Thorne** (Swindon), **Simon Barnard** (Worcester C, Portsmouth), **Andy Tucker** (Cheltenham T), **Jon Holloway** (Swindon)

Midfielders: Simon Cooper (Cheltenham T), **Shaun Rouse** (Weston-S-M, Carlisle, Weston-S-M, Bristol C, Glasgow Rangers), **Ade Adebowale** (Merthyr Tydfil, Chesham U, Bishop's Stortford, Hertford T, Balls Park), **David Webb** (Trowbridge T, Gloucester C, Stroud, Devizes T, Wantage T, Supermarine), **Ian Howell** (Cheltenham T, Gloucester C, Trowbridge T, Hungerford T, Trowbridge T, Swindon Ath, Swindon), **Adie Mings** (Bath C, Chippenham T, Melksham T), **Steve Fergusson** (Worcester C, Telford U, Gloucester C, Worcester C, Redditch U, Alvechurch, Redditch U, Bromsgrove R)

Forwards: Paul Milsom (Oxford U, Cardiff, Bristol C), **Dale Watkins** (Rushden & D, Grantham T, Peterborough C, Peterborough, Sheffield U (T)), **Steve Mardenborough** (Newport AFC, Colchester, Stafford R, Lincoln, Darlington, Hereford, Cardiff, Newport Co, Swansea, Wolves, Coventry), **Deion Vernon** (Bath C, Bristol C), **Keith Knight** (Trowbridge T, Yeovil T, Trowbridge T, Gloucester C, Reading, Cheltenham T), **Leroy Rosenior** (Fleet T, Bristol C, West Ham, Fulham, QPR, Fulham), **Henry Wright** (Hednesford T, Halesowen T, Bilston T, Sprinvale-Tranco, Stourbridge, Hednesford T)

1946 **GRAVESEND & NORTHFLEET** The Fleet

Gravesend FC. after match with Aston Villa. *Photo - K Gillard*

Chairman: L G F Ball **Vice Chairman/Chief Executive:** David Stevens.
Secretary: Bill Hornby c/o the club (H - 01474 363424). **Manager:** Chris Weller.
Press Officer: Lionel R H Ball (01474 569985). **Physio:** Micky Ward
Ground: Stonebridge Road, Northfleet, Kent DA11 9BA (01474 533796)
Directions: From A2 take Northfleet/Southfleet exit (B262), follow to Northfleet then B2175 (Springhead Rd) to junc A226, turn left (The Hill, Northfleet), rd becomes Stonebridge Rd, grd on right at bottom of steep hill after 1 mile - car parking behind for 400-500 cars. 2 mins walk from Northfleet BR station.
Capacity: 3,300 **Cover:** 2,200 **Seats:** 400 **Floodlights:** Yes **Metal Badges:** Yes
Club Shop: Yes, progs, hats, scarves etc, & other memorabilia. Contact Mick Hills or Angela Still.
Colours: Red/white/red **Change colours:** White/black/white
Sponsors: Mister Ham Man. **Previous Names:** Gravesend Utd/ Northfleet Utd (merged 1946).
Previous Leagues: Kent (as Gravesend Utd)/ Southern 1946-79/ Alliance Prem. 79-80.
Previous Ground: Central Avenue (as Gravesend United) *(Northfleet Utd always played at Stonebridge Rd).*
Midweek home matchday: Tuesday **Reserves' Lge:** Kent Midweek League
Best FA Cup season: 4th Rd Replay 1963 (lost 2-5 at Sunderland after 1-1 draw at home).
Best FA Trophy season: 3rd Rd 88-89.
Record win: 8-1 v Clacton Tn, Sth Lge 62-63, 7-0 Godalming 95-96 FAC
Record defeat: 0-9 v Trowbridge Tn, Southern Lge Prem Div 91-92.
Record Fees - Paid: £8,000 for Richard Newbery (Wokingham, 1996).
Received: £17,500 for Steve Portway from Gloucester C 94.
Record Attendance: 12,036 v Sunderland, FA Cup 4th Rd 62-63.
Players progressing to Football League: J Wilson (Chelsea 47), F Pincott (Newport 47), S Aldows & H Hawkins (Orient 50 & 51), H Gunning (West Ham 52), J Hills (Spurs 53), N Lewis (Newport 54), K Baron (Aldershot 60), R Dwight (Coventry 62), R Cameron (Southend 63), R McNichol (Carlisle 65), A Humphreys (Mansfield 64), B Thornley (Brentford 65), P Jeavons (Lincoln 66), B Fry (Orient 66), B Gordine (Sheffield Utd 68), T Baldwin (Brentford 77), L Smelt (Nottm Forest 80), T Warrilow (Torquay 87)
Clubhouse: Fleet Social Centre open every day. Hot and cold food available at tea bars on matchdays.
Club Record Goalscorer (career): Bert Hawkins.
Club Record Goalscorer (two seasons): Steve Portway,113 (92-94).
Club Record Appearances: Ken Burrett 537.
95-96 Captain: Colin Blewden **95-96 P.o.Y.:** Jimmy Jackson.
95-96 Top scorer: Mark Munday 27.
Local Newspapers: Gravesend & Dartford Reporter, Kent Evening Post, Gravesend Extra, Leader
Local Radio Stations: Invicta Radio, Radio Kent, RTM.
Hons: Southern Lg 57-58 (Southern Div 94-95, Div 1 Sth 74-75 (R-up 70-71 88-89), Lg Cup 77-78 (R-up 57-58), Champ Cup 77-78), Kent Sen Cup 48-49 52-53 80-81 (R-up 47-48 76-77 90-91), Kent Floodlit Cup 69-70 (R-up 72-73), Kent Sen Shield R-up 47-48 51-52, Kent Interm Cup R-up 87-88, Kent Midweek Lg 95-96, R-up 92-93 93-94 94-95. Kent Youth Lg Cup 82-83 86-87, Kent Youth Lg 95-96, John Ullman Cup 82-83.

PROGRAMME DETAILS:
Pages: 32 **Price:** £1.20
Editor: Lionel R H Ball
(01474 569985)

GRAVESEND & NORTHFLEET'S 1995-96 CAMPAIGN

DATE		OPPONENTS	COMP	RESULT		GATE	GOALSCORERS
Aug 19	H	Gresley Rovers	BHL	D	1-1	527	Cotter
22	A	Hastings Town	BHL	W	3-1	584	Cotter, Best, Munday
26	A	Atherstone Utd.	BHL	L	0-2	286	
28	H	Sudbury Town	BHL	D	3-3	536	Munday, Blewden, Lamb
Sept 2	A	Gloucester City	BHL	L	1-3	851	Powell
5	H	Cambridge City	BHL	W	2-0	471	Cotter 2
9	H	Godalming	FAC	W	7-0	443	Munday 2, Powell 2, Cotter, Mortley, Thomas
16	A	V. S.Rugby	BHL	W	1-0	384	Munday
19	H	Hastings Town	BHL	W	4-0	500	Powell 2, Munday, Mortley
23	A	Molesey	FAC 2Q	W	6-0	295	Munday 3, Powell 2, Jackson
30	A	Salisbury City	BHL	L	0-2	425	
Oct 3	H	Chelmsford	DMC	W	3-1	386	Gooding, Munday, Cotter
7	H	Carshalton	FAC	W	2-1	685	Lamb, Mortley
14	H	Ilkeston Town	BHL	W	3-1	595	Munday, Powell, og
17	A	Sudbury Town	BHL	L	3-5	411	Munday 2, Cotter
21	H	Marlow	FAC	D	1-1	814	Munday
24	A	Marlow	FAC R	D	3-3	767	Powell, Lamb, Blewden
28	H	Burton Albion	BHL	L	1-2	609	Cotter
30	H	Marlow	FAC 2R	W	4-0	1346	Powell 3, Jackson
Nov 4	A	Hendon	FAT	L	0-3	291	
7	H	Margate	FKSC	W	2-1	241	Powell, Gibbs
11	H	Colchester	FAC 1R	W	2-0	3128	Jackson, Mortley
14	A	Cambridge City	BHL	L	1-2	212	Munday
18	H	Rushden & Diamonds	BHL	L	1-3	658	Gooding
20	A	Chelmsford	DMC	L	0-1	534	
Dec 2	A	Cinderford Town	FAC 2R	D	1-1	2067	Blewden
9	A	Gresley Rovers	BHL	L	1-3	537	Jackson
14	H	Cinderford	FAC 2R 2R	W	3-0	2851	Best, Munday, Powell
16	H	Stafford Rangers	BHL	L	0-3	462	
19	H	Crawley	DMC 2R	L	1-2	189	Best
30	A	Dorchester Town	BHL	D	2-2	607	Munday 2
Jan 1	H	Crawley Town	BHL	W	3-1	633	Gibbs, Cotter, Munday
6	A	Aston Villa	FAC 3R	L	0-3	26018	
13	H	Cheltenham Town	BHL	W	1-0	884	Mortley
20	A	Baldock Town	BHL	D	2-2	360	Jackson 2
23	A	Fisher	FKSC QF	L	0-2	136	
Feb 3	A	Halesowen Town	BHL	L	1-2	675	Powell
10	A	Rushden & Diamonds	BHL	W	3-2	1841	Munday, Cotter, Mortley
12	A	Chelmsford	BHL	L	1-6	618	Powell
17	H	Atherstone Utd.	BHL	W	2-1	511	Jackson, Mortley
24	A	Merthyr Tydfil	BHL	D	2-2	411	Mortley, Cotter
27	H	VS Rugby	BHL	W	2-0	426	Cotter, Munday
Mar 3	A	Cheltenham	BHL	D	0-0	549	
5	H	Salisbury	BHL	D	1-1	424	Powell
9	A	Stafford Rangers	BHL	L	0-1	635	
16	H	Worcester City	BHL	L	0-1	472	
23	A	Newport AFC	BHL	W	1-0	777	Cotter
26	H	Gloucester City	BHL	D	0-0	377	
30	H	Dorchester Town	BHL	W	4-1	427	Cotter 2, Jackson, Newbery
Apr 2	H	Merthyr Tydfil	BHL	W	1-0	395	Jackson
6	A	Crawley Town	BHL	L	0-1	884	
8	H	Baldock Town	BHL	D	1-1	506	Powell
13	A	Ilkeston Town	BHL	D	1-1	598	Munday
16	H	Newport AFC	BHL	W	4-0	449	Munday 3, Jackson
20	H	Halesowen Town	BHL	L	0-1	679	
23	A	Burton Albion	BHL	W	2-1	444	Powell, Munday
27	H	Chelmsford City	BHL	L	0-1	610	
May 4	A	Worcester City	BHL	L	1-3	702	Munday

GRAVESEND & NORTHFLEET PLAYING SQUAD 1996-97

Goalkeepers: Lee Turner (Bury T, Corinthian, Sittingbourne, Corinthian, Leyton O), **Luke Hills** (Margate)
Defenders: Paul Lamb (Ramsgate, Margate, Dartford, Ramsgate), **Peter Mortley** (Sittingbourne, Erith & Belvedere, Ipswich), **David Walker** (Dover Ath, West Ham), **Matt Gubbins** (Ashford T, Canterbury C), **Ian Gibbs** (Youth team), **Mark Leahy** (Hitchin T, Bishop's Stortford, Gravesend, Gillingham, Ashford T)
Midfielders: Mark Munday (Herne Bay, Ramsgate, Ashford T, Thanet U), **Clint Gooding** (Ashford T), **Jimmy Jackson** (Charlton), **Lee Spiller** (Gillingham (T)), **Danny Eede** (Margate, Lordswood), **Mark Robinson** (Whitstable T)
Forwards: Richard Newbery (Wokingham T, Woking, Wokingham T, Hampton, Staines T, Farnborough T), **Colin Blewden** (Dover Ath, Gravesend, Tonbridge, Gillingham), **David Powell** (Hastings T, Margate, Bromley), **Dave Arter** (Ashford T, Sittingbourne, Hythe T, Ashford T, Tonbridge, Herne Bay, Ashford T)

GRESLEY ROVERS

Formed: 1882 | The Moatmen

Back Row (L/R): Gordeon Ford (Physio), Paul Futcher (Mgr), Richard Denby, Stuart Evans, Andy Garner, Stuart Ford, Kevin Allsop, Paul Cox, Paul Wardle, Scott Gnyett, Garry Birtles (Asst Mgr). Front Row: Mack Hurst, Gary Castledine, Graeme Fowkes, Richard Wardle, Kick Master, Tony Marsden, Darren Turner, Brian Horseman. *Photo - Derrick Kinsey.*

Chairman: Peter Hall **Vice Chairman:** Dennis Everitt **President:** Gordon Duggins.
Secretary: Neil Betteridge, 88 Midway Road, Midway, Swadlincote, Derbys DE11 7PG (01283 221881).
Manager/Coach: Paul Futcher **Asst Manager:** Garry Birtles **Physio:** Gordon Ford.
Press Officer: Secretary **Commercial Manager:** Frank McArdle.
Ground: Moat Ground, Moat Street, Church Gresley, Swadlincote, Derbys DE11 9RE (01283 216315).
Directions: To A444 via either the A5, A38, A5121 or M42 North to Appleby Magna. On reaching A444 head for Castle Gresley. Turn onto A514 to Derby; at island 2nd exit (Church St), then 2nd left (School St) then 1st left into Moat St. 5 miles Burton-on-Trent (BR). Buses from Swadlincote and Burton.
Capacity: 2,000 **Cover:** 1,200 **Seats:** 400 **Floodlights:** Yes **Metal Badges:** Yes
Club Shop: Yes - progs and other merchandise. Contact Shelley Holmshaw (01283 224493).
Cols: Red & white/red/red **Change colours:** Blue/navy/navy **Sponsors:** Hepworth Building Products.
Previous Lges: Burton lgs 1892-95 97-01 09-10 43-45/Derbyshire Sen 1895-97 02-03/Leics Sen 1890-91 98-99 08-09 10-12 15-16 35-42 45-49/Notts 01-02/Midland 03-06/Central All 11-15 19-25 49-53 59-67/Birmingham Comb 25-33 53-54/Birmingham (now West Mids) 54-59 75-92/Central Comb 33-35/East Mids 67-75
Prev. Grounds: Mushroom Lane, Albert Village 1882-95/ Church Str., Church Gresley 95-1909.
Midweek matchday: Tuesday **Reserve's Lge:** Midland Comb (Res. Div.)
Record Attendance: 3,950 v Burton Albion, Birmingham (now West Mids) Lg Division One, 57-58.
Best F.A. Cup season: 1st Rd Proper 30-31 (lost 1-3 at York City).
1st Rd Proper 94-95 (lost 1-7 at Crewe Alex.)
League clubs defeated in F.A. Cup: None.
Record win: 23-0 v Holy Cross Priory, Leics Jun Cup 1889-90.
Record defeat: 1-15 v Burton Crusaders, 1886-87.
Record fees received: £30,000 for Justin O'Reilly (Port Vale 1996)
Players progressing to Football League: Phil Gee (Derby County 85), Mark Blount (Sheffield Utd 94), Colin Loss (Bristol City 94), Justin O'Reilly (Port Vale 96)
Clubhouse: Inside ground, open Mon, Tues & Thurs evenings and matchdays. **Club Record Goalscorer:** Gordon Juggins 306.
Club Record Appearances: Dennis King 579.
95-96 Captain: Richard Denby.
95-96 P.o.Y.: Tony Marsden.
95-96 Top scorer: David Taylor & Justin O'Reilly
Local Newspapers: Derby Evening Telegraph, Burton Mail.
Hons: FA Vase R-up 90-91 (SF 92-93); West Mids Lg 90-91 91-92 (R-up 85-86 88-89); Lg Cup 88-89 R-Up. 86-87 91-92; Southern Lg Mid Div R-up 92-93; Derbys Snr Cup 87-88 88-89 89-90 90-91 93-94 95-96 (R-Up 01-02 02-03); Leics Snr Cup 1898-99 46-47 (R-Up 1899-90 45-46); Leics Sen Lg 00-01 46-47 47-48 R-Up 1898-99 11-12 15-16 37-38 38-39 41-42 48-49; Coalville Charity Cup 46-47; Derby Senior Cup (S) 01-02,02-03 R-Up 00-01; Bass Vase 10-11 28-28 30-31 48-49 49-50 66-67; Cent All 64-65 66-67 R-Up 49-50 62-63 65-66 (Lg Cup 52-53); East Mids Reg Lg 67-68 69-70 R-Up 71-72 74-75; Dr.Martens (S Lge) Cup Fin 93-94.

PROGRAMME DETAILS:
Pages: 36 **Price:** £1.00
Editor: Brian Spare
(01332 862812)

GRESLEY ROVERS 1995-96 CAMPAIGN

DATE		OPPONENTS	COMP	RESULT		GATE	GOALSCORERS
Aug 19	A	Gravesend & N'fleet	BHL	D	1-1	527	Taylor
22	H	Halesowen Town	BHL	D	1-1	704	Mann
26	H	Merthyr Tydfil	BHL	W	3-1	580	Mann 2, Taylor
28	A	Ilkeston Town	BHL	D	0-0	979	
Sept 2	A	Baldock Town	BHL	W	1-0	277	Fowkes
5	H	Atherstone Utd.	BHL	W	1-0	702	Taylor
9	H	Dudley Town	FAC	L	1-2	541	Taylor
16	H	Chelmsford City	BHL	L	0-2	545	
19	A	Halesowen Town	BHL	D	1-1	584	Mann
30	H	Newport AFC	BHL	L	1-3	788	Taylor
Oct 3	A	Burton Albion	DMC 1L	W	2-0	1143	Marsden, Taylor
7	A	Cheltenham Town	BHL	L	0-2	607	
14	H	Rushden & Diamonds	BHL	L	0-3	808	
24	H	Ilkeston Town	BHL	L	2-3	637	Horseman, Taylor
28	A	Stafford Rangers	BHL	W	5-3	582	O'Reilly 3, Taylor 2
31	H	Burton Albion	DMC 2L	L	1-2	990	Marsden
Nov 4	A	Chelmsford City	BHL	W	2-1	947	Denby, R. Wardle
11	H	VS Rugby	BHL	W	4-0	689	Marsden, Garner, Taylor 2
14	A	Atherstone Utd	BHL	W	2-1	454	Fowkes, Garner
18	A	Merthyr Tydfil	BHL	L	1-2	336	Foster
25	A	Accrington Stanley	FAT	W	3-2	542	Garner 2, Marsden
Dec 2	H	Cheltenham Town	BHL	L	0-2	662	
6	A	Paget Rangers	DMC 2R	W	3-2	127	O'Reilly 3
9	H	Gravesend & N'fleet	BHL	W	3-1	537	Fowkes, O'Reilly 2
13	A	Staveley	DSC	W	4-1	180	Taylor 4
16	A	Newport AFC	BHL	W	1-0	655	Garner
Jan 1	A	Burton Albion	BHL	D	1-1	1609	O'Reilly
6	H	Worcester City	BHL	W	1-0	677	O'Reilly
9	A	Cheltenham Town	DMC 3R	D	3-3	308	Cas'dine, Taylor 2
13	A	Salisbury City	BHL	W	4-1	337	Cas'dine, Marsden, O'Reilly, Stanburgh
20	A	Stalybridge	FAT	D	1-1	638	O'Reilly
23	H	Stalybridge	FAT R	W	1-0	603	Marsden
Feb 10	A	Blyth Spartans	FAT	W	2-1	626	Garner, O'Reilly
13	H	Buxton	DSC	W	2-0	401	O'Reilly
17	H	Dorchester Town	BHL	L	0-2	650	
24	H	Worcester City	BHL	D	3-3	632	Fowkes 2, Marsden
Mar 2	A	Guiseley	FAT	W	2-1	790	Evans, O'Reilly
5	H	Cheltenham Town	DMC R	D	2-2	407	Marsden, Garner
9	H	Baldock Town	BHL	W	3-0	657	Marsden, Garner, O'Reilly
12	H	Sudbury Town	BHL	W	5-2	402	Allsop 3, Marsden, Garner
14	A	Nuneaton Borough	DMC	L	1-4	606	Taylor
16	H	Burton Albion	BHL	W	2-1	1172	P. Wardle. Garner
19	H	Gloucester City	BHL	W	1-0	511	O'Reilly
23	H	Macclesfield	FAT	L	0-2	1727	
26	A	Crawley Town	BHL	L	0-2	437	
30	A	Gloucester City	BHL	W	2-1	613	Allsop, Fowkes
Apr 2	H	Hastings Town	BHL	D	1-1	538	Allsop
6	H	Stafford Rangers	BHL	D	1-1	656	Allsop
8	A	VS Rugby	BHL	W	2-1	364	Evans, Fowkes
10	H	Glossop	DSC	W	3-0	363	Master, Allsop, Bryant, og
13	H	Salisbury City	BHL	D	2-2	582	Allsop 2
16	A	Rushden & Diamonds	BHL	L	1-2	2250	Fowkes
20	A	Hastings Town	BHL	W	4-2	380	Marsden 2, Garner, Cox
23	A	Dorchester Town	BHL	L	1-2	536	Allsop
25	H	Cambridge City	BHL	D	2-2	483	Allsop, Garner
27	A	Sudbury Town	BHL	L	1-3	320	Marsden
30	A	Cambridge City	BHL	W	3-2	303	? ? ?
May 4	H	Crawley Town	BHL	W	1-0	611	Marsden

GRESLEY ROVERS PLAYING SQUAD 1996-97

Goalkeepers: Stuart Ford (Scarborough, Doncaster, Bury, Scarborough, Rotherham), **Mark Wheatley** (Burton A)

Defenders: Paul Futcher (Droylsden, Grimsby, Halifax, Barnsley, Derby, Oldham, Manchester C, Luton, Chester), **Paul Cox** (Kettering T, Notts Co), **Brian Horseman** (Notts Co), **Duane Brown** (Derby), **Stuart Evans** (Wolves), **Mark Wood** (Burton A, Mansfield, Derby (T)), **Mark Blount** (Peterborough, Sheffield U, Gresley R, Derby)

Midfielders: Gary Castledine (Oakham U, Cork C, Gainsborough T, Telford U, Mansfield T, Shirebrook MW), **Graeme Fowkes** (Weymouth, Birmingham (T)), **Tony Marsden** (Grantham T, Belper T, Burton A), **Roger Sallis** (Rocester, Belper T, Burton A, Manchester U), **Darren Turner** (Notts Co), **Richard Wardle** (Tamworth), **Richard Denby** (Alfreton T, Huthwaite, Sutton T, Boston U, Chesterfield), **Steve Owen** (Derby)

Forwards: Mark Hurst (Leicester U, Grantham T, Huddersfield, Nottingham F), **Chris Hanks** (Bromsgrove R, Studley Sporting), **Carl Cunningham** (Derby), **Andy Garner** (Blackpool, Derby), **Steve Bradshaw** (Hereford), **Ian Clark** (Barlestone St.Giles, Hinckley T), **Steve McGinty** (Stapenhill, Heanor T, Sandiacre T), **Kevin Allsop** (Stapenhill, Harrstad (Nor), Hinckley T), **Gareth Jennings** (Hednesford T, Gresley R, Sutton Coldfield T, Stoke)

Formed: 1961

HALESOWEN TOWN

Halesowen Town FC:

Chairman: Brian Beasley **Match Secretary:** Malcolm Pearce.
Secretary: Mrs Christine Beasley, 43 Hawne Lane, Haleowen, West Midlands B63 3RN.
Manager: Derek Beasley **Asst Manager:** Neil Beasley **Physio:** D Bowen.
Ground: Hayes Park, Park Rd, Colley Gate, Halesowen (01384 896748. Club Newsline: 0891 66 42 52).
Directions: On A458 Birmingham to Stourbridge Rd (B'ham 10 miles, Stourbridge 4 miles) - main bus route. M5 Jct 3 (towards Kidderminster), right at 1st island (towards Dudley), turn left at island (towards Stourbridge), straight over next island then 3m to grd on left-hand side, 200yds past Park Lane. Just over a mile from Lye BR station.
Seats: 350 **Cover:** 500 **Capacity:** 4,000 **Floodlights:** Yes **Club Shop:** No.
Colours: White with blue trim/black/white **Change colours:** Yellow/Blue/Yellow
Sponsors: Bevan Contracts
Midweek home matchday: Tuesday or Wednesday.
Record Attendance: 750; friendlies v Walsall and Wolves in 1985. Competitive; 450 v Lye, Lge 1988.
Previous Leagues: Festival (Sunday)/ West Midlands (pre-1994).
Clubhouse: Open every evening. Limited range of hot snacks, but full cold snack kitchen.
95-96 Captain:
95-96 P.o.Y.: Rob Shilvock
95-96 Top Scorer: Charlie Blakemore
Club Record Goalscorer:
Club Record Appearance:
Honours: West Mids Lg Div 1 85-86 (Div 2 84-85, Div 2 Cup 84-85), Inter City Bowl 67-68 68-69, Festival Lg(5)(R-up(9)), FA Sunday Cup SF 79-80, Midland Sunday Cup, Birmingham Sunday Cup.

PROGRAMME DETAILS:
Pages: 24 **Price:** £1.00
Editor: Rob Shinfield
(01384 850819)

HALESOWEN TOWN'S 1995-96 CAMPAIGN

DATE		OPPONENTS	COMP	RESULT		GATE	GOALSCORERS
Aug 19	H	Sudbury Town	BHL	D	3-3	660	Bradley, Wright, Crisp
22	A	Gresley Rovers	BHL	D	1-1	704	Harrison
28	H	Cheltenham Town	BHL	L	0-1	843	
Sept 2	A	VS Rugby	BHL	W	1-0	443	Crisp
5	H	Gloucester City	BHL	W	2-1	679	Crisp 2
9	H	Blakenall	FAC	W	3-2	618	Bradley, Snape, Wright
16	A	Ilkeston Town	BHL	W	3-1	597	Owen, Harrison, Crisp
19	H	Gresley Rovers	BHL	D	1-1	584	Crisp
23	H	Moor Green	FAC	W	1-0	620	Crisp
30	A	Chelmsford City	BHL	L	0-1	1,185	
Oct 3	A	Worcester City	DMC	L	0-2	441	
7	A	Telford United	FAC	L	1-4	905	Rodwell
14	H	Newport AFC	BHL	W	3-1	355	Harrison, Crisp, Hackett
21	H	Stafford Rangers	BHL	D	2-2	678	Harrison, Wright
24	A	Cheltenham Town	BHL	D	2-2	534	Wright, Crisp
26	H	Atherstone United	BHL	W	5-4	694	Rodwell, Harrison 2, Wright 2
30	A	Worcester City	DMC	L	1-4	627	Owen
Nov 7	A	Bridgnorth Town	WSC	W	3-0	180	Harrison, Wright 2
11	H	Ilkeston Town	BHL	W	3-2	636	Owen, Harrison, Shearer
14	A	Gloucester City	BHL	W	2-0	578	Wright, Crisp
16	A	Salisbury City	BHL	W	3-2	391	Wright 3
25	H	Bilston Town	FAT	D	0-0	601	
2a	A	Bilston Town	FAT	W	4-1	307	Snape, Wright 2, Crisp
Dec 2	H	Hastings Town	BHL	L	0-1	627	
5	A	Tamworth	BSC	D	1-1	264	Massey
9	A	Sudbury Town	BHL	W	2-1	345	Wright 2
12	H	Tamworth	BSC	L	1-2	275	Bradley
16	H	Dorchester Town	BHL	W	1-0	534	Harrison
23	A	Merthyr Tydfil	BHL	W	2-0	703	Crisp, Williams
26	H	Worcester City	BHL	D	3-3	1,119	Harrison, Williams 2
Jan 6	H	Salisbury City	BHL	W	2-0	652	Coates, Williams
9	A	Stourbridge	WSC	L	0-1	421	
13	A	Cambridge City	BHL	W	1-0	409	Wright
20	A	Dudley Town	FAT	L	2-4	769	Snape, Wright
Feb 3	H	Gravesend & Northfleet	BHL	W	2-1	718	Wright, Shearer
10	H	Crawley Town	BHL	W	2-0	681	Wright 2
13	A	Stafford Rangers	BHL	L	0-1	602	
17	A	Hastings Town	BHL	W	2-0	512	Bradley, Wright
24	H	VS Rugby	BHL	D	0-0	737	
Mar 2	A	Burton Albion	BHL	D	1-1	816	Wright
9	H	Chelmsford City	BHL	W	3-0	693	Harrison 3
12	A	Baldock Town	BHL	W	2-0	164	Wright, Crisp
16	A	Atherstone United	BHL	W	1-0	339	Wright
19	H	Rushden & Diamonds	BHL	D	0-0	1,725	
23	H	Merthyr Tydfil	BHL	W	2-1	680	Wright, Hopcroft
26	A	Dorchester Town	BHL	D	0-0	454	
30	A	Rushden & Diamonds	BHL	W	2-1	3,481	Bradley, Harrison
Apr 6	H	Burton Albion	BHL	D	1-1	902	Crisp
8	A	Worcester City	BHL	W	1-0	1,121	Wright
13	H	Cambridge City	BHL	W	2-1	952	Crisp 2
20	A	Gravesend & Northfleet	BHL	W	1-0	679	Bellingham
27	H	Baldock Town	BHL	W	1-0	1,053	Crisp
30	A	Crawley Town	BHL	W	3-1	802	Hackett, Crisp, Wright
May 4	A	Newport AFC	BHL	W	2-1	1,180	Wright, Wood

HALESOWEN TOWN PLAYING SQUAD 1996-97

Goalkeepers: Danny McDonnell (Lye T, Stourbridge, Lye T), **Mark Hart** (Coleshill T, Stratford T, Moor Green)
Defenders: Matthew Clarke (Halesowen H, Cradley T), **Phil Wood** (Pelsall V, Bilston T, Dudley T, Bilston T, Rushall O, Bilston T), **Jason Owen** (Stourbridge, Halesowen T, West Bromwich T), **Steve Hopcroft** (West Mids Police, Worcester C, Redditch U, Triplex, Shrewsbury (A)), **Danny Collier** (Crewe, Wolves)
Midfielders: Gary Hackett (Chester, Peterborough, WBA, Stoke, Aberdeen, Shrewsbury, Bromsgrove R), **John Snape** (Stourbridge, Northfield T, Bromsgrove R, WBA (A)), **Andy Bradley** (Tividale), **Richard Crisp** (Telford U, Aston Villa), **Mick Shearer** (Gloucester C, Nuneaton B, Kettering T, VS Rugby, Nuneaton B, Coventry Sporting, AP Leamington, Luton, Birmingham (A)), **Sean Small** (WM Police)
Forwards: Kevin Harrison (Stourbridge, Tividale), **Evran Wright** (Bilston T, Stafford R, Barry T, Walsall, Halesowen T, Stourbridge, Oldbury U, Stourbridge, Springvale-Tranco), **Nick Colley** (Chasetown), **Julian Alsop** (Tamworth, RC Warwick, VS Rugby, Nuneaton B)

Formed: 1894

HASTINGS TOWN

The Town

Hastings Town FC. Back Row (L-R): Steve Ferguson, Mathew Ball, Tony Burt, Stuart Playford, Danny Simmonds, Richard Callaway, Phillip Henderson, Steve Cuggy, Ray Tuppen (Physio). Front Row: Joe Lambert, Lee Issac, Kieran O'Shaughnessy, Steve Smith, James Creed, Garry Wilson (Mgr), Peter Carman, Adam Kerry, Steve Willard, Liam Barham, Paul Tuppenney.

Chairman: David Nessling. **Vice Chairman:** Charles Pilbeam **President:** David Harding.
Secretary/Press Officer: R A Cosens, 22 Baldslow Road, Hastings TN34 2EZ (01424 427867).
Manager: Garry Wilson. **Asst Manager:** Peter Carman. **Physio:** Ray Tuppen
Newsline: 0891 664 356.
Ground: The Pilot Field, Elphinstone Road, Hastings TN34 2AX (01424 444635).
Directions: From A21 turn left at 1st mini-r'bout into St Helens Rd, left after 1 mile into St Helens Park Rd, this leads into Downs Rd, at end of Downs Rd (T-junction) turn left, ground 200yds on right. From town centre take Queens Road (A2101). Right at roundabout into Elphinstone Road - ground 1 mile on right. One and a half miles from Hastings BR station - infrequent bus service from town centre to ground.
Capacity: 4,050. **Cover:** 1,750 **Seats:** 800 **Floodlights:** Yes **Metal Badges:** Yes
Club Shop: Yes, selling replica kits, scarves, programmes, pens, key-rings etc.
Colours: All white **Change colours:** Yellow & Blue
Sponsors: MT Newlite.
Previous Leagues: South Eastern 04-05/ Southern 05-10/ Sussex County 21-27 52-85/ Southern Amateur 27-46/ Corinthian 46-48.
Previous Name: Hastings & St Leonards Amateurs
Previous Ground: Bulverhythe Recreation Ground (until about 1976).
Midweek home matchday: Tuesday **Reserve Team's League:** Winstonlead Kent Div 2.
Record Attendance: 2,248 v Arsenal, friendly 25/7/92. *Competitive: 1,774 v Dover Athletic, Southern League Premier Division 12/4/93.*
Best FA Cup season: 4th Qualifying Rd 85-86, lost 2-3 at Farnborough Town.
League clubs defeated in FA Cup: None.
Players progressing to Football League: Peter Heritage (Gillingham and Hereford United).Paul Smith (Notts Forest).
Clubhouse: Open matchdays and Tues, Thurs and Fri evenings from 7pm.
Club Record Goalscorer: Dean White 28
Club Record Appearances:
95-96 Captain: Simon Beard.
95-96 P.o.Y.: Simon Ullathorne.
95-96 Top scorer: Steve Cuggy 24.
Local Newspapers: Hastings Observer & News (01424 854242), Evening Argus (01273 606799).
Local Radio Stations: Radio Sussex, Southern Sound.
Hons: FA Vase 5th Rd rep. 90-91, FA Amateur Cup 3rd Rd 38-39, Southern Lg Southern Div 91-92 (Div 2 R-up 08-09 (Div 2(B) 09-10)), Sussex County Lg R-up 21-22 25-26 (Lg Cup 80-81, Div 2 79-80 (R-up 59-60), Div 2 Cup 79-80), Sussex Senior Cup 35-36 37-38 95-96, AFA Snr Cup 37-38, Gilbert Rice Floodlit Cup 89-90.

PROGRAMME DETAILS:
Pages:64.**Price:**£1.0.
Editor: Tony Cosens
(01424 427867)

HASTING TOWN'S 1995-96 CAMPAIGN

DATE		OPPONENTS	COMP	RESULT		GATE	GOALSCORERS
Aug 19	A	Burton Albion	BHL	D	1-1	627	Cuggy
22	H	Gravesend & N'fleet	BHL	L	1-3	584	White (pen)
26	A	Salisbury City	BHL	W	4-3	334	White 2, (1 pen) Cuggy, Ullathorne
28	H	Baldock Town	BHL	D	2-2	527	White (pen)
Sept 2	H	Rushden & Dmds.	BHL	L	0-1	552	
5	A	Sudbury Town	BHL	D	0-0	320	
9	A	Croydon	FAC	W	3-2	166	O'Shaughnessy, White (pen), Simmonds
16	A	Dorchester T.	BHL	D	1-1	466	O'Shaughnessy
19	A	Gravesend & N'fleet	BHL	L	0-4	500	
23	A	Ashford Town	FAC	L	1-3	966	Simmonds
30	H	Cambridge City	BHL	W	3-1	441	Tuppenney, Playford, O'Shaughnessy
Oct 3	A	Crawley Town	DMC	D	1-1	425	Cuggy
7	A	Worcester City	BHL	L	0-1	731	
14	H	Havant Town	FAT	D	2-2	392	Ullathorne, Beard
18	A	Havant Town	FAT	L	0-1	141	
21	H	Merthyr Tydfil	BHL	W	2-1	381	Parris, Cuggy
24	A	Baldock Town	BHL	W	3-1	183	Ullatorne 2, Simmonds
28	A	Gloucester C.	BHL	W	2-0	712	White, Cuggy
31	H	Crawley Town	DMC	L	1-2	328	Cuggy
Nov 4	H	Burton Albion	BHL	L	0-3	421	
11	H	Salisbury City	BHL	W	6-2	444	Cuggy 4, (2 pens), Ullathorne, White
18	A	VS Rugby	BHL	D	1-1	389	Parris
25	A	Peacehaven & T.	SSC	W	2-1	269	White, Beard
Dec 2	A	Halesowen Town	BHL	W	1-0	627	White
16	A	Rushden & Dmds.	BHL	D	1-1	1024	Playford
23	H	Cheltenham Town	BHL	W	4-1	523	Callaway 2, Cuggy 2
26	A	Crawley Town	BHL	L	2-3	757	Playford, Smith
Jan 1	H	Chelmsford City	BHL	L	2-3	616	Beard, Ullathorne
6	A	Dorchester Town	BHL	W	4-1	510	Ullathorne 2, Cuggy, O'Shaughnessy
9	H	Stamco	SSC	W	2-1	1418	Cuggy, Playford
13	H	VS Rugby	BHL	D	2-2	530	Cuggy, Playford
20	H	Atherstone Utd.	BHL	W	5-1	407	Ullathorne 2, Cuggy, Smith, Burt
Feb 3	H	Ilkeston Town	BHL	W	2-1	402	Ullathorne, Smith
10	H	Burgess Hill	SSC	W	4-0	361	Willard, Beard, Playford, Parris
17	H	Halesowen Town	BHL	L	0-2	512	
Mar 2	A	Ilkeston Town	BHL	L	0-1	413	
5	A	Cambridge City	BHL	W	3-0	139	Cuggy 2, Simmonds
9	H	Worcester City	BHL	D	0-0	440	
13	A	Langney Sports	SSC	W	6-0	430	Cuggy 2, Ullathorne, Simmonds, Playford, White.
16	H	Stafford Rangers	BHL	L	0-2	451	
23	A	Cheltenham Town	BHL	W	2-1	608	Cuggy, Playford
26	A	Stafford Rangers	BHL	D	1-1	500	Playford
30	H	Newport AFC	BHL	D	1-1	463	O'Shaughnessy
Apr 2	A	Gresley Rovers	BHL	D	1-1	538	Willard
6	A	Chelmsford City	BHL	W	3-0	658	Tuppenney, Playford, Cuggy
8	H	Crawley Town	BHL	L	0-1	713	
13	A	Atherstone United	BHL	L	0-1	301	
20	H	Gresley Rovers	BHL	L	2-4	380	Cuggy, White
23	H	Sudbury Town	BHL	W	2-1	363	Cuggy, Hume
27	A	Merthyr Tydfil	BHL	D	1-1	387	White (pen)
28	A	Newport AFC	BHL	D	1-1	611	Callaway
May 4	H	Gloucester City	BHL	W	2-0	504	Playford 2
6	A	Crawley Town	SSC	W	1-0	1153	Simmonds (final)

HASTINGS TOWN PLAYING SQUAD 1996-97

Goalkeepers: James Creed (Faversham T, Hastings T), **Peter Carman** (Ashford T, Herne Bay, Ashford T, Maidstone U)

Defenders: Lloyd Hume (Sittingbourne, Whitstable T, Chatham T, Tonbridge, Ashford T, Gillingham (A)), **Steve Smith** (Lewes, Hastings T, Southwick, Hastings T, Brighton (A)), **Steve Ferguson** (Youth team), **Matt Ball** (Worthing, Bexhill T), **Phil Henderson** (Eastbourne T, Wivenhoe T, Northampton), **Adam Kerry** (Youth team), **Paul Tuppenney** (Stamco, Hastings T), **Tony Burt** (Hastings U), **Steve Willard** (Sidley U), **Danny Simmonds** (Brighton), **Justin Gregory** (Worthing, Shoreham)

Midfielders: Simon Beard (Sittingbourne, West Ham U (T)), **Terry White** (Hythe T, Hastings T, Bexhill T), **Liam Barham** (Wealdstone, Hastings T, Grays Ath, Kingstonian, VV Veendam (Holl), Dover Ath, Dunstable, Windsor & Eton, Dunstable, Hastings U, Brighton (A)), **Richard Calloway** (Tunbridge Wells, Yate T, Wokingham T, Chester, Bristol C), **Keiran O'Shaughnessy** (Local football), **Joe Lambert** (Youth team)

Forwards: Steve Cuggy (Margate, Dover Ath, Maidstone U, Blyth Spartans, Sunderland), **Stuart Playford** (Rye U), **Simon Ullathorne** (Gloucester C, Sittingbourne, Gravesend, Croydon, Cleator Moor Celtic, Workington, Windscale U), **Dave Benson** (Youth team)

Formed: 1879

KING'S LYNN

The Linnets

Back Row (L-R); J Hawthorn, L Cooper, A Stanhope, C Hopkins, H Purvis (Physio), B McNamara, J Pascoe, D Bloodworth, R Curtis. Front; M Hales, R Skelly, M Matthews, M Lynn, P Morris (Mgr), L Harrison, L Hudson, I Stringfellow, S Lewis.

Chairman: John Scales. **President:** Jim Chandler.
Secretary: John Franks, c/o Club, (01733 267272)
Manager: Peter Morris. **Asst Manager/Coach:** N/A **Physio:** H Purvis
Ground: The Walks Stadium, Tennyson Road, King's Lynn PE30 5PB (01553 760060).
Directions: At mini r-about arriving from A10/A47 take Vancouse Avenue. Ground on left after a half mile. Quarter mile from King's Lynn (BR), half mile from bus station.
Capacity: 8,200 **Cover:** 5,000 **Seats:** 1,200 **Club Shop:** Yes **Metal Badges:** Yes
Colours: Royal Blue with gold trim/Blue/Blue & Gold hoops. **Change colours:** All red
Prev Lges: Norfolk & Suffolk/Eastern C'ties 35-39 48-54/UCL 46-48/Midland C'ties 54-58/ NPL 80-83.
Previous Name: Lynn Town **Previous Ground:** None. **Sponsors:** TBA.
Midweek home matchday: Tuesday **Reserve Team's League:**
Record Attendance: 12,937 v Exeter, FA Cup 1st Rd 50-51. *(44,916 saw the Cup tie at Everton (below)).*
Best FA Cup season: 3rd Rd 61-62 (lost 0-4 at Everton). Competition Proper on 14 occasions; 05-06 37-38 49-50 51-52 58-63 64-65 68-69 71-72 73-74 84-85.
Best FA Trophy season: 2nd Rd 78-79.
Best FA Vase season: 5th Rd 94-95 (lost 0-2 at Diss Town).
League clubs defeated in FA Cup: Aldershot 59-60, Coventry 61-62, Halifax 68-69.
Players progressing to Football League: Norman Rowe (Derby 1949), Brian Taylor & Polly Ward (Bradford Park Avenue 54 & 55), Tom Reynolds (Darlington 54), Graham Reed (Sunderland 55), Peter McCall (Bristol City 55), John Neal (Swindon 57), Tom Dryburgh (Oldham 57), John Hunter (Barrow 59), John Stevens (Swindon), George Catleugh (Watford), George Walters (Chesterfield 64), Peter McNamee (Notts County 1966), Wayne Biggins (Burnley & Manchester City), Jackie Gallagher (Peterborough 80), Andy Higgins (Rochdale 83), Neil Horwood (Grimsby 86), Darren Rolph (Barnsley 87), Mark Howard (Stockport 88).
Clubhouse: Normal hours, extension for matchdays.
Club Record Appearances: Mick Wright 1,152 (British Record)
Club Record Goalscorer: Malcolm Lindsay 321.
95-96 Captain: Garry Harrison **95-96 P.o.Y.:** Darren Bloodworth
95-96 Top scorer: Brett McNamara
Local Newspapers: Lynn News & Advertiser (01553 761188), Eastern Daily Press (01603 628311).
Honours: FA Amateur Cup R-up 1900-01, Southern Lg R-up 84-85 (Div 1 R-up 63-64), NPL Presidents Cup 82-83, Eastern Co's Lg 53-54 (R-up 49-50 52-53 (Lg Cup 53-54), Norfolk & Suffolk Lg(8)(R-up(6)), E Anglian Lg R-up(2), Norfolk Snr Cup(19)(R-up(20), Norfolk Invitation Cup 94-95, Norfolk Premier Cup 68-69(jt) 73-74, East Anglian Cup(4)(R-up(3), Eastern Prof Floodlit Lg 68-69, Southern Lg Midland R-up 95-96.

PROGRAMME DETAILS:
Pages: 24 **Price:** £1
Editor: Gary Hart.

KING'S LYNN'S 1995-96 CAMPAIGN

DATE		OPPONENTS	COMP	RESULT		GATE	GOALSCORERS
Aug 19	A	Moor Green		W	2-0		McNamara, Setchell (p)
22	H	Rothwell Town		W	2-0		McNamara, Hudson
28	A	Grantham Town		W	1-0		McNamara
Sept 2	A	Racing Club Warwick		L	2-1		McNamara
5	H	Hinckley Town		W	3-1		McNamara, Setchell, Munton
16	A	Bridgnorth Town		W	3-2		McNamara, Skelly, Setchell
19	A	Rothwell Town		W	2-1		Pascoe, McNamara
30	A	Solihull Borough		D	2-2		McNamara (p), Dolby
Oct 24	H	Grantham Town		W	6-2		McNamara 2, Dolby, og 3
28	A	Nuneaton Borough		D	1-1		Hudson
Nov 4	H	Buckingham Town		L	1-4		Munton
11	H	Racing Club Warwick		W	2-0		Pascoe, Munton
14	A	Hinckley Town		A	3-4		Bloodworth, McNamara (p), Matthews
18	A	Stourbridge		W	2-1		Setchell, Skelly
21	H	Tamworth		L	0-3		
28	A	Leicester United		W	3-0		McNamara 2, Hudson
Dec 2	H	Sutton Coldfield Town		W	2-1		McNamara 2
16	H	Dudley Town		W	2-1		McNamara 2
23	H	Paget Rangers		W	2-0		McNmara, Cooper
26	A	Bury Town		W	5-1		Munton, Hudson, Stanhope 2, McNamara
Jan 1	H	Corby Town		W	1-0		Stanhope
6	A	Buckingham Town		W	4-0		Munton, Stanhope 2, Setchell
13	H	Solihull Borough		W	3-0		Hudson, Munton, og
20	A	Tamworth		L	0-1		
Feb 10	H	Leicester United		D	0-0		
17	A	Dudley Town		D	2-2		Setchell, Hopkins
Mar 2	H	Moor Green		W	2-0		McNmara. McLaughlin
5	A	Redditch United		L	1-2		Hudson
9	A	Sutton Coldfield Town		W	4-1		McLaughlin, Hudson 2, Skelly
12	H	Bilston Town		L	1-3		Pascoe
16	H	Bedworth United		W	2-0		Skelly, Hudson
23	A	Paget Rangers		W	2-0		Hudson, Setchell
26	A	Evesham United		W	3-2		Hudson 2, McNamara
30	H	Evesham United		W	2-0		McLaughlin
Apr 2	H	Redditch United		W	3-0		McLaughlin (p), McNamara, Stanhope
6	H	Bury Town		W	3-0		McNamara 2, Hudson
8	A	Corby Town		D	1-1		Hudson
13	H	Nuneaton Borough		L	0-1		
20	A	Bedworth United		L	0-1		
27	A	Bilston Town		L	0-2		
30	H	Bridgnorth Town		W	4-0		Harrison, Pascoe, Hudson, Cooper
May 4	H	Stourbridge		W	2-1		Hudson, McNamara

KING'S LYNN PLAYING SQUAD 1996-97

Goalkeepers: Steve Lewis (Cambridge U), **Mark Hales** (Shirebrook T)

Defenders: Robbie Curtis (Northampton, Boston U, Shirebrook Coll), **Richard Skelly** (Northampton, Cambridge U, Newmarket T), **Darren Bloodworth** (Boston U, Kuitan (HK), King's Lynn, Kettering T, Bourne T, Holbeach U, Peterborough, Leicester C), **Jamie Hawthorn** (Corby T, Bedford T, Newport Pagnell T, Wootton BC, Woverton T)

Midfielders: Martin Matthews (Derby (T)), **Garry Harrison** (Northampton, Aston Villa), **Gary Setchell** (Youth team), **Jason Pascoe** (Northampton, Boston U, Ashfield U, Worksop T, Sutton T, Oakham U), **Andy Stanhope** (Peterborough (T)), **Lee Cooper** (Holbeach U, Lincoln U, Boston, Boston U), **Steve McLaughlin** (Wisbech T, Holbeach U, Boston U, King's Lynn, Boston U, Lincoln U, Grimsby), **Ian Stringfellow** (Dag & Red, Kettering T, Mansfield), **Mickey Gynn** (Kettering T, Hednesford T, Stoke, Coventry, Peterborough)

Forwards: Brett McNamara (Northampton, Stamford), **Lee Hudson** (Boston, Spalding U, Moulton Harrox), **Andy Hawes** (Downham T, King's Lynn), **Craig Hopkins** (Shirebrook T), **Wayne Spencer** (Corby T, Buckingham T, Milton Keynes B, Dunstable, Leighton T), **Darren Munton** (Boston U, Bourne T, Pedigree Petfoods, Melton T, Oakham U)

Formed: 1945

MERTHYR TYDFIL

The Martyrs

Merthyr Tydfil (L-R): Gareth Astley, Ian Jones, Anthony Jenkins, Paul Evans, Ross Knight, Colin Loss, Chris Summers, Andy York, Gary Wager (Cpt), Andy Evans, Steve Williams, Lyn Jones (Mgr), Andy Beattie, Neil O'Brien. Full squad not available due to injury.

Chairman: Ken Gunter **Football Secretary:** Peter Hunt.
Joint Presidents: The Archbishop of Cardiff, His Grace John Aloysious Ward, The Lord Bishop of Llandaff, The Right Rev. Roy Davies.
Manager: Lyn Jones **Asst Manager:** **Physio:** Ken Davey
Press Officer: Anthony Hughes **Commercial Manager:** Howard King.
Ground: Pennydarren Park, Merthyr Tydfil, Mid Glamorgan (01685 384102)
Directions: South A470 Express Way to Merthyr through Town Centre to Pontmorlais (traffic lights) turn left then first right, first right at Catholic Church and right again into Park Terrace to ground. North Heads of the Valley road to Town Centre, to Pontmorlais (traffic lights) turn right, then as above.
Capacity: 10,000 **Seats:** 1,500 **Cover:** 5,000. **Floodlights:** Yes
Colours: Black & White **Change colours:** Yellow/black & Sky Blue
Club Shop: Yes, sells replica kits, club souvenirs & programmes. Contact Mel Jenkins 01443 692336.
Record Gate: 21,000 v Reading FA Cup 2nd Rnd 1949/50
Previous Leagues: Southern League, Beazer Homes (Midland Division), Beazer Homes (Premier Division), G M Conference.
Best FA Cup season:
Best F.A.Trophy season: 3rd Rd v Northwich Vic 95-96
Beat F.A.Vase season:
Sponsors: Hoover PLC **Previous Ground:** None.
Midweek home matchday: Tuesday
Reserve team's League:
Record win: 11-0 **Record defeat:** 9-2
Record transfer fee paid: £ 10,000 to Cardiff City for Robbie James 1992
Received: £12,000 for Ray Pratt from Exeter City 1981).
Clubhouse: Open Monday to Sunday 6.30 to 11.00pm. Two club cafes open on match days for hot food.
Captain 95-96: Gary Wager
Top Scorer 95-96: Lge P Evans 23
P.o.Y. 95-96:
Past players who progressed to the Football League: Syd Howarth (Aston Villa), Cyril Beech, Gilbert Beech, Bill Hullet, Ken Tucker (Cardiff City), Nick Deacy (Hereford United), Gordon Davies (Fulham), Ray Pratt (Exeter City), Peter Jones, Paul Giles (Newport County).
Club Honours: Welsh FA Cup Winners 1948/49, 1950/51, 1986/87; Southern League 1947/48, 1949/50, 1950/51, 1951/52, 1953/54; Southern League (Midland) Winners 1987/88; Southern League (Premier) Winners 1988/89; Southern League Cup Winners 1947/48, 1950/51.

PROGRAMME DETAILS:
Pages: 32 **Price:** £1.00
Editor: Anthony Hughes
(01685 359921)

MERTHYR TYDFIL'S 1995-96 CAMPAIGN

DATE		OPPONENTS	COMP	RESULT		GATE	GOALSCORERS
Aug 19	H	Baldock Town	BHL	W	1-0	453	Pearson
23	A	Salisbury City	BHL	D	0-0	402	
26	A	Gresley Rovers	BHL	L	1-3	580	P. Evans
28	H	Worcester City	BHL	L	0-1	423	
Sept 2	H	Stafford Rangers	BHL	W	3-1	323	P. Evans 2, Pearson
5	A	Dorchester Town	BHL	L	1-7	502	Loss
9	A	Bridport	FAC	W	3-0	300	Loss, L. Jones, P. Evans
16	A	Cambridge City	BHL	W	2-1	300	P. Evans, og
19	H	Salisbury City	BHL	W	1-0	257	Mitchell
24	A	Newport AFC	FAC	D	3-3	1816	Williams, Abraham 2
26	H	Newport AFC	FAC	L	1-2	887	Mitchell
30	H	Ilkeston Town	BHL	W	10-1	321	Mitchell 3, Jenkins 3, Loss 2, P. Evans, M. Williams
Oct 3	A	Cinderford T.	DMC	W	4-1	177	Loss, Jenkins 2, Evans (P)
14	H	Burton Albion	BHL	W	4-3	451	Mitchell, M.Williams, Jenkins, Abraham
21	A	Hastings Town	BHL	L	1-2	381	Mitchell
23	A	Worcester City	BHL	L	2-4	1094	P. Evans,Jenkins
28	H	Rushden & Diamonds	BHL	L	0-3	464	
Nov 4	H	VS Rugby	BHL	L	2-3	312	Mitchell, Loss
7	H	Cinderford T.	DMC	W	4-3	144	Evans (P) 4
11	A	Sudbury Town	BHL	W	2-1	324	Nicholls, L. Jones
14	H	Dorchester Town	BHL	W	3-1	222	Beattie 3
18	H	Gresley Rovers	BHL	W	2-1	336	P. Evans, M. Williams
22	A	Newport AFC	DMC	L	1-2	452	Walker
25	A	Baldock Town	BHL	D	1-1	187	Jenkins
28	H	Newport AFC	DMC	D	1-1	347	Evans (P)
Dec 2	A	Stafford Rangers	BHL	W	2-1	487	P. Evans, Summers
9	H	Chelmsford City	BHL	L	0-1	512	
16	A	Burton Albion	BHL	W	3-1	658	Summers 2, P. Evans
23	H	Halesowen Town	BHL	L	0-2	703	
Jan 6	H	Sudbury Town	BHL	W	2-1	431	M. Williams 2
13	A	Gloucester City	BHL	L	1-3	756	P. Evans
20	A	Oxford City	FAT	W	2-1	251	Williams, Evans (P)
Feb 3	A	Cambridge City	BHL	W	2-1	238	Jenkins, L. Jones
10	A	Dudley Town	FAT	W	2-1	321	Jenkins, Evans (P)
17	A	Ilkeston Town	BHL	W	1-0	318	Perrett
24	H	Gravesend & N'fleet	BHL	D	2-2	411	P. Evans 2
27	A	Atherstone United	BHL	W	2-0	229	Summers, Jenkins
Mar 2	H	Northwich Victoria	FAC	D	1-1	528	Summers
5	A	Northwich Victoria	FAC	D	2-2	838	Evans (P) 2
9	H	Gloucester City	BHL	W	1-0	438	Beattie
11	A	Northwich Victoria	FAC	L	0-3	811	
16	A	VS Rugby	BHL	W	2-1	328	P. Evans, A. Evans
23	A	Halesowen Town	BHL	L	1-2	850	P. Evans
26	H	Cheltenham Town	BHL	L	0-1	277	
30	H	Atherstone United	BHL	W	4-0	403	Summers 2, A. Evans, O'Brien
Apr 2	A	Gravesend & N'fleet	BHL	L	0-1	365	
6	A	Cheltenham Town	BHL	L	0-1	552	
8	H	Newport AFC	BHL	L	0-1	753	
13	A	Chelmsford City	BHL	W	4-1	728	Summers 3, S. Williams
16	A	Crawley Town	BHL	L	0-1	534	
20	H	Crawley Town	BHL	L	1-1	404	P. Evans
24	A	Newport AFC	BHL	D	0-0	839	
27	H	Hastings Town	BHL	D	1-1	504	P. Evans
May 4	A	Rushden & Diamonds	BHL	L	2-3	4664	P. Evans, Knight

MERTHYR TYDFIL PLAYING SQUAD 1996-97

Goalkeepers: Gary Wager (Bridgend T), **Kevin Creedon** (Swansea)

Defenders: Neil O'Brien (Inter Cardiff, Aberystwyth T, Llanelli), **Phil Evans** (Inter Cardiff, Merthyr Tydfil, Swansea), **Gareth Abraham** (Hereford, Cardiff), **Mark Williams** (Aston Villa), **Ross Knight** (Sandwell B, Halesowen T, Barry T, Evesham U, Barry T, Northfield T), **Andy Yorke** (Chesham U, Merthyr Tydfil, Ebbw Vale, Exeter), **Kevin Richards** (Ton Pentre)

Midfielders: Colin Loss (Bristol C, Gresley R, Derby, Norwich), **Andy Evans** (Cardiff), **Lee Jones** (Inter Cardiff), **Andy Beattie** (Inter Cardiff, Newport AFC, Mangotsfield U, Bridgend T, Newport Co), **Lee Walker** (Cardiff), **Gareth Astley** (Ebbw Vale), **David Barnhouse** (Swansea), **Russell Wigley** (Inter Cardiff, Bath C, Inter Cardiff, Barry T), **Lee Street** (Cardiff C)

Forwards: Paul Evans (Ton Pentre, Newport AFC, Merthyr Tydfil, Barry T, Auckland (NZ), Barry T, Bridgend T, Newport Co, Brecon, Ferndale, Barry T, Cardiff), **Darren Perrett** (Torquay, Swansea, Cheltenham T), **Tony Jenkins** (Chesham U, Merthyr Tydfil), **Ian Mitchell** (Chesham U, Hereford, Merthyr Tydfil, Newport Co), **Chris Summers** (Inter Cardiff, Barry T, Cardiff), **Chris Ingram** (Cardiff C), **Tony Rees** (WBA, Grimsby, Barnsley, Birmingham, Aston Villa)

Formed: 1989

NEWPORT A.F.C.

The Exiles

Newport AFC Back Row (L-R): Darren Porretta, Phil Coyne, Jason Price, Jon Roberts, Tom Johansen, Jason Donovan, David Webley, Linden Jones (Asst Mgr). Middle Row: David Williams (Trainer), Steve Lowndes, Nigel Vaughan, Will Foley, Ray John, Danny Street, Kevin Rogers, Tony Gilbert (Physio). Front Row: Mark Price, Steve Williams Mark Spencer, Graham Rogers (Mgr), Brendan Dowd, Mark Tucker, Ceri Williams, Craig Evans.

Chairman: David Hando **Vice-Chairman:** Wallace Brown **President:** Brian Toms, MBE.
Secretary: Mike Everett, 66 Gibbs Rd, Newport, Gwent NP9 8AU (01633 280932).
Manager: Graham Rogers **Asst Manager:** Linden Jones **Physios:** T Gilbert & D Williams
Trainer: David Williams **Press Officer:** Wallace Brown (01633 265500).
Community Director: Ray Taylor (01443 237545).
Club Headquarters: The King, 76 Somerton Road, Newport, Gwent NP9 0JX (01633 271771).
Ground: Newport Stadium, Spytty Park, Langland Way, Newport, Gwent (01633 280802).
Directions: From Severn Bridge on M4 take 1st exit signed Newport (jct 34), 1st left at r'bout follow signs for industrial area, left at r'bout after 2 1/2 miles, over 2 r'bouts, next left for ground.
Capacity: 3,300 **Cover:** 1,236 **Seats:** 1,236 **Floodlights:** Yes.
Club Shop: Yes. Open matchdays, selling badges, scarves, pennants, replica shirts, back issues of programme, videos, mugs, bookmarks etc.
Colours: All Amber with black trim **Change colours:** All Green with White Trim
Sponsors: Empress Carsales **Previous Leagues:** Hellenic 89-90.
Previous Grounds: London Road, Moreton-in-the-Marsh 89-90/ Somerton Park, Newport 90-92/ Gloucester City FC 92-94 *(period in exile due to dispute with FAW over the League of Wales).*
Previous Names: None. Newport AFC were formed after the demise of Newport County in 1988-89.
Midweek matchday: Wednesday
Reserve Team's League: Avon Insurance Football Combination.
Record Attendance: 2,475 v Redditch United,Beazer (Midland) 24,8,04.
Best FA Cup season: 4th Qualifying Rd 92-93.
Best FA Trophy season: 2nd Rd Proper 95-96.
Record win: 9-0 v Pontlottyn Blast Furnace (A), Welsh Cup First Round 1/9/90.
Record defeat: 0-5 v Trowbridge Town (H), FA Cup 1st Qualifying Round replay 15/9/93, 1-6 v Stafford Rangers(A) BHL 6/1/96
Clubhouse: Open 2 hours before kick-off and three hours after (approx). Pasties available in club. Burgers, hot dogs, hot drinks etc available within ground. Limited bar accomodation at stadium.
Club Record Goalscorer: Chris Lilygreen 93.
Club Record Appearances: Chris Lilygreen 274 (222 Lg + 52 cup)
95-96 Captain: Brendan Dowd **95-96 P.o.Y.:** David Webley
95-96 Top scorer: David Webley
Local Newspapers: South Wales Argus, South Wales Echo.
Local Radio Stations: Red Dragon.
Hons: Hellenic Lge 89-90 (Lge Cup 89-90); Gloucs Sen Cup 93-94; Beazer Homes Lge Mid Div Champ 94-95; Beazer Merit Cup Jnt Win 94-95:

PROGRAMME DETAILS:
Pages: 42 **Price:** £1.20
Editor: Wallace Brown
(01633 265500)

NEWPORT AFC'S 1995-96 CAMPAIGN

DATE		OPPONENTS	COMP	RESULT		GATE	GOALSCORERS
Aug 19	A	VS Rugby	BHL	W	3-1	648	Foley, Webley, og
23	H	Gloucester C.	BHL	W	1-0	1524	Vaughan
26	H	Stafford R.	BHL	W	2-1	1279	Lowndes, Webley
28	A	Dorchester T.	BHL	W	3-0	944	Spencer, Tucker, Webley
Sept 2	A	Cambridge C.	BHL	W	1-0	495	Webley
6	H	Worcester C.	BHL	D	1-1	1407	Tucker
9	H	Brockenhurst	FAC	W	5-0	1011	Tucker 2, Lowndes, John, Vaughan
16	A	Sudbury T.	BHL	L	1-3	454	Tucker
19	A	Gloucester C.	BHL	D	1-1	1412	Donovan
24	H	Merthyr Tydfil	FAC	D	3-3	1816	Jones, Tucker, C. Williams
26	A	Merthyr Tydfil	FAC R	W	2-1	887	Tucker, Jones
30	A	Gresley R.	BHL	W	3-1	788	Tucker 3
Oct 7	A	Trowbridge T.	FAC	L	0-2	623	
14	A	Halesowen T.	BHL	L	1-3	855	Jones
21	H	VS Rugby	BHL	W	5-2	921	C. Williams 2,Spencer, Webley,Rogers
25	H	Dorchester T.	BHL	W	3-2	1077	C. Williams, Webley,Lowndes
28	A	Crawley T.	BHL	D	0-0	853	
Nov 4	H	Fleet	FAT	W	2-1	679	Evans 2
11	A	Cheltenham T.	BHL	L	0-2	1092	
13	A	Worcester C.	BHL	L	0-2	1501	
18	H	Chelmsford C.	BHL	L	1-2	896	S. Williams
22	H	Merthyr Tydfil	DMC	W	2-1	572	Dowd, Hall
26	H	Grays Athletic	FAT	W	1-0	679	Jones (P)
28	A	Merthyr Tydfil	DMC	D	1-1	347	Jones
Dec 2	H	Burton Albion	BHL	L	0-1	817	
6	A	Forest Green R.	DMC	W	4-2	185	C. Williams 2, Jones (P), Price
9	A	Ilkeston T.	BHL	D	1-1	564	Jones
16	H	Gresley Rovers	BHL	L	0-1	655	
Jan 6	A	Stafford R.	BHL	L	1-6	634	??
10	H	Waterlooville	DMC	W	1-0	418	Lowndes
13	H	Crawley Town	BHL	D	1-1	827	Webley
20	A	Chelmsford C.	FAT	W	1-0	1121	Evans
Feb 10	A	Carshalton A.	FAT	L	1-2	682	Tucker
17	H	Sudbury T.	BHL	W	5-1	576	Tucker 3, Webley, Nicholls
24	H	Rushden & Diamonds	BHL	D	1-1	1170	Webley
26	H	Salisbury C.	DMC	L	1-2	541	Webley
28	A	Salisbury C.	BHL	W	3-1	340	Webley 2, Porretta
Mar 2	A	Atherstone U.	BHL	D	0-0	328	
9	H	Cambridge City	BHL	L	1-2	828	Tucker
16	A	Baldock Town	BHL	W	2-1	307	Lowndes, Webley
18	H	Cheltenham T.	BHL	L	2-3	646	Donovan, Webley
23	H	Gravesend & N'fleet	BHL	L	0-1	777	
27	H	Ilkeston T.	BHL	L	2-3	542	Brown, Nicholls
30	A	Hastings T.	BHL	D	1-1	463	Webley
31	A	Chelmsford C.	BHL	D	0-0	804	
Apr 2	H	Atherstone U.	BHL	L	1-2	504	Porretta
6	H	Salisbury C.	BHL	D	1-1	648	Nicholls
8	A	Merthyr Tydfil	BHL	W	1-0	735	Tucker
13	A	Rushden & Diamonds	BHL	L	0-4	449	
20	H	Baldock T.	BHL	D	1-1	724	Webley
24	H	Merthyr Tydfil	BHL	D	0-0	839	
27	A	Burton Albion	BHL	W	1-0	599	Webley
28	H	Hastings Town	BHL	D	1-1	611	Brown
May 4	H	Halesowen T.	BHL	L	1-2	1184	Brown

NEWPORT AFC PLAYING SQUAD 1996-97

Goalkeepers: Jon Roberts (Barry T, Cardiff), **Leigh Hall** (Ross T, Worcester C)

Defenders: Steve Lowndes (Hereford, Barnsley, Millwall, Newport Co), **Brendan Dowd** (Clevedon T, Mangotsfield U, Barry T, Caerleon, Newport Co), **Mark Spencer** (Albion R), **Phil Coyne** (Abergavenny Thursdays, Pill), **Ray John** (Inter Cardiff, Barry T, Ton Pentre, Happy Valley (HK), Plymouth, Cardiff Corinthians), **Derek Brazil** (Cardiff, Manchester U)

Midfielders: Mark Tucker (Merthyr Tydfil, Abergavenny Thursdays), **Ryan Nicholls** (Merthyr Tydfil, Cardiff, Leeds), **Mark Pice** (Albion R), **Jason Donovan** (Cardiff, Llanwern), **Darren Porretta** (Cardiff Corinthians), **Linden Jones** (Reading, Newport Co, Cardiff), **Nigel Vaughan** (Worcester C, Hereford, Cardiff, Newport Co)

Forwards: Dave Webley (Merthyr Tydfil, Newport AFC, Chesham U, Inter Cardiff, Merthyr Tydfil, Abertillery T, Pontllanfraith), **Craig Evans** (Aberbargoed, Salisbury C, Luton), **Danny Street** (Cardiff), **Paul Burton** (Westfields)

1937 # NUNEATON BOROUGH The Boro

Nuneaton Borough celebrate after lifting the Dr Martens Southern League Cup to complete a memorable double

Chairman: Howard Kerry **Life President:** Alf Scattergood.
Secretary: Peter Humphreys, 29 Amington Rd, Shirley, Solihull, West Mids B90 2RF (0121 745 2031).
Manager: Brendan Phillips. **Asst Manager:** Colin Welsh. **Physio:** Richie Norman.
Press Officer: Gordon Chislett (01203 222106) **Comm Mgr:** Phil Wright (01203 385738).
Ground: Manor Park, Beaumont Road, Nuneaton, Warks CV11 5HD (01203 342690/385738. Fax: 342690).
Directions: A444 to Nuneaton from M6 junction 3, 2nd exit at 1st roundabout, 2nd exit at 2nd r'about, left at 3rd r'bout, 2nd right into Greenmoor Rd, turn right at the end, grd on left. Parking 100 cars Manor Park Schl, Beaumont Rd, 50p each. Grd 1 mile Nuneaton Trent Valley (BR).
Capacity: 6,500 **Cover:** 3,500 **Seats:** 520 **Floodlights:** Yes **Metal Badges:** Yes.
Club Shop: Yes, souvenirs, progs. Contact Andy Pace (01203 374043).
Colours: Royal & white stripes **Change colours:** Red & white **Sponsors:** Wainfleet Coaches
Previous Leagues: Central Amateur 37-38/ B'ham Comb 38-52/ West Mids (B'ham) 52-58/ Southern 58-79 81-82/ GM Conference (Alliance Premier & Gola) 79-81 82-87.
Midweek matchday: Tuesday **Res Lge:** Ansells Midland Comb.
Record Gate: 22,114 v Rotherham, FA Cup 3rd Rd 1967
Best FA Cup season: 3rd Rd rep. 66-67. 1st Rd 19 times;
Record Fees - Paid: £9,500 for Richard Dixey (Scarborough, 1981)
Received: £60,000 for D Bullock (Huddersfield Tn 93)
Record win: 11-1 (45-46 & 55-56) **Record defeat:** 1-8 (55-56 & 68-69).
Players progressing to Football League: R Mason/P Culpin (Coventry 46/85), E Betts (Walsall 49), F Cruickshank (Notts Co 50), K Plant (Bury 50), J Schofield (Birmingham 50), R Howells (Wolves 52), R Dickinson/M Gibson (Shrewsbury 53/60), G Cattleugh (Watford 54), T Wright (Barrow 62), K Satchell/B Holbutt (Walsall 65), T Bell (Hartlepool 66), A Morton (Fulham 70), R Edwards Port Vale 72), K Stephens (Luton 78), T Peake (Lincoln 79), P Sugrue (Man City 80), M Hartland/M Shotton & T Smithers (Oxford 63/80), D Thomas (Wimbledon 81), P Richardson (Derby 84), F Upton/R Hill/T Morley/E McGoldrick/ A Harris (Northampton 53/85/86), D Bullock (Huddersfield 93).
Clubhouse: Open every evening, weekend lunchtimes and matchdays (inc Reserve & Youth).
Club Record Scorer: Paul Culpin 201.
Record Record Scorer in one season: Paul Culpin 55 (92-93).
Club Record Appearances: Alan Jones 545 (1962-74).
95-96 Players P.o.Y.: Dave Crowley
Hons: FA Tphy QF 76-77(replay) 79-80 86-87, Alliance Premier Lge R-up(2) 83-85, Southern Lg R-up 66-67 74-75, Sth Lg Cup Win 95-96, Midland Div 81-82 92-93, Champ 95-96, Lg Cup R-up 62-63, Merit Cup 92-93(joint)), Birmingham Lg 55-56 (Nth Div 54-55), Birmingham Comb. R-up 3; Birmingham Snr Cup 6, (R-up 3)

PROGRAMME DETAILS:
Pages: 40 **Price:** £1
Editor: Editorial team (contact Comm Mgr

NUNEATON BOROUGH'S 1995-96 CAMPAIGN

DATE		OPPONENTS	COMP	RESULT		GATE	GOALSCORERS
Aug 19	H	Sutton Coldfield Tn	BHL	L	1-2	1002	Statham
23	A	Dudley Town	BHL	W	1-0	357	Drewitt
26	A	Solihull Borough	BHL	W	1-0	340	Drewitt
28	H	Racing Club Warwick	BHL	W	1-0	1010	Drewitt
Sept 2	A	Moor Green	BHL	W	2-0	571	Drewitt 2
5	H	Redditch United	BHL	W	4-1	1056	Williams, Drewitt 2, Clark
9	A	Hinckley Town	BHL	W	3-0	895	Drewitt, Straw 2
16	H	Evesham United	BHL	W	6-3	1049	Straw 3, Crowley, Drewitt, Clark
19	H	Dudley Town	BHL	L	3-4	1186	Drewitt (P), Straw, Smith
23	A	Grantham Town	BHL	W	2-1	543	Drewitt, Donald
30	A	Bridgnorth Town	BHL	L	0-1	475	
Oct 3	A	VS Rugby	DMC 1R 1L	W	4-2	651	Smith, Simpson, Drewitt (P), Carr
7	H	Corby Town	BHL	W	1-0	1075	Drewitt (P)
21	H	Evesham United	FAC 4Q	W	6-1	1415	Drewitt (P), Statham 2, Simpson, Andersen, Straw (P)
24	A	Racing Club Warwick	BHL	D	2-2	450	Drewitt, Straw
28	H	King's Lynn	BHL	D	1-1	1202	Simpson
31	H	VS Rugby	DMC 1R 2L	W	2-1	629	Donnelly, Williams
Nov 4	H	Knowsley United	FAT 2Q	W	3-2	1017	Donnelly, Straw, Simpson
11	A	Barrow	FAC 1	L	1-2	2869	Simpson
14	A	Redditch United	BHL	W	5-1	385	Straw, Car, Drewitt (PO), Culpin 1 + 1(P)
18	H	Buckingham Town	BHL	D	1-4	1103	Drewitt
25	A	Spennymoor Utd.	FAT 3Q	W	2-0	486	Straw, Donnelly
Dec 2	H	Bilston Town	BHL	W	2-1	942	Straw, Statham
5	A	Burton Albion	BSC2	L	1-2	343	Carr
9	A	Sutton Coldfield Town	BHL	W	3-0	498	Straw 2, Drewitt (P)
12	A	Atherstone United	DMC2	W	3-1	467	Straw, Simpson, Drewitt
16	H	Solihull Borough	BHL	W	2-1	869	Andersen, Straw
23	H	Stourbridge	BHL	W	1-0	975	Drewitt
Jan 1	H	Bedworth United	BHL	L	1-2	1936	Carr
6	H	Bury Town	BHL	W	5-1	935	Carr, Statham, Straw, Simpson 2
10	A	Buckingham Town	DMC3	W	3-1	127	Straw2, Statham
13	A	Paget Rangers	BHL	D	2-2	760	Simpson, Drewitt (P)
20	A	Gainsborough Trinity	FAT 121	L	1-4	867	Straw
Feb 3	H	Hinckley Town	BHL	W	1-0	1061	Straw
10	A	Evesham United	BHL	W	3-0	460	Simpson, Straw 2
17	H	Grantham Town	BHL	W	2-0	1031	Simpson, Andersen
20	A	Leicester United	BHL	W	2-1	223	Simpson, Straw
24	A	Bilston Town	BHL	W	2-0	489	Straw 2 (1P)
27	A	Bury Town	BHL	W	3-1	218	Statham, Straw 2
Mar 2	A	Corby Town	BHL	W	3-1	602	Straw (P), Simpson, Hardwick
9	H	Paget Rangers	BHL	L	0-2	1179	
14	H	Gresley Rovers	DMC4	W	4-1	606	Straw, Simpson, Burton 2
16	H	Moor Green	BHL	W	3-1	937	Drewitt 2, Straw
19	H	Moor Green	DMCSF 1L	W	2-0	528	Simpson, Straw
23	A	Stourbridge	BHL	W	1-0	507	Straw
26	A	Tamworth	BHL	W	3-0	1635	Straw 2, Drewitt
30	H	Rothwell Town	BHL	D	0-0	901	
Apr 1	A	Moor Green	DMCSF 2L	D	1-1	340	Straw
6	A	Bedworth United	BHL	L	0-1	1540	
8	H	Tamworth	BHL	W	1-0	1388	Simpson
13	A	King's Lynn	BHL	W	1-0	3635	Drewitt
17	A	Baldock Town	DMCF 1L	W	3-1	386	Andersen, Straw 2
20	H	Bridgnorth Town	BHL	W	2-0	1245	Drewitt 2
23	A	Rothwell Town	BHL	L	0-2	443	
27	H	Leicester United	BHL	W	2-0	1055	Williams, Massey
30	H	Baldock Town	DMCF 2L	W	2-1	1248	Drewitt (P), Simpson
May 4	A	BuckinghamTown	BHL	W	3-2	472	Massey, Stathem, Simpson

NUNEATON BOROUGH PLAYING SQUAD 1996-97

Goalkeepers: Paul Hayward (Bromsgrove R, Hednesford T, Bilston T, Blakenall, Redditch U, Kidderminster H, Worcester C, Paget R)
Defenders: Tom McGinty (VS Rugby, Moor Green, Coventry Sporting), **Gary Statham** (VS Rugby, Hinckley T, Shepshed A, Hinckley, Barlestone St. Giles, Barwell), **Seamus Luby** (Tamworth, Stafford R, Armitage, Cradley T, Redditch U, Chelmsley T, Hinckley T, Chelmsley T, Coleshill T), **Barry Williams** (Redditch U, Ely C, Alvechurch), **Jon Davidson** (Ilkeston T, Dag & Red, Telford U, Preston, Derby), **Warren Donald** (Kettering T, Colchester, Northampton, West Ham)
Midfielders: Richard Massey (Stafford R, Halesowen T, Stourbridge, Kettering T, Exeter C), **Richard Lavery** (Hinckley Ath, Bedworth U), **Dave Crowley** (Stafford R, Bedworth U), **Scott Clamp** (Youth team), **Craig Dean** (Hinckley T, Tamworth, Manchester U (T), **Chris Moss** (Tamworth, Redditch U, Solihull B), **Keith Sievewright** (Tamworth, Bedworth U, Redditch U, Barri, Redditch U, Tamworth, Hinckley T, Nuneaton B, Solihull B, Stratford T, Moor Green), **Danny Martin** (VS Rugby, Nuneaton B, Stoke (T))
Forwards: Ian Drewitt (Stafford R, Merthyr Tydfil, Weymouth, Ton Pentre, Ferndale Ath), **Rob Straw** (Bedworth U, Tamworth, Bedworth U, Nuneaton B, Stafford R, Derby), **Tony Simpson** (Tamworth, Nuneaton B, Grantham T, Nottingham F), **Stuart Taylor** (WBA (T))

Formed: 1947

SALISBURY CITY

The Whites

Salisbury City FC:

Chairman: Mr P R McEnhill **Vice-Chairmam:** Mr R Brocksom.
Secretary: Sean Gallagher, 49 Sunnyhill Road, Salisbury, Wilts SP1 3JQ (01722 324932 FAX 01722 500132.
Manager: Geoff Butler **Physio:** Kim Sturgess **Press Officer:** David Macey (01264 773765)
Youth Development Officer: John Trollope
Commercial Manager: Geoff Butler, 38 Endless House, Salisbury (01722 326454).
Ground: Victoria Park, Castle Road, Salisbury SP1 3ER (01722 336689).
Directions: A345 (Amesbury) road north from city centre/ring-road, Victoria Park is on the left 800 yds after the ring road. One mile from Salisbury (BR). Buses 208 & 209 run every 15 mins from city centre.
Capacity: 3,400 **Cover:** 1,100 **Seats:** 320 **Floodlights:** Yes **Metal Badges:** Yes
Colours: White/black/white **Change colours:** All Blue.
Sponsors: Buddens Coaches.
Previous Leagues: Western 47-68. **Previous Name:** Salisbury FC (pre-1992).
Midweek home matchday: Wednesday **Reserve Team's League:** None.
Club Shop: Yes,replica shirts,memorabilia, programmes, scarves, metal badges, souvenirs. Contact Mr David Beavon (01747 828624).
Previous Ground: Hudson Field, Castle Rd, Salisbury - 1947-51.
Record Attendance: 8,902 v Weymouth, Western League 1948.
Best FA Amtr Cup year: 2nd Rd 49-50 **Best FA Trophy season:** 1st Rd 85-86 90-91 91-92.
Best FA Cup season: 2nd Rd 59-60, lost 0-1 at home to Newport County.
Record win: 9-0 v Westbury United (H), FA Cup 1st Qualifying Round 1972.
Record defeat: 0-7 v Minehead, Southern League 1975.
Record Fees - Paid: £5,750 for Peter Loveridge (Dorchester Town, 1990)
Received: £16,000 for Ian Thompson (AFC Bournemouth, 1983).
Players progressing to Football League: Eric Fountain (Southampton 1948), Cyril Smith (Arsenal & Southampton 1948), Graham Moxham (Exeter 1975), Tony Alexander (Fulham 1975), Eric Welch (Chesterfield) 1976), Ian Thompson (Bournemouth 1983), Trevor Wood (Port Vale 1988), Denny Mundee (B'mouth 1988), Matthew Carmichael (Lincoln 1990).
Clubhouse: Small bar on ground open matchdays. Main Supporters Club situated in Chatham Close, some 500yds from ground - normal pub hours. Two bars and a seperate function room, snooker, satellite TV, Discos etc.
Club Record Goalscorer: Allan Green 113 (Southern Lg)
Club Record Appearances: Barry Fitch 713.
95-96 Captain: Roger Emms.
95-96 P.o.Y.: Ian Chalk.
95-96 Top scorer: Gary Manson 19.
Local Newspapers: Salisbury Journal, Southern Evening & Sports Echo, Western Gazette, Western Daily Press.
Local Radio Stations: Wiltshire Sound, Radio Solent, Spire F.M.
Club Information Line: Cityline, 0891 122 905 (Sponsored by Spire F.M.).
Honours: Southern Lg Southern Div Champions 94-95,R-up 85-86 92-93, Western Lg 57-58 60-61 (R-up 58-59 59-60 60-61 61-62 67-68, Div 2 47-48, Lg Cup 55-56), Hants Senior Cup 61-62 63-64, Alan Young Cup 59-60 60-61 62-63, Wilts Premier Shield 56-57 59-60 60-61 61-62 66-67 67-68 70-71 77-78 78-79 95-96.

PROGRAMME DETAILS:
Pages: 48 **Price:**£1.
Editor: David Macey
(01831 395756)

SALISBURY CITY'S 1995-96 CAMPAIGN

DATE		OPPONENTS	COMP	RESULT		GATE	GOALSCORERS
Aug I9	A	Rushden & Diamonds	BHL	L	0-3	1,532	
23	H	Merthyr Tydfil	BHL	D	0-0	402	
26	H	Hastings Town	BHL	L	3-4	334	Manson, Emms, Chalk
26	A	Gloucester City	BHL	L	0-2	1,576	
Sep 2	H	Sudbury Town	BHL	W	3 0	345	Harbut, Paskins 2
5	A	Crawley Town	BHL	L	0 2	722	
9	H	Hungerford Town	FAC 1Q	W	5-2	373	Brown, Guy, Harbut, Chalk, Manson
16	H	Stafford Rangers	BHL	W	2-1	379	Chalk, Manson
19	A	Merthyr Tydfil	BHL	L	0-1	321	
23	H	Newport IOW	FAC 2Q	L	I-3	412	Browne p
30	H	Gravesend & Northfleet	BHL	W	2-0	425	Manson 2
Oct 4	H	Poole Town (1st Leg)	DMC 1	W	5-0	239	Blackler, Emms, Hewitt, Paskins, Clements
14	H	Fisher 93	FAT 1a	W	2-0	319	Emms, Chalk
18	A	Pools Town (2nd Leg)	DMC 1	W	6-0	117	Brown p, Emms, Chalk 3, Clements
25	H	Gloucester City	BHL	D	3 3	483	Manson 3
26	H	Cheltenham Town	BHL	D	3 3	547	Browne, Noble, Clements
Nov 4	H	Sudbury Town	FAT2a	D	2-2	332	Paskins, Carroll
7	A	Sudbury Town 1st re	FAT 2a	D	2-2	251	Nobb p, Chalk
11	A	Hastings Town	BHL	L	2-6	444	Blackler, Manson
13	A	Sudbury Town 2nd re	FAT 2Q	L	2-3	213	Nobb p
18	H	Halesowen Town	BHL	L	2-3	213	Hobson, Manson
Dec 2	H	Atherstone United	BHL	L	2-3	333	Manson, Clements
6	H	Dorchester Town	DMC 2	W	2-1	145	Sandrey, Chalk
9	A	Stafford Rangers	BHL	L	1-2	433	Browne
13	H	Westbury United	WPS2	W	3-2	84	Browne p, De Gordon, Manson
16	H	VS Rugby	BHL	W	1-0	302	Masters
19	A	Burton Albion	BHL	W	1-0	466	Manson
23	H	Baldock Town	BHL	W	1-2	351	Hobson
26	A	Dorchester Town	BHL	W	2-0	1,032	Sandrey, Masters
Jan 6	A	Halesowen Town	BHL	L	0 2	652	
13	H	Gresley Rovers	BHL	L	1-4	337	Carroll
20	H	Crawley Town	BHL	W	2-1	272	Lovell, Browne p
Feb 10	A	Cambridge City	BHL	W	3-1	257	Lovell, Browne p, Manson
13	A	Trowbridge Town	DMC 3	D	1-1	303	
17	H	Burton Albion	BHL	W	2-0	376	Emms, Chalk
21	H	Trowbridge Town (re)	DMC 3	W	2-1	236	Carroll 2
24	A	Atherstone United	BHL	L	1-3	238	Chalk
26	A	Newport AFC	DMCO/F	W	2-1	571	Sandrey, Manson
26	H	Newport AFC	BHL	L	1-3	340	Chalk
Mar 2	H	Cambridge City	BHL	W	1-0	272	Carroll
5	A	Gravesend & Northfleet	BHL	D	1-1	481	Lovell
9	A	Sudbury Town	BHL	D	3-3	325	Sanders, Carroll, Chalk
11	A	Chelmsford City	BHL	D	0-0	556	
16	A	Ilkeston Town	BHL	L	1-2	340	Carroll
18	A	Worcester City	BHL	L	0 2	435	
20	A	VS Rugby	BHL	W	1-0	250	Sandrey
23	A	Baldock Town	BHL	L	2-4	280	Manson, Guy
27	H	Trowbridge Town	WPS S F	W	2-1	168	De Gordon 2
30	H	Chelmsford	BHL	D	0-0	355	
Apr 3	A	Baldock Town 1st Leg	DMS S/F	D	0-0	104	
6	A	Newport AFC	BHL	D	1-1	648	Manson
8	H	Dorchester Town	BHL	W	1-0	422	Carroll
10	H	Baldock Town	DMCS/F	D	1-1	355	
13	A	Gresley Rovers	BHL	D	2-2	582	Webb
20	H	Ilkeston Town	BHL	L	0-2	381	
24	H	Rushden & Diamonds	BHL	L	0-2	569	
27	H	Worcester City	BHL	W	3-1	316	Brown, Webb, Spencer
May 1	N	Chippenham Town	WPS F	W	2-0	170	Harbut 2
4	A	Cheltenham Town	BHL	D	3-3	548	Emms, Carroll, Spencer

SALISBURY CITY PLAYING SQUAD 1996-97

Goalkeepers: John Simpkins (Newport IOW, Bashley, Basingstoke T, East Cowes V (IOW))

Defenders: Roger Emms (Andover, Newbury T, Swindon Ath, Devizes T), **Simon Browne** (Dorchester T, Swanage, Weymouth), **Gavin Sandrey** (Fareham T, Weymouth, Dorchester T, Weymouth, Swindon T, Weymouth), **Matthew Lovell** (Cheltenham T, AFC Bournemouth), **Sandy Baird** (Bashley, Gosport B, Basingstoke T, Weymouth, Horndean, Fareham T, Horndean, Fareham T)

Midfielders: Paul Batty (Bath C, Yeovil T, Exeter, Chesterfield, Swindon), **Robbie Harbut** (Bashley, Southampton (T)), **Andy Leader** (Newport IOW, Cove, Newport IOW, Frimley Green, Bracknell T, Egham T, Newbury T, Windsor & Eton, Bracknell T, Newbury T, Reading, Crystal Palace), **Robbie Carroll** (Bashley, Crawley T, Worthing, Woking, Yeovil T, Fareham T, Brentford, Gosport B, Southampton), **Peter Conning** (Trowbridge T, Yeovil T, Dorchester T, Bashley, Yeovil T, Weymouth, Altrincham, Rochdale), **Chris Shaw** (Poole T, Salisbury C, Weymouth, Salisbury C, Bath C, AFC Bournemouth)

Forwards: Gary Manson (Dorchester T, Poole T, Parley Sports, Wimborne T), **Ian Chalk** (Warminster T, Bemerton Ath, Swindon, Peterborough, Wrexham), **Matthew Guy** (Warminster T), **Sean Sanders** (Andover, Salisbury C, Andover), **Lee Webb** (Poole T, Salisbury C, Westbury U, Trowbridge T, Westbury U, Devizes T), **Mickey Spencer** (Bath C, Yeovil T, Wokingham T, Bury)

Formed: 1881

SITTINGBOURNE

Brickies

Sittingbourne's Tom Planck fires in a shot past Fisher's Billy Logan *Photo - Alan Coomes*

Chairman: B.Bright **President:** E H Bennett.
Secretary: Mrs Nina Hadaway,c/o Sittingbourne F.C. **Manager:** Steve Lovell
Youth Team Manager: Alan Walker **Coaches:** Alan Walker & Paul Haylock **Physio:** Kevin Manser
Newsline: 0891 88 44 34. **Commercial Manager:** Kevin Illand (c/o the club).
Ground: Central Park, Eurolink, Sittingbourne, Kent ME10 3SB (0795 475547. Fax: 0795 430776).**Clubhouse:** The Cabin (Club's Tel No.)
Directions: Through Sittingbourne on main A2, club signposted clearly and regularly from both east and west. 1 mile from Sittingbourne BR station.
Capacity: 8,000 **Cover:** 3,300 **Seats:** 2,000 **Floodlights:** 420 lux **Metal Badges:** Yes
Club Shop: Yes, selling match videos, action photos, college scarves, bar scarves, t-shirts, flat hats, bobble hats, badges, mugs, rosettes, tankards, pennants, car pennants & stickers, key rings, pens, coasters, replica home & away kits, club ties, programmes etc. Open matchdays, otherwise contact Ann Morrison (0795 664436) or Clive Phillips (0795 477108).
Colours: Red & Black Stripes/Black/Red. **Change colours:** All yellow.
Sponsors: Medway Galvanizing.
Previous Leagues: Kent 1894-1905 09-27 30-39 46-59 68-91/ South Eastern 05-09/ Southern 27-30 59-67.
Previous Names: Sittingbourne United 1881-86.
Previous Grounds: Sittingbourne Recreation Ground 1881-90/ Gore Court Cricket Ground 90-92/ The Bull Ground 1892-1990.
Midweek home matchday: Wednesday
Other Teams: Reserves, Two youth teams, under13s.
Record Attendance: 5,951 v Tottenham Hotspur, friendly 26/1/93.
Record transfer paid: £20,000 to Ashford Town for Lee McRobert, 1993.
Record transfer received: £210,000 from Millwall for Neil Emblen and Michael Harle, 1993.
Best FA Cup season: Second Round Proper 25-26 (lost 0-7 at Swindon Town), 28-29 (lost 1-2 at Walsall). Also First Round Proper 26-27 30-31 62-63.
Players progressing to Football Lge: Jason Lillis (Walsall 93), Neil Emblen & Michael Harle & Steve Forbes & Lee McRobert (Millwall 93/93/94/95, Jimmy Case (Brighton 93), Lee Harper (Arsenal 94).
95-96 Captain: **95-96 P.o.Y.:**
95-96 Top scorer:
Local Newspapers: East Kent Gazette, Kent Today, Kent Messenger Extra, Sittingbourne & Maidstone Post, The Word Is Out.
Local Radio Stations: Invicta Supergold, BBC Radio Kent, Invicta FM.
Hons: Southern Lg Southern Div 92-93, Kent Lg 1897-98 1902-03 57-58 58-59 75-76 83-84 90-91 (Lg Cup 25-26 58-59 73-74 80-81, Div 2 Cup 54-55 57-58 83-84 86-87 87-88), Kent Senior Cup 01-02 28-29 29-30 57-58, Kent Senior Shield 25-26 27-28 53-54, Kent Senior Trophy 89-90, Thames & Medway Cup 55-56 58-59, Thames & Medway Comination 02-03 07-08 11-12 24-25 25-26, Chatham Charity Cup 03-04 19-20. Kent Midweek Lg(res) 91-92 (Lg Cup 90-91). *Unbeaten in Kent Lg 90-91.*

PROGRAMME DETAILS:
Pages: 48 **Price:** £1
Editor: William Rickson
(c/o the club)

SITTINGBOURNE'S 1995-96 CAMPAIGN

DATE		OPPONENTS	COMP	RESULT		GATE	GOALSCORERS
Aug 19	H	Bashley	BHL				
22	A	Ashford Town	BHL	D	0-0	891	
26	A	Cinderford Town	BHL	L	2-3	229	Miller 2
28	H	Tonbridge	BHL	W	3-1	749	Walker, Miller, Hearn
Sept 2	A	Weymouth	BHL	W	3-0	711	Kimble 2, Planck
6	H	Erith & Belvedere	BHL	W	1-0	526	Planck
9	A	Horsham	FAC	W	5-0	376	Kimble 2, Thompson, Lovell, Seager
16	A	Yate Town	BHL	D	2-2	155	Lovell, Walker
20	H	Ashford Town	BHL	W	4-0	947	Walker 2, Planck, Hearn
20	A	Erith & Belvedere	FAC	D	2-2	247	Lovell, Planck
27	H	Erith & Belvedere	FAC	W	6-1	556	Starle, Planck, Lovell, Kimble, Walker 2
30	H	Fleet Town	BHL	W	3-2	646	Planck 2, Kimble
Oct 4	H	Margate	DMC	L	1-3	467	Donoghue
7	A	Bromley	FAC	D	1-1	692	Planck
11	H	Bromley	FAC	W	3-2*	1,032	Lovell, Walker, Kimble
14	A	Forest Green Rovers	FAT	W	2-1	101	Hearn, Lovell
18	H	Erith & Belvedere	KSC	D	3-3*	249	Miller 2, Seager
21	H	Dorchester Town	FAC	L	1-2	1,232	Walker
24	A	Tonbridge	BHL	W	4-1	588	Walker 2, Miller, Searle
28	H	Waterlooville	BHL	L	1-2	701	Pearson
31	A	Margate	DMC	L	0-1	154	
Nov 4	A	Bognor Regis Town	FAT	D	2-2	520	
8	H	Bognor Regis Town	FAT	L	1-2	674	Planck
11	A	Poole Town	BHL	W	5-0	102	Planck, Lovell 3, Hearn
18	H	Clevedon Town	BHL	W	5-1	598	Walker, Eeles, Lovell, Seager, Kimble
25	A	Forest Green Rovers	BHL	L	0-2	169	
Dec 2	H	Yate Town	BHL	L	0-1	547	
9	A	Fareham Town	BHL	W	2-0	104	Seager, Lovell
14	A	Havant Town	BHL	L	0-1	546	
21	H	Newport IOW	BHL	L	1-2	675	Lovell
28	A	Margate	BHL	W	2-1	506	Walker, Kimble
Jan 1	H	Braintree Town	BHL	W	2-1	674	Hearn, Lovell
6	H	Cinderford Town	BHL	W	4-0	597	Lovell, Seager 2, Kimble
16	A	Trowbridge Town	BHL	L	0-3	243	
20	H	Poole Town	BHL	W	8-0	611	Lovell 4, Pearson, Kimble, Walker 2
29	H	Charlton Athletic	KSC	L	1-3	476	Planck
Feb 3	H	Trowbridge Town	BHL	W	2-1	629	Pearson, Planck
6	A	Erith & Belvedere	BHL	W	3-0	213	Lovell, Planck, Seager
13	A	Weston-super-Mare	BHL	W	2-1	220	Donoghue 2
17	A	Waterlooville	BHL	L	0-1	276	
24	H	Forest Green Rovers	BHL	W	5-1	750	Lovell, Seager, Donoghue, Planck, Searle
Mar 2	A	Bashley	BHL	W	1-0	171	Planck
9	H	Weymouth	BHL	W	2-1	805	Miller, Kimble
16	A	Clevedon Town	BHL	W	3-2	218	Lovell, Kimble, Walker
20	H	Weston-super-Mare	BHL	W	2-0	554	Planck, Lovell
23	A	Newport IOW	BHL	L	1-3	385	Walker
30	H	Fisher '93	BHL	W	3-0	647	Lovell, Eeles, Kimble
Apr 6	A	Braintree Town	BHL	W	7-0	303	Planck 3, Kimble, Walker, Eeles, Seager
8	H	Margate	BHL	W	3-0	1,085	Walker, Searle, Planck
13	A	Fleet Town	BHL	L	1-3	388	Planck
16	A	Witney Town	BHL	W	2-0	124	Bourne, Lovell
20	H	Fareham Town	BHL	W	3-0	795	Walker, Lovell, Planck
23	A	Fisher '93	BHL	W	2-0	411	Kimble, Pearson
27	H	Witney Town	BHL	W	4-2	1,072	Pearson, Planck 3
May 4	A	Havant Town	BHL	D	2-2	465	Planck, Seager

SITTINGBOURNE PLAYING SQUAD 1996-97

Goalkeepers: Andy Hough (Sheppey U), **Gareth Williams** (From YTS)

Defenders: Paul Haylock (Barnet, Shrewsbury, Maidstone U, Gillingham, Norwich), **Alan Walker** (Barnet, Mansfield, Plymouth, Gillingham, Millwall, Lincoln, Telford U, Bangor C, Stockport), **Scott Saunders** (Greenwich B, Charlton), **Roy Clarke** (Youth team), **Ricky Pearson** (Margate, Ashford T, Erith & Belvedere, Fisher Ath, Ashford T, Gillingham), **Garry Kimble** (Welling U, Dag & Red, Grays Ath, Purfleet, Hendon, Dag & Red, Peterborough, Gillingham, Doncaster, Cambridge U, Charlton)

Midfielders: Steve Searle (Youth team), **Andy Blondrage** (Hastings T, Gravesend, Ashford T, Gravesend), **Dave Bourne** (Gravesend, Sittingbourne), **Tony Eeles** (Dover Ath, Gillingham),

Forwards: Steve Lovell (Hastings T, St.Albans C, Braintree T, Sittingbourne, Gillingham, Millwall, Crystal Palace), **Tom Planck** (Youth team), **Damon Verrall** (Gillingham (T)), **Marc Seager** (Local football), **Tyrone King** (Youth team), **Lee Thompson** (Chatham T, Sheppey U, Chatham T, Tonbridge)

Formed: 1885

SUDBURY TOWN

The Borough

Sudbury's Chris Tracey defends against Macclesfield's Phil Power.

Chairman: Graeme Garden **President:** H D J Yallop.
Secretary: David Webb, 6 Melford Road, Sudbury, Suffolk CO10 6LS (01787 372352).
Manager/Press Officer: Richie Powling. **Asst Mgr/Coach:** David Crown. **Physio:** Tony Brightwell
Commercial Manager/Press Officer: Richie Powling, c/o the club (01787 370957).
Ground: Priory Stadium, Priory Walk, Sudbury, Suffolk (01787 379095).
Directions: Take Friars Street from town centre, pass cricket ground and continue to the 'Ship & Star'. Left into Priory Walk and continue to ground. Half mile and three quarters of a mile from bus and rail stations respectively.
Capacity: 5,000 **Cover:** 1,000 **Seats:** 300 **Floodlights:** Yes **Metal Badges:** Yes
Colours: All yellow **Change colours:** All red.
Sponsors: Fairview Homes & Wheelers (Timber & Building).
Club Shop: Open before and after 1st team games and at half-time. League and non-League programmes, scarves, hats, rosettes, badges, etc. Managed by Darren Witt, 4 Highfield Rd, Sudbury, Suffolk CO10 6QJ.
Previous Leagues: Suffolk & Ipswich/ Essex & Suffolk Border/ Eastern Counties 55-90.
Previous Ground: Friars Street (until 1951).
Midweek home matchday: Tuesday **Reserve Team's League:** Jewson Eastern Cos.Premier Div 1.
Record Attendance: 4,700 v Ipswich Town, testimonial 1978.
Record win: 14-1 v Leiston (H), FA Cup First Qualifying Rd 24/9/55.
Record defeat: 0-9 v Tottenham Hotspur 'A', Eastern Counties League 25/2/61.
Record Transfer Fee Received: £10,000 for Steve McGavin (Colchester United, 1991).
Best F.A.Vase Season: Losing Finalists 88-89.
BEat F.A.Trophy Season : 3rd Rd.Proper 95-96.
Best FA Cup season: Fourth Qualifying Rd on five occasions.
Players progressing to Football League: Gilbert Dowsett (Tottenham Hotpur 52), John Taylor (Cambridge Utd 88), Steve McGavin (promoted with Colchester Utd 92).
Clubhouse: Open on matchdays and for other functions. Pool, darts and dancehall.(01787 379095)
95-96 Captain: Murray Osman. **95-96 P.o.Y.:** Brett Girling
95-96 Top scorer: Ian Brown.
Local Newspapers: Suffolk Free Press, East Anglian Daily Times.
Hons: FA Vase R-up 88-89 (SF 87-88 91-92),Beazer Championship Match Winners 93-94,Southern Lg Cup 93-94 (Southern Div R-up 93-94), Eastern Counties Lg 73-74 74-75 75-76 85-86 86-87 88-89 89-90 (R-up 65-66 72-73 76-77 80-81 81-82 84-85, Lg Cup 69-70 76-77 82-83 86-87 88-89 89-90 R-Up 75-76, Suffolk Premier Cup 72-73 73-74 75-76 80-81 81-82 82-83 84-85 86-87 87-88 88-89 89-90 91-92 92-93 (R-up(7)), Suffolk Senior Cup 50-51 52-53 53-54 56-57 86-87, East Anglian Cup 85-86 86-87(retained - final not played) 91-92, R-up 83-84 95-96, Essex & Suffolk Border Lg 48-49 49-50 51-52 52-53 53-54. E.S.B.L.Cup Winners 49-50,R-Up 46-47..Eastern Floodlit Group Winners 93-94 94-95.

PROGRAMME DETAILS:
Pages: 48 **Price:** £1.
Editors Darren Witt

SUDBURY TOWN'S 1995-96 CAMPAIGN

DATE		OPPONENTS	COMP	RESULT		GATE	GOALSCORERS
Aug 19	A	Halesowen Town	BHL	D	3-3	660	Girling, Brown, Wallace
22	H	Crawley Town	BHL	L	1-2	370	Brown
26	H	Burton Albion	BHL	W	3-0	380	Stafford, Greaves, Wallace
28	A	Gravesend & N'fleet	BHL	D	3-3	536	Hammond 2, Smith (P)
Sept 2	A	Salisbury City	BHL	L	0-3	345	
5	H	Hastings Town	BHL	D	0-0	320	
9	H	Tiptree United	FAC 1Q	W	3-0	334	Brown 3
16	H	Newport AFC	BHL	W	3-1	454	Stafford, McClean, Brown
19	A	Crawley Town	BHL	D	2-2	822	Ashdjian, Smith (P)
23	H	Heybridge Swifts	FAC 2Q	W	2-1	502	Smith, French
30	H	Gloucester City	BHL	L	0-2	421	
Oct 3	A	Cambridge City	DMC	D	1-1	180	Reilly
7	A	Wisbech Town	FAC 3Q	L	0-1	705	
11	H	Bury Town	SPC	L	1-2	154	Smith (P)
14	A	Ashford Town	FAT 1Q	W	2-0	569	Brown, McClean
17	H	Gravesend & N'fleet	BHL	W	5-3	411	Tracey, Brown, Thompson 2, Reilly
21	A	Atherstone United	BHL	D	0-0	243	
28	H	Baldock Town	BHL	W	2-1	406	Brown, Wallis (P)
31	H	Cambridge City	DMC	L	1-3	225	Cutmore
Nov 4	A	Salisbury City	FAT 2Q	D	2-2	332	Smith 2
7	H	Salisbury City	FAT 2QR	D	2-2	251	Osman, McIntosh
11	H	Merthyr Tydfil	BHL	L	1-2	324	Smith (P)
13	H	Salisbury City	FAT 2QR2	W	3-2	249	Brown 3
18	H	Cheltenham Town	BHL	L	3-4	349	Osman, Thompson, McIntosh
25	H	Tooting & Mitcham	FAT 3Q	W	2-0	418	Stafford, Thompson
Dec 2	H	Ilkeston	BHL	W	1-0	349	McIntosh
9	H	Halesowen Town	BHL	L	1-2	345	Brown
12	A	Cambridge City	BHL	L	0-1	141	
16	A	Chelmsford City	BHL	L	1-2	771	Ashdjian
Jan 6	A	Merthyr Tydfil	BHL	L	1-2	417	Ashdjian
13	H	Dorchester Town	BHL	W	2-1	344	Tracey, Brown
20	A	Trowbridge Town	FAT 1	D	2-2	319	McClean, Smith (P)
23	H	Trowbridge Town	FAT 1R	D	1-1	224	Brown
Feb 5	S	Trowbridge Town	FAT 1R2	D	1-1	327	Smith (P)
10	H	Trowbridge Town	FAT 1R3	W	4-3	368	McClean 2, French, Greaves
15	H	Gloucester City	FAT 2	W	3-1	262	McClean, Smith 2
17	A	Newport AFC	BHL	L	1-5	576	Brown
24	H	Chelmsford City	BHL	W	2-0	604	Brown, Grice?
27	H	Cambridge City	BHL	D	1-1	279	Smith
Mar 2	A	Macclesfield Town	FAT 3	L	0-1	1140	
5	A	Rushden & Diamonds	BHL	L	1-3	1409	Ashdjian
9	H	Salisbury City	BHL	D	3-3	325	McClean, Brown 2
12	A	Gresley Rovers	BHL	L	2-5	402	Callihan, Brown
16	A	Gloucester City	BHL	L	0-1	509	
19	A	Dorchester Town	BHL	L	0-2	408	
23	H	Stafford Rovers	BHL	W	3-1	347	McClean, Smith (P), Brown
25	A	Worcester City	BHL	D	1-1	448	Tracey
30	A	VS Rugby	BHL	W	2-0	302	Ball, Crown
Apr 2	A	Stafford Rovers	BHL	W	1-0	440	Brown
6	A	Baldock Town	BHL	W	3-1	382	Brown, Crown, Reilly
8	H	Rushden & Diamonds	BHL	W	4-1	918	Brown 4
13	A	Cheltenham Town	BHL	D	1-1	602	McClean
16	H	VS Rugby	BHL	W	3-2	301	Ball, Crown 2
20	H	Atherstone Utd.	BHL	L	0-1	390	
23	A	Hastings Town	BHL	L	1-2	363	Crown
27	H	Gresley Rovers	BHL	W	3-1	320	Smith, Brown, Adams
30	H	Worcester City	BHL	D	0-0	263	
May 4	A	Ilkeston Town	BHL	L	2-4	534	Brown 2

SUDBURY TOWN PLAYING SQUAD 1996-97

Goalkeepers: Steve Mokler (Harwich & Parkeston, Newmarket T, Harwich & Parkeston, Thetford T)

Defenders: Christian McLean (Wivenhoe T, Braintree T, Wivenhoe T, Chelmsford C, Northampton, Swansea, Bristol R, Clacton T, Zeebrugia (Belg), Colchester), **Brett Girling** (Woodbridge T), **Chris Tracey** (Harwich & Parkeston, Stanway R), **Murray Osman** (Harwich & Parkeston, Ransomes), **Andy Taylor** (Bury T, Long Melford), **Mark Adams** (Peterborough), **Clive Stafford** (Bury T, Colchester, Diss T, Ipswich), **Kirk Hammond** (Ipswich Wanderers), **Steve Callinan** (Cambridge C, Bury T), **Tony English** (Colchester, Coventry)

Midfielders: Steve Ball (Colchester, Norwich, Colchester, Arsenal), **Nicky Smith** (Wycombe W, Colchester, Southend), **Trevor Quow** (Hong Kong Rangers, Instant Dict (HK), Northampton, Peterborough), **Steve Greaves** (Dag & Red, Scunthorpe, Ipswich, Preston, Fulham), **Neil Grice** (Braintree T, Bayswater (Aust), Braintree T, Witham T, Fisher Ath, Braintree T, Chelmsford C, Braintree T, Ipswich)

Forwards: **Jamie Reilly** (Ashford T, Margate, Maidstone U (T)), **David Crown** (Aylesbury U, Purfleet, Dag & Red, Gillingham, Southend, Cambridge U, Reading, Portsmouth, Brentford, Walthamstow Ave), **Gary Thompson** (Ipswich), **Ian Brown** (Northampton, Bristol C, Chelmsford C, Harwich & Parkeston, Stowmarket T, Sudbury T, Felixstowe T, Colchester, Birmingham), **John Ashdjian** (Cambridge C, Kettering T, Scarborough, Northampton), **Dave Pirie** (Ipswich)

WORCESTER CITY

Formed: 1902 The City

Worcester City FC Back Row (L-R): Paul Molloy, Steve Walker, Danny Hilditch, Steve Fergusson, Ian Cottrill, Melvin Watson, Joe Jackson, Ian Brown, Dave Benton. Front Row: Kieran Hemstock, Danny Williams, Steve Norris. *Photo - Tim O'Grady*

Chairman: Dr Michael Sorenson **Vice Chairman:** L.Brown **President:**
Secretary: Steve Bond, 4 Ferry Close, Worcester, Worcs WR2 5PQ (01905 423120/617887).
Manager: George Rooney **Chief Coach:** Graham Selby
Newsline: 0898 884476. **Physio:** Peter O'Connell & R McConnell
Ground: St Georges Lane, Barbourne, Worcester WR1 1QT (01905 23003 (fax: 26668)).
Directions: M5 jct 6 (Worcester North), follow signs to Worcester, right at first lights, St Georges Lane is 3rd left. 1 mile from Foregate Street (BR) station.
Capacity: 4,749 **Cover:** 2,000 **Seats:** 1,223 **Floodlights:** Yes **Metal Badges:** Yes
Club Shop: Yes, selling programmes and souvenirs. Contact Mr.Widdison c/oClub.
Colours: Blue & white/blue/blue **Change colours:** All red **Sponsors:** Worcester Tools & Fixings
Prevs Lgs: West Mids (Birmingham) 1902-38/ Southern 38-79/ Alliance Premier 79-85.
Prevs Names: Worcester Rovers, Berwick Rangers **Prevs Grds:** Severn Terrace/ Flagge Meadow.
Record Attendance: 17,042 v Sheff Utd (lost 0-2), FA Cup 4th Rd 24/1/59.
Best FA Cup year: 4th Rd 58-59. 1st Rd (10) 05-06 25-26 28-29 50-51 57-58 60-61 78-79 82-84 87-88.
Midweek matchday: Monday **Reserve Lge:** Skol Mid Comb
Record win: 18-1 v Bilston, Birmingham League 21/11/31.
Record defeat: 0-10 v Wellington, Birmingham League 29/8/20.
Record Fees - Paid: £8,500 for Jim Williams (Telford United, 1981)
Received: £27,000 for John Barton (Everton, 1979).
Players progressing to Football League: J Goodwin (Birmingham 46), T Brown/A Awford (Portsmouth 46/91), G Medd (Birmingham 46), H Horton (Blackburn 47), R Baynham (Luton 51), A Lawless (Plymouth 55), H Knowles/P King/K Ball/J Williams/M Gayle (Walsall 59/60/6579/91), J Fairbrother (Peterborough 65), D Tennant (Lincoln 66), R Davies (Derby 71), N Merrick (Bournemouth 74), J Barton (Everton 78), A Preece (Wrexham 90), D Lyttle (Swansea 92).
Clubhouse: Open every evening and Saturday and Sunday daytime. Cold snacks available.
Club Record Goalscorer: John Inglis 189 (1970-77).
Club Record Appearances: Bobby McEwan 596 (1959-75).
95-96 Captain: **95-96 P.o.Y:**
95-96 Top Scorer:
Local Press: Berrows Journal, Worcester Evening News, W/ster Source.
Local Radio Stations: Radio Wyvern & BBC Hereford & Worcester
Hons: Southern Lg 78-79 (Div 1 67-68, Div 1 Nth 76-77, Lg Cup R-up 45-46 59-60, Chal. Cup 39-40, Champs Cup 78-79), West Mids (B'ham) Lg(4) 13-14 24-25 28-30 (R-up(3) 31-34), Worcs Snr Cup(25) 07-14 28-30 32-33 45-46(jt) 48-49 55-59 60-61 62-63 64-65 69-70 77-78 79-80 81-82 83-84 87-88, B'ham Snr Cup 75-76, Staffs Snr Cup 76-77, Inter Lg Champs Cup 78-79, Welsh Cup SF 78-79, FA Tphy QF 69-70 73-74 80-81 81-82.

PROGRAMME DETAILS:
Pages: 32 **Price:** £1
Editor: Julian Pugh
(01905 25844)

WORCESTER CITY'S 1995-96 CAMPAIGN

DATE		OPPONENTS	COMP	RESULT		GATE	GOALSCORERS
Aug 19	A	Ilkeston Town	BHL	W	3-2	606	Molloy, Williams, Fergusson
21	H	Stafford Rangers	BHL	W	4-0	775	Jackson, Hemstock 2, Norris
26	H	Yate Town	BHL	L	1-2	595	Norris
28	A	Merthyr Tydfil	BHL	W	1-0	424	Norris
Sept 2	H	Cheltenham Town	BHL	L	1-2	1,212	Norris
6	A	Newport AFC	BHL	D	1-1	1,407	Fergusson
16	H	Rushden & Diamonds	BHL	D	0-0	960	
19	A	Stafford Rangers	BHL	W	2-0	463	Hemstock, Norris
23	A	Crawley Town	BHL	W	3-1	1,004	Hicks, Jackson, Norris
30	H	Burton Albion	BHL	D	1-1	968	Williams
Oct 3	A	Halesowen Town	DMC	W	2-0	441	Norris, Cottrill
7	H	Hastings Town	BHL	W	1-0	723	Fergusson
14	A	Gloucester City	BHL	L	1-2	1,235	Norris
21	H	Cambridge City	BHL	W	2-1	825	Fergusson, Norris
23	H	Merthyr Tydfil	BHL	W	4-2	1,018	McGrath, Heeley, Fergusson, Cottrill
28	A	VS Rugby	BHL	D	0-0	548	
30	A	Halesowen Town	DMC	W	4-1	627	Williams, Norris 2, Hemstock
Nov 4	A	Clevedon Town	FAT	W	4-0	420	Jackson, Fergusson, Norris, Cottrill
11	H	Crawley Town	BHL	W	2-0	887	Hicks, Fergusson
13	H	Newport AFC	BHL	W	2-0	1,501	Norris 2
18	A	Burton Albion	BHL	L	0-2	968	
25	H	Aylesbury United	FAT	W	3-0	902	Williams, Fergusson, Norris
Dec 2	H	Gloucester City	BHL	L	1-3	1,109	Heeley
4	H	Stourbridge	BHL	W	3-0	305	Fergusson, Norris 2
16	A	Cheltenham Town	BHL	W	3-1	1,010	Jackson, Fergusson, Norris
18	H	West Midlands Police	BSC	W	3-1	224	Helley, Hemstock 2
26	A	Halesowen Town	BHL	D	3-3	1,119	Williams, Jackson, Norris
Jan 6	A	Gresley Rovers	BHL	L	0-1	677	
8	H	Hinckley Town	DMC	L	2-3	256	Hemstock, Norris
13	H	Ilkeston Town	BHL	W	4-3	690	McGrath, Jackson 2, Fergusson
15	H	Aston Villa	BSC	L	1-2	1,229	Hemstock
20	A	Bognor Regis Town	FAT	L	0-1	524	
Feb 3	A	Rushden & Diamonds	BHL	L	0-1	2,197	
10	H	Atherstone United	BHL	W	1-0	588	Fergusson
17	H	Chelmsford City	BHL	D	0-0	742	
24	H	Gresley Rovers	BHL	D	3-3	632	Williams, Fergusson, Wright
26	H	Solihull Borough	WSC	L	0-2	262	
Mar 2	A	Chelmsford City	BHL	L	0-1	710	
5	A	Baldock Town	BHL	W	1-0	220	Wright
9	A	Hastings Town	BHL	D	0-0	440	
16	A	Gravesend & N'fleet	BHL	W	1-0	472	Scott
18	H	Salisbury City	BHL	W	2-0	435	McGrath, Molloy
23	A	Dorchester Town	BHL	W	2-1	705	Molloy, Hemstock
25	H	Sudbury Town	BHL	D	1-1	448	Hemstock
30	H	Baldock Town	BHL	D	0-0	555	
Apr 6	A	Atherstone United	BHL	D	1-1	326	Benton
8	H	Halesowen Town	BHL	L	0-1	1,216	
13	H	VS Rugby	BHL	W	4-0	613	Molloy, Walker, Scott, Hemstock
15	H	Dorchester Town	BHL	L	0-1	543	
20	A	Cambridge City	BHL	L	2-4	234	Hemstock, Greenman
27	A	Salisbury City	BHL	L	1-3	319	Fergusson
30	A	Sudbury Town	BHL	D	0-0	263	
May 4	H	Gravesend & N'fleet	BHL	W	3-1	702	Fergusson 2, Hicks

WORCESTER CITY PLAYING SQUAD 1996-97

Goalkeepers: Melvyn Watson (Upton T, Crewe (T))
Defenders: Carl Heeley (Sutton C, Bilston T, Dudley T, Bilston T, Alvechurch, Great Wyrley), **Mark Burrow** (Youth team), **Chris Greenman** (Bromsgrove R, Peterborough, Coventry), **John McGrath** (Kidderminster H, Worcester C, Shrewsbury), **Trevor Whittington** (Redditch U, Solihull B, Evesham U, Telford U, Redditch U, Northfield T), **Dave Richards** (Walsall (T)), **Billy Campbell** (Shrewsbury (T)), **Darren Williams** (Stoke (T)), **Andy Power** (Bromsgrove R)
Midfielders: Paul Molloy (Redditch U, Stafford R, Redditch U, Bromsgrove R), **Gareth McCarthy** (Youth team), **Scott Morrell** (Shrewsbury (T)), **Stuart Clarke** (Walsall), **Gary Pick** (Hereford, Stoke, Leicester U)
Forwards: Keiran Hemstock (Youth team), **Steve Norris** (Chesterfield, Halifax, Carlisle, Scarborough, Telford U, VS Rugby, Long Buckby), **Anton Thomas** (Kettering T, Corby T, Leicester U, Bedworth U, Northampton), **Ian Scott** (Kettering T, Hinckley T), **Richard Evans** (Trowbridge T, Yeovil T, Bristol R, Weymouth)

BEAZER HOMES LEAGUE Midland Division Ten Year Records

	86/7	87/8	88/9	89/0	90/1	91/2	92/3	93/4	94/5	95/6
Alvechurch	-	-	-	-	20	21	-	-	-	-
Armitage '90	-	-	-	-	-	-	-	22	22	-
Atherstone United	-	4	2	-	-	-	-	-	-	-
Banbury United	12	10	16	21	-	-	-	-	-	-
Barri (ex Barry Town)	-	-	-	5	6	4	4	-	-	-
Bedworth United	-	-	-	15	13	5	6	17	13	3
Bilston Town	18	17	13	17	14	12	14	8	13	12
Bridgnorth Town	14	11	17	12	17	17	16	12	5	22
Buckingham Town	13	12	-	-	-	-	-	-	6	9
Bury Town	-	-	-	-	-	-	-	-	-	21
Clevedon Town	-	-	-	-	-	-	-	5	-	-
Corby Town	-	-	-	-	2	-	-	-	-	20
Coventry Sporting	8	20	20	-	-	-	-	-	-	-
Dudley Town	-	8	9	9	19	22	17	14	11	10
Evesham United	-	-	-	-	-	-	15	10	14	19
Forest Green Rovers	9	9	12	10	18	19	19	15	18	-
Gloucester City	7	7	1	-	-	-	-	-	-	-
Grantham Town	11	3	5	14	9	13	13	11	21	14
Gresley Rovers	-	-	-	-	-	-	2	-	-	-
Halesowen Town	5	6	4	1	-	-	-	-	-	-
Hednesford Town	6	18	15	16	3	2	-	-	-	-
Hinckley Town	-	-	-	-	11	15	20	18	15	17
Ilkeston Town	-	-	-	-	-	-	-	-	2	-
King's Lynn	-	13	19	13	8	14	21	20	9	2
Leamington	19	-	-	-	-	-	-	-	-	-
Leicester United	2	-	-	11	15	16	12	19	20	16
Merthyr Tydfil	3	1	-	-	-	-	-	-	-	-
Mile Oak Rovers & Youth	16	19	22	-	-	-	-	-	-	-
Moor Green	4	2	-	-	-	-	-	-	4	4
Newport AFC	-	-	-	-	7	10	5	4	1	-
Nuneaton Borough	-	-	6	3	5	6	1	-	7	1
Paget Rangers	-	22	-	-	-	-	-	-	-	5
Racing Club Warwick	-	-	-	19	16	18	22	13	10	18
Redditch United	-	-	-	18	10	20	9	6	19	15
Rothwell Town	-	-	-	-	-	-	-	-	8	8
Rushden & Diamonds	-	-	-	-	-	-	3	1	-	-
Rushden Town	20	15	17	2	-	8	-	-	-	-
Sandwell Borough	-	-	14	22	-	-	-	-	-	-
Solihull Borough	-	-	-	-	-	1	-	-	-	7
Spalding United	-	-	8	6	22	-	-	-	-	-
Stourbridge	10	21	18	8	1	9	7	9	16	11
Sutton Coldfield Town	17	5	10	7	12	3	8	16	17	13
Tamworth	-	-	3	4	4	7	10	7	3	6
Trowbridge Town	-	16	-	-	-	-	-	-	-	-
V S Rugby	1	-	-	-	-	-	-	2	-	-
Wellingborough Town	15	14	21	-	-	-	-	-	-	-
Weston Super Mare	-	-	-	-	-	-	11	3	-	-
Willenhall Town	-	-	11	20	21	-	-	-	-	-
Yate Town	-	-	-	-	-	11	18	21	-	-
No of Clubs Competing	20	22	22	22	22	22	22	22	22	22

MIDLAND DIVISION FINAL LEAGUE TABLES 1995/96

Midland Division	*P*	*W*	*D*	*L*	*F*	*A*	*Pts*
1. Nuneaton Borough	42	30	5	7	82	35	95
2. Kings Lynn	42	27	5	10	85	43	84*
3. Bedworth United	42	24	10	8	76	42	81*
4. Moor Green	42	22	8	12	81	47	74
5. Paget Rangers	42	21	9	12	70	45	72
6. Tamworth	42	22	3	17	97	64	69
7. Solihull Borough	42	19	9	14	77	64	66
8. Rothwell Town	42	17	14	11	79	62	65
9. Buckingham Tn	42	18	9	15	74	62	63
10. Dudley Town	42	15	16	11	83	66	61
11. Stourbridge	42	17	8	17	60	63	59
12. Bilston United	42	16	9	17	61	62	57
13. Sutton Coldfield T	42	16	9	17	62	67	57
14. Grantham Town	42	17	5	20	71	83	56
15. Redditch United	42	14	11	17	57	77	53
16. Leicester Utd	42	13	13	16	58	72	52
17. Hinckley Town	42	14	7	21	62	83	49
18. R C Warwick	42	10	13	19	67	90	43
19. Evesham Utd	42	11	6	25	59	94	39
20. Corby Town	42	9	7	26	52	95	34
21. Bury Town	42	8	8	26	57	95	32
22. Bridgnorth Tn	42	7	6	29	53	112	27

** Bedworth Utd 1pt deducted, Kings Lynn 2pts deducted*

LEADING LEAGUE & CUP GOALSCORERS 1995-96

R Straw	Nuneaton Borough	34	G Piggott	Dudley Town	33
I Bennett	Tamworth	31	I Drewitt	Nuneaton Borough	27
K McGuire	Rothwell Town	26	B McNamara	Kings Lynn	25
P Davies	Moor Green	24	I Perry	Bilston Town	22
J Symonds	Bedworth United	21	J Dowling	Solihull Borough	19
J Graham	Bedworth United	19	R Whitehorse	Tamworth	19

MIDLAND DIVISION RESULTS CHART 1995-96

HOME TEAM	1	2	3	4	5	6	7	8	9	10	11	12	13	14	15	16	17	18	19	20	21	22
1. Bedworth Utd	*	3-1	3-0	1-1	3-2	3-0	3-1	1-2	2-2	3-1	1-0	2-1	0-2	1-0	1-1	2-1	5-0	4-1	5-0	1-1	3-2	1-2
2. Bilston Town	0-1	*	1-0	0-0	2-1	1-0	0-3	3-1	3-4	4-3	2-0	3-0	0-4	0-2	0-2	1-1	2-2	3-0	2-1	3-0	0-1	0-3
3. Bridgnorth T	0-5	1-0	*	0-3	2-1	3-3	1-2	3-1	4-1	2-5	2-3	3-3	2-3	1-0	0-2	2-4	1-4	1-3	1-4	2-4	1-2	1-4
4. Buckingham	0-2	0-2	3-0	*	2-2	5-0	0-2	3-1	1-0	1-2	0-4	3-3	2-0	2-3	2-4	2-2	0-0	1-1	3-1	0-2	3-0	2-1
5. Bury Town	0-1	0-1	5-1	2-1	*	1-2	1-3	2-2	2-4	1-3	1-5	0-1	0-1	1-3	1-2	2-5	2-0	1-4	2-0	1-0	1-5	1-1
6. Corby Town	2-3	3-1	0-0	2-3	2-2	*	6-1	0-1	2-4	1-1	1-1	0-1	0-2	1-3	1-2	4-0	1-2	0-2	2-1	1-5	2-2	1-0
7. Dudley Town	2-3	2-2	0-0	4-2	1-1	1-1	*	5-1	4-1	3-0	2-2	6-3	2-1	0-1	0-0	3-3	2-2	2-2	1-1	2-2	2-1	1-0
8. Evesham Utd	0-0	3-2	0-3	1-4	1-2	2-1	1-1	*	4-0	5-1	2-3	3-0	0-5	0-3	2-2	2-4	1-1	3-1	1-2	2-1	2-3	2-6
9. Grantham Tn	1-1	1-1	4-1	2-1	3-2	4-1	2-0	1-0	*	0-1	0-1	0-3	3-0	1-2	1-3	1-1	5-3	0-6	3-4	1-3	1-0	3-1
10. Hinckley Tn	0-0	2-4	2-0	0-4	1-1	1-3	1-1	0-1	2-0	*	4-3	1-0	4-3	0-3	1-2	4-1	1-2	2-2	2-3	1-1	2-1	3-2
11. Kings Lynn	2-0	1-3	4-0	1-4	3-0	1-0	2-1	2-0	6-2	3-1	*	0-0	2-0	0-1	2-0	2-0	3-0	2-0	3-0	2-1	2-1	0-3
12. Leicester U	0-1	1-1	4-0	2-0	2-4	3-2	0-5	2-2	0-1	1-0	0-3	*	0-2	1-2	1-1	1-1	3-4	1-1	1-0	2-0	2-2	1-0
13. Moor Green	0-0	1-1	7-0	1-2	2-1	1-0	2-2	1-0	1-0	2-0	0-2	3-2	*	0-2	1-1	2-2	3-1	1-1	1-1	3-0	3-0	0-1
14. Nuneaton Bor	1-2	2-1	2-0	1-1	5-1	1-0	3-4	6-3	2-0	1-0	1-1	2-0	3-1	*	0-2	1-0	4-1	0-0	2-1	1-0	1-2	1-0
15. Paget Ranger	1-1	0-0	3-2	1-2	5-1	10-0	2-0	1-0	0-1	1-2	0-2	0-1	3-2	2-2	*	1-0	0-2	1-0	1-3	2-0	3-0	1-0
16. R C Warwick	2-1	1-2	2-1	0-5	4-1	3-4	0-0	0-4	3-2	2-1	2-1	1-1	2-3	2-2	1-1	*	1-3	2-4	0-3	3-5	4-1	3-7
17. Redditch Utd	1-0	2-1	0-5	0-1	0-1	4-1	2-6	1-0	1-1	1-2	2-1	2-3	1-1	1-5	2-0	1-1	*	0-0	0-0	1-1	1-1	2-3
18. Rothwell Tn	2-2	2-2	4-4	3-1	3-3	1-0	2-1	4-1	3-0	2-1	1-2	5-0	3-2	2-0	0-2	2-1	2-1	*	1-4	1-1	3-1	0-1
19. Solihull Bor	1-3	2-0	2-2	3-2	1-1	0-2	4-2	3-0	4-2	3-0	2-2	1-1	0-2	0-1	2-1	3-2	4-0	2-1	*	4-0	3-2	1-3
20. Stourbridge	3-0	2-1	2-1	0-2	3-2	2-0	1-0	1-0	1-5	1-1	1-2	1-1	0-2	0-1	3-2	0-0	1-2	2-0	2-1	*	0-1	3-2
21. S/Coldfield T	2-0	1-0	3-0	0-0	2-1	4-0	1-1	3-0	0-2	6-1	1-4	2-2	0-5	0-3	0-1	0-0	1-0	2-2	1-1	3-2	*	2-0
22. Tamworth	1-2	3-5	4-0	6-0	3-0	7-0	3-2	7-2	3-2	3-2	1-0	2-4	1-5	0-3	3-1	2-0	1-2	2-2	1-1	1-2	3-0	*

BEDWORTH UNITED

1947 Greenbacks

Bedworth United FC Back Row (L-R): Andrew Penny, Dean Thomas (Mgr), Ian Blyth, John Symonds, Robert Wood (Res Goalkeeper), Gary Banks, Nicky Platnauer (Asst Mgr), Scott Stackman, Wayne Starkey (1st Team Goalkeeper). Front Row: Robert Beard, Kevin Wilson, Paul Lamb, Matthew Wileman, Andy Mee, Richard Lavery, Jon Graham, Lloyd Morrison.

Chairman: Alan Robinson **Vice Chairman:** Roy Whitehead
Secretary: Graham Bloxham, 43 Mount Pleasant Road, Bedworth, Nuneaton, Warks CV12 9EX (01203 317940).
Manager: Dean Thomas **Asst Mgr:** Nicky Platnauer **Physio:** John Roberts.
Press Officer: Alan Robinson
Ground: The Oval, Miners Welfare Park, Coventry Road, Bedworth CV12 8NN (01203 314302).
Directions: M6 jct 3, into Bedworth on B4113 Coventry to Bedworth road, ground 200yds past past Bedworth Leisure Centre on this road. Coaches should park at this Leisure Centre. Buses from Coventry and Nuneaton pass ground.
Capacity: 7,000 **Cover:** 300 **Seats:** 300 **Floodlights:** Yes **Metal Badges:** Yes
Club Shop: Yes, selling badges, scarves, programmes, shirts, hats, caps, club coats. Contact Tom Ison-Jacques (01203 314884).
Colours: Green & white/white/white **Change colours:** Yellow & green.
Sponsors: Cassidy Construction
Previous Leagues: Birmingham Comb. 47-54/ West Mids (at first Birmingham) Lg 54-72.
Previous Name: Bedworth Town 47-68 **Previous Ground:** British Queen Ground 11-39.
Midweek home matchday: Tuesday **Reserve's Lge:** Midland Floodlit Youth League.
Record Attendance: 5,127 v Nuneaton Borough, Southern Lg Midland Division 23/2/82.
Record win: 11-0 **Record defeat:** 1-10.
Record Fees - Paid: £1,750 for Colin Taylor (Hinckley Town, 1991-92)
Received: £30,000 for Richard Landon (Plymouth Argyle, January 1994).
Best FA Trophy season: Second Round 80-81.
Best FA Cup season: 4th Qualifying Rd 1983/89/90
League clubs defeated in F.A. Cup: None.
Players progressing to Football League: Phil Huffer (Derby County 1953), Geoff Coleman (Northampton Town 1955), Ian Hathaway (Mansfield Town 1989), Richard Landon (Plymouth Argyle 1994).
Clubhouse: Social club open every day 7.30-11pm and weekend lunchtimes noon-3pm. Hot and cold bar food, pool, darts.
Club Record Goalscorer: Peter Spacey (1949-69)
Club Record Appearances: Peter Spacey.
95-96 Captain: Simon Williams
95-96 P.o.Y.: Nicky Platnauer
95-96 Top scorer: John Symonds 21.
Local Newspapers: Bedworth Echo (312785/319548), Coventry Evening Telegraph (01203 633633)
Local Radio Stations: Mercia Sound, BBC CWR.
Hons: Birmingham Comb.(2) 48-50, Birmingham Snr Cup(3) 78-79 80-82, Midland Floodlit Cup 81-82 92-93.

PROGRAMME DETAILS:
Pages: 18 **Price:** 80p
Editor: Peter Thompson
(01203 311538)

BILSTON TOWN

Formed: 1895 | Steelmen or Boro

Bilston Town's Queen Street ground.

Chairman: Mr I K Wymer **Vice-Chairman:** Mr A K Hickman **President:** Dennis Turner MP.
Secretary: Mr Jeff Calloway, 4 Mervyn Rd, Bradley, Bilston, West Midlands WV14 8DF (01902 491799).
Manager: Ian Painter. **Asst Manager:** Alan Potts **Coach:** I Painter/B Pope
Physio: Reg Pickering **Press Officer:** Mr A Owen.
Ground: Queen Street, Bilston WV14 7EX (01902 491498).
Directions: M6 junction 10, A454 towards Wolverhampton then pick up A563 towards Bilston and turn left into Beckett Street after a little over a mile, ground at bottom. 3 miles from Wolverhampton (BR), bus 45 from bus station passes ground. Buses 78 and 79 from Birmingham stop within quarter of a mile of ground.
Capacity: 4,000 **Cover:** 350 **Seats:** 350 **Floodlights:** Yes **Metal Badges:** Yes
Club Shop: Yes, selling badges, pennants, key rings, pens, old and new non-League progs. Contact Paul Galloway, 4 Mervyn Rd, Bradley, Bilston, West Mids WV14 8DF.
Colours: Tangerine & white **Change colours:** White/black/white.
Club Sponsors: Stowlawn Ltd and Second City.
Previous Names: Bilston Utd 1895-1932/ Bilston
Previous Ground: Pounds Lane 1895-1921.
Previous Leagues: Birmingham Comb. 07-21 48-54/ (Birmingham) West Mids 21-32 54-85.
Midweek home matchday: Tuesday **Reserve Team's League:** N/A.
Record Attendance: 7,500 v Wolverhampton Wanderers, floodlight opening 1953. *Competitive: 7,000 v Halifax Town, F.A. Cup First Round 1968.*
Record win: 12-2 v Tipton Town
Record defeat: 0-8 v Merthyr Tydfil.
Best F.A. Cup season: 2nd Rd replay 72-73 (lost 0-1 at Barnet after 1-1 draw). Also 1st Rd 68-69.
League clubs defeated in F.A. Cup: None.
Record Fees - Paid: for Steve Gloucester.
Received: From Southend United for Ron Poutney, 1975.
Players progressing to Football League: R Ellows (Birmingham), James Fletcher (Birmingham 1950), Stan Crowther (A Villa 1955), Ron Pountney (Southend 1975), K Price (Gillingham), Campbell Chapman (Wolves 1984).
Clubhouse: Open every night and weekend lunchtimes (normal pub hours). Usual club activities.
Club Record Scorer: Ron McDermott 78.
95-96 Captain:
95-96 P.o.Y.:
95-96 Top scorer:
Local Newspapers: Express & Star, Evening Mail.
Local Radio Stations: Radio West Mids, WABC (Wolverhampton), Beacon (Wolverhampton), BRMB.
Honours: F.A. Tphy 2nd Rd 70-71 74-75, F.A. Vase QF 92-93, West Mids Lg 60-61 72-73 (R-up 22-23 70-71 73-74 74-75 75-76 84-85, Lg Cup 72-73 (R-up 65-66), Div 2 56-57), Birmingham Comb R-up 07-08 53-54, Staffs Senior Cup 57-58 59-60 60-61 61-62 (R-up 56-57 64-65 85-86), Birmingham Junior Cup 1895-96, Wednesbury Charity Cup 1981-81 81-82 82-83 84-85 (R-up 83-84).

PROGRAMME DETAILS:
Pages: 24 **Price:** 70p
Editor: Secretary

CORBY TOWN

Formed: 1948 The Steelmen

Action between Corby Town and Rothwell *Photo - Gordon Whittington*

Chairman: T Howarth **President:** H Hqtterley.
Secretary: Roger Abraham, 68 Cornwall Rd, Kettering, Northants NN16 8PE (01536 522159).
Manager: Paul Fitzpatrick **Coach:** Simon Mason **Physio:** Mick Mackie.
Ground: Rockingham Triangle Stadium, Rockingham Road, Corby NN17 2AE (01536 406640).
Directions: On northern outskirts of town at junction of A6003 and A6116, opposite entrance to Rockingham Castle grounds. One and a half miles from Corby (BR).
Capacity: 3,000 **Cover:** 1,150 **Seats:** 960 **Floodlights:** Yes **Metal Badges:** Yes
Club Shop: Yes, selling metal badges & programmes etc. Contact C Woolmer (01536 260900).
Colours: White with black trim,black,black. **Change colours:** All yellow.
Midweek matchday: Wednesday **Previous Leagues:** United Counties 35-52/ Midland 52-58.
Sponsor: Commision for New Towns. **Reserve Lge:** Hereward Sports Utd Count Lge Res Div
Record Attendance: 2,240 v Watford, pre-season friendly 86-87. At Old Ground; 10,239 v Peterborough United, FA Cup Third Qualifying Round 52-53.
Record win: 14-0 v Gainsborough Trinity, 56-57.
Record defeat: 0-10 v Paget Rangers, 95-96.
Best FA Trophy season: 3rd Rd, 1986-87.
Best FA Cup season: 3rd Rd 65-66 (lost to Plymouth). 1st Rd on five occasions; 54-55 63-66 67-68.
League clubs defeated in F.A. Cup: Luton Town 65-66.
Record Fees - Paid: £2,700 for Elwyn Roberts (Barnet, 1981)
Received: £20,000 for Matt Murphy (Oxford Utd 93).
Players progressing to Football League: A McCabe (Chesterfield 55), L Claimers (Leicester City 56), K Brown (Nottm Forest 56), P Kearns (Aldershot 62), N Dean (Southampton 63), H Curran (Millwall 64), D McNeil/A McGowan/G Reilly (Northampton 69/75/76), P Chard (Peterborough 79), T Morley (West Ham), J Flower (Sheffield Utd, Aldershot), M Murphy (Oxford Utd 93), C McKenzie (Hereford 94).
Clubhouse: Yes, VP Lounge open matchdays and during the week.
Club Record Scorer: David Hofbauer 141 (1984-95)
Club Record Appearances: Derek Walker 600 (78-92).
95-96 Captain: Noel Luke. **95-96 Player of the Year:** Noel Luke.
95-96 Top scorer: Wayne Spencer 12
Local Newspapers: Northampton Evening Telegraph (01536 81111).
Local Radio Stations: BBC Radio Northampton, Hereward and KCBC.
Hons: UCL 50-51 51-52 (R-up 37-38), Midland Lg R-up 52-53, Southern Lg Midland Div R-up 90-91 (Merit Cup 63-64 90-91), Northants Snr Cup 6; Maunsell Cup 83-84, Daventry Charity Cup 94-95, Midland Floodlit Cup 74-75, Evans Halshaw F'lit Cup 91-92, Anglia Floodlit Trophy 68-69 72-73, Chelmsford Invitation Cup 63-64 64-65 65-66(joint), Kettering & Dist Samaritan Cup 60-61(joint) 68-69, Wellingborough Charity Cup 50-51, Desborough Nursing Cup 48-49 50-51(joint), Bob Cumning Cup 6:

PROGRAMME DETAILS:
Pages: 32 **Price:** £1
Editor: C Smith
(01536 522159)

DUDLEY TOWN

Formed: 1893

The Robins

Back Row (L-R): David Thomas (Trainer), Steve Shaw, Toby Hall, Donald Bailey, Chris Jones, Andy Crannage, Nigel Richards, Robert Grant, Mick Williams, Gary Piggott, Alan Moore (Coach). Front: Dean Harrison, Nick Henley, John Horne, John Chambers (Mgr), Richard Evans, Brian Agar, Curtis Barnes.

Chairman: Trevor Lester **Vice Chairman:** Philip Edwards **President:** N D Jeynes.
Secretary: Tony Turpin, 24 Andrew Drive, Short Heath, Willenhall WV12 5PP (01922 475541).
Manager: John Chambers. **Asst Manager/Coach:** Alan Moore. **Press Officer:** Secretary
Ground: The Grove, Old Hawne Lane, Halesowen, West Midlands B63 3TB (0121 550 2179).
Directions: Leave M5 Motorway at Junc 3, follow A456 Kidderminster Rd to t island, turn right signposted A459 Dudley. Turn left at next island singposted Stourbridge. At next island take 3rd turn on left into Grammar School Lane/old Hanne Lane, ground 500 yds on left.
Capacity: 5,000 **Cover:** 1000 **Seats:** 380 **Floodlights:** Yes **Metal Badges:** Yes
Club Shop: Yes,progs & badges etc.(Frank Whitehouse.01902-674068)
Colours: Red/black/black **Change colours:** All yellow.
Sponsors: Crest Homes & Thornleigh Freight Ltd
Previous Leagues: West Mids (previously Birmingham) 1898-1915 35-38 53-82/ Midland (Worcs) Combination 29-32/ Birmingham Combination 32-35 45-53.
Previous Grounds: The Sports Centre, Birmingham Rd 1936-85, The Round Oak Stadium 1985-96
Midweek home matchday: Tuesday 7.45pm **Reserves' League:** None.
Record Fee Received: £25,000 for Gary Piggott (West Bromwich Albion, March 1991).
Record Gate: 3,000 v West Bromwich Albion, pre-season friendly 91. *(At old grd; 16,500 the official opening (a representative game) 36).*
Best F.A. Cup season: 1st Rd replay 76-77 (v York).
League clubs defeated in F.A. Cup: None.
Record win: 8-0 v Banbury, 1965.
Players progressing to Football League: Albert Broadbent (Notts Co 1952), Joe Mayo (Walsall 1972), Ken Price (Southend 1976), Andy Reece (Bristol Rovers 1987), Russell Bradley (Nottm Forest 1988), John Muir (Doncaster 1989), Gary Piggott (West Bromwich Albion 1991).
Clubhouse: Dudley Town Sports & Social Club, John Street, Brierley Hill. Open nightly, all day Saturday and Sunday lunchtimes. Bar, lounge bar, ballroom, bowling green etc. Bar snacks available.
Club Record Scorer: Frank Treagust, 56 (47-48).
Club Record Appearances: Brendon Hackett & John Muir, 55.
Captain 95-96: **P.o.Y. 95-96:** Gary Piggott
Top scorer 95-96: Gary Piggott 43.
Local Newspapers: Express & Star, Dudley Evening Mail, Birmingham Post, Sunday Mercury.
Local Radio Stations: Beacon Radio, BRMB, BBC Radio West Midlands.
Honours: FA Trophy 2nd Rd 84-85, Southern Lg Midland Div 84-85, Birmingham Comb 33-34 (R-up 34-35 47-48), Midland (Worcs) Comb 31-32 (R-up 29-30 30-31), West Mids Lg Cp R-up 75-76 (Div 2 Cp R-up 80-81), Birmingham Senior Cp 85-86 (R-up 64-65 83-84), Worcs Senior Cp 45-46(joint)(R-up 84-85), Camkin Cp 64-65, Worcs Junior Cp 83-84.

PROGRAMME DETAILS:
Pages: 36 **Price:** 80p
Editor: David Lawrence
c/o the club

EVESHAM UNITED

Formed: 1945 | The Robins

Action as both teams battle for possession; Evesham United v Nuneaton Borough

Chairman: Stuart Reeves **Vice Chairman:** Jim Cockerton.
President: M E H Davies **Treasurer:** Dave Wright.
Secretary: Mike J Peplow, 68 Woodstock Rd, St Johns, Worcester WR2 5NF (01905 425993).
Manager: Nick Jordan **Asst Manager:** Paul Collicott
Physio: K Sullivan **Press Officer:** Mp Peplow (01905 425993)
Ground: Common Road, Evesham, Worcestershire WR11 4PU (01386 442303).
Ground Directions: From Evesham High Street turn into Swan Lane, continue down hill between Willmotts factory called Conduit Hill into Common Rd, ground 200yds down on right just before railway bridge. 5 minutes walk from Evesham BR station.
Seats: 350 **Capacity:** 2,000 **Cover:** 600 **Floodlights:** Yes **Metal Badges:** No
Club Shop: Yes, selling programmes, pennants, scarves and ties. Contact John Hawkins c/o the club.
Colours: Red & white/black/black **Change Colours:** All blue **Club Sponsors:** Safeway.
Midweek matches: Wednesday **Reserves' League:** No reserve team.
Prev Name: Evesham Town **Prev Grd:** The Crown Meadow (pre-1968).
Previous Lges: Worcester/ Birmingham Combination/ Midland Combination 51-55 65-92/ West Midlands Regional 55-62.
Record Gate: 2,338 v West Bromwich Albion, friendly 18/7/92.
Record win: 11-3 v West Heath United.
Record Fee Paid: £1,500; to Hayes for Colin Day, 1992.
Record Fee Received: £5,000 for Simon Brain (to Cheltenham Town).
Players who have progressed to Football League: Billy Tucker, Gary Stevens (Cardiff 1977), Kevin Rose (Lincoln 1978), Andy Preece (Northampton 1986), Simon Brain (Hereford, via Cheltenham Town).
Clubhouse: Open matchdays and training nights. Cold food available in club, and hot food from tea hut on matchdays.
Club Record Scorer: Sid Brain.
Club Record Appearances: Rob Candy.
95-96 Captain: Sean Cotterill **95-96 P.o.Y:** Richard Clark
95-96 Top Scorer: Kacey Johnstone
Local Press: Evesham Journal (01386 765678), Worcester Evening News (01905 748200), Gloucester Echo.
Local Radio Stations: Radio Wyvern, BBC Hereford & Worcester.
Hons: FA Amateur Cup R-up 23-24, FA Vase QF 91-92, Worcestershire Snr Urn(2) 76-78 (R-up 90-91), Midland Combination(6) 52-53 54-55 65-66 67-69 91-92 (Chal. Cup 53-54 87-88 91-92 (R-up(5) 54-55 71-72 83-84 88-90)), Worcestershire Combination 52-53 54-55; B'gham Combination R-up 30-31, Evesham Hosp. Cup 89-90, Tony Allden Mem. Cup 1973 1988 1992.

EVESHAM UNITED
FOOTBALL CLUB
Official Programme 95/96
75p
BEAZER HOMES LEAGUE
(MIDLAND) DIVISION
EVESHAM UNITED
v
SUTTON COLDFIELD TOWN

PROGRAMME DETAILS:
Pages: 24 **Price:** 50p
Editor: Graham Hill
(01905 351653)

Formed: 1874

GRANTHAM TOWN

Gingerbreads

Action between Grantham Town and Peterborough United. *Photo - Grantham Journal*

Chairman: Alan Prince **President:** Baroness Thatcher of Kesteven.
Secretary: Mr Pat Nixon, 72 Huntingtower Road, Grantham, Lincs NG31 7AU (01476 564408).
Manager: Gary Mills **Asst Mgr:** Paul Buckthorpe **Physio:** Nigel Marshall.
Ground: The South Kesteven Sports Stadium, Trent Road, Grantham, Lincs (01476 562177)
Directions: Midway between A1 and A52 on edge of Earlesfield Industrial Estate; from A1 take A607 to Earlsfield Ind. Est and continue into Trent Rd.
Capacity: 7,500 **Cover:** 1,950 **Seats:** 750 **Floodlights:** Yes **Metal Badges:** Yes
Club Shop: Yes, selling programmes and a wide range of souvenirs. Contact Paul Wilson (01476 562177).
Colours: Black & white stripes black/black **Change colours:** All red **Sponsors:** Crystal Motors.
Prev Lgs: Mid Amat All/ Cent All 11-25 59-61/ Midland Co's 25-59 61-72/ Sthn 72-79/ Nth Prem. 79-85.
Prev. Name: Grantham FC, pre-80 **Prev Grd:** London Road up to 90.
Midweek matchday: Tuesday **Reserve Lge:** Lincolnshire.
Record Attendance: 1,402 v Ilkeston Town, FA Cup Preliminary Rd 91-92
Record win: 13-0 v Rufford Colliery (H), FA Cup Preliminary Rd 15/9/34.
Record defeat: 0-16 v Notts County Rovers (A), Midland Amateur Alliance 22/10/1892.
Record Fees - Paid: £1,000 for Gary Jones (Doncaster Rovers, 1989)
Received: £20,000 for Gary Crosby (Notts Forest 87)
Best FA Cup season: 3rd Rd 1883-84 86-87 1973-74. Comp Proper on 23 occasions;
Players progressing to Football League: E Morris (Halifax 50), P Thompson/R Cooke (Peterborough 64/80), J Rayner (Notts County 64), D Dall (Scunthorpe 79), N Jarvis/H Wood (Scunthorpe 80), D White (Bristol Rvrs 86), T Curran (Grimsby 87), G Crosby (Nottm Forest 87), A Kennedy (Wrexham 87), R Wilson (Lincoln 87).
Clubhouse: (01476 593506) Open evenings and weekends. Bar, darts, pool etc. Frequent live entertainment. Available for functions.
Club Record Goalscorer: Jack McCartney 416
Club Record Appearances: Chris Gardiner 664.
95-96 Captain: Adrian Speed **95-96 P.O.Y:** Andrew Bullimore
95-96 Top scorer: Andrew Bullimore
Local Newspapers: Grantham Journal (01476 62291), Nottingham Evening Post (01602 482000), Melton & Grantham Trader (01476 74433), Grantham Citizen, Lincolnshire Echo (01522 525252).
Local Radio Stations: Radio Lincolnshire, Lincs FM.
Hons: FA Tphy QF 71-72, Southern Lg R-up 73-74 (Div 1 Nth 72-73 78-79, Merit Cup 72-73), Midland Co's Lg(3) 63-64 70-72 (R-up 37-38 64-65 69-70, Lg Cup 68-69 70-71), Midland Amtr Lg 10-11 (Lg Cup R-up 10-11), Central All. 24-25 (Southern Div R-up 59-60), Lincs Snr Cup 1884-85 1936-37 (R-up(5) 34-36 39-40 45-47), Lincs Co. 'A' Cup(3) 53-54 60-62 (R-up 49-50 52-53 57-58), Lincs Co. Snr Cup 71-72 82-83 (R-up 80-81).

PROGRAMME DETAILS:
Pages: 36 **Price:** 70p
Editor: M Koranski

HINCKLEY TOWN

Formed: 1958 | The Town

Hinckley Town's main stand and social club. *Photo - Keith Clayton*

Chairman: Kevin Downes **Vice Chairman:** Geoffrey Sutton. **President:** Frank Downes.
Secretary: Stuart Millidge, 25 Elizabeth Rd.,Hinckley,Leics.LE10 OQY (01455 635808)
Manager: David Grundy **Assistant Manager:** Martin Sockett. **Coach:** Jeavon Payne.
Physio: TBA **Commercial Manager:** TBA
Ground: Leicester Road Sports Ground, Leicester Road, Hinckley, Leics (01455 615062).
Directions: From M69 junction 1 take A447 then A47 towards Leicester. Ground on A47 about 2 miles from town centre (half way between Earl Shilton and Hinckley).
Capacity: 2,000 **Cover:** 200 **Seats:** 200 **Floodlights:** Yes
Club Shop: Yes, selling programmes, books, vidoes, badges, mugs. Contact Mr Brian Blockley (01455 635148).
Colours: Maroon,Sky Blue and White shirts,maroon,maroon and sky. **Change colours:** All Yellow.
Sponsors: F E Downes Ltd. **Previous Name:** Westfield Rovers 1958-66.
Previous Grounds: Westfield Playing Field 58-60/ Coventry Road Recreation Ground 60-68.
Previous Lges: Sth Leicester & Nuneaton Amtr/ Leics Snr 72-86/ Central Mids 86-88/ West Mids 88-90.
Midweek home matchday: Tuesday
Reserve Team's League: None.
Record Attendance: 2,000 v Real Sociedad, floodlight opening, 1986. *Competitive: 1,022 v Nuneaton Borough, Southern League Midland Division 1/1/91.*
Best FA Vase season: Third Round 85-86.
Best FA Cup season: 4th Qualifying Rd replay 1988-89 (lost 0-3 after 1-1 draw at Welling United).
League clubs defeated in FA Cup: None.
Record win: 10-0 v Kettering Town Reserves, Central Midlands League B.E. Webbe Cup.
Record defeat: 0-10 v Barry Town, Southern League Midlands Division.
Record Fees - Paid: £1,600 for John Lane (V.S. Rugby)
Received: £1,750 for Colin Taylor (Bedworth United).
Clubhouse: Bar with facilities for functions. Open matchdays and training nights (Tuesday & Thursday). Sandwiches available.
Club Record Scorer: Paul Purser.
95-96 Captain: **95-96 P.o.Y.:**
95-96 Top scorer:
Local Newspapers: Hinckley Times (0455 238383), Leicester Mercury (512512)
Local Radio Stations: Radio Leicester.
Honours: West Midlands (Regional) Lg 89-90, Central Midlands Lg 86-87 (R-up 87-88, B E Webbe Cup R-up 86-87 87-88, Gerry Mills Cup R-up 87-88), Leics Senior Lg R-up 83-84 (Div 2 72-73, Div 2 Cup 72-73), Leicestershire Challenge Cup 89-90 (R-up 90-91 93-94), Leics Senior Cup (Jelson Holmes) R-up 87-88, Leics Senior Cup 88-89, Midland Floodlit Cup 88-89 (R-up 91-92 93-94).

PROGRAMME DETAILS:
Pages: 16 **Price:** 60p
Editor: Alan Mason

ILKESTON TOWN

ReFormed: 1945 The Robins

Back Row (L-R): Brindley (Mgr), Woolley (Trainer), Fletcher. Rigby, Igoe, Antenbring, Thompson, Gunn, Collier (Asst Mgr). Middle Row: Clark, Bailey, Harbottle, Campbell, Beckford, P Robinson. Front Row: D Robinson, Maddison, Williams, Stark. Early Season Photo. By the end only Harbottle & D Robinson were in the 1st team. *Photo - John Shiels.*

Chairman: Paul Millership **President:** Robert Lindsay
Secretary: Anthony Cuthbert, 8 Darwin Road, Long Eaton, Nottingham NG10 3NW (0115 9731531).
Manager: Keith Alexander. **Asst Manager:** Gary Simpson. **Coach:** Keith Alexander.
Commercial Manager: Contact secretary
Ground: New Manor Ground, Awsworth Rd, Ilkeston (0115 9324094).
Directions: M42 to M1 junc 23A, continue on M1 to junc 26, exit left onto A610 towards Ripley, take 1st exit signed Awsworth and Ilkeston (A6096), continue thru Awsworth, right at top of hill into Newtons Lane (signed Cotmanhay & Heanor) - grd 1/2 mile left before canal bridge.
Capacity: 3,500 **Seats:** 270. **Cover:** 1,100. **Floodlights:** Yes
Colours: Red/black/black **Change colours:** White/white/white. **Sponsors:** Sportsworld
Club Shop: Yes, selling shirts, T-shirts, jumpers, caps, badges, programmes, scarves, 'Team Talk' magazine. Contact Manager (0115 9305 622) or club secretary
Record Gate: 2,349 Kidderminster H (F.A.Trophy 3rd Rd) 94-95.
Previous Leagues: Midland 1894-1902 25-58 61-71/Notts and Derby Senior Lg.1945-47/ Central Alliance 47-61/Midland CountiesLg.1961-71/Southern League 1971-73/ Midland Co.Lg.1973-82/ Northern Co.East Lg.1982-86/ Central Midlands 86-90/ West Midlands (Regional) 90-94.
Best FA Cup season: 1st Rd 51-52 (lost 0-2 at home to Rochdale), 56-57 (1-5 at home to Blyth).
Best F.A.Trophy season: 3rd Rd v Enfield 1-5 82-83,v Kidderminster H 2-2,1-2 94-95.
Beat F.A.Vase season: 4th Rd.v Tamworth 88-89 1-2.
Previous Ground: Manor Ground, Manor Rd (1945-92).
Midweek home matchday: Tuesday
Reserve team's League: Mids Regional Alliance.
Record win: 14-2 v Codnor M.W 46-47: 13-0 v Swanwick OB 46-47
Record defeat: 1-11 v Grantham T. 47-48: 0-10 v VS Rugby 85-86.
Record transfer fee paid: £5,000 for Mark Hallam (Gloucester C 96)
Received: £11,750 for Chris Brookes (Luton Town, 1992).
Clubhouse: Open Wed-Fri 7-11pm, Sat-Sun noon-3 & 7-11pm, and Mon or Tue if there is a match. Snacks behind bar. Large tea bar open matchdays 2-5pm (6.30-9pm for night games).
Captain 95-96: Dave Harbottle **Top Scorer 95-96:** Mark Harbottle 9
P.o.Y. 95-96:
All Time Top Scorer: Jackie Ward 141.
Most Appearances in Career: Terry Swincoe 377
Most Goals in a Season: Barry Jepson 62, 1952-53.
Hons: Beazer Homes League,Midland Division 94-95,West Mids (Regional) Lg 93-94 (Div 1 91-92, Lg Cup 93-94 Div 1 Lg.Cup 91-92, Central Mids Lg Cup 87-88, Midland Lg 67-68 (R-up 1898-99), Midland Co.Lg.67-68,Central All. 51-52 52-53 53-54 54-55 (R-up 47-48 55-56).

PROGRAMME DETAILS:
Pages: 32 **Price:** 80p
Editor: Mic Capill
J.Shiels,D.Payne.

Formed: 1900

LEICESTER UNITED

United

Leicester United against Bury Town *Photo - Chris Ball*

A SAD PAGE

Farewell to United Park, Winchester Road as sadly Leicester United have disbanded.

MOOR GREEN

Formed: 1901 | The Moors

Home of Moor Green & Solihull Borough *Photo - Paul Dennis*

Chairman: Geoff Hood **Vice-Chairman:** Martyn Alcott.
Secretary: Martyn Davis, 22 Collingdon Ave., Sheldon, Birmingham B26 3YL (0121 694 8405)
Manager: Bob Faulkner **Asst Manager:** Barry Powell **Coach:** Doug Griffith
Press Officer: Peter Clynes (0121 745 3262) **Physio:** Steve Shipway.
Commercial Manager: Commercial Dept.(0121 777 8961)
Ground: 'The Moorlands',Sherwood Rd.,Hall Green. B28 OEX (0121 624 2727).
Directions: Off Highfield Rd, which is off A34 (B'ham to Stratford). Hall Green & Yardley (BR) half mile.
Capacity: 3,250 **Cover:** 1,200 **Seats:** 250 **Floodlights:** Yes **Metal Badges:** Yes
Club Shop: Yes, selling scarves, mugs, stickers, programmes.
Colours: Light and Dark Blue Halves/Navy/Light Blue. **Change colours:** All yellow **Sponsors:** T.B.A.
Previous Leagues: (friendlies only 1901-21) Birmingham & Dist. A.F.A. 1908-36/ Central Amateur 36-39/ Birmingham Comb 45-54/ West Mids 54-65/ Midland Comb 65-83.
Previous Grounds: Moor Green Lane 1901-02/ numerous 02-22/ Windermere Road 1910-30.
Midweek matchday: Tuesday **Reserve League:** None.
Best F.A. Cup season: 1st Rd Proper 79-80 (lost 2-3 Stafford Rgs).
Record Gate: 5,000 v Romford, FA Amtr Cup 1951
Record Fees - Paid: £1,000 for Adrian O'Dowd (Alvechurch)
Received: £90,000 for In Taylor(Port Vale.
Players progressing to Football League: H Smith/R Jefferies (Aston Villa 47/50), F Pidcock (Walsall 53), P Woodward/B Mack (W B Abion 54), S Cooper (Birmingham City 83), K Barnes (Manchester City), P Brogan (Mansfield Town), I Taylor (Pt Vale 92), S Talbot (Port Vale 94).
Clubhouse: Two bars, dance floor. Open nightly & weekend lunch.
95-96 Captain: Guy Russell. **95-96 P.o.Y.:** Guy Russell.
95-96 Top scorer: Phil Davies 51.
Local Newspapers: Solihull News (0121 626 6635), Solihull Times (0121 704 3338), Birmingham Post & Mail (0121 236 3366), Express & Star (01902 319461).
Local Radio Stations: Radio WM, BRMB.
Hons: Sthn Lg Mid Div R-up 87-88, Mids Comb 80-81 (R-up(4) 74-76 79-80 82-83, Div 1 85-86, Presidents Cup(2) 66-68 78-79), Mids Comb Chall Cup 80-81 (R-up 69-70 82-83), Lord Mayor of B'ham Charity Cup 90-91, Mids F'lit Cup(2) 90-92, Tony Allden Tphy 81-82, B'ham Snr Cup 57-58, Worcs Snr Cup R-up 86-87, B'ham Jnr Cup 66-67, Worcs Jnr Cup 85-86, Solihull Charity Cup 85-86, Smedley Crook Memorial Cup 87-88, Cent Amat Lg 36-37 37-38 38-39, Verviers (Belg) Tphy 32-33 36-37, AFA Chall Cup 38-39, AFA Snr Cup 26-27 35-36, Mids F'lit Yth Lg Cup R-up 87-88, B'ham County Yth Lg Cup R-up 83-84.

PROGRAMME DETAILS:
Pages: 52 **Price:** 80p
Editor: Peter Denham
(0121 777 3356)

PAGET RANGERS

Formed: 1938 The 'P's'

Paget Rangers:

Chairman: R R Ruddick **Vice-Chairman:** Derek Culling
Secretary: Ian T Price, 754A Alum Rock Road, Alum Rock, Birmingham, B8 3PP. (0121 327 3746).
Manager/Physio: Eddie Caulfield **Asst Manager:** Paul Edwards **Coach:** Chris Sharpe
Press Officer: Chris Inman **Commercial Manager:** Rob Wilkinson (0121 749 5660)
Ground & Directions: As Sutton Coldfield (see page 497)
Capacity: 4,500 **Cover:** 500 **Seats:** 200 **Floodlights:** Yes **Metal Badges:** Yes
Club Shop: No, metal badges available from chairman or secretary.
Colours: Gold/black/gold. **Change colours:** All red **Sponsors:** Delaware Communications
Previous Leagues: Birmingham Suburban/Central Amateur/Midland Combination 50-81/Southern 86-88/West Midlands (Regional) 88-94/ Interlink Midland Alliance 94-95.
Previous Grounds: Pype Hayes Park 38-46/ Springfield Road, Walmley 46-93
Midweek home matchday: Wednesday **Reserve Team's League:** None.
Best F.A. Cup season: Third Qual Round 94-95
Record Gate: 2,000 v Aston Villa, F'light opening 1971
Record Fees - Paid: N/A
Received: John Gittens (Southampton) £10,000
Players progressing to Football League:
John Gittens (Southampton for £ 10,000)
Clubhouse: Open daily, brick built lounge and concert room, fully carpeted and extensively decorated. Food available
95-96 Captain: Stuart Tucker
95-96 P.o.Y.: Richard Brown
95-96 Top scorer: Ian Bennett
Local Newspapers: Sutton Coldfield News, Sutton Observer.
Local Radio Stations: Radio WM, BRMB.
Hons: West Mids Lg R-up 91-92 (Lg Cup 91-92); Midland Comb.(6) 59-61 69-71 82-83 85-86 (R-up 77-78, Lg Cup 59-60 66-67, Div 1 Cup 70-71, Div 3 82-83(res)); B'ham Jnr Cup 51-52; Walsall Snr Cup 85-86; Midland Alliance 94-95; Lord Mayor Birmingham Charity Cup 94-95; Staffs Sen Cup R-up 94-95.

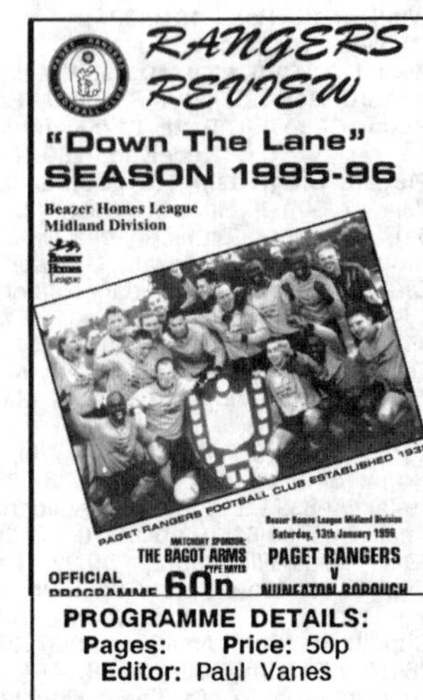

PROGRAMME DETAILS:
Pages: **Price:** 50p
Editor: Paul Vanes

1919 # RACING CLUB WARWICK Racing

Back Row (L-R): Andy Green, Robert Gould, Ben Foost, Richard Anstiss, Kieran Sullivan, Matt Haywood. Front; Richard Wade. Liam O'Neil, Barry Wilcox, Gary Hardwick, Mick Walker. Photo: Keith Clayton.

Chairman: Mr J Wright **Vice Chairman:** Mr E Jenkins.
Secretary: Patrick Murphy, 20 Dadglow Rd, Bishops Itchington, Leamington Spa CV33 0TG (01926 612675).
Manager: Wilson Barrett **Asst Manager:** Russell Ashendon.
Press Officer: Secretary **Commercial Manager:** Robin Lamb.
Ground: Townsend Meadow, Hampton Road, Warwick CV34 6JP (01926 495786).
Directions: On the B4095 Warwick to Redditch road (via Henley in Arden) next to owners' & trainers' car park of Warwick Racecourse. From M40 jct 15 (one and a half miles) take A429 into Warwick, left into Shakespeare Ave., straight over island, right at T-junction into Hampton Rd, ground 300yds on left. 2 miles from Warwick BR station.
Capacity: 1,000 **Cover:** 200 **Seats:** 200 **Floodlights:** Yes **Metal Badges:** Yes
Club Shop: Scarves, mugs, badges, programmes - contact Robin Lamb.
Colours: Gold/black/black **Change colours:** Red/white/white **Sponsors:** N/A.
Previous Leagues: Birmingham & West Midlands Alliance/ Warwickshire Combination/ West Midlands (Regional) 67-72/ Midland Combination 72-89.
Previous Name: Saltisford Rovers 1919-68/ Warwick Saltisford 68-70.
Midweek home matchday: Tuesday
Reserve Team's League: No Reserve team.
Record Attendance: 1,000 v Halesowen Town, FA Cup 1987.
League clubs defeated in FA Cup: None.
Record Fees - Paid: £1,000 for Dave Whetton (Bedworth United)
Received: £2,000 for Ian Gorrie (Atherstone Utd).
Record win: 9-1 **Record defeat:** 2-6.
Clubhouse: (01926 495786). Open every evening and and Fri/Sat/Sun & Mon lunchtimes.
Club Record Goalscorer: Steve Edgington.
Club Record Appearances: Steve Cooper 600.
94-95 Captain:
94-95 P.o.Y.:
94-95 Top scorer:
Local Newspapers: Warwick Advertiser, Leamington Courier, Coventry Evening Telegraph.
Local Radio Stations: BBC Radio Coventry.
Hons: FA Vase 4th Rd 77-78, Midland Combination 87-88 (R-up 88-89), Warwick Lg 33-34 34-35 35-36, Birmingham & West Mids Alliance 48-49, Birmingham & Dist Alliance Senior Cup 49-50, Leamington & Dist Lg 37-38 45-46 46-47 47-48, Leamington Hospital Cup 37-38 46-47, Warwick Cinderella Cup 35-36 36-37 37-38 38-39 46-47, T G John Cup 36-37, Leamington Junior Cup 38-39 46-47.

PROGRAMME DETAILS:
Pages: 20 **Price:** TBA
Editor: Robin Lamb

RAUNDS TOWN FC

1946 Shopmates

Back Row (L-R): Shaun Keeble, Peter Green, John Fowler, Kevin Fox, Darryl Page, Stan Hardy, Ian Pearce, Ashley Carr. Front Row: Paul Hill, Paul York, Martin Lewis, Darryl Wilson, Ian McInerney, Matt Freeman.
Photo - Tony Reavey

Chairman: George Hagan **President:** R Woods
Secretary: Mick Jones,14 Welland Close,Raunds,Northants.NN9 6SQ.(01933 625429)
Manager: Keith Burt **Asst Manager:** Glen Burdett
Ground: Kiln Park, London Road, Raunds, Northants NN9 6EQ (01933 623351).
Directions: Take Raunds turning at roundbout on A45 and ground is first left.
Capacity: 3,000 **Seats:** 250 **Cover:** 600 **Floodlights:** Yes
Press Officer: Mick Jones
Colours: Red & black **Change Colours:** White.
Midweek matchday: Wednesday **Club Shop:** Yes.
Clubhouse: On ground, open every day
Sponsors: Jubilee Enterprises **Reserve Team's League:** UCL Reserve Division One.
Record Attendance: 1,500 v Crystal Palace, ground opening 23/7/91.
Previous Leagues: Rushden & District, Central Northants Combination, United Counties League Prem Div.
Previous Grounds: Greenhouse Field (until 1948), The Berristers (1948-91).
Best FA Cup season: 92-93 (0-4 at Nuneaton Borough), 93-94 (0-4 v Telford United).
Players to progress to Football League: Greg Downs (Norwich, Coventry, Birmingham, Hereford).
Local Newspapers: Northants Evening Telegraph, Wellingborough Post, Chronicle & Echo.
Captain 1995-96: Paul York. is
Hons: UCL Prem Champions 95-96, UCL Div 1 82-83 (R-up 91-92, KO Cup 90-91 (R-up 83-84 93-94), Reserve Div 1 88-89 95-96 (R-up 86-87 87-88 89-90 90-91 91-92), Reserve KO Cup 84-85 88-89 93-94), Northants Snr Cup 90-91, Hunts Premier Cup R-up 92-93, Daventry Charity Cup R-up 83-84, Northants Jnr Cup 82-83 91-92(res) 92-93(res).

PROGRAMME DETAILS:
Pages: 68 **Price:** 50p
Editor: Mick Jones
(01933 625429)

Formed: 1900

REDDITCH UNITED

The Reds

Redditch United's Valley Stadium

Chairman: Malcolm Jones. **President:** Bob Thompson.
Secretary: M A Langfield, 174 Harport Road, Redditch, Worcs B98 7PE (0527 526603).
Manager: Mick Tuohy. **Asst Manager:** Ivor Chambers. **Physio:** Ginger Jordan.
Commercial Mgr: Dave Roberts **Press Officer:** R Newbold (0527 27516).
Ground: Valley Stadium, Bromsgrove Road, Redditch B97 4RN (0527 67450).
Directions: Access 7 on town centre ring-road takes you into Bromsgrove Road (via Unicorn Hill) - ground entrance 400yds past traffic lights on right. Arriving from Bromsgrove take first exit off dual carriageway. Ground 400 yds from Redditch BR station and town centre.
Capacity: 9,500 **Cover:** 2,000 **Seats:** 400 **Floodlights:** Yes **Club Shop:** No.
Colours: All red with white trim on shirts. **Change colours:** Royal Blue/Sky Blue/Royal Blue.
Sponsors: TBA.
Previous Leagues: Birmingham Combination 05-21 29-39 46-53/ West Midlands 21-29 53-72/ Southern 72-79/ GMV Conference (then Alliance Premier League) 79-80.
Previous Name: Redditch Town
Prev. Ground: HDA Spts Ground, Millsborough Rd.
Midweek home matchday: Tuesday
Reserves' League: Ansells Midland Comb. Res Div.
Record Attendance: 5,500 v Bromsgrove, league match 54-55.
Best FA Cup season: 1st Rd replay 71-72 (lost 0-4 at P'boro after 1-1 draw). Also 1st Rd 71-72.
League clubs defeated in FA Cup: None.
Record Fees - Paid: £3,000 for Paul Joinson
Received: £42,000 for David Farrell (Aston Villa, 1991).
Players progressing to Football League: N Davis (Aston Villa), Hugh Evans (Birmingham 1947), Trevor Lewes (Coventry 1957), David Gilbert (Chesterfield 1960), Mike Tuohy (Southend Utd 1979), Neil Smith (Liverpool), David Farrell (Aston Villa 1992).
Clubhouse: Large clubroom and lounge boardroom. Open matchdays and for private hire. Food availsable on matchdays; hot dogs, burgers, chips etc.
95-96 Captain:
95-96 P.o.Y.:
95-96 Top scorer: .
Local Newspapers: Redditch Indicator (0527 63611), Redditch Advertiser, Birmingham Evening Mail, Redditch Weekly Mail.
Local Radio Stations: BBC Hereford & Worcester.
Hons: FA Trophy 1st Rd 78-79, Southern Lg Div 1 Nth 75-76 (Midland Div R-up 85-86), West Mids (B'ham) Lg Southern Sect. 54-55, Birmingham Comb. 13-14 32-33 52-53 (R-up 06-07 14-15 51-52), Staffs Snr Cup 90-91, Birmingham Snr Cup 24-25 31-32 38-39 76-77, Worcs Snr Cup 1894-95 1930-31 74-75 76-77 (R-up 1888-89 1929-30 52-53 73-74), Worcs Jnr Cup 90-91.

Redditch United Football Club Limited

PROGRAMME DETAILS:
Pages: 48 **Price:** TBA
Editor: Roger Newbold (0527 27516)

1895 **ROTHWELL TOWN** The Bones

ROTHWELL TOWN

Rothwell's Kevin McGuire scores in their match against Bridgnorth. *Photo - Neil Whittington.*

Chairman: Stuart Andrews **Vice-Chairman:** Jeremy Freestone **President:**
Secretary: Roger Barratt, 18 Norton Street, Rothwell, Northants NN14 2DE (01536 711244).
Manager: Jack Murray **Asst Manager/Physio:** Graham Simmonds **Coach:** Kim Davies.
Press Officer/Comm Mgr: Peter Bradley (01536 710925). **Newsline:** 0891 88 44 14.
Ground: Cecil Street, Rothwell, Northants NN14 2EZ (01536 710694).
Directions: A14/A6 to Rothwell. At town centre roundabout turn into Bridge Street (right if northbound, left if southbound), take 3rd left into Tresham Street, ground is at top on left. Three miles from Kettering (BR); Rothwell is served by Kettering to Market Harborough buses.
Capacity: 3,000 **Seats:** 264 **Cover:** 1,000 **Floodlights:** Yes **Club Shop:** No.
Colours: Blue (white trim)/blue/blue **Change Colours:** Red (white trim)/red/red **Metal Badges:** Yes
Midweek matchday: Tuesday **Club Sponsors:** N P S Healthcare
Previous Grounds: Harrington Road, Castle Hill **Previous Name:** Rothwell Town Swifts.
Previous Leagues: Northants 1896-1911 21-33/ Kettering Amateur 11-21 33-48/ Leicestershire Senior 48-50/ United Counties 50-56 61-94/ Central Alliance 56-61.
Record Attendance: 2,508 v Irthlingborough Diamonds, United Counties League 1971.
Reserve Team's League: Hereward Sports United Counties League Reserve Division.
Players progressing to Football League: Lee Glover (Nottingham Forest, Barnsley & Scotland under-21) 1987, Matty Watts (Charlton Athletic) 1990.
Best FA Cup season: Never past Second Qualifying Round.
Best FA Trophy season: Second Round Proper 94-95.
Best FA Vase season: Fifth Round 92-93 (lost 1-2 v Bridlington Town).
Record transfer fee paid: Undisclosed for Andy Wright (Aylesbury 1992).
Record transfer fee received: Undisclosed for Matty Watts (Charlton 1990).
Record win: 17-0 v Stamford, FA Cup Preliminary Round replay 1927.
Record defeat: 1-10 v Coalville Town, Leicestershire Sen Lge 49.
Clubhouse: Rowellian Social Club, open every evening and weekend lunchtimes. Crisps and rolls available on matchdays (hot food and drinks available in ground). 'Top of the Town Ballroom', lounge seats 200.
Local Newspapers: Northants Evening Telegraph (01536 81111), Chronicle & Echo (01604 231122), Herald & Post.
Local Radio Stations: Radio Northants, KCBC.
95-96 Captain: Kevin McDonald. **95-96 Top Scorer:** Kevin McGuire 29.
95-96 Player-of-the-Year: Danny Liquerish
Hons: United Counties Lg 92-93 94-95 (R-up 69-70 70-71 87-88 89-90 90-91, KO Cup 55-56 70-71 71-72 91-92 92-93 (R-up 77-78 79-80 82-83), Div 2 52-53 53-54, Div 2 Cup 52-53 53-54, Benevolent Cup 92-93 94-95 (R-up 89-90 90-91)), Northants Lg 1899-1900 (R-up 1895-96 96-97 97-98), Northants Snr Cup 1899-1900 23-24 59-60 88-89 95-96 (R-up 24-25 71-72 87-88).

PROGRAMME DETAILS:
Pages: 52 **Price:** 80p
Editor: Mark Southon
(01162 774877)

SHEPSHED DYNAMO

1890 | The Raiders

Shepshed Dynamo: *Photo - Martin Wray*

Chairman/Comm. Mgr: Paul Mitchell **Vice Chairman:**
Secretary: Mr Peter Bull, 17 Welland Rd, Barrow-on-Soar, Leicestershire LE12 8NA (01509 413338).
Manager: Mark O'Kane **Assistant Manager:** Keith Milner.
Physio: John Watson. **Press Officer:** Maurice Brindley (01509 267922)
Ground: The Dovecote, Butthole Lane, Shepshed, Leicestershire (01509 502684).
Directions: M1 junction 23, A512 towards Ashby, right at first lights, right at garage in Forest Street, right into Butthole Lane opposite Black Swan. Five miles from Loughborough (BR).
Capacity: 5,000 **Cover:** 1,500 **Seats:** 209 **Floodlights:** Yes
Colours: Black & white **Change colours:** All red.
Previous Leagues: Leicestershire Senior 07-16 19-27 46-50 51-81/ Midland Counties 81-82/ Northern Counties (East) 82-83/ Southern 83-88/ Northern Premier 88-93/ Midland Combination 93-94.
Previous Grounds: Ashby Road (pre-1897)/ Little Haw Farm.
Previous Names: Shepshed Albion 1890-1975 91-94/ Shepshed Charterhouse 75-91.
Midweek home matchday: Tuesday **Record Attendance:** 1,672.
Club Shop: TBA
Best FA Vase season: Semi-Finalists 78-79.
Best FA Trophy season: 1st Rd Replay 85-86 89-90.
Best FA Cup season: 1st Rd 82-83 (lost 1-5 at Preston North End).
Rec. fee paid: £2,000 for Doug Newton **Received:** £10,000 for John Deakin.
Players progressing to Football League: Neil Grewcock (Burnley 1984), Gordon Tucker (Huddersfield 1987), Devon White (Bristol Rovers 1987), John Deakin (Birmingham City).
Clubhouse: Accomodates 120 in main room, 50 in others.
Club Record Scorer: Jeff Lissaman **Club Record Appearances:** Austin Straker 300.
Honours: Southern League Midland Division Runners-up 83-84, Northern Counties (East) League 82-83 (League Cup 82-83), Midland Counties League 81-82 (League Cup 81-82), Leicestershire Senior League 10-11 20-21 78-79 79-80 80-81 (Runners-up 21-22, Div 2 53-54 65-66 77-78, Div 2 Cup 77-78), Leicestershire Senior Cup 77-78 79-80 81-82 83-84 84-85 85-86 87-88, FA Vase SF 78-79, Loughborough Charity Cup 92-93.

PROGRAMME DETAILS:
Pages: Price:
Editor:

1951 **SOLIHULL BOROUGH** Boro

Back Row (L-R): P Dyson, D Houghton, J Muir, J Mulders, M Crisp. Middle Row: R Phillps, D Lachford (Coach), J Price (Physio), J Pearson, R Hopkins, B Palgrave, K Green, D Griffiths. Front Row: T Whitington, K Casey, R Judd, M Coogan, J Morris (Mgr), C Gillett, R Martin, J Dowling.

Chairman: John Hewitson **Vice Chairman:** T Stevens **President:** Joe McGorian.
Secretary: John A France, 22 Swallows Meadow, Shirley, Solihull B90 4QB (0121 733 6584).
Manager: Paul Dyson **Asst Manager:** Kevin Sweeney **Coach:** Robert Hopkins
Physio: John Price **Press Officer:** Richard Crawshaw (01564 702746).
Ground: Moor Green FC (see Midland Division section). Solihull are groundsharing at Moor Green whilst awaiting planning permission for a stadium of their own
Directions & Capacity: See Moor Green **Club Shop:** Yes **Metal Badges:** Yes.
Colours: Red/white/red. **Change colours:** Yellow/black/black.
Sponsors: Mitchells & Butlers. **Previous Leagues:** Mercian/ Midland Combination 69-91.
Previous Name: Lincoln FC **Previous Grounds:** Widney Stadium, Solihull 65-88.
Midweek matchday: Wednesday **Reserve's League:** Midland Combination Reserve Division.
Record Attendance: 1,360 v VS Rugby, FA Cup First Round 14/11/92. *At previous ground: 400 v Moor Green, Midland Combination Division Two, 1971.*
Best FA Cup season: 1st Rd 92-93 (lost 1-3 at VS Rugby after 2-2 draw).
Best FA Vase season: 5th Rd 74-75
Best FA Trophy season: 3rd Qualifying Rd 92-93.
Record win: 6-1 v Hednesford (H), Southern Lge Midland Div 91-92.
Record defeat: 1-7 v VS Rugby (A), Birmingham Senior Cup.
Record Fees - Paid: £5,000 for Robin Judd (Atherstone United).
Received: £30,000 for Andy Williams (from Coventry).
Players progressing to Football League: Kevin Ashley (Birmingham City, Wolverhampton Wanderers), Andy Williams (Coventry City, Rotherham United, Leeds United, Notts County), Geoff Scott (Leicester City, Birmingham City, Stoke City), Danny Conway (Leicester City), Alan Smith (Leicester City, Arsenal), Dean Spink (Aston Villa, Shrewsbury Town).
Clubhouse: The Borough Club, Tanworth Lane, Shirley; opened June 16th 1990. Two bars, dance floor, meeting room available for hire. Open every night, Sunday and bank holiday lunchtimes. **Steward:** Mark Dumelow.
Club Record Goalscorer: Chris Burton.
Club Record Appearances: Darrell Houghton.
95-96 Captain: Jan Mulders **95-96 Top scorer:** Joe Dowling
Local Press: Solihull Times, Solihull News, Sunday Mercury, Sports Argus.
Local Radio Stations: Radio WM, BRMB.
Hons: Southern Lg Midland Div 91-92, Midland Comb. R-up 90-91 (Chall. Cup R-up 74-75 90-91, Presidents Cup R-up 69-70), Lord Mayor of Birmingham Charity Cup 91-92 92-93 94-95, Worcs Senior Cup R-up 92-93.

PROGRAMME DETAILS:
Pages: 32 **Price:** £1
Editor: Richard Crawshaw
(01564 702746)

Formed: 1876

STAFFORD RANGERS

Boro

Stafford's Richard Mitchell about to make a cross as Hasting's Simon Ullathorne closes in.
Photo - Roger Turner

Chairman: John Horton **Vice-Chairmam:** C Went
Secretary: Michael Hughes, 1 Rambleford Way, Parkside, Stafford ST16 1TW (01785 54879)
Manager: Robert Horton **Physio:** B. Whittaker **Press Officer:** Chris Godwin
Commercial Manager: George Berry
Ground: Marston Road Stafford ST16 3BX (01785 42750) (Fax 01785 54050)
Directions: From M6 junction 14, A34 (Stone) to roundabout, straight over into Beaconside, take third right into Common Road, ground one mile ahead. From Town Centre, follow signs for B5066 (Sandon) turn left by Lotus shoe factory. Two miles from railway station.
Capacity: 6,000 **Cover:** 3,000 **Seats:** 426 **Floodlights:** Yes **Metal Badges:** Yes
Colours: White & black/black/black **Change colours:** All Yellow **Sponsors:** Sentinal Newspapers
Previous Leagues: Shropshire 1891/93, Birm 1893/96, 21/40, N Staffordshire 1896/1900, Cheshire 00/01, Birm Comb 00/12, 46/52, Cheshire Cnty 52/69, Nthn Prem 69/79, 83/85, Alliance Prem 79/83.
Midweek home matchday: Tuesday **Reserve Team's League:**
Club Shop: Two shops, one old programmes and one souvenirs run by Jim & Irene Dalglish.
Prev Grd: Lammascotes, Stone Rd, Newtown, Doxey (until 1896)
Record Attendance: 8,536 v Rotherham Utd FA Cup 3rd Rd 75
Record win: 11-0 v Dudley Town FA Cup 6.9.58
Record defeat: 0-12 v Burton Town Birmingham Lge 13.12.30
Record Fees - Paid: £13,000 for S Butterworth from VS Rugby 90
Received: £100,000 for Stan Collymore from Crystal Palace 1990
Players progressing to Football League: M Alckisie (Plymouth, Luton, Spurs), J Arnold (Blackburn, Everton, Port Vale), R Williams, M Cullerton, T Bailey (all Port Vale), K Barnes (Man. City), A Lee (Tranmere Rovers), E Cameron, (Exeter), W Blunt (Wolves), G Bullock (Barnsley), K Mottershead (Doncaster), McIlvenny (WBA), S Collymore (C Palace), P Devlin (Notts County), R Price (Birmingham City).
Clubhouse: Yes
Club Record Goalscorer: M Cullerton 176
Club Record Appearances: Jim Sargent
95-96 Captain: **95-96 P.o.Y.:**
95-96 Top scorer:
Local Newspapers: Staffordshire Newsletter, Express & Star, Evening Sentinel
Local Radio Stations: Radio Stoke, Beacon Radio, Signal Radio.
Hons: Birm Comb Champions 12-13; Birm Lge Champ 25-26; Nthn Prem Lge Champ 71-72, 84-85; FA Trophy Win 71-72, 78-79, R-up 75-76; Bob Lord Trophy 85-86; Wednesday Charity Cup 20-21; Midland Floodlight Cup 70-71; NPL Champ Shield 84-85; Jim Thompson Shield 86-87; Staffs Sen Cup 54-55, 56-57, 62-63, 71-72, 77-78, 86-87, 91-92.

PROGRAMME DETAILS:
Pages: 40 **Price:** £ 1.00
Editor: C & W Bedford

STOURBRIDGE

Formed: 1876 — The Glassboys

Back Row (L-R): A Bastable, C Guest, T Davies, A Johnson, R Tivey, T Bryne. Middle; L Palmer, N Henley, M Gardner, W Houghton, J Smith, S Downing. Front; M Clarke, R Walker, C Gordon, A Webb, S Ball, J Lowe, J Jeavons — *Photo - Marshall Sports*

Managing Director: Nick Pratt **Chairman:** Morton Bartleet **Vice Chairman:** Nick Pratt
Secretary/Press Off.: Hugh Clark, 10 Burnt Oak Drive, Stourbridge, West Mids DY8 1HL (01384 392975).
Manager: Morton Bartlett **Coach:** Dale Rudge. **Physio:** Steve Ball.
Ground: War Memorial Athletic Ground, High Street, Amblecote, Stourbridge DY8 4EB (01384 394040).
Directions: Take A491, signposted Wolverhampton, from Stourbridge ring-road - ground 300yds on left immediately beyond traffic lights and opposite 'Royal Oak' pub. Buses 311, 313 from Dudley, and 256 from Wolverhampton, pass ground. One mile from Stourbridge Town (BR).
Capacity: 2,000 **Cover:** 1,250 **Seats:** 250 **Floodlights:** Yes **Metal Badges:** Yes
Colours: Red & white stripes **Change colours:** Yellow & blue.
Club Shop: Yes. Thousands of programmes and souvenirs. Contact Nigel Gregg (01384 838334).
Previous Leagues: West Midlandss (previously Birmingham) 1892-1939/ Birmingham Combination 45-53.
Previous Grounds: None **Previous Name:** Stourbridge Standard
Sponsors: Spar, Wordsley Green **Midweek home matchday:** Tuesday
Record Attendance: 5,726 v Cardiff City, Welsh Cup final 1st leg 1974.
Best F.A. Cup season: 4th Qual. Rd 3 times this century: v Arnold 67-68, v V.S. Rugby 84-85 & 85-86.
Record Fee Received: £20,000 for Tony Cunningham (Lincoln C 79).
Players progressing to Football League: D Pinbley/B Farmer (Birmingham City 46/54), H Edwards (Derby Cnty 47), J Pemberton (Luton Town 47), J Boxley (Bristol City 50), A Rowley (Liverpool 53), C Taylor/K Ball (Walsall 58/72), P Clark (Stockport Cnty 65), P Freeman (W B A 68), C Bates/R Harwood (Shrewsbury Tn 74), L Lawrence (Shrewsbury Tn 75), S Cooper (Torquay 78), T Cunningham (Lincoln 79), M Gwinnet (Peterborough 81).
Clubhouse: Open every evening from 8pm and Sunday lunchtimes.
Club Record Scorer/Appearances: Ron Page 269/427.
95-96 Captain Ron Walker. **95-96 Top scorer:** Les Palmer 20
95-96 Player of the Years: Albert Johnson/Matt Gardiner
Local Newspapers: Stourbridge News & County Express, Express & Star, Dudley Evening Mail.
Local Radio Stations: Radio West Wids, B.R.M.B., Beacon.
Honours: Welsh Cup R-up 73-74, FA Trophy QF 70-71, Southern Lg Midland Div 90-91 (Lg Cup 92-93, Div 1 North 73-74, Merit Cup 73-74), West Mids (prev. Birmingham) Lg 23-24 (R-up 4), Birmingham Comb. R-up 51-52, Birmingham Snr Cup 49-50 45-46 75-76 (R-up 3), Worcs Snr Cup 9, (R-up 12), Herefordshire Snr Cup 54-55, Camkin Cup R-up 69-70, Camkin Presidents Cup 70-71, Albion Shield 43-44, Keys Cup 37-38 62-63, Worcs Comb. R-up 27-28, Worcester Jnr Cup R-up 27-28, Tillotson Cup R-up 39-40, Brierley Hill Lg R-up 44-45 (Lg Cup R-up 44-45), Brierley Hill Yth Lg Coronation Cup 56-57.

PROGRAMME DETAILS:
Pages: **Price:** 70p
Editor: Secretary

1897 **SUTTON COLDFIELD TOWN** Royals

Sutton Coldfield Town's ground. *Photo - Keith Clayton*

Chairman: Kevin Holt **Vice Chairman:**
Secretary: Fred Rought, 25 Lebanon Grove, Chase Terrace, Burntwood Staffs. WS7 8BE (01543 685029).
Manager: Chris Wright **Asst Mgr:** Alan Hampton **Physio:** Reg Brassington
Press Officer: Brian Turner **Commercial Manager:** Peter Young.
Ground: Central Ground, Coles Lane, Sutton Coldfield B72 1NL (0121 354 2997/0121 355 5475).
Directions: A5127 into Sutton, right at Odeon cinema (Holland Road), then first right into Coles Lane - ground 150 yds on left. 10 mins walk from Sutton Coldfield (BR), bus 104 from Birmingham.
Capacity: 4,500 **Cover:** 500 **Seats:** 200 **Floodlights:** Yes **Metal Badges:** Yes
Club Shop: Yes, selling metal badges, scarves, hats, pens, rosettes, progs. Contact Paul Vanes (0121 770 9835).
Colours: Royal/white/royal **Change colours:** Red & black/red/ red & black
Previous Leagues: Central Birmingham/ Walsall Senior/ Staffs County/ Birmingham Combination 50-54/ West Mids (Regional) 54-65 79-82/ Midlands Combination 65-79.
Previous Grounds: Meadow Plat 1879-89/ Coles Lane (site of current ambulance station) 90-1919.
Reserve Team's League: None. **Previous Name:** Sutton Coldfield FC 1879-1921.
Midweek home matchday: Tuesday
Record Fees - Paid: £1,500 twice in 1991, for Lance Morrison (Gloucester) & Micky Clarke (Burton A.)
Received: £25,000 for Barry Cowdrill (WBAI 1979).
Record Attendance: 2,029 v Doncaster Rovers, F.A. Cup 80-81 (Receipts £2,727).
Best FA Cup season: 1st Rd 80-81 (lost 0-1 to Doncaster), 92-93 (1-2 at Wanderers).
Players progressing to Football League: Arthur Corbett (Walsall 1949), Paul Cooper (Manchester City), Noel Blake (Leeds), Steve Cooper (Barnsley), Peter Latchford (WBA & Celtic), Mark Smith (Wolves), John Barton (Everton), Barry Cowdrill (WBA 1979), Colin Dryhurst (Halifax 1979), Dale Belford (Notts County 1987), Ellis Laight (Torquay 1992).
Clubhouse: Brick built lounge and concert room, fully carpeted and extensively decorated. Open daily, food available.
Club Record Goalscorer: Eddie Hewitt 288
Club Record Apps: Eddie Hewitt 465
95-96 Captain: Carl Bannister. **95-96 P.o.Y.:** Royston Richardson.
95-96 Top scorer: Darren Brown.
Local Newspapers: Sutton Coldfield News, Sutton Observer.
Local Radio Stations: BRMB, Radio WM.
Honours: Southern Lg Midland Div R-up 82-83, West Mids Lg 79-80 (Lg Cup 80-81 81-82), Midland Comb.(2) 77-79 (R-up(2) 69-71, Lg Cup 69-70), Walsall Senior Lg 46-47, Walsall Senior Cup(3) 77-80 (R-up 80-81), Staffs Senior Cup R-up 89-90 (SF 84-85 86-87), Lord Mayor of Birmingham Charity Cup Winners 95-96, R-up 93-94, Worcs Snr Cup SF 88-89, Walsall Challenge Cup R-up 46-47 47-48, Sutton Charity Cup 46-47 65-66 71-72 86-87 89-90 90-91, F.A. Trophy 1st Rd Replay 89-90, FA Amateur Cup 2nd Rd 70-71, Express & Star Cup 44-45.

PROGRAMME DETAILS:
Pages: 20 **Price:** 80p
Editor: Peter Young

TAMWORTH

Formed: 1933 | Lambs or Town

Tamworth's Julian Alsop rises above the Bolehall defence to crash a header against the crossbar in the FA Cup 1st Rd Qu. Bolehall Swifts 0, Tamworth 1 *Photo - Paul Barber.*

Chairman: Bob Andrews **Vice Chairman:** Tony Reeves **President:** Len Gendle.
Secretary: Rod A Hadley, 38 Godolphin, Riverside, Tamworth B79 7UF (01827 66786).
Manager: Paul Hendrie. **Asst Manager:** Andy Dwyer. **Physio:** Peter Smith
Press Officer: Sam Holiday. **Commercial Manager:** Buster Belford.
Ground: The Lamb Ground, Kettlebrook, Tamworth, Staffs B79 1HA (01827 65798).
Directions: Follow the signs for Town Centre/Snowdone,then for Kettlebrook.The entrance to the ground and car parks is in Kettlebrook Road,50yards from the traffic island by the railway viaduct.
Capacity: 2,500 **Cover:** 1,191 **Seats:** 391 **Floodlights:** Yes **Metal Badges:** Yes
Colours: Red/black/black (red trim) **Change colours:** White/red/white **Sponsors:** Alco Heating
Previous Leagues: Birmingham Combination 33-54/ West Midlands (initially Birmingham Lg) 54-72 84-88/ Southern 72-79 83-84/ Northern Premier 79-83.
Midweek home matchday: Tuesday **Club Shop:** Yes.
Previous Grounds: Jolly Sailor Ground 33-34.
Record Attendance: 4,920 v Atherstone Tn, Birm Comb 48.
Best FA Cup season: 2nd Rd 69-70 (lost 0-6 at Gillingham).
Record Fees - Paid: £5,000 for Steve Cartwright (Colchester Utd, 88).
Received: £7,500 for Martin Myers (Telford Utd, 90).
Record Win: 14-4 v Holbrook Institute (H), Bass Vase 34.
Record Defeat: 0-11 v Solihull (A), Birmingham Comb. 40.
Players progressing to Football League: P Hilton (WBA 49), A Godridge (Swansea 50), W Ealing (Doncaster), Higgins (Fulham), P Weir (Cardiff), S Fox (Wrexham), S Cartwright (Colchester 88), S Ryder(Walsall).
Clubhouse: Club on grd open matchdays, training nights and tote night (Monday) only.
Club Record Goalscorer: Graham Jessop 195
Club Record Scorer in single season: Percy Vials 64 (36-37)
Club Record Appearances: Dave Seedhouse 869.
95-96 Captain: Jon Howard/Paul Brogan **95-96 P.o.Y.:** Ian Michael
95-96 Top scorer: Mark Whitehouse
Local Newspapers: Tamworth Herald (01827 60741).
Local Radio Stations: Radio WM, BRMB Radio, Extra AM.
Hons: FA Vase 88-89, West Mids Lg 63-64 65-66 71-72 87-88 (R-up(2) 67-69, Div 2 55-56, Lg Cup(5) 64-66 71-72 85-86 87-88 (R-up 70-71)), Birmingham Snr Cup 60-61 65-66 68-69 (R-up 36-37 63-64), Staffs Snr Cup 58-59 63-64 65-66 (R-up 55-56 66-67 70-71), Midland F'lit Cup R-up 71-72 72-73, Camkin Cup 71-72 (R-up 70-71),

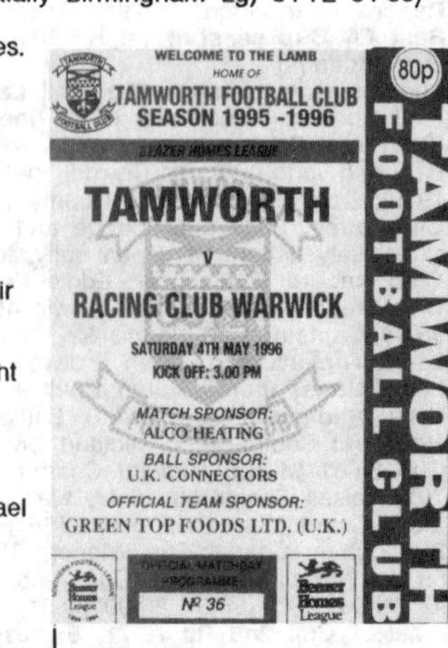

PROGRAMME DETAILS:
Pages: 28 **Price:** 80p
Editor: Secretary

Formed: 1956

V.S. RUGBY

The Valley

V.S. Rugby FC. *Photo - Andrew Chitty.*

Chairman: Peter Kilvert.
Secretary: Trevor Osborne, 37 Park Leys, Daventry, Northants NN11 4AS (01327 77866)
Manager: David Jones **Asst Manager:** Steve Hunt
Physio: Alan Cooke. **Press Officer:** Derek Jenkins (01788 576804).
Ground: Butlin Road, Rugby, Warks CV21 3ST (01788 543692).
Directions: 1 mile walk from station. Ground off Clifton (B5414) on north side of Rugby.
Capacity: 6,000 **Cover:** 1,000 **Seats:** 240 **Floodlights:** Yes **Metal Badges:** Yes
Club Shop: Yes.
Colours: Sky & white stripe/navy/sky
Change colours: All Red
Sponsors: T.B.A. **Previous Name:** Valley Sports/ Valley Sports Rugby.
Previous Leagues: Rugby & District 1956-63/ Coventry & Partnership/ North Warks 63-69/ United Counties 69-75/ West Midlands 75-83
Midweek matchday: Wednesday
Record Attendance: 3,961 v Northampton FA Cup 1984
Best FA Cup season: 1st Rd 84-85 85-86 86-87 94-95, 2nd Rd 87-88
League clubs defeated in FA Cup: None
Record Fees - Paid: £3,500 R Smith, I Crawley, G Bradder
Received: £15,000 T Angus (Northampton)
Players progressing to Football League: S Storer (Birmingham 1985), S Bicknell (Leicester), S Norris (Scarborough), T Angus (Northampton Town), Ashley Walker (Peterborough), Ian King (Stoke City).
Clubhouse: Every night and weekend lunchtimes. Entertainment Saturday nights. Excellent facilities include Long Alley Skittles, darts and pool.
Club Record Goalscorer: Danny Conway, 124
Club Record Appearances: Danny Conway, 374
95-96 Captain: Les Hornby
95-96 P.o.Y.: Les Hornby
95-96 Top scorer: Matt Owen
Local Newspapers: Rugby Advertiser (01788 535363), Coventry Evening Telegraph (01203 633633), Rugby Observer (01788 535147).
Local Radio Stations: Mercia Sound, CWR
Club Newsline: 0891 10 1999.
Hons: Southern Lg Midland Div 86-87 (R-up 94-95, Lg Cup 89-90), FA Vase 82-83, Midland F'lit Cup 84-85 89-90 (R-up 86-87), Birmingham Snr Cup 88-89 91-92, Utd Co's Lg Div 3 Cup 69-70. (all-time record FA Trophy win; 10-0 away to Ilkeston Town, Preliminary Rd 85-86).

Atherstone United

PROGRAMME DETAILS:
Pages: 30 **Price:** £1
Editor: Bob Pinks

BEAZER HOMES SOUTHERN DIVISION Ten Year Records

	86/7	87/8	88/9	89/0	90/1	91/2	92/3	93/4	94/5	95/6
Andover	16	6	18	18	9	7	20	-	-	-
Ashford Town	2	-	-	-	5	9	8	6	5	2
Baldock Town	-	15	6	10	4	11	13	7	2	-
Bashley	-	-	-	1	-	-	-	-	7	16
Braintree Town	-	-	-	-	-	4	9	13	14	5
Buckingham Town	-	-	16	3	1	5	12	12	-	-
Burnham	17	8	5	11	11	10	16	16	22	-
Bury Town	-	9	4	9	12	17	22	22	18	-
Canterbury City	20	20	13	15	18	21	17	20	-	-
Chatham Town	9	21	-	-	-	-	-	-	-	-
Chelmsford City	-	-	1	-	-	-	-	-	-	-
Cinderford Town	-	-	-	-	-	-	-	-	-	14
Clevedon Town	-	-	-	-	-	-	-	-	11	17
Corinthian	14	18	22	21	21	-	-	-	-	-
Dorchester Town	1	-	-	-	-	-	-	-	-	-
Dover Athletic	5	1	-	-	-	-	-	-	-	-
Dunstable	13	7	15	4	17	16	21	18	-	-
Erith & Belvedere	8	10	17	20	19	20	7	19	19	21
Fareham Town	-	-	-	12	20	19	15	14	21	20
Fisher 93	-	-	-	-	-	-	19	17	17	15
Fleet Town	-	-	-	-	-	-	-	-	-	19
Folkstone Town	-	17	11	17	w/d	-	-	-	-	-
Forest Green Rangers	-	-	-	-	-	-	-	-	-	8
Gosport Borough	-	-	-	-	15	22	-	-	-	-
Gravesend & Northfleet	6	4	2	-	-	-	4	1	-	-
Hastings Town	4	12	7	8	7	1	-	-	-	-
Havant Town	-	-	-	-	-	3	5	5	3	7
Hounslow	-	16	8	19	-	-	-	-	-	-
Hythe Town	-	-	-	6	8	13	-	-	-	-
Margate	10	5	20	16	10	14	10	9	13	11
Newport Isle of Wight	-	-	-	-	14	15	18	8	9	4
Poole Town	18	14	3	2	-	-	14	15	20	22
Ruislip	19	19	22	-	-	-	-	-	-	-
Salisbury	-	3	9	5	3	12	2	4	1	-
Sheppey United	15	11	19	22	-	-	-	-	-	-
Sittingbourne	-	-	-	-	-	6	1	-	-	1
Sudbury Town	-	-	-	-	13	8	6	2	-	-
Tonbridge AFC	7	13	21	-	-	-	-	11	12	18
Trowbridge Town	12	-	10	7	2	-	-	-	-	9
Waterlooville	11	2	-	-	-	-	-	-	4	3
Wealdstone	-	-	-	-	-	-	11	21	15	-
Weston Super Mare	-	-	-	-	-	-	-	-	6	13
Weymouth	-	-	-	-	-	2	-	10	8	6
Witney Town	-	-	14	14	16	18	3	3	10	12
Woodford Town	3	-	-	-	-	-	-	-	-	-
Yate Town	-	-	-	13	6	-	-	-	16	10
No of Clubs Competing	20	21	22	22	21	22	22	22	22	22

FINAL LEAGUE TABLE 1995/96

Southern Div	*P*	*W*	*D*	*L*	*F*	*A*	*Pts*
1. Sittingbourne	42	28	4	10	102	44	88
2. Ashford Town	42	25	9	8	75	44	84
3. Waterlooville	42	24	8	10	87	44	80
4. Newport IOW	42	24	6	12	75	58	78
5. Braintree Town	42	24	8	10	93	70	77*
6. Weymouth	42	24	4	14	75	55	76
7. Havant Town	42	23	11	8	73	42	74*
8. Forest Green Rov	42	22	8	12	85	55	74
9. Trowbridge Tn	42	18	8	16	86	51	62
10. Yate Town	42	17	8	17	85	71	59
11. Margate	42	18	5	19	68	62	59
12. Witney Town	42	16	11	15	60	54	59
13. Weston Super Mare	42	16	9	17	78	68	57
14. Cinderford Town	42	16	8	18	74	77	56
15. Fisher 93	42	14	13	15	58	59	55
16. Bashley	42	14	11	17	63	61	53
17. Clevedon Town	42	15	6	21	70	80	51
18. Tonbridge Angels	42	13	10	19	58	79	49
19. Fleet Town	42	14	5	23	58	79	47
20. Fareham Town	42	12	5	25	71	97	41
21. Erith & Belve	42	4	4	34	38	111	16
22. Poole Town	42	0	1	41	17	188	1

** Braintree Town 3pts deducted, Havant Town 6pts deducted*

LEADING LEAGUE & CUP GOALSCORERS

M Buglione	Margate	34	P Odey	Fareham Town	33
D Mitchell	Trowbridge Town	31	D Arter	Ashford Town	27
W Falana	Braintree Town	27	S Tate	Waterloovile	25
C Moore	Forest Grn Rovs	24	E Fearon	Newport IOW	23
D Powell	Weymouth	22	T Planck	Sittingbourne	21
S Lovell	Sittingbourne	20			

SOUTHERN DIVISION RESULTS CHART 1995-96

HOME TEAM	1	2	3	4	5	6	7	8	9	10	11	12	13	14	15	16	17	18	19	20	21	22
1. Ashford Town	*	1-4	7-1	4-0	2-1	2-0	2-1	1-0	1-0	3-0	1-1	2-0	4-2	1-0	0-0	0-0	1-0	3-2	2-2	1-0	2-0	4-2
2. Bashley	2-0	*	0-1	1-0	2-0	2-1	3-0	2-0	2-1	1-2	2-3	3-0	0-1	2-0	0-1	0-2	1-1	2-2	1-2	2-3	0-1	1-2
3. Braintree T	1-1	2-2	*	3-2	2-0	4-0	1-0	2-1	4-0	1-4	3-0	3-0	1-2	7-1	0-7	5-2	1-0	1-1	2-2	2-1	2-1	4-4
4. Cinderford T	0-1	3-0	3-4	*	2-0	3-1	1-2	0-1	3-2	2-1	1-2	1-3	2-2	7-1	3-2	1-2	2-0	0-4	1-1	3-4	1-0	3-3
5. Clevedon Tn	4-2	1-2	1-0	2-2	*	1-2	4-1	2-1	0-2	1-1	2-2	1-4	5-3	3-0	2-3	0-2	1-3	2-0	1-2	2-3	4-3	1-1
6. Erith & Belv	2-3	1-1	1-4	2-2	1-2	*	3-4	1-3	0-3	0-3	1-3	0-2	2-4	4-1	0-3	0-1	0-5	1-3	0-0	3-4	0-5	2-1
7. Fareham Tn	0-3	1-2	1-2	2-1	2-1	5-1	*	0-2	0-3	2-2	1-3	2-1	2-7	5-0	0-2	3-3	0-3	0-3	0-3	1-1	3-3	2-1
8. Fisher '93	0-0	3-3	2-2	2-2	3-0	4-3	2-2	*	2-2	1-1	0-0	0-2	0-1	4-0	0-2	0-3	1-2	3-0	1-2	1-2	1-0	3-3
9. Fleet Town	3-2	2-2	2-4	1-2	1-2	3-0	3-2	1-2	*	0-3	0-3	0-4	1-1	2-1	3-1	1-1	2-1	0-3	2-1	0-1	1-2	3-1
10. Forest Green	2-3	2-1	1-1	3-1	5-2	2-0	4-5	2-2	4-0	*	0-1	3-1	5-2	6-0	2-0	3-0	2-2	0-3	4-0	2-0	0-0	1-0
11. Havant Town	2-1	1-2	0-2	0-1	0-0	1-0	4-3	1-2	1-0	1-1	*	2-0	0-5	7-1	2-2	4-1	2-0	4-2	3-3	2-0	5-1	1-0
12. Margate	0-1	2-1	0-1	1-1	1-2	1-0	2-0	2-2	3-1	3-1	3-2	*	2-2	6-0	1-2	2-2	1-0	0-1	1-0	2-1	1-1	2-1
13. Newport IOW	2-1	1-1	3-0	1-3	3-1	1-0	1-0	4-2	1-0	0-1	0-2	1-0	*	1-0	3-1	2-0	1-3	2-1	0-3	2-0	0-0	1-0
14. Poole Town	0-4	0-0	1-6	0-4	0-3	2-4	0-3	0-1	0-3	1-2	0-3	1-2	0-5	*	0-5	0-1	0-8	0-3	1-8	2-4	1-3	0-8
15. Sittingbourn	4-0	2-2	2-1	4-0	5-1	1-0	3-0	3-0	3-2	5-1	0-1	3-1	1-2	8-0	*	3-1	2-1	1-2	2-0	2-1	4-2	0-1
16. Tonbridge	2-1	2-3	1-0	0-3	1-2	1-0	1-8	1-1	1-2	2-3	1-1	1-2	1-2	5-0	1-4	*	3-1	2-2	3-2	0-1	0-0	3-4
17. Trowbridge T	1-1	5-2	1-5	2-3	1-1	4-0	5-0	1-1	4-0	2-0	0-0	3-1	0-2	9-1	3-0	1-1	*	0-2	1-0	1-2	0-1	2-2
18. Waterlooville	1-1	2-2	3-0	3-0	2-1	6-0	1-0	0-1	3-0	1-2	0-0	0-4	1-1	8-0	1-0	4-1	1-2	*	3-1	1-0	3-2	1-1
19. Weston S M	1-1	2-0	2-3	2-0	3-2	3-0	1-6	0-1	2-3	0-3	0-0	4-3	5-0	7-0	1-2	2-0	1-5	0-3	*	1-1	2-2	6-1
20. Weymouth	0-2	2-0	5-1	2-0	2-4	3-1	2-1	2-0	2-1	2-1	1-2	2-0	2-1	6-0	0-3	1-2	0-1	2-1	2-2	*	1-0	1-0
21. Witney Town	1-2	2-1	2-3	4-1	2-1	1-1	5-1	1-0	1-1	1-0	0-0	3-2	2-0	2-0	0-2	1-1	2-1	0-1	0-1	1-1	*	2-0
22. Yate Town	0-1	0-3	1-1	4-1	1-4	4-0	2-0	1-2	3-1	2-0	2-1	3-2	3-0	8-0	2-2	4-0	2-1	1-3	2-1	1-5	3-0	*

Formed: 1947

BASHLEY

The Bash

Bashley FC 95-96: *Photo - Andrew Chitty*

Chairman: Trevor Adams **Vice Chairman:** Richard Eastwood **President:** Len Farebrother
Secretary: Ray Murphy, Flat 10, Richmond Court, 122 Richmond Park Rd, Bournemouth BH8 8TH (01202 517607).
Manager: Frank Whitman **Asst Manager/Coach:** Paul Arnold.
Commercial Mgr: David Groom **Physio:** Kim Sturgess. **Newsline:** 0891-424 112.
Press Officer: Tony Adams (01425 613859)
Ground: Recreation Ground, Bashley, Hants BH25 5RY (01425 620280)
Directions: A35 Lyndhurst towards Christchurch, turn left down B3058 towards New Milton, ground on left in Bashley village. Half hour walk from New Milton (BR) station
Capacity: 4,250 **Cover:** 1,200 **Seats:** 200 **Floodlights:** Yes **Metal Badges:** Yes
Colours: Yellow & black **Change colours:** Blue & white.
Club Shop: Open matchdays - contact Mrs L Murphy (address as secretary).
Club Sponsors: Sport livewire UK Ltd.
Previous Leagues: Bournemouth 50-83/ Hants 83-86/ Wessex 86-89.
Midweek home matchday: Tuesday
Record Attendance: 3,500 v Emley, F.A. Vase S.F. 1st Leg 1987-88
Best FA Cup season: 2nd Rd Proper,1994-95(Lost0-1 v Swansea City)
Record win: 21-1 v Co-operative (A), Bournemouth League, 1964.
Record defeat: 2-20 v Air Speed (A), Bournemouth League, 1957.
Record Fee Paid: £7,500.
Record Fee Received: £5,000 from Havant Town for John Wilson, 1990.
Past Players who have progressed into The Football League: Wayne Brown (Bristol City, 1994).
Clubhouse: Usual licensing hours. Snacks available.
Record Goalscorer: Colin Cummings
Record Appearances: John Bone
94-95 Captain: Andy Bye.
94-95 P.o.Y.: Jimmy Sheppard.
94-95 Top scorer: Richie Paskins. **Local Newspapers:** Bournemouth Echo, Southern Pink, New Milton Advertiser.
Local Radio Stations: 2CR Solent, Ocean Sound.
Honours: Southern Lg Southern Division 89-90 (Lg Cup SF 89-90), Wessex Lg 86-87 87-88 88-89, Hants Lg Div 3 84-85, Hants Lg Combination 88-89, Russell Cotes Cup 88-89 90-91 92-93, FA Vase SF 87-88 (QF 88-89), FA Tphy 2nd Rd 91-92.

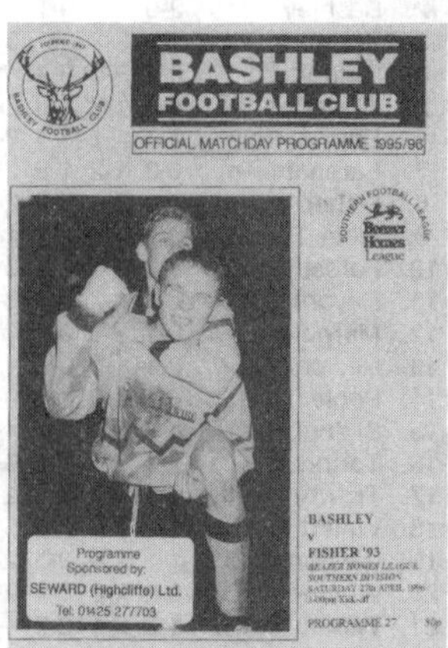

PROGRAMME DETAILS:
Pages: 36 **Price:** 70p
Editor: Mark Barlow
(c/o Bashley FC)

1883 BUCKINGHAM TOWN The Robins

Buckingham Town FC

Chairman: Gerald Sean **President:** Robin Taylor
Secretary: Philip Bettles,20 Lime Avenue,Buckingham MK18 7JJ(01280 823076)
Manager/Coach: Steve Cunley **Assistant Manager/Physio:** John Horsley
Press Officer: Vic West **Commercial Manager:** Trevor Millington
Ground: Ford Meadow, Ford Street, Buckingham (01280 816257).
Directions: From town centre take Aylesbury (A413) road and turn right at Phillips Garage after 400yds. By public transport: train to Milton Keynes, then bus to Buckingham.
Capacity: 4,000 **Cover:** 420 **Seats:** 420 **Floodlights:** Yes **Metal Badges:** Yes.
Club Shop: Yes, selling scarves, hats, badges and programmes. Contact Dave Newton at ground.
Colours: All red **Change colours:** All blue. **Sponsors:** Wipac.
Previous Lges: Aylesbury & Dist/ Nth Bucks/ Hellenic 53-57/ Sth Mids 57-74/ Utd Co's 74-86.
Midweek matchday: Tuesday 7.30pm
Reserve Team's League: None.
Record Attendance: 2,451 v Orient, FA Cup 1st Rd 84-85.
Best FA Cup season: 1st Rd 84-85.
League clubs defeated in FA Cup: None.
Record Fees - Paid: £7,000 for Steve Jenkins (Wealdstone, 1992)
Received: £1,000 for Terry Shrieves (Kettering).
Players progressing to Football League: None.
Clubhouse: Open every evening 7-11pm (4-11pm on Sat) and weekend lunchtimes 12-3pm. Concert room with stage for hire, capacity 150. Bingo, dominoes, ladies and mens darts, pool. Rolls ect available matchdays only.
95-96 Captain: Barry Grant Jess Mansfield.
95-96 Players P.o.Y.: Mike Marshall
95-96 Supporters P.o.Y.: Jess Mansfield
95-96 Top scorer: Mike Marshall.
Local Newspapers: Buckingham Advertiser, MK Citizen, Herald & Post.
Local Radio Stations: Chiltern Radio, Fox FM (102.6 fm), 3 Counties Radio.
Newsline: 0891 884 431.
Hons: FA Vase QF 90-91 92-93, Southern Lg Southern Div 90-91, Utd Co's Lg 83-84 85-86 (Div 1 R-up 75-76, Div 2 R-up 74-75, Lg Cup 83-84, Div 2 Cup R-up 74-75), Nth Bucks Lg(8) 24-25 28-29 33-34 35-37 38-39 48-49 49-50, Aylesbury & Dist. Lg 02-03, Berks & Bucks Snr Cup 83-84, Berks & Bucks Jnr Cup 02-03 48-49 (R-up 38-39 72-73), Berks & Bucks Minor Cup 32-33, Buckingham Snr Charity Cup(18) 32-33 35-36 37-38 47-50 52-55 72-73 75-77 78-79 80-81 83-87 (R-up 31-32 36-37 39-40 73-74 81-82).

THE ROBINS 1995/96 Season
Programme sponsored by

PROGRAMME DETAILS:
Pages: 32 **Price:** 80p.
Editor: Vic West

CINDERFORD TOWN

Formed: 1922 Town

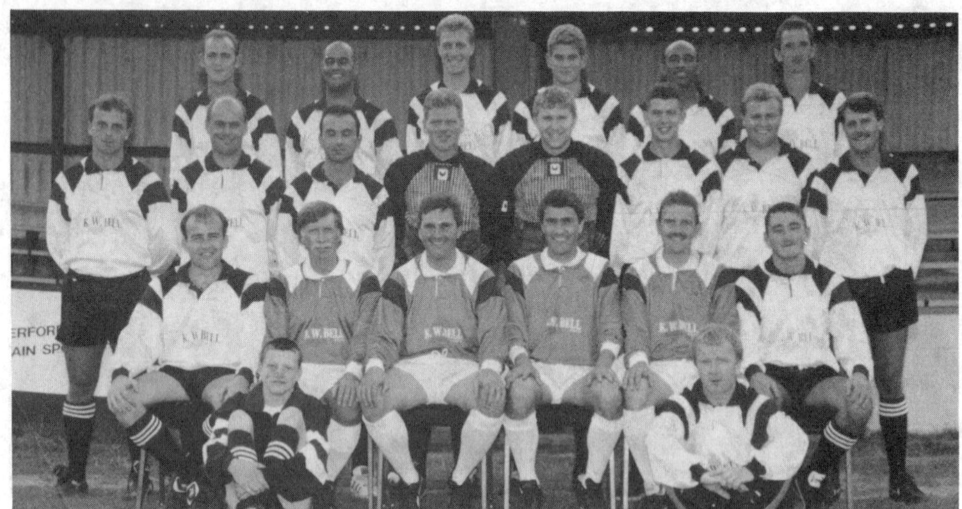

Back Row (L-R): Paul Wilband, John Hamilton, David Cole, Danny Hill, Eston Chiverton, Terry Price. Middle Row: Chris Smith, Chris Price, Richard Criddle, Russell Bowles, Terry Stevenson, Mark Lee, Gareth Howells, Russell Wilton. Front Row: Steve Crouch, Brian Godfrey (Coach), Tim Harris (Mgr), Clive Boxall (Asst Mgr), Keith Marfell (Physio), Dean Powell. Foreground: Andrew Jenkins (Kit), Adrian Harris.

Chairman: A Saunders **Vice Chairman:** R.Reed. **President:** S Watkins.
Secretary: C Warren, 9c Tusculum Way, Mitcheldean, Glos GL17 0HZ (01594 543065).
Manager: Tim Harris **Physio:** Keith Marfell.
Press Officer: A Peacey **Asst.Manager & Coach:** Chris Hyde.
Ground: The Causeway, Hilldene, Cinderford, Glos (01594 822039).
Directions: From Gloucester take A40 to Ross-on-Wye, then A48 - Chepstow. In 10 miles turn right at Elton garage onto A4151 signed Cinderford, thru Littledean, up steep hill, right at crossroads, second left into Latimer Rd. Ground 5 mins walk from town centre.
Capacity: 3,500 **Cover:** 1,000 **Seats:** 250 **Floodlights:** Yes
Club colours: White & Black. **Change colours:** Jade/Red.
Club Shop: Souvenirs: Club badges (£2), ties, mugs etc. Programme exchanges welcome - contact secretary.
Clubhouse: Open every day. 2 bars, kitchen, 2 skittle alleys, darts, dancehall, committee room.
Record Attendance: 4,850 v Minehead, Western League, 1955-56.
Midweek matchday: Tuesday. **Reserve's League:** None.
Previous Leagues: Western 46-59/ Glos Northern Snr 60-62/ Warwickshire Combination 63-64/ West Midlands 65-69/ Gloucestershire County 70-73 85-89/ Midland Comb. 74-84.Hellenic 90-95.
Best F.A. Cup Results: 2nd Rd v Gravesend 1996
Captain 95-96: Clive Boxall.
Top Scorer 95-96: Danny Hill.
Players P.o.Y. 95-96: Clive Boxall.
Supporters P.o.Y.: Brad Thomas.
Hons: Hellenic Lg Premier Champions 94-95,Premier Lg.Cup 94-95,Hellenic Floodlit Cup 93-94, Div 1 90-91, Glos Northern Snr Lg Div 1 38-39 60-61 (R-up(6) 35-37 61-63 66-67 80-81), Nth Glos Lg Div 1 38-39 60-61, Glos Snr Amtr Cup (Nth)(6) 49-50 54-56 68-69 70-71 76-77 (R-up 34-35 57-58 80-81), Western Lg Div 2 56-57, Warwickshire Comb. 63-64, W Mids Lg Prem Div Cup 68-69, Glos Jnr Cup (Nth) 80-81, Midland Comb. 81-82, Glos Co. Lg R-up 69-70 71-72 73-74, Glos F.A. Tphy R-up 92-93.Hungerford Cup 94-95

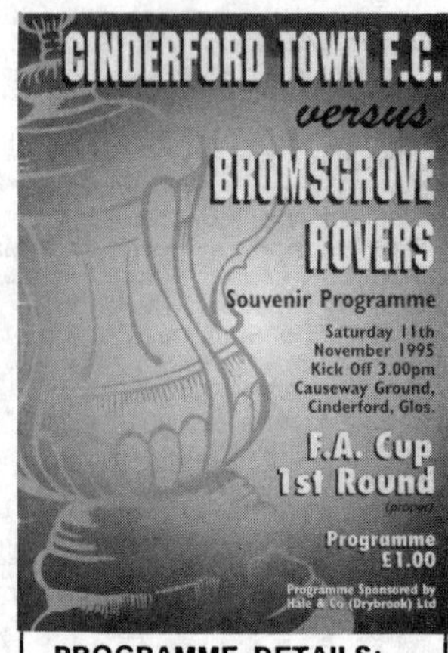

PROGRAMME DETAILS:
Pages: 50 **Price:** £1
Editor: M Bradley/C Warren

Founded: 1889

CIRENCESTER TOWN

Ciren

Cirencester Town FC 95-96:

Chairman: Stephen Abbley. **President:**
Secretary: Brian Davis, 97 Golden Farm Rd, Cirencester, Glos GL7 1DG (01285 654274).
Manager: Ray Baverstock **Coach:** Gary Goodwin **Physio:** Jim Saunders
Ground: The Stadium, Smithsfield, Chesterton Lane, Cirencester (01285 645783).
Directions: Follow By-pass towards Bristol. The ground is signposted on the left approx quarter of a mile from town. 3 miles from Kemble (BR).
Seats: 236 **Cover:** 500 **Capacity:** 3,000 **Floodlights:** Yes **Club Shop:**
Colours: Red & black/black/red **Change colours:** All blue.
Sponsor: Swindon Computing Services
Press Officer: Dave Barnes
Midweek Matchday: Tuesday
Youth League: Allied Count. S W Counties
Record Attendance: 2,500 v Fareham 1969
Previous Leagues: Hellenic Premier Lge
Clubhouse: Open 5 nights
95-96 Captain:
95-96 Top Scorer:
95-96 P.o.Y.:
Honours: Glos Sen Amt Cup 89-90; Hellenic Div One Chall Cup 90-91; Hellenic Prem Lge 95-96, Cup 95-96; Glos County Cup 95-96.

PROGRAMME DETAILS:
Pages: Yes **Price:** £1
Editor:

Formed: 1880

CLEVEDON TOWN

The Seasiders

Back Row (L-R); Matthew Walker, Pete Bailey, Jeff Meacham, Lee Jefferies, Steve Weaver, Ian Weston, Richard Hill, Nathan Rudge, Dave Singleton. Front; Andy Hogg, Toby Jackson, Paul Terry, Steve Lester, Eddie Gregg, Matt Parkinson, Wayne Noble, Dave Palmer.

President: J.Croft. **Chairman:** P.Haden.
Secretary: Mike Williams, 34 Robinia Walk, Whitchurch, Bristol BS14 0SH (01275 833835).
Manager: Steve Fey **Physio:** T.Banks.
Ground: Hand Stadium, Davis Lane, Clevedon (01275 341919 ground 341641 office).
Directions: M5 Jct 20 - follow signs for Clevedon Town Sports Complex; first left into Central Way (at island just after motorway), 1st left at mini-r'bout into Kenn Rd, 2nd left Davis Lane; ground half mile on right. Or from Bristol (B3130) left into Court Lane (opposite Clevedon Court), turn right after 1 mile, ground on left. Nearest BR station: Nailsea & Backwell. Buses from Bristol.
Seats: 300 **Cover:** 1,600 **Capacity:** 3,650 **Floodlights:** Yes
Club colours: Blue . **Change colours:** Yellow. **Metal Badges:** Yes.
Midweek Matches: Tuesday. **Reserve Team's League:** Somerset Senior.
Club Sponsors: T B A
Club Shop: Yes, selling all types of souvenirs, programmes and replica kit. Exchanges welcome: Contact J Anderson.
Previous Leagues: Weston & District/ Somerset Senior/ Bristol Charity/ Bristol & District/ Bristol Suburban/ Western 74-93.
Previous Grounds: Dial Hill (til early 1890's)/ Teignmouth Road (til 1991).
Previous Names: Clevedon FC, Ashtonians (clubs merged in 1974).
Record Gate: 1,295 v Tiverton Town, Western League Premier Division 17/4/93 *(At Teignmouth Road: 2,300 v Billingham Synthonia, FA Amateur Cup, 52-53).*
Record win: 18-0 v Dawlish Town (H), Western League Premier Division 24/4/93.
Best FA Cup season: 3rd Qual. Rd second replay 92-93 (lost 2-4 after two 1-1 draws with Newport AFC).
Football league Clubs defeated in FA Cup: None.
Best FA Amateur Cup season: 3rd Round Proper, 52-53.
Best FA Vase season: 5th Round 92-93 (lost 0-1 at Canvey Island).
Clubhouse: Open every day and evening. Separate function suite & lounge bar. Hot food available. Matchday refreshment bar within ground sells confectionary, teas & hot food.
95-96 Captain: Dave Singleton.
95-96 P.o.Y.: Toby Jackson/Matt Walker
95-96 Top scorer: Gareth Morgan
Local Radio Stations: Radio Bristol
Local Newspapers: South Avon Mercury
Hons: Western League 92-93 (R-up 91-92, League Cup R-up 92-93), Bristol Charity League, Somerset Snr Cup 01-02 04-05 28-29 76-77, Somerset Snr League Div 1(reserves) 92-93.

PROGRAMME DETAILS:
Pages: 36 **Price:** 75p
Editor: Terry Colley.
(c/o club)

DARTFORD

1888 **DARTFORD** Darts

Dartford celebrate with The Kent Senior Trophy *Photo - Roger Turner*

Chairman: D M Skinner **Vice-Chairman:** R W Mace **Secretary:** Mike Brett-Smith, 83 Wellcome Avenue, Dartford, Kent DA1 5JL. Tel. 01322 277243.
Manager: Tony Burman **Assistant-Manager:** Trevor Timms **Coach:** Dave Wadhams
Physio: Terry Skelton
Ground: Erith & Belvedere FC, Park View, Lower Road, Belvedere, Kent DA17 6DF (0181 311 4444).
Directions: From Dartford bridge follow signs for Crayford to Erith and follow A206. Ground half mile from Erith Blackwall tunnel: head for Abbey Wood and on to Belvedere. Entrance in Station Road, adjoining Belvedere (BR) station. Bus No.469.
Capacity: 1,500 **Cover:** 1,000 **Seats:** 500 **Floodlights:** Yes **Metal Badges:** Yes
Club Shop: Yes, open matchdays. Mail Order: Norman Grimes 01474 815236.
Colours: Black/White halves/Black/Black. **Change colours:** Red & White/White/White.
Previous Leagues: Kent 1894-96, 97-98, 99-1902, 09-14, 21-26, 92-96/ Southern Lg 1896-98, 99-1900, 27-81, 82-84, 86-92/ GMVC 1981-82, 84-86.
Midweek home matchday: Wednesday. **Best FA Trophy season:** Runners-up in 1974.
Best FA Vase season: 1995/96.
Best FA Cup season: 3rd Round Proper 35-36 & 36-37.
League clubs defeated in FA Cup: Cardiff (1935), Exeter (1961), Aldershot (1968).
Players progressing to Football League: Fred Dall (West Ham 1936), Riley Cullum (Charlton 1947), Ted Croker (Charlton 1948), Frank Coombs (Bristol C 1949), James Kelly (Gillingham 1951), Tom Ritchie (Grimsby 1958), Dave Underwood (Watford 1960), Derek Hales (Luton 1972), Andy Hessenthaler (Watford via Redbridge F).
Record Fee Paid: £6,000 for John Bartley (Chelmsford 1988)
Record Fee Received: £25,000 for Andy Hessenthaler (Watford via Redbridge F).
Top scorer 95-96: Dean Bowey
Local Newspapers: Kentish Times, Kentish Independant.
Local Radio Stations: Radio Kent, Radio Thamesmead.
Honours: Southern Lg 1930-31, 31-32, 73-74, 83-84, R-up 87-88, 88-89, Eastern Div 30-31, 31-32, Southern Div 80-81, Southern Lg Div 2 1896-97, Lg Cup 76-77, 87-88, 88-89, Championship Shield 83-84, 87-88, 88-89; Kent Lg 1995-96, Lg Cup 24-25, Kent Snr Cup 29-30, 34-35, 38-39, 69-70, Snr Trophy 95-96, Inter Lg Chall 1974; FA Trophy R-up 1974.

PROGRAMME DETAILS:
Pages: 36 **Price:** 50p
Editor: Mike Brett-Smith

1922 **ERITH & BELVEDERE** Deres

ERITH & BELVEDERE

Desperate defending by Erith & Belvedere against Waterlooville. *Photo - Andrew Chitty.*

Chairman: J McFadden **Vice Chairman:** R E Cowley **President:** L O'Connell.
Secretary: Miss Kellie Discipline,30 Chatsworth Road,Dartford,Kent DQ1 5AT. (01322 275766)
Manager: Tom Hake. **Asst Manager:** **Physio:** Ron Bates
Ground: Park View, Lower Road, Belvedere, Kent DA17 6DF (0181 311 4444).
Directions: From Dartford bridge follow signs for Crayford to Erith and follow A206. Ground half mile from Erith Blackwall tunnel: head for Abbey Wood and on to Belvedere. Entrance in Station Road, adjoining Belvedere (BR) station. Bus No. 469.
Capacity: 1,500 **Cover:** 1,000 **Seats:** 500 **Floodlights:** Yes **Metal Badges:** Yes
Club Shop: Yes, selling programmes, badges and pens.
Colours: Blue & white/Blue/White **Change colours:** All red.
Previous Leagues: Kent 22-29 31-39 78-82/ London 29-31/ Corinthian 45-63/ Athenian 63-78.
Previous Names: Erith FC/ Belvedere & District FC (clubs amalgamated in 1922).
Midweek home matchday: Tuesday **Reserves' League:** None.
Record Attendance: 8,000 v Coventry City, FA Cup First Round Proper 1932.
Best FA Trophy season: Third Qualifying Round second replay 89-89.
Best FA Vase season: Third Round 76-77.
Best FA Cup season: First Round Proper 24-25 32-33.
League clubs defeated in FA Cup: None.
Players progressing to Football League: Geoff Bray (Oxford Utd 1971), Tommy Ord (Chelsea 1972).
Clubhouse: Licensed social club open matchdays and weekends. Cold snacks available available, separate canteen provides hot food on matchdays.
95-96 Captain: **95-96 P.o.Y.:**
95-96 Top scorer:
Local Newspapers: Kentish Times, Kentish Independant.
Local Radio Stations: Radio Kent, Radio Thamesmead.
Honours: FA Amat Cup R-up 23-24 37-38, Athenian Lge Div 1 R-up 70-71 (Lge Cup 73-74, Memorial Shield 67-68), Corinthian Lge R-up 62-63 (Lge Cup 47-48 48-49 49-50), Kent Lge 81-82 (Lge Cup R-up 81-82), London Sen Cup 44-45 (R-up 38-39), Kent Amat Cup 6, (R-up 4), Bromley Hospital Cup 38-39, Kent Floodlit Lge R-up 67-68, Kent Interm Cup R-up 90-91, Kent Jun Cup 67-68, Essex & Herts Border Comb Cup 73-74, Kent County Yth Lge 90-91, Kent Yth Cup 87-88.

PROGRAMME DETAILS:
Pages: 30 **Price:** 50p
Editor: Peter Bird

FAREHAM TOWN

Formed: 1947 The Town

Fareham Town *Photo - Roy Rogers*

Chairman: Chris Solen. **President:** Vacant.
Secretary: K F Atkins, 4 Cedar Close, Elson, Gosport PO12 4AT (01705 583049).
Manager: Phil Simkin **Asst Manager/Coach:** None
Press Officer: M Willis **Physio:** James McKay
Commercial Manager: None.
Ground: Cams Alders, Highfield Avenue, Fareham, Hants PO14 1JA (01329 231151).
Directions: From Fareham station follow A27 towards Southampton and take second left into Redlands Avenue. Turn right at Redlands Inn then left into Highfields Avenue.
Capacity: 5,500 **Cover:** 500 **Seats:** 450 **Metal Badges:** Yes
Colours: Red/black/red **Change colours:** All white.
Sponsors: Hellyers Coaches.
Club Shop: Yes, selling programmes, scarves & fanzines.
Previous Name: Fareham FC **Previous Leagues:** Portsmouth 47-49/ Hants 49-79.
Previous Ground: Bath Lane.
Midweek home matchday: Wednesday **Reserve Team:** None.
Record Gate: 2,650 v Wimbeldon, FA Cup 1965. *(at Southampton F.C.; 6,035 v Kidderminster Harriers, FA Trophy Semi Final Second leg 86-87).*
Best FA Cup season: 1st Rd replay 88-89 (lost 2-3 at home to Torquay after 2-2 draw).
League clubs defeated in FA Cup: None.
Record Fees - Paid: £1,000 for Peter Baxter (Poole)
Received: £43,000 for David Leworthy (Spurs).
Players progressing to Football League: Ray Hiron (Portsmouth 1964), John Hold (AFC Bournemouth), David Leworthy (Spurs 1984), Steve Claridge (AFC Bournemouth 1984), Darren Foreman (Barnsley), Kevin Bartlett (Cardiff City 1986), Domenyk Newman (Reading 1990).
Clubhouse: Open every evening except Sundays.
95-96 Captain:
95-96 P.o.Y.:
95-96 Top scorer:
Local Newspapers: Portsmouth Evening News, Southampton Evening Echo.
Hons: FA Trophy SF 86-87, FA Amateur Cup 2nd Rd 63-64 66-67 73-74, Hants Lg(8) 59-60 62-67 72-73 74-75 (R-up 55-56 60-61 67-68 71-72 76-77 78-79, Div 2 R-up 52-53, Eastern Div 24-25, Div 3 East 49-50), Hants Snr Cup 56-57 62-63 67-68 92-93, Russell Cotes Cup(6) 64-65 72-77, Gosport War Memorial Cup, SW Co's Cup(2), Pickford Cup(2),

PROGRAMME DETAILS:
Pages: 36 **Price:** 50p
Editor: Roy Grant

Formed: 1908 **FISHER ATHLETIC (LONDON)** The Fish

Fisher'93 FC;

President: Barry Albin-Dyer **Life President:** Lord Mellish **General Manager:** TBA
Secretary: M J Wakefield, 146 Layard Square, Drummond Rd, Bermondsey SE16 0JG (0171 237 2819).
Manager: Neil Norman **Coachs:** Micky Stead & Ian Dawes
Press Officer: **Physio:** T J Salih **Commercial Co-ordinator:** P Merrett
Ground: The Surrey Docks Stadium, Salter Road, London SE16 1LQ (0171 231 5144. Fax: 0171 2520060).
Directions: 8 minutes walk from Rotherhithe (tube), 2 miles from London Bridge (main line). Buses 188, P11, P14.
Capacity: 5,300 **Cover:** 4,283 **Seats:** 400 **Floodlights:** Yes **Club Shop:** Yes.
Colours: Black & white stripes/black/black **Change colours:** All red. **Metal Badges:** Yes
Previous Leagues: Parthenon/ West Kent/ Kent Amateur/ London Spartan 76-82/ Southern 82-87/ GMV Conference 87-91.
Midweek home games: Tuesday **Reserve Team's League:** Kent Midweek.
Club Sponsors: Intercell Communications **Record Gate:** 4,283 v Barnet, GMV Conference 4/5/91.
Previous Names: Fisher Athletic 08-93, Fisher'93 93-96.
Previous Ground: London Road, Mitcham.
Record win: 7-0 v Lewes Sept 95, FA Cup
Record defeat: 0-6 v Salisbury, 21/8/93.
Best FA Cup season: 1st Rd 84-85 (0-1 at home to Bristol City), 88-89 (0-4 at Bristol Rovers).
League Clubs Defeated in FA Cup: None.
Record Fees: Paid: £500 each for Sean Devine & Jamie Kempster (Erith & Belvedere 1995)
Received: £45,000 for Paul Gorman (Charlton 1991)
Players progressing to The Football League: John Bumstead (Chelsea), Trevor Aylott (Bournemouth), Paul Shinners (Orient 1984), Dave Regis (Notts County - via Barnet), Paul Gorman (Charlton 1991), Sean Devine (Barnet via Okonia Nicossia), George Barry (Leyton Orient).
Clubhouse: (0171 252 0590). Luxury clubhouse, Vice-President's club. Bar open 11am-3 & 5-11pm. Sandwiches, pies, sausage rolls, chips etc available.
cold food.
Club Record Scorer: Paul Shinners 205
Club Record Appearances: Dennis Sharp 720.
95-96 Captain: _Paul Robets.
95-96 P.o.Y.: Seãn Devine
95-96 Top scorer: Sean Devine 28
Honours: Southern Lg 86-87 (R-up 83-84, Southern Div 82-83, Lg Cp 84-85, Championship Cup 87-88, Merit Cup), London Spartan Lg 80-81 81-82 (R-up 78-79, Senior Div 77-78, Div 2 R-up 76-77), Parthenon Lg 61-62 (Lg Cup 63-64 65-66), Kent Amateur Lg 73-74 74-75 (R-up 72-73), London Senior Cup 84-85 87-88 88-89, London Intermediate Cup 59-60 (R-up 75-76), Kent Senior Cp 83-84, Kent Senior Trophy 81-82 82-83, Surrey Intermediate Cup 61-62, FA Trophy 3rd Rd 3rd replay 87-88, FA Vase 2nd Rd replay 82-83.

PROGRAMME DETAILS:
Pages: 32 **Price:** 70p
Editor: John O'Grady

Formed: 1947

FLEET TOWN

The Blues

Back Row (L-R); Tony Phillips, Steve Hyde, Paul Woller, Kevin Betsy, Paul Mills,, Andy Taylor, Vernon Pratt, Russ Watkinson, Neil Roberts, Jess Bone (Asst Mgr). Front; Jamie Horton, Mark Frampton, Chris Ferrett, Derek Holloway, Ricky Jones, Derek Traylen, Steve Kerbey.

Photo - Andrew Chitty

Chairman: Anthony Cherry **Vice Chairman:** Bob Worthington **President:** Les Hocking
Secretary: Stephen Hyde, 163 Quilter Road, Brighton Hill, Basingstoke, Hants RG22 4HE. Tel.01256 59675.
Manager: Alan Manville **Assistant Manager:**
Coach: **Physio:** Steve Hyde
Ground: Calthorpe Park, Crookham Road, Fleet, Hants (01252 623804).
Directions: M3 jct 4A, into Fleet past BR station to town centre. Ground clearly marked at Oatsheaf pub crossroads.
Seats: 200 **Cover:** 250 **Capacity:** 2,000 **Floodlights:** Yes **Founded:** 1890.
Midweek Matches: Tuesday **Sponsors:** Hart Dist Council
Colours: Dark & Pale Blue. **Change colours:** Yellow & Blue.
Club Shop: Yes.
Clubhouse: Yes. Hot & cold food served.
Reserves' League: Suburban
Previous Lges: Hants/ Athenian/ Combined Co's/ Chiltonian.
Record win: 7-0
Record transfer paid: £1,500 to Farnborough, 1991.
Club Record Scorer: John Smith.
Club record appearances: Steve Hodge/ Paul Dear.
Top Scorer 95-96: John Smith.
Hons: Wessex Lg 93-94, Lg Cup R-up 92-93, Hants Lg Div 2 R-up 61-62 (Div 1 R-up 60-61), Aldershot Snr Cup 92-93, Simpsonair Challenge Shield 1993, Hants Yth Lg Div 3 92-93.

PROGRAMME DETAILS:
Pages: 20 **Price:** 50p
Editor: Secretary

1890

FOREST GREEN ROVERS

Rovers

Forest Green's striker Gary Marshall whose career was nearly ended by serious burns after a road accident in April 1996

Chairman: Trevor Horsley **President:** E.G.Smith.
Managing Director: Colin Peake, Club Admin Office, Unit 14 Springfield Bus. Centre. Stonehouse, Gloucester GL10 3SX (01453 791232, Fax 791305)
Manager: Frank Gregan **Asst Manager:** Tommy Callinan **Physio:** Dave Tyrrell.
Press Officer: Heather Cook (01453 823281, Mob 0385 940981)
Ground: 'The Lawn', Nympsfield Road, Forest Green, Nailsworth, Glos. GL6 0ET (01453 834860).
Directions: About 4 miles south of Stroud on A46 to Bath. In Nailsworth turn into Spring Hill off mini r'bout - ground approximately half mile up hill on left. The nearest BR station is Stroud.
Capacity: 3132. **Cover:** 980 **Seats:** 332
Floodlights: Yes **Club Shop:** Yes - open matchdays.
Colours: Black & white stripes/black/red **Change colours:** All Yellow.
Sponsors: Sponsors Cind.
Previous Lges: Stroud & Dist. 1890-1921/ Glos Northern Snr 22-67/ Glos Co. 67-73 /Hellenic 73-82.
Previous Name: Stroud FC, 1989-92. **Previous Ground:** None.
Midweek matchday: Wed **Youth League:** Glos Co. Yth.
Record Attendance: 2,200 v Wolvers, floodlight inauguration 81.
Best FA Cup season: 3rd Qualifying Rd 87-88.
Best FA Trophy season: 3rd Round Proper 90-91.
Best FA Vase season: Winners 81-82.
Players progressing to Football League: G Rogers/K Gill (Newport Cnty 85), M England (Bristol Rov 85).
Clubhouse: (01453 833295). Bar and lounge, open every night.
95-96 Captain: Paul Underhill. **95-96 P.o.Y.:** Don Forber
95-96 Top scorer: Christian Moore
Local Newspapers: Stroud News & Journal, Gloucester Citizen.
Local Radio Stations: Severn Sound, BBC Radio Gloucestershire.
Hons: FA Vase 81-82, Hellenic Lg 81-82, Gloucs Nthn Sen Lg 37-38 49-50 50-51, Gloucs Sen Cup 84-85 85-86 86-87, Gloucs Sen Amat Cup (N) 26-27 45-46 71-72 75-76 77-78, Gloucs Sen Prof Cup 84-85 85-86.

PROGRAMME DETAILS:
Pages: 36 **Price:** 60p
Editor: Julie Davis.

Formed: 1958

HAVANT TOWN

Havant Town FC 96-97: *Photo - Andrew Chitty*

Chairman: Ray Jones **President:** George Jones.
Directors: Derek Pope, Paul Cummins, Ian Craig, Trevor Brock.
Secretary/Press Officer: Kevin Moore, 68 St Ronan's Rd, Southsea, Hampshire. PO4 OPX(01705 731530)
Manager: Tony Mount **Physio:** Gary Buckner
Ground: West Leigh Park, Martin Road, West Leigh, Havant PO9 5TH (0705 470918).
Directions: Take B2149 to Havant off the A27 (B2149 Petersfield Rd if coming out of Havant). 2nd turning off dual carriageway into Bartons Road then 1st right into Martins Road. 1 mile from Havant BR station.
Capacity: 6,000 **Cover:** 1,500 **Seats:** 240 **Floodlights:** Yes **Metal Badges:** Yes
Club Shop: Yes, selling various souvenirs and programmes.
Colours: Yellow & Black/Black/Black **Change colours:** Black & White/Black/Black **Sponsors:** G. A. Day.
Previous Leagues: Portsmouth 58-71/ Hants 71-86/ Wessex 86-91.
Previous Names: Leigh Park/ Havant & Leigh Park.
Previous Grounds: Front Lawn 1958-83.
Midweek home matchday: Wednesday **Reserves' Lge:** Jewson Wessex Combination.
Record Attendance: 3,500 v Wisbech Town, FA Vase QF 85-86.
Best FA Cup season: Third Qualifying Round 92-93 (lost 2-3 at Sittingbourne).
Record win: 10-0 three times; v Sholing Sports (H), FA Vase 4th Rd 85-86, v Portsmouth Royal Navy (H), Wessex League 90-91; v Poole Town, Southern League Southern Division 94-95.
Record defeat: 1-7 v Camberley Town (H), FA Vase 3rd Rd 88-89.
Record Fees - Paid: £5,750 for John Wilson (Bashley, 1990)
Received: £7,000 for Steve Tate (Waterlooville, 1993).
Players progressing to Football League: Bobby Tambling (Chelsea).
Clubhouse: Open every day, lunchtime and evening. 2 bars, function suites, hot & cold food available.
Club Record Goalscorer: Unknown.
Club Record Appearances: Tony Plumbley.
95-96 Captain: **95-96 P.o.Y.:**
95-96 Top scorer:
Local Newspapers: News (Portsmouth)(0705 664488).
Local Radio Stations: Ocean Sound, Radio Solent.
Honours: FA Sunday Cup 68-69, FA Vase QF 85-86, Wessex Lg 90-91 (R-up 88-89), Hampshire Lg Div 3 72-73 (Div 4 71-72), Hampshire Senior Cup R-up 91-92 94-95, Hampshire Intermediate Cup, Hampshire Junior Cup, Russell Cotes Cup 91-92, Portsmouth Senior Cup 83-84 84-85 91-92, Gosport War Memorial Cup 74-75 91-92 92-93 94-95, Southern Counties Floodlit Cup R-up 91-92, Hampshire Floodlit Cup 85-86, Portsmouth Lg.

PROGRAMME DETAILS:
Pages: 24 **Price:** 50p
Editor: Steve Cox
(0705 269072)

Formed: 1896

MARGATE

The Gate

Margate FC's Karl Emerice surrounded by Corinthian-Casuals defenders goes close, FA Cup 1st Rd.
Photo - Peter Lirettoc.

Chairman: Keith Piper **Vice Chairman:** Richard Piper **President:** Mr R W Griffiths
Secretary: K E Tomlinson, 65 Nash Road, Margate CT9 4BT (01843 291040).
Managers: Chris Kinnear **Coach:** Mark Weatherly **Press Officer:** Chairman
Ground: Hartsdown Park, Hartsdown Road, Margate CT9 5QZ (01843 221769).
Directions: A28 into Margate, turn right opposite hospital into Hartsdown Road, proceed over crossroads and ground is on left. Ten mins walk from Margate (BR).
Capacity: 6,000 **Cover:** 3 sides **Seats:** 400 **Floodlights:** Yes **Metal Badges:** Yes
Club Shop: Yes. Progs, books, magazines, fanzines etc. Contact Paul Bates, (01304 367257).
Colours: Royal/royal &white/royal & white **Change colours:** Amber/amber & black/amber
Previous Grounds: Margate College/ Dreamland, Northdown Rd/ Garlinge.
Previous Leagues: Kent 11-23 24-28 29-33 37-38 46-59/ Southern 33-37.
Midweek matchday: Tuesday **Reserve Lge:** Winstonlead Kent Lg. Div 2 **Sponsors:** Westons Dairies.
Previous Name: Thanet Utd 1981-89 **Record Gate:** 14,500 v Spurs, FA Cup 3rd Rd 1973.
League clubs defeated in F.A. Cup: Gillingham 29-30, Queens Park Rangers, Crystal Palace 35-36, Bournemouth & Boscombe Athletic 61-62, Swansea 72-73.
Best FA Cup season: 3rd Rd 72-73 (lost 0-6 to Spurs), 36-37 (lost 1-3 at Blackpool).
Record transfer fees paid: £5,000 for Steve Cuggy (Dover Athletic, 1993)
Record transfer fee received: Undisclosed for Martin Buglione (St Johnstone 92-93).
Players progressing to Football League: J Yeomanson (West Ham 47), D Bing/G Wright (West Ham 51), T Bing (Spurs 56), J Roche (Millwall 57), D Hodgkinson (Man City 61), S Foster (C Palace 61), J Fraser (Watford 62), R Walker (Bournemouth 65), K Bracewell (Bury 66), T Jenkins/R Flannigan (Reading 69-70), M Blyth (Millwall 78), M Buglione (St Johnstone 92).
Clubhouse: Flexible hours, private functions, matchday facilities.
Steward: Pam & Mark Weatherly.
Club Record Goalscorer: Dennis Randall 66 (season 1966-67).
Club Record Appearances: Bob Harrop.
95-96 Captain: Phil Handiford **95-96 P.o.Y.:** Kevin Hudson
95-96 Top scorer: Martin Buglione 38
Local Newspapers: Isle of Thanet Gazette, Thanet Times (01843 221313), Thanet Extra, Adscene.
Local Radio: Radio Kent, Invicta Radio. **Newsline:** 0898 800 665.
Hons: Southern Lg 35-36 (Lg Cp 67-68 (R-up 61-62 74-75), Div 1 62-63 (R-up 66-67), Div 1 Sth 77-78, East Div R-up 33-34, Merit Cp 66-67 77-78, Midweek Sect. 36-37), Kent Lg(4), (R-up 5, Div 2 4, Lg Cp 4), Kent Snr Cup(4), Kent Snr Shield(8), Kent F'lit Cp 62-63 66-67 75-76, FA Tphy 3rd Rd rep 78-79.

PROGRAMME DETAILS:
Pages: 28 **Price:** 80p
Editor: TBA

Formed: 1888

NEWPORT I.O.W.

The Port

Back Row (L-R): Roger Sanders (Kit suplier), Lisa McKinney (Physio), Chris Cheverton (Sec), Kenny Hughes, Clifton Soares, Joe McCormack,Neil Wickens, Andy Wollen, Dave Vale, Nick Williams. Front; Hilton Bunday (Pres), Jamie Webb, Lee Phillips, Chris Male, Stuart Ritchie, Steve Mellor (Mgr), Graeme Gee, Mike McEvoy, Dave Puckett, Adam Barsdell, Alan White (Sthn Vectis).

Chairman: Martin Edwards **Vice Chairman:** Peter Ranger **President:** W H J Bunday.
Secretary/Press Off.: Chris Cheverton, 127 Westhill Road, Ryde, Isle of Wight PO33 1LW (01983 567355).
Manager: Steve Mellor **Asst Manager:** Dave Wakefield **Coach:** Dave Puckett
Commercial Manager: Dave Hiscock. **Physio:** Marcus Elie
Ground: St George's Park, St George's Way, Newport, Isle of Wight PO30 2QH (01983 525027).
Directions: Roads from all ferry ports lead to Coppins Bridge R-about at eastern extremity of town. Take Sandown/Ventnor exit, proceed to small r-about, St George's way is first exit (straight on), ground immediately visible on left. Five minute walk from Newport bus station; along Church Litten (past old ground), turn left then right at r-about.
Capacity: 5,000 **Cover:** 1,000 **Seats:** 300 **Floodlights:** Yes **Metal Badges:** Yes.
Club Shop: Yes, selling clothes, programmes and novelties. Contact M Reader at ground.
Colours: Gold,Blue trim. **Change colours:** All Mauve.
Previous Ground: Church Litten (previously Well's Field) 1888-1988.
Previous Leagues: Isle of Wight 1896-1928/ Hants 28-86/ Wessex 86-90.
Midweek home matchday: Tuesday **Reserve Team's Lge:** Isle of Wight League.
Record Attendance: 2,217 FA Cup 1st Rd Nov 1994 v Aylesbury Utd, *(6,000 v Watford, FA Cup 1st Round 56-57, at Church Litten, old ground)).*
Record win: 14-1, home to Thornycroft Athletic, Hampshire League Division One, 22/12/45.
Record defeat: 2-10, home to Basingstoke Town, Hampshire League Division One, 12/10/68.
Players progressing to Football League: Gary Rowatt (Cambridge City, Everton).
Best FA Cup season: 2nd Rd 35-36 45-46. 1st Rd another eight times; 45-46 52-55 56-59 94-95 95-96.
League clubs defeated in FA Cup: Clapton Orient 45-46.
Record Fees - Paid: £3,000 for Stuart Ritchie (Bashley, May 1991)
Received: £2,250 for Mick Jenkins (Havant, March 1992).
Clubhouse: Open normal licensing hours. 2 bars, full range of hot and cold bar snacks. Buffet inside ground.
Club Record Goalscorer: Eddie Walder.
Club Record Apps: Jeff Austin 540 (69-87).
95-96 Captain: Dave Puckett.
95-96 Player of Year: Dave Puckett.
95-96 Top scorer: Eurshall Fearon.
Local Newspapers: Portsmouth Evening News, I.O.W. County Press, Southampton Evening Echo.
Local Radio Stations: Solent, Isle of Wight Radio, Ocean Sound.
Honours: FA Vase 5th Rd 91-92 93-93, Wessex Lg R-up 89-90 (Comb. 91-92(reserves)), Hants Lg(11),(R-up(7), Div 2 R-up 70-71), Hants Snr Cup(7) 31-33 54-55 60-61 65-66 79-81, Russell Cotes Cup(3) 77-80, Pickford Cup(4) 47-50 52-53, Isle of Wight Snr (Gold) Cup(30) 29-30 35-36 37-38 39-40 44-47 48-49 52-54 55-56 57-58 65-66 67-68 70-76 77-79 80-81 86-88 89-90 91-94 95-96, Hants F'lit Cup 76-77 77-78, Isle of Wight Lg(4) 07-10 23-24, Hants I'mediate Cup 31-32, Hants Comb. Cup 38-39.

PROGRAMME DETAILS:
Pages: **Price:** £1
Editor: Peter Ranger
(01983 526144)

St LEONARDS STAMCROFT

The Blues

Formed: 1971

St Leonards Stamcroft FC

Chairman: Leon Shepperdson **Vice-Chairman:** Terry Henham. **President:** Mrs K Shepperdson
Secretary: Ms.Wynne Mould, 142 Seddlescombe Gdns. St Leonards-on-Sea, East Sussex TN38 0YW (01424 420244).
Manager: Micky Reed **Physio:** Peter Butcher **Coach:** Mike Trusson.
Commercial Mgr: John Huggett (01424 456885) **Press Officer:** Peter High
Ground: The Firs, Elphinstone Road, Hastings, East Sussex (01424 434755).
Directions: Adjacent to Hastings Town FC - see Beazer Homes League section for directions.
Seats: 250 **Cover:** 500 **Capacity:** 2,500 **Floodlights:** Yes
Sponsors: Croft Glass Ltd **Metal Badges:** Yes.
Colours: Blue/white/blue **Change colours:** White/blue/white
Prev. Grounds: Council pitches 71-76/ Pannel Lane, Pett 1971-93.
Record Gate: 1,798v Tiverton Town, F.A.Challenge Vase 4th Rd. 25/8/93. At old ground: 527 v Hastings Town, Sussex Senior Cup Second Round 92-93.
Previous Leagues: Southern Counties Combination/ East Sussex/ Hastings.
Midweek Matchday: Tuesday or Wednesday.
Record win: 10-1 v Portfield (H), Sussex County League Division One 4/12/93.
Record defeat: 2-6 v Pagham (A), Sussex RUR Charity Cup 22/1/94.
Clubhouse: Licensed bar open normal pubhours. Hot foof from tea bar.
Local Newspaper: Hastings Observer.
Club record appearances: Gary Cawkill.
Club Record Scorer: Dean Kewley
95-96 Captain:
95-96 Top Scorer: Keith Miles 52.
94-95 P.o.Y.: Keith Miles.
Hons: Sussex Co. Lg Div 1 R-Up 94-95, Div 2 R-up 92-93 (Div 2 Cup R-up 89-90 90-91, Div 3 R-up, Div 3 Cup R-up, Reserve Section East 92-93), Hastings Snr Invitation Cup 89-90, R-up 95-96. Hastings Intermediate Cup 79-80 81-82 82-83 85-86 86-87 87-88.Sussex R.U.R. Cup Finalists 94-95.

PROGRAMME DETAILS:
Pages: 72 **Price:** 50p
Editor: Peter High
(01424 420244)

TONBRIDGE ANGELS

Founded: 1948

The Angels

Back Row (L-R): Phil Walker, Paul Emblen, Craig Wilkins, Steve Williams, Joe Radford, Alan Tutton, Mark Freeman, Brian Frampton, Bill Roffey (Mgr). Front; Adrian Le Moine, Jason Fenton, Matt Le Moine, Dave Forster, Danny Tindley, Graham Benton, Simon Colbran.

Photo - Toni Jarrett.

Chairman: Nigel Rimmer **Vice Chairman:**
Secretary: Ken Jarrett, 8 Farraday Ride, Tonbridge, Kent. TN10 4RL. (01732 351856)
Manager: Bill Roffey **Physio:** Peter Battell/Chris Dunk **Coach:**
Press Officer: Simon Piper **Commercial Manager:**
Ground: Longmead Stadium, Darenth Avenue, Tonbridge, Kent TN10 3JW (01732 352417/ 358868).
Directions: From Tonbridge BR station, through High Street, north up Shipbourne Rd (A227 Gravesend road) to 2nd mini-r'bout ('The Pinnacles' pub), left into Darenth Avenue, ground at bottom approx. 1 mile at far side of sports ground car park.
Seats: 202 **Cover:** 640 **Capacity:** 5,000 **Metal Badges:** Yes. **Club Shop:** Yes.
Colours: Black & blue/black/black **Change Colours:** All red.
Midweek matchday: Tuesday **Sponsors:** Tonbridge Coachworks
Reserve Team's League: Winstonlead Kent Division Two.
Previous Leagues: Southern 48-89/ Kent 89-93.
Previous Ground: The Angel 48-80.
Previous Names: Tonbridge Angels, Tonbridge F.C., Tonbridge A.F.C.
Record Gate: 1,463 v Yeovil Town, FA Cup 4th Qualifying Round 26/10/91. *At the Angel Ground: 8,236 v Aldershot, FA Cup 1st Round 1951.*
Players progressing to Football League: R Saunders, M McMcDonald, T Burns, I Seymour, G Moseley, T Morgan, Neil Emblen.
Clubhouse: Open Mon-Sat evenings and Sunday lunchtimes. Hot food on matchdays from burger bar.
Club Record Goalscorer: Unknown
Club Record Appearances: Mark Gillham, 520 to date.
95-96 Captain: Alan Tutton
95-96 P.o.Y.: Danny Tingley
95-96 Top scorer: Craig Wickens
Local Newspapers: Kent Messenger, Courier, Sevenoaks Leader.
Local Radio Stations: Invicta, Radio Kent.
Honours: Kent League 94-95 (League Cup(2)), Southern League Cup Runners-up(2)(SF(1)), Kent Senior Cup 64-65 74-75 (Runners-up(2)), Kent Senior Shield 51-52 55-56 57-58 58-59 63-64, FA Cup 1st Rd Proper 50-51 51-52 52-53 67-68 72-73.

PROGRAMME DETAILS:
Pages: 38 **Price:** £1
Editor: Ian White

TROWBRIDGE TOWN

Formed: 1880 | The Bees

Back Row (L-R); Chris Jones, Peter Tagg, Jason Lunt, Ian Harris, Chris Hamblin, Neil Cole, Lee Darby, Jeremy Christopher. Front; Tommy Taylor, Russell Fishlock, David Mitchell, Lee James, Phil Ferns, Darren Lush, Gerry Pearson, Darren Young.

Chairman: A I Moore **Vice Chairman:** C Belcher **President:** A M Townley.
Secretary: Colin Elliott,40 Eastbourne Rd., Trowbridge,Wilts.BA14 7HW(01225 760619)
Manager: Steve Rutter **Asst Manager:** T Parker **Physio:** James Marshall.
Press Officer: A Meaden (01225 755752). **Commercial Manager:** T.B.A..
Ground: County Way, Trowbridge, Wilts BA14 0DB (01225 752076).
Directions: On entering town, follow inner relief road (County Way) signs towards Frome, ground on left, Ground on right if entering from Frome.
Capacity: 5,000 **Cover:** 2,000 **Seats:** 250 **Floodlights:** Yes **Metal Badges:** £1.55
Club Shop: Yes, selling hats, scarves, badges, mugs, sweaters, jumpers, replica kits, programmes.
Colours: Old gold/black/black **Change colours:** All white. **Sponsors:** Bowyers (Wiltshire) Ltd.
Previous Leagues: Somerset Senior/ Trowbridge & Dist/ Western 1892-98 1901-07 13-58/ Wiltshire/ Southern 58-81/ Alliance Premier (GMV Conference) 81-84.
Previous Name: Trowbridge F.C.
Previous Grounds: Timbrell Street 1880-87/ Flower Show Field 87-1923/ Bythesea Rd 23-34.
Midweek matchday: Tuesday. **Reserve Lge:** Wiltshire County.
Record Attendance: 9,009 v Weymouth, F.A 4th Qualifying Rd 49-50.
Best F.A. Cup season: 1st Rd replay (v Brighton) 47-48. 1st Rd 45-46 57-58 63-64.
Record win: 17-1 v Yeovil & Petters **Record defeat:** 0-10 v Barnet.
Record Fees - Paid: £7,000 for John Freegard (Gloucester City, 1991).
Received: £10,000 for Paul Compton (B'mouth),
Players progressing to Football League: A Eisentrager (Bristol C 50), D Townsend (Charlton 50), C Dixon (Cardiff 54), D Pyle/J Meacham (Bristol Rovers 55/87), E Weaver/K Skeen/B Wade (Swindon 61/64/85), P Compton (Bournemouth 80), J Layton (Newport 84), A Feeley (Leicester 84), R Cashley (Chester 85).M Fishlock (Hereford U).
Clubhouse: Open before & after games. Hot & cold snacks.
95-96 Captain: Paul Thorpe. **95-96 P.o.Y.:** Russell Fishlock.
95-96 Top scorer: Dave Mitchell.
Local Newspapers: Wiltshire Times (01225 777292), Bath Evening Chronicle, Western Daily Press.
Local Radio Stations: Radio Bristol, Wilts Radio, Wilts Sound.
Hons: F.A. Vase SF 90-91, F.A. Tphy 1st Rd rep 83-84, F.A. Amateurr Cup 2nd Rd 30-31, Sthn Lg Sthn Div R-up 90-91 (Lg Cup R-up 85-86), Western Lg(7) (R-up 4) Lg Cup 56-57), Wilts Lg Div 2 11-12 30-31(jt)(R-up 5), Trowbridge & Dist Lg(3) 09-11 13-14, Wilts Snr Cup 1884-85 95-96(jt with Swindon T) 97-98 1921-22 25-26 33-34 37-38 (R-up 7), Wilts Prof. Shield(8), Wilts F'lit Lg Cup(3) 91-94, Bristol Charity Cup 25-26, Wilts Jnr Cup 10-11 12-13, Trowbridge & Dist Jnr Cup 19-20, Allen Palmer Cup 23-24 24-25(joint), Swanborough Cup 33-34 34-35 35-36(jt), Somerset Snr Lg 30-31 (R-up 11-12 33-34 35-36), Western Co's F'lit Lg Cup 80-81 85-86, Coronation Cup 92-93.

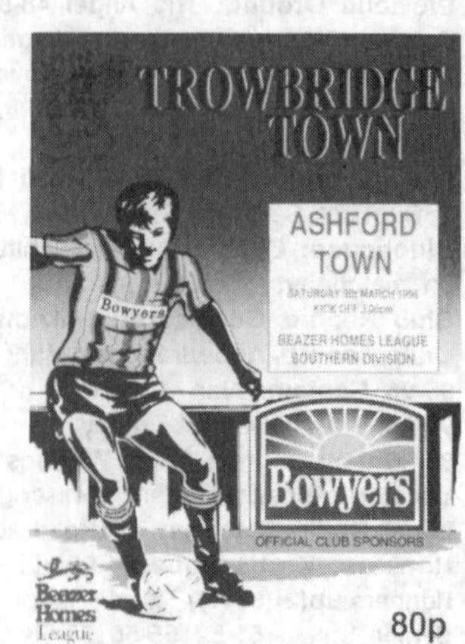

PROGRAMME DETAILS:
Pages: 48 **Price:** 80p
Editor: A Meaden
(01225 752076)

WATERLOOVILLE

Formed: 1905 The Ville

Waterlooville FC 1995-96: *Photo - Andrew Chitty*

Chairman: D.J.Jobe. **Vice Chairman:** K L Ashman **President:** M Hibberd
Secretary: P Elley, 139 Chichester Rd, North End, Portsmouth, Hampshire PO2 0AQ (01705 665885).
Manager: Billy Gilbert **Asst Manager/Coach:** John Waugh **Physio:** Bill Pizey
General Manager: D Armstrong **Commercial Manager:** Terry Diddymus (01705 230114).
Ground: Jubilee Park, Aston Road, Waterlooville PO7 7SZ (01705 263867).
Directions: Turn right off town by-pass (B2150) at Asda r-about. Dual carriage to next island, and return back towards town (ground signposted). Aston Road is first left. Nearest stations; Havant (4 miles), Cosham (5).
Capacity: 7,000 **Cover:** 1,500 **Seats:** 480 **Floodlights:** Yes **Metal Badges:** Yes
Club Shop: Yes, selling usuals items. Contact Mrs B Tomkins.
Colours: White & navy **Change colours:** Yellow & green.
Previous Leagues: Waterlooville & District/ Portsmouth 38-53/ Hants 1953-71.
Club Sponsors: None.
Previous Grounds: Convent Ground 10-30/ Rowlands Avenue Recreation Ground 30-63.
Midweek home matchday: Tuesday **Reserve Team's League:** Wessex Combination.
Record Attendance: 4,500 v Wycombe Wanderers, FA Cup 1st Rd 1976-77.
Best FA Cup season: 1st Rd 2nd replay 83-84 (lost 0-2 at Northampton Town after two 1-1 draws. Also 1st Rd 68-69 76-77 88-89.
League clubs defeated in FA Cup: None
Record Fees: Paid: £6,000 for Steve Tate (Havant Town, 1993)
Received: £6,000 for Dave Boyce (Gravesend & Northfleet, 1993).
Players progressing to Football League: Phil Figgins (Portsmouth 1973), Paul Hardyman (Portsmouth 1983), Guy Whittingham (Portsmouth via Yeovil Town 1988), Paul Moody (Southampton 1991).
Clubhouse: Jubilee Club, open to all for all games (first team and reserves). Food available.
95-96 Captain:
95-96 P.o.Y.:
95-96 Top scorer:
Local Newspapers: The News & Sports Mail.
Local Radio Stations: BBC Solent, Ocean Sound.
Hons: Southern Lg Div 1 Sth 71-72 (Lg Cup 86-87, R-up 82-83), Hants Lg R-up 69-70 (Div 2 59-60 64-65, Div 3 (East) R-up 53-54), Hants Snr Cup 69-70 72-73 84-85 (R-up 75-76 90-91), Russell Cotes Cup 88-89, Portsmouth Lg 49-50 50-51 51-52 (Div 2 46-47, Div 3 38-39), Portsmouth Snr Cup 68-69, Portsmouth Victory Cup 59-60 69-70, FA Tphy 2nd Rd 76-77, FA Amtr Cup 1st Rd 59-60.

PROGRAMME DETAILS:
Pages: 32 **Price:** 50p
Ed.: Universal Leisure Ltd

1948 # WESTON-SUPER-MARE Seagulls

Weston-super-Mare FC. Back Row (L/R): David Mehew, Jon Bowering, Stewart Jones, Danny O'Hagan, Wayne Brown, Lee Rogers, Leigh White, Karl Madge. Front; Ryan Souter, Jamie Boulton, Robbie James, Paul McLoughlin, Lee Jones, Andy Llewellyn, Neil Reeves.

President: D A Usher **Chairman:** P T Bliss
Secretary/Press Officer: Keith Refault, 7 Somerdale Close, Weston-s-Mare BS22 8EB (01934 628068).
Manager: Peter Amos **Asst Manager:**Phil Chant. **Coach:** Keith Christie.
Physio: Gary Cox. **Commercial Manager:** Dave Percy.
Ground: Woodspring Park, Winterstoke Road, Weston-super-Mare BS23 2YG (01934 6355665/621618).
Directions: M5 Jct 21.A370 along new dual carriageway to fourth roundabout.First left and immediately rightr at new roundabout,club on right.
From South:M5 Jct 22, follow Weston signs for approx 7 miles, right at first r'bout (by Hospital), left at next r'bout, ground 1 mile on left. Twenty minutes walk from Weston-super-Mare (BR).
Seats: 350 **Cover:** 1,000 **Capacity:** 4,000 **Metal Badges:** Yes
Club Shop: Yes, selling programmes, club ties, pullovers, badges, scarves, pens, pennants, Sweat Shirts and T-shirts. Contact Mrs Aileen Milsom, 12 Greenland Road, Milton, Weston-s-Mare BS22 8JP (01934 413059).
Club colours: White/blue/blue **Change colours:** All yellow
Midweek matches: Tuesday **Reserve Team's Lge:** Somerset Snr Lge Division One.
Previous Name: Borough of Weston-super-Mare.
Previous Grounds: The Great Ground, Locking Road 48-55, Langford Road 55-83.
Record Attendance: 2,623 v Woking, FA Cup First Round Proper replay 23/11/93. *At Langford Road: 2,500 v Bridgwater Town, FA Cup First Round Proper replay 1961-62.*
Best FA Cup season: First Round Proper replay 1961-62 (lost 0-1 after 0-0 draw at Bridgwater Town) 1994-95 (lost 0-1 after 2-2 draw at Woking).
Players progressing to Football League: Shaun Rowse (Carlisle United, March 1994), Ian Maine, John Palmer.
Previous League: Western 1948-92.
Club Sponsors: Uphill Motor Company.
Record win: 11-0 v Paulton Rovers
Record defeat: 1-12 v Yeovil Town Reserves.
Clubhouse: Mon-Fri 7-11pm, Sat 12-11pm, Sun 12-3 & 7-11pm. 2 skittle alleys, 3 bars. Bar meals available and cooked meals on matchdays.
Club Record Goalscorer: Matthew Lazenby, 180
Club Record Appearances: Harry Thomas, 740.
95-96 Captain: **95-96 P.o.Y.:**
95-96 Top scorer:
Local Newspapers: Bristol Evening Post,Western Daily Press.
Local Radio Stations: Somerset Sounds,Radio Bristol.
Hons: Somerset Snr Cup 23-24 26-27, Western Lg,Champions,91-92 (R-up 76-77, Lg Cup 76-77 (R-up 89-90), Merit Cup 76-77 77-78), Somerset Snr Lg (Reserves) Div 1 87-88 (R-up 90-91), Div 2 R-up 85-86, Div 3 84-85).

PROGRAMME DETAILS:
Pages: 32 **Price:** 60p

WEYMOUTH

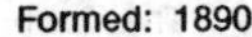

Formed: 1890 | The Terras

Back Row (L-R); Neil Housley, Tom Kelly, Lee Bradford, Darren Powell, Paul Mayers, Martin Shepherd, Richard Bartlett, Alex Brown. Front; John Waldock, David Laws, Nicky Limber, Ian Hutchinson.
Photo - Andrew Chitty

Chairman: Matthew McGowan **Vice Chairman:** Peter Sapsworth.
Secretary: Terry Northover, 2 Stoke Rd, Weymouth, Dorset DT4 9JF (01305 771480).
Manager: Graham Carr **Physio:** Bob Lucas. **Commercial Manager:** Fred Dunford.
Ground: Wessex Stadium, Radipole Lane, Weymouth, Dorset DT4 0TJ (01305 785558).
Directions: Arriving from Dorchester on A354, turn right following signs to Granby Industrial Estate at Safeway r'bout - ground on right as you enter estate.
Capacity: 10,000 **Cover:** All sides **Seats:** 900 **Floodlights:** Yes **Metal Badges:** Yes.
Club Shop: Yes, open matchdays. During week contact Andrew Millar at 4 Franklin Rd, Weymouth DT4 0JR (01305 772743). Progs & souvenirs.
Colours: Claret & sky/claret & sky. **Change colours:** Gold/claret trim. **Sponsors:** Marlboro.
Best FA Cup season: 4th Rd 61-62, 0-2 at Preston. 1st rd on 29 occasions
League clubs defeated in FA Cup: Merthyr 24-25, Aldershot 49-50, Shrewsbury Town 56-57, Newport County 61-62, Cardiff City 82-83.
Previous Lges: Dorset Lge/ Western 1907-23 28-49/ Southern 23-28 49-79/ Alliance Premier 79-89.
Previous Ground: Recreation Ground (until 1987).
Midweek matchday: Tuesday **Reserve Lge:** Dorset Comb
Record Attendance: 4,995 v Manchester Utd, ground opening, 21/10/87.
Record Fees: Paid: £15,000 for Shaun Teale (Northwich)
Received: £100,000 for Peter Guthrie (Spurs, 1988)
Players progressing to Football League: R Pickett/B Carter (Portsmouth 49/56), S Northover (Luton 50), E Grant (Sheffield Utd 50), D Clelland (Scunthorpe 50), A Corbett (Hartlepool 53), W Holt (Barrow 54), A Smith (Accrington 61), G Bond/T Spratt/A Donnelly/M Cave (Torquay 61/65/67/68), P Leggett (Swindon 62), R Fogg (Aldershot 63), B Hutchinson (Lincoln 65), T Gulliver/R Hill (Bournemouth 66/67), A Wool (Reading 71), A Beer (Exeter 74), B Iles (Chelsea 78), G Roberts (Spurs 80), N Townsend, P Morrell/J Smeulders (Bournemouth 79/83/84), T Agana (Watford), A Townsend/D Hughes (Southampton), S Claridge (C Palace), B McGorry/S Teale (Bournemouth), T Pounder/R Evans (Bristol Rvrs), R Pethick (Portsmouth 93)
Clubhouse: Matchdays & functions. Hot & cold food available.
Club Record Goalscorer: W Farmer, Haynes. 275
Club Record Appearances: Tony Hobson 1,076
95-96 Captain: **95-96 P.o.Y:**
95-96 Top scorer:
Local Press: Dorset Evening Echo. **Local Radio:** Wessex FM.
Honours: All Prem Lg R-up 79-80 (Lg Cup 81-82), Prem Inter Lg Cup R-up 87-88 (QF 90-91), Sthn Lg 64-65 65-66 (R-up 54-55 77-78, Lg Cup 72-73 (R-up 5), Sthn Div R-up 91-92), Wstn Lg 22-23 (Div 2 33-34 36-37 (R-up 35-36 47-48)), Dorset Sen. Cup(25), Mark Frowde Cup (12), FA Tphy 4th Rd rep. 76-77, FA Amat Cup 1st Rd 1900.

PROGRAMME DETAILS:
Pages: 44 **Price:** 70p
Editor: Fred Danford (784133)

WITNEY TOWN

Formed: 1885 The Town

Back Row (L-R): S Ovens, K Knight, G Murphy, C Maguire, C Pettis. Middle; B Hughes (Coach), J Murphy (Mgr), J Cole, A Bird, K Alder, S Cook, D Williams, D Nichols, B Baird (Asst Mgr). Front; S Crouch, S Holt, S Tavinor, S Tapp, M Adams, J Caffel.

Chairman: Brian Constable **Vice-Chairman:** Adrian Dunsby **President:** Sir Peter Parker
Secretary: Adrian Bircher, 13 Colwell Drive,,Witney ,Oxon.OX8 5FQ (01993 700634).
Manager: John Murphy **Asst Manager:** Bob Baird **Coach:** Brian Hughes
Physio: Bob Baird **Press Officer:** Jon Adaway (01628 603612)
Commercial Mgr/Public Relations: Dermot Gallagher
Ground: Marriott Stadium, Downs Rd, Witney, Oxon OX8 7LY. (01993 702549).
Directions: From West on A40; take B4047 at island past Burford, follow signs for Witney West & N.W. Industrial Estates, thru Minster Lovell to West Witney, right into Downs Rd, ground on right. From the East on A40, 2nd turn off to Witney and follow signs for South & S.W. Industrial Estates, right at r'bout to traffic lights, left and proceed to r'bout, straight over, signs to West Witney Industrial Estate, left at lights onto B4047, left into Downs Rd, ground on right. Nearest BR station is Oxford 12 miles away.
Capacity: 3,500 **Cover:** 2,000 **Seats:** 280 **Floodlights:** Yes **Metal Badges:** Yes
Club Shop: Yes, selling programmes, t-shirts, sweatshirts, hats, scarves etc. Contact secretary.
Colours: All Yellow **Change colours:** Blue/white/white.
Sponsors: Regal (Witney) Ltd. **Previous Name:** Witney F.C.
Previous Leagues: Reading & Dist./ Oxfordshire Senior/ Hellenic 53-73.
Previous Ground: Marriotts Close, Welch Way (pre-1992).
Midweek matchday: Tuesday **Reserve Lge:** Applied for Suburban
Record Attendance: 2,000 (approx) v Aston Villa, ground opening 1992. Competitive: 544 v Salisbury, F.A. 4th Qual. Rd 24/10/92.
Best F.A. Cup season: 1st Rd 71-72 (lost 0-3 at home to Romford).
Record Fees - Paid: £3,000 for Steve Jenkins (Cheltenham Town)
Received: £5,000 for John Bailey (Worcester City).
Players progressing to Football League: Herbert Smith, Frank Clack (Birmingham City), Arthur Hall (Bristol Rovers 1959), David Moss (Swindon 1969), Jack Newman.
Clubhouse: Members bar open seven days a week except Christmas Day 6.30-11pm. Open all day Saturday. Hot food on matchdays.
Club record scorer: Kenny Clarke 133.
Club record appearances: Peter Hutter 384 (+21 sub).
95-96 Captain: Jason Caffel **95-96 Top scorer:** Danny Nichols 19
Players' Player of the Year 95-96: Steve Tavinor
Supporters' Player of the Year 95-96: Steve Tavinor
Local Newspapers: Witney Gazette (01993 704265), West Oxon Standard (01993 702175), Oxford Mail & Oxford Times (01865 244988).
Local Radio Stations: BBC Radio Oxford, Fox (FM) Oxford.
Hons: FA Tphy 2nd Rd 78-79, FA Amtr Cup 2nd Rd rep.(3) 66-67 71-73, Southern Lg Div 1 Nth 77-78, Hellenic Lg(8) 54-55 57-58 64-67 70-73 (R-up 53-54 67-68 69-70, Lg Cup(6), Prem Div Benevolent Cup 59-60 63-64), Oxon Snr Lg(5), Oxon Snr Cup(11)

PROGRAMME DETAILS:
Pages: 40 **Price:** £1
Editor: Adrian Bircher
(01993 703257)

YATE TOWN

Formed: 1946 | The Bluebells

Yate Town FC. Back Row (L/R): Mike Garland (Physio), Danny Idles, Lee Jefferies, Richard Jones, Paul Weeks, Paul Howse, Colin Towler, Matt Leonard, Phil Purnell (Asst Mgr). Front; Carl Rutter, Danny Rofe, ASlan Theobald, Ian Alexander (Mgr), Paul Mortimore, Kriss Lee, Paul Dempsey

Chairman: R G Hawkins **Vice Chairman:** D A Phillips **President:** R Hewetson.
Secretary: Terry Tansley, 1Tyning Close,Yate,Bristol Avon.BS17 5BH (01454 311029)
Manager: Ian Alexander **Asst Manager:** Phil Purnell **Coach:** Phil Purnell
Press Officer: Ian Alexander **Physio:** Mike Garland
Commercial Manager: Ian Alexander
Ground: Lodge Road, Yate, Bristol BS17 5LE (0454 228103).
Directions: M4 jct 18, A46 towards Stroud, then A432 to Yate. Turn right at top of railway bridge into North Road, first left past traffic lights. Five miles from Bristol Parkway BR main line station, half mile from Yate BR station. Buses 329, X68 and 328.
Capacity: 2,000 **Cover:** 236 **Seats:** 236 **Floodlights:** Yes **Metal Badges:** Yes
Club Shop: Yes, selling programmes, metal badges, pens, rosettes, shirts, key rings etc. Contact: Bob Chester (0117 9563674)
Colours: White & Navy pinstripes/navy/navy **Change colours:** All tangerine.
Sponsors: Carlsberg/ Tetley.
Previous Leagues: Gloucestershire County 68-83/ Hellenic 83-89.
Previous Name: Yate YMCA 1946-70.
Previous Grounds: Yate Aerodrome 50-54/ Newmans Field 54-60/ Sunnyside Lane 60-84.
Midweek home matchday: Wednesday **Reserve Team's League:** Bristol Suburban.
Record Attendance: 2,000 for Bristol Rovers v Bristol Rovers Past, Vaughan Jones testimonial 1990.
Record Fees - Paid: None.
Received: £7,500; for Darren Tilley (York, 1991); for Mike Davis (Bristol Rovers, 1993).
Record win: 13-3 v Clevedon, Bristol Premier Combination 1967-68.
Players progressing to Football League: Richard Thompson (Newport County & Exeter City), Phil Purnell (Bristol Rovers), Darren Tilley (York City), Steve Winter (Walsall), Mike Davis (Bristol Rovers) 1993.
Clubhouse: Open every night and weekend lunchtimes. Skittles, darts, pool, live entertainment.
Club Record Scorer: Kevin Thaws.
Club Record Appearances: Gary Hewlett.
95-96 Captain: Colin Towler
95-96 P.o.Y.:
95-96 Top scorer:
Local Press: Bristol Evening Post, Western Daily Press, North Avon Gazette.
Local Radio Stations: GWR, Radio Bristol.
Honours: FA Vase 5th Rd 91-92, Hellenic Lg(2) 87-89 (Div 1 R-up 84-85, Lg Skol Cup R-up 87-88), Glos Chal. Tphy 88-89 (R-up 78-79), Glos Snr Amtr Cup Sth 77-78 91-92(res) 92-93(res), Glos Snr Chal. Cup (Nth) R-up 89-90 92-93 94-95, Stroud Charity Cup R-up 74-75 81-82 84-85 (Sect. A Winners(6) 76-78 79-80 82-83 87-89), Berkeley Hosp. Prem. Cup(3) 73-75 80-81, S.W. Co's Sutton Vase 85-86.

PROGRAMME DETAILS:
Pages: 32 **Price:** 70p
Editor: Bob Chester

JEWSON EASTERN COUNTIES Premier Division Ten Year Records

	86/7	87/8	88/9	89/0	90/1	91/2	92/3	93/4	94/5	95/6
Braintree Town	2	2	2	3	2	-	-	-	-	-
Brantham Athletic	19	20	17	8	19	17	21	-	-	-
Brightlingsea United	-	-	-	-	-	20	22	-	-	-
Bury Town	3	-	-	-	-	-	-	-	-	-
Chatteris Town	15	7	19	21	21	19	16	12	22	-
Clacton Town	12	12	18	20	12	21	-	-	-	15
Colchester Utd Res.	7	14	-	-	-	-	-	-	-	-
Cornard United	-	-	-	-	8	3	4	13	20	22
Diss Town	-	-	-	-	-	-	5	4	4	2
Ely City	22	22	20	-	-	-	-	-	-	-
Fakenham Town	-	-	-	-	-	-	7	17	6	13
Felixstowe Town	17	17	11	13	13	13	9	8	13	8
Gorleston	18	18	10	5	17	12	10	21	-	-
Gt. Yarmouth Town	6	4	5	6	18	14	11	16	16	16
Hadleigh United	-	-	-	-	-	-	-	-	15	17
Halstead Town	-	-	-	14	3	9	15	2	1	1
Harwich & Parkeston	14	13	14	4	5	6	6	11	5	7
Haverhill Rovers	13	10	7	15	4	8	14	10	17	21
Histon	21	5	6	7	10	15	20	20	21	-
Lowestoft Town	9	8	12	18	9	11	17	9	7	14
March Town United	4	1	4	9	15	10	18	19	14	19
Newmarket Town	16	15	16	17	20	7	3	3	8	6
Norwich United	-	-	-	-	-	4	8	22	-	-
Soham Town Rangers	20	21	21	-	-	-	-	18	18	12
Stowmarket Town	10	19	8	11	11	2	13	5	11	4
Sudbury Town Reserves	1	3	1	1	-	-	-	-	9	18
Sudbury Wanderers	-	-	-	-	-	-	-	7	-	9
Thetford Town	23	16	9	2	14	22	-	-	-	-
Tiptree United	5	11	15	19	16	16	12	14	12	10
Watton United	8	9	13	16	6	18	19	15	19	20
Wisbech Town	11	6	3	10	1	5	2	6	3	11
Woodbridge Town	-	-	-	-	-	-	-	-	10	5
Wroxham	-	-	-	12	7	1	1	1	2	3
No of Clubs Competing	23	22	21	21	21	22	22	22	22	21

Premier Division Champions Halstead Town take the lead at Hadleigh on the stroke of half time, as Andy Smile's header beats Dickie Mann in the home goal.

EASTERN COUNTIES LEAGUE

FEEDER TO: BEAZER HOMES LEAGUE

FOUNDED: 1935

Hon. Patron: Derek Needham **President:** Roger Pauley

Secretary: Colin Lamb, 3 Land Close, Clacton-on-Sea, Essex CO16 8UJ (01255 436398)

FINAL LEAGUE TABLES 1995/96

Premier Div	P	W	D	L	F	A	Pts
1. Halstead Town	42	31	8	3	110	50	101
2. Diss Town	42	29	9	4	94	32	96
3. Wroxham	42	26	10	6	97	39	88
4. Stowmarket Tn	42	23	7	12	69	47	76
5. Woodbridge Tn	42	22	5	15	73	50	71
6. Newmarket Tn	42	18	13	11	78	58	67
7. Harwich & Park	42	25	8	9	102	55	*64
8. Felixstowe Tn	42	16	11	15	60	57	59
9. Sudbury Wand	42	17	8	17	53	58	59
10. Tiptree Utd	42	17	8	17	56	67	59
11. Wisbech Tn	42	16	9	17	76	67	57
12. Soham T Rang	42	16	9	17	76	78	57
13. Fakenham Tn	42	17	5	20	67	67	56
14. Lowestoft Tn	42	13	14	15	73	59	53
15. Clacton Tn	42	14	10	18	72	84	52
16. Gt Yarmouth T	42	11	11	20	34	61	44
17. Hadleigh Utd	42	10	9	23	33	85	39
18. Sudbury Tn R	42	9	11	22	49	86	38
19. March Tn Utd	42	10	7	25	39	67	37
20. Watton United	42	8	13	21	41	73	37
21. Haverhill Rov	42	8	10	24	36	78	34
22. Cornard Utd	42	5	7	30	38	108	22

Div One	P	W	D	L	F	A	Pts
1. Gorleston	32	26	4	2	100	30	82
2. Warboys Town	32	22	7	3	79	33	73
3. Ely City	32	19	6	7	82	40	63
4. Thetford Town	32	20	2	10	72	52	62
5. Ipswich Wand	32	17	8	7	87	41	59
6. Whitton Utd	32	15	10	7	67	43	55
7. Norwich Utd	32	14	7	11	58	46	49
8. Mildenhall T	32	14	5	13	53	61	47
9. Swaffham Tn	32	10	8	14	53	54	38
10. Brighlingsea U	32	8	11	13	44	61	35
11. Somersham Tn	32	10	5	17	41	62	35
12. Downham Tn	32	9	7	16	46	80	34
13. Histon	32	8	4	20	54	73	28
14. Kings Lynn Res	32	8	4	20	46	91	28
15. Stanway Rov	32	6	9	17	35	67	27
16. Chatteris Tn	32	7	4	21	41	82	25
17. Bury Tn Res	32	6	5	21	54	96	23

** 19 points deducted -incorrectly registered players*

Great Yarmouth FC: Back Row (L-R); Matt Bailsey, Jon White, Brian Payne, Paul Mayne, Mark Grealy, Marck Vincent, Ian George. Front Row; Martin Moy, Luke Price, Tim Ellis, Martyn Sinclair, Paul Thompson, Zac Colman, Steve Ellis

LEADING GOALSCORERS 1995-96

Premier Division:

Clacton	Alan Day	18.	Sid Edwards	17.	Ian Daly	10.
Diss	Paul Smith	32.	Paul Warne	14.	Shaun Curtis	13.
Fakenham	Luther Blissett	15.	Mark Howard	13.	Wayne Coe	13.
Felixstowe	Richard Barber	20.				
Halstead	Andy Smiles	27.	Steve Parnell	22.	Mark Farthing	21.
Harwich	Brendan Tuck	22.	David Fleming	14.		
Lowestoft	Stuart Jopling	25.				
Newmarket	Lee Sharp	24.				
Soham	Andy Morton	14.	David Braybrooke	11.		
Stowmarket	Tony Gayfer	16.	Dave King	13.		
Sudbury Town	Andy Orvis	10.				
Sudbury Wanderers	Adrian Bullett	12.				
Tiptree	Gary Hollocks	12.	Lee Sonnex	11.		
Wisbech	Peter Munns	17.	Steve McLaughlin	15.		
Woodbridge	Simon Fryatt	19.	Paul Leech	14.		
Wroxham	Simon Barnes	18.	Paul Reeve	11.	Jon Rigby	11.

JEWSON SPORTSMANSHIP TROPHY 1995-96

Winners: Histon **Second:** Sudbury Wanderers **Third:** Diss Town

JEWSON FAIR PLAY TROPHY 1995-96

Winners: Gorleston **Second:** Fakenham Town **Third:** Whitton United

Wroxham Captain Stuart Larter receiving the February Club of the Month award from Jewson League Assistant Secretary Keith Johnson:

(L-R); Paul Reeve, Neil Bennett, Chris Clement, Gavin Pauling, Darren Gill, Adrian Harris, Ryan Lemmon, Stuart Larter, Robbie Price, Stuart Youngman, Keith Johnson (Jewson League), Jason Gorman, Simon Barnes, Tristan Everitt (Trainer).

PREMIER DIVISION CLUBS 1996-97

BURY TOWN

Formed: 1872 The Blues
Chairman: Colin Hurley **Vice Chairman:** Brian Lafflin **President:** Cyril Elsey.
Secretary: Mrs Wendy Turnmer, 64 Winthrop Rd., Bury-St-Edmunds, Suffolk. IP33 3UF (01284 753688)
Manager/Coach: Tony Godden **Asst Manager:** Keith Vince **Physio:** John Chandler
Ground: Ram Meadow, Cotton Lane, Bury St Edmunds, Suffolk IP33 1XP, (01284 754721).
Directions: Leave A14 at sign to central Bury St Edmunds, follow signs to town centre at exit r'bout, at next r'bout 1st exit into Northgate Street, left at 'T' junct. (traffic lights) into Mustow Street and left immediately into Cotton Lane - ground 350 yds on right, through 'Pay & Display' car park (n.b. fine for not displaying a 50p ticket is £25). 10 mins walk from station.
Capacity: 3,500 **Cover:** 1,500 **Seats:** 300 **Floodlights:** Yes **Club Shop:** Yes
Programme: 40 pages 80p **Editor:** TBA **Press Officer:** Ron Kent
Colours: Blue/white/blue **Change colours:** Red/black/red. **Sponsors:** Greene King Plc.
Midweek home matchday: Tuesday **Reserves' Lge:** Jewson (Eastern Co's) Div 1.
Record Attendance: 2,500 v Enfield, FA Cup 3rd Qualifying Rd 1986.
Best FA Cup season: 1st Rd replay 68-69 (lost 0-3 at AFC Bournemouth after 0-0 draw).
Previous Lges: Norfolk & Suffolk/ Essex & Suffolk Border/ Eastern Co's 35-64 76-87/ Metropolitan 64-71.
Players progressing to Football League: D Lewis (Gillingham, Preston), Larry Carberry (Ipswich & England), Terry Bly (Norwich 1956, Peterborough), Terry Pearce (Ipswich), Gary Stevens (Brighton, Spurs & England), Simon Milton (Ipswich 1990).
Clubhouse: Members'/Public Bars open at matchdays
95-96 Captain: Mike Henry **95-96 P.o.Y.:** Paul England **95-96 Top scorer:** Matthew Metcalf
Club Record Goalscorer: Doug Tooley 58. **Club Record Appearances:** Doug Tooley.
Honours: FA Vase QF 88-89, FA Trophy 2nd Rd 70-71, Eastern Counties Lg 63-64 (R-up 37-38, Lg Cup 61-62 63-64), Metropolitan Lg 65-66 (R-up 67-68 70-71, Lg Cup 67-68, Prof Cup 65-66), Suffolk Prem Cup 58-59 59-60 60-61 61-62 63-64 64-65 70-71 77-78 95-96, Suffolk Sen Cup 36-37 37-38 38-39 44-45 84-85.

CLACTON TOWN

Chairman: Fred Lawrence **President:** R Manning **Manager:** Paul Duley.
Secretary: Mrs Sandra Harris, 57 Coopers Lane, Clacton-on-Sea, Essex CO15 2BY (01255 476133).
Ground: The Rushgreen Bowl, Rushgreen Road, Clacton-on-Sea (01255 432590).
Directions: A133 to Clacton, at r'bout right into St Johns Rd, 4th left Cloes Lane, 3rd right Rushgreen Rd, ground approximately half mile on right. From B1027 take main Jaywick turn off (Jaywick Lane), then 2nd left (after about a mile) into Rushgreen Rd. Ground 400 yds. 2 miles from Clacton (BR), buses 3, 5 or 5a to Coopers Lane/Rushgreen Rd.
Seats: 200 **Cover:** Yes **Capacity:** 2,500 **Floodlights:** Yes **Founded:** 1892.
Colours: Royal blue **Change colours:** All red **Club Shop:** Yes
Previous Grounds: Clacton Stadium, Old Road 06-87/ Gainsford Av (temp). **Metal Badges:** Yes.
Midweek Matches: Tuesday **Pennants:** Yes.
Record Attendance: 3,505 v Romford, FA Cup 1st Qualifying Rd 1952 (at Old Road).
Previous Leagues: Eastern Co's 35-37 38-58/ Southern 58-64.
Programme: 40 pages, 50p **Local Paper:** Clacton Gazette **Nickname:** Seasiders.
Clubhouse details: Licensed club. Open 7-11pm Mon-Sat, 12-3pm Sat-Sun.
Matchday food & drink: Tea, coffee, cold drinks, confectionary, burgers, hotdogs, soup, rolls.
Players progressing to Football League: Vivian Woodward (Spurs, Chelsea, England), Mick Everitt (Arsenal, Northampton), Christian McLean (Bristol Rovers).
Honours: Southern Lg Div 1 59-60, Eastern Co's Lg R-up 36-37 53-54 64-65 74-75 (Lg Cup 73-74), East Anglian Cup 53-54, Worthington Evans Cup 56-57 67-68 74-75, FA Cup 1st Rd (v Southend) 60-61.

DISS TOWN

Chairman: Des Tebble **President:** R A Gooderham **Treasurer:** Noel Mullenger.
Secretary: R Upson, Bamburgh House, Brewers Green Lane, Diss, Norfolk IP22 3QP (01379 642923).
Manager: Bill Punton **Asst Manager:** Paul Tong **Physio:** Mick Mundey/Nigel Wilson
Ground: Brewers Green Lane, Diss (01379 651223).
Directions: Just off B1066 Diss-Thetford road, near Roydon School. One and a half miles from Diss (BR).
Seats: 280 **Cover:** Yes **Capacity:** 2,500 **Floodlights:** Yes **Club Shop:** Yes
Programme: 16 pages, 50p **Programme Editor:** G Enderby
Colours: Tangerine/navy/tangerine **Change colours:** White/navy/tangerine.
Founded: 1888. **Nickname:** Tangerines. **Sponsors:** Diss Fasteners
Midweek Matches: Tuesday **Reserve Team's League:** Anglian Combination.
Record Attendance: 1,731 v Atherton LR, FA Vase SF 1st leg 19/3/94
Previous Leagues: Norwich & District/ Norfolk & Suffolk 35-64/ Anglian Combination 64-82.
Players progressing to the Football League: Alec Thurlow (Man City), Mervyn Cawston (Norwich), Trevor Whymark (Ipswich), Clive Stafford (Colchester),Paul Gibbs.
Clubhouse: Open evenings (except Sunday), Sat/Sun lunchtimes, and matchdays.
95-96 Captain: Garry Smith **95-96 Top Scorer:** Paul Smith **95-96 P.o.Y.:** Garry Smith,
Honours: FA Vase 94-95 (QF 91-92), Eastern Co's Lg Div 1 91-92, Anglian Comb. 76-77 78-79 (R-up 74-75, Div 1 67-68 73-74, Lg Cup 67-68 79-80 81-82), Norfolk & Suffolk Lg R-up 55-56 (Applegate Cup 56-57 57-58(joint)(R-up 55-56)), Norfolk Snr Cup 74-75 95-96, Norfolk Jnr Cup 1891-92, Jewson Prem Lge R-up 95-96.

FAKENHAM TOWN

Chairman: Tony Fisher **President:** B E Woodhouse **Manager:** Nolan Keeley
Secretary: E V Linnell, 40 Warren Avenue, Fakenham, Norfolk NR21 8NP (01328 855445).
Press Officer: J Cushion **Commercial Manager:** R Lane.
Ground: Clipbush Lane, Fakenham (01328 856222).
Directions:
Seats: 80 **Cover:** 300 **Capacity:** 1,500 **Floodlights:** Yes **Founded:** 1884.
Colours: Amber & black/black/black. **Change colours:** Red/white/red. **Club Shop:** Yes.
Midweek Matchday: Tuesday. **Sponsors:** English Garages **Nickname:** Ghosts.
Previous Grounds: Hempton Green 1884-89/ Star Meadow 89-1907
Previous Leagues: North Norfolk 1884-1910/ Norwich & District 10-35/ Norfolk & Suffolk 35-64/ Anglian Combination 64-87.
Reserves' League: Anglian Comb. **Record Gate:** 1,000 v Norwich City, floodlight inauguration.
Clubhouse details: Bar, colour TV and pool table.
Matchday food & drink: Tea, coffee, cold drinks, confectionary, soup.
Programme: 32 pages (Barnes Print), 20p **Local Newspapers:** Fakenham & Wells Times.
Players progressing to the Football League: Nolan Keeley (Scunthorpe & Lincoln).
Honours: Norfolk Snr Cup 70-71 72-73 73-74 91-92 94-95, Eastern Co's Lg Div 1 R-up 91-92, Anglian Comb. Cup 78-79.

FELIXSTOWE TOWN

Chairman: Dave Ashford **President:** TBA **Manager:** Doug Wade.
Secretary: Steve Page, 11A Lonsdale Close, Ipswich, Suffolk (01473 712613).
Ground: Dellwood Avenue, Felixstowe (01394 282917).
Directions: A45 to Felixstowe. Turn right at 3rd r'bout then 1st left - ground 100 yds on left. 5 mins from Felixstowe (BR) and town centre.
Seats: 200 **Cover:** 200 **Capacity:** 2,000 **Floodlights:** Yes **Founded:** 1890.
Colours: White/blue/gold. **Change:** Blue/white/yellow & blue **Nickname:** Seasiders.
Prev. Leagues: Essex & Suffolk Border/ Ipswich & Dist. **Midweek Matches:** Tuesday
Record Attendance: 1,500 v Ipswich Town, floodlight inauguration 25/1/91.
Programme: 16 pages, 30p **Programme Editor:** P Griffiths.
Clubhouse details: Bar, snack bar, TV, darts, pool table. **Local Newspaper:** East Anglia Daily Times.
Matchday food & drink: Tea, coffee, cold drinks, confectionary, hotdogs, burgers, soup, rolls.
Honours: Suffolk Senior Cup 66-67 74-75. **Club Shop:** Yes **Enamel Badges & Pennants:** Yes.

GORLESTON

Chairman: Kevin Antcliffe **President:** Jimmy Jones **Manager:** M.Hubble & Steve Foyster
Secretary: A Ottley, 60 Peterhouse Ave., Gorleston, Gt Yarmouth, Norfolk NR31 7PL (01493 603353).
Ground: Emerald Park, Woodfarm Lane, Gorleston, Great Yarmouth (01493 602802).
Directions: On Magdalen Estate - follow signs to Crematorium, turn left and follow road to ground. Five and a half miles from Great Yarmouth Vauxhall (BR).
Seats: 250 **Cover:** 4,000 **Capacity:** 5,000 **Floodlights:** Yes **Club Shop:** Yes
Programme: 56/60 pages 70p **Editor:** Brian Bunn **Press Officer:**
Colours: All Green. **Change colours:** All white.
Sponsor: **Nickname:** Greens. **Founded:** 1884.
Midweek Matchday: Tuesday. **Record Attendance:** 4,473 v Orient, FA Cup 1st Rd 29/11/51.
Previous Leagues: Gt Yarmouth & Dist/Norfolk & Suffolk/ Anglian Comb.
Past players progressing to the Football League: J Joblins (Norwich), Mike Bailey (Wolves), Dave Stringer (Norwich), Roger Carter (Aston Villa), D Carter (Man City), A Brown (Charlton), S Morgan (Cambridge), Paul Gibbs (Colchester).
Clubhouse: Bar, TV, pool table, darts, snacks.
Honours: Eastern Co's Lg 52-53 72-73 79-80 80-81; Lge Cup 55-56; Norf. Snr Cup(13)(R-up 25); Anglian Comb. 68-69, Norf. & Suf. Lg (7); E Anglian Cup (3); Jewson Lge Div 1 95-96; FA Cup 1st Rd 51-52 57-58;

GREAT YARMOUTH TOWN

Chairman: Colin Smith **President:** **Manager:** Paul Chick.
Secretary: Michael Capon, 16 Orchard Way, Fleggburgh, Gt Yarmouth, Norfolk NR29 3AY (01493 369530).
Ground: Wellesey Recreation Ground, Wellesey Road (01493 842936).
Directions: Just off Marine Parade, 200 yds north of Britannia Pier. Half a mile from Vauxhall (BR).
Seats: 500 **Cover:** 2,100 **Capacity:** 3,600 **Floodlights:** Yes **Club Shop:** No.
Programme: 20 pages, 50p **Editor:** **Press Officer:**
Colours: Amber & black stripes/black/black. **Change colours:** White/red/red.
Sponsor: **Founded:** 1897. **Nickname:** Bloaters.
Midweek Matches: Tuesday **Reserve League:**
Record Attendance: 8,944 v Crystal Palace, FA Cup 1st Rd 52-53.
Previous Leagues: Norfolk & Suffolk
Players progressing to the Football League: Roy Hollis (Norwich), Mel Blyth & Nolan Keeley (Scunthorpe), Steven Davy (West Ham), Kevin Ready (Aston Villa), Gary Butcher (Blackburn).
Clubhouse details: (01493 8443373). Dancehall, Committee Room, darts, pool.
Matchday food & drink: Tea, coffee, cold drinks, confectionary, hotdogs, burgers, soup, sandwiches, rolls.

95-96 P.o.Y.: **95-96 Captain:** **95-96 Top Scorer:**
Honours: Eastern Co's Lg 68-69 (R-up 56-57 67-68 77-78 78-79, Lg Cup 37-38 74-75 80-81), East Anglian Cup(3), Norfolk Snr Cup(12)(R-up(22)), Norfolk Premier Cup(twice shared), Norfolk & Suffolk Lg 13-14 26-27 27-28, FA Vase SF 82-83, FA Cup 2nd Rd(2)(1st Rd(1)), Anglian Comb. Cup 65-66(res), E Anglian Lg 56-57(res).

HADLEIGH UNITED

President: H Claireaux, Esq **Chairman:** S R King **Vice-Chairman:** T.B.A.
Secretary: Barrie Stokes, 27 Martin Road, Ipswich, Suffolk IP2 8BJ (01473 405103).
Manager: Scott Clarke. **Assistant Manager:** Stuart Ayles.
Physio: Stuart Ayles. **Press Officer:** Terry Adams.
Ground: Millfield, Tinkers Lane, Duke Street, Hadleigh, Suffolk (01473 822165).
Directions: Turn off A12 approx halfway between Ipswich & Hadleigh. Take B1070 & follow signs to Hadleigh. Duke Street is off the High Street - turn left by Library.
Seats: 250 **Cover:** 500 **Capacity:** 3,000 **Floodlights:** Yes **Founded:** 1892.
Colours: White/navy/navy **Change colours:** All yellow
Programme: 12 pages, 50p **Programme Editor:** Alvin Jarrald (01473 311798).
Reserves' Lge: Essex & Suff. Border **Player progressing to Football Lge:** Perry Groves (Arsenal).
Midweek Matches: Tuesday. **Prev. Lge:** Suffolk & Ipswich (prev. Ipswich & D.)(pre-1991).
Sponsors: Fontana. **Previous Grounds:** Grays Meadow, Ipswich Roa.
Record Gate: 518 v Halstead Town,F.A.Vase Replay 17.1.95
Record win: 8-1 v Chatteris(A) 17/1/95. **Record defeat:** 1-7 v Fakenham Town (A) 4/1/92.
Nickname: Brettsiders. **Clubhouse:** Open matchdays, Fridays & Sunday lunchtimes.
Honours: Ipswich & Dist./Suffolk & Ipswich Lg 53-54 56-57 73-74 76-77 78-79 (Mick McNeil Lg Cup 76-77 80-81 81-82 86-87)), Suffolk Senior Cup 68-69 71-72 82-83.Eastern Co.Lg Champions 93-94.

HALSTEAD TOWN

Chairman: Steve Marszal **Vice-Chairman:** D Hume **President:** Mr E J R McDowell
Secretary: Stephen Webber, 12 Ravens Ave, Halstead, Essex CO9 1NZ (01787 476959).
Caretaker Player Coach: I.Phillips **Manager:** Ian Phillips.
Physio: B Dunster.
Ground: Rosemary Lane, Halstead, Essex (01787 472082).
Directions: A131 Chelmsford to Braintree - follow signs to Halstead. In Halstead, 1st left after Police Station, then 1st right, and first left to ground.
Seats: 312 **Cover:** 400. **Capacity:** 2,000 **Floodlights:** Yes **Founded:** 1879.
Colours: White/black/white **Change colours:** Red/white/red
Previous Lges: Nth Essex/ Halstead & Dist./ Haverhill/ Essex & Suffolk Border/ Essex Snr 80-88.
Previous Grounds: Three Gates 1879-1948, Coggeshall Pieces, Ravens Meadow, King George Playing Field.
Record Attendance: 4,000 v Walthamstow Avenue, Essex Senior Cup 1949.
Clubhouse details: Open evenings and matchdays. **Programme:** 30p **Editor:** D Osborne.
Players progressing to the Football League: Steve Allen (Wimbledon Physio).
Midweek Matches: Tuesday **Local Newspaper:** Halstead Gazette.
Hons: Eastern Co's Lg 94-95 R-up 94-95 (Div 1 R-up 89-90), Essex Senior Trophy 94-95, Knight Floodlit Cup R-up 90-91, Essex & Suffolk Border Lg(4) 57-59 77-78
94-95(res)(R-up 49-50 54-55 60-61, Lg Cup(4) 57-59 73-74 94-95(res), Div 1(res) 94-95), Essex Snr Lg Cup R-up 79-80, Essex Jnr Cup 01-02 46-47 (R-up 00-01).

HARWICH & PARKESTON

Chairman: Paul Revell **Vice-Chairman:** T.B.A. **President:** J Whitmore
Secretary: Graham Firth, 24 Glebe Close, Wix, Essex CO11 2SD (01255 870805).
Manager: Tony Kinsella. **Assistant Manager:** Don James.
Physio: John Nicholls. **Press Officer:** Carl Allan
Ground: Royal Oak, Main Road, Dovercourt, Harwich (01255 503649).
Directions: On main road into Dovercourt. 600 yds from Dovercourt (BR).
Seats: 350 **Cover:** 1,000 **Capacity:** 5,000 **Floodlights:** Yes **Founded:** 1877.
Colours: White with Black trim/Black. **Change colours:** Red. **Nickname:** Shrimpers.
Previous Lges: Eastern Co's 35-37 38-64/ Essex County 37-38/ Athenian 64-73 83-84/ Isthmian 73-83.
Midweek Matches: Tuesday **Previous Ground:** Phoenix Field, Seafront.
Record Attendance: 5,649 v Romford, FA Amateur Cup 4th Rd 19/3/38. **Club Shop:** Yes
Clubhouse details: Open every day. Dances, bingo, darts, pool, function room.
Players progressing to the Football League: I Gillespie (C Palace, Ipswich), G Waites, K Sanderson, Ian Brown (Bristol City 1991).
Prog.: 28 pages, 40p (Ed.: C.Allen.) **Reserve Lge:** Essex & Suffolk Border Prem. Div.
Honours: FA Amateur Cup R-up 1898-99 1952-53, FA Vase QF 90-91, Eastern Counties Lg 35-36(joint)(Lg Cup 35-36 36-37), Essex County Lg 37-38, Athenian Lg Div 1 R-up 65-66 (Div 2 64-65, Lg Cup 64-65), Essex Senior Cup 1898-99 1936-37, Essex Senior Trophy 89-90, AFA Senior Cup 35-36 36-37, Worthington Evans Cup 80-81.

LOWESTOFT TOWN

Chairman: Roy Harper **Vice-Chairman:** Rex Butcher **President:** W Yates
Secretary: Mike Pearce, 46 Teesdale, Carlton Colvile, Lowestoft, Suffolk NR33 8TG (01502 519229).
Manager: Michael Chapman **Press Officer:** Michael Pearce.
Ground: Crown Meadow, Love Road, Lowestoft (01502 573818).
Directions: Just off A12, 10 mins walk from Lowestoft (BR).
Seats: 466 **Cover:** 500 **Capacity:** 4,000 **Floodlights:** Yes **Founded:** 1890.
Colours: Royal/white/royal **Change colours:** Yellow/red/yellow **Nickname:** Blues.
Prev. Lge: Norfolk & Suffolk 1897-1935 **Midweek Matches:** Tuesday **Metal Badges:** Yes
Programme: 20 pages, 30p **Programme Editor:** Secretary
Club Shop: Yes, selling programmes, badges, scarves, pennants, pens, key-rings, mugs. Contact Dave Brooks (0502 531998).
Reserves' Lge: Anglian Combination **Record Attendance:** 5,000 v Watford, FA Cup 1st Rd 9/12/67.
Record win: 19-0 v Thetford Town (H), Eastern Counties League.
Players progressing to Football League: Eddie Spearitt (Ipswich 1965), Nigel Cassidy (Norwich 1967), Richard Money (Scunthorpe 1973), Graham Franklin (Southend 1977).
Club Sponsors: John Grose **Clubhouse details:** Pub hours
Matchday food & drink: Tea, coffee, cold drinks, confectionary, hotdogs, burgers, soup.
Record Scorer: M Tooley 383 **Record appearances:** C Peck 629.
Honours: Eastern Co's Lg(8) 35-36(joint) 37-38 62-63 64-65 67-68 69-71 77-78 (Lg Cup(7) 38-39 54-55 65-67 68-69 75-76 83-84), Norf. & Suffolk Lg(8) 1897-99 1900-04 28-29 30-31, Suffolk Prem. Cup(5) 66-67 71-72 74-75 78-80, Suffolk Snr Cup(10) 02-03 22-24 25-26 31-32 35-36 46-49 55-56, E Anglian Cup(10), FA Cup 1st Rd 26-27 38-39 66-67 77-78, Anglian Comb. (Reserves) 77-78 79-80 (Lg Cup 76-77), E Anglian Lg (Reserves) 57-58 63-64.

MARCH TOWN UNITED

Chairman: David Swift. **President:** D Wilkinson **Manager:** Stephen Spendlow.
Secretary: R S Bennett, 47 Ellingham Ave, March, Cambs PE15 9TE (01354 653271)
Ground: GER Sports Ground, Robin Goodfellows Lane, March (01354 653073).
Directions: 5 mins from town centre, 10 mins from BR station.
Seats: 500 **Cover:** 2,000 **Capacity:** 4,000 **Floodlights:** Yes **Founded:** 1885.
Club colours: Yellow & blue/blue/yellow. **Change colours:** Black & white/black/black.
Previous Ground: The Avenue (prior to 1946). **Nickname:** Hares
Previous Leagues: Peterborough/ Isle of Ely/ Utd Co's 48-54.
Midweek Matches: Tuesday **Record Gate:** 7,500 v King's Lynn, FA Cup 1956.
Programme: 30p **Prog. Editor:** Miss D Frost **Clubhouse:** On ground, seating 150.
Matchday food & drink: Tea, coffee, cold drinks, soup, sandwiches, rolls.
Honours: Eastern Co's Lg 87-88 (Lg Cup 60-61), Utd Co's Lg 53-64, FA Cup 1st Rd 53-54 (lost to Brentford) 77-78 (to Swindon), Cambs Invitation Cup 54-55, East Anglian Cup 53-54(jt with Barking).

NEWMARKET TOWN

Chairman: K Sheppard **President:** M J Nicholas **Manager:** Richard Datson.
Secretary: Mr Eddie Leafhead, 56 Churchill Court, Rowley Drive, Newmarket CB8 0JZ (01638 669503).
Ground: Cricketfield Road, off New Cheveley Road, Newmarket (01638 663637).
Directions: 400 yds from Newmarket (BR) - turn right into Green Road, right at crossroads New Cheveley Road - ground at top on left.
Seats: 144 **Cover:** 150 **Capacity:** 1,750 **Floodlights:** Yes **Club Shop:**
Programme: 50p **Editor:** Tony Pringle **Press Officer:**
Colours: Yellow/navy/blue **Change Colours:** All maroon
Sponsor: **Founded:** 1877. **Nickname:** Jockeys.
Midweek Matches: Tuesday **Reserve League**
Record Attendance: 2,701 v Abbey Utd (now Cambridge Utd), FA Cup 1st Qualifying Rd 1/10/49.
Best F.A. Cup year: 4th Qualifying Rd 92-93 (lost 0-2 at home to Hayes).
Previous League: Bury Snr/ Ipswich Snr/ Essex & Suffolk Border/ Utd Co's 34-37/ Eastern Co's 37-52.
Players progressing to the Football League: Mick Lambert (Ipswich), M Wright (Northampton), G Tweed (Coventry), R Fuller (Charlton).Colin Vowden(Camb.Utd.)
Clubhouse: Matchdays only. Tea, coffee, cold drinks, confectionary, burgers, hotdogs, soup, sandwiches, rolls.
95-96 Captain: **95-96 TopScorer:** **95-96 P.o.Y.:**
Honours: Suffolk Snr Cup 34-35 93-94; Cambs Invitation Cup 58-59; Cambs Challenge Cup 21-22 26-27; Cambs Snr Lg, 19-20; Ipswich Snr Lg 30-31 31-32 32-33 33-34; Peterborough Lg 57-58; Suffolk Premier Cup 93-94 94-95.

Newmarket Town's Steve Low fires in a volley, during the second half against Southend Manor.
Photo - Martin Wray.

Sudbury Wanderers FC:
Back Row (L-R); Lee Wilson, Robert Sims, Darren Pratt, Jayson Haygreen, Adam Crofton, Richard Codling, Scott Mills, Stephen Day.
Front Row; Chris Wilde, Adrian Bullett, Jamie Howe, Darren Judd, Danny Hill, Andrew Southgate,
Photo - Andrew Chitty.

SOHAM TOWN RANGERS

Chairman: M Robinson **President:** J Mann
Secretary: Mrs Wendy Gammon, 32 Broad Piece, Soham, Cambs CB7 5EL (01353 722139).
Manager: R Goodjohn/ G Grogan **Asst Manager:** **Coach:** Mick Drury
Ground: Julius Martins Lane, Soham, Cambs (01353 720732).
Directions: A142 between Newmarket and Ely - Julius Martins Lane.
Seats: 200 **Cover:** 1,500 **Capacity:** 2,000 **Floodlights:** Yes **Shop:**
Programme: 50p **Editor:** Graham Eley.
Colours: Green/white **Change colours:** Blue/black
Sponsors: Clark & Butcher & Able Acess Ltd **Nickname:** Town or Rangers. **Founded:** 1947.
Midweek Matchday: Wednesday **Reserves League:** Cambs Prem. B.
Record Attendance: 3,000 v Pegasus, FA Amateur Cup 1963.
Previous Leagues: Peterborough & Dist.
Clubhouse: General bar, Stud Bar, Lounge Bar.
95-96 Captain: Darren Hayward **95-96 P.o.Y.:** Darren Hayward **95-96 Top Scorer:**
Honours: Eastern Co's Lg Div 1 R-up 92-93; P'boro. Lg(3).

STOWMARKET TOWN

Chairman: Derek Barnard. **Vice-Chairman:** T.B.A. **President:** Brian Crascall
Secretary: John Doward, Deepland House, Stowupland, Stowmarket, (01449 612003)
Manager: Trevor Wardlaw **Coach:** David King **Physio:** John Chandler
Ground: Green Meadows Stadium, Bury Road, Stowmarket (01449 612533).
Directions: About 800 yds from Stowmarket BR station - turn right at 1st lights and head out of town over r'bout into Bury Road - ground on right.
Seats: 200 **Cover:** 450 **Capacity:** 2,000 **Floodlights:** Yes **Club Shop:** Yes
Programme: 20 pages, 50p **Editor:** John Gillingham (01449 674507). **Press Officer:**
Colours: Old gold & black **Change colours:** Red & black
Sponsor: **Founded:** 1883. **Nickname:** Stow
Midweek Matches: Wednesday **Reserves' Lge:** Essex & Suffolk Border
Record Attendance: 1,200 v Ipswich Town, friendly July 1994. At Cricket Meadow: 3,800 v Romford, FA Amtr Cup 1st Rd 15/12/51.
Previous Leagues: Ipswich & Dist./ Essex & Suffolk Border 25-52.
Players progressing to Football League: Craig Oldfield (Colchester), Les Tibbott, Ted Phillips & Brian Klug (Ipswich).
Clubhouse: Bar open 6.30pm onwards Mon-Fri, weekends 12.0pm onwards. Matchday food available.
95-96 Captain: Roger Aldis. **95-96 P.o.Y.:** Darren Scoulding **95-96 Top Scorer:** Tony Gayfer 21
Honours: Eastern Co's Lg R-up 91-92, Suffolk Premier Cup(4), Suffolk Snr Cup(10), Suffolk Jnr Cup.

SUDBURY TOWN Reserves

Chairman: Graeme Garden **President:** H D J Yallop.
Secretary: David Webb, 6 Melford Road, Sudbury, Suffolk CO10 6LS (01787 372352).
Manager/Press Officer: Richie Powling. **Asst Mgr/Coach:** David Crown. **Physio:** Tony Brightwell
Commercial Manager/Press Officer: Richie Powling, c/o the club (01787 370957).
Ground: Priory Stadium, Priory Walk, Sudbury, Suffolk (01787 379095).
Directions: Take Friars Street from town centre, pass cricket ground and continue to the 'Ship & Star'. Left into Priory Walk and continue to ground. Half mile and three quarters of a mile from bus and rail stations respectively.
Capacity: 5,000 **Cover:** 1,000 **Seats:** 300 **Floodlights:** Yes **Metal Badges:** Yes
Colours: All yellow **Change colours:** Red.
Previous Ground: Friars Street (until 1951).
Midweek home matchday: Wednesday

SUDBURY WANDERERS

Chairman: N Smith **President:** **Manager:** Mick Mills.
Secretary: Brian Tatum, 4 Beaconsfield Close, Sudbury, Suffolk CO10 6JR (01787 375840).
Ground: Brundon Lane, Sudbury, Suffolk (01787 376213).
Directions: From Sudbury centre follow Halstead/Chelmsford signs for about 1 mile. Take 1st right after railway bridge at foot of steep hill, and 1st right after sharp lefthand bend.
Seats: 200 **Cover:** 150 **Capacity:** 2,500 **Floodlights:** Yes **Founded:** 1958
Midweek Matchday: Tuesday **Programme:** With entry **Nickname:** Wanderers
Colours: Yellow/blue/blue **Change Colours:** All Red
Record Attendance: 248 v Woodbridge Town, Jewson Eastern Counties League Division One 20/4/93.
Clubhouse: Matchdays/ training nights.
Hons: Eastern Co's Lg Div 1 92-93, Ess. & Suff. Border Lg(2) 89-91 (R-up 88-89), Suffolk Snr Cup 90-91.

TIPTREE UNITED

Chairman: Frederick Byles **President:** Len Foakes **Manager:** Steve Sutton.
Secretary/Press Officer: Peter G Fidge, 77 Chelmer Road, Chelmsford, Essex CM2 6AA (0245 353667).
Ground: Chapel Road, Tiptree, Essex (0621 815213).
Directions: Enter town on B1023 - Chapel Road is left at second crossroads, ground 200yds on left. 3 miles from Kelverdon (BR). Served by Eastern National Colchester to Maldon bus.
t sa/(0/(01 **Cover:** 300 **Capacity:** 2,500 **Floodlights:** Yes
Founded: 1933.
Club colours: Red & white/black/black **Change colours:** All white. **Nickname:** Strawberries.
Midweek Matchday: Tuesday. **Previous Lges:** Essex & Suffolk Border/ Essex Snr 78-84
Record Attendance: 1,210 v Spurs, floodlight inauguration Dec 1990.
Programme: 30 pages, 30p **Editor:** Secretary
Sponsors: S Smith (Transport) **Reserves' Lge:** Essex & Herts Comb. **Club Shop:** No.
Local Newspapers: Colchester Evening Gazette, Essex County Standard.
Clubhouse details: Large bar, two snooker tables, pool, darts, netball, badminton, pigeon club, bingo. Dance hall seats 180, small hall seats 60. Open daily 7-11pm (all day Fri & Sat) and noon-2.30, 7-10.30 Sun.
Captain 95-96: . **Top Scorer 95-96:** **P.o.Y. 95-96:**
Honours: Essex Snr Tphy 80-81, Eastern Co's Lg 81-82 (Lg Cup 81-82 84-85), Essex Snr Lg R-up 75-76 77-78, Harwich Charity Cup(4).

WARBOYS TOWN

Chairman: Richard Kelly. **President:** G C Bowd **Manager:** Robbie Cook.
General Manager: Geoff Tuff.
Secretary: Brian Lewis, 29 Vinery Court, Ramsey, Cambs, PE17 1JZ (01487 710653)
Ground: Sports Field, Forge Way, off High Street, Warboys, Cambs (01487 823483).
Directions: Access through Forge Way, half way along south side of High Street.
Seats: None **Cover:** 200 **Capacity:** 2,000 **Floodlights:** Yes **Founded:** 1885.
Colours: Red & white/Black/Red. **Change colours:** White/maroon/maroon. **Nickname:** Witches.
Midweek Matches: Tuesday
Previous Leagues: Peterborough & District 46-48 56-88/ Utd Co's 50-56/ Huntingdonshire 48-50.
Record Attendance: 500 v Ramsey Town, Hunts Senior Cup Semi Final.
Programme: 12 pages, 30p **Programme Editor:** Martin England
Local Newspaper: Hunts Post (01480 411481).
Clubhouse: Bar, lounge, function hall. Open every evening & Sunday lunchtime. Various entertainments.
Matchday food & drink: Tea, coffee, cold drinks, confectionary, sandwiches, rolls.
Past Players progressing to Football League: Alex Chamberlain (Ipswich, Everton, Colchester).
Honours: Utd Co's Lg Div 2 R-up 54-55, P'boro Lg R-up(2) 59-60 61-62, P'boro Snr Cup 63-64, Hunts Snr Cup 26-27 28-29 31-32 32-33,94-95. (R-up 92-93), Hunts Scott Gatty Cup 30-31. Reserves: Hunts Benevolent Cup 57-58, Hunts Junior Cup 24-25 27-28 52-53, Hunts Lower Junior Cup 75-76 77-78. .gap 5

WATTON UNITED

Chairman: Dick Jessup **Vice-Chairman:** Phil Scott **President:** Malcolm Warner.
Secretary: D M Bealey, 11 Hickling Close, Swaffham, Norfolk PE37 7SE (01760 721869).
Manager: Dominic McCallam
Physio: M Kay.
Commercial Manager: Committee **Press Officer:** R Wordon
Ground: Watton Sports Centre, Dereham Road, Watton, Norfolk (01953 881281).
Directions: On A1075 towards Dereham about half a mile from junction with B1108.
Seats: 50 **Cover:** 150 **Capacity:** 2,000 **Floodlights:** Yes **Founded:** 1888.
Club colours: All white **Change colours:** Green/black/green **Nickname:** Brecklanders.
Midweek Matchday: Tuesday. **Previous Lges:** East Anglian/ Anglian Combination.
Club Sponsors: Style Windows **Record Gate:** 1,200 v Norwich City, floodlight inauguration 1985.
Programme: 25p **Programme Editor:** D M Bealey **Club Shop:** No.
Clubhouse: Watton 881281. **Reserve Team's League:** Anglian Combination.
Matchday food & drink: Tea, coffee, cold drinks, confectionary, burgers, soup, sandwiches, rolls.
Players progressing to Football League: Chris Watts (Norwich), Robert Taylor (Leyton Orient, Brentford).
95-96 Captain: **95-96 P.o.Y.:** **95-96 Top Scorer:**
Honours: Anglian Combination 66-67 67-68 85-86 (Lg Cup 66-67 69-70).

WISBECH TOWN

Chairman: E Anderson **Vice Chairman:** J D Patch **President:** J W A Chilvers
Secretary: J D Petch, 34 Walton Road, Wisbech, Cambs PE13 3EN, (01945 584333)
Manager: I Jones **Asst Manager:** S Shelton **Physio:** M Miller
Ground: Fenland Park, Lerowe Road, Wisbech, Cambs (01945 584176).
Directions: On Lerowe Road, a right turn off the B198 Lynn Road. Twenty minutes walk from town centre. Irregular bus services to Wisbech from Peterborough or March.
Seats: 258 **Cover:** 3,000 **Capacity:** 7,500 **Floodlights:** Yes **Club Shop:** Yes.
Programme: 40 pages, 75p **Editor:** C Smith **Press Officer:** R Green
Club colours: All red. **Change colours:** Yellow/green/yellow
Nickname: Fenmen. **Founded:** 1920. **Midweek Matchday:** Wednesday
Record Attendance: 8,004 v Peterborough United, Midland League 25/8/57.
Previous Lges: Peterborough/ Utd Co's 35-50/ Eastern Co's 50-52/ Midland 52-58/ Southern 58-70.
Players progressing to Football League: Chris Watts and Robert Taylor (both Norwich City).
Clubhouse: Open every day. Matchday food & drink; Tea, coffee, cold drinks, confectionary, burgers, hotdogs, soup, sandwiches, rolls.
Honours: FA Cup 2nd Rd 57-58 (1st Rd(5) 45-46 58-60 64-66), FA Vase SF 84-85 85-86, Southern Lg Div 1 61-62, Utd Co's Lg(4) 46-48 49-50 61-62(reserves)(R-up 48-49, Lg Cup 35-36 (R-up 46-47)), Midland Lg R-up 57-58, Eastern Co's Lg 71-72 76-77 90-91 (R-up 70-71 73-74 83-84 92-93, Lg Cup 50-51 70-71 71-72 (R-up 73-74 76-77 86-87), Cambs Invitation Cup(8) 52-53 55-56 57-58 74-76 81-83 91-92, East Anglian Cup 87-88 (R-up 40-41 48-49), Peterborough Lg 24-25 27-28 28-29 31-32 32-33, Peterborough Snr Cup 32-33 76-77 89-90.

WOODBRIDGE TOWN

Chairman: K Dixon **President:** J Coates
Secretary: JohnBennett, 67 Cumberland St, Woodbridge, Suffolk IP12 4AQ (01394 385973).
Manager/Coach: Malcolm Mackenzie **Asst Manager:** **Commercial Manager:** David Leech
Ground: Notcutts Park, Seckford Hall Road, Woodbridge, Suffolk (01394 385308).
Directions: Turning into Woodbridge off last r'bout from Lowestoft, or 1st r'bout from Ipswich. Take 1st turning left and 1st left again. Drive to ground at end of road on left.
Seats: 50 **Cover:** 200 **Capacity:** 3,000 **Floodlights:** Yes **Club Shop:**
Programme: 36p with entry **Editor:** D Crowley/K Dixon **Press Officer:** M Banthorpe
Colours: Black & white stripes/white/white **Change colours:** Blue/white/blue.
Sponsors: Posh Windows & Doors **Nickname:** The Woodpeckers. **Founded:** 1885.
Midweek Matcheday: Tuesday. **Reserves League:** Suff. & Ipswich
Record Attendance: 3,000 v Arsenal, floodlight opener 2/10/90.
Previous Leagues: Suffolk & Ipswich
Clubhouse: Visitors bar, lounge bar, function hall.Matchday Tea, coffee, cold drinks, hotdogs, soup, burgers, sandwiches, rolls. Also cooked meals after match.
95-96 Captain: Gary Barker. **95-96 Top Scorer:** Simon Fryatt **95-96 P.o.Y.:**
Honours: Suffolk Senior Cup(4); Eastern Counties Lg Cup 93-94, Lge Div 1 R-up 93-94; Suffolk Jun Cup (4); Ipswich Sen Lge (2).

WROXHAM

Chairman: Ray Bayles **President:** L King
Secretary: Chris Green, 24 Keys Drive, Wroxham, Norfolk NR12 8SS (01603 783936).
Manager: Bruce Cunningham **Asst Manager:** Keith Robson **Physio:** G Christmas
Ground: Trafford Park, Wroxham, Norfolk (01603 783583).
Directions: Arriving from Norwich turn left at Castle PH and keep left to ground. One and a half miles from Wroxham+Hoveton (BR). Buses 722, 724 and 717.
Seats: 50 **Cover:** 250 **Capacity:** 2,500 **Floodlights:** Yes **Club Shop:** No.
Programme: 20 pages with entry **Editor:** Ray Bayles (01603 403555). **Press Officer:** Secretary
Colours: Blue/white **Change colours:** Red/black. **Founded:** 1892.
Nickname: Yachtsmen. **Midweek Matchday:** Tuesday. **Reserve Lge:** Anglian Combination.
Record Attendance: 1,011 v Wisbech Town, Eastern Counties League Premier Division 16/3/93.
Players progressing to Football League: Matthew Metcalf (Brentford) 1993.
Previous Leagues: Norwich City/ East Anglian/ Norwich & Dist./ Anglian Comb. 64-88.
Clubhouse: Bar, pool, darts, carpet bowls etc. Matchday, Tea, coffee, cold drinks, burgers, hotdogs, soup, sandwiches, rolls.
95-96 Captain: Stu Larter. **95-96 P.o.Y.:** Darren Gill **95-96 Top Scorer:** Jon Rigby.
Club Record Goalscorer: Matthew Metcalf **Club Record Appearances:** Mark Halsey.
Honours: Eastern Co's Lg 91-92 92-93 94-95,R-Up: 94-95.(Lg Cup 92-93 (R-up 90-91), Div 1 88-89), Norfolk Snr Cup 92-93, Anglian Combination (6)(Lg Cup(7)The reserves completed the double in 94-95.

Warboys Town FC: Last seasons Division 1 second place, promoted to Premier.

Action from the match between Sudbury Wanderers & Clacton Town *Photo - Richard Brook*

DIVISION ONE CLUBS 1996-97

BRIGHTLINGSEA UNITED

Chairman: Graham Steady **Manager:** Frank Thompson.
Secretary: H J Beere, 108 Regent Road, Brighlingsea, Essex CO7 0NZ (01206 303122).
Ground: North Road, Brightlingsea, Essex (01206 304199).
Directions: B1027 Colchester-Clacton, B1029 from Thorrington Cross - follow Church Road into town, left into Spring Road, left into Church Road. Nearest station; Colchester then bus 78 to Brighlingsea.
Seats: 50 **Cover:** 250 **Capacity:** 2,000 **Floodlights:** Yes **Club Shop:** Yes.
Colours: Red+white/red/red. **Change colours:** Blue+White/blue/blue. **Nickname:** Oystermen.
Previous Leagues: Tendring Hundred, Essex & Suffolk Border, Essex Senior 1972-90.
Midweek Matches: Tuesday. **Record Gate:** 1,200 v Colchester, friendly 68-69.
Programme: 24 pages, 30p **Prog. Editor:** M Cole (01206 304430) **Founded:** 1887
Clubhouse details: Open matchadays and all evenings bar Sunday.
Matchday food & drink: Tea, coffee, cold drinks, confectionary, hotdogs, sandwiches, rolls.
Local Newspapers: Essex County Standard, Evening Gazette.
Honours: Essex Snr Lg 88-89 89-90 (Harry Fisher Mem. Tphy 89-90 (R-up 88-89), Lg Cup R-up 78-79), Eastern Co's Lg Div 1 R-up 90-91, Essex & Suffolk Border Lg Prem. Div Cup 71-72, Harwich Charity Cup 87-88, Worthington Evans Cup 76-77 77-78 78-79.

CAMBRIDGE CITY Reserves

See Cambridge City main entry in Dr Martens League page 440

CHATTERIS TOWN

Chairman: A Parish **President:** J Chambers **Manager:** Steve Taylor and Ian Edwards
Secretary: Anthony Summers, 41 The Elms, Chatteris, Cambs PE16 6JN (01354 692062).
Ground: West Street, Chatteris (01354 692139).
Directions: Entering Chatteris on A141 from Huntingdon turn right into West Street after by-pass roundabout.
Seats: 250 **Cover:** 400 **Capacity:** 2,000 **Floodlights:** Yes **Founded:** 1920.
Colours: White/sky/sky. **Change colours:** Red & black/black/black. **Nickname:** Lillies.
Previous League: Peterborough **Midweek Matches:** Wednesday **Pennants:** Yes.
Clubhouse details: Bar & tea bar. **Record Gate:** 2,000 v March Town Utd, League 5/5/88.
Programme: 12 pages, 20p **Previous Ground:** First Drove
Matchday food & drink: Tea, coffee, cold drinks, confectionary, burgers, hotdogs, sandwiches, soup, rolls.
Players progressing to Football League: Andy Rogers (Reading, Southend, Plymouth), Dave Gregory (Plymouth).
Honours: Eastern Counties Lg Cup 67-68, Peterborough Premier Lg(3).

CORNARD UNITED

Chairman: David Nichells. **Vice-Chairman:** Jim McLoughlin. **President:** Len Hodgson
Secretary: Richard Powell, 14 North Rise, Great Cornard, Sudbury, Suffolk CO10 0DE (01787 371671).
Manager: Chris Symes. **Asst Manager:** **Physio:** Mike Ford.
Ground: Blackhouse Lane Sportsfield, Great Cornard, Suffolk (01787 376719).
Directions: Left off r'bout on A134 coming from Ipswich/Colchester into Sudbury, follow signs for Country Park - ground is immediately opposite along Blackhouse Lane.
Seats: 250 **Cover:** 500 **Capacity:** 2,000 **Floodlights:** Yes **Club Shop:** No.
Programme: 16 pages **Editor:** TBA
Colours: Blue/white **Change colours:** All white.
Sponsors: Angelo Smith. **Nickname:** Ards. **Founded:** 1964.
Midweek Matches: Tuesday. **Reserve League:** Essex & Suffolk Border.
Record Attendance: 330 v Sudbury Town, Eastern Floodlit League 4/2/92.
Previous Leagues: Sudbury Sunday 64-65/ Bury St Edmunds & District 65-72/ Colchester 71-78/ Essex & Suffolk Border 78-89.
Clubhouse: Open matchdays & Sunday lunchtimes. Matchday Tea, coffee, cold drinks, confectionary, hotdogs, burgers, soup, sandwiches, rolls.
95-96 Captain: Andy McLoughlin **95-96 Top Scorer:** Andy McLoughlin **95-96 P.o.Y.:** Steven Arnold
Club Record Appearances: Malcolm Fisher. **Club Record Goalscorer :** Andy Smiles.
Honours: Eastern Co's Lg Div 1 89-90 (Lg Cup R-up 92-93), Essex & Suffolk Border Lg 88-89 (Lg Cup 88-89), Suffolk Snr Cup 89-90, Suffolk Jnr Cup R-up 84-85.

DOWNHAM TOWN

Chairman: John Fysh **President:** T G Barker **Manager:** Steve Tyres.
Secretary: F.Thorne, 6 Maple Rd., Downham Market, Norfolk, PE38 9PY. (01366 382563)
Ground: Lynn Road, Downham Market, Norfolk (01366 388424).
Directions: One and a quarter miles from Downham Market (BR) - continue to town clock, turn left and ground is three quarters of a mile down Lynn Road.
Seats: None **Cover:** Yes **Capacity:** 1,000 **Floodlights:** Yes **Founded:** 1881.
Colours: Red & white/red/red **Change colours:** Sky/Navy/sky. **Nickname:** Town
Midweek Matches: Wednesday. **Previous Leagues:** Peterborough
Record Attendance: 292 v Diss Town, Jewson League Division One 1991/92.
Clubhouse: Open matchdays **Programme:** By Barnes Promotions, with entry
Matchday food & drink: Tea, coffee, cold drinks, confectionary, hotdogs, burgers, soup, sandwiches, rolls.
Honours: P'boro Lg(5) 62-63 73-74 78-79 86-88, Norfolk Senior Cup 63-64 65-66 (R-up(3) 66-69).

ELY CITY

Chairman: Brian Jordan **Manager:** David Pinkowski & Tony Lyes
Secretary: Derek Oakey, 37 Fordham Road, Soham, Nr Ely, Cambs CB7 5AH (01353 722141).
Ground: Unwin Sports Ground, Downham Road (01353 662035).
Directions: A10 Ely by-pass turn off for Downham. 3 miles (approx) from Ely (BR).
Seats: 150 **Cover:** 350 **Capacity:** 1,500 **Floodlights:** Yes **Founded:** 1885
Colours: All red **Change colours:** All jade. **Nickname:** Robins
Metal Badges: Yes.
Previous Lges: Peterborough/ Central Alliance 58-60. **Midweek Matches:** Tuesday
Record Gate: 260 v Soham, Eastern Co's Lg Div 1, 12/4/93. *At old ground: 4,260 v Torquay, FA Cup 56-57*
Clubhouse details: Open matchdays **Local Press:** Ely Standard (01353 667831)**Programme:** 20p
Matchday food & drink: Tea, coffee, cold drinks, confectionary, hotdogs, burgers, sandwiches, rolls.
Hons: Cambs Snr Cup 47-48, Eastern Co's Lg R-up 69-70 (Lg Cup 79-80), FA Cup 1st Rd 56-56 (2-6 v Torquay).

HAVERHILL ROVERS

Chairman: Terry McGerty **President:** N Haylock **Secretary:** Chris Rice, 23 Ovington Place, Haverhill, Suffolk. CB9 0BA. (01440 712396)
Manager: Derek Richardson. **Asst Mgr:** Paul Gaffin. **Physio:** Stan Goodall.
Press Officer: Ray Esdale
Ground: Hamlet Croft, (0440 702137). **Directions:** Centre of Haverhill.
Seats: 200 **Cover:** 200 **Capacity:** 3,000 **Floodlights:** Yes **Founded:** 1886.
Colours: All red **Change colours:** All blue **Prev. League:** Essex & Suffolk Border.
Record Attendance: 1,537 v Warrington Town, FA Vase QF 86-87. **Nickname:** Rovers.
Midweek Matches: Tuesday **Programme:** 24 pages, 40p **(Editor:** C.Nunn)
Clubhouse details: Open matchdays and functions.
Matchday food & drink: Tea, coffee, cold drinks, confectionary, burgers, hotdogs.
Local Paper: Haverhill Echo. **Players progressing to the Football League:** R Wilkins (Colchester).
Honours: Eastern Co's Lg 78-79 (Lg Cup 64-65), E & S Border Lg 62-63 63-64, East Anglian Cup 90-91.

HISTON

Chairman: Gareth Baldwin **President:** G P Muncey **Manager:** Graham Daniels.
Secretary: Gareth Baldwin, Tanglewood, 5 Caxton Lane, Foxton, Cambridgeshire CB2 6SR (01223 872246).
Ground: Bridge Road, Impington, Cambridge (01223 232301).
Directions: Leave A45 northern Cambridge bypass on B1049 (signposted Histon and Cottenham). Ground half a mile on right. 5 miles from Cambridge (BR). Bus No. 104.
Seats: 250 **Cover:** 200 **Capacity:** 2,250 **Floodlights:** Yes **Founded:** 1904.
Programme: 16 pages, 30p **Editor:** Gareth Baldwin.
Colours: Red and black/black/black. **Change colours:** Blue and white/blue/blue.
Midweek Matches: Tuesday
Record Attendance: 2,400 v K. Lynn, FA Cup.
Previous Leagues: Cambridgeshire 04-48/ Spartan 48-60/ Delphian 60-63/ Athenian 63-65.
Clubhouse details: Bar/lounge open Tues-Sun evenings, Sun lunctimes and matchdays. Matchday food & drink: Tea, coffee, cold drinks, soup, rolls.
Honours: Eastern Co's Lg Cup 90-91; Cambridge Invitation Cup 77-78 79-80 (R-up 50-51 52-53 53-54); Spartan Lg Div 1 (East) 50-51; Cambs Chall Cup; Cambs Lg Section; Kershaw Sen A:

IPSWICH WANDERERS

Chairman: A.Haste. **President:** P.Emmerson. **Manager:** Alan Dilloway
Secretary: Martin Head, 246 Sidelate Lane, Ipswich, Suffolk. IP4 3DH (01473 273811)
Ground: Humberdoucey Road, Ipswich, Suffolk (01473 728581).
Directions: Take Woodbridge Road out of Ipswich,then left fork into Playford Road.Take first left into Humberdoucy Lane Ground 300yds on right.
Seats: 50 **Cover:** Yes **Capacity:** 2,000 **Floodlights:** Yes **Club Shop:**
Programme: Yes. **Editor:**
Colours: Blue/blue/white **Change colours:** Red & black/red/red.
Sponsors: Car Glass & Trim. **Nickname:** Wanderers. **Founded:** 1983.
Midweek Matches: Wednesday
Previous Leagues: Little David Sunday
Record Attendance: 335 v Woodbridge, ECL Div 1 4/4/94.
Clubhouse: Bar, Tea, coffee, cold drinks, confectionary, burgers, hotdogs, sandwiches, rolls.
95-96 Captain: Murray Osmay **95-96 Top Scorer:** Roy Edwards **95-96 P.o.Y.:** Roy Edwards
Club Record Goalscorer: **Club Record Appearances:**

MALDON TOWN

Chairman: Bob Large. **Manager:** Ben Embery.
Secretary: Phil Robinson.9 Lyndhurst Drive, Bicknarce, Essex CM3 4XL (01245 222633)
Commercial Manager: Eddie Hawkins.
Ground: Wallace Binder Ground, Park Drive, Maldon CM9 7XX (01621 853762).
Seats: **Cover:** **Capacity:** **Floodlights:** **Founded:** 1946.
Colours: Blue & white/blue/blue & white **Change colours:** Red & black/black/red **Programme:** Yes
Previous Lges: Eastern Counties, Essex & Suffolk Border. **Previous Ground:** Fambridge Road (pre-1994).
Top Scorer 94-95: Nail Harris 16.
Hons: Essex Snr Lg 84-85 (Sportsmanship Award 87-88,88-89,94-95, Reserve Shield 93-94), Reserve Cup:94-95, Essex & Suffolk Border Lg 55-56 (Cup 64-65), Essex Intermediate Cup 51-52, Tolleshunt D'Arcy Cup 93-94.

MILDENHALL TOWN

Chairman: B Brigden **President:** J E Butcher **Manager:** Mark Goldsack.
Secretary: B W Hensby, 14 Sanderling Close, Mildenhall, Suffolk IP28 7LF (01638 715772).
Ground: Recreation Way, Mildenhall, Suffolk (01638 713449).
Directions: Next to swimming pool/car, quarter of a mile from town centre.
Seats: None **Capacity:** 2,000 **Midweek Matchday:** Tuesday **Founded:** 1890.
Club colours: Amber/black/black. **Change colours:** All white **Nickname:** Town or yellows.
Previous Leagues: Bury & District/ Cambs Lg 2B, 1B & Premier.
Record Attendance: 350 v Norwich City, friendly 22/7/89.
Programme: Free with admission **Editor:** F Marshall **Clubhouse:** Open matchdays & functions.
Matchday food & drink: Tea, coffee, cold drinks, confectionary, sandwiches, rolls.
Local Newspapers: Bury Free Press, Newmarket Journal, Cambridge Evening News.
Honours: Suffolk Junior Cup 1899-1900.

NEEDHAM MARKET

Chairman: P Coleman **Managers:** Jim Fitzgerald & Wayne Leggett
Secretary: D Bloomfield, 33 Quinton Road, Needham Market, Suffolk IP6 8DA (01449 720693)
Fixture Secretary: I Croft, (01449 676517)
Ground: Bloomfields, Quniton Road, Needham Market, Suffolk (01449 721000)
Colours: All Green & White **Change Coloures:** White/navy/navy
Midweek Matchday: Tuesday **Programme Editor:** P Coleman (01449 711295)

NORWICH UNITED

Chairman: John Hilditch **Vice-Chairman:** J Cubitt **President:** Michael Miles
Secretary: M Barber, Plantation Park Blofield, (01603 716963)
Manager: S Rushbrook/ M Brown **Coach:** **Physio:** Mike Chapman.
Ground: Plantation Road, Blofield, Norwich, Norfolk NR13 4PL (01603 716963).
Directions: Half a mile from Blofield village - coming from Norwich on Yarmouth Road turn left in Blofield

at Kings Head pub and follow to Plantation Rd (ground on right after bridge over bypass). Half-hour walk Brundall BR (Norwich-Yarmouth line).
Seats: 100 **Cover:** 1,000 **Capacity:** 3,000 **Floodlights:** Yes **Club Shop:**
Programme: 24 pages, 50p **Editor:** Secretary
Colours: Yellow & blue **Change colours:** All red
Sponsor: **Nickname:** Planters. **Founded:** 1903.
Midweek Matches: Tuesday
Record Attendance: 401 v Wroxham, League match, 2/10/91.
Clubhouse: Matchday food & drink: Tea, coffee, cold drinks, hotdogs, burgers, soup, sandwiches, rolls.
95-96 Captain: Graham Holden. **95-96 Top Scorers:** Terry Parke **95-96 P.o.Y.:**
Club Record Goalscorer: M Money **Club Record Appearances:** Tim Sayer.
Honours: Eastern Co's Lg Div 1 90-91 (R-up 89-89, Lg Cup 91-92), Anglian Combination 88-89.

SOMERSHAM TOWN

Chairman: Bill Bailey. **Vice-Chairman:** Norman Burkett **President:** Jack Marjason
Secretary: Norman Burkett, 6 West Leys, St Ives, Cambs. PE17 3SX (01480 464411).
Managers: Ian Boon **Coach:** Jim Wallace **Physio:** Alan Magnus
Ground: West End Ground, St Ives Road, Somersham, Cambs (01487 843384).
Directions: On A604 St Ives to Somersham on right as you enter town.
Seats: None **Cover:** 200 **Capacity:** 1,500 **Floodlights:** Yes **Club Shop:**
Programme: 76 pages, 30p **Editor/Press Officer:** Dave Hardy (01487 840441)
Colours: All old gold **Change colours:** Sky/maroon/sky
Sponsors: Rapidtech (UK) Ltd. **Nickname:** Westenders **Founded:** 1893.
Midweek Matchday: Tuesday. **Reserve League:** Kershaw Senior A.
Record Attendance: 538 v Norwich City, floodlight inauguration 19/11/91.
Previous League: Peterborough & Dist.
Clubhouse: Open Friday, Sat/Sun lunchtimes.
95-96 Captain: Ian Wilson. **95-96 Top Scorer:** Jamie Donald **95-96 P.o.Y.:** Martin Parr
Club Record Goalscorer & Appearances: Terry Butcher
Honours: Hunts Snr Cup 72-73 94-95, Peterboro Snr Cup 84-85, Hinchingbrooke Cup 53-54, Cambs Lg Premier B Div 94-95(reserves).

Robbie Cook's last minute goal gives Warboys a 2-1 win over Kings Lynn Resreves and an eighth cosecutive league win

STANWAY ROVERS

Chairman: B.Peachey. **President:** Colin Henson.
Secretary: Alan Brierley, 19 Barleyb Way, Stanway, Colchester, Essex CO3 5YD (01206 572439).
Manager: Phil Bloss. **Physios:**John Chandler/Barry Wreford.
Ground: 'Hawthorns', New Farm Road, Stanway, Colchester, Essex (01206 578187).
Directions: Take turn off marked Stanway off A12. Turn right and go over flyover to Tollgate r'bout, 1st right into Villa Rd, after 25 yards turn left into Church Rd, 200 yards on left into New Farm Rd, ground 400 yards on left. Nearest BR station is Colchester North.
Seats: None **Cover:** 200 **Capacity:** 1,500 **Floodlights:** Yes **Founded:** 1955
Colours: Yellow/black/yellow **Change colours:** White/black/red **Nickname:** Rovers.
Reserves' Lge: Essex & Suff. Border **Record Gate:** 156 v Hadleigh, ECL Division One 10/7/94.
Club Shop: Club pennants, ties sold
Prev. Lges: Colchester & E Essex/ Essex & Suff. Border (pre-1992).
Previous Ground: Stanway Secondary School, Winstree Road (20 years).
Programme: 12 pages, 50p **Programme Editor:** Alan Brierley (Stanway Sid).
Midweek matchday: Wednesday **Sponsors:** Collier & Catchpole.
Record win: 8-1 v Swaffham Town (H), Eastern Counties League Division One 26/3/94.
Record defeat:0-10 v Sudbury Townt (A), E.C.L. Cup.
Players progressing to Football League: Andy Farrell(Colchester,Burnley,Wigan).
Clubhouse: 6.45-11pm evenings, noon-11pm Sats. Rolls, soup, tea, coffee etc available matchdays.
Honours: Essex Intermediate Cup R-up 89-90 90-91, Essex & Suffolk Border Lg R-up 91-92 (Div 1 86-87, Div 2 81-81 85-86), Essex Junior Cup R-up 74-75 (QF 73-74).

SWAFFHAM TOWN

Chairman: S Choppen. **President:**j.Smith. **Manager:** M.Simmons.
Secretary: David Ward, 2 Princes Street, Swaffham, Norfolk PE37 7BX (0760 722516).
Ground: Shoemakers Lane, Swaffham, Norfolk (0760 722700).
Seats: None **Cover:** **Capacity:** 2,000 **Floodlights:** Yes **Founded:** 1892.
Colours: Black & white/black/black. **Change:** Blue/blue/yellow. **Nickname:** Pedlars
Midweek Matchay: Tuesday. **Previous Leagues:** Dereham, Anglian Combination
Record Attendance: 250 v Downham Town, Jewson Eastern Co's League Cup 3/9/91.
Clubhouse details: Open Tuesday, Thursday, Saturday & Sunday lunchtimes & evenings.
Matchday food & drink: Tea, coffee, cold drinks, confectionary, rolls (occasionally).
Programme: 36 pages, 30p **Hons:** Norfolk Snr Cup(2), Anglian Comb. 89-90 (Div 1 88-89).

THETFORD TOWN

Chairman: M Bailey **Vice-Chairman:** B Richards
Secretary: John Wordley, 4 Claxton Close, Thetford, Norfolk IP24 1BA (01842 762530).
Manager: G Hughes S Allen **Coach:** John Denniss. **Physio:**
Ground: Mundford Road, Thetford, Norfolk (01842 766120).
Directions: Turn off bypass (A11) at A143 junction - ground 800yds next to sports ground
Seats: 400 **Cover:** 400 **Capacity:** 2,000 **Floodlights:** Yes **Club Shop:** No.
Programme: 48 p, with entry **Editor:** G Mills (01480 385425). **Press Officer:** Mick Burgess.
Colours: Claret+blue/sky/royal blue. **Change:** Sky & navy checks/black/white.
Sponsors: Sportscene **Nickname:** **Founded:** 1884.
Midweek Matches: Tuesday **Reserves League:** Anglian Comb.
Record Attendance: 394 v Diss Town, Norfolk Snr Cup 23/1/91.
Players progressing to Football League: Dick Scott (Norwich City, Cardiff City), Kevin Seggie (Leeds United), Simon Milton (Ipswich Town).
Previous Leagues: Norfolk & Suffolk
Clubhouse: Bar, teas, refreshments, light meals & snacks
95-96 Captain: Clive Denniss. **95-96 P.o.Y.:** Morgan Crane **95-96 Top Scorer:** Marcus Hawkin
Honours: Eastern Co's Lg R-up 89-90, Norfolk & Suffolk Lg 54-55, Norfolk Snr Senior Cup 47-48 90-91.

WHITTON UNITED

Chairman: John Watkins
Secretary: David Gould, 7 Karen Close, Ipswich, Suffolk IP1 4LP (0473 253838).
Fixture Secretary: Mark Woodward, (01473 742805)
Ground: King Geore V Playing Field, Norwich Road, Ipswich, Suffolk.
Colours: Green & white/green/green **Change Colours:** All orange.
Previous Name: Whitton FC **Programme Editor:** Ian Vernau (0473 680592).
Midweek Matchday: Wednesday

Norwich United FC:

Whitton United FC:
Back Row (L-R); Chris Wells (Trainer), Colin Macrow, Damian Pryke, Andy Callaghan, Mick Clement, Carl Henry, Paul Wade, John Green (Trainer), Brian Swift (Manager).
Front Row; Daniel Abbott, Daniel Eaton, Graham Pooley, Kevin Leathers, Daniel Wade (Mascot), Gary Hart, Jason Bixby, Micky Squirrel, Glen Read (Mascot).

HELLENIC FOOTBALL LEAGUE

FEEDER TO:

Beazer Homes League

President: Morman Matthews **Chairman:** G Poole

Press Officer: T G Cuss

Secretary: M J Jenkins,

3 Leamington Drive, Faringdon, Oxon. SN7 7JZ (01367 240042)

The significant alterations to the Constitution relate to the promotion of Cirencester Town FC to The Southern League now known as the Doc Martins League and the retention of Bicester Town FC and Didcot Town FC both of whom finished in relagation positions, in the Premier Division. Purton FC, the Champions of Division One have been unable to fulfill the facilities criteria for promotion to the Premier Division and in consequence are not able to be promoted. Runners-up in Division One Wantage Town have been admitted to the Premier Division subject to payment of a bond of £500 to have their facilities in accordance with the division's criteria by the start of the season. Wantage Town FC are presently engaged in discussions with the Local Authority as to the planning aspects of their floodlights.

The clubs in danger of relegation from Division One into the Feeder Leagues namely Cirencester United and Yarnton will retain their postions within the League because no suitable clubs have applied from the feeder leagues. Rayners Lane have withdrawn from the League due to travelling and other difficulties but Ross Town have been admitted to the league. They have their own facilities but have signed a one year ground sharing agreement with Cinderford Town until their own have been completed and approved by the League Management Committee.

The leagues Floodlight Competition will again be run as a Knock-Out Cup competition.

There has been a reorganisation of the Reserve Section Football. Cirencester Town Reserves will remain with the league despite the promotion of their first team. Banbury United, Carterton Town and Didcot Town who finished in the bottom three of Reserve Premier Division will take places in the new Reserve Division Two. Cirencester United, Kidlington and Easington Sports who finished in that order at the top of Reserve Division One will take their places in the new Reserve Division One. Circester Town will play in Reserve Division One and there are two new clubs admitted to Division Two namely Lambourn Sports and Wootton Bassett Town.

The meeting also heard that a number of clubs presently in membership of the Senior Division have complied with the latest stages of the ground grading criteria. The clubs who had until 1st June 96 for compliance were not named named at the meeting. They will be required to deposit a Bond with the League Management Committee pending completion of the required works.

The Hungerford Cup awarded to Clubs showing the most improvement on and off the field, was awarded to Cirecester Town. Bicester Town were awarded the Premier Division Sportsmanship Trophy with Letcombe winning The Division One award. The Clubs Linesmans Award for Reserve Teams was won by W Monell of Almondsbury.

Trevor Cuss

HELLENIC LEAGUE ROLL of HONOUR 1995-96

Premier Division Champions	Cirencester Town
Premier Division Runner-up	Brackley Town
Premier Division Challenge Cup Winners	Cirencester Town
Premier Division Challenge Cup Finalists	Shortwood United
Division One Champions	Purton
Division One Runners-up	Wantage Town
Division One Challenge Cup Winners	Ardley United
Division One Challenge Cup Finalists	Milton United

COUNTY CUPS

Berks and Bucks Senior Trophy Finalist	Lambourn Sports
Gloucestershire Trophy Winners	Cirencester Town
Gloucestershire Trophy Finalist	Endsleigh
Gloucestershire Senior Amateur Cup Winners	Endsleigh Reserves
Wiltshire Senior Cup Winners	Highworth Town

FINAL LEAGUE TABLES 1995/96

Premier Div	P	W	D	L	F	A	Pts
1. Cirencester Tn	34	24	8	2	69	24	80
2. Brackley Town	34	19	12	3	60	32	69
3. Lambourn Spts	34	21	5	8	71	41	68
4. Tuffley Rovers	34	20	7	7	78	46	67
5. Burnham	34	20	4	10	66	37	64
6. Swindon S/mar	34	20	3	11	82	33	63
7. Endsleigh	34	16	7	11	56	41	55
8. North Leigh	34	15	4	15	66	62	49
9. Carterton Tn	34	13	9	12	57	59	48
10. Abingdon Utd	34	13	4	17	49	55	43
11. Fairford Town	34	10	10	14	49	52	40
12. Almondsbury T	34	10	7	17	53	54	37
13. Shortwood Utd	34	10	5	19	53	82	35
14. Kintbury Rang	34	8	9	17	45	74	33
15. Banbury United	34	8	6	20	40	66	30
16. Highworth Tn	34	9	3	22	36	80	30
17. Didcot Town	34	7	7	20	39	88	28
18. Bicester Town	34	6	4	24	37	80	22

Div One	P	W	D	L	F	A	Pts
1. Purton	34	22	6	6	79	40	72
2. Wantage Town	34	21	8	5	66	34	71
3. Milton United	34	18	8	8	102	63	62
4. Hallen	34	16	9	9	75	49	57
5. Harrow Hill	34	16	9	9	57	38	57
6. Pegasus Juns	34	15	7	12	76	62	52
7. Kidlington	34	13	9	12	73	59	48
8. Cheltenham Ss	34	14	6	14	71	71	48
9. Ardley United	34	13	6	15	47	60	45
10. Wootton Bass T	34	12	9	13	50	64	45
11. Clanfield	34	9	12	13	54	61	39
12. Bishops Cleeve	34	10	9	15	50	65	39
13. Rayners Lane	34	9	11	14	51	66	38
14. Easington Spts	34	9	10	15	45	64	37
15. Headington A	34	10	5	19	51	72	35
16. Letcombe	34	9	8	17	38	65	35
17. Yarnton	34	9	6	19	45	84	33
18. Cirencester Utd	34	8	8	18	53	66	32

HELLINIC FOOTBALL LEAGUE PREMIER DIVISION CUP 95-96

First Round;

Almondsbury Town v Abingdon United 3-2
Kintbury Rangers v Cirencester Town 0-4

Second Round;

Bicester Town v Carterton Town 0-3
Almondsbury Town v Shortwood United 2-3(aet)
North Leigh v Lambourn Sports 1-0
Fairford Town v Cirencester Town 2-3
Didcot Town v Burnham 1-3
Endsleigh v Brackley Town 2-2, 0-1
Gighworth Town v Swindon Supermarine 0-6
Banbury United v Tuffley Rovers 1-3

Third Round;

Burnham v Brackley Town 2-3
North Leigh v Cirencester Town 0-2
Swindon Supermarine v Shortwood Utd 1-2
Tuffley Rovers v Carterton Town 0-3

Semi-Finals;

Cirencester Town v Brackley Town 1-0, 3-2
Carterton Town v Shortwood United 2-2, 0-1

Final: Cirencester Town v Shortwood United 2-1

HELLENIC FOOTBALL LEAGUE DIVISION ONE CUP 95-96

First Round;

Kidlington v Cheltenham Saracens 2-3
Pegasus Juniors v Yarnton 2-1

Second Round;

Hallen v Headington Amateurs 0-3
Pegasus Juniors v Cheltenham Saracens 3-1
Wantage Town v Ardley United 0-2
Harrow Hill v Bishops Cleeve 1-2
Cirencester United v Easington Sports 2-3
Wootton Bassett v Purton 2-0
Clanfield v Rayners Lane 1-3
Milton United v Letcombe 4-2

Third Round;

Ardley United v Rayners Lane 5-3
Easington Sports v Milton United 0-4
Pegasus Juniors v Headington Amateurs 2-1(aet)
Bishops Cleeve v Wootton Bassett 2-5

Semi-Finals;

Ardley United v Wootton Bassett 3-1, 5-0
Milton United v Pegasus Juniors 0-0, 4-2(aet)

Final; Ardley United v Milton United 1-0

HELLENIC LEAGUE Premier Division Ten Year Records

	86/7	87/8	88/9	89/0	90/1	91/2	92/3	93/4	94/5	95/6
Abingdon Town	1	2	-	-	-	-	-	-	-	-
Abingdon United	6	4	3	3	7	6	15	12	11	10
Almondsbury Town	-	-	-	7	10	3	15	4	15	17
Banbury United	-	-	-	-	8	10	11	3=	8	15
Bicester Town	14	10	6	6	3	9	9	7	10	18
Bishops Cleeve	-	16	10	16	14	18	-	-	-	-
Brackley Town	-	-	-	-	-	-	-	-	14	2
Burnham	-	-	-	-	-	-	-	-	-	5
Carterton Town	-	-	-	-	12	17	-	-	13	9
Cinderford Town	-	-	-	-	-	5	5	6	1	-
Cirencester Town	-	-	-	-	-	2	4	13	6	1
Didcot Town	-	5	8	15	4	7	18	-	-	17
Endsleigh	-	-	-	-	-	-	-	-	-	7
Fairford Town	15	8	4	5	2	11	12	5	2	11
Headington Amateurs	-	-	-	12	5	12	13	16	-	-
Highworth Town	-	-	-	-	-	-	-	-	15	16
Hounslow Town	2	-	-	-	9	-	-	-	-	-
Kintbury Rangers	-	-	15	8	11	14	14	18	16	14
Lambourn Sports	-	-	-	-	-	-	-	-	-	3
Milton United	-	-	-	-	1	4	3	11	-	-
Moreton Town	8	12	7	13	17	16	2	1	-	-
Morris Motors	7	14	-	-	-	-	-	-	-	-
Newport AFC	-	-	-	1	-	-	-	-	-	-
North Leigh	-	-	-	-	-	-	-	14	4	8
Pegasus Juniors	12	17	5	9	15	13	17	-	9	-
Rayners Lane	13	13	13	11	13	15	10	9	-	-
Ruislip Manor	-	-	-	18	-	-	-	-	-	-
Sharpness Athletic	5	7	2	4	-	-	-	-	-	-
Shortwood United	3	3	11	2	6	1	7	2	5	13
Supermarine	11	15	14	17	-	-	-	-	-	-
Swindon Athletic	9	6	9	10	16	8	-	-	-	-
Swindon Supermarine	-	-	-	-	-	-	8	8	3	6
Thame United	17	9	-	-	-	-	-	-	-	-
Tuffley Rovers	-	-	-	-	-	-	-	10	7	4
Viking Sports	4	11	17	-	-	-	-	-	-	-
Wallingford	16	18	16	-	-	-	-	-	-	-
Wantage Town	18	-	12	14	18	-	16	3=	-	-
Wollen Sports	-	-	-	-	-	-	1	17	-	-
Yate Town	10	1	1	-	-	-	-	-	-	-
No of Clubs Competing	18	18	17	18	18	18	18	18	16	18

The NORMAN MATTHEWS FLOODLIGHT CUP 1995-96

First Round;

Endsleigh v Highworth Town 3-1, 5-0

Didcot Town v North Leigh 0-1, 0-2

Second Round:

Bicester Town v Kintbury Rangers 2-0, 2-3

Fairford Town v Endsleigh 1-1, 0-3

Lambourn Sports v Almondsbury Town 2-0, 2-2

Tuffley Rovers v Swindon Supermarine 1-0, 0-5

Carterton Town v Brackley Town 1-0, 4-0

Burnham v North Leigh 2-1, 0-2

Abingdon United v Banbury United 3-0, 5-0

Cirencester Town v Shortwood United 0-1, 4-0

Third Round;

Cirencester Town v Endsleigh 1-1, 1-0

Swindon Supermarine v Lambourn Spts 3-0, 4-0

Abingdon Utd v Bicester Tn 1-0, 1-2, (6-7pen)

Carterton Tn v North Leigh 2-1, 1-2, (4-2pen)

Semi-Finals;

Bicester Town v Carterton Town 2-1, 3-2

Cirencester Tn v Swindon Supermarine 1-2, 2-1, (4-5pen)

Final; Swindon Supermarine v Bicester Town 2-2, (4-5 penalties)

PREMIER DIVISION CLUBS 1996-97

ABINGDON UNITED

Chairman: John Blackmore **Vice-Chairman:** A White **President:**
Secretary: Terry Hutchinson, 41 Austin Place, Dunmore Farm Estate, Abingdon, Oxon OX14 1LT (01235 559019)
Manager: R Hayward **Coach:** P Storey **Physio:** A Wise
Press Officer: W Fletcher (0235 520255.
Ground: Northcourt Road, Abingdon OX14 1PL (01235 520255).
Directions: From north (Oxford) leave A34 at Abingdon north sign and Northcourt Rd is 1st major turning after r'bout. From South, East or West leave Abingdon on A4183 and turn left into Northcourt Rd after 1 mile. 2 miles from Redley (BR)
Seats: 52 **Cover:** 120 **Capacity:** 2,000 **Floodlights:** Yes **Founded:** 1946
Colours: Blue & yellow/blue/blue **Change colours:** All yellow **Nickname:** The U's
Reserves' Lge: Hellenic Res section **Previous league:** North Berks **Prev. Grnds:** None
Programme: 30p **Programme Editor:** W Fletcher, ACJI (0235 20255).
Midweek home matchday: Tuesday **Record Gate:** 500 v Newport AFC 1990.
Clubhouse: Two bars, food available. Open normal pub hours every day.
Club record appearances: D Webb.
Honours: N Berks Lg 53-54 (Lg Cup R-up 53-54, Charity Shield 52-53), Hellenic Div 1 R-up 76-77 81-82 (Lg Cup R-up 89-90, Div 1 Cup 65-66 81-82 (R-up 66-67, Reserve Cup R-up 93-94), Berks & Bucks Snr Cup R-up 83-84, Berks & Bucks Snr Tphy R-up 93-94.

ALMONDSBURY TOWN

Chairman: F David Pick **President:** Peter Howarth
Secretary: D W Winstone, 30 Cherington, Yate, Bristol BS17 4UZ (01454 323877)
Manager: Steve Jefferies **Physio:** Steve Watkins
Ground: Oaklands Park, Almondsbury, Bristol (01454 612220).
Directions: Adjacent to M5 junction 16 - follow A38 Thornbury - ground first left. 4 miles from Bristol Parkway (BR). County bus services to Thornbury, Stroud and Gloucester.
Seats: None **Cover:** No **Capacity:** 2,000 **Floodlights:** Yes **Founded:** 1897
Colours: All blue **Change colours:** White/blue/blue.
Record Gate: Hellenic Cup Final replay 89-90.
Previous Leagues: Bristol Weslyan/ Bristol Suburban/ Bristol Premier Comb./ Glos Co.
Previous Ground: Almondsbury Rec. (until 1986). **Programme:** 20 pages 25p
Nickname: Almonds. **Midweek Matchday:** Tuesday
Clubhouse: 7 days, all sports, refreshments, function room, entertainment, skittles.
Hons: FA Vase R-up 78-79 (SF 77-78), Glos Co. Lg(4) 76-78 79-81 (R-up 75-76 81-82), GFA Chal. Tphy 78-79 (R-up 80-81), Avon Prem. Comb. 74-75, Glos Snr Amtr Cup 87-88, Hellenic Lg 83-84 (R-up 82-83, Lg Cup(2) 83-85).

BANBURY UNITED

Chairman: J Breslin **Vice Chairman:** N/A **President:** D K Jesson
Secretary: B Worsley, c/o Sol Systems, Unit 4 Mallorie Hse, Beaumont Rd, Banbury, OX16 7RH (01295 255536)
Manager: Ian Bowyer **Asst Manager:** Tony Rose **Physio:** John Source
Ground: The Stadium, off Station Rd, Banbury, Oxon (01295 263354).
Directions: M40 jct 11, follow signs for Banbury then BR station, turn right down narrow lane before entering station forecourt; eastern end of town.
Seats: 240 **Cover:** 800 **Capacity:** 6,500 **Floodlights:** Yes **Club Shop:** Yes
Programme : 24 pages 50p **Editor:** Kevin Hicklin **Press Officer:** Barry Worsley.
Colours: Blue & White/Blue/Blue **Change colours:** Green/white/green
Midweek matches: Tuesday. **Reserves' Lge:** Hellenic Res. section **Nickname:** Puritans.
Founded: 1933 **Reformed:** 1965 **Club Sponsors:** Timms Homes.
Record Attendance: 7,160 v Oxford City, FA Cup 3rd Qualifying Round, 30/10/48.
Best FA Cup season: 1st Rd replay 73-74 (Also 1st Rd 47-48 61-62 72-73).
Best FA Trophy year: 3rd Rd 70-71 73-74.
Prev. Lges: Banbury Jnr 33-34/ Oxon Snr 34-35/ Birmingham Comb. 35-54/ W. Mids 54-66/ Southern 66-90.
Players progressing to Football League: Ollie Kearns (Reading), Kevin Wilson & Richard Pratley (Derby), Mick Kearns & Terry Muckleberg (Oxford), Martin Singleton (Coventry).
Clubhouse: Match days & week-ends. Mid-week on hire. Hot food available during aftermatches.
95-96 Captain: Kevin Hicklin **95-96 P.O.Y.:** Martin Singleton **95-96 Top Scorer:** Martin Singleton
Club Record Goalscorer: Dick Pike (1935-48), Tony Jacques (65-76) - both 222.
Club Record Appearances: Dave Matthews.
Honours: Oxon Snr Cup 78-79 87-88 (R-up 6), Birmingham Comb. R-up 47-48, Oxon Prof. Cup 52-53(jt) 70-71(jt) 72-73 77-78 79-80(jt) Hellenic Lg.Cup R-Up 91-92, Birmingham Snr.Cup R-Up 48-49,59-60(S.F.46-47, Oxon Snr Lg. 34-35 39-40 47-48(res), Oxon Hosp. Cup 46-47 (R-up 45-46), Oxon Benev. Cup R-up 77-78 80-81 82-83, Daventry Charity Cup 88-90, Smiths Mem. Cup 68-70 (R-up 66-68), Hitchin Centenary Cup 68-69 (R-up 67-68), Leamington Charity Cup 51-52, Warks Comb. R-up 57-58 60-61 (Presidents Cup R-up 60-61), Midland Floodlit Cup 67-68, Wallspan Comb. 85-86.

BICESTER TOWN

Chairman: Bill Hammond. **Vice Chairman:** Ray Honour. **President:** Mike Staniford.
Secretary/Press Officer: Phil Allen, 38 Bassett Avenue, Bicester OX6 7TZ (01869 252125).
Manager: Aiden McKay **Ground:** Sports Ground, Oxford Rd, Bicester (01869 241936)
Directions: From Oxford; past Tescos on outskirts of Bicester - ground on right. From Aylesbury; turn left at first island on outskirts of Bicester onto bypass, right at next island, pass Tescos & ground on right.
Seats: 250 **Cover:** 550 **Capacity:** **Floodlights:** Yes **Founded:** 1876
Colours: Red & white/red/red **Change:** Yellow/black/black.
Previous Lge: Oxon Senior **Reserve team's league:** Hellenic Lge Reserve Division.
Programme: With admission **Programme Editor:** Secretary
Nickname: Foxhunters **Previous Name:** Slade Banbury Road (pre-1923).
Clubhouse: One bar **Record Gate:** 955 v Portsmouth, floodlight inauguration 1/2/94.
Hons: Hellenic Lg 60-1 77-78 (Lg Cup 90-91 (R-up 92-93), Div 1 76-77).

BRACKLEY TOWN

Chairman: Kim Golding **President:** Miss C Billingham
Secretary: Pat Ashby, 17 Manor Rd, Woodford Halse, Daventry, Northants. NN11 3QP (01327 262955).
Manager: Phil Lines. **Coach:** Brian Robinson **Physio:** Charlie Busby
Ground: St James Park, Churchill Way, Brackley, Northants (0280 704077).
Directions: Churchill Way, east off A43, south end of town
Capacity: 3,500 **Seats:** 400 **Cover:** 50 **Floodlights:** Yes **Founded:** 1890.
Colours: All white **Change Colours:** All yellow **Nickname:** Saints
Programme: Yes. **Midweek matchday:** Tuesday
Clubhouse details: Lounge & main hall. Open all week
Record Attendance: 600 v Kettering, Northants Senior Cup 1989
Previous Leagues: Banbury & District/ North Bucks/ Hellenic 77-83/ United Counties 83-94.
Previous Grounds: Banbury Road, Manor Road, Buckingham Road (upto 1974).
Players to progress to Football League: Jon Blencowe (Leicester)
Hons: UCL 88-89 (Div 1 83-84), N'hants Snr Cup R-up, Buck'ham Charity Cup, Hellenic Lg Div 1 Cup 82-83.

BURNHAM

Chairman: Malcolm Higton **Vice Chairman:** M.A.Beavis. **President:** R J Laverick.
Secretary/Press Officer: M J Boxall, 6 Goose Green, Farham Royal, Slough SL2 3DU (01753 648091).
Manager: Andy Lyne. **Asst Manager:** Derek Sweetman **Physio:** Mark Green.
Ground: The Gore, Wymers Wood Road, Burnham, Slough SL1 8JG (01628 602467/602697).
Directions: North west of village centre, 2 miles from Burnham BR station, 2 miles from M4 junction 7, 5 miles from M40 junction 2, 100yds north of Gore crossroads - fork right into Wymers Wood Rd and ground is immediately on right. Bee Line bus 66.
Capacity: 2,500 **Cover:** 250 **Seats:** 250 **Floodlights:** Yes **Club Shop:** Yes
Press Officer: Secretary **Programme:** 30 pages **Editor:** Cliff Sparkes
Colours: Blue & white **Change colours:** All yellow.
Midweek matchday: Tuesday **Reserve Team's Lge:** Suburban.
Sponsors: Caflon International,Waterside Associates.
Record Attendance: 2,400 v Halesowen Town, FA Vase 2/4/83.
Best FA Cup season: 3rd Qualifying Rd. **Best FA Trophy season:** Third Qualifying Rd replay 89-90.
Previous Leagues: Sth Bucks & East Berks/ Maidenhead Intermediate/ Windsor, Slough & Dist./ Gt Western Comb. 48-64/ Wycombe Comb. 64-70/ Reading Comb. 70-71/ Hellenic 71-77/ Athenian 77-84/ London Spartan 84-85.Southern 85-95.
Players progressing to Football League: D Hancock (Reading), R Rafferty (Grimsby Town, Portsmouth), D Payne (Barnet, Southend United,Watford).
Clubhouse: Open every evening and weekend lunchtimes. Darts and pool, two bars, usual matchday food.
95-96 Captain: Jamie Jarvis. **95-96 P.o.Y.:** Paul Brett. **95-96 Top Scorer:** Steve Bunce, 16.
Club Record Scorer: Fraser Hughes 65, 69-70
Hons: FA Vase SF 82-83 (QF 77-78), Athenian Lg R-up(2) 78-80, Hellenic Lg 75-76 (Div 1 R-up 72-73, Lg Cup 75-76, Div 1 Cup 71-72), London Spartan Lg 84-85 (Lg Cup 84-85), Reading Comb. Lg Cup 70-71 (All Champions Cup 70-71), Wycombe Comb. R-up(4) 65-67 68-70, various local cup competitions.

CARTERTON TOWN

President: Mr G Fox **Chairman:** Mr G Maxwell **Vice-Chairman:**
Secretary/Physio: Mr R Stephens, 40 Shillbrook Avenue, Carterton, Oxfordshire (01993 843135).
Manager: A Sinnott **Physio:** D Buckby **Press Officer:** P King.
Ground: Kilkenny Lane, Carterton, Oxfordshire (0993 842410)
Directions: Enter Swinbrook Rd which off the Burford-Carterton road, proceed into Kilkenny Lane (one track road), ground car park 200yds on left before sharp corner. Hourly buses to Carterton from Oxford.
Seats: 50 **Cover:** 100 **Capacity:** 1,500 **Floodlights:** Yes **Founded:** 1922
Colours: Black & white/black/white **Change colours:** Yellow/blue/yellow **Reformed:** 1946/1983
Previous Leagues: Witney & District **Record Gate:** 600 v Oxford Utd, Oxon Snr Cup 93-94.
Programme: 20 pages with admission **Programme Editor:** Jenny Maxwell (0993 841301).
Sponsors: Morlands Brewery **Reserve League:** Hellenic Reserve section.
Midweek home matches: Wednesday. **Club record goalscorer:** Tim Dorrington.
Clubhouse: Lounge & fully licensed bar open every day 7.30-11pm, Sat & Sun noon-2pm, Sat 4-6pm. Snacks & meals available.
95-96 Top Scorer: **95-96 Captain:** **95-96 P.o.Y.:**
Hons: Oxon Junior Shield 85-86, Oxon Snr Cup R-up 90-91, Witney & Dist. Lg 65-66 (Div 1 84-85 76-77), Hellenic Lg Div 1 89-90 93-94 (Reserve Div 1989-90 (R-up 93-94)), Oxon Intermediate Cup R-up 93-94(res.)

DIDCOT TOWN

President: **Chairman:** John Bailey **Manager:**
Secretary: N Bennett, 75 Churchill Road, Didcot, Oxon. OX11 7BU (01235 813016).
Ground: Station Road, Didcot (01235 813212).
Directions: Midway down Station Rd, Didcot, on right quarter mile from Railway Station towards town centre.
Seats: 50. **Cover:** 200 **Capacity:** 5,000 **Floodlights:**Yes. **Founded:** 1907
Colours: Red/white/red **Change colours:** All blue
Prev. Lges: Hellenic 53-57/ Metropolitan 57-63.
Nickname: Railwaymen. **Midweek Matchday:** Wednesday
Record Attendance: 550 v Wycombe Wanderers, 1956.
Programme: 50p **Programme Editor:** Peter Swain.
Clubhouse: Every evenings and Sunday lunchtimes.
Honours: Hellenic Lg 53-54,Lg Cup 1965-66 66-67 92-93 Div 1 76-77,Div1 Cup 76-7

ENDSLEIGH

Chairman: Michael Alcock
Secretary: Graham Ayers, 7 Oakbrook Drive, The Reddings, Cheltenham, Glos GL51 6SB (01452 548556)
Manager: Gary Leeds
Ground: Cheltenham Town FC Whaddon Rod (see page 444)
Colours: Blue/blue/white **Change colours:** All white.
Previous Ground: The Folley, Swindon Road, Cheltenham (pre-1993)
Prev. Lge: Glos Northern Snr (pre'93) **Hons:** Glos Northern Snr Lg 92-93 (Div 1 91-92).

Midfield action during this Easters Monday Hellenic League fixture between Abingdon United (stripes) and Endsleigh

Photo - Martin Wray

Letcombe Sport's Mike Brendel slide tackles Purton's Brian Cant.

Photo - Ray Pruden

FAIRFORD TOWN

Chairman: M B Tanner **President:** B W Wall
Secretary: M J Cook, "Bow Wow" Down Ampney, Cirencester GL7 5QU (01793 751240).
Ground: Cinder Lane, Fairford, Cirencester (01285 712071).
Manager: Paul Richardson **Asst Manager:** Gerry Kelly. **Physio:** C Tye
Directions: Entering Fairford on A417 from Lechlade turn left down Cinder Lane 150yds after 40mph sign. From Cirencester on same road, follow thru village and turn right down Cinder Lane 400yds after Railway Inn. Buses from Swindon, Lechlade and Cirencester.
Seats: 100 **Cover:** 150 **Capacity:** 2,000 **Floodlights:** Yes **Club Shop:** No.
Programme: 20 pages with admission **Editor/Press Officer:** Chairman
Colours: Red/white/red **Change colours:** White/blue/blue
Club Sponsors: Jewson **Founded:** 1891 **Nickname:** Town.
Midweek matchday: Wednesday **Reserve Team's League:** Hellenic Reserve section.
Record Attendance: 1,500 v Swindon Town, friendly 18/7/92.
Previous Leagues: Cirencester & District (pre-1946)/ Swindon & District 46-70.
Clubhouse: Open each evening, weekend lunches & before and after all games
95-96 Captain: John Hathaway **95-96 Top Scorer:** Chris Panter. **95-96 P.o.Y.:** Martin Gullis
Club Record Goalscorer: Pat Toomey. **Club Record Appearances:**
Hons: Glos Challenge Trophy 79-80 (R-up 82-83), Hellenic Lg R-up 78-79 79-80 90-91 (Premier Div Cup 78-79, Div 1 71-72, Div 1 Cup 71-72), Glos Jnr Cup 62-63, Swindon & Dist Lg 64-65 68-69.

HIGHWORTH TOWN

President: Alan Vockins **Chairman:** Steven Leppard **Vice Chairman:**
Secretary: Fraser Haines, 222 Windrush, Highworth, Swindon SN6 7EB (01793 861109).
Manager: Keith Skinner **Coach:** Fraser Haines **Asst Manager:** Tony Garland
Physio: Graham Ashby
Commercial Manager/Press Officer: David Evans.
Ground: Elm Recreation Ground, Highworth. (01793 766263)
Directions: Enter on A361 from Swindon, past Simpsons Garage, straight over island, next sharp left into Green by Vet's Surgery - ground & car park 60yds on left next to Sports Hall.
Seats: 50 **Cover:** 250 **Capacity:** 2,000 **Floodlights:** Yes **Founded:** 1894.
Colours: Red & white/white/red **Change colours:** Blue & white/black/blue **Club Shop:** No.
Programme: 16 pages, 60p **Editor:** George Ranson (Shrivenham 782808).
Prev. Lges: Wilts/Swindon & Dist. **Club Sponsors:** Smart Movers.
Midweek matchday: Wednesday **Reserves Lge:** Hellenic Reserve Div. **Nickname:** Worthians
Record win: 12-0 v Beeches, Arthur Shipway Cup 1992.
Record defeat: 2-8 v Milton United, Hellenic League Division One, 1987.
Record Gate: 300 v Swindon Supermarine, Wiltshire Senior quarter-final, 1994.
Clubhouse: Sat 12-2.30 & 4.30-11pm. Mon, Wed & Fri 7-11pm. Rolls & Hot food.
Record scorer: Kevin Higgs **Record appearances:** Rod Haines.
95-96 Top Scorer: **95-96 Captain:** **95-96 P.o.Y.:**
Hons: Wilts Snr Cup 63-64 72-73 (R-up 88-89), Hellenic Div 1 Cup 88-89, Arthur Shipway Cup 88-89 93-94, Swindon & District Lg 63-64 64-65 65-66 68-69.

KINTBURY RANGERS

President: **Chairman:** P Angell
Secretary: A K Plank, 26 Kennet Road, Kintbury, Hungerford, RG17 9XW (01488 658460).
Manager: D Angell **Res Manager:** W Bailey **Press Officer:** C Angell
Ground: Recreation Ground, Inkpen Road, Kintbury (0488 57001).
Directions: Turn off A4 (signed Kintbury) between Newbury/Hungerford. 2nd left after level crossing into Inkpen Road, entrance 200yds on right by Jubilee Centre. Half mile from Kintbury (BR).
Seats: None **Cover:** No **Capacity:** 1,000 **Floodlights:** Yes **Founded:** 1890
Colours: Amber/black **Change colours:** White/blue
Nickname: Rangers **Reformed:** 1943.
Reserves' Lge: Hellenic Res. sect. **Previous Leagues:** Newbury District/ Nth Berks.
Programme: 16 pages, 50p **Programme Editor:** Colin Godfrey (0635 874209)
Record Gate: 550 v Newport AFC, 1990.
Clubhouse: Open every nightl 7.30-11. Hot & cold meals matchdays.
95-96 Captain: **95-96 Top Scorer:** **95-96 P.o.Y.:**
Club record appearances: Nigel Llewellyn.
Hons: Nth Berks Lg 77-78 81-82, Hellenic Lg Div 1 R-up 87-88, Berks & Bucks I'mediate Cup 60-61 (R-up 87-88).

LAMBOURN SPORTS

Chairman: M.Killick. **Vice Chairman:** E O'Neill. **President:** N L Fraser
Secretary: Clive Bettison, 11 Foxbury, Lambourn, Berks RG17 8PT (01488 73537).
Manager: Don Rogers. **Coach:** Colin Moyle **Physio:** Kevin Retter
Ground: Bockhampton Rd, Lambourn, Berks (01488 72214).
Directions: From Lambourn Church take Newbury St, then 1st right into Station Rd, left at T junction into Bockhampton Rd, ground on left.
Seats: 50 **Cover:** 100 **Capacity:** 2,000 **Floodlights:** Yes **Club Shop:**
Programme: 12 pages **Editor:**
Colours: Red & white/white/white **Change colours:** All blue
Sponsor: **Nickname:** **Founded:** 1889
Midweek Matchday: **Reserve League:** North Berks.
Previous Leagues: Newbury & Dist. 11-51/ Swindon & Dist. 51-61/ Hellenic 61-72/ Nth Berks 72-77.
Clubhouse: Bars, lounge, dancehall, billard room, kitchen, open 7 nights, & matchdays
95-96 Captain: Mick Casey **95-96 Top Scorer:** Barry Flippance **95-96 P.o.Y.:** Mick Casey.
Club Record Goalscorer: Stan Fisher 634 **Club Record Appearances:**
Honours: Berks & Bucks Interm Cup 61-62 79-80; Berks & Bucks Sen Trophy 94-95; Hellenic Lg Div 1 81-82 (R-up 61-62), Div 1 Cup 61-62 79-80.

NORTH LEIGH

President: Mrs C Smith **Chairman:** P.King. **Vice Chairman:** B.Shepperd.
Secretary: Mr P J Dix, 8 Windmill Close, North Leigh, Nr Witney, Oxon OX8 6RP (0993 881199).
Manager: A Buckingham/P Hutter **Asst Manager:** Mr P King **Physio:** Mr R Keen
Ground: Eynsham Hall Park Sports Ground, North Leigh, nr Witney, Oxon (0993 881427).
Directions: Ground is situated off A4095 Witney to Woodstock road 3 miles east of Witney. Entrance to ground is 300yds east of Main Park Entrance.
Seats: 100 **Cover:** 200 **Capacity:** 2,000 **Floodlights:** Yes **Club Shop:** No.
Programme: 20 pages, £1 with entry **Editor:** J Fogg **Press Officer:** B Norton (0993 881777).
Colours: Sky/navy **Change colours:** All orange
Club Sponsors: Various **Founded:** 1908 **Nickname:** None.
Midweek home matches: Wednesday
Previous Leagues: Witney & District 08-89.
Clubhouse: Bar open matches. Snacks available.
Club record scorer: P Coles **Club record appearances:** P King.
Hons: Hellenic Lg Div 1 R-up 92-93 (Reserves Cup 93-94), Oxon Jnr Shield 56-57 83-84, Oxon Charity Cup 84-85 88-89, Witney & Dist. Lg(13) 50-57 84-90 (Lg Cup(10) 47-48 51-52 53-55 56-57 81-82 85-89), Oxon Yth Cup 93-94 94-95, Oxon Yth u-17 Lg & Cup 93-94. Oxford Senior Cup R-Up 94-95. Marriott Cup 95-96.

SHORTWOOD UNITED

Chairman: Peter Webb **Vice C'men:** C.Rivers,G.Benton,J Humphrys **President:** Bob Tanner
Secretary: Mark Webb, 1 The Bungalow, Shortwood, Nailsworth, Stroud, Glos GL6 0SD (01453 833204).
Manager: Simon Stroud **Asst Manager:** Mike Stratford. **Physio:** Adrian Brown
Ground: "Meadow Bank", Shortwood, Nailsworth, Gloucestershire (01453 833936).
Directions: In Nailsworth turn into Spring Hill then first left. Continue past shop and and keep left past "Britannia" (signposted Shortwood) - continue to end for ground. 4 miles from Stroud (BR).
Seats: 50 **Cover:** 150 **Capacity:** 5,000 **Floodlights:** Yes **Club Shop:** No.
Programme: 18 pages, 30p **Editor:** Keith Sheppard **Press Officer:**
Colours: All red **Change:** All blue
Sponsors: Richard Lacey Insurance **Nickname:** The Wood. **Founded:** 1900
Midweek matchday: Wednesday **Reserves' League:** Glos Northern Snr
Record Attendance: 1,000 v Forest Green Rovers, FA Vase 5th Rd 81-82.
Previous Leagues: Stroud/ Glos Northern Snr/ Glos Co.
Clubhouse: Mon-Sat 7-11pm, Sun noon-12 & 7-10.30pm. Crisps etc in bar, hot food kitchen on matchdays.
95-96 Captain: James Darby. **95-96 P.o.Y.:** Scott Thomas. **95-96 Top Scorer:** Ian Freebry 21.
Club Record appearances: Peter Grant. **Club Record Goalscorer:** Peter Grant
Hons: Glos.Co.Lg 81-82 (R-up 80-81), Glos Tphy 83-84 91-92,94-95,(R-up 79-80), Hellenic Lg 84-85 91-92 (R-up 85-86 89-90 94-95, Div 1 R-up 83-84, Div 1 Cup 83-84), Prem Lge Cup R-up 95-96, Hungerford Merit Cup, Glos Snr Amtr Cup 85-86 (R-up 79-80), Stroud Charity Cup 91-92 92-93 94-95 (R-up 95-96), Stroud Lg 27-28 (Div 2 26-27 64-65(res), Div 3 25-26 49-50(res) 62-63(res)), Glos Northern Snr Lg R-up 67-68 91-92(res)(Div 2 62-63 80-81(res) 90-91(res)), Arthur Shipway Cup 78-79 79-80.

SWINDON SUPERMARINE

Chairman: Steve Lodge **President:** Cliff Puffit
Secretary: Eric Stott, 43 Stanier Street, Swindon, Wilts SN1 5QU (0793 521301).
Ground: Highworth Road, South Marston, Swindon (0973) 824828
Directions: On A361 Swindon/Highworth road, adjoining Marston Industrial Estate. 6 miles from Swindon (BR) - buses in direction of Highworth, Fairford & Lechdale. If lost ask for Vickers Sports Ground.
Seats: 75 **Cover:** 120 **Capacity:** 1,000 **Floodlights:** Yes **Founded:** 1992.
Colours: White & blue/blue/white **Change colours:** Yellow/blue/blue **Programme:** Yes
Previous Names: Supermarine (prev. Vickers Armstrong 46-81), Swindon Athletic (prev. Penhill Yth Centre 70-84/ Penhill 84-84-89) amalgamated in 1992.
Previous Leagues: Wilts. **Midweek Matchday:** Wednesday
Previous Ground: Supermarine: Vickers Airfield (until mid-1960s), *Swindon Ath.: Merton 70-84/ 'Southbrook', Pinehurst Road 84-92.*
Hons: Wilts Snr Cup R-up 93-94, Hellenic Lg Reserve Section 93-94. As Supermarine: Wilts Snr Cup 85-86 (R-up 74-75 84-85), Hellenic Div 1 R-Up 82-83 (Res Section West R-up 84-85 (Challenge Cup 83-84), Wilts Comb Snr 75-76, Swindon & District Lg Div 3 55-56, Dr Elliott Cup(5), Faringdon Thursday Memorial Cup(3). *Swindon Ath.: Wilts Snr Cup 82-83 86-87 89-90 (R-up 83-84 85-86 90-91), Hellenic Lg Div 1 85-86 86-87, Wilts Co. Lg 82-83 83-84).*

TUFFLEY ROVERS

President: A W Purdy **Chairman:** Andrew Gregory
Secretary: Graham Moody, 50 Giles Cox, Quidgley, Gloucester GL2 4YL (01452 724083).
Manager: D Foxwell. **Coach:** C Gardner **Physio:** S Tracey
Ground: Glevum Park, Lower Tuffley Lane, Gloucester (01452 423402).
Directions: Follow Gloucester city ring-rd to r'bout signed M5 South & Bristol, take 4th exit signed Hempsted & city centre, after 200yds turn right (McDonalds on corner) into Lower Tuffley Lane, ground 400yds on left.
Seats: 50 **Cover:** Yes **Capacity:** **Floodlights:** Yes **Founded:** 1929
Colours: Claret & blue/white/claret **Change colours:** Yellow/white/claret **Nickname:** Rovers
Previous Grounds: Stroud Rd, Gloucester/ Randwick Park, Tuffley. **Club Shop:** No.
Previous Leagues: Stroud/ Glos Northern Senior/ Glos County (pre-1991).
Midweek Matchday: Wednesday
Programme: approx 10 pages with entry **Editor:** Mr A Purdy, 43 Ermin Park, Brockworth.
Club Sponsors: Ermin Plant. **Reserve League:** Glos.Northern Senior Stroud Lge.
Clubhouse: 800 yds from ground. Open before & after matches, and normal pub hours at other times. Snacks.
95-96 Captain: **95-96 Top Scorer:** **95-96 P.o.Y.:**
Hons: Hellenic Lg Div 1 92-93 (Div 1 Cup 92-93), Glos Co. Lge 90-91, Glos Snr Amtr Cup 87-88, Stroud Lg 72-73,94-95, Glos Northern Senior Lg. Div 1 87-88 Div2 79-80.

WANTAGE TOWN

Chairman: Kevin O'Hanlon **Vice-Chairman:** A Woodward **President:** Ernie Smart
Secretary: Nick Morris, 27 Cherburg Green, Grove, Wantage, Oxon OX12 0DB. (01235 766419).
Manager: Fred Bint **Asst Manager:** Jon Hawkins **Physio:**
Ground: Alfredian Park, Manor Park, Wantage, Oxon (01235 764781).
Directions: Take Hungerford Road from Wantage, ground signposted on right oppsite recreation ground.
Seats: 50 **Cover:** 300 **Capacity:** 1,500 **Floodlights:** Yes **Club Shop:** No
Programme: 28 pages, 50p **Editor:** Andy Wells (0235 767291).
Colours: Green & white hoop/white **Change colours:** White/green
Sponsors: Broadway Motors **Nickname:** **Founded:** 1892
Midweek Matchday: Wednesday **Record Attendance:** 1,800
Previous Leagues: Swindon & Dist. 1901-12 30-35 47-56/ N Berks 12-22 38-40 46-47/ Reading & D. 22-30 35-38.
Players progressing to Football League: Roy Burton and Colin Duncan (both Oxford United).
Clubhouse: Mon-Fri 7.30-11pm, Sat noon-2.30, 4-7pm.
95-96 Captain: **95-96 P.o.Y.:** Jamie Alexander **95-96 Top Scorer:** John Cully 20
Club Record Goalscorer: A Rolls **Club Record Appearances:**
Honours: Hellenic Lg R-up 81-82, Div 1 80-81 (R-up 69-70 87-88 91-92 95-96), Div 1 Cup R-up 91-92; Oxon Snr Cup 82-83; Berks & Bucks Intermediate Cup 54-55; Swindon & District Lg 07-08 33-34 52-53 55-56.

Wantage Town: Back Row (L-R); Ian Howard, Fred Bint (Mgr), James Butler, Peter Broad, Jon Hawkins, John Culley, Derek Burke, Jamie Alexander. Front Row; Lorenzo Easen, Roy Clark, Nick Roberts, Jeb Gampoli, Frankie Dorrian, Phil Padbury, Jason Champion.

Abingdon United FC: Back Row (L-R); A Wise (Physio), R Green, K Crooks, S Green, L Coweybear, S Brierty, B Spiero, W Morbu, R Haywood (Mgr). Front Row; S Collins, D Romain, S Bloomfield, P Storey, R McNeill, A Jones, A Wise.

Photo - Martin Wray

Endsleigh F C

Photo - Martin Wray

DIVISION ONE CLUBS 1996-97

ARDLEY UNITED

Chairman: Norman Stacey
Secretary: Nigel Adams, 139 Willow Drive, Bicester, Oxon, OX6 9XF (01869 325734)
Manager: Peter Foley **Coach:** David Underwood **Physio:** Norman Stacey
Press Officer: Ron Jones (01869 246717)
Ground: Ardley Sports Ground (01869 346429)
Directions: M40 junc 10 take A43 towards Middleton Stoney on the right after 1/2 mile.
Colours: Claret & blue/claret/claret **Change colours:** Yellow/black/black
Midweek matchday: Tuesday **Prev. Lge:** Oxon Snr (pre-1993)
Hons: Oxon Snr Lg R-up 92-93 (Pres. Cup R-up 90-91 91-92).

BISHOPS CLEEVE

President: John Davies **Chairman:** David Lewis
Secretary: Phil Tustain, 7 Dale Walk, Bishops Cleeve, Glos GL52 4PQ (01242 674968).
Manager: David Lewis **Coach:** G Samuels **Physio:** Philip Tustain
Ground: Stoke Rd, Bishops Cleeve (01242 676257)
Directions: 3 miles north of Cheltenham on A435. 3rd left in village into Stoke Rd - ground on right. 4 miles from Cheltenham (BR); served by Cheltenham to Tewkesbury buses.
Seats: None **Cover:** 50 **Capacity:** 1,500 **Floodlights:** No **Founded:** 1892.
Colours: Green & black/black/black **Change colours:** Blue/white/red.
Midweek Matchday: Wednesday **Nickname:** Skinners
Prev. Lges: Cheltenham, Nth Glos **Prev. Grnds:** The Skiller (pre-1913), Village Field (pre-1950)
Record Gate: 1,000 v Newport AFC.
Clubhouse: Full facilities, bar, dance area **Honours:** Hellenic Lg Cup R-up 90-91.

CHELTENHAM SARACENS

Chairman: J Utteridge **Manager:** Ian Ford
Secretary: R Attwood, 179 Arle Road, Cheltenham GL51 8LJ (011242 515855).
Asst Manager: Clive Shatford. **Coach:** John Caskton **Physio:** Jim Utteridge
Press Officer: Terry Coates (01242 692320).
Ground: Petersfield Park, Tewkesbury Road, Cheltenham (011242 589134).
Directions: 1 mile from Cheltenham centre on A4019 Tewksbury Road (next to B & Q) - 1st left over railway bridge, 1st left and follow service road.
Seats: None **Cover:** 100 **Capacity:** 2,000 **Floodlights:** No **Founded:** 1964.
Colours: All blue **Change colours:** Black & white/black/black
Club Shop: No **Nickname:** Saras. **Midweek Matchday:** Wednesday
Prog.: 20 pages, 50p (Ed: Secretary) **Previous League:** Cheltenham 1964-86.
Reserve Team's League: Hellenic Reserve section.
Players progressing to Football League: S Cotterill (Wimbledon, B/mouth) 88, K Knight (Reading) 89.
Hons: Glos Snr Cup 91-92. **Clubhouse:** 2 mins away at 16-20 Swindon Rd, Cheltenham.
95-96 Captain: **95-96 Top Scorer:** **95-96 P.o.Y.:**

CIRENCESTER UNITED

President: A Day **Chairman:** J Austin **Vice Chairman:** Paul King.
Secretary/Press Officer: G Varley, 95 Vaisey Rd, Cirencester, Glos GL7 2JW (01285 657836).
Manager: **Coach:** **Physio:**
Ground: Four Acres P.F., Chesterton Lane (01285 651726).
Directions: Dual carriageway towards Bristol, under footbridge, first left after Cirencester Town F.C., ground 200yds on left hand side.
Seats: None **Cover:** No **Programme:** Yes **Floodlights:** No **Founded:** 1970
Colours: Red & white/black/red **Change colours:** Green & yellow/green/green
Nickname: Herd. **Previous Grounds:** None **Previous Name:** The Herd (pre-1990)
Previous Leagues: Cirencester & District (4 years)/ Cheltenham (8 years).
Programme: 16 pages, 50p **Editor:** N Warriner (01285 656187) **Club Shop:** No.
Midweek Matchday: Wednesday **Sponsors:** D G Sunner (Builders)
Clubhouse: Training nights & matchdays. Rolls & sundries available.
95-96 Captain: **95-96 Top Scorer:** **95-96 P.o.Y.:**
Club record scorer: M Day **Club record appearances:** A Smith.
Hons: Glos Snr Amtr Cup R-up 86-87 89-90, Cirencester Lg 72-73 74-75 (Div 2(3) 71-73 74-75, Lg Cup 74-75, Res. Cup 74-75), Cheltenham Lg 76-77 83-84 (Div 2 75-76, Lg Cup 83-84 (R-up 86-87), Snr Charity Cup 86-87), Stroud Charity Cup 86-87 (Section A 82-83 83-84), Arthur Shipway Cup 86-87 (R-up 87-88 92-93), Fairford Hospital Cup R-up(4) 83-85 90-91 92-93.

CLANFIELD

President: B Wallis **Chairman:** J Osborne
Secretary: J Osborne, 70 Lancut Road, Witney, Oxon OX8 5AQ (01993 771631).
Manager: Bill Pirie/Mark Light **Physio:**
Ground: Radcot Road, Clanfield, Oxon (01367 810314)
Directions: On A4095 8 miles west of Witney & 4 miles east of Faringdon on south side of Clanfield. Buses from Witney - contact Thames Transit for details.
Seats: No **Cover:** 300 **Capacity:** 2,000 **Floodlights:** No **Club Shop:** No.
Prev. Grnds: None **Prev. Lges:** Nth Berks/ Witney & Dist.
Colours: Red & black/black/red **Change colours:** Yellow & Black/black/black
Programme: 8 pages, with admission **Editor:** Secretary
Sponsors: Morelands Brewery **Nickname:** Robins **Founded:** 1890
Reserves' Lge: Hellenic League Reserve section.
Clubhouse: Every evening & Sat/Sun lunch
95-96 Captain: **95-96 Top Scorer:** **95-96 P.o.Y.:**
Hons: Oxon Jnr Shield 32-33, Oxon I'mediate Cup 67-68, Witney & Dist. Lg 66-67 (Div 1 65-66, Div 2 64-65), Hellenic Lg Div 1 69-70 (Premier Div Cup 72-73, Div 1 Cup 69-70 85-86), Jim Newman Mem. Tphy 83-84 87-88, Faringdon Thursday Memorial Cup 69-70 71-72.

EASINGTON SPORTS

President: **Chairman:** Terry Horley
Secretary: Terry Horley, 65 Grange Road, Banbury, Oxon OX16 9AT (01295 254950).
Manager: Jim Hay **Physio:** Alan Gardner **Press Officer:** G Lines.
Ground: Addison Road, Easington Estate, Banbury, Oxon (01295 257006).
Directions: From Oxford A423. After passing under flyover on the outskirts of Banbury take first turning left into Grange Road then third right into Addison Rd. Ground at top on left. One and a half miles from Banbury (BR).
Seats: 50 **Cover:** 100 **Capacity:** 1,000 **Floodlights:** No **Founded:** 1946
Cols: Red & white/red/red **Change colours:** White & blue/blue/blue.
Programme: Yes, 25p **Record Gate:** 250 v Witney Town 68
Previous Ground: Bodicote. **Prev. Lges:** Banbury Jnr/ Oxon Snr/ Warkwick Combination.
Reserves' Lge: Hellenic Res. section **Clubhouse:** Changing rooms, showers, bar facilities and food.
95-96 Captain: Karlton Stratford **95-96 Top Scorer:** Darren Deeley.
Honours: Oxon Snr Cup R-up, Oxon Intermediate League & Cup, Oxon Snr Lg.

HALLEN

Chairman: Barry Phillips **Manager:**
Secretary: Charmaine Phillips, 145A Station Road, Henbury, Bristol BS10 7LZ (0117 9501754)
Ground: Hallen Playing Fields, Moorhouse Lane, Hallen, Nr Bristol (0272 504610).
Directions: M5 jct 17, A4018 to Henbury r'bout, right, right again at junction, next right to Station Road, left into Avonmouth Road at r'bout. One mile to Hallen, ground first left, then right into lane to ground.
Seats: No **Cover:** No **Clubhouse:** Yes **Programme:** No **Founded:** 1949
Colours: Royal/black/black **Change Colours:** Green & black/red/red
Previous Names: Lawrence Weston Athletic (80's), Lawrence Weston Hallen (pre-1991).
Record Gate: 250 **Midweek Matchday:** Wednesday
Prev. Grnd: Kings Weston (early 1980's) **Previous League:** Glos County (pre-1993)
Hons: Glos County Lg 92-93, Glos Snr Trophy 92-93.

HARROW HILL

Chairman: Reg Taylor **President:** Ken Jones
Secretary: Geoff Tuffley, 19 Westfield Court, Hetwood Road, Cinderford GL14 2RU (01594 542421)
Manager/Coach: R White **Physio:** R Taylor
Ground: Larksfield Road, Harrow Hill (01594 543873)
Directions: Take A40 west out of Gloucester, follow A40 for 8 miles then take A4136 to Longhope, pass by on the outskirts of Michealdean, up steep hill (plump Hill), then second turn on the right signed Harrow Hill. At phone box on the left turn right into Larksfield Road, ground on right at top of hill.
Colours: Claret & blue/sky/sky **Change Colours:** Black & white/black/black
Record Gate: 350 v Cinderford Town 92 **Midweek Matchday:** Tuesday

HEADINGTON AMATEURS

President: John Dunne **Chairman:** Donald Light **Vice Chairman:** Paul Sammons.
Secretary: C Barrett, 6 Holland Place, Wood Farm, Oxford OX3 8QT (01865 750828).
Manager: J Light. **Physio:** Chris Gillick **Press Officer:** Paul Sammons
Ground: Barton Rec., Barton Village Road, Barton, Oxon (01865 60489).
Directions: From Green Rd r'bout, Headington, (on A40) take Barton/Islip exit (1st exit coming from Witney, last coming from London), turn left into North Way, follow road for half mile - ground at bottom of hill on left.
Seats: None **Cover:** None **Floodlights:** No **Founded:** 1949. **Nickname:** A's.
Colours: All red **Change:** Yellow & Black
Midweek matchday: Tuesday **Prevs Lgs:** Oxford City Junior 49-66/ Oxford Senior 67-88.
Programme: 8 pages, £1 with entry **Editor:** Stan Hawkswood (01865 65546) **Club Shop:** No.
Sponsors: Oxford Marquees **Previous Ground:** Romanway, Cowley (pre-1990).
Reserves' Lge: Hellenic Res. sect.
Player progressing to Football Lge: James Light (Oxford) 1970s.
Record win: 6-0 v Carterton (H) 1991 **Record defeat:** 1-8 v Banbury United (A), February 1994.
Clubhouse: Open Tues & Thurs 6-11pm, Sat matchdays 4.45-11pm. Rolls, chips, burgers, hot dogs, sweets etc.
95-96 Captain: **95-96 Top Scorer:**
Club record scorer: Tony Penge **Club record appearances:** Keith Drackett.
Hons: Oxon Snr League(4) 72-74 75-77 (R-up 71-72 74-75 77-78 81-82 84-85, Div 1 68-69, Presidents Cup(2) 72-74 (R-up 71-72 77-78 84-85)), Oxon Charity Cup 75-76 (Intermediate Cup 88-89), Hellenic League Div 1 R-up 87-88 (Res. Sect. 92-93, Res. Cup 91-92).

KIDLINGTON

President: Gordon Norridge. **Chairman:** Peter Walton. **Manager:** K Grossman
Secretary: Kathleen Walton, 3 Azalea Ave, Kidlington, Oxon. OX5 1HQ (01865 377226)
Coach/Physio: S Dickens **Commercial Manager:** Peter Walton.
Ground: Yarnton Rd, Kidlington, Oxford (01865 375628)
Directions: From Kidlington r'bout (junction of A4260 & A34) A423 north to Kidlington; after 1st lights take 2nd left (Yarnton Road), ground is 200yds on the left.
Colours: Green & black/white/green **Change colours:** Red & blue/blue/red **Floodlights:** No
Programme: 20 pages, 20p **Programme Editor:** M A Canning **Founded:** 1920
Midweek Matchday: Wednesday **Previous League:** Oxon Snr 47-54.
Record Attendance: 2500 v Showbiz XI 1973
Clubhouse: Two bars open after matches
Honours: Oxon Snr Lg 53-54 (R-up 47-48), Hellenic Lg Cup 74-75 (R-up 68-69 73-74 74-75, Div 1 R-up 63-64 78-79), Oxon Intermediate Cup 52-53 84-85 (R-up 68-69 73-74 74-75), FA Vase 5th last sixteen 76-77.

LETCOMBE SPORTS

President: D.McDowell. **Chairman:** D Stock **Vice-Chairman:** P.Allen.
Secretary: Mr D Williams, 8 Larkdown, Wantage OX12 8HE (01235 764130).
Manager: Brian Monnery. **Commercial Manager:** R Stock.
Ground: Bassett Road, Letcombe Regis, Wantage, Oxon (012357 68685).
Directions: B4507 Swindon road from Wantage, left for Letcombe Regis, follow road thru Letcombe Regis; ground on right on far side of village.
7Life Member:G.Oliver.
Seats: No **Cover:** No **Floodlights:** No **Nickname:** None **Founded:** 1960.
Colours: yellow/blue/yellow. **Change colours:** White/blue/blue
Sponsors: Autotype/ D McDowell **Previous Lges:** North Berks 60-90/ Chiltonian 90-93.
Programme: £1 with entry **Editor:** R.Stock.(01235 762387) **Club Shop:** No.
Reserves' Lge: Hellenic Res. sect. **Midweek Matchday:** Wednesday
Clubhouse: Open evenings except Monday. Rolls & hot food sold.
Record scorer: R Taylor **Record appearances:** P Davies.
95-96 Top Scorer: **95-96 P.o.Y.:** **95-96 Captain:**
Hons: Chiltonian Lg Div 1 90-91, North Berks Lg 89-90 (Lg Cup 87-88, War Memorial Cup 89-90, A G Kingham Cup 89-90.

Wantage Town's D Burke (No 11) is denied by a great save by Rayners Lane keeper P Randall.
Photo - Mr N Thaler

Shortwood United; Players, Committee and Supporters.

Carterton Town (stripes) and Swanage battle out a FA Vase Qualifying Round tie. *Photo - D Nicholson*

MILTON UNITED

Chairman: Mr K Tull **Vice-Chairman:** Mr P Mitchell **President:** Mr J Cannon
Secretary: Mel James, 45 Whitehorns Way, Drayton, Abingdon, Oxon, OX14 4LH. (01235 531789)
Manager: Alan Hyatt **Asst Manager:** Glyn Evans **Physio:** John Belcher
Ground: The Sportsfield, High Street, Milton, Abingdon, Oxon (01235) 832999
Directions: Use A34 bypass approx 10 miles north of M4 jct.13 & 10 miles south of Oxford. Leave A34 at Milton Hill roundabout and follow signs to Milton Park.
dabout follow road over railway bridge, take 1st left, ground immediately on left.
Capacity: **Seats:** None **Cover:** None **Floodlights:** No **Club Shop:** No.
Programme: Yes **Editor/Press Officer:** David Taylor(01235 816376)
Colours: Claret & sky/sky/sky **Change cols:** All white or all sky
Sponsors: Morlands Brewery **Founded:** 1926
Midweek matchday: Tues/Wed **Reserve Team's League:** Hellenic Lge Res sect
Record Attendance: 500 v Almondsbury Picksons, Hellenic Lg 90-91.
Clubhouse: On ground, open matchdays.
95-96 Captain: **95-96 Top Scorer:** **95-96 P.o.Y.:**
Club Record Goalscorer: Nigel Mott **Club Record Appearances:**
Honours: Hellenic Lg 90-91 (Div 1 89-90 R-Up.94-95)), Nth Berks Lg(4) 85-86 87-89 (R-up 84-85 86-87, Lg Cup(3) 84-86 88-89, Div 2 80-81, Charity Shield(4) 84-86 87-89 (R-up 82-83), Nth Berks War Mem. Cup(3) 83-85 87-88, Berks & Bucks I'mediate Cup 90-91.

PEGASUS JUNIORS

President: **Chairman:** R W Pasley
Secretary: Brian James, 7 Loder Drive, Hereford HR1 1DS (01432 274982).
Manager: M.Williams. **Physio:** D Smith.
Ground: Essex Arms,Widemarsh St.,Hereford.
Directions:A49 past Hereford United ground into Widemarsh St.,straight over mini roundbout.Ground 75 yds on left.
Seats: None **Cover:** None **Capacity:** **Floodlights:** No. **Founded:** 1955
Programme: 20p **Editor:** D.Llewellyn
Colours: All red. **Change colours:** Blue & white/blue/blue.
Previous Leagues: Leisure Centre.
Prev. Grnds: Hereford Utd FC/ Essex Arms Spts Ground, Widemarsh Str.
Clubhouse: 48 Stowens Street. **Midweek Matchday:** Tuesday
Hons: Herefordshire Snr Amtr Cup 71-72, Herefordshire Co. Chal. Cup(5) 81-83 84-85 87-88 89-90 (R-up 93-94), Worcs Snr Urn 85-86, Hellenic Lg Div 1 84-85 (R-up 93-94, Div 1 Cup R-up 93-94).

PURTON

President: Graham Price **Chairman:** John Hayden **Press Officer:** Alan Eastwood
Secretary: Nick Webb, 4 Glevum Close, Purton, Swindon, Wilts SN5 9HA (0793 770242).
Ground: The Red House, Purton (0793 770262 - Saturday afternoons only).
Directions: Purton is on B4041 Wootton Bassett to Cricklade Road. Ground near village hall.
Seats: **Capacity** **Cover:** **Floodlights:** No **Founded:** 1923
Colours: All red **Change colours:** White & blue/blue/blue
Programme: 40 pagesp **Editor:** Alan Eastwood (0793 694036).
Sponsors: Courtoulds. **Midweek Matchday:** Wednesday
Clubhouse: Open after matches
95-96 Captain: **95-96 Top Scorer:** **95-96 P.o.Y.:**
Hons: Wilts Lg 48-49 85-86 (Div 2 83-84, Div 3 86-87), Wilts Snr Cup(6) 38-39 48-49 50-51 54-55 87-89, Wilts Yth Cup 77-78 85-86 88-89, Fairford Hosp. Cup(3) 87-89 93-94.

ROSS TOWN

President: Mrs E Saunders **Chairman:** Geof Jones **Press Officer:** Chris Parsons
Secretary: Tim Barnard, Apsley House, Whitchurch, Ross-on-Wye, HR9 6DJ (01600 890722)
Manager: Clive Saunders **Coach:** Phil Davies **Physio:** Neil Rhodes
Ground: Cinderford Town FC, Causeway Ground, Hilldene, Cinderford
Directions: From Gloucester take A40 to Ross-on-Wye, then A48 - Chepstow. In 10 miles turn right at Elton garage onto A4151 signed Cinderford, thru Littledean, up steep hill, right at crossroads, second left into Latimer Rd. Ground 5 mins walk from town centre.
Capacity: 3,500 **Cover:** 1,000 **Seats:** 250 **Floodlights:** Yes
Colours: Red & white/red/red & white **Change colours:** Yellow & sky/black/yellow
Midweek Matchday: Various **Nickname:** Riversiders
Record Attendance: 102 v St Marks CA 1996
95-96 Captain: **95-96 Top Scorer:** **95-96 P.o.Y.:**

WOOTTON BASSETT TOWN

Chairman: John Reynolds **President:** Keith Lodge
Sec./Press Officer: Mr R Carter, 14 Blackthorn Close, Wootton Bassett, Swindon, Wilts SN4 7JE (01793 851386).
Manager: Dave Warren **Coach:** Dave Warren.
Ground: Gerard Buxton Sports Ground, Rylands Way, Wootton Bassett, Swindon (0793 853880).
Directions: M4 jnct 16 to Wootton Bassett (A3102), left at 2nd r'bout (Prince of Wales pub on right), 2nd left into Longleaze (just after Mobil garage) and Rylands Way is 3rd right by shops, ground 100yds on right. Coming from Calne/Devizes proceed thru town centre and turn right into Longleaze after Shell petrol station on right - Rylands Ave. is 3rd left. Coming from Malmesbury take last exit off r'bout by Prince of Wales pub and Longleaze is 2nd left.
Seats: None **Cover:** 350 **Capacity:** 4,000 **Floodlights:** Due **Founded:** 1882
Colours: All Blue **Change colours:** All Red
Programme: 12 pages, free **Editor:** T.B.A. **Club Shop:** No.
Previous Grounds: None **Record Gate:** 2,103 v Swindon T., friendly 91.
Sponsors: Cathy Moore Recruitment **Previous Leagues:** Wilts (pre-1988).
Midweek home matchday: Wednesday **Reserve team's League:** Wiltshire.
Record win: 11-2 **Record defeat:** 0-9
Clubhouse: Open every matchdays, usual opening hours. Usual type of bar food available together with filled rolls. Tea & coffee available over bar. Matchday refreshments - teas, coffees, soups with light snacks.
95-96 Captain: **95-96 Top Scorer:** **95-96 P.o.Y.:**
Record scorer: Brian (Toby) Ewing **Record appearances:** Steve Thomas.
Hons: Hellenic Lg Div 1 Cup 89-90 93-94, Wilts Lg 87-88 (Div 2 84-85, Subsidiary Cup 78-79), Wilts Snr Cup R-up 02-03 03-04 87-88, Ghia Snr 83-84, Ghia Jnr Cup R-up 88-89, FA Amateur Cup QF 26-27.

YARNTON

Chairman: Michael Staniford **President:** Susan Staniford
Secretary: Amanda Kirk, 11 Saw Close, Chalgrove, Oxon OX44 7TW (01865 891088)
Manager: Peter Wright **Coach:** Andy Slater **Press Off.:** Brian Kirk
Ground: Marsh Road Sports Ground, Yarnton, Oxon (01865 842037).
Directions: North of Oxford on A44 - head for Woodstock/Evesham. Ground situated behind The Grapes pub. Entrance on right before roundabout. Oxford-Woodstock buses stop near ground, Oxford-Kidlington stop 30mins walk from ground.
Seats: None **Cover:** None **Capacity:** Unknown **Floodlights:** No **Founded:** 1947
Colours: Royal & white/blue/blue **Change colours:** Yellow & green/black/black **Club Shop:** No.
Previous Grounds: None **Previous Lges:** Witney & Dist. 47-80/ Oxon Snr 80-91.
Programme: 12 pages, £1 with admission **Clubhouse:** No.
Midweek matchday: Tuesday **Sponsors:** Woodstock Felt Roofing & Red Lion, Yarnton
Record Gate: 45 v Wantage Town 1996
95-96 Captain: **95-96 Top Scorer:** **95-96 P.o.Y.:**
Hons: Oxford Jnr Shield 76-77, Witney & Dist. Lg Div 2 72-73 (Supplementary Cup 65-66), Oxon Snr Lg Div 1 80-81 (Ben Turner Cup 90-91), Oxon Jnr Chal. Cup 56-57 72-73, Fred Ford Mem. Cup 76-77, Burford Spts Cup 76-77.

WINSTON LEAD DIVISION ONE Ten Year Records

	86/7	87/8	88/9	89/0	90/1	91/2	92/3	93/4	94/5	95/6
Alma Stanley	3	12	6	5	8	5	5	5	-	-
Beckenham Town	15	8	17	12	14	14	9	7	10	16
Canterbury City	-	-	-	-	-	-	-	-	13	13
Chatham Town	-	-	19	16	12	19	6	3	2	3
Corinthian	-	-	-	-	-	13	20	8	12	17
Cray Wanderers	10	7	7	18	2	18	17	17	19	12
Crockenhill	2	19	13	15	15	16	21	18	16	18
Darenth Heathside	9	11	4	10	13	21	19	20	20	-
Dartford	-	-	-	-	-	-	-	6	11	2
Deal Town	16	16	2	4	5	3	4	10	8	5
Faversham	17	2	3	1	6	2	15	13	18	20
Folkstone Invicta	-	-	-	-	-	-	13	12	4	10
E Cowes Vict. Ath.	-	15	14	17	18	20	7	2	3	1
Greenwich Borough	1	1	16	6	17	9	16	14	15	11
Herne Bay	5	18	20	14	3	1	2	1	7	4
Hythe Town	11	5	1	-	-	-	-	-	-	-
Hythe United	-	-	-	-	-	-	-	-	-	19
Kent Police	18	6	12	11	19	11	18	21	21	-
Met Police (Hayes)	14	13	15	19	20	-	-	-	-	-
Ramsgate	4	10	9	20	10	10	12	9	5	14
Sheppey United	-	-	-	-	21	6	3	11	1	7
Sittingbourne	6	4	5	2	1	-	-	-	-	-
Slade Green	12	14	10	9	9	8	11	19	17	6
Thamesmead Town	-	-	-	-	-	17	8	4	6	9
Thames Polytechnic	13	17	18	13	16	15	-	-	-	-
Tonbridge FC	-	-	-	3	4	4	1	-	-	-
Tunbridge Wells	7	9	11	7	11	12	14	16	14	15
Whitstable Town	8	3	8	8	7	7	10	15	9	8
No of Clubs Competing	18	19	20	20	21	21	21	21	21	20

Furness: Back Row (L-R); Ronnie Knox (Coach), Mark Quamina, Barry Jeffreys, Tony Haynes, Bobby Gibbons, Denis Chambers, Alfie Charlton, Steve Brown (Mgr). Front Row; Tony McKenzie, Steve Frampton, Paul Roberts, Steve O'Brien, James Halsey, Paul Brown, Gary Ware. *Photo - Steve Holland*

FEEDER TO:
BEAZER HOMES LEAGUE

President: D D Baker
Chairman: P C Wager, **Vice Chairman:** E V Ward
Hon.Secretary: A R Vinter, The Thatched Barn,
Catt's Wood Road, Lower Hardress, Canterbury CT4 5PG, (01227 700108)

The past twelve months have seen a momentous period in the history of the League, the Centenary celebrations. a League and Cup 'double' for Furness, good runs in the FA Carlsberg Vase by Thamesmead Town and Furness and the promotion of Dartford to the Southern League. The Centenary was celebrated in style and we were honoured by the presence of Graham Kelly, Chief Executive of the Football Association, Guest Speaker, Bob 'The Cat' Bevan, Officers of the Kent County Football Association and representatives of other Leagues.

Throughout the season we have witnessed some excellent football but at the start of the season no one could have predicted the final outcome to the League Championship when both Furness and Dartford, both level on points at the top, met in the final league game of the season at Furness's Green Court Road ground. Both sides, after a hard fought campaign, had put together an excellent run of results and in front of 1,055 spectators, the biggest crowd for a Kent League game for over a decade, the match ended in a 1-1 draw, which saw Furness lift the Division One Championship for the first time in their history on goal difference. For Dartford, to finish runners-up with only one defeat all season and that against Furness in their first meeting, their consolation was that they were accepted into the Dr. Martens Southern League after just three seasons in the Winstonlead Kent League, we wish them all the best in their new venture. Two days after clinching the Championship, Furness met Sheppey United in the Final of the Division One Cup at Sittingbourne's Central Park and a two one success, after extra time, saw Furness complete a unique 'League and Cup Double', the first since Greenwich Borough's achievement in 1986/87.

In Division Two of the Winstonlead Kent League, we had another close fought race for the title with four teams battling it out in the final weeks but eventually Hastings Town won the Championship for the first time with Furness (Div 2) and Dover Athletic finishing second and third respectively. The Final of the Division Two Cup saw a 'local derby' match between Folkstone Invicta and Dover Athletic at Hythe United's ground, a game watched by over 300 spectators who saw Folkstone lift the Cup for the second time after a 2-0 victory. In the other Cup Competitions, Dartford defeated Chatham Town by 3-0 in the final of the Plaaya Kent Senior Trophy, watched by over 900, and Bromley beat Fisher 93 to lift the Kent Intermediate Cup.

Nationally, the FA Carlsberg Vase drew great interest for the Kent clubs with Whitstable Town and Slade Green doing well but Thamesmead Town and Furness went one better. Furness played ten Vase matches including three games against Raunds Town before departing from the competition whilst Thamesmead reached the Fifth Round. Earlier they had defeated the holders Arlesey Town and produced other good results before losing, by a late goal, to Canvey Island. In the FA Cup, Dartford lost narrowly to the Conference side Farnborough Town.

Throughout the year we have seen improvements taking place on and off the field, Deal Town have had new floodlights installed and other clubs have plans for similar benefits. Sadly, during the year we have lost a long serving member of the League in Cyril Nicholls who was a Life Member and the loss of Kent Police from the League who have resigned due to 'operational reasons'. Norman Barney, the League Fixture Secretary, has decided to take a rest after twenty four consecutive years of League Management service.

For a number of seasons we have praised our sponsors, Winstonlead Cables Ltd, and would like to thank them for their continued support for Kent Football.
Paul Rivers; Press Officer.

Highest Scorers:	Div One	Furness 87 goals
	Div Two	Hastings Town & Sittingbourne 127 Goals
Golden Boot Award:	Div One	Lee Bosson 36 Goals (Whitstable Town)
	Div Two	Steve Jones 33 goals (Dover Athletic)

FINAL LEAGUE TABLES 1995/96

Div One	P	W	D	L	F	A	Pts
1. Furness	38	27	8	3	87	19	89
2. Dartford	38	26	11	1	71	21	89
3. Chatham Town	38	24	5	9	79	48	77
4. Herne Bay	38	18	10	10	74	44	64
5. Deal Town	38	17	13	8	72	52	64
6. Slade Green	38	17	12	9	66	46	63
7. Sheppey United	38	19	5	14	66	49	62
8. Whitstable Tn	38	17	7	14	85	61	58
9. Thamesmead T	38	17	7	14	59	51	58
10. Folkstone Inv	38	15	11	12	82	56	56
11. Greenwich Boro	38	15	7	16	60	66	52
12. Cray Wanderers	38	16	5	17	70	70	50*
13. Canterbury City	38	14	6	18	48	59	48
14. Ramsgate	38	13	6	19	62	81	45
15. Tunbridge Wells	38	10	10	18	45	64	40
16. Beckenham Tn	38	9	9	20	45	60	36
17. Corinthian	38	9	7	22	53	84	34
18. Crockenhill	38	8	8	22	51	92	32
19. Hythe United	38	8	6	24	58	101	30
20. Faversham Tn	38	3	3	32	33	142	12

* Cray Wanderers 3 points deducted

Div Two	P	W	D	L	F	A	Pts
1. Hastings Tn	36	26	6	4	127	49	84
2. Furness Res	36	24	5	7	121	36	77
3. Dover Ath	36	23	5	8	104	52	74
4. Tonbridge	36	22	7	7	108	48	73
5. Whitstable R	36	22	5	9	107	46	71
6. Sittingbourne	36	22	4	10	127	57	70
7. Thamesmead R	36	18	6	12	63	48	60
8. Folkstone Res	36	18	6	12	84	73	60
9. Chatham Tn R	36	15	10	11	56	59	55
10. Corinthian Res	36	16	4	16	63	58	52
11. Beckenham R	36	15	7	14	62	67	52
12. Ramsgate Res	36	14	4	18	79	84	46
13. Margate	36	10	9	17	57	76	39
14. Herne Bay R	36	12	3	21	49	86	39
15. Deal Tn Res	36	12	3	21	73	114	39
16. Canterbury R	36	11	5	20	58	86	38
17. Crockenhill R	36	6	4	26	49	104	22
18. F/sham Tn R	36	5	3	28	41	138	18
19. Kent Police	36	2	2	32	28	175	8

DIVISION ONE RESULTS CHART 1995-96

HOME TEAM	1	2	3	4	5	6	7	8	9	10	11	12	13	14	15	16	17	18	19	20
1. Beckenham Town	*	1-1	1-3	4-0	1-5	2-3	0-0	0-3	5-0	2-2	0-2	0-1	0-2	4-2	1-2	0-1	1-1	0-1	1-0	0-2
2. Canterbury City	1-2	*	1-2	1-3	2-0	2-2	1-1	1-2	2-0	2-0	0-2	2-1	0-1	4-0	0-1	2-1	0-1	1-2	1-1	1-2
3. Chatham Town	2-0	2-0	*	2-1	4-1	1-2	0-2	9-1	2-0	2-2	1-1	4-2	0-2	3-1	1-3	0-4	4-2	2-0	5-3	1-0
4. Corinthian	1-2	2-3	1-2	*	2-3	2-2	0-3	2-0	5-2	1-4	1-5	0-3	1-1	0-1	2-2	0-2	3-0	2-1	1-0	0-3
5. Cray Wanderers	4-1	1-2	0-1	2-1	*	5-2	0-1	1-3	6-1	3-1	0-1	1-1	2-2	4-2	5-3	1-2	1-1	2-2	2-0	0-4
6. Crockenhill	1-0	0-1	1-1	1-4	0-1	*	0-2	3-1	2-0	1-4	0-3	3-1	1-6	6-2	2-2	2-2	1-5	0-1	1-1	1-1
7. Dartford	1-1	1-0	1-0	2-0	5-2	1-0	*	1-1	2-1	1-0	0-1	1-0	2-0	2-1	3-0	3-0	4-1	4-3	3-1	2-0
8. Deal Town	1-0	3-0	0-2	0-0	4-2	2-2	0-0	*	3-3	0-0	2-2	0-1	1-0	5-1	3-1	0-0	0-0	3-1	4-1	3-0
9. Faversham Tn	1-0	2-3	1-2	1-2	0-5	3-1	1-4	0-6	*	2-7	0-8	0-6	0-6	1-3	2-0	2-3	2-4	0-3	0-3	0-5
10. Folkstone Inv	2-0	1-2	5-2	6-1	0-0	1-2	1-1	3-1	9-0	*	0-1	0-3	3-3	4-0	4-1	1-2	1-1	2-2	1-0	0-2
11. Furness	1-0	2-0	1-1	1-0	4-1	7-0	1-1	0-0	3-0	2-2	*	5-0	1-1	2-0	4-0	2-1	1-1	1-0	2-1	1-2
12. Greenwich Boro	0-2	2-1	0-3	1-2	1-0	4-3	0-0	4-0	1-1	2-4	0-5	*	1-0	4-2	4-0	0-1	2-0	3-2	1-2	1-7
13. Herne Bay	2-0	5-0	1-2	4-3	2-4	3-0	0-0	2-1	3-2	0-1	0-2	1-1	*	5-1	2-1	2-0	0-0	3-0	0-1	5-2
14. Hythe United	2-4	2-2	3-4	4-1	0-1	3-0	0-0	2-6	5-2	1-1	0-3	2-2	0-2	*	4-3	0-3	0-1	1-1	1-0	4-3
15. Ramsgate	0-0	1-2	1-4	5-3	0-1	4-3	1-3	2-3	4-0	1-1	1-0	3-1	0-1	3-2	*	1-0	1-1	1-2	0-4	2-1
16. Sheppey Utd	4-3	1-0	1-3	5-1	3-0	2-1	1-3	2-2	2-2	0-1	1-3	4-1	3-0	3-1	2-2	*	0-1	1-0	2-1	1-2
17. Slade Green	3-3	2-3	0-0	2-2	3-0	3-0	0-2	1-1	4-0	3-0	0-1	4-0	3-2	3-1	3-1	2-1	*	3-2	4-1	2-1
18. Thamesmead Tn	2-2	0-3	2-0	1-0	5-1	2-0	1-2	1-2	4-0	2-1	1-0	0-0	1-1	3-1	3-1	0-3	1-0	*	0-0	2-1
19. Tunbridge Wells	1-1	1-1	1-0	0-0	0-2	2-1	0-5	0-3	4-0	1-5	0-2	1-1	3-3	2-2	2-3	2-1	2-0	3-2	*	0-0
20. Whitstable Tn	0-1	6-0	0-2	3-3	3-1	5-1	2-2	2-2	5-1	6-2	1-4	0-4	1-1	4-1	2-5	2-1	1-1	1-3	3-0	*

LEAGUE DIVISION ONE CUP 1995-96

First Round;

Beckenham Town v Faversham Town	2-1
Canterbury City v Folkstone Invicta	4-5
Whitstable Town v Herne Bay	2-1
Dartford v Cray Wanderers	0-2

Second Round:

Beckenham Town v Chatham Town	0-2
Cray Wanderers v Furness	1-2
Sheppey United v Deal Town	3-2
Slade Green v Thamesmead Town	4-2
Whitstable Town v Folkstone Invicta	2-1
Crockenhill v Greenwich Borough	1-1, 1-1, (4-3p)
Hythe United v Tunbridge Wells	1-2
Corinthian v Ramsgate	5-5, 4-1

Third Round:

Crockenhill v Furness 1-6
Chatham Town v Whitstable Town 1-1, 1-3
Sheppey United v Tunbridge Wells 2-0
Slade Green v Corinthian 2-0

Semi-Finals;

Whitstable Tn v Furness 1-1, 1-3, (1-4ag)
Sheppey United v Slade Green 1-1, 2-1, (3-2ag)

Final: Furness v Sheppey United 2-1

DIVISION TWO RESULTS CHART 1995-96

HOME TEAM	1	2	3	4	5	6	7	8	9	10	11	12	13	14	15	16	17	18	19
1. Beckenham Tn	*	2-2	1-2	4-3	2-2	10-0	0-5	1-0	1-2	0-2	2-4	1-0	*-*	3-2	2-1	5-4	0-4	0-3	3-1
2. Canterbury City	2-4	*	0-1	3-0	3-2	1-5	0-3	2-1	0-1	0-2	2-4	0-2	6-0	1-3	5-2	0-3	1-0	1-1	0-0
3. Chatham Town	1-0	0-2	*	1-0	0-0	1-1	3-1	1-0	3-1	2-1	0-3	0-3	5-0	1-1	2-2	0-3	3-1	4-1	0-3
4. Corinthian	2-0	4-1	3-0	*	1-0	3-0	2-2	1-3	3-2	2-0	1-2	2-1	1-0	3-0	1-0	1-1	0-1	3-2	0-2
5. Crockenhill	4-3	2-6	2-4	0-2	*	3-1	1-2	5-0	1-0	0-5	1-9	2-3	5-0	3-0	0-3	1-2	1-1	0-5	0-4
6. Deal Town	3-1	2-3	3-4	3-2	2-1	*	1-5	5-1	3-2	0-3	1-1	4-1	12-1	2-0	3-4	0-0	1-3	0-5	1-5
7. Dover Athletic	1-1	2-2	2-0	3-1	5-0	6-1	*	9-1	1-2	0-2	0-5	4-1	6-1	5-1	4-2	2-1	1-2	3-1	3-2
8. Faversham Town	0-3	2-1	2-3	1-1	3-2	2-3	1-5	*	1-2	1-16	0-5	0-1	3-3	1-2	0-2	1-4	1-0	1-3	1-4
9. Folkstone Invicta	1-1	1-1	2-2	2-3	2-1	5-1	0-2	4-0	*	1-6	2-0	3-1	5-3	5-0	7-2	6-3	0-0	2-5	1-0
10. Furness	3-0	3-1	3-0	1-0	4-0	7-1	1-2	5-0	12-2	*	1-4	3-1	6-0	1-0	1-1	3-1	2-0	1-3	2-0
11. Hastings Town	1-1	4-2	3-3	2-0	5-2	5-1	6-1	12-1	3-3	1-1	*	7-2	2-0	3-1	2-0	4-3	0-1	2-3	2-2
12. Herne Bay	2-1	0-2	1-1	1-1	2-1	2-0	2-4	3-3	1-2	1-5	0-5	*	4-0	3-1	0-1	0-5	3-2	0-3	1-1
13. Kent Police	0-4	2-5	1-2	0-10	2-0	2-4	1-4	0-5	0-5	1-11	1-3	3-1	*	1-2	0-3	0-9	1-4	2-2	0-9
14. Margate	0-0	7-0	2-2	3-3	2-2	0-2	1-1	2-0	2-3	1-1	2-6	0-2	8-1	*	2-1	0-2	4-3	1-1	1-1
15. Ramsgate	1-2	4-1	5-1	3-4	3-0	3-1	0-3	4-1	2-0	1-1	3-5	6-2	6-0	3-4	*	4-4	0-2	1-0	0-1
16. Sittingbourne	7-0	7-0	2-0	2-0	5-2	9-1	3-5	6-0	0-2	1-2	0-3	5-1	7-0	1-2	8-3	*	4-2	3-3	4-2
17. Thamesmead Town	0-1	4-2	1-1	3-0	2-1	2-1	1-1	4-2	3-1	2-2	0-2	2-1	1-0	2-0	3-2	0-2	*	0-3	5-1
18. Tonbridge FC	1-1	2-0	2-2	3-1	4-2	8-2	2-1	6-0	4-4	4-1	5-0	4-0	6-0	4-0	3-0	0-1	2-1	*	2-3
19. Whitstable Town	1-2	4-0	1-0	5-0	6-0	3-2	1-0	8-2	2-1	2-1	1-2	3-0	9-1	3-0	9-1	2-5	1-1	5-2	*

. Match not played three points awarded to Beckenham Town

DIVISION TWO CUP 1995-96

First Round;

Chatham Town v Ramsgate 4-0
Whitstable Town v Crockenhill 6-1
Canterbury City v Furness 0-4

Second Round;

Chatham Town v Thamesmead Town 2-0
Whitstable Town v Sittingbourne 2-1
Margate v Kent Police 1-2
Furness v Dover Athletic 0-2
Corinthian v Deal Town 2-0
Beckenham Town v Hastings Town 1-4
Herne Bay v Folkstone Invicta 2-4
Faversham Town v Tonbridge FC 0-4

Third Round:

Chatham Town v Whitstable Town 1-2
Kent Police v Dover Athletic 0-3
Corinthian v Hastings Town 2-3
Folkstone Invicta v Tonbridge FC 2-0

Semi-Finals;

Whitstable T v Dover Ath 0-1, 1-1, (1-2ag)
Hastings Tn v Folkstone 2-3, 0-1, (2-4ag)

Final; Dover Athletic v Folkstone Invicta 0-2

PLAAYA SENIOR TROPHY 1995-96

Quarter Finals:

Whitstable Town v Dartford 1-2
Furness v Greenwich Borough 2-0
Thamesmead Town v Tunbridge Wells 2-1
Chatham Town v Herne Bay 2-1

Semi-Finals:

Dartford v Furness 1-0
Thamesmead Town v Chatham Town 0-4

Final: Dartford v Chatham Town 3-0

KENT INTERMEDIATE CUP 1995-96

Semi-Finals:

Fisher 93 v Thamesmead Town 4-0
Whitstable Town v Bromley 2-4

Final: Fisher 93 v Bromley 1-3

DIVISION ONE CLUBS 1996-97

BECKENHAM TOWN

Chairman: T.B.a. **Vice Chairman:** B Hollaway.
Secretary: Peter Palmer, 107 Wentworth Rd, West Croydon, Surrey CR0 3HZ (0181 689 2134).
Manager: Kevin Sugrue **Asst Manager:**J.Moore.
Ground: Eden Park Avenue, Beckenham, Kent (0181 650 1066).
Directions: M25, A21 to Bromley then follow signs to Beckenham. Ground 1 mile west of town off A214, 2 mins walk from Eden Park (BR) station - trains from London Bridge. Bus 264.
Seats: 120 **Cover:** 120 **Capacity:** 4,000 **Floodlights:** Yes **Reformed:** 1971.
Colours: Red & white/red/white **Change Colours:** Yellow/black/black. **Nickname:** Reds.
Midweek matchday: Tuesday. **Record Gate:** 720 v Berkhamstead .F.A.Cup.1994-95.
Sponsors: **Prev. Ground:** Stanhope Grove, Beckenham (60 yrs)
Previous Leagues: South East London Amtr 71-73/ Metropolitan 73-75/ London Spartan 75-82.
Programme: 8 pages, 50p **Programme Editor:** Bob Chilvers (0181 301 2624)
Clubhouse: All day opening at weekends. Hot & cold food, teas, coffees, hotdogs, burgers, crusty rolls, bread pudding etc on matchdays. Bar and dance area. Pool tables and fruit machines.
Record Scorer: Ricky Bennett **Record appearances:** Lee Fabian.
95-96 Captain: **Club Shop:** Yes - contact secretary.
95-96 P.o.Y.: **95-96 Top Scorer:**
Hons: London Spartan Lg Cup R-up 77-78 78-79, Kent Snr Tphy R-up 81-82 93-94, Kent Lg Cup R-up 84-85 92-93 (Div 2 Cup R-up 90-91).

CANTERBURY CITY

Chairman: Paul Gladwish **Vice Chairman:** Geoff Bradley **President:** V H Heslop.
Secretary: Keith J Smith, 7 Knight Ave, London Rd Est, Canterbury, Kent CT2 8PZ (0227 456116).
Manager: Martin Farnie **Asst Manager:** Gary Allen. **Physio:** Brian Ball
Ground: Kingsmead Stadium, Kingsmead Road, Canterbury CT2 7PH (01227 457245)
Directions: A28 out of city centre into Military Road. At 1st r-about turn left into Tourtel Rd, proceed to next r-about and head straight over into Kingsmead Rd - stadium on right opposite Canterbury swimming pool. Half mile from Canterbury West (BR). Bus service 624 or 625 from Canterbury bus station
Capacity: 5,000 **Cover:** 200 **Seats:** 200 **Floodlights:** Yes **Club Shop:** Yes
Programme: 24 pages, 50p **Editor:** Roy Twyman (01227 375774) **Press Officer:** Roy Twyman
Colours: Green & white/green/green **Change:** Navy/red/navy
Nickname: The City. **Sponsors:** Parker Tools. **Founded:** 1947.
Midweek home matchday: Thursday. **Reserve Team's League:** Winstonlead Kent Div 2
Record Attendance: 3,001 v Torquay, FA Cup 1st Rd 1964.
Best FA Cup season: 1st Rd 64-65 (lost 0-6 to Torquay), 68-69 (lost 0-1 to Swindon).
Previous Leagues: Kent 47-59/ Metropolitan 59-60/ Southern 60-94.
Players progressing to Football League: Ron Gawler (Southend 1949), Arthur Hughes (Grimsby 1954), Arthur Nugent (Darlington 1956), John Richardson (Southport 1956), Tommy Horsfall (Cambridge Utd), Jimmy Murray (Wolves), Kenny Hill (Gillingham), Terry Norton (Brighton), Mark Weatherly (Gillingham), Pat Hilton (Brighton 1973), David Wiltshire (Gillingham 1974), Gary Pugh (Torquay 1984).
Clubhouse: Lounge bar open on matchdays. Snack bar,burgers,hot-dogs, pies, chips, tea, coffee, etc
95-96 Captain: Sammy Spence **95-96 Top scorer:** Darren Hare 8.
95-96 P.o.Y.: Julian Beal. **95-96 Supporters' P.o.Y.:** Sammy Spence
Record Scorer: Wilf Heathcote 113 (48-51) **Record Appearances:** John Carragher 413 (60-70)
Honours: FA Trophy 2nd Rd replay 74-75, Kent Lg Cup, 49-50, (Div 2 (Reserves)90-91, Div 2 Cup (Reserves)48-49, 89-90), Kent Senior Cup 53-54, Kent Senior Trophy 79-80, Kent Intermediate Cup 73-74, Kent Messenger Trophy 74-75, Frank Norris Memorial Shield 88-89 89-90.Kent League Div 2 Champions(reserves0 90-91.

CHATHAM TOWN

Chairman: P Enright **President:**
Secretary: Brian Burcombe, 4 Hallwood Close, Parkwood, Rainham, Kent ME8 9NT (01634 363419).
Manager: John Adams **Asst Manager:**
Ground: Maidstone Road Sports Ground, Maidstone Road, Chatham, Kent (01634 812194).
Directions: M2, A229 Chatham turn-off, follow signs to Chatham, ground one and a half miles on right opposite garage. 1 mile from Chatham (BR).
Seats: 500 **Cover:** 1,000 **Capacity:** 5,000 **Floodlights:** Yes **Founded:** 1882.
Colours: Red & black halves/black/black. **Change Colours:** Yellow & green **Nickname:** Chats.
Midweek matchday: Tuesday **Record Gate:** 5,000 v Gillingham, 1980.
Sponsors: Topps Scaffolding **Previous Ground:** Great Lines, Chatham 1882-90.
Previous Lges: Southern (several spells)/ Aetolian 59-64/ Metropolitan 64-68/ Kent (Sev. spells).
Programme: 12 pages, 50p **Programme Editor:** Trevor Busby
Clubhouse: Matchdays and functions **Previous Names:** Chatham FC/ Medway FC (1970s).
95-96 Captain: **95-96 P.o.Y.:** **95-96 Top Scorer:**
Hons: Kent Lg(9) 1894-95 03-05 24-25 26-27 71-72 73-74 76-77 79-80 (R-up 02-03 23-24 25-26 70-71 74-75 80-81, Lg Cup 71-72 76-77 (R-up(3)), Thames & Medway Comb.(5) 1896-97 04-06 19-20 23-24, FA Cup QF (beat Nottm Forest 2-0 en route) 1888-89, FA Tphy 3rd Rd 70-71, Kent Snr Cup 1888-89 1904-05 10-11 18-19, Kent Snr Shield 19-20.

CORINTHIAN

Chairman: R J Billings **Manager:** Tony Sitford
Secretary: Dave Roff, 79 Edwin Street, Gravesend, Kent DA12 1EJ (01474 569457).
Ground: Gay Dawn, Valley Road, Fawkham, Nr Dartford, Kent DA3 8LZ (01474 707559/702335 fax:708431).
Directions: A2 off Longfield, take Fawkham Road - ground one mile on left. Or, A20 to Fawkham Green then ground one and a half miles on right. One and a quarter miles from Longfield (BR).
Seats: 134 **Cover:** 175 **Capacity:** 2,000 **Floodlights:** Yes **Club Shop:** Yes
Programme: 12 pages, 30p **Editor:** TBA **Press Officer:** Secretary
Colours: Green & white hoops/white **Change Colours:** Sky & white
Sponsors: None **Founded:** 1972. **Nickname:** None.
Midweek matchday: Tuesday **Reserves' League:** Wintonlead Kent Div 2
Record Attendance: 480 v Spurs, friendly 1979.
Players progressing to Football League: Andy Hessenthaler (Watford).
Clubhouse: Bar, cafeteria & restaurant
95-96 Captain: Allan Clarke **95-96 P.o.Y.:** Danny Pedley. **95-96 Top Scorer:**
Club Record Appearances: Gavin Tovey **Club Record Goalscorer:** Lee Annett
Hons: Essex AFA Snr Cup 82-83, Kent Snr Tphy 83-84 86-87, Fort Lauderdale International Tournament 84-85, Kent Intermediate Cup 89-90 90-91.

CRAY WANDERERS

Chairman: Gary Hillman **President:** Bill Faulkner
Secretary: Mr Kerry Phillips, 15 Watling Street, Bexleyheath, Kent DA6 7QJ (01322 554108).
Manager: Glen Cooper. **Asst Manager:** Peter Little **Coach:**
Ground: Oxford Road, Sidcup, Kent (0181 300 9201).
Directions: Between Sidcup High Street and Footscray High Street; from A20 turn off for Footscray, left at lights, Oxford Rd is 5th left. Three quarters of a mile from Sidcup (BR) station - buses 492 21 51 233 R11 stop at top of Oxford Rd
Seats: 106 **Cover:** 300 **Capacity:** 2,000 **Floodlights:** Due **Club Shop:** Yes
Programme: 20 pages, 50p **Editor/Press Officer:** Greg Mann (0181-318 9604)& (w)0171 438 1735.
Colours: Amber & black **Change Colours:** Purple & white
Sponsors: N.Hillman & Sonsd **Founded:** 1860. **Nickname:** Wands.
Midweek matchday: Tuesday
Record Gate: 1,523 v Stamford, F.A. Vase QF 79-80.
Previous Leagues: Kent 1894-1903 6-7 9-14 34-38/ W Kent 03-06 07-09/ London 20-34 51-59/ Kent Amtr 38-39 46-51/ S London All 43-46/ Aetolian 59-64/ Gtr London 64-66/ Metropolitan 66-71/ London Metropolitan 71-75/ London Spartan 75-78.
Clubhouse: Open pub hours (freehouse). Hot & cold food available.
95-96 P.o.Y.: Peter Coupland **95-96 Captain:** Ian Jenkins **95-96 Top Scorer:** Phil Collins 23
Club Record Goalscorer: Ken Collishaw, 272. **Club Record Appearances:** John Dorey c500, 61-72
Hons: London Lg(2) 56-58 (Lg Cup 54-55), Aetolian Lg 62-63 (Lg Cup 63-64), Gtr London Lg 65-66 (Lg Cup(2) 64-66), Metropolitan Lg Cup 70-71 (Amtr Cup(2) 66-68), London Spartan Lg(2) 76-78, Kent Lg 01-02 80-81 (R-up 79-80 90-91, Lg Cup 83-84), Kent Snr Tphy 92-93, Kent Amtr Cup(4) 30-31 62-65.

CROCKENHILL

President: Mr H Miller **Chairman:** Alan Parkin **Vice-Chairman:** Brian Perfect
Secretary: Alan Parkin, 15 Greenside, Swanley, Kent. BR8 7ER (01322 663319)
Commercial Manager: Mike Floate (01322 668275).
Manager: Alan Whitehead **Asst Manager:** Glen Cooper **Coach:** Brian Crimmen.
Ground: 'Wested', Eynsford Road, Crockenhill, Kent (01322 662097).
Directions: Just off M25 junction 3, B2173 towards Swanley, left after 200yds into Wested Lane, ground 1 mile on right (Ord. Survey grid Ref: 516669 sheet 177). Just over a mile from Swanley (BR) station - trains from Victoria. Kentish Bus 477 to Crockenhill - at village shops turn left at T-juntion - ground 1 mile up narrow lane on left.
Seats: 200 **Cover:** 200 **Capacity:** 2,000 **Floodlights:** No **Founded:** 1946.
Cols: Red & white stripes/red/red **Change Colours:** Blue/Black/Blue. **Nickname:** Crocks.
Programme: 8 pages + cover/ads **Programme Editor:** Mike Floate/ Bill Bamforth.
Midweek matchday: Tuesday **Reserve Lge:** Sevenoaks & Dist. (Crockenhill Dundee).
Club Shop: To open September 1994, selling old programmes, club strip, scarves, pocket annuals, action photos, ground photos, framed photos of League grounds. Contact Mike Floate (0322 668275).
Record Gate: 800 v Maidstone, Kent Amtr Cup 1948. *3,500 at Raleys Field, Sevenoaks, for Sevenoaks Charity Cup final v Bromley Green in 1949. Crockenhill won 2-1.*
Previous Grounds: None **Prev. Lgs:** Kent Amtr 46-59/ Aetolian 59-64/ Gtr London 64-68
Players progressing to Football Lge: Tony Cascarino (Gillingham) 1982, Steve Bruce (Gillingham via other clubs) late 70s.
Clubhouse: Open matchdays, Sunday lunchtimes, many evenings. Wide range of food always available.
95-96 Captain: **95-96 Top Scorer:** **95-96 P.o.Y.:**
Hons: Kent Lg 82-83 (R-up 84-85), Kent Snr Tphy 80-81, Kent Jnr Cup R-up 48-49, West Kent Amtr Cup 56-57, Sevenoaks Charity Cup 48-49, Kent Amtr Lg 56-57 (R-up 54-55, Prem Div 53-54 (R-up 52-53), Div 1 48-49 (R-up 46-47), Snr Div Cup R-up 56-57, Div 1 Cup R-up 46-47).

DEAL TOWN

Chairman: Roy Smith. **Vice-Chairman:** Bill Bennett.
Secretary: Mrs Anne Lewis, Silver Hill, Northbourne Rd, Mongeham, Deal, Kent CT14 0LF (01304 373918).
Manager: Dave Dadd. **Asst Manager:** T.B.A. **Physio:** T.B.A.
Ground: Charles Sports Ground, St Leonards Road, Deal, Kent (01304 375623).
Directions: A258 through Walmer, left into Cornwell Road, continue into Hamilton Road, veer left into Mill Rd, follow round to right into Manor Road, right into St Leonards Road, ground 100 yards on right. 1 mile from both Walmer and Deal BR stations. Local buses stop near ground.
Seats: 150 **Cover:** 500 **Capacity:** 2,000 **Floodlights:** Yes **Club Shop:** No
Programme: 28 pages, 50p. **Editor:** Peter Humphries (01304 367031) **Press Officer:** Colin Adams
Colours: Black & white hoops/black **Change Colours:** Yellow & Blue quarters/blue/blue.
Founded: 1908. **Nickname:** Town. **Sponsors:** Greene King.
Midweek matchday: Tuesday **Reserves' Lge:** Wintonlead Div 2
Record Gate: 4,000 v Billy Wright showbiz XI, Feb '61.
Previous Leagues: Kent 09-59/ Aetolian 59-63/ Southern 63-66/ Gtr London 66-71
Player progressing to Football Lge: Danny Wallace (Southampton)
Clubhouse: Matchdays & functions. Bar. Tea bar with hot & cold food.
95-96 Captain: Colin Gilmore. **95-96 Top Scorer:** Joe Lewis 21. **95-96 P.o.Y.:** Gary Miller.
Club Record Scorer: Joe Brayne 147. **Club Record Appearances:** Alan Barrow 543 (recent times).
Hons: Kent Lg 53-54 (R-up 88-89, Lg Cup 57-58 81-82 (R-up 94-95, SF 88-89 89-90), Kent Snr Tphy 94-95 R-up 82-83 90-91, Gtr London Lg Cup 68-69, Aetolian Lg R-up 59-60.

FAVERSHAM TOWN

Chairman: Brian Mulherne **Vice-Chairman:** Richard Stebberds **President:** Mr R W B Neame
Secretary: K F Hammond, 8 Sherwood Close, Faversham, Kent ME13 7QS (0795 535612).
Manager: Hughie Stinson **Asst Manager:** Steve Wren **Physio:** Andy Potterton.
Coach: Bob Mason **Commercial Manager:** Chris Turner.
Ground: Shepherd Neame Stadium, Salters Lane, Faversham, Kent (0795 532738).
Directions: On A2 (Canterbury road) just west of town.
Seats: 350 **Cover:** 1,500 **Capacity:** 2,000 **Floodlights:** Yes **Founded:** 1901.
Colours: White/blue/red **Change Colours:** Red/white/blue **Nickname:** Town.
Midweek matchday: Tuesday **Record Gate:** 1,400 v Sheppey Utd, 1949.
Sponsors: Shepherd Neame Master Brewers
Previous Leagues: Aetolian 59-64/ Metropolitan 64-71/ Athenian 71-76.
Programme: 16 pages, 40p **Editor:** John Barrett (0795 535500).
Reserves' Lge: Kent Lg Div 2 **Prev. Grounds:** Ashford Rd 1901-46/Gordon Square 46-58
Rec. win: 8-0 v Greenwich B., Aug'89 **Record defeat:** 0-9 v Sittingbourne, Jan '82.
Clubhouse: Open matchdays (Sat/Sun/Tues) Wed/Thurs. Snacks sold.
Club Record Scorer: Tony Rudd 43. **Club Record Appearances:** Bob Mason.
95-96 Top Scorer: **95-96 Captain:**
95-96 P.o.Y.:
Hons: Kent Lg 69-70 70-71 77-78 89-90 (R-up 87-88, Lg Cup 70-71 90-91 (R-up 82-83)), Kent Snr Tphy 76-77 77-78 (R-up 87-88 88-89), Kent Amtr Cup 56-57 58-59 71-72 72-73 73-74.

FOLKESTONE INVICTA

Chairman: Tommy Guiver. **President:** Wilfred Armory.
Secretary: Neil Pilcher, 25 Pavilion Road, Folkestone, Kent. CT19 5RW (01303 245066)
Player/Manager: Tim Hulme. **Asst Manager:** Micky Dix. **Coach:** Dennis Hunt.
Ground: The New Pavilion, Cheriton Road, Folkestine, Kent CT20 5JU (01303 257461).
Directions: On the A20 behind Safeway foodstore, midway between Folkestone central and Folkestone West BR stations.
Seats: 900 **Cover:** 3,500 **Capacity:** 6,500. **Floodlights:** Yes **Founded:** 1936.
Colours: Amber & black/black/amber. **Change Colours:** Blue & green/green/blue**Nickname:**
Midweek matchday: Tuesday **Sponsors:**Eurotunnel(Le Shuttle).
Previous Lges: Kent County (pre-1991).
Rec. Gate: 1,211 v Brighton, Friendly 91.
Programme: 44 pages, 50p **Editor:** Neil Pitcher.
Previous Ground: South Rd, Hythe (pre-1991).Kent County Lg matches wer played on council pitches.
Clubhouse: Yes, The Invicta Club **95-96 Top Scorer:**
Honours:(since joining Winstonlead Kent League)Plaaya Kent Senior Trophy R-Up 93-94,94-95.

Beckenham Town FC: Team line up before their 4-0 home victory against Corinthian *Photo - Martin Wray*

Chatham Town: Back Row (L-R); Micky Wells, Derek Reid, Paul Hobbs, Matt Glennon, Carl Webb, Gary Wallace. Front Row: John Adamss, Eddie Lund, Dennis Reid, Lol Ward, Ricky Harris, Paul Collins, Dave Samwell

Deal Town FC: Back Row (L-R); Assistant Manager, Paul Stevens, Julian Homes, Spencer Creedon, John Rigden, John Lewis, Paul Cureton, Jim Brannon, Eddie Pickford. Front Row; Phil Hancock, John McManus, Colin Gilmore, Paul Murray, Kevin Marsden, Darren Loarring.

Photo - Andrew Chitty

FURNESS

Chairman: Alan Sutherland
Secretary: Richard Ayling, 22 Houston Rd, London SE23 2RN (0181 699 1052).
Manager: Steve Brown **Physio:** Bob Pearson
Commercial Manager: Alan Simmonds. **Press Officer:** David Skeel (0181 464 8571)
Ground: Green Court Road, Swanley, Kent BR8 8JG (01322 666442).
Directions: From junction of M25 & M20 follow signs for Swanley. Left at Crockenhill turning, then first right after motorway crossing. 500 yards from Swanley (BR).
Seats: 100 **Cover:** 200 **Capacity:** 1,500 **Floodlights:** No **Founded:** 1991.
Colours: All white **Change Colours:** All red **Nickname:** None.
Midweek matchday: Tuesday **Record Gate:** 350 v Newport IOW, FA Vase 1980.
Previous Names: Danson (Bexley Borough)(founded 1941) and Furness United merged in 1991. Danson Furness United 91-93.
Previous Grounds: Randell Down Road 41-53/ Eltham Road 53-60/ Crook Log, Brampton Road 60-92.
Prev. Lges: Sidcup & Dist./ S.E. London Amtr/ London Spartan 82-87. *Furness: Sth London Alliance (pre-1991).*
Record win: 11-0 v Kent Police, Kent Lge 94-95.
Programme: 12 pages, 50p **Editor:** Alan Sutherland (0171 537 2817).
Clubhouse: Matchdays and functions **Club Sponsors:** S H E Printers
Player progressing to Football Lg: Darren Adams (Cardiff 94-95).
95-96 Captain: **95-96 Top Scorer:** **95-96 P.o.Y.:**
Hons: Kent Lg R-up 94-95, SE Amteur Lg Cup R-up 60-61.

GREENWICH BOROUGH

President: T H M Edwaards **Chairman:** Martin Dillnut
Secretary: Ms Denise Richmond, 7 Castlecombe Rd, Mottingham, London SE9 6BA (0181 850 5360).
Manager: Dave Waight **Asst Manager:** Doug Francis
Ground: Harrow Meadow, Eltham Green Rd, Eltham, London SE9 (0181 850 3098).
Directions: South Circular (A205) to Yorkshire Grey pub, ground opposite. 1 mile from both Eltham and Kidbrooke BR stations.
Seats: 50 **Cover:** 50 **Capacity:** 2,500 **Floodlights:** Yes **Founded:** 1928.
Colours: All Red **Change Colours:** Blue/Black/Blue. **Nickname:** Boro.
Midweek matchday: Tuesday **Previous Ground:** Erith & Belvedere F.C. 1992-93.
Record Gate: 2,000 v Charlton, floodlight opening, 1978.
Record defeat: 0-8 v Faversham Town, August 1989.
Sponsors: Pelgary Ltd **Previous Name:** London Borough of Greenwich.
Previous Leagues: South London Alliance/ Kent Amateur/ London Spartan 77-84.
Programme: 8 pages, 20p **Programme Editor:** Denise Richmond. **Clubhouse:** Yes.
Hons: London Spartan Lg 79-80 (Lg Cup 82-83), Kent Lg 86-87 87-88 (Lg Cup 84-85 86-87), Kent Snr Tphy 84-85, FA Vase 5th Rd 89-90.

HERNE BAY

Chairman: M Todd **Vice Chairman:** R.Gibson. **President:** J Hodkinson
Secretary: T Sampson, 33 Sharp's Field, Headcorn, Kent Tn27 9UF, (01622 891784)
Manager: Tom Sampson **Asst Manager:** Keith Lissenden **Physio:**J.Hodkinson.
Ground: Winch's Field, Stanley Gardens, Herne Bay, Kent (01227 374156).
Directions: Leave A299 at Herne Bay r'bout, 2nd left, 1st left. Half mile from Herne Bay (BR); down Station Approach (half mile), 1st right (Spencer Road), 2nd right.
Seats: 250 **Cover:** 2,000 **Capacity:** 5,000 **Floodlights:** Yes **Club Shop:** Due.
Programme: 36 pages, 60p **Editor:** Doug Smith **Press Officer:** Doug Smith.
Colours: Blue & white . **Change Colours:** Red & black halves
Sponsors: Abik Leisure/Waterways. **Nickname:** The Bay. **Founded:** 1886.
Midweek matchday: Tuesday **Reserve Team's League:** Kent Lge Div Two.
Record Attendance: 2,303 v Margate, FA Cup 4th Qual. Rd 1970.
Previous Leagues: Kent Amtr/ Thanet/ East Kent/ Kent 53-59/ Aetolian 59-64/ Athenian 64-74.
Clubhouse: Open evenings and matchdays.
95-96 Captain: Terry Martin **95-96 P.o.Y.:** Steve Best. **95-96 Top Scorer:** Roly Graham
Honours: Kent Lg 91-92 94-95 (R-up 92-93, Div 2 62-63 63-64 (R-up 92-93(res) 94-95(res)), Lg Cup R-up 78-79, Div 2 Cup 53-54), Kent Snr Tphy 78-79, Kent Amtr Cup 57-58 (R-up 58-59 63-64 68-69 72-73), Aetolian Lg Div 2 62-63 63-64 (Lg Cup R-up 62-63, Div 2 Cup 62-63 63-64), Athenian Lg Div 2 70-71 (Lg Cup 66-67), Kent Amtr Lg Cup 53-54 54-55, Thames & Medway Comb. Cup R-up 61-62, FA Cup 4th Cup Qual. Rd 70-71 86-87.

HYTHE UNITED (1992)

Chairman: Steve Walker **Vice Chairman;** **President:** Jim Robb
Secretary: A.Maycock, 86 Dymchurch Rd, Hythe, Kent. CT21 6LH (01303 268346)
Manager: Michael Dix **Asst Manager:** Dave Linstrem **Physio:** Dave Murphy
Ground: Reachfields, Fort Rd, Hythe (01303 264932)
Directions: On A259 west out of Hythe, turn left after light railway lights (Fort Road), entrance at end
Capacity: 3,000 **Seats:** 400 **Cover:** 2,400 **Floodlights:** Yes **Club Shop:** No
Programme: Free with entry **Editor:** A J Maycock **Press Officer:** M R Giles
Colours: All Red **Change Colours:** Green.
Sponsor: Colin A Morgan **Nickname:** **Founded:** 1992
Midweek Matchday: Tuesday **Youth League:** Kent Youth
Record Attendance: 422 v Folkstone 1996
Previous Leagues: Nuclear Elec Kent Lge
Clubhouse: Bar open weekends/matchdays & training nights
95-96 Captain: **95-96 Top Scorer:** **95-96 P.o.Y.:**
Honours: None as Hythe United

LORDSWOOD

Secretary: Steve Lewis, Sunnybrook, Gorsewood Road, Hartley, Longfield, Kent DA3 7DF (01474 708233 H, 01474 708233 B
Ground: Lordswood Sports & Social Club, North Dane Way, Walderslade, Chatham, Kent ME5 9XX (01634 669138)
Colours: Orange/black/black **Change Colours:** White/black/black

RAMSGATE

Chairman: R Lawson **Vice Chairman:** C Payne **President:** Tom Pendry M.P.
Secretary/Press Officer: Steve Lancaster.66 Park Avenue,Birchington,Kent(o1843 597703). (0843 595632).
Manager/Coach: Lennie Lee **Asst Manager:** Dave Bostock **Physio:** John Burroughs
Commercial Manager: Martin Power(01843 597703).
Ground: Southwood Stadium, Prices Avenue, Ramsgate, Kent (0843 591662).
Directions: From London on A229, A253 into Ramsgate - left into Netherhill at r'bout, right into Ashburnham Rd, right into Southwood Rd. 15 mins walk from Ramsgate BR station; walk thru Warre Recreation Ground, along St Lawrence High Str., left at 'White Horse', follow Southwood Rd and turn right into Prices Avenue.
Seats: 400 **Cover:** 600 **Capacity:** 5,000 **Floodlights:** Yes **Founded:** 1946.
Colours: Red & white. **Change Colours:** White/blue/blue **Nickname:** Rams.
Midweek matchday: Tuesday **Record Gate:** 5,200 v Margate, 56-57.
Sponsors: Hoverspeed. **Reserve Team's League:** Winstonlead Kent Div. Two.
Programme: 28 pages. **Editor:** Steve Redford(01843 596138). **Club Shop:** No.
Previous Name: Ramsgate Athletic **Previous Leagues:** Southern 59-75.
Record win: 9-1 v Crockenhill, Kent League Cup 22/1/94.
Clubhouse: Open matchdays & private functions. Two bars, two pool tables, darts. Hot & cold food on matchdays.
Club Record Scorer: Mick Williamson.
95-96 Top Scorer: **95-96 P.o.Y.:**
Hons: Kent Lg 49-50 55-56 56-57 (Lg Cup 48-49 92-93 93-94 94-95)
Kent I'mediate Cup 54-55, Kent Snr Cup 63-64, Thames & Medway Cup 60-61, Kent Snr Shield 60-61, Kent Floodlit Tphy 69-70, Kent Snr Tphy(2) 87-89.

SHEPPEY UNITED

Chairman: Peter Sharrock **Manager:** Johnny Roseman.
Secretary: Mr Barry H Bundock, Dunedin, 104 Southsea Ave., Minster, Sheerness, Kent ME12 2NH (0795 876025).
Ground: Shepherd Neame Stadium, Salters Lane, Faversham, Kent (0795 532738).
Directions: On A2 (Canterbury road) just west of town.
Seats: 350 **Cover:** 1,500 **Capacity:** 2,000 **Floodlights:** Yes **Founded:** 1890.
Colours: Red & white/white **Change colours:** All blue
Midweek matchday: Tuesday **Nickname:** Islanders or Ites.
Previous Name: Sheppey Athletic. **Programme:** 20 pages, 40p
Previous Ground: Botany Road, St Georges Avenue, Sheerness (pre-1992).
Record Gate: 4,000 v Sittingbourne, Kent Senior Trophy 1927 (at Botany Road).
Previous Leagues: Southern 1894-1901 84-91/ Kent 01-27 32-59 72-84/ Aetolian 59-64/ Gtr London 64-65/ Metropolitan Lg 65-71.
Players progressing to Football League: E C Harper (England, Blackburn, Spurs, Preston).
Hons: Kent Lg(6) 05-07 27-28 72-73 74-75 78-79 (R-up 03-04 04-05 77-78 83-84, Lg Cup 75-76 78-79, Div 2(reserves) 32-33 84-85 (R-up 1894-95 1979-80)), Thames & Medway Comb. 08-09 12-13 22-23 25-26 28-29 55-56, Kent Amtr Cup 45-46 51-52, Kent Snr Shield 77-78, Kent Snr Cup R-up(3), Gtr London Lg 64-65, FA Cup 6th Qual. Rd 19-20, FA Tphy 1st Rd Proper 85-86.

SLADE GREEN

Chairman: Brian Smith. **President:** William Dudley
Secretary: Bruce Smith, 15 Gumping Rd, Orpington, Kent BR5 1RX (01689 858782).
Joint Managers: M Watts/T Carley. **Coach:** Tony Pruce. **Physio:** Alan Martin.
Ground: The Small Glen, Moat Lane, Slade Green, Erith, Kent (01322 351077).
Directions: Off A206 between Erith & Dartford. 400 yards from Slade Green BR station. Buses 89 & B13.
Capacity: 3,000 **Seats:** 150 **Cover:** 400 **Floodlights:** Yes **Club Shop:**
Programme: 24 pages, with admission **Editor/Press Officer:** Robert Smith (01322 287982).
Colours: White & green **Change Colours:** All yellow
Sponsor: **Founded:** 1946. **Nickname:** The Green
Midweek matchday: Tuesday **Reserve League:**
Record Attendance: 3,000 v Millwall, friendly 25/7/92.
Previous Leagues: Dartford 46-52/ Kent Amateur 52-62/ Greater London 62-70.
Players pogressing to Football League: Roy Dwight (Nottm Forest), Alan Clark (Charlton), Fred Lucas (Charlton).
Clubhouse:
95-96 Captain: Graham Hall **95-96 Top Scorer:** Kelly Penfold 24 **95-96 P.o.Y.:** Trevor Lee.
Club Record Goalscorer: Colin Dwyer **Club Record Appearances:** Colin Dwyer.
Honours: Kent Snr Tphy 91-92 (R-up 80-81), Kent Lg Cup 82-83, Kent Amtr Lg 52-53 60-61 (Lg Cup 60-61), Kent Intermediate Cup 61-62, Kent Benevolent Cup 46-47, West Kent 60-61 65-66, Dartford Lg R-up 48-49 (Lg Cup 47-48 (R-up 46-47)), Erith Hospitals Cup 46-47 48-49, Gtr London Lg R-up 68-69, Plumstead Challenge Cup 48-49.

THAMESMEAD TOWN

Chairman: Brian Morris. **Vice Chairman:** Keith Dunsmore. **President:**
Secretary: Albert Panting, 97 Sydney Road, Bexleyheath Kent DA6 8HQ (0181 303 1350)
Manager: Terry Hill. **Coach:** Keith Gurr. **Physio:** Shaun Edwards
Ground: Bayliss Avenue, Thamesmead, London SE28 8NJ (0181 311 4211).
Directions: From Abbey Wood (BR) north east along Harrow Manor Way, into Crossway at 3rd r'bout, Bayliss Av. is 3rd right (Bexley bus 272 stops in Crossway near Bayliss Av. By road: From Dartford tunnel A2 to London, exit Danson Interchange and follow signs for Thamesmead and Abbey Wood. From Blackheath tunnel exit on south side and follow signs to Woolwich, to Plumstead and then to Thamesmead.
Seats: 125 **Cover:** 125 **Capacity:** 400 **Floodlights:** Yes **Club Shop:**
Programmes: Yes. 50p **Ediotor:** **Press Officer:** Matthew Panting.
Colours: Green & black **Change Colours:** All red
Sponsors: Courage Brewery **Nickname:** The Mead. **Founded:** 1970.
Midweek matchday: Tuesday. **Reserves League:** Winstonlead Kent D2
Record Attendance: 400 v Wimbledon, ground opening 1988.
Previous Leagues: London Spartan 80-91.
Clubhouse: Mon-Fri 6-11pm, Sat 12-11pm, Sun 12-3 & 7-10.30pm. Double bar, lounge, dance-floor, children's games room, video machines, hot & cold food. New members Bar.
95-96 Captain: Sean Rush. **95-96 Top Scorer:** Dean Burns 25. **95-96 P.o.Y.:** Garry Dreher
Club Record Appearances: Delroy D'Oyley. **Club Record Goalscorer:**
Honours: Spartan Lg Div 3 79-80 (Lg Cup 84-85 86-87; I'mediate champs 85-86); Kent I'mediate Cup 83-84 94-95; 4 promotions, and 9 trophies (inc London FA and Kent FA Cups) in progress thru Spartan I'mediate Divs, 1980-87; Winstonlead Kent Div 2 94-95, Div 2 Cup 94-95.

Corinthian FC; *Photo - Martin Wray*

Cray Wanderers: Back Row (L-R); Barrie Smith, John Allwright, Jack Charlton, Dave Clark, Craig Townsend, Gary Wilders, Alan Willis, Peter Coupland, Steve Yardley, Mark Twiner, Peter Cappuccio, Alan Whitehead (Mgr). Seated; Glen Cooper (Asst Mgr), Jason Head, Ian Jenkins, Gary Hillman (Chr), Lee Allchorn, Paul Turner, Peter Little (Coach). *Photo - R Carey*

Thamesmead Town *Photo - Eric Marsh*

TUNBRIDGE WELLS

Chairman: R J Bonny **Vice Chairman:** P C Wager.
Secretary: P C Wager, 46 Mereworth Rd, Tunbridge Wells, Kent TN4 9PL (01892 524182).
Manager: Rob Dobereiner **Asst Manager:** Shaun Lovett **Coach:** Dean Woodward
Ground: Culverden Stadium, Culverden Down, Tunbridge Wells, Kent TN4 (01892 520517).
Directions: Leaving town on main Tonbridge rd (A26), turn left opposite 'Spanner in the Works' pub - grd half mile. 1 mile from Tunbridge Wells Central (BR). Served by any Tunbridge Wells-Tonbridge bus - to St Johns.
Seats: 350 **Cover:** 1,000 **Capacity:** 3,750 **Floodlights:** Yes **Club Shop:** Yes
Programme: 16 pages, 30p **Editor:** Secretary. **Press Officer:** R Bonny (01892 531898).
Colours: Red/White/Red. **Change Colours:** Yellow/navy/navy.
Sponsors: Private Patients Plan. **Nickname:** Wells. **Founded:** 1886. **Reformed:** 1967.
Midweek Matchday: Tuesday **Reserve League:**
Record Attendance: 967 v Maidstone United, FA Cup 1969.
Clubhouse: Open matchdays and as required.
95-96 Captain: **95-96 P.o.Y.:** **95-96 Top Scorer:**
Club Record Goalscorer: John Wingate 151 **Club Record Appearances:** Tony Atkins 410.
Honours: Kent Lg 84-85 (R-up 68-69, Lg Cup 74-75 77-78 85-86 87-88), Kent Snr Tphy R-up 85-86 91-92.

WHITSTABLE TOWN

Chairman: Joe Brownett **Vice Chairman:** Peter Dale **President:** George Gifford.
Secretary: Mrs Sylvia J Davis, 5 Old Bridge Rd, Whitstable, Kent CT5 1RJ (01227 265646).
Manager: Wayne Godden **Asst Manager:** John Crabbe **Physio:** Micky West.
Ground: Belmont Road, Belmont, Whitstable, Kent (01227 266012).
Directions: From Thanet Way (A299), left at Tescos r'bout and down Millstrood Rd - ground at bottom of road, 400yds from Whitstable (BR) station. Car park at Grimshall Rd entrance.
Capacity: 2,000 **Cover:** 1,000 **Seats:** 500 **Floodlights:** Yes **Club Shop:** Yes
Programme: 48 pages, 50p **Editor/Press Officer:** Trevor Myhill (01227 277297).
Colours: Red/white/red **Change colours:** Yellow/blue
Sponsors: D & J Tyres **Nickname:** Oystermen, Reds, Natives **Founded:** 1885.
Midweek matchday: Tuesday
Record Gate: 2,500 v Gravesend & Northfleet, FA Cup 3rd Qualifying Rd, 19/10/87.
Previous Leagues: E. Kent 1897-1909/ Kent 09-59/ Aetolian 59-60/ Kent Amtr 60-62 63-64/ Seanglian 62-63/ Gtr London 64-67/ Kent Premier 67-68 (also in New Brompton, Thanet and Faversham & Dist. Lges over the years).
Clubhouse: Social & recreation purposes, open all matchdays. Bar. Hot food & drinks at tea-bar.
95-96 Captain: Lee Bosson **95-96 P.o.Y.:** Mick Cadmore **95-96 Top Scorer:** Lee Bosson.
Club Record Goalscorer: Barry Godfrey **Club Record Appearances:** Frank Cox 429 (1950-60).
Honours: Kent Lg Div 2 27-28 33-34 49-50 (Lg Cup 79-80 (R-up 89-90 91-92)), Kent Amtr Lg East 60-61, Kent Amtr Cup 28-29, Kent Snr Tphy R-up 78-79 89-90 92-93, Gtr London Lg Cup R-up 65-66, Kent Amtr Cup 28-29, Kent Midweek Lg Cup 92-93.

WOOLWICH TOWN

Chairman: Phillip Legg
Secretary: J R Kelly, 88 Hook Lane, Welling, Kent DA16 2DP (0181 303 8977)
Ground: Shared with Greenwich Borough, Harrow Meadow, Eltham Green Rd, Eltham, London SE9 (0181 850 3098).
Directions: South Circular (A205) to Yorkshire Grey pub, ground opposite. 1 mile from both Eltham and Kidbrooke BR stations.
Seats: 50 **Cover:** 50 **Capacity:** 2,500 **Floodlights:** Yes
Colours: Red & blue/black/black **Change Colours:** Yellow/black/black
Previous Ground: Flamingo Park, Sidcup (pre 1994)

UNIJET SUSSEX COUNTY LEAGUE

FEEDER TO: BEAZER HOMES LEAGUE

FOUNDED: 1920

President: P H Strange

Chairman: Peter Bentley

Secretary: Peter Wells, 37 Bewley Road, Angmering, BN16 4JL (01903 771146)

FINAL LEAGUE TABLES 1995/96

	Division One	*P*	*W*	*D*	*L*	*F*	*A*	*Pts*
1.	Peacehaven & Telscombe	38	32	5	1	133	23	101
2.	Stamco	38	29	3	6	130	38	90
3.	Shoreham	38	25	8	5	91	37	83
4.	Wick	38	23	6	9	95	52	75
5.	Hailsham Town	38	21	10	7	84	48	73
6.	Pagham	38	20	3	15	59	59	63
7.	Arundel	38	19	4	15	80	61	61
8.	Hassocks	38	18	7	13	71	62	61
9.	Langney Sports	38	17	9	12	70	52	60
10.	Ringmer	38	16	6	16	70	59	54
11.	Burgess Hill Tn	38	14	10	14	66	66	52
12.	Horsham YMCA	38	15	7	16	56	75	52
13.	Portfield	38	15	5	18	65	81	50
14.	Eastbourne Town	38	12	4	22	51	89	40
15.	Southwick	38	10	9	19	38	75	39
16.	Whitehawk	38	10	6	22	49	71	36
17.	Mile Oak	38	9	6	23	48	93	33
18.	Three Bridges	38	6	6	26	46	101	24
19.	Oakwood	38	5	2	31	30	113	17
20.	Crowborough Ath	38	4	4	30	40	117	16

UNIJET SUSSEX COUNTY DIV ONE RESULTS CHART 1995-96

HOME TEAM	1	2	3	4	5	6	7	8	9	10	11	12	13	14	15	16	17	18	19	20
1. Arundell	*	1-1	5-2	2-1	2-4	0-1	2-2	1-1	6-0	6-0	3-1	0-3	2-1	2-0	2-3	1-2	0-1	3-1	3-2	2-2
2. Burgess Hill Town	1-0	*	2-1	6-3	1-6	1-2	2-2	0-3	4-1	3-2	3-1	0-2	5-1	4-1	1-3	0-2	2-1	5-3	6-1	1-1
3. Crowborough Athletic	1-6	2-3	*	1-6	0-3	2-4	2-1	1-4	2-5	2-0	1-2	1-8	1-2	0-0	1-4	0-1	1-4	2-1	1-1	1-0
4. Eastbourne Town	1-3	1-1	5-2	*	1-2	2-1	1-4	0-1	1-0	1-1	1-0	2-7	0-0	2-1	0-2	0-1	1-2	5-3	2-2	5-4
5. Hailsham Town	0-2	3-0	2-1	0-1	*	4-2	1-1	2-0	0-0	4-1	4-0	1-1	0-1	1-1	3-3	1-0	1-3	4-1	1-0	0-0
6. Hassocks	3-1	0-0	2-1	0-1	4-4	*	4-2	0-0	4-1	3-1	1-0	3-5	3-2	1-2	1-3	5-2	1-2	5-0	2-0	1-2
7. Horsham YMCA	0-4	1-0	2-0	0-2	1-4	2-2	*	0-0	3-2	3-0	0-2	1-2	1-0	0-1	0-3	2-0	1-2	1-1	2-1	1-4
8. Langney Sports	2-3	2-0	4-1	1-0	1-1	1-3	3-6	*	7-0	5-0	1-2	1-3	2-3	2-1	1-1	1-1	0-1	2-0	1-1	2-2
9. Mile Oak	1-3	2-2	3-2	2-1	1-1	0-1	1-2	1-5	*	2-0	0-2	0-6	0-3	2-2	0-2	5-1	0-5	1-0	1-3	0-1
10. Oakwood	0-3	0-3	0-0	2-0	1-5	0-3	0-4	0-4	4-2	*	0-1	0-2	2-3	1-4	0-3	0-1	0-8	2-1	2-0	1-5
11. Pagham	1-2	1-0	3-2	2-0	2-3	2-1	1-2	3-1	2-1	1-0	*	0-0	0-0	4-1	0-3	3-0	4-3	3-0	2-1	1-2
12. Peacehaven & Tel	3-2	3-1	6-0	6-0	4-0	4-0	5-0	5-0	0-0	4-1	2-1	*	2-0	3-0	0-0	4-*0	2-0	5-0	2-1	5-1
13. Portfield	5-2	3-1	5-1	5-1	0-4	1-2	0-2	0-1	3-0	4-3	2-3	0-6	*	4-3	4-2	0-0	2-4	0-4	4-2	0-4
14. Ringmer	2-1	0-1	5-0	5-0	5-1	0-0	0-0	2-1	1-2	4-1	5-0	0-5	1-1	*	0-1	2-1	0-1	5-1	3-2	0-2
15. Shoreham	1-0	1-0	5-0	3-0	0-2	1-0	2-3	2-3	2-0	2-0	0-0	2-2	9-1	5-0	*	5-1	1-1	2-0	1-1	2-1
16. Southwick	0-1	2-2	1-1	1-0	1-4	0-0	2-0	1-3	1-1	3-0	2-1	2-6	2-0	1-4	4-4	*	0-2	1-1	0-1	1-3
17. Stamco	6-0	5-1	4-1	9-0	4-0	6-0	9-0	3-1	4-2	4-0	4-0	2-1	1-1	2-5	1-3	7-0	*	6-2	3-1	4-1
18. Three Bridges	3-1	2-2	1-0	1-3	1-6	3-3	1-1	1-2	1-4	2-0	3-4	0-4	2-1	0-3	0-2	0-0	0-4	*	2-0	2-5
19. Whitehawk	1-2	1-1	2-1	4-1	1-1	0-3	3-1	1-2	1-2	1-4	1-3	0-1	0-1	2-1	3-0	2-0	2-1	4-2	*	0-2
20. Wick	2-1	0-0	5-2	2-0	0-1	4-0	7-2	0-1	5-3	7-1	4-1	1-4	3-2	2-0	1-3	3-0	1-1	2-1	4-0	*

LEADING GOALSCORERS 1995-96

Division One

Keith Miles	Stamco	43.	Martin Spiers	Arundel	30.
Howard Stevens	Hailsham Town	30.	Mark Sherriff	Peacehaven	26.
Anton Romasz	Portfield	19.	Andy Blythe	Peacehaven	18.
Ashley Carr	Shoreham	18	Simon Pierce	Whitehawk	18.
Steve Norris	Burgess Hill	17.	Phil Churchill	Horsham YMCA	17.
Leighton Allen	Ringmer	16.	Mark Vickers	Wick	16.

Division Two:

Marc Shaw	Saltdean United	39.	Jason Reed	Selsey	37.
Paul Forfar	Bosham	24.	Nigel Waller	Worthing United	24.
Gerald Moyse	Bexhill Town	22.	Paul Lee	Selsey	21.
Jon Scrivens	Saltdean Utd	18.	Dave Agnew	East Preston	17.
Ricky Geddes	Redhill	17.	Micky Dorrill	Newhaven	16.

Division Three:

Andy West	Ifield	35.	Robbie Warner	Shinewater	34.
Tim De Castro	Crawley Down	22.	Jim Cowie	Franklands	19.
Richard Tilford	Lindfield Rang	19.	Simon Hatton	St Francis Hosp	18.
Mark Aldred	Crawley Down	15.	Dave Heath	Forest	15.

FINAL LEAGUE TABLES 1995/96

Div Two	P	W	D	L	F	A	Pts
1. Saltdean Utd	34	25	6	3	87	40	81
2. Selsey	34	24	6	4	113	33	78
3. Chichester City	34	19	8	7	71	35	65
4. E Grinstead	34	19	8	7	76	53	65
5. Redhill	34	15	6	13	67	54	51
6. Newhaven	34	16	3	15	63	62	51
7. East Preston	34	13	10	11	63	55	49
8. Lancing	34	11	10	13	62	70	43
9. Worthing Utd	34	10	12	12	67	61	42
10. Steyning Tn	34	11	9	14	61	76	42
11. Sidley Utd	34	10	10	14	45	56	40
12. Bexhill Tn	34	11	6	17	65	59	39
13. Midhurst & E	34	11	6	17	55	69	39
14. Withdean	34	11	6	17	57	81	39
15. Littlehampton	34	8	14	12	48	58	38
16. Broadbridge H	34	10	7	17	55	82	37
17. Bosham	34	10	4	20	65	103	34
18. Eastbourne U	34	3	7	24	33	106	16

Div Three	P	W	D	L	F	A	Pts
1. Ifield	30	22	6	2	77	37	72
2. Crawley Down	30	22	3	5	83	32	69
3. Shinewater A	30	21	5	4	90	35	68
4. Sidlesham	30	18	6	6	73	34	60
5. Franklands	30	17	8	5	60	37	59
6. Lindfield R	30	15	3	12	64	59	48
7. Forest	30	11	10	9	43	42	43
8. Hurstpierpoint	30	12	5	13	48	55	41
9. Haywards Hth	30	9	8	13	37	50	35
10. Thomson Ath	30	9	6	15	44	53	33
11. Buxted	30	9	5	16	38	57	32
12. Storrington	30	8	4	18	36	54	28
13. Seaford Tn	30	7	5	18	50	75	26
14. St Francis H	30	8	1	21	37	74	25
15. Sun Alliance	30	5	6	19	35	68	21
16. Lingfield	30	5	3	22	30	83	18

MANAGER OF THE MONTH AWARDS 1995-96

August:
Division 1: Peter Edwards (Peacehaven)
Division 2: Peter Burdett (Redhill)
Division 3: John Wort (Ifield)

September:
Division 1: Steve Richardson (Hailsham)
Division 2: Gerry Green (Saltdean)
Division 3: G Standen/A Watson (Crawley)

October:
Division 1: Carl Stabler (Wick)
Division 2: David Kew (Selsey)
Division 3: John Wort (Ifield)

November:
Division 1: Steve Dove (Burgess Hill)
Division 2: Peter Knee (Steyning Tn)
Division 3: Chris Snelling (Franklands)

December:
Division 1: Peter Edwards (Peacehaven)
Division 2: John Finneran (East Preston)
Division 3: Alan Walsh (Shinewater)

January:
Division 1: Brian Donnelly (Shoreham)
Division 2: Gerry Green (Saltdean)
Division 3: Alan Walsh (Shinewater)

February:
Division 1: Peter Cherry (Langney Spts)
Division 2: Dickie Day (Sidley Utd)
Division 3: G Standen/A Watson (Crawley)

March:
Division 1: Peter Edwards (Peacehaven)
Division 2: Bruce Kendall (Chichester)
Division 3: Peter Cleverley (Sidlesham)

April/May:
Division 1: Peter Edwards (Peacehaven)
Division 2: David Kew (Selsey)
Division 3: Graham Standen (Crawley)

Season Overall Winner:
Division 1: Peter Edwards (Peacehaven)
Division 2: Gerry Green (Saltdean Utd)
Division 3: John Wort (Ifield)

SUSSEX COUNTY LEAGUE Division One Ten Year Record

	86/7	87/8	88/9	89/0	90/1	91/2	92/3	93/4	94/5	95/6
Arundel	1	12	16	16	8	11	12	10	17	7
Bexhill Town	-	-	-	-	15	16	11	19	-	-
Burgess Hill Town	11	9	5	4	6	6	14	7	8	11
Chichester City	15	-	-	-	-	15	16	20	-	-
Crowborough Athletic	-	-	-	-	-	-	-	16	14	20
Eastbourne Town	5	4	15	15	16	12	17	17	13	14
East Grinstead	-	-	-	-	-	-	-	15	20	-
Hailsham Town	14	6	4	13	13	8	10	6	5	5
Hassocks	-	-	-	-	-	-	-	-	-	8
Haywards Heath	3	7	13	12	14	18	-	-	-	-
Horsham YMCA	13	16	-	-	-	-	-	-	-	12
Lancing	10	13	12	17	-	-	-	-	-	-
Langney Sports	-	-	10	3	3	2	4	3	11	9
Littlehampton Town	6	14	7	2	1	3	7	13	19	-
Midhurst & Easebourne	16	-	-	-	-	-	18	-	-	-
Mile Oak	-	-	-	-	-	-	-	-	-	17
Newhaven	-	-	-	-	-	10	6	8	18	-
Oakwood	-	-	17	-	9	14	8	11	15	19
Pagham	-	1	1	8	4	4	2	5	7	6
Peacehaven & Telscombe	7	8	8	5	2	1	1	4	1	1
Portfield	12	15	18	-	-	-	13	14	9	13
Redhill	-	-	11	18	-	-	-	-	-	-
Ringmer	-	-	-	10	12	9	15	18	6	10
Seaford	-	-	-	11	17	-	-	-	-	-
Selsey	-	11	9	14	18	-	-	-	-	-
Shoreham	8	10	14	9	11	17	-	-	4	3
Southwick Borough	-	-	-	-	-	-	-	-	16	15
Stamco	-	-	-	-	-	-	-	9	2	2
Three Bridges	4	2	2	7	7	7	9	12	12	18
Whitehawk	2	5	3	6	10	13	5	2	10	16
Wick	9	3	6	1	5	5	3	1	3	4
No of Clubs Competing	16	16	18	18	18	18	18	20	20	20

Peacehaven & Telscombe FC. Division One League winners for the fourth time in five years.

ARUNDEL

Chairman: Michael Peters **Vice Chairman:** S Brennan.
Secretary/Press Officer: Doud Feest, 342 Goring Road, Worthing. BN12 4PD (01903 249276)
Manager: Roger Kent
Ground: Mill Road, Arundel (01903 882548).
Directions: A27 from Worthing to Arundel town centre, 1st right into Mill Road, ground thru large car park (on right). 1 mile from Arundel (BR).
Seats: 100 **Cover:** 200 **Capacity:** 2,200 **Floodlights:** 206 lux **Founded:** 1889
Colours: Red & white halves/white/red **Change colours:** All yellow **Nickname:** Mulletts
Programme: 8 pages, free **Programme Editor:** Secretary **Sponsors:** None
Midweek matchday: Tuesday. **Record Gate:** 2,200 v Chichester, League 67-68
Previous Lge: West Sussex 1896-1975 **Previous Grounds:** Castle Park/ Station Rd Ground.
Players progressing to Football League: John Templeman (Brighton & Hove Albion 1966).
Reserves' Lge: Sussex Co. Res Div (West)
Record win: 13-0 v Horsham YMCA (H), Sussex Co. Lge Div 1 21/12/85.
Clubhouse: 2 bars, kitchen, toilets, telephone, pool, darts, Sky TV. Normal pub hours. No food.
Record Scorer: Paul J Bennett **Record appearances:** 537, Paul Bennett (goalkeeper).
Captain 93-94: S Bates **Player of the Year:** R Hellen.
Local Press: Arun Gazette
Hons: Sussex County Lg 57-58 58-59 86-87 (Lg Cup 86-87, Div 2 Cup 76-77, Reserve Section 78-79, Reserve Section Cup 78-79, Merit Table winners 80-81, Sussex Fives 1984 1987), Sussex RUR Charity Cup 68-69 72-73 78-79 79-80, Sussex Jnr Cup 07-08, West Sussex Lg (Reserves) 70-71 (Malcolm Simmonds Cup 70-71).

BURGESS HILL TOWN

Chairman: Jim Collins. **President:** Jack Lake **Manager:** Alan Pook
Secretary: Martin Waner, 26 Hamilton Close, Mile Oak, Brighton BN41 2WY (01273 439849)
Ground: Leylands Park, Burgess Hill, West Sussex RH15 8AW (01444 242429).
Directions: Wivelsfield Station (BR out of Victoria), turn right, first left, ground on right.
Seats: 100 **Cover:** Yes **Capacity:** 2,000 **Floodlights:** Yes **Club badges:**Yes
Programme: Yes with Admission **Editor:** **Admission:** £3.00
Colours: Yellow/black/black **Change colours:** Purple.
Sponsors: None **Nickname:** Hillians **Founded:** 1882
Midweek matchday: Tuesday
Record Gate: 600 v Carshalton A., FA Cup 3rd Qual. 1981.
Previous Lges & Grounds: None
Clubhouse: Bar & social facilities. Tea bar.
95-96 Captain: Chris Ridley **95-96 Top Scorer:** Steve Norris 30 **95-96 P.o.Y.:**
Honours: Sussex County Lg 75-76 (Div 2 74-75, Lg Cup 73-74 79-80 (R-up 90-91), Div 2 Cup 73-73, Reserve Section 76-77 77-78 91-92, Reserve Sect. East 77-78 82-83 84-85, Reserve Cup 82-83, Yth Sect. West 91-92 East 95-96, Sussex Fives 1980), Mid-Sussex Lg 00-01 03-04 39-40 46-47 56-57 (Div 2 03-04(res), Div 3 20-21 36-37, Div 4(res) 56-57, Montgomery Cup 39-40 56-57, Mowatt Cup 45-46, Sussex Snr Cup 1883-84 84-85 85-86, Sussex RUR Charity Cup 91-92, Sussex I'mediate Cup 76-77, Sussex Jnr Cup 1889-90, Sussex Yth Cup 91-92.

EASTBOURNE TOWN

Chairman: Stuart Higgins **Manager:** Rob Thorley
Secretary: Kevin Moore, 27 Chesterton Drive, Seaford. BN25 3RJ (01323 897369)
Ground: The Saffrons, Compton Place Road, Eastbourne, East Sussex (01323 723734).
Directions: Turn south west off A22 into Grove Road (opposite BR station), and the ground is situated a quarter of a mile on the right.
Seats: 100 **Cover:** Yes **Capacity:** 3,000 **Floodlights:** No **Founded:** 1882
Colours: Yellow/blue/blue **Changes:** White & black/white/white **Nickname:** 'Bourne'
Programme Editor: Sid Myall (01323 728096) **Admission:** £1.50/80p
Previous Leagues: Southern Amtr 07-46/ Corinthian 60-63/ Athenian 63-76.
Record Gate: 7,378 v Hastings U. 1953 **Prev. Ground:** Devonshire Park 1881-85 **Metal Badges:** Yes
Sponsors: Eastbourne Car Auctions **Local Press:** Eastbourne Gazette & Herald Chronicle
Prev. Name: Eastbourne FC (pre-1970) **Clubhouse:** Fully licensed bar. Board room. Tea bar.
Hons: Sussex County Lg 76-77, Sussex Snr Cup(12) 1889-91 93-95 98-1901 02-03 21-22 31-33 52-53, Sussex RUR Charity Cup 32-33 47-48 49-50, Southern Amtr Lg(2), AFA Snr Cup 21-22 24-25 (R-up 22-23 23-24), AFA Invitation Cup 69-70 (R-up 56-57 68-69 70-71).

HAILSHAM TOWN

President: J Whippy **Chairman:** Dave Challinor **Manager:** Pete Roberts.
Secretary/Press Officer: Derek York, 59 Anglesey Avenue, Horsebridge, Hailsham BN27 3BQ (01323 848024).
Ground: The Beaconsfield, Western Road, Hailsham, East Sussex (01323 840446).
Directions: A22 to Arlington Road, turn east, then left into South Road - left into Diplocks Way until Daltons. Four miles from Polegate (BR - Brighton-Eastbourne line); regular bus service from Eastbourne.
Seats: None **Cover:** 300 **Capacity:** 2,000 **Floodlights:** Yes
Programme: Yes **Editor:** Secretary **Admission:** £2.50
Colours: Yellow & green **Change colours:** All white
Founded: 1885 **Nickname:** None **Midweek matchday:** Tuesday.
Record Gate: 1,350 v Hungerford, FA Vase Feb '89
Previous League: E Sussex, Southern Comb.
Clubhouse: Hot and cold snacks. Open every evening, matchdays and Sundays, tea bar.
Honours: FA Vase 5th Rd 88-89, Sussex County Lg Div 2 R-up 80-81, Southern Co's Comb. 74-75, Sussex RUR Charity Cup, Sussex I'mediate Cup, Hastings Snr Cup, Sussex Jnr Cup, E Sussex Lg Cup, Hailsham Charity Cup, John O'Hara Cup 95-96.

HASSOCKS

President: Maurice Boxall **Chairman:** Jim Goodrum
Secretary: Bob Preston, 65 Oak Hall, Burgess Hill, West Sussex RH15 0DA (01444 245695).
Manager: Nick Greenwood / Peter Liddell **Press Off.:** Paul Elphick (01444 454492) **Physio:** Norman Dodds
Ground: The Beacon, Brighton Rd, Hassocks (01273 846040)
Directions: Off A273 Pyecombe - Burgess Hill 300yds south of Stonepound crossroads (B2116) to Hurstpierpoint or Hassocks.
Seats: None **Cover:** 100 **Capacity:** **Floodlights:** No **Founded:** 1902
Colours: Red/white/red **Change colours:** All yellow.
Programme: Yes **Editor:** Paul Elphick (0444 454492) **Admission:** £1.50 **Metal Badges:** No.
Previous Leagues: Mid Sussex/ Brighton Hove & Dist./ Southern Co's Comb. **Nickname:** Robins
Record Gate: 340 v Bognor Regis Town, Sussex Senior Cup 92-93. *At previous ground: 400 v Nottingham University, AFA Snr Cup January 1978.*
Midweek Matchday: Wednesday **Clubhouse:** Clubroom, bar, kitchen.
Sponsors: Benwood Copiers **Local Press:** Burgess Hill Times, Evening Argus
Previous Ground: Adastra Park, Hassocks (pre-1992).
Hons: Sussex County Lg Div 3 91-92 (Res. Sect. East R-up 92-93), Southern Counties Comb. 76-77 (Lg Cup 79-80), Brighton Hove & Dist. Lg 71-72, Sussex Intermediate Cup 74-75 (R-up 80-81).

HORSHAM

Chairman: Frank King **Vice Chairman:** Jeff Barratt **President:** Geoff Holtom
Secretary: Eric Mallard, 6 Morrell Avenue, Horsham, West Sussex RH12 4DD (01403 267687 H; 0181 643 6406 B)
Manager: Mark Dunk **Asst Mgr/Coach:** Sam Chapman. **Physio:** Geoff Britta1n.
Ground: Queen Street, Horsham RH13 5AD (01403 252310).
Directions: From the station turn left into North Street. Pass the Arts Centre to the traffic lights and turn left. At the next set of lights (200 yards) turn left again into East Street. East Street becomes Queen Street after the Iron Bridge and the ground lies opposite Queens Head public house.
Capacity: 4,500 **Seats:** 300 **Cover:** 3,000 **Floodlights:** Yes **Club Shop:** Yes.
Programme: 40 pages, £1 **Editor:** Adam Hammond (01403 217316). **Press Officer:**
Colours: Yellow & green halves/green/yellow. **Change colours:** White/blue/white
Founded: 1885 **Nickname:** Hornets **Club Sponsors:** Persimmon Homes.
Midweek Matchday: Tuesday **Reserve League:** Sussex County.
Record Attendance: 8,000 v Swindon, FA Cup 1st Rd, November 1966.
Best FA Cup year: 1st Rd 47-48 (lost 1-9 at Notts County), 66-67 (lost 0-3 v Swindon).
Previous Leagues: W Sussex Sen/ Sussex County 26-51/ Metropolitan 51-57/ Corinthian 57-63/ Athenian 63-73.
Players progressing to Football League:
Jamie Ndah (Torquay Utd), Darren Freeman (Gillingham), Paul Smith (Barnet).
Clubhouse: Normal licensing hours. Hot and cold snacks. Dancehall.
95-96 Captain: Steve Breach. **95-96 P.O.Y.:** Rodney Prosper. **95-96 Top scorer:** Rodney Prosper
Hons: Sussex Snr Cup 33-34 38-39 49-50 53-54 71-72 73-74 75-76, Sussex RUR Cup 1899-1900 30-32 33-34(jt with Worthing) 34-37 37-38(jt with Southwick) 45-46 48-49(jt with Worthing) 50-52 56-57. Sussex Floodlight Cup 77-78. Sussex County Lg 31-33 34-38 46-47 (R-up 29-30 30-31 47-48 48-49, Lg Cup 45-46 46-47), Metropolitan Lg 51-52, Athenian Lg Div 1 72-73, Div 2 69-70 72-73. West Sussex Sen Lge 1899-90 1900-02 25-26. ICIS Div 3 95-96.

LANGNEY SPORTS

Chairman: Mr Len Smith **President:** Mr J Stonestreet **Secretary:** Mrs Myra Stephens, 7b Erica Close, Langney, Eastbourne, East Sussex BN23 8BT (01323 766050).
Manager: Steve Richardson **Physio:** T.B.A.
Ground: Priory Lane, Eastbourne, East Sussex (01323 766265).
Directions: A22 to Polegate, A27 to Stone Cross, right onto B32104 to Langney Shopping Centre, then left and first right. One mile from Pevensey & Westham (BR). Buses from Eastbourne.
Seats: 900 **Cover:** 400 **Capacity:** 2,500 **Floodlights:** Yes **Club Shop:** Yes
Programme: Yes **Editor:** Mike Spooner (01323 461003) **Press Officer:**
Colours: All red **Change:** Sky & navy stripes/navy
Sponsors: Nobo Group Plc. **Nickname:** None **Founded:** 1966
Midweek Matchday: Tuesday **Reserve League:**
Record Attendance: 1,000+ v Crystal Palace, f'light opener 90-91.
Previous League: Eastbourne & Hastings
Clubhouse: Open every evening & lunchtime with adjoining sports hall, board room, matchday tea bar.
Club Record Goalscorer: Nigel 146 **Club Record Appearances:** Steve Dell 386.
Honours: Sussex Co. Lg R-up 91-92 (Div 2 87-88, Lg Cup 89-90, Div 3 86-87, Div 3 Cup 86-87, 5-aside comp. 1990), Sussex I'mediate Cup 85-86, Eastbourne Challenge Cup 85-86 86-87.

MILE OAK

Manager: Tony Gratwicke **Chairman:** R A Kearly **President:** D Bean
Secretary: C D Brown, 19 The Crescent, Southwick, West Sussex BN42 4LB (0273 591346).
Ground: Mile Oak Recreation Ground, Graham Avenue, Mile Oak(01273 423854)
Directions: From A27 take Mile Oak Road or Locks Hill & Valley Road to Chalky Road, ground 500yds on right along Graham Avenue which runs up valley from centre of Chalky Road.
Seats: None **Cover:** Yes **Capacity:** **Floodlights:** Yes. **Founded:** 1960
Colours: All tangerine **Change colours:** All white **Nickname:** The Oak
Programme: Yes **Editor:** C Tew (01273 416036) **Admission:** £1.50 **Metal Badges:** No
Previous Leagues: Southern Counties Combination/ Brighton Hove & District
Record Gate: 186 **Previous Ground:** Victoria Rec., Portslade.
Midweek Matchday: Tuesday **Clubhouse:** Mile Oak Pavillion; Hall and tea bar.
Local Press: Brighton Evening Argus, Shoreham Herald
Hons: Sussex Co.Lg.Div 2 Champions, Div 3 R-up 91-92 (Div 2 Cup R-up 92-93), Southern Counties Combination 86-87, Brighton Hove & District Lg 80-81, Vernon Wentworth Cup 85-86, Sussex Intermediate Cup R-up 88-89.

OAKWOOD

President: TBA **Chairman:** A T Bridges
Secretary: Gerry Martin, 'Singlegate', Tinsley Green, Crawley RH10 3NS (01293 882400).
Manager: Alan Gould **Asst Mgr:** Terry Aller **Coach:** Neil Blackwell / John Yemms
Physio: Ms S Widy **Press Officer:** Simon Milham (01293 615043).
Ground: Tinsley Lane, Three Bridges, Crawley, West Sussex (01293 515742).
Directions: From A23 to Gatwick, take 1st set of lights into Manor Royal, pass next lights, over r'bout to warehouse marked Canon, turn right signposted Oakwood. Last clubhouse down lane. Two miles north of Three Bridges (BR).
Seats: 20 **Cover:** Yes **Capacity:** 3,000 **Floodlights:** Yes **Founded:** 1966
Colours: Red/black/black **Change colours:** Blue/black/black **Nickname:** Oaks
Programme: 24 pages, 50p **Editor:** Simon Milham (01293 615043) **Club Shop:** Yes
Previous Ground: Park pitches. **Previous Lgs:** Crawley & Dist., Southern Co's Comb.
Record Gate: 367 **Midweek Matchday:** Tuesday **Metal Badges:** Yes
Sponsors: Linden Plc. **Reserve Team's League:** Sussex County Reserve section.
Clubhouse: Pool tables, multidart boards, large bar area. Board room & tea bar.
Record appearances: Peter Brackpool **Local Press:** Crawley Observer, Crawley News
Hons: Sussex Snr Cup R-up 92-93, Sussex Co. Lg Div 2 R-up 89-90 (Div 2 Cup 89-90, Div 3 84-85), Southern Comb. Cup 83-84.

Southwick FC: *Photo - Andrew Chitty*

Portfield FC: *Photo - Andrew Chitty*

Arundel FC: *Photo - Andrew Chitty*

PAGHAM

Chairman: Graham Peach **Vice-Chairman:** D Abburon **President:** A Peirce
Secretary: Mr Alan Seal, 6 Greenlea Ave., Pagham, West Sussex PO21 3LH (01243 262944 Mobile: 0850 707932)
Manager/Coach: Graham Peach **Asst Manager:** P Gilbert **Comm. Manager:** A Dixon
Press Officer: Mr Eric G Nunn (0243 262879).
Ground: Nyetimber Lane, Pagham, West Sussex (0243 266112).
Directions: Turn off A27 Chichester by-pass (signposted A259 Pagham). Ground in village of Nyetimber. Three miles from Bognor (BR). Buses 260 & 240.
Seats: 200 **Cover:** 200 **Capacity:** 2,000 **Floodlights:** Yes **Founded:** 1903
Colours: White/black/black **Change colours:** Yellow/green **Nickname:** Lions.
Midweek Matchday: Tuesday **Reserve Team's League:** Unijet Sussex Co. Reserve Div.
Programme: 12 pages, 50p **Programme Editor:** Secretary **Club Shop:** No.
Record Gate: 1,200 v Bognor, 1971. **Sponsors:** Nyetimber Mazda.
Previous Grounds: None **Previous Leagues:** Chichester 1903-50/ West Sussex 50-69.
Record win: 10-1 v Seaford Town (A), Sussex County League Division Two, 1970.
Record defeat: 0-7 v Newport IOW (H), FA Amateur Cup, mid-1970s.
Clubhouse: Bar open to members and visitors matchdays and some evenings. Hot food, pool, darts, satellite TV. Tea bar.
Local Press: Bognor Observer **Club Record Scorer:** Mark Vickers/ R Deluca.
Hons: Sussex Co. Lg R-up 80-81 87-88 88-89 92-93 (Div 2 78-79 86-87, Lg Cup 88-89, Div 2 Cup 71-72 85-86, Res. Sect. West 80-81, Res Sect. Cup 80-81, Res Section Cup 77-78 80-81 87-88 88-89 90-91), Sussex F'lit Cup R-up 88-89, Sussex RUR Charity Cup 88-89 (R-up 93-94), West Sussex Lg 65-66 68-69 69-70, Malcolm Simmonds Cup 67-68, Sussex I'mediate Cup 66-67.

PEACEHAVEN & TELSCOMBE

Chairman: Mr Jim Edwards **President:** Mr W Parris **Manager:** P Edwards
Secretary: Mr F Parris, 17A Piddinghoe Ave, Peacehaven, E. Sussex BN10 8PF (01273 587297).
Ground: Piddinghoe Avenue, Peacehaven, East Sussex (01273 582471).
Directions: Arriving from Brighton on A259, cross r'bout and Piddinghoe Avenue is next left after 2nd set of lights - ground at end. From Newhaven Piddinghoe Avenue is first right after first set of lights. Three miles from Newhaven (BR). Peacehaven is served by Brighton to Newhaven and Eastbourne buses.
Seats: None **Cover:** 250 **Capacity:** 3,000 **Floodlights:** Yes **Club Shop:**
Programme: Yes **Editor:** Secretary **Press Officer:** Secretary
Colours: All white with black trim **Change colours:** All sky
Sponsors: Anchor Garage **Founded:** 1923 **Nickname:** The Tye
Midweek Matches: Wednesday **Record Gate:** 1,420 v Littlehampton, League 11/5/91.
Previous Leagues: Lewes/ Brighton
Clubhouse: Bar open evenings and weekends, pool darts, hot and cold food available. Tea bar.
Hons: Sussex Co. Lg 78-79 81-82 82-83 91-92 92-93 94-95 95-96 (R-up 77-78 80-81 90-91, Lg Cup 91-92 92-93, Div 2 R-up 75-76, Div 2 Cup 75-76, Norman Wingate Tphy 82-83 91-92 92-93, Hayden Tphy 82-83 92-93, Div 2 Invitation Cup 69-70, Res. Sect. 83-84 92-93 (R-up 91-92), Res Sect. Cup 81-82 83-84 85-86 86-87 87-88, Res Sect East R-up 90-91), Sussex Snr Cup R-up 81-82 92-93, Sussex RUR Charity Cup 77-78 81-82 92-93 (R-up 80-81 89-90 90-91 94-95 95-96), Brighton Charity Cup 91-92 92-93 93-94, Vernon Wentworth 91-92 92-93, FA Cup 4th Qual. Rd 90-91, FA Vase 5th Rd 92-93, Qtr Fin 95-96.

PORTFIELD

President: C Newell **Chairman:** T Rustell **Manager:** Richard Reynolds
Secretary: Mr Gary Rustell, 102 Churchwood Drive, Tangmere, Chichester, West Sussex PO20 6GB (01243 537978).
Ground: Church Road, Portfield, Chichester, West Sussex PO19 4HN (01243 779875)
Directions: A27 from Arundel to Chichester, take road to signposted city centre then 1st left (Church Rd) after supermarket r'bout. 1 mile from Chichester (BR).
Seats: 8 **Cover:** 200 **Capacity:** 2,000 **Floodlights:** Yes **Club Shop:**
Programme: Yes **Editor:** TBA **Admission:** £2.00 & £1
Colours: Amber/black/amber. **Change colours:** All Blue
Sponsors: T.B.A **Founded:** 1896 **Nickname:** Field.
Midweek Matchday: Tuesday **Record Attendance:** Unknown **Previous League:** West Sussex.
Clubhouse: 2 bars, pool, snooker, seating for 100, dance floor, darts, and tea bar selling hot & cold food.
95-96 Top Score: Anton Romazz 41
Hons: Sussex Co. Lg Div 2 72-73 83-84 91-92 (Div 2 Cup 70-71 72-73, Reserve Sect. Premier lg. 94-95,Cup 91-92, 5-aside comp. 1991), W Sussex Lg 46-47 48-49 (Malcolm Simmonds Cup 46-47), Sussex Jnr Cup 45-46, Benevolent Cup 46-47.

RINGMER

President: Sir G Christie **Chairman:** Richard Soan
Secretary: Pam Howard, 29 Mill Rd., Ringmer, Sussex. BA8 3HD (01273 813818).
Manager: Gary Allen. **Press Officer:** Alan Harper (01323 764263)
Ground: Caburn Ground, Anchor Field, Ringmer (01273 812738).
Directions: From Lewes road turn into Springett Avenue opposite Ringmer village green. Anchor Field first left. Three miles from Lewes (BR).
Seats: 100 **Cover:** Yes **Capacity:** 1,000 **Floodlights:** Yes **Founded:** 1906.
Colours: Sky & navy blue **Change colours:** All yellow **Nickname:** None
Programme: Yes **Editor:** James Boyce (01270 812742). **Admission:** £2 **Club ties:** Yes.
Previous League: Brighton **Previous Names:** None. **Metal Badges:** No
Record Gate: 1,200 in FA Cup **Previous Grounds:** None.
Midweek Matchday: Tuesday **Clubhouse:** 2 bars, function room, boardroom, tea bar.
Local Press: Sussex Express
Hons: FA Cup 1st Rd Proper 70-71 (lost 0-3 at Colchester Utd), Sussex Co. Lg 70-71 (Div 2 68-69, Div 2 Invitation Cup 66-67, Res. Sect. 80-81, Res. Sect. East 79-80 80-81 (R-up 89-90), Yth Section 87-88, Yth Section East 87-88), Sussex Snr Cup 72-73 (R-up 80-81), Sussex Jnr Cup 25-26.
ussex Express Sne.Charity Cuop 94-95.

SALTDEAN UNITED

Chairman: Mike Walker **Vice Chairman:** Rod Flavell **President:** Jim Bower
Secretary: I S Fielding, 40 Rowan Way, Rottingdean, Brighton BN2 7FP (01273 304995).
Manager: G Green **Asst Manager:** Mark Hammond **Physio:** Keith Gray
Ground: Hill Park, Combe Vale, Saltdean, Brighton (01273 309898).
Directions: A259 coast road east from Brighton to Saltdean Lido, left into Arundel Drive West, and Saltdean Vale to bridle path at beginning of Combe Vale. Club 200yds along track.
Seats: 50 **Cover:** Yes **Capacity:** 2,000 **Floodlights:** Yes **Club Shop:**
Programme: Yes **Editor:** Bob Thomas (01273 309898) **Press Officer:** Julian Appleton.
Colours: Red & black **Change colours:** Blue & yellow
Sponsors: Marat **Nickname:** Tigers **Founded:** 1966.
Midweek Matchday:
Record Attendance: 250
Previous League: Brighton Hove & Dist.
Clubhouse: Licensed bar, lounge, juke box, video games, board room, tea bar. Pool table.
95-96 Captain: Mark Hammond **95-96 Top Scorer:** Mark Shaw. **95-96 P.o.Y.:** Mark Hammond
Honours: Sussex Co. Lg Div 3 88-89, Div 2 95-96.

SELSEY

Chairman: Roger Slade **Manager:** John Davies / Dave Kew **President:** Roy Glew
Secretary: Denny Lee, 29 Malthouse Cottages, West Wittering, Chichester, West Sussex PO20 8QJ (01243 513788 Mobile: 0585 074890).
Press Officer: Mr P Emms. **Ground:** High Street Ground, Selsey, Chichester, West Sussex (0243 603420)
Directions: Through Selsey High Street to fire station. Take turning into car park alongside the station. Entrance is in the far corner. Regular buses from Chichester.
Seats: 50 **Cover:** Yes **Capacity:** 2,250 **Floodlights:** Yes **Founded:** 1923
Colours: Blue/white/blue **Change colours:** White/red/red **Metal Badges:** No
Programme Editor: Mrs D Hayers (0243 604013) **Admission:** £1.50 **Nickname:** Blues
Midweek Matchday: Wednesday **Record Gate:** 750-800 v Chichester or Portfield, 1950's
Clubhouse: Bar, hospitality room, lounge, toilets, kitchen. **Sponsors:** Allslade Welding & Fabrications Ltd
Local Newspapers: Chichester Observer, Evening Argus, Portsmouth Evening News.
Previous Leagues: Chichester & Dist./ West Sussex.
Hons: Sussex Co. Lg R-up 89-90 (Div 2 63-64 75-76 (R-up 86-87), Div 2 Cup 86-87 (R-up 84-85), Div 2 Invitation Cup 63-64, Sussex 5-aside 88-89), Sussex Snr Cup R-up 63-64, Sussex I'mediate Cup 58-59, Sussex Jnr Cup(Reserves) 76-77, West Sussex Lg 54-55 55-56 57-58 58-59 60-61 (Malcolm Simmonds Cup 55-56 56-57 57-58 58-59).

Shoreham celebrate beating Hailsham Town 3-2 in the John O'Hara League Cup final. Photo: Roger Turner.

SHOREHAM

President: Mr Alf Bloom **Chairman:** Mr John Bell.
Secretary: Mrs Anne Harper, 66 Willow Crescent, Worthing. BN13 2SX (01903 267672).
Manager: Brian Donnelly **Press Officer:** Mr Michael Wenham (01273 596009).
Ground: Middle Road, Shoreham-by-Sea, West Sussex (01273 454261).
Directions: Half mile from Shoreham-by-Sea (BR) - east across level crossing, up Dolphin Road, ground 150yds on right. Or, A27 to Shoreham. At Southlands Hospital turn left down Hammy Lane, left at end, ground opposite. **Record Gate:** 1,342 v Wimbledon (floodlight opening 1986).
Seats: 20 **Cover:** 1 stand **Capacity:** 1,500 **Floodlights:** Yes **Founded:** 1892
Colours: Blue / white / blue. **Change colours:** Red & white **Nickname:** Musselmen
Programme: Yes **Editor:** Mr M Wenham (0273 596009) **Admission:** £1.50
Previous League: West Sussex **Midweek Matchday:** Wednesday **Metal Badges:** No
Sponsors: Len German Wholesalers. **Previous Ground:** Buckingham Park (pre-1970)
Local Press: Shoreham Herald **Clubhouse:** Seats 70. Bar, pool, darts, tea bar.
Hons: Sussex Co. Lg 51-53 77-78 (R-up 34-35, Div 2 61-62 76-77 84-85 93-94, Div 2 Cup 74-75 82-83, Invitation Cup 57-58), Sussex Snr Cup 01-02 05-06, Sussex F'lit Cup R-up 89-90, Sussex RUR Charity Cup 02-03 05-06, Vernon Wentworth Cup 86-87.

SOUTHWICK

Chairman: Roy Pollard **Vice-Chairman:** Dave Cook **President:** Dr D W Gordon.
Secretary: Peter Hallett, 10 Hawkins Close, Shoreham-by-Sea, West Sussex BN43 (01273 700474)
Manager: Mick Fogden. **Asst Manager:** Colin Smart. **Coach:** Colin Smart
Ground: Old Barn Way, off Manor Hall Way, Southwick, Brighton BN43 4NT (01273 701010).
Directions: Five minutes walk from either Fishergate or Southwick BR stations. By A27 from Brighton take 1st left after 'Southwick' sign to Leisure Centre. Ground adjacent.
Seats: 220 **Cover:** 1,220 **Capacity:** 3,500 **Floodlights:** Yes
Programme: Yes **Editor/Press Officer:** Paul Symes (01273 594142). **Midweek matchday:** Tuesday
Colours: Red & black stripes/black/red **Change Colours:** Yellow/red/red
Sponsors: Ninex. **Nickname:** Wickers **Founded:** 1882
Reserve League: Sussex Co. Res Div **Record Attendance:** 3,200 v Showbiz side 1971
Best FA Cup season: 1st Rd Proper 74-75 (lost 0-5 at AFC Bournemouth).
Best FA Amtr Cup season: 3rd 28-29 **Best FA Vase season:** 3rd Rd 79-80 85-86
Previous Leagues: West Sussex 1896-1920/ Sussex County 20-52 54-84/ Metropolitan 52-54/ Combined
Players progressing to Football League: Charles & William Buttenshaw (Luton 1948).
Clubhouse: Weekdays noon-3 & 6-11pm, all day Saturday, normal hrs Sunday. Members bar & boardroom with bar. Snacks on matchdays from tea bar.
95-96 Captain: Tony Flowers. **95-96 P.O.Y.:** Richard Waters. **95-96 Top Scorer:** Dave Wills.
Honours: Isthmian Lg Div 2 Sth 85-86, Sus. Co. Lg 25-26 27-28 29-30 47-48 68-69 74-75 (R-up(9) 23-24 28-29 36-37 39-40 70-71 76-77 78-80 82-83, Lg Cup 77-78, Div 1 Invit. Cup 65-66, Div 2 R-up 65-66), Combined Co's Lg R-up 84-85, Sus. Snr Cup 1896-97 1910-11 12-13 24-25 27-28 29-30 30-31 36-37 47-48 67-68, Sus. RUR Charity Cup(10) 1896-97 08-09 10-11 24-26 27-30 37-38 76-77, W. Sus. Lg 1896-97 97-98 1908-09 10-11, Sus. Jnr Cup 1891-92.

THREE BRIDGES

President: Mr Jim Steele **Chairman:** Alan Bell
Secretary: Chris Merson, 19 Bradbury Road, Maidenhead, Crawley. RH10 7HY (01293 887137).
Manager: Steve Dove **Press Officer:** Mr Alf Blackler
Ground: Jubilee Field, Three Bridges, Crawley, West Sussex (01293 530540).
Directions: From West Three Bridges station, turn second right into Three Bridges Road and first left 75 yds down, opposite the Plough Inn.
Seats: None **Cover:** 400 **Capacity:** 3,500 **Floodlights:** Yes **Founded:** 1901
Colours: Amber & black / black / black. **Change colours:** All white **Nickname:** Bridges
Programme: Yes **Editor:** Mark Stacy (0293 885864) **Admission:** £1.50
Previous Lgs: Mid Sussex/ Redhill & District **Previous Grounds:** None.
Record Gate: 2,000 v Horsham, 1948 **Midweek Matchday:** Tuesday **Metal Badges:** No
Clubhouse: Bar, dance floor, pool, darts **Sponsors:** Auto Body Care
Local Press: Crawley Observer, Crawley News
Hons: Sussex Co. Lg R-up 85-86 87-88 88-89 (Div 2 54-55, Invitation Cup 70-71, Div 2 Invitation Cup 62-63), Sussex RUR Charity Cup 82-83.

WHITEHAWK

President: Ron Wiltshire **Chairman/Comm. Mgr:** Ken Powell **Vice-Chairman:** David Powell
Secretary: John Rosenblatt, 25 Arundel Street, Brighton BN2 5TH (01273 680322).
Manager: Butch Reeves **Asst Manager:** Vic Standen **Coach:** Paul Hubbard.
Ground: The Enclosed Ground, East Brighton Park (01273 609736).
Directions: Follow Brighton seafront road towards Newhaven, turn inland (Arundel Road) opposite Marina, 3rd right into Roedean Road, 1st left into Wilson Avenue. Three miles from Brighton (BR); take Newhaven, Eastbourne or Saltdean bus to Marina, then as above.
Seats: None **Cover:** 500 **Capacity:** 3,000 **Floodlights:** Yes **Founded:** 1945
Colours: All red **Change colours:** All blue **Nickname:** Hawks
Midweek Matchday: Wednesday
Programme: £2 with admission **Programme Editor:** Tony Kelly (0273 698203)
Local Press: Evening Argus **Sponsors:** Brighton Co-operative Society.
Record Gate: 2,100 v Bognor Regis Town, FA Cup 4th Qualifying Rd replay 88-89.
Clubhouse: Licensed bar, pool, darts. Board room. Tea bar.
Previous League: Brighton Hove & Dist. **Previous Grounds:** None **Metal Badges:** No
Previous Name: Whitehawk & Manor Farm Old Boys (until 1958).
Club record scorer: Billy Ford **Club record appearances:** Ken Powell 1,103.
Hons: Sussex Co. Lg 61-62 63-64 83-84 (Div 2 67-68 80-81, Lg Cup 82-83 93-94, Invitation Cup 60-61 69-70, Div 2 Cup 80-81), Sussex Snr Cup 50-51 61-62, Sussex RUR Charity Cup 54-55 58-59 90-91, Sussex I'mediate Cup 49-50, Sussex Jnr Cup 48-49 51-52, Brighton Charity Cup 51-52 59-60 61-62 82-83 87-88 88-89, Worthing Charity Cup 82-83, FA Vase 5th Rd 93-94.

WICK

Chairman & Gen Mgr: Norman Cairns **Vice-Chairman:** J Burnett **President:** B Wadsworth
Secretary: Paul Beard, 2 Van Gogh Place, Bersted, Bognor Regis, West Sussex PO22 9BG (01243 822063).
Manager: Jimmy Quinn. **Asst Manager:** Jim Thompson **Physio:**
Ground: Crabtree Park, Coomes Way, Wick, Littlehampton, West Sussex (01903 713535).
Directions: A27 to Crossbush, left at traffic lights signed Littlehampton, after 1 mile cross level crossing, turn left into Coombes Way next to Locomotive PH - ground at end. One and a half miles from Littlehampton (BR).
Seats: 50 **Cover:** 200 **Capacity:** 2,000 **Floodlights:** Yes **Club Shop:**
Programme: Yes **Editor/Press Officer:** Thomas Cairns (01903 501857)
Colours: Red & black / black / black. **Change colours:** Blue & White.
Sponsors: Swandean **Nickname:** Wickers **Founded:** 1892
Midweek Matchedays: Tuesday **Reserve League:** Unijet Sussex Co. Reserve Div.
Record Attendance: 900. **Previous League:** West Sussex
Clubhouse: First floor. Capacity 120. Tea bar.
Honours: Sussex Snr Cup 92-93, Sussex Co. Lg 89-90 93-94 (Lg Cup 87-88 (R-up 93-94 94-95), Div 2 81-82 85-86, Div 2 Cup R-up 81-82, Norman Wingate Tphy 88-89 90-91, Res. Sect West 87-88 90-91 94-95,, Sussex 5-aside R-up 85-86), Sussex RUR Charity Cup 89-90, Gilbert Rice F'lit Cup R-up 80-81 81-82, Sussex Jnr Cup 59-60, Brighton Charity Cup 85-86.Sussex Floodlit Cop R-Up 94-95.

UNIJET SUSSEX COUNTY LEAGUE - DIVISION TWO CLUBS

BEXHILL TOWN

President: Barry Woodcock **Chairman:** Elwyn Hughes **Manager:** Glen Sully/Steve Johnson
Secretary: Mrs Leigh Quinn, 37 Colebrook Road, Bexhill-on-Sea. TN39 3PX (01424 214197).
Ground: The Polegrove, Brockley Rd, Bexhill-on-Sea, East Sussex (0424 220732).
Directions: At Little Common r'bout take 3rd exit to Cooden Sea Rd, left into Cooden Drive for one and a half miles, Brockley Rd on the right. Three quarters of a mile from Bexhill Central (BR).
Seats: 250 **Cover:** 250 **Capacity:** 2,000 **Floodlights:** No **Founded:** 1926
Colours: Green & white/white/white **Change colours:** Black & white **Nickname:** Green Machine
Previous Name: Bexhill Town Athletic.
Programme: Yes **Programme Editor:** Mr G Sully **Admission:** £1.50/£1/50p
Record Gate: 2,000 **Clubhouse:** Clubroom and bar. **Local Press:** Bexhill Observer
Hons: Sussex Co. Lg 56-57 65-66 (Invit. Cup 55-56), Sussex RUR Char. Cup 57-58 73-74, Hastings Challenge Cup 93-94, Sussex Midweek Cup 25-26.

BOSHAM

President: D. M. Fowler. **Chairman:** Richard Doncaster **Manager:** Lloyd Fowler
Secretary: Richard Doncaster, 61 Manor Way, Southborne, Emsworth, Hampshire. (01243 375184).
Ground: The Receation Ground, Walton Lane, Bosham, W. Sussex PO18 8QF (01243 574011).
Directions: Half mile from Bosham (BR) - walk south down station road, over A259. r'bout, left at T-junction, ground entrance 50 yds on left.
Seats: None **Cover:** 50 **Capacity:** 2,000 **Floodlights:** No **Founded:** 1901
Colours: Red/white/red **Change colours:** White/black/white **Nickname:** Robins
Programme: Yes **Programme Editor:** Secretary **Admission:** None **Metal Badges:** No
Previous Leagues: Chichester & Dist Jnr/ Chichester & Bognor/ Chichester & Dist./ West Sussex
Midweek Matchday: Tuesday. **Sponsors:** None.
Clubhouse: Lounge bar, open evenings & weekends. Tea bar.
Local Press: Portsmouth News, Chichester Observer.
Hons: Sussex Co. Lg Div 3 R-up 84-85 (Div 3 Cup 84-85 (R-up 92-93), Reserve Sect. West R-up 92-93), Sussex Jnr Cup 55-56, West Sussex Lg 77-78 (Div 2 56-57), Chichester & Dist. Jnr Lg 06-07, Chichester & Bognor Lg 11-12 12-13 (Lg Cup 11-12), Chichester & Dist. Lg 53-54 55-56, Chichester Charity Cup 55-56.

BROADBRIDGE HEATH

Chairman: Roger Weekes **President:** G W Manketelow
Joint Managers: Tony Beckenham, Kevin Moyse
Secretary: Andy Crisp, 19 Church Rd, Broadbridge Heath, Horsham, West Sussex RH12 3LD (01403 252273).
Ground: Broadbridge Heath Sports Centre, Wickhurst Lane, Horsham (01403 265871).
Directions: Alongside A24, Horsham north/south bypass.
Seats: 300 **Cover:** 300 **Capacity:** 1,300 **Floodlights:** Not full
Programme: Yes **Editor:** Roy Neilson(01403 218318) **Admission:** £1.50.
Colours: All royal blue **Change colours:** All red
Sponsors: Mark Woodham, Painter &Decorator **Nickname:** Bears
Founded: 1919 **Midweek matches:** Tuesday.
Record Attendance: 240
Previous Leagues: Horsham, West Sussex, Southern Co's Comb.
Clubhouse: Bar. Kitchen serving meals, pool, darts, social club etc.

CHICHESTER CITY

President: G Redford **Chairman:** Tony Muncaster
Secretary: John F Hutter, 28 Stockbride Gdns, Donnington, Chichester, West Sussex PO19 2QT (01243 785839).
Manager: Adrian Girdler **Physio:** Wally Lightfoot **Press Officer:** T Wallis (01705 464438).
Ground: Oaklands Park, Chichester (01243 785978).
Directions: Half mile north of city centre adjacent to Festival Theatre. Turn into Northgate car park from Oaklands Way and entrance is beside Tennis and Squash club. 1 mile from Chichester (BR) - walk north through city centre.
Seats: 50 **Cover:** 500 **Capacity:** 2,500 **Floodlights:** No **Founded:** 1873
Colours: White/black/black **Change colours:** All red **Nickname:** Lilywhites
Programme Editor: T Wallis (0705 464438) **Club Shop:** No **Midweek home matchday:** Tuesday.
Prev. Name: Chichester FC (pre-1960). **Record Gate:** 2,500 v Dorchester, FA Cup 1960
Local Press: Chichester Observer **Previous Lgs:** Chichester/ West Sussex 1886-1920
Previous Grounds: New Park Rec. 1873-81/ Priory Park 1881-1956.
Clubhouse: Licensed, open matchdays and some evenings. Tea bar & boadroom.
Club record scorer: David Green **Club record appearances:** Neal Holder.
Hons: Sussex Co. Lg(5) 59-61 67-68 72-73 79-80 Invitation Cup 47-48 54-55 56-57 63-64, Div 2 Cup 84-85 87-88 90-91, Sussex Snr Cup 25-26, Sussex RUR Charity Cup 60-61(jt with Brighton & HA) 63-64, Sussex I'mediate Cup 67-68.

CRAWLEY DOWN VILLAGE

Chairman: Robert Pearce (01342 712964) **Manager:** G Standen/Alan Watson
Secretary: Stuart Frier, 30 Squires Close, Crawley Down, Surrey. RH10 4JQ (01342 714507 or 0181 667 2752 (B)).
Ground: The Haven Sportsfield, Hophurst Lane, Crawley Down. (01342 717140)
Simple Directions: From B2028, follow signpost for village to War Memorial, turn left into Hophurst Lane, ground 100 yards on left. From A22, Felbridge, left into Crawley Down Road, ground 2 miles uphill on right.
Colours: Red & white/red/red & white.

CROWBOROUGH ATHLETIC

President: Mr Peter Taylor **Chairman:** Barry J Sykes
Match Secretary: David Mackellow, 38 Eridge Drive, Crowborough, Sussex. (01892 653122)
Manager: Tony Atkins. **Press Officer:** Peter Crisp (01892 655470).
Ground: Alderbrook Recreation Ground, Fermor Road, Crowborough (01892 661893).
Directions: Turn east off A26 at Crowborough. Cross traffic lights, through High Street, right into Croft Rd, continue into Whitehall Rd and Fermor Rd, Alderbrook is second right after mini-r'bout.
Seats: None **Cover:** 200 **Capacity:** 1,000 **Floodlights:** Yes. **Founded:** 1894
Colours: Blue and White striped shirts/blue/blue. **Change colours:** All red. **Nickname:** Crows.
Programme Editor: Bert Collick(01892 655565) **Sponsors:** Blackden Enterprises Ltd.
Previous League: Brighton **Clubhouse:** Bar facilities & tea bar on matchdays
Midweek Matchday: Tuesday **Local Press:** Kent & Sussex Courier,Sussex Express.
Club badges: Yes. **Previous Grounds:** None
Record Gate: 439 v Stamco, Sussex County League Division Two 1/5/93.
Hons: Sussex Co. Lg Div 1 92-93 (Div 2 Cup 77-78, Div 3 R-up), Sussex Intermediate Cup 86-87.

EAST GRINSTEAD

Chairman: Mark Arnold **Vice-Chairman:** **President:** Colin Dixon
Secretary: Hugh Roberts, 37 Parham Road, Ifield, Crawley, West Sussex RH11 0ET (01293 526805)
Manager: Bryn Marshall **Gen Manager:** Paul O,Donnell **Physio:** Andy Peppercorn.
Ground: East Court, East Grinstead
Directions: A264 Tunbridge Wells road (Moat Road) until mini-r'bout at bottom of Blackwell Hollow, turn immediately right by club sign then 1st left, ground 200yds down lane past rifle club on right.
Seats: None **Cover:** 400 **Capacity:** 3,000 **Floodlights:** Yes **Club Shop:** No
Programme: 36 pages, 50p **Editor/Press Officer:** Bruce Talbot (01293 543809).
Change colours: Navy & L/blue **Colours:** Amber & black
Sponsors: Rydon Group. **Nickname:** Wasps **Founded:** 1890
Midweek Matchday: Tuesday. **Reserves League:** Sussex County Reserve Div. (Prem).
Record Attendance: 2,006 v Lancing, FA Amateur Cup 8/11/48
Previous Leagues: Mid-Sussex 1900-15 35-37/ Sussex County 20-32/ Southern Amateur League 32-35.
Players progressing to Football League: None
Clubhouse: Open 1.30-10.30 matchdays (6-11 midweek matches). Available for hire. Darts, pool, satellite TV. Hot food available Saturdays matcdays, hot snacks rolls etc available at midweek matches.
Honours: Sussex RUR Charity Cup (R-up 74-75); Sussex Co. Lg Invitation Cup 51-52; Sussex Jnr Cup (jointly) 07-08; Sussex Youth Cup 86-87; Southern Amtr Lg Snr Div 3 31-32; Mid-Sussex Lg(6),Lg Cup(7); Brighton Lg(3),Lg Cup(3);

EAST PRESTON

President: Greg Stanley **Chairman:** Greg Stanley **Vice-Chairman:** Don Pryke.
Secretary: Keith Freeman, 41 Ambersham Cres., East Preston, West Sussex BN16 1AJ (01903 771158).
Manager: John Finneran **Assistant Manager:** Ian Cole.
Coach: Adie Cooper **Physio:** Natasha Finneran.
Ground: Roundstone Rrecreation Ground, East Preston, West Sussex (01903 776026).
Directions: Less than a mile from Angmering (BR) station. A259 from Worthing to Roundstone Hotel (6 miles), turn south over railway crossing, left past Centurion garage, right into Roundstone Drive.
Seats: None **Cover:** 40 **Capacity:** **Floodlights:** No **Reformed:** 1966
Colours: White/black/black **Change:** Green/sky/sky **Nickname:** None
Programme: Yes, six pages **Editor:** Mick Miles (0903 787615) **Sponsors:** Focus DIY
Previous Lges: Worthing / W Sussex **Reserve Team's League:** Unijet Sussex Co. Res. Div (West).
Local Press: Littlehampton Gazette. **Clubhouse details:** 4 dressing rooms. Licensed bar open Tues-Fri evenings, Sat noon-3pm, Sun noon-3 & 7-11pm. Kitchen serves light refreshments on matchdays.
Hons: Sussex Co. Lg Div 3 83-84 (R-up 90-91, Div 3 Cup 87-88 (R-up 89-90)), West Sussex Lg 77-78 80-81 81-82 82-83 (Malcolm Simmonds Cup 80-81 82-83, Div 2 Sth 81-82, Div 3 Sth 79-80, Div 5 Sth 82-83, Chichester Cup 87-88, Div 4 Cup 86-87, Boreham Tphy 77-78 90-91 (R-up 93-94)), Vernon Wentworth Cup 80-81 89-90, Worthing Lg 67-68 (Div 2 68-69(res), Benev. Tphy 66-67 68-69), Worthing Charity Cup 68-69.

EASTBOURNE UNITED

Chairman: Ian Botting **Vice-Chairman:** B Winter **President:** N Hampson. **Manager:** Neil Ivemy.
Secretary: Maurice Stevens, 21 Brookside Avenue, Polegate. Bn26 6DL. (01323 484644).
Ground: The Oval, Channel View Rd, Eastbourne, East Sussex (011323-726989) **Directions:** To seafront and turn left. Turn left into Channel View Rd at Princess Park and ground 1st right. 2 miles from Eastbourne (BR).
Seats: 160 **Cover:** 160 **Capacity:** 3,000 **Floodlights:** Yes **Club Shop:**
Programme: 36 pages **Editor:** R.Adcock. **Press Officer:** M Stevens
Colours: White/black/black **Change colours:** Tangerine/white/white. **Sponsors:** Lincoln National.
Nickname: The Raiders. **Founded:** 1894 **Midweek Matchday:** Tuesday
Reserve League: Sussex County Res. Div. (East). **Record Attendance:** 11,000 at Lynchmere
Previous Leagues: Sussex Co. 21-28 35-56/ Metropolitan 56-64/ Athenian 64-77/ Isthmian 77-92.
Players progressing to Football League: B Salvage, T Funnell, M French.
Clubhouse: Bar, lounge, dancefloor, stage, tea bar, board room.
95-96 Captain: G Holder **95-96 Top Scorer:** G Thacker.
Honours: Sussex Co. Lg 54-55, Sussex Snr Cup(5) 60-61 62-64 66-67 68-69 (R-up 89-90), Sussex RUR Charity Cup 55-56, Metropolitan Lg Cup 60-61, Athenian Lg Div 2 66-67 (Div 1 R-up 68-69), Sussex I'mediate Cup 65-66 68-69.

LANCING

Chairman: R J Brown **President:** R G Steele **Manager:** John Bailey **Physio:** Peter Towell.
Secretary: J Chisnall, 15 Orchard Way, Lancing, West Sussex BN15 9ED (01903 763048).
Ground: Culver Road, Lancing, West Sussex (01903 764398).
Directions: From A27 turn south at Lancing Manor r'about into Grinstead Lane, 3rd turning on right North Farm Rd. Turn left then immed. right into Culver Rd. From railway station take 3rd turning on left heading north.
Seats: 350 **Cover:** 350 **Capacity:** 2,400 **Floodlights:** Yes **Club Shop:**
Programme: Yes **Editor:** Jim Thompson (01273 880073) **Press Officer:** John Rea (01903 521593
Colours: Yellow/blue/yellow **Change colours:** All red
Sponsors: Gold Arts **Nickname:** Yellows **Founded:** 1941 **Midweek Matches:** Wednesday
Record Attendance: 2,591 v Tooting, FA Amtr Cup 22/11/47. At Culver Road: 2,340 v Worthing 25/10/52.
Previous League: Brighton Hove & Dist. **Clubhouse:** Open matchdays & training nights.
95-96 Captain: Tim Fletcher. **95-96 Top Scorers:** Derren Woods 20
Honours: Sussex Co. Lg R-up 49-50 64-65 (Div 2 57-58 69-70 (R-up 82-83), Div 2 Cup 81-82 92-93, Invitation Cup), Sussex RUR Charity Cup 65-66, Brighton Lg 46-47 47-48, Sussex Intermediate Cup 46-47, Brighton Charity Cup 83-84 84-85 86-87.

LITTLEHAMPTON TOWN

President: Ian Cunningham **Chairman:** Andy Baumfield **Manager:** Carl Stabler
Secretary: John Savage, 66 Nelson Road, Worthing. BN12 6EN. (01903 502850).
Ground: The Sportsfield, St Flora's Road, Littlehampton (0903 713944).
Directions: 10 minutes walk from Littlehampton station (BR) - turn left along Terminus Rd, continue through High Street and Church Rd to junction with St Flora's Rd (left).
Seats: 260 **Cover:** 260 **Capacity:** 4,000 **Floodlights:** Yes **Founded:** 1894
Colours: Gold/black/black. **Change:** Blue/white/white **Nickname:** Marigolds
Programme Editor: Mr C Scrimshaw (0903 713466) **Local Press:** Littlehampton Gazette
Record Gate: 4,000 v Northampton, FA Cup 1st Rd Proper 90-91
Midweek Matches: Tuesday **Metal badges:** Yes **Clubhouse:** Sportsman (Private Club). Separate board room & tea bar. **Hons:** FA Vase SF 90-91, FA Cup 1st Rd 90-91, Sussex Co. Lg 90-91 (Lg 58-59(jt with Shoreham) 75-77 84-85 90-91), Sussex Snr Cup 73-74.

MIDHURST & EASEBOURNE

Chairman: Pat Perry **President:** Andy Robertson.
Secretary: Ted Dummer, 14 Nine Acres, June Lane, Midhurst, West Sussex GU29 9EP (01730 813887).
Manager: Stuart Groves **Assistant Manager:** Wayne Hyde. **Press Officer:** Rex Lane (01730 812839).
Ground: Rotherfield, Dodsley Lane, Easebourne, Midhurst, West Sussex (01730 816557)
Directions: Ground one mile out of Midhurst on London Road (A286) opposite BP Garage. Ample car parking. Buses pass ground every hour.
Seats: 60 **Cover:** 200 **Capacity:** 800 **Floodlights:** No **Founded:** 1946
Colours: All royal blue **Change colours:** Red/black/black **Nickname:** None
Programme: 8 pages, free **Editor:** Secretary **Club Shop:** No.
Reserves' Lge: Sussex Co. Res. sect. **Record Gate:** 300 in local Gingell Cup, 1989.
Clubhouse: Clubhouse with canteen and bar. Open matchdays & training nights only.
Previous Leagues: West Sussex 46-79/ Southern Co's Combination 79-81. **Previous Grounds:** None
Players progressing to Football League: Colin Gibson (Aston Villa, Man Utd, Leicester).
Hons: Sussex Co. Lg Div 2 Cup 88-89, Div 3 94-95, Southern Co's Comb. Div 2 80-81 (Chal. Cup 80-81), W Sussex Lg 67-68 76-77 79-80 (Div 1 55-56 62-63 64-65, Malcolm Simmonds Cup 59-60 73-74 77-78 79-80, Bareham Tphy 70-71), Sussex I'mediate Cup(5) 54-57 62-63 77-78.

Saltdean United FC display The County League and Cup Trophies Division 2,1995-96

Chichester City FC: *Photo - Eric Marsh*

East Grinstead FC:

NEWHAVEN

Chairman: Alan Baker **Managers:** Martin Langley
Secretary: Frank D Dixon, 39 Southdown Avenue, Peacehaven, East Sussex BN10 8RX (01273 585514).
Ground: Fort Road, Newhaven, East Sussex (01273 513940).
Directions: A275 from Lewes, or A259 coast rd, to Newhaven 1-way system. 1 mile from Newhaven Town (BR).
Seats: 50 **Cover:** Yes **Capacity:** 4,000 **Floodlights:** Yes **Founded:** 1887
Colours: Red & Amber/red/red. **Change colours:** Yellow/green **Nickname:** Dockers
Programme: Yes **Editor:** S.Cox. **Admission:** £1.50 **Metal Badges:** No
Previous Leagues: None (founder members of SCFL) **Previous Name:** Newhaven Town.
Record Gate: 3,000 **Previous Ground:** None (Lewes FC temporarily 90-91)
Midweek Matchday: Tuesday **Clubhouse:** Being redeveloped **Sponsors:** Long Dis Cabs. **Local Press:** Evening Argus, Sussex Express
Hons: Sussex County Lg 53-54 (Div 2 71-72 90-91, Invitation Cup 48-49, Lg Cup R-up 92-93, Reserve Section East R-up 92-93), Sussex Snr Cup R-up 53-54, Sussex RUR Charity Cup 93-94.

REDHILL

President: Malcolm Chatfield **Chairman:** Eric Lee. **Manager:** Peter Burdett.
Secretary: Mr Neil Hoad, 'Braeside', 2b Earlswood Rd, Redhill, Surrey RH1 6HE (01737 213847).
Ground: Kiln Brow, Three Arch Road, Redhill, Surrey (01737 762129).
Directions: On left hand side of A23, two and a half miles south of Redhill.
Seats: 100 **Cover:** 100 **Capacity:** 3,100 **Floodlights:** Yes **Founded:** 1894
Cols: Red & white stripes/red/red. **Change colours:** White/black.
Metal Badges: Yes **Club Shop:** Yes
Record Gate: 1,200 v Crystal Palace & All Star XI, Brian Medlicott Testimonial 1989
Programme: 36 pages **Editor:** Secretary **Nickname:** Reds/Lobsters **Midweek matchday:** Tuesday.
Clubhouse: Social club, bar, canteen, board room, club shop, tanoy, toilets.
Hons: FA Amtr Cup SF 25-25, FA Cup 1st Rd 57-58, Athenian Lg 24-25 83-84 (Lg Cup 69-70 70-71),East & West Surrey Lg. 1902-03,Southern Suburban Senior West Lg. 1902-03,, Surrey Snr Cup 28-29 65-66 , Gilbert Rice F'lit Cup 80-81, Sussex County Lg Div 2 Cup 91-92, Southern Co's Comb. Cup 90-91.

SIDLEY UNITED

President: Tibby Adams **Chairman:** Paul Tidd (01424 2223040 **Manager:** Mick Day/Paul Haffenden
Secretary: Tom Hyland, 12 Penland Court, 56 College Rd. Bexhill. TN49 1TL. (01424 217547).
Ground: Gullivers Sports Ground, North Road, Glovers Lane, Sidley, Bexhill-on-Sea (0424 217078).
Directions: From Brighton on A259 to Bexhill bypass traffic lights, left into London Road, continue into Sidley, right into Glovers Lane and 1st left into North Road. One mile from Bexhill (BR).
Seats: None **Cover:** 150 **Capacity:** 1,500 **Floodlights:** No **Founded:** 1906
Colours: Royal & sky blue **Change colours:** All red **Nickname:** Blues
Programme: Yes **Editor:** Peter Snow **Metal Badges:** Yes
Previous Leagues: East Sussex/ Hastings & District
Record Gate: 1,300 in 1959 **Previous Grounds:** None. **Sponsors:** J Burke
Midweek Matchday: Tues/ Weds **Clubhouse:** Large bar area & function room. Tea bar.
Local Press: Bexhill Observer, Bexhill News
Hons: Suss. Co. Lg Div 2 58-59 64-65 (Div 2 Invit. Cup 57-58), Suss. I'mediate Cup 47-48, Suss. Jnr Cup 24-25.

STEYNING TOWN

Chairman: Graham Matthews (01903 812689) **Manager:** Vic Gretton
Secretary: Mrs Helen Ellis, 15 Breach Close, Steyning, West Sussex BN44 3RZ (01903 816495).
Ground: The Shooting Field, Steyning, West Sussex (01903 812228).
Directions: A27 east then A283 turn off - town centre turning at r'bout, right into Church Street, straight into Church Lane, straight into Shooting Field, ground on left by Grammar School. Bus 10 from Shoreham-by-Sea BR station stops at end of road.
Seats: None **Cover:** 400 **Capacity:** 2,000 **Floodlights:** Yes **Club Shop:** No.
Programme: 28 pages, 50p **Midweek home matchday:** Wednesday **Founded:** 1900
Colours: Red/white/red **Change colours:** All blue
Record Attendance: 1,100 v Halesowen Town, FA Vase QF 84-85.
Previous Leagues: Sussex County 64-86/ Wessex 86-88/ Combined Counties 88-93.
Clubhouse: Tues-Fri 7-11pm, Sat 12-3 & 4.30-11pm, Sun 12-3 & 7-10.30pm. Snacks available.
Club record scorer: D Deans, 42 **Club record appearances:** N Manvell, 800.
Hons: FA Vase QF 84-85, Sussex Snr Cup 85-86 88-89, Sussex Co. Lg 84-85 85-86 (Lg Cup 77-78 83-84 85-86, Div 2 Invitation Cup 65-66, Reserve Section West 88-89), Sussex RUR Charity Cup 79-80, Vernon Wentworth Cup 33-34, Sussex Jnr Cup 01-02 37-38.

WITHDEAN

Chairman: Phil Bond **President:** Graham Spicer
Secretary: Simon Pattenden, 37 Stanmer Road, Brighton. BN1 7JL. (01273 507128 or 01273 541102 (B))
Manager: Paul Norland
Ground: Withdean Stadium, off Valley Drive, Brighton (01703 551638).
Directions: Off main London - Brighton road.
Seats: 100. **Cover:** 1,000. **Capacity:** 10,000 **Floodlights:** No **Founded:** 1984.
Colours: Green & black/black/black **Change Colours:** All white **Metal Badges:** No.
Programme Editor: Dave Bull **Clubhouse:** Pub on ground **Club Shop:** No.
Prev. Leagues: Brighton Hove & Dist. **Prev. Ground:** Council pitch.
Local Newspaper: Brighton Evening Argus **Sponsors:** Computer & Network Consultants Ltd.
Honours: Sussex Co. Lg Div 3 92-93 (Div 3 Cup 91-92).

WORTHING UNITED

President: Ken Higson **Chairman:** Len Killpatrick
Secretary: Mr Malcolm Gamlen, 1 Westbourne Ave., Worthing, West Sussex BN14 8DE (01903 263655).
Manager: Mr Brian Woolmer **Press Officer:** Mr Brian Woolmer.
Ground: Beeches Avenue, Lyons Way, Worthing, West Sussex (0903 234466).
Directions: From west on A27, Beeches Avenue is 4th left past Barn Hill r'bout. From east take 2nd left past lights at Downlands Hotel and proceed to Beeches Avenue - go to and follow concrete road to cap park.
Seats: 100 **Cover:** 500 **Capacity:** 1,000 **Floodlights:** No **Founded:** 1988
Colours: Sky & white/navy/blue **Change colours:** All white **Nickname:** None **Metal badges:** Yes
Programme: Yes **Editor:** N Woolmer (0903 772698) **Sponsors:** Tinsley Robor.
Previous Names: Wigmore Athletic (founded 1948) merged with Southdown in 1988.
Previous Grounds: Harrison Road, Worthing. **Record Gate:** 180 v Northwood, FA Vase 3rd Rd 91-92.
Clubhouse: Bar (capacity 80), refreshment facilities (tea bar). **Local Newspapers:** Worthing Herald.
Hons: *As Wigmore Athletic prior to 1988.* Sussex Co. Lg Challenge Cup 74-75 (Invitation Cup 59-60, Div 2 52-53, Div 2 Invitation Cup 59-60, Div 3 89-90, Reserve Section West 92-93, 5-aside comp. R-up 1993), Sussex Jnr Cup 49-50.

UNIJET SUSSEX COUNTY LEAGUE - DIVISION THREE CLUBS

ANSTY RANGERS

Secretary: Tina Derbyshire, 6 Faulkners Way, Burgess Hill. RH15 8SB. 01444 233030.
Ground: Mill Road, Arundel. 01903 882548
Simple Directions: On A27 from Worthing, over railway bridge to r'about. 2nd exit into Queen St. to town centre. Right over bridge. Car park leading to ground 100yds on right.
Manager: Roger Kent **Colours:** Red & white halves/white/red.

BUXTED

Secretary: Peter J Durrant, 'Haven', Station Road, Isfield. TN22 5XB. 01825 750449.
Ground: Buxted Recreation Ground, Buxted. 01825 763593.
Simple Directions: A272 to Buxted, 1st right, Framfield Rd., opposite Buxted Inn, ground 500 yds. on right.
Manager: Neil Thornicroft **Colours:** Red & Black/black/red & black.

FOREST

Secretary: Gill Hultquist, 117 ifield Drive, Ifield. RH11 0EA. 01293 522846.
Ground: Roffey Sports & Social Club, Spooners Rd., Roffey. 01403 210221.
Simple Directions: spooners Rd. is off the main Crawley road, 100 yds from the 'Star' PH, towards Crawley.
Manager: Russell Pentecost. **Colours:** Claret & blue/blue/white.

FRANKLANDS VILLAGE

Secretary: Mrs Linsey Worsfold, 151a Franklands Village, Haywards Heath. RH16 3RF. 01444 416475.
Ground: Hardy Memorial Playing Field, Franklands Village. 01444 440138
Simple Directions: A272 (Haywards H. to Uckfield). Left at Princess Royal Hosp. r'about. 2nd left & ground at rear of social club.
Manager: Chris Snelling. **Colours:** Royal blue/royal blue/royal blue.

HAYWARDS HEATH TOWN

Secretary: Pat Bucknell, 79 Priory Way, Haywards Heath. RH16 3NS. 01444 457726
Ground: Hanbury Park Stadium, Haywards Heath. 01444 412837.
Simple Directions: A272 to town centre. At Sussex r'about, north on B2078 (Hazlegrove). 1st right (New England Rd) then 4th right (Allen Rd.) to ground.
Manager: Dudley Christensen. **Colours:** Blue, white trim/blue/blue.

HURSTPIERPOINT

Secretary: Paul A John, 16 Church Close, Burgess Hill. RH15 8EZ. (01444 247183).
Ground: Fairfield Recreation Ground, Cuckfield Road. (01273 834783) **Simple Directions:** At Hurstpierpoint crossroads, proceed north into Cuckfield Road (B2117) for 1km. Entrance to ground between houses nos. 158 & 160.
Manager: Steve Marchant. **Colours:** Blue & black/black/blue.

IFIELD

Secretary: Robert Anderson, 1 Old Orchards, Church Rd., Worth, Crawley. RH10 7QA. (01293 886215).
Ground: Ifield Sports Club, Ifield Green, Rusper Road. (01293 536569). **Simple Directions:** From A23 Crawley by-pass going north, left at r'about signed Charlwood. Third left into Ifield Green, first right past Royal Oak (PH) into Rusper Rd.
Manager: john Wort **Colours:** Red/black/red.

LINGFIELD

Secretary: Tracey weston, 1 Arden Mead, Tandridge Lane, Lingfield, Surrey. RH7 6LL. (01342 835082).
Ground: Godstone Road, Lingfield, Surrey. (01342 834269).
Simple Directions: A22, 4 miles north of E Grinstead, to Mormon Temple r'about, take exit Lingfield (B2028) Newchapel Rd. for 1 1/2 miles. Left at T junction into Godstone Rd. (B2029) & ground 1/2 mile on left.
Manager: Ali Rennie **Colours:** Scarlet & amber stripes/black/yellow.

ST. FRANCIS HOSPITAL

Secretary: Colin Mansbridge, 9 Pinehurst, Burgess Hill. Rh15 0DG. (01444 244197).
Ground: St. Francis Hospital, Colwell Lane, Haywards Heath. (01444 441881). **Simple Directions:** Enter through main entrance of Princess Royal Hospital on Lewes road, A272 Haywards Heath. Follow signs to Sports Complex.
Manager: Craig Stewart. **Colours:** Green & white shirts/green/green.

SEAFORD TOWN

Secretary: Mick Webster, 113 Lexden Drive, Seaford. Bn25 3JF. (01323 899218)
Ground: East Street, Crouch Gardens, Seaford. (01323 892221). **Simple Directions:** From A529, turn into Warwick Rd., opposite library by pedestrian crossing. Continue into East St. & ground at end of Crouch Lane.
Manager: Steve Palmer. **Colours:** All red.

SHINEWATER ASSOCIATION

Secretary: Brian Dowling, 79 Harebeating Drive, Hailsham. BN27 1JE. (01323 442488).
Ground: Shinewater Lane, Eastbourne. (01323 765880). **Simple Directions:** From A27, B2104 to Eastbourne. At Stone Cross go under railway br., 1st rt (Larkspur Dr.), 1st left (Milfoil Dr.), 3rd left into Shinewater Lane.
Manager: Alan Walsh. **Colours:** Sky blue/navy/navy.

SIDLESHAM

Secretary: Peter Turner, 64 Hawthorn Rd., Bognor Regis, W. Sussex. PO21 2DD. (01243 822860).
Ground: Sidlesham Recreation Ground. (01243 641538). **Simple Directions:** Signposted Hunston/Selsey (B2145) from r'about towards Selsey for 4 miles. Ground on right between houses.
Manager: Peter Cleverley. **Colours:** Yellow & green/black/black.

STORRINGTON

Secretary: Keith Dalmon, 4 End Cottages, Storrington Rd., Amberley. BN18 9LX. (01798 831887).
Ground: Recreation Ground, Storrington. (01903 745860).
Simple Directions: Turn west on A283 (off A24). Ground opposite pond to west of village centre.
Manager: Malcolm MacMichael **Colours:** All blue.

SUN ALLIANCE

Secretary: Steve Jenkins, 33 Owlscastle Close, Horsham. RH12 5YA. (01403 256697).
Ground: Sunallon Sports Club, North Heath Lane. ()1403 253814). **Simple Directions:** Into Horsham on Warnham road, left at 1st set of lights, over mini-r'about to North Heath Lane. Ground is on the L.H.S.
Manager: Dave Roberts. **Colours:** Yellow/blue/blue.

THOMSON ATHLETIC

Secretary: Mrs Tracy Lucas, 24 Manorfields, Bewbush, Crawley. RH11 8GN. (01293 851800 pm only).
Ground: Tinsley Lane, Crawley. (01293 442000). **Simple Directions:** From south on 123, right at traffic lights (Manor Rd.), past traffic lights, r'about, then 1st right into Tinsley Lane. 1st entrance.
Manager: John Smith. **Colours:** Black & white stripes/black/black.

UCKFIELD TOWN

Secretary: Ian Bohemen, 32 farriers way, Uckfield. TN22 5BY. (01825 767781).
Ground: Victoria Pleasure Grounds, Uckfield. (01825 769400). **Simple Directions:** Take Eastbourne road (old A22) south of Uckfield town centre. Entrance to ground 1/2 mile on right (just after Police station).
Manager: David Miller. **Colours:** Red/black/black.

uhlsport

UNITED COUNTIES LEAGUE

FEEDER TO: BEAZER HOMES LEAGUE

FOUNDED: 1895

Chairman: Geoffrey Paul

Hon.Secretary: R J Gamble, 8 Bostock Avenue, Northampton (01604 494121 [B])

Press Secretary: J Biggs, (01780 63048, 01123 702917)

The league's centenary campaign 1994-95 had been one of the most dramatic in the competition's 100 years but 1995-96 wasn't far behind in terms of excitement, both Premier and First division title races going to the seasons final day.

In the top flight Mirrlees Blackstone were surprising early pacesetters with the goals of Dave Scotney putting them in contention, the likes of Cogenhoe, Eynesbury and Stamford all had their moments when threatening to join the race but in the second half of the season three clubs pulled away. Desborough, enjoying their best season for years, were left to rue a series of early season defeats in the final analysis, but could be delighted with the progress made under Willie Kell's command during the season. Stotfold and Raunds matched each other stride for stride in the closing weeks and when they met at Kiln Park on the final Wednesday of the season, Stotfold - unbeaten in 20 outings- held a three point lead over their hosts who boasted a 21 game sequence without loss. Raunds, who had suffered heartbreak aplenty on numerous fronts during the last two years, rose to the occasion and raced to a 5-2 victory. That win left them ahead on goal difference and the contenders both had one game left.

Stotfold's final match was at Holbeach, who had beaten them at Roker on the season's opening day. The Carters Park clash kicked off early as the Tigers had a reserve game to fit in on the same afternoon - but the Eagles kept up their challenge with a 2-1 success. Back at Kiln Park, Raunds were holding an interval lead against Long Buckby but within five minutes of the restart the Bucks were on terms. As the match moved into injury time the Denham Parker Trophy looked to be heading south - but four minutes into time added on, top scorer Shaun Keeble's close range header gave Raunds a 2-1 win and their first Premier Division Championship.

After the disappointment of rejection by the Southern League twelve months before, the programme of ground improvements carried out during the season did the trick and Raunds become the latest UCL side to graduate to the next level of the pyramid.

At the foot of the Premier Division Kempston struggled throughout and mustered just a single victory, at local rivals Wooton on Easter Monday. Just above them Newport Pagnell whose youthful squad found the going tough, the good news for both clubs is that Raunds' promotion prevented relegation from the Premier once again.

In passing it seems appropriate to mention a sporting legend who briefly played in our competition during 1995-96 - double Olympic decathlon champion Daley Thompson. He joined Stamford in October and spent three months with the Daniels before moving on to try his luck in the Football League with Mansfield. Even at the age of 37 this remarkable athlete caught the eye and his spell at Wothorpe Road brought excellent publicity to both Stamford and the League.

In Division One there was another excellent title race. Half a dozen clubs were in contention at Christmas and in the mid season the top five clubs were covered by a single point. Ramsey's challenge collapsed after manager Steve Jackson's Boxing day departure, Whitworth's challenge faded as attention switched to their county cup challenge, while newboys Rothwell Corinthians couldn't quite match their early season in the new year, but could nonetheless be pleased with fourth place in their debut campaign.

Ford Sports, Higham and Bugbrooke were left to fight it out for the crown, the Badgers were always the outsiders and despite their fine late season form their blend of experienced players and exciting youngsters had to settle for third place. Higham looked to have blown their chances with a 4-1 defeat by Bugbrooke in the spring but the Lankies didn't lose thereafter and finished runners-up for a fourth season in succession. Ford Sports lifted the Championship for the second time in four seasons, clinching the championship with a 7-2 drubbing of Cottingham on the season's last day. While the team were doing their stuff on the field, hard work behind the scenes including construction of a stand and floodlights paid off and the Motormen were rewarded with promotion to the Premier for 1996-97.

At the other end of the table a frantic finish saw Irchester finish bottom just below surprise strugglers ON Chenecks as Harrowby produced another of their last gasp escapes.

Turning to the season's cup football, the Knockout Cup brought its share of surprises not least the early departure of Raunds, beaten at home by Higham who enhanced their giant killing reputation with a 1-0 success at Kiln Park. By the semi-final stage all the Division One contenders were out. Stewarts & Lloyds ended Spalding's reign, Derek Walker's last minute winner the only goal of the two hours at Occupation Road. In the other half of the draw Cogenhoe went through against Stotfold on the away goals rule, their 1-1 Roker draw followed by a goalless stalemate at Compton Park.

The first leg of the final saw S & L notch up a surprise 2-1 away win, that set up the tie for the Occupation Road return which proved an all time classic. The first half was all Cogenhoe down the slope, two goals saw them in front on aggregate with 45 minutes left. In the second half the tie turned spectacularly as S & L tore the Cooks apart, Dave Beazeley scoring three of their four goals. With just nine minutes left S & L led 6-3 on agregate, but a penalty gave them a glimmer of hope. The league's top scorer Kevin Slinn tucked away the spot kick and then produced a superb volley to square the match on the night. With the seconds ticking away it didn't seem enough, but in injury time Cooks sub Chris Nicholson's stunning blast from a wide position took the tie into extra time. Neil Westland completed Cogenhoe's comeback, 6-4 on the night and 7-6 on aggregate. What a way for Cogenhoe to win their first senior trophy for the League's longest serving manager Dave Conlon.

Over the years the Benevolent Cup has brought its share of controversy and this time it ended in the removal of Raunds from the competition as they fielded 'on the day' signing Juilian Capone as a substitute in the final at Stotfold. The player did not meet the eligibility qualification, so Stotfold, beaten 3-1 on the field by Peter Green's hat-trick, were awarded the trophy.

Moving away from the domestic action, Raunds again shone in the FA Carlsberg Vase, they claimed highly prized scalps Hinckley Athletic, Furness and Taunton before losing 1-0 to a last minute Mangotsfield winner in a home 6th round replay. In the FA Cuo six clubs reached the Second Round Qualifying, the league's best representation at that stage in two decades. All six lost at that hurdle but there were some highlights to look back on, most notably Boston's 5-2 replay thrashing of ICIS League Premier Division Bishop Stortford, not far behind was Eynesbury's 7-1 defeat of Halstead who went on to win the Jewson League Championship.

It was Boston and Eynesbury who were our best county cup performers. The Poachers were Lincs Senior Cup A runners-up for a second consecutive season, losing 2-1 to Unibond side Lincoln United in the final, while Eynesbury won both Senior and Premier Cups in Huntingdonshire, beating Warboys and Langford in the respective finals. The League's domination of the Northants Junior Cup continued with Whitworths winning the cup for the first time beating Rothwell Reserves 3-2 in a replayed final.

Looking ahead we welcome Huntingdon United back to the league after a 3 year absence. They are the latest graduates from our junior pyramid having swept the board in the West Anglia League last season.

1996-97 will see the league under new sponsorship, "uhlsport" linking up with the league for a three year period. This means we bid farewell to Hereward Sports after a lenghty six year sponsorship which has proved mutually successful to both parties. Our thanks are due to Hereward Sports and in particular Davod Oxer, for their interest and support since 1990.

Jeremy Biggs

FINAL LEAGUE TABLES 1995/96

PREMIER DIVISION

		Home					Away					
	P	*W*	*D*	*L*	*F*	*A*	*W*	*D*	*L*	*F*	*A*	*Pts*
1. Raunds	38	14	4	1	60	14	12	5	2	51	14	87
2. Stotfold	38	13	4	2	45	16	13	5	1	49	21	87
3. Desborough	38	13	3	3	63	33	12	1	6	41	23	79
4. Cogenhoe	38	13	5	1	47	22	8	3	8	37	34	71
5. Eynesbury	38	11	4	4	37	19	8	5	6	27	20	66
6. Spalding	38	8	4	7	25	25	11	4	4	37	26	65
7. Stamford	38	11	4	4	51	27	7	6	6	37	29	64
8. Long Buckby	38	9	6	4	41	29	8	4	7	39	34	61
9. Holbeach	38	9	4	6	32	20	7	8	4	36	25	60
10. Boston	38	11	2	6	45	22	4	10	5	29	27	57
11. Mirrlees Blackstone	38	11	4	4	39	30	5	5	9	31	41	57
12. Stewarts & Lloyds	38	10	3	6	53	39	5	5	9	37	38	53
13. North Spencer	38	5	4	10	34	51	7	2	10	33	37	42
14. Wootton	38	4	7	8	28	34	7	2	10	26	44	42
15. St Neots	38	8	3	8	40	39	3	1	15	19	57	37
16. Potton	38	5	5	9	25	33	4	4	11	21	43	36
17. Wellingborough	38	6	5	8	35	38	4	1	14	22	50	36
18. Bourne	38	5	5	9	24	40	3	4	12	25	63	33
19. Newport Pagnell	38	4	3	12	19	54	0	4	15	18	74	19
20. Kempston	38	0	2	17	14	48	1	2	16	18	57	7

PREMIER DIVISION RESULTS CHART 1995-96

HOME TEAM	1	2	3	4	5	6	7	8	9	10	11	12	13	14	15	16	17	18	19	20
1. Boston Town	*	0-0	1-3	1-2	0-1	1-2	6-2	2-3	2-1	5-0	1-0	1-0	1-1	8-1	2-0	3-2	3-2	0-2	1-0	7-0
2. Bourne Town	1-1	*	1-0	0-2	0-2	0-4	0-0	1-1	1-6	3-3	4-1	1-3	0-2	1-1	1-2	0-6	4-2	0-2	2-1	4-1
3. Cogenhoe United	2-2	6-0	*	3-2	1-1	1-1	3-1	1-0	3-0	4-2	3-1	3-1	1-3	3-0	2-2	3-2	2-1	2-2	1-0	3-1
4. Desborough Town	1-1	5-0	5-2	*	2-1	3-1	5-1	4-0	3-1	4-1	3-3	4-2	1-3	5-2	3-2	4-1	1-1	1-5	7-1	2-5
5. Eynesbury Rovers	2-0	4-0	0-2	2-1	*	3-1	2-1	1-1	3-0	3-0	4-2	2-1	2-2	3-0	0-1	1-0	2-2	0-0	2-3	1-2
6. Holbeach United	1-1	3-1	1-1	1-2	2-1	*	3-1	2-3	4-1	5-0	1-0	1-1	0-1	1-0	1-2	0-1	1-1	1-2	3-1	1-0
7. Kempston Rovers	1-5	1-2	1-2	0-5	1-2	0-4	*	1-2	0-1	0-0	1-1	1-2	0-2	2-3	1-3	1-2	1-7	1-2	1-2	0-1
8. Long Buckby	1-1	4-1	2-2	2-0	2-1	2-2	4-0	*	2-2	3-0	2-3	2-2	0-2	3-0	1-1	1-4	3-2	2-5	2-0	3-1
9. Mirrlees Blackstone	2-1	1-2	3-2	2-5	0-2	1-0	2-1	1-8	*	4-1	3-0	5-0	2-1	3-1	1-1	0-0	2-2	1-1	5-2	1-0
10. Newport Pagnell Tn	1-1	1-1	2-1	0-3	1-4	0-5	5-2	0-4	0-4	*	1-4	0-0	0-8	2-1	1-3	1-4	1-4	0-2	3-1	0-2
11. Northampton Spencer	0-0	9-5	2-2	1-3	2-3	0-4	1-0	1-1	2-2	5-1	*	2-1	0-7	1-4	3-2	1-4	0-5	2-3	2-3	0-1
12. Potton United	0-4	3-0	0-1	1-0	1-2	1-1	6-3	3-4	2-2	0-0	0-4	*	0-4	4-1	0-0	0-0	0-1	0-3	3-0	1-3
13. Raunds Town	1-1	5-0	1-2	1-0	1-1	5-1	2-1	2-1	3-0	2-1	5-1	9-0	*	4-0	4-1	1-1	0-3	5-2	5-0	1-1
14. St Neots Town	1-2	2-2	2-6	1-4	1-3	1-2	2-0	4-1	2-2	5-1	1-3	2-1	0-0	*	2-4	2-1	3-1	1-3	3-1	5-2
15. Spalding United	1-1	1-2	2-1	0-2	1-0	1-1	3-0	2-1	0-2	4-1	2-1	3-0	0-2	1-0	*	2-2	0-2	0-4	1-1	1-2
16. Stamford	5-1	6-2	3-1	2-3	0-0	1-1	4-2	3-2	4-1	7-2	1-0	2-1	0-4	6-0	0-3	*	5-1	1-1	0-1	1-1
17. Stewarts & Lloyds	3-2	5-4	1-4	1-2	2-1	2-2	4-0	3-1	1-2	8-3	2-3	3-0	2-2	5-1	0-3	1-1	*	1-6	4-2	5-0
18. Stotfold	2-1	3-1	2-1	4-2	2-1	1-2	3-0	0-0	1-1	9-0	1-0	0-0	2-0	2-0	1-2	2-2	4-1	*	3-2	3-0
19. Wellingborough Tn	1-3	2-2	2-3	0-2	1-0	1-0	1-0	1-2	3-2	2-1	1-4	1-3	3-3	3-2	1-2	4-0	1-0	2-3	*	5-3
20. Wootton Blue Cross	1-1	2-0	3-1	1-1	0-0	1-1	1-2	2-4	5-1	1-1	2-1	1-3	0-4	0-2	2-3	2-4	2-2	1-1	2-1	*

FINAL LEAGUE TABLES 1995/96

DIVISION ONE		Home					Away					
	P	*W*	*D*	*L*	*F*	*A*	*W*	*D*	*L*	*F*	*A*	*Pts*
1. Ford Sports	36	15	2	1	57	18	12	3	3	48	24	86
2. Higham	36	14	1	3	48	17	13	3	2	46	16	85
3. Bugbrooke	36	13	3	2	38	13	12	3	3	53	18	81
4. Rothwell Cor	36	12	3	3	49	19	10	5	3	30	10	74
5. Olney	36	12	1	5	41	22	12	1	5	44	25	74
6. North. Vanaid	36	12	2	4	53	28	7	6	5	36	35	65
7. Whitworths	36	13	1	4	47	13	7	3	8	25	22	64
8. Ramsey	36	7	5	6	33	22	9	2	7	27	25	55
9. Burton P W	36	8	1	9	29	25	5	7	6	21	21	47
10. Yaxley	36	4	7	7	26	37	6	5	7	25	30	42
11. Thrapston	36	8	3	7	47	33	4	2	12	17	37	41
12. Daventry	36	5	4	9	23	43	7	1	10	32	42	41
13. Cottingham	36	5	6	7	18	27	4	2	12	23	41	35
14. St Ives	36	2	8	8	19	27	5	4	9	31	35	33
15. Blisworth	36	4	3	11	31	53	4	5	9	28	50	32
16. Harrowby	36	8	0	10	25	46	1	3	14	17	69	30
17. Sharnbrook	36	5	3	10	27	47	3	2	13	23	54	29
18. On Chenecks	36	4	4	10	21	32	2	3	13	17	40	25
19. Irchester	36	3	5	10	18	45	3	2	13	24	56	25

Leading Goalscorers:

Premier Division		**Lge**	**KO**	**Ben**	**Total**
Kevin Slinn	Cogenhoe	32	15	-	47
Jamie Cunningham	Desborough	34	4	-	38*
(* includes 2 lge for Cogenhoe)					
John Coley	Stotfold	25	5	2	32
Shaun Keeble	Raunds	31	-	-	31
Dave Scotney	M. Blackstone	29	1	-	30
Dave Beazeley	Stewarts & Lloyds	21	5	-	26
Division One:					
Andrew Green	Ford Sports	33	-		33
Jon Ogden	Higham	27	2		29
Clive Woodland	Olney	28	-		28

DIVISION ONE RESULTS CHART 1995-96

HOME TEAM	1	2	3	4	5	6	7	8	9	10	11	12	13	14	15	16	17	18	19
1. Blisworth	*	2-2	1-3	3-1	1-4	1-3	3-3	2-3	3-3	3-6	1-4	2-6	0-5	1-2	1-3	3-1	2-0	0-3	2-1
2. Bugbrooke St Michaels	2-0	*	2-0	1-3	3-1	1-1	3-1	1-1	5-1	5-1	3-0	1-0	0-2	1-0	1-0	4-0	3-1	1-0	1-1
3. Burton Park Wanderers	3-4	0-1	*	0-1	0-2	1-2	2-0	1-4	3-0	2-0	1-0	3-1	1-2	0-2	2-4	4-1	3-0	1-1	2-0
4. Cottingham	0-0	0-4	2-2	*	1-0	2-2	3-1	0-4	1-2	1-1	1-1	2-3	0-2	0-1	1-0	1-0	1-0	0-2	2-2
5. Daventry Town	1-1	0-7	0-0	2-0	*	0-7	3-2	0-4	3-0	3-4	4-1	0-3	2-3	1-0	1-1	2-6	0-2	0-0	1-2
6. Ford Sports	9-0	1-0	3-2	7-2	2-1	*	1-0	1-2	3-1	3-1	2-1	3-3	1-0	1-1	4-1	8-0	2-1	2-0	4-2
7. Harrowby United	0-3	1-3	1-5	3-2	2-0	0-3	*	0-4	3-2	1-3	3-1	4-2	0-2	0-5	0-7	2-0	2-1	3-0	0-3
8. Higham Town	3-0	1-4	1-2	1-0	4-0	4-2	9-0	*	3-1	2-2	4-0	0-3	2-0	2-1	2-0	2-1	3-0	2-1	3-0
9. Irchester United	2-4	0-7	1-0	0-4	2-6	0-2	2-0	0-4	*	1-3	1-1	0-2	1-2	0-0	1-5	2-2	3-1	1-1	1-1
10. Northampton Vanaid	3-3	4-3	2-1	2-0	3-1	1-2	7-2	2-0	6-1	*	4-0	1-2	3-1	1-1	2-0	5-3	3-4	3-0	1-4
11. ON Chenecks	1-2	1-2	0-0	2-1	0-3	1-4	6-0	1-1	3-1	0-5	*	1-2	0-1	0-3	1-1	1-2	1-0	1-3	1-1
12. Olney Town	3-2	3-1	0-1	6-0	2-2	0-4	5-0	3-2	4-0	1-3	1-0	*	1-2	0-1	2-1	1-0	3-1	2-1	4-1
13. Ramsey Town	2-2	2-2	1-1	1-2	2-1	0-2	7-2	0-2	4-0	0-0	4-1	0-1	*	0-1	0-0	2-1	5-1	2-1	1-2
14. Rothwell Corinthians	1-0	0-2	1-1	2-1	4-3	2-3	9-1	0-2	3-0	0-0	3-1	3-2	2-1	*	3-0	8-0	1-1	3-0	4-1
15. St Ives Town	4-0	2-2	1-1	1-1	1-2	2-2	1-2	1-2	0-0	0-2	1-1	1-4	2-0	1-4	*	0-2	0-0	0-1	1-1
16. Sharnbrook	4-3	0-6	2-1	2-1	0-1	1-2	4-0	1-5	1-7	1-0	1-2	0-4	3-3	0-0	5-5	*	1-2	1-3	0-2
17. Thrapston Venturas	7-1	0-2	0-1	4-2	7-0	4-0	1-1	1-3	8-2	4-4	2-1	1-5	1-1	0-5	5-0	2-1	*	0-3	0-1
18. Wellingborough Whit	3-1	1-2	3-0	1-1	5-1	3-1	1-0	1-2	3-0	7-0	2-1	0-1	4-0	1-2	2-0	5-1	3-0	*	2-0
19. Yaxley	2-2	0-3	0-0	3-1	3-4	1-6	2-2	1-1	0-3	1-1	2-1	3-0	2-0	1-1	2-3	2-2	1-2	0-5	*

LEAGUE KNOCKOUT CUP 1995-96

Preliminary Round:

Raunds v Higham	0-1	Stotfold v St Ives	0-0, 9-2
Burton PW v Kempston	3-4	On Chenecks v Cogenhoe	1-2
Boston v Yaxley	7-0	Northampton Spencer v Ford Sports	2-1
Newport Pagnell v Rothwell Cor	0-1		

First Round:

Holbeach v Wellingborough	5-1	WQootton v Whitworths	2-1
Stamford v Bugbrooke	1-0	Daventry v Higham	1-5
Harrowby v Sharnbrook	6-1	Mirrlees Blackstone v St Neots	1-2
Stewarts & Lloyds v Blisworth	2-1	Eynesbury v Ramsey	4-0
Thrapston v Spalding	0-1	Long Buckby v Cottingham	0-1
Olney v Irchester	2-4	Northampton Vanaid v Bourne	0-4
Potton v Cogenhoe	0-3	Desborough v Rothwell Cor	3-1
Kempston v Stotfold	0-4	Boston v Northampton Spencer	4-0

Second Round:

Spalding v Holbeach	1-1, 3-1	Stamford v Stewarts & Lloyds	1-2
Irchester v Eynesbury	0-6	Stotfold v Wootton	3-2 (aet)
Bourne v Cottingham	2-1	Higham v St Neots	1-3
Boston v Harrowby	5-0	Desborough v Cogenhoe	4-4, 1-5

Third Round:

Stewarts & Lloyds v Bourne	10-3	Boston v Cogenhoe	1-5
St Neots v Stotfold	0-1 (aet)	Spalding v Eynesbury	3-2

Semi-Finals:

Stewarts & Lloyds v Spalding	1-0 (aet)	Stotfold v Cogenhoe	1-1, 0-0. Cogenhoe won on away goals

Final: Cogenhoe v Stewarts & Lloyds 1-2, 6-4.

BENEVOLENT CUP 1995-96

Semi-finals:

Raunds v Higham	2-0	Ford Sports v Stotfold	2-3

Final: Stotfold v Raunds 1-3, (Raunds fielded an ineligible player, trophy awarded to Stotfold.

BOSTON TOWN

Chairman: Mick Vines **Vice Chairman:** J Rose. **Treasurer:** J Rose
Secretary: A Crick, Daisy Cottage, Shore Rd, Freiston, Boston, Lincs PE22 0LU (01205 760162. Fax:760162).
Manager: Bob Don-Duncan **Asst Manager:** Shaughan Farrow. **Physio:**
Ground: Tattershall Road, Boston, Lincs (01205 365470). **Directions:** A52 Grantham-Sleaford, 2nd left into Brotherton Rd., Argyle St.to bridge, immediately over left into Tattersall road, ground 3/4 mile on left.
Capacity: 6,000 **Seats:** 450 **Cover:** 950 **Floodlights:** Yes **Club Shop:** Yes.
Programme: 40 pages, 50p **Editor/Press Officer:** Bob Whitaker (01205 368445)
Colours: Blue & white/white **Change:** Yellow/blue/yellow **Sponsors:** Keystone Fabricators
Nickname: Poachers **Founded:** 1963. **Midweek Matchday:** Tuesday **Reserves League:** None 94-95.
Record Attendance: 2,700 v Boston Utd, FA Cup 3rd Qual. Rd 1970.
Best season - FA Cup: 1st Rd Proper 76-77 (lost 1-3 at Barnsley). **FA Trophy:** Second Round 79-80 (lost 3-6 at Mossley after 0-0 draw). **FA Vase:** Semi-Finals 94-95 (lost 0-2 on aggregate to Taunton Town).
Previous Leagues: Lincs 63-65/ Central Alliance 65-66/ Eastern Co's 66-68/ Midland 68-82/ Northern Co's East 82-87/ Central Midlands 87-91.
Players progressing to Football League: Julian Joachim (Leicester City), Neil Mann (Hull City).
Clubhouse: Open evenings (except Sunday), matchdays & functions. Bar & Lounge. Darts & pool.
95-96 Captain: Pat Clark. **95-96 Top Scorer:** Carl Smaller **95-96 P.o.Y.:** Lee Rippen.
Club Record Goalscorer (in a season): Carl Smaller 48, 1994-95.
Honours: Midland Co's Lg 74-75 78-79 80-81 (Lg Cup 76-77); Lincs Snr 'A' Cup (5) 73-74 79-82 89-90 (Snr 'B' Cup 65-66); Central Mids Lg 88-89; Central All 65-66; Lincs Lg 64-65; Hereward Spts Unt.Co.Lg.Prem Div Champ 94-95.

BOURNE TOWN

Chairman: Ivor Turner **Vice-Chairman:** Roger Atkins **President:** Ray Ferrer
Secretary: Roger Atkins, 106 Stephenson Way, Bourne PE10 9DD (01778 424882)
Manager: Mick Bloodworth **Coach:** Stuart Hodson **Physio:** Colin Notley
Ground: Abbey Lawn, Abbey Road, Bourne, Lincs (01778 422292). **Directions:** In market place take A151 Spalding Road, ground 500 yds on right. Public transport from Peterborough, Stamford and Grantham.
Capacity: 3,000 **Seats:** 300 **Cover:** 750 **Floodlights:** Yes **Club Shop:** Contact sec.
Programme: 50 pages, 50p **Editor:** Tony Gout (01778 425548) **Press Officer:** Secretary
Colours: Claret/sky/claret **Change Colours:** White and Blue. **Sponsors:** Jaychem
Nickname: Wakes **Founded:** 1883. **Midweek matchday:** Wednesday **Reserves' Lge:** HSUCL Res Div 1
Record Attendance: 3,000 v Chelmsford, FA Tphy 1970 **Club Record Goalscorer:** David Scotley
Previous Leagues: Peterborough/ UCL 47-56/ Central Alliance 58-61/ Midland Counties 61-63.
Players to progress to Football League: Peter Grummit (Nottm Forest), Shaun Cunnington (Wrexham, Grimsby, Sunderland), David Palmer (Wrexham).
Clubhouse: Small, open matchdays and specific events. Food, confectionary available.
95-96 Captain: Tony Cook **95-96 P.o.Y.:** Paul Pearson. **95-96 Top Scorer :** Paul Pearson
Honours: Utd Co's Lg 68-69 69-70 71-72 90-91 (KO Cup 69-70, Benevolent Cup 90-91, Res Div 2 94-95), Lincs Snr 'A' Cup 71-72 (R-up 92-93), Central Alliance Division 1 South 59-60, Lincs Intermediate Cup 85-86.

COGENHOE UNITED

Chairman: Derek Wright **Vice Chairman:** Bob Earl **President:** Steve Brockwell
Sec./Press Off.: Mick Marriott, 14 Corn Kiln Close, Cogenhoe, Northants NN7 1NX (01604 890043).
Manager: Dave Conlon **Asst Man.:** Micky Donnelly **Physio:** Ian Blair. **Coach:** Stuart Robertson
Ground: Compton Park, Brafield Rd, Cogenhoe, Northants (01604 890521). **Comm. Man.:** Robert Jones.
Directions: Turn off A428 at Brafield-on-the-Green, first turn right to Cogenhoe or A45 to Billing Aquadrome. Carry on, take second Cogenhoe turn on left.
Capacity: 5,000 **Seats:** 100 **Cover:** 200 **Floodlights:** Yes **Founded:** 1967
Programme: 32 pages with Admission **Programme Editor:** Mick Marriott **Nickname:** Cooks.
Club Colours: Sky Blue. **Change:** All White. **Club Shop:** No.
Midweek home matchday: Tuesday **Previous Ground:** Cogenhoe Village PF 1967-84.
Sponsors: Cogenhoe Dairy/ Ying Wa **Previous League:** Central Northants Combinatiom 1967-84.
Reserves' Lge: UCL Res. Div 1 **Record Gate:** 1,000 v Eastenders XI, Charity match 8/7/90.
Record win: 22-0 v Ravensthorpe, Central Northants Comb. Premier Division KO Cup, 79-80.
Record defeat: 0-6 v Yardley United, Central Northants Combination Division One, 1976-77.
Players to progress to Football League: Darren Bazeley (Watford 1989), Darren Harmon (Notts Co., Shrewsbury, Northampton 1989), Matt Murphy (Oxford Utd 1993), Gary Leonard (Northampton 1978).
Clubhouse: Open Tues-Fri 7-11pm, Sat 12-3 & 4-11pm, Sun 12-3 & 7-10.30pm. Snacks. Hot food on matchdays.
Local Newspapers: Chronicle & Echo, Northants Evening Telegraph.
Record scorer & appearance maker: Tony Smith.
Hons: UCL Div 1 R-up 86-87 (Reserve Div 2 88-89), Daventry Charity Cup 91-92 (R-up 79-80), Central Northants Comb 80-81 82-83 83-84 (R-up 81-82, Prem Div Cup 82-83 (R-up 78-79), Div 1 Cup R-up 77-78, Charity Shield 82-83 83-84).

DESBOROUGH TOWN

Chairman: Bryan Walmsley **President:** Ernie Parsons.
Secretary: John Lee, 85 Breakleys Road, Desborough, Northants NN14 2PT (01536 760002).
Manager: Willie Kelly **Asst Manager:** Terry Madox **Physio:** TBA
Ground: Waterworks Field, Braybrooke Rd, Desborough (01536 761350).
Directions: Half a mile west of A6 following signs for Braybrooke.
Capacity: 8,000 **Seats:** 250 **Cover:** 500 **Floodlights:** Yes **Club Shop:**
Programme: 40 pages with entry **Editor:** Robert Bindley **Press Officer:** John Lee
Colours: All blue **Change Colours:** Red/White/Navy **Previous Leagues:** None.
Sponsors: Wincanton Transport/R Fox **Nickname:** Ar Tarn **Founded:** 1896.
Midweek matchday: Tuesday **Record Attendance:** 8,000 v Kettering Town.
Players progressing to Football League: Wakeley Gage (Northampton, Chester, Peterborough and Crewe), Jon Purdie & Campbell Chapman (Wolves), Andy Tillson (Grimsby, QPR & Bristol Rvrs).
Clubhouse: Lounge & main hall, 2 bars, games room. Open every evening, weekend lunchtimes.
95-96 Captain: Paul Murphy **95-96 P.O.Y.:** Jamie Cunningham
Honours: Utd Co's (Prev. Northants) Lg 00-01 01-02 06-07 20-21 23-24 24-25 27-28 48-49 66-67 (R-up 02-03 10-11 19-20 22-23 79-80 (Div 2 10-11(Res) 28-29(Res) (R-up 09-10(Res) 26-27(Res) 51-52(Res)), KO Cup 77-78), Northants Snr Cup 10-11 13-14 28-29 51-52.

EYNESBURY ROVERS

Chairman: Deryck Irons **President:** Bill Stephenson
Secretary/Press Officer: Patrick Worrall, 22 Blea Water, Huntingdon, Cambs. PE18 6XH. (01480 431257)
Manager: Barry Cavilla **Asst Manager/Coach:** Dave Mountford.
Ground: Hall Road, Eynesbury, St Neots (01480 477449).
Directions: Approx 2 miles from A1, on South side of St Neots urban area, near Ernulf School.
Capacity: 3,000 **Seats:** 270 **Cover:** 270 **Floodlights:** Yes **Founded:** 1897
Programme: 24 pages, 30p **Editor:** Patrick Worrall **Club Shop:**
Colours: Royal blue & white **Change Colours:** All yellow. **Nickname:** Rovers.
Midweek matchday: Tuesday **Clubhouse:** Large bar, capacity 150, committee room
Sponsors: National Power/Terosons **Reserve Team's League:** United Counties Reserve Div. One.
Record Gate: 5,000 v Fulham 1953 **Previous Lges:** Sth Mids 34-39/ UCL 46-52/ Eastern Co's 52-63.
Best FA Vase season: 2nd Rd 85-86 88-89 **Best FA Cup season:** 4th Qual. Rd 54-55 (1-3 at Camb. Utd)
Players to progress to Football Lge: Chris Turner (P'boro, Luton, Cambridge), Denis Emery (P'boro)
Local Newspapers: Hunts Citizen, Cambridge Evening News, St Neots Weekly News.
Hons: UCL Div 1 76-77, Hunts Snr Cup(12) 13-14 46-47 48-51 54-55 56-57 69-70 84-85 90-93, Hunts Premier Cup 50-51 90-91, Hinchingbrooke Cup(7) 46-47 48-52 57-58 66-67, Cambs Invitation Cup 61-62, E Anglian Cup R-up 90-91 91-92, Hunts Scott Gatty Cup 35-36 56-57 84-85 89-90 (R-up 93-94(res)), Hunts Jnr Cup 21-22 26-27, S Mids F'lit Cup 90-91(Res).

FORD SPORTS

Chairman: Mel Knowles **Managers:** Richard Green & Kevin Flear
Secretary: David Hirons, 53 Armull Cres., Daventry, Northants NN11 5AZ (01327 71461).
Ground: Royal Oak Way South, Daventry, Northants (01327 709219).
Directions: Enter Daventry on A45 or A361 and follow signs for Royal Oak Way
Capacity: 1,000 **Seats:** Yes **Cover:** Yes **Floodlights:** Yes **Founded:** 1968
Programme: 12 pages **Reserves' Lge:** UCL Res Div 2 **Clubhouse:** Yes
Colours: Yellow & Blue **Change colours:** All Blue. **Nickname:** Motormen
Prev. Lge: Central Northants Comb **Sponsors:** Zurich.
Player progressing to Football League: Martin Aldridge (Northampton).
Player of the Year 1994-95: Paul Beauchamp.
Hons: UCL Div 1 92-93, 95-96 (Benevolent Cup R-up 92-93, Highest Aggregate Goalscoring Trophy 92-93).

Raunds Town: Champions of the Hereward Sports United Counties League

Photo - G Whittington

Stotfold FC: Runners-up in the Herward Sports United Counties League

Photo - G Whittington

HOLBEACH UNITED

President: John King **Chairman:** John Crunkhoen
Secretary: Mr John Crunkhorn, The Old Nurseries, Bakers Corner, High Rd, Whaplode, Spalding, Lincs PE12 6UA (01406 422540).
Manager: Dominico Genovese/ Milton Graham.
Ground: Carters Park, Park Road, Holbeach (01406 424761. **Directions:** Second left at traffic lights in town centre, 220 yds down road on left. From King's Lynn; sharp right at traffic lights.
Capacity: 4,000 **Seats:** 200 **Cover:** 450 **Floodlights:** Yes **Founded:** 1929.
Programme: 44 pages, 50p **Programme Editor:** Alan Wright **Club Shop:**
Colours: Old gold & black **Change Colours:** Blue & white **Nickname:** Tigers
Reserves' Lge: Peterborough **Clubhouse:** Large bar, lounge & kitchen, open every night.
Midweek matchday: Wednesday **Record Gate:** 4,094 v Wisbech 1954.
Sponsors: J F Buffham Transport/ Rings Quality Homes/ Anchor Produce '90.
Previous Leagues: Peterborough/ Utd Co's 46-55/ Eastern Co's 55-62/ Midland Co's 62-63.
Players progressing to Football League: Peter Rawcliffe (Lincoln).
Best FA Cup season: 1st Rd Proper 82-83 (lost 0-4 v Wrexham at Peterborough).
Best FA Trophy season: 2nd Qualifying Round 69-70 71-72.
Best FA Vase season: 5th Round 88-89 (lost 2-4 v Wisbech Town).
Local Newspapers: Lincs Free Press, Spalding Guardian, Peterborough Evening Telegraph.
Honours: Utd Co's Lg 89-90 (KO Cup 64-65 89-90, Benevolent Cup), Lincs Snr Cup 'A' 83-84 84-85 86-87 (Senior Cup 'B' 57-58)

KEMPSTON ROVERS

President: H Gilbert **Chairman:** Peter Burnage **Vice-Chairman/Comm. Mgr:** Ian Davis.
Press Officer/Secretary: Alan Scott, 26 King William Rd, Kempston, Bedford MK42 7AT (01234 854875).
Manager: Russell Shreeves **Assistant Manager:** Bobby Folds.
Ground: Hillgrounds Leisure, Hillgrounds Rd, Kempston, Bedford (01234 852346). **Directions:** M1 jct 13, A421 to Kempston, Hillgrounds Rd is off the B531 main Kempston-Bedford road. Entrance to Hillgrounds Road is opposite Sainsburys on the B531 - ground can be found just over twi miles from Sainsburys entrance. British Rail to Bedford Thameslink/Midland then bus No.103 from Bedford town centre stops outside ground.
Capacity: 2,000 **Seats:** 100 **Cover:** 250 **Floodlights:** Yes **Founded:** 1884.
Programme: 24 pages, 40p **Programme Editor:** Alan Scott.
Colours: Red/white/black **Change Colours:** All yellow.
Nickname: Walnut Boys **Club record scorer:** Doug Jack.
Midweek matchday: Tuesday **Club Sponsors:** Kempston Bedding/ Dings Entertainment.
Record Attendance: unknown **Previous League:** Sth Mids 27-53.
Reserves's Lge: HUCL Res Div. **Club Shop:** No, but old programmes available from clubhouse.
Previous Grounds: Bedford Rd 1900s-1973/ Hillgrounds Road 74-86 *(three grounds in same road!).*
Players progressing to Football League: Ernie Fenn (WBA, Aston Villa), Matthew Woolgar (Luton 1994).
Clubhouse: Open 7-11pm every evening except Monday and weekend lunctimes noon-3pm. Sky TV, pool, fruit machines, hot pies & pasties.
Local Newspapers: Bedfordshire Times, Herald & Post.
Hons: Utd Co's Lg 73-74 (R-up 56-57 59-60 (Div 1 57-58 85-86, Div 2 55-56 (R-up 67-68), KO Cup 55-56 57-58 59-60 74-75 76-77), Beds Senior Cup 08-09 37-38 76-77 91-92 (R-up 92-93).

LONG BUCKBY

President: Alister Bruce **Chairman:** Ted Thresher
Secretary: Dave Austin, 6 Jubilee Close, Long Buckby NN6 7NP (01327 843286).
Manager: Mick Emms **Asst Manager:** Les Thurbon **Press Officer:** Dave Derrig
Ground: Station Rd, Long Buckby (01327 842682).
Directions: On Daventry - Long Buckby road. 400 yds from station (Northampton - Rugby line).
Capacity: 1,000 **Sseats:** 200 **Cover:** 200 **Floodlights:** Yes **Founded:** 1945
Programme: 8 pages **Programme Editor:** Rod Peyor. **Sponsors:** Ned.
Colours: All blue **Change colours:** Yellow & black **Nickname:** Bucks
Reserves' Lge: HSUCL Res Div 1 **Clubhouse:** Bar & concert room. Open matchdays.
Midweek matchday: Tuesday **Record Gate:** 750 v Kettering, Northants Snr Cup Final 1984.
Prev. Name: Long Buckby Nomads 1936. **Previous Lges:** Rugby & D./ Central Northants Comb. (pre-1968).
Best FA Vase season: 2nd Rd 85-86 **Best FA Cup season:** 1st Qualifying Rd 92-93..
Players progressing to Football League:
Gary Mills (Nottingham Forest, Derby, Notts County, Leicester), Vince Overson (Burnley, Birmingham), Des Waldock (Northampton), Steve Norris (Scarborough, Carlisle, Halifax, Chesterfield).
Local Newspapers: Chronicle & Echo, Daventry Weekly News.
Honours: UCL KO Cup 84-85 (UCL Div 2 70-71 71-72, Div 3 69-70, Div 2 KO Cup 71-72), Northants Snr Cup R-up.

MIRRLEES BLACKSTONE

Chairman: Bill Sewell **President:** Darren Laughton
Secretary: Derek Hall, 67 Ringwood, South Bretton, Peterborough PE3 9SR (01733 332074).
Manager: Steve Blades **Press Officer:** Kevin Bloor.
Ground: Lincoln Road, Stamford (01780 57835).
Directions: A6121 Stamford to Bourne road, 2nd left past MB works.
Capacity: 1,000 **Seats:** 100 **Cover:** Yes **Floodlights:** Yes **Founded:** 1920.
Programme: 32 pages with entry **Editor:** Kevin Boor
Local Newspapers: Stamford Mercury, Herald & Post, Peterborough Evening Telegraph.
Club Colours: Blue & black. **Change Colours:** Red
Clubhouse details: Open evenings, lunchtimes & matchdays.
Sponsors: Dolpin Inn **Midweek matchday:** Tuesday **Nickname:** Stones
Record Gate: 700 v Glinton. **Record win:** 11-0 v Brackley, 22/1/94 (A Dunn 6 goals).
Previous Leagues: Peterborough Works/ Peterborough/ Stamford & District.
Previous Names: Rutland Ironworks/ Blackstone (until 1975).
Players to progress to Football League:
Craig Goldsmith (Peterborough, Carlisle), Alan Neilson (Newcastle & Wales).
Club record scorer (in one game): A Dunn; 6 v Brackley Town, 22/1/94.
Hons: UCL Div 1 R-up 87-88 (Benevolent Cup R-up), Lincs Snr Cup 'A' 92-93.

NEWPORT PAGNELL TOWN

President: Ken Inch. **Chairman:** Bill Burke
Secretary: John Anderson, 59 Willen Road, Newport Pagnell, Bucks MK16 0DE (01908 610440).
Manager: Terry Ashton/D Janes (joint).
Ground: Willen Road, Newport Pagnell (01908 611993).
Directions: Adjacent to A442 Newport Pagnell by-pass.
Capacity: 2,000 **Seats:** 100 **Cover:** 100 **Floodlights:** Yes **Club Shop:**
Programme: 56 pages **Editor:** Ernie Print **Press Officer:**
Colours: Green & white stripes/green/white **Change colours:** Yellow & black
Sponsors: Charles Wells **Nickname:** Swans **Founded:** 1963.
Midweek Matchday: **Reserve Team's League:**
Previous Leagues: Nth Bucks 63-71/ South Mids 71-73
Best FA Vase year: 2nd Rd 84-85
Clubhouse: Open every evening
95-96 Captain: Des Cook **95-96 P.o.Y.:** Paul Stokes **95-96 Top Scorer:**
Honours: UCL Div 1 82-83 (R-up 91-92, Div 1 Cup 77-78), Daventry Charity Cup R-up 93-94.

NORTHAMPTON SPENCER

President: P.A.Frost. **Chairman:** Graham Wrighting
Secretary: R Linnell, 53 Muscott Lane, Duston, Northampton (01604 751731).
Manager: Gary Sargent **Asst Manager:** Keith Bowen
Ground: Kingsthorpe Mill, Studland Rd, Northampton NN3 1NF (01604 718898).
Directions: Turn off Kingsthorpe Rd at traffic lights into Thornton Rd, 1st right into Studland Rd, ground at end.
Capacity: 2,000 **Seats:** 100 **Cover:** 350 **Floodlights:** Yes **Founded:** 1936
Programme: 48 pages, 50p **Programme Editor/Press Officer:** Andy Goldsmith
Colours: Yellow & green **Change Colours:** White & green **Nickname:** Millers
Midweek matchday: Tuesday **Clubhouse:** Lounge and bar, open normal licensing hours.
Club Sponsors: Doc Martens **Record Gate:** 800 v Nottm F., dressing-room opener 1993.
Previous Lge: Northampton Town 36-68 **Previous Name:** Spencer School Old Boys.
Reserves' Lge: HSUCL Res. Div. One **Prev. Grnds:** Dallington Park 1936-70, Duston High School 70-72.
Best FA Cup year: 1st Qual. Rd 93-94 **Best FA Vase year:** 4th Round 87-88 (lost 1-2 v Gresley Rovers)
Players to progress to Football League:
Paul Stratford (Northampton), Wakeley Gage (Northampton, Chester, Peterborough, Crewe)
Local Newspapers: Chronicle & Echo, Northampton Post, Northants Advertiser.
Hons: United Counties Lg 91-92 (R-up 92-93, Div 1 84-85, KO Cup 88-89 93-94 (R-up 87-88), Benevolent Cup 91-92), Northants Snr Cup R-up 90-91 93-94.

POTTON UNITED

President: Peter Hutchinson. **Chairman:** Claude Munns
Secretary/Press Officer: Derek Inskip, 3 Bellevue Close, Potton, Beds SG19 2QA (01767 260355).
Manager: Ken Davidson **Asst Manager:** Alan Biley
Ground: The Hollow, Biggleswade Road, Potton (01767 261100).
Directions: Outskirts of Potton on Biggleswade Road (B1040). Three and a half miles from Sandy (BR). United Counties buses from Biggleswade.
Capacity: 2,000 **Seats:** 200 **Cover:** 250 **Floodlights:** Yes **Founded:** 1943
Programme: 28 pages, 50p **Pogramme Editor:** Bev Westhorpe **Club Shop:**
Club Sponsors: Darlows **Local Press:** Biggleswade Chronicle, St Neots Weekly News.
Colours: Blue & white **Change Colours:** All yellow **Nickname:** Royals
Midweek matchday: Tuesday **Clubhouse details:** Large (capacity for 100), opened 1985.
Reserves' Lge: HSUCL Res. Div. Two **Record Attendance:** 470 v Hastings Town, FA Vase 1989
Prev. Grnd: Recreation Grnd pre-1947 **Previous Lges:** Sth Mids 46-55/ Central Alliance 56-61
Best FA Trophy year: 3rd Qualifying Round 71-72 72-73.
Best FA Vase year: 5th Round 89-90 (lost 1-2 to Billericay Town).
Best FA Cup year: 3rd Qualifying Round 74-75 (lost 1-2 to Bedford Town).
Hons: Utd Co's Lg 86-87 88-89 (KO Cup 72-73, Benevolent Cup 88-89), Beds Snr Cup(5) 47-49 63-64 75-76 77-78 (R-up 94-95), Wallspan Floodlit Cup 87-88, Hinchingbrooke Cup 51-52 84-85 89-90 90-91 91-92, Hunts Premier Cup 89-90 91-92 94-95(joint), Beds I'mediate Cup 43-44, Southern Comb. Cup 92-93, Nth Beds Charity Cup(9) 58-60 65-67 70-72 85-86 87-88 89-90.

ST NEOTS TOWN

Chairman: Bob Page **Press Officer:** Mike Birch.
Secretary: John Carroll, 95 St Neots Rd, Sandy, Beds SG19 1BP (01767 680709).
Manager: Guy Loveday **Asst Manager:** Tony McGovern**Coach:** Pete Brown.
Ground: Rowley Park, Cambridge Rd, St Neots, Cambs (01480 470012).
Directions: Through town centre, under railway bridge, 1st left.
Capacity: 3,000 **Seats:** TBA **Cover:** 250 **Floodlights:** Yes **Founded:** 1879
Programme: Yes **Programme Editor:** Mike Birch **Nickname:** Saints
Reserves' Lge: UCL Res Div 2 **Clubhouse:** Built 1994. **Sponsors:** TBA
Club colours: Sky & navy **Change colours:** Blue & gold.
Previous Ground: Shortsands **Best FA Cup year:** 1st Rd 66-67 (lost 0-2 at Walsall).
Best FA Vase year: 3rd Rd 78-78 **Best FA Trophy year:** Second Qualifying Round 69-70 72-73.
Record Gate: 2,000 v Wisbech, 1966 **Previous Name:** St Neots & District 1879-1957.
Previous Lges: South Midlands 27-36 46-49/ United Counties 36-39 51-56 66-69 73-88/ Metropolitan 49-51 60-66/ Central Alliance 56-60/ Eastern Counties 69-73/ Huntingdonshire 90-94.
Players progressing to Football League:
Frank Atkins (Cambridge), John Gregory (Aston Villa) and Matthew Oakle (Southampton).
Honours: Hunts Snr Cup(33), UCL 67-68 (KO Cup 67-68 68-69), Metropolitan Lg 49-50 (Lg Cup 79-80), South Midlands Lg 32-33, Huntingdonshire Lg 90-91 92-92 92-93 94-95.

SPALDING UNITED

Chairman: Rod Quinton **President:** John Chappell
Secretary: Jack Grimwood, 29 Moons Green, Moulton, Spalding, Lincs. PE12 6QW (01406 370698)
Manager: Alan Day **Asst Manager:** Phil Ward **Physio:**
Ground: Sir Halley Stewart Field, Winfrey Avenue, Spalding (01775 713328).
Directions: Town centre off A16, adjacent to bus station. 250 yds from Spalding (BR) station.
Capacity: 7,000 **Seats:** 350 **Cover:** 2,500 **Floodlights:** Yes **Shop:**
Programme: 36 pages, 50p **Editor:** Bernard Holmes **Press Officer:** Ray Tucker
Colours: Tangerine & black/black/tangerine **Change:** All Blue
Sponsors: Foremost Supplies **Nickname:** Tulips **Founded:** 1921
Midweek matchday: Tuesday **Reserve League:** Utd Counties Lge Res Div Two.
Record Attendance: 6,972 v Peterborough, FA Cup 1952.
Previous Leagues: Peterborough/ Utd Co's 31-55 68-78 86-88/ Eastern Co's 55-60/ Central Alliance 60-61/ Midland Co's 61-68/ Northern Co's (East) 82-86/ Southern 88-91.
Best FA Cup year: 1st Round 57-58 (1-3 at Durham City), 64-65 (3-5 at Newport County).
Best FA Trophy year: 2nd Qualifying Round 69-70 70-71 71-72 74-75 76-77 81-82.
Best FA Vase year: Quarter-Finals 89-90 (lost 1-3 to Guiseley).
Players progressing to Football League: Carl Shutt (Sheffield Wednesday, Bristol City, Leeds).
95-96 P.o.Y.: Nick Keeble. **Clubhouse:** Open matchdays, and events.
Honours: Utd Co's Lg 54-55 74-75 87-88 (R-up 50-51 51-52 52-53 72-73 75-76); KO Cup 54-55 94-95; Northern Co's East Lg 83-84; Lincs Snr Cup 52-53; Lincs Snr 'A' Cup 87-88; Lincs Snr 'B' Cup 50-51; Evans Halshaw F'lit Cup 89-90.

Holbeach United FC: Back Row (L-R); Glen Eldridge, Ronnie Fortune, Brian Small, Derek Nutall, Simon Hart, RobertSpeechlep, Lee Cooper, Fred McDonnell. Front Row; Andy Creakhorn, Dominic Genovese, Des Lawrence, Shaun Brothwell. Steve Thompson. Angus Heplourn. *Photo - Martin Wray.*

Raund's Shaun Keeble heads home the last minute goal which beat Long Bockby and made Raunds Champions *Photo - G Whittington*

The Celebrations after Shaun Keeble's last minute winner for Raunds *Photo - G Whittington*

STAMFORD

Chairman: Arthur Twiddy **Vice-Chairman:** Bill Warrington **President:** Vacant
Secretary: Phil Bee,3 Launde Gardens,Sramford,Lincs. (01780 56665)
Manager: Steve Evans. **Asst Manager:** P O'Keeffe **Physio:** Gerard Evans
Ground: Wothorpe Road, Stamford, Lincs (01780 63079).
Directions: Off A43 Kettering Rd, 1 mile east of A1. 200 yds from station.
Capacity: 5,000 **Seats:** 250 **Cover:** 1,250 **Floodlights:** Yes **Club Shop:** Yes
Programme: 36 pages, 60p **Editor:** Andrew Eason **Press Officer:** Andrew Eason
Colours: Red/White/red **Change Colours:** Yellow/black/yellow
Sponsors: Wilpave **Nickname:** Daniels **Founded:** 1896
Midweek matchday: Tuesday **Reserves League:** UCL Res Div 2
Record Attendance: 4,200 v Kettering, FA Cup Third Qual. Rd 1953.
Previous Leagues: Peterborough/ Northants (UCL) 08-55/ Central Alliance 55-61/ Midland Co's 61-72.
Players to progress to Football League: Alan Birchenall (Chelsea, Crystal Palace, Leicester), Reg Chester (Aston Villa), Teddy Tye (Chelsea), Gerry Fell (Brighton, Southend, Torquay, York), Campbell Chapman (Wolves), Steve Collins (Peterborough), Keith Alexander (Grimsby, Stockport, Lincoln), Andy Tillson (Grimsby, QPR, Bristol Rovers), Brian Stubbs (Notts Co.), Domenico Genovese (Peterborough).
Clubhouse: Open matchdays, Sunday lunchtimes & evenings (bingo). Food available matchdays - hot and cold.
95-96 Captain: Dean Elston **95-96 P.o.Y.:** Milton Graham **95-96 Top Scorer:** Daren Edey
Honours: FA Vase 79-80 (R-up 75-76 83-84), Utd Co's Lg 75-76 77-78 79-80 80-81 81-82 (KO Cup 51-52 75-76 79-80 81-82 85-86, Northants Lg 11-12, Lincs Snr 'A' Cup 78-79 82-83, Lincs Snr 'B' Cup 51-52 53-54, Hinchingbrooke Cup, William Scarber Mem. Cup 70-71 82-83 85-86 88-89 94-95, Stamford Chal. Cup 89-90, Lincs Jnr Cup 48-49.

STEWARTS & LLOYDS

Chairman: Peter Webb
Manager: Elwyn Roberts.
Ground: Recreation Ground, Occupation Road, Corby (01536 401497).
Directions: On Occupation Rd at rear of Stewart & Lloyds Leisure Club, next to old Corby Town F.C. ground.
Capacity: 1,500 **Seats:** 100 **Cover:** 200 **Floodlights:** Yes **Club Shop:**
Programme: 12 pages with admission **Editor/Press Officer:** Dave Foster
Colours: Yellow & blue **Change Colours:** Red & white
Sponsor: Hamlet Circuits **Nickname:** None **Formed:** 1935
Midweek matchday: Tuesday **Previous Leagues:** Kettering Amateur
Players to progress to Football League: Andy McGowan (Northampton), Willie Graham (Brentford)
Clubhouse: Licensed bar.
95-96 Captain: Derek Walker **95-96 P.o.Y.:** Stewart Mar**Club Record Goalscorer:** Joey Martin 46 (92-93).
Honours: UCL R-up 85-86, Div 1(2) 73-75; UCL KO Cup, Prem 95-96, Div 1 Cup(2) 73-75, Div 2 KO Cup(2) 75-77)

STOTFOLD

Chairman: Jerry Watson **Vice Chairman:** Graham Jarman **President:** Charles Hyde
Secretary: W Clegg, 12 Common Rd, Stotfold, Hitchin, Herts SG5 4BX (0462 730421).
Manager: Ian Allinson **Asst Manager:** Gordon Allinson
Physiotherapist: Keith Allinson **Press Officer:** Miss J Longhurst
Ground: Roker Park, The Green, Stotfold, Hitchin, Herts (0462 730765).
Directions: A507 from A1, right at lights, right at T-jct. A507 from Bedford via Shefford, left at lights, right at T-jct.
Capacity: 5,000 **Seats:** 50 **Cover:** 300 **Floodlights:** Yes **Nickname:** Eagles
Programme: 22 pages with entry **Programme Editor:** Keith Mayhew **Founded:** 1904.
Club Colours: Amber & black **Change Colours:** Sky blue **Reformed:** 1945.
Midweek matchday: Tuesday **Reserve Team's League:** UCL Reserve Division One.
Club Sponsors: Motorola **Record Attendance:** 1,000 v Letchworth Town, FA Amtr Cup.
Previous Leagues: Biggleswade & District/ North Herts/ South Midlands 51-84.
Local Newspapers: Comet, Biggleswade Chronicle.
Clubhouse details: Clubroom, bar, refreshment bar, dressing rooms, physio room.
Record appearances: Roy Boon/Dave Chellew.
Hons: Utd Co's Lg R-up 93-94 (KO Cup R-up 91-92, Res Div 1 87-88), Sth Mids Lg 80-81 (R-up 55-56 57-58 58-59 59-60 63-64 65-66 77-78, Div 1 53-54, Chal. Tphy 81-82, Beds Snr Cup 64-65 93-94, Beds Premier Cup 81-82, Beds I'mediate Cup 58-59, Nth Beds Charity Cup 55-56 56-57 61-62 81-82 87-88 90-91, Beds Colts Lg 88-89.

WELLINGBOROUGH TOWN

Chairman: Corville Brown. **President:**
Secretary: Mike Walden, 5 Fernie Way, Wellingborough, Northants NN8 3LB (01933 279561).
Manager: Brian Knight.
Ground: Dog & Duck, London Road, Wellingborough, Northants (01933 223536).
Directions: 200yds off A45 by-pass, by Dog & Duck PH. 1 mile from Wellingborough (BR).
Capacity: 5,000 **Seats:** 300 **Cover:** 500 **Floodlights:** Yes **Club Shop:** No
Programme: 16 pages 30p **Editor:** Secretary **Press Officer:** Secretary
Colours: Blue & gold **Change Colours:** All red.
Sponsors: Overstone Park School **Nickname:** Doughboys **Founded:** 1867
Midweek matchday: Tuesday **Reserve League:** HSUCL Res. Div. Two
Record Attendance: 4,013 v Kettering Town.
Best FA Cup season: 1st Round 28-29 (v Bristol Rovers) 65-66 (1-2 v Aldershot Town).
Best FA Trophy season: 1st Round 71-72 (lost 0-3 to Dartford after 1-1 and 0-0 draws).
Best FA Vase season: 95-96.
Previous Leagues: Midland 1895-97 98-1901/ Southern 01-05 71-89/ Northants (Utd Co's) 19-34 36-56 61-68/ Central Alliance 56-61/ Metropolitan 68-70/ West Midlands Regional 70-71.
Players progressing to Football Lge: Phil Neal (N'hampton, L'pool & Eng.), Fanny Walden (Spurs & Eng.)
Clubhouse: Full facilities. Open evenings & Sat lunchtimes.
95-96 Captain: Adam Sandy **95-96 Top Scorer:** **95-96 P.o.Y.:** Adam Sandy
Club Record Goalscorer: S Hill **Club Record Appearances:** P Hayes 165, 1985-89.
Honours: Utd Co's Lg 10-11 62-63 64-65, Metropolitan Lge 69-70, Northants Snr Cup 1896-97 1901-02 02-03 33-34 47-48 49-50 81-82, Maunsell Cup 20-21 21-22.

WOOTTON BLUE CROSS

President: J Clarke. **Chairman:** D Peters
Secretary: Trevor Templeman, 13 Spring Gardens,Newport Pagnell,Bucks MK16OEE
Manager: Ken Goodeve **Asst Manager:** Neil Simms.
Press Officer: Secretary
Ground: Weston Park, Bedford Road, Wootton (01234 767662).
Directions: Four miles south of Bedford on main road through village at rear of Post Office.
Capacity: 2,000 **Seats:** 50 **Cover:** 250 **Floodlights:** Yes **Founded:** 1887
Programme: 24 pages **Programme Editor:** Secretary. **Club Shop:**
Colours: Blue & black. **Change:** Yellow & Blue. **Sponsors:** Marshall
Nickname: Blue Cross. **Reserve Team's League:** United Counties Reserve Div. Two.
Midweek matchday: Tuesday **Record Gate:** 838 v Luton, Beds Prem. Cup 1988.
Best FA Vase year: 3rd Rd 74-75 **Best FA Cup year:** 2nd Qual. Rd 50-51 (3-4 v Hitchin (H)).
Previous Leagues: Bedford & District/ South Midlands 46-55.
Previous Grounds: Recreation Ground, Fishers Field, Rose & Crown, Cockfield.
Players progressing to Football Lge: Tony Biggs (Arsenal).
Local Newspapers: Bedfordshire Times, Bedford Herald, Beds Express, Beds on Sunday.
Clubhouse details: Main hall, bar, darts, pool, bingo. Open every evening and weekend lunchtimes.
Hons: Utd Co's Lg Div 2 67-68 69-70 (KO Cup 82-83, Div 2 Cup 64-65), South Midlands Lg 47-48 (R-up 49-50), Beds Senior Cup 70-71, Hinchinbrooke Cup(5).

uhlsport UNITED COUNTIES LEAGUE - DIVISION ONE CLUBS

BLISWORTH

Chairman: Pete Edwards **President:** L Piggott.
Secretary: Terry Jeyes, 33 Buttmead, Blisworth, Northampton NN7 3DQ (01604 858750).
Manager: Phil Holding. **Assistant Manager/Coach:** Paul Smith.
Ground: Blisworth Playing Field, Courteenhall Road, Blisworth (01604 858024).
Directions: Courteenhall Road off A43.
Capacity: 1,000 **Seats/Cover:** No **Floodlights:** No **Clubhouse:** Yes **Programme:** No.
Colours: Yellow & green **Change colours:** Blue & Black. **Founded:** 1890.
Reserves' Lge: UCL Res. Div. 2 **Previous Lge:** Central Northants Combination 1978-87.
Player progressing to Football Lge: Dave Johnson (N'pton 83-84)
Hons: Northants Junior Cup 88-99

BUGBROOKE St MICHAELS

Chairman: Tom Treacy. **President:** Jack Holt
Secretary: Roger Geary, 31 Kislingbury Rd, Bugbrooke, Northampton NN7 3QG (01604 831678).
Manager: Nick Verity **Asst Manager:** Tony Bonner. **Press Officer:** Rose Harris.
Ground: Birds Close, Gayton Road, Bugbrooke (01604 830707).
Directions: A45 Northampton to Daventry road, onto B4525 (Banbury Lane) at Kislingbury, left into Gayton Road, ground on left.
Capacity: 1,500 **Seats:** None **Cover:** Yes **Floodlights:** Yes **Founded:** 1929
Reserves' Lge: UCL Res. Div. 1 **Clubhouse:** Yes - normal licensing hours.
Programme: Eight pages. **Programme Editor:** Rose Harris **Nickname:** Badgers
Club colours: Blue & yellow **Change colours:** All green. **Record Gate:** 1,156
Previous Ground: School Close **Previous Lge:** Central Northants Combination 1952-87.
Players progressing to Football League: Kevin Slinn (Watford), Craig Adams (Northampton).
Club Sponsors: Church & Newman Builders.
Club Record Scorer: Vince Thomas **Club Record Appearances:** Jimmy Nord.
Hons: Northants Junior Cup 89-90, Central Northants Comb. 68-69 69-70 70-71 71-72 76-77 85-86, UCL Res Div 2 R-up 94-95.

BURTON PARK WANDERERS

Chairman: Bernard Lloyd **Manager:** Colin Neill.
Secretary: David Haynes, 125 Churchill Way, Burton Latimer, Northants NN15 5RT (01536 724871).
Ground: Latimer Park, Polwell Lane, Burton Latimer (01536 725841).
Directions: Entering Burton Latimer, turn off A6 Station Rd and right into Powell Lane; ground on the right.
Capacity: 1,000 **Seats:** 100 **Cover:** 150 **Floodlights:** No **Founded:** 1961
Local Newspapers: Northants Evening Telegraph, Northants Post.
Colours: Green and White. **Change Colours:** Green,Yellow and Black.
Prog: 16 pages with entry **Nickname:** The Wanderers **Midweek matchday:** Tuesday
Previous Lge: Kettering Amateur **Record Attendance:** 253 v Rothwell, May 1989
Past Players to progress to Football League: Shaun Wills (Peterborough)
Honours: UCL Div 1 R-up, Benevolent Cup R-up

COTTINGHAM

Chairman: Mike Beadsworth **Manager:** Rob Dunion. **Asst Manager:** Neil Burns.
Secretary: Lindsay Brownlie, 30 Bancroft Rd, Cottingham, Market Harborough LE16 8XA (01536 771009).
Ground: Berryfield Rd, Cottingham (01536 770051).
Directions: One and a half miles from Corby on A427 turn right to Cottingham. At junction of B670 turn left; Berryfield Road 200 yds on right.
Capacity: 1,000 **Seats:** None **Cover:** Yes **Floodlights:** No **Programme:** No
Reserves' Lge: UCL Res. Div. 2 **Clubhouse:** Bar & changing rooms **Founded:**
Colours: Yellow & Green **Change colours:** Orange & Black **Nickname:**
Sponsors: Sportsworld-Pipeline Construction.
Previous Leagues: Market Harborough/ Kettering Amateur/ East Midlands Alliance.
Honours: UCL Div 1 runners-up, Northants Junior Cup

DAVENTRY TOWN

Chairman: Ray Humphries **Manager/Coach:** Tony Perry **Asst Manager:** Jim Henderson
Secretary/Press Officer: Cliff Farthing, 45 The Fairway, Daventry, Northants NN11 4NW (01327 72149).
Ground: Elderstubbs Farm, Leamington Way, Daventry, Northants (01327 706286).
Directions: Adjacent to A45 by-pass at top of Staverton Road Sports Complex.
Capacity: 2,000 **Seats:** 250 **Cover:** 250 **Floodlights:** Yes **Founded:** 1886.
Programme: 4 Pages. **Local Newspapers:** Daventry Weekly Express, Herald & Post.
Colours: Black & white **Change colours:** Red & White **Nickname:** None.
Midweek Matchday: Tuesday **Reserve Team's League:** Central Northants Comb.
Clubhouse: Large bar/kitchen **Record Attendance:** 350 v Ford Sports 1991.
Best FA Cup year: Prel. Rd 94-95 **Best FA Vase year:** Preliminary Rd 91-92 94-95.
Previous Leagues: Northampton Town (pre-1987)/ Central Northants Combination 87-89.
Players Progressing to Football League: Martin Aldridge (Northampton).
Hons: UCL Div 1(2) 89-91 (Lg Cup R-up 92-93, Highest Aggregate Cup), Northants Junior Cup 36-37 60-61 91-92.

HARROWBY UNITED

Chairman: Robert Wilson **Manager:** Charlie Harvey **Coach:** Allan Bond
Secretary: Charlie Harvey, 64 Queensway, Grantham, Lincs NG31 9QD (01476 70255).
Ground: Harrowby Playing Fields, Harrowby Lane, Grantham (01476 590822).
Directions: From A1 take B6403, go past A52 roundabout, past Ancaster turn and take road to Harrowby. Continue into Grantham, ground on right opposite Cherry Tree public house.
Capacity: 1,500 **Seats:** 100 **Cover:** 150 **Floodlights:** No **Founded:** 1949.
Programme: 12 pages **Clubhouse:** Large bar open normal licensing hours.
Colours: Blue & white **Change colours:** Red & white. **Nickname:** Arrows.
Reserves' League: Grantham **Best FA Vase season:** Preliminary Round 91-92.
Previous Leagues: Grantham/ Lincs/ East Mids Regional Alliance (pre-1990).
Players progressing to Football League: Richard Liburd (Middlesbrough).
Hons: Utd Co's Lg Div 1 91-92 (Benev. Cup R-up 91-92), Mids Regional All. 89-90 (Lg Cup 89-90), Lincs Snr 'B' Cup(2) 90-92.

HIGHAM TOWN

Chairman: Richard Williams **Vice Chairman:** Robin James **President:** Robin James.
Secretary: Chris Ruff, 23 Queensway, Higham Ferrers NN10 8BU (01933 58862).
Manager: Gary Savage **Assistant Manager:** Alan Strickland
Coach: Kevin Roberts **Physio:** Keith Bates.
Ground: Recreation Ground, Vine Hill Drive, Higham Ferrers (01933 53751).
Directions: From Kettering 1st right on A6 after A45 junction to St Neots. From Bedford, 3rd left after entering town on A6 from Rushden. Higham is served by London-Bedford-Corby United Counties Coachlines, and United Counties local services Northampton-Raunds and Bedford-Kettering.
Capacity: 1,000 **Seats:** Nil **Cover:** 100 **Floodlights:** No **Founded:** 1895.
Programme: 12 pages with admission **Editor:** Secretary **Reformed:** 1920 & 1946
Colours: Sky/navy **Change colours:** Olive/white **Nickname:** Lankies.
Midweek home matches: Tuesday **Reserves' Lge:** UCL Reserve Div. **Sponsors:** Alpha Tankers
Previous Lges: Wellingborough 20-21/ Northants (now Utd Co's) 21-36/ Rushden 46-50.
Record Attandance: 5,700 v Chesterfield, FA Cup final qualifying round replay 22-23.
Previous Ground: Duchy Farm Field 20-24.
Record win: 15-0 v Towcester Town (H), United Counties League Division One 3/4/93.
Record defeat: 0-12 v Kettering Town (A), United Counties League 8/2/36.
Clubhouse: Open during season 8.30-11pm Tues, Thurs & Fri, after Saturday games & 12-1.30pm Sundays. Light refreshments available after Saturday games.
Record scorer: Stuart Sinfield 136 **Record appearances:** Brian Harbour 485.
Hons: UCL Div 1 R-up 70-71 71-72 92-93 94-95, Northants Lg 21-22 22-23 (R-up 23-24 26-27), Northants Snr Cup 21-22 (R-up 30-31 32-33), Maunsell Premier Cup 22-23 33-34.

HUNTINGDON UNITED

Chairman: John Hope **Manager:** Andy Ross
Secretary: Stephen Taresh, 41 maple drive, Huntingdon, Cambs. PE18 7JE. (01480 417146)
Ground: Sapley Park, Stoveley Close, Huntingdon. (01480 417202).
Capacity: 750 **Covered:** 100 **Seating:** No **Floodlights:** No **Year Formed:** 1949
Colours: Green/red/red. **Change Colours:** Red/green/green. **Club Captain 1995-96:** Gary Ling
Programme: Yes **Clubhouse:** Yes **Nickname:** None **Midweek matchday:** Tuesday

IRCHESTER UNITED

Chairman: Geoff Cotter
Secretary: Perry Mayhew, 52 Castle Way,Barton Seagrave,Northants (01536 518542)
Manager: Alan Ambridge. **Asst. Managers:** Derek Atkinson & Roy Geeves
Ground: Alfred Street, Irchester (01933 312877).
Directions: Off Rushden Road to Wollaston Road, next to recreation ground.
Capacity: 1,000 **Seats:** None **Cover:** Yes **Floodlights:** No **Programme:** No
Colours: Red & Blue **Change colours:** White & claret **Clubhouse:** Yes
Reserves' Lge: UCL Res. Div. 2 **Previous Leagues:** Rushden & District 1936-69.
Best FA Cup year: Prel. Rd 34-35 **Best FA Vase year:** Preliminary Round 77-78.
Hons: Northants Lg Div 2 30-31 31-32, Northants Snr Cup 29-30 48-49 75-76, Rushden & District Lg 28-29 29-30 36-37 46-47 50-51 51-52 56-57.

NORTHAMPTON O.N. CHENECKS

Chairman: John Wilson **Manager:** Tony Pancoust.
Secretary: John Goodger, 74 Beech Avenue, Northampton NN3 2JG (0604 717224).
Ground: Billing Road, Northampton (0604 34045).
Directions: South ring road, exit A43 Kettering, left at lights, top of hill, ground 200 yds on right.
Capacity: 1,350 **Seats:** Yes **Cover:** Yes **Floodlights:** No **Founded:** 1946.
Prog.: 16 pages with entry **Reserves' Lge:** UCL Res Div 1 **Clubhouse:** Yes
Colours: White & blue **Change colours:** All red
Prev. Lge: N'pton Town (pre-1969) **Hons:** UCL Div 1 77-78 79-80, Northants Jnr Cup R-up 93-94

NORTHAMPTON VANAID

Chairman: Rob Clarke **Manager:** Dick Underwood **Asst Manager:** Mick Calvert.
Secretary: Tony Loveday, 28 Rickyard Rd, The Arbours, Northampton NN3 3RR (0604 412502).
Ground: Fernie Fields, Moulton, Northampton (0604 670366).
Directions: R'bout at Lumbertub pub take turn to Moulton, 1st right signposted.
Capacity: 700 **Seats:** 100 **Cover:** Yes **Floodlights:** **Founded:** 1968
Programme: Yes **Programme Editor:** Tony Asker **Clubhouse:** Large bar. Hot food/bar meals
Colours: Blue/black/black **Change colours:** White & blue **Nickname:** Vans.
Prev. Lge: N'pton Town (pre-1993) **Reserves' Lge:** UCL Res Div 2 **Record Gate:** 78
Club Sponsors: Vanaid/ Crisis Couriers.
Honours: UCL Div 1 93-94 (Benevolent Cup R-up 93-94), Northants Jnr Cup 93-94, Northampton Town Lg 88-89 89-90.

OLNEY TOWN

Chairman: Peter Shipton **Manager:** Alan Byron **Asst Manager:** Barry Simons
Secretary: Andrew Baldwin, 49 Midland Road, Olney, Bucks MK46 4BP (0234 711071)
Ground: East Street, Olney (0234 712227)
Directions: Enter Olney on A509 from Wellingborough, 100yds on left enter East St, ground 200 yds on left.
Capacity: 2,000 **Seats:** None **Cover:** Yes **Floodlights:** No **Prog.:** 32 pages
Club colours: White & black **Change colours:** Green & yellow. **Clubhouse:** Yes
Prev. Lges: Nth Bucks, Rushden & Dist. **Hons:** UCL Div 1 72-73, Berks & Bucks I'mediate Cup 92-93

RAMSEY TOWN

Chairman: Ian Cooper **Vice-Chairman:** Syd Mortlock **President:** Albert Jones
Secretary: Mike Baldwin, 19 Slade Close, Ramsey, Cambs PE17 1LF (0487 814084).
Manager: Steve Jackson **Asst Manager:** Steve Long **Coach:** Simon Ward.
Physio: Danny Richardson **Press Officer:** Ian Cooper **Comm. Manager:** Hazel Dawson.
Ground: Cricketfield Lane, Ramsey, Huntingdon, Cambridgeshire PE17 1BG (0487 814218)
Directions: 100 yds off B1040 Ramsey to Warboys road.
Capacity: 1,000 **Seats:** None **Cover:** 50 **Floodlights:** Yes **Founded:**
Programme: 12 pages with admission **Editor:** Barry Colam (0487 812709) **Club Shop:** No.
Club colours: Amber & black **Change colours:** Red & white. **Nickname:** Rams
Sponsors: Burton Brothers Vauxhall **Previous Lge:** Peterborough & Dist. **Prev. Grounds:** None
Reserves' Lge: P'boro & Dist.
Player progressing to Football Lge: Alec Chamberlain (Sunderland)
Clubhouse: Weekdays 6-11pm, Sat 11am-11pm, Sun noon-10.30pm.
Record scorer: Jim Barron **Honours:** UCL Div 1, Hunts Senior Cup(3).

Irchester United FC: *Photo - Martin Wray*

Rothwell Corinthians *Photo - Martin Wray*

Boston Town FC:

ROTHWELL CORINTHIANS:

Chairman: Brian Johnson **President:**Terry Smith **Manager:** Dave McNish
Secretary: Bob Clelland, 5 Drake Close, Rothwell, Northants NN14 6DJ (01536 710134).
Ground: Seargeant's Lawn, Desborough Road, Rothwell (01536 418688)
Directions: A6 towards Desborough, on right opposite Greening Road.
Capacity: 100 **Seats:** Yes **Cover:** 100 **Floodlights:** No **Nickname:** Corinthians
Programme: Yes **Club House:** Yes **Club Shop:** No **Previous Lge:** East Midlands Alliance
Club colours: Red/white/black **Change colours:** Green/black **Honours:** East Midlands Alliance (2).

St IVES TOWN

President: Ken Booth **Chairman:** Stewart White **Manager:** Tony Coulson
Secretary: Jim Stocker, 23 Townsend Rd, Needingworth, St Ives, Cambs PE17 3SE (0480 492680).
Ground: Westwood Rd, St Ives, Cambs (0480 63207). **Directions:** From Huntingdon: A1123 thru Houghton, right at 2nd lighs into Ramsey Rd, after quarter mile turn right opp. Fire Station into Westwood Rd. From A604: Follow Huntingdon signs past 5 r'bouts, left into Ramsey Rd at lights then follow as above.
Capacity: 5,000 **Seats:** 130 **Cover:** 300 **Floodlights:** Yes **Founded:** 1887.
Club colours: White & black **Change cols:** Blue & white. **Club Shop:** No. **Nickname:** Saints
Reserves' Lge: UCL Res Div 2 **Clubhouse:** Bar and entertainment room. Normal licensing hours.
Midweek home matchday: Tuesday **Record Gate:** 400 v Saffron Walden Town, FA Vase.
Previous Ground: Meadow Lane **Prev. Lges:** Cambs/ Central Amtr/ Hunts/ P'boro. & D. (pre-1985).
Honours: Hunts Snr Cup 00-01 11-12 22-23 25-26 29-30 81-82 86-87 87-88, Cambs Lg 22-23 23-24 24-25.

SHARNBROOK

Chairman: Peter Butler **Manager:** Dick Williams **Asst Manager:** Roy Boulton
Secretary: Rob Stanton, 4 Towns End Rd, Sharnbrook, Beds (0234 782052).
Ground: Lodge Rd, Sharnbrook (0234 781080). **Directions:** Second sign to Sharnbrook from Rushden on A6, under railway bridge, right at T-junction, left past church, right into Lodge Road.
Capacity: 1,000 **Seats:** None **Cover:** Yes **Floodlights:** No **Programme:** 12 pages
Colours: Claret & blue **Change colours:** Yellow & black. **Clubhouse:** Yes
Reserves' Lge: UCL Res Div 2 **Previous Leagues:** Bedford & District (pre-1968).
Hons: Beds I'mediate Cup 73-74 **Player progressing to Football Lge:** Matt Jackson (Luton, Everton)

THRAPSTON TOWN

President: Denis Barber **Chairman:** David Morson
Secretary: Derek Pickard, 9 Springfield Ave., Thrapston, Northants (0832 734102)
Manager: Gary Petts **Asst Manager:** Peter Wills. **Press Officer:** Mark James.
Ground: Chancery Lane, Thrapston, Northants (08012 732470).
Directions: Chancery Lane off A605 in town centre.
Capacity: 1,000 **Seats:** Yes **Cover:** Yes **Floodlights:** No **Founded:** 1960.
Programme: Yes **Programme Editor:** Mrs A J Petts **Prev. Lge:** Kettering Amtr (pre-1978)
Colours: Blue & white **Change colours:** All yellow **Nickname:** Venturas **Clubhouse:** Yes
Honours: Northants Junior Cup 87-88, Kettering Amateur Lg 70-71 72-73 73-74 77-78.

WELLINGBOROUGH WHITWORTHS

Chairman: B Jarvis **Manager:** Ian Young **Asst Manager:** Martin Goodes.
Secretary: Ron Edwards, 15 James Rd, Wellingborough NN8 2LR (0933 227765).
Ground: London Road, Wellingborough, Northants (0933 227324). **Clubhouse:** Yes
Directions: Off London Road at Dog & Duck public house
Capacity: 700 **Seats:** None **Cover:** Yes **Floodlights:** No **Programme:** No
Colours: Blue & white **Change colours:** Green & white **Reserves' Lge:** UCL Res Div 2
Prev. Lges: Rushden & Dist./ E. Mids All. (pre-1985). **Honours:** Rushden & District Lg 76-77.

YAXLEY

President: F.S. Clark **Chairman:** Malcom Whaley **Manager:** Jimmy Watson
Secretary: Malcom Larrington, 70 Main Street, Yaxley, Peterborough PE7 3DB (01733 243276)
Ground: Holme Road, Yaxley (01733 244928). **Directions:** A1, then A15 at Norman Cross up to traffic lights, turn right then immediately right, follow road approx. 1 mile turn right into Holme Rd., ground approx. 200 yards on left.
Capacity: 1,000+ **Seats:** 150 **Cover:** Yes **Floodlights:** Yes **Programme:** Yes
Prev. Lge: Peterborough & District, Jewson Huntingdonshire, West Anglia.
Colours: Yellow/black **Change colours:** Blue/white
Honours: Hunts Senior Cup (4), Peterborough League (2), Peterborough Senior Cup (2), West Anglia League, Scott-Gatty Cup.

BOSTON TOWN F.C. 1996-97 (L-R) Back: *Bob Don-Duncan, Paul Martin, Paul Ward, Mark Collingwood, James Morgan, Richard Shaw, Lee Rippin, Ross Don-Duncan, Tom Watson, Andy Sandall, Shaughan Farrow.* FRONT: *Andy Mundell, Stuart Burns, Jason Callaby, Ian Shooter, Shaun Hanket, Gary Walters, Simon Dunlop. Photo: Bob Whitaker.*

WIMBORNE TOWN F.C. 1996-97 (L-R) Back: *Ryon Haigh, Steve Staples, Brett Phillips, Gareth Randall, Robbie Beacham, Peter Howard, Andy Taplin, Mark Turner, Kriastian Weller, Matty White.*
Front: *Mike Glavin, Richard Glenister, Michael White, Martin Beardsley, Andy Frost, Ossie O"Hara, Kevin Leonard. Photo: Keith Clayton.*

JEWSON WESSEX LEAGUE

FEEDER TO: BEAZER HOMES LEAGUE

President/Chairman: Alf Peckham

Vice Chairman: Cyril Hurlock

Hon: Secretary: Trevor Brock, 2 Betula Close, Waterloovile, Hampshire, PO7 8EJ (01705 262367)

It seems an awfully long time ago that the League programme commenced on August 19th and I remember the "shock" of the opening day being, newcomers Whitchurch United making a winning return to the JWL by beating Wimborne 4-3, since when a great deal has happened.

As usual in August and September interest centred around the FA Cup, AFC Totton provided an early giant killing when they saw off last years champions Fleet Town but by the 2nd Qualifying Round our last hopes Thatcham had bowed out to Buckingham Town. In the Vase our hopes lasted much longer but only as a result of the resilience of AFC Lymington who made it to Round 4 before losing to Cornish side Torpoint. Our standing in the Pyramid is often judged by our clubs performances in the two major FA competitions and being blunt we didn't do ourselves justice in 1995-96!

The League table as at the last Saturday in September makes interesting reading, in the First Division Bournemouth are placed first with Lymington second and Ryde third. Eventual champions were Thatcham stranded in mid-table. Eastleigh didn't take over top-spot in the Combination Division until early December but from that date there was no doubt that they would win the division. Thatcham went to the top of Division One on the first Saturday in November and stayed there until a spell of bad weather allowed Lymington to take over.

The weather was reasonably kind to us this year and several clubs and officials were muttering that fixtures would be over by March but Derek Hawkins experience proved itself again and almost everyone was playing right up to the end. The race for the Championship started in earnest at the end of January with AFC Lymington and Thatcham Town out in the clear but with Ryde in contention. Eastleigh Res still led the Combination Division with many games in hand, and they wrapped up the title a month before the season closed. By May 4th Division One was a two horse race, Lymington had to win their final game at Aerostructures, which they duly accomplished but eventually lost out to Thatcham Town who clinched their first ever League crown in front of 400 excited fans at Waterside Park. Unfortunately the League was unable to recommend our Champions, on grounds of grading, for promotion to the Southern League but 3rd placed Ryde would have "got the nod" had they finished in the top two.

The Wessex League Cup Final was staged at Bemerton on the May Bank Holiday and was won by Downton, on penalties, thus upsetting the majority of the crowd of 420 supporting runners-up Wimborne. BAT Res won a one-sided Combination Cup Final 7-0 over Downton Res.

On a sadder note, two stalwarts of this League were mourned in the second half of the season. Jack Barter, our Past President, and one of the founders of the League was a great loss as his experience and advice wll be sadly missed. Within weeks we were hit by the death of Joe Reed, 'Mr East Cowes Vic'. Both these Gentlemen of Football were known and respected throughout our League and we are the poorer for their passing.

Thatcham Town - Jewson Wessex League Champions at the 10th attempt. *Photo - Newbury Weekly News*

FINAL LEAGUE TABLE 1995/96

DIVISION ONE		Home					Away					
	P	*W*	*D*	*L*	*F*	*A*	*W*	*D*	*L*	*F*	*A*	*Pts*
1. Thatcham Town	40	13	4	3	30	13	15	4	1	43	14	92
2. AFC Lymington	40	14	4	2	54	15	14	3	3	46	16	91
3. Ryde	40	15	2	3	65	20	10	6	4	27	21	83
4. Eastleigh	40	12	6	2	38	19	9	7	4	45	31	76
5. Christchurch	40	9	6	5	31	23	12	2	6	35	26	71
6. Wimborne Town	40	12	3	5	52	28	8	3	9	33	33	66
7. Bournemouth	40	9	8	3	44	20	8	5	7	41	20	64
8. Bemerton Hth Har	40	12	4	4	43	25	6	4	10	24	38	62
9. Andover	40	8	4	8	61	43	10	3	7	40	27	61
10. East Cowes Vic	40	12	3	5	34	21	5	5	10	26	39	59
11. Gosport Borough	40	4	6	10	20	31	12	3	5	39	27	57
12. Downton	40	8	3	9	31	34	8	3	9	34	39	54
13. Whitchurch United	40	6	6	8	39	42	6	7	7	27	34	49
14 A F C Totton	40	4	6	10	24	35	6	7	7	31	31	43
15. B.A.T.	40	8	4	8	25	29	2	8	10	19	29	42
16. Cowes Sports	40	5	6	9	18	26	6	1	13	20	50	40
17. Portsmouth R N	40	4	3	13	19	39	6	5	9	33	45	38
18. Aerostructures	40	3	6	11	19	36	6	4	10	22	35	37
19. Brockenhurst	40	9	0	11	27	30	2	4	14	15	44	37
20. Petersfield Town	40	4	3	13	23	40	4	1	15	30	53	28
21. Swanage & Her	40	3	1	16	16	77	3	3	14	16	61	22

DIVISION ONE RESULTS CHART 1995-96

HOME TEAM	1	2	3	4	5	6	7	8	9	10	11	12	13	14	15	16	17	18	19	20	21
1. A/structures	*	0-5	1-2	1-2	0-0	3-0	0-5	1-1	0-0	5-0	1-2	1-1	1-1	0-1	1-0	0-6	0-1	1-3	1-2	2-2	0-2
2. Lymington	0-0	*	0-1	1-0	0-0	5-1	2-1	0-0	3-0	7-1	4-2	3-1	2-0	2-0	6-3	5-0	3-0	6-0	1-2	1-1	3-2
3. AFC Totton	1-1	1-2	*	0-2	2-1	1-2	0-2	1-2	0-6	0-3	3-1	3-3	2-2	2-3	2-1	0-0	0-0	6-0	0-2	0-0	0-2
4. Andover	1-2	4-2	3-3	*	1-1	4-5	2-0	5-0	3-4	3-4	5-0	2-1	3-7	1-2	5-1	8-2	2-2	8-0	0-4	1-1	0-2
5. BAT Sports	1-3	1-4	2-1	1-1	*	1-0	2-0	1-0	1-3	3-0	2-1	0-2	1-2	3-4	0-0	0-0	2-0	2-1	0-2	0-3	2-2
6. Bemerton HH	4-0	0-3	1-0	1-1	1-1	*	1-1	4-2	2-1	2-0	3-1	4-0	2-4	1-0	1-0	4-0	4-3	3-1	2-3	1-2	2-2
7. Bournemouth	5-1	1-1	1-1	1-2	0-0	4-0	*	2-0	2-3	5-0	2-2	3-1	1-3	5-0	2-1	0-0	1-1	4-0	1-1	1-1	3-2
8. Brockenhurst	2-0	0-1	1-3	0-3	3-2	2-0	0-2	*	0-3	1-2	2-0	2-0	0-1	0-2	4-2	4-3	0-1	2-0	0-3	1-2	3-0
9. Christchurch	1-2	1-0	3-1	3-3	0-2	1-1	0-0	2-0	*	3-1	0-0	1-1	3-2	2-2	2-1	2-0	0-1	2-0	2-4	1-2	2-0
10. Cowes Sports	2-0	0-2	0-0	1-0	1-1	0-0	3-4	3-1	0-1	*	0-1	0-0	1-0	0-0	1-4	0-4	2-2	2-0	0-2	0-1	2-3
11. Downton	3-3	0-3	1-1	2-4	1-0	3-0	0-4	1-0	0-1	0-1	*	4-2	1-1	1-2	2-0	1-3	0-2	5-2	1-3	3-2	2-0
12. East Cowes V	1-0	0-4	3-2	2-0	1-0	2-1	0-1	2-1	4-0	1-0	1-2	*	2-2	1-2	6-1	1-1	0-1	2-0	2-2	2-1	1-0
13. Eastleigh	1-0	1-1	1-1	3-1	1-1	2-0	0-4	4-0	2-1	1-1	3-0	2-1	*	0-0	3-2	3-2	1-3	4-0	0-0	3-0	3-1
14. Gosport Boro	1-2	0-3	0-0	3-2	2-1	2-0	1-1	2-5	0-0	0-1	0-0	0-3	1-3	*	0-2	0-2	0-0	1-2	0-2	5-0	2-2
15. Petersfield T	0-2	0-3	4-5	1-4	2-0	1-3	1-0	1-1	0-1	1-3	1-3	0-1	2-1	0-2	*	5-1	0-2	2-2	1-4	1-1	0-1
16. Portsm/th RN	0-2	1-2	1-2	0-1	2-1	1-4	1-0	1-1	0-1	2-1	1-3	2-3	1-2	0-5	0-5	*	1-3	0-0	0-1	2-2	3-0
17. Ryde Sports	3-1	2-0	2-1	1-4	4-1	3-2	3-3	7-0	6-1	3-0	2-1	5-1	1-1	1-2	6-0	4-0	*	5-0	0-1	3-1	4-0
18. Swanage T	2-2	0-3	1-5	0-5	1-5	0-1	0-11	2-1	0-4	3-0	1-9	0-2	0-5	2-6	0-4	1-3	1-3	*	0-3	2-1	0-4
19. Thatcham Tn	3-0	1-3	1-0	3-0	0-0	0-0	1-0	2-0	1-0	3-0	0-1	2-0	2-2	1-0	2-1	3-1	0-0	2-0	*	2-0	1-5
20. Whitchurch	2-1	1-1	2-2	0-4	3-0	1-2	1-1	2-0	2-4	5-1	3-4	3-1	3-4	0-4	3-1	3-3	1-2	3-3	1-1	*	0-3
21. Wimborne	2-0	2-3	3-0	3-1	4-2	2-2	2-1	1-0	0-1	2-1	5-1	2-2	2-2	5-2	7-1	1-2	3-0	1-2	2-1	3-4	*

Leading Goalscorers:

Division One;	Darren Pitter	AFC Lymington	44
	Andy Sampson	Ryde	27
	Jamie Sturgess	Wimborne Town	24
	Darren McBride	Bournemouth	23
	Gareth Barnes	Christchurch	23
	Jamie O'Rourke	Ryde	22
Combination;	Steve Jones	AFC Totton	23

JEWSON WESSEX Ten Year Records

	86/7	87/8	88/9	89/0	90/1	91/2	92/3	93/4	94/5	95/6
Aerostructures Spts & Soc	-	13	10	12	16	9	12	19	17	18
AFC Lymington	-	-	5	5	9	2	1	3	8	2
AFC Totton	3	8	14	6	14	17	16	21	9	14
Andover	-	-	-	-	-	-	-	2	7	9
Bashley	1	1	1	-	-	-	-	-	-	-
BAT Sports	-	-	-	3	8	16	18	9	13	15
Bemerton Heath Harl.	-	-	-	8	18	8	3	7	5	8
Bournemouth	15	10	12	10	3	6	7	11	2	7
Brockenhurst	17	18	16	17	7	12	10	8	6	19
Christchurch	-	5	13	15	15	13	13	10	18	5
Cowes Sports	-	-	-	-	-	-	-	-	15	16
Downton	-	-	-	-	-	-	-	16	20	12
E Cowes Vict. Ath.	-	9	8	13	13	14	20	14	16	10
Eastleigh	8	12	9	14	12	10	9	15	14	4
Fleet Town	-	-	-	18	10	11	8	6	1	-
Gosport Borough	-	-	-	-	-	-	5	5	10	11
Havant Town	5	2	2	11	1	-	-	-	-	-
Horndean	14	14	11	16	20	18	11	17	22	-
Lymington Town	10	19	(See AFC Lymington)							
Newport IOW	4	4	3	2	-	-	-	-	-	-
Petersfield Town	-	-	-	-	-	-	-	18	21	20
Portals Athletic	12	-	-	-	-	-	-	-	-	-
Portsmouth Royal Navy	13	16	17	19	17	19	17	13	11	17
Romsey Town	16	3	7	1	4	4	21	-	-	-
Road Sea Southampton	2	-	-	-	-	-	-	-	-	-
Ryde Sports	-	-	-	-	11	7	6	12	12	3
Sholing Sports	9	7	15	9	19	15	19	w/d		
Steyning Town	11	17	-	-	-	-	-	-	-	-
Swanage Town & Her.	-	-	-	-	2	5	14	20	19	21
Thatcham Town	6	11	4	7	6	3	4	4	3	1
Wellworthy Ath.	7	11	(See AFC Lymington)							
Whitchurch United	-	-	-	-	-	-	15	22	-	13
Wimborne Town	-	6	6	4	5	1	2	1	4	6
No of Clubs Competing	17	19	17	19	20	19	21	22	22	21

JEWSON WESSEX LEAGUE CUP 1995-96

First Round Aggreagate Results;

Andover v Whitchurch United	6-2	Downton v Swanage Town & Hersham	3-1
Gosport Borough v Cowes Sports	7-3	Thatcham Town v AFC Totton	5-2
Wimborne Town v Bournemouth	8-2		

Second Round Aggregate Results;

Aerostructures v Bemerton Heath Harl.	2-0	Brockenhurst v Petersfield Town	7-4
Downton v Gosport Borough	5-2	East Cowes Victoria v Christchurch	6-2
AFC Lymington v Andover	8-3	Portsmouth RN v B.A.T. Sports	4-2
Thatcham Town v Eastleigh	3-2	Wimborne Town v Ryde	5-4

Quarter Final Aggregate Results;

Brockenhurst v Thatcham Town	5-3	Downton v Aerostructures	*2-2
Portsmouth RN v East Cowes Victoria	4-1	Wimborne Town v AFC Lymington	4-2

** Away goals rule applied.*

Semi-Final Aggregate Results;

Downton v Brockenhurst	4-2	Wimborne Town v Portsmouth RN	4-1

FINAL; Downton v Wimborne Town 1-1, (3-2 penalties).

AEROSTRUCTURES SPORTS & SOCIAL CLUB

Chairman: Alastair Tritten, 51 Coach Road, Hamble, Southampton. SO31 4LA. 01703 452432
Secretary: Richard Phippard, 198 Butts Road, Sholing, Southampton. SO19 1BP.
01703 438413 (H) 01703 338286 (B)
Manager: Steve Beck **General Manager:** Nigel Kent
Ground: Folland Park, Kings Avenue, Hamble (01703 452173).
Directions: M27 junction 8, then B3397 to Hamble. One and a half miles from Hamble (BR); turn right out of station, proceed for one mile then turn right into Queens Avenue. Ground 50 yards on right.
Midweek Matches: Tues (1st team), Wed (Res) **Previous Name:** Folland Sports (pre-1990).
Colours: White/white/red **Change colours:** Red/black/white. **Floodlights:** Yes
Record defeat: 1-10 v Andover (A), Wessex League 93-94.
Clubhouse: 300 capacity social club. Tennis, bowls, hockey.
Honours: Hants Lg Div 3 80-81 (Div 4 79-80), Hants Intermediate Cup 79-90, Southampton Snr Cup(4).

(A.F.C.) LYMINGTON

Chairman: John Mills **V-Chairmen:** R.Millbery. **President:** Jack Holliday
Secretary: John Osey, 9 Samphire Close, Lymington, Hants SO41 6EB (01590 676995).
Manager: Derek Binns **Asst Manager:** Tony Morris. **Physio:** Alan Farrar
Ground: Lymington Sports Ground, Southampton Road, Lymington (01590 671305).
Directions: M27 jct 1, follow signs (A337) to Lymington via Lyndhurst and Brockenhurst, ground 250yds on left after 1st set of lights on entering town. 1 mile from Lymington Town BR station.
Seats: 200 **Cover:** 200 **Capacity:** 3,000 **Floodlights:** Yes **Club Shop:** Yes
Programme: 48 pages, 60p **Editor/Press Officer:** John Mills (01590 682830).
Colours: Red & black/Black/Red. **Change colours:** Yellow/green/green.
Founded: 1988 **Nickname:** Linnets **Sponsors:** Monitor Business Magazine.
Midweek Matches: Tuesday. **Reserve Team's League:** Jewson Wessex Combination.
Record Attendance: 2,900 v Karen Mills Memorial Day 12.3.95
Best FA Cup season: 3rd Qualifying Rd 92-93 (lost 0-1 at home to Cheltenham).
Players progressing to Football League: Stuart Doling (Doncaster Rovers), Russell Perrett (Portsmouth).
Clubhouse: Sat 2-7pm training and match nights. Rolls, hot pies.
95-96 Captain: Graham Kemp. **95-96 P.o.Y.:** Graham Kemp. **95-96 Top Scorer:** Darren Pitter 54.
Club Record Scorer: Darren Pitter 173. **Club Record Appearances:** Glen Limburn 329.
Honours: Wessex Lg 92-93 (R-up 91-92 95-96), Wessex Lg Cup 88-89 (R-up 94-95), Wessex Comb. 92-93, Hants Snr Cup R-up 89-90, Texaco Cup 91-92, Bournemouth Snr Cup 92-93, Russell Cotes Cup 93-94 94-95 (R-up 91-92 92-93), Pickford Cup R-up 92-93. As Lymington Town: Russell Cotes Cup 35-36. Bournemouth Snr Cup 83-84 (R-up 69-71 84-85), Hants Lg Div 2 R-up 83-84, Hants Lg Div 3 67-68 (Div 2 R-up 82-83). As Wellworthy Ath: Bournemouth Snr Cup 87-88 (R-up 53-54), Hants Intermediate Cup 56-57 84-85, Pickford Cup 84-85, Bournemouth Lg 84-85, Hants Lg Div 3 R-up 85-86.

(A.F.C.) TOTTON

Chairman: Bob Devoy 01703 324477 **Vice Chairman:** Mr P Maiden **President:** Mr D Maton.
Secretary: Mrs Sheila Benfield, 35 Fishers Rd, Totton, Southampton SO4 4HW (01703 865421).
Manager: Eddie Harper **Asst Manager/Coach:** TBA
Commercial Mgr: Mr E Ffister **Press Officer:** Mr P Chilcott (01703 860453).
Ground: Testwood Park, Testwood Place, Totton, Southampton (01703 868981).
Directions: 5 mins walk from Totton station. Turn off r'bout in Totton centre into Library Rd, then 1st left & 2nd rd.
Seats: 200 **Cover:** 250 **Capacity:** 2,500 **Floodlights:** Yes **Founded:** 1886
Record Gate: 600 v Windsor & Eton, F.A. Cup 4th Qualifying Rd 82-83.
Sponsors: Burger Rack **Midweek Matches:** Wednesday **Nickname:** Stags.
Colours: Blue & white halves/blue/blue **Change colours:** Green & White/Black/Green
Club Shop: No **Programme:** 30 pages with admission
Previous Name: Totton FC (until merger with Totton Athletic in 1979).
Previous League: Hants 1886-1986 **Previous Grounds:** Downs Park/ Mayfield Park.
Clubhouse: Open for matches and training sessions. Burgers, sandwiches, tea, coffee, biscuits etc available.
Honours: Hants Lg(2)

ANDOVER

Chairman: Trevor Mitchell **President:** R Coleman
Secretary: Chris Jeremy, 23 Stubbs Court, Artists Way, Andover, Hampshire. SP10 3QR.
01264 361973 (H) 01980 678643 (B) Fax: 01264 391341.
Manager: Ken Cunningham-Brown **Asst Manager:** Mike Burford **Physio:** Terry Carr.
Ground: Portway Stadium, West Portway Industrial Estate, Andover SP10 3LF (01264 333052).
Directions: From the Andover By-pass A303 follow the signs to Portway Industrial estate. On exiting the A303 turn right at r/about and over bridge, bear off left at next mini r/about and after 150yards turn right onto estate. head straight on until you enter Hopkinson Way, ground on left 400/500 yards.
Capacity: 3,000 **Cover:** 250 **Seats:** 250 **Floodlights:** Yes **Club Shop:** No.
Programme: 50 pages, 50p **Editor:** **Metal Badges:** Yes.
Colours: Red & black shirts/black/red **Change cols:** Blue & white/white/white
Founded: 1883. **Nickname:** The Lions. **Sponsors:** Hospital Saving Association.
Midweek home matchday: Tuesday **Reserve Team's League:** None.
Record Attendance: 1,100 v Leicester, ground opening. *(3,484 v Gillingham at Walled Meadow, previous ground).*
Best FA Cup season: 1st Rd 62-63 (lost 0-1 to Gillingham).
Best FA Trophy season: 3rd Qualifying Rd 69-70 70-71.
Best FA Vase season: Fourth Round 94-95 (lost 1-3 at Falmouth Town)
Prev. Lges: Salisbury & D./ Hants 1896-98 99-1901 02-62/ Southern 1898-99 1971-93/ Western 1962-71.
Players progressing to Football League: Keith Wilson (Soton 1959), Nigel Spackman (B'mouth 1980), Colin Court (Reading 1981), A Kingston (Soton), P Brown (Soton, Walsall), Emeka Nwajiobi (Luton).
Clubhouse: Open matchdays & private functions
Club Record Scorer: T Randall 73 **Club Record Appearances:** P Pollard 469
Honours: Wessex Lg R-up 94-95, Western Lg R-up 69-70 70-71, Hants Lg 13-14 24-25 33-34 44-45 48-49 50-51 61-62 (R-up 42-43, Northern Div 13-14, Div 2 R-up 37-38, Salisbury & Dist Lg 1894-95 95-96 96-97 99-1900 03-04 07-08 12-13, Hants Sen Cup 48-49 50-51 55-56 64-65, Russell Cotes Cup 23-24 31-32 37-38 44-45 52-53 58-59 60-61 61-62, Pickfords Cup 50-51, Hants Interm Cup 59-60 60-61, Hants Junior Cup 19-20 (R-up 1894-95 1910-11 12-13).

B.A.T. SPORTS

Chairman: Mr D Batt **Manager:** Derek Dempsey & Gary Grant
Secretary: M.Geddes 136 Regents Park Rd,Southampton SO15 8PD (01703 325224(h) 01703 793420(w)
Ground: BAT Sports Ground, Southern Gdns, off Ringwood Road, Totton (01703 862143).
Directions: Into centre of Totton, proceed up Ringwood Rd past small r'bout, 2nd left into Southern Gardens. Half mile from Totton (BR), bus X2 (Southampton-Bournemouth).
Seats: 150. **Cover:** 150. **Capacity:** 3,000 **Floodlights:** Yes
Colours: All Blue **Change:** Coral & Purple stripes/purple/purple.
Programme: 8-10 pages, 30p
Founded: 1925 **Midweek Matches:** Tuesday
Best FA Vase year: Extra-Preliminary Rd 91-92
Clubhouse: Normal licensing hrs, all day for members' sports facilities. Darts, pool, CD player. Hot & cold snacks.

BEMERTON HEATH HARLEQUINS

Chairman: George Parker **President:** Peter Say.
Secretary: Andy Hardwick, 2 Ashley Rd., Salisbury, Wilts. SP2 7LW. 01722 333015.
Manager: Steve Slade **Coach:** Gary Cross
Asst. Manager: Kevin Franklyn. **Physio:** Andy Nash
Ground: Western Way, Bemerton Heath, Salisbury, Wilts (01722 331925).
Directions: Turn off A36 Salisbury-Bristol Rd at Skew Bridge (right turn if coming out of Salisbury), 1st left into Pembroke Rd for half mile, 2nd left along Western Way - ground quarter mile at end. 40 mins walk from Salisbury (BR) station. Bus 351 or 352 from city centre stops at junction of Pembroke Rd/ Western Way.
Clubhouse: Yes **Seats:** 155. **Cover:** 350 **Floodlights:** Yes **Founded:** May 1989
Previous Names: Bemerton Athletic, Moon FC & Bemerton Boys; all merged in 1989.
Previous Leagues: B'ton Ath.: Salis. & Wilts Comb., Moon: Salis. & Andover Sunday, B'ton Boys: Mid Wilts.
Colours: Black & white/black/black & white **Change colours:** Amber/white/white
Nickname: Quins **Programme:** 32 pages, 50p **Midweek Home Matches:** Tuesday
Record Gate: 1,118 v Aldershot Town F.A.Cup Ist Qual.RD.Aug.94.
Club record appearances: Keith Richardson.
Hons: Wilts Snr Cup 92-93. *Wilts Lg(3) as Bemerton Athletic*

BOURNEMOUTH

Chairman: Vic C Dominey **Vice Chairman:** J B Wood **President:** D Nippard
Secretary: D. Hawkins, 12 Bloomfield Avenue, Moordown, Bournemouth. BH9 1UA (01202 525914)
Manager: Alex Pike **Asst Manager:** Nick Jennings **Coach:** Chris Weller
Physio: Irvin Brown **Comm. Manager:** Alex Pike **Press Officer:** Mark Willis.
Ground: Victoria Park, Namu Rd., Winton, Bournemouth, Dorset (01202 515123).
Directions: Any bus to Wimborne Road, Winton. 2 miles from Bournemouth Central (BR).
Seats: 250 **Cover:** 250 **Capacity:** 3,000 **Floodlights:** Yes **Founded:** 1875.
Colours: Red & White Shirts/Red/Red **Change colours:** Green & Yellow/Green/Green
Programme: 58 pages, 50p **Programme Editor:** Mark Willis **Club Shop:** No.
Sponsors: Chapel Carpets **Midweek Matches:** Tuesday **Prev. Lge:** Hants.
Previous Ground: Dene Park 1888-90 **Local Newspaper:** Evening Echo. **Rec. Gate:** Unknown
Reserves' Lge: Jewson Wessex Comb. **Record fee rec.:** £1,500 for Chike Onourah (Wimborne 93-94)
Previous Names: Bournemouth Rovers 1875-88/ Bournemouth Dene Park 1888-90.
Clubhouse: Open daily 7-11pm. Sandwiches & hot snacks (burgers, chips etc).
Nickname: Poppies. **Club record scorer:** B Head
Hons: Hants Lg 13-13 21-22, B'mouth Snr Cup 66-67 89-90, Texaco F'lit Cup R-up 91-92, Hant I'mediate Cup 49-50 69-70, Hants Yth Cup 54-55 57-58 67-68.

BROCKENHURST

Chairman: Bob Philpott **Manager:** Cliff Huxford.
Secretary: Peter Lawford, 22 Fathersfield, Brockenhurst, Hampshire. (01590 623772)
Ground: Grigg Lane, Brockenhurst, Hants (01590 23544).
Directions: 400 yds from Brockenhurst station, just off main shopping area.
Seats: 200 **Cover:** 300 **Capacity:** 2,000 **Floodlights:** Yes **Founded:** 1898
Midweek Matches: Wednesday. **Clubhouse:** Every evening plus Tues, Sat & Sun lunchtimes.
Colours: White with navy pin stripe/navy/navy **Change colours:** All red.
Programme: 12 pages, 20p, **Editor:** C Fisher **Prev. League:** Hants 24-26 47-86
Hons: Hants I'mediate Cup 61-62, B'mouth Snr Cup 60-61, Hants Lg 75-76 (R-up 73-74 79-80, Div 2 70-71 (R-up 60-61), Div 3 59-60), F.A. Amateur Cup 2nd Rd 73-74.

CHRISTCHURCH

Chairman: Mick Ryan. **Vice Chairman:** Jan Bridle. **President:** Dennis James.
Secretary: Mrs D Page, 87 Albany Manor Road, Bournemouth BH1 3EJ (01202 551977).
Manager: Ian Kelly. **Asst Manager:** No appointment. **Physio:** Brian Finch
Ground: Christchurch Sporting Club, Hurn Bridge, Avon Causeway, Christchurch (0202 473792).
Directions: A338 from Ringwood, turn off signed Hurn Airport on left. Before Airport use mini roundabout & take exit signed to Sopley and ground is immediately on the right. 3 miles from Christchurch (BR).
Seats: 215 **Cover:** 265 **Capacity:** 2,000 **Floodlights:** Yes
Programme: 16 pages, 50p **Editor:** Phil Old **Press Officer:** Dennis James.
Colours: All royal blue (white trim) **Change colours:** All yellow
Sponsors: Franklin Transport **Nickname:** Priory **Founded:** 1885
Midweek Matches: Wednesday **Previous League:** Hampshire.
Players progressing to Football Lge: Jody Craddock (Cambridge Utd 1993), Dan West (Aston Villa, 1994).
Clubhouse: Normal pub hours. Cooked food at lunchtimes.
95-96 Captain: Steve Joyce **95-96 Top Scorer:** Gareth Barnes **95-96 P.o.Y.:** Neil Massie
Club record appearances: John Haynes.
Honours: Hants Jnr Cup 1892-93 1911-12 20-21, Hants Int. Cup 86-87, Pickford Cup 1991, Hants Lg Div 2 37-38 47-48 85-86 (Div 3 56-57), B'mouth Snr Cup(5) 56-57 59-60 67-70, B'mouth Page-Croft Cup 94-95.

Cowes Sports: Back Row (L-R); Danny Case, James Hutchinson, Calum McInnes, Malcolm Cole, Steve Mumford, Lee Dent, Pete Jeffery (Trainer), Pete Young (Coach). Front Row; Dale Young (Player/Mgr), Glynn Taylor, Andy Watson, Iain Stevens, Shaun North, Kevin Morris, Ashley Wright. *Photo - Roger Turner*

Petersfield Town FC *Photo - Andrew Chitty*

Andover: Back Row (L-R); P O'Riordan, J Collins, D Fern, S Wiltshire, M Barrett. Front Row; C Goddard, G Lewis, P Hunt, S Wheeler, J Gomersall, J Purkiss.

COWES SPORTS

Chairman: Ray Sleep, 100 Upper Moor Green Rd., Cowes, I.o.W. PO31 7LY. (01983 294445).
Secretary: Mr W G Murray, 53 Park Rd, Cowes, Isle of Wight PO31 7LY (01983 294445).
Manager: Dale Young.
Ground: Westwood Park, Reynolds Close, off Park Rd, Cowes, Isle of Wight (01983 293793).
Directions: Take Park Road out of Cowes centre. Reynolds Close is a right turn half mile up hill.
Capacity: **Seats:** Yes **Cover:** Stand **Floodlights:** Yes **Founded:**
Cols: Blue & white stripes/black/blue **Change colours:** All red
Previous League: Hampshire (pre-1994) **Previous Grounds:** None **Midweek Fixtures:** Wednesday
Best FA Cup season: Fourth Qualifying Round replay 57-58 (lost 1-4 at Trowbridge after 2-2 draw).
Honours: Hampshire Lg 93-94.

DOWNTON

Chairman: Trevor Halski. **President:** R Tanner
Secretary: Brian Trent, 21 Fison Walk, Bishopdown, Salisbury, Wilts. SP1 3JF. (01722 323097 H & B)
Manager: P Moore **Coach:** E Lane **Physio:** T Ship
Ground: Brian Whitehead Sports Ground, Wick Lane, Downton (01725 512162)
Directions: Travelling south from Salisbury on A338, 7 miles, turn right into Wick Lane (opposite the turn for village centre). Ground is 1/4 mile on left.
Capacity: 1600 **Seats:** 250 **Cover:** Nil **Flodlights:** Yes **Club Shop:** No
Programme: Yes **Editor:** J Blake **Press Officer:**
Colours: All red **Change colours:** All blue.
Sponsor: Lex Vauxhall Salisbury **Nickname:** The Robins **Founded:** 1905
Midweek Matchday: Wednesday **Youth League:** Southampton Yth Lge
Previous League: Bournemouth, Hants (pre-1993).
Clubhouse: Bar with kitchen facilities.
Honours: Wilts Sen Cup 79-80 80-81, (R-up 55-56 91-92 94-95); Wilts Jun Cup 49-50; Bournemouth Sen Lge 60 61 62 64 65 67 68, Sen Lge Cup 61-62 63-64 66-67, Cup 62-63 79-80; Wessex Lge Cup 95-96; Wessex Comb Cup (R-up 95-96); Russell Cotes Cup 95-96; Hayward Cup 64-65.

EAST COWES VICTORIA ATHLETIC

President: T. Thomas. **Chairman:** Steve Stay. **Vice-Chairman:** M Everett.
Secretary: Lee Bray, 57 Grange Road, East Cowes, I.O.W. PO32 6DY (01983 200276).
Ground: Beatrice Avenue Ground, East Cowes, I.O.W. (01938 297165).
Manager: D'Ohren. **Coach:** D. Bardell. **Physios:** M. Reed & R. Mitchell.
Directions: From the ferry: 1 mile from town centre on lower main road to Newport or Ryde, near Whippingham Church adjacent to Osborne Middle School.
Seats: 200 **Cover:** 400 **Capacity:** 4,000 **Floodlights:** Yes **Founded:** 1968.
Midweek Matches: Wednesday **Sponsors:** Bishops Insurance. **Club Shop:** No.
Previous Names: East Cowes Victoria (founded 1888) merged with East Cowes Athletic in 1968.
Previous Leagues: (E.C. Vics): I.O.W. 1898-19 21-47/ Hants 14-21 47-87.
Record win: 9-0 v Brading Town (A), Hampshire Lg 86-87.
Record defeat: 0-10 v Andover (A), Wessex Lg 94-95.
Colours: Red & white stripes/black/red **Change colours:** Blue/white/blue. **Nickname:** Vics.
Programme: 14 pages, 30p **Programme Editor:** Darren Dyer (01983 297488).
Record Gate: 2,000 v Poole Town, FA Cup 1954
Clubhouse: Yes, open most evenings and matchdays. Crisps and confectionary available.
Midweek home matchday: Wednesday **Reserve team's League:** Isle of Wight Lge.
Player progressing to Football League: Gareth Williams (Aston Villa, via Gosport Borough, 1987).
Club record appearances: Joe Reed.
Honours: (as East Cowes Vics pre-'68): Wessex Lg Cup 87-88, IOW Senior Gold Cup 79-80 81-82 82-83 83-84 84-85 85-86 88-89, Hants Lg 85-86 86-87 (Div 2 52-53 82-83, Div 3 63-64 71-72, Div 3 West 47-48), IOW Lg 1898-99 99-1900 30-31 34-35 78-79 82-83 86-87 87-88 94-95 (Div 2 1898-99 1904-05 06-07, Div 3 28-29 32-33, Comb Div 2 87-88 90-91,94-95 IOW Chal. Cup 1899-1900 00-01 01-02 19-20 47-48 50-51 51-52 52-53 80-81 84-85 87-88 90-91 91-92, IOW Mem. Cup 19-20 32-33 82-83 87-88 90-91, Brooklyn Cup 86-87 87-88 89-90 91-92, IOW Charity Cup 23-24 25-26, IOW Centenary Cup 89-90 91-92.

EASTLEIGH

Chairman: Bruce McLaren. **President:** Phil Fernandez.
Secretary: Reg G Kearslake, 10 Binsey Close, Millbrook, Southampton, Hants SO16 4AQ (01703 779545).
Manager: Roger Sherwood. **Asst Manager:** Paul Smith. **Physio:** Barry Wilkinson.
Press Officer: Tommy Whale. **Commercial Manager:** Vic Holland.
Ground: 'Ten Acres', Stoneham Lane, North Stoneham, Eastleigh SO50-9HT(01703 613361).
Directions: M27 to Jct 5, to r'bout - exit marked Stoneham Lane, ground on left but carry on to r'bout and come back down Stoneham Lane, turning right opposite Concord Club. Ground 400 yds on left. Three quarters of a mile from Southampton Parkway (BR). Bus 48 (Southampton-Winchester) to Stoneham Church stop.
Seats: 150 **Cover:** 210 **Capacity:** 4,300 **Floodlights:** Yes **Founded:** 1946.
Midweek home matches: Wednesday. **Prev. Lges:** Southampton Jnr & Snr 46-59/ Hants 50-86.
Colours: Blue & white/blue/blue **Change cols:** Yellow (green sleeves)/green/green **Nickname:** None.
Programme: 32 pages with admission **Programme Editor:** John Pothecary **Club Shop:** No.
Record Gate: 2,500 v Southampton, floodlight opener 30/9/75.
Club Sponsors: Various **Previous Names:** Swaythling Ath. 46-73/ Swaythling 73-80
Previous Grounds: Southampton Common 46-47/ Walnut Avenue, Swaythling 47-75.
Clubhouse: Licence 11am-11pm Mon-Sat plus Sundays. Extensive facilities for weddings, parties, skittles and seminars. All catering undertaken.
Record win: 12-1 v Hythe & Dibden, home 11/12/48 **Record defeat:** 0-11 v Austin Spts, away 1/1/47.
Club record scorer: Johnny Williams, 177 **Club record appearances:** Ian Knight, 611.
Hons: FA Vase 4th Rd 90-91, Wessex Lg Cup R-up 91-92, Hants Lg Div 2 69-70, Div 3(W) 50-51 53-54 70-71(Res), Hants Midweek F'lit Cup 78-79, Soton Snr Lg(W) 49-50 (R-up 51-52(Res), Div 1 56-57(Res) 57-58(Res)), Russell Cotes R-up 76-77 80-81 89-90,

GOSPORT BOROUGH

Chairman: I T Hay **President:** W J Adams.
Secretary: B V Cosgrave, 2 Cavanna Close, Rowner, Gosport PO13 0PE (01329 314117).
Manager: John Hawes. **Coaches:** Dave Pitt & Barry Cook. **Physio:** Dave Topliss
Ground: Privett Park, Privett Road, Gosport, Hants (01705 583986).
Directions: M27 junct 11, then A32 Fareham to Gosport, at Brockhurst r-about (after about 3 miles) right into Military Road passing thru H.M.S. Sultan, left into Privett Road at next r-about, ground 300 yds on left signed 'Privett Park Enclosure'. 2 miles from Portsmouth Harbour (BR) or Fareham (BR).
Capacity: 4,500 **Cover:** 500 **Seats:** 450 **Floodlights:** Yes **Club Shop:** No
Programme: 20 pages, 50p **Editor:** Ian Hay (01329 314601)
Colours: Yellow/blue/blue **Change colours:** Red/Black/Black.
Sponsors: Cougar Marine **Founded:** 1944. **Nickname:** The Boro'
Midweek matchday: Tuesday. **Reserve Team's League:** Jewson Wessex Combination.
Record Attendance: 4,770 v Pegasus, FA Amtr Cup 1951.
Best FA Trophy year: 1st Rd 88-89 **Best FA Amateur Cup year:** 3rd Rd 47-48 66-67
Best FA Vase year: 6th Rd rep 77-78 **Best FA Cup year:** 4th Qual. Rd 80-81 (lost to Windsor & Eton).
Previous Leagues: Portsmouth 44-45/ Hants 45-78/ Southern 78-92
Clubhouse: (01705 583986). Open matchdays from 1.30pm Saturday, 6.30pm Wednesday. Refreshment hut sells hot food and drinks.
95-96 Captain: Dave Taviner. **95-96 P.o.Y.:** Nicky Goater **95-96 Top scorer:** Martin Harper
Club Record Scorer: Richie Coulbert 192 **Club Record Appearances:** Tony Mahoney 764.
Honours: Wessex Lg Cup 92-93, Southern Lg Div 1 South R-up 84-85, Hants Lg 45-46 76-77 77-78 (Div 3 (Reserves) 70-71 75-76), Portsmouth Lg R-up 44-45, Hants Senior Cup 87-88, Russell Cotes Cup R-up 94-95, Hants Intermediate Cup 70-71, Portsmouth Senior Cup 61-62 69-70 70-71 94-95, South West Counties Pratten Challenge Cup 77-78.

PETERSFIELD TOWN

Chairman: G. W. Goad. **Manager:** Tony Adams & Mick Jenkins
Secretary: M Nicholl, 49 Durford Rd, Petersfield, Hants GU31 4ER (01730 261735).
Asst Manager:
Ground: Love Lane, Petersfield, Hants (01730 233416).
Directions: On A3 circulatory system. 10 mins walk from Petersfield BR station heading towards London.
Seats: 150 **Cover:** 50 **Capacity:** 2,500 **Floodlights:** Yes **Club Shop:** No.
Colours: Red & Black/Black/Black. **Change cols:** White/blue/white
Club Sponsors: Tarrant Specialist Contracting Services **Reformed:** 1993
Midweek Matches: Wednesday. **Youth Team League:** Hampshire Yth Lge Div 2
Previous Leagues: None
Record Attendances: 1,500 - Gary Stevens All-Stars v Aston Villa, Tony Barton memorial match 10/11/93.
Best F.A. Cup season: Not entered to date.
Clubhouse: Yes. **Hons:** None.

PORTSMOUTH ROYAL NAVY

Chairman: Cdr A S Miklinski
Secretary: Roy Newman, 8 Kimpton Close, Lee-on-Solent, PO13 8JY (01705 799198)
Manager: M Marsh **Physio:** F Cripps **Coach:** R Brady/A Maher
Ground: RN Stadium, Burnaby Road, West Portsmouth, (01705 724235).
Directions: From Portsmouth Harbour (BR), turn right onto The Hard, pass under the rail bridge and turn left into Park Road, after approx 200yards take 1st right into Burnaby Road. Entrance to ground 100 mtrs on the right.
Seats: 500 **Cover:** 500 **Capacity:** 1,500 **Floodlights:** Yes **Club Shop:** No
Programme: Yes free with entry **Editor:** **Press Officer:**
Colours: All Royal blue **Change colours:** All Red
Club Sponsors: Federation Brewery **Formed:** 1962 **Nickname:** Sailors
Midweek Matches: Monday **Reserve Team's League:** Portsmouth & Dist.
Previous Leagues: Hampshire 62-86
Clubhouse: Open 1.5hrs before k.o. & 2hrs after game on matchdays and by arrangement only.
95-96 Captain: Kev Crellin. **95-96 Top Scorer:** Jon Wallsgrove **95-96 P.o.Y.:** Kev Crellin
Honours: Russell-Cotes Cup 67-68, Basingstoke Lg Div 2, Hants Lge Div 2 67-68 77-78 80-81.

ROMSEY TOWN

Chairman: Derek Edwards, 'Deer Park Farm', Hursley, Winchester. 01703 260376.

Secretary: Bill Clouder, 15 Malmesbury Road, Romsey. SO51 8FS. 01794 518556

Ground: The By-Pass Ground, South Front, Romsey. 01794 512003.

Directions: The ground is adjacent to the roundabout at the junction of the A31 and the A27.

Nearest Railway station: Romsey (BR) is about 3/4 mile away.

Colours: Yellow & black stripes/black/black. **Change colours:** Red & black stripes/red/red.

Midweek Home Matchday: Wednesday

RYDE SPORTS

President: John Keynes **Chairman:** Steve Rann
Secretary: Mark Firmin, c/o Ground. (01983 740113).
Manager: Dennis Probee **Asst Manager:** Tony Newman.
Physio: Tom Kennedy **Commercial Manager:** Mark Firmin (01983 812906).
Ground: Smallbrook Stadium, Ashley Rd., Ryde, I.o.W. PO33 4BH. (01983 812906).
Directions: From the Pier Head follow directions to the Royal Isle of Wight Hospital, carry on past the hospital turning left at the Partlands Hotel - ground is one mile along Ashey Road. Not served by public transport.
Seats: 450 **Cover:** 1,500 **Capacity:** 5,000 **Floodlights:** 246 lux **Founded:** 1888.
Midweek Matches: Wednesday **Previous League:** Hants.
Colours: All Red. **Change colours:** All Blue. **Metal Badges:** Yes.
Programme: 20 pages, 50p. **Editor:** Mark Firmin (01983 812906) **Nickname:** The Reds.
Previous Ground: Partlands (pre-1990). **Club Sponsors:** Wight Sports/ Hoevertravel.
Reserve Team's League: Isle of Wight League.
Best FA Vase season: Prel. Rd 90-91 **Best FA Cup season:** 3rd Rd Proper 35-36.
Record Gates: 3,100 v Aston Villa 17/12/90. 2,400 v Sheffield Wednesday 26/3/90.
Players pogressing to Football League: Roy Shiner (Sheff Wed), Keiron Baker & Kevin Allen (Bournemouth). *(Also Wally Hammond played for Ryde before achieving fame in cricket).*
Clubhouse: Open every day. 2 bars, function suite, balcony overlooking stadium, restaurant, fitness centre, gym, treatment room.Also Table Tennis Centre and Floodlit Astro Turf Football and Hockey pitch.
Club shop: Yes, selling old & new programmes, metal badges, scarves & pennants, sportswear.
Honours: Hants Lg 1899-00 25-26 89-90 (Div 2 88-89, Div 3 64-65), Hants Snr Cup(8) 1899-00 03-04 25-26 34-39, IOW Gold Cup(7) 26-27 46-47 48-49 55-56 61-64, IOW Snr Challenge Cup 1898-99, IOW Gold Cup(7) 26-27 46-47 48-49 55-56 61-64, IOW Challenge Cup 27-28 80-81, P'mouth Snr Cup 1899-00 00-01 05-06 19-20 53-54 66-67 89-90, IOW Charity Cup(7) 18-22 44-47, Ryde & Dist Cup 89-90, Westwood Cup 84-85, IOW Lg 20-21 (Div 2 80-81), Memorial Cup 93-94.

Portsmouth Royal Navy FC: Back Row (L-R); Arnie Ormston (Manager), Bob Brady, Paddy Snodgrass,Pete Houkes, Jamis Cook, Jimmy Mullen, Kev Crellin, Jon Wallsgrove, Shaun Parker, Fred Cripps (Physio). Front Row; Kenny Kennedy, Robbie Shankland, Ivan Sadd, Chris Marshall, Dave Smith, Jake Cripps (Mascot).

AFC Lymington FC: Back Row (L-R); Derek Binns (Manager), Jimmy Sheppard, Nick Drewitt, Dave Perrett, Nigel Mottashed, Graham Kemp, Kevein Green, Darren Pitter, Garry Penhaligon, Eric Corlett (Coach). Front Row; Danny Adams, Paul Sims, Jason Brookes (Mascot), Paul Morris, Andy Knighton, Dave Knighton, David Adams, Alan Farrar (Physio).

THATCHAM TOWN

Chairman: Phil Holdway, 68 Park Lane, Thatcham, Berks. RG18 4JS. 01635 867803
General Secretary: John Haines (01635 40845)
Football Secretary: Charles Heaver, 32 Baily Avenue, Thatcham, Berks. RG13 3DU. 01635 868179
Manager: Jim Greenwood. **Press Off:** Dave Ware. 01635 861000 **Coach:** Dave Cox
Ground: Waterside Park, Crookham Rd, Thatcham, Berks (01635 862016/873912).
Directions: 2 mins walk from from Thatcham BR station.
Seats: 300 **Cover:** 300 **Capacity:** 3,000 **Floodlights:** Yes **Founded:** 1895
Midweek Matches: Tuesday **Best FA Vase season:** QF 88-89
Colours: Blue & white stripes/blue/blue **Change colours:** All Red.
Programme: 28 pages, 50p **Programme Editor:** Dave Ware
Previous Ground: Station Road 46-52/ Lancaster Close 52-92.
Clubhouse: Open every evening & lunchtimes. **Record Gate:** 1,400 v Aldershot, F.A.Vase.
Honours: Wessex Lg Cup 90-91 91-92 94-95. (R-up.93-94)

WHITCHURCH UNITED

Chairman: Chris Rowland, 17 Rose Close, Kempshott, Basingstoke, Hants. RG22 5FN.
01256 55731 (H) 01793 541541 (B)
Secretary: Mr N Spencer, 54 Winchester Rd, Whitchurch, Hants RG28 7HP
01256 896895 (H) 01264 3443336 (B)
Ground: Long Meadow, Winchester Road, Whitchurch (01256 892493).
Directions: From Whitchurch (BR) station; turn left after Railway Inn, follow road to end, turn right into main road, arriving in town turn left along Winchester Road. Ground three quarters of a mile on left.
Seats: 200 **Cover:** Yes **Capacity:** **Floodlights:** Yes **Founded:**
Midweek Matches: Thursday (Monday for Reserves).
Colours: Red & white/black/red **Change colours:** All Blue.
Programme: 24 pages **Previous Leagues:** Hants (pre-1992).
Best FA Vase season: Extra-Preliminary Rd 93-94 (lost 1-3 at home to Peppard).
Clubhouse: Hot food on matchdays. Sports hall incorporating squash courts and indoor bowling green

WIMBORNE TOWN

Chairman: Mike Sturgess **Vice Chairman:** Steve Churchill **President:** Brian Maidment
Secretary: Mark Willis, 63 Victoria Close, Corfe Mullen, Wimborne, Dorset. BH21 3TX (01202 605089)
Manager: Alex Pike. **Coach:** Chris Weller **Physio:** Irvin Brown
Ground: The Cuthbury, Cowgrove Road, Wimborne, Dorset BH21 4EL (01202 884821).
Directions: Wimborne to Blandford Road, behind Victoria Hospital.
Seats: 150 **Cover:** 500 **Capacity:** 3,250 **Floodlights:** Yes **Club Shop:** Yes
Programme: 32 pages, 50p **Editor:** Secretary **Press Officer:** Secretary.
Colours: Black & white stripes/black/black **Change colours:** Green & white/white/green & white.
Club Sponsors: Fisks. **Nickname:** Magpies **Founded:** 1878
Midweek Matches: Tuesday **Reserve League:** Dorset
Record Attendance: 3,250 v Bamberbridge FA Vase Semi-Final 28/3/92
Best FA Vase season: Winners 91-92
Best FA Cup season: 1st Rd Proper 82-83.
Previous Leagues: Dorset Lge, Dorset Comb, Western 81-86.
Clubhouse: Evenings 7-11pm, Sat noon-11pm, Sun noon-3pm & 7-10.30pm. Bar. Skittle alley.
95-96 Top Scorer: J Sturgess 26
Club Record Goalscorer: Jason Lovell. **Club Record Appearances:** Danny Saxby
Honours: Wessex Lg 91-92 93-94 (R-up 92-93), Lg Cup 93-94 (R-up 90-91 95-96); Dorset Lg Div 1 80-81 81-82 (R-up 38-39 72-73), Div 2 31-32 34-35 36-37 (R-up 35-36), Lg Cup R-up(4) 72-74 80-82; Dorset Snr Cup 91-92, (R-up 80-82 85-86); Mark Frowde Cup 92-93 94-95; Dorset Snr Amateur Cup 36-37 63-64; Dorset Jnr Cup 31-32 36-37 (R-up 13-14 34-35); Dorset Minor Cup 12-13; Dorset Jnr Amateur Cup(3) 34-36 38-39; Bankes Charity Cup 89-90 94-95 95-96, Texaco F/Light Cup 90-91

SCREWFIX DIRECT WESTERN LEAGUE

FEEDER TO: BEAZER HOMES LEAGUE

President: Stan Priddle

Chairman: R J Webber **Vice Chairman:** C D Ashton

Hon. Secretary: M E Washer, 16 Heathfield Road, Nailsea, Bristol BS19 1EB, (01275 851314)

In the eyes of many of the so called experts, this last season should have been thoroughly predictable, so much so that little interest would be generated. However, in true Western League fashion , events dispelled all theories, and very few would have foreseen the emphasis on Somerset clubs for the successes. Only the Les Phillips Cup eluded a Somerset club, being fought out rather disappointingly by Tiverton Town and Barnstable Town in a one sided game in which Barnstable did not do themselves justice.

The Premier Division honours went to Taunton Town who were rewarded for consistency all season, and equalling the record lowest goals conceded in a season since Bideford in 1981-82. Tiverton eventually were runners-up, as the inevitable toll of fixtures caught up with Mangotsfield who went so very close in the FA Vase losing at Clitheroe in the Semi-Fimnal.

First Division honours eventually went to Bridgwater who truimphed over Chard Town by means of goal difference, in what was a runaway season for both clubs. History was made again here though, since Chard created a new lowest goals conceded in that division beating the previous record of 19 held by Taunton in 1973.

The Combination League and Cup double was attained by Wellington which completed the Somerset stronghold. Will it continue next season?

Off the field, we were sadly informed that Great Mills Retail would end their connection with our League after fifteen years sponsorship, a record for Non League Football if not professional football as well. This League and its club could not have had better sponsors during that time and we record our grateful and appreciative thanks to that Company for their support and continued interest. The end of the season aslso brought us a new Chairman, as Stan Priddle decided to hand over the reins to Rod Webber after eleven years as Chairman, and suitable presentations were made at our convention weekend in May at Dawlish, and also at our AGM. Stan will remain as our President, and the progress our League has attained over the last decade is in no small way attributable to his work and guidance.

During the close season, we were fortunate indeed to obtain new sponsors in the form of Screwfix Direct Ltd. who have quaranteed us a starting period of three years and I am sure that the relationship will prove to be as fruitful as previously, and we all look forward to the new season with high hopes and enthusiasm. Heres hoping that this time next year we are not disappointed. **Maurice Washer.**

Taunton Town FC: Winners of the Great Mills League Premier Championship.
Back Row (L-R); Dave Kendall (Trainer), Ben Rowe, Keith Graddon, Mark Coombe, Steve Kidd, Paul West, Alex Crook, Paul Topping (Physio).
Front Row; Damon Palfrey, Mark Loram, Ian Down, Russell Musker (Player/Mgr), Tom Harris (Chairman), Derek Fowler (Asst Player/Mgr), Tiv Lowe, Darren Cann.

FINAL LEAGUE TABLES 1995/96

Premier Division	P	W	D	L	F	A	Pts
1. Taunton Town	34	25	7	2	84	20	82
2. Tiverton Town	34	25	4	5	101	34	79
3. Mangotsfield	34	22	7	5	88	23	73
4. Torrington	34	23	4	7	65	37	73
5. Brislington	34	17	4	13	60	41	55
6. Bideford	34	16	7	11	63	47	55
7. Backwell United	34	15	7	12	54	46	52
8. Paulton Rovers	34	14	10	10	59	53	52
9. Calne Town	34	14	9	11	41	40	51
10. Chippenham Town	34	11	12	11	53	41	45
11. Bridport	34	13	5	16	51	60	44
12. Bristol Manor Farm	34	11	6	17	55	69	39
13. Westbury United	34	9	9	16	39	54	36
14. Barnstable Town	34	10	6	18	61	78	36
15. Odd Down	34	6	6	22	39	77	24
16. Elmore	34	6	6	22	30	91	24
17. Frome Town	34	5	7	22	31	85	22
18. Crediton United	34	3	6	25	18	96	15

Div One	P	W	D	L	F	A	Pts
1. Bridgwater Tn	36	29	3	4	93	29	90
2. Chard Town	36	28	6	1	65	17	90
3. Keynsham Tn	36	22	7	7	67	35	73
4. Bishop Sutton	36	18	9	10	48	36	63
5. Clyst Rovers	36	18	7	11	74	52	61
6. Welton Rovers	36	15	11	10	52	44	56
7. Devizes Town	36	15	10	11	61	50	55
8. Dawlish Town	36	14	9	13	56	53	51
9. Melksham Tn	36	13	11	12	59	54	50
10. Warminster Tn	36	14	6	16	51	57	48
11. Glastonbury	36	12	10	14	45	54	46
12. Wellington	36	12	8	16	47	52	44
13. Pewsey Vale	36	10	6	20	35	69	36
14. Heavitree Utd	36	9	8	19	64	81	35
15. Larkhall Ath	36	10	4	22	50	78	34
16. Amesbury Tn	36	7	10	19	37	67	31
17. Minehead	36	8	7	21	41	73	31
18. Exmouth Town	36	9	3	24	44	67	30
19. Ilfracombe Tn	36	6	11	19	43	64	29

Combination Lge	P	W	D	L	F	A	Pts
1. Wellington	36	25	8	3	92	33	83
2. Heavitree Utd	36	23	7	6	90	46	76
3. Elmore	36	22	3	11	84	61	69
4. Chard Town	36	17	9	10	80	44	60
5. Crediton Utd	36	16	7	13	70	63	55
6. Bideford	36	15	9	12	69	52	54
7. Tiverton Tn	36	16	6	14	80	70	54
8. Barnstable	36	15	4	17	81	75	49
9. Clyst Rovers	36	13	8	15	66	77	47
10. Exmouth Tn	36	13	5	18	63	67	44
11. Taunton Tn	36	12	2	22	53	97	38
12. Dawlish Tn	36	5	4	27	43	124	19
13. Ottery St M	36	3	6	27	29	91	15

LEADING GOAL SCORERS 1995-96

G Ross	Dawlish	27
K Smith	Tiverton	23
M Grimshaw	Tiverton	22
R Hill	Barnstable	21
A Perrett	Mangotsfield	26
A Gibson	Chard Town	22
P Everett	Tiverton	22
N Hawkins	Bridgwater	20

HIGHEST LEAGUE ATTENDANCES 1995-96

1,303	Taunton Town	v	Tiverton Town	18.03.96
757	Tiverton Town	v	Barnstable Town	04.05.96
680	Tiverton Town	v	Taunton Town	30.09.95
672	Tiverton Town	v	Bristol Manor Farm	18.11.95
633	Bridgwater Town	v	Chard Town	20.04.96
521	Tiverton Town	v	Elmore	05.04.96
517	Tiverton Town	v	Mangotsfield	06.04.96
508	Barnstable Town	v	Tiverton Town	13.05.96

Premier Division Ten Year Records

	86/7	87/8	88/9	89/0	90/1	91/2	92/3	93/4	94/5	95/6
Backwell United	-	-	-	-	-	-	-	-	-	7
Barnstable Town	11	12	9	18	20	-	-	-	4	14
Bideford	6	10	16	16	12	4	14	9	15	6
Bridport	-	-	-	-	-	-	-	-	13	11
Brislington	-	-	-	-	-	-	-	-	-	5
Bristol City Reserves	3	7	-	-	-	-	-	-	-	-
Bristol Manor Farm	5	8	6	12	14	16	13	13	9	12
Calne Town	-	-	-	-	-	-	-	14	14	9
Chard Town	22	-	15	15	16	18	19	-	-	-
Chippenham Town	9	20	12	13	17	14	16	8	8	10
Clandown	20	22	-	-	-	-	-	-	-	-
Clevedon Town	12	13	11	10	11	2	1	-	-	-
Crediton United	-	-	-	-	-	-	-	11	16	18
Dawlish Town	14	15	19	14	9	13	20	-	-	-
Elmore	-	-	-	-	-	9	12	16	2	16
Exmouth Town	2	6	2	5	19	17	11	17	-	-
Frome Town	19	18	17	20	13	19	15	15	18	17
Liskeard Athletic	4	1	4	2	8	12	18	7	10	-
Mangotsfield United	10	3	18	3	1	8	5	3	6	3
Melksham Town	18	21	-	-	-	-	-	-	-	-
Minehead	21	19	21	-	-	11	17	18	-	-
Odd Down Athletic	-	-	-	-	-	-	-	10	12	15
Ottery St Mary	-	-	-	-	18	21	-	-	-	-
Paulton Rovers	16	14	8	11	10	10	8	4	7	8
Plymouth Argyle Reserves	7	4	5	7	3	6	10	-	-	-
Radstock Town	17	16	14	19	21	-	-	-	-	-
Saltash United	1	2	1	8	6	5	3	5	11	-
Swanage Town & Herston	-	11	10	9	-	-	-	-	-	-
Taunton Town	8	9	3	1	7	7	4	2	3	1
Tiverton Town	-	-	-	4	4	3	2	1	1	2
Torquay United Reserves	-	-	-	-	-	-	9	-	-	-
Torrington	15	17	20	17	2	15	6	6	17	4
Welton Rovers	-	-	13	21	15	20	-	-	-	-
Westbury United	-	-	-	-	-	-	7	12	5	13
Weston Super Mare	13	5	7	6	5	1	-	-	-	-
No of Clubs Competing	22	22	21	21	21	21	20	18	18	18

LES PHILLIPS CHALLENGE CUP 1995-96

First Round:

Bridgwater Town Clyst Rovers	4-5	Odd Down v Devizes Town	2-5
Larkhall Athletic v Paulton Rovers	1-2	Melksham Town v Bridport	2-1
Tiverton Town v Welton Rovers	7-1		

Second Round:

Taunton Town v Elmore	6-1	Warminster Town v Chard Town	2-1
Brislington v Ilfracombe Town	8-0	Devizes Town v Wellington	6-3
Heavitree Utd v Mangotsfield Utd	0-4	Westbury Utd v Amesbury Town	3-0
Frome Town v Clyst Rovers	3-1	Calne Town v Keynsham Town	4-0
Dawlish Town v Pewsey Vale	1-0	Backwell Utd v Glastonbury	0-2
Bishop Sutton v Exmouth Town	1-2	Torrington v Chippenham Tn	3-0
Barnstable Tn v Paulton Rovers	4-2	Bideford v Melksham	3-0
Tiverton Town v Crediton Utd	1-0	Bristol Manor Farm v Minehead	0-1

Third Round:

Calne Town v Dawlish Town	2-1	Glastonbury v Devizes Town	1-0
Brislington v Frome Town	8-0	Torrington v Barnstable Town	1-2
Tiverton Town v Bideford	4-2	Exmouth Town v Westbury Utd	0-5
Warminster Town v Elmore	2-3	Mangotsfield v Minehead	5-1

Quarter Finals;

Calne Town v Tiverton Town	0-2	Westbury Utd v Brislington	0-2
Barnstable Town v Elmore	1-0	Glastonbury v Mangotsfield	0-1

Semi-Finals;

Tiverton Town v Mangotsfield	1-0	Barnstable Town v Brislington	4-2

Final; Tiverton Town v Barnstable 4-0

GREAT MILLS WESTERN LEAGUE Division One Ten Year Records

	86/7	87/8	88/9	89/0	90/1	91/2	92/3	93/4	94/5	95/6
Amesbury Town	-	-	-	-	-	-	-	-	12	16
Backwell United	9	10	9	2	16	12	8	7	3	-
Barnstaple Town	-	-	-	-	-	17	9	1	-	-
Bath City Reserves	3	4	15	18	12	4	-	-	-	-
Bishop Sutton	-	-	-	-	-	13	13	12	8	4
Bridgwater Town	-	-	-	-	-	-	-	-	6	1
Bridport	-	-	3	4	6	9	10	2	-	-
Brislington	-	-	-	-	-	8	4	3	1	-
Calne Town	19	13	4	12	3	7	2	-	-	-
Chard Town	-	2	-	-	-	-	-	10	5	2
Clandown	-	-	14	13	14	18	-	-	-	-
Clyst Rovers	-	-	-	-	-	-	6	6	11	5
Crediton United	-	-	-	-	10	3	3	-	-	-
Dawlish Town	-	-	-	-	-	-	-	17	20	8
Devizes Town	6	6	5	10	8	20	12	9	17	7
Elmore	14	18	20	14	2	-	-	-	-	-
Exmouth Town	-	-	-	-	-	-	-	-	9	18
Glastonbury	22	19	19	19	21	14	16	13	2	11
Heavitree United	21	16	11	11	20	22	11	18	15	14
Ilfracombe Town	20	15	8	3	9	10	18	11	14	19
Keynsham Town	13	7	10	8	13	6	7	5	7	3
Larkhall Athletic	7	5	1	6	19	15	17	14	19	15
Melksham Town	-	-	12	9	15	21	21	-	10	9
Minehead	-	-	-	20	1	-	-	-	21	17
Odd Down Athletic	12	14	6	5	4	11	1	-	-	-
Ottery St Mary	11	9	13	1	-	-	19	20	-	-
Pewsey Vale	-	-	-	-	-	-	-	4	18	13
Portway-Bristol	2	-	-	-	-	-	-	-	-	-
Radstock Town	-	-	-	-	-	16	20	19	-	-
Swanage Town & Herston	1	-	-	-	-	-	-	-	-	-
Tiverton Town	16	3	2	-	-	-	-	-	-	-
Torquay Utd Reserves	-	-	-	-	7	2	-	-	-	-
Warminster Town	10	11	18	15	18	5	5	15	4	10
Wellington Town	18	12	7	17	11	19	15	16	13	12
Welton Rovers	8	1	-	-	-	-	14	8	16	6
Westbury United	15	8	16	7	5	1	-	-	-	-
Weymouth Reserves	17	-	-	-	-	-	-	-	-	-
Wimborne Town	5	-	-	-	-	-	-	-	-	-
Yeovil Town Reserves	4	17	17	16	17	-	-	-	-	-
No of Clubs Competing	22	19	20	20	21	22	21	20	21	19

COMBINATION KNOCK OUT CUP 1995-96

First Round;

Heavitree Utd v Ottery St Mary 5-1

Bideford v Taunton Town 4-2

Dawlish Town v Tiverton Town 1-5

Wellington v Exmouth Town 3-1

Barnstable Tn v Crediton Utd 7-6

Second Round;

Heavitree Utd v Clyst Rovers 2-0

Chard Town v Barnstable Town 5-1

Elmore v Tiverton Town 6-5

Wellington v Bideford 2-1

Semi-Finals;

Elmore v Wellington 0-2

Chard Town v Heavitree Utd 0-2

Final; Wellington v Heavitree United 3-1

BACKWELL UNITED

Chairman: Dick Cole. **Vice-Chairman:** Peter Higgins. **President:** John Southern
Secretary: Bill Coggins, 34 Westfield Road, Backwell, Bristol BS19 3ND (01275 463424).
Manager: Adrian Britton **Asst Manager:** Martin Finn. **Physio:** Ian Pinkney
Ground: Recreation Ground, Backwell, Avon (01275 462612).
Directions: Near centre of Backwell on main A370 Bristol to Weston-super-Mare road. Buses from Bristol or Weston, or 20 mins walk from Nailsea & Backwell (BR) station; turn right out of station, right at traffic lights (half mile), ground quarter mile on right just past car sales.
Seats: 60 **Cover:** 150 **Capacity:** 1,000 **Floodlights:** Yes **Club Shop:** No.
Club colours: All red **Change colours:** All Gold **Nickname:** Stags
Programme: 42 pages, 50p. **Editor:** Dick Cole (01275 463627) **Press Officer:** Peter Higgins.
Midweek Matches: Tuesday **Club Sponsors:** C W Jones Carpets. **Founded:** 1911.
Record attendance: 487 v Brislington, Gt Mills Lg. 2/5/94.
Previous Lges: Clevedon & Dist/ Bristol Church of England/ Bristol Surburban (pre 1970)/ Somerset Snr 70-83
Clubhouse: Open 6-11pm weekdays, 12.30-11pm Sat. Sausage & chips, hot pasties, rolls, crisps etc. available.
95-96 Captain: Ian Davis. **95-96 Top Scorer:** Darren Pool. **95-96 P.o.Y.:** Nathan Brown.
Club Record Goalscorer: Steve Spalding **Club Record appearances:** Wayne Buxton.
Honours: Somerset Snr Lg 77-78 79-80 80-81 81-82 82-83 (Lg Cup 82-83 (R-up 79-80) Div 1 72-73); Somerset Snr Cup 81-82; SW Co.'s Sutton Transformer Cup 81-82. Gt.Mills Div 1 89-90 Champions,94-95 promoted in third place.

BARNSTAPLE TOWN

President: Wilf Harris **Chairman:** Vic Hamilton-Philip 01271 861093
Secretary: David Cooke, 51 Walnut Way, Whiddon Valley, Barnstaple, Devon. EX32 7RF. (01271 328088)
Ground: Mill Road, Barnstaple, North Devon (01271 743469). **Manager:** Phil Lloyd 01803 552796
Directions: A361 towards Ilfracombe (from M5 Jct 26), in Barnstaple follow A361 Ilfracombe signs, second left after crossing small bridge is Mill Road.
Seats: 250 **Cover:** 1,000 **Capacity:** 5,000 **Floodlights:** Yes **Year Formed:** 1906
Colours: Red/white/red. **Change colours:** Yellow/black/black. **Nickname:** Barum.
Sponsors: Pearce Construction. **Prev. Lges:** Nth Devon, Devon & Exeter, S. Western
Prev. Grounds: Town Wharf (Pre 1920's); Highfield Rd, Newport (until 1935), Pilton Pk, Rock Pk.
Previous Name: Pilton Yeo Vale. **Rec. Gate:** 6,200 v Bournemouth, FA Cup 1st Rd, 1954
Midweek Matches: Tuesday **Local Press:** N. Devon Journal Herald **Club Shop:** Yes
Reserve Team's League: Great Mills Combination.
Record win: 12-1 v Tavistock (H), FA Cup Third Qualifying Round 1954.
Record defeat: 1-10 v Mangotsfield United (A), Western League Premier Division 90-91.
Record transfer fee paid: £4,000 for Joe Scott (Hungerford Town, 1980).
Record transfer fee received: £6,000 for Ian Doyle (Bristol City).
Clubhouse: Full license. Bar snacks. **Club record appearances:** Trevor Burnell
Past players progressing to Football League: Len Pickard (Bristol Rovers 1951), John Neale (Exeter 1972), Barrie Vassallo (Torquay 1977), Ian Doyle (Bristol City 1978), Ryan Souter (Swindon 1994), Jason Cadie (Reading 1994).
Hon: Western Lg 52-53 79-80 (R-up 80-81 81-82, Div 1 49-50 94-95, Merit Cup 74-75 83-84 84-85, Combination 92-93), FA Cup 1st Rd replay 51-52, Devon Professional Cup 62-63 64-65 67-68 69-70 71-73 74-75 76-81, Devon Lg, Devon St Lukes Cup 87-88, Devon Snr Cup 92-93, Devon Youth Cup 48-49 51-52.

BIDEFORD

President: C C Prust **Chairman:** J McElwee (01237 475967)
Secretary: Mr Ron Ackland, Korna House, Shebbear, North Devon EX21 5RU (01409 281451).
Manager: Peter Buckingham **Coach:** G Waldron **Reserve Manager:** K Ebsworthy.
Ground: The Sports Ground, Kingsley Road, Bideford (01237 274974).
Directions: A361 for Bideford - ground on right as you enter the town.
Seats: 120 **Cover:** 1,000 **Capacity:** 6,000 **Floodlights:** Yes **Founded:** 1946
Colours: Red/white/red. **Change colours:** Yellow/white/yellow. **Nickname:** Robins
Previous Name: Bideford Town **Prev. Lges:** Devon & Exeter 47-49/ Western 49-72/ Southern 72-75
Prev. Ground: Hansen Ground (1 season) **Record Gate:** 6,000 v Gloucester C., FA Cup 4th Qual. Rd 1960
Programme: 32 pages, 50p **Programme Editor:** Ian Knight.
Midweek Matchday: Wednesday. **Club record appearances:** Derek May 528.
Record win: 16-0 v Soundwell 50-51 **Record defeat:** 0-10 v Bristol City 51-52.
Players progressing to Football League: Shaun Taylor (Swindon Town).
Clubhouse: 'Robins Nest' - on ground. Open lunchtimes and evenings, snacks and bar menu available. Manager: Mrs Sue Tyrell.
Record scorer: Tommy Robinson. **Record appearances:** Derek May 527.
Top Scorer 1994-95: Neil Gauntlett. **Hons:** Western Lg 63-64 70-71 71-72 81-82 82-83 (Div 1 51-52, Div 3 49-50, Lg Cup 71-72 84-85, Alan Young Cup 64-65 69-70, Merit Cup 68-69, Subsidiary Cup 71-72), Devon Snr Cup 79-80, Devon St Lukes Cup 81-82 83-84 85-86 (R-up 86-87 91-92 94-95), FA Cup 1st Rd 64-65(replay) 73-74 77-78 81-82.

BRIDGWATER TOWN '84

Chairman: Keith Setter. **President:** T Pearle
Secretary: Miss S A Wright, 37 Kidsbury Road, Bridgwater TA6 7AQ (01278 421189)
Manager: Alan Hooker. **Physio:** M Brown
Ground: Fairfax Park, Fairfax Road, Bridgwater (01278 446899 - matchdays only).
Directions: M5 jct 23, follow signs to Glastonbury (A39), turn right for Bridgwater (A39).Look for sign to Bridgwater College-College Way. One mile from Bridgwater (BR).
Seats: 150 **Cover:** Yes **Capacity:** **Floodlights:** Yes **Club Shop:** Yes
Programme: Yes. **Editor:** G Nelson **Press Officer**
Colours: Red/black/red **Change colours:** Blue/blue or white/blue.
Sponsor: TMB Patterns **Founded:** 1984.
Nickname: The Robins
Midweek Matchday: Tuesday **Youth Team's League:** U18 Floodlight
Previous League: Somerset Snr (pre-1994)
Clubhouse: 'The Sportsman' Bath Road.
Honours: Somerset Snr Cup 93-94, Somerset Snr Lge 90-91 91-92, GMWL Div 1 95-96.

BRIDPORT

President: B Williams **Chairman:** David Fowler (01308 456142)
Secretary: Keith Morgan, 95 Orchard Crescent, Bridport DT6 5HA (01308 425113).
Manager: Phil Simkin (01305 262021) **Asst Manager/Physio:** Alan Newey.
Ground: The Beehive, St Mary's Field, Bridport, Dorset (01308 423834).
Directions: Take West Bay road from town centre, turn right immediately before Palmers Brewery.
Seats: 200 **Cover:** 400 **Capacity:** 2,000 **Floodlights:** Yes **Founded:** 1887
Cols: Red & black/black/red & black **Change:** Blue/white/blue **Nickname:** Bees
Midweek Matches: Wednesday **Reserve Team's League:** Dorset Combination.
Programme: 32 pages, 30p **Programme Editor:** John Hallett (01308 868795).
Club Shop: Yes, selling programmes, jerseys, ties etc. Contact John Hallett (above).
Previous Grounds: Pymore (pre 1930s); Crown Field (pre 1953)
Previous Leagues: Perry Street/ Western 61-84/ Dorset Combination 84-88.
Record transfer fee received: £2,000 for Tommy Henderson.
Record transfer fee paid: £1,000 for Steve Crabb.
Record Attendance: 1,150 v Exeter City, 1981; 3,000 v Chelsea, at Crown, 1950
Clubhouse: Yes, open matchdays and for functions. Hot and cold snacks available.
Club record scorer (in a season): Eric Hoole 36.
Hons: Western Lg Cup 70-71 72-73 77-78 (R-up 76-77, Div 1 R-up 94-95, Merit Cup 69-70 71-72 73-74); FA Vase 5th Rd 88-89; Dorset Comb.(3) 85-88 (Lg Cup 86-87 87-88); Dorset Snr Cup(8) 63-64 69-71 75-76 78-81 87-88; Dorset Snr Amtr Cup(6) 48-50 54-55 56-57 70-72; W. Dorset Chal. Bowl 07-08; Perry Str. Lg 22-23; Mark Frowde Cup 76-77 88-89

BRISLINGTON

President: C Elston **Chairman:** Paul Bishop (0117 986 8482) **Vice-Chairman:** P K Brake
Secretary: Frank G Durbin, 52 Arlington Road, St Annes, Bristol BS4 4AJ (0117 985 4107 (H) 0117 921 2261 (B))
Manager: Jamie Patch (0117 907 6257) **Asst Manager:** Dave Payne **Physio:** Art Rowland/Dave Gould
Ground: Ironmould Lane, Brislington, Bristol (0117 977 4030)
Directions: Four miles out of Bristol on main A4 to Bath – turn left up lane opposite Garden Centre
Capacity: **Seats:** 144 **Cover:** 100 **Floodlights:** No **Club Shop:** No
Programme: 50p **Editor:** Laserset (0117 9695487). **Nickname:** Bris.
Colours: Red & black stripes/white/red & black **Change colours:** All Yellow
Midweek matches: Wednesday **Reserve's League:** Somerset Senior
Best FA Vase year: 3rd Rd 89-90 (lost 2-3 at Abingdon T.)
Clubhouse: Yes - on ground, open matchdays. **Previous League:** Somerset Senior (pre-1991).
Honours: Somerset Snr Cup 92-93 (R-up 93-94), Som. Snr Lge, Les Phillips Cup SF 93-94 95-96, Prem Cup 95-96.

Bridgwater Town: Back Row (L-R); Colin Paczowski (Physio), Nick Hawkins, Paul Rich, David Pope, Neil Seymour, Shaun Pople, Nigel Williams, Matt Lazenby, Dave Kitchiner, Ben Aherne. Front Row; Steve Nicholls, Neal Tucker, Paul Skinner, Alan Hooker (Mgr), Andy Howe, Paul Elson, Craig Laird.

Photo - Sunday Independant

Tiverton Town FC: Back Row (L-R); Jimmy Giles (Asst Mgr), Dai Morgan, Anthony Thirlby, Steve Daley, Mike Taylor,Paul Edwards, Phil Everett, Steve Rowlands, Kevin Smith, Phil Hucker, Martyn Rogers (Mgr). Front Row; Steve Hynds, Nick Campbell, Dave Leonard, Martin Tregedeon, Hedley Steele, Neil Saunders, Paul Edwards, Graham Walters.

Photo - Sunday Independant

Chard Town: Back Row (L-R); Pete Smith (Asst Mgr), Gary McAuley, Nick Flory, Ashley Gibson, Gary French, Brent Ireland, Jason Manlet, Gordon Bennett, Pete Copland, Bob Russell (Mgr). Front Row; Harry Sayers, Paul Meare, Jamie Manley, Matt Francis, Mark Rolls, Rob Clement, Rob Walker.

Photo - Sunday Independant

BRISTOL MANOR FARM

Chairman: F Wardle **Vice Chairman:** Brian Bartlett. **President:** Fred Wardle
Press Officer/Secretary: John Coles, 33 Jubilee Cres., Mangotsfield, Bristol BS17 3BB (0117 956 3075)
Manager: Chris Rex **Asst Mgr:** Barry Fry **Physio:** Alan Williams.
Ground: 'The Creek', Portway, Sea Mills, Bristol BS9 2HS (0117 982 6952).
Directions: M5 jct 18 (Avonmouth Bridge), follow A4 for Bristol - U-turn on dual carriageway by Bristol & West sports ground and return for half mile on A4 - ground entrance is down narrow lane on left (hidden entrance). Near to Sea Mills station (BR Temple Meads-Severn Beach line).
Seats: 84 **Cover:** 350 **Capacity:** 2,000 **Floodlights:** Yes **Club Shop:** No.
Programme: 28 pages, 50p **Editor:** Steve Price (0117 982 6952).
Colours: Red & black stripes/black/black **Change colours:** White/red/red
Club Sponsors: Wardle Fencing. **Nickname:** The Farm **Formed:** 1964
Midweek Matchday: Tuesday 7.30pm **Reserve League:** Somerset Senior.
Record Attendance: 500 v Portway, Western Lg 1974.
Previous Leagues: Bristol Suburban 64-69/ Somerset Snr 69-77.
Players progressing to Football League: Ian Hedges (Newport) 88-89, Gary Smart (Bristol Rovers).
Clubhouse: Lounge bar, entertainments, skittle alley, bar meals. Open every night and lunchtime Sat & Sun.
95-96 Captain: Matt Baird. **95-96 P.o.Y.:** Tony Bennett **95-96 Top Scorer:** Natham Baird
Club Record Goalscorer: Chris Rex, 222 **Club Record Appearances:** Paul Williams, 821.
Honours: Western Lg Div 1 82-83, Glos Tphy 87-88, Glos Amtr Cup 89-90, Somerset Snr Lg Div 1 (Lg Cup, Div 2).

CALNE TOWN

President: Fred Rutty **Chairman:** David Heath **Vice Chairman:** N/A.
Press Officer/Secretary: Laurie Drake, 22 Falcon Rd, Calne, Wilts SN11 8PL (01249 819186).
Manager: Tom Saunders. **Coach:** Colin Bush.
Ground: Bremhill View, Lickhill Rd., North End, Calne (01249 816716).
Directions: From Bristol to Chippenham, on entering town keep left all the way taking slip road to North End, off main Swindon Road.
Seats: 78 **Cover:** 250 **Capacity:** 2,500 **Floodlights:** Yes **Club Shop:** No.
Programme: 20 pages, 50p **Editor:** Laurie Drake (01249 819186).
Colours: White/black/white **Change colours:** Yellow/blue/yellow
Sponsors: Montreux Developements **Nickname:** Lilywhites **Founded:** 1887.
Midweek Matcheday: Wednesday **Reserves League:** None. **Record Attendance:** 1,100 v Swindon, Friendly 25/7/1987.
Previous League: Wilts Co. (pre-1986)
Clubhouse: Mon-Fri 7-11pm, Sat-Sun 12-11pm. Filled rolls, hot food, tea, coffee, sweets etc.
95-96 Captain: John Woods **95-96 Top Scorer:** **95-96 P.o.Y.:** Ian Murphy
Club record scorer: Robbie Lardner **Club record appearances:** Gary Swallow, 259.
Hons: Western Lg Div 1 R-up 92-93, Wilts Snr Cup 12-13 34-35 84-85 (R-up 1894-95 94-95 1911-12 49-50), Wilts Lg 33-34 ('Ghia' Cup 8)1-81 85-86, Div 2 79-8)1, Div 3 85-86, Div 4 81-82).

CHARD TOWN

Chairman: Brian Beer **Vice Chairman:** Roy Goodland. **President:**
Secretary: Colin Dunford, 27 Manor Gardens, Ilchester, Yeovil, Somerset BA22 8LE (01935 841217).
Manager: Bob Russell **Coach:** Peter Smith. **Physio:** Peter Smith
Ground: Town Ground, Zembard Lane, Chard (014606 61402).
Directions: 150 yards from the town centre, off Combe Street. 8 miles from Crewkerne BR station.
Seats: 60 **Cover:** 200 **Capacity:** 1,500 **Floodlights:** Yes
Programme: 24 pages with entry **Editor:** Secretary. **Press Officer:** Secretary
Colours: Scarlet/black/scarlet **Change colours:** White/black.
Founded: 1920 **Nickname:** Robins. **Sponsors:** Annual Competition.
Midweek matches: Tuesday. **Reserve Team's League:** Great Mills Combination.
Prev. Lges: Somerset Snr 20-24 48-75/ Perry Street 25-48.
Clubhouse: Matchdays & most evenings. Snacks served
95-96 Captain: Dave Platt. **95-96 P.o.Y.:** Ashley Gibson **95-96 Top Scorer:** Ashley Gibson
Honours: Som. Snr Lg 49-50 53-54 59-60 67-68 69-70 (Lg Cup 61-62 71-72 76-77); Western Lg Div 1 R-up 83-84 87-88 95-96, (Merit Cup 82-83, Comb. Cup(Res) 91-92 (R-up 92-93)); Som. Snr Cup 52-53 66-67; S W Co's Cup 88-89

CHIPPENHAM TOWN

Chairman: Malcolm Lyus **Vice-Chairman:** Andy Russell **President:** G W Terrell
Secretary: Chris Blake, 28 Sadlers Mead, Chippenham, Wilts SN15 3PB (01249 658212).
Manager: John Freegard **Assistant Manager:** Vic Flippance **Physio:** Paul Christopher
Ground: Hardenhuish Park, Bristol Road, Chippenham (01249 650400).
Directions: M4 jct 17, A429 into Chippenham, follow signs for Trowbridge/Bath until r'bout, left onto A420 into town, ground 400yds on left. 5 mins walk from railway station on main A420 Bristol Road.
Seats: 100 **Cover:** 300 **Capacity:** 4,000 **Floodlights:** Yes **Club Shop:** Yes
Programme: 32 pages, 50p **Editor:** Sandie Webb (01249 653142**Press Officer:** Barry Fulker
Club colours: All blue **Change colours:** Old Gold/Black/Black.
Midweek matches: Wednesday **Nickname:** The Bluebirds **Formed:** 1873
Sponsors: Cifer Ltd, Kingston Smith, Supreme Video, Shoestrings Food Services, Vanitec Computers.
Record Gate: 4,800 v Chippenham Utd, Western Lg, 1951.
Previous Leagues: Hellenic, Wiltshire Senior, Wiltshire Premier.
Clubhouse: Yes, open matchdays. Food available. **95-96 Top Scorer:** Richard Lardner.
Club Record Goalscorer: Dave Ferris **Club Record Appearances:** Ian Monnery.
Honours: FA Cup 1st Rd 51-52, Western Lg 51-52 (Div 1 80-81, Div 2 52-53(Res) 80-81), Wilts Shield, Wilts Snr Cup, Wilts Snr League.

ELMORE

Chairman: A J Cockram **Vice Chairman:** P J Garnsworthy
Secretary: Alan Cockram, 1 Church Path, Halberton, Tiverton, Devon. Ex16 7AR. (01884 820959).
Manager: N Crocker. **Asst Manager:** R Moore. **Physio:** M Crocker.
Ground: Horsdon Park, Tiverton, Devon EX16 4DE (01884 252341). **Directions:** M5 Jct 27, A373 towards Tiverton, leave at 1st sign for Tiverton & Business Park, ground 500yds on right.
Seats: 200 **Cover:** **Capacity:** 2,000 **Floodlights:** Yes **Club Shop:** Yes.
Programme: 12 pages, 30p **Editor:** Richard Tapp(01884 252341) **Midweek matches:** Tuesday
Club Sponsors: Ken White Signs. **Nickname:** Eagles. **Founded:** 1947
Colours: Green & white/green/green. **Change colours:** Red/black/black
Previous Leagues: Devon & Exeter 47-74/ South Western 74-78.
Record Attendance: 1,713 v Tiverton Town Fri.April 14th 95.
Clubhouse: 11am-11pm Mon-Sat. Full canteen service - hot & cold meals & snacks.
95-96 Captain: P Lloyd. **95-96 P.o.Y.:** Mike Coysh. **95-96 Top Scorer:** B Walters
Club Record Appearances: P Webber. **Club Record Goalscorers:**
Hons: East Devon Snr Cup 72-73 75-76, Western Lg Cup 90-91,Les Philips(Lg Cup)94-95 (Div 1 R-up 90-91, Prem Div Merit Cup R-up 91-92, Div 1 Merit Cup 86-87 89-90 90-91), Devon St Lukes Cup R-up 90-91, Devon Snr Cup 87-88, Devon Intermediate Cup 60-61, Football Express Cup 60-61, Devon & Exeter Lg Div 2A 73-74 86-87(res)(Div 1A 76-77(res)), Devon Yth Cup 77-78.Great Mills Western League Runners Up 94-95.

MANGOTSFIELD UNITED

President: A J Hill **Chairman:** R Davis **Vice Chairman:** P Selway
Secretary: R Gray, 105 Chiltern Close, Warmley, Bristol BS15 5UW (01179 616523).
Manager: Terry Rowles. **Asst Manager:** Andy Perrett **Physio:** Ken Dodd.
Ground: Cossham Street, Mangotsfield, Bristol BS17 3EW (01179 560119).
Directions: M4 jct 19, M32 jct 1; A4174 marked Downend, through lights, over double mini-r'bout to Mangotsfield, left by village church onto B4465 signposted Pucklechurch, ground quarter mile on right. From central Bristol take A432 thru Fishponds, Staple Hill, to Mangotsfield and turn right by village church onto B4465. From Bath/Keynsham follow A4175, right at island at Willsbridge onto A431, then rejoin A4175 at next island (Cherry Garden Hill) to Bridge Yate, straight over double mini-r'bout and take 1st left, right into Carsons Rd after 1 mile and follow to Mangotsfield village & turn right by church onto B4465.
Seats: 300 **Cover:** 800 **Capacity:** 2,500 **Floodlights:** Yes **Club Shop:** Yes
Programme: 32 pages, 50p. **Editor:** Bob Smale (01179 401926). **Press Officer:** Secretary
Colours: Maroon/white/white **Change colours:** All white
Sponsors: Aaron Roofing Supplies **Nickname:** The Field **Founded:** 1950
Reserve League: Somerset Senior. **Record Attendance:** 2,386 v Bath City, FA Cup 77-78
Previous Leagues: Bristol & District 50-67/ Avon Premier Combination 67-72.
Players to progress to Football League: G.Megson, S.White, G.Penrice, P.Purnell, N.Tanner, M.Hooper.
Clubhouse: Open 11am-11pm. Snacks - hot food on matchdays. Lounge bar for official functions etc.
95-96 P.o.Y.: Richard Thompson **95-96 Top Scorer:** Andy Perrett **Midweek matchday:** Tuesday
Honours: FA Vase Semi-fin 95-96; Western Lg 90-91 (Lg Cup 73-74 (R-up 86-87) Div 1 R-up 82-83); Somerset Prem. Cup 87-88 (R-up 88-89 95-96); Glos Snr Cup 68-69 75-76; Glos FA Trophy 84-85 86-87 90-91 94-95; Hungerford Invitation Cup 74-75; Rothmans National Cup R-up 77-78; Hanham Invitation Charity Cup 84-85 85-86; Somerset Snr Lg(Reserves) Div 2 75-76 (Div 3 74-75); Somerset Comb. Cup 74-75; Glos Yth Shield 81-82 84-85 (R-up 82-83); Somerset Floodlit Yth Lg 81-82 82-83 83-84 84-85 87-88; Somerset Yth Shield 76-77.

ODD DOWN ATHLETIC

President: P A L Hill **Chairman:** N Fenwick (01225 834394) **Vice Chairman:** Mike Wilkins
Secretary: Mike Mancini, 36 Caledonian Rd., East Twerton, Bath BA3 2RD (01225 423293).
Manager: Alan Pridham (0117 983 3768)
Ground: Combe Hay Lane, Odd Down, Bath (01225 832491).
Directions: On main Bath/Exeter road - leaving Bath turn left into Combe Hay Lane opposite Lamplighters Pub. 40 mins walk from Bath (BR).
Seats: 160 **Cover:** 250 **Capacity:** 1,000 **Floodlights:** Yes. **Founded:** 1901
Colours: White/black/black. **Change colours:** Green/white/green
Programme: 12 pages with admission **Programme Editor:** Secretary **Club Shop:** No.
Sponsors: Streamline Coaches **Prev. Lges:** Wilts Premier, Bath & District, Somerset Senior
Midweek Matches: Tuesday **Reserve Team's League:** Somerset Senior
Record win: 11-1 v Minehead (H), Western League Premier Division 19/3/94.
Clubhouse: Yes, open noon-3 & 7-11pm. Hot & cold food available.
Record Scorer: Joe Matano 89 **Record appearances:** L Burns and T Ridewood, both 291.
Hons: Western Lg Div 1 92-93, Somerset Snr Cup 91-92.

PAULTON ROVERS

President: Mr T Pow **Chairman:** David Bissex **Vice Chairman:** Mr D Carter
Secretary: Mr John E Pool, 111 Charlton Park, Midsomer Norton, Avon BA3 4BP (01761 415190).
Manager: John Goss (0117 964 1191) **Physio:** John Pool.
Press Officer: D Bissex (01761 412463) **Commercial Manager:** M. Maule.
Ground: Athletic Ground, Winterfield Road, Paulton (01761 412907).
Directions: Leave A39 at Farrington Gurney (approx 15 miles south of Bristol), follow A362 marked Radstock for two miles, left at junction B3355 to Paulton, ground on right. Bus services from Bristol and Bath.
Seats: 138 **Cover:** 200 **Capacity:** 5,000 **Floodlights:** Yes **Founded:** 1881
Colours: White/maroon/maroon **Change colours:** Green & navy stripes/navy/navy **Nickname:** Rovers.
Midweek matches: Tuesday 7.30pm **Previous Leagues:** Wilts Premier/ Somerset Snr.
Previous Grounds: Chapel Field/ Cricket Ground/ Recreation Ground 1946-48.
Record Gate: 2,000 v Crewe, FA Cup, 1906-07
Programme: 20 pages, 50p **Programme Editor:** D Bissex (01761 412463).
Club Shop: Old programmes available - contact Chairman.
Clubhouse: 3 bars, lounge, skittle alley, dance hall. Capacity 300. Catering facilities.
Club Sponsors: BPC Catalogues/Design Windows/ Berkley Coaches.
Reserves' League: Somerset Snr. **Record appearances:** Mike Deeks. **Record scorer:** D Clark.
Hons: Western Lg Div 2 R-up 1900-01, Somerset Snr Cup 00-01 02-03 03-04 07-08 08-09 09-10 34-35 67-68 68-69 71-72 72-73 74-75, Somerset Snr Lg 00-01 03-04 04-05 70-71 71-72 72-73 73-74
Local Newspapers: Bath Evening Chronicle, Bristol Evening Post, Western Daily Post.

TAUNTON TOWN

Chairman: T F Harris **Vice Chairman:** A J Rutland. **Treasuer:** Joan Ellis
Secretary: The Secretary, C/O the club (see below).
Manager: Russell Musker. **Asst Manager:** Derek Fowler. **Physio:** Paul Topping
Ground: Wordsworth Drive, Taunton, Somerset TA1 2HG (01823 278191).
Directions: Leave M5 Jct 25, follow signs to town centre, at 2nd set of lights turn left into Wordsworth Drive; ground on left. 25 mins walk from Taunton (BR); turn left out of station and follow road right through town centre bearing left into East Reach. Follow road down and turn right into Wordsworth Drive shortly after Victoria pub.
Seats: 250 **Cover:** 1,000 **Capacity:** 4,000 **Floodlights:** Yes **Club Shop:** Yes
Programme: 28 pages, 50p **Editor:** Tom Harris. **Press Officer:**
Colours: Sky blue & claret/claret/sky blue **Change colours:** Yellow/blue/yellow.
Club Sponsors: Taunton Cider Co. **Formed:** 1947 **Nickname:** Peacocks
Midweek matches: Monday **Reserve Team's League:** Great Mills Combination.
Best FA Cup season: 1st Rd Proper 81-82 (lost 1-2 at Swindon Town).
Best FA Trophy season: 1st Rd Proper 80-81 (lost 1-5 v Hendon at Queens Park Rangers).
Best FA Vase season: Finalists 93-94.
Players progressing to Football League: Charlie Rutter (Cardiff), Stuart Brace (Southend & Grimsby).
Previous Leagues: Western 54-77/ Southern 77-83.
Clubhouse: Social club to accommodate 300, full bar facilities, separate bar & hall for private functions.
96-97 Captain: David Ewens. **95-96 P.O.Y.:** Keith Graddon
Club Record Appearances: Tony Payne **Club Record Scorer** (in a season): Reg Oram 67.
Honours: FA Vase R-up 93-94, Western Lg 68-69 89-90 (R-up 93-94, Les Phillips Cup R-up 93-94, Alan Young Cup 73-74 75-76(jt with Falmouth), Charity Challenge Cup 49-50 50-51), Somerset Snr Lg 52-53, Somerset Prem. Cup R-up 82-83 89-90 92-93.

Paulton Rovers:
Back Row (L-R); Dave Bissex (Chairman), Alan Bull (Coach), Graham Colborne, Mike Godwin, Steve Phillips, Steve Tovey, Simon Culliford, Mark James, Craig Harding, John Harvey, John Poole (Sec).
Front Row; Barry Young, Lee Evans, Andy Culliford, Lee Burns, Mark Evans, Trevor O;Neil, Wayne Gay.
Photo - Sunday Independant

Mangotsfield United:
Back Row (L-R); Steve Cross, Stuart Minall, Gary Smart, Jason Matthews, Dean Radford, Dave Bright, Simon Winstone, Andy Perrett.
Front Row; Carl Saunders, Matthew Rawlings, Richard Thompson, Wayne Morris, Gary Hewlett, Nigel Gillard, Joe Mogg, Ryan Perrett (Mascot).
Photo - Sunday Independant

TIVERTON TOWN

President: Dan McCauley **Chairman:** Gordon Anderson **Vice-Chairman:** Dave Wright.
Secretary: Ramsay Findlay, 35 Park Road, Tiverton, Devon EX16 6AY (01884 256341).
Manager: Martyn Rogers **Asst Manager:** Jimmy Giles **Physio:** Alan Morgan
Ground: Ladysmead, Bolham Road, Tiverton, Devon EX16 8SG (01884 258840).
Directions: M5 Jct 27, west towards Tiverton on A373, continue to end of dual carriageway and turn left at r'about; ground entrance 300yds on right alongside BP petrol station.
Seats: 300 **Cover:** 1,200 **Capacity:** 3,500 **Floodlights:** Yes **Club Shop:** Yes
Programme: 40 pages, 60p **Editor/Press Officer:** Nigel Davis
Colours: All Yellow **Change:** All white (black facings)
Sponsor: **Nickname:** Tivvy. **Formed:** 1920
Midweek matches: Wednesday **Previous League:** Devon & Exeter
Record Attendance: 3,000 v Leyton Orient, FA Cup First Round Proper 1994-95.
Players progressing to Football League: Jason Smith (Coventry City, 1993).Mark Saunders(Plymouth Argyle,1995).
Clubhouse: Lunctimes, evenings. All day Sat during the season. 3 bars. Food (burgers, hot dogs, chips etc).
95-96 Captain: Hedley Steele **95-96 Top Scorer:** Kevin Smith. **95-96 P.o.Y.:** Kevin Smith
Hons: FA Vase R-up 92-93 (QF 94-95); FA Cup 1st Rnd 90-91 91-92 94-95; Western Lg 93-94 94-95 (R-up 92-93 95-96); Les Phillips Cup 92-93 94-95 95-96; Amateur Trophy 77-78 78-79, Div 1 R-up 88-89; Devon St Lukes Cup 90-91 91-92 92-93 94-95 (R-up 89-90); Devon & Exeter Lg 51-52 66-67 70-71 84-85; Devon Snr Cup 55-56 65-66; East Devon Snr Cup 35-36 37-38 52-53 55-56 60-61 62-63 66-67; North Devon Charity Cup 72-73 86-87.

TORRINGTON

President: Frank Morris **Chairman:** Robert Dymond (01805 623569 (H) 01805 622853 (B)
Secretary: David Priscott, 6 Highfield Terrace, Bishops Tawton, Barnstaple. EX32 0AN. 01271 328316 (H & Fax).
Manager: Frank Howart (01395 446480)
Ground: Vicarage Field, School Lane, Great Torrington (01805 622853).
Directions: (From North, Barnstaple, Exeter, South Molton) In town centre turn left by parish church, turn right at swimming pool, ground behind swimming pool. Good parking. Red Bus from Bideford and Barnstaple (nearest BR station). Bus stop 300yds from ground.
Seats: None **Cover:** 2,000 **Capacity:** 4,000 **Floodlights:** Yes **Year Formed:** 1908
Midweek Matches: Wednesday **Club Sponsors:** Bideford Tool **Club Shop:** No.
Colours: Green & white hoops/green/green & white **Change cols:** Sky blue & white stripes/navy/light blue.
Previous Grounds: None **Nickname:** Torrie or Supergreens **Record win:** 18-0.
Previous Leagues: North Devon/ Devon & Exeter/ South Western 77-84.
Clubhouse: Weekdays 7-11pm, Sat 11am-11pm, Sun 12-3 & 7-10.30pm. Two bars. Light snacks available. New kitchen lounge,toilets and offices have been built.
Local Newspapers: North Devon Journal, Bideford Gazette
Record transfer fee paid: Nil **Received:** £3,000 for Dave Walter (Yeovil Town).
Best F.A.Vase Season: Fifth Round 1984-85.
Club record scorer: Trevor Watkins, 254 **Club record appearances:** Nigel Reed, 450+.
Hons: Western Lg R-up 90-91 (Lg Cup R-up 91-92, Div 1 R-up 84-85) Merit Cup 91-92 93-94. South Western Lg R-up 80-81 82-83 (Lg Cup 80-81 82-83), Devon Cup, Devon & Exeter Lg & Cup double, various local cup wins inc. Torridge Cup 92-93.

WESTBURY UNITED

Chairman: Philip Alford (01373 826327 (H) 01373 826275 (B) **President:** George Nicholls.
Secretary: Ernie Barber, 7 Farleigh Close, Westbury, Wilts. BA13 3TF (01373 822117).
Manager: Nigel Tripp (01225 782853)
Ground: Meadow Lane, Westbury (01373 823409).
Directions: In town centre, A350, follow signs for BR station, Meadow Lane on right (club signposted). Ten mins walk from railway station (on main London-South West + South Coast-Bristol lines).
Seats: 150 **Cover:** 150 **Capacity:** 3,500 **Floodlights:** Yes **Year Formed:** 1921
Colours: Green & white/green/white. **Change colours:** Sky blue/navy blue/nvay blue.
Midweek Matches: Tuesday **Prev. Leagues:** Wilts Comb./ Wilts Co. (pre-1984)
Nickname: White Horsemen **Previous Ground:** Redland Lane (pre-1935).
Club Shop: Yes. Shirts, scarves, hats, badges and various programmes.
Reserve Team's league: Trowbridge League.
Record Gate: 4,000 v Llanelli, FA Cup 1st Rd 1937 (match was on Littlewoods coupon!).Also 4,000 vWalthamstow Avenue.F.A.Cup 1937.
Players progressing to Football League: John Atyeo (Bristol City and England).
Clubhouse: Evenings 7-11pm, Fri, Sat & Sun lunctimes 12-3pm.
Honours: Western Lg Div 1 91-92, Wilts Senior Cup 31-32 32-33 47-48 51-52, Wilts Combination, Wilts Lg 34-35 37-38 38-39 49-50 50-51 55-56, Wilts Premier Shield R-up 92-93.

SCREWFIX WESTERN LEAGUE - DIVISION ONE CLUBS

AMESBURY TOWN

Chairman: Peter Taylor **President:** Sammy Dunford
Secretary: Tony Hinchliffe, 12 Lanes Close, Amesbury, Wilts. SP4 7RW. (01980 62445 (H) 01980 678425 (B).
Manager: Derek Graham **Coach:** John Hollis **Physio:** John Loftus/John Marshall
Ground: Amesbury Recreation Ground, Amesbury, Wiltshire (01980 623489).
Directions: Amesbury is nine miles north of Salisbury, off A303 through traffic lights, right at mini roundabout, left at Lloyds Bank, over bridge, as road bears right left into ground.
Capacity: 1,500 **Seats:** None **Cover:** 100 **Floodlights:** Yes **Club Shop:** No
Programme: £1 **Editor/Press Officer:** Tony Hinchliffe.
Colours: Blue/blue/white **Change colours:** All red **Record Attendance:** 753
Midweek home matches: Tuesday **Sponsors:** A K Motors **Nickname:**The Town **Founded:** 1905
Players progressing to Football League: Adrian Randall (Bournemouth/Burnley/York City), Mick Channon (Southampton/Manchester/England), David Coleman (Bournemouth).
Prev. Lgs: Salisbury & D., Wilts (pre-'94) **Clubhouse:** Bar on Matchdays.
Honours: Wilts Sen Cup 83-84 93-94, Wilts Lg 59-60 79-80 89-90 91-92.

BISHOP SUTTON

Chairman: Bob Redding **Vice Chairman:** Roy Penney **President:** Bob Redding.
Secretary: Mr Roy Penney, 33 Ridgway Lane, Whitchurch, Bristol BS14 9PN (01275 541392).
Manager: Chris Mountford **Coach:** Chris Stutt **Physio:** Vernon Ashton
Ground: Lakeview Football Field, Bishop Sutton (01275 333097).
Directions: On A368 at rear of Butchers Arms pub - Ground signposted on left entering village from the West.
Seats: None **Cover:** 200 **Capacity:** 1,500 **Floodlights:** No **Club Shop:** No.
Programme: Yes **Editor:** Mr G Williams **Colours:** All blue **Change colours:** Green/white/white.
Sponsors: Crown Insulation. **Nickname:** Bishops. **Founded:** 1977.
Youth team's League: Somerset Mid Week **Midweek Matches:** Tuesday **Record Attendance:** 410
Previous Leagues: Weston & Dist. Yth/ Bristol & Avon/ Somerset Snr (pre 1991)
Players progressing to Football League: David Lee (Chelsea), S Williams (Southampton), J French (Bristol Rovers).
Clubhouse: Open matchdays. Rolls, pies and usual pub food available.
Honours: Somerset Snr Lg R-up 89-90 (Div 1 83-84 (R-up 81-82), Div 2 82-83), Bristol & Avon Lg 80-81 (Div 2 79-80), Somerset Jnr Cup 80-81, Weston Yth Lg 77-78, Chew Valley Cup 83-84, Mid-Somerset Lg(Res) R-up 82-83 (Div 3 81-82).

CLYST ROVERS

Secretary: Bob Chamberlain, Orchard Cottage, Clyst St. George, Exeter. EX3 0NZ. (01392 873498 (H) 01392 59786 (B)
Manager: Dean Roberts / Nick Thomas (01392 462692) **Physio:** Bill Wreford.
Ground: Waterslade Park, Clyst Honiton, Devon (01884 259152). **Directions:** A30 following signs for Exeter Airport. From Exeter take 1st right after airport turning (ground signposted), 200yds past Duke of York Pub.
Seats: 130 **Cover:** 300 **Capacity:** 3,000 **Floodlights:** Yes **Founded:** 1926.
Colours: All Blue. **Change colours:** Red & White/White/Black. **Reformed:** 1951.
Midweek Matches: Tuesday. **Previous Grounds:** Fair Oak 1926-44. **Nickname:** Rovers.
Previous Leagues: Exeter & District 26-44 51-66/ Exeter & District Sunday 67-82/ South Western 81-92.
Programme: Yes. **Editor:** Ray Dack (01392 215075) **Club Shop:** Yes. Programmes, souvenirs etc.
Record Gate: 768 v Tiverton, Devon St Lukes final 11/5/93. **Record win:** 6-0 v Heavitree United, 1993.
Record defeat: 0-12 v Torpoint Athletic, South Western League, October 1990.
Clubhouse: Open one and a half hours before kick off and after game. Excellent food available.
Hons: Devon St Lukes Cup R-up 92-93, Western Lg Cup SF 92-93.

CREDITON UNITED

Chairman: D J Blanchford **Vice Chairman:** C R Gillard **President:** W J Ash.
Secretary: A Sherriff, 17 Churchill Drive, Crediton, Devon, EX17 3DW, (01363 774002)
Manager: Bob Calderhead/Rob England **Coach:** Dave Evans **Founded:** 1946
Ground: Lord's Meadow Sports Centre, Crediton (01363 774671-club, 777930-commercial dept.).
Directions: A337 to Crediton from Exeter, right onto A3072 (signposted Tiverton) at Crown of Crediton restaurant, turn right into Commercial Rd for Lord's Meadow Ind. Est.- Sports Centre car park 250 metres on left.
Seats: 150 **Cover:** 150 **Capacity:** 2,000 **Floodlights:** Yes **Club Shop:** No.
Programme: Yes **Colours:** Sky & Navy/Navy/Navy. **Change colours:** Red & Black/Black/Black.
Midweek Matches: Wednesday **Previous League:** Devon & Exeter (pre-1990) **Sponsors:** Graphic Electronics
Honours: Devon & Exeter Lg 87-88 (R-up 88-89, Harry Wood Tr. 88-89, Snr Div 1 62-63 66-67, Jnr Div 3 48-49(jt) 49-50, Snr Div 2b(res) 70-71, Snr Div 3(res) 86-87, Jnr Div 3(res) 56-57, I'mediate 1 Winners 94-95, I'mediate Div 3('A') 91-92, I'mediate Div 4 R-up('B') 92-93, I'mediate Div 5 R-up('B') 91-92), E. Devon Snr Cup 33-34, Okehampton Chal. Cup 72-73 74-75, Whitbread Flowers Cup 78-79, Bill Rees Trophy 86-87, Geary Cup(res) 84-85 86-87, Liddon Cup('A') 84-85 86-87.

DAWLISH TOWN

President: Bob Webster **Chairman:** Tony Darby **Vice-Chairman:** Peter Burridge
Secretary: Graham Jones, 133 Kingsdown Cres., Dawlish, Devon EX7 0HB (01626 866004).
Managers: Ian Hill & Tony Bowker. (01803 526362)
Ground: Sandy Lane, off Exeter Road, Dawlish (01626 863110).
Directions: Approx 1 mile from centre of town, off main Exeter road (A379).
Seats: 200 **Cover:** 200 **Capacity:** 2,000 **Floodlights:** Yes **Founded:** 1889
Programme: 34 pages, 30p **Programme Editor:** Roy Bolt.
Colours: Green & white/white/green & white **Change colours:** Blue & white/blue/blue & white.
Midweek home matchday: Tuesday **Previous League:** Devon & Exeter.
Record Gate: 1,500 v Heavitree Utd, Devon Prem. Cup Q-Final
Clubhouse: Open nightly, situated in car park opposite ground.
Hons: Western Lg Cup 80-81 83-84, Devon Premier Cup 69-70 72-73 80-81, Devon Snr Cup 57-58 67-68, Devon St Lukes Cup 82-83 (R-up 81-82), FA Vase Quarter Finals 86-87.

DEVIZES TOWN

Secretary: Andy Pearce, 66 Avon Road, Devizes, Wilts. SN10 1PT. (01380 727625 (H) 01380 729080 (B)).
Ground: Nursteed Road, Devizes. (01380 722817). **Manager:** Brian Newlands (01380 728991)
Directions: Off Nursteed Road (A342 signposted Andover); leaving town ground on right opposite Eastleigh Rd.
Seats: 130. **Cover:** 400 **Capacity:** 2,500 **Floodlights:** Yes **Founded:** 1883
Cols: Red & white stripes/black/black **Change colours:** Yellow & Blue/Blue/Yellow.
Previous Ground: London Rd (pre 1946) **Previous Name:** Southbroom (until early 1900s)
Previous Leagues: Wilts Comb./ Wilts Premier.
Hons: Wilts Snr Cup 07-08 49-50 56-57 57-58 58-59 60-61 61-62 62-63 65-66 67-68 70-71 71-72 73-74 78-79.

EXMOUTH TOWN

President: Brian Bradley **Chairman:** Paul Marshall (01395 276219)
Secretary: John S Edwards, Lamorna, 5 Pinn Lane, Pinhoe, Exeter EX1 3QX. (01392 468633 (H) 01404 850691 (B)).
Manager: Robert Green (01392 51781) **Physio:** Julian Bennett
Ground: King George V Ground, Southern Road, Exmouth (01395 263348).
Directions: On right side of main Exeter to Exmouth road (A376). Half mile from Exmouth (BR) station.
Seats: 100 **Cover:** 250 **Capacity:** 2,500 **Floodlights:** Yes **Year Formed:** 1933
Colours: Blue & white/blue/blue. **Change col:** Green & yellow/green/yellow. **Nickname:** 'Town' or 'Blues'
Programme: 36 pages, 30p **Editor:** J Dibsdall. **Previous Lge:** Devon & Exeter 1933-73.
Midweek home matchday: Tuesday **Reserves' League:** Gt Mills Comb.
Previous Grounds: Maer Cricket Field 33-38 48-64; Raleigh Park, Withycombe 38-39
Club Shop: Yes. Selection of non-League programmes (up to 20,000 in stock) and other club souvenirs.
Record Gate: 2,395 v Liverpool XI, friendly in 1987. **Record win:** 8-1 v Bristol Manor F., 1986
Record defeat: 0-10 v Tiverton (A), Devon St Lukes Cup QF 16/2/94.
Clubhouse: Open every night and weekend lunchtimes. Snacks available.
Club Record Scorer: Mel Pym, 117 **Record Appearances:** Keith Sprague, Geoff Weeks 410 (Western Lg)
Hons: FA Vase SF 84-85; Western Lg 83-84 85-86 (R-up 86-87 88-89; Lg Cup 88-89; Div 1 R-up 81-82; Sportmanship Tphy 86-87 92-93); Devon Premier Cup 70-71 79-80; Devon St Lukes Cup 84-85 88-89 89-90; Devon Snr Cup 50-51; East Devon Snr Cup 50-51 82-83; Harry Wood Mem. Cup 81-82; Exmouth Chal. Cup 64-65 65-66 66-67 68-69 70-71 71-72 73-74

FROME TOWN

President: Mr C W M Norton. **Chairman:** Colin Skirton (01225 423810)
Secretary: Mrs Sue J Merrill, 56 Nightingale Ave., Frome, Somerset BA11 2VW (011373 473820).
Manager: Mike Leeson (01225 706527) **Coach:** Mark Jones **Physio:** Shaun Baker
Ground: Badgers Hill, Berkeley Road, Frome (011373 453643). **Directions:** Locate "Vine Tree Inn", Bath Road; ground 100 yds from Inn (1 mile from town centre and Frome BR station).
Seats: 250 **Cover:** 800 **Capacity:** 5,000 **Floodlights:** Yes **Founded:** 1904
Colours: All red. **Change colours:** Green & yellow/black/green. **Nickname:** Robins.
Prev. Grounds: None **Prev. League:** Somerset Snr, Wilts Lge & Wilts Prem. **Club Shop:** No.
Midweek home matchday: Wednesday **Reserve team's League:** Somerset Senior.
Clubhouse: Evenings & weekends. Cold food only.
Record Attendance: 8,000 v Leyton Orient, F.A.Cup 1st Rd. 20-11-58. **Record Victory:** 15-0 v Glastonbury, Somerset Senior League (h) 1906-07. **Record Defeat:** 1-11 v Dorchester, Western League (a) 1958-59.
Best Season - F.A.Cup: 1st Rd Proper v L.Orient 1954-55. **F.A.Trophy:** 2nd. Rd. Proper v Boston United (a) 0-4, 1984-85. **F.A.Vase:** 2nd.Rd.Proper v Paulton R (a) 1-2.
Hons: Wiltshire League 1909-10,1910-11,Western Lg 78-79 (Div 2 19-20, Div 2 R-up 54-55, Lg Cup 79-80 82-83, Merit Cup 82-83, Alan Young Cup 79-80, Subsidiary Cup 59-60), FA Cup 1st Rd 54-55, Somerset Premier Cup 66-67 68-69 82-83, Wilts Premier Lg 62-63, Western Co's F'lit Cup 83-84, Somerset Snr Cup 32-33 33-34 50-51, Somerset Snr Lg 06-07 08-09 10-11 (Div 1(res) 90-91, Div 3(res) 85-86, Lg Cup(res) 91-92).

Exmouth Town: Back Row (L-R); K Lammacroft, C Tillett, J Harkness, H Richardson, N Montandon, N James, G Lucas (Trainer), R Green (Mgr), P Tricker, M Clatworthy. Front Row; K Hawkins, B Zoetemerk, S West, Daniel Green (Mascot), S Tonkins, N Skinner, I Harris. *Photo - Sunday Independant*

Frome Town: Back Row (L-R); S Baker (Trainer), L Aycliffe, S Rose, S Eade, L Cole, M Ford, D Turner, K Hunt (Asst Mgr), K Ball, M Leeson (Mgr). Front Row; D Keen, R Burr, J Edwards, J Burr, S Ratcliffe, G Baker, S Baker, K Chalice. *Photo - Sunday Independant*

Devizes Town: Back Row (L-R); N Taylor, J Alexander, D Hunt, Romans, D Lloyd, A Coombes, B Newland (Mgr). Front Row; M Allen, N Mooney, J Gale, A Doel, G Hopper, J King.

Photo - Sunday Independant

GLASTONBURY

Chairman: Terry Wolfe **President:** Mr L R Reed **Life President:** Les Heal
Secretary: Mrs L.Harmon,'Barleys',Bere Lane,Glastonbury,Somerset(011458 833221)
Ground: Abbey Moor Stadium, Godney Road, Glastonbury, Somerset (011458 831460).
Directions: From Bristol take by-pass from Tin Bridge r/about turning right at Northload Bridge r/about, then 1st right. From Taunton take by-pass at 'B&Q' turning, left at Northload Bridge r/about, then 1st right.
Seats: 80 **Cover:** 300 **Capacity:** 1,500 **Floodlights:** Yes **Nickname:** None
Manager: Dave Sheeham. **95-96 Top Scorer:** Mike Hole. **95-96 P.o.Y.:** Andy Howe.
Programme: 24 pages, 30p **Editor/Press Officer:** Les Heal (011458 832037) **Founded:** 1890.
Colours: Old gold/black/old gold **Change colours:** White/white/orange **Midweek Matches:** Wednesday
Prev. Lges: Bristol & District, Bristol Suburban **Clubhouse:** Hot snacks from tea bar on matchdays.
Club Record scorer: Jim Allaway 42 **Club Record Appearances:** Brian Mortimer 496.
Honours: Western Lg 48-49 50-51 69-70 (R-up 47-48 51-52)Great Mills Div 1 94-95 Lg Cup 65-66 (SF 83-84), Alan Young Cup 67-68 (jt with Minehead) 70-71); Somerset Professional Cup 37-38 48-49; Somerset Snr Cup 35-36; Somerset Charity Cup 32-33; Somerset Jnr Cup 12-13 13-14; Somerset Lg 49-50 50-51

HEAVITREE UNITED

President: Mr E Drew **Chairman:** Denis Bray. **Nickname:** Heavies.
Secretary: Keith Gilbert, 9 Dean St., St. Leonards, Exeter, Devon. (01392 438637).
Manager: Steve Riley (01392 424593) **Physio:** R Channing.
Ground: Wingfield Park, East Wonford Hill, Exeter, Devon (01392 73020).
Directions: Leave M5 at Exeter Granada Services, follow signs for City Centre/ Heavitree for approx. 3 miles and ground is situated on left at top of East Wonford Hill.
Seats: 150 **Cover:** 150 **Capacity:** 500 **Floodlights:** No **Founded:** 1885.
Colours: Black & jade/black & jade/black. **Change colours:** Black & white stripes/black/black.
Prev. Ground: Heavitree Park (pre-1950) **Previous Lges:** Exeter & Dist./ Devon & Exeter.
Records - Gate: 350 v Exeter City, friendly 1989. **Win:** 6-0 v Ilfracombe Town. **Defeat:** 0-13 v Larkhall Athletic.
Top scorer: John Laskey. **Most appearances:** Alan Kingdom.
Clubhouse: 12am-12pm daily. Wide range of matchday hot food. **Midweek home matchday:** Tuesday
Hons: Exeter & Dist Lg 46-47 51-52 (Snr Div 2 56-57 59-60 60-61 67-68), Devon & Exeter Lg 70-71 76-77, Devon Snr Cup 46-47 60-61 70-71, E Devon Snr Cup 46-47 70-71 76-77, Wheaton Tphy 87-88.

ILFRACOMBE TOWN

Chairman: Mike Edmunds **Vice-Chairman:** Bob Martin. **President:** Bob Martin.
Secretary/Press Officer: Tony Alcock, 2 Worth Road, Ilfracombe, North Devon EX34 9JA (01271 862686).
Manager: Ian Cornish **Asst Manager:** Mark Richards **Coach/Physio:** Eric Hayhurst
Ground: Marlborough Park, Ilfracombe, Devon (01271 865939).
Directions: A361 to Ilfracombe, 1st right in town after lights, follow Marlborough Rd to top, ground on left.
Seats: 60 **Cover:** 450 **Capacity:** 2,000 **Floodlights:** Yes **Club Shop:** No.
Programme: The Bluebird 8 pages, 40p **Editor:** Peter Bidgood (0271 864756)
Colours: Blue **Change colours:** Coral & purple **Sponsors:** Park View. **Nickname:** Bluebirds
Midweek home matchday: Tuesday **Reserve team's League:** North Devon. **Founded:** 1902
Previous Leagues: North Devon 04-14 20-22 60-84/ East Devon Premier 22-31/ Exeter & District 32-39 46-49/ Western 49-59/ South Western League (Reserves) 53-54.
Clubhouse: Every night 7-11pm and weekend lunchtimes. Hot & cold meals on matchdays.
95-96 P.o.Y.: Mark Creek. **95-96 Top Scorer:** Troy Roach. **Record attendance:** 3,000 v Bristol City, Ground opening, 2/10/24. **Club Record Goalscorer:** Darren Bryant. **Record Appearances:** Paul Jenkins 410.
Honours: East Devon Premier Lg 25-26 28-29 29-30, North Devon Senior Lg, North Devon Premier Lg 66-67 70-71 81-82 82-83, Western Lg Div 2 R-up 52-53.

KEYNSHAM TOWN

Chairman: Mike Lambern **President:** K Dowling
Secretary: Iain Anderson, 195 Mount Hill Road, Hanham, Bristol BS15 2SU (0117 9616426)
Manager: Graham Bird. **Physio:** A Weaver **Founded:** 1895
Ground: Crown Field, Bristol Road, Keynsham (01272 865876).
Directions: A4 from Bristol to Bath, ground on left before entering village opposite Crown Inn. Bus service every 30 mins from Bristol passes ground. 10 mins walk from Keynsham BR station.
Seats: 120 **Cover:** 500 **Capacity:** 2,000 **Floodlights:** Yes **Club Shop:** No.
Programme: 32 pages, 25p **Editor:** Alan Sale (0117 9499672) **Press Officer:** D Brassington
Colours: All Yellow. **Change colours:** All white. **Sponsors:** Ace Building Services Ltd. **Nickname:** K's.
Midweek matchday: Tuesday **Reserve team's League:** Somerset Senior.
Record Attendance: 3,000 v Chelsea, floodlight opening 88-89. Competitive: 2,160 v Saltash, Amateur Cup, Oct 1952.
Previous Leagues: Bristol District, Bristol Comb., Bristol Premier, Somerset Senior.
Clubhouse: Evenings & before & after games. Sunday lunch. Snacks.
95-96 Captain: Steve Clarke **95-96 Top Scorer:** Sean Day **95-96 P.o.Y.:** Jamie Boulton.
Honours: Somerset Lg Div 1 77-78; Somerset Snr Cup 51-52 57-58; GFA Jnr Cup 25-26, Somerset & Avon (South) Premier Cup 79-80 (SF 93-94), FA Cup 4th Qualifying Rd.

Melksham Town: Back Row (L-R); A Gingell, S Price, D Kilmurray, D Whiting, M Pearce, S Burns, A Hunt, B Moses. Front Row; S Irons, S Perkins, G Sanderson, G Burns, D Perrin (Pl/Mgr), M Howard, C Bishop.
Photo - Sunday Independant

Wellington: Back Row (L-R); M Darby (Mgr), K Pearson (Phy), N Pring, N Stone, M Jenkins, S Parrish, K Bryant, G Chaffey, I Blake, K Matthews (Train). Front Row; E Silva, R Lowe, A Payne, D Bryant, N Bowrah, N Woon.
Photo - Sunday Independant

Welton Rovers: Back Row (L-R); J CArver, I Dixon, P Griffiths, N Young, D Stock, A Doel, S Gurner, A Weeks, D James, M Beck (Mgr). Front Row; M Rogers, I Morrison, S Nethercott, J Bryan, P Antell, M Shields, J Bidmead.
Photo - Sunday Independant

LARKHALL ATHLETIC

President: Tony Rhymes **Chairman:** Jim McLay **Manager:** P Rankin/P Miles
Secretary: Mervyn Liles, 9 Eastbourne Ave., Claremont Rd., Bath BA1 6EW (01225 319427).
Ground: "Plain Ham", Charlcombe Lane, Larkhall, Bath (01225 334952).
Directions: A4 from Bath, 1 mile from city centre turn left into St Saviours Rd. In Larkhall square fork left, and right at junction, road bears into Charlcombe Lane. Ground on right as lane narrows.
Seats: None **Cover:** 50 **Capacity:** 1,000 **Floodlights:** No **Club Shop:** No
Programme: Yes **Colours:** All royal blue **Change colours:** All red
Nickname: Larks. **Founded:** 1914 **Midweek Matches:** Tuesday **Previous League:** Somerset Snr
Honours: Som. Snr Cup 75-76, Som. Snr Lg, Western Lg Div 1 88-89 93-94 94-95(Div 1 Merit Cup(4) 83-86 87-88(jt with Yeovil Res).

MELKSHAM TOWN

President: H J Goodenough **Chairman:** Mike J Perrin (01225 704523).
Secretary: Paul R Macey, 30 Wellington Square, Bowerhill, Melksham SN12 6QX (01225 706876 (H).
Manager: Darren Perrin (01225 704523)
Ground: The Conigre, Melksham. (01225 702843).
Directions: Just off main square in grounds of Melksham House.
Capacity: 3,000 **Seats:** 100. **Cover:** 1,500 **Floodlights:** Yes **Founded:** 1876.
Colours: Amber & royal blue/royal blue/royal blue. **Change colours:** Gold & black/black/black.
Previous Leagues: Wiltshire 1894-1974 93-94/ Western 74-93.
Previous Grounds: Challymead/ Old Brighton Road Field.
Record Gate: 2,821 v Trowbridge Town, FA Cup 57-58.
Clubhouse: Inside ground, open every evening & weekend lunchtimes.
Hons: Wilts Lg 03-04 93-94 (R-up 24-25 29-30 59-60 67-68 68-69 71-72), Western Lg Div 1 79-80, Wilts Snr Cup 03-04 69-70 77-78 (R-up 57-58 67-68 68-69), Wilts Shield 80-81 81-82 84-85 (R-up 86-87), FA Amateur Cup 1st Rd 68-69.

MINEHEAD

Chairman: Kyran Jesson. **Secretary:** Peter Bate, Meadow Cottage, Venniford, Minehead, Som. TA24 8ST. (01643 704063 (H) 0585 361207 (Mobile).
Manager: C Porter (01278 457583)
Ground: The Recreation Ground, Irnham Road, Minehead, Somerset (01643 704989).
Directions: Entering town from east on A39 turn right into King Edward Road at Police station, first left into Alexandra Rd and follow signs to car park; ground entrance within. Regular buses to Minehead from Taunton, the nearest railhead.
Seats: 350 **Cover:** 400 **Capacity:** 3,500 **Floodlights:** Yes **Founded:** 1889.
Club colours: Navy & sky blue/navy/navy. **Change colours:** Yellow & green/sky blue/yellow & green.
Programme: 24 pages, 50p **Editor:** Secretary. **Midweek Matches:** Tuesday 7.45pm.
Previous Leagues: Somerset Senior / Southern 72-83.
Record Gate: 3,600 v Exeter City, FA Cup 2nd Rd, 17/12/77.
Record defeat: 1-11 v Odd Down (A), Western League Premier Division 19/3/94.
Hons: Southern Lg R-up 76-77 (Div 1 Sth 75-76, Merit Cup 75-76), Western Lg R-up 66-67 71-72 (Div 1 90-91, Alan Young Cup 67-68 (jt with Glastonbury), Somerset Premier Cup 60-61 73-74 76-77.

PEWSEY VALE

Chairman: Mr J Noyes, 9 Easterton Lane, Pewsey, Wiltshire. (01672 563665).
Secretary: Mrs Barbara Flippance, 17 Slater Rd, Pewsey SN9 5EE (01672 63665).
Manager: N Offer (01672 563785)
Ground: Recreation Ground, Ball Rd, Pewsey (01672 62990).
Directions: On entering Pewsey from A345, at the Market Place proceed to end of High Street and turn right into Ball Rd, entrance to ground on right opposite pub. BR to Pewsey station.
Seats: **Cover:** Yes **Capacity:** **Floodlights:** No **Year Formed:**
Colours: White/blue/white **Change colours:** All Red.
Previous League: Wiltshire County (pre-1993).
Previous Name: Pewsey Y.M. (until late 1940s).
Midweek home matchday: Wednesday **Hons:** Wiltshire County League 92-93.

WARMINSTER TOWN

President: Bob Peaty **Chairman:** Colin Ball **Vice-Chairman:** Rod Kitley.
Secretary: Dave Carpenter, Cley View, 46 Upper Marsh Rd, Warminster, Wilts BA12 9PN (01985 212198).
General Manager: Derek Wesley **Coach:** Peter Russell.
Ground: Weymouth Street, Warminster, Wilts BA12, (01985 217828).
Directions: Take A350 for Weymouth from lights at centre of town - ground on left at brow of hill.
Seats: 75 **Cover:** 150 **Capacity:** 2,000 **Floodlights:** Yes **Club Shop:** No.
Programme: 36 pages, 40p **Editor:** Chris Finch (01985 217326)
Colours: Red & black stripes/black/black **Change:** All sky
Sponsors: Lyons Seafoods. **Nickname:** Red & blacks **Founded:** 1878
Midweek Matchday: Wednesday **Previous League:** Wiltshire
Clubhouse: Opened 22/7/94. Evenings/matchdays/as required
95-96 Captain: Paul Newman **95-96 P.o.Y.:** Gordon Saunderson. **95-96 Top Scorer:** Gary Lewis.
Honours: Wilts Snr Cup 1900-01 02-03 10-11 (R-up 09-10 26-27 32-33 53-54); Wilts Prem. Lg 56-57; Wilts Jnr Cup R-up 21-22 27-28 55-56 58-59; Central Wilts Lg 08-09

WELLINGTON

Chairman: Selwyn Aspin **Vice-Chairman:** **President:** Alan Shire
Secretary: Tony Brown, 6 Courtland Rd, Wellington, Somerset TA21 8ND (01823 662920).
Manager: Martin Darby. **Res. Manager:** Graham Aspin **Physio:** Ken Pearson.
Ground: Wellington Playing Field, North Street, Wellington, Somerset (01823 664810).
Directions: At town centre traffic lights turn into North St., then first left by Fire Station into the public car park that adjoins the ground.
Seats: None **Cover:** 200 **Capacity:** 3,000 **Floodlights:** Yes **Club Shop:**
Programme: Yes **Editor:** Jeff Brown
Colours: Tangerine/black/tangerine **Change colours:** Blue & claret stripes/blue/blue
Sponsors: A J Shire & Wadham Fencing **Nickname:** **Founded:** 1892
Midweek Matches: Wednesday **Reserves League:** Combination
Previous Leagues: Taunton Saturday, Somerset Senior
Players progressing to Football League: Nick Jennings (Plymouth).
95-96 Captain: Ian Jackson. **95-96 P.o.Y.:** Andy Payne. **95-96 Top Scorer:** Don Johnson.
Club Record Goalscorer: Ken Jones **Club Record Appearances:**
Honours: Western Lg Div 1 R-up 80-81 (Merit Cup 91-92); Western Comb Lge 95-96; Western Comb Lge KO Cup 95-96; Somerset Snr Lg Div 1 R-up; Rowbarton & Seward Cup;

WELTON ROVERS

Chairman: Ray James **President:**
Secretary: Geoff Baker, 6 Longfellow Road, Westfield, Radstock, Bath BA3 3YZ (01761 413742).
Manager: Malcolm Beck. **Asst Manager:** **Physio:** John Carver
Ground: West Clewes, North Road, Midsomer Norton, Somerset (01761 412097).
Directions: A367 Bath to Radstock – right at lights at foot of hill onto A362, ground on right.
Seats: 300 **Cover:** 300 **Capacity:** 2,400 **Floodlights:** Yes **Club Shop:** No.
Programme: 12 pages, 25p **Editor:** M Brown
Colours: Green & white/green/green **Change colours:** All Red
Sponsors: Maximum FX **Nickname:** Rovers. **Formed:** 1887
Midweek matchday: Monday **Reserve League:** Somerset Senior.
Record Attendance: 2,000 v Bromley, FA Amateur Cup 1963 **Previous Leagues:** None
Clubhouse: 7.30-11pm daily, Sat matchdays 1.30-2.45pm, Sun noon-2pm.
95-96 Captain: Mark Bartlett **95-96 Top Scorer:** Ian Dixon 18 **95-96 P.o.Y.:** Paul Antell
Club Record Appearances: **Club Record Goalscorer:** Ian Henderson, 51
Hons: Western Lg 11-12 64-65 65-66 66-67 73-74 (Div 1 59-60 87-88; Amateur Cup 56-57 57-58 58-59 59-60; Alan Young Cup 65-66 66-67 67-68(joint)); Somerset Snr Cup 06-07 11-12 12-13 13-14 19-20 24-25 25-26 60-61 61-62 62-63, Somerset I'mediate Cup 77-78, Somerset Jnr Cup 06-07(joint) 24-25 30-31, WBC Clares City of Wells Cup 78-79.

YEOVIL TOWN

Chairman: John Fry **President:** S N Burfield **Secretary:** Roger Brinsford c/o Club.
Manager: **Physio:** Tony Farmer
Ground: Huish Park, Lufton Way, Yeovil Somerset, BA22 8YF. (01935 23662, Fax 73956
Directions: Leave A303 at Cartgate roundabout and take A3088 signposted Yeovil. Take first exit at next roundabout and first exit at next roundabout into Lufton Way. Railway station - Yeovil Pen Mill (Bristol/Westbury to Weymouth) 2.5 miles from ground. Yeovil Junction (Waterloo to Exeter) 4 miles. Bus service from both stations on Saturday - matchdays.
Capacity: 8,720 **Seats:** 5,212 **Terracing:** 3,508 **Floodlights:** Yes **Metal Badges:** Yes.
Club Shop: Open on matchdays selling full range of souvenirs, match programmes, scarves, hats, replica kits *Team Talk Magazine* etc.
Colours: Green & white/green/white **Change colours:** All blue.
Midweek home matchday: Wednesday
Clubhouse: Matchdays hot + cold food available. Meals can be ordered provided advance notice is given. All weather astro turf pitch available for bookings 9am-10pm.
Hons:

Bristol Manor Farm:

Bridport 96-97: *Photo - Keith Clayton*

INTERLINK EXPRESS MIDLAND FOOTBALL ALLIANCE

FEEDER TO: BEAZER HOMES LEAGUE

President: Neville D Jeynes

Chairman: P Fellows **Vice-Chairman:** M W Lycett

Gen.Secretary: P G Dagger,
49 Bristol Way, Wellesbourne,
Warwickshire CV35 9TJ (01789 470236)

Publicity Officer: David Jenkin, (01203 593679)

The 1995-96 season has been one of consolidation following the League's formation in the previous season. The two teams that joined the League for their first season, Blakenhall, who were promoted from the West Midlands Regional League and Armitage relegated from the Beazer Homes League had very differing seasons. Blakenhall continued their success, winning the Industrial Rewind League Cup, the Walsall Senior Cup and finshing runners up in the League. Armitage were top of the League until the beginning of December when quite unexpectedly their owner decided to close the club having previously purchased another club in the Beazer Homes League.

Shepshed Dynamo, winners of the 95-96 Interlink Express MFA League receive the Championship Shield from Julie Roy- Financial controller of Interlink Express at the Welland Road ground

This meant that the results of matches played br Armitage had to be expunged and the season completed with the League's constitution one club short. If there is a lesson to be learned from the demise of Armitage it is of what can happen when the finances of a club are totally dependent on one person. This matter caused a lot of unnecessary work for the Officers of the League, brought the game of football into disrepute and was one sad episode in an otherwise successful season.

From Christmas omwards it became obvious that the League Champions would come from Shepshed Dynamo, Hinckley Athletic, Blakenhall, Knypersley Victoria and Rocester. Shepshed Dynamo and Hinckley Athletic were in first and second place for most of this period and it was only in the last two weeks of the season that Shepshed Dunamo were able to be confirmed as Champions. After a poor end to the season Hinckley Athletic lost the runners up position to Blakenhall on the last day of the season.

The league Cup sponsored by Industrial Rewind was keenly contested, the semi-finalists being Blakenhal, Oldbury United, Sandwell Borough and West Midlands Police. The final Played on May bank holiday Monday was won by Blakenhall who defeated Oldbury United 1-0.

The Midland Triangular Cup, sponsored by Polymac Services, is a competition for clubs in the Midland Football Alliance, the Premier Divisions of the Midland Football Combination and the West Midlands Regional League. The final was played between Pelsall Villa of the West Midlands Regional League and Oldbury United and resulted in a 1-0 victory for Pelsall Villa.

I must mention Oldbury United who unfortunately not only lost in the finals of the League Cup and the Midlands Triangular Cup but also in the final of the Birmingham Lord Mayor's Charity Cup. Any club which loses three finals in ten days deserves some sympathy but at least they were successful enough to reach the finals.

Other clubs achieving success this season were Pershore Town who won the Worcestershire Senior Urn and Barwell who reached the last sixteen of the FA Vase.

The Midland Football Alliance is proud that it retains its Contributory League status for Referees and Linesmen. Many of our officials received prestigious appointments during the season including Tony Bates and Peter Walton who were the two linesmen for the FA Cup final, Mark Warren FA Cup Semi-Final linesman, Alan Wiley and Paul Rejer who refereed FA Trophy and FA Vase Semi-Finals respectively and Tom Nicholls, Kevin Ingram and Andy Penn who were all linesmen for the FA Trophy and Vase Semi-Finals. Particular congratulations to Tony Bates who was appointed as a referee by the Football League at the end of the season. Tony together with Peter Walton and Mark Warren were also appointed linesmen for the European Cup (Euro 96).

The League continue's to be indebted to its main sponsors Interlink Express, whose support gives us the necessary resources to not only administer the League in an effective manner but also to provide member clubs with excellent financial rewards at the end of the season.

P G Dagger.

FINAL LEAGUE TABLE 1995/96

Division One	P	W	D	L	F	A	Pts
1. Shepshed Dynamo	36	22	10	4	90	37	76
2. Blakenhall	36	19	11	6	60	35	68
3. Hinckley Athletic	36	21	4	11	78	54	67
4. Rocester	36	19	9	8	55	50	66
5. Knypersley Victoria	36	18	8	10	73	43	62
6. Boldmere St Michael	36	18	5	13	73	51	59
7. Sandwell Borough	36	17	5	14	56	50	56
8. Willenhall Town	36	16	7	13	52	62	55
9. Barwell	36	15	6	15	57	53	51
10. Oldbury United	36	14	8	14	49	41	50
11. Halesowen Harriers	36	13	7	16	54	62	46
12. Rushall Olympic	36	15	5	16	56	65	46*
13. Stratford Town	36	12	9	15	56	54	45
14. Pershore Town	36	12	9	15	58	73	45
15. West Midlands Police	36	11	11	14	49	55	44
16. Chasetown	36	10	10	16	44	52	40
17. Shifnal Town	36	8	9	19	38	60	33
18. Stapenhill	36	5	6	25	38	87	21
19. Bolehall Swifts	36	5	5	26	30	82	20

** Rushall Olympic 4pts deducted*

LEADING GOALSCORERS (Lge only).

Mick Biddle	Knypersley Victoria	30	Lee Jinson	Sandwell Borough	26
Craig Martin	Hinckley Athletic	20	Neil Hesson	Oldbury United	19
Phil Haywood	Boldmere St Michael	18	Martin Dean	Boldmere St Mich	17
Mark Hodgkins	Hinckley Athletic	17	Paul James	Knypersley Victoria	16
Dave King	Shepshed Dynamo	16	Nick Kirk	Stratford Town	16
Shane Riddell	Shepshed Dynamo	16	Charlie Blakemore	Halesowen Harriers	14
Lee McGlinchey	Shepshed Dynamo	14	Antony Dixon	Chasetown	13
Carl Dwyer	Willenhall Town	13	Martin Hallam	Pershore Town	13
Andy McRobbie	Stapenhill	13	Russell Peake	Rocester	13

INTERLINK MIDLAND ALLIANCE LEAGUE RESULTS CHART 1995-96

HOME TEAM	1	2	3	4	5	6	7	8	9	10	11	12	13	14	15	16	17	18	19
1. Barwell	*	2-1	0-3	3-2	3-0	3-0	1-2	1-3	1-0	8-0	0-2	4-1	6-3	0-0	0-1	1-1	2-4	2-0	2-1
2. Blakenhall	2-0	*	3-2	2-1	0-0	1-0	2-0	1-1	0-1	2-2	0-0	4-2	2-1	3-3	2-1	2-0	2-2	3-0	3-0
3. Boldmere St Mich	3-0	2-3	*	0-1	5-1	3-0	4-2	1-6	1-1	4-0	0-1	1-2	3-0	1-4	3-1	3-1	1-1	3-3	4-0
4. Bolehall Swifts	0-4	0-0	1-4	*	0-2	2-5	1-3	1-1	1-2	0-2	0-2	0-3	0-1	1-3	0-0	2-0	2-0	3-5	2-2
5. Chasetown	1-0	1-0	0-2	0-1	*	0-1	1-2	0-1	1-0	1-2	2-3	2-0	0-1	3-3	2-2	7-1	1-2	4-0	4-2
6. Halesowen Harr	2-2	1-1	2-0	3-1	4-2	*	3-2	0-2	4-1	1-3	2-1	2-2	1-2	5-1	1-2	1-3	2-2	1-1	2-1
7. Hinckley Athletic	0-1	1-4	5-2	4-0	5-1	3-0	*	3-1	3-2	3-0	5-2	4-3	3-0	0-2	2-0	4-1	0-0	0-0	3-2
8. Knypersley Victoria	4-0	1-2	0-1	4-1	5-1	1-2	4-3	*	1-0	1-4	2-2	4-1	2-0	0-2	3-1	3-1	2-0	0-1	2-2
9. Oldbury United	0-0	2-1	0-1	2-0	2-0	2-0	0-2	0-0	*	2-0	5-1	0-1	3-2	1-6	1-2	6-0	5-0	1-0	2-0
10. Pershore Town	0-2	1-1	1-3	2-1	0-0	2-4	6-1	1-1	1-1	*	0-0	2-0	0-1	0-5	5-1	2-1	4-4	0-0	1-4
11. Rocester	2-0	1-0	2-1	2-1	1-1	5-0	1-0	1-4	0-0	3-1	*	2-1	3-2	0-2	2-1	2-2	2-1	2-1	1-2
12. Rushall Olympic	4-1	0-0	0-4	3-1	0-1	2-0	0-0	3-2	1-1	3-4	2-0	*	0-5	1-2	0-2	3-0	4-2	1-0	1-1
13. Sandwell Boro	3-1	0-1	3-2	1-1	1-1	3-1	0-1	1-0	3-2	3-2	0-1	0-1	*	1-0	0-0	2-0	2-1	2-0	1-2
14. Shepshed Dynamo	1-1	4-1	0-0	4-0	1-1	2-0	0-2	3-1	0-0	2-2	7-1	3-2	3-0	*	3-2	2-0	2-0	2-0	6-1
15. Shifnal Town	2-0	1-1	2-3	4-1	0-0	0-0	0-3	1-4	2-1	0-2	0-1	0-1	0-3	3-5	*	0-2	1-1	1-2	1-2
16. Stapenhill	0-1	1-2	2-2	0-1	0-2	0-2	4-1	0-3	1-1	1-2	2-2	3-4	1-6	1-5	0-0	*	0-3	2-0	0-1
17. Stratford Town	2-3	0-2	2-0	1-0	0-0	0-0	5-2	2-2	0-1	3-1	1-2	5-0	3-0	2-1	0-1	3-1	*	0-2	2-3
18. West Midlands Pol	1-1	1-3	0-1	6-0	1-1	2-1	1-1	0-2	2-0	3-2	1-1	3-1	3-3	1-1	2-2	2-3	1-0	*	2-1
19. Willenhall Town	2-1	0-3	1-0	2-1	1-0	2-1	0-3	0-0	3-1	3-1	1-1	0-3	0-0	0-0	2-1	4-3	0-2	4-2	*

INDUSTRIAL REWINDS LEAGUE CUP 1995-96

First Round;

Bolehall Swifts	v	Hinckley Athletic	2-1	
Chasetown	v	Shifnal Town	2-1	
Halesowen Harriers	v	Barwell	1-1, 1-0	
Rocester	v	Willenhall Town	0-0, 0-1	

Second Round;

Armitage	v	Blakenhall	1-5	
Boldmere St Michaels	v	Oldbury United	0-1	
Halesowen Harriers	v	Willenhall Town	1-1, 1-1	Willenhall won on penalties
Knypersley Victoria	v	Chasetown	4-4, 1-2	
Pershore Town	v	Stratford Town	2-2, 0-1	
Rushall Olympic	v	West Midlands Police	0-3	
Shepshed Dynamo	v	Sandwell Borough	3-3, 2-2	Sandwell win on away goals
Stapenhill	v	Bolehall Swifts	1-3	

Quarter Finals;

Blakenhall	v	Willenhall Town	2-0	
Oldbury United	v	Chasetown	2-0	
Sandwell Borough	v	Bolehall Swifts	3-1	
Stratford Town	v	West Midlands Police	1-3	

Semi-Finals 2 legs;

Blakenhall	v	Sandwell Borough	1-0	
Sandwell Borough	v	Blakenhall	2-1	Blakenall win on away goals
Oldbury United	v	West Midlands Police	5-1	
West Midlands Police	v	Oldbury United	1-3	Oldbury win 8-2 on agg.

Final: **Blakenall** B **Oldbury United 1-0**

CLUB DIRECTORY 1996-97

BARWELL

Chairman: David Laing. **Vice Chairman:** Ron Borman. **President:** Bob Gee
Secretary: Mrs Sue Boorman, 40 Charnwood Road, Barwell Leics. (01455 845749)
Manager: Bill Moore **Asst Manager:** Paul Purser. **Physio:** Viv Coleman/Mark Moore
Ground: Kirkby Rd, Barwell, Leics (01455 843067).
Directions: M42 jct 10 (Tamworth Services), A5 towards Nuneaton. Remain on A5 for approx 11 miles, go straight on at traffic lights at the Longshoot Motel the 400 yards at r/about take 1st exit left sign A47 Earl Shilton, in 3 miles at traffic lights go straight ahead and in 1 mile at r/about take first left exit sign Barwell in village centre 1/2 mile go straight over mini r/about, 20 yards turn right into Kirkby Rd, ground 400 yards on right.
Capacity: 2,500 **Seats:** 140 **Cover:** 750 **Floodlights:** Yes **Club Shop:** Unknown
Programme: 36 pages, 50p **Editor:** Mr Ron Boorman **Press Officer:** Merv Nash.
Colours: Yellow/green/yellow **Change colours:** Blue & white/blue/Blue. **Nickname:** Kirkby Roaders
Midweek home matchday: Tuesday **Club Sponsors:** Leicester Windows **Founded:** 1992.
Previous Lges: Midland Combination 92-94. *Barwell Ath.: Leics Senior. Hinckley: Central Midlands 86-88.*
Clubhouse: Evenings & lunchtimes. Snacks available.
95-96 Captain: Mark Orton **95-96 Top Scorer:** Nick Buff/Paul Purser **95-96 P.o.Y.:** Paul Purser
Club Record Goalscorer: Scott Kempin **Club Record Appearances:** Kevin Johnson.
Honours: Barwell Athletic: Leics Snr Lg Tebbutt Brown Cup 91-92.

BLAKENALL

President: J Bridgett **Chairman:** P Langston **Vice-Chairman:** D Cotterill
Secretary: David Birch, 64 Wimperis Way, Great Barr, Birmingham B43 7DF (0121 360 3574).
Manager: Bob Green **Asst Manager:** Graham Callaghan **Coach:** Brian Taylor
Commercial Mgr: Jeff Husted **Press Officer:** Russell Brown (01902 787853).
Ground: Red Lion Ground, Somerfield Rd, Bloxwich, Walsall, West Mids (01922 405835).
Directions: M6 jct 10, follow signs for Walsall centre. At 1st lights turn left (about 200yds from Motorway junction) into Bloxwich Lane. Keep following this lane to the 'T' junction and turn right into Leamore Lane, at this island turn left into Somerfield Road. Ground is approx. 400yds on the right.
Seats: 250 **Cover:** 250 **Capacity:** 2,500 **Floodlights:** Yes **Founded:** 1946.
Colours: Blue & white/white/blue & white. **Change colours:** Red & Black/White/Blue & White.
Clubhouse: Yes **Midweek home matchday:** Tuesday. **Nickname:** Lions.
Programme: 52 pages **Editor:** Russell Brown (01902 787853).
Previous Leagues: Bloxwich Comb./ Staffs County/ Midland Comb. 60-79.
Record transfer fee received: £10,000 for Darren Simkin (Wolverhampton Wanderers, 1992).
95-96 Captain: **95-96 Top Scorer:**
Hons: West Midlands (Regional) Lg 88-89, Midland Comb. 76-77, Walsall Snr Cup (6).Banks's Premier League Cup,94-95,Midland Football Alliance Tri-Angular cup 94-95.

BLOXWICH TOWN

President: M M Ross **Chairman:** C S Sanghera/ A S Bain.
Secretary: S Clarke, 10 Sandhill Str., Bloxwich, Walsall WS3 2JH (011922 492463).
Manager: M Folland/P Knox **Coach:** Jim Skidmore. **Physio:** R.Pickering.
Ground: Abbey Park, Glastonbury Crescent, Bloxwich, Walsall. (011922 77640)
Directions: A34 Walsall-Bloxwich, then west onto A4124. Ground 2-3 miles on right, s.p. Mossley Estate.
Capacity: 1,000 **Seats:** 200 **Covered:** 400 **Floodlights:** Yes **Club Shop:** No.
Programme: 16 pages 20p **Editor:** R S Badesha
Colours: Blue/white/blue **Change Colours:** Red & Black/Black/Black.
Sponsors: Leamore Windows. **Nickname:** Kestrels **Founded:** 1977.
Midweek Matches: Tues/Thurs
Players progressing to Football League: Martin O'Connor (Crystal Palace & Walsall).
95-96 Captain: Paul Wilde **95-96 Top Scorer:** Robert Wilson 40 **95-96 P.o.Y.:**
Honours: Bloxwich Comb.(2), Staffs Co. Lg Div 1, Walsall Snr Cup R-up 86-87, Invitation Cup 89-90, Midland Combination Premier Div. 95-96 R-Up.94-95.
Midland Combination Div 1 89-90, Alan Peck Cup (3), Carlsberg Challenge Cup 95-96.

BOLDMERE St MICHAELS

Manager: Alan Parsons
Secretary: John D. Shaw, 176 Springthorpe Rd.,Erdington, Birmingham B24 OSN (01213 505869)
Ground: Church Road, Boldmere, Sutton Coldfield (01213 374435/01213 847531)
Directions: A38 & A5127 from City towards S. Coldfield, left at Yenton lights onto A452 (Chester Rd), Church Rd is 6th turning on the right. 400yds from Chester Road (BR).
Capacity: 2,500 **Seats:** 100 **Covered:** 100 **Floodlights:** Yes **Nickname:** Mikes.
Colours: Black & White stripes/black/black **Change Colours:** All blue **Founded:** 1882
Midweek matches: Tues/Thurs **Previous Leagues:** West Mids 49-63/ Midland Combination 63-94.
Programme: 28 pages, 30p **Editor:** Dave Tolley (0121 382 7130)
Clubhouse: Bar & lounge, every evening and four lunchtimes
Hons: Birmingham AFA 36-37, Birmingham AFA Snr Cup, Birmingham Jnr Cup, FA Amtr Cup SF 47-48, AFA Snr Cup 47-48, Central Amtr Lg 48-49, Midland Comb.(3) 85-86 88-90 (Challenge Cup 77-78 89-90, Tony Allden Memorial Cup 78-79 88-89 91-92, Challenge Trophy 86-87).
Players who progressed to Football League: John Barton (Everton, Derby County), Kevin Collins (Shrewsbury), Jack Lane (Birmingham City, Notts Co.), John Lewis (Walsall), Don Moss (Cardiff, C Palace), Harry Parkes (Aston Villa), Wally Soden (Coventry).

CHASETOWN

Chairman: G Rollins **Vice Chairman:** B Simpson **President:** A Scorey.
Secretary: P E Dixon, c/o Club
Manager: Cliff Painter **Asst Manager:** Brian Fox **Physio:** E Highfield.
Ground: The Scholars, Church Street, Chasetown (01543 682222/684609).
Directions: Follow Motorways M5, M6 or M42 and follow signs for A5. A5 to White Horse Road/Wharf Lane, left into Highfields Rd (B5011), left into Church Street at top of hill, ground at end just beyond church. Buses 394 or 395 W Mids Travel, 94 Chase Bus,from Walsall, 860 Midland Red from Cannock.
Seats: 112 **Cover:** 250 **Capacity:** 2,000 **Floodlights:** Yes **Club Shop:** Yes
Programme: 26 pages, 50p **Editor/Press Officer:** Mike Fletcher
Colours: All blue **Change Colours:** All Red.
Sponsors: Aynsley Windows **Nickname:** Scholars **Founded:** 1954.
Midweek matchday: Tuesday **Reserves League:** West Midlands
Record Attendance: 659 v Tamworth, FA Cup 2nd Qualifying Rd 1/10/88.
Previous Leagues: Cannock Yth 54-58/ Lichfield & Dist. 58-61/ Staffs Co. 61-72/ West Mids 72-94.
Clubhouse: Mon-Fri 7.30-11pm, Sat 11.30am-11pm, Sun 8-10.30pm. Basic snacks.
95-96 Captain: Peter Perry. **95-96 Top Scorer:** T Dixon. **95-96 P.o.Y.:** Peter Perry.
Club Record Goalscorer: T Dixon 172 **Club Record Appearances:** A Cox 469 (+15 sub).
Honours: West Mids Lg R-up 90-91 92-93 (Lg Cup 89-90 90-91, Div 1 77-78 (R-up 73-74 74-75 75-76 80-81 82-83), Div 1 Cup R-up 80-81 82-83, Div 2 R-up 87-88, Div 2 Cup R-up 86-87); Walsall Snr Cup 90-91 92-93; Staffs Snr Cup R-up 91-92.

HALESOWEN HARRIERS

Chairman: Brian Beasley **Match Secretary:** Malcolm Pearce.
Secretary: Mrs Christine Beasley, 43 Hawne Lane, Haleowen, West Midlands B63 3RN.
Manager: Derek Beasley **Asst Manager:** Neil Beasley **Physio:** D Bowen.
Ground: Hayes Park, Park Rd, Colley Gate, Halesowen (01384 896748. Club Newsline: 0891 66 42 52).
Directions: On A458 Birmingham to Stourbridge Rd (B'ham 10 miles, Stourbridge 4 miles). M5 Jct 3 (towards Kidderminster), right at 1st island (towards Dudley), turn left at island (towards Stourbridge), straight over next island then 3m to grd left side, 200yds past Park Lane. 1 mile Lye BR
Seats: 350 **Cover:** 500 **Capacity:** 4,000 **Floodlights:** Yes **Club Shop:** No.
Programme: 24-28 pages **Editor:** Rob Shinfield (01384 850819)
Colours: White with blue trim/black/white **Change colours:** Yellow/Blue/Yellow
Sponsors: Bevan Contracts **Founded:** 1961 **Nickname:** None
Midweek home matchday: Tuesday or Wednesday.
Record Attendance: 750; friendlies v Walsall and Wolves in 1985. Competitive; 450 v Lye, Lge 1988.
Previous Leagues: Festival (Sunday)/ West Midlands (pre-1994).
Clubhouse: Open every evening. Limited range of hot snacks, but full cold snack kitchen.
95-96 Captain: **95-96 P.o.Y.:** Rob Shilvock **95-96 Top Scorer:** Charlie Blakemore
Honours: West Mids Lg Div 1 85-86 (Div 2 84-85, Div 2 Cup 84-85), Inter City Bowl 67-68 68-69, Festival Lg(5)(R-up(9)), FA Sunday Cup SF 79-80, Midland Sunday Cup, Birmingham Sunday Cup.

HINCKLEY ATHLETIC

Chairman: Mick Voce **Vice Chairman:** Rob Mayne **President:** Derek Loakes.
Secretary: Mr John Colver, 18 Portland Drive, Hinckley, Leics LE10 1SE (01455 613936).
Manager: John Hanna **Asst Manager:** Bill Nally **Physio:** Buster Kendall
Ground: Middlefield Lane, Hinckley. Leics (01455 613553 or 01455 615012)
Directions: A47 Coventry Rd towards Hinckley. Keep on Inner Ring Rd to lights top of Upper Bond St, junc of Ashby Rd/Derby Rd. Turn left grd bottom of Middlefield Lane. 2 miles Hinckley (BR).
Seats: 320 **Cover:** 1,000 **Capacity:** 5,000 **Floodlights:** Yes **Club Shop:** No.
Programme: 36 pages, 50p **Editor:** A Mason (0116 2891 899) **Press Officer:** Andy Gibbs.
Colours: Red/black/red **Change colours:** All blue
Sponsors: Vend Fabrics **Nickname:** Robins. **Founded:** 1889
Midweek matchday: Tuesday **Reserves League:** Endsleigh Midland Comb.
Record Attendance: 5,410 v Nuneaton Borough, Birmingham Combination 26/12/49.
Best FA Cup season: 2nd Rd Proper 54-55 (lost 1-2 at Rochdale), 62-63 (2-7 at Queens Pk Rgrs).
Best FA Trophy season: 1st Qualifying Rd 69-70 72-73 73-74.
Best FA Vase season: 5th Rd 89-90 (lost to Guiseley),93-94 (lost to Newbury Tn)
Previous Leagues: Leicestershire & Northants/ Leicestershire Senior/ Birmingham Combination 14-39 47-54/ West Midlands (Regional) 54-59 64-94/ Southern 63-64.
Players progressing to Football League: John Allen (Port Vale), Keith Scott (Wycombe,Swindon,Stoke,Norwich), Gary Pick (Hereford), Mike Love (Wigan).
Clubhouse: Social club with lounge, games room, and concert room. Open each evening, Sunday lunch and matchdays. Hot & cold food available (01455 615012).
95-96 Captain: Gareth Williams **95-96 Top Scorer:** Craig Martin **95-96 P.o.Y.:** Craig Martin
Club Record Goalscorer: M Hodgkins **Club Record Appearances:** Steve Markham 455 86-96
Honours: Leics Snr Cup 4, West Mids (Reg.) Lg R-up 82-83, Birmingham Snr Cup 54-55(jt with Brush Sports), Leics Challenge Cup 6.

KNYPERSLEY VICTORIA

Chairman: Philip Leese **Vice Chairman:** Peter Freeman **President:** G Quinn.
Secretary: J.A.Shenton, 27 Portland Drive, Biddulph, Stoke on Trent, ST8 6RY (01782 517962).
Manager: Dave Nixon **Coach:** Greg Clowes **Physio:** N Gregory
Ground: Tunstall Road, Knypersley, Stoke-on-Trent, (01782 522737 club).
Directions: M6 Jct 15 join A500, 4th exit, pick up A527, follow through Tunstall, Chell, to Biddulph. Grd on A527 just before Biddulph. Bus 61 Congleton-Tunstall passes ground.
Seats: 200 **Cover:** 200 **Capacity:** 1,200 **Floodlights:** Yes **Club Shop:** Yes
Programme: 40 pages, 50p. **Editor/Press Officer:** J A Shenton (01782 517962).
Colours: Claret & Sky Stripes/sky/Claret & sky. **Change Colours:** White & Navy/Navy/White.
Sponsors: KMF Precision Sheetmetal Ltd. **Nickname:** The Vics. **Founded:** 1969.
Midweek matchday: Tues/Thurs **Reserve League:** Staffs Senior.
Record Attendance: 1,100 v Pt Vale, friendly 1989.
Prevs Lgs: Leek & Moorlands 69-78/ Staffs Co. (Nth) 78-83/ Staffs Sen 83-90/ W Mid (Reg) 90-94.
Clubhouse: Open from 1pm on Saturdays and 7pm weekdays. Burgers, hot dogs, crisps etc
95-96 Captain: **95-96 P.o.Y.:** Carl Woolhouse **95-96 Top Scorer:** Mick Biddle 36
Club Record Goalscorer: J Burndred **Club Record Appearances:** David Shallcross 475
Honours: West Mids Lg Div 1 92-93, Staffs Snr Lg 84-85 (Lg Cup 84-85 85-86), Staffs Co. Lg R-up 79-80, Staffs FA Vase 83-84 86-87, Sentinel Cup 86-87, Leek & Moorlands Lg 72-73 (Div 2 71-72).

OLDBURY UNITED

Chairman: Roy Keeling. **Vice Chairman:** Ken Harris.
Secretary: Michael Stanley, 32 Junction St, Oldbury, Warley, West Mids B69 3HD (0121 544 5091).
Manager: Kevin Hadley. **Asst Mgr:** Graham Jones. **Physio:** Tony Dandy
Ground: The Cricketts, York Road, Rowley Regis, Warley, West Midlands (0121 559 5564).
Directions: M5 jct 2, follow Blackheath & Halesowen signs, 1st left at lights & 4th left into York Rd, grd 200yds left. 1 1/2 miles Sandwell & Dudley and Rowley Regis BR. Bus 404 from West Bromwich, Oldbury and Blackheath.
Seats: 300 **Cover:** 1,000 **Capacity:** 3,000 **Floodlights:** Yes **Founded:** 1958
Cols: All blue (white flashes/trim) **Change colours:** Tangerine/Black/Black.
Cricketts,The Blues. **Nickname:**
Previous Names: Queens Colts 58-62/ Whiteheath Utd 62-65.
Record Gate: 2,200 v Walsall Wood, Walsall Snr Cup Final 1982.
Prev. Lges: Oldbury 58-62/ Warwick & W Mids All. 62-65/ Worcs (later Midland) Comb. 65-82/ Southern 82-86.
Players progressing to F'ball Lge: C Gordon, L Conoway, J Scott, R O'Kelly, G Nardiello, Dakin, T Reece.
Programme: 28 pages, 50p **Programme Editor:**Football Secretary. **Club Shop:** No
Midweek home matchday: Tuesday **Club Sponsors:** Beswick Paper Group, Oldbury.
Clubhouse: Mon-Fri 7.30-11pm, Sat-Sun 12-2.30 (12-11pm Sat matchdays). Hot snacks.
Hons: West Mids Lg 92-93, Staffs Snr Cup 87-88, Midland Comb. R-up 78-79, Walsall Snr Cup 82-83, B'ham Snr Amtr Cup, Oldbury Lg Div 2 61-62, Worcs Snr Urn 86-87, Sandwell Charity Cup 86-87.

Barwell FC:
Back Row (L-R); Andy Lucas, Jevon Payne, Jason Gotch, Mark Orton (Capt), Paul Bray, Darren Ratcliffe, Ian Munroe, Jeff Lissaman, Scott Mackay, Darren Hill, Wayne Nimblette. Front Row; Paul Purser, Nick Buff, Anthony Hopewell, Terry Smith, Tim Warner. Mascot of the Day, Adam Withers

Boldmere St Michaels FC: Team photo taken before the "Mikes" 3-0 home victory over Stapenhill in the MFA.

PELSALL VILLA

Chairman: C V Dolphin **Vice Chairman:** J H Gough **President:** B J Hill
Secretary: Gareth J Evans, 72 St Pauls Crescent, Pelsall, Walsall WS3 4ET (01922 693114).
Manager: Reg Priest **Asst Manager:** Kevin Gough. **Physio:** J.Lancaster.
Ground: The Bush, Walsall Rd, Heath End, Pelsall, Walsall (01922 682018 or 692748 matchdays only).
Directions: M6 jct 7 marked A34 B'gham. Take A34 towards Walsall to 1st island, turn right (marked Ring Road), cross two islands. At large island at bottom of hill take last exit marked Lichfield, up hill, cross next island to lights. Continue to next set of lights and turn left (B4154 Pelsall). Go over railway bridge to Old Bush pub on right (next to Pelsall Cricket and Sports Club).
Seats: Yes **Cover:** 624 **Capacity:** 2,000 **Floodlights:** Yes **Club Shop:** Yes
Programme: 52 pages, 50p **Editor:** Secretary **Press Officer:** B J Hill
Colours: Red & black/black/black **Change colours:** Blue & white/blue/blue
Sponsor: **Nickname:** Villians **Reformed:** 1961.
Midweek home matchday: Tuesday. **Record Gate:** 1,800 v Aston Villa 28/11/91.
Best FA Cup season: 3rd Qualifying Rd 92-93 (lost 2-4 at Gainsborough Trinity).
Best FA Vase season: 5th Rd 92-93 (lost 0-1 at Buckingham Town).
Previous League: Staffs County (South) 61-81.
Clubhouse: Mon-Fri 7.00-11pm, Sat noon-11pm, Sun noon-3 & 7.00-10.30pm. Hot & cold meals.
95-96 Captain: Adrian Horne. **95-96 Top Scorer:** Hardip Singh **95-96 P.o.Y.:**
Club Record Goalscorer: Kevin Gough 109. **Club Record Appearances:** Kevin Gough 435.
Honours: West Mids Lg Div 1 Cup 88-89 (R-up 89-90, Div 2 Cup R-up 83-84, Walsall Snr Cup R-up 89-90 92-93, Wednesbury Charity Cup 6, (R-up 7), D Stanton Shield(2) 73-75 (R-up 75-76), Sporting Star Cup 76-77 (R-up 61-62), Prem Div Tphy(res)89-90), Rugeley Charity Cup 78-79 (R-up 69-70), Bloxwich Charity Cup(2), Edge Cup 83-84, Ike Cooper Tphy R-up 89-90. Banks's Brewery League Champions 94-95 (R-up 95-96) Div Cup 95-96, Midland Triangle Cup 95-96.

PERSHORE TOWN '88

Chairman: T.B.A. **Vice Chairman:** C.Brimmell.
Secretary: Mr A J Barnett, 8 Croft Cottages, Cropthorne, Nr Pershore, Worcs WR10 3LX (01386 860243).
Manager: Gary Aldington. **Asst Mgr:**Ricky Hooman. **Physio:** Rick Harber/Mark Palfrey
Ground: King George XI Playing Fields, High Street, Pershore, Worcs (01386 556902).
Directions: M5 jct 7, A44 to Pershore (8 miles) cross 1st lights in Pershore, at 2nd lights turn left & fold road round into King Georges Way, ground immediately on left.
Seats: 120 **Cover:** 120 **Capacity:** 4,000 **Floodlights:** Yes **Founded:** 1988.
Colours: Blue & white/blue/blue **Change colours:** Yellow/green/yellow.
Previous League: Midland Combination 90-94.
Programme: 20 pages, 50p **Editor:** Mr T S Conway (01386 554390) **Club Shop:** No
Reserves' Lge: Banks's W.Mid.Lg.Div.1. **Midweek home matchday:** Tuesday **Nickname:** The Town
Best FA Cup season: 4th Qualifying Round 94-95 (lost 1-3 to Yeading).
Best FA Vase season: Preliminary Rd 92-93 (lost 0-1 at Stewarts & Lloyds).
Record Gate: 1,356 v Yeading, FA Cup 4th Qualifying Round 23/10/93.
Clubhouse: Bar open Tue-Thur 7.30-11pm, Fri 2-6 & 7.30-11pm, Sat noon-11pm, Sun noon-3 & 7-10.30pm. Coffee, tea, soup,. hot pies and rolls available during matches.
Record scorer: Simon Judge 76. **Record appearances:** Ian Aldington, 192 + 5 sub.
Hons: Midland Combination 94-95 (Div 2 89-90), Worcs Jnr Cup 90-91, Robert Biggart Cup(2) 90-92 94-95 (R-up 89-90), Worcs Snr Urn R-up 92-93, Jack Mould Cup 90-91, Alfred Terry Cup 90-91, Martley Hosp. Cup('A') 90-91, Pershore Hosp. Cup(Res) 92-93 94-95, Evesham Hosp. Minor Cup R-up('A') 94-95.

ROCESTER

Chairman: A.Hawksworth.
Secretary: Mr Gilbert Egerton, 23 Eaton Road, Rocester, Uttoxeter, Staffs ST14 5LL (01889 590101).
Manager: Mick Collins. **Asst Mgr:** P.Fernihough. **Reserves' Mgr:** Mick Collins
Ground: The Rivers Field, Mill Street, Rocester, Uttoxeter, Staffs (01889 590463).
Directions: From A50 r'bout adjoining Little Chef restaurant at Uttoxeter take B5030 towards Rocester and Alton Towers, right into Rocester village after 3 miles over narrow bridge, in village centre bear right at sharp left-hand bend into Mill Str., ground 500yds on left just past former cotton mill.
Seats: 200 **Cover:** 500 **Capacity:** 4,000 **Floodlights:** Yes **Founded:** 1876
Colours: Amber/black/black **Change colours:** All sky blue **Nickname:** Romans
Programme: 32 pages, 50p **Programme Editor:** Ian Cruddas (01889 564173)**Club Shop:** Yes
Players progressing to Football League: George Shepherd (Derby County), Mark Sale (Birmingham).
Record Gate: 1,026 v Halesowen Town, FA Vase 4th Rd January 1987 (at Leek Town FC).
Previous Lges: Ashbourne/ Leek & Moorland/ Cheadle & Distrist/ Uttoxeter Amateur/ Stafford 53-57/ Staffs County Nth 57-84/ Staffs Senior 84-87/ West Mids 87-94.
Reserves Lge: W Midlands **Midweek matchday:** Tuesday **Sponsors:** H.K.B. Steels Ltd.
Players progressing to Football League: Bert Carpenter (Manchester Utd), Joe Carpenter (Brighton), George Shepherd (Derby), Mark Sale (Birmingham, Torquay), Tony Hemmings (Wycombe (via Northwich)).
Clubhouse: On matchdays (normal licensing hours) and other special events. Hot drinks & snacks.
Club record scorer: Mick Collins **Club record appearances:** Peter Swanwick.
Hons: West Mids Lg R-up 89-90 (Div 1 87-88, Div 1 Cup 87-88), Staffs Snr Lg(2) 85-87, Staffs FA Vase 85-86 87-88.

Halesowen Harriers:
Back Row (L-R): Paul Probert, Kevin Thompson, Gary Gibbs, Duncan Brown, Robert Shilvock, Lee Humphries, Danny Philpotts. Front Row; Dennis Brown, Richard Madeley, Charlie Blakemore, Steve Shaw, Neal Meredeth, Ian Guise.

Knypersley Victoria FC:
Back Row (L-R); Adam Royall, Danny Higgins, Mick Biddle, Robert Powner, Peter Wilcox, Terry Stanway, Paul Shenton, Paul James. Middle Row; Greg Clowes (Coach), Peter Hall, Mark Timms, David Shallcross (Capt), Brian Hall, Dave Nixon (Mgr). Front Row; Wayne Atkinson, Nicky Bedson.

RUSHALL OLYMPIC

Chairman: John Burks **Vice Chairman:** Trevor Westwood **President:** Brian Greenwood.
Secretary: Barry Hall, 10 Miles Meadow Close, Willenhall WV12 5YE (01922 446822)
Manager: Martin Sweeny/Carlo Rossi **Asst Manager:** **Physio:** Eddie Judge
Ground: Dales Lane, off Daw End Lane, Rushall, Nr Walsall (01922 641021).
Directions: From Rushall centre (A461) take B4154 signed Aldridge. Approx., 1 mile on right, directly opposite Royal Oak Public House, in Daw End Lane. Grd on right. 2 miles Walsall (BR) station.
Seats: 200 **Cover:** 200 **Capacity:** 2,500 **Floodlights:** Yes **Club Shop:** No
Programme: 36 pages **Editor/Press Officer:** Darren Stockall (01922 379153).
Colours: Amber/black/black **Change colours:** White/red/red
Sponsors: WM Print **Founded:** 1951 **Nickname:** Pics.
Midweek matchday: Tuesday **Reserves' League:** West Mids (Reg.)
Record Attendance: 2,000 v Leeds Utd Old Boys, charity match 1982.
Previous Leagues: Walsall Amateur 52-55/ Staffs County (South) 56-78/ West Midlands (Regional) 78-94.
Players progressing to Football League: Lee Sinnott (Watford), Lee Palin (Aston Villa, Nottingham Forest, Bradford City), Stuart Watkiss (Walsall), Steve Taylor (Crystal Palace).
Clubhouse: Bar/lounge, open every night 8-11pm, Sat matchdays, Sunday noon-2.30pm.
95-96 Captain: **95-96 Top Scorer:** **95-96 P.o.Y.:**
Club Record Goalscorer: Graham Wiggin **Club Record Appearances:** Alan Dawson (400+ apps).
Hons: West Mids League Div 1 79-80, Walsall Amtr League Div 1 55-56 (Div 2 52-53, Snr Cup 54-55 55-56, Jabez Cliff Cup 55-56), Staffs Co. League Div 1 60-61 61-62 62-63 64-65 (Div 2 56-57), Walsall Charity Cup 52-53, Walsall Chal. Cup 54-55 56-57, Walsall Memorial Charity Cup 55-56 56-57 57-58 58-59 59-60 60-61 61-62, W Preston Chal. Cup 56-57, Cannock & Dist. Charity Cup 56-57, Wednesbury Snr Cup 58-59 59-60 60-61, Sporting Star Cup 59-60 60-61(joint) 64-65 65-66 67-68, J W Edge 62-63 66-67, Walsall Snr Cup 64-65, Lichfield Charity 64-65 66-67, Staffs Yth Cup 81-82.

SANDWELL BOROUGH

Manager: Paul Molesworth. **Founded:** 1918.
Secretary: Ken Jones, 19 Henn Drive, Princes End, Tipton, West Mids DY4 9NN (0121 557 9429).
Ground: Oldbury Sports Centre, Newbury Lane, Oldbury (0121 552 1759).
Directions: Follow A4123 B'ham-Wolverhampton Rd, past island at jnt 2 M5, after half mile turn left into Newbury Lane and stadium is on the right. 2 miles from Sandwell & Dudley (BR).
Capacity: 3,000 **Seats:** 200 **Cover:** 600 **Floodlights:** Yes **Nickname:** Trees
Midweek matches: Wednesday **Previous Grnd:** Londonderry, Smethwick 18-81
Colours: Green & white stripes/green/green **Change Colours:** Amber & black
Record Gate: 950 v Halesowen T., FA Cup 1987
Programme: 12 pages 25p **Programme Editor:** R Unitt.
Previous Leagues: B'ham Suburban/ Central Amtr/ Worcs (Midlands Comb.) 48-88 90-94/ Southern 88-90.
Clubhouse: Licensed bar overlooking pitch. Open everyday
Players who have progressed to Football League: Andy Micklewright (Bristol Rov, Bristol City, Swindon, Exeter), Gary Bull (Southampton, Cambridge Utd)
Hons: Mids Comb. Chal. Cup R-up(5) 49-50 51-53 67-68 74-75, Chal. Tphy R-up 88-89, Pres. Cup 79-80 (R-up 76-77), Div 2 R-up 79-80), B'ham Jnr Cup.

SHIFNAL TOWN

Chairman: Mr L Jones **Vice Chairman:** R Owen **President:** R Arnold
Secretary: Mr D Groucott, 4 Idsall Cres., Shifnal, Shropshire, TF11 8ES (01952 402255).
Manager: Mervyn Rowe **Asst Manager:** M.Humphreys. **Physio:** Danny Wedge
Ground: Phoenix Park, Coppice Green Lane, Shifnal, Shropshire.
Directions: M54 jct 3, A41 towards Newport, 1st left for Shifnal (3 miles), in Shifnal take 1st right, and sharp right again up Coppice Green Lane, ground 800yds on left past Idsall School. 1 mile from Shifnal BR station.
Seats: 104 **Cover:** 300 **Capacity:** 3,000 **Floodlights:** Yes **Club Shop:** No
Programme: 32 pages, 60p **Editor:** J.Wilson (01952 274855). **Press Off:** G Davies (01952 460326).
Colours: Red/white/black **Change colours:** Yellow/green
Sponsors: Associated Cold Stores & Transport Ltd. **Nickname:** None. **Founded:** 1964
Midweek matchday: Tuesday **Reserves' League:** None at present
Record Attendance: 1,002 v Bridgnorth Town, F.A. Vase 3rd Rd 83-84 (at Admirals Park).
Previous Leagues: Wellington (East Dist.) 64-69/ Shropshire County 69-77 85-93/ West Midlands 77-85/ Midland Combination 94-95.
Clubhouse: Not on ground but in Newport Rd, Shifnal. Open Mon-Fri 7.30-11pm, noon-11pm Sat matchdays, noon-2.30 & 7.30-11pm Sat non-matchdays, Sun noon-3 & 7.30-11pm.
95-96 Captain: Mick Flanell **95-96 Top Scorer:** Shaun Bradbury 14 **95-96 P.o.Y.:** Shaun Bradbury
Club Record Goalscorer: Steve Kelly 35. **Club Record Appearances:**
Honours: West Mids Lg 80-81 81-82 (Div 1 78-79), Shropshire Snr Cup 80-81 90-91 92-93.

STAPENHILL

Chairman: Tony Smith **Vice Chairman:** **President:** Fred Sleigh.
Secretary: David Coulson, The Flat, 117 Calais Road, Burton-on-Trent DE13 0UN (01283 516725)
Manager: Bob Sykes **Asst Manager:** John Wayte **Physio:** Ken Hulland.
Ground: Edge Hill, Maple Grove, Stapenhill, Burton-on-Trent (01283 562471).
Directions: 3 miles from Burton on A444 Measham Rd, turn right (coming from Burton) at Copperhearth Pub Hse into Sycamore Rd, Maple Grove is 5th left. 3 miles from Burton-on-Trent (BR) buses 15, 16 from opposite station.
Capacity: 2,000 **Seats:** 100 **Covered:** 500 **Floodlights:** Yes **Club Shop:** No
Programme: 60p **Editor:** Secretary **Press Officer:** Secretary.
Colours: Red & white trim/red **Change Colours:** Sky/navy/navy/navy
Sponsors: TAG Football Kits **Nickname:** Swans. **Founded:** 1947.
Midweek matcheday: Tuesday **Reserves League:** Midland Comb.
Record Attendance: 2,000 v Gresley, Derbys Snr Cup final 88-89.
Previous League: Leics Snr 58-89/ Midland Combination 89-94.
Clubhouse: In ground. Pub hours. Matchday tea bar.
95-96 Captain: **95-96 Top Scorer:** **95-96 P.o.Y.:**
Club Record Goalscorer: Brian Beresford 123 **Club Record Appearances:** Ian Pearsall 172.
Honours: Midland Combination R-up 92-93 (Div 1 89-90, Challenge Cup 92-93 93-94), Leics Snr Lg 59-60 86-87 88-89 (Tebbutt Brown Cup(2) 87-89), Leics Snr Cup 69-70 86-87, Derby Snr Cup R-up 88-89 91-92.

STRATFORD TOWN

Chairman: G Cutler **Vice-Chairman:** T.B.A **President:** P Chatburn
Secretary: R.Liggins, 17 Hammerton Way, Wellesboure, Warwicks. CV35 9NS. (01789 840755)
Manager: S Dixon **Physio:** N Dixon **Commercial Mgr:** J Carruthers.
Ground: Masons Road, off Alcester Road, Stratford-upon-Avon, Warks (01789 297479).
Directions: Follow Alcester/Worcester A422 signs from town centre - Masons Rd is 1st right afterrailway bridge. 400 yards from Stratford-on-Avon (BR) station. Local buses for West Green Drive.
Capacity: 1,100. **Seat/Cover:** 200 **Floodlights:** Yes **Club Shop:** No.
Programme: 20 pages, 50p **Editor:**
Colours: Tangerine/black/tangerine **Change Colours:** White/white/black
Sponsors: Porters Precision Products **Nickname:** The Town **Founded:** 1944
Midweek Matches: Tuesday **Reserves' League:** Midland Comb. Reserve Division.
Record Attendance: 1,078 v Aston Villa, Birmingham Snr Cup, Oct 1996
Previous Leagues: W Mids 57-70/ Mid Com. 70-73 75-94/ Hellenic 70-75.
Players progressing to Football League: Martin Hicks (Charlton, Reading, Birmingham), Roy Proverbs (Coventry, Bournemouth, Gillingham), Richard Landon (Stockport Co.,Plymouth Argyle (via Bedworth Utd).
Clubhouse: Open every night except Sunday
95-96 Captain: G Hannam. **95-96 P.o.Y.:** G Hannam. **95-96 Top Scorer:** N Kirk.
Honours: Midland Comb 56-57 86-87; Chal. Cup 86-87 88-89 (R-up 55-56); Chal. Vase 81-82; Jack Mould Tphy 81-82; Tony Allden Mem. Cup 86-87; B'ham Snr Cup 62-63.

WEST MIDLANDS POLICE

President: Chief Constable R Hadfield OBE
Chairman: Asst Chief Constable D G Ibbs MBE **Vice Chairman:** Jim Swingeford
Secretary: John Black,57 Grosvenor Close,Sutton Coldfield,W.Mids.B75 6RP.(0121 308 7673)
Manager: Colin Brookes/Mark Fogarty
Commercial Manager: John Black. **Press Officer:** Tony Pearson.
Ground: Police Spts Ground, 'Tally Ho', Pershore Road, Edgbaston, Birmingham B5 7RN (0121 472 2944).
Directions: 2 miles south west of city on A441 Pershore Road. Ground is on the left 50yds past Priory Road lights (Warks County Cricket Ground). 3 miles from Birmingham New Street (BR) - buses 41, 45 & 47 from city.
Capacity: 2,500 **Seats:** 224 **Covered:** 224 **Floodlights:** Yes **Founded:** 1974
Midweek matches: Tues/Thurs. **Reserve Team's League:** Midland Combination.
Programme: 16 pages, 50p **Editor:** K Horrigan (0121 626 4020x6100) **Club Shop:** No.
Colours: Red & black stripes/black/black
Change Cols: Yellow/green/green. **Record Gate:** 1,072 v Sudbury Town, FA Vase QF 29/2/92.
Previous Leagues: B'ham Wednesday 28-38/ Mercian 46-53/ B'ham Works 53-69/ Mid Comb 74-94.
Clubhouse: Complex of 3 bars including snooker room, ballroom, kitchen. Hot & cold food. Open all day.
Hons: FA Vase QF 91-92, Mids Comb 90-91 (R-up 94-95, Chal. Cup 74-75 (R-up 85-86)), Tony Allden Mem. Cup 75-76 (R-up 91-92), B'ham Jnr Cup, Worcs Snr Urn 84-85 90-91 91-92 (R-up 81-82 85-86), National Police Cup(12) 61-65 66-67 69-70 73-76 80-81 87-88 91-92 (R-up(7) 67-68 70-72 76-78 88-89 94-95), Aston Villa Cup 60-61 64-65 65-66.

WILLENHALL TOWN

President: Jack Williams **Chairman:** Don Crutchley **Vice Chairman:** David Homer.
Secretary: Malcom Skitt, 52 Longwood Rise, Willenhall, West Midlands WV12 4AX (01902 632557).
Manager: Kenny Drakeford. **Asst Manager:** Phil Embury. **Physios:** Mike Andrews & Steve Hooper.
Ground: Noose Lane, Willenhall, West Midlands (01902 605132-club, 636586-office).
Directions: M6 Jnc 10 follow 'new' Black Country route and then 'Keyway'. On leaving 'Keyway' follow signs to Wolverhampton(A454). At 'Neachells' P H house right into Neachells Lane, and first right again into Watery Lane. At island turn left onto Noose Lane, ground is 200yds on left.
Seats: 324 **Cover:** 500 **Capacity:** 5,000 **Floodlights:** Yes **Club Shop:** Yes
Programme: 40 pages, 60p **Editor:** Bill Taylor(01902 843435).
Colours: All red **Change colours:** Yellow & blue.
Sponsors: Aspray Transport. **Nickname:** Reds **Founded:** 1953
Midweek matchday: Tuesday. **Reserves League:** Midland Comb.
Record Attendanc: 3,454 v Crewe Alexandra, FA Cup 1st Rd 1981.
Previous Leagues: Wolverhampton Amateur/ Staffs County/ West Mids 75-82 91-94/ Southern 82-91.
Players progressing to Football League: Sean O'Driscoll (Fulham & Bournemouth), Joe Jackson (Wolves), Stuart Watkiss (Wolves & Walsall), Tony Moore (Sheff Utd), Andy Reece (Bristol Rovers), Wayne O'Sullivan (Swindon).
Clubhouse: Open Mon-Thurs 12-3 & 7-11pm, Fri-Sat 11am-11pm, Sun 12-2 & 7-10.30pm. Pies, cobs, crisps etc available.
95-96 Captain: Carl Dwyer. **95-96 P.o.Y.:** Gary Chadwick. **95-96 Top Scorer:** Carl Dwyer
Club Record Goalscorer: Gary Matthews **Club Record Appearances:** Gary Matthews.
Honours: FA Vase R-up 80-81, West Mids Lg 78-79 (Div 1 75-76, Prem. Div Cup 79-80, Div 2 Cup 78-79(res)), Birmingham Snr Cup R-up 82-83, J W Hunt Cup 73-74.

FA Vase 5th Round Flixton v Barwell

The massed Barwell defence takes on the Flixton attack. *Photo - Martin Wray.*

Flixton's Rob Jackson attacks the Barwell Goal *Photo - Colin Stevens*

ENDSLEIGH MIDLAND FOOTBALL COMBINATION

FEEDER TO: MIDLAND ALLIANCE

Chairman: Ian Johnson

Hon. Secretary: Norman Harvey, 115 Millfield Road, Handsworth Wood, Birmingham B20 1ED (01213 574172)

Bloxwich Town completed the transformation from Cinderella club to Champions as they were the outstanding side in the Premier. They emphasised their quality by defeating Alvechurch 8-1 in the final of the Challenge Cup. Off the field the committee did their bit to clinch a place in the Midland Alliance next season. They go with our best wishes. Coventry Climax did well to finish runners-up in their first season. Massey Ferguson won the Coventry Telegraph Cup and Handrahan Timbers runners-up in the J W Hunt Cup.

In Division One Richmond Swifts were deserved Champions, they were runners-up in the Birmingham County Vase and won the J W Hunt Cup. The Presidents Cup final was a high scoring affair as Polesworth North Warwick beat Kenilworth Town 8-5. Kenilworth won the Birmingham County Vase and on the last day of the season clinched a point to give them 2nd place edging out Bilston CC but all three sides will play Premier Division football next season. Spare a thought for Northfield Town champions 1994-95, relegated 95-96. Chelmsley Town were relegated due to ground facilities.

In Division Two Continental Star took the title with Enville Athletic 2nd, sadley Enville's ground was not up to division one standards, Cheslyn Hay and Brownhills Town were promoted. Fairfield Villa and Badsey Rangers were relegated from Division One. In the Challenge Vase Bromsgrove Rangers defeated West Midlands Police 4-0. Feckenham had a stunning debut season in the Combination , winning the league from Richmond Swifts Reserves, they also beat the latter on penalties in the Challenge Urn Final. Feckenham also won the Worcester Junior Cup and the Smedley Crooke Cup Final. Third place Tipton S+S were also promoted.

Rushden & Diamonds won the Reserve Division Double winning the league and Challenge Trophy, Tamworth reserves won the Fazeley Cup, Gresley Reserves were runners-up in the league, Divisional Cup and Fazeley Cup.

Steve Davies

FINAL LEAGUE TABLES 1995/96

Premier Div	*P*	*W*	*D*	*L*	*F*	*A*	*Pts*
1. Bloxwich Tn	38	31	4	3	122	45	97
2. C/try Climax	38	25	5	8	87	43	80
3. M Ferguson	38	23	8	7	77	36	77
4. Knowle	38	21	10	7	87	49	73
5. Studley BKL	38	17	11	10	93	64	62
6. Kings Heath	38	18	6	14	63	65	60
7. Meir K A	38	15	10	13	77	72	55
8. Wellesbourne	38	15	10	13	55	60	55
9. Southam Utd	38	13	14	11	69	63	53
10. Coleshill Tn	38	14	9	15	76	66	51
11. Chelmsley Tn	38	14	8	16	65	62	50
12. Upton Town	38	14	6	18	68	72	48
13. Ansells	38	12	10	16	64	81	46
14. Olton Royale	38	12	8	18	56	71	44
15. W Mids Fire	38	11	9	18	51	70	42
16. Alvechurch V	38	10	10	18	57	84	40
17. Highgate Utd	38	9	10	19	56	81	37
18. Handrahan Tim	38	9	10	19	46	71	37
19. Shirley Town	38	8	8	22	51	74	32
20. Northfield T	38	3	6	29	33	124	15

Div One	*P*	*W*	*D*	*L*	*F*	*A*	*Pts*
1. Richmond Sw	32	26	5	1	92	18	83
2. Kenilworth T	32	17	10	5	75	31	61
3. Bilston C C	32	18	7	7	78	41	61
4. Colletts Gr	32	18	7	7	76	54	61
5. GPT Coventry	32	19	3	10	84	47	60
6. Dudley Spt	32	16	8	8	63	39	56
7. Alveston	32	14	7	11	63	48	49
8. Polesworth NW	32	12	9	11	60	69	45
9. Newhall Utd	32	11	10	11	68	63	43
10. Monica Star	32	11	8	13	55	56	41
11. Holly Lane	32	9	11	12	43	53	38
12. Hams Hall	32	11	4	17	55	68	37
13. Kings Norton	32	12	1	19	49	82	37
14. Thimblemill	32	8	4	20	38	73	28
15. Barlestone S G	32	8	3	21	44	91	27
16. Fairfield V	32	6	4	22	27	75	22
17. Badsey Rang	32	2	7	23	30	92	13

PREMIER DIVISION RESULTS CHART 1995-96

HOME TEAM	1	2	3	4	5	6	7	8	9	10	11	12	13	14	15	16	17	18	19	20
1. Alvechurch Villa	*	3-1	0-6	1-2	2-2	3-4	3-0	2-2	0-2	1-3	0-1	0-1	1-3	1-0	1-1	0-4	0-2	4-1	1-0	2-2
2. Ansells	2-3	*	1-8	2-2	1-4	0-0	5-1	1-2	4-0	1-1	2-2	2-0	4-0	0-3	2-2	2-0	1-5	1-0	4-2	0-0
3. Bloxwich Town	6-2	0-2	*	2-1	1-0	3-0	3-0	4-2	4-3	3-1	3-1	4-0	5-0	2-2	1-0	4-1	6-2	3-1	0-1	4-2
4. Chelmsley Town '94	1-1	3-2	3-4	*	3-3	0-1	5-2	0-3	0-0	1-3	0-0	3-0	3-0	0-1	3-2	4-2	2-1	2-0	2-0	2-1
5. Coleshill Town	2-2	1-1	0-1	3-3	*	2-1	1-2	2-3	3-0	1-2	0-0	5-4	2-0	6-2	1-0	5-3	1-4	0-1	1-3	0-3
6. Coventry Sphinx	3-1	2-0	1-1	1-5	2-2	*	4-2	0-1	5-0	3-1	0-1	3-0	2-0	2-1	2-0	3-2	2-3	1-1	1-2	2-1
7. Handrahan Timbers	0-1	1-0	0-2	1-0	0-2	0-2	*	2-2	0-0	2-1	1-2	1-1	1-1	3-0	6-2	1-2	4-0	0-2	1-3	4-2
8. Highgate United	2-2	1-3	1-2	3-2	0-2	0-2	2-2	*	2-0	3-3	1-1	1-3	1-0	3-0	0-1	0-2	0-4	1-3	1-1	1-1
9. Kings Heath	1-0	2-3	2-5	3-0	2-0	0-2	1-0	2-1	*	2-2	3-2	1-1	4-0	3-0	0-0	1-1	1-3	3-2	3-4	2-0
10. Knowle	0-0	2-3	1-3	2-1	1-0	4-0	3-0	2-1	4-2	*	1-1	5-1	4-0	2-1	1-2	1-1	3-2	2-2	5-0	3-1
11. Massey-Ferguson	6-2	3-0	5-0	1-0	2-0	1-2	1-0	2-1	5-0	0-2	*	0-2	5-0	3-1	1-0	1-1	1-1	3-2	2-0	2-1
12. Meir K A	6-0	3-3	2-2	5-2	2-6	0-4	1-1	4-2	0-2	1-2	0-1	*	6-1	1-3	1-0	2-2	2-1	5-0	4-1	1-2
13. Northfield Town	2-2	4-3	2-8	0-3	1-5	0-3	0-1	2-5	0-3	1-3	1-6	1-2	*	2-2	4-0	0-2	0-5	0-2	0-3	0-3
14. Olton Royale	1-5	4-2	0-4	0-1	1-1	0-3	2-2	5-2	3-4	0-0	1-3	1-3	1-1	*	2-2	1-2	0-0	1-2	2-1	4-1
15. Shirley Town	1-2	4-0	0-4	1-1	4-2	1-3	1-1	3-2	1-2	0-4	1-3	0-2	6-0	0-1	*	2-3	2-3	0-5	1-3	1-2
16. Southam United	2-3	1-2	1-2	2-2	3-1	2-1	2-2	4-1	2-3	1-2	2-1	1-2	2-2	2-1	1-1	*	1-1	1-1	1-1	2-0
17. Studley BKL	2-2	5-0	2-2	3-2	3-3	1-7	6-0	6-1	1-3	2-2	2-2	0-0	3-2	1-2	0-2	2-2	*	7-2	2-2	2-0
18. Upton Town	3-0	3-0	1-3	2-1	0-3	1-2	4-1	4-0	2-0	0-5	2-1	3-3	8-0	0-3	3-3	3-4	0-3	*	0-0	0-1
19. Wellesbourne	3-1	3-3	1-2	1-0	2-1	0-3	1-1	1-1	0-1	1-4	0-3	2-2	2-0	1-2	2-1	1-1	2-1	3-1	*	1-0
20. W Midlands Fire Ser	3-3	1-1	0-5	3-0	1-3	1-3	1-0	1-1	3-2	1-0	1-2	4-4	3-3	0-2	0-3	1-1	0-2	2-1	1-1	*

FINAL LEAGUE TABLES 1995/96

Div Two	P	W	D	L	F	A	Pts
1. C/tinental St	32	24	6	2	89	28	78
2. Enville Ath	32	21	5	6	71	31	68
3. Brownshill T	32	20	5	7	73	46	65
4. Cheslyn Hay	32	19	4	9	76	54	61
5. Earlswood Tn	32	16	9	7	56	30	57
6. W Mid Pol R	32	13	8	11	47	41	47
7. Bromsgrove R	32	13	8	12	63	59	44
8. Ledbury Tn	32	11	9	12	71	50	42
9. Alvis	32	10	12	10	52	41	42
10. Coleshill T R	32	12	6	14	49	61	42
11. Cadbury Ath	32	11	6	15	36	49	39
12. W/hampton CR	32	11	4	17	46	79	37
13. Blackheath ED	32	8	8	16	40	49	32
14. Archdale	32	7	8	17	46	60	29
15. Burntwood	32	7	7	18	41	64	28
16. Albright & W	32	6	6	20	35	81	24
17. Wellesbourne R	32	6	5	21	33	101	23

Rugby Town FC resigned records expunged

Div Three	P	W	D	L	F	A	Pts
1. Feckenham	34	27	5	2	102	26	86
2. Richmond S R	34	25	4	5	89	29	79
3. Tipton S & S	34	21	5	8	68	30	68
4. Birmingham V	34	20	8	6	62	38	68
5. Mitchells & B	34	16	9	9	74	44	57
6. Studley Utd	34	16	6	12	64	56	54
7. Cradley Hth	34	13	8	13	53	46	47
8. Kenilworth W	34	13	7	14	51	56	46
9. Dudley S R	34	14	3	17	48	55	45
10. Kings Hth R	34	13	2	19	53	79	41
11. Enville A R	34	10	8	16	47	60	38
12. Birchfield Sp	34	10	8	16	46	71	38
13. Tipton Rov	34	10	7	17	51	59	37
14. Swan Spts	34	10	6	18	76	85	36
15. Studley BKL R	34	9	6	19	45	71	33
16. Alvechurch VR	34	9	4	21	45	85	31
17. Barlestone R	34	8	7	19	35	81	31
18. Park Rangers	34	5	11	18	51	89	26

CHALLENGE CUP 1995-96

First Round:

Barlestone St Giles v Coventry Sphinx 1-2
Massey Ferguson v Fairfield Villa 8-0
Coleshill Town v Kenilworth Town 1-1, 2-2. *Coleshill won on away goals*
Highgate United v Handrahan Timbers 2-0
Northfield Town v West Midlands Fire Service 0-2

Second Round;

Alvechurch Villa v Dudley Sports 3-1
Chelmsley Town v Thimblemill REC 2-3
Coventry Sphinx v Coleshill Town 0-1
Kings Heath v Badsey Rangers 4-1
Massey Ferguson v GPT Coventry 2-0
Richmond Swifts v Knowle 2-1
Southam United v Alveston 3-0
Upton Town v Holly Lane 0-1
Bloxwich Town v Olton Royale 3-1
Colletts Green v Bilston Comm Coll 2-2, 5-1
Highgate United v Newhall United 0-1
Kings Norton Ex Serv v W Midlands Fire 2-0
Meir KA v Ansells 2-1
Shirley Town v Hams Hall 3-1
Studley BKL v Polesworth North Warwick 5-3
Wellesbourne v Monica Star 0-1

Third Round:

Alvechurch Villa v Meir KA	3-2	Bloxwich Town v Richmond Swifts	2-1
Coleshill Town v Newhall United	5-0	Colletts Green v Southam United	4-1
Kings Heath v Thimblemil REC	3-0	Studley BKL v Massey Ferguson	2-2, 3-1
Kings Norton Ex Service v Holly Lane	3-1	Monica Star v Shirley Town	0-2*

Shirley Town disqualified Monica Star go through

Fourth Round;

Coleshill Town v Bloxwich Town	1-2	Alvechurch Villa v Kings Norton E S	2-2, 2-0
Colletts Green v Kings Heath	2-0	Monica Star v Studley BKL	1-2

Semi-Finals;

Bloxwich Town v Colletts Green	1-0	Alvechurch Villa v Studley BKL	4-3 (aet)

Final; Alvechurch Villa v Bloxwich Town 1-8

PRESIDENTS CUP 1995-96

Second Round;

Badsey Rangers v Colletts Green	1-3	Dudley Sports v Kenilworth	1-2
GPT Coventry v Bilston Community College	4-2	Holly Lane v Barlestone St Giles	3-0
Kings Norton Ex Ser v Polesworth N Warwick	0-1	Monica Star v Hams Hall	1-0
Newhall United v Fairfield Villa	4-0	Thimblemill Rec v Richmond Swifts	3-0 (aet)

Third Round;

Colletts Green v Newhall United	1-2	GPT Coventry v Holly Lane	0-3
Polesworth N Warwick v Monica Star	7-1	Thimblemill Rec v Kenilworth Town	4-6

Semi-Finals;

Polesworth N Warwick v Newhall Utd	2-0 (aet)	Holly Lane v Kenilworth Town	1-1, 3-2

Holly Lane disqualified

Final; Kenilworth Town v Polesworth North Warwick 4-6

CHALLENGE VASE 1995-96

Quarter Finals;

Archdale v Earlswood Town	2-3	Blackheath Electrodrives v Bromsgrove Rangers	1-2
Ledbury Town v Brownhills Town	2-1 (aet)	W Midlands Police R v Cheslyn Hay	1-0

Semi-Finals;

Bromsgrove Rangers v Ledbury Town	3-0	Earlswood Town v W Midlands Police	1-2

Final; Bromsgrove Rangers v West Midlands Police Reserves 4-0

CHALLENGE TROPHY 1995-96

Quarter Finals;

Atherstone United v Gresley Rovers	1-0 (aet)	Bridgnorth Town v Hednesford Town	2-1
Burton Albion v Kidderminster Harriers	0-3	Rushden & Diamonds	1-0

Semi-Finals;

Kidderminster H v Bridgnorth Town	0-2	Rushden & Diamonds v Atherstone United	3-0

Final; Bridgnorth Town v Rushden & Diamonds 0-4

CHALLENGE URN 1995-96

Quarter Finals;

Birmingham Vaults v Dudley Sports Res	1-1, 1-2	Feckenham v Kenilworth Wardens	1-0
Richmond Swifts Res v Studley United	1-0	Studley BKL Res v Tipton Spts & Soc	1-3

Semi-Finals;

Feckenham v Dudley Sports Res	2-0	Richmond Swifts Res v Tipton Spts & Soc	1-0

Final; Feckenham v Richmond Swifts Reserves 2-2 (aet), 4-3 pen

PREMIER DIVISION CLUBS 1996-97

ALVECHURCH FC

Manager: Paul Madders **Vice-Chairman:** **President:**
Secretary: Alan Deakin, 58 Chesterfield Close, Northfield, Birmingham, B31 3TR (0121 552 8427)
Ground: Lye Meadow, Redditch Rd, Alvechurch, Worcs (0121 445 2929).
Directions: M42 jct 2, left for Alvechurch (A441) at 1st island, pass right thru Alvechurch - ground on left half mile after village. 10 mins walk from Alvechurch BR station. Birmingham-Redditch buses pass ground.
Seats: TBA **Cover:** Yes **Capacity:** 3,000 **Floodlights:** No **Founded:** 1994
Colours: Gold/Black/Gold. **Change colours:** TBA
Club Sponsors: Quazer Sports **Nickname:** The Church.
Midweek home matchday: TBA
Best FA Cup year: Not entered to date *(predessors: 3rd Rd 73-74 beating Exeter en route. Also 1st Rd 71-72).*
Club record scorer: **Club record appearances:**
Hons:

ANSELLS

Manager: Bernard Cronin
Secretary: J Cronin, 32 Whittleford Grove, Castle Bromwich, Birmingham B36 9SL (0121 747 9925).
Ground: Ansells Sports Club, Aldridge Rd, Perry Barr, Birmingham (0121 356 4296).
Directions: Coming from city centre Aldridge Rd is a right turn (just before Perry Barr stadium) off the main Birmingham to Walsall road. Ground entrance almost immediately on right.
Capacity: TBA **Seats:** No **Cover:** Yes. **Floodlights:** No
Previous League: Birmingham Works (pre-1992).
Clubhouse: Large Social Club.
Colours: Blue & White/Blue & White/red.
Hons: Midland Combination Div 2 92-93, Birmingham Works Lg (numerous occasions).

BILSTON COMMUNITY COLLEGE

Chairman: Mr Earl Laird **Manager:** Brian Waldron.
Secretary: J Calloway, 4 Mervyn Rd, Bradley, Bilston, West Midlands WV14 8DF (01902 491799).
Ground: Queen St.,Bilston,West Midlands.(01902 491498)
Colours: All green. **Change:** Green & gold/green. **Programme:** No.
Previous League: Staffs County (South) (pre-1993)
Previous Ground: Springvale Spts & Social Club, Millfields Rd, Bilston (pre-1993).
Hons: Midland Comb. Chall. Urn 93-94 94-95, Staffs Co. (Sth) Lg(4) 89-93, J W Hunt Charity Cup 90-91.

BOLEHALL SWIFTS

President: Mr Dennis Baker **Chairman:** Mr G Mulvey **Vice-Chairman:** Mr W Gould.
Secretary: Michael Simpkins, 22 Brambling, Wilnecote, Tamworth, Staffs B77 5PQ (01827 283004).
Manager: Ron Tranter **Player/Coach:** Mick Thurman. **Physio:** Barry Davis.
Commercial Mgr: Mike Fletcher. **Press Officer:** Mr L Bretherton/ Mr W Gould (01827 64530).
Ground: Rene Road, Bolehall, Tamworth (01827 62637).
Directions: A51 signs south to Bolebridge island, left under railway arches into Amington Rd, 4th left into Leedham Ave, fork right into Rene Rd, ground on right by school. From Tamworth BR station walk up Victoria Road for three quarters of a mile and catch No.3 or No.6 mini-bus to Bolehall. Alight at Leedham Avenue or Rene Road and follow as above.
Capacity: 2,000 **Seats:** 500 **Cover:** 600 **Floodlights:** Yes **Founded:** 1953
Midweek matches: Wednesday **Youth Team :** Play Sundayafternoons. **Nickname:** Swifts
Colours: Yellow/Black/Green. **Change Colours:** All green **Club Shop:** No.
Programme: 32 pages, 70p **Editor:** W Gould (01827 64530).
Previous Leagues: Sutton Lge/ Staffs County 74-80/ Midland Combination 80-94.
Previous Grounds: None **Club Sponsors:** Walton Homes.
Clubhouse: Large Social Club - 2 rooms. Open every evening (7-11) and lunchtimes. Entertainment Saturday nights. Cobs and crisps etc available.
Record Scorer: Billy Oughton **Record appearances:** Duane Mellors 196.
Hons: Midland Combination Div 2 84-85 (Challenge Vase 84-85, Presidents Cup R-up 85-86), Fazeley Charity Cup 84-85 (R-up 85-86), Ernie Brown Memorial Cup R-up 89-90 90-91 91-92 92-93 94-95, Jack Mould Cup R-up 85-86.

Highgate United *Photo - Martin Wray*

Olton Royale keeper makes an excellent stretching save from the Highgate United attack during the first half at "The Coppice". *Photo - Martin Wray*

Olton Royale FC: *Photo - Martin Wray*

COLESHILL TOWN

Manager: Msartin Sockett **Founded:** 1894.
Secretary: Neil Hamilton, 31 Fourfields Way, New Arley, N Warwicks, CV7 8PX (01676 54088)
Ground: Pack Meadow, Packington Lane, Coleshill, Birmingham B46 3JQ (01675 63259).
Directions: A446 to A4117 towards Coleshill, Packington Lane forks from A4117, south of village and ground is 150 yds on right. M6 jct 4, 1 mile away.
Capacity: 3,000 **Seats:** 50 **Cover:** 50 **Floodlights:** Yes **Nickname:** Coalmen.
Midweek matches: Tues/Thurs **Record Gate:** 1,000.
Colours: All green. **Change Colours:** Green/white/green
Clubhouse: Bar open 7 nights a week. Bar manager resident. **Programme:** 30p, **Editor:** Mavis Gordon
Players who have progressed to Football League: Gary Shaw (Aston Villa, Walsall)
Hons: Mercian Lg 75-76, Walsall Snr Cup 82-83 (R-up 83-84), Midland Comb. R-up 83-84 (Div 2 69-70 (R-up 74-75), Invitation Cup 1970, Presidents Cup R-up(2) 67-69).

COVENTRY SPHINX

Manager: Willie Knibbs
Secretary: K Whitehall, 34 Engleton Road, Radford, Coventry CV6 1JE (01203 598148).
Ground: Sphinx Drive, off Siddeley Avenue, Stoke Aldermoor, Coventry (01203 451361).
Colours: Sky blue & navy/Navy & sky blue/navy & sky blue.

HANDRAHAN TIMBERS

Chairman: E J Smith **President:** W J Handrahan
Secretary: Stuart Fereday, 93 Millfield Cres., Kidderminster (01562 820385).
Manager: Glen Taylor/Nigel Kirkham **Asst Manager:** Phillip McNally
Press Officer: E J Smith (01384 295394).
Ground: The Mile Flat Sports Ground, Mile Flat, Wallheath, Kingswinford, West Mids (01381 484755).
Cover: 200 **Seats:** 40 **Floodlights:** No **Nickname:** Timbers **Founded:** 1982.
Colours: Red/black/black. **Change colours:** Sky/navy/navy **Club Shop:** No.
Previous Grounds: None **Previous Leagues:** Staffs County Lg (South) 82-86.
Programme: All games except outside cups).
Clubhouse: Teas and refreshments. **Sponsors:** W J Handrahan & Son
Midweek home matchday: Wednesday
95-96 Captain: **95-96 Top Scorer:** **95-96 P.o.Y.:**
Club record scorer: Paul Baker **Club record appearances:** Jonathan Pole.
Hons: Midland Combination Div 1 R-up 93-94, Birmingham Challenge Vase R-up 93-94, Wednesbury Charity Cup 91-92, J W Hunt Cup 92-93 (R-up 93-94).Invitation Cup(Mid.Comb.Champios v Vup Winners)94-95.

HIGHGATE UNITED

Chairman: T G Bishop **Treasurer:** F H Drennan **Founded:** 1947.
Secretary: G Read, 23 Southam Rd, Hall Green, Birmingham B28 8DQ (0121-777-1786)
Manager: Mick Neville **Assistant Manager:** TBA
Physio: Garry Bishop **Press Officer:** N C Sawyer.
Ground: The Coppice, Tythe Barn Lane, Shirley, Solihull B90 1PH (0121 7444194).
Directions: A34 from City through Shirley, fork right B4102 (Tanworth Lane), half mile then right into Dickens Heath Rd, then first right and the ground is on the left. 100yds from Whitlocks End (BR).
Capacity: 5,000 **Seats:** 250 **Covered:** 750 **Floodlights:** Due 1996
Colours: All red **Change Colours:** All white **Nickname:** The Gate.
Midweek matches: Tuesday **Record Gate:** 4,000 v Enfield, FA Amateur Cup QF 1967.
Programme: 28 pages, 40p **Programme Editor:** Terry Bishop (0676 22788).
Clubhouse: Members Club open Tues, Wed, Thurs, Sat & Sun. Light refreshments available at weekends.
Players progressing to Football League: John Gayle (W'ledon), Keith Leonard (A Villa, P Vale), Geoff Scott (Leic.)
95-96 Captain: . **95-96 P.o.Y.:** **95-96 Top Scorer:**
Hons: Midland Comb.(3) 72-75 (Div 2 66-67 68-69 71-72, Lg Cup(5) 72-74 75-77 84-85 (R-up 78-79 92-93), Presidents Cup 70-71 85-86), Tony Allden Mem. Cup 74-75, Invit. Cup 68-69 71-72 85-86, West Mids All. 63-64, Birmingham Snr Cup 73-74 (SF 91-92).

KENILWORTH TOWN

Manager: John Clarke **Asst Mgr:** Tony Hudson **President:** Bernard Jones.
Secretary: F.Breese, 188 Winsford Avenue, Allesley Park, Coventry CV5 9NH.
Ground: Gypsey Lane (off Rouncil Lane), Kenilworth, Warks (01926 50851).
Seats: No **Cover:** Yes **Club Shop:** No **Floodlights:** No **Programme:** Yes
Cols: All Red with white trim. **Previous Name:** Kenilworth Rangers (pre-1992).
Midweek home matchday: Tuesday **Previous Grounds:** Scott Road/ Glasshouse Lane.
Sponsors: Davies Bakery, Kenilworth **Founded:** 1936
Clubhouse: Open matchdays. Hot food available.
Record win: 17-0 v Bubbenhall, Coventry & North Warks Lge Prem Div 25/2/89
95-96 Captain: **95-96 Top Scorer:**
Hons: Birmingham Challenge Vase 92-93.

KINGS HEATH

Manager: Clive Seeley **Founded:** 1964.
Secretary: Dennis Ellis, 2 Willsbridge Covert, Druids Heath, Birmingham B14 5YD (0121 625 6019)
Ground: Triplex Sports Ground, Eckershall Road, Kings Norton (0121 422 1087).
Previous Names: Horse Shoe FC/ Kings Heath Amateur.
Cols: Gold shadow stripes/black/gold **Change Colours:** All red **Nickname:** The Kings
Programme: 12 pages **Programme Editor:** M Kite
95-96 Top Scorer: Mark Cartwright. **95-96 Player P.o.Y.:** Dean Donaghy
95-96 Manager P.o.Y.: John Price
95-96 Clubman: Perry Deakin
Previous Ground: Shirley Town (pre-1994).
Players progressing to Football League: Geoff Scott (Stoke, Leicester, Birmingham).
Hons: Midland Combination Div 1 R-up 92-93 (Div 2 R-up 82-83, Presidents Cup R-up 79-80 81-82 92-93), Birmingham Challenge Vase R-up 86-87.

KNOWLE

Manager: Paul Aldridge **Assistant Manager:** Stan Tims **Founded:** 1926.
Secretary: George Phillips, 49 Circus Avenue, Chelmsley Wood, Birmingham B37 7NG (0121 770 9513).
Ground: Hampton Rd, Knowle, Solihull (01564 779807).
Directions: A41 Warwick Rd from City, left at Wilsons Pub into Hampton Rd, ground 200 yds on right. 1 mile from Dorridge (BR). Buses from Solihull.
Capacity: 3,000 **Seats:** 72 **Cover:** 200 **Floodlights:** No **Nickname:** Robins.
Midweek matches: Wednesday **Record Gate:** 1,000 in FA Vase 1980.
Programme: 20 pages, 25p **Editor:** Dave Radburn
Colours: Red/white/red **Change Colours:** Yellow/black/yellow
Previous Lges: Birmingham Yth O.B./ Birmingham Alliance. **Previous Name:** Knowle North Star 80-87
Previous Ground: Bentley Heath Village
Clubhouse: Seating for 60, tea bar, recently exstended
Players who have progressed to Football League: Guy Russell (Birmingham City)
95-96 Top Scorer: John Mitchell
Hons: B'gham Jnr Cup R-up 70-71, FA Vase QF 81-82, Midland Combination Div 2 R-up 68-69.

MASSEY-FERGUSON

Manager: Geoff Brassington, Steve Gibbs
Secretary: Lee Thomas, 730 Broad Lane, Coventry, West Midlands CV5 7BB (01203 465476).
Ground: Massey-Ferguson Sports Ground, Banner Lane, Tile Hill, Coventry.(01203 694400)
Seats: 70 **Cover:** 200 **Programme:** Yes
Previous League: Coventry Alliance (pre-1993).
Colours: Red & Black,Black,Red.
Clubhouse: Not on ground
Honours: Midland Comb. Div 2 93-94 (Chall. Vase 93-94), Coventry Evening Telegraph Cup 95-96.

MEIR K.A.

President: John Whitfield **Chairman:** Des Reaney **Vice Chairman:** Graham Lovatt.
Secretary: Stanley Tooth, 29 Colclough Road, Meir, Stoke-on-Trent ST3 6DH (01782 310145).
Manager: Terry Greer **Asst Manager:** **Coach:** Terry Turner.
Press Officer: Graham Birks (01782 395647)
Ground: Stanley Park, Hilderstone Road, Meir Heath, Stoke-on-Trent (01782 388465)
Directions: M6 jct 14, A34 to Stone, A520 from Stone, right (B5066) at Meir Heath, ground on right. 2 miles from Blythe Bridge (BR).
Capacity: 5,000 **Seats:** 400 **Cover:** 1,000 **Floodlights:** Yes **Founded:** 1976.
Colours: Yellow/red/grey. **Change colours:** All red **Nickname:** Kings.
Previous Ground: Normacot Rec. **Previous Name:**'The Station'&'Shoulder of Mutton.'
Programme: 32 pages 50p **Programme Editor:** Steve Osbourne .oneline 2
Midweek home matchday: Wednesday **Club Sponsors:** John Whitfield & Sons.
Previous Leagues: Staffs Alliance/ Staffs Snr 84-92.
Clubhouse: Built in 1982, open matchdays. Hot food.
Club Record Scorer: W J Anderson **Club Record Appearances:** David Preston, 500+
95-96 P.o.Y.: Darren Rearey **95-96 Top Scorer:** Martin Wood
Hons: Staffs Snr Lg 88-89, 90-91, Staffs FA Vase 93-94 95-96, Walsall & Dist Sen Cup 89-90.

RICHMOND SWIFTS

Chairman: M Rowley **Vice-Chairman:** S Sanders.
Secretary: Mike Rowley, 61 Derwent Drive, Priorslee, Telford, Shrops TF2 9QZ (01952 200020)
Manager: Pete Dunbavin **Assistant Manager:**
Coach: Morris Gittens **Commercial Manager/Press Office:** Fred Evans
Ground: Triplex Sports Ground, Eckershall Road, Kings Norton (021 422 1087).
Seats: None **Cover:** None **Floodlights:** No **Founded:** 1994 **Nickname:** Nomads
Colours: White (red trim) **Change colours** Blue (white trim).
Programme: Yes, for 94-95 **Midweek home matchdays:** Tuesday.
Previous Names: Swift Personalised Products (founded 1979)/ Richmond Amateurs - clubs merged in 1994. All historical entries below pertain to Swift PP except those *italicised.*
Previous League: Birmingham Works. *Richmond Amateurs: Birmingham AFA, pre-1994.*
Sponsors: Swift Personalised Products/ BGR Financial Consultants.
Previous Grounds: Shirley Town FC (pre-'92)/ Wythall Park, Silver Street, Wythall (Wythall FC) 92-93/ Alvechurch FC 93-94 (pre-Xmas)/ British Gas Sports Ground, Woodacre Rd, Erdington 93-94.
Record win: 6-0 v Burntwood, 93-94 **Record defeat:** 0-6 v Archdales, 92-93.
95-96 Captain: **95-96 P.o.Y.:** **95-96 Top Scorer:**
Club Record Scorer: A Dunkley (21, 93-94).
Hons: Midland Comb Div 1 95-96, Challenge Vase R-up 93-94, Kings Norton Lg Divs 1 + 2 & Lg Cup, J W Hunt Cup 95-96, Mercian Lg Div 1, Birmingham Works Lg, Birmingham Jnr Cup R-up, Birmingham Vase R-up 95-96.

SHIRLEY TOWN

Manager: Pete Sysum.
Secretary: B Fox, 26 Claines Road, Northfield, Birmingham B31 2EE (0121 475 4465)
Ground: Shirley Stadium, Tile House Lane, Shirley, Solihull (0121 744 1560).
Directions: A34 B'gham to Shirley, right onto B4025 towards Shirley (BR) - ground one and a half miles on left.
Colours: All maroon. **Previous League:** B'ham Comb. 35-38. **Founded:** 1926
95-96 Top Scorer: **Hons:** Midland Combination Division 2 R-up 92-93.

SOUTHAM UNITED

Chairman: N Srmstrong **Vice-Chairman:** T Frost.
Secretary: R J Hancocks, 18 Warwick Road, Southam, Leamington Spa CV33 0HN (01926 813483).
Manager: Jason Cadden **Asst Manager:** Dave Sharpe **Physio:** Barry Cramp
Ground: Banbury Road Ground, Southam, Leamington Spa (01926 812091).
Directions: On righthand side of A423 Banbury Road heading south from Southam.
Capacity: 2,000 **Seats:** 50 **Cover:** 100 **Floodlights:** No **Nickname:** Saints
Colours: White & Black/Black/Black. **Change:** Red & white/red/red **Club Shop:** No.
Programme: Av. 50 pages, 50p **Programme Editor:** Mrs A Hancocks.
Prev. Lge: Coventry & North Warks **Record Gate:** 1,500 v Coventry City, friendly 1990.
Midweek matchday: Tues or Thurs. **Reserve Team's League:** Coventry & District.
Sponsors: B & M Sleeper Coaches **Player progressing to Football Lge:** Stephen Bicknell (Leicester).
Record win: 10-0 v Studley **Record defeat:** 1-7 v Kings Heath.
Clubhouse: Open every evening and matchdays. Hot pies, rolls, tea & coffee available at matches.
95-96 Captain: **Club record scorer & appearances:** Bob Hancocks.
95-96 Top Scorer: **95-96 P.o.Y.:**
Hons: Mids Comb. Div 3 80-81 (Div 2 R-up 82-83, Chal. Vase 80-81).

STUDLEY B.K.L.

Chairman: D Robinson **Vice-Chairman:** Alec James **President:** N/A
Secretary: K Addis, 16 Ansley Close, Matchborough, East Redditch, Worcs, B98 0AX (01527 526454)
Manager: John Adams **Assistant Manager:** Alan Scarfe.
Physio: Derrick Mutton **Press Officer:** Dave Chiswell.
Ground: 'Beehive', BKL Spts Ground, Abbeyfields, Birmingham Rd, Studley, Warks (01527 853817)
Capacity: **Seats:** None **Cover:** Yes **Floodlights:** No **Founded:** 1971.
Colours: Sky/navy/navy **Change colours:** White/red **Nickname:** Bees.
Sponsors: BKL Fittings **Previous Name:** BKL Works **Clubhouse:** Yes, on ground
Reserve Team's League: Skol Midland Combination Division Two.
Programme: 30p **Ed.:** Alec James, 14 Eldersfield Close, Churchill, Redditch B98 9NG
Previous League: Redditch & South Warwickshire Sunday Combination 71-87.
Club record appearances: Lee Adams.
Club Record Scorer: Kevin Rowlands.
Hons: Midland Comb. Div 1 91-92 (Chal. Cup R-up 91-92, Presidents Cup R-up 91-92, Div 2 Cup 87-88), Smedley Crooke Charity Cup 90-91 91-92.

WELLESBOURNE

Chairman: Mr C Keyes **Manager:** T B A **Asst Manager:** Allan Stacey.
Secretary: Ted Forster (01926 494507)
Ground: The Sports Field, Loxley Close, Wellesbourne (01789 841878).
Seats: 80 **Cover:** 100 **Floodlights:** No **Nickname:** Bourne **Founded:** 1932.
Programme: 30 pages, 80p **Programme Editor:** Mr A Mason **Club Shop:** No.
Colours: Blue & White Halves/blue/blue **Sponsors:** Various
Change colours: Yellow/black/black
Midweek home matchday: Tuesday **Previous Grounds:** None
Previous Leagues: Covenrty & North Warks/ Stratford Alliance.
Reserve Team's League: Midland Combination Division Three
Clubhouse: Open all day matchdays. Sandwiches, crisps, drinks, tea, coffee available.
95-96 P.o.Y.: **95-96 Captain:** **95-96 Top Scorer:**
Hons: Midlands Comb. Div 1 92-93 (Presidents Cup 91-92, Invitation Cup 92-93 94-95.

WEST MIDLANDS FIRE SERVICE

Chairman: Mr R Jefferies **President:** Chief Fire Officer.
Secretary: Mr J Clarke, 51 Stonebury Ave., Eastern Green, Coventry CV5 7FW (01203 467997).
Manager: T B A **Asst Manager:** Clive Mason.
Ground: 'The Glades', Lugtrout Lane, Solihull (0121 705 8602).
Directions: M42 jct 5, A45 towards B'ham Airport, leave at next junction and at island take 1st exit (Catherine de Barnes Lane) - ground half mile on left. Nearest station is Birmingham International. No buses pass ground.
Seats: None **Cover:** 150 **Floodlights:** No **Club Shop:** No **Founded:** 1947
Colours: Red with black pin stripe/Black/Black. **Change colours:** White/navy/navy
Previous Grounds: None. **Previous Leagues:** Birmingham AFA (pre-1986).
Programme: 12 pages, 25p **Editor:** J Kempson (01922 408464)
Sponsors: Contract Fire Sytems Ltd **Record defeat:** 1-14 v West Heath United.
Midweek home matchday: Tues/Thurs **Nickname:** None.
Clubhouse: No. **Club record appearances:** Brian Farrell.
95-96 Captain: **95-96 Top Scorer:** **95-96 P.o.Y.:**
Hons: Midland Combination Div 1 94-95 (Div 2 87-88, Presidents Cup 94-95, Jack Mould Trophy 87-88), Fire Services National Cup 89-90, Fire District Cup 90-91.

WORCESTER ATHLETICO

Chairman: Bill Jones. **Vice Chairman:** Bill Jones **President:** Steve Goode.
Secretary/Press Officer: Don Roberts, 6 Gardens Close, Upton-on-Severn, Worcs WR8 0LT (01684 593439).
Manager: Dave Boddy **Coach:** M Lowe **Physio:** A Pugh.
Commercial Manager: Les Wadley.
Ground: Malvern Town FC (see West Mids Lge) **Founded:** 1904
Colours: Green & white **Change:** Red & black stripes **Nickname:** Emeralds
Programme: 16 pages, 50p **Editor:** Graham Hill (01905 351653) **Club Shop:** No.
Sponsors: The Bankhouse. **Prev. Ground:** Old Street, Upton-on-Severn (pre'92)
Previous Leagues: Malvern 04-71/ Worcester & Dist. 72-85/ Kidderminster 85-88.
Midweek home matchday: Tuesday **Record Gate:** 350 v Colletts Green, Mids Comb. Div 1, 7/4/94.
Record win: 13-1 **Record defeat:** 0-17.
Clubhouse: Evenings 7.30-11pm, Saturday matchdays 12.30-11pm. Food (hamburgers etc), tea, coffee, squash available on matchdays.
95-96 Captain: **95-96 P.o.Y.:** Glenn Burrows
95-96 Top Scorer: Matt Henning 25.
Club record scorer: Paul Buckley **Club record appearances:** Keith Aingel.
Hons: Midland Combination Div 2 89-90 (Jack Mould Tphy 89-90, Presidents Cup R-up 89-90), Worcs Jnr Cup 73-74 88-89 (R-up 74-75), Worcs Minor Cup 24-25 86-87.

DIVISION ONE CLUBS 1995-96

ALVESTON

Secretary: P Beese, 36 Bishops Close, Stratford-upon-Avon, Warks CV37 9ED (01789 267966).
Ground: Home Guard Club, Main Street, Tiddington, Stratford-upon-Avon.(01789 297718)
Colours: All Maroon and Sky Blue.

BARLESTONE St GILES

Secretary: T Wentworth, 3 Rush Close, Newbold Verden, Leicester LE9 9LX (01455 822602).
Ground: Barton Road, Barlestone, Nuneaton.(01455 822602) **Colours:** Gold/black/black

BROWNHILLS TOWN

Secretary: Alan Payne, 7 Norton Grange, Norton Canes, Cannock, Staffs WS11 3Qz (01543 279080)
Ground: Walsall Wood FC.
Cols: Sky & white stripes/royal/sky **Change colours:** Red & white/red

CHELMSLEY TOWN '94

Secretary: M J.Harris,149 Wyckham rd., Castle Bromwich,Birmingham B36 OHU (0121 747 4589)
Ground: The Pavilion, Coleshill Road, Marston Green, West Midlands (0121 779 5400).
Colours: Yellow & Green/Sky Blue/White. **Change Colours:** Yellow/black/black

CHESLYN HAY

Secretary: Mr Ivor Osborne, 16 Littlewood Lane, Cheslyn Hay, Walsall WS6 7EJ (01922 414755).
Ground: As Walsall Wood FC (see West Midlands League section).
Colours: Orange/white/orange

COLLETTS GREEN

Secretary: Brian Scott, 3 Blagdon Close, St Peters, Worcester, (01905 767386)
Ground: Victoria Park, Pickersleigh, Malvern Link (01905 830442)
Colours: All green with white trim. **Change colours:** All white

CONTINENTAL STAR

Secretary: Noel O'Donnell, 4 Fern Rd, Erdington, Birmingham B24 9DE (0121 354 2277).
Ground: Holly Lane Sports Ground.
Colours: Yellow/Blue/Yellow

DUDLEY SPORTS

Secretary: John Lewis, 6 Hern Road, Brieley Hill, West Mids DY5 2PW (01384 895782)
Ground: High Ercal Avenue, Brierley Hill, West Mids (01384 826420).
Colours: Red+Blue/Blue/Red. **Change colours:** All blue

G.P.T. (COVENTRY)

Secretary: P Scanlon, 61 Norton Hill, Wyken, Coventry, West Mids CV2 3AX (01203 616576).
Ground: GEC Sports Ground, Allard Way, Copsewood, Coventry.(01203 451157)
Colours: White with blue trim/blue/blue. **Change colours:** All red

HAMS HALL

General Mgr/Press Officer: Bob Ringrose, 6 Holly Drive, Hurley, Atherstone, Warks CV9 2JY (0827 872747).
Ground: Hams Hall Generating Station, Lea Marston, Sutton Coldfield B76 0BG (0675 463223).
Colours: White/black/black **Change colours:** Sky & navy

HOLLY LANE '92

Secretary: R G Ashton, 19 Grange Road, Erdington, Birmingham B24 0DG (0121 350 2352).
Ground: Holly Sports & Social Centre, Holly Lane, Erdington, Birmingham B24 9LH.(01213 730979)
Colours: Yellow/green/green. **Change colours:** yellow/black

LEICESTER YMCA

Secretary: Colin Chappell, 132 South Knighton Road, Leicester LE2 3LE (0116 247 8989)
Ground:
Colours:

MONICA STAR

Secretary: A Rourke, 35 Fairlands, Yardley, Birmingham B26 2DT (0121 789 6695).
Ground: Sedgmere Sports & Social Club, Sedgmere Road, Yardley, Birmingham (0121 [illegible]) **Colours:** Red & black Stripes/Red/Red.

NEWHALL UNITED

Secretary: David Wain, 26 Willow Drive, Newhall, Swadlincote, Derbys DE11 0NW (01283 225188 Business)
Ground: Hawfields Ground, St Johns Drive, Newhall, Swadlincote (01283 551029).
Colours: All Blue. **Change colours:** All white.

NORTHFIELD TOWN

Secretary: Monty Patrick, 38 Pensford Rd, Northfield, Birmingham B31 3AG (0121 475 2057).
Ground: Shenley Lane, Selly Oak, Birmingham B29 (0121 478 3900).
Colours: Yellow/blue/yellow **Change Colours:** Blue & yellow/blue

POLESWORTH NORTH WARWICK

Secretary: E Guild, 43 Station Road, Polesworth, Tamworth, Staffs B78 1BG (01827 8936(011).
Ground: North Warwick Sports Ground, Hermitage Hill, Tamworth Road, Polesworth (01827 892482).
Colours: All Green. **Change colours:** Tangerine & black

THIMBLEMILL R.E.C.

Secretary: G M Houten, 86 Gower Road, Lapal, Halesowen, West Mids B62 9BT (0121 442 3357).
Ground: Thimblemill Recreation, Thimblemill Road, Smethwick, Warley (0121 4292459).
Colours: White (blue trim)/white/navy blue

DIVISION TWO CLUBS 1996-97

ALBRIGHT & WILSON

Secretary: Andrew Such, 29 Bristnall Hall Road, Oldbury, Warley, West Midlands. B68 9TS (0121 552 8427)
Ground: Albright & Wilson Spts Club, Tat Bank, Oldbury, Warley (0121 552 1048).
Colours: Blue and Black Stripes/Black/Black. **Change colours:** Gold/black/black

ALVIS S.G.L.

Secretary: D A Leslie, 9 Stephenson Close, Milverton, Leamington Spa CV32 6BS (01926 336700).
Ground: Alvis Spts & Social Club, Green Lane, Finham, Coventry.(01203 692576)
Colours: Blue and White/White/Blue.

ARCHDALE '73

Secretary: R T Widdowson, 33 Mayfield Avenue, Worcester WR3 8LA (01905 27866).
Ground: Windermere Drive, Worcester (01905 451410)

BADSEY RANGERS

Secretary: M J Loram, 39 Synehurst, Badsey, Evesham, Worcs WR11 5UI (01386 832040).
Ground: Badsey Recreation Ground, Sands Lane, Badsey, Evesham (01386 830867).
Cols: Red & black stripes/black/black

BIRMINGHAM VAULTS

Secretary: S Johal, 41 Roebuck Lane, West Browich, B70 6QP (0121 553 1758)
Ground: Bloxwich Town AFC
Cols: Red/black/black

BLACKHEATH ELECTRODRIVES

Secretary/Press Officer: G.Ellison, 12 Meadowhill Drive,Wordsley, West Midlands.DY8 5AF.(01384 836112)
Ground: Electrodrives Sports Ground, Cakemore Road, Rowley Regis, Warley (0121 559 1500 Security)(01215 599105 Social Club)
Colours: All red **Change colours:** All blue

BURNTWOOD

Secretary: S.Ropbinson, 74 Oakdene Road, Burntwood.(01543 677869)
Ground: Memorial Institute, Rugeley Rd, Burntwood.(01543 675578)
Colours: Red and Blue /Blue/Red.

CADBURY ATHLETIC

Secretary: G.Boyle, 1 Greenway Gardens, Kings Norton, Birmingham B38 9RY (0121 628 6533)
Ground: Bournville Recreation Ground, Bournville Lane, Bournville, Birmingham.90121 458 2000 Ext 3316)
Cols: Blue & white halves/white/blue.

EARLSWOOD TOWN

Secretary: Jim Jones, 22 Antony Road Shirley, Solihull, B90 2NX (0121 603 4436)
Ground: Malthouse Lane, Earlswood, near Solihull (015646 703989).
Colours: Red/black/red **Change:** Green & yellow/green/green

ENVILLE ATHLETIC

Secretary: c/o Ian Williams (01384 377764)
Ground: Hall Drive Ground, Hall Drive, Enville, Stourbridge (01384 872368).
Colours: Sky Blue/Maroon/Maroon.

FAIRFIELD VILLA

Secretary/Press Officer: C W Harris, 7 Churchill Road, Catshill, Bromsgrove B61 0PE (01527 831049).
Ground: Recreation Ground, Stourbridge Road (B4091), Fairfield, Bromsgrove (01527 77049).
Colours: Red/Black/Black **Change colours:** All blue

FECKENHAM

Secretary: M G Hawkes 23 High Street, Astwood Bank, Redditch, Worcs (01527 893341)
Ground: Feckenham Playing Fields, Mill Lane, Feckenham
Colours: All green **Change colours:**

LEDBURY TOWN '84

Secretary: M.Cluett, 55 Lawnside Rd., Ledbury,Herefordshire. HR8 2AE (01531 633182)
Ground: New Street, Ledbury (01531 6314630
Colours: White and Black/Black/Black.

RICHMOND SWIFTS

Secretary: Tony Moogan, 6 George Arthur Rd, Saltley, Birmingham B8 1LW (0121 328 9720).
Ground: Triplex Sports Ground, Eckershall Road, Kings Norton (0121 458 4570).
Colours: Red and White Halves/Red/White. **Change colours** Blue (white trim).

TIPTON SPORTS & SOCIAL

Secretary: Bill Andrews, 42 Ambleside, Bradley, Bilston, West Midlands WV14 0SN (01902 497404)
Ground: Coneygre Leisure Centre.
Colours: **Change colours:**

WEST MIDLANDS POLICE RESERVES

Secretary: John Black,57 Grosvenor Close,Sutton Coldfield,W.Mids.B75 6RP.(0121 308 7673)
Ground: Police Spts Ground, 'Tally Ho', Pershore Road, Edgbaston, Birmingham B5 7RN (0121 472 2944).
Colours: Red/black/black

DIVISION THREE CLUBS 1996-97

Alvechurch Reserves
Barlestone St Giles Reserves
Birchfield Sports
Cradley Heath
Dudley Sports Reserves
Enville Athletic Reserves
Kenilworth Town Reserves
Kenilworth Wardens
Mitchells & Butler
Studley BKL Reserves
Swan Sports
Tipton Rovers
Tipton Town Reserves

RESERVE DIVISION 1996-97

Atherstone United
Barwell
Boldmere St Michaels
Bridgnorth Town
Bromsgrove Rovers
Burton Albion
Gresley Rovers
Hednesford Town
Hinckley Athletic
Nuneaton Borough
Rushden & Diamonds
Solihull Borough
Stapenhill
Stratford Town
Tamworth
Willenhall Town
Worcester City

BANK'S BREWERY WEST MIDLANDS (REGIONAL) LEAGUE

FEEDER TO: MIDLAND ALLIANCE

Hon. Secretary: Neil Juggins
14 Badgers Lane, Blackwell, Bromsgrove.

The Premier Division has Proved to be a little predictable in recent seasons, in that the eventual champions generally emerge from an anticipated group of contenders. It is therefore pleasing to report that this was not the case in the 1995-96 season, with the League winners coming in the unlikely form of Wednesfield, whose previous best final placing had been 3rd back in 1987.

Nevertheless, the leading pack contained some familiar names; Pelsall Villa, Stafford Town and Stourport Swifts all held the lead at various times, as did Bloxwich Strollers whilst Gornal Athletic also featured prominently in the leading pack. Wednesfield's challenge was founded on the back of a 20 game unbeaten league run from the start of the season, though they had played fewer games than all of their rivals and didn't reach top spot for the firt time until the beginning of March. At this stage Pelsall and Wednesfield broke away from the pack, with top spot changing hands several times, and the decisive game took place at Pelsall's Bush Ground on April 27th. Pelsall had put together a tremendous run of just 1 defeat in 18 league games, the previous 10 having all been victories, culminating in an 11-0 victory at struggling Wolverhsampton Casuals. Wednesfield's form was only marginally less impressive with 5 consecutive victories behind them. Vill's last minute goal came too late to preserve that run, however, and Wednesfield's 2-1 victory decided the destination of the title. This was confirmed a few days later with a nervous 3-1 win over Lichfield City. Wednesfield's final record of 28 victories and just 2 defeats was the best ever recorded in a 36 match programme - not bad for a cub with no reported wage-bill! Reigning champions Pelsall therfore had to make do with the Keys Cup (awarded to the runners-up) and the League Cup, which they won for the first time with a comfortable 3-1 win near neighbours Walsall Wood. The real consolation, however, came with the news of the Club's acceptance into the Midland Alliance for the1996-97 season. Having been turned down in each of the two previous years Pelsall were this time able to take advantage of the unsuitability of Wednesfield's Cottage ground.

Elsewhere in this section, Lye Town claimed 3rd place, the best finish in 8 Years for the WMRL's longest serving club. Lye had been considered championship outsiders for much of the campaign but the fixture backlog caused by their FA Vase exploits meant that they remained in mid-table until the closing weeks of the season. Neither of the promoted clubs, Wolverhampton Casuals and Lichfield City, made much of an impression but it was Darlaston (surprisingly) and Hill Top Rangers who occupied the bottom 2 places for virtually the whole season.

Division One was a much more open affair with a variety of clubs leading at various stages and the eventual outcome not being decided until the first week of May. Rushall Olympic Reserves started well again, 10 wins in their opening 11 games, and were accompanied by newcomers Bandon, Mordea United and the reserve sides of Chasetown and Rocester. The arrival of December saw Rushall's challenge start to fade and Morda took over top spot until Easter, when they were finally overhauled by Rocester who had put together a run of 12 victories in 15 unbeaten league games. Ultimately the top 2 sides were not from any of those mentioned so far. Even as late as March 9th work's side Goodyear and Wolverhampton United lay 9th and 10th respectively, Goodyear some 13 points adrift of Morda. Beaten 7 times in their openig 13 games, United put together an impressive run of 21 wins and just 3 defeats in 27 games and defeat for Goodyear by fellow contenders Rocester on April 20th seemed to pave the way for United to claim the title. However, a draw with Rushall and defeat in their final game against Morda whilst Goodyear were disposing of wooden-spoonists Sikh Hunters left the tyre men with the comfortable task of avoiding defeat 27 goals in their last game to clinch the championship. Goodyear had finished the season with their own impressive run of 15 wins and a single defeat in 17 games.

Member clubs had varying degrees of success in outside cup competitions. The FA Cup is becoming progressively more difficult with each reorganisation further up the pyramid and this season saw just 3 clubs make it as far as the 1st Qualifying Round. Lye Town went down at Eastwood Hanley after winning at Stapenhill, whilst Wednesfield were beaten at Paget Rangers following a replay victory at Banbury United. Stafford Town actually had a bye to this stage but were beaten 4-0 by Burton Albion and thus missed out on a lucrative tie against landlords Stafford Rangers. One other tie which warrants a mention was Westfields Preliminary Round tie at Corby Town which they lost 5-7.

Pride of place in the FA vase went to Lye Town who reached the 4th Round after a string of impressive away victories against Sandwell Borough, Blakenhall, Oakham and Cheste-le-Street. Sadly the first home tie of the run ended in elimination, beaten by 0-2 by Barwell.

FINAL LEAGUE TABLES 1995/96

Premier Div	P	W	D	L	F	A	Pts
1. Wednesfield	36	28	6	2	95	30	90
2. Pelsall Villa	36	27	5	4	97	30	86
3. Lye Town	36	20	11	5	80	34	71
4. Stafford Town	36	19	10	7	79	35	67
5. S/port Swifts	36	19	10	7	74	50	67
6. Bloxwich St	36	17	9	10	67	50	60
7. Walsall W	36	16	8	12	61	42	56
8. Westfields	36	16	6	14	86	73	54
9. Gornal Ath	36	16	6	14	54	42	54
10. Ludlow Tn	36	14	9	13	68	71	51
11. Ettingshall	36	11	9	16	62	80	42
12. Tividale	36	11	8	17	65	79	41
13. Lichfield C	36	9	10	17	43	65	37
14. Malvern Tn	36	9	9	18	34	67	36
15. Brierley Hill T	36	10	4	22	49	73	34
16. Cradley Tn	36	8	7	21	55	82	31
17. W/hampton C	36	9	4	23	53	108	31
18. Darlaston	36	5	11	20	40	86	26
19. Hill Top Rang	36	4	6	26	34	99	18

* 3 points deducted

Div One	P	W	D	L	F	A	Pts
1. Goodyear	40	27	6	7	110	45	87
2. W/hampton U	40	27	3	10	85	50	84
3. Rocester R	40	24	10	6	109	46	82
4. Morda Utd	40	26	4	10	87	54	82
5. Chasetown R	40	23	6	11	92	69	75
6. Bandon	40	22	7	11	94	57	73
7. Tipton Tn	40	21	10	9	78	42	73
8. Rushall O R	40	21	4	15	98	70	64*
9. Bilston Utd	40	17	10	13	92	84	61
10. Brereton Soc	40	14	12	14	66	62	54
11. Moxley Rang	40	16	8	16	70	64	53*
12. Bromyard Tn	40	16	5	19	70	67	53
13. Hinckley A R	40	15	4	21	71	84	49
14. Gornal A R	40	13	5	22	42	91	44
15. Gt Wyrley	40	13	4	23	55	103	43
16. Mahal	40	12	6	22	61	89	42
17. Oldbury U R	40	11	7	22	68	87	40
18. Pershore T R	40	10	7	23	47	82	37
19. Tividale R	40	10	6	24	51	92	36
20. Cannock C R	40	7	9	24	54	97	30
21. Sikh Hunters	40	6	5	29	50	115	20*

PREMIER DIVISION RESULTS CHART 1995-96

HOME TEAM	1	2	3	4	5	6	7	8	9	10	11	12	13	14	15	16	17	18	19
1. Bloxwich Strollers	*	3-0	2-0	0-0	3-2	1-2	2-0	3-0	1-2	1-0	5-0	0-1	2-2	2-3	3-1	0-1	3-1	6-2	1-0
2. Brierley Hill Town	1-1	*	0-0	1-4	4-1	2-0	3-1	1-1	3-2	1-2	2-0	0-1	0-1	1-1	1-2	2-1	0-1	0-2	1-4
3. Cradley Town	0-2	1-0	*	5-1	0-2	2-3	2-1	1-1	2-5	0-3	2-1	4-7	1-6	1-3	6-2	2-2	0-3	1-3	4-0
4. Darlaston	1-1	1-5	1-1	*	0-1	0-3	2-2	1-3	1-1	0-4	2-1	0-2	2-0	0-4	3-1	0-4	0-2	2-3	4-0
5. Ettingshall Holy Trin.	3-3	1-2	2-0	1-1	*	0-3	3-0	1-2	7-2	1-1	4-2	3-3	0-1	1-1	2-1	2-0	1-1	3-3	4-0
6. Gornal Athletic	1-1	1-0	1-0	1-0	2-1	*	6-1	1-0	1-2	0-1	1-1	3-0	0-1	1-3	1-2	2-0	0-3	1-3	2-3
7. Hill Top Rangers	1-3	2-1	4-1	1-1	0-2	0-3	*	0-1	2-2	0-4	0-0	0-7	0-2	1-4	2-2	0-2	1-5	1-4	0-3
8. Lichfield	1-3	3-2	1-4	4-2	0-1	1-1	1-3	*	1-3	0-4	2-1	1-0	0-2	1-1	1-3	1-2	3-4	1-4	1-1
9. Ludlow Town	0-1	3-0	1-1	5-0	5-0	1-3	3-1	1-1	*	0-2	1-2	0-3	2-2	0-0	2-2	1-1	0-4	2-6	2-1
10. Lye Town	2-2	3-2	1-1	2-0	2-0	3-1	1-2	3-0	4-0	*	5-1	1-0	4-4	0-0	0-2	3-1	1-4	4-0	4-1
11. Malvern Town	1-1	1-0	1-0	2-2	1-0	1-1	2-1	1-0	2-0	0-3	*	0-2	0-3	0-1	2-4	1-1	1-3	0-0	1-1
12. Pelsall Villa	6-0	3-2	2-0	6-0	3-1	1-0	3-0	2-0	3-0	1-1	3-1	*	1-0	4-1	1-1	3-2	1-2	3-1	3-0
13. Stafford Town	5-0	7-0	3-1	1-1	6-0	2-1	5-1	1-1	3-4	2-2	0-0	0-1	*	1-2	2-0	1-1	1-2	1-0	1-3
14. Stourport Swifts	3-2	2-1	1-1	2-1	6-3	2-3	6-2	3-3	1-3	1-1	0-1	0-0	1-1	*	4-1	1-0	0-3	5-1	4-1
15. Tividale	1-2	6-2	3-0	2-2	2-2	1-0	2-2	1-2	3-3	1-1	4-1	2-3	1-3	1-2	*	0-4	0-4	3-2	0-2
16. Walsall Wood	1-0	1-2	4-3	5-0	5-1	2-0	3-0	1-1	0-1	1-1	3-1	1-3	0-2	3-1	2-1	*	1-2	2-1	0-1
17. Wednesford	1-0	4-2	4-2	5-2	4-0	0-0	1-0	3-1	1-2	1-1	5-1	2-2	0-0	2-0	3-2	0-0	*	3-0	2-0
18. Westfield	2-4	4-0	5-2	1-1	6-1	1-1	5-1	0-0	2-4	2-1	3-0	1-2	0-5	1-2	5-1	2-2	2-5	*	7-2
19. Wolverhampton Cas	3-3	2-5	1-4	4-2	5-5	0-4	2-1	0-3	4-3	1-5	2-3	0-11	1-2	2-3	2-4	0-2	0-5	1-2	*

PREMIER DIVISION LEAGUE CUP 1995-96

First Round;

Bloxwich Strollers v Lye Town 0-2
Ludlow Town v Hill Top Rangers 5-0
Darlaston v Stourport Swifts 0-3

Second Round;

Ettingshall H T v Pelsall Villa 2-3
Gornal Athletic v Wednesfield 1-2
Stourport Swifts v Stafford Town 1-0
Walsall Wood v Cradley Town 3-1
Brierley Hill Town v Lye Town 0-0, 1-4
Malvern Town v Lichfield City 2-0
Tividale v Wolverhampton Casuals 1-2
Westfields v Ludlow Town 1-0

Third Round;

Lye Town v Malvern Town 7-0
Westfields v Pelsall Villa 0-2
Stourport Swifts v Wednesfield 2-2, 2-1
Wolverhampton Casuals v Walsall Wood 3-3, 1-2

Semi-Finals;

Lye Town v Walsall Wood 0-1, 0-3, (0-4)

Pelsall Villa v Stourport Sw 3-1, 2-1, (5-2)

Final; Pelsall Villa v Walsall Wood 3-1

DIVISION ONE RESULTS CHART 1995-96

HOME TEAM	1	2	3	4	5	6	7	8	9	10	11	12	13	14	15	16	17	18	19	20	21
1. Bandon	*	0-0	3-1	0-1	3-0	0-0	5-1	0-3	3-1	2-2	3-1	1-2	2-2	3-2	3-1	2-5	3-1	6-1	0-1	2-1	4-1
2. Bilston Utd	4-1	*	0-1	2-1	2-2	0-2	2-3	0-4	4-1	0-3	3-3	5-1	2-0	4-2	5-1	1-1	1-7	5-1	2-0	1-3	2-1
3. Brereton Social	0-0	3-3	*	3-2	1-0	2-3	1-2	0-1	1-2	3-1	0-0	3-4	1-1	2-1	1-1	2-0	3-1	2-2	1-0	2-1	4-1
4. Bromyard Town	4-3	4-5	1-0	*	2-0	3-2	2-1	1-2	3-1	5-1	3-1	0-2	5-1	2-2	3-0	0-2	2-2	1-3	0-1	2-0	0-2
5. Cannock Chase	3-1	1-3	0-0	1-3	*	1-1	3-4	1-2	0-1	3-1	3-2	1-4	3-2	1-3	0-0	1-1	1-4	2-2	1-3	5-0	4-3
6. Chasetown Res	1-6	3-5	4-4	4-2	5-1	*	3-0	2-1	3-1	3-2	2-0	2-3	3-1	3-1	3-0	2-1	2-1	3-1	0-4	0-0	2-3
7. Gornal Ath Res	1-5	2-0	0-3	0-0	2-1	2-6	*	2-0	0-3	1-3	1-1	0-3	0-4	1-1	5-1	0-6	0-5	2-1	0-1	0-3	0-2
8. Goodyear	4-1	3-1	3-3	0-3	2-2	1-2	5-0	*	6-2	7-0	2-1	4-2	2-0	1-0	5-1	1-2	6-1	6-0	0-4	3-0	4-2
9. Gt Wyrley	1-4	3-3	1-1	2-4	1-0	1-5	0-2	2-6	*	2-1	1-1	3-1	1-1	0-2	2-0	0-4	0-7	0-2	0-4	4-0	1-6
10. Hinckley Ath Res	1-1	2-3	1-3	1-0	4-2	2-1	5-0	0-2	3-0	*	3-1	0-1	1-2	0-3	4-1	6-3	2-1	4-2	1-6	3-2	1-3
11. Mahal	0-8	4-2	2-1	1-4	1-0	0-1	3-0	0-3	0-3	3-0	*	1-3	2-2	4-2	3-1	1-4	0-1	4-0	3-0	3-3	1-5
12. Morda United	0-3	2-1	2-0	1-0	4-1	5-0	2-0	0-2	7-1	3-2	7-2	*	2-2	2-0	1-2	1-3	3-2	3-1	0-2	1-1	1-3
13. Moxley Rangers	2-3	3-3	3-0	1-1	3-0	4-2	2-0	0-2	4-0	1-0	1-0	0-1	*	5-2	0-1	4-1	3-2	3-2	2-2	0-2	0-1
14. Oldbury Utd Res	2-3	2-3	2-2	3-0	7-1	1-5	1-0	1-1	1-2	2-5	0-7	0-0	0-2	*	3-0	0-3	2-3	1-1	0-4	1-3	0-3
15. Pershore Tn Res	1-2	2-2	2-1	1-0	2-0	2-4	0-2	0-1	0-3	0-0	6-0	0-0	1-3	2-2	*	1-2	3-4	2-1	1-1	3-1	1-3
16. Rocester Res	2-2	4-4	1-1	1-0	7-1	1-1	1-1	2-2	3-1	4-0	3-0	1-2	2-1	3-1	5-1	*	7-0	1-1	0-1	5-1	3-1
17. Rushall Oly Res	0-1	2-0	1-0	7-2	3-3	1-0	0-1	0-3	5-3	4-2	0-1	2-1	7-0	3-0	1-0	0-4	*	3-0	1-4	4-0	1-2
18. Sikh Hunters	1-3	0-5	2-3	2-1	2-3	0-1	1-3	1-5	1-2	1-0	1-3	1-2	0-3	1-5	3-4	0-6	0-4	*	1-3	5-0	0-1
19. Tipton Town	1-0	2-3	6-1	3-1	1-1	3-3	1-1	3-3	1-0	0-0	2-0	1-3	1-0	0-2	0-1	1-2	1-1	2-2	*	4-1	3-1
20. Tividale Res	1-2	1-1	0-5	1-1	3-1	0-2	1-2	1-0	1-2	1-4	2-1	1-4	2-1	2-5	2-1	0-2	2-4	7-0	1-1	*	0-3
21. W/hampton Utd	1-0	3-0	2-1	2-1	2-0	3-1	4-0	2-2	3-1	2-0	3-0	0-1	2-1	0-3	0-1	1-1	2-2	1-4	2-0	2-0	*

DIVISION ONE LEAGUE CUP 1995-96

First Round:

Bandon v Morda United 1-0

Cannock Chase v Rocester Res 1-1, 0-1

Rushall Olympic Res v Mahal 1-0

Sikh Hunters v Goodyear 0-0, 0-4

Wolverhampton United v Moxley Rangers 1-2

Second Round;

Chasetown Res v Brereton Social 2-0

Gornal Ath Res v Bandon 0-1

Hinckley Ath Res v Bilston United 0-3

Moxley Rangers v Rocester Res 1-5

Oldbury United Res v Bromyard Town 1-2

Pershore Tn Res v Rushall Olym Res 3-1

Tipton Town v Great Wyrley 3-1

Tividale Res v Goodyear 2-5

Third Round;

Chasetown Res v Bandon 1-3

Goodyear v Tipton Town 4-1

Pershore Tn Res v Bromyard Town 3-1

Rocester Res v Bilston United 5-0

Semi-Finals;

Pershore Tn R v Bandon 2-0, 2-2, (4-2)

Rocester Res v Goodyear 1-0, 0-1, (1-1) 4-3pen

Final; Pershore Town Reserves v Rocester Reserves 1-2

POLYMAC SERVICES MIDLAND TRIANGULAR CUP 1995-96

Third Round;

Bloxwich Strollers v Haleowen Harriers 1-3

Boldmere St Michael v Hinckley Athletic 1-0

Cradley Town v Kypersley Victoria 1-7

Knowle v Coleshill Town 1-0

Lye Town v Willenhall Town 1-2

Pelsall Villa v Upton Town 2-0

Shepshed Dynamo v Oldbury United 1-3

Westfields v Stratford Town 0-1

Quarter Finals;

Halesowqen Harriers v Willenhall Town 1-0

Knypersley Victoria v Boldmere St Michael 1-3

Statford Town v Oldbury United 1-2

Knowle v Pelsall Villa 1-2

Semi-Finals;

Pelsall Villa v Halesown Harriers 3-0

Boldmere St Michael v Oldbury United 2-5

Final; Pelsall Villa v Oldbury United 1-0

BLOXWICH STROLLERS

Chairman: Ronald Brant
Secretary: George A Llewellyn, 7 Birchover Road, Walsall WS2 8TU (0922 614595).
Manager: Leigh Taylor **Assistant Manager:** Gavin Stanton.
Ground & Directions: Blakenall FC (see page 678).
Colours: Black & white/black/black **Change colours:** All yellow **Founded:** 1888.
Programme: Yes **Programme Editor:** Neil Morris.
Previous Leagues: Walsall/ Birmingham Combination 13-32/ West Mids 52-55/ Bloxwich Combination/ West Mids Metropolitan/ Staffs Co. (Sth)/ Midland Combination (pre-1988).
Previous Grounds: The Red Lion (originally)/ T P Riley Community Centre, Lichfield Rd (pre'87).
Previous Name: Little Bloxwich Strollers **Top Scorers 93-94:** Ricky Watson & Jason Marsden.
Hons: Birmingham Comb. 24-25 (R-up 22-23), West Mids Lg Div 2 R-up 92-93 (Div 2 Cup R-up 92-93), Staffs Co. Lg Sth, Edge Cup, Lg Shield 84-85, Walsall Challenge Cup 92-93, Walsall Charity Cup, Staffs Jnr Cup, Walsall Lg.

BRIERLEY HILL TOWN

Chairman: Anthony Purchase **Vice-Chairman:** Terry Baker.
Secretary: Bill Hughes, 13 Barnett Close, Kingswinford West Midlands, DY6 9PW (01384 288855)
Manager: Richard Gwinnett **Asst Manager:** Steve Scott **Coach:** Chris Conway.
Ground: The Dell Sports Stadium, Bryce Rd, Pensnett, Brierley Hill, West Mids (0384 77289).
Directions: At lights in Brierley Hill High St turn into Bank St by Police Station. Over bridge into Pensnett Rd, ground 3/4 mile on left Paddy's Garage. Entrance 120yds in Bryce Rd.
Seats: 300 **Cover:** 300 **Capacity:** 5,000 **Floodlights:** Yes **Founded:** 1955
Colours: Blue & white/blue/blue/ **Change colours:** All Yellow **Club Shop:** No.
Programme: 20 pages, 50p **Programme Editor:** Secretary **Previous Name:** Oldswinford F & SC 1955-93.
Previous Leagues: Kidderminster (eight seasons)/ Staffs County (South)(seven seasons)/ West Midlands Regional (pre-1994).
Club Sponsors: Various **Record Gate:** 800 v Wolverhampton Wdrs, friendly.
Midweek matchday: Mon or Wed. **Nickname:** Lions.
Clubhouse: Open Mon, Wed & Fri. Hot foods & drinks on matchdays - Best hot dogs in the Midlands!
Hons: West Mids Lg Prem. Div Cup R-up 84-85 (Div 1 80-81 (Div 1 Cup 80-81)).

CRADLEY TOWN

Chairman: Graham Taylor **Vice Chairman:** R Gosling **President:** W Forrest
Secretary: David Attwood, 4 Birch Coppice, Quarry Bank, Brierley Hill, W Midlands DY5 1AP.
Manager: Trevor Thomas **Asst Manager:** T Hetheridge **Physio:** S Ward
Ground: Beeches View, Beeches View Avenue, Cradley, Halesowen, Cradley Heath (01384 569658)
Directions: M5 jct 3, take A456, right at 2nd island, left into Rosemary Rd after Fox Hunt pub, Landsdown Rd, Dunstall Rd, left at T-junction, left again at next T-junction (Beecher Rd East), 1st left (Abbey Rd), right at end, ground 50yds on left. Nearest BR station is Cradley Heath.
Seats: 200 **Cover:** 1,500 **Capacity:** 3,000 **Floodlights:** Yes **Club Shop:** No.
Programme: Yes **Editor:** **Press Officer:** A Hills (01384 69585)
Colours: Red & black stripes/black/black **Change colours:** All blue
Sponsors: Adstone Structural Ltd **Founded:** 1944. **Nickname:** Lukes
Midweek home matchday: Tuesday **Reserve team's League:** West Mids Lge Division Two.
Record Gate: 1,000 v Aston Villa, friendly.
Previous Leagues: Metropolitan/ Brierley Hill/ Kidderminster/ West Mids Amtr/ Midland Comb. 71-82.
Players progressing to Football Lge: Alan Nicholls (Plymouth (via Cheltenham)), John Williams, Jon Ford, Andy McFarlane (all Swansea), Duane Darby (Torquay).
Clubhouse: Open all day every day. Food available.
95-96 Captain: Chris Turner **95-96 Top Scorer:** Jason Marsden **95-96 P.o.Y.:** Wayne Bache
Club Record Goalscorer: Jim Nugent **Club Record Apearances:** R J Hayward.
Hons: West Mids Lg Div 1 90-91, Midland Comb. Div 2 72-73 (R-up 75-76 77-78, Presidents Cup 74-75 75-76, Invitation 72-73), Metropolitan Lg 70-71, Wednesbury Charity Cup 90-91, Dudley Guest Hosp. Cup 71-72 72-73 75-76 90-91.

DARLASTON

Chairman: Mike Howls **Vice-Chairman:**
Secretary: Andrew Hickman, 31 Willenhall Street, Darlaston WS10 8NE (0121 568 7514).
Manager: David Downing. **Assistant Manager:** Martin Seal. **Physio:**
Ground: City Ground, Waverley Rd, Darlaston (0121 526 4423).
Directions: M6 Jct 10, onto A454 towards Willenhall, left at lights outside 'Lane Arms' into Bentley Rd North, follow this down hill and over the railway and canal bridges to traffic lights. Cross over the lights into Richards St and along into Victoria Rd, 1st right into Slater St and ground on left but entrance is next left in Waverley Rd.
Seats: Yes **Cover:** Yes **Capacity:** **Floodlights:** Yes. **Club Shop:** Yes
Programme: Yes **Editor:** Dave Stevenson (0121 526 2465). **Press Officer:** Neil Chambers
Colours: Blue & white stripes/blue/blue **Change colours:** All yellow
Sponsors: Metafin Holdings **Nickname:** Blues. **Founded:** 1874
Midweek matches: Tuesday **Reserves League:**
Prevs Lgs: Jun lges (inc Wednesbury Lge) pre-1908/ B'gham Comb. 08-11 28-54/ W Mids 11-28.

Players progressing to Football League: J Burkett (Nottingham For), A McFarlane (Swansea C).
Clubhouse: Open matchdays. Tues/Wed/Thur evenings & Sunday Lunch. Hot/cold drinks/snacks.
95-96 Captain: Jon Chapman. **95-96 Top Scorer:** Chris Marriott. **95-96 P.o.Y.:** Matt Abley.
Honours: West Mids Lg Div 1 89-90 (R-up 91-92 92-93, Div 1 Cup Cup 89-90), Birmingham Snr Cup 72-73, Birmingham Vase 90-91 91-92, Birmingham Jnr Lg 07-08, Birmingham Comb. 10-11 37-38 45-46 (Tillotson Cup 36-37 37-38 38-39 45-46), Keys Cup 11-12), Wednesbury Lg(5) 1896-1901.

ETTINGSHALL HOLY TRINITY

Chairman: John O'Dell. **Vice-Chairman:** T.B.A. **President:** David Gadd.
Secretary: Graham Mills, 27 Ashen Close, Sedgley, Dudley, West Mids DY3 3UZ (0902 662222(01.
Manager: David Caddick. **Asst Manager:** Mark King. **Coach:** Graham Mills.
Ground: Aldersley Stadium.
Directions: From Wolverhampton take A41 Tettenhall Rd 1.5miles turn right into Lower St. then Rt Aldersley Rd Ground on Rt. **Founded:** 1920.
Colours: Green/white **Change colours:** Yellow/blue **Nickname:** Trins.
Previous League: Wednesbury Church & Chapel (early 1900s(01/ Bilston Youth (1950s(01/ Wolverhampton & District Amateur (1960s(01/ Staffs County (South(01.
Programme: Yes **Programme Editor:** Geoff Little (0902 883121(01.
Midweek home matchday: Wednesday **Club Sponsors:** Direct Batteries/ DKB Electric.
Record win: 13-0 v Chubbs Sports, Hunt Cup.
Hons: West Mids Lg Div 1 Cup R-up 85-86 (Div 2 R-up 84-85, Sporting Award 85-86, Staffs Co. Lg R-up 82-83 (Lg Shield 82-83 83-84), Ike Cooper Cup 82-84 83-84, Sporting Club Award 81-82, Wolverhampton & District Amateur Lg 80-81 (Div 1 65-66, Div 2 64-65), Div 1/2 Cup 64-65 65-66, A H Oakley Cup 80-81, J W Hunt Cup 82-83 83-84 (R-up 79-80), Wolverhampton Cup 83-84 (R-up 82-83).

GORNAL ATHLETIC

Chairman: Ken Taylor
Secretary: Paul Westwood, 18 The Close, Lower Gornal, Dudley DY3 2JY (01902 664209).
Manager: John Gwinnell **Coach:** Ian Clark/ Ross Hill.
Reserves' Manager: Ian Davies **Commercial Manager:** Martin Wedgebury.
Ground: Garden Walk Stadium, Lower Gornal, Dudley, West Midlands (01384 252285).
Directions: From Dudley take A459 to Sedgley past the Burton Rd Hospital. 1st on left at the Green Dragon public house on the B4175 (Jews Lane). Follow the road until you come to the Old Bull's Head, turn left into Rednall Road, 2nd left to Garden Walk.
Seats: 100 **Cover:** 500 **Capacity:** 3,000 **Floodlights:** Yes **Founded:** 1945.
Colours: Yellow&green/black/black **Change colours:** All sky blue. **Club Shop:** No.
Previous Name: Lower Gornal Ath. **Previous Lge:** Midland Comb. 51-63 **Nickname:** Peacocks
Sponsors: Jasper Steels **Reserve Team's League:** West Mids (Regional) Lge Res. Div.
Record transfer fees received: £1,500 for Gary Bell and for George Andrews both to Cardiff City, 1965.
Hons: West Mids Lg Div 1 R-up 83-84 (Div 1 Cup 92-93), Birmingham Vase 91-92.

HILL TOP RANGERS

Chairman: Mr J Scott
Secretary: Mr Paul Allen, 14 Queen Street, Wednesbury, West Midlands WS10 7PT.
Managers: Paul Rushton & Steve Dale. **Asst Manager:** Dave Scott **Coach:** T.B.A.
Physio: J Scott **Press Officer:** Mrs S Allen.
Ground: Hadley Stadium,Wilson Road,Smethwick,West Midlands. **Founded:** 1980.
Colours: Yellow/black/yellow **Change Colours:** Red/navy/red **Club Shop:** No.
Previous Leagues: West Bromwich & Dist. 80-84/ West Mids Metropolitan 84-86/ Mercian FA 86-88.
Programme: With entry, or 50p **Programme Editor:** Secretary
Midweek home matchday: Tuesday **Record Gate:** 165 v Darlaston, W Mids Lg Div 1 12/4/94.
Players progressing to Football League: Andy Pearce (Coventry City, Sheffield Wednesday via Stourbridge and Halesowen Town).
Clubhouse: Inside ground. Hot food from Sportsmans Bar. Snacks (crisps, chocolate) and hot and cold drinks available from tea bar at top of ground.
Club record scorer: Dean Cadman 175 **Club record appearances:** Dave Scott 399.
Hons: West Midlands (Regional) Lg Div 2 89-90, West Midlands Metropolitan Lg R-up 85-86, Mercian FA 86-87, West Bromwich District Charity Cup.

LUDLOW TOWN

Chairman: P.Gwilliam.
Secretary: Miss K Evans, Riddings Park, Riddings Road, Ludlow, Shropshire SY8 1HZ.
Manager: Robert Hicks. **Asst Manager:** Derek Mulliner. **Coach:** Bob Bodenham.
Ground: The Riddings, Riddings Road, Ludlow, Shropshire (01584 875103).
Directions: From Kidderminster A4117; straight over r'bout into Henley Rd, 2nd left into Sandpits Rd, follow road for 1/4 mile until road bears round to the left into Ridding Rd - grd on right.
Seats: No **Cover:** 150 **Floodlights:** Yes **Clubhouse:** Yes **Programme:** No
Cols: Red (white pin stripes)/black/black (red tops) **Change colours:** White/Black/Black.
Previous League: Kidderminster.
Hons: Wes Mids Lg Div 1 Cup 90-91, Shropshire County Challenge Cup 93-94,94-95.
Presteigne-Otway Cup 90-91.94-95.West Mids.Lg Premier Lg.Cup:Finalists 94-95. .gap 3

LYE TOWN

Chairman: Geoff Ball **President:** Ian Cole. **Comm. Manager:** TBA.
Secretary: Mrs Audrey Ball, 79 Aretha Close, Crestwood Park, Kingswinford, West Mids DY6 8SW (01384 839216).
Manager: David Beasley. **Asst Manager:**
Coach: Alan Moore **Physio:** Harry Hill.
Ground: Stourbridge Road, Lye (01384 422672).
Directions: On A458 Birmingham-Stourbridge road about 400yds after lights/crossroads at Lye. From M5 jct 3 take road marked Kidderminster as far as lights at bottom of Hagley Hill, right at island, 3rd turn off at next island,turn off left at crossroads/lights, ground about 400yds on left. Quarter mile from Lye (BR).
Seats: 200 **Cover:** 600 **Capacity:** 5,000 **Floodlights:** Yes **Founded:** 1930.
Colours: Red & black/black/red & black **Change Colours:** Blue & white/blue/blue **Nickname:** Flyers.
Programme: 24 pages, 40p **Programme Editor:** J.Galloway. .oneline 2
Clubhouse: Yes (01384 822672).
Previous Leagues: Midland Combination 31-39.
Record Gate: 6,000 v Brierley Alliance. **Hons:** West Mids Lg R-up 76-77 78-79 79-80 80-81 (Prem. Div Cup 75-76), Midland Comb. 35-36 (R-up 32-33 34-35 37-38), B'ham Snr Cup R-up 80-81.

MALVERN TOWN

Chairman: R C Tandy **President:** R H Mann **Manager:** Martyn Day
Secretary: G F Knapper, 27 Alexandra Lane, Malvern, Worcs WR14 1JF (01684 574861).
Ground: Langland Stadium, Langland Avenue, Malvern, Worcs (01684 574068).
Directions: From Worcester take main road to Malvern. When reaching Malvern turn left at 1st lights into Pickersleigh Ave., follow to Langland Arms Pub on left, left into Madresfield Rd, 2nd left into Langland Ave., ground 100yds on right. 1 mile from Malvern (BR).
Seats: 140 **Cover:** 310 **Capacity:** 4,000 **Floodlights:** Yes **Founded:** 1947.
Colours: Claret/white/sky **Change colours:** White/black/maroon.
Prog: 12 pages 20p (special matches) **Programme Editor:** Dave Liley
Clubhouse: 2 bars, large dance area **Previous League:** Midland Comb. 55-79.
Hons: Worcester/ Midland Comb. 55-56. **Record Gate:** 1,221 v Worcester, FA Cup

STAFFORD TOWN

President: T Logan **Chairman:** A Bowers.
Secretary: Dave Rowley, 32 Lodge Road, Brereton, Rugely, Staffs WS15 1HG (01889 583000)
Manager: Chris Curtiss **Press Officer:** David Howard (01785 222686).
Ground: As Stafford Rangers FC (see page 495).
Programme: 28 pages, 50p **Editor:** David Howard (0785 222686) **Founded:** 1974
Colours: All red **Change colours:** All blue.
Nickname: Reds or Town **Previous Names:** Stafford Town 74-90/ Stafford MSHD 90-92.
Prev. Grnds: Silkmore Lane 74-77/ Burton Manor Spts 77-88/ Riverway 88-91/ Rowley Park Stad 91-94.
Previous Leagues: Staffs County (North) 74-77 82-84/ Midland Combination 77-82/ Staffs Senior 84-93.
Midweek home matches: Mon/Wed **Club Shop:** No - just old programmes available.
Record win: 14-0 v Leek CSOB (H), Staffs Senior League 8/10/88.
Hons: WMRL Div 1 93-94, Staffs Snr Lg R-up 91-92, Midland Comb. Div 2 78-79, Staffs Vase 84-85 92-93 (R-up 87-88), Bourne Sports Trophy 84-85, Walsall Senior Cup SF 91-92.

STOURPORT SWIFTS

Chairman: Chris Reynolds **Vice Chairman:** Trevor Roberts **President:** Roy Crowe.
Secretary: John McDonald, 65 Princess Way, Stourport-on-Severn (01299 822088).
Physio: Ginger Jorden **Managers:** Rod Brown **Coach:** Ian Brown.
Ground: Walshes Meadow, off Harold Davis Drive, Stourport-on-Severn (01299 825188).
Directions: Follow one-way system through Stourport sign posted Sports Centre. Go over River Severn Bridge, turn left into Harold Davies Drive. Ground is at rear of Sports Centre. Nearest rail station is Kidderminster.
Seats: 250 **Cover:** 150 **Capacity:** 2,000 **Floodlights:** Yes **Club Shop:** No.
Programme: 40 pages, 50p **Editor:** Dave Watts (01299 823349)
Press Officer: Dave Watts (01299 823349).
Colours: Black & gold/black/black **Change colours:** All Red
Club Sponsors: T. & J. Joinery **Founded:** 1882. **Nickname:** Swifts.
Midweek home matchday: Tuesday **Reserve team's League:** Kidderminster.
Record Attendancee: 4,000 v Birmingham, charity match.
Previous Leagues: Kidderminster/ Worcester/ Midland Combination.
Clubhouse: Clubhouse open matchdays. Hot snacks available. Licensed bar.
95-96 Captain: Kevin Nokes. **95-96 Top Scorer:** Darren Tafft 38 **95-96 P.o.Y.:** Kevin Nokes
Club Record Goalscorer: Gary Crowther **Club Record Appearances:** Ian Johnson
Hons: West Mids Prem Div.R-Up.94-95,Lg Div 1 R-up 87-88 (Prem Div Cup 92-93, Div 2 Cup R-up 82-83), Worcs Snr Urn 92-93 93-94 94-95, Worcs Infirmary Cup 94-95 95-96.

Gornal Athletic FC: Back Row (L-R); R Green, I Clift, K Freeth, R Hill, K Salmon, J Carmichael, D Townsend, P Smith, C Banks, K Birch, J Gwinnell. Front Row; P Wells, D Brookes, N Smith, T Kettle, A Patterson, S Worley, P Bradley.

Pelsall Villa: Back Row (L-R); K Gough, S Beech, D Wilkinson, M Iqbal, N Jones, A Horne, M Cartwright, N Coles, S Hughes, R Priest (Mgr). Front Row; D Walters, M O'Sullivan, I Patel, C Duffus, H Singh, C Hodges, J Lancaster.

Walsall Wood: Back Row (L-R); B Morgan, M Speake, T Siverns, M Sylvester, D Thompson, S Bamford, W Essen, G Slide, J Hewitt, G Tonks. Front Row; D Roper, T Carson, T Gwynne, D Oliver, A Roper, R Malliband, A Cox, P Welburn, D Roper.

TIVIDALE

Chairman: Don Ashton **President:** Lord Peter Archer.
Secretary: Paul Boswell, 34 Princes Rd, Tividale, Warley, W.Mids. B69 2LR (0121 520 3618)
Manager: Terry Jones **Asst Manager:** Kevin Mullinder **Physio:** J Cotton/K Nicklin
Ground: The Beeches, Packwood Rd, Tividale, Warley, West Midlands B69 1UL (01384 211743).
Directions: Dudley Port Station to Burnt tree, left towards Birmingham, ground 1 mile on right. Or, M5 jct 2, follow Dudley signs A4123, after approx 2 miles turn left into Regent Rd and left again into Elm Terraces, first left into Birch Crescent. Packwood Rd is second left - ground at end of cul-de-sac.
Seats: 200 **Cover:** 1,000 **Capacity:** 3,500 **Floodlights:** Yes **Club Shop:** No.
Programme: 40 pgs, £1.75 inc entry **Editor:** c/o Club **Press Officer:** T Clark.
Colours: All Yellow. **Change colours:** All Red.
Sponsors: Midland & North Security Consultants **Nickname:** Dales **Founded:** 1954
Midweek matchday: Tuesday **Reserves League:** Div. One.
Record Attendance: 2,400 v Telford United, FA Cup.
Previous Leagues: Handsworth & District 56-60/ inactive 60-62/ West Mids Alliance 62-66.
Players progressing to Football League: G Hughes, L May.
Clubhouse: Mon-Fri 8-11pm, Sat 12-11pm, Sun 12-3 & 8-10.30. Cobs, rolls, sandwiches available.
95-96 Captain: **95-96 Top Scorer:** **95-96 P.o.Y.:**
Hons: W Mids Lg Div 1 72-73 (Prem. Div Cup 76-77, Div 1 Cup 72-73), Wednesbury Charity Cup 76-77.

WALSALL WOOD

Chairman: Robert Thomas **Manager:** Michael Speake
Secretary: John Rousel, 19 Kinver Avenue, Willenhall, Walsall, West Midlands, WV12 4LS (011902 637711) 373180).
Ground: Oak Park, Lichfield Rd, Walsall (01543 361084).
Directions: Off A461 Walsall-Lichfield Rd, 4 miles from Walsall town centre and 100yds south of junction with A4152 Aldridge-Brownhills. If travelling via M6/M5 exit motorway at jct 7 (Post House) and continue on A34 towards Walsall before joining A4148 which connects with the A461. 4 miles from Walsall (BR) station - regular buses pass ground.
Capacity: 3,000 **Seats:** 400 **Cover:** 400 **Floodlights:** Yes **Founded:** 1928.
Colours: Red & white/white/red **Change colours:** All blue **Programme:** Yes
Previous Grounds: None **Previous Leagues:** Mids Comb. 51-92/ Staffs Snr 92-93.
Previous Names: Walsall Wood, Walsall Sportsco merged in 1982 to form Walsall Borough. Name later reverted.
Record Gate: 800 v Aston Villa, 1980.
Clubhouse: Evenings, matchdays and Sunday lunchtimes. Darts, pool. Hot snacks on matchdays.
Hons: Midland Comb. 51-52 (R-up 53-54 54-55 57-58 58-59 60-61, Lg Cup 54-55 60-61 (R-up 56-57 58-59)), B'ham Jnr Cup 76-77.

WEDNESFIELD

Chairman: R Thomas **Vice Chairman:** J Massey
Secretary: Roger Thomas, 21 Stubley Drive, Fallings Park, Wolverhampton. WV10 9YB (01902 725656)
Manager/Coach: Ken Hall **Asst Manager:** TBA **Physio:** M Andrews
Commercial Mgr: D Clayton **Press Officer:** J Massey (0902 781819).
Ground: Cottage Ground, Amos Lane, Wednesfield, Wolverhampton (01902 735506).
Directions: From Wolverhampton on the A4124 Wednesfield Rd. Stay on road right through Wednesfield until island. Leave island at 1st exit (Wood End Rd), left after 200yds into Amos Lane. Ground on right, approx. 400yds along. 3 miles Wolverhampton BR station. Bus 559 to Wood End or 560 to Red Lion.
Seats: 148 **Cover:** 250 **Capacity:** 1,000 **Floodlights:** Yes **Founded:** 1961.
Colours: Red & white/black/black **Change colours:** Green & yellow/green/yellow
Programme: 50p **Programme Editor:** TBA **Club Shop:** No.
Record Gate: 480 v Burton Albion, FA Cup 1981.
Previous Ground: St Georges PF 61-76
Previous Name: Wednesfield Social 61-89.
Previous League: Wolverhampton & District Amateur 61-76.
Club Sponsors: Ansells **Midweek home matchday:** Tuesday **Nickname:** Cottagers.
Clubhouse: Evenings 7-11pm. Food (burgers, chips etc) on 1st team matchdays.
95-96 Captain: **95-96 Top Scorer:** **95-96 P.o.Y.:**
Hons: West Mids Lg Div 1 76-77 (R-up 77-78).

WESTFIELDS

Chairman: Alan Dunsford **Vice Chairman:** **President:** Graham Preece.
Secretary: Andrew Morris, 17 Fayre Oaks Green, Kings Acre, Hereford HR4 0QT (01432 264711 H)
Manager: Gary Stevens **Coach:** Sean Edwards/Phil Dean **Physio:** Peter Boulton
Ground: Thorn Lighting, Holme Lacy Rd, Rotherwas, Hereford (01432 268131)
Directions: Proceed 1.5 mile south from Hereford on A49, left in Home Lacy Rd at Broadleys Inn, proceed 1 mile to Thorn Lighting Rotherwas, ground on the right on Rotherwas Ind. Estate. 2 miles from Hereford (BR).
Seats: 100 **Cover:** 150 **Capacity:** 2,000 **Floodlights:** Yes **Club Shop:** Yes
Programme: Yes **Editor:** Andy Morris **Press Officer:** Secretary
Colours: Maroon & sky **Change colours:** Sky & white
Sponsors: Hereford Times **Founded:** 1966 **Nickname:** The Fields.
Midweek matchday: Tuesday **Youth team's League:** W Midlands Youth Lge Floodlite
Record Attendance: 1,057 v Hereford Utd, t'monial 1980.
Previous Leagues: Herefordshire Sunday 66-74/ Herefordshire 72-74/ Worcester & Dist. 74-77.
Players progressing to Football League: Alex Sykes (Mansfield Town 92), Gary Bowyer (Nottingham Forest 89), John Layton (Hereford Utd 74).
Clubhouse: 'Gamecock Inn' Holme Lacey Rd. Hereford (1/2 mile from ground).
95-96 Captain: Darren Preece. **95-96 Top Scorer:** Paul Burton 46 **95-96 P.o.Y.:**
Club Record Goalscorer: Paul Burton. **Club Record Appearances:** Phil Powell/ Mark Tabb.
Hons: West Mids Lg Div 1 86-87, Div 2 R-up 83-84 (Div 2 Cup 79-80 83-84), Herefordshire Snr Cup 85-86 88-89 91-92 95-96 (Yth Cup 92-93 95-96), Kington Chall. Cup 83-84 85-86 86-87 89-90 91-92, Kington Invitation Cup 84-85 85-86 86-87 95-96, Presteigne Ottway Cup 78-79 81-82 84-85 93-94, Worcs Jnr Cup 79-80, Wye Guild Cup 74-75 77-78, Hereford Sunday Lg Prem 75-76 76-77 (Div 1 71-72, Div 2 76-77, Div 3 75-76, Prem Div Cup 75-76 76-77, Div 1 Cup 73-74 74-75, Div 3 Cup 72-73), Smart Brown Cup 67-68, Fair Play Cup 67-68. Dennis Hartland Mem Trophy 95-96, Robert Biggart Trophy 95-96.

WOLVERHAMPTON CASUALS

Chairman: B.Austin. **President:** Clive Hammond **Manager:** Gary Walters.
Secretary: Michael Green, 63 St Philip's Ave., Pennfields, Wolverhampton WV3 7GD (01902 333677).
Ground: Brinsford Lane, Coven, Wolverhampton (01902 783214).
Directions: Onto M54 from M6 North, at jct 2 turn right (A449 to Stafford). Ground half a mile, turn right into Brinsford Lane. 2 miles from Billbrooke (BR). Stafford-Wolverhampton buses pass ground.
Seats: 50 **Cover:** 50 **Capacity:** 2,000 **Floodlights:** No **Founded:** 1896
Colours: White & green/green/green. **Change colours:** Gold/black/gold
Programme: 28 pages, 30p **Programme Editor:** G Smith
Previous Name: Staffs Casuals (pre-1981) **Previous Ground:** Aldersley Stadium.
Clubhouse: Bar and snacks, open Tues, Wed, Thurs, Sat, Sun & alternative Mon.
Players progressing to Football League: David Heywood (Wolves),Chris Lewis(Leicester C),Des Lyttle (Nottm.F).
Prev. Lges: B'gham AFA, W'hampton Amtr
Hons: W Mids Lg Div 1 R-up(3) 85-88 (Div 1 Cup 85-86).Banks's Brewery Div 1. Champions 1994-95.

WOLVERHAMPTON UNITED

Chairman: Geoffrey Lee
Manager: Micky Ward.
Secretary: Liz Blatherwick, 38 Sharpe Road, Wednesfield, Wolverhampton WV11 2NP (01902 728611).
Ground: Prestwood Rd Spts Centre, Prestwood Rd West, Wednesfield (01902 730881).
Directions: Situated between Nos. 44 and 46 Prestwood Rd West, approached by way of a drive between the two houses. From Wolverhampton centre Ring Road, follow round to Stafford Str. (A449), join Cannock Rd (A460), after 1 mile bear right into Victoria Road, cross over into Thorneycroft Lane/Prestwood Rd West - ground on right 200yds from pedestrian crossing.
Seats: 200 **Cover:** Yes **Programme:** Yes **Clubhouse:** Yes **Founded:** 1976.
Colours: Gold/black/gold **Change colours:** All Blue.
Hons: WMRL Div 1 Section B 76-77 (R-up 81-82, Div 1 Cup 76-77 81-82 93-94), Birmingham Co. Vase 93-94.

Brierley Hill:
Back Row (L-R); Lee Smith, Trevor Davis, Colin Horne, Tracey Davies, Dave Hughes, Dean English, Derrick Rhodes. Front Row; Andy Mole, Sylvester Phillips, Adam Smith, Neil Foxall, John Street, Jason Downing, Craig Myatt.

Stourport Swifts:
Back Row (L-R); Martin Bennett, Neil Walters, Jason Fellows, Wayne Lancett, David Herrington, Paul Vaughan, Craig Whiston, Kevin Nokes, Paul Danks, Matt Greaves. Front Row; David Brookes, Trevor Kirby, Duncan Flowers, Neil Eggington, John Holmes, Ian Brown, Darren Tafft, Russell Parmentor, Clive Bishop.

DORSET COMBINATION LEAGUE

FOUNDED: 1957

President: A P Humphries

Chairman: R E Maidment

Hon. Secretary: G A Theobald,
41 South Road, Corfe Mullen, Wimborne, Dorset BH21 3HZ (01202 697994).

The League Championship was won by Hamworthy Engineering and thereby completing a hat-trick of League titles. The runners-up position was a closely fought contest with Bridport Reserves finishing behind Hamworthy, leaving Portland United in third place and Weymouth Sports in fourth. At the other end of the table Flight Refuelling were experiencing their worst season ever in the Combination League and looking very much like candidates for relegation to the Dorset League. However, a string of good results in the last few weeks lifted Flights to 18th position, leaving Swanage Town & Herston Reserves and Holy United in 19th and 20th place respectively.

The Combination Cup Final saw Sturminster Newton beating Sherborne Town by 2-1 to take the honours for the second time. Bournemouth Sports kept the League's hopes alive in the Dorset Senior Cup, reaching the semi-final and only losing 1-0 to Dorchester Town (Premier Div Beazer Homes League) after three games. Sherborne Town, the league's only representative in this season's FA Vase, won through to the First Round, narrowly losing at Torrington (Premier Div Great Mills League), having beaten Portsmouth RN and Christchurch (both Jewson Wessex League) in the Preliminary rounds.

The Representative team under manager Pat Notley (Hamworthy Engineering) drew 1-1 with the Hampshire League at Shaftsbury. Whilst the annual fixture with the Wiltshire League was postponed because of bad weather and due to the backlog of fixtures suffered by both Leagues, another suitable date could not be found. The Trevor Williams Fair Play Trophy was won by newcomers Allendale, narrowly beating last season's joint winner Bournemouth Sports.

A lot of people locally knock our League, saying that the standard is not what it used to be, but results acheived by our Clubs against opposition from higher leagues tend to dispel this theory. This is also backed up by the success of the County Senior squad, consisting almost entirely of Combination League players. enjoying one of their most successful seasons for a long time.

The 1996-97 season sees a number of changes in the League with both Weymouth Reserves and Holt United withdrawing and two new teams joining the League. Swanage Town & Herston, relegated from the Jewson Wessex League, are replacing their Reserves, whilst Sturminster Marshall (runners-up Dorset League), who are promoted under the new agreement are returning to the Combination League after an absense of 20 years.

Geoff Theobald.

FINAL LEAGUE TABLES 1995/96

		P	*W*	*D*	*L*	*F*	*A*	*Pts*
1.	Hamworthy Engineering	38	27	9	2	109	31	90
2.	Bridport	38	23	6	9	69	51	75
3.	Portland United	38	22	7	9	79	41	73
4.	Weymouth Sports	38	21	5	12	76	59	68
5.	Wareham Rangers	38	20	7	11	86	69	67
6.	Bournemouth Sports	38	19	6	13	103	63	63
7.	Shaftsbury	38	19	6	13	76	60	63
8.	Dorchester Town	38	18	8	12	75	61	62
9.	Sherborne Town	38	18	7	13	95	60	61
10.	Blandford United	38	15	11	12	61	51	56
11.	Allendale	38	16	6	16	68	70	54
12.	Sturminster Newton	38	14	5	19	64	77	47
13.	Weymouth	38	13	9	16	64	63	45*
14.	Westland Sports	38	13	6	19	59	78	45
15.	Hamworthy United	38	12	8	18	57	57	44
16.	Parley Sports	38	13	5	20	61	84	44
17.	Gillingham Town	38	8	11	19	52	74	35
18.	Flight Refuelling	38	10	3	25	54	81	33
19.	Swanage Town	38	8	1	29	33	140	25
20.	Holt United	38	7	2	29	42	113	23

** 3points deducted ineligible player*

LEADING GOALSCORERS (League Matches only)

C Morison	Bournemouth Sports	28	D Pritchett	Hamworthy Engineering	27
D Alford	Shaftsbury	26	P Selby	Wareham Rangers	25
G Bardell	Weymouth Reserves	22	J Westlake	Sherborne Town	21
S Manuel	Hamworthy Engineering	20	J Lewis	Portland United	19
S Mulcock	Hamworthy Engineering	19	D Blenman	Parley Sports	18
R Fox	Sturminster Newton	18	R Sweetlove	Flight Refuelling	17
D Mears	Wareham Rangers	16	M Town	Bournemouth Sports	16
G Trevett	Allendale	16			

COMBINATION CUP 1995-96

First Round;

Bournemouth Spts v Dorchester Tn Res	4-0	Hamworthy Eng v Westland Sports	6-0
Portland United v Swanage T & H Res	5-0	Sturminster Newton v Blandford Utd	3-1

Second Round;

Allendale v Bournemouth Sports	0-1	Flight Refuelling v Portland United	0-1
Gillingham Town v Bridport Res	0-1	Holt United v Hamworthy United	3-5
Sherborne Town v Wareham Rangers	3-1	Sturminster Newton v Shaftsbury	2-0
Weymouth Res v Hamworthy Eng	0-1	Weymouth Sports v Parley Sports	3-6

Third Round;

Bournemouth Sports v Portland United	4-1	Hamworthy Eng v Hamworthy United	1-0
Parley Sports v Sturminster Newton	0-1	Sherborne Town v Bridport Res	0-0, 1-0

Semi-Finals;

Sturminster Newton v Bournemouth Spt	1-0	Hamworthy Eng v Sherborne Town	2-3 (aet)

Final; Sherborne Town v Sturminster Newton 1-2

DORSET COMBINATION LEAGUE RESULTS CHART 1995-96

HOME TEAM	1	2	3	4	5	6	7	8	9	10	11	12	13	14	15	16	17	18	19	20
1. Allendale	*	0-2	1-1	0-3	0-0	3-1	2-2	0-2	1-1	2-0	3-1	1-3	3-3	1-2	4-3	3-0	2-4	3-2	4-0	1-3
2. Blandford United	2-0	*	3-3	3-1	1-1	2-1	2-2	0-4	1-1	4-1	3-1	2-1	1-3	2-3	1-0	3-0	0-2	1-1	1-2	0-2
3. Bournemouth Sports	2-1	2-1	*	2-2	1-2	2-0	1-1	1-2	2-1	3-1	3-2	3-0	1-3	7-1	9-0	7-0	1-3	5-0	3-1	6-1
4. Bridport Reserves	3-1	0-2	3-2	*	0-0	2-1	3-0	0-0	3-1	3-2	1-3	4-0	4-1	3-1	2-0	1-0	2-1	2-1	1-1	0-1
5. Dorchester Res	2-1	2-2	1-3	8-0	*	3-0	2-0	1-3	3-1	4-1	1-3	2-1	3-2	1-1	3-1	3-1	3-3	2-1	0-1	1-3
6. Flight Refuelling	0-3	0-2	0-5	4-0	2-3	*	2-0	1-3	1-2	1-2	2-1	0-1	1-4	1-3	3-1	4-0	2-2	2-2	2-1	2-1
7. Gillingham Town	1-2	4-2	3-2	0-3	0-3	1-0	*	1-1	0-3	2-3	2-2	0-1	2-3	3-2	2-2	9-0	2-0	2-4	0-1	0-3
8. Hamworthy Eng.	0-1	3-2	3-2	6-3	1-1	3-1	1-1	*	2-1	8-1	0-0	2-2	2-1	2-1	4-0	2-1	3-5	2-0	2-1	4-0
9. Hamworthy United	4-0	0-1	1-1	0-1	3-2	0-3	1-2	0-1	*	3-1	1-1	0-2	1-2	1-2	1-0	4-0	1-2	2-1	2-0	0-2
10. Holt United	1-3	0-2	2-5	0-3	4-3	1-0	2-2	0-7	1-1	*	3-1	0-2	1-3	0-3	0-1	2-3	1-2	1-2	1-2	1-5
11. Parley Sports	3-4	2-1	4-3	0-4	3-3	2-3	3-1	0-5	0-0	5-0	*	0-2	0-1	2-1	0-4	3-1	2-6	4-1	0-4	1-0
12. Portland United	4-2	0-0	4-1	0-1	5-0	3-1	2-0	1-1	3-3	4-0	4-1	*	1-1	2-4	3-0	5-0	2-1	3-2	1-2	3-0
13. Shaftesbury	4-2	0-0	2-5	2-0	0-2	4-2	0-3	1-2	0-0	4-2	5-0	1-0	*	0-2	0-2	1-4	4-0	2-3	3-0	2-2
14. Sherbourne Town	1-3	1-1	0-1	0-1	2-4	4-0	1-1	0-5	5-0	5-0	3-0	0-0	5-0	*	2-2	8-0	4-1	4-0	4-0	6-1
15. Sturminster Newton	0-2	0-3	2-3	3-1	4-1	5-3	4-1	0-0	1-3	4-1	2-1	0-3	1-0	1-1	*	5-1	2-4	5-0	1-0	1-2
16. Swanage T&H Res	0-3	3-2	3-0	0-2	1-2	2-1	2-0	0-14	0-6	1-4	2-1	0-5	1-3	0-5	2-0	*	2-2	0-2	0-4	2-4
17. Wareham Rangers	5-1	0-3	2-0	1-2	3-0	4-1	1-1	1-1	2-4	2-0	1-2	4-2	0-3	4-1	2-2	1-0	*	4-1	1-1	2-1
18. Westland Sports	4-2	0-0	3-2	1-2	1-0	2-1	4-0	0-3	3-2	4-0	1-4	1-1	0-5	3-1	1-2	3-0	2-3	*	0-1	2-4
19. Weymouth Res	1-3	2-2	2-2	1-1	1-0	1-4	1-1	1-3	3-1	3-0	1-3	1-2	2-2	2-2	4-1	10-1	3-4	1-1	*	2-3
20. Weymouth Sports	0-0	3-1	2-1	2-2	1-3	1-1	3-0	0-2	2-1	1-2	2-0	0-1	0-1	5-4	4-2	6-1	5-1	0-0	1-0	*

DORSET COMBINATION CLUBS 1995-96

ALLENDALE F.C.

Chairman: E Case (01202 887920 H, 01258 857191 B)
Secretary: Rod Pope, 51 Dalkeith Road, Corfe Mullen Wimborne, BH21 3PQ (01202 602922 H, 01929 424601 B)
Ground: Redcotts Recreation Ground, School Lane, Wimborne
Colours: White/blue/white
Change Colours: Blue & white/white/blue

BLANDFORD UNITED

Chairman: John Radford **Secretary:** David Upshall, 18 Ramsbury Court, Ramsbury Gdns, Blandford Forum, Dorset DT11 7UL (01258 456125).
Ground: Recreation Ground, Park Lane, Blandford Forum, Dorset. (HQ Tel: 01258 456374).
Colours: All Royal Blue **Change colours:** All red
Cover: No **Programme:** Yes **Clubhouse:** No

BOURNEMOUTH SPORTS CLUB

Chairman: T Bloor.
Secretary: Mrs Lorraine Samson, 42 Mallard Close, Bournemouth, BH8 9PG (01202 532723)
Ground: Chapel Gate, East Parley, Christchurch, Dorset BH23 6BD (01202 581933).
Colours: Gold/black/gold **Change colours:** All red
Cover: No **Programme:** Yes **Clubhouse:** Yes

BRIDPORT RESERVES

Chairman: D Fowler
Secretary: Keith Morgan, 95 Orchard Crescent, Bridport DT6 5HA (01308 425113)
Ground: St Mary's Field, Bridport (01308 423834)
Cols: Red & blacl/black/red & black **Change:** Blue/white/blue
Cover: Yes **Floodlights:** Yes **Programme:** Yes **Clubhouse:** Yes

DORCHESTER TOWN RESERVES

Chairman: P Aitken
Secretary: Albert Miller, 29 Shaston Crescent, Dorchester DT1 2EB (01305 264843)
Ground: The Avenue Stadium, Dorchester. (01305 262451)
Cols: Black & white/black/black **Change:** SAky/white/sky
Cover: Yes **Floodlights:** Yes **Programme:** Yes **Clubhouse:** Yes

FLIGHT REFUELLING

Chairman: A Miles
Secretary: Harry W Doyle, 27 Fairview Cres., Broadstone, Poole BH18 9AP (01202 698393).
Ground: Merley Park, Merley, Wimborne, Dorset (01202 885773).
Colours: Blue & black stripes/black/blue **Change colours:** All yellow
Cover: No **Programme:** Yes **Clubhouse:** Yes

GILLINGHAM TOWN

Chairman: E Murphy.
Secretary: David J Ayles, 37 Sylvan Way, Bay Road, Gillingham SP8 4EQ (01747 822065).
Ground: Hardings Lane, Gillingham (01747 823673).
Colours: Tangerine/black/black **Change colours:** Yellow & green/green/green
Cover: Yes **Programme:** Yes **Clubhouse:** Yes

HAMWORTHY ENGINEERING

Chairman: M Robson.
Secretary: Ray Willis, 52 Heckford Rd, Poole BH15 2LY (01202 677063).
Ground: Hamworthy Rec. Club, Magna Rd, Canford Magna, Wimborne, Dorset BH21 3AE (01202 881922).
Colours: Green & white/green/green
Change colours: Blue & white/navy/navy
Cover: No **Programme:** No **Clubhouse:** Yes

HAMWORTHY UNITED

Chairman: D.Manmuel
Secretary: Roy Mitchener, 68 St Mary's Rd, Poole, Dorset BH15 2LL (01202 676128).
Ground: The County Ground, Blandford Close, Hamworthy, Poole, Dorset (01202 674974).
Colours: Maroon & sky/maroon/sky & maroon
Change colours: Green & black stripes/black/black
Cover: Yes **Floodlights:** Yes **Programme:** Yes **Clubhouse:** Yes

PARLEY SPORTS

Chairman: N.Coombes
Secretary: Mrs Pat Coombes, 332 Christchurch Road, West Parley, Ferndown.BH22 8SN (01202 578546)
Ground: Parley Sports Club, Christchurch, West Parley, Bournemouth, Dorset (01202 573345).
Colours: Yellow/blue/yellow & blue **Change colours:** Blue/burgundy/burgundy
Cover: No **Programme:** No **Clubhouse:** Yes

PORTLAND UNITED

Chairman: P.Laming
Secretary: David M Camp, 23 Four Acres, Weston, Portland DT5 2LG (01305 821816).
Ground: *New ground for 1994-95*
Colours: All blue. **Change colours:** White/black/red.
Cover: Yes **Programme:** Yes **Clubhouse:** Yes

SHAFTESBURY

Chairman: A P Humphries.
Secretary: Mrs Alison Marsh, 16 Jeanneau Close,Shaftesbury SP7 8PQ (01747 855832)
Ground: Cockrams, Coppice Street, Shaftesbury (01747 53990).
Colours: Red & white/black/red **Change colours:** Green/white/green
Cover: Yes **Floodlights:** Yes **Programme:** No **Clubhouse:** Yes

SHERBORNE TOWN

Chairman: K Mullins.
Secretary: Roger V Woolmington, 27 Harbour Rd, Sherborne DT9 4AL (01935 814354).
Ground: Raleigh Grove, The Terrace Playing Fields, Sherborne (01935 816110).
Colours: Black & white/white/white **Change colours:** All tangerine
Cover: Yes **Programme:** Yes **Clubhouse:** Yes

STURMINSTER MARSHALL

Chairman: R Copeland
Secretary: David Miller, 8 Blaney Way, Corfe Mullen, Wimborne BH21 3HG (01202 602366)
Ground: Churchill Close, Sturminster Newton
Cols: Jade/black/black **Change:** Yellow/blue/white
jade

STURMINSTER NEWTON

Chairman: D Walters
Secretary: Richard Frear, 44 Green Close,Sturminster, Newton DT10 1BL (01258 473036)
Ground: Ricketts Lane, Sturminster Newton, Dorset. (HQ (RBL) Tel:(01258 473753)
Colours: Red/black/black **Change colours:** All green
Cover: Yes **Programme:** Yes **Clubhouse:** No

SWANAGE TOWN & HERSTON

President: Mayor of Swanage **Chairman:** Leonard Marsh
Secretary: Eric Webster, 24 James Day Mead Ulwell Road, Swanage BH19 1NQ (01929 423522)
Ground: Days Park, off De Moulham Road, Swanage, Dorset (01929 424633).
Colours: Black & white/black/black. **Change colours:** Red/white/red
Cover: Yes **Floodlights:** Yes **Programme:** Yes **Clubhouse:** Yes

WAREHAM RANGERS

Chairman: A.White
Secretary: Mrs Carol White, 9 Bere Road, Wareham, Dorset BH20 4DB (01929 551765).
Ground: Wareham Recreation Ground, Worgret Rd, Wareham, Dorset.
Colours: Amber & black/black/black **Change colours:** All sky blue
Cover: No **Programme:** Yes **Clubhouse:** No

WESTLAND SPORTS

Chairman: N.Boucher.
Secretary: Tony Kent, c/o Yeovil Town FC (01935 23662)
Ground: Westland Sports Ground, Westbourne Close, Yeovil (01935 703810).
Colours: Blue & Black stripes/Black/Black.**Change colours:** Red/white/red.
Cover: No **Programme:** Yes **Clubhouse:** No

WEYMOUTH SPORTS

Chairman: B. King
Secretary: Alan Burt, 32 Preston Road, Wyke Regis,Weymouth DT4 9JF (01305 771480)
Ground: Weymouth College, Cranford Ave., Weymouth, Dorset (01305 208859/208860).
Cols: Yellow & black stripes/black/yellow **Change:** Blue & white/blue/blue
Prev. Lge: Dorset (champs 1993) **Previous Name:** Weymouth Taxi Co. (pre-1993).

GLOUCESTERSHIRE COUNTY LEAGUE

FOUNDED: 1968

Chairman: A C Barrett **Vice Chairman:** J D Hart

Hon. Treasurer: P T McPherson, 36 St Andrews Road, Avonmouth, Bristol BS11 9EU (0117 982 7035)

Hon. Secretary: D J Herbert, 8 Fernhurst Road,St George, Bristol BS5 7TQ (0117 951 7696)

"Heath give way to D.R.G. to take the title in style"

D.R.G., made it a first in the Club's history in lifting the League Title, they maintained their position all throughout the season, ensuring the title on Saturday 20th April. Cadbury Heath gained the runners-up spot, finishing with the same points as Brockworth who took third place on goal difference, an exciting end to the season.

At the foot of the table it was as interesting with Stapleton recording their first win of the season on Saturday 20th January and looked favourites to be relegated, but that win inspired them to take five more victories to pull clear of the last two. Leaving Smiths Athletic and Winterbourne United, on the same points as each other, relegated, although they both put together a late rally.

In the Gloucestershire Challenge Trophy the League had two losing semi-finalists in Bitton, in their first season, and Winterbourne United. The Sportsmanship Award went to Pucklechurch Sports for the second consecutive season.

Promoted to the League are Dursley Town (Gloucester Northern Senior Lge Champions), Oldland (Bristol Premier Comb. Lge Champions) who were relegated last season.

D J Herbert

FINAL LEAGUE TABLE 1995/96

		P	*W*	*D*	*L*	*F*	*A*	*Pts*
1.	D.R.G.	34	23	7	4	74	30	76
2.	Cadbury Heath	34	19	6	9	70	36	63
3.	Broad Plain House	34	18	9	7	68	46	63
4.	Brockworth	34	19	5	10	62	42	62
5.	Bitton	34	15	11	8	63	37	56
6.	Frampton Athletic	34	14	9	11	53	49	51
7.	Wotton Rovers	34	14	7	13	54	53	49
8.	Old Georgians	34	11	12	11	49	60	45
9.	Patchway Town	34	13	6	15	51	62	45
10.	Henbury O B	34	11	10	13	49	55	43
11.	St Marks C A	34	11	10	13	68	76	43
12.	Totterdown P O B	34	11	8	15	58	62	41
13.	Ellwood	34	9	12	13	35	49	39
14.	Broadwell Amateur	34	9	9	16	38	60	36
15.	Pucklechurch Sports	34	8	11	15	39	63	35
16.	Stapleton	34	8	10	16	38	52	34
17.	Smiths Athletic	34	8	5	21	45	62	29
18.	Winterbourne United	34	6	11	17	43	63	29

Leading Goalscorers:

I Day	Cadbury Heath	25	B Anderson	Broad Plain House	20
A Kissoon	D.R.G.	20	N Hooke	St Marks C A	20
A Bateman	Broad Plain House	19	J Healey	D.R.G.	18
D Thacker	Smiths Athletic	18	C Brain	Broadwell Amateurs	16
K Morse	Bitton	16	J Higgs	Bitton	14
N Smith	Totterdown P O B	14	P Williams	Brockworth	14

RESULTS CHART 1995-96

HOME TEAM	1	2	3	4	5	6	7	8	9	10	11	12	13	14	15	16	17	18
1. Bitton	*	1-2	1-1	4-1	0-1	0-0	0-0	0-3	1-0	0-2	2-2	3-1	8-0	0-0	2-1	1-1	0-0	1-2
2. Broad Plain House	0-2	*	2-0	0-3	3-2	1-1	1-4	1-2	3-0	3-2	0-3	2-0	2-0	2-1	2-2	4-1	3-1	3-1
3. Broadwell Amateurs	2-1	2-4	*	0-1	4-3	1-0	1-1	0-1	1-0	0-0	2-2	1-1	3-1	2-0	0-4	1-3	4-2	1-1
4. Brockworth	4-1	2-1	5-1	*	0-1	0-2	3-2	0-3	0-2	2-0	5-2	3-1	2-2	4-0	5-0	1-2	1-1	2-1
5. Cadbury Heath	1-5	0-0	2-1	2-1	*	3-1	0-0	4-0	1-2	0-0	5-0	6-0	2-0	3-0	0-2	0-1	1-0	2-0
6. D.R.G.	2-2	2-2	2-0	5-1	1-0	*	3-0	2-1	2-1	3-3	3-0	2-0	4-3	3-1	2-0	3-1	1-1	0-1
7. Ellwood	0-4	1-2	2-0	1-1	0-6	0-0	*	0-0	1-0	1-2	0-1	1-0	2-2	0-3	2-0	0-0	2-0	4-0
8. Frampton Athletic	2-1	0-4	1-1	2-0	2-2	1-4	0-0	*	4-1	1-3	5-0	0-2	3-2	6-4	3-1	3-1	0-0	2-0
9. Henbury Old Boys	3-3	1-1	3-1	0-2	2-0	0-2	2-3	4-2	*	0-0	2-0	3-2	1-1	4-3	4-1	3-2	2-2	1-1
10. Old Georgians	0-2	2-2	2-0	0-2	0-5	2-1	3-3	0-0	1-1	*	1-1	0-1	1-4	1-1	1-5	0-4	4-1	2-4
11. Patchway Town	0-2	1-3	2-0	1-2	1-6	0-1	5-0	1-3	1-1	1-2	*	0-0	2-0	4-1	2-0	3-5	4-2	1-0
12. Pucklechurch Sports	0-4	0-0	3-2	2-3	0-1	1-2	1-0	0-0	1-1	1-3	3-2	*	1-6	3-1	2-2	2-1	4-1	2-2
13. St Marks C A	2-3	2-1	2-2	0-2	5-2	1-8	2-1	3-1	3-1	4-4	1-2	2-2	*	2-0	2-0	3-3	5-3	0-2
14. Smiths Athletic	1-3	0-1	3-0	0-0	2-4	1-2	4-1	2-0	3-0	0-1	1-1	1-1	1-2	*	1-0	3-1	2-1	1-2
15. Stapleton	1-2	1-4	0-1	0-0	1-2	0-2	1-1	1-1	1-0	1-1	2-0	0-0	1-1	1-0	*	3-2	2-1	0-1
16. Totterdown P O B	1-1	2-2	1-1	2-0	1-2	1-3	1-0	0-0	2-3	1-2	1-2	2-0	3-3	1-0	3-2	*	2-3	1-5
17. Winterbourne United	1-1	2-2	4-0	1-2	0-0	0-2	0-1	2-1	0-0	1-2	1-3	1-1	2-1	2-1	1-1	2-5	*	4-0
18. Wotton Rovers	0-2	2-5	0-2	0-2	1-1	1-3	1-1	3-0	4-1	4-2	0-1	5-1	1-1	4-3	1-1	1-0	3-0	*

Wotton's Ian Shepherd disputes possession with Henbury's Eddie Gregg.
Photo - Ken Gregory

GLOUCESTERSHIRE COUNTY LEAGUE CLUBS 1996-97

BITTON

Secretary: Michael Hall, 14 Pillingers Road, Kingswood Bristol, BS15 2DE (0117 9603627)
Ground: Recreation Ground, Bath Road, Bitton Bristol.
Colours: Red & White/black/red **Change colours:** Black & white/black/red

BROAD PLAIN HOUSE

Secretary: Larry Hartrey, 11 Smythe Croft, Whitchurch, Bristol BS14 0UB (01275 835247)
Ground: Filwood Playing Fields, Creswicke Road Knowle, Bristol.
Colours: Red & black/black/black **Change colours:** Yellow/blue/blue

BROADWELL AMATEURS

Secretary: Steve Turner, 2 South Road, Sunnybank, Coleford, Glos. GL16 8EJ (01594 834391)
Ground: The Hawthorns, Poolway Road, Broadwell, near Coleford (01594 837347).
Directions: B4228 to Coleford then B4028 out of Coleford, B4226 into Broadwell ground on right.
Colours: Claret & blue/claret/blue **Change colours:** Yellow/blue/blue
Prev. Lge: Glos Northern Snr (pre-1994) **Honours:** Glos Northern Snr Lg 93-94 (R-up 92-93).

BROCKWORTH (1958)

Secretary: Geoffrey Bick, 18 The Wend, Longhope, Gloucester GL17 0QR (01452 830889)
Ground: Brockworth Rugby & Assc. Football Club, Mill Lane, Brockworth Glos.
Colours: Black & white/black/black. **Change colours:** Blue & black/black/black

CADBURY HEATH

Secretary: C Thomas, 73 Ridgeway Rd, Fishponds, Bristol BS16 3ED (01179 518097).
Ground: 'Springfield', Cadbury Heath Rd, Warmley, Bristol (01179 675730).
Directions: A420 from Bristol through Kingswood, across new r'bout, right into Tower Rd North, past school, right into Cadbury Heath Rd, ground immediately on right down alley.
Colours: Red/black/red & black **Change Colours:** Yellow/black/black.
Hons: Glos Co. Lg 70-71 71-72 72-73 73-74 93-94 (R-up 74-75 90-91 91-92), Glos Amtr Cup Sth(3), FA Vase QF.

D.R.G.

Secretary: Robert Wakefield, 101 Wellsway, Keynsham, Bristol. BS18 1HZ (0117 9865516)
Ground: 'Shortwood', Carsons Road, Mangotsfield, Bristol (01179 560390).
Directions: M4 jct 19 onto M32, off at jct 1 onto A4174 follow signs for Downend then Mangotsfield. Continue through town, road becomes Carsons Road, ground on right after factory.
Seats: None **Cover:** No **Capacity:** 1,000 **Clubhouse:** Yes **Founded:** 1962
Colours: Maroon & sky/maroon/maroon **Change Colours:** Yellow/black/black
Previous Name: R.W.P. (pre-1986) **Previous Ground:** St Johns Lane 62-66. **Clubhouse:** Yes.
Record Gate: 500 v Pucklechurch Sports, Bristol Combination 1/4/86.

DURSLEY TOWN

Secretary: Phil James, 8 Meadow Vale, Tilsdown, Dursley, Glos. GL11 6HJ (01453 547413).
Ground: Recreation Ground, Kingshill Road, Dursley, Glos. (01453 546122)
Founded: 1893.
Colours: Red & black/black/black **Change Colours:** Blue & black/black/black

ELLWOOD

Secretary: Ian Edwards, 24 Forest Road, Milkwall, Coleford, Glos Gl16 7LB (01594 833585)
Ground: Bromley Rd, Ellwood, Coleford, Glos (01594 832927).
Directions: B4234 to Parkend then B4431 up hill to next crossroads, turn left - ground half mile on left.
Colours: Blue & white/blue/blue & white **Change Colours:** Red/blue/blue

FRAMPTON ATHLETIC

Secretary: Keith Potter 117 Goldcrest Road, Chipping Sodbury, Bristol BS17 6XN
Ground: Beesmoor Road, Frampton Cotterill, Bristol
Colours: Red/black/red **Change colours:** Black & white/black/black

HENBURY OLD BOYS

Secretary: C B Barron, 126 Charlton Rd, Westbury-on-Trym, Bristol BS10 6NL (01179 504002).
Ground: Arnall Drive Playing Fields, Henbury, Bristol (01179 590475). **Founded:** 1962
Directions: M5 jct 17, down Cribbs Causeway, into Station Road, left into Henbury Rd, ground on left.
Colours: Amber & black/black/amber & black **Change Colours:** Red & Black/black/black.
Hons: Avon Combination 82-83 (Lg Cup 83-84), Glos Snr Amtr Cup South, Fry Club Cup 92-93.

OLD GEORGIANS

Secretary: B M Latchem, 87 Vicarage Rd, Whitehall, Bristol BS5 9AQ (01179 556292).
Ground: St George's School PF, Johnsons Lane, Whitehall, Bristol (01179 516888).
Directions: M32 jct 2, left, left, right at lights, right behind Kings Head. Buses 6 or 7 from central Bristol. One mile from Stapleton Road (BR).
Seats: None **Cover:** No **Capacity:** 1,500 **Clubhouse:** Yes **Founded:** 1905.
Colours: Sky/navy/sky & navy **Change Colours:** Red/navy/red
Record Gate: 770 v Stansted, FA Vase QF 4/3/84. **Manager:** Brian Tufton.
Hons: Glos Co. Lg 82-83 84-85 (R-up 83-84 92-93), Glos Chal. Tphy, Glos Snr Amtr Cup Sth, FA Vase QF 83-84.

OLDLAND

Secretary: Reg Hamblin, 152 Stockwood Lane, Stockwood, Bristol BS14 8TA (01275 8352033)
Ground: Aitchinson Playing Field, Castle Road, Oldland Common, (0117 932 8263)
Founded: 1898.
Colours: Blue & white/blue/blue **Change Colours:** Yellow & blue/blue/yellow

PATCHWAY TOWN

Secretary: R Stewart, 22 Arlingham Way, Patchway, Bristol, BS12 5NQ (01179 792983).
Ground: 'Scott Park', Coniston Rd, Patchway, Bristol (01179 691203)
Directions: M5 jct 16, A38 towards Bristol, right into Coniston Road, ground signposted Scott Park.
Colours: Black & white stripes/black/black **Change Colours:** Red/black/black
Hons: Glos County Lg 91-92

PUCKLECHURCH SPORTS

Secretary: R B Savage, 54 Shortwood Rd, Pucklechurch, Bristol BS17 3RN (01179 373972).
Ground: Pucklechurch Recreation Ground, Pucklechurch, Abson (01275 822102).
Directions: M32 jct 1 follow A4174 through Downend to Mangotsfield, left signposted Pucklechurch, continue to village, turn right, ground on left.
Seats: No **Cover:** None **Clubhouse:** Yes **Prog:** 32 pages,40p **Editor:** M Dowse.
Colours: All green **Change Colours:** White/green/green.
Hons: Avon Comb. 77-78 78-79 87-88 (Div 2 66-67, Lg Cup 77-78 78-79 87-88), Glos Jnr Cup 65-66 82-83, Bristol & District Lg 72-73.

St MARKS C.A.

Secretary: W Pember, 11 Linworth Rd, Bishops Cleeve, Cheltenham, Glos GL52 4PF (01242 673800).
Ground: King George V Playing Fields,Brooklyn Rd., Cheltenham,Glos.901378 839210)
Directions: In Cheltenham follow signs for GCHQ. Ground adjacent. **Clubhouse:** Yes
Colours: Royal/royal/red **Change Colours:** Red/blue/red
Prev. Ground: Cheltenham Town FC **Hons:** Glos Northern Snr Lg 74-75 78-79 83-84.

STAPLETON

Secretary: M Dodd, 108 Downend Rd, Fishponds, Bristol BS16 5BH (01179 400544).
Ground & Directions: Frenchay Park Playing Field, Frenchay, Bristol. M32 jct 1, A4174, follow signs to Frenchay Hospital - ground opposite. Or M32 jct 2, follow signs for Frenchay through Stapleton, ground on left.
Seats: No **Cover:** No **Clubhouse:** Yes **Programme:** Yes **Founded:** 1932.
Colours: Blue & Black Stripes/Black/Black**Change Colours:** All Burgundy.

TOTTERDOWN P.O.B.

Secretary: Brian Truman, 10 Elmore Road, Patchway, Bristol BS12 5LL (0117 976 0386)
Ground: City & Port of Bristol Sports Ground, Nibley Rd, Shirehampton, Bristol.
Directions: 5 mins walk from Shirehampton (BR) station (Temple Meads-Severn Beach line).
Colours: Red/navy/navy. **Change Colours:** Yellow/blue/blue.
Prevous Names: Totterdown Ath., Port of Bristol - clubs merged 1994. *Notes below apply to Totterdown.*
Prev. Lge: Bristol & Suburban (pre'93) **Hons:** Bristol & Suburban Lg R-up 92-93.
Previous Ground: Bristol & West Indian Cricket Ground, Gordon PF, Gordon Rd, Whitehall, Bristol (pre-1994).

WOTTON ROVERS

Secretary: M P Excell, 94 Bearlands, Wotton-under-Edge, Glos. GL12 7SB (01453 845178).
Ground: Synwell Playing Field, Synwell Lane, Wotton-under-Edge (01453 842929).
Directions: From Wotton war memorial down hill and follow Synwell Lane. Ground on left.
Seats: None **Cover:** No **Capacity:** 2,000 **Clubhouse:** Yes **Founded:** 1959.
Colours: All royal **Change Colours:** White/blue/red
Record Gate: 2,000 **Programme:** 20 pages, 50p
Previous Names: Synwell Rovers (pre-1959)/ Wotton-under-Edge FC.

THE JEWSON SOUTH WESTERN LEAGUE

FOUNDED; 1951

Chairman; Mr Tristan Scott

Secretary; Mr M Goodenough, Rose Cottage, Horrels Ford, Milton Damerel, Holsworthy, Devon EX22 7NU (01409 261402)

Truro City won the League Championship five points clear of runners-up Torpoint Athletic, and Launceston won the League Cup for the first time in their history, defeating Bodmin Town in the final. Torpoint Athletic won both the Cornwall Senior Cup and the Cornwall Charity Cup, and also enjoyed a very successful run in the FA Vase, while Appledore BAAC reached the semi-final stage of the Devon Premier Cup. Okehampton Argyle were awarded the League's Sporting Trophy for a second consecutive year, and Truro City took the best kept ground award. Andy Waddell (Falmouth Town) again finished the season as the leading goalscorer for a fourth consecutive year with 38 goals, and also for a second consecutive year the Top Match Referee was Alan Johns fron Ivybridge.

The League Representative team played 2 fixtures defeating the Plymouth & District League 5-0 at Liskeard, but went down 2-1 to a Cornwall X1 at Bodmin.

Hon.Tresurer Mike Wilson reached a milestone this year when he completed 25 years service to the League. For the forth coming season the league will be reduced to 16 member Cclubs following the withdrawal of both Appledore BAAC and Okehampton Argyle.
Mel Goodenough

FINAL LEAGUE TABLE 1995/96

		P	*W*	*D*	*L*	*F*	*A*	*Pts*
1.	Truro City	34	26	4	4	99	27	82
2.	Torpoint Athletic	34	23	8	3	81	32	77
3.	Falmouth Town	34	22	4	8	89	37	70
4.	Launceston	34	20	9	5	95	29	69
5.	Bodmin Town	34	18	10	6	91	36	64
6.	Penzance	34	18	5	11	64	43	59
7.	Newquay	34	18	4	12	73	54	58
8.	Holsworthy	34	17	5	12	58	43	56
9.	Wadebridge Town	34	16	5	13	65	55	53
10.	Saltash United	34	14	8	12	66	67	50
11.	Porthleven	34	13	5	16	61	64	44
12.	St Austell	34	10	5	19	57	78	35
13.	Millbrook	34	9	7	18	60	58	34
14.	Liskeard Athletic	34	9	6	19	58	96	33
15.	Appledore BAAC	34	7	7	20	43	80	28
16.	Tavistock	34	6	6	22	55	99	24
17.	St Blazey	34	4	4	26	38	106	16
18.	Okehampton Argyle	34	4	2	28	24	143	14

Leading League Goalscorers 1995-96

A Waddell	Falmouth Town	38	A Cusack	Holworthy	29
S Wherry	Truro City	24	D Stocker	Bodmin Town	23
D Downing	Appledore BAAC	22	C Legg	Newquay	22
G Nardiello	Torpoint Athletic	22			

JEWSON SOUTH WESTERN LEAGUE RESULTS CHART 1995-96

HOME TEAM	1	2	3	4	5	6	7	8	9	10	11	12	13	14	15	16	17	18
1. Appledore BAAC	*	0-2	0-4	2-3	2-2	0-2	0-4	2-4	1-1	0-1	1-1	4-3	2-1	3-3	1-1	3-5	0-4	2-4
2. Bodmin Town	3-0	*	2-1	4-1	0-0	7-0	0-0	4-2	4-0	3-3	6-1	4-1	7-0	2-1	6-0	4-0	2-3	0-1
3. Falmouth Town	2-2	1-1	*	2-1	1-3	2-1	3-0	0-1	9-0	1-0	0-1	4-0	2-3	2-1	10-0	0-0	2-1	4-2
4. Holsworthy	2-0	1-4	2-3	*	1-0	1-1	1-2	0-1	7-0	0-0	3-0	4-0	4-1	5-2	3-1	1-1	2-0	0-0
5. Launceston	0-0	2-2	0-1	4-1	*	4-1	1-0	2-0	10-0	7-1	4-0	2-2	3-2	4-1	5-0	1-2	0-1	3-1
6. Liskheard Athletic	4-1	1-2	2-6	1-1	0-2	*	3-2	2-3	4-0	1-4	0-2	0-5	0-7	6-2	1-6	2-2	2-4	2-5
7. Millbrook	0-3	0-0	0-3	0-1	0-1	1-1	*	2-0	2-0	0-2	1-3	0-1	2-1	0-1	3-1	0-2	0-1	2-2
8. Newquay	1-0	2-1	3-3	2-0	1-1	0-2	4-2	*	8-0	2-2	2-1	1-1	7-1	6-0	3-1	2-3	0-3	0-3
9. Okehampton	2-3	0-7	1-3	0-2	1-4	1-2	0-2	1-2	*	2-0	0-5	4-2	2-1	2-1	0-7	0-12	0-9	1-3
10. Penzance	1-2	2-2	2-0	2-3	1-3	2-0	1-2	2-0	2-0	*	1-0	1-2	1-2	6-0	3-0	1-1	1-2	2-1
11. Porthleven	7-1	1-0	0-2	1-0	0-7	2-3	1-1	2-3	5-0	0-1	*	0-3	3-3	2-0	6-3	3-1	1-4	2-4
12. Saltash United	3-1	2-2	5-2	2-0	2-2	2-0	1-1	2-1	4-2	3-6	0-0	*	4-0	3-0	1-2	0-5	1-1	0-3
13. St Austell	2-1	2-3	2-3	0-1	0-4	3-3	6-1	2-0	5-2	0-2	3-3	2-1	*	4-0	2-1	1-2	0-1	0-2
14. St Blazey	0-1	1-1	0-4	0-2	0-5	7-4	1-2	0-1	4-0	0-3	2-5	2-3	0-0	*	4-2	0-3	0-6	3-3
15. Tavistock	1-5	3-2	0-3	0-1	1-4	4-2	2-2	1-4	1-1	0-3	2-3	4-4	1-1	3-0	*	1-2	1-3	2-2
16. Torpoint Athletic	3-0	0-0	0-2	3-1	2-1	2-2	3-1	2-0	3-0	2-1	2-1	4-0	1-0	5-1	4-1	*	0-0	1-0
17. Truro City	3-0	4-2	2-4	2-0	1-1	4-0	3-1	5-3	9-0	1-2	1-0	2-0	6-0	5-1	2-1	0-0	*	2-0
18. Wadebridge Town	2-0	0-2	1-0	2-3	1-1	0-3	4-3	1-4	4-1	0-1	2-0	1-3	3-0	2-0	4-1	2-3	0-4	*

CHALLENGE CUP 1995-96

Preliminary Round;

Liskeard Athletic v Tavistock 1-0

St Austell v Launceston 0-3

First Round;

Holsworthy v Appledore BAAC 2-1

Millbrook v Newquay 2-3

Porthleven v Bodmin Town 1-2

St Blazey v Launceston 2-6

Falmouth Town v Penzance 3-0

Okehampton Argyle v Truro City 0-4

Saltash United v Torpoint Athletic 3-2

Wadebridge Town v Liskeard Athletic 2-1

Quarter Finals;

Bodmin Town v Saltash United 7-1

Launceston v Truro City 1-1, 2-1

Holsworthy v Falmouth Town 2-2, 2-3

Newquay v Wadebridge Town 3-1

Semi-Finals;

Bodmin Town v Falmouth Town 2-1

Launceston v Newquay 2-0

Final; Launceston v Bodmin Town 3-1

Laaunceston Challenge Cup Winners: Back Row (L-R); Keith Ellacott (Gen Mgr), Dave Trott, Ian Saunders, Craig Hodge, Lee Wakeham, Dave Ellis, Graham Kimberley, Steve Anbany, Chris Visick, Lee Fox, Roger Wakeham (Mgr). Front Row; Jason Trott (Mascot), Clinton Tedder, John Best, Darren Butcher, Trevor Griffiths, Neil Carter, Jordan Trott and Channon Hodge (Mascots).

CLUB DIRECTORY 1996-97

BODMIN TOWN

Chairman: C.Hooper. **Vice-Chairman:** P.Lee. **President:** A.Gynn.
Secretary: Martin Mullis, 24 Jubilee Terrace, Bodmin PL31 2QE (01208 77685).
Manager: Ricky Cardew. **Asst Manager:** Phil Brown. **Physio:** Jim Brewer
Ground: Priory Park (01208 78165) - Just off town centre in large park complex, at rear of town car park.
Capacity: **Cover:** Grandstand **Seats:** Yes **Floodlights:** Yes **Founded:** 1889
Colours: Yellow/black & yellow/yellow **Change colours:** All sky
Programme: 20 pages, 30p **Programme Editor:** Secretary **Club Shop:** No.
Sponsors: Gynn Construction **Nickname:** Black & Ambers
Midweek home matchday: Tuesday **Reserve team's League:** East Cornwall Premier.
Clubhouse: Mon-Fri 6.30-11pm (matchdays 6-11), Fri-Sat noon-11pm, Sun noon-3 & 7-10.30pm (except when Sky matches are on then 12 noon-10.30 p.m.). Bar snacks available most times.
Honours: South Western Lg 90-91 93-94 (R-up 76-77,92-93,94-95,Lg Cup 93-94 (R-up 77-78 88-89 94-95), Cornwall Snr Cup R-up 93-94, Cornwall Charity Cup 86-87 89-90.Cornish Guardian E.C.P.L.Supplimentary Cup 91-92 (R-Up. 93-94),Gordon Sweet Cup 90-91,92-93.

FALMOUTH TOWN

Chairman: Malcolm Newland **Vice Chairman:** Paul Ashburn **President:** Seb Coe.
Secretary: David Woon,Llamedos,Mount Stephens Lane,Falmouth,Cornwall TR11 2LJ (01326 315151(H)
Manager: Ray Nicholls **Asst Manager:** Dave Ball. **Coach:** Keith Barker
Ground: Bickland Park, Bickland Vale, Falmouth, Cornwall (01326 375156).
Directions: Follow A39 to Tregoniggie Industrial Estate - will pass ground on left. One and a half miles from Penmere Halt (BR) on Falmouth-Truro branch line. Bus service from town centre.
Seats: 300 **Cover:** 1,200 **Capacity:** 6,000 **Floodlights:** Yes **Club Shop:** TBA
Programme: 16 pages, 30p **Editor/Press Officer:** Mike Odgers (01209 715766).
Colours: Amber/black **Change colours:** Red/white.
Nickname: Town **Club Sponsors:** Stralfors/ Diadora. **Founded:** 1949.
Midweek home matchday: Tues/Wed **Reserve team's League:** Jollys Cornwall Comb.
Record Gate: 6,300 v Oxford United, FA Cup 1st Round 3/11/62.
Best FA Cup season: 1st Round 62-63 (lost 1-2 v Oxford United) 67-68 (lost 2-5 at Peterborough Utd).
Best FA Vase season: Quarter-Final replay 86-87 (lost 0-1 after 1-1 draw at St Helens Town).
Best FA Trophy season: 2nd Round proper 77-78.
Previous Leagues: Cornish Snr 50-51/ South Western 51-74/ Western 74-83.
Players progressing to Football League: Roy Carter (Hereford 1975), Joe Scott (Bournemouth 1978), Tony Kellow (Exeter 1976), John Hodge (Exeter 1991).
Clubhouse: Mon-Fri 7-11pm, Sat 12-11pm, Sun 12-3 & 7-10.30pm. Meals available.
95-96 Captain: **95-96 Top Scorer:** **95-96 P.o.Y.:**
Club Record Scorer: Joe Scott 198, 72-78 **Club Record Appearances:** Keith Manley 580 (appr) 70-83.
Honours: Cornish Snr Cup(10) 61-62 64-66 67-68 70-71 73-74 75-79 (R-up(7) 66-67 72-73 81-83 89-92), Western Lg(4) 74-78 (Lg Cup 74-75, Alan Young Cup 74-75 75-76 77-78(joint)), South Western Lg(12) 61-62 65-66 67-68 70-74 85-87 88-90 91-92 (R-up 58-59 64-65 69-70 87-88, Lg Cup(10) 57-59 61-63 67-68 70-71 85-86 90-92 (R-up(5) 59-60 71-72 86-88 92-93)), Pratten Cup 73-74, Cornwall Charity Cup 59-60 94-95, Cornwall Comb.(res) 83-84 (Supplementary Cup 93-94 (R-up 90-91)).

HOLSWORTHY

Manager: Peter England. **Assistant Manager:** Alan Mayes.
Secretary: Rob Moores, Rydon View, Central Avenue, Holsworthy, EX22 6DB (01409 253982).
Ground: Upcott Field (01409 254295) **Nickname:** The Magpies. **Cover:** Yes **Floodlights:** No.
Programme:28 pages, £2 with entry **Editor:** Terry Trewin.& Bob Thomson.
Colours: Black & White/Black/black & white **Change colours:** Gold/white/gold. **Nickname:** Magpies
Hons: Devon Snr Cup 53-54 (Prem. Cup 71-72 78-79),Devon Junior Cup 38-39.

LAUNCESTON

Chairman: D Redstone **Vice Chairman:** D Heard **President:** D Viggers.
Secretary: Chris Martin, 3 Tavistock Road, Launceston, Cornwall PL15 9HA (01566 776175).
Manager: Roger Fice **General Manager:** Keith Ellacott.
Physio: D James **Ground:** Pennygillam, Launceston (0566 773279)
Directions: Follow signs to Pennygillam Industrial Est., just off main A30 - ground 400yds on left.
Programme: Yes **Seats:** 150 **Cover:** 150 **Floodlights:** Yes **Nickname:** Clarets
Cols: Claret & blue/blue/claret **Change:** Sky/Sky/claret
Midweek matchday: Tues/Wed **Club Shop:** No.
Sponsors: D Viggers Coal **Reserve team's League:** Plymouth & Dist.
Clubhouse: Open after every game. Bar meals.
Hons: S. Western Lg R-up 84-85, Cornish Snr Cup 1899-1900 00-01 82-83 (R-up 92-93, Charity Cup R-up 88-89).

LISKEARD ATHLETIC

Chairman: David Hick **Vice Chairman:** Dave Rawlings **President:** R.D.Burt.
Secretary: Adrian Wilton, Martina, Dawes Close, Dobwalls, Liskeard, Cornwall PL14 6JD (01579 20980).
Manager: Phil Sullivan. **Asst Manager:** Geof Battams. **Physio:**
Ground: Lux Park, Liskeard, Cornwall (01579 42665).
Directions: Take Tavistock Road (A390) from town centre, after 1/2 mile turn left on St Cleer Road (following signs to Lux Park Sports Complex) and the ground is 200 yards on left. Half mile from Liskeard BR station.
Seats: 100 **Cover:** 300 **Capacity:** 2,000 **Floodlights:** Yes **Club Shop:** No.
Programme: 40 pages, 50p **Editor:** D.J.Rawlings.
Colours: Blue & White/blue/blue & white **Change colours:** All white.
Sponsors: Aviation C.B.International/ Gilbert Outfitters**Nickname:** Blues. **Formed:** 1889
Midweek matchday: Tuesday
Previous Leagues: East Cornwall Premier, Plymouth & District, South Western 66-79, Great Mills 79-95.
Players progressing to Football League: Bradley Swiggs.
Clubhouse: (01579 342665) Normal licensing hours. Hot & cold food available.
95-96 Captain: Roger Quaintance. **95-96 Top Scorer:** Paul Webber. **95-96 P.o.Y.:** Mark Peard.
Club Record Goalscorer: Not known **Club Record Appearances:** Brian Bunney, 500+.
Hons: South Western Lg 76-77 78-79 (R-up 75-76 77-78; Lg Cup 76-77 78-79) Western Lg 87-88 (R-up 85-86 89-90, Merit Cup 80-81); Cornwall Snr Cup 04-05 83-84 84-85 85-86 88-89 89-90 93-94 (R-up 70-71 75-76 76-77 78-79 94-95); Cornwall Charity Cup 21-22 79-80, Cornwall Jnr Cup 05-06 13-14 26-27; SW Pratten Cup 78-79; E Cornwall Prem RAOB Cup 67-68, Plymouth & Dist. Lg 60-61 (Div 1 59-60 (R-up 54-55 73-74), Div 2 76-77(Res)), Victory Cup 60-61, Charity Cup 59-60), E Cornwall Prem. Lg (Reserves) 84-85 92-93 93-94(Lg.Cup 88-89 93-94).

MILLBROOK

President: Mrs E Weekes **Chairman:** Mr J Weekes **Vice Chairman:** Mr K Townsend.
Secretary: Bob Bell, 15 Carew Close, Crafthole, Cornwall PL11 3EB (01503 230953)
Manager: Mr J Bennett **Asst Manager:** Mr S Matthews **Press Officer:** Mr W Linney.
Ground: Mill Park, Millbrook, Cornwall (0752 822113)
Directions: From Torpoint Ferry - 3 miles to Antony on A374, fork left, after 1 mile turn left again and follow B3247 to Millbrook (3 miles), take road marked 'Town Centre Southdown', right at mini-r'bout after quarter mile, ground clearly visible. From Tamar Bridge - follow signs for Torpoint, 2 miles after Polbathic take right turning marked Millbrook, 5 miles to Millbrook then proceed as above.
Capacity: **Seats:** None **Cover:** 200 **Floodlights:** Yes **Founded:** 1973.
Colours: White & Black/black/red **Change colours:** Sky/white/white **Nickname:** The Brook
Prev. Ground: Insworke Pk (14yrs) **Prev. Lges:** Plymouth Comb.(8yrs)/ Plymouth & Dist.(6yrs).
Programme: 20 pages, 10p **Editor:** Mr J Weekes (0752 822637) **Club Shop:** No.
Club Sponsors: Plymouth Boat Cruises Ltd.
Midweek home matchday: Tuesday **Reserve team's League:** Plymouth & District.
Clubhouse: Weekdays 7-11pm, Sat 11am-11pm, Sun noon-3 & 7.30-10.30. Hot food (chips, burgers etc) available during and after matchdays.
Club record scorer: Unknown **Club record appearances:** John Horne 215.
Hons: South Western Lg R-up 81-82, Cornwall Snr Cup R-up 83-84 (Charity Cup 84-85, Jnr Cup 75-76), Plymouth & District Lg 80-81 (Div 1 R-up 76-77).

NEWQUAY

Chairman: A Kendall **Vice-Chairman:** J.Lugg. **President:** J L Parker
Secretary: John Hawkey, 16 Higher Tower Rd, Newquay, Cornwall.TR7 1QL (01637 871884)
Mgr/Coach: Graham Nicholls **Asst Manager:** Andy Mattock **Physio:** Ross McOpie
Ground: Mount Wise, Newquay (01637 872935)
Directions: 1/2 mile from Newquay BR, follow 1-way system for 1/2 miles - grd signed on left before Windsor Hotel.
Seats: 250 **Cover:** 500 **Capacity:** 4,000 **Floodlights:** Yes **Club Shop:** No
Programme: 16 pages, 30p **Editor:** M Lowry **Press Officer:**
Colours: Red & white stripes **Change colours:** Sky & navy
Sponsors: Studs Sports **Nickname:** Peppermints **Founded:** 1890.
Midweek Matchday: **Reserve League:** Cornwall Combination.
Previous Leagues: West Cornwall/ Plymouth & District 21-27/ Cornish Senior 31-51.
Players progressing to Football League: Chris Morris (Sheffield Wednesday, Celtic & Eire), David Philp (Plymouth Argyle), Kevin Miller (Exeter City,Birmingham C,Watford), John Hodge (exeter City,Swansea).
Clubhouse: 7-11pm w/days, 12-11pm Sat, 12-3 & 7-10.30pm Sun. Hot & cold snacks after matchs.
95-96 Captain: Phil Dingle **95-96 P.o.Y.:** Charlie Legg **95-96 Top Scorer:** Charlie Legg
Hons: FA Vase 3rd Rd 90-91, Cornish Snr Cup 34-35 52-53 54-55 56-57 91-92 (R-up(9) 05-07 08-09 25-26 33-34 35-36 57-58 69-70 84-85), S. Western Lg(7) 58-60 77-78 79-80 81-82 83-84 87-88 (R-up 57-58 85-86 94-95, Lg Cup 55-56 88-89 (R-up(4) 56-58 79-81), Cornish Charity Cup(13) 06-07 08-09 53-56 57-59 62-63 69-70 74-75 76-78 88-89 (R-up(9) 07-08 20-21 56-57 60-61 73-74 75-76 81-82 84-86), W. Cornwall Lg 06-07 (R-up(2) 07-09), Cornish Snr Lg Herald Cup 34-35 (R-up(7) 33-34 35-36 49-51 55-57 58-59).

PENZANCE

President: Len Stanbury **Chairman:** Jim Dann
Secretary: Jim Dann (Acting) Carthew Farm, Newbridge, Penzance, Cornwall, TR20 8QL (01736 62749)
Manager: Martin Smith **Coach:** T.B.A. **Trainer:** Ken Prowse.
Ground: Penlee Park (0736 61964) **Floodlights:** Yes **Seats:** Yes **Founded:** 1888.
Directions: Seafront road past harbour, after amusement arcade turn right at r'bout (Alexander Rd), ground second right. Fifteen minutes walk from Penzance (BR); directions as above.
Colours: Black & white/black/black **Change colours:** All yellow **Nickname:** Magpies.
Clubhouse: Yes **Reserve team's league:** Cornwall Comb.
Captain 93-94: **Top Scorer 93-94:**
Players progressing to Football League: Gerry Gazzard (Brentford), Tony Kellow (Exeter).
Hons: Cornish Snr Cup 1892-93 95-96 97-98 98-99 1903-04 07-08 47-48 60-61 72-73 80-81 (R-up 1896-97 99-1900 00-01 04-05 48-49 49-50 54-55 56-57 74-75), South Western Lg 55-56 56-57 74-75 (Lg Cup R-up 60-61), Cornwall Charity Cup 47-48 48-49 (R-up 21-22 63-64), Cornwall Snr Lg Div 2 57-58 (Div 2 Cup 53-54 54-55), Cornwall Comb. R-up 65-66 (Lg Cup 69-70 (R-up 81-82)), Cornwall Jnr Cup (West) 03-04 04-05 05-06 07-08 09-10.

PORTHLEVEN

President: Mr W O Allen **Chairman:** Mr W Tearney **Vice Chairman:** Mr L Williams
Secretary: Vidal James, 11 Primrose Close, Weeth Park, Camborne, TR14 7HS (01209 710618) 561160).
Manager: Trevor Mewton **Coach:** Paul Christie **Comm. Mgr:** Mr V James.
Ground: Gala Parc, Mill Lane, Porthleven (0208 574754).
Directions: From Penzance on A394, B3304 into Porthleven, ground on left immediately before town. From Helston on B3304 ground on right as you exit town. Buses from Helston and Penzance.
Capacity: **Seats:** None **Cover:** Yes **Floodlights:** No. **Programme:** 20p
Colours: Amber/black **Change colours:** All blue **Nickname:** Fishermen
Previous Leagues: West Penwith/ Cornwall Snr/ South Western 66-77/ Cornwall Combination 77-89.
Reserves' Lge: Cornwall Comb. **Previous Grounds:** Treza Downs/ Sunset Farm.
Clubhouse: Mon-Fri 7-11pm, Sat 11am-8pm, Sun 11am-3 & 7-10.30pm. Full food menu.
Hons: Sth Western Lg R-up 72-73, Cornwall Comb.(6),(Lg Cup(6), Cornwall Charity Cup 70-71, Cornwall Snr Cup R-up 68-69, George Evely Cup 64-65 65-66 83-84 86-87, West Penwith Lg, Penzance Hosp. Cup, Penzance Charity Cup.

SALTASH UNITED

President: P Skinnard **Chairman:** M Howard **Manager:** Phil Towl
Secretary: P J Gammage, 23 Spire Hill Park, Saltash, Cornwall, PL12 4SR (01752 844046).
Ground: Kimberley Stadium, Callington Road, Saltash, Cornwall (01752 845746).
Directions: First left after crossing Tamar Bridge, through town centre, at top of town fork right at mimi r'bout, ground 400 yds ahead on left.
Seats: 250 **Cover:** 250 **Capacity:** 3,000 **Floodlights:** Yes **Shop:**
Programme: 40 pages, 40p **Editor:** Marian Gammage.
Colours: Red/Black/Black **Change:** Black & white stripes/black/black
Sponsor: **Nickname:** The Ashes **Formed:** 1945.
Midweek Matcheday: Wednesday
Previous Leagues: Cornwall Snr/Sth Western 51-59 62-76/E Cornwall Prem 59-62/Gt Mills West 76-95.
Clubhouse: Club attached to stand and caters for dancing and club activities.Saphire Lounge caters for wedding receptions,quiz nights and private functions etc.
Hons: Cornwall Snr Lg 49-50 50-51, Western Lg 84-85 86-87 88-89 (R-up 83-84 87-88, Lg Cup 86-87 87-88 (R-up 88-89), Div 1 76-77, Merit Cup 79-80 87-88), Sth Western Lg 53-54 75-76 (R-up 3), Lg Cup 3, Cornwall Snr Cup 6.

St AUSTELL

Chairman: Colin Marshall **Asst Chairman:** Derek Silk
Secretary: Peter Beard, 24 Alexandra Rd, St Austell, Cornwall PL25 4QP (01726 64138).
Manager: John Peters **Asst Manager:** Colin Bunney **Physio:** N McKenna
Ground: Poltair Park (0726 77099). **Directions:** 5 mins walk north of St Austell (BR).
Seats: 200 **Cover:** 300 **Capacity:** 8,000 **Floodlights:** No **Founded:** 1890.
Colours: White/black/black **Change colours:** Blue/black/blue.
Previous Leagues: Rocky Park (1890s) **Record Gate:** 15,000 v Penzance, Senior Cup 49.
Hons: S West Lg 68-69 (R-up 4), Lg Cup 64-65 71-73 87-88 (R-up 4), Cornish Snr Cup(11)

St BLAZEY

Vice Chairman: Mr P Clemow. **President:** K.Cocks. **Chairman:** Mr H Cooke
Secretary: Martin Richards, 14 Landreath Place, St Blazey, Par, Cornwall PL24 2JX (01726 817419).
Manager: Kenny Cook. **Coach:** Gareth Lobb. **Physio:** T.B.A.
Ground: Blaise Park, Station Road, St Blazey (01726 814110).
Directions: A390 Liskeard-St Austell road, turn into Station Road at lights in St Blazey village; ground 100 yards on left. One and a half miles from Par (BR).
Seats: 200 **Cover:** 700 **Capacity:** 3,500 **Floodlights:** Yes **Founded:** 1896.
Colours: Green/black **Change colours:** All white **Nickname:** Saints
Programme: 24 pages, 30p **Editor:** M.Newcombe(011726 815964) **Club Shop:** No.
Sponsors: Express Joinery **Record Gate:** 6,500 v St Austell, Cornwall Snr Cup 48-49.
Midweek home matchday: Tues/Wed **Reserve team's League:** East Cornwall Premier.
Clubhouse: Mon-Thurs 11am-3pm & 7-11pm,Fri-Sat11-11.45pm, Sun noon-3.0 & 7.11pm. Bar snacks.
Club record scorer: B Tallamy **Club record appearances:** W Isbell.
Hons: South Western Lg 6, (R-up 9), Lg Cup 5, (R-up 5), Cornish Snr Cup 8, Cornish Charity Cup 35-36 56-57 83-84, Cornwall Snr Lg Cup (Herald Cup) 35-36 48-49.

TAVISTOCK

President: **Chairman:** R A Fenner **Vice Chairman:** D R D Pethick
Secretary: Philip Lowe, 1 Bainbridge Court, Colebrook, Plympton, PL7 4HH (01752 335273).
Manager: Steve Metters **Asst Manager:** Jerry Collins. **Coach:** Les Mewton.
Physio: Les Mewton **Press Officer:** Chairman.
Ground: Langsford Park, Crowndale Rd, Tavistock (01822 614447)
Directions: A386 from Plymouth, left after Ford garage into Crowndale Rd, ground half mile on left.
Capacity: 2,000 **Seats:** 200 **Cover:** 200 **Floodlights:** Yes **Founded:** 1888.
Colours: Red & Black/black/black. **Change colours:** All Blue
Programme: 32 pages, with entry **Editor:** Secretary **Club Shop:** No.
Sponsors: Dave Carter Spts, Plymouth **Record Gate:** 5,000 v Calstock, Bedford Cup final 1952.
Midweek home matchday: Wednesday. **Reserve team's League:** Plymouth & District.
Nickname: 'Tavy' or 'Lambs'
Players progressing to Football League: Peter, Neil Langman (Plymouth, 51 53).
Clubhouse: Open all day Saturday and evenings 6.30-10.30 or 11pm. Hot & cold food
Club record appearances: A Pethick 1,000+.
Hons: Devon Premier Cup 90-91 (R-up 94-95), Devon Snr Cup 1889-90 1968-69 77-78 81-82, South Western Lg Cup 68-69 (R-up 76-77 83-84), Bedford Cup on numerous occasions.

TORPOINT ATHLETIC

Manager: Phil Cardew
Secretary: Vic Grimwood, 43 Henerdon Heights, Plympton PL7 3EY (01752 81344).
Ground: Mill Field (01752 812889)
Directions: Bear left from Torpoint ferry, ground down hill on left after half a mile.
Clubhouse: Yes **Programme:** Yes **Seats:** Yes **Cover:** Yes **Floodlights:** No
Colours: Gold & black stripes/black/gold **Change colours:** White & Black/White/White.
Previous League: Plymouth & District League.(Premier)
Best FA Vase season: 4th Round 93-94 (lost 0-3 at home to Diss Town, eventual winners).
Hons: South Western Lg 64-65 66-67 (Lg Cup R-up 65-66), Cornish Snr Cup 8.

TRURO CITY

Manager: Leigh Cooper.
Secretary: Roy Rowe, 5 Alverton Gardens, Truro, Cornwall TR1 1JA (01872 78853).
Ground: Treyew Road, Truro, Cornwall (01872 78853) **Seats:** Yes **Floodlights:** Yes.
Directions: On A39 by-pass south of city. 10 mins walk from BR station; up hill and left at junction.
Colours: Red & black/black/black **Change colours:** White/Black/Black.
Reserve Team's League: Jolly's Cornwall Combination.
Hons: South Western Lg 60-61 69-70 92-93 (R-up 54-55 62-63 66-67 67-68 70-71, Lg Cup 59-60 66-67(joint) 92-93 (R-up 54-55 58-59 67-68 93-94)), Cornish Snr Cup 12, Cornish Charity Cup 7, Cornish Snr Lg 31-32 32-33, Cornwall Comb. .gap 3

WADEBRIDGE TOWN

Manager: Robbie Black.
Secretary: Barry Cudmore, 3 Marine Terrace, Wadebridge, Cornwall PL27 7AJ (0208 813826).
Ground: Bodieve Park (0208 812537) **Seats:** Yes **Cover:** Ample **Floodlights:** No
Directions: At junction of A39 and B3314 to east of Wadebridge. **Nickname:** Bridgers.
Colours: Red & White/red/red **Change colours:** All blue.
Reserve Team's League: East Cornwall Premier.
Hons: South Western Lg R-up 68-69 78-79 79-80 (Lg Cup 5), (R-up 3), Cornish Snr Cup 79-80, Cornish Charity Cup 8,

CLUBSAVER HAMPSHIRE LEAGUE

FOUNDED: 1896

Chairman: N White

League Secretary: J Moody, 13 Tadfield Crescent, Romsey, Hampshire, SO51 5AN (01794 514073)

During the League's long history I don't suppose that any two seasons have been alike and the one just completed is no exception - unique in its own way.

The League welcomed the addition of Sherborne St John who joined us from the North Hants Senior League and Yateley Green from the Aldershot Senior League. Horndean made a return to the Hampshire League after a period in the Jewson Wessex League, being relegated under the Pyramid system.

The League said goodbye to Whitchurch United who took promotion to the Jewson Wessex League and Nursling FC who resigned to join the Southampton Premier League.

The season opened during one of the hottest summers on record and as a consequence most of our Clubs suffered from lack of grass on their pitches. Some, Netley Central Sports in particular, were dustbowls with not a blade of grass in sight.

Fixtures Secretary Ian Craig was presented with an immediate fixture problem as some Clubs were unable to start the season due to the state of their pitches. After he had sorted that out, the rains came and with them more cancellations due to flooding. As the winter progressed he and the Clubs had to contend with severe frosts and several falls of snow. As Ian struggled with fixture re-arrangements he was beset with computer and printer problems. Due to his dedication and the co-operation of the clubs, the season ended more or less on time - congratulations to all concerned.

Congratulations as always go to our League Champions. Colden Common tooke the Division One crown, coming from behind to pip Netley Central Sports. The Division title race provided interest all season with Fleetlands, Moneyfield and Romsey Town all topping the table and all having a chance to win the crown going into the last few weeks of the season.

The Division Two title was ample reward for Locksheath who just missed the title the season before whilst in Division Three Ringwwod Town dominated the league all season.

Otterbourne, the underdogs, won the Trophyman League Cup defeating Division One New Milton Town at Cams Alders in a tense game. The trophyman was added to Otterbourne's trophy cabinet alongside the Southampton Senior Cup the club won at the Dell a few weeks previously, again, against senior opposition in Jewson Wessex League B.A.T. - a unique double. Our clubs were also prominent in County Cups and Local Association Cup competitions and we are proud to record that Malshanger won the North Hants Senior Cup.

It is always pleasant to record progress within the League and during the season Bass Alton Town unveiled a superb new set of floodlights and Ecchinswell took the gigantic leap from their village ground to the old Newbury Town ground which can only be described as magnificent. Bishops Waltham Town als moved into a new ground at Priory Park and despite some drainage problems, which are being worked on, they have a facility as good as any in the league. As usual the programme of ground inspections was carried out and I am pleased to report that overall standards are gradually improving and our new entrants Sherbourne St John and Yateley Green certainly set the standards with their splendid new clubhouses.

At the start of the season the League were fortunate in acquiring sponsorship from Clubsaver Foreman-Bassett Insurance and we thank the company for their valuable support. We also thank Trophyman of Southampton for their continuing sponsorshp of our League Cup.

Off the field progress was also made, with, after two years of productive negotiation with the Local Senior Leagues, the process for the formation of the Hampshire Combination Division is now underway with a timetable aimed at the season 1997-98

John Moody

FINAL LEAGUE TABLES 1995/96

Division One	*P*	*W*	*D*	*L*	*F*	*A*	*Pts*
1. Colden Common	38	26	5	7	80	39	83
2. Netley Central Sports	38	26	3	9	91	49	81
3. Romsey Town	38	23	6	9	95	43	75
4. Moneyfields	38	24	3	11	95	48	75
5. Fleetlands	38	23	6	9	84	45	75
6. New Street	38	21	7	10	71	52	70
7. Hayling United	38	21	6	11	58	42	69
8. Blackfield & Langley	38	18	6	15	85	71	59
9. Pirelli General	38	18	3	17	59	59	57
10. Malshanger	38	12	11	15	58	70	47
11. Horndean	38	13	7	18	54	60	46
12. Wincester City	38	12	9	17	62	75	45
13. Ecchinswell	38	11	9	18	59	78	42
14. Bass Alton Town	38	10	11	17	64	84	41
15. A C Delco	38	12	5	21	54	88	41
16. New Milton Town	38	9	10	19	46	70	37
17. Liss Athletic	38	9	10	19	60	93	37
18. Overton United	38	10	5	23	39	76	35
19. Paulsgrove *	38	9	5	24	61	84	29
20. Verwood Town	38	7	6	25	30	82	27

** 3 points & 3 goals deducted*

Div Two	*P*	*W*	*D*	*L*	*F*	*A*	*Pts*
1. Locks Heath	34	21	10	3	79	22	73
2. Stockbridge	34	20	10	4	87	51	70
3. Bishopstoke S	34	21	5	8	92	51	68
4. Brading Town	34	22	1	11	96	44	67
5. Vos.Thornycroft	34	21	4	9	91	56	67
6. Fleet Spurs	34	18	6	10	76	53	60
7. Esso Fawley	34	16	10	8	79	44	58
8. Hilsea Club	34	16	7	11	84	56	55
9. B Waltham T	34	17	7	11	84	53	55*
10. Otterbourne	34	15	7	12	69	58	52
11. Broughton	34	13	4	17	63	67	43
12. Hythe & Dib	34	12	5	17	58	74	41
13. St Mary's	34	12	4	18	60	71	40
14. Hedge End	34	11	3	20	56	98	36
15. Ludgershall St	34	7	7	20	58	104	28
16. Alresford Tn	34	7	7	20	56	78	27#
17. Compton	34	6	0	28	32	108	18
18. Basing Rovers	34	1	3	30	34	157	6

** 3 points & 4 goals deducted*

 # 1 point deducted

Div Three	*P*	*W*	*D*	*L*	*F*	*A*	*Pts*
1. Ringwood Tn	34	23	5	6	90	46	74
2. Tadley	34	22	6	6	80	43	71*
3. Mayflower	34	18	8	8	84	43	62
4. Fleetlands Res	34	18	8	8	68	45	62
5. Yateley Green	34	16	11	7	57	33	59
6. Hamble Club	34	16	10	8	55	33	58
7. Swanmore	34	15	9	10	53	57	54
8. Moneyfields R	34	11	12	11	60	52	45
9. W/ster Castle	34	12	8	14	68	68	44
10. Aldermaston	34	12	8	14	60	70	44
11. Awbridge	34	11	10	13	46	42	43
12. Sherborne S J	34	11	7	16	64	70	40
13. Covies	34	11	4	10	52	80	37
14. Four Marks	34	9	9	16	60	84	36
15. Braishfield	34	7	13	14	40	61	34
16. Netley C S R	34	6	9	19	53	82	27
17. Winchester CR	34	7	6	21	45	89	27
18. Bass Alton TR	34	7	5	22	45	90	26

** 1 point & 3 goals deducted*

DIVISION ONE CLUBS 1996-97

A.C. DELCO

Secretary: Brian Cook, 17 Hickory Gardens, West End, Southampton.SO30 3RN (01703 613334)
Ground: AC Delco Spts Ground, Stoneham Lane, Eastleigh (01703 613334).
Colours: Royal Blue & white stripes/black/blue. **Change:** Red & Black stripes/White/Black.
Programme: No **Midweek home matchday:** Wednesday.

AFC NEWBURY

Secretary: Damien Hayden, 10 Nideggen Close, Thatcham, Berkshire RG19 (01635 826540)
Ground: Faraday Road, Newbury.
Colours: Green & white/green/green **Change:** White/navy/white.
Programme: Yes **Midweek home matchday:** Tuesday or Wednesday.

BASS ALTON TOWN

Secretary: A J M Hillman, 19a Beechwood Rd, Alton, Hants GU34 1RL (01420 87103).
Ground: Bass Spts Ground, Anstey Rd, Alton (01420 82465).
Colours: Black & red/black/black **Change:** Blue & Yellow/Blue/Blue.
Programme: No **Midweek home matchday:** Any.

BISHOPSTOKE SOCIAL

Secretary: Tony Boland, 34 Fryern Close, Chandlers Ford, Hants SO50 2LF (01703 262763).
Ground: Chicken Hall Lane, Bishopstoke, Eastleigh, Hants (01860 612038).
Colours: Green & Black/Black/Black. **Change:** All Blue.

BLACKFIELD & LANGLEY

Secretary: Ian Hore, 5 Foxhayes Lane, Blackfield, Southampton, Hants SO45 2QD (01703 893325).
Ground: Gang Warily Rec., Newlands Rd, Blackfield, Southampton, Hants (01703 893603).
Colours: All Green. **Change:** Yellow/blue/blue
Programme: Yes **Midweek home matchday:** Wednesday.

COLDEN COMMON

Secretary: M.Budden, 44 Orchard Close, Colden Common, Winchester, Hampshire.SO21 1ST (01962 713813)
Ground: Colden Common Recreation Ground, Main Road, Colden Common (01962 712365).
Colours: Red & white/black/red **Change:** All yellow
Programme: Yes **Midweek home matchday:** Wednesday.

FLEETLANDS

Secretary: David Bell, 72 White Hart Lane, Portchester, Hants. PO16 9BQ.(01705 321781)
Ground: Lederle Lane, Gosport, Hants (01329 239723).
Colours: Red & black/white/white **Change:** All white.
Programme: Yes **Midweek home matchday:** Any.

HAYLING UNITED

Secretary: Mrs S Westfield, 14 Harold Road, Hayling Island, Hants PO11 9LT (01705 463305).
Ground: Hayling Park, Hayling Island, Hants.
Colours: Red & navy/navy/navy **Change:** Blue & white/blue/blue
Programme: No **Midweek home matchday:** Tuesday.

HORNDEAN

Secretary: Mrs Gladys Berry, 74 Five Heads Road, Horndean PO8 9NZ (01705 591698).
Ground: Five Heads Park, Five Heads Road, Horndean (01705 591363).
Colours: Black & Red/black/black **Change colours:** Navy & white/white/navy.

LISS ATHLETIC

Secretary: W.E.Moseley, 3 Yew Tree Place, Liss, Hants. GU33 7ET (01730 894631)
Ground: Newman Collard PF, Hill Brow Rd, Liss, Hants (01730 894022).
Colours: All Blue & White. **Change:** All yellow
Programme: No **Midweek home matchday:** Thursday.

LOCKSHEATH

Secretary: Michael Harrison, 30 Whitebeam Road, Hedge End, Southampton, Hants. SO30 OPZ (01489 784470)
Ground: Locksheath Rec, Warsash Rd, Titchfield Common, Eastleigh (01489 600932).
Colours: Red/black/black. **Change:** All white

MALSHANGER

Secretary: Fred Norris, 9 Goddards Firs, Oakley, Basingstoke, Hants. RG23 7JL (01256 781697)
Ground: The Sportsfield, Malshanger, Basingstoke (01256 780285).
Colours: Tangerine/Black/Tangerine. **Change:** Purple/Purple/White.
Programme: **Midweek home matchday:** Tuesday.

MONEYFIELDS

Secretary: Peter Shires, 242 Grafton Street, Mile End, Portsmouth, (01705 645813)
Ground: Moneyfields Sports Ground, Moneyfield Avenue, Copnor Road, Portsmouth, Hampshire.
Colours: Yellow/blue/blue. **Change:** Jade & white/jade/jade

NETLEY CENTRAL SPORTS

Secretary: Mr R W Crompton, 47 Station Rd, Netley Abbey, Southampton SO31 5AE (01703 452049).
Ground: Netley Rec, Station Rd, Netley Abbey, Southampton (01703 452267).
Colours: Royal & white/royal/royal **Change:** All red
Programme: Yes **Midweek home matchday:** Wednesday.

NEW MILTON TOWN

Secretary: Malcom Smith, 4 Kestral Drive, Mudeford, Christchurch Dorset BH23 4DE (01425 277565)
Ground: Fawcetts Spts Ground, Christchurch Rd, New Milton, Hants BH25 6QF (01425 628191).
Colours: Yellow & blue/black/yellow **Change:** White/navy/navy.
Programme: Yes **Midweek home matchday:** Wednesday.

NEW STREET

Secretary: Mrs F J Waterman, 'Jorin Bay' 2 Pine Walk, Andover, Hants SP10 3PW (01264 362751)
Ground: Foxcotte Park, Charlton Down, Andover.(01264 358358)
Colours: Green & black/black/green **Change colours:** Red/white/red.
Programme: Yes **Midweek home matchday:** Tuesday or Wednesday.

OVERTON UNITED

Secretary: Mrs A Wheeler, 3 Lordsfield Gardens, Overton, Hants RG25 2EW (01256 771241).
Ground: Recreation Centre, Bridge Street, Overton (01256 770561).
Colours: Blue & white stripes/white/blue **Change:** Green & purple/purple/purple
Programme: No **Midweek home matchday:** Tuesday or Thursday

PIRELLI GENERAL

Secretary: Miss Bernice Fox 31 Spring Close, Fair Oak, Eastleigh, Hants SO50 7BB (01703 693537).
Ground: Jubilee Spts Ground, Chestnut Ave., Eastleigh (01703 612721).
Colours: Blue & white/white/white **Change:** Yellow/black/yellow
Programme: Yes **Midweek home matchday:** Tuesday.

POOLE TOWN

Secretary: Bill Read, 15 Addison Close, Romsey, Hants SO51 7TL (01794 517991)
Ground: Petersham Lane, Gants Common, Holt, Wimborne, Dorset (01258 840379)
Colours: Red & white/red/white **Change Colours:** Yellow & black/blue/yellow

STOCKBRIDGE

Secretary: Graham Howard, 1 Moat Cottages, Longstock,Stockbridge, Hants.SO20 6EP (01264 810753)
Ground: The Recreation Ground, High Street, Stockbridge, Hants.
Colours: All red **Change:** All blue

WINCHESTER CITY

Secretary: Geoffrey Cox, 9 Burnetts Gdns, Horton Heath, Eastleigh, Hants SO5 7BY (01703 693021).
Ground: Hillier Way, Abbotts Barton, Winchester (01962 863553).
Colours: Red & white/black/red **Change:** White/green/green

DIVISION TWO CLUBS 1996-97

BISHOPS WALTHAM TOWN

Secretary: Mrs Margaret Weavil, 69 Oak Road, Ridgemede, Bishops Waltham, Hants SO32 1ER (01489 894952)
Ground: Priory Park, School Hill, Bishops Waltham (01489 892179).
Colours: Amber/Black/Black & Amber. **Change:** Blue/Blue/Blue & White.

BRADING TOWN

Secretary: Mick Edmondston, Seawinds, Nunwell St., Sandown.I.O.W. PO36 9DE (01983 404770)
Ground: Vicarage Lane, Brading, Isle of Wight (01983 405217).
Cols: All red. **Change:** All blue **Programme:** Yes

BROUGHTON

Secretary: A R Hammerton, 19 Plough Gdns, Broughton, Stockbridge, Hants SO20 8AF (01794 301495).
Ground: The Sports Field, Buckholt Rd, Broughton, Stockbridge, Hants.
Colours: Blue & white /blue/blue. **Change:** All Green.

ESSO (FAWLEY)

Secretary: Mr A Haws, 40 Hollybank Rd, Hythe, Southampton, Hants SO45 5FQ (01703 843402).
Ground: Esso Recreation Club, Long Lane, Holbury, Southampton, Hant (01705 893750).
Colours: White/blue/red **Change:** Red/white/white

FLEET SPURS

Secretary: C R Filkins, 5 Byron Close, Fleet, Hants GU13 9QD (01252 627385).
Ground: Ancells Farm, Fleet, Hants.
Colours: Red & black/black/red **Change:** Blue or green or purple/turqu/white.

HEDGE END

Secretary: M J Oliver, 25 Blossom Close, Botley, Southampton, Hants SO3 2FR (01489 786308).
Ground: Norman Ridaway Playing Fields, Heathouse Lane, Hedge End, Southampton.
Colours: Black & white/black/black **Change:** Blue & white/blue/blue.

HILSEA CLUB

Secretary: Mr Terry Harwood, 147 Manners Rd, Southsea, Hants PO4 0BD (01705 785140).
Ground: Portsmouth Sailing Centre, Eastern Rd, Portsmouth PO3 5LY (01705 670119).
Colours: Yellow/blue/white **Change:** Blue/blue/white

HYTHE & DIBDEN

Secretary: Mr A Moyst, 105 Hobart Drive, Hythe, Southampton, Hants SO40 6FD (01703 847335).
Ground: Ewart Rec Ground, Jones Lane, Hythe, Southampton (01703 845264 - matchdays only).
Colours: Green/green/yellow **Change:** Blue & white stripes/blue/black.

LUDGERSHALL SPORTS CLUB

Secretary: Steve Winstone, 57 Wood Park, Ludgershall, Andover, Hants SP11 9NS (01264 791193).
Ground: Astor Cres., Ludgershall (01264 398200).
Change Colours: Yellow/green/green **Colours:** All maroon
Midweek home matchday: Wednesday.

MAYFLOWER

Secretary: Mr C J Papadatos, 5 Albion Close, Porchester, Fareham, Hants PO16 9EW (01329 510623)
Ground: Clarence Gardens, Southsea (01705 824246 - FAX 01705 727273)
Colours: Blue & black stripes/black/black **Change:** Yellow & green/green/yellow

OTTERBOURNE

Secretary: R J Broom, 249 Passfield Rd, Eastleigh, Hants SO5 5DE (01703 328992).
Ground: Oakwood Park, off Oakwood Ave., Otterbourne (01962 714681).
Colours: Red/white/red & white
Change: Blue & white/blue/blue.

PAULSGROVE

Secretary: S J Cox, 22 Alameda Road, Purbrook, Waterlooville, Hants. PO7 5HD (01705 785110)
Ground: The Grove Club, Marsden Rd (off Allaway Avenue), Paulsgrove, Portsmouth (01705 324102).
Colours: Red & black stripes/black/red **Change:** Blue & white/blue/black
Programme: **Midweek home matchday:** Wednesday.

PORTSMOUTH CITY

RINGWOOD TOWN

Secretary: Mrs S Crewe, 278 Windham Rd, Bournemouth, Dorset BH1 4QU (01202 398975).
Ground: Long Lane, Ringwood, Hants (01425 473448).
Colours: Red & white stripes/black/red **Change:** All blue

TADLEY

Secretary: Mike Miller, Meadow View, West Heath, Baughurst, Hants RG26 5LE (01256 850700).
Ground: The Green, Tadley, Hants.
Cols: Blue & maroon stripes/maroon/maroon **Change:** Yellow/blue/blue

VERWOOD TOWN

Secretary: Mrs J A Fry, 19a Noon Hill Rd, Verwood, Dorset BH31 7DB (01202 822826).
Ground: Pottern Park, Pottern Way, Verwood, Dorset.
Colours: All red **Change:** All blue
Programme: Yes **Midweek home matchday:** Tuesday.

VOSPER THORNYCROFT

Secretary: Peter Prin, 454 Bursledon Road, Sholing, Southampton, Hants. SO19 8QQ (01703 403829)
Ground: Vosper Thornycroft Spts Ground, Portsmouth Rd, Sholing, Southampton (01489 403829).
Colours: All royal **Change:** Red & black/black/black

YATELEY GREEN

Secretary: Alan Baynes, 7 Borderside, Yateley, Camberley Surrey GU17 7LJ
Ground: Yateley Recreation Ground, Reading Road, Yateley, Camberley, Surrey
Colours: Green/black/black **Change:** Red/black/black

DIVISION THREE CLUBS 1996-97

A.F.C. ALDERMASTON

Secretary: Mr Gareth Dew, 58 Portway, Baughurst, Hants RG26 5PE (01734 811271).
Ground: Aldermaston, Recreation Society, Awe, Aldermaston (01734 814111 ex4544).
Colours: Blue/Blue/White. **Change colours:** Red & white/white/red.

AFC BASINGSTOKE

Secretary: T Purnell, 1 Byfleet Avenue, OLd Basing, Basingstoke, Hants RG24 7HD (01256 23239)
Ground: War Memorial Park, Crossborough Hill, Basingstoke, Hants.
Colours: Blue & black/black/black **Change Colours:** Green & white/green/white

AWBRIDGE

Secretary: Mike Caws, 2 Copsewood Road, Bitterne Park, Southampton, Hants SO18 1QU (01703 551880).
Ground: The Village Hall Field, Cross Roads, Awbridge, nr Romsey, Hants.
Colours: Red & black/black/black **Change:** Light Blue & white/white/white

BASING ROVERS

Secretary: Mr C J Dale, 13 Howard View, Basingstoke, Hants RG22 6LF (01256 26604).
Ground: Old Basing Rec, The Street, Old Basing (01256 844254).
Colours: All red **Change:** Yellow/blue/blue

BASS ALTON TOWN RESERVES

BRAISHFIELD

Secretary: Mick Tanner, 10 Avon Cres., Romsey, Hants.SO51 5PY (01794 523180)
Ground: Braishfield Recreation Ground, Braishfield, Hants.
Colours: Royal & yellow/royal/yellow. **Change:** Yellow & green/green/green.

COMPTON

Secretary: M Allerton, 28 Keats Close, Olivers Battery, Winchester SO22 4HR (01962 869574).
Ground: Shepherds Lane, Compton Down, nr Winchester (01962 712083).
Colours: Red/black/red **Change:** All blue.

COVIES

Secretary: Mr John Marchment, 4 Linstead Rd, Cove, Farnborough, Hants GU14 9HH (01276 34254).
Ground: Queens Road Recreation Ground, North Camp, Farnborough, Hants.
Colours: Yellow & green/green/yellow **Change:** All red

FLEETLANDS RESERVES

FOUR MARKS

Secretary: Mr Simon C Annetts, 5 Thorn Court, Four Marks, nr Alton, Hants (01420 562570).
Ground: The Recreation Ground, Uplands Lane, Brislands Lane, Four Marks, nr Alton, Hants.
Colours: Tangerine/black/tangerine **Change colours:** Navy/white/red

HAMBLE CLUB

Secretary: H.J.Noice, 55 The Oaks, Bitterne,Southampton, Hants. SO19 7RP(01703 398370)
Ground: Mount Pleasant Rec, Hamble Lane, Hanble, Southampton, Hants (01703 452327).
Colours: All Red **Change:** All Blue.

LAVERSTOCK & FORD

Secretary: Chris Dare, 22 Beechcroft Road, Laverstock, Salisbury, Wilts SP1 1PF (01722 329395)
Ground: 23 Church Road, Laverstock, Salisbury, Wilts (01722 327401)
Colours: White & orange/white/white **Change Colours:** All white

MONETFIELD RESERVES

NETLEY CENTRAL SPORTS RESERVES

OVERTON UNITED RESERVES

QUEENS KEEP

Secretary: Donald Campbell, 81 Lumsden Avenue, Shirley, Southampton, Hants SO15 5EJ (01703 781362)
Ground: Civil Service Club, off Malmesbury Road, Shirley, Southampton, (01703 771950)
Colours: Yellow & green/emerald/emerald **Change Colours:** Royal & maroon/royal/royal

SHERBORNE ST JOHN

Secretary: Mrs Jean Barton, 34 Pitcairn Close, Basingstoke, Hampshire RG24 9BD (01256 819802)
Ground: Charles Chute Recreation Ground, Vyne Road, Sherborne St John, Basingstoke, Hampshire.
Colours: Green/black/black **Change:** Yellow/green/green

SWANMORE

Secretary: Mrs L Chapman, Green Brae, Swanmore Road, Swanmore, Hants (01489 894246)
Ground: The Recreation Ground, New Road, Swanmore, Hants.
Colours: White/blue/white **Change:** All yellow.

WINCHESTER CASTLE

Secretary: A J Rutter, 79 South Ham Road, Basingstoke, Hants RG22 6AA (01256 842689)
Ground: Hants County Council Spts Ground, Petersfield Rd, Chilcomb, Winchester (01962 866989).
Colours: Red & black/black/red **Change:** Blue & white/white/blue.

WINCHESTER CITY RESERVES

ICIS LEAGUE

FOUNDED: 1905

President: B D East.

Chairman: Alan C F Turvey.

Hon. Secretary: Nicholas Robinson,
226 Rye Lane, Peckham, London SE15 4NL.

The race for the Premier Division championship was the closest for many years. Indeed, up until just a few weeks before the end of the season, around six clubs were still in with a chance of taking the title, including reigning champions Enfield, promoted Boreham Wood, relegated Yeovil Town and surprise packages Dulwich Hamlet and Hayes, although the latter would perhaps refute that comment after finishing in third spot last season.

In the end it came down to the very last game of the season and Hayes clinched the title, and promotion to the Vauxhall Conference, by the narrowest of margins possible - one goal difference. The Church Road outfit have done remarkabley well during the past couple of years and certainly benefitted from the sell-on clause, which earned the Middlesex club a massive sum following the transfer of their former player, Les Ferdinand, to Newcastle United. Most of that money was spent on up-grading their stadium which meant that promotion to the Conference for the first time was a formality. Enfield had to be content with runners-up spot and Boreham Wood can feel well satisfied with third place in their first season back in the Premier Division since 1982.

Other Premier division winners were Aylesbury United, who achieved the 'double' of Berks & Bucks Senior Cup finalists and Charity Shield winners, Bromley, who narrowly avoided relegation but won the London Challenge Cup, Kingstonian lifted the Guardian Insurance Cup after beating Aldershot Town in the final, and Sutton United, who beat Boreham Wood to lift the Carlton Cup.

It was goodbye to Premier Division football. at least for the time being, for Molesey, Walton & Hersham and Worthing. They are replaced by Oxford City, Heybridge Swifts and Staines Town. For Oxford it capped a magnificent achievement, having only returned to the Isthmian League in 1993. Successive promotions have brought City back to the top division for the first time since 1980. Staines return to the Premier Division after a three year gap but it is Heybridge Swifts first tilt at the top section and it will be interesting to chart the Essex club's progress.

Division One sadly lost Ruislip Manor, who decided to drop down a standard due to financial difficulties, therfore only Wembley and Barking suffered relegation whilst Canvey Island, Croydon and Hampton moved up from Division Two.

Dorking's sad demise continued with a third consecutive relegation. However along with Hungerford Town and Witham Town, they were reprieved due to the fact that Harefield United and Cove joined Ruislip Manor in resigning from the League, and with Braintree Town being allowed to switch over from the Southern League, it leaves Division Three with just seventeen clubs just for one season.
Steve Witney

Hayes's clinching goal for the Championship against Carshalton *Photo - Mark Sandom*

Action between Aldershot Town's Mark Butler (white) and Kingstonian's David Stevens, in the Guardian Insurance Cup Final.

Photo - Andrew Chitty

PREMIER DIVISION FINAL LEAGUE TABLE 1995/96

		P	W	D	L	F	A	Pts
1.	Hayes	42	24	14	4	76	32	86
2.	Enfield	42	26	8	8	78	35	86
3.	Boreham Wood	42	24	11	7	69	29	83
4.	Yeovil Town	42	23	11	8	83	51	80
5.	Dulwich Hamlet	42	23	11	8	85	59	80
6.	Carshalton Ath	42	22	8	12	68	49	74
7.	St Albans	42	20	12	10	70	41	72
8.	Kingstonian	42	20	11	11	62	38	71
9.	Harrow Borough	42	19	10	13	70	56	67
10.	Sutton United	42	17	14	11	71	56	65
11.	Aylesbury United	42	17	12	13	71	58	63
12.	Bishops Stortford	42	16	9	17	61	62	57
13.	Yeading	42	11	14	17	48	60	47
14.	Hendon	42	12	10	20	52	65	46
15.	Chertsey Town	42	13	6	23	45	71	45
16.	Purfleet	42	12	8	22	48	67	44
17.	Grays Athletic	42	11	11	20	43	63	44
18.	Hitchin Town	42	10	10	22	41	74	40
19.	Bromley	42	10	7	25	52	91	37
20.	Molesey	42	9	9	24	46	81	36
21.	Walton & Hersham	42	9	7	26	42	79	34
22.	Worthing	42	4	7	31	42	106	19

LEADING LEAGUE GOALSCORERS:

Mark Xavier	Harrow Borough	29
Paul Whitmarsh	Dulwich Hamlet	25
Warren Patmore	Yeovil	24
Dominic Feltham	Sutton United	21
Andy Salako	Carshalton Athletic	21

PREMIER DIVISION RESULTS CHART 1995-96

HOME TEAM	1	2	3	4	5	6	7	8	9	10	11	12	13	14	15	16	17	18	19	20	21	22
1. Aylesbury U	*	0-0	1-3	3-0	0-1	2-0	0-3	2-3	2-2	2-0	1-3	1-0	2-1	0-2	1-1	1-0	1-1	4-1	0-0	1-1	1-1	3-1
2. B/Stortford	3-6	*	0-2	1-1	0-2	3-1	1-2	0-1	2-0	2-3	1-2	3-1	2-2	2-3	4-0	1-1	3-2	1-3	2-0	0-0	3-1	2-2
3. Boreham Wd	2-2	0-1	*	3-1	2-3	2-0	2-2	4-1	2-0	3-2	0-0	4-0	1-0	0-0	0-1	2-1	2-0	0-1	1-1	3-1	1-1	0-2
4. Bromley	0-3	0-2	0-1	*	1-2	3-3	0-2	0-1	2-2	5-1	0-1	2-5	0-2	1-1	1-3	0-2	1-0	2-3	3-2	3-2	1-0	1-5
5. Carshalton A	3-1	2-0	0-0	0-0	*	3-1	2-2	1-1	3-1	0-1	0-3	1-1	1-1	0-3	4-0	3-1	1-1	1-2	5-2	4-0	2-0	2-1
6. Chertsey Tn	0-3	3-0	0-3	0-2	0-1	*	0-1	0-3	2-0	1-6	1-3	3-1	2-1	2-1	3-0	2-1	1-2	1-1	1-3	2-1	1-1	1-3
7. Dulwich Ham	1-0	4-1	0-2	4-1	2-1	0-0	*	1-1	3-5	3-2	1-1	1-0	3-3	1-3	2-0	1-1	3-1	2-2	1-1	4-1	3-0	2-1
8. Enfield	3-3	0-1	0-2	5-0	4-0	0-0	1-0	*	3-0	3-0	1-1	2-0	3-0	2-1	2-0	3-0	2-2	0-2	4-0	5-1	2-0	2-1
9. Grays Ath	2-0	0-2	1-2	0-3	1-0	2-1	1-4	0-3	*	0-2	3-3	0-0	1-0	1-1	1-0	2-0	0-3	1-2	3-1	6-0	0-0	0-2
10. Harrow Boro	3-3	0-0	1-1	1-3	0-1	3-1	1-2	3-1	3-0	*	1-1	2-2	1-2	2-1	3-1	2-2	0-0	0-0	2-3	3-1	4-1	0-1
11. Hayes	0-1	3-1	1-1	5-1	1-2	4-0	2-2	3-1	5-1	2-1	*	3-1	1-1	2-1	2-0	2-1	0-0	0-0	2-0	2-0	0-0	1-1
12. Hendon	4-2	1-1	1-1	2-0	0-0	0-0	1-2	0-1	0-0	0-2	0-2	*	1-2	0-3	2-0	2-4	1-2	0-4	4-0	3-0	1-1	1-3
13. Hitchin Tn	0-3	1-1	1-2	2-1	2-5	2-0	1-3	1-0	1-0	1-5	1-3	0-1	*	1-1	0-1	2-0	0-0	1-0	0-2	2-2	0-3	1-2
14. Kingstonian	1-1	2-1	1-0	0-1	2-1	0-2	0-2	0-1	1-0	0-1	1-0	0-1	0-1	*	1-1	1-1	4-1	2-2	1-0	1-1	3-1	2-2
15. Molesey	1-4	2-1	1-2	3-2	0-1	2-0	1-2	1-4	0-0	0-0	0-2	1-2	2-1	0-2	*	2-3	1-1	0-5	2-2	3-1	1-2	2-3
16. Purfleet	1-2	1-2	1-0	1-1	2-1	1-3	3-1	1-1	1-0	0-1	0-0	2-3	1-1	1-3	0-2	*	0-1	2-1	2-1	3-1	1-2	0-3
17. St Albans C	2-0	3-0	0-0	5-0	3-0	2-0	4-1	1-0	1-1	0-2	0-3	3-1	5-1	1-2	1-0	3-0	*	2-2	3-0	2-0	0-1	2-2
18. Sutton Utd	2-3	2-1	0-3	1-3	2-1	2-1	1-1	2-4	0-0	4-0	2-2	2-3	4-0	0-1	2-0	1-0	0-1	*	2-1	3-1	2-2	1-1
19. Walton & Her	2-1	0-2	0-4	3-1	0-1	0-1	0-2	0-1	1-4	1-2	0-1	1-0	4-1	0-2	3-3	1-2	1-2	1-1	*	1-0	0-0	1-3
20. Worthing	1-3	0-1	0-2	2-2	2-3	1-2	1-3	0-1	1-1	1-2	0-3	0-5	2-0	0-5	4-4	1-2	1-5	5-2	0-2	*	2-1	3-2
21. Yeading	0-0	2-4	0-3	3-0	1-3	1-3	5-3	1-1	0-1	1-2	0-1	0-0	2-0	0-2	2-2	3-1	2-1	2-2	3-0	1-0	*	1-1
22. Yeovil Town	3-2	1-3	0-1	4-3	2-1	1-0	5-3	0-1	1-0	0-0	3-0	4-1	1-1	1-1	3-2	2-1	1-1	0-0	4-1	3-1	2-0	*

GUARDIAN INSURANCE FOOTBALL LEAGUE CUP 1995-96

Preliminary Round;

Banstead Athletic v E Thurrock Utd	2-0	Bedford Town v Met Police	2-1
Bracknell Town v Cheshunt	3-1	Collier Row v Canvey Island	0-0, 2-0*
Croydon v Camberley Town	4-0	Dorking v Aveley	3-2
Edgware Town v Harlow Town	2-1	Egham Town v Hertford Town	2-0
Epsom & Ewell v Barton Rovers	2-3	Flackwell Heath v Wingate & Finchley	2-1
Hemel Hempstead v Tilbury	3-1 (aet)	Horsham v Oxford City	3-6
Kingsbury Town v Cove	2-0	Leatherhead v Clapton	3-2 (aet)
Leighton Town v Hampton	1-2 (aet)	Lewes v Witham Town	1-2
Northwood v Harefield United	0-1	Saffron Walden Town v Hornchurch	1-2
Thame United v Chalfont St Peter	0-1	Ware v Tring Town	3-5
Windsor & Eton v Southall	2-1 (aet)	Wivenhoe Town v Wealdstone	2-5
Hungerford Town v Newbury Town	W/O		

Newbury Town suspended by Football Association — ** Collier Row disqualified for ineligible player*

First Round;

Aldershot Town v Chertsey Town	3-2	Aylesbury United v Maidenhead United	3-0
Banstead Athletic v Windsor & Eton	6-1	Berkhamsted Town v Kingsbury Town	1-2
Billericay Town v Hampton	3-1	Bracknell Town v Wokingham Town	3-5
Chesham United v Harrow Borough	4-1	Croydon v Witham Town	3-0
Dorking v Barton Rovers	1-5	Edgware Town v Bishops Stortford	0-2
Enfield v Leyton Pennant	4-2	Egham Town v Ruislip Manor	1-1, 0-2
Flackwell Heath v Dulwich Hamlet	1-3 (aet)	Harefield United v Bromley	0-3
Hayes v Grays Athletic	0-1	Hitchin Town v Canvey Island	4-1
Hornchurch v Bedford Town	1-4	Kingstonian v Abingdon Town	2-1
Leatherhead v Hungerford Town	2-1	Marlow v Hemel Hempstead	2-1
Molesey v Basingstoke Town	0-1	Purfleet v Boreham Wood	0-1
St Albans City v Worthing	2-3	Staines Town v Oxford City	3-1 (aet)
Sutton United v Tring Town	2-0	Tooting & Micham Utd v Wealdstone	4-3
Uxbridge v Barking	0-1	Walton & Hersham v Chalfont St P	2-2, 5-3
Wembley v Carshalton Athletic	1-3	Whyteleafe v Heybridge Swifts	1-2
Yeading v Bognor Regis Town	0-3	Yeovil Town v Hendon	1-3

Second Round;

Aldershot Town v Grays Athletic	2-1	Barking v Kingstonian	0-6
Barton Rovers v Dulwich Hamlet	0-1	Basingstoke Town v Ruislip Manor	2-2, 3-2
Bedford Town v Tooting & Mitcham Utd	3-2	Bishops Stortford v Staines Town	3-1
Bromley v Boreham Wood	3-3, 0-1	Carshalton Athletic v Bognor Regis Town	2-0
Chesham United v Aylesbury United	2-3 (aet)	Hendon v Croydon	0-1 (aet)
Heybridge Swifts v Billericay Town	4-3	Kingsbury Town v Walton & Hersham	1-1, 1-3
Leatherhead v Marlow	0-2	Sutton United v Hitchin Town	0-1
Wokingham Town v Banstead Athletic	0-3*	Worthing v Enfield	1-4

** Banstead Athletic removed for playing ineligible player.*

Third Round;

Aldershot Town v Boreham Wood	1-0	Aylesbury United v Carshalton Athletic	3-1
Basingstoke Town v Marlow	6-0	Bedford Town v Wokingham Town	1-2
Croydon v Walton & Hersham	2-1	Enfield v Kingstonian	2-2, 0-3
Heybridge Swifts v Dulwich Hamlet	3-2 (aet)	Hitchin Town v Bishops Stortford	4-1 (aet)

Fourth Round;

Aldershot Town v Basingstoke Town	1-0	Aylesbury United v Croydon	2-1 (aet)
Heybridge Swifts v Kingstonian	2-2, 0-2	Wokingham Town v Hitchin Town	2-3

Semi-Finals; First Leg;		**Second Leg;**	
Aylesbury United v Kingstonian	1-3	Kingstonian v Aylesbury Utd	2-1, **5-2 agg**
Hitchin Town v Aldershot Town	0-1	Aldershot Town v Hitchin Town	2-0, **3-0 agg**

Final; Aldershot Town v Kingstonian 1-4

Kingstonian pictured with the Guardian Insurance Cup after their 4-1 victory over Aldershot Town in the final played at Aldershot's Recreation Ground, 6/5/96.

Photo - Andrew Chitty

CARLTON CUP 1995-96

First Round;

Match	Score
Aldershot Town v Bromley	3-0
Barton Rovers v Heybridge Swifts	3-2 *(Match Void)*
Basingstoke Town v Whyteleafe	4-1
Chertsey Town v Yeovil Town	0-2
Molesey v Kingstonian	0-3
Staines Town v Walton & Hersham	0-1
Uxbridge v Harrow Borough	1-0
Aylesbury United v Chesham United	3-1 (aet)
Barton Rovers v Heybridge Swifts	0-1
Berkhamsted Town v Yeading	0-3
Hendon v St Albans City	3-4
Purfleet v Hayes	2-0
Thame United v Marlow	4-1

Second Round;

Match	Score
Aldershot Town v Maidenhead United	3-1
Bishops Stortford v Hitchin Town	3-0
Boreham Wood v Barking	3-1
Enfield v Yeading	1-2 (aet)
Heybridge Swifts v Uxbridge	3-1
St Albans City v Ruislip Manor	1-2
Thame United v Dulwich Hamlet	3-0
Walton & Hersham v Kingstonian	1-3
Aylesbury United v Purfleet	0-1
Bognor Regis Town v Worthing	6-0
Carshalton Athletic v Yeovil Town	2-1
Grays Athletic v Billericay Town	1-2 (aet)
Oxford City v Basingstoke Town	1-0
Sutton United v Abingdon Town	3-0
Tooting & Mitcham Utd v Wokingham Town	4-3
Wembley v Leyton Pennant	2-3

Third Round;

Match	Score
Carshalton Athletic v Thame United	4-0
Heybridge Swifts v Boreham Wood	0-2
Leyton Pennant v Purfleet	5-1
Tooting & Mitcham United v Sutton United	1-3
Aldershot Town v Bognor Regis Town	2-2, 3-5pen
Kingstonian v Oxford City	5-3
Ruislip Manor v Billericay Town	1-4
Yeading v Bishops Stortford	0-1

Fourth Round;

Match	Score
Billericay Town v Bishops Stortford	0-2
Boreham Wood v Leyton Pennant	5-1
Bognor Regis Town v Sutton United	1-2 (aet)
Kingstonian v Carshalton Athletic	2-3

Semi-Finals;

Match	Score
Boreham Wood v Bishops Stortford	4-1
Sutton United v Carshalton Athletic	1-1, 4-1 (aet)

Final; Sutton United v Boreham Wood 2-2 (aet), 4-3 penalties.

CARLTON TROPHY 1995-96

First Round;

Aveley v Harlow Town	6-2	Banstead Athletic v Windsor & Eton	2-0
Bracknell Town v Horsham	1-0	Chalfont St Peterv Croydon	1-0
Cove v Flackwell Heath	2-0	Hertford Town v East Thurrock United	0-2
Newbury Town v Metropolitan Police	**	*(Newbury Town removed from competition)*	
Southall v Saffron Walden Town	3-1	Wingate & Finchley v Harefield United	0-1
Witham Town v Clapton	1-4	Wivenhoe Town v Hornchurch	5-2

Second Round;

Aveley v Ware	0-1	Banstead Athletic v Camberley Town	6-1
Bracknell Town v Harefield United	2-1 (aet)	Canvey Island v Collier Row	3-2
Cove v Hampton	0-4	Dorking v Hungerford Town	1-6
East Thurrock United v Cheshunt	3-2	Egham Town v Leatherhead	1-2
Epsom & Ewell v Lewes	0-1	Hemel Hempstead v Edgware Town	3-0
Kingsbury Town v Clapton	2-5	Met Police v Chalfont St Peter	2-6
Northwood v Southall	6-1	Tring Town v Tilbury	1-5
Wealdstone v Bedford Town	1-0	Wivenhoe Town v Leighton Town	5-3

Third Round;

Banstead Athletic v Leatherhead	2-0	Bracknell Town v Lewes	2-0
Canvey Island v Clapton	1-0	E Thurrock Utd v Tilbury	2-2 *Abandoned*
Hungerford Town v Hampton	1-0	Northwood v Wealdstone	0-2
Ware v Hemel Hempstead	3-1 (aet)	Wivenhoe Town v Chalfont St Peter	5-1
Tilbury v East Thurrock United (Replay)	*2-0*		

Fourth Round;

Banstead Athletic v Bracknell Town	1-0	Tilbury v Ware	2-1
Wealdstone v Hungerford Town	1-2	Wivenhoe Town v Canvey Island	1-3

Semi-Finals;

Banstead Athletic v Tilbury	2-1 (aet)	Canvey Island v Hungerford Town	1-1, 2-1

Final; Canvey Island v Banstead Athletic 2-1

ICIS LEAGUE PREMIER DIV ATTENDANCE CHART 1995-96

HOME TEAM	1	2	3	4	5	6	7	8	9	10	11	12	13	14	15	16	17	18	19	20	21	22
1. Aylesbury U	*	451	855	703	469	501	424	859	440	531	809	396	503	739	259	402	426	606	715	778	895	812
2. B/Stortford	308	*	360	386	340	286	408	879	306	285	427	323	265	422	264	189	487	384	308	242	202	466
3. Boreham Wd	324	432	*	252	552	263	586	507	315	224	308	307	348	522	292	302	821	427	247	428	245	784
4. Bromley	264	208	231	*	637	201	584	469	264	204	419	259	310	636	326	254	298	361	205	401	285	357
5. Carshalton A	236	251	373	365	*	376	365	823	313	283	1025	501	389	842	352	404	603	794	429	245	374	641
6. Chertsey Tn	434	317	283	316	416	*	449	731	292	337	603	366	361	518	280	387	418	638	603	260	342	766
7. Dulwich Ham	324	260	402	706	457	380	*	1604	322	262	448	417	411	629	414	261	385	559	442	296	289	1289
8. Enfield	1344	773	777	1006	834	611	939	*	731	870	1023	802	982	904	765	744	1006	823	603	714	806	1117
9. Grays Ath	274	205	196	251	171	239	271	305	*	168	226	217	197	261	255	341	212	318	264	215	167	251
10. Harrow Boro	417	221	324	205	308	365	295	605	249	*	1212	253	260	338	198	111	318	339	243	360	256	489
11. Hayes	393	243	707	267	283	505	227	625	583	716	*	347	303	431	318	371	238	516	293	240	473	1537
12. Hendon	253	183	252	234	246	262	301	346	239	273	262	*	182	274	197	227	357	275	225	249	241	443
13. Hitchin Tn	418	436	511	373	384	291	281	611	369	304	164	209	*	365	292	299	443	313	331	256	201	523
14. Kingstonian	598	259	523	602	707	422	418	940	325	302	431	321	524	*	390	397	501	747	402	399	421	642
15. Molesey	150	120	125	120	180	220	190	405	115	120	200	190	142	310	*	180	190	275	240	130	110	300
16. Purfleet	156	173	174	268	210	238	293	517	231	162	181	169	156	248	129	*	163	262	127	102	123	302
17. St Albans C	695	603	727	485	702	551	751	1102	441	620	756	425	626	465	368	492	*	651	454	503	452	853
18. Sutton Utd	653	469	521	627	784	512	697	887	392	448	611	529	490	944	494	334	640	*	483	461	455	537
19. Walton & Her	266	215	202	238	245	409	232	451	239	247	302	267	186	402	212	170	281	445	*	203	185	406
20. Worthing	289	321	339	417	531	540	370	627	425	338	305	336	353	334	304	275	562	575	223	*	298	561
21. Yeading	181	148	262	183	170	356	260	432	104	189	405	202	160	281	155	110	245	260	136	120	*	403
22. Yeovil Town	2008	1629	1283	1869	1920	2417	1960	3804	1668	1942	2025	2306	1789	1953	1870	2267	2758	2818	1563	1602	1281	*

ICIS (Isthmian) LEAGUE Premier Division Ten Year Records

	86/7	87/8	88/9	89/0	90/1	91/2	92/3	93/4	94/5	95/6
Aylesbury United	-	-	-	3	3	7	10	12	4	11
Barking	8	19	10	20	21	-	-	-	-	-
Basingstoke Town	-	22	-	8	18	14	11	21	-	-
Bishop's Stortford	10	13	7	9	13	22	-	-	19	12
Bognor Regis Town	5	16	9	19	17	21	22	-	-	-
Boreham Wood	-	-	-	-	-	-	-	-	-	3
Bromley	11	2	14	21	-	12	17	15	6	19
Carshalton Athletic	15	9	4	10	9	8	4	6	12	6
Chertsey Town	-	-	-	-	-	-	-	-	-	15
Chesham United	-	-	-	-	-	4	1	4	20	-
Croydon	7	18	22	-	-	-	-	-	-	-
Dagenham	-	-	18	6	14	9	-	-	-	-
Dorking	-	-	-	-	-	-	-	20	-	-
Dulwich Hamlet	18	20	16	22	-	-	14	16	11	5
Enfield	-	-	-	-	2	2	3	2	1	2
Farnborough Town	3	9	8	2	-	-	-	-	-	-
Grays Athletic	-	-	5	5	6	15	6	14	18	17
Harrow Borough	6	12	19	18	20	18	8	9	10	9
Hayes	16	6	8	14	8	19	9	13	3	1
Hendon	4	10	12	12	15	17	11	11	17	14
Hitchin Town	20	21	-	-	-	-	-	8	5	18
Kingstonian	12	14	6	4	5	10	13	10	13	8
Leytonstone-Ilford	-	4	1	-	-	-	(see Redbridge)			
Leyton-Wingate	-	17	15	7	22	-	-	-	-	-
Marlow	-	-	20	17	7	6	15	3	21	-
Molesey	-	-	-	-	-	-	-	18	8	20
Purfleet	-	-	-	-	-	-	-	-	16	16
Redbridge Forest	-	-	-	11	1	-	-	-	-	-
St Albans City	14	15	17	15	16	13	2	7	7	7
Slough Town	3	3	3	1	-	-	-	-	2	-
Staines Town	-	-	-	16	19	20	20	-	-	-
Stevenage Borough	-	-	-	-	-	-	7	1	-	-
Sutton United	-	-	-	-	-	3	5	5	15	10
Tooting & Mitcham United	19	11	21	-	-	-	-	-	-	-
Walthamstow Avenue	22	-	-	-	-	-	(see Redbridge)			
Walton & Hersham	-	-	-	-	-	-	-	-	14	21
Windsor & Eton	13	7	13	13	12	11	21	-	-	-
Wivenhoe Town	-	-	-	-	10	16	18	22	-	-
Woking	-	-	-	-	4	1	-	-	-	-
Wokingham Town	17	5	11	2	11	5	16	19	22	-
Worthing	21	-	-	-	-	-	-	-	-	22
Wycombe Wanderers	1	-	-	-	-	-	-	-	-	-
Yeading	-	-	-	-	-	-	19	17	9	13
Yeovil Town	2	1	-	-	-	-	-	-	-	4
No of clubs competing	22	22	22	22	22	22	22	22	22	22

AYLESBURY UNITED

Formed: 1897 The Ducks

Back Row (L-R); Luke Longman, Ricky Sullivan, Matt Carmichael, Matt Hayward, Andy Hopping, Carl Hoddle, Kevin Davies, Mick Danzey, Stacy Joseph, Robert Boyce. Front; Paul Thawley (PHysio), Mark Newson, Robert Sharpe, Justin Skinner, Gary Phillips (Coach), Danny Honeyball, Gary Smith, Kieran Gallagher, Ron Schmidt (Kit). *Photo - The Bucks Herald*

Chairman: K.T. Arnold. **President:** J Durban **Vice Chairman:** R. Enright.
Secretary/Press Officer: Tony Graham c/o the club. (01296 88178 H / 436350 or 436525 B)
Coach: Gary Phillips **Football Development Manager:** Peter Wright **Physio:** Paul Thorley
Ground: The Stadium, Buckingham Road, Aylesbury HP20 2AQ (01296 436350/436525).
Directions: On A413 to Buckingham, just off ring road opposite Horse & Jockey PH. Arriving from Buckingham ground is on left - from all other directions follow Buckingham signs and ground on right. Half hour walk from Aylesbury rail and bus stations.
Capacity: 4,500. **Cover:** 1000. **Seats:** 400 **Floodlights:** Yes **Metal Badges:** Yes
Club Shop: Yes, selling prog, magazines, leisurewear, etc. Contact Debbie Gamage c/o The Club.
Colours: Green with white sleeves/Green/Green. **Change colours:** Amber& black.
Newsline: 0891 446 824 **Midweek home matchday:** Tuesday
Club Sponsors: Thrifty Car Rental. **Reserve Team's League:** No reserve team.
Previous Leagues: Bucks Contiguous 1897-1903/ South Eastern 03-07/ Spartan 07-51/ Delphian 51-63/ Athenian 63-76/ Southern 76-88/ GMV Conference 88-89.
Previous Grounds: Printing Works Ground 1897-1935/ Sports Stadium, Wendover Rd (ground name changed to The Stadium, Turnfurlong Lane) 35-85/ shared grounds 85-86.
Previous Name: Night School, Printing Works (merged in 1897).
Record Attendance: 6,000 v England 1988 *(at old ground: 7,500 v Watford, FA Cup 1st Rd 1951).*
Best FA Trophy season: Quarter-Final replay 80-81.
Best FA Cup season: 2nd Rd 88-89 89-90 91-92 (1st Rd 51-52 85-86 86-87 87-88 91-92).
League clubs defeated in FA Cup: Southend Utd 89-90.
Record Fees - Paid: £15,000 for Glenville Donegal (Northampton, 1990)
Received: £35,000 for Glenville Donegal (Maidstone Utd, 1991).
Players progressing to Football League: Ray Mabbutt (Bristol Rovers), Phil Barber (Crystal Palace 1986)
Clubhouse: Pub hours, but shut during matches. Function room available for hire (01296 436891). Bar snacks available.
Club Record Scorer: Cliff Hercules
Record Appearances: Cliff Hercules.
95-96 P.o.Y.: Michael Danzey.
95-96 Top scorer: Michael Danzey.
Local Newspapers: Bucks Herald, Bucks Advertiser, Herald & Post.
Local Radio Stations: Three Counties Radio, Chiltern Radio, Fox FM, Mix 96.
Honours: Southern Lg 87-88 (Mids Div R-up 84-85, Sth Div R-up 79-80), Athenian Lg Div 2 R-up 67-68, Delphian Lg 53-54 (R-up 52-53, Lg Cup 59-60), Spartan Lg 08-09 (R-up 52-53, West Div 28-29 (R-up 45-46), Div 1 38-39 (R-up 34-35)), Berks & Bucks Snr Cup 13-14 85-86),Isthmian League Cup 94-95, Isthmian Charity Shield 95-96.

PROGRAMME DETAILS:
Pages: 36 **Price:** £1.20.
Editor: Dave Gamage
(01844 342308)

AYLESBURY UNITED'S 1995-96 CAMPAIGN

DATE		OPPONENTS	COMP	RES		GATE	GOALSCORERS
Aug 12	A	Dulwich Hamlet	IL	L	0-1	394	
19	H	Yeovil Town	IL	W	3-1	812	Bashir, Danzey, Pluckrose
23	A	Harrow Borough	IL	D	3-3	417	Williams, Hercules, Caesar
26	A	Molesey	IL	W	4-1	150	Shea, Hobbs, Caesar, Bashir
29	H	Bromley	IL	W	3-0	703	Danzey, Pluckrose, Caesar
Sept 2	H	Walton & Hersham	IL	D	0-0	713	
16	H	Yeading	IL	D	1-1	875	Caesar
23	A	Hitchen Town	IL	W	3-0	418	Pluckrose, Hobbs, Hercules
30	A	Sutton United	IL	W	3-2	653	Hayward, Cobb, Hercules
Oct 3	A	Chertsey Town	IL	W	3-0	434	Shea, Cobb, Hercules
7	H	Boreham Wood	IL	L	1-3	855	Caesar
14	H	Kingstonian	IL	L	0-1	739	
21	H	Stevenage Borough	FAC	L	1-3	1480	Pluckrose
28	H	Grays Athletic	IL	D	2-2	490	Cobb, Caesar
31	A	Chesham United	GIC	W	3-2	339	Smart, Caesar, Sullivan
Nov 11	H	Chesham United	CC	W	3-1	455	Heard, Williams, Hercules
18	A	St. Albans City	IL	L	0-2	695	
25	A	Worcester City	FAT	L	0-3	863	
28	H	Purfleet	CC	L	0-1	242	
Dec 2	A	Hayes	IL	W	1-0	393	Caesar
9	H	Worthing	IL	D	1-1	778	Crown
16	A	Purfleet	IL	W	2-1	156	Hayward, Crown
Jan 3	H	Bishop's Stortford	IL	D	0-3	455	
6	A	Walton & Hersham	IL	L	1-2	266	Crown
9	H	St. Albans City	IL	W	2-0	531	Heard, Caesar
Feb 3	A	Bromley	IL	W	3-0	264	Caesar 2, Davies
10	H	Sutton United	ICIA	W	4-1	606	Sullivan, Crown, Davies 2
13	A	Carshalton Athletic	GIC	D	0-0	181	
24	A	Grays Athletic	IL	L	0-2	274	
Mar 2	H	Chertsey Town	IL	W	2-0	501	Hayward, Caesar
5	H	Croydon	GIC	W	2-1	246	Pluckrose 2
9	H	Hitchin Town	IL	W	2-1	503	Cobb, Haworth
12	H	Hendon	IL	W	1-0	396	Pluckrose
16	A	Boreham Wood	IL	D	2-2	324	Newman, Davies
23	A	Kingstonian	IL	D	1-1	598	Caesar
28	H	Kingstonian	GIC	L	1-3	260	Heard
30	H	Carshalton Athletic	IL	L	0-1	469	
Apr 2	A	Kingstonian	GIC	L	1-2	292	Heard
4	A	Dulwich Hamlet	IL	L	0-3	242	
6	A	Bishop's Stortford	IL	W	6-3	308	Smart, Pluckrose, Danzey, Cobb, Haworth, Caesar
8	H	Enfield	IL	L	2-3	859	Cobb 2
13	A	Hendon	IL	L	2-4	253	Newman, Davies
16	A	Yeovil Town	IL	L	2-3	2003	Pluckrose, Davies
20	H	Hayes	IL	L	1-3	809	Caesar
23	H	Molesey	IL	D	1-1	259	Hayward
27	A	Worthing	IL	W	3-1	289	Caesar, Haworth 2
30	A	Enfield	IL	D	3-3	1344	Newman, Shea, Haworth
May 2	A	Carshalton Athletic	IL	L	1-3	236	Bashir

AYLESBURY UNITED PLAYING SQUAD 1996-97

Goalkeepers: Gary Phillips (Barnet, Reading, Brentford, Barnet, WBA, Brighton)
Defenders: Mark Newson (Barnet, Fulham, AFC Bournemouth, Maidstone U, Charlton), **Justin Skinner** (Wimbledon), **Matt Hayward** (Leighton T, Aylesbury U, Thame U, Pitstone & Ivinghoe, Aylesbury U), **Ricky Sullivan** (Barton R, Aylesbury U, Hertford Heath)
Midfielders: Gary Smith (Barnet, Welling U, Wycombe W, Enfield, Colchester, Fulham), **Marc Field** (Baldock T), **Carl Hoddle** (Enfield, Woking, Barnet, Leyton O, B Stortford)
Forwards: Matt Carmichael (Darlington, Scunthorpe, Lincoln, Basingstoke T, Army), **Michael Danzey** (Camb.U, St. Albans C, Peterborough, Nottingham F), **Wayne Jones** (Local football, Aylesbury U)

1874 **BISHOP'S STORTFORD** Blues

Back Row (L-R): Matt Barnaby, Chris Moore, Karl Shuttlewood, Lee Claridge, Gavin King, Graeme Paxton, Ian Hollamby, Andy Walker, Martin Gardener, Roy Parkyn. Front Row: Russell Jackson, Dean Parratt, Pat Jackman, Will Cooper, Justin Cockman (Mascot), Andy Edmonds, Kevin Jordan.

Chairman: Gordon Lawrence **Vice-Chairman:** Mick Hancock **President:** B W A Bayford
Secretary: Graeme Auger, 58 Braziers Quay, South Street, Bishop's Stortford, Herts. CM23 3YW.
Team Manager: Dave Edwards **Coach:** Ray Wickenden. **Physio:** Micky Stevens
Gen Manager: John Radford **Press Officer:** Edward Stalley (01279 658536).
Ground: George Wilson Stadium, Rhodes Ave., Bishop's Stortford CM23 3JN (01279 654140(club)
Directions: M11 jct 8, A1250 towards town centre, left at crossroads into London Rd (A1184), right at mini-r'bout and cross railway bridge, right at next island (by garage), Rhodes Ave is 2nd left (5-10 mins from M11). By rail: BR W Anglia Line (London Liverpool Str.-Cambridge)
Capacity: 6,000 **Cover:** 1,770 **Seats:** 270 **Floodlights:** Yes **Metal Badges:** Yes
Club Shop: Full stock inc. scarves, badges and other souvenirs. Massive stock of programmes and books etc. Contact Andy Stalley (01279 658536).
Cols: White & blue stripes/blue/blue **Change colours:** Yellow/white/yellow. **Sponsors:** TBA
Previous Leagues: East Herts 1896-97 02-06 19-21/ Stansted & Dist. Lg 06-19/ Herts County 21-25 27-29/ Herts & Essex Border 25-27/ Spartan 29-51/ Delphian 51-63/ Athenian 63-73.
Midweek matchday: Tuesday **Reserve League:** Essex & Herts Border Comb.
Record Attendance: 6,000 v Peterborough United, F.A. Cup 2nd Rd 1972 & v Middlesbrough FA Cup 3rd Rd replay, 1983
Best FA Cup season: 3rd Rd replay (see above). 1st Rd 70-71 72-73 74-76 81-83 84-87.
League clubs betean in FA Cup: Reading 82-83.
Record win: 11-0; Nettleswell & Butntmill, Herts Jun Cup 2nd Rd 1911
Record defeat: 0-13 v Cheshunt (H), Herts Senior Cup 1st Rd 9/1/26.
Record Fees - Paid: £1,500 for Phil Hopkins (Walthamstow Ave., 1984)
Received: £10,000 for Carl Hoddle (Leyton Orient, 1989)
Players progressing to Football Lge: B Atkinson (Watford) 54), R Johnson (Chelsea) 54, P Burridge (Crystal Pal.) 56, P Phelan (Southend) 61, M Hollow (Orient 62), P Phillips (Luton 69), T Baker (Colchester) 86, T Sorrell (Maidstone, Colchester, Barnet) 88, C Hoddle (Leyton O., Barnet) 89, T English (Colchester) 89.L Fortune-West (Gillingham) 95, L Braithwaite (Exeter City) 96.
Clubhouse: Open matchdays and Mondays (bingo). Available for hire (weddings/functions).
Club Record Scorer: (Since 1929) Jimmy Badcock 123
Club Record Appearances: Phil Hopkins 543.
95-96 Captain: Lee Claridge
95-96 P.o.Y.: Dean Parratt. **95-96 Top scorer:** Andy Walker.
Press: B.Stortford Gazette, Herts & Essex Observer, Herald & Post.
Radio Stations: BBC Essex, Essex Radio, Breeze AM, 1017.
Honours: FA Tphy 80-81, FA Amtr Cup 73-74, Isthmian Lg Div 1 80-81 94-95 (Lg Cup 88-89, Full Mem. Cup 90-91), Prem. Inter Lg Cup 89-90, Athenian Lg 69-70 (R-up 66-67, Div 1 65-66, Div 2 R-up 64-65), Delphian Lg 54-55, London Snr Cup 73-74, Herts Snr Cup 58-59 59-60 63-64 70-71 72-73 73-74 75-76 86-87, E Anglian Cup 81-82, Herts Charity Cup 62-63 65-66 73-74 81-82 82-83 84-85 87-88, Herts Charity Shield 54-55, Herts I'mediate Cup(res) 94-95, Eastern F'lit Cup 84-85, Essex F'lit Cup 67-68, Essex & Herts Border Comb(W) 81-82 88-89 (R-up(2) 92-94), Fred Budden Tphy R-up 78-79 90-91 92-93.

PROGRAMME DETAILS
Pages: 32 **Price:**£1.
Editor: Roy Kemp.
(01279 659856)

BISHOPS STORTFORD'S 1995-96 CAMPAIGN

DATE		OPPONENTS	COMP	RESULT		GATE	GOALSCORERS
Aug 15	H	Boreham Wood	HCC	L	0-2	183	
19	H	Sutton United	IL	L	1-3	384	Cooper
22	A	Dulwich Hamlet	IL	L	1-4	260	Burns
26	A	Walton & Hersham	IL	W	2-0	215	Walker, Parkyn
Sept 2	H	Bromley	IL	D	1-1	386	Braithwaite
5	A	Edgeware Town	LC	W	2-0	137	Hollamby 2
9	H	Boston Town	FAC	D	2-2	352	Cooper, Hollamby
12	A	Boston Town	FAC	L	2-5	183	Hollamby 2
16	H	Worthing	IL	D	0-0	242	
23	A	Yeovil Town	IL	W	3-1	1,629	Hollamby, Braithwaite, Walker
26	H	Purfleet	IL	D	1-1	189	Walker
30	A	Hendon	IL	D	1-1	183	Jordan
7	A	Molesey	IL	L	1-2	120	Cooper
14	A	Abingdon Town	FAT	D	1-1	182	Braithwaite
17	H	Abingdon Town	FAT	W	5-1	208	Hollamby 2, Forbes, Parratt
21	A	Grays Athletic	IL	W	2-0	205	Braithwaite, Walker
28	H	Enfield	IL	L	0-1	879	
31	H	Staines Town	LC	W	3-1	192	Barnaby, Parkyn, Braithwaite
Nov 4	A	Trowbridge Town	FAT	L	0-1	361	
11	H	St. Albans City	IL	W	3-2	487	Adekola, Walker, Jordan
18	H	Kingstonian	IL	L	2-3	422	Adekola 2
21	H	Hitchin Town	CC	W	3-0	201	Adekola, Cooper, og
25	H	Walton & Hersham	IL	W	2-0	308	Adekola 2
Dec 2	H	Boreham Wood	IL	L	0-2	360	
9	A	Harrow Borough	IL	D	0-0	221	
12	A	Hitchin Town	LC	L	1-4	121	Walker
16	H	Yeading	IL	W	3-1	202	Walker, Cooper
23	A	Bromley	IL	W	2-0	208	Claridge, Edmonds
Jan 3	A	Aylesbury United	IL	D	0-0	451	
6	H	Yeovil Town	IL	D	2-2	466	Jackman, Walker
13	H	Dulwich Hamlet	IL	L	1-2	408	Edmonds
16	A	Yeading	CC	W	1-0	71	Edmonds
20	A	Sutton United	IL	L	1-2	469	Walker
30	A	Hitchin Town	HSC	L	1-4	192	Edmonds
Feb 3	A	Purfleet	IL	W	2-1	173	Hollamby, Parkyn
10	H	Hendon	IL	W	3-1	323	Hollamby, Shuttlewood, Conroy
17	A	Worthing	IL	W	1-0	321	Conroy
24	A	Enfield	IL	W	1-0	773	Shuttlewood
27	A	Billericay Town	CC	W	2-0	202	Claridge, Wardley
Mar 2	H	Grays Athletic	IL	W	2-0	306	Parratt, Cooper
5	A	Hayes	IL	L	1-3	243	Wardley
9	A	Chertsey Town	IL	L	0-3	317	
16	H	Molesey	IL	W	4-0	264	Cooper 2, Roberts, Wardley
19	A	Carshalton Athletic	IL	L	0-2	251	
23	H	Hayes	IL	L	1-2	427	Shuttlewood
26	A	Boreham Wood	IL	L	1-4	182	Parratt
30	A	St. Albans City	IL	L	0-3	603	
Apr 2	H	Hitchin Town	IL	D	2-2	265	Conroy, Cooper
6	H	Aylesbury United	IL	L	3-6	308	Shuttlewood 2, Walker
8	A	Hitchin Town	IL	D	1-1	436	Roberts
13	H	Carshalton Athletic	IL	L	0-2	340	
16	A	Kingstonian	IL	L	1-2	259	Claridge
20	A	Boreham Wood	IL	W	1-0	432	Parratt
23	H	Chertsey Town	IL	W	3-1	246	Cooper, Conroy 2
27	H	Harrow Borough	IL	L	2-3	285	Roberts, Conroy
May 4	A	Yeading	IL	W	4-2	148	Cooper 2, Walker, Forbes

BISHOP'S STORTFORD PLAYING SQUAD 1996-97

Goalkeepers: Gavin King (Cheshunt)
Defenders: Kevin Jordan (Southend, Tottenham (T)), **Karl Shuttlewood** (Worthing, Saffron Walden T, Sawbridgeworth T, B Stortford, Stansted, Saffron Walden T), **Graham Paxton** (Sawbridgeworth T, Norwich, QPR), **Lee Claridge** (Stansted, Harlow T), **Stuart Wardley** (Saffron Walden T), **Pat Jackman** (Enfield, Chesham U, Harrow B, St. Albans C, Dagenham, B Stortford, Leyt & Ilf, Kingsbury T)
Midfielders: Scott Forbes (Youth team), **Will Cooper** (Dag & Red), **Russell Jackson** (Egham T, RC Warwick, Hinckley, Hinckley T, Nuneaton B, Coventry), **John Ridout** (Enfield, Purfleet, Enfield, Harrow B, Parmitarians, Leyton O)
Forwards: Andy Walker (Saffron Walden T, B Stortford, Stevenage B, Harlow T, Boreham Wood, Grays A, Harlow T, San Diego Sockers (USA), Harlow T), **Steve Conroy** (Hitchin T, Aylesbury U, Stevenage B, Hitchin T, Harrow B, Kingstonian, Hitchin T, Chesham U, St. Albans C, Hemel Hempstead, Colchester), **Ian Hollamby** (Clavering, B Stortford), **Richard Cherry** (Canvey Is, Bromley, Grays A, Purfleet, Enfield, Hendon, Kingstonian, Redbridge F, Grays A, Barking, Woodford T, Colchester, Gillingham)

Formed: 1948

BOREHAM WOOD

The Wood

Marc Liburd, of Boreham Wood, cuts in from the right during the match against Dover.

Photo: Clive Butchins.

Chairman: Phil Wallace **President:** W F O'Neill.
Secretary: Bob Nicholson, 56 Newcombe Road, Shenley, Radlett, Herts WD7 9EJ (01923 856077).
Manager: Bobby Makin **Asst Manager:** Alan Carrington **Coach:** Nick Ironton.
Press Officer: John D Gill (0181 723 6407) **Physio:** Dave Dickens
Ground: Meadow Park, Broughinge Road, Boreham Wood, Herts WD6 5AL (0181 953 5097).
Directions: A1 towards London from M25, 1st turn off for Boreham Wood, head for town centre, into into Brook Rd at r'bout before town centre, Broughinge Rd is 1st left. 1 mile from Elstree & Boreham Wood station (Thameslink), then bus 292 or 107 to Red Lion (5 minutes walk).
Capacity: 4,502 **Cover:** 1,568. **Seats:** 500. **Floodlights:** Yes **Metal Badges:** Yes
Club Shop: Yes, selling old and new programmes, replica shirts, scarves, hats, magazines, club badges etc. Contact: Dell Ward.(0181363 7345).
Colours: White/black/red **Change colours:** Red/red/black
Previous Leagues: Mid Herts 48-52/ Parthenon 52-57/ Spartan 56-66/ Athenian 66-74.
Previous Ground: Eldon Avenue 1948-63
Previous Names: Boreham Wood Rovers and Royal Retournez, amalgamated in 1948
Midweek home matchday: Tuesday **Sponsors:** L. & M. Foods/ Wansons.
Record Attendance: 2,500 v St Albans, F.A. Amateur Cup 70-71.
Best F.A. Cup season: 1st Rd replay (v Swindon) 77-78. Also 1st Rd (v Southend) 73-74.
Best F.A.Trophy season: Quarter Finals 1995-96. Replay at Chorley 3-4.
Players progressing to Football League: Colin Franks (Watford & Sheff Utd), Charles Ntamark (Walsall).
Clubhouse: (0181 953 5097). Holds 250, open normal pub hours. Hall available for hire. Sandwiches, filled rolls, hot pasties etc available.
Club Record Goalscorer: Micky Jackson 208
Club Record Appearances: Steve Waller 575
95-96 Captain: Billy Harrigan.
95-96 Player of the Year: Billy Harrigan.
95-96 Top scorer: Tony Samuels.
Local Newspapers: Boreham Wood Times, Watford Observer, Herts Advertiser.
Local Radio Stations: Chiltern Radio.
Honours: FA Amateur Cup 3rd Rd replay 70-71, Isthmian Lg.Div I Champions 94-5, Isthmian Lg Div 2 76-77 (Yth Cup R-up 80-81), Athenian Lg 73-74 (Div 2 68-69, Div 1 R-up 69-70), Spartan Lg R-up 65-66, Herts Senior Cup 71-72 (R-up 66-67 74-75 79-80 87-88), Herts Junior Cup 51-52, Parthenon Lg 55-56 (R-up(2) 53-55 56-57, Herts Charity Shield 64-65, Herts Intermediate Cup 69-70, Herts Charity Cup(5) 80-81 83-84 85-86 88-90 (R-up 71-72 84-85 86-87 90-91 91-92 92-93), London Senior Cup R-up 89-90, London Intermediate Cup 70-71, Neale Trophy 69-70, Essex & Herts Border Comb 72-73 (Lg Cup 72-73, Western Div R-up 82-83 89-90), Mithras Cup 76-77, Middx Border Lg 81-82 (Lg Cup 79-80), Wallspan Floodlit 86-87.

PROGRAMME DETAILS:
Pages: 32 Price: £1.
Editor: J D Gill
(0181 723 6407)

BOREHAM WOOD'S 1995-96 CAMPAIGN

DATE		OPPONENTS	COMP	RESULT		GATE	GOALSCORERS
Aug 19	H	Yeading	IL	D	1-1	245	Harrigan
23	A	Molesey	IL	W	2-1	125	Joyce, Liburd
26	A	Hendon	IL	D	1-1	252	D.Samuels
Sept 2	H	Sutton United	IL	L	0-1	472	
4	A	Purfleet	GIC1	W	1-0	127	A.Samuels
9	H	Chalfont St.Peter	FAC 1Q	W	1-0	151	Joyce
16	H	Bromley	IL	W	3-1	252	Nisbet, Stein, Prutton
19	A	Enfield	IL	W	2-0	777	Joyce 2
23	H	Staines Town	FAC 2Q	L	0-1	314	
26	H	Harrow Borough	IL	W	3-2	224	Joyce, Ashenden
30	A	Yeovil Town	IL	W	1-1	1283	A.Samuels
Oct 7	A	Aylesbury United	IL	W	3-1	855	Heffer, Stein, A.Samuels
14	H	Grays Athletic	IL	W	2-0	315	Joyce, Heffer
24	A	Leyton Pennant	LCC1	D	5-5	101	Joyce, Stein, Prutton, Samuels, og
28	H	Kingstonian	IL	D	0-0	522	
31	A	Bromley	GIC2	D	3-3	101	Joyce, A.Samuels, D.Samuels
Nov 4	A	Hitchin Town	IL	W	2-1	511	Stein 2
6	A	Purfleet	IL	L	0-1	176	
11	H	Carshalton Athletic	IL	L	2-3	552	Joyce, A.Samuels
14	H	Bromley	GIC2 rep	W	1-0	119	OG
18	A	Chertsey Town	IL	W	3-0	283	Hatchett, Joyce, A.Samuels
21	H	Hayes	IL	D	0-0	308	
25	H	Heybridge Swifts	FAUT 3Q	W	3-0	204	Joyce 2, A.Samuels
28	H	Barking	CC2	W	3-1	93	Joyce, Nisbet, Stein
30	H	Leyton Pennant	LCC1 rep	L	2-3	88	A.Samuels, Ahsenden
Dec 2	A	Bishops Stortford	IL	W	2-0	360	Nisbett 2
16	A	Worthing	IL	W	2-0	339	Stein, Prutton
19	A	Aldershot Town	GIC3	L	0-1	954	
23	H	Purfleet	IL	W	2-1	302	Hatchet, Stein
Jan 1	H	Dulwich Hamlet	IL	D	2-2	586	Nisbett, A.Samuels
6	A	Sutton United	IL	W	3-0	521	Stein, A.Samuels
13	H	Molesey	IL	L	0-1	292	
20	A	Cambridge City	FAUT1	W	2-1	287	Gentle2
23	A	Heybridge Swifts	CC3	W	2-0	116	Joyce, Heffer
Feb 3	A	Harrow Borough	IL	D	1-1	276	Gentle
10	H	Dover Athletic	FAUT2	W	2-1	506	Harrigan, Gentle
13	H	Walton & Hersham	IL	D	1-1	247	Gentle
17	A	Bromley	IL	W	1-0	231	Daly
24	A	Kingstonian	IL	L	0-1	523	
27	H	Leyton Pennant	CC4	W	5-1	102	Nisbet, Shaw, Miles 3
Mar 2	H	Chorley	FAUT3	D	1-1	525	Prutton
5	A	Chorley	FAUT3 rep	L	4-3	833	Fox, Hatchett, Heffer
16	H	Aylesbury United	IL	D	2-2	324	Harringan, Hatchett
19	H	Enfield	IL	W	4-1	507	Stein 2, A.Samuels 2
23	A	Carshalton Athletic	IL	D	0-0	373	
26	H	Bishops Stortford	CCSF	W	4-1	182	Fox 2, Nisbet, Miles
30	H	Hitchin Town	IL	W	1-0	348	Heffer
Apr 2	A	St.Albans City	IL	D	0-0	727	
6	A	Dulwich Hamlet	IL	W	2-0	402	Shaw, A.Samuels
8	H	St.Albans City	IL	W	2-0	821	Shaw, A.Samuels
10	A	Yeading	IL	W	3-0	266	Liburd, A.Samuels, Prutton
13	A	Hayes	IL	D	1-1	707	Liburd
16	H	Chertsey Town	IL	W	2-0	263	Liburd, Fox
20	H	Bishops Stortford	IL	L	0-1	432	
23	H	Hendon	IL	W	4-0	307	Gammons, Stein, A.Samuels 2
25	A	Grays Athletic	IL	W	2-1	196	A.Samuels, og
27	A	Walton & Hersham	IL	W	4-0	202	Stein 2, A.Samuels, Prutton
30	H	Yeovil Town	IL	L	0-2	784	
May 4	H	Worthing	IL	W	3-1	428	Stein 2, Liburd

BOREHAM WOOD PLAYING SQUAD 1996-97

Goalkeepers: Martin Taylor (B Stortford, Epping T, Woodford T, Hendon, Jyderup (Den), Charlton, Arsenal)

Defenders: Tony Joyce (Stevenage B, Staines T, Woking, Aldershot, QPR), **Gary Nisbet** (Collier Row, Walthamstow Pennant, Collier Row), **Steve Daly** (Wembley, Chalfont St. Peter, Ruislip Manor), **Barry Fox** (Grays A, Millwall), **Andy Pask** (Grays A, Dartford, Redbridge F, West Ham (T)), **Billy Harrigan** (B Stortford, Chesham U, Leyt & Ilf, Walthamstow Ave, B Stortford, Camb.U), **Dave Hatchett** (Enfield), **Paul Ferry** (Edgware T)

Midfielders: Andy Prutton (Harrow B, Dartford, Cheshunt, Wormley R), **Scott Ashenden** (Hendon, Southend), **Jason Shaw** (Harrow B, Dartford, Redbridge F, West Ham), **Steve Heffer** (Hendon, Grays A, Swindon, Southend, West Ham), **Robbie Gammons** (Heybridge S, Dag & Red, Barking, Purfleet, Aveley, Barking, Chesham U, Chelmsford C, Barking, Arsenal), **Paul Jordan** (Watford)

Forwards: Marc Liburd (Millwall, Watford (T)), **Dean Samuels** (Sutton U, Leyton, Collier Row), **Damon Miles** (Ware, Camb.C, Ware, Baldock T, Ware, B Stortford, Ware, Saffron Walden T, Ware, Stansted), **Tony Samuels** (Leyton, Collier Row, Bromley, Leyton-Wingate, Leyt & Ilf), **Terry Robbins** (Barnet, Welling U, Crawley T, Maidstone U, Gillingham, Tottenham)

Formed: 1892

BROMLEY

The Lilywhites

Bromley F.C. 1995-96: Back row,left to right: Carl Richards, Ian Rawlings, Steve Campbell, Curtis Hayes, Richard Cherry, Olue Adedijl. Front row: Dean Francis, Frank Coles, Andy Silk, Mark Loveday, Ian Dawes. Photo: Andrew Chitty

Chairman: Glyn Beverly. **President:** G T Ransom, AM Inst BE, MHTTA
Secretary: Ron McLean, 60 Fawkham Ave., New Barn, Nr.Longfield, Kent.DA3 7HE. (01474 709495).
Manager: George Wakeling **Asst Manager:** N/A **Coach:** John Kane.
Press Officer: N/A **Physio:** J De Palma
Ground: Hayes Lane, Bromley, Kent BR2 9EF (0181 460 5291 or 0181-313-3992).
Directions: One mile from Bromley South (BR). Buses 316, 146 and 119 pass ground. Junction 4 off M25, then A21 towards London.
Capacity: 8,500 **Cover:** 4,000 **Seats:** 2,000 **Floodlights:** Yes **Club Shop:** Yes.
Colours: White/black/black. **Change colours:** All red
Previous Leagues: South London - 1894/ Southern 94-96/ London 96-98 99-1901/ West Kent 01-04/ Southern Suburban 04-07/ Kent 1898-99 11-14/ Spartan 07-08/ Isthmian 08-11/ Athenian 19-52.
Prev. Grounds: White Hart Field Cricket Ground, Widmore Rd (pre-1904)/ Plaistow Cricket Field 1904-37.
Midweek home matchday: Tuesday **Reserve Team's League:** Suburban
Record Attendance: 12,000 v Nigeria, 1950.
Newsline: 0891 122 904.
Best FA Trophy season: Second Round 91-92.
Best FA Cup season: 2nd Rd replay v Scarborough 37-38, Lincoln 38-39, Watford 45-46.
Record Fees - Paid: Undisclosed
Received: £50,000 for Jon Goodman (from Millwall 90)
Players progressing to Football League: Roy Merryfield (Chelsea), Stan Charlton (Arsenal 1952), Ron Heckman (Orient 1955), John Gregory (West Ham 1951), Bill Lloyd (Millwall 1956), Brian Kinsey (Charlton 1956), Harold Hobbs (Charlton & England), Matt Carmichael (Lincoln 1990), Leslie Locke (QPR 1956), Jon Goodman (Millwall).
Clubhouse: Open matchdays. Food available.
Club Record Goalscorer: George Brown 570 (1938-61)
Club Record Appearances: George Brown
95-96 Captain: Frank Coles. **95-96 P.o.Y.:** Ollie Adeiji.
95-96 Top scorer: Dean Wordsworth.
Local Newspapers: Bromley Times (01474 363363).
Local Radio: Radio Kent, Bromley Hospital Radio, Bromley Local Radio.
Honours: FA Amateur Cup 10-11 37-38 48-49, Isthmian League(4) 08-10 53-54 60-61 (R-up 52-53 55-56 87-88, Div 1 R-up 79-80 85-86 90-91, Prince Phillip 5-a-side Cup 1979), Athenian League 22-23 48-49 50-51 (R-up 35-36), London League Div 2 1896-97, Spartan League 07-08, London Snr Cup 09-10 45-46 50-51, Kent Senior Cup 49-50 76-77 91-92, Kent Amateur Cup(12) 07-08 31-32 35-37 38-39 46-47 48-49 50-51 52-53 53-55 59-60. London Challenge Cup 1995-96.

PROGRAMME DETAILS:
Pages: 32 **Price:** 80p
Ed: John Self.
(0181 402 2391)

BROMLEY'S 1995-96 CAMPAIGN

DATE		OPPONENTS	COMP	RESULT		GATE	GOALSCORERS
Aug 12	H	Hayes	IL	L	0-1	419	
19	A	Grays Athletic	IL	W	3-0	251	J. Francis (P) 2, Sharman
22	H	Kingstonian	IL	D	1-1	661	Rawlings
26	H	Carshalton A.	IL	L	1-2	637	Quail
29	A	Aylesbury U.	IL	L	0-3	703	
Sept 2	A	Bishop's Storford	IL	D	1-1	397	J. Francis (P)
9	H	Herne Bay	FAC	W	3-1	386	Coles, Quail, J. Francis (P)
16	A	Boreham Wood	IL	L	1-3	252	Quail
23	A	Welling United	FAC	D	2-2	722	J. Francis (P), Quail
26	H	Welling United	FAC	D	3-3	451	Brown 2, J. Francis (P)
30	H	Hitchin Town	IL	L	0-2	310	
Oct 2	A	Welling United	FAC	W	2-1	701	Adedeji, Brown
7	H	Sittingbourne	FAC	D	1-1	692	Keen
11	A	Sittingbourne	FAC	L	2-3	1030	J. Francis (P), Silk
14	H	Molesey	IL	L	1-3	326	Brown
21	A	Hendon	IL	L	0-2	236	
28	H	Yeovil Town	IL	L	1-5	376	Coles
Nov 4	A	Enfield	IL	L	0-5	1006	
7	A	Aldershot	IL	L	0-3	1193	
11	H	Yeading	IL	W	1-0	280	Dennis
18	A	Walton & Hersham	IL	L	1-3	242	Dennis
25	H	Oxford City	FAT	D	1-1	183	Cherry
28	A	Oxford City	FAT	L	2-3	248	D. Francis, Cherry
Dec 2	A	Worthing	IL	D	2-2	417	Richards 2
5	A	Dulwich Hamlet	LCC	W	2-1	137	Cherry, Coles
16	A	St. Albans City	IL	L	0-5	485	
19	H	Millwall	RSC	D	1-1	88	Cherry
23	H	Bishop's Stortford	IL	L	0-2	208	
26	A	Dulwich Hamlet	IL	L	1-4	626	Coles
Jan 6	A	Hayes	IL	L	1-5	267	Antone
9	H	Millwall	KSC	W	4-1	183	J. Francis (P), Gordon, Campfield
13	A	Kingstonian	IL	W	1-0	602	Richards
16	H	Barking	KSC	W/O			
20	H	Grays Athletic	IL	D	2-2	264	Cherry (P), Brown
31	A	Harrow Borough	IL	W	3-1	206	Coles, Cherry, Samuels
Feb 3	H	Ayelsbury Utd	IL	L	0-3	264	
10	A	Hitchin Town	IL	L	1-2	373	Dennington
13	H	Gillingham	KSC	D	1-1	96	Keen (P), (lost 2-4 on pens)
17	H	Boreham Wood	IL	L	0-1	231	
24	A	Yeovil Town	IL	L	3-4	1869	Bunter, Coles, Silk
27	H	Purfleet	IL	L	0-2	262	
Mar 2	H	Hendon	IL	L	2-5	258	Wordsworth 2
5	H	Sutton	IL	L	2-3	341	Wordsworth, Silk
9	A	Molesey	IL	L	2-3	160	Campfield, Coles
16	H	Harrow Borough	IL	W	5-1	207	Wordsworth 3, Tomkins, Coles
19	H	Chertsey Town	IL	D	3-3	201	Wordsworth, Timkins, Antone
23	A	Yeading	IL	L	0-3	183	
26	H	Walton & Hersham	IL	W	3-2	205	Dennington (P), Brown, Wordsworth
30	H	Enfield	IL	L	0-1	469	
Apr 1	A	Tooting & Mitcham	LCC	W	1-0	270	Silk
6	A	Chertsey	IL	W	2-0	216	Tompkins, Dennington
8	H	Dulwich Hamlet	IL	L	0-2	584	
13	A	Sutton United	IL	W	3-1	627	Brown, Tompkins, Dennington
16	H	St. Albans City	IL	W	1-0	298	Tompkins
20	H	Worthing	IL	W	3-2	401	Tompkins 2, Uvieghara
22	A	Carshalton A.	IL	D	0-0	365	
27	A	Purfleet	IL	D	1-1	268	Wordsworth
May 1	N	Leyton Pennant	LCC	W	3-2		J. Francis, Rawlings, Brown

BROMLEY PLAYING SQUAD 1996-97

Goalkeepers: Dave Wietecha (Millwall), **Curtis Hayes** (Metrogas)

Defenders: Keith Sharman (Barking, Leyton O, Clapton), **Dean Francis** (Youth team), **John Raffington** (Molesey, Dulwich Hamlet, Bromley, Carshalton A, Sutton U, Hendon, Carshalton A, Epsom & Ewell, Carshalton A, Croydon), **Ollie Adedeji** (Boreham Wood, Bromley, Finchley), **Ricky Antoine** (Charlton (T)), **Steve Campfield** (Tonbridge, Bromley), **Ian Rawlings** (Leyton-Wingate, Leyton O), **Paul Campbell** (Charlton)

Midfielders: Bobby Dennington (Tooting & Mitcham U, Bromley, Tooting & Mitcham U, Bromley, Leyton-Wingate), **Frank Coles** (Enfield, Leyton-Wingate, Leyt & Ilf, Dagenham, Leyt & Ilf, Charlton), **Paul Bunter** (Clapton, Fisher A, Horley T, Crystal Palace)

Forwards: Dean Wordsworth (Welling U, Dag & Red, Greenwich B), **Liburd Henry** (Welling U, Dag & Red, Welling U, Woking, Gillingham, Maidstone U, Watford, Leyt & Ilf, Millwall, Rainham T, Colchester), **Micky Brown** (Sutton U, Bromley, Wealdstone, Tooting & Mitcham U, Dulwich Hamlet, Croydon), **Mark Tompkins** (Tooting & Mitcham U, Fisher A, Corinthian, Dulwich Hamlet, Darenth Heathside, AFC Eltham), **Neil Wareham** (Greenwich B)

1903 CARSHALTON ATHLETIC Robins

Robins before the victory over holders Woking in the FA Trophy. *Photo - Eric Marsh.*

Chairman: Mike Dawes. **Vice Chairman:** Keith Dawes.
Joint-Presidents: Wally Stephenson and Bill Plumbridge.
Secretary: Bill Miller, 94 Craddocks Avenue, Ashtead, Surrey KT21 1PG (01372-272992).
Manager: Tony Jennings. **General Manager:** Fred Callaghan. **Coach:** TBA
Press Officer: Clive Allard. **Physio:** TBA **Commercial Manager:** John Carpentiere.
Ground: War Memorial Sports Ground, Colston Av, Carshalton SM5 2PW (0181 642 8658).
Directions: Turn right out of Carshalton BR Station, and Colston Avenue is first left. Entrance 150 yards on right. London Transport bus 151 from Morden to Wrythe Green Lane.
Capacity: 8,000 **Cover:** 4,500 **Seats:** 240 **Floodlights:** Yes **Metal Badges:** Yes.
Club Shop: Yes, selling hats, scarves, T-shirts, programmes and various football souvenirs.
Colours: White (maroon trim)/maroon/maroon. **Change colours:** Maroon/white.
Prev. Lges: Southern Sub (pre-1911)/ Surrey Snr 22-23/ London 23-46/ Corinthian 46-56/ Athenian 56-73.
Previous Grounds: Wrythe Recreation Ground 1907-14/ Culvers Park 19-20.
Midweek matchday: Monday **Reserve League:** Suburban. **Club Sponsors:** T C Cleaning.
Record Attendance: 7,800 v Wimbledon, London Senior Cup.
Best FA Trophy season: 3rd Rd 80-81 (lost 0-3 at home to Mossley (eventual Runners-up)).
Best FA Cup season: 2nd Rd 82-83, lost 1-4 at Torquay. (1st Rd 69-70 87-88).
Record win: 13-0 v Worthing, Loctite Cup Third Round 28/2/91.
League clubs defeated in FA Cup: None.
Record Fees - Paid: £2,000 for Jimmy Bolton, 1990.**Received:** £15,000 for Curtis Warmington (Enfield).
Players progressing to Football League: Ernie Taylor (Newcastle, Blackpool, Manchester United), Billy Barragon (QPR), John McDonald (Notts County 1948), Frank George (Orient 1954), Thomas Williams (Colchester 1956), Alan Eagles (Orient 1957), Derek Razzell (QPR), Terry Stacey (Plymouth 1959), Roy Lunnes (Crystal Palace 1960), Les Burns (Charlton 1967), Ron Walker (Watford), Nobby Warren (Exeter), Gus Caesar (Arsenal), Darren Annon (Brentford) 1994, Ian Cox (Crystal Palace) 1994.
Clubhouse: Open every evening and lunchtime. Licenced bar, pool, darts, machines, discos on Saturday. Separate function hall (bookings taken). Food: sandwiches, rolls, burgers, hot dogs, teas, coffees and soft drinks. (0181 642 8658).
Club Record Goalscorer: Jimmy Bolton
Club Record Appearances: Jon Raffington and Jon Warden.
95-96 Captain: Andy Riley. **95-96 P.o.Y.:** Gary Bowyer.
95-96 Top scorer: Jimmy Bolton.
Club Newsline: 0891 446849.
Local Newspapers: Wallington & Carshalton Advertiser (668411), Carshalton Herald (6612221).
Local Radio Stations: Capital.
Hons: Isthmian League Div 2 Runners-up 76-77, Corinthian League 52-53 53-54, Surrey Senior League Runners-up 22-23, Surrey Senior Cup(3) 88-90 91-92, Surrey Senior Shield (Runners-up(2)), London Challenge Cup 91-92.

PROGRAMME DETAILS:
Pages: 14 Price: 80p
Editor: Andy Hill.

CARSHALTON ATHLETIC'S 1995-96 CAMPAIGN

DATE		OPPONENTS	COMP	RESULT		GATE	GOALSCORERS
Aug 19	H	Molesey	IL	W	4-0	352	Bassey, Hazel 2, og
22	A	Yeading	IL	W	3-0	170	Underwood, Vines, Salako
26	A	Bromley	IL	W	2-1	637	Lunn, Vines
29	A	Enfield	IL	L	0-4	836	
Sept 2	H	Hendon	IL	D	1-1	501	Vines
9	H	Sheppey United	FAC 1Q	W	3-1	283	Underwood, Vines, Salako
12	A	Walton and Hersham	IL	W	1-0	245	Hazel
16	H	Purfleet	IL	W	3-1	403	Bassey, Vines, Salako
23	H	Windsor and Eton	FAC 2Q	W	4-3	354	Hazel, Vines 2, Salako
25	H	Yeovil Town	IL	W	2-1	640	Salako 2
30	A	Harrow Borough	IL	W	1-0	279	Lunn
Oct 7	A	Gravesend & Northfleet	FAC 3Q	L	1-2	685	Salako
9	H	Kingstonian	IL	L	0-3	834	
14	H	Dulwich Hamlet	FAT 1Q	D	1-1	499	Hanlan
17	A	Dulwich Hamlet	FAT 1QR	D	1-1	295	Saunders
21	A	Worthing	IL	W	3-2	513	Vines, Ugbah, Salako
23	A	Dulwich Hamlet	FAT 1QR2	W	2-1	301	Bowyer, Vines
28	H	Hitchin Town	IL	D	1-1	389	Salako
Nov 4	H	Weymouth	FAT 2Q	W	5-1	379	Vines 3, Salako 2
11	A	Boreham Wood	IL	W	3-2	552	Vines, Salako 2
16	A	Dulwich Hamlet	IL	L	1-2	457	Salako
25	H	Braintree Town	FAT 3Q	D	1-1	309	Vines
28	A	Braintree Town	FAT 3QR	W	5-0	260	Robson, Vines, Salako, Brady, og
Dec 2	A	St Albans City	IL	L	0-3	702	
9	H	Chertsey Town	IL	W	3-1	376	Underwood, Vines, Salako
11	H	Kingstonian	SSC 1	D	1-1	301	Ugbah
16	A	Hayes	IL	W	2-1	283	Saunders, Clark
19	A	Kingstonian	SSC 1R	W	2-1	307	Hanlan, Salako
23	H	Walton and Hersham	IL	W	5-2	429	Ugbah, Vines, Hanlan 2, Salako
Jan 1	H	St Albans City	IL	D	1-1	603	Hanlan
6	A	Hendon	IL	D	0-0	249	
8	H	Yeovil Town	CC 2	W	2-1	336	Hanlan 2
13	H	Yeading	IL	W	2-0	372	Ugbah, Vines
15	H	Thame United	CC 3	W	4-0	252	Underwood, Clark, Hazel, Hanlan
20	H	Woking	FAT 1	W	3-1	1485	Ugbah, Vines, Salako
23	A	Corinthian Casuals	SSC 1	W	3-2	200	Underwood, Hazel, Vines
Feb 3	A	Yeovil Town	IL	L	1-2	1920	Salako
10	H	Newport AFC	FAT 2	W	2-1	682	Ugbah, Salako
13	A	Aylesbury United	GIC 3	L	1-2		Clark
17	A	Purfleet	IL	L	1-2	210	Robson
24	A	Hitchin Town	IL	W	5-2	384	Hazel, Vines, Salako 3
Mar 2	A	Hyde United	FAT 3	L	2-3	854	Clark 2
5	A	Totting & Mitcham U.	SSC SF	L	2-4	150	Clark, Salako
9	A	Kingstonian	IL	L	1-2	707	Salako
12	A	Sutton United	IL	L	1-2	784	Vines
14	A	Kingstonian	CC 4	W	3-2		Bassey, Ugbah 2
16	H	Grays Athletic	IL	W	3-1	313	Vines, Salako 2
19	H	Bishop's Stortford	IL	W	2-0	251	Vines 2
23	H	Boreham Wood	IL	D	0-0	373	
26	A	Sutton United	CC SF	D	1-1		Vines
30	A	Aylesbury United	IL	W	1-0	469	Vines
Apr 1	H	Sutton United	CC SFR	L	1-4	564	Ugbah
4	H	Harrow Borough	IL	L	1-0	283	
8	H	Sutton United	IL	L	1-2	764	Daly
13	A	Bishop's Stortford	IL	W	2-0	340	Saunders, Daly
15	A	Grays Athletic	IL	L	0-1	179	
17	A	Molesey	IL	W	1-0	180	Salako
20	H	Enfield	IL	D	1-1	823	Hazel
22	H	Bromley	IL	D	0-0	365	
25	H	Worthing	IL	W	4-0	248	Saunders, May, Salako 2
27	A	Chertsey Town	IL	W	1-0	416	Kingsford
29	H	Dulwich Hamlet	IL	D	2-2	365	May, Saunders
May 2	H	Aylesbury United	IL	W	3-1	236	Salako, May, Vines
4	H	Hayes	IL	L	0-3	1025	

CARSHALTON ATHLETIC PLAYING SQUAD 1996-97

Goalkeepers: Les Cleevely (Yeovil T, Welling U, Carshalton A, Epsom & Ewell, Farnborough T, Wealdstone, Kungsbaka (Swe), Crystal Palace (A), Southampton (A)), **Adrian Blake** (Chertsey T, Kingstonian, Walton & H, Yeading, Feltham, Walton & H)
Defenders: Luke Morrish (Southend) **Eddie Saunders** (Civil Service FC), **Danny Bower** (Fulham), **Michael Brady** (Leatherhead, Carshalton A), **Solomon Eriemo** (Aldershot T, Kingstonian, Wealdstone, Leyton-Wingate, Walthamstow Ave, Leyt & Ilf)
Midfielders: Sean Daly (Sutton U, Croydon), **Gary Wilgoss** (Molesey, Dulwich Hamlet, Carshalton A, Whyteleafe), **Gary Bowyer** (Kingstonian, Carshalton A, Bromley, Whyteleafe, Carshalton A, Crystal Palace (T)), **Robin Beste** (Warlingham, Dulwich Hamlet, Chelsea (A)), **Simon Bassey** (Charlton (T)), **Mark Harmsworth** (Molesey, Yeading, Walton & H, Yeading, Hayes, Fisher A, Hampton, Kingstonian, Hampton, Epsom & Ewell), **Neil Robson** (Molesey, Carshalton A, Dorking, Sutton U, Epsom & Ewell, Sutton U)
Forwards: Francis Vines (Dulwich Hamlet, Kingstonian, Molesey), **Andy Salako** (Bromley, Tonbridge, St. Albans C, Croydon, Welling U, Charlton), **Matthew Hanlan** (Molesey, Dorking, Farnborough T, Dorking, Wycombe W, Sutton U), **Mark Wiggins** (Kingstonian, Carshalton A, Epsom & Ewell, Carshalton A), **Carl Williams** (Collier Row & Romford, Fulham), **Rod Braithwaite** (Chertsey T, Wealdstone, Kingstonian, Farnborough T, Fulham)

Formed: 1890

CHERTSEY TOWN

Curfews

Chertsey Town FC: Players included; Adrian Blake, Johnson Hippolyte, Jamie Beer, Trevor Argrave, Stuart Cash, Mark Nicholls, Chris Sparks, Byron Walton, Bradley Pratt, Paul Kelley, Jason Tucker, Mark Harper, Eamon O'Connor, Hamid Harrak. Mascots; Samuel Hyam & Adam Blake.

Photo - Andrew Chitty

Chairman: David Rayner **Vice Chairman:** Chris Mason **President:** Cllr Chris Norman
Press Officer/Secretary: Chris Gay, 23 Richmond Close, Frimley, Camberley, Surrey GU16 5NR (01276 20745).
Manager: Allan Cockram. **Physio:** Jean Lewis **Commercial Mgr:** Brian Walker
Ground: Alwyns Lane, Chertsey, Surrey KT16 9DW (01932 561774).
Directions: Alwyns Lane is off Windsor Street at north end of shopping centre. 10 mins walk from Chertsey (BR). London Country bus.
Capacity: 3,000 **Seats:** 250 **Cover:**1000 **Floodlights:** Yes
Colours: Blue & white stripes/white/white **Change colours:** All red.
Club Shop: Yes (manager - Martin Gay 0276 20745) **Sponsors:** Hayes Express Services.
Previous Ground: The Grange (pre-World War 1)/ The Hollows (pre-1929).
Midweek Matchday: Tuesday
Previous Leagues: West Surrey (pre-1899)/ Surrey Jnr 1899-1920/ Surrey Intermediate 20-46/ Surrey Snr 46-63/ Metropolitan 63-66/ Gtr London 66-67/ Spartan 67-75/ London Spartan 75-76/ Athenian 76-84/ Isthmian 84-85/ Combined Counties 85-86.
Club Metal Badges: Yes, priced at £2
Record Gate: 2,150 v Aldershot, Isthmian Lge Division Two 4/12/93.
Best FA Cup year: 3rd Qualifying Rd 92-93 (lost 1-3 at home to Kingstonian).
Record win: 10-1 v Clapton (H), Isthmian Lge Division Three, 91-92.
Record defeat: 1-12 v Bromley (H), FA Cup Preliminary Rd, 82-83.
Players progressing to Football League: Rachid Harkouk (Crystal Palace, Queens Park Rangers & Notts County), Peter Cawley (Wimbledon 1987), Lee Charles (Queens Park Rangers 1995).
Clubhouse: Open weekday evenings and weekend lunchtimes.
Club Record Goalscorer: Alan Brown 54, 1962-63.
95-96 P.o.Y.:
95-96 Top scorer: Johnson Hippolyte.
Local Press: Surrey Herald.
Hons: FA Vase QF 87-88 91-92, Isthmian League Cup 94-95 (Associate Members Trophy 94-95, Div 2 R-up 94-95, Div 3 R-up 91-92), Surrey Snr League 59-60 61-62 62-63 (League Cup 59-60 61-62), Combined Co's League R-up 85-86 (Concours Tphy 85-86), Surrey Snr Cup R-up 85-86, Spartan League & League Cup R-up 74-75.

PROGRAMME DETAILS:
Pages: 36 **Price:** £1.20.
Editor: Secretary

CHERTSEY TOWN'S 1995-96 CAMPAIGN

DATE		OPPONENTS	COMP	RES		GATE	GOALSCORERS
Aug 12	A	Yeading	IL	W	3-1	356	Harrak, Nabil, Tucker
19	H	Walton & Hersham	IL	L	1-3	603	Dawber
21	A	Purfleet	IL	W	3-1	203	Dawber, Walton, Hippolyte
26	A	Worthing	IL	W	2-1	540	Walton, Tucker
29	H	Sutton United	IL	D	1-1	638	Hippolyte
Sept 2	H	Yeovil Town	IL	L	1-3	766	Sparks
5	A	Aldershot Town	LC	L	2-3	1388	Tucker, Argrave
9	H	Shoreham	FAC	D	2-2	272	og, Hippolyte
12	A	Shoreham	FAC	W	3-1	236	Argrave, Nabil 2
16	H	Hendon	IL	W	3-1	366	Argrave 2, Sparks
23	A	Tooting & Mitcham	FAC	D	2-2	280	Savage, Walton
26	H	Tooting & Mitcham	FAC	L	1-2	327	Harrak
30	A	Dulwich Hamlet	IL	D	0-0	380	
Oct 3	H	Aylesbury United	IL	L	0-3	356	
7	H	Enfield	IL	L	0-3	731	
14	H	Poole Town	FAT	W	9-0	328	Hippolyte, Sparks 2, Savage 2, Argrave 2, B. Walton, og
24	H	Hayes	IL	L	1-3	603	Savage
28	A	St Albans City	IL	L	0-2	551	
Nov 4	H	Chesham United	FAT	D	2-2	518	Cash 2
7	A	Chesham United	FAT	W	3-2	395	Hippolyte, Tucker, O'Connor
11	A	Harrow Borough	IL	L	1-3	365	Tucker
14	A	Hitchin	IL	L	0-2	291	
18	H	Boreham Wood	IL	L	0-3	283	
21	H	Yeovil	Carltn	L	0-2	255	
25	H	Purfleet	FAT	L	0-1	266	
Dec 2	H	Grays Athletic	IL	W	2-0	292	B. Walton, Hippolyte
9	A	Carshalton Athletic	IL	L	1-3	386	Tucker
14	A	Egham Town	SSC	W	4-2	96	Savage, Nabil, Tucker, og
16	H	Molesey	IL	W	3-0	280	Argrave 2, Pratt
23	A	Yeovil Town	IL	L	0-1	2418	
26	H	Kingstonian	IL	W	2-1	518	Argrave 2
Jan 6	H	Yeading	IL	D	1-1	342	Nicholls
13	H	Purfleet	IL	W	2-1	387	Nicholls, Argrave
20	A	Walton & Hersham	IL	W	1-0	409	Tucker
23	H	Tooting & Mitcham	SSC	L	1-3	284	Kelly
Feb 3	A	Sutton United	IL	L	1-2	512	Argrave
10	H	Dulwich Hamlet	IL	L	0-1	449	
17	A	Hendon	IL	D	0-0	262	
24	H	St Albans City	IL	L	1-2	418	Nabil
Mar 2	A	Aylesbury United	IL	L	0-2	501	
9	H	Bishops Stortford	IL	W	3-0	317	Kelly, Tucker, Furnell
12	H	Worthing	IL	W	2-1	260	Argrave, Sparks
16	A	Enfield	IL	D	0-0	611	
19	A	Bromley	IL	D	3-3	201	Tucker, Argrave, Furnell
23	H	Harrow Borough	IL	L	1-5	337	Walton
30	A	Hayes	IL	L	0-4	507	
Apl 6	H	Bromley	IL	L	0-2	321	
8	A	Kingstonian	IL	W	2-0	422	Hippolyte, Argrave
13	H	Hitchin Town	IL	W	2-1	361	Sparks, Hippolyte
16	A	Boreham Wood	IL	L	0-2	263	
20	A	Grays Athletic	IL	L	1-2	239	Hippolyte
23	A	Bishop's Stortford	IL	L	1-3	246	Hippolyte
27	H	Carshalton Athletic	IL	L	0-1	416	
May 4	A	Molesey	IL	L	0-2	220	

CHERTSEY TOWN PLAYING SQUAD 1996-97

Goalkeepers: Michael Whittaker (St. Albans C), **John Cotter** (Brentford, Chertsey T)

Defenders: Stuart Cash (Stevenage B, Wycombe W, Chesterfield, Nottingham F, Halesowen T, Stourbridge, Bilston T), **Simon Webster** (St. Albans C, West Ham, Charlton, Sheffield U, Huddersfield, Tottenham H), **Chris Sparks** (Yeading, Brentford), **Mark Harper** (Egham T, Hampton, Bedfont), **Colin Davis** (Egham T, Chertsey T, Cove, Chertsey T), **Jamie Beer** (Brentford (T))

Midfielders: Hamid Harrak (Edgware T, Charlton, Southall), **Marco Ellerker** (Local football), **Detzi Kruszynski** (Crawley T, Hayes, St. Albans C, Coventry, Peterborough, Homburg (Ger), Saarbrucken (Ger), Brentford, Wimbledon, Homburg (Ger)), **Steve Scott** (Ruislip M, St. Albans C, Ruislip M, Chesham U, Yeading, Slough T, Hibernians (Malta), Harrow B, Farnborough T, Friska Viljor (Swe), QPR), **Allan Cockram** (St. Albans C, Farnborough T, Woking, Reading, Brentford, St. Albans C, Farnborough T, Bristol R, Tottenham H)

Forwards: Youness Nabil (F.A.S.(Morocco)), **Rod McKane** (St. Albans C, Tottenham H (J)), **Rob Peters** (St. Albans C, Woking, Carlisle, Brentford), **Johnson Hippolyte** (Yeading, Wealdstone, Chalfont St. Peter, Uxbridge, Hounslow), **David Pearce** (Hayes, Kingstonian, Hayes, Kingstonian, Wokingham T, Dagenham, Barnet, Harrow B, Wealdstone, Millwall)

1992 **DAGENHAM & REDBRIDGE** Reds or Daggers

Back Row (L-R); John Stannard (Physio), Nigel Hewes, Robin Taylor, Graham Reed, Steve Conner, Darren Williams, Paul Hague, Haul Gothard, Dominic Crookes, Neil Matthews, David Culverhouse, Kelly Haag, Clive Walker (Asst Mgr). Front; Bill Edmans (Kit), Jonathan Davidson, Deiniol Graham, Jason Broom, Gary Stebbing, Graham Carr (Mgr), Garry Bennett, Lee Wilson, Jay Devereux, Kenny Dyer.

Chairman: Dave Andrews **President:** Barry East
Secretary: Derek Almond, 149 Kings Head Hill, Chingford, London E4 7JG (0181 524 2689)
Manager: Ted Hardy **Asst Manager:** Clive Walker **Physio:** John Stannard
Press Officer: Steve Warren (0181 252 9417) **Safety Officer:** David Simpson
Ground: Victoria Road, Dagenham RM10 7XL (0181 592 7194. Fax: 0181 593 7227).
Directions: On A112 between A12 & A13. Buses 103 & 174 or, exit Dagenham East tube station, turn left and after approximately 500 yards take 5th turning left into Victoria Road.
Capacity: 5,500 **Seated:** 700 **Covered:** 3,000 **Floodlights:** Yes **Club Shop:** Yes
Club colours: Red & Blue/red/red
Change colours: Yellow/blue/yellow
Previous Grounds: None **Previous Leagues:** None
Club Sponsors: Barking & Dagenham Post
Reserve team league: Essex & Herts Border Combination.
Midweek home matchday: Monday
Record Attendance: 5,300 v Leyton Orient - FA Cup 1st Rnd - 14.11.92.
Record win: 8-1 v Woking (A), GMV Conference 19/4/94.
Record defeat: 0-5 v Stalybridge Celtic (A), GMV Conference 31/4/94, 0-5 v Northwich Victoria, GMV Conference 3/9/94.
Record transfer fee: £30,000 to Boston United for Paul Cavell & Paul Richardson - 1991.
Record transfer fee received: £65,000 from Watford for Andy Hessenthaler - 1991.
Past players progressed to the Football League: Juan Mequel DeSouza (Birmingham City) 1994; Ian Richardson (Birmingham City) 1995.
Daggersline: 0891 101965.
Fanzline: 0891 101955.
Local Newspapers: Dagenham Post, Waltham Forest Gazette,, Ilford Recorder
Local Radio: Breeze AM, BBC Radio Essex, Capital Radio.
Clubhouse: Open 11.00am -11.00pm on match days. Hot & cold food available.
95-96 Captain:
95-96 Top scorer:
95-96 Player of the Year:
Club record goalscorer: Paul Cavell - 47; Ian Richardson - 31; Jason Broom - 26.
Record appearances: Paul Watts -174; Steve Corner - 154; Jason Broom - 130.
Club Honours: None since amalgamation.

PROGRAMME DETAILS:
Pages: 36 Price: £1.20
Editor: John Hillier

DAGENHAM & REDBRIDGE'S 1995-96 CAMPAIGN

DATE		OPPONENTS	COMP	RES		GATE	GOALSCORERS
Aug 19	?	Stalybridge Celtic	GMVC	L	1-2	647	Haag
21	?	Farnborough Town	GMVC	D	2-2	784	Conner, Haag
26	?	Altrincham	GMVC	W	1-0	662	Shipp
28	?	Macclesfield Town	GMVC	L	1-3	1172	Shipp
Sept 2	?	Runcorn	GMVC	L	0-2	461	
4	?	Hednesford Town	GMVC	L	1-2	837	Greene
9	?	Hornchurch	FA Cup 1Q	W	4-0	589	Culverhouse, Greene, McDonough, Brown
12	?	Bromsgrove Rovers	GMVC	L	0-2	781	
16	?	Morecambe	GMVC	D	2-2	884	Haag, og
18	?	Slough Town	SC 1/1	L	0-2	408	
23	?	Berkhamsted	FA Cup2Q	W	2-1	350	Haag 2
26	?	Farnborough Town	GMVC	L	0-2	427	
30	?	Northwich Victoria	GMVC	L	0-3	646	
Oct 3	?	Slough Town	SC 1/2	D	0-3	456	
7	?	Purfleet	FA Cup 3Q	D	1-1	758	Dyer
9	?	Purfleet	FA3Q replay	L	1-2	688	Haag
14	?	Gateshead	GMVC	L	0-2	587	
28	?	Kidderminster Harriers	GMVC	W	4-2	756	Dyer, Matthews (2) Wilson
31	?	Dover Athletic	GMVC	W	1-0	1167	Howes
Nov 4	?	Kettering Town	GMVC	L	0-2	1616	
11	?	Gateshead	GMVC	L	0-4	712	
18	?	Halifax Town	GMVC	D	1-1	701	Bennett
20	?	Slough Town	GMVC	L	1-3	712	Prindiville
25	?	Telford United	GMVC	D	0-0	721	
Dec 2	?	Welling United	GMVC	D	1-1	806	Bennett
4	?	Leyton Orient	ESC	L	1-3	298	Crookes
9	?	Dover Athletic	GMVC	W	3-0	862	Derry, Worthington, Aldridge
11	?	Stevenage Borough	GMVC	L	1-2	762	Taylor
16	?	Southport	GMVC	L	1-2	904	Taylor
26	?	Woking	GMVC	D	2-2	2874	Worthington, Taylor
30	?	Bromsgrove Rovers	GMVC	D	2-2	1020	Worthington, Taylor
Jan 1	?	Woking	GMVC	D	0-0	1368	
6	?	Halifax Town	GMVC	L	0-8	729	
13	?	Southport	GMVC	L	1-2	964	Prindiville
20	?	Stevenage Borough	FAT 1	L	2-3	1348	Prindiville, Dyer
Feb 3	?	Kidderminster Harriers	GMVC	L	1-5	1439	
10	?	Morecambe	GMVC	D	2-2	787	Stringfellow, Taylor
17	?	Stalybirdge Celtic	GMVC	W	4-1	707	Derry, Worthington, Stringfellow, Wilson
24	?	Northwich Victoria	GMVC	L	0-1	727	
Mar 9	?	Slough Town	GMVC	L	0-5	912	
16	?	Telford United	GMVC	D	1-1	665	Stringfellow
23	?	Welling United	GMVC	D	0-0	823	
25	?	Bath City	GMVC	L	0-1	814	
Apr 6	?	Kettering Town	GMVC	L	1-2	22	
8	?	Bath City	GMVC	W	2-0	541	Crookes, Stringfellow
13	?	Hednesford Town	GMVC	D	0-0	946	
20	?	Runcorn	GMVC	L	2-3	755	Stringfellow
27	?	Macclesfield Town	GMVC	W	3-0	660	Broom, Stringfellow
29	?	Stevenage Borough	GMVC	L	0-1	2379	
May 4	?	Altrincham	GMVC	L	1-3	748	Prindiville

DAGENHAM & REDBRIDGE PLAYING SQUAD 1996-97

Goalkeepers: Darren Williams (Dover A, Welling U, Chelmsford C, Sorrento (Aust), Wealdstone, Barnet, Dagenham), **Paul Gothard** (Grays A, Chelmsford C, Colchester)

Defenders: Steve Conner (Dartford, Tilbury, East Thurrock U), **Glyn Creaser** (Rushden & D, Wycombe W, Barnet, Wolverton T, Kettering T, Milton Keynes C, Wolverton T), **Craig Davidson** (Chelmsford C, Southend, Aldershot), **Dean Johnson** (Youth team), **Dave Culverhouse** (Maidstone U, Southend, Tottenham)

Midfielders: Bartholomew Mas (Billericay T, Barking, Dag & Red, Maidstone U), **Gus Caesar** (Colchester, Airdrie, Bristol C, Camb.U, Arsenal), **John Stimson** (Aveley, Dag & Red, Leyt & Ilf), **Jason Broom** (Billericay T, Eton Manor), **Darren Barry** (Wembley, B Stortford, Cork C, Nottingham F), **Dean Parratt** (B Stortford, Purfleet, Dag & Red, Wimbledon, Arsenal)

Forwards: Dave Derry (Youth team), **Matthew Bird** (Leyton O), **Kurt Davidson** (Cheshunt, B Stortford, Grays A, Sutton U, Chelmsford C, Hendon, Redbridge F, Dartford, Billericay T, Leyt & Ilf, Hornchurch, Barking, Ford U), **Gordon Hendricks** (IFK Stockholm (Swe), Barnet, Dag & Red, Wycombe W), **Vinny John** (Clapton, Wimbledon)

Formed: 1893

DULWICH HAMLET

The Hamlet

Back Row (L-R); E Allen. W Lillington, L Anderson, D Brace, T Jones, C Kane, K Thomas, R Edwards. Middle; G Clark (Kit), G Hewitt, L Akers, P Whitmarsh, D Holness, C Gartell, M Middleton. Front; K Holland, M Eede (Chairman), E Smart, Caroline Brouwer (Physio), F Murphy (Mgr), B Simmonds (Asst Mgr), J Johnson (Coach), N Gray, A Peck, J Lawrence. *Photo - Dennis Nicholson*

Chairman: Martin Eede. **Vice Chairman:** Glyn Beverley **President:** Tommy Jover
Secretary: Paul Hobdell,c/o Ground. Tel. 01712 748707 (club).
Manager: Frank Murphy **Physio:** Caroline Brower.
Press Officer: John Lawrence (0171 733 6385) **Commercial Mgr:** Ian Woodley.
Ground: Champion Hill Stadium, Dog Kennel Hill, East Dulwich, London SE22 8BD (0171 274 8707).
Directions: East Dulwich station, 200yds. Denmark Hill station, 10 mins walk. Herne Hill station then bus 37 stops near ground. Also buses 40 & 176 from Elephant & Castle, 185 from Victoria.
Capacity: 3,000 **Cover:** 1,000 **Seats:** 500 **Floodlights:** Yes **Metal Badges:** Yes
Club Shop: Yes, selling programmes, pennants, badges, scarves, baseball caps, replica shirts (by order only). Contact Mishi D Morath at club.
Previous Grounds: Woodwarde Road 1893-95/ College Farm 95-96/ Sunray Avenue 96-1902/ Freeman's Ground, Champion Hill 02-12/ Champion Hill (old ground) 1912-92/ Sandy Lane (groundshare with Tooting & Mitcham F.C.) 91-92.
Colours: Navy Blue & Pink stripes, Navy, Navy. **Change colours:** Green & white stripes/green/green.
Previous Leagues: Camberwell 1894-97/ S/thern Sub 1897-1900 01-07/ Dulwich 00-01/ Spartan 07-08.
Midweek matchday: Tuesday **Reserve League:** Suburban. **Sponsors:** BCA Music Clubs.
Record Attendance: 20,744, Kingstonian v Stockton, FA Amateur Cup Final 1933 *(at refurbished ground: 744 v Hendon, 3/10/94).*
Best FA Cup season: 1st Rd replay 30-31 33-34. 1st Rd on 13 occasions; 25-31 32-38 48-49.
Record Fees - Paid: T Eames, G Allen **Received:** E Nwajiobi (Luton).
Record win: 13-0 v Walton-on-Thames, 37-38.
Record defeat: 1-10 v Hendon, 63-64.
Players progressing to Football League: W Bellamy (Spurs), A Solly (Arsenal), J Moseley & E Tozer (Millwall), G Pearce (Plymouth), G Jago (Charlton 51), R Crisp (Watford 61), J Ryan (Charlton 63), E Nwajiobi (Luton 83), A Gray (Crystal Palace 84), C Richards (Bournemouth), P Coleman (Millwall 86), A Perry (Portsmouth 86).
Clubhouse: Open 7 days a week, 3 bars. Function rooms and meeting room available for hire. Gymnasium, squash courts (0171 274 8707).
Club Record Goalscorer: Edgar Kail 427 (1919-33)
Club Record Appearances: Reg Merritt 571 (50-66).
95-96 Captain: Lee Akers. **95-96 P.o.Y.:** Gary Hewitt.
95-96 Top scorer: Joseph Odegbami.
Local Newspapers: South London Press (0181 769 4444), S.E. London & Kentish Mercury (0181 692 1122).
Honours: FA Amateur Cup 19-20 31-32 33-34 36-37, Isthmian League 19-20 25-26 32-33 48-49 (R-up(7) 21-22 23-24 29-31 33-34 46-47 58-59, Div 1 77-78), London Senior Cup 24-25 38-39 49-50 83-84 (R-up 05-06 07-08 20-21 27-28), Surrey Senior Cup(16) 04-06 08-10 19-20 22-23 24-25 27-28 33-34 36-37 46-47 49-50 57-59 73-75 (R-up(6) 11-12 31-33 37-38 50-51 67-68), London Chal. Cup R-up 91-92, London Charity Cup(12) 10-11(jt) 19-21 22-23 23-24(jt) 25-26 27-29 30-31(jt) 47-48 56-58, Surrey Senior Shield 72-73, Surrey Centen. Shld 77-78, Sth of the Thames Cup(4) 56-60, Southern Comb Cup 73-74, FA Trophy QF 79-80.

PROGRAMME DETAILS:
Pages: 36 **Price:** £1
Editor: John Lawrence

DULWICH HAMLET'S 1995-96 CAMPAIGN

DATE		OPPONENTS	COMP	RES		GATE	GOALSCORERS
Aug 12	H	Aylesbury United	IL	W	1-0	324	Odegbami
19	A	Hayes	IL	D	2-2	327	Whitmarsh, Lillington
22	H	Bishop's Stortford	IL	W	4-1	260	Witmarsh 2, Kerrins 2
26	H	St Albans City	IL	W	3-1	385	Whitmarsh 2, Akers
29	A	Hitchin Town	IL	W	3-1	281	Whitmarsh, Akers, Odegbami
Sept 2	A	Grays Athletic	IL	W	4-1	270	Whitmarsh, Odegbami 2, Lillington
5	A	Flackwell Heath	GIC	W	3-1*		
9	H	Southwick	FACIQ	W	7-1		Whitmarsh 2, Odegbami 2,Akers, Murphy, Lillington
16	A	Enfield	IL	L	0-1	939	
23	H	Chatham Town	FAC2Q	W	2-1		Allen, Odegbami
30	H	Chertsey Town	IL	D	0-0	380	
Oct 7	A	Bognor Regis Town	FAC3Q	L	3-4		Whitmarsh, Akers
10	A	Walton & Hersham	IL	W	2-0	232	Lillington, Odegbami
14	A	Carshalton Athletic	FAT1Q	D	1-1		Whitmarsh
17	H	Carshalton Athletic	FAT1Q	D	1-1		Lillington
21	A	Molesey	IL	W	2-1	190	Lillington, Odegbami
23	H	Carshalton Athletic	FAT1Q	L	1-2		Anderson
28	H	Worthing	IL	W	4-1	296	Whitmarsh 3, Odegbami
Nov 4	A	Sutton United	IL	D	1-1	697	Akers
7	A	Barton Rovers	FAT2Q	W	1-0		
11	H	Purfleet	IL	D	1-1	261	Odegbami
18	H	Carshalton Athletic	IL	W	2-1	457	Edwards, Allen
21	A	Thame United	CC	L	0-3		
25	A	Yeovil Town	IL	L	3-5	1960	Anderson 2, Whitmarsh
Dec 2	H	Yeading	IL	W	3-0	289	Holness 2, Allen
12	A	Heybridge Swifts	GIC	L	2-3*		
16	H	Harrow Borough	IL	W	3-2	262	Whitmarsh, Lillington, Odegbami
26	H	Bromley	IL	W	4-1	706	Whitmarsh, patullo, Odegbami 2
Jan 1	A	Boreham Wood	IL	D	2-2	586	Whitmarsh, Lillington
6	H	Grays Athletic	IL	L	3-5	320	Lillington, Holness
13	A	Bishop's Stortford	IL	W	2-1	408	Whitmarsh
20	H	Hendon	IL	W	1-0	417	Odegbami
Feb 3	H	Hitchin Town	IL	D	3-3	411	Whitmarsh 2, Lillington
10	A	Chertsey Town	IL	W	1-0	449	Lillington
17	H	Enfield	IL	D	1-1	1604	Whitmarsh
24	A	Worthing	IL	W	3-1	370	Lillington 2, Garter
Mar 2	H	Chertsey	IL	W	2-0	414	Kerrins, Holness
9	H	Walton & Hersham	IL	D	1-1	442	Whitmarsh
12	A	St Albans City	IL	L	1-4	751	Kerrins
16	H	Hendon	IL	W	2-1	301	Allen, Bartley
19	H	Hayes	IL	D	1-1	448	Akers
23	A	Purfleet	IL	L	1-3	293	Allen
30	H	Sutton United	IL	D	2-2	539	Whitmarsh, Bartley
Apl 4	A	Aylesbury United	IL	W	3-0	424	Whitmarsh, Akers, Lillington
6	H	Boreham Wood	IL	L	0-2	402	
8	A	Bromley	IL	W	2-0	584	Hewitt, Akers
13	H	Yeovil Town	IL	W	2-1	1289	Anderson, Lillington
18	A	Kingstonian	IL	W	2-0	418	Holness, Whitmarsh
20	A	Yeading	IL	L	3-5	260	Lillington 2, Hewitt
27	H	Kingstonian	IL	L	1-3	629	Lillington
29	A	Carshalton	IL	D	2-2	365	Whitmarsh 2
May 4	A	Harrow Borough	IL	W	2-1	276	Holness, Anderson

DULWICH HAMLET PLAYING SQUAD 1996-97

Goalkeepers: Gary McCann (Sutton U, Chesham U, Walton & H, Enfield, Sutton U, Fulham)

Defenders: Matthew Middleton (Chesham U, Millwall), **Russell Edwards** (Barnet, Crystal Palace), **Erskine Smart** (St. Albans C, Enfield, Hendon, Kingsbury T, Watford (A)), **Lee Dooley** (Youth team), **Dave Pattulo** (Molesey, Sutton U, Molesey, Sheen A), **Steve Moss** (Worthing, Enfield, Worthing, Shoreham, Worthing, Walton & H, Basingstoke T, Carshalton A, Worthing, Woking, Camberley T, Woking, Southampton), **John Phillips** (Youth team), **Dave Coppin** (Molesey, Whyteleafe, Carshalton A)

Midfielders: Lee Akers (Tonbridge, Croydon, Erith & B, Croydon, Dulwich Hamlet, Malden Vale, Dulwich Hamlet, Bromley, Greenwich B, Bromley, Dulwich Hamlet, Arsenal), **Gary Hewitt** (Erith & B, Bromley, Margate, Bromley, Gravesend, Hendon, Dulwich Hamlet, Erith & B, Gateway), **Ben Kamara** (Youth team), **Kelvin Thomas** (Croydon, Dulwich Hamlet, Bromley), **Luke Anderson** (Kingstonian, Horsham, Dulwich Hamlet), **Paul Haigh** (Youth team), **Martin Ferney** (Dover A, Fulham), **Paul Kember** (Chipstead, Whyteleafe, Croydon, Dulwich Hamlet, Molesey, Whyteleafe)

Forwards: Conrad Kane (Kingstonian, Carshalton A, Dulwich Hamlet, Bromley, Dulwich Hamlet, Merstham), **Joseph Odegbami** (St. Polten (Aus), Paralimon (Cyp), EPA Larnaca (Cyp), Leventis U (Nig), **Paul Whitmarsh** (Stevenage B, Doncaster, West Ham), **Willie Lillington** (Molesey, Wimbledon), **Steve McKimm** (Molesey, Hendon, Malden V), **Dean Holness** (Bromley), **Frank Murphy** (Cray W, Kettering T, Cray W, Barnet, Kettering T, Nuneaton B, Kettering T, Desborough T)

ENFIELD

Formed: 1893 The E's

Back Row (L-R); Lee Marshal, Steve Terry, Steve Cox, Jim Carstairs, Gary Fitzgerald, Steve West, John Richardson, Martin St Hikaire, Dominic Gentle. Front; Justin Gentle, Paul Underwood, Shaun Marshall, David May, Matt Edwards, Paul Moran, Joe Francis, Shaun Flemming.

.gap 10

Chairman: A Lazarou **President:** T F Unwin.
Secretary: Alan Diment, 30 Apple Grove, Enfield, Middx EN1 3DD (0181 363 6317).
Manager: George Borg **Coaches:** Paul Siani/ Andy Pape.
Press Officer: John Jefferson Tel.Physio:366273Reddon **Marketing Mgr:** Jonathon Moreland.
General Manager: Dee Curran. **Newsline:** 0891 122920.
Ground: The Stadium, Southbury Road, Enfield EN1 1YQ (0181 292 0665).
Directions: At junction of A10 & A110. 800 yards from Southbury Road station. Buses from town centre.
Capacity: 8,500 **Cover:** 3,500 **Seats:** 820 **Shop:** Yes
Colours: All White **Change colours:** Blue (white & red trim)
Sponsors: Cable London Plc. **Record Gate:** 10,000 (10/10/62) v Spurs, floodlight opener.
Previous Leagues: Tottenham & Dist 1894-95/Nth Middx 96-1903/ London 03-13 20-21/Middx 08-12 19-20/ Athenian 12-14 21-39 45-63/Herts & Middx Comb 39-42/ Isthmian 63-81/ GMV Conference 81-90.
Previous Name: Enfield Spartans 1893-1900. **Metal Badges:** Yes.
Previous Grounds: Baileys Field 1893-96/ Tuckers Field 96-1900/ Cherry Orchard Lane 1900-36.
Midweek matchday: Tuesday **Reserve Team's League:** Capital.
Best FA Cup season: 4th Rd replay 80-81 (lost 0-3 to Barnsley at Spurs (Att 35,244) after 1-1 draw).
League clubs beaten in F.A. Cup: Wimbledon, Northampton 77-78, Hereford, Port Vale 80-81, Wimbledon 81-82, Exeter 84-85, Orient 88-89, Aldershot 91-92.
Record Fees - Paid: For Gary Abbott (Barnet) **Received:** For Paul Furlong (Coventry City)
Players progressing to Football League: John Hollowbread & Peter Baker (Spurs 1952), Terry McQuade (Millwall 1961), Roger Day (Watford 1961), Jeff Harris (Orient 1964), Peter Feely (Chelsea 1970), Carl Richards (B'mouth 1980), Paul Furlong (Coventry 1991), Andy Pape (Barnet 1991), Greg Heald (Peterborough 1994), Jon Bailey (AFC Bournemouth 1995).
Clubhouse: Starlight Suite. Bar open every lunch & evening. Snacks. Starlight nightclub, cabaret, dinner & dance.
Club Record Scorer: Tommy Lawrence
Club Record Appearances: Steve King 617
95-96 Captain: Paul Turner.
95-96 P.o.Y.:
95-96 Top scorer: Gary Abbott.
Local Press: Enfield Gazette (0181 367 2345), Enfield Advertiser, Enfield Independent, Enfield Town Express.
Hons: FA Trophy 81-82 87-88, FA Amtr Cup R-up 66-67 69-70 (R-up 63-64 71-72), Alliance Premier League 82-83 85-86 (R-up 81-82, Lg Cup R-up 81-82), Isthmian Lg(8) 67-70 75-78 79-80 94-95 (R-up(7) 64-65 71-72 74-75 80-81 90-92 95-96, Lg Cup(2) 78-80 (R-up 91-92 94-95)), Athenian Lg(2) 61-63 (R-up 34-35), London Lg Div 1 11-12 (R-up 04-05 06-07, Middx Snr Cup(13) 13-14 46-47 61-62 65-66 68-71 77-81 88-89 90-91 (R-up(12) 10-11 20-21 47-48 51-52 57-60 62-63 66-67 72-73 75-76 84-85), London Snr Cup(6) 34-35 60-61 66-67 71-73 75-76 (R-up 63-64 67-68 70-71), Middx Lg (West) 09-10 (R-up 10-11), European Amtr Cup Winners Cup 69-70.

PROGRAMME DETAILS:
Pages: 24 **Price:** £1.20.
Editor: Lee Harding

ENFIELD'S 1995-96 CAMPAIGN

DATE		OPPONENTS	COMP	RES		GATE	GOALSCORERS
Aug 12	A	Molesey	IL	W	4-1	405	Terry, Gentle, Abbott, og
19	H	Hendon	IL	W	2-0	802	Nolon, Abbott
22	A	Sutton United	IL	W	4-2	887	Abbott 3, Sayer
26	A	Purfleet	IL	D	1-1	517	Abbott
29	H	Carshalton Athletic	IL	W	4-0	834	Abbott, Sayer 2, Kerr
Sept 2	H	Harrow Borough	IL	W	3-0	870	Richardson, Abbot, Gentle
4	H	Leyton Pennant	GIC	W	4-2		
9	A	Yeading	IL	D	1-1	432	Sayer
16	H	Dulwich Hamlet	IL	W	1-0	939	Terry
19	H	Boreham Wood	IL	L	0-2	777	
30	A	Worthing	IL	W	1-0	627	Abbott
Oct 3	H	Walton & Hersham	IL	W	4-0	603	Abbott 2, Terry, Fleming
7	A	Chertsey Town	IL	W	3-0	731	Richardson 2, Sayer
10	A	St Albans City	IL	L	0-1	1102	
14	H	Hayes	IL	D	1-1	1023	Kerr
28	A	Bishop's Stortford	IL	W	1-0	879	Gentle
31	A	Worthing	GIC	W	4-1		
Nov 4	H	Bromley	IL	W	5-0	1006	Sayer 2, Nolan, Adams, Gentle
11	A	Newport IOW	FAC 1	D	1-1	?	Abbott
18	H	Grays Athletic	IL	W	3-0	73	Abbott, Gentle, Sayer
21	H	Newport IOW	FAC 1	W	2-1	1804	Abbott 2
25	A	Kingstonian	IL	W	1-0	940	Sayer
Dec 2	H	Woking	FAC 2	D	1-1		Gentle
9	A	Hitchin Town	IL	L	0-1	611	
12	A	Woking	FAC 2	L	1-2		Abbott
16	H	Yeovil Town	IL	W	2-1	1177	Ridout, Fleming
19	H	Yeading	CC	L	1-2		
23	A	Harrow Borough	IL	L	1-3	603	
Jan 6	H	Molesey	IL	W	2-0	765	Abbott 2
13	H	Sutton United	IL	L	0-2	823	
20	A	Hayes	FAT 1	D	0-0		
23	H	Hayes	FAT 1	D	2-2		Abbott, Carstairs
29	H	Hayes	FAT 1	D	2-2		Abbott, Carstairs
31	A	Hayes	FAT 1	L	0-2		
Feb 3	A	Walton & Hersham	IL	W	1-0	451	Abbott
10	H	Worthing	IL	W	4-0	714	Grazioli 3, Morgan
17	A	Dulwich Hamlet	IL	D	1-1	1604	Terry
24	H	Bishop's Stortford	IL	L	0-1	733	
27	H	Kingstonian	GIC	D	2-2		
Mar 5	A	Kingstonian	GIC	L	0-3		
9	A	Hayes	IL	L	1-3	625	Richardson
12	A	Grays Athletic	IL	W	3-1	305	Abbott 2, Richardson
16	H	Chertsey Town	IL	D	0-0	611	
19	A	Boreham Wood	IL	L	1-4	507	Abbott
23	H	St Albans City	IL	D	2-2	1006	Carstairs, Terry
26	A	Hendon	IL	W	1-0	346	Blackford
30	A	Bromley	IL	W	1-0	469	Sayer
Apr 6	H	Yeading	IL	W	2-0	806	Edwards, Richardson
8	A	Aylesbury United	IL	W	3-2	859	Richardson 2, Gentle
13	H	Kingstonian	IL	W	2-1	904	Underwood, Richardson
16	H	Purfleet	IL	W	3-0	744	Terry, Abbott, West
20	A	Carshalton Athletic	IL	D	1-1	823	West
27	H	Hitchin Town	IL	W	3-0	982	Terry, Abbott, West
30	H	Aylesbury United	IL	D	3-3	1344	Richardson, Morgan, Terry
May 4	A	Yeovil Town	IL	W	1-0	3804	Richardson

ENFIELD PLAYING SQUAD 1996-97

Goalkeepers: Andy Pape (Barnet, Enfield, Harrow B, Feltham, Charlton, Crystal Palace, Ikast (Den), QPR), **Darryl Trigg** (Colchester)
Defenders: Steve Terry (Walton & H, Aylesbury U, Northampton, Hull, Watford), **Andy Kerr** (Wycombe W, Telford U, Cardiff, Shrewsbury), **Jim Carstairs** (Stockport, Camb.U, Arsenal), **Gary Fitzgerald** (Yeading, Watford), **David May** (Barking), **Paul Underwood** (Carshalton A, Sutton U, Kingstonian)
Midfielders: Paul Hobson (St. Albans C, Newcastle KB (Aust), Burnley), **Joe Francis** (Bromley, Welling U, Erith & B, Canterbury C, Dartford, Epsom & Ewell, Charlton, Millwall (A)), **John Richardson** (Slough T, Chesham U, Papatoetoe (NZ), Chalfont St. Peter, Chesham U, Amersham T), **Mark Bentley** (Youth team)
Forwards: Justin Gentle (Chesham U, Colchester, Luton, Boreham Wood, Cockfosters, Swindon, Wimbledon), **Paul Moran** (Peterborough, Tottenham), **Matthew Edwards** (Walton & H, Kettering T, Brighton, Tottenham), **Martin St. Hilaire** (Yeovil T, Enfield, Harrow B, Harlow T, Chesham U, Aveley), **Steve West** (Concord R, Aveley, East Thurrock U, Tilbury, Aveley, Tilbury, Purfleet, Arsenal (T)), **Dominic Gentle** (Grays A, Boreham Wood, Cockfosters, ICL Letchworth), **Shaun Marshall** (Stevenage B, Hitchin T, Stevenage B)

GRAYS ATHLETIC

Formed: 1890 | The Blues

Grays Athletic F.C. - Back Row: Donovan Wilson, Russell Penn, Peter Hickles, Richard Cherry, Andy Marsh, Malcom Stewart, Lee Double, Andy Alexander, John Ray. Front Row: Danny Wallace, Darryl Heffer, Barry Roberts, Phil Sammons, Jason Walker, Dean Cox, Kamal Bahbra.

Chairman: Frank Harris **Twin Managers:** Fred & Jeff Saxton
Secretary: Jeff Saxton, 216 Thundersley Park Road, South Benfleet, Essex SS7 1HP (01268 756964).
Asst Manager: Vince Craven **Physio:** Dave Lawson. **Coach:** P Carey
Commercial Mgr: Bill Cherry **Press Officer:** Gordon Norman (014024 51733)
Ground: Recreation Ground, Bridge Road, Grays RM17 6BZ (01375 391649).
Directions: Seven minutes walk from Grays station - turn right round one way system, right into Clarence Road, and at end into Bridge Road. Bus No. 370. By road - A13 towards Southend from London, take Grays exit and follow signs to town centre, keep left on one-way system, continue up hill for about half a mile, turn right into Bridge Road, ground half mile on right.
Capacity: 4,500 **Cover:** 1,200 **Seats:** 300 **Floodlights:** Yes **Metal Badges:** Yes
Club Shop: Yes, selling official club history 'The First Hundred Years' (priced £6.95), club sweaters, T-shirts, replica shirts, mugs, scarves, ties, pennants, pens, key fobs, lapel badges, bookmarks, stickers, diaries. Contact Bill Grove & Dave Smith (01375 377753/391649.
Colours: Royal & white **Change colours:** All yellow.
Sponsors: Roehlig & Co (UK) Ltd. London Advertising Centre Ltd, Harris Commercials, McDonalds.
Previous Leagues: Athenian 12-14 58-83/ London 14-24 26-39/ Kent 24-26/ Corinthian 45-58.
Record Attendance: 9,500 v Chelmsford City, FA Cup Fourth Qualifying Round 1959.
Best FA Cup season: 1st Rd 51-52 88-89. **Midweek home matchday:** Tuesday
Record Fees - Paid: For Ian Durant (Canvey Island)
Rec'd: Undisclosed for Tony Witter (C. Palace) and Dwight Marshall (Plymouth 1991).
Players progressing to Football League: J Jordan (Spurs 47), R Kemp (Reading 49), B Silkman & T Banfield (Orient), G O'Reilly (Spurs), W Entwhistle (Bury 83), M Welch (Wimbledon 84), T Witter (C Palace 90), D Marshall (Plymouth 91).
Clubhouse: Bar, pool, darts, bar snacks available. Indoor sports hall,
Stewardess: Sue Riley (01375 377753)
Club Record Goalscorer: Harry Brand 269 (1944-52)
Club Record Appearances: Phil Sammons, 601.
95-96 Captain: Malcolm Stewart. **95-96 P.o.Y.:** Russell Penn.
95-96 Top scorer: Dominic Gentle.
Local Newspapers: Thurrock Gazette (01375 372293)
Local Radio: BBC Essex, Radio Essex.
Hons: Isthmian Div 1 R-up 87-88 (Div 2 Sth 84-85, Lg Cup 91-92), Athenian Lg R-up 82-83 (Reserve Section R-up 58-59 (Cup R-up 59-60)), Corinthian Lg 45-46 (R-up 51-52 54-55 56-57, Lg Cup(2) 45-47, Mem. Shield(4) 45-47 77-78 79-80), Essex Snr Cup (4 plus) 56-57 87-88 93-94 94-95 (R-up(6 plus) 57-58 65-66 88-89), East Anglian Cup 44-45 (R-up 43-44 54-55), Essex Thameside Tphy(6) 47-48 78-79 80-81 87-89 90-91 (R-up(7) 45-46 58-59 61-62 68-69 84-86 94-95), Essex Elizabeth Trophy 76-77 (R-up 65-66), Claridge Tphy 87-88 88-89, Mithras Cup 79-80, Essex Int Cup(3) 56-57 58-60 (Junior Cup 19-20 (R-up 58-59)), Essex & Herts Border Comb. East 87-88 (Ancillary Cup 78-79, Comb Cup 82-83), Fred Budden Tphy 86-87, Hornchurch Charity Cup 78-79 86-87, Neale Tphy 50-51, Ford Rate Tphy 83-84 85-86 87-88 (R-up 84-85 86-87). Stan Veness Memorial Trophy (8) 87-96.

PROGRAMME DETAILS:
Pages: 48 **Price:** 80p
Editor: Jeremy Mason
(01375 376428)

GRAYS ATHLETIC'S 1995-96 CAMPAIGN

DATE		OPPONENTS	COMP	RESULT		GATE	GOALSCORERS
Aug 12	A	Worthing	IL	D	1-1	1125	Wallace
19	H	Bromley	IL	L	0-3	251	
22	A	Walton & Hersham	IL	W	4-1	239	Wilson 2, Cherry, Heffer
26	A	Yeovil Town	IL	L	0-1	1668	
29	H	Yeading	IL	D	0-0	167	
Sept 2	H	Dulwich Hamlet	IL	L	1-4	270	Walker
5	A	Hayes	GIC	W	1-0	110	Heffer
9	H	Wealdstone	FAC	D	2-2	262	Cherry, Double
12	A	Wealdstone	FAC	L	3-4	291	Cherry 2, Wilson
16	H	Harrow Borough	IL	L	0-2	168	
30	A	Molesey	IL	D	0-0	115	
Oct 3	A	Kingstonian	IL	L	0-1	420	
14	A	Boreham Wood	IL	L	0-2	315	
21	H	Bishop's Stortford	IL	L	0-2	205	
28	A	Aylesbury United	IL	D	2-2	490	Roberts, Ray
Nov 4	H	St Albans City	IL	L	0-3	212	
31	A	Aldershot Town	GIC	L	1-2	1177	Walker
18	A	Enfield	IL	L	0-3	731	
25	A	Newport AFC	FAT	L	0-1	679	
Dec 2	A	Chertsey Town	IL	L	0-2	292	
5	A	Harwich & Parkeston	ESC	W	3-2	80	Penn, Cox, og
12	H	Billericay Town	CC	L	1-2	102	D Roberts
16	A	Sutton United	IL	D	0-0	392	
23	H	Worthing	IL	W	6-0	215	McIntyre, Lawrence 2, Ray 2, Gentle
Jan 2	H	Hayes	IL	D	3-3	226	Sammons, Gentle 2
6	A	Dulwich Hamlet	IL	W	5-3	320	Ray, Lawrence, Gentle 2, Deleon
9	H	Ford United	ESC	W	3-2	106	Risley, Gentle, Wallace
13	H	Walton & Hersham	IL	W	3-1	264	Penn, Gentle, Mitchell
20	A	Bromley	IL	D	2-2	264	Goldstone 2
30	H	Romford	ETT	W	3-0	118	Penn, Mitchell, Deleon
Feb 3	A	Yeading	IL	W	1-0	104	Mitchell
6	H	Witham Town	ESC	W	4-0	85	Tripp, Penn 2, Wallace
10	H	Molesey	IL	W	1-0	255	Penn
13	H	Hitchin Town	IL	W	1-0	197	Mitchell
17	A	Harrow Borough	IL	L	0-3	250	
24	H	Aylesbury United	IL	W	2-0	274	Southon, S Lawrence
27	H	Hendon	IL	D	0-0	217	
Mar 2	A	Bishop's Stortford	IL	L	0-2	306	
4	A	Purfleet	IL	L	0-1	231	
12	H	Enfield	IL	L	0-3	305	
16	A	Carshalton Athletic	IL	L	1-3	313	Southon
19	H	Billericay Town	ESC	L	0-2	120	
23	A	Hitchin Town	IL	L	0-1	369	
26	H	Yeovil Town	IL	L	0-2	251	
30	H	Kingstonian	IL	D	1-1	261	Gentle
6	A	Hayes	IL	L	1-5	583	Gentle
8	H	Purfleet	IL	W	2-0	341	Alexander, Southon
11	H	Great Wakering Rovers	ETT	W	2-1	85	Ashenden, Gentle
13	A	St Albans City	IL	D	1-1	441	Southon
15	H	Carshalton Athletic	IL	W	1-0	179	Gonzague
20	H	Chertsey Town	IL	W	2-1	239	Gentle, Gonzague
25	H	Boreham Wood	IL	L	1-2	196	Charles
27	A	Hendon	IL	D	0-0	239	
May 4	H	Sutton United	IL	L	1-2	318	Alexander
6	H	Canvey Island	ETT	L	0-2	110	

GRAYS ATHLETIC PLAYING SQUAD 1996-97

Goalkeepers: Andy Marsh (Clapton, West Ham)
Defenders: Steve Ward (Youth team), **Billy Goldstone** (Purfleet, Enfield, Grays A, Chesham U, Chelmsford C, Barking, East Ham U, Woodford T, Barking), **Danny Tripp** (Dag & Red, Southend), **Andy Alexander** (Chesham U, Grays A, Brimsdown R, Haringey B, Fulham (T)), **Russell Penn** (Norwich (T)), **John Ray** (Tilbury, Billericay T, Ford U, Barking, Wycombe W, Colchester)
Midfielders: Jamie Southon (Sing Tao (HK), **Phil Sammons** (Hornchurch, Walthamstow Ave, Tilbury, Dagenham), **Jason Walker** (Wingate & Finchley), **Adam Bloss** (Southend, Leyton O, Arsenal (T)), **Dean Cox** (Dag & Red), **Malcolm Stewart** (Boreham Wood, Hendon, B Stortford, Harlow T, Redbridge F, Maidstone U, Dartford, Maidstone U, Dagenham, Hoddesdon T)
Forwards: Dominic Gentle (Boreham Wood, Cockfosters, ICL Letchworth), **Julian Charles** (Cheshunt), **Barry Roberts** (Dag & Red, Heybridge S, Uxbridge, Harrow B, Wivenhoe T, Braintree T, Chelmsford C), **Godfrey Obebo** (Kingstonian, Grays A, Collier Row, Leyton-Wingate, Leyton O, Halifax T, Royal Club de Charleroi (Belg))

HARROW BOROUGH

1933 | The Boro

Back Row (L-R): Andy McDade (Physio), Cliff Rapley (Coach), Christian Metcalfe, Paul Fishenden, David Hook, Neil Fraser, Frank Appiah, Robert Marshall, Brian Jones, David Clarke. Front Row: Nko Ekoku, Lee Endersby, Gary Ellis, Mark Xavier, Harry Manoe (Mgr), Jason Court, John Hurlock, Grant Robinson, Sean James.

Chairman: Jim Ripley **Vice Chairman:** **President:** Jim Rogers
Secretary/Press Off.: Peter Rogers, 21 Ludlow Close, South Harrow, Middx HA2 8SR (0181 248 8003).
Manager: Harry Manoe **Asst Manager:** **Physio:** Andy McDade.
Coach: Cliff Rapley **Commercial Manager:** Bill Porter c/o the club.
Ground: Earlsmead, Carlyon Avenue, South Harrow, Middx HA2 8SS (0181 422 5989/5221).
Directions: Underground to Northolt (Central Line) then 140 or 282 bus, or to South Harrow (Piccadilly Line) then 114 or H10. By road leave A40 at Macdonalds roundabout towards Northolt station (A312 north), left at lights, right at next island, ground 5th turning on right.
Capacity: 3,070 **Cover:** 1,000 **Seats:** 350 **Floodlights:** Yes **Metal Badges:** Yes.
Club Shop: Yes. Progs, scarves, badges, mugs, T-shirts, etc. Contact Don Crowhurst c/o Club.
Colours: Red & white **Change colours:** Black& White Stripes/Black.
Sponsors: Don Bruce Bookmakers.
Previous Leagues: Harrow & Dist 33-34/ Spartan 34-40,45-58/ W Middx Comb 40-41/ Middx Sen 41-45/ Delphian 58-63/ Athenian 63-75/ Isthmian 75-96
Previous Names: Roxonian 1933-38/ Harrow Town 38-66.
Previous Ground: Northolt Road 33-34.
Midweek matchday: Wednesday **Best FA Cup season:** 2nd Rd 83-84 (1-3 at home to Newport Co).
Record Attendance: 3,000 v Wealdstone, F.A. Cup 1st Qualifying Round 1946.
Record Fees - Paid: To Dagenham for George Duck & Steve Jones
Received: £15,000 for Chris Hutchings (Chelsea)
Record win: 13-0 v Handley Page (A), Middlesex Snr Lg 18/10/41.
Rec. loss: 0-8 5 times: Wood Green T. (A) Middx Lge 40, Met Police (A) Spartan Lg 52, Briggs Spts (A) Spartan Lg 53, Hertford T. (A) Spartan Lge 53, Hendon (A) Middx Snr Cup 65.
Players progressing to Football League: D Russell (Arsenal 46), M Lucas (Leyton Orient & Wales), R Shaw (Torquay 47), T Eden (Raith Rovers 48), T Carpenter (Watford 50), M Bottoms (QPR 60), C Hutchings (Chelsea 80), R Holland (Crewe 85), J Kerr (Portsmouth 87), D Howell, A Pape & E Stein (Barnet), D Byrne (Gillingham), R Rosario (Norwich), D Kemp (Crystal Palace), M Doherty (Reading), D Bassett (Wimbledon), G Borthwick (Bournemouth), B Laryea (Torquay).
Clubhouse: Open every day with normal licensing hours. Four bars, games room, varied entertainment venue for major sporting and social events. Hot and cold food available, buffets by prior request.
Club Record Scorer: Dave Pearce, 153
Club Record Appearances: Steve Emmanuel 522 (1st team only), Les Currell 582, Colin Payne 557.
95-96 Captain: Bob Dowie. **95-96 P.o.Y.:** Sean James.
95-96 Top scorer: Mark Xavier 32.
Local Newspapers: Harrow Observer (0181 427 4404).
Honours: Isthmian Lg 83-84 (Div 1 R-up 78-79), Athenian Lg Div 2 R-up 63-64, Spartan Lg R-up 57-58, Spartan Lg R-up 57-58 (Div 2 West 38-39 (R-up 37-38)), Middx Senior Cup 82-83 92-93, Harrow & Dist. Lg Div 1 R-up 33-34, Middx Charity Cup 79-80 92-93 (R-up 78-79), F.A. Trophy SF 82-83.Middx Intermediate Cup 55-56,Middx Premier Cup 81-82.

PROGRAMME DETAILS:
Pages: 28 **Price:** £1
Editor: Jim Rogers
(0181 248 8003)

HARROW BOROUGH'S 1995-96 CAMPAIGN

DATE		OPPONENTS	COMP	RESULT		GATE	GOALSCORERS
Aug 19	A	Hitchin Town	IL	W	5-1	304	Xavier 2, Jones 2, Egbe
23	H	Aylesbury United	IL	D	3-3	417	Xavier 3
26	H	Kingstonian	IL	W	2-1	338	Jones (pen), Xavier
Sept 2	A	Enfield	IL	L	0-3	870	
5	A	Chesham United	GIC	L	1-4		Biggins
9	H	Leatherhead	FAC	W	2-1	198	Jones, Davies
13	H	St Albans City	IL	D	0-0	318	
16	A	Grays Athletic	IL	W	2-0	168	Xavier, Davies
23	A	Bracknell	FAC	L	1-2		Endersby
26	A	Boreham Wood	IL	L	2-3	224	Xavier 2
30	H	Carshalton Athletic	IL	L	0-1	308	
Oct 10	A	Yeading	IL	W	2-1	189	Hurlock 2
14	H	Marlow	FAT	D	1-1	244	Clarke
17	A	Marlow	FAT R	W	4-1		Hurlock, Seabrook, Clarke, Xavier
24	A	Sutton United	IL	L	0-4	452	
28	H	Molesey	IL	W	3-1	198	og, Xavier, Metcalfe
Nov 4	A	Braintree	FAT	L	0-4		
7	A	Uxbridge	CC	L	0-1		
11	H	Chertsey Town	IL	W	3-1	365	Xavier 3
18	A	Hendon	IL	W	2-0	273	Endersby 2
Dec 2	A	Walton & Hersham	IL	W	2-1	247	Xavier 2
9	H	Bishop's Stortford	IL	D	0-0	221	
13	H	Purfleet	IL	D	2-2	111	Endersby, James
16	A	Dulwich Hamlet	IL	L	2-3	262	Endersby, Xavier
23	H	Enfield	IL	W	3-1	605	Endersby, Fraser 2
Jan 1	H	Worthing	IL	W	3-1	360	Ekoku 2, Endersby
6	A	St Albans City	IL	W	2-0	620	Ekoku, Endersby (pen)
10	H	Wembley	MSC	D	2-2	131	Hurlock, Dowie
13	A	Aylesbury United	IL	L	0-2	531	
16	A	Wembley	MSC R	D	1-1		James
20	H	Hitchin Town	IL	L	1-2	260	Fraser
23	A	Wembley	MSC R	W	3-2		Jones, Endersby 2
31	H	Bromley	IL	L	1-3	205	Hurlock
Feb 3	H	Boreham Wood	IL	D	1-1	324	og
10	A	Yeovil Town	IL	D	0-0	1942	
14	H	Uxbridge	MSC	D	2-2	110	Ekoku, Metcalfe
17	H	Grays Athletic	IL	W	3-0	249	Endersby, Hurlock 2
24	A	Molesey	IL	D	0-0	120	
27	A	Uxbridge	MSC R	W	1-0		Fishenden
Mar 2	H	Sutton United	IL	D	0-0	339	
9	H	Yeading	IL	W	4-1	256	Xavier 3, Endersby
12	A	Hayes	MSC	L	1-2		Fishenden
16	A	Bromley	IL	L	1-5	204	Fishenden
23	A	Chertsey Town	IL	W	6-1	351	Fishenden, Xavier 4, Endersby
26	A	Kingstonian	IL	W	1-0	302	Xavier
30	H	Yeovil Town	IL	L	0-1	489	
Apr 4	A	Carshalton Athletic	IL	W	1-0	283	James
6	A	Worthing	IL	W	2-1	338	Ekoku, Xavier
13	A	Purfleet	IL	W	1-0	162	Xavier
17	H	Hendon	IL	D	2-2	253	Clarke, Hurlock
20	H	Walton & Hersham	IL	L	2-3	243	Xavier, Clarke
23	A	Hayes	IL	L	1-2	716	Bensted
27	A	Bishop's Stortford	IL	W	3-2	285	Xavier, Fraser, Fishenden
May 1	H	Hayes	IL	D	1-1	1212	Xavier (pen)
4	H	Dulwich Hamlet	IL	L	1-2	295	Marshall

HARROW BOROUGH PLAYING SQUAD 1996-97

Goalkeepers: David Hook (Hampton, Feltham)

Defenders: Dave Bensted (Dartford, Redbridge F, Brimsdown R), **Steve Palmer** (Luton), **Dave Clarke** (Eastwood T, Notts Co), **Sean James** (Bedfont), **Bob Dowie** (Leighton T, Enfield, Aylesbury U, Hendon, St. Albans C, Hendon, St. Albans C, Hertford T, Cheshunt, Hatfield T, B Stortford), **Jason Court** (Leverstock Green, Harrow B, Hayes, Leverstock Green, Hayes, Boreham Wood, Chalfont St. Peter, St. Albans C)

Midfielders: Neil Fraser (Hayes, Harrow B), **Frank Appiah** (Hayes, Charlton), **John Hurlock** (Droylsden, Altrincham, Nuneaton B, Bedworth U, Stockport), **Tommy Evans** (Sheffield U), **Brian Jones** (Bedfont, Yeading)

Forwards: Lee Endersby (Wembley, Brimsdown R), **Uche Egbe** (Hendon, Wembley, Hendon, Watford), **Nko Ekoku** (Hampton, Malden Vale, Sutton U), **Mark Xavier** (Hendon, Ruislip Manor, Hendon), **Christian Metcalfe** (Chelsea (T)), **Paul Fishenden** (Crawley T, Wokingham T, Crewe, Wimbledon, Hillingdon), **Dwane Ackerman** (Croydon, Feltham & H, Ruislip Manor, Hendon, Dagenham)

HENDON

Formed: 1908 Dons or Greens

Back Row (L-R): JS White, L Francis, D Adams, S Powell, P Kelly, D Stephenson, A Kennedy, H Altinok. Middle; T Neill (Exec), M Dawber, D Brodrick, S Clarke, S Achcroft, D Murphy, A O'Brien, T Wells, M Banton, L Lindo, S Smart, J Wheeldon (Chief Exec). Front; N Price (Mgr), J Price, S Heard, D Speedie, I Arbiter (Chr), P Kelly, M Biggins, M Duffield, G Etchell (Sec).

Chairman: Ivor Arbiter. **Presidents:** Monty Hyams and Bobbie Butlin
Secretary: Graham Etchell, c/o Hendon FC.
Manager: Neil Price **Asst Manager:** Richard Parkin **Coach:** Andy O'Brien
Press Officer: David Ballheimer **Physio:** Sam Old B.Sc. MCSP,SRP. **Commercial Manager:** T.B.A.
Ground: Claremont Road, Cricklewood, London NW2 1AE (0181 201 9494 (Fax: 0181 9055966)).
Directions: From Brent Cross tube station (Northern Line) to the east take first left after flyover on North Circular - Claremont Rd is then left at 3rd mini-r'bout. Buses 102, 210, 226 and C11 pass ground.
Capacity: 8,000 **Cover:** 5,119 **Seats:** 381 **Floodlights:** Yes **Metal Badges:** Yes.
Club Shop: (Contact Derek Furmedge 01814 552219(shop) 01814 592042(H)
Sells kit, bags, badges, pens, mugs, scarves, ties, programmes and other football souvenirs.
Colours: White & green stripe/green/green & wh **Change:** White with tang. stripe/tang./tang.& wh
Previous Leagues: Finchley & Dist. 08-11/ Middx 10-11/ London 11-14/ Athenian 14-63.
Previous Names: Christ Church Hampstead to 08, H/stead Tn to 26, H/stead to 33, Golders Green to 46.
Previous Grounds: Kensal Rise 08-12/ Avenue Ground, Cricklewood Lane 12-26.
Sponsors: Fender Guitars. **Midweek matchday:** Tuesday **Reserve League:** Suburban (North)
Record defeat: 2-11 v Walthamstow Avenue (A), Athenian League 9/11/35.
Record win: 13-1 v Wingate (H), Middx Senior Cup 2/2/57.
Record Gate: 9,000 v Northampton, FA Cup 1st Rd 1952.
Best F.A. Cup season: 3rd Rd replay 73-74 (lost 1-4 to Newcastle at Watford after 1-1 draw away).
Record Fees - Paid: £5,000 twice. **Received:** £30,000 for Iain Dowie (Luton).
Players progressing to Football League: Arnold Siegel (Orient 1946), William Dare (Brentford 1948), Roy Stroud (West Ham 1952), Miles Spector (Chelsea 1950), Jeff Darey (Brighton), Doug Orr (QPR 1957), Peter Shearing (West Ham 1960), Iain Dowie (Luton 1988), Peter Anderson (Luton), Jeff Harris (Orient), Phil Gridelet (Barnsley 1990), Gerry Soloman (Leyton Orient 1991), Junior Hunter & Micah Hyde (both Cambridge 94-95), Simon Clark (Peterborough 94-95).
Clubhouse: (0181 455 9185 - contact Pat Hunt). Two bars and function hall open licensing hours 7 days a week. Hot & cold food, pool, darts, bingo, members club, satelite TV, entertainments. Available for hire.
Club Record Goalscorer: Freddie Evans 176 (1929-35)
Club Record Apps: Bill Fisher 787 (1940-62).
95-96 Captain: Paul Hobbs. **95-96 P.o.Y.:** Dave Stephenson.
95-96 Top scorer: Michael Banton.
Local Newspaper: Hendon Times,Willesden & Brent Chronicle. (0181 203 0411).
Local Radio Stations: Capital,London News Radio,GLR, LBC.
Hons: FA Amtr Cup 59-60 64-65 71-72 (R-up 54-55 65-66), European Amtr Champions 72-73, Isthmian Lg 64-65 72-73 (R-up 63-64 65-66 73-74, Lg Cup 76-77 (R-up 86-87), Full Members Cup 94-95), Premier Inter-Lge Cup R-up 86-87, Middx Lge 12-13 13-14, Athenian Lg 52-53 55-56 60-61 (R-up 28-29 32-33 47-48 48-49 51-52), London Lg Div 1 R-up 12-13 (Amtr Div 13-14), Finchley & Dist. Lg 10-11, London Snr Cup 63-64 68-69 (R-up 35-36 50-51 54-55 58-59 71-72), Middx Snr Cup(11) (R-up 83-84), Middx Charity Cup(14); FA Tphy 3rd Rd replay 76-77 77-78, London Interm Cup 64-65 72-73 75-76 79-80 (R-up 63-64 68-69), Middx Interm 64-65 66-67 72-73, Suburban Lg 92-93 (R-up 84-85).

PROGRAMME DETAILS:
Pages: 64 **Price:** £1.20p
Editor: Secretary

HENDON'S 1995-96 CAMPAIGN

DATE		OPPONENTS	COMP	RESULT		GATE	GOALSCORERS
Aug 19	A	Enfield	IL	L	0-2	802	
22	H	Hayes	IL	L	0-2	262	
26	H	Boreham Wood	IL	D	101	252	Haynes
29	A	St.Albans	IL	L	1-3	425	Hunter
Sept 2	A	Carshalton Athletic	IL	D	1-1	501	Haynes
5	A	Yeovil Tn	GICi	W	3-1	1092	Haynes
9	H	Flackwell Heath	FAC 1QR	W	8-0		Pike, Sweetman, Haynes 3, Gallagher 2 McKimm
16	A	Chertsey Town	IL	L	1-3		Clarke
23	A	Clapton	FAC 2QR	W	3-2		Stephenson, Gallagher, Haynes
30	H	Bishops Stortford	Isic	D	1-1	183	Haynes
Oct 7	H	Hayes	FAC-3QR	L	0-3		
10	H	Sutton United	IL	L	0-4	275	
14	H	Waterlooville	FAT-1QR	D	2-2		Stephenson, Haynes
17	A	Waterlooville	(replay)	W	1-0		Gallagher
21	H	Bromley	IL	W	2-0	234	Gallagher, Haynes
28	A	Purfleet	IL	W	3-2	169	Stephenson, Gallagher
31	H	Croydon	GIC2	L	0-1		
Nov 4	H	Gravesend & Northfleet	FAT-2QR	W	3-0		Deadman 2, Fiori
11	A	Walton & Hersham	IL	L	0-1	207	
14	H	Ruislip Manor	MSC1	L	2-5		Pike, Fiori
18	H	Harrow Borough	IL	L	0-2	273	
21	H	St. Albans City	CC1	L	3-4		Dowson 3
25	A	Cambridge City	FAT2Q	L	0-2		
Dec 2	H	Molesey	IL	W	2-0		Turner, Haynes
19	H	Hitchen Town	IL	L	1-2	182	Dawber
26	H	Yeading	IL	D	1-1		Fiori
Jan 1	A	Yeovil Town	IL	L	1-4	2306	Price
6	H	Carshalton Athletic	IL	D	0-0	246	
13	A	Hayes	IL	L	1-3	347	Banton
20	A	Dulwich Hamlet	IL	L	0-1	417	
Feb 3	H	St. Albans City	IL	L	1-2	317	Bolton
10	A	Bishops Stortford	IL	L	1-3	323	Bolton
17	H	Chertsey Town	IL	D	0-0	202	
24	H	Purfleet	IL	L	2-4		Price, Banton
27	A	Grays Athletic	IL	D	0-0	217	
Mar 2	A	Bromley	IL	W	5-2	259	Stephenson, Duffield, Banton, Clarke
5	A	Hitchen Town	IL	W	1-0	209	Hobbs
9	H	Sutton United	IL	W	3-2	529	Banton 2, Duffield
12	A	Aylesbury United	IL	L	0-1	346	
16	H	Dulwich Hamlet	IL	L	1-2	301	Banton
23	H	Walton & Hersham	IL	W	4-0	225	Banton 2, Dawber 2
26	H	Enfield	IL	L	0-1	346	
30	A	Worthing	IL	W	5-0	336	Stephen, Banton, Dawber 3
Apr 2	A	Yeading	IL	D	0—0	202	
6	H	Yeovil Town	IL	L	1-3	443	Duffield
9	H	Worthing Town	IL	W	3-0	249	Driscoll, Duffield, Dawber
13	H	Aylesbury United	IL	W	4-2	253	Banton, Dawber, Clarke, Powell
17	A	Harrow Borough	IL	D	2-2	253	Banton 2
20	A	Molesey	IL	W	2-1	190	Price, Dawber
23	A	Boreham Wood	IL	L	0-4	307	
27	H	Grays Athletic	IL	D	0-0	239	
May 4	A	Kingstonian	IL	W	1-0	421	Stephenson

HENDON PLAYING SQUAD 1996-97

Goalkeepers: Scott Ashcroft (Berkhamsted T)

Defenders: Darren Brodrick (Walton & H, Kingstonian, Carshalton A, Kingstonian, Fulham (T)), **Dave Stephenson** (Malden Vale, Croydon, Tooting & Mitcham U, Dorking, Croydon), **Dean Murphy** (St. Albans C, Wokingham T, Barnet, Harpenden T), **Steve Smart** (Aylesbury U, Sutton U, Wealdstone, Barnet, Tottenham Hotspur (J)), **Mark Turner** (Chesham U, Staines T, Hayes, Walton & H, Chertsey T, Slough T, Brentford (T)), **John White** (Watford), **Lee Francis** (Yeovil T, Grays A, Boreham Wood, Enfield, Chesterfield, Arsenal)

Midfielders: Jonathan Price (Aylesbury U, Chesham U, Walton & H, Chertsey T, Berkhamsted T, Staines T, Sutton U, Staines T, Wycombe W, Watford), **Simon Clarke** (Kettering T, West Ham), **Mark Dawber** (Chertsey T, Sutton U, Chesham U, Staines T, Wycombe W, Woking, Virginia Water), **Steve Heard** (Aylesbury U, Eynesbury R, Rushden & D, Silkaborge (Den), Camb.U), **Danny Adams** (Enfield, Walton & H, St. Albans C, Enfield, St. Albans C, Watford (T)), **Paul Kelly** (Chertsey T, Chesham U, Fulham), **Martin Duffield** (St. Albans C, Sutton U, Hendon, Enfield, QPR, Tottenham)

Forwards: Micky Banton (Walton & H, Chesham U, Barnet, Windsor & Eton, Hellenic (SA), **Tony Kelly** (Hayes, Wealdstone, Hayes, Harefield U, Hillingdon, Wealdstone), **Mark Biggins** (St. Albans C, Harrow B, Wealdstone, Aldershot T, Woking, Windsor & Eton, St. Albans C, Maidenhead U, Feltham, Hanwell T, Hampton), **Hakan Altinok** (Turkish football)

Formed: 1880

HEYBRIDGE SWIFTS

Swifts

Heybridge Swifts FC 95-96; *Photo - Eric Marsh*

Chairman: Michael Gibson **Vice Chairman:** Paul Wilkinson **President:** Ronnie Locker.
Secretary: Dennis Fenn, 31 Saxon Way, Maldon, Essex CM9 7JN (01621 854798).
Manager: Garry Hill **Asst Manager:** Mick Loughton **Coach:** N/A
Press Officer: Tim Huxtable. **Physio:** Barry Anthony **Commercial Manager:** Peter Fenn.
Ground: Scraley Road, Heybridge, Maldon, Essex (01621 852978).
Directions: Leave Maldon on main road to Colchester, pass through Heybridge then turn right at sign to Tolleshunt Major (Scraley Road). Ground on right. Six miles from nearest station (Witham). By bus via Chelmsford and Maldon.
Capacity: 4,500 **Cover:** 1,200 **Seats:** 550 **Floodlights:** Yes **Metal Badges:** Yes
Club Shop: Yes. Club sweaters, shirts, scarves, baseball hats, enamel badges, old programmes etc. Contact Chris Fenn, 40 Drake Avenue, Mayland CM3 6TY (01621 740878).
Colours: Black & white stripes/black/black & white **Change colours:** All Red
Sponsors: Balham Electrical Wholesalers
Previous Leagues: North Essex/ South Essex/ Essex & Suffolk Border/ Essex Senior 1971-84.
Midweek home matchday: Tuesday **Reserve Team's League:** Essex & Herts Border Comb.
Record Attendance: 4,614 Gillingham FA Cup 1st Rd Proper 94.
Best FA Cup season: First round v Gillingham (H),played at Colchester.Lost 0-2
League clubs defeated in FA Cup: None.
Best FA Trophy season: 2nd Rd Proper 92-93 (lost at Gateshead).
Record Fees - Paid: None
Received: £12,000 for Simon Royce (Southend United).
Players progressing to Football League: Simon Royce (Southend United), Peter Cawley & Ben Lewis (Colchester Utd), Jonathan Hunt, Dominic Naylor, Derek Payne & Eddie Stein (Barnet).
Clubhouse: Two bars open every night. Games room, boardroom, kitchen (on matchdays).
Club Record Goalscorer: J Lamb 115
Club Record Appearances: H Askew 500+.
95-96 Captain: Keith Bain.
95-96 P.o.Y.:
95-96 Top scorer: Mitchell Springett.
Local Newspapers: Maldon & Burnham Standard (01621 8522233).
Local Radio Stations: BBC Essex, Essex FM.
Honours: Isthmian Lg Div 2 North 89-90, Div 1 R-up 95-96, Essex Senior Trophy 81-82, Essex Senior Lg 81-82 82-83 83-84 (Lg Cup 82-83), JT Clarke Cup 82-83, Thorn EMI National Floodlit Competition R-up 82-83, Essex & Herts Border Combination R-up 88-89 90-91.Eastern Floodlit Cup 93-94,East Anglian Cup 93-94 94-95.

PROGRAMME DETAILS:
Pages: 40 **Price:** £1
Editor: Peter Fenn
(01621 740878)

HEYBRIDGE SWIFT'S 1995-96 CAMPAIGN

DATE		OPPONENTS	COMP	RESULT		GATE	GOALSCORERS
Aug 12	A	Aldershot Town	BHL	D	1-1		G. Caldon
19	H	Marlow	BHL	W	3-1		Matthews, Pollard, Jones
22	A	Barking	BHL	W	2-1		Pollard 2
28	H	Bognor Regis T.	BHL	W	5-1		Matthews 2, Adcock 2, Jones
Sept 2	H	Billericay Town	BHL	W	3-2		Springett 3
5	A	Whyteleafe	GIC	W	2-1		Jones, O'Dea
9	A	Diss Town	FAC	W	2-0		Adcock 2
12	A	Basingstoke Town	BHL	W	3-1		Adcock 2, Jones
16	H	Uxbridge	BHL	W	4-0		Adcock, Matthews, Jones, Rolfe
19	H	Maldon Town	EFC	W	2-0		Bain, Abrehart
23	A	Sudbury Town	FAC	L	1-2		Rolfe
30	A	Tooting & Mitcham Utd	BHL	W	1-0		G. Caldon
Oct 3	A	Maldon Town	EFC	W	2-1		G. Caldon, Rolfe
7	A	Wokingham Town	BHL	L	0-1		
10	H	Harwick & Parkes'	EFC	W	3-1		Matthews, Adcock, Game
17	H	Maidenhead United	BHL	D	1-1		Springett
21	H	Thame United	BHL	W	5-1		Adcock 2, G. Caldon, Game, Jones
24	A	Burnham Ramblers	EAC	W	3-0		Adcock 2, Springett
28	A	Wembley	BHL	W	3-0		Springett, Jones, Pollard
31	H	Billericay Town	GIC	W	4-3		Matthews 2, Rolfe 2
Nov 4	A	Yate Town	FAT	W	2-1		Matthews, Rolfe
11	A	Berkhamsted Town	BHL	W	2-1		Adcock, Vickers
18	A	Barton Rovers	BHL	W	4-1		G. Caldon, Matthews, Adcock, Bain
21	H	Tiptree United	ESC	W	5-1		G. Caldon 2, Springett, Rolfe, Jones
25	A	Boreham Wood	FAT	L	0-3		
28	A	Barton Rovers	CC	W	1-0		G. Caldon
Dec 2	A	Chesham United	BHL	D	1-1		G. Caldon
9	H	Abingdon Town	BHL	W	3-0		Adcock, Vickers, Jones
12	H	Dulwich Hamlet	GIC	W	3-2		G. Caldon 2, Matthews
16	A	Whyteleafe	BHL	L	1-4		G. Caldon
19	H	Uxbridge	CC	W	3-1		Adcock 2, G. Caldon
Jan 1	H	Ruislip Manor	BHL	W	3-0		G. Caldon, Springett, Cook
6	A	Billericay Town	BHL	L	0-2		
9	A	Halstead Town	ESC	W	3-0		Matthews 2, G. Caldon
13	H	Barking	BHL	W	7-0		Matthews 3, G. Caldon 3, Jones
20	A	Marlow	BHL	L	0-1		
23	H	Boreham Wood	CC	L	0-2		
Feb 3	A	Bognor Regis Town	BHL	W	3-1		G. Caldon 2, Matthews
6	H	Staines Town	BHL	W	3-0		G. Caldon 3
8	A	Aveley	EAC	L	2-3		Springett, Cutbush
10	H	Tooting & Mitcham	BHL	L	1-2		Pollard
13	H	Billericay Town	ESC	L	1-3		Bain
15	A	Harwich & Parkes'	EFC	L	0-1		
17	A	Uxbridge	BHL	L	0-1		
24	H	Wembley	BHL	W	4-1		Bain 2, G. Caldon, Springett
Mar 2	A	Thame United	BHL	D	1-1		Cook
5	A	Leyton Pennant	BHL	W	1-0		Springett
9	A	Maidenhead United	BHL	W	4-1		G. Caldon 2, Pollard, Springett
12	H	Kingstonian	GIC	D	2-2		Matthews, Jones
16	H	Wokingham Town	BHL	W	2-0		Springett, Pollard
19	H	Aldershot Town	BHL	W	2-0		G. Caldon, Jones
21	A	Kingstonian	GIC R	L	0-2		
23	H	Berkhamsted Town	BHL	W	4-2		G. Caldon, Matthews, Jones, Pollard
30	A	Oxford City	BHL	L	3-4		Matthess, McDonough, og
Apr 2	H	Barton Rovers	BHL	W	3-1		Matthews, Adcock, Game
6	A	Ruislip Manor	BHL	W	2-1		Matthews, Hewes
8	H	Leyton Pennant	BHL	D	0-0		
13	A	Staines Town	BHL	D	2-2		Adcock, Springett
16	H	Oxford City	BHL	D	2-2		Matthews, Cranfield
20	H	Chesham United	BHL	W	2-0		Matthews, Adcock
27	A	Abingdon Town	BHL	L	1-3		Vickers
May 2	H	Basingstoke Town	BHL	W	3-1		Matthews, Springett, Pollard
4	H	Whyteleafe	BHL	W	2-0		Springett 2

HEYBRIDGE SWIFTS PLAYING SQUAD 1996-97

Goalkeepers: Kingsley Banks (Witham T, Barking, Enfield, Basildon U, Dartford, Gillingham, Tottenham)
Defenders: Mark Cranfield (Braintree T, Brightlingsea U), **Kirk Game** (Great Wakering R, Stambridge, Chelmsford C, Homburg (Ger), Colchester, Southend), **David Rolfe** (Baldock T, Braintree T, Chelmsford C, Eton Manor), **Ashley Vickers** (Worcester C, Sheffield U, Sheffield Wed), **Keith Bain** (Wivenhoe T, Sudbury T, Wivenhoe T, Tiptree U, Wivenhoe T), **Wayne Adcock** (Witham T, Braintree T, Chelmsford C, Eton Manor)
Midfielders: Matt Jones (Chelmsford C, Southend, Arsenal (T)), **Darren Southgate** (Romford, Collier Row, Ford U, Billericay T, Collier Row, Sheffield U, Tottenham, Millwall), **Lee Abrehart** (Harwich & P, Brantham A), **Barry O'Dea** (Melbourne U (Aust), Witham T, Chelmsford C), **Mark Keen** (Chelmsford C, Enfield, Dartford, Witham T), **Nigel Hewes** (Dag & Red)
Forwards: Mitchell Springett (Wivenhoe T, Bury T, Chelmsford C, Braintree T, Wivenhoe T, Braintree T, Halstead T, Camb.U), **John Pollard** (Bury T, Colchester), **Gary Caldon** (Maldon T, Basildon U, Billericay T), **Dave Matthews** (East Thurrock U, Billericay T, Purfleet, Dagenham, Southend, Walsall, Basildon U, Aveley, West Ham (A))

Formed: 1928

HITCHIN TOWN

The Canaries

Hitchin Town F.C. - Back Row: Gary Roberts, Gary Williams, Tim Allpress, James Robinson, Gerald Sylvester, Jon Bone, Ian Scott, Dave Cooper, Adam Parker, Ken Gillard. Front Row: Steve Maylin, Gavin Covington, Neil Ryan, Chris McMenamin, Darren Thompson, Steve Conroy, Mark Burke, Lee Burns.

Chairman: Terry Barratt **General Manager:** Andy Melvin
Secretary: Roger Austin, 22 St Katherine's Close,Ickleford,Hitchin,Herts.SG5 3XS (01462 457811).
Manager: Micky Hazard & Paul Price **Asst Mgr:** Robin Wainwright **Coach:** Rob Johnson.
Fix Sec: Alan Sexton **Press Officer:** Bary Swain (01462 455096). **Physio:** Peter Prince.
Ground: Top Field, Fishponds Road, Hitchin SG5 1NU (01462 459028-matchdays only).
Directions: On A505 near town centre opposite large green. 1 mile from Hitchin (BR).
Capacity: 4,148 **Cover:** 1,000 **Seats:** 420 **Floodlights:** Yes **Metal Badges:** Yes.
Club Shop: Yes, Contact I Morgan & M Williams **Sponsors:** Bristol & West Building Society.
Colours: Yellow/green/green **Change:** Black & white/black/black. **Clubcall Line:** 0891 122 934
Previous Lges: Spartan 28-39/ Hert & Middx 39-45/ Athenian 39,45-63.
Record win: Spartan Lge 29-30 13-0 v Cowley, 13-0 v RAF.
Record defeat (in Isthmian League): 0-10; v Kingstonian, 65-66; v Slough Town, 79-80. Both away.
Record Attendance: 7,878 v Wycombe Wanderers, FA Amateur Cup 3rd Rd 18/2/56.
Midweek matchday: Tuesday **Reserve Team:** No (youth team).
Best FA Cup season: 2nd Rd (v Swindon, lost 1-3 (A)) 76-77, 2nd Rd (v Boston Utd, lost 0-1(A)) 73-74, 2nd Rd (v Wycombe Wand. lost 0-5 (H)) 94-95, 2nd Rd (v Gillingham lost 0-3 (A)) 95-96
Record Fees - Paid: £2,000 for Ray Seeking (Potton United, July 1989)
Received: £5,750 for Steve Conroy (Kingstonian, 90).
Players progressing to Football League: R Smith (Millwall & England), L Garwood (Spurs 46), C J Walker, W Odell, S Foss, R Stevens, T Clarke, G Goodyear, L Harwood, P Burridge, R Kitchener (Chelsea 54), D Bumstead, M Dixon, D Pacey (Luton 56), M Dixon & B Whitby (Luton 57), K Abiss (Brighton 57), D Hille, G Ley, R Morton, L Payne (Newcastle & Reading), M Small (Brighton), R Nugent (Barnet).
Clubhouse: (01462 434483). Members bar, Function Hall (hireable). Open every day. Steward: Eamonn Watson
Club Record (Isthmian Lge) Appearances: Paul Giggle 950+ 67-88.
Club Record (Isthmian Lge) goals: Paul Giggle, 129.
95-96 Captain: Mark Burke. **95-96 P.o.Y.:** Mark Burke.
95-96 Top scorer: Gary Williams 16 Lge & Cup goals.
Local Papers: Hitchin Gazette/Hitchin Comet - Home Counties Newspapers (01727 866166), Hitchin Herald & Post (01727 846866)
Local Radio: Chiltern (01582 666001), Three Counties (01582 454748).
Hons: FA Amateur Cup SF 60-61 62-63, Isthmian Lge R-up 68-69 (Div 1 92-93), Spartan Lge 34-35, AFA Sen Cup 30-31, Herts Snr Cup(18-record) London Sen Cup 69-70 (R-up 72-73), E Anglian Cup 72-73, Herts Charity Cup(16) Herts I'mediate Cup(8) Woolwich Trophy 82-83, Televised Sport International Cup 88-89 90-91, Southern Comb. Senior Floodlit Cup 90-91, FA Trophy 3rd Rd replay 76-77.

PROGRAMME DETAILS:
Pages: 48 **Price:** £1
Editor: Barry Swain

HITCHIN TOWN'S 1995-96 CAMPAIGN

DATE		OPPONENTS	COMP	RESULT		GATE	GOALSCORERS
Aug 15	A	Stevenage Borough	HCC2	L	0-3	818	
19	H	Harrow Borough	IL	L	1-5	304	Burke
26	A	Yeading	IL	L	0-2	160	
29	H	Dulwich Hamlet	IL	L	1-3	281	G. Williams
Sept 2	H	Worthing	IL	D	2-2	250	McMenamin, Ryan pen
9	A	Yeovil Town	IL	D	1-1	1739	G.Williams
12	H	Canvey Island	GICI	W	4-1	185	Conroy 2,Scott,Burke
16	H	Molesey	IL	L	0-1	292	
23	H	Aylesbury	IL	L	0-3	418	
30	A	Bromley	IL	W	2-0	310	G.Williams, Parker
Oct 07	A	Kingstonian	IL	W	0-1	524	Burns
21	H	St.Albans City	FAC4q	W	2-1	1147	Burns, G.Williams
24	H	St.Albans City	IL	D	0-0	443	
28	A	Carshalton Athletic	IL	D	1-1	379	G.Williams
31	A	Sutton United	GIC2	W	1-0	229	G.Williams
Nov 4	H	Boreham Wood	IL	L	1-2	511	Covington
11	H	Bristol Rovers	FAC1	W	2-1	3101	Conroy, Burns
14	H	Chertsey Town	IL	W	2-0	291	Burns, Gillard
18	A	Hayes	IL	D	1-1	303	Ryan
21	A	Bishops Stortford	CATLC2	L	0-3	201	
25	H	Bognor Regis Town	FAUT3q	L	1-2	394	Gillard
Dec 2	A	Gillingham	FAC2	L	0-3	7142	
5	A	Hertford Town	HSC2	W	6-0	60	Conroy 3, Issott 2, Roberts
9	H	Enfield	IL	W	1-0	611	G.Williams
12H	H	Bishops Storford	GIC3	W	4-1	121	G.Williams, Roberts 2, Cooper pen
16	A	Walton & Hersham	IL	L	1-4	186	Roberts
19	A	Hendon	IL`	W	2-1	182	Brett, Roberts
Jan 2	H	Sutton United	IL	W	1-0	303	Roberts
6	A	Worthing	IL	L	0-2	353	
13	H	Yeovil Town	IL	L	1-2	523	Conroy
20	A	Harrow Borough	IL	W	2-1	276	Clarke 2
23	A	Wokingham Town	GICQF	W	3-2	110	Clarke, Burke,G.Williams
30	H	Bishops Stortford	HSCQF	W	4-1	192	G.Williams 2, Burke, og
Feb 3	A	Dulwich Hamlet	IL	D	3-3	411	G.Williams 3
10	H	Bromley	IL	W	2-1	373	G.Williams, Clark
13	A	Grays Athletic	IL	L	0-1	197	
17	A	Molesey	IL	L	1-2	142	G.Williams
21	H	Hayes	IL	L	1-3	164	og
24	H	Carshalton Athletic	IL	L	2-5	384	Clark, Parker
27	H	Aldershot Town	GICSF(1)	L	0-1	654	
Mar 2	A	St.Albans City	IL	L	1-5	626	McMenamin pen
5	H	Hendon	IL	L	0-1	209	
9	A	Aylesbury United	IL	L	1-2	503	Clark
12	A	Aldershot Town	GICSF	L	0-2	1965	
16	H	Kingstonian	IL	D	1-1	364	Clark
18	A	Purfleet	IL	D	1-1	156	Parker
23	H	Grays Athletic	IL	W	101	369	Parker
26	A	Barnet	HSCSF	L	0-1	284	
30	A	Boreham Wood	IL	L	0-1	348	
Apr 2	A	Bishop Stortford	IL	D	2-2	265	Burke,G.Williams
6	A	Sutton United	IL	L	0-4	490	
8	H	Bishops Stortford	IL	D	1-1	436	Parker
13	A	Chertsey Town	IL	L	1-2	361	McMenamin
16	H	Yeading	IL	L	0-3	201	
20	H	Purfleet	IL	W	2-0	299	Dunlop, Gillard
27	A	Enfield	IL	L	0-3	982	
May 4	H	Walton & Hersham	IL	L	0-2	331	

HITCHIN TOWN PLAYING SQUAD 1996-97

Goalkeepers: Gerald Sylvester (Eynesbury R, Haverhill R, Northampton), **Lee Pearce** (Barnet)

Defenders: Mark Parsons (Kettering T, Northampton), **Steve Miller** (Vauxhall Motors, Stevenage B, St. Albans C, Hitchin T), **Ken Gillard** (Chesham U, Northampton, Luton), **Mark Burke** (Luton, QPR (A)), **Jon Bone** (Baldock T, Hitchin T, Luton), **Lee Henry** (Youth team), **Gavin Covington** (Wycombe W, Hitchin T, Barnet, Dunstable), **Danny Swale** (West Ham)

Midfielders: Ian Scott (St. Albans C, Aylesbury U, Luton), **Darren Thompson** (Luton), **Adam Parker** (Stevenage B, Hoddesdon T), **Dave Drury** (Stotfold, Langford, Stotfold), **Micky Hazard** (Tottenham, Swindon, Portsmouth, Chelsea, Tottenham), **Mick Wilson** (Monaghan U, Linfield), **Neil Ryan** (Luton), **Barry Dellar** (Arlesey T), **Sam Turner** (Luton)

Forwards: Paul Olney (Barton R, Hitchin T, Bedford T, Baldock T, Hitchin T), **David Fenton** (Olney T), **David Cooper** (Exeter, Luton), **John Coley** (Stotfold, Langford), **Bradley Anderson** (Leighton T, Hendon, Hertford T, Stevenage B, St. Albans C, Boreham Wood, Watford), **Marvin Bates** (Stevenage B), **Godfrey Ingram** (San Jose (USA), St. Albans C, Peterborough, San Jose (USA), Luton)

KINGSTONIAN

Formed: 1885 The K's

Kingstonian FC. *Photo: Andrew Chitty.*

Chairman: G M Child **Vice Chairman:** Peter Gellard. **President:** J Webster.
Chief Executive: Chris Kelly.
Football Secretary: W R McNully, 71 Largewood Ave., Tolworth, Surbiton KT6 7NX (0181 391 4552).
Manager: Bill Smith. **Asst Manager:** John Broughton. **Coach:** Gavin Nebbling.
Press Officer: B P Frawley (0181 541 5250) **Physio:** Steve Wells.
Commercial & Administration Manager: Mrs A Dickinson (0181 547 3336).
Ground: Kingsmeadow Stadium, Kingston Road, Kingston-on-Thames KT1 3PB (0181 547 3335).
Directions: From town centre - Cambridge Rd on to Kingston Rd (A2043) to Malden Rd. From A3, turn off at New Malden, turn left on to A2043 - grd 1 mile on left. Half mile from Norbiton (BR)
Capacity: 9,000 **Cover:** 3,500 **Seats:** 690 **Floodlights:** Yes **Metal Badges:** Yes.
Club Shop: Sells programmes, shirts, souvenirs. Contact Mrs Ann Dickinson (0181 747 3336).
Cols: Red & white hoops/black/black **Change colours:** Black & blue stripes **Fanzine:** Yes.
Club Sponsors: Cherry Red Records. **Newsline:** 0891 884 441.
Previous Lges: Kingston & Dist./ West Surrey/ Southern Suburban/ Athenian 1919-29.
Previous Names: Kingston & Surbiton YMCA 1885-87/ Saxons 87-90/ Kingston Wanderers 1893-1904/ Old Kingstonians 08-19.
Prev. Ground: Various to 1921/ Richmond Rd 21-89.
Midweek matchday: Tuesday **Reserve League:** Suburban.
Record win: 15-1 v Delft, friendly 5/9/51 (competitive: 10-0 v Hitchin (H), Isthmian Lge 19/3/66).
Record defeat: 0-11 v Ilford (A), Isthmian Lge 13/2/37.
Record Attendance: 4,582 v Chelsea (Friendly) 22.7.95.
Best FA Cup season: 2nd Rd Proper v Aylesbury U lost after beating Brighton 1-0 1st Rd 94-95.
Record Fees - Paid: £10,000 for R Cherry (Redbridge Forest 91)
Received: £10,000 for D Harlow Farnborough 95.
Players progressing to Football League: C Nastri (C Palace), H Lindsay (Southampton 65), G Still (Brighton 79), D Byrne (Gillingham 1985), J Power (Brentford 87).
Clubhouse: (0181 547 3336) + banqueting centre, open 7 days a week. 3 bars capacity 400.
Club Record Goalscorer: Johnny Whig 295
Club Record Appearances: Micky Preston 555.
95-96 Captain: Andy Riley. **95-96 P.o.Y.:** Andy Riley.
95-96 Top scorer: Jon Warden.
Local Newspaper: Surrey Comet (0181 546 2261).
Local Radio Stations: County Sound.
Hons: FA Amtr Cup 32-33 (R-up 59-60), Isthmian Lg 33-34 36-37 (R-up 47-48 62-63, Div 1 R-up 84-85), Icis Lg Cup winners 95-96, Athenian Lg 23-24 25-26 (R-up 26-27), London Snr Cup 62-63 64-65 86-87 (R-up 23-24 25-26 30-31 46-47 83-84), Surrey Snr Cup(9) 25-26 30-32 34-35 38-39 51-52 62-64 66-67 (R-up 90-91).

PROGRAMME DETAILS:
Pages: 36 **Price:** £1
Editor: Brian Giffard
(0181 940 6448)

KINGSTONIAN'S 1995-96 CAMPAIGN

DATE		OPPONENTS	COMP	RESULT		GATE	GOALSCORERS
Aug 19	H	Worthing	IL	D	1-1	389	Wiggins
22	A	Bromley	IL	D	1-1	664	Warden
26	A	Harrow Borough	IL	L	1-2	338	Bolton
29	H	Molesey	IL	D	1-1	394	Riley
Sept 2	H	Purfleet	IL	D	1-1	397	Bolton
9	A	Sutton Utd	IL	W	1-0	944	Bolton
16	H	Yeovil Town	IL	D	2-2	642	Bowyer, Jasper
23	H	Sutton Utd	IL	D	2-2	747	Bowyer, Broderick
30	A	Yeading	IL	W	2-0	281	Stevens, Wingfield
Oct 3	H	Grays Athletic	IL	W	1-0	???	Brooker
7	H	Hitchin Town	IL	L	0-1	524	
9	A	Carshalton Ath	IL	W	3-0	843	Warden, Luckett, ??
14	A	Aylesbury Utd	IL	W	2-0	739	Brooker, Wingfield
28	A	Boreham Wood	IL	D	0-0	522	
31	H	Hayes	IL	W	1-0	432	Luckett
Nov 18	A	Bishops Stortford	IL	W	3-2	422	Warden 2, Wingfield
25	H	Enfield	IL	L	0-1	940	
Dec 16	A	Hendon	IL	W	3-0	278	Walden, Brooker, Fisher
26	A	Chertsey Town	IL	L	1-2	518	Riley
Jan 2	H	Walton & Hersham	IL	W	1-0	402	Jones
6	A	Purfleet	IL	W	3-1	248	Brooker 2, Bolton
13	H	Bromley	IL	L	0-1	602	
23	A	Worthing	IL	W	5-0	334	Stevens, Luckett 2, Akuamoah 2
Feb 3	A	Molesey	IL	W	2-0	310	Nebbling
10	H	Yeading	IL	W	3-1	419	Jasper, Warmington, Warden
17	A	Yeovil Town	IL	D	1-1	1953	Warden
24	H	Boreham Wood	IL	W	1-0	523	Annon
Mar 2	A	Hayes	IL	L	1-2	431	Warden
9	H	Carshalton Ath	IL	W	2-1	707	Warden, Nebbling
16	A	Hitchin Town	IL	D	1-1	365	Warden
19	A	St Albans	IL	W	2-1	469	Warden, Jones
23	H	Aylesbury Utd	IL	D	1-1	598	Danzey (og)
26	H	Harrow Borough	IL	L	0-1	302	
30	A	Grays Athletic	IL	D	1-1	261	Warden
Apr 6	A	Walton & Hersham	IL	W	2-0	402	M Jones, Warden
8	H	Chertsey Town	IL	L	0-2	422	
13	A	Enfield	IL	L	1-2	904	Bolton
16	H	Bishops Stortford	IL	W	2-1	259	D.Jones, Warden
18	H	Dulwich Hamlet	IL	L	0-2	418	
20	H	St. Albans	IL	W	4-1	501	Bolton 4
27	A	Dulwich Hamlet	IL	W	3-1	629	Bolton 3
May 4	H	Hendon	IL	L	0-1	421	

KINGSTONIAN PLAYING SQUAD 1996-97

Goalkeepers: Dave Root (Hendon, Eton Manor, Hendon, Walthamstow Ave, Barking, Launceston T), **Richard Morgan** (Carshalton A)
Defenders: Andy Riley (Carshalton A, Leatherhead, Whyteleafe, Malden Vale), **Andy Fisher** (Carshalton A, Dulwich Hamlet, Dorking, Molesey, Leatherhead, Carshalton A), **John Finch** (Fulham, Dorking, Molesey, Leatherhead, Chelsea), **Matt Elverson** (Walton & H), **Gavin Nebbeling** (Preston, Fulham, Crystal Palace, Arcadia Shepherds (SA)), **Dave Stevens** (Carshalton A, Crystal Palace), **Danny Lavender** (Hampton)
Midfielders: Jon Warden (Carshalton A, Tooting & Mitcham U, Croydon), **David Jones** (Sutton U, Staines T, Walton & H, Epsom & Ewell, Kingstonian, Epsom & Ewell, Wimbledon), **Lionel Best** (Croydon, Dulwich Hamlet, Elms, Fisher A), **Scott Corbett** (Hampton), **Danny Brooker** (Sutton U, Dorking, Wimbledon (T))
Forwards: Jimmy Bolton (Carshalton A, Harrow B, Farnborough T, Kiruna (Swe), Farnborough T, Tooting & Mitcham U, Farnborough T, Wimbledon, Hillingdon, Tottenham), **Tim Hope** (Barking, Croydon, Tooting & Mitcham U), **Darren Annon** (Brentford, Carshalton A), **Steve Darlington** (Wokingham T, Staines T, Windsor & Eton, Chalfont St. Peter, Hounslow), **Eddie Akamoah** (Carshalton A)

OXFORD CITY

1882 | City

Back Row: Alan Thorne (Asst Mgr), Andy Smith, Martin Brown, David Summer, Graham Bowerman (Physio), Mick Torres, Andy Martin, Richard Peirson, Andy Thomas (Player/Mgr). Front Row: Stuart Beavon, Liam Herbert, Steve Fontaine, Neil Greig, Stewart McCleary, Kurt Douglas, Mark Hewitson, Howard Kemp.

Chairman: M Woodley **Vice Chairman:** R Holt **President:** J Grosvenor
Press Officer/Secretary: John Shepperd, 20 Howe Close, Wheatley, Oxford OX33 1SS (01865 872181).
Manager: Andy Thomas **Asst Manager:** Alan Thorne **Physio:** G Bowerman.
Ground: Court Place Farm, Marsh Lane, Marston, Oxford (01865 744493).
Directions: From London M40/A40, ring-road to North, take 1st slip road, follow signs to John Radcliffe hospital, ground on left after leaving flyover. From the north same ring-road.
Capacity: 3,000 **Seats:** 300 **Cover:** 400 **Floodlights:** Yes
Colours: White & blue hoops **Change colours:** Yellow/black/black**Club Shop:** Yes.
Midweek Matchday: Tuesday **Sponsors:** Unipart O.C.M.
Prev. Grnds: The White House 1882-1988/ Cuttleslowe Pk 90-91/ Pressed Steel, Romanway 91-93.
Previous League: Isthmian 07-88/ South Midlands 90-93.
Record Gate: 9,500 v Leytonstone, FA Amateur Cup 1950.
Record Fees - Paid: £3,000 for S Adams (Woking)
Received: £2,000 for P Dallaway (Witney Town).
Best FA Cup year: Second Round 69-70 (lost 1-5 at home to Swansea Town).
Reserve Team's League: 'Minerva' South Midlands Reserve Section.
Players progressing to Football League: A Blakeman (Brentford 1946), C Holton (Arsenal 1950), K Savin (Derby 1950), E Wilcox (WBA 1948), R Adams (Blackpool 1948), A Jeffries (Brentford 1949), P James (Luton 1949), D Gordon (WBA 1947), V Mobley (Sheffield Wednesday 1963), J Varney (Hull 1950), P Lee (Hereford 1973), H Poole (Port Vale 1955), G Parker (Luton 1981), M Keown (Arsenal 1984), D Meeson (Wolves 1952).
Record win: 9-0 v Harlow Town, Isthmian League 9/10/76.
Record defeat: 0-8 v Wycombe Wanderers, Isthmian League - date unknown.
Clubhouse: Open matchdays, most refreshments available.
Club Record Scorer: John Woodley
Club Record Appearances: John Woodley.
95-96 Captain: Jon Muttock.
95-96 P.o.Y.: Terry Morrisey.
Local Press: Oxford Mail
Local Radio: Radio Oxford Thames Valley FM, Fox FM.
Hons: FA Amteur Cup 05-06 (R-up 02-03 12-13),F.A.Vase R-Up 94-95, Isthmian Lg R-up 34-35 45-46 (Div 1 R-up 77-78), Icis Lg Div 1 Champions 95-96,South Midlands Lg 92-93, Oxon Snr Cup(27).

PROGRAMME DETAILS:
Pages: 60 **Price:** 50p
Editor: Secretary

OXFORD CITY'S 1995-96 CAMPAIGN

DATE		OPPONENTS	COMP	RESULT		GATE	GOALSCORERS
Aug 12	H	Basingstoke Town	IL	W	3-2		Herbert, Thomas, Pierson
20	A	Chesham United	IL	W	2-0		Martin, Pierson
29	H	Marlow	IL	L	1-6		Kemp
Sept 2	H	Ruislip Manor	IL	D	2-2		C. Fontaine, S. Fontaine
5	A	Staines Town	GIC	L	1-3		
9	H	Witney Town	FAC	D	1-1		A. Thomas
12	A	Witney Town	FAC	L	1-3		S. Fontaine
16	H	Tooting & Mitcham	IL	W	3-1		Hewitson, Pierson, Morrissey
30	A	Barking	IL	W	3-2		Douglas, Herbert, Charles
Oct 7	A	Maidenhead United	IL	W	2-0		Herbert, Martin
10	H	Berkhamsted Town	IL	W	1-0		Brown
14	A	Aldershot Town	IL	W	2-0		S. Fontaine, Hewitson
21	A	Abingdon Town	IL	L	2-4		S. Fontaine, Charles
28	H	Wokingham Town	IL	W	2-0		Douglas
Nov 4	A	Walton & Hersham	FAT	D	0-0		
7	H	Walton & Hersham	FAT	W	5-2		Herbert 2, Thomas, Morrissey, S. Fontaine
11	H	Wembley	IL	W	5-1		McLeary 2, Kemp, Herbert, Martin
18	A	Staines Town	IL	W	2-1		Martin, Thomas
21	A	Uxbridge	IL	D	2-2		Herbert, og
25	A	Bromley	FAT	D	1-1		Thomas
28	H	Bromley	FAT	W	3-2		Charles, Morrissey, Brown
Dec 2	A	Leyton Pennant	IL	W	3-1		McLeary 3
9	H	Whyteleafe	IL	W	2-0		McLeary, Charles
12	H	Basingstoke Town	CC	W	1-0		
16	A	Billericay Town	IL	L	0-1		
23	H	Chesham United	IL	W	1-0		McLeary
Jan 3	H	Bognor Regis Town	IL	W	1-0		Hewitson
6	A	Ruislip Manor	IL	W	5-4		McLeary 2, Muttock, S. Fontaine, Martin
13	H	Uxbridge	IL	W	1-0		Martin
15	A	Kingstonian	CC	L	3-5		
20	H	Merthyr Tydfil	FAT	L	1-2		Herbert
28	H	Aldershot Town	IL	L	1-3		S. Fontaine
Feb 3	A	Marlow	IL	W	4-2		S. Fontaine 2, C. Fontaine, Thomas
10	H	Barking	IL	W	1-0		Herbert
Mar 2	H	Abingdon Town	IL	D	3-3		McLeary, Thomas, S. Fontaine
9	A	Berkhamsted Town	IL	W	3-2		McLeary 2, Thomas
12	H	Barton Rovers	IL	W	3-0		McLeary, Smith, Pierson
16	H	Maidenhead United	IL	D	2-2		Smith, Herbert
19	A	Tooting & Mitcham	IL	W	3-1		McLeary, Greig, S. Fontaine
23	A	Wembley	IL	W	2-0		Muttock, S. Fontaine
26	A	Basingstoke Town	IL	L	1-3		Lee
30	H	Heybridge Swifts	IL	W	4-3		S. Fontaine 2, McLeary 2
Apr 6	A	Bognor Regis Town	IL	L	1-3		McLeary
8	H	Thame United	IL	W	5-0		McLeary 3, Pierson, Herbert
13	A	Barton Rovers	IL	L	0-1		
16	A	Heybridge Swifts	IL	D	2-2		McLeary, Morrissey
20	H	Leyton Pennant	IL	D	2-2		S. Fontaine 2
23	H	Staines Town	IL	D	1-1		Herbert
27	A	Whyteleafe	IL	W	5-3		Thomas, Herbert, Phillips, Beckham, Smart
30	A	Wokingham Town	IL	W	4-2		S. Fontaine 2, Smith, McLeary
May 4	H	Billericay Town	IL	W	4-1		S. Fontaine 2, Morrissey, Martin

OXFORD CITY PLAYING SQUAD 1996-97

Goalkeepers: Mick Torres (Local football), **Lee Perkins** (Brackley T, Thame U, Bicester T, Thame U, Easington Sports)
Defenders: Kurt Douglas (Abingdon T, Thame U, Abingdon U, Bicester T), **Richard Pierson** (Local football), **Terry Morrissey** (Wokingham T, Oxford U), **Andy Smith** (Local football), **Jon Muttock** (Thame U, Carterton T, Oxford C, Wycombe W, Oxford U), **Stuart Fisher** (Abingdon T, Oxford U (T)), **Martin Brown** (Abingdon T), **Andy Martin** (Abingdon T, Bicester T, Woodstock T)
Midfielders: Justin Lee (Abingdon T, Arsenal), **Roger Charles** (Abingdon T, Oxford U (T)), **Andy Thomas** (Plymouth, Bradford C, Newcastle, Oxford U), **Liam Herbert** (Abingdon T, Oxford C, Abingdon T, Bicester T, Banbury U, Bicester T, Abingdon T, Thame U)
Forwards: Chris Fontaine (Abingdon U), **Stewart McCleary** (Local football), **Steve Fontaine** (Abingdon U, Oxford C), **Keith Holmes** (Marlow, Oxford U (T)), **Howard Forinton** (Abingdon T, Oxford U (T))

PURFLEET

1985 Fleet

Purfleet FC. *Photo: P C W Barnes.*

Chairman: Harry South **Vice Chairman:** Ken Worrall **President:** Keith Parker.
Secretary/Press Officer: Norman Posner, 1 Chase House Gdns, Hornchurch, Essex RM11 2PJ (01708 458301).
Manager: Gary Calder **Asst Manager:** Chris King **Coach:** Trevor Moore
Commercial Manager: Bob Andrews (01268 415149). **Physio:** Bob Johnson.
Ground: Thurrock Hotel, Ship Lane, Grays, Essex (01708 868901) (Fax 01708 866705)
Directions: M25 or A13 to Dartford tunnel r'bout. Ground is fifty yards on right down Ship Lane. Nearest station is Purfleet, two miles from ground.
Capacity: 4,500 **Cover:** 1,000 **Seats:** 300 **Floodlights:** Yes
Club Shop: Yes, selling programmes and magazines. Contact Tommy South (01708 868901).
Colours: Green/yellow **Change colours:** Claret/blue.
Main Sponsors: Mann Enterprises **Team Sponsors:** Scantruck Ltd
Prog Sponsors: London Container Services
Previous Grounds: None. **Previous League:** Essex Senior 85-89.
Midweek home matchday: Monday **Reserve Team's League:** Essex & Herts Border Combination.
Record Attendance: 950 v West Ham United, friendly 1989.
Best FA Cup season: Third Qualifying Rd 94-95 (lost 1-2 at home to Yeading).
Record win: 10-0 v Stansted (H) 86-87, v East Ham Utd (A) 87-88 (both Essex Senior League).
Record defeat: 0-5 v Kingsbury Town (H), Isthmian Lge Division One 89-90.
Players progressing to Football League:
Paul Cobb & Lee Williams (Leyton O.)
Clubhouse: 10am-11pm every day. Snooker, squash, weights room, aerobics, a-la carte restaurant, steam room.Three Bars.56 Bedroom Hotel.
Steward: Tommy South.
Club Record Goalscorer: Terry Bellamy, 59.
Club Record Appearances: Colin McBride, 234.
95-96 Captain:
95-96 P.o.Y.:
95-96 Top scorer:
Local Newspapers: Thurrock Recorder, Thurrock Gazette.
Local Radio Stations: Essex Radio, BBC Radio Essexx.
Hons: Isthmian Lg Div 2 91-92 (Div 1 R-up 93-94, Div 2 Nth R-up 88-89, Associate Members Tphy 91-92), Essex Snr Lg 87-88 (Lg Cup(2) 86-88), Stanford Charity Cup 87-88 (R-up 85-86).Essex Thames-Side Trophy 1994-95. Loctite Trophy 91-92. Essex Bus Houses Sen L/Cup 93-94. F Budden Trophy 94-95. Essex & Herts Border Comb R-up 94-95.

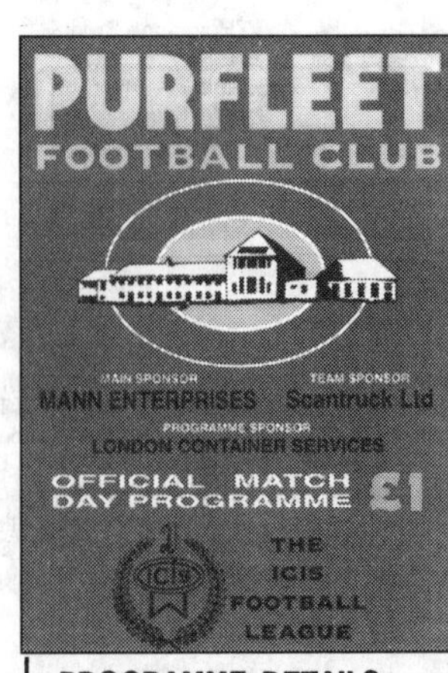

PROGRAMME DETAILS:
Pages: 44 **Price:** £1
Editor: Secretary

PURFLEET'S 1995-96 CAMPAIGN

DATE		OPPONENTS	COMP	RESULT		GATE	GOALSCORERS
Aug 19	A	St Albans C.	IL	L	0-3		
21	H	Chertsey Town	IL	L	1-3		Bourne
26	H	Enfield	IL	D	1-1		Crown
Sept 2	A	Kingstonian	IL	D	1-1		Reilly
4	H	Boreham Wood	GIC	L	0-1		
9	H	Felixstowe T.	FAC	W	4-0		Rees McFarlane Leslie Crown
16	A	Carshalton A.	IL	L	1-3		Jeyes
23	H	Chesham United	FAC	W	3-1		Rees Crown Matthews
26	A	Bishop's S.	IL	D	1-1		Crown
30	H	Hayes	IL	D	0-0		
Oct 7	A	Dagenham & R.	FAC	D	1-1		McFarlane
9	H	Dagenham & R.	FAC	W	2-1		Bourne Jeyes
14	A	Berkhamsted T.	FAT	W	2-1		Jeyes Matthews
17	A	Yeading	IL	L	1-3		McFarlane
21	H	Rushden & D.	FAC	D	1-1		Crown
24	A	Rushden & D.	FAC	L	1-3		Donovan
28	H	Hendon	IL	L	2-3		Crown 2
Nov 4	H	Corby Town	FAT	W	6-1		Crown 3 Jeyes Bates Comer
6	H	Boreham Wood	IL	W	1-0		Southon
11	A	Dulwich Hamlet	IL	D	1-1		Goldstone
13	H	Hayes	CC	W	2-0		Southon Cobb
18	H	Yeovil Town	IL	L	0-3		
21	A	Aveley	ESC	W	3-0		Cobb Jeyes Rees
25	A	Chertsey Town	FAT	W	1-0		Bourne
28	A	Aylesbury Utd.	CC	W	1-0		Cobb
Dec 13	A	Harrow Borough	IL	D	2-2		Rees 2
16	H	Aylesbury Utd.	IL	L	1-2		Rees
19	A	Billericay T.	ETT	W	2-0		Cobb Rees
23	A	Boreham Wood	IL	L	1-2		Nesling
Jan 1	A	Molesey	IL	W	3-2		Bourne Deadman Jeyes
6	H	Kingstonian	IL	L	1-3		Deadman
8	A	Collier Row	ESC	W	1-0		Bourne
13	A	Chertsey Town	Il	L	1-2		Bourne
20	A	Rushden & D.	FAT	W	1-0		Jeyes
23	A	Leyton Pennant	CC	L	1-5		Schneider
30	A	Sutton United	IL	L	0-1		
Feb 3	H	Bishop's S.	IL	L	1-2		Rees
5	H	Southend Utd.	ESC	L	2-4		Jeyes Brown
10	A	Macclesfield T.	FAT	L	1-2		own goal
12	H	St. Albans C.	IL	L	0-1		
17	H	Carshalton A.	IL	W	2-1		Bourne Portway
19	H	Worthing	IL	W	3-1		Portway 2 Cobb
24	A	Hendon	IL	W	4-2		Cobb 2 Donovan Bourne
27	A	Bromley	IL	W	2-0		Cobb Bourne
Mar 2	H	Yeading	IL	L	1-2		Portway
4	H	Grays Athletic	IL	W	1-0		Jeyes
9	A	Worthing	IL	W	2-1		Portway 2
11	H	Walton & H.	IL	W	2-1		Portway 2
16	H	Sutton United	IL	W	2-1		Portway 2
18	H	Hitchin Town	IL	D	1-1		Cobb
23	H	Dulwich Hamlet	IL	W	3-1		Portway 2 Cobb
26	A	Hayes	IL	L	1-2		Rees
30	A	Walton & H.	IL	W	2-1		Rees Deadman
Apr 2	A	Yeovil Town	IL	L	1-2		Cobb
6	H	Molesey	IL	L	0-2		
8	A	Grays Athletic	IL	L	0-2		
13	H	Harrow Borough	IL	L	0-1		
16	A	Enfield	IL	L	0-3		
20	A	Hitchin Town	IL	L	0-2		
25	A	Leyton Pennant	ETT	L	2-6		McFarlane Jeyes
27	H	Bromley	IL	D	1-1		Deadman
May 4	A	Aylesbury Utd.	IL	L	0-1		

PURFLEET PLAYING SQUAD 1996-97

Goalkeepers: Micky Desborough (Canvey Is, Dag & Red, Braintree T, Chelmsford C, Purfleet, Aveley, Hornchurch, Clapton)

Defenders: Jim McFarlane (Clapton, Millwall Wanderers), **Graham Daly** (Aveley, Walthamstow Ave, Woodford T), **Steve Dickinson** (QPR (T)), **Steve Mosely** (Dover A, Chelmsford C, Enfield, Dartford, Barking, Billericay T, Stambridge), **John Deadman** (Hendon, Grays A), **Martin Carthy** (Erith & B, Fisher`93, Erith & B)

Midfielders: John Rees (Aveley), **Danny Snowsill** (Youth team), **Paul Donovan** (Dagenham, Fulham (T)), **John Nestling** (Youth team), **Lee Matthews** (Southend)

Forwards: Steve Portway (Romford, Gloucester C, Gravesend, Barking, Boreham Wood, Witham T, Brentwood, B Stortford, Walthamstow Ave, Dagenham), **Paul Cavell** (Macclesfield T, Gateshead, Dag & Red, Boston U, Stafford R, Goole T, Worksop T), **Paul Cobb** (Enfield, Purfleet, Leyton O, Purfleet), **Nigel Jeyes** (Aveley, Basildon U, Billericay T, Tilbury, Barking, Dartford)

Formed: 1908

ST ALBANS CITY

The Saints

St Albans City photographed with Coventry City prior to a friendly match. *Photo - Brian Hubball*

Chairman: Bernard Tominey **Vice Chairman:** John Adams **President:** Cllr Malcolm MacMillan
Secretary: Steve Trulock, 42 Heath Road, St Albans AL1 4DP (01727 834920).
Manager: Alan Randall. **Physio:** Judith Monteath **Newsline:** 0891 664354
Press Off.: Dave Tavener (01582 401487) **Comm. Director:** Graham McDougall (01727 864296/866819).
Ground: Clarence Park, York Rd, St Albans, Herts AL1 4PL (01727 866819).
Directions: Left out of St Albans station - Clarence Pk 200yds ahead across Hatfield Rd. M25 - jct 21 to Noke Hotel island, straight on thru Chiswell Green towards St Albans, straight over 2 mini-r'bouts and one larger island, thru two sets of lights and right at island at far end of city centre (St Peters Str.) into Hatfield Rd, over 1 mini-r'bout, left at 2nd lights into Clarence Rd, ground on left.
Capacity: 6,000 **Cover:** 1,900 **Seats:** 904 **Floodlights:** Yes **Metal Badges:** Yes
Club Shop: Managed by Terry Edwards (01727 833685) and Ray Stanton. Large selection of club merchandise and League and non-League programmes. Magazines, videos etc.
Colours: Blue/gold trim. **Change cols:** All white.
Previous Leagues: Herts County 08-10/ Spartan 08-20/ Athenian 20-23.
Midweek home matchday: Tuesday **Record Gate:** 9,757 v Ferryhill Ath., FA Amtr Cup QF 27/2/26.
Record win: 14-0 v Aylesbury United (H),
Record loss: 0-11 v Wimbledon (H), Isthmian Lg 9/11/46.
Best FA Cup season: 2nd Rd replay 68-69 (lost 1-3 at Walsall after 1-1 draw), 80-81 (lost 1-4 at Torquay after 1-1 draw).
Record Fees - Paid: £4,500 for Martin Duffield (Sutton United, March 1992)
Rec.: £92,750 for Dean Austin (Southend 90/Spurs).
Players progressing to Football League: A Grimsdell (Spurs 11), R Burke (Man Utd), J Meadows (W'ford 51), M Rose (Charlton 63), J Kinnear (Spurs 65), J Mitchell (Fulham 72), A Cockram (Brentford 88), D Austin (Southend 90), T Kelly (Stoke 90), M Danzey (Cambridge 92), D Williams (Brentford 93).
Clubhouse: Tea bar within ground serves hot food. Clubhouse open matchdays and available for daytime and evening functions.
Clubhouse manager: Ray McCord (01727 866819 or 837956).
Club Record Goalscorer: W H (Billy) Minter 356 (top scorer for 12 consecutive seasons 1920-32).
Club Record Appearances: Phil Wood 900 (62-85)
95-96 Captain: Kevin Mudd **95-96 P.o.Y.:** Gareth Howells
95-96 Top scorer: Steve Clark 28, (Total 191, 2nd highest in club)
Local Newspapers: St Albans & District Observer, St Albans Herald.
Local Radio Stations: Chiltern Radio, Super Gold Sport, BBC Three Counties.
Hons: Isthmian Lg 23-24 26-27 27-28 (R-up 54-55 92-93, Div 1 85-86, Div 2 R-up 83-84, Lg Cup R-up 89-90, Res. Sect. R-up 48-49 60-61 61-62), Athenian Lg 20-21 21-22 (R-up 22-23), Spartan Lg 11-12 (R-up 12-13, East Div 09-10), Herts Co. Lg 09-10 (West Div 08-09, Aubrey Cup(res) 61-62), London Snr Cup 70-71 (R-up 69-70), AFA Snr Cup 33-34 (R-up 30-31 32-33 34-35), E Anglian Cup 92-93, Herts Snr Cup(12) (R-up 10), Herts Snr Tphy 86-87, Herts Charity Cup(25) (R-up(18), Mithras Cup 64-65 71-72 (R-up 76-77), Wycombe F'lit Cup(2) 68-70, St Albans Hosp Cup 45-46, Hitchin Centenary Cup 70-71 (R-up 71-72), Victory Cup 25-26 27-28, Liege Cup 26-27, Billy Minter Invit. Cup 90-91 91-92 92-93, FA Amtr Cup SF(4) 22-23 24-26 69-70, FA Tphy 2nd Rd 81-82 92-93.

PROGRAMME DETAILS:
Pages: 40 **Price:** £1.30
Editor: Ray Stanton
(0181 561 6830

ST. ALBANS CITY'S 1995-96 CAMPAIGN

DATE		OPPONENTS	COMP	RESULT		GATE	GOALSCORERS
Aug 12	H	Purfleet	IL	W	3-0	492	Howell, Daly, Clark
22	A	Worthing	IL	W	5-1	562	Daly, Clark, Attrell
26	A	Dulwich Hamlet	IL	L	1-3	385	Clark
29	H	Hendon	IL	W	3-1	425	Daly, og 2
Sept 2	H	Yeading	IL	L	0-1	456	
9	H	Barton Rovers	FAC 1Q	W	4-1	407	Clark, Blackman, Howell, Blake
13	A	Harrow Borough	IL	D	0-0	324	
16	H	Sutton United	IL	D	2-2	651	Gurney, Blake
23	A	Woodbridge Town	FAC 2Q	D	1-1	292	Howell
26	H	Woodbridge Town	FAC 2QR	W	2-0	358	Howell, Gurney
30	A	Walton & Hersham	IL	W	2-1	281	Duffield, Attrell
Oct 7	H	Romford	FAC 3Q	W	3-1	649	Daly, Duffield, Clark
10	H	Enfield	IL	W	1-0	1102	Clark
14	H	Yeovil Town	IL	D	2-2	853	Clark, Blake
21	A	Hitchin Town	FAC 4Q	L	1-2	1147	Mudd
24	A	Hitchin Town	IL	D	0-0	443	
28	H	Chertsey Town	IL	W	2-0	551	Clark, Howell
31	A	Sawbridgeworth Town	EFC	D	1-1	105	Howell
Nov 4	A	Grays Athletic	IL	W	3-0	212	Howell, Clark 2
8	A	Collier Row	LCC 1	L	1-2	163	Mudd
11	A	Bishop's Stortford	IL	L	2-3	487	Howell, Clark
14	H	Sawbridgeworth Town	EFC	D	2-2	121	Clark 2
18	H	Aylesbury United	IL	W	2-0	695	Biggins, Clark
21	A	Hendon	CC 1	W	4-3	125	Connor, Hagg, Blake, Howard
25	H	Thame United	FAT 3Q	W	4-2	407	Daly 2, Howell, Driscoll
28	H	Ruislip Manor	CC 2	L	1-2	146	Daly
Dec 2	H	Carshalton Athletic	IL	W	3-0	702	Biggins, Howell, Gurney
5	A	Barnet	HSC 2	L	0-3	192	
16	H	Bromley	IL	W	5-0	485	Biggins 3, Howell, Clark
19	A	Hayes	IL	D	0-0	238	
23	A	Yeading	IL	L	1-2	245	Clark
Jan 1	A	Carshalton Athletic	IL	D	1-1	603	Coleman
6	H	Harrow Borough	IL	L	0-2	620	
9	A	Aylesbury United	IL	D	1-1	421	Clark
13	H	Worthing	IL	W	2-0	503	Coleman, Biggins
20	A	Kettering Town	FAT 1	D	1-1	1577	Clark
23	H	Kettering Town	FAT 1R	L	2-3	785	Howell, Gurney
30	A	Harpenden	EAC 2	W	2-1	65	Howell, Gurney
Feb 3	A	Hendon	IL	W	2-1	397	Clark, Blake
10	H	Walton & Hersham	IL	W	3-0	454	Clark, Peters 2
12	A	Purfleet	IL	W	1-0	163	Clark
14	H	Chelmsford City	EFC	L	0-2	60	
17	A	Sutton United	IL	W	1-0	640	Blake
24	A	Chertsey Town	IL	W	2-1	418	Clark, Peters
26	H	Barking	EAC 3	W	1-0	78	og
28	A	Molesey	IL	D	1-1	190	Blake
Mar 2	H	Hitchin Town	IL	W	5-1	626	Biggins, Blake 2, Gurney 2
6	A	Chelmsford City	EFC	D	3-3	137	Gurney, Saintauran, Blackman
9	A	Yeovil Town	IL	D	1-1	2758	Cockram
12	H	Dulwich Hamlet	IL	W	4-1	751	Cockram, Biggins, Clark, Blackman
16	H	Hayes	IL	L	0-3	765	
19	H	Kingstonian	IL	L	1-2	469	Biggins
23	A	Enfield	IL	D	2-2	1006	Cockram, Peters
30	H	Bishop's Stortford	IL	W	3-0	603	Cockram, Howell, Blake
Apr 2	H	Boreham Wood	IL	D	0-0	727	
6	H	Soham Town Rangers	EAC QF	W	1-0	194	Clark
8	A	Boreham Wood	IL	L	0-2	821	
13	H	Grays Athletic	IL	D	1-1	441	Peters
16	A	Bromley	IL	L	0-1	298	
18	A	Braintree Town	EAC SF	L	0-2	152	
20	A	Kingstonian	IL	L	1-4	501	Peters
24	H	Boreham Wood	HCC SF	W	2-0		Gurney, Blake
27	H	Molesey	IL	W	1-0	378	Martin

ST. ALBANS CITY PLAYING SQUAD 1996-97

Goalkeepers: Gareth Howells (Dorking, Hellenic (SA), Torquay, Tottenham), **Richard Watkiss** (Stevenage B, Slough T, St. Albans C, Luton)

Defenders: Andy Polston (Hendon, Brighton, Tottenham), **Peter Risley** (Dagenham, B Stortford, Ware, Hoddesdon T), **Darren Coleman** (Chesham U, Edgware T, Kingsbury T, Finchley, Forest U), **Kevin Mudd** (Sittingbourne, St. Albans C, Harrow B, Finchley, Enfield, St. Albans C, Mount Grace), **Joel Swain** (Romford, St. Albans C, Enfield, Arsenal (T)), **Paul Clark** (Carshalton A, Molesey, Walton & H, St. Albans C, Camb.U (T))

Midfielders: Greg Howell (Enfield, Stevenage B, Southend, Tottenham (T)), **Gary Cobb** (Aylesbury U, Chesham U, Fulham, Luton), **Jon Daly** (Kingstonian, Hendon, Dulwich Hamlet, Whyteleafe, Croydon, Tooting & Mitcham U, Croydon, Crystal Palace), **Richard Blake** (Saffron Walden T, Enfield)

Forwards: Steve Clark (Wivenhoe T, Saffron Walden T, Stansted), **Barry Blackman** (Kingstonian, Hendon, Dulwich Hamlet, Gloucester C, Wealdstone, Yeovil T, Tooting & Mitcham U, Edsbro (Swe), Croydon, Uppsala (Swe), Charlton (A)), **Ron Haworth** (Aylesbury U, Kettering T, Millwall, Fulham), **Naseem Bashir** (Aylesbury U, Chesham U, Chalfont St. Peter, Slough T, Reading)

STAINES TOWN

Formed: 1892 | The Swans

Staines Town F.C. 96-97. *Photo - Andrew Chitty*

Chairman: Alan Boon **Vice Chairman:** Ken Williams **President:** Nigel Iggulden
Secretary: Steven Parsons, 3 Birch Green, Staines, Middx TW18 4HA (01784 450420).
Manager: Chris Wainwright **Asst Manager:** Keith Bristow **Physio:** Mick Minter/Jug Stephen
Commercial Mgr: Ken Williams **Press Officer:** Secretary + Stuart Moore (01784 421118)
Ground: Chertsey Town FC. Alwyns Lane, Chertsey, Surrey KT16 9DW (01932 561774).
Directions: Alwyns Lane is off Windsor St N end of shopping centre. 10 mins Chertsey (BR).
Capacity: 3,000 **Cover:** 1000 **Seats:** 250 **Metal Badges:** £2.50
Colours: Old gold (blue trim)/blue/blue (old gold trim). **Change colours:** All white.
Club Shop: Souvenirs available from Harry Trim, 23 Grosvenor Rd, Staines, Middx TW18 2RN.
Previous Leagues: W London All (pre-1900)/ W London/ W Middx (pre-1905)/ Gt Western Suburban 05-13 20-24/ Gt Western Comb/ Munitions Lg (World War 1)/ London Works (World War 1)/ Hounslow & Dist 19-20/ Spartan 24-35 58-71/ Middx Sen 43-52/ Parthenon 52-53/ Hellenic 53-58/ Athenian 71-73.
Previous Names: Staines Albany and St Peters Institute (merged) in 1895/Staines 05-18/Staines Lagonda 18-25/Staines Vale (2nd World War).
Previous Grounds: Edgell Rd (St Peters Inst); The Lammas, Shortwood Common, Mill Mead (Hammonds/Wicks/Pursers Farm); Shepperton Road (to 1951); Wheatsheaf Lane (1951-96).
Record Gate: 2,750 v Banco di Roma (Barassi Cup) 1975 *(70,000 saw 1st leg in Rome).*
Best FA Cup year: 1st Rd 84-85 (0-2 at Burton Alb) & 1879-80 & 80-81 (as St Peters Institute).
Sponsors: Barratt Homes. **Midweek matchday:** Tuesday **Reserve league:** Suburban (since 72).
Record win: 14-0 v Croydon (A), Isthmian League Division One 19/3/94.
Record defeat: 1-18 v Wycombe Wanderers (A), G West Sub Lge 1909.
Record Fees - Paid: Undisclosed for R Teale (Slough 81)
Received: Undisclosed for Scott Taylor (Millwall 95-96).
Players progressing to Football League: R Bennett (Southend 72), J Love (C Palace 75), P Shaw (Charlton 77), E Young (Wolves, Brighton, W'don), G Hill (M'wall, Man Utd, Derby), W Stemp (Brighton), M Ferney (Fulham), S Taylor (Millwall, Bolton).
Clubhouse: Fully furnished clubhouse & function hall, open 7-11 matchdays and every evening. Rolls and other snacks available.
Club Record Goalscorer: Alan Gregory 122 & Neville Warner 100+
Club Record Appearances: Dickie Watmore 840
95-96 Captain: Joe O'Shea. **Dick Watmore' P.o.Y. 95-96:** Mark Fleming.
95-96 Top scorer & Players P.o.Y.: Steve Becks 24
Local Newspapers: Staines & Ashford News, Middx Chronicle, Informer.
Local Radio Stations: County Sound, GLR, Capital, Star FM, Radio Wey
Hons: Isthmian Lg Div 1 74-75 88-89 (Div 2 74-75), Athian Lg Div 2 71-72 (Div 1 R-up 72-73), Spartan Lg 59-60 (R-up 70-71, Lg Cup 68-69 (R-up 60-61 70-71)), Hellenic Lg R-up 55-56 (Lg Cup R-up 53-54 55-56), Gt Western Suburban Lg Div 1 R-up 11-12 22-24 (Div 2 (Middx) 20-21), W London All Div 1 1899-1900, W London Lg Div 1 00-01, W Middx Lg 04-05 (R-up 03-04), London Snr Cup R-up 76-77 80-81, Middx Snr Cup(6) 74-77 87-88 89-90 94-95 (R-up 09-10 32-33 79-80), Middx Snr Charity Cup 94-95, Barassi Cup 1976, Southern Comb. Chall. Cup 64-65 66-67 68-69 94-95,(R-up 67-68 94-95), W Middx Cup 23-24, Staines Cottage Hosp Cup 24-25, Merthyr Middx Charity Shield 90-91,(R-Up 94-95)FA Amtr Cup 3rd Rd 23-24, FA Trophy 2nd Rd 2nd rep 76-77. El Canuelo Trophy: 32-33,34-35,94-95. Carlsberg Cup:94-95.

PROGRAMME DETAILS:
Pages: 44 **Price:** £1
Editor: Sec. & Stuart Moore (01784 421118)

STAINES TOWN'S 1995-96 CAMPAIGN

DATE			OPPONENTS	COMP	RESULT		GATE	GOALSCORERS
Aug	6	A	Blackpool	fr	L	0-4	478	
	12	A	Basingstoke Town	IL	L	0-5	399	
	19	H	Whyteleafe	IL	D	2-2	157	Beeks, Ulasi
	26	A	Billericay Town	IL	L	1-2	290	O'Shea
Sept	2	H	Barking	IL	D	2-2	173	Williams, Grainger
	5	H	Oxford City	GIC 1	W	3-1*	199	Williams, K Philips, Fleming
	9	A	Hampton	FAC 1q	W	2-1	255	Ulasi, Grainger
	13	A	Chesham United	IL	L	0-2	336	
	16	H	Aldershot Town ('92)	IL	W	3-2	839	Williams, Beeks, Fleming
	23	A	Boreham Wood	FAC 2q	W	1-0	293	Wheatley
	30	A	Bognor Regis Town	IL	L	1-3	554	Williams
Oct	3	A	Ashford Town (Middx)	fr	W	2-0	162	Williams, O'Shea
	7	A	Stevenage Borough	FAC 3q	L	0-2	1176	
	10	H	Ruislip Manor	IL	D	3-3	253	Anderson, Beeks, O'Shea
	14	H	Wokingham Town	FAT 1q	W	2-1	304	Bygrave, Beeks
	17	A	Leyton Pennant	IL	W	3-1	173	O'Shea, P Lucas, Grainger
	21	H	Maindenhead United	IL	W	2-1	265	Beeks, Williams
	28	A	Thame United	IL	W	2-1	155	Anderson, Grainger
	31	A	Bishop's Stortford	GIC 2	L	1-3	223	og (Moore)
Nov	4	H	Havant Town	FAT 2q	w	3-1	329	Reilly, Williams, Grainger
	11	A	Marlow	IL	W	3-2	272	Grainger, Evans, Reilly
	14	A	Croydon Athletic	SCC 1	L	0-2	34	
	18	H	Oxford City	IL	L	0-2	226	
	21	H	Walton and Hersham	CC 1	L	0-1	314	
	25	A	Molesey	FAT 3q	D	2-2	214	Reilly, Grainger
	28	H	Molesey	FAT rep	W	5-0	235	Beeks 3, Williams 2
Dec	2	H	Berkhamsted Town	IL	W	2-1	242	Grainger, Williams
	9	A	Wembley	IL	W	1-0	146	Beeks
	16	H	Uxbridge	IL	W	3-1	198	Anderson 2, Livey
Jan	2	A	Tooting & Mitcham Utd	IL	D	1-1	196	Anderson
	6	H	Basingstoke Town	IL	W	3-1	288	Evans 2, Beeks
	13	H	Chesham United	IL	D	3-3	388	Evans 2, Beeks
	16	H	Barton Rovers	IL	W	3-2	188	og (McNally), Beeks, Anderson
	20	A	Gloucester City	FAT 1	L	0-5	1150	
	30	H	Abington Town	IL	W	6-0	163	Evans, Beeks 2, Williams 2, Anderson
Feb	3	A	Ruislip Manor	IL	W	2-0	162	Evans 2
	6	A	Heybridge Swifts	IL	L	0-3	185	
	17	A	Aldershot Town (1992)	IL	D	3-3	2034	Grainger, Walters, Beeks
	24	H	Thames United	IL	D	1-1	280	Evans
Mar	2	A	Maidenhead United	IL	L	0-1	198	
	9	H	Leyton Pennant	IL	L	1-2	283	P Lucas
	12	A	Edgware Town	MCC rep	W	1-0*	73	Walters
	16	A	Abingdon Town	IL	W	2-0	180	Evans, O'Shea
	19	H	Wokingham Town	IL	W	2-1	252	Williams, Evans
	23	H	Marlow	IL	W	3-1	292	Anderson, Livey, Evans
	26	A	Barking	IL	W	2-1	82	Gasson, Evans
	30	A	Barton Rovers	IL	W	2-0	120	Gasson 2
Apr	2	H	Billercay Town	IL	W	4-1	267	Evans, Beeks, Grainger, Anderson
	6	H	Tooting & Mitcham U	IL	W	2-1	324	Beeks 2
	8	A	Wokingham Town	IL	W	3-0	430	Livey, Evans, Grainger
	13	H	Heybridge Swifts	IL	D	2-2	393	Beeks 2
	16	A	Whyteleafe	IL	W	2-0	112	Beeks, Evans
	20	A	Berkhamsted Town	IL	W	2-1	246	Gasson, og (Bartlett)
	23	A	Oxford City	IL	D	1-1	365	Gasson
	27	H	Wembley	IL	W	1-0	391	Anderson
	30	H	Bognor Regis Town	IL	D	2-2	433	Beeks, Pentland
May	4	A	Uxbridge	IL	D	1-1	177	Gasson
	11	H	C.D. Mijas '92	ECT	W	7-1	136	B Collins, Nunkoo (4), Reilly, Townsend

STAINES TOWN PLAYING SQUAD 1996-97

Goalkeepers: Dave Brace (Dulwich Hamlet, Molesey, Walton Casuals, Molesey, Fulham (A)), **Trent Phillips** (Walton & H, Staines T, Camberley T, Wimbledon)

Defenders: John Gasson (Walton & H), **Derek Walters** (Farnborough T, Windsor & Eton, Egham T, Staines T), **Chris Wheatley** (Walton & H, Egham T, Slough T, Staines T), **Darren Anderson** (Sutton U, Slough T, Aldershot, Charlton), **Spencer Collins** (Walton & H, Walton Casuals), **Mark Keadell** (Crystal Palace (T))

Midfielders: Mark Fleming (Aylesbury U, Woking, Farnborough T, Brentford, QPR), **Steve Beeks** (Sutton U, Woking, Aldershot, Egham T), **Geoff Taylor** (Walton & H, Woking, Banstead A, Kingstonian, Wimbledon (T)), **Danny Bygrave** (Walton & H, Malden Vale), **Craig Reilly** (Fulham)

Forwards: Phil Grainger (Sutton U, Dorking, Winterton R, Goole T, Hull C), **Justin Mitchell** (Walton & H, Chelsea), **Richard Evans** (Marlow, Sutton U, Windsor & Eton, Harrow B, Wokingham T, Reading), **Grant Hutchinson** (Walton & H, Woking, Aldershot, Chelsea), **Alan Gregory** (Uxbridge, Staines T, Walton & H, Egham T, Ruislip Manor, Staines T, Gillingham), **Kelly Phillips** (Walton & H, Staines T, Hampton, Staines T)

SUTTON UNITED

Formed: 1898 | The U's

Back Row (L-R); G Berry, M Jones, B Pratt, A Harris, N Golley, J Vansittart, S Watson, B Laker. Front; J Dack, S Payne, D Feltham, C Gartell, D Everitt, T Argrave, (Mascots) M Nock, D Watts.

Photo - Andrew Chitty

Chairman: Bruce Elliott **President:** Andrew W Letts.
Secretary: Brian Williams, 49 Panmure Rd, Sydenham, London SE26 6NB (0181 699 2721).
Managers: John Rains **Asst Manager:** Tony Rains **Coach:** Bobby Mapleson
Commercial Manager: Mike Baker. **Press Officer:** Tony Dolbear (0171 782 8644 daytime)
Grd: Borough Sports Ground, Gander Green Lane, Sutton, SM1 2EY (0181 644 4440 Fax: 5120).
Directions: Gander Green Lane runs between A232 (Cheam Road - turn by Sutton Cricket Club) and A217 (Oldfields Road - turn at 'Gander' PH lights). Ground opposite 'The Plough' 50 yards from West Sutton BR station. Bus 413 passes ground.
Capacity: 6,200 **Cover:** 1,800 **Seats:** 765 **Floodlights:** Yes **Metal Badges:** Yes.
Club Shop: Open on matchdays selling full range of souvenirs, etc, contact Tony Cove via club.
Colours: Amber/chocolate **Change colours:** All white (chocolate trim). **Sponsors:** Securicor.
Previous Leagues: Sutton Jun/ Southern Sub 10-21/ Athenian 21-63/ Isthmian 63-86/ GMVC 86-91.
Previous Names: Sutton Association, Sutton Guild Rovers.
Best FA Cup season: 4th Rd 69-70 88-89. **Midweek matchday:** Tuesday **Reserve Lge:** Suburban.
Record Attendance: 14,000 v Leeds United, FA Cup 4th Rd 24/1/70.
Record Fees - Paid: To Malmo FF for Paul McKinnon
Received: For E Ekoku (Bournemouth)
Players Progressing to Football Lge: C Vaughan (Charlton 47), R Hancox & L Coules & R Colfar & S Galloway & M Robinson (C Palace 50/51/58/84), T Barton (Fulham), P Woosnam (Orient 55), D Gamblin (Portsmouth 65), M Pentecost (Fulham 66), J Faulkner (Leeds 70), M Mellows (Reading 70), M Fillery (Chelsea & QPR), F Cowley (Derby 77), P McKinnon (Blackburn 86), R Fearon (I'wich 87), P Harding (Notts Co), E Ekoku (Bournemouth 91), M Golley (Maidstone), A Barnes (C Palace 91), P Rogers (Sheff U 92), S Massey (C Palace 92), A & R Scott (Sheff U 93), O Morah (Cambridge 94), M Watson (West Ham 95).
Clubhouse: Open every day, food. Available for hire.
Club Record Scorer: Paul McKinnon
Club Record Appearances: Larry Pritchard 781 (1965-84)
95-96 Captain: Nigel Golley **95-96 Top scorer:** Dominic Feltham
95-96 Players P.o.Y.: Mark Hynes
Local Newspapers: Sutton Herald, Sutton Guardian.
Hons: Alliance Prem. Lg Bob Lord Trophy 90-91, FA Trophy R-up 80-81 (SF 92-93), FA Amtr Cup R-up 62-63 68-69 (SF 28-29 36-37 67-68), Isthmian Lg(3) 66-67 84-86 (R-up 67-68 70-71 81-82, Lg Cup(3) 82-84 85-86 (R-up 79-80), Loctite Cup 91-92), Athenian Lg 27-28 45-46 57-58 (R-up 46-47, Lg Cup 45-46 55-56 61-62 62-63, Res Sec 61-62 (R-up 32-33)), Anglo Italian Semi-Pro Cup 79 (R-up 80 82), London Snr Cup 57-58 82-83, London Charity Cup 69-70 (R-up(3) 67-69 72-73), Surrey Snr Cup(13) (R-up(9), Surrey Intermediate Cup (4) (R-up (6), Surrey Jnr Cup R-up 09-10, Surrey Snr Charity Shield(3) (R-up (6), Surrey Interm Charity Cup 31-32 (R-up 34-35 38-39), Dylon Charity Shield 84 (R-up 80 82 83 85), Groningen Yth tournament 83 85 (R-up 79 81 89 91), John Ullman Invitation Cup 88-89, Carlton Cup 95-96

PROGRAMME DETAILS:
Pages: 48 **Price:** £1.20
Editor: Tony Dolbear

SUTTON UNITED'S 1995-96 CAMPAIGN

DATE		OPPONENTS	COMP	RESULTS		GATE	GOALSCORERS
Aug 19	A	Bishops Stortford	IL	W	3-1	384	Vansittart, Feltham 2
22	H	Enfield	IL	L	2-4	887	Feltham, Dennis
26	H	Hayes	IL	D	2-2	611	Feltham 2
29	A	Chertsey Town	IL	D	1-1	638	Vansittart
Sept 2	A	Boreham Wood	IL	W	1-0	427	Golley
5	H	Tring Town	GIC1	W	2-0	263	Lempriere, Shepherd
9	H	Kingstonian	IL	L	0-1	944	
16	A	St. Albans City	IL	D	2-2	651	Vansittart 2
23	A	Kingstonian	IL	D	2-2	747	Vansittart, Feltham
30	H	Aylesbury United	IL	L	2-3	653	Vansittart, Hynes
Oct 7	A	Worthing	IL	L	2-5	575	Vansittart, Feltham
10	A	Hendon	IL	W	4-0	275	Costello, Payne 2, Vansittart
14	A	Yeading	IL	D	2-2	260	Vansittart, Feltham
21	H	Crawley Town	FAC	W	4-1	1,637	Hynes 2, Feltham 2
24	H	Harrow Borough	IL	W	4-0	452	Hynes, Vansittart, Feltham 2
28	A	Walton & Hersham	IL	D	1-1	445	Feltham
31	H	Hitchin Town	GIC2	L	0-1	228	
Nov 4	H	Dulwich Hamlet	IL	D	1-1	697	Watson
11	A	Kidderminster Harriers	FAC1	D	2-2	2,513	Hynes, Vansittart
18	H	Molesey	IL	L	2-0	494	Hynes, Dack
21	H	Kidderminster Harriers	FAC1	D	1-1	1,304	Payne
25	H	Trowbridge Town	CT3	L	0-1	612	
Dec 2	A	Hereford United	FAC2	L	0-2	2,908	
12	A	Tooting & Mitcham Utd	CC	L	1-2	132	Payne
16	H	Grays Athletic	IL	D	0-0	392	
19	H	Abingdon Town	CC	W	3-0	166	Payne, Hynes, Watson
Jan 2	A	Hitchin	IL	L	0-1	303	
6	H	Boreham Wood	IL	L	0-3	521	
9	A	Tooting & Mitcham Utd	CC	W	3-1	201	Dack, Feltham, (og)
13	A	Enfield	IL	W	2-0	B23	Hynes, Feltham
17	A	Molesey	IL	W	5-0	275	Green, Hynes, Dennis, Feltham, Dack
20	H	Bishops Stortford	IL	W	2-1	469	Payne, Hynes
30	H	Purfleet	IL	W	1-0	334	Hynes
Feb 3	H	Chertsey Town	IL	W	2-1	512	Golley, Feltham
10	A	Aylesbury United	IL	L	1-4	606	Hynes
17	H	St. Albans City	IL	L	0-1	640	
21	A	Bognor Regis Town	CC	W	2-1	250	Hynes, Dennis
24	H	Walton & Hersham	IL	W	2-1	4a3	Hynes 2
27	H	Yeovil Town	IL	D	1-1	537	Green
Mar 2	A	Harrow Borough	IL	D	0-0	339	
5	A	Bromley	IL	W	3-2	361	Hynes, Dennis, Dack
9	H	Hendon	IL	L	2-3	529	Hynes, Feltham
12	H	Carshalton Athletic	IL	W	2-1	7e4	Payne, Watson
16	A	Purfleet	IL	L	1-2	262	Golley
23	H	Worthing	IL	W	3-1	461	Feltham 2, Dack
26	H	Carshalton Athletic	CC	D	1-1	719	Feltham
30	A	Dulwich Hamlet	IL	D	2-2	559	Hynes, Feltham
Apr 1	A	Carshalton Athletic	CC	W	4-1	565	Hynes 2, Costello, Feltham
6	H	Hitchin Town	IL	W	4-0	490	Payne 2, Feltham
8	A	Carshalton Athletic	IL	W	2-1	794	Dack 2
13	H	Bromley	IL	L	1-3	627	Feltham
16	A	Hayes	IL	D	0-0	516	
20	A	Yeovil Town	IL	D	0-0	2,a1	
27	H	Yeading	IL	D	2-2	455	Feltham, Haynes
May 4	A	Grays Athletic	IL	W	2-1	318	Vansittart, Hynes
7	A	Boreham Wood	CC	D	2-2	612	Dack (pen), Green
		Kidderminster Harriers	FA1r	D	1-1		Sutton won 3-2 on penalties
		• Carlton Cup Final					
		Purfleet	IL	W	1-0		Sutton won 4-3 on Penalties

SUTTON UNITED PLAYING SQUAD 1996-97

Goalkeepers: Andy Harris (Welling U, Worthing, Sutton U)

Defenders: Nigel Golley (Whyteleafe), **Barry Laker** (Banstead A, Wimbledon), **Mark Costello** (Youth team), **Chris Green** (Dulwich Hamlet), **Paul Gates** (Chipstead, Whyteleafe), **Gary Elliott** (Youth team), **Gwynne Berry** (Welling U, Sutton U, Woking, Sutton U, Whyteleafe), **Dave Everitt** (Walton & H, Leyton O), **Clive Gartell** (Dulwich Hamlet, Molesey, Dulwich Hamlet, Molesey, Leatherhead, Epsom & Ewell), **Bradley Pratt** (Chertsey T, Farnborough T, Chertsey T, Woking, Nth.Shore (NZ), Farnborough T, Egham T, Bracknell T, Wokingham T, Camberley T)

Midfielders: Jimmy Dack (Carshalton A, Crawley T, Sutton U, Epsom & Ewell), **Steve Watson** (Croydon, Whyteleafe), **Warren Pritchard** (Youth team), **Jamie Earp** (Leatherhead), **Stuart Channon** (Walton & H), **Carl Procopi** (Hendon, Malden V), **Lee Tierling** (Welling U, Woking, Fulham, Portsmouth)

Forwards: Joff Vansittart (Crawley T, Brighton), **Dominic Feltham** (Baltimore Blasts (USA), Chelsea), **Mark Hynes** (Whyteleafe, Fisher A, Croydon A, Merstham, Croydon, Brentford (T)), **Steve Payne** (Crawley T, Ringmer, Ware), **Murray Jones** (Kingstonian, Welling U, Exeter, Bristol C, Crystal Palace, Carshalton A, Whyteleafe), **Trevor Argrave** (Chertsey T, Burnham, Chertsey T)

YEADING

Formed: 1965 The Dinc

Yeading's Nathan Bunce outjumps two Purfleet defenders, but puts his header just wide.
Photo - Alan Coomes

Chairman: Philip Spurden **Vice Chairman:** Steve Perryman **President:** Mr R Carter
Secretary: Peter Bickers, 140 Hercies Rd, Hillingdon, Middlesex (01895 203562).
Manager: Steve Cordery. **Asst Manager:** Leo Morris **Coach:** Leo Morris.
Comm Mgr: Neil Roberts **Press Officer:** Peter Bickers (as above) **Physio:** Edward Cole.
Ground: The Warren, Beaconsfield Road, Hayes, Middx (0181 848 7362/7369. fax: 081 561 2222).
Directions: Two miles from Hayes (BR) - take Uxbridge Road and turn right towards Southall, right into Springfield Road and then left into Beaconsfield Road. Bus 207 stops half mile from ground.
Capacity: 3,500 **Cover:** 1,500 **Seats:** 250 **Shop:** Planned **Metal Badges:** Yes
Colours: Red & black stripes/black/black **Change colours:** All white. **Sponsors:** Heineken.
Previous Leagues: Hayes & District Yth/ Uxbridge/ S W Middx 1967-74/ Middx 74-84/ Spartan 1984-87.
Midweek matchday: Tuesday **Reserve League:** None.
Record Attendance: 3,000; v Hythe Town, FA Vase SF 1990; v Tottenham Hotspur, friendly.
Best FA Cup season: Third Qualifying Round 90-91.
Record Fees - Paid:
Received: £45,000 for Andrew Impey (QPR).
Players progressing to Football League: Andrew Impey (QPR & England u-21).
Clubhouse: Open normal pub hours. Social Secretary: William Gritt.
Club Record Goalscorer: Dave Burt 327
Club Record Appearances: Norman Frape.
95-96 P.o.Y.: Phil Dicker.
Local Newspapers: Hayes Gazette.
Honours: FA Vase 89-90, Isthmian League Div 2 Sth 89-90 (Div 1 R-up 91-92), Spartan League 86-87 (R-up 85-86, Senior Div R-up 84-85, League Cup 85-86 86-87), Middlesex Snr League(6) 71-73 74-76 81-82 83-84 (R-up 73-74 74-75 78-79, League Cup(6) 72-73 75-76 79-83), South West Middlesex League(2) 69-71, Middlesex Snr Cup 89-90 91-92, Middlesex Prem. Cup 80-81, Middlesex I'mediate Cup(5) 70-72 74-76 77-78, Middlesex Jnr Cup(4) 68-69 70-72 74-75, Uxbridge League 66-67, Middlesex Border League Cup 86-87 (AJA Cup 86-87), Suburban League Nth 87-88, Allied Counties Yth League 89-90 (League Cup 89-90).

PROGRAMME DETAILS:
Pages: 32 **Price:** £1
Editor: David Low.

YEADING'S 1995-96 CAMPAIGN

DATE		OPPONENTS	COMP	RESULT		GATE	GOALSCORERS
Aug 12	H	Chertsey Town	IL	L	1-3	356	Dicker
19	A	Boreham Wood	IL	D	1-1	245	Bowder
22	H	Carshalton Athletic	IL	L	1-3	170	McGrath
26	H	Hitchin Town	IL	W	2-0	160	Cordery, Graham
29	A	Grays Athletic	IL	D	0-0	167	
Sept 2	A	St Albans City	IL	W	1-0	456	Bowder
5	H	Bognor Regis Town	GIC	L	0-3		
9	H	Enfield	IL	D	1-1	432	Graham
16	A	Aylesbury United	IL	D	1-1	875	Graham
30	H	Kingstonian	IL	L	0-2	281	
Oct 7	A	Yeovil Town	IL	L	0-2	1,281	
10	H	Harrow Borough	IL	L	1-2	189	Gell
14	H	Sutton United	IL	D	2-2	260	McGrath 2
17	H	Purfleet	IL	W	3-1	110	Evans, Wallace, og
28	A	Hayes	IL	D	0-0	437	
Nov 4	H	Molesey	IL	D	2-2	155	Grill, Cordery
7	A	Berkhamsted Town	CC	W	3-0		
11	A	Bromley	IL	L	0-1	285	
18	A	Worthing	IL	L	1-2	210	Graham
25	A	Chelmsford City	FAT	L	1-2		Graham
Dec 2	A	Dulwich Hamlet	IL	L	0-2	289	
16	A	Bishops Stortford	IL	L	1-3	202	Gell
19	A	Enfield	CC	W	2-1		
23	H	St Albans City	IL	W	2-1	245	Houghton, Carter
26	A	Hendon	IL	D	1-1	241	Gell
Jan 6	A	Chertsey Town	IL	D	1-1	342	McGrath
13	A	Carshalton Athletic	IL	L	0-2	372	
16	H	Bishops Stortford	CC	L	0-1		
20	H	Worthing	IL	W	1-0	120	Fitzgerald
Feb 3	H	Grays Athletic	IL	L	0-1	104	
10	A	Kingstonian	IL	L	1-3	419	McGrath
17	H	Aylesbury United	IL	D	0-0	181	
24	H	Hayes	IL	L	0-1	405	
Mar 2	A	Purfleet	IL	W	2-1	123	Allen 2
9	A	Harrow Borough	IL	L	1-4	256	Ripley
16	H	Yeovil Town	IL	D	1-1	403	Ripley
23	H	Bromley	IL	W	3-0	183	Kellman, Carter, Ripley
30	A	Molesey	IL	W	2-1	110	Carter, Roddis
Apr 2	H	Hendon	IL	D	0-0	202	
6	A	Enfield	IL	L	0-2	806	
10	H	Boreham Wood	IL	L	0-3	262	
13	A	Walton & Hersham	IL	D	0-0	185	
16	A	Hitchin Town	IL	W	3-0	201	Kellman, Gell, Carter
20	H	Dulwich Hamlet	IL	W	5-3	260	Roddis 2, Kellman 2, Graham
23	H	Walton & Hersham	IL	W	3-0	136	Kellman 2, Witter
27	A	Sutton United	IL	D	2-2	455	Graham, Witter
May 4	H	Bishops Stortford	IL	L	2-4	148	Sewell, Kellman

YEADING PLAYING SQUAD 1996-97

Goalkeepers: Danny Honey (Aylesbury U, Newbury T, Reading (T))

Defenders: Matthew Flitter (Hayes, Brentford), **Tony Houghton** (Brentford (T)), **Phil Dicker** (St. Albans C, Southall, Harrow B, Hanwell T, Brentford), **Steve McGrath** (Shamrock FC), **Mark Woods** (Basingstoke T, Farnborough T, Windsor & Eton, Walton & H, Tooting & Mitcham U, Windsor & Eton, Addlestone, QPR)

Midfielders: Steve Graham (Stevenage B, Wembley, Basildon U, Tottenham), **Stan Bowder** (Chelsea (T)), **Paul Cooper** (Hayes, Brentford), **Paddy McCarthy** (Chertsey T, Yeading, Chesham U, Farnborough T, Yeovil T, Weymouth, Wealdstone, Chelsea), **Paul Ford** (Brentford (T)), **Steve Cordery** (Chesham U, Windsor & Eton, Egham T, Maidenhead U, Hayes, Feltham, Southall, Hillingdon B)

Forwards: Paul Ripley (Northwood, Ruislip Manor, Hitchin T, Harrow B, Ruislip M, Harrow B, Finchley, Ruislip Manor, Harrow B), **Martin Carter** (Hayes), **Dave Kellman** (Hayes, Harlow T, Stevenage B, Willesden Hawkeye), **Eben Allen** (Dulwich Hamlet, Hampton, Marlow, Staines T, Godalming & Guildford, WBA, Arsenal)

Formed: 1895

YEOVIL TOWN

Glovers

Back Row: Rob Cousins, Kevin Braybrooke, Tony Pennock, James Smith, Dean Birkby, Chris White. Middle: Terry Cotton (Asst Mgr), Lee Groves, Jamie Laidlow, Chris Seymour, Jerry Gill, Tony Pounder, Leroy Whale, Terry Hardwell (Physio). Front; Warren Patmore, Graham Kemp, Graham Roberts (Player/Mgr), Mickey Engwell, Lee Harvey

Chairman: John Fry **President:** S N Burfield **Secretary:** Jean Cotton c/o Club.
Manager: Graham Roberts **Asst Manager:** Terry Cotton **Physio:** Terry Hardwell
Ground: Huish Park, Lufton Way, Yeovil Somerset, BA22 8YF. (01935 23662, Fax 73956
Directions: Leave A303 at Cartgate r'about, take A3088 signposted Yeovil. 1st exit at next r'about, 1st exit at next r'about into Lufton Way. Railway station - Yeovil Pen Mill (Bristol/Westbury to Weymouth) 2.5 miles from ground. Bus service from stations on Saturday.
Capacity: 8,720 **Seats:** 5,212 **Terracing:** 3,508 **Floodlights:** Yes **Metal Badges:** Yes.
Club Shop: Open on matchdays selling full range of souvenirs, match programmes, scarves, hats, replica kits *Team Talk Magazine* etc.
Colours: Green & white/green/white
Change colours: Cerise/navy/navy
Previous Leagues: Western Lge, London Comb, Southern Lge, Alliance Premier, Isthmian, GMVC.
Midweek matchday: Tuesday **Previous Names:** Yeovil & Petters Utd
Reserve Lge: Screwfix Direct, Western Lge Div 1
Record Attendance: 8,612 v Arsenal 3rd Rd FA Cup 02/1/93.
Record Fees - Paid: £15,000 to Worcester City for Joe Jackson 1990
Received: £75,000 for Mark Shail from Bristol City
Players Progressing to Football Lge: Over 40 players + 18 managers including, since 1985, Nigel Jarvis (Torquay), Ian Davies (Bristol Rovers), Alan Pardew (Crystal Palace), Paul Miller (Wimbledon) John McGinlay (Bolton), Guy Whittingham (Portsmouth), Mark Shail (Bristol City), Malcom McPherson (West Ham).
Clubhouse: Matchdays hot + cold food available. Meals can be ordered provided advance notice is given. All weather astro turf pitch available for bookings 9am-10pm.
Club Record Scorer: Dave Taylor 285 1960-69
Club Record Appearances: L Harris
95-96 Captain: Mickey Engwell **95-96 P.o.Y.:** Mickey Engwell
95-96 Top scorer: Warren Patmore
Local Newspapers: Western Daily Press
Hons: Southern Lge 54-55,63-64,70-71, R-up 23-24,31-32,34-35,69-70,72-73. Southern Lge Cup 48-49,54-55,60-61,65-66. Vauxhall-Opel Lge 87-88, R-up 85-86,86-87. AC Delco Cup 87-88. FA Cup 5th Rd 48-49. Bob Lord Trophy 89-90, R-up 93-94.

PROGRAMME DETAILS:
Pages: 50 **Price:** £1.20
Editor: Bayan Moore

YEOVIL TOWN'S 1995-96 CAMPAIGN

DATE		OPPONENTS	COMP	RESULT		GATE	GOALSCORERS
Aug 19	A	Aylesbury United	IL	L	1-3	812	St Hilaire
26	H	Grays Athletic	IL	W	1-0	1668	St Hilaire
28	H	Walton & Hersham	IL	W	4-1	1563	Patmore 4
Sept 2	A	Chertsey Town	IL	W	3-1	766	St Hilaire 3
5	H	Hendon	ILC	L	1-3	1092	Groves
9	H	Hitchin Town	IL	D	1-1	1739	Patmore
16	A	Kingstonian	IL	D	2-2	642	Engwell, St Hilaire
23	H	Bishop's Stortford	IL	L	1-3	1629	Whale
25	A	Carlshalton Athletic	IL	L	1-2	641	St Hilaire
30	H	Boreham Wood	IL	L	0-1	1283	
Oct 7	H	Yeading	IL	W	2-0	1281	Whale, Patmore
14	A	St Albans City	IL	D	2-2	853	Browne, Patmore
17	A	Chard Town	SPC	W	2-0	495	Burton, Patmore
21	A	Farnborough Town	FAC 4QR	L	1-2	1409	Patmore
28	A	Bromley	IL	W	5-1	357	Dillon, Patmore 2, St Hilaire, Burton
Nov 4	H	Worthing	IL	W	3-1	1602	Grazioli, Dillon, Patmore
11	A	Molesey	IL	W	3-2	300	Seymour, Grazioli 2
15	A	Brislington	SPC	L	1-2	175	Doherty
18	A	Purfleet	IL	W	3-0	302	Patmore, Grazioli 2
21	A	Chertsey	CC	W	2-0	215	Grazioli, Patmore
25	H	Dulwich Hamlet	IL	W	5-3	1960	Browne, Patmore 2, Grazioli, Kemp
Dec 9	H	Hayes	IL	W	3-0	2025	Seymour, Grazioli 2
16	A	Enfield	IL	L	1-2	1177	Patmore
23	H	Chertsey Town	IL	W	1-0	2417	Burton
26	A	Worthing	IL	L	2-3	561	Grazioli, Patmore
Jan 1	H	Hendon	IL	W	4-1	2306	Grazioli 2, Patmore, St Hilaire
6	A	Bishop's Stortford	IL	D	2-2	466	Grazioli 2
8	A	Carshalton Athletic	CC	L	1-2	346	Birkby
13	A	Hitchin Town	IL	W	2-1	523	Grazioli 2
21	A	Bath City	FAT 1R	D	1-1	2225	Patmore
23	H	Bath City	FAT 1RR	L	2-3	2731	Whale 2
Feb 3	H	Carshalton Athletic	IL	W	2-1	1920	Whale, Birkby
10	H	Harrow Borough	IL	D	0-0	1942	
17	H	Kingstonian	IL	D	1-1	1953	
24	H	Bromley	IL	W	4-3	1869	Braybrooke, Whale, Patmore, St Hilaire
27	A	Sutton United	IL	D	1-1	537	Whale
Mar 2	A	Walton & Hersham	IL	W	3-1	407	Engwell, Seymour, Birkby
9	H	St. Albans City	IL	D	1-1	2758	Seymour
16	A	Yeading	IL	D	1-1	403	Whale
23	H	Molesey	IL	W	3-2	1870	Patmore 2, St Hilaire
26	A	Grays Athletic	IL	W	2-0	251	og, Birkby
30	A	Harrow Borough	IL	W	1-0	489	
Apr 2	H	Purfleet	IL	W	2-1	2267	Patmore, Birkby
6	A	Hendon	IL	W	3-1	443	Nugent, Patmore 2
13	A	Dulwich Hamlet	IL	L	1-2	1289	Birkby
16	H	Aylesbury United	IL	W	3-2	2008	Birkby, Lynch, Laidlaw
20	H	Sutton United	IL	D	0-0	2818	
27	A	Hayes	IL	D	1-1	1537	Roberts
30	A	Boreham Wood	IL	W	2-0	784	White, Laidlaw
May 4	H	Enfield	IL	L	0-1	2818	

YEOVIL TOWN PLAYING SQUAD 1996-97

Goalkeepers: Tony Pennock (Hereford, Wigan, Stockport)
Defenders: Micky Engwell (Grays A, Enfield, Harrow B, Chesham U, Crewe, Barking, Chelmsford C, Southend), **Chris White** (Exeter, Peterborough, Portsmouth), **Graham Roberts** (Stevenage B, Slough T, Enfield, WBA, Chelsea, Glasgow Rangers, Tottenham, Weymouth, Dorchester T, Portsmouth, AFC Bournemouth, Sholing Sports, Southampton), **Lee Harvey** (Slough T, Aylesbury U, Hemel Hempstead), **Jerry Gill** (Bath C, Weston-super-Mare, Leyton O), **Danny Burwood** (From YTS)
Midfielders: Graham Kemp (Newbury T, Reading, Shrewsbury), **Jamie Laidlaw** (Swindon), **Chris Seymour** (Newbury T, Reading), **Steve Browne** (Walton & H, Wealdstone, Yeading, Sutton U, Kingstonian, Sutton U, Wealdstone, Barking, Wealdstone, Newmont Travel, Grays A, Dartford, Maidstone U, Fulham, Charlton), **Rob Cousins** (Bath C, Bristol C), **Tony Pounder** (Hereford, Bristol R, Weymouth, Westlands Sports), **Paul Turner** (Enfield, Farnborough T, Camb.U, Arsenal (T))
Forwards: Warren Patmore (Ards, Northampton, Millwall, Camb.U, Northwood), **Kevin Braybrooke** (Portsmouth), **Dean Birkby** (Bath C, Yate T, Gloucester C, Mangotsfield U, Clevedon T, Mangotsfield U), **Leroy Whale** (Enfield, Bashley, Basingstoke T, Rotherham, Southampton (A)), **Kevin Doherty** (Southampton)

ICIS (Isthmian) LEAGUE Division One Ten Year Records

	86/7	87/8	88/9	89/0	90/1	91/2	92/3	93/4	94/5	95/6
Abingdon Town	-	-	-	-	-	6	6	7	10	16
Aldershot Town	-	-	-	-	-	-	-	-	4	5
Aveley	-	-	-	-	4	21	21	-	-	-
Barking	-	-	-	-	-	12	19	14	15	22
Barton Rovers	-	-	-	-	-	-	-	-	-	18
Basildon United	12	7	21	-	-	-	-	-	-	-
Basingstoke Town	-	-	2	-	-	-	-	-	7	9
Berkhamsted Town	-	-	-	-	-	-	-	18	19	17
Billericay Town	13	20	-	-	-	-	8	6	5	6
Bishop's Stortford	-	-	-	-	-	-	5	1	-	-
Bognor Regis Town	-	-	-	-	-	-	-	12	18	7
Boreham Wood	8	4	11	7	14	4	11	10	1	-
Bracknell Town	3	19	20	-	-	-	-	-	-	-
Bromley	-	-	-	2	-	-	-	-	-	-
Chalfont St Peter	-	-	16	11	11	13	18	20	-	-
Chertsey Town	-	-	-	-	-	-	-	-	3	-
Chesham United	-	18	14	10	1	-	-	-	-	12
Collier Row	-	-	19	-	-	-	-	-	-	-
Croydon	-	-	-	17	17	18	17	22	-	-
Dorking	-	-	-	6	10	11	3	-	22	-
Dulwich Hamlet	-	-	-	-	12	3	-	-	-	-
Epsom & Ewell	20	-	-	-	-	-	-	-	-	-
Finchley	22	-	-	-	-	-	-	-	-	-
Grays Athletic	6	2	-	-	-	-	-	-	-	-
Hampton	11	9	17	19	-	-	-	-	-	-
Harlow Town	-	-	-	8	13	17	-	-	-	-
Heybridge Swifts	-	-	-	-	18	19	16	5	16	2
Hitchin Town	-	-	4	4	5	8	1	-	-	-
Kingsbury Town	7	14	8	22	-	-	-	-	-	-
Leatherhead	10	10	12	20	-	-	-	-	-	-
Lewes	15	16	6	15	20	-	20	-	-	-
Leytonstone-Ilford	1	-	-	-	-	-	-	-	-	-
Leyton Pennant	2	-	-	-	-	14	13	9	14	4
Maidenhead United	21	-	-	-	16	-	12	17	12	14
Marlow	-	1	-	-	-	-	-	-	-	8
Metropolitan Police	-	-	13	9	21	-	-	-	-	-
Molesey	-	-	-	-	8	10	2	-	-	-
Newbury Town	-	-	-	-	-	-	-	-	20	-
Oxford City	17	12	-	-	-	-	-	-	-	1
Purfleet	-	-	-	21	-	-	4	2	-	-
Ruislip Manor	-	-	-	-	-	-	-	19	17	21
Southwick	4	11	15	3	19	-	-	-	-	-
Staines Town	14	5	1	-	-	-	-	11	6	3
Stevenage Borough	16	21	-	-	1	-	-	-	-	-
Thame United	-	-	-	-	-	-	-	-	-	13
Tilbury	19	-	-	-	-	-	-	-	-	-
Tooting & Mitcham United	-	-	-	12	6	7	7	4	8	19
Uxbridge	9	17	9	18	16	15	15	15	13	10
Walthamstow Avenue	-	15	-	-	-	-	-	-	-	-
Walton & Hersham	18	8	7	5	7	9	10	3	-	-
Wembley	5	6	10	16	15	5	9	13	9	20
Whyteleafe	-	-	-	14	9	20	14	16	11	15
Windsor & Eton	-	-	-	-	-	-	-	21	-	-
Wivenhoe Town	-	-	5	1	-	-	-	-	21	-
Woking	-	3	3	2	-	-	-	-	-	-
Wokingham Town	-	-	-	-	-	-	-	-	-	11
Wolverton Town	-	22	-	-	-	-	-	-	-	-
Worthing	-	13	18	13	22	-	-	8	2	-
Yeading	-	-	-	-	3	2	-	-	-	-
No of clubs competing	22	22	21	22	21	22	21	22	22	22

ICIS DIVISION ONE FINAL LEAGUE TABLE 1995/96

Division One		P	W	D	L	F	A	Pts
1.	Oxford City	42	28	7	7	98	60	91
2.	Heybridge Swifts	42	27	7	8	97	43	88
3.	Staines Town	42	23	11	8	82	59	80
4.	Leyton Pennant	42	22	7	13	77	57	73
5.	Aldershot Town	42	21	9	12	81	46	72
6.	Billericay Town	42	19	9	14	58	58	66
7.	Bognor Regis Town	42	18	11	13	71	53	65
8.	Marlow	42	19	5	18	72	75	62
9.	Basingstoke Town	42	16	13	13	70	60	61
10.	Uxbridge	42	16	12	14	46	49	60
11.	Wokingham Town	42	16	10	16	62	65	58
12.	Chesham United	42	15	12	15	51	44	57
13.	Thame United	42	14	13	15	64	73	55
14.	Maidenhead United	42	12	14	16	50	63	50
15.	Whyteleafe	42	12	13	17	71	81	49
16.	Abingdon Town	42	13	9	20	63	80	48
17.	Barton Rovers	42	12	10	20	69	87	46
18.	Berkhamsted Town	42	11	11	20	52	68	44
19.	Tooting & Mitcham	42	11	10	21	45	64	43
20.	Ruislip Manor	42	11	9	22	55	77	42
21.	Wembley	42	11	8	23	49	66	41
22.	Barking	42	4	12	26	35	90	24

LEADING LEAGUE GOALSCORERS

Steve Darlington	Wokingham Town	28
Paul Coombe	Basingstoke Town	26
Mark Butler	Aldershot Town	24
Matthew McDonnell	Marlow	26

DIVISION ONE RESULTS CHART 1995-96

	HOME TEAM	1	2	3	4	5	6	7	8	9	10	11	12	13	14	15	16	17	18	19	20	21	22
1.	Abingdon Tn	*	1-2	4-0	4-2	1-0	2-0	1-2	1-2	0-0	3-1	2-2	1-1	3-4	4-2	2-2	0-2	1-2	2-1	0-2	0-2	1-3	3-1
2.	Aldershot T	5-1	*	5-1	6-2	1-1	2-1	0-1	1-1	1-0	1-1	4-1	0-1	2-3	0-2	0-1	3-3	1-0	3-1	4-0	0-3	3-0	2-2
3.	Barking	1-5	0-4	*	1-4	2-2	1-2	0-1	1-1	0-2	1-2	1-2	1-1	2-0	2-3	1-2	1-2	1-4	1-1	0-2	1-0	2-2	1-3
4.	Barton Rovers	0-1	0-3	0-0	*	1-2	5-2	1-1	0-5	0-0	1-4	2-2	4-0	2-1	1-0	1-0	0-2	3-3	2-0	1-1	5-1	4-0	2-2
5.	Basingstoke	0-0	4-1	1-0	3-1	*	1-1	2-1	4-2	2-1	1-3	2-1	2-2	0-1	3-1	1-1	5-0	3-3	2-0	0-1	2-0	2-2	0-2
6.	Berkhamstead	4-2	0-0	0-1	1-2	0-3	*	2-0	0-2	0-1	1-2	1-1	2-2	1-1	2-3	1-1	1-2	4-1	0-1	1-3	1-0	1-1	2-1
7.	Billericay	1-3	1-2	3-0	1-6	2-2	3-0	*	3-1	2-0	2-0	0-3	1-1	2-0	1-0	4-1	2-1	1-2	1-0	0-0	0-1	1-1	0-0
8.	Bognor Regis	2-0	0-0	1-1	3-0	4-1	1-1	4-0	*	3-0	1-3	3-2	0-0	0-1	3-1	1-1	3-1	0-1	3-2	0-2	1-1	2-2	2-0
9.	Chesham Utd	4-0	1-0	1-1	4-0	2-2	0-1	0-1	0-1	*	1-1	0-1	1-0	1-1	0-2	3-2	2-0	0-0	1-2	1-0	3-0	2-2	2-0
10.	Heybridge S	3-0	2-0	7-0	3-1	3-1	4-2	3-2	5-1	2-0	*	0-0	1-1	3-1	2-2	3-0	3-0	5-1	1-2	4-0	4-1	2-0	2-0
11.	Leyton Penn	0-2	1-0	3-0	4-2	3-1	3-1	1-2	3-2	2-2	0-1	*	5-1	2-4	1-3	1-2	1-3	1-0	4-1	2-1	4-2	4-0	1-1
12.	Maidenhead	4-0	1-1	0-2	3-4	0-0	0-2	2-2	0-1	1-0	1-4	0-2	*	4-1	0-2	2-1	1-0	2-1	2-2	1-2	1-0	2-1	0-3
13.	Marlow	2-1	0-3	2-0	2-0	3-3	1-1	1-4	3-0	1-2	1-0	2-1	3-0	*	2-4	3-2	2-3	4-6	3-1	2-3	0-2	2-0	1-1
14.	Oxford City	3-3	1-3	1-0	3-0	3-2	1-0	4-1	1-0	1-0	4-3	2-2	2-2	1-6	*	2-2	1-1	5-0	3-1	1-0	5-1	2-0	2-0
15.	Ruislip Man	1-0	1-2	3-1	3-1	1-0	2-3	2-2	2-0	1-0	1-2	0-1	0-1	0-1	4-5	*	0-2	2-3	2-1	0-1	0-5	0-1	1-2
16.	Staines Tn	6-0	3-2	2-2	3-2	3-1	2-1	4-1	2-2	3-3	2-2	1-2	2-1	3-1	0-2	3-3	*	1-1	2-1	3-1	1-0	2-2	2-1
17.	Thame United	1-1	2-2	1-1	3-1	1-0	2-2	0-1	2-3	1-2	1-1	2-0	2-5	0-3	0-2	2-0	1-2	*	0-0	3-1	1-0	1-1	4-3
18.	Tooting & M	1-0	0-2	5-1	0-0	1-3	3-2	0-1	1-0	1-1	0-1	2-3	1-1	2-0	1-3	1-1	1-1	1-0	*	1-0	1-1	0-5	1-2
19.	Uxbridge	1-1	0-2	1-0	3-2	0-1	1-2	0-1	0-0	0-0	1-0	1-0	0-0	4-0	2-2	2-1	1-1	2-2	1-1	*	0-4	1-0	1-1
20.	Wembley	1-1	1-2	2-2	3-0	0-2	2-0	2-2	2-1	0-2	0-3	0-1	0-1	1-2	0-2	2-2	0-1	2-2	1-0	0-2	*	2-2	3-1
21.	Whyteleafe	4-2	0-6	2-0	3-3	2-0	1-1	2-1	2-4	3-4	4-1	1-3	2-1	3-1	3-5	8-3	0-2	1-2	0-2	1-1	2-0	*	1-2
22.	Wokingham T	3-4	1-0	1-1	1-1	3-3	1-2	3-0	0-5	3-2	1-0	0-1	2-1	2-0	2-4	0-1	0-3	2-0	2-1	3-1	3-1	1-1	*

ABINGDON TOWN

Formed: 1870 — Over The Bridge

Adingdon's keeper M Cummings gathers a corner under pressure from Lee Cormack. *Photo - A Relton*

Chairman: Phil Evans **Vice Chairman:** Craig Norcliffe **President:** Dr Tim Reynolds
Secretary: Ted Quail, 107 Park Lane, Thatcham, Newbury, Berks RG18 3BZ (01635 868967).
Manager: Paul Lee **Asst Manager:** Roger Nicholls. **Physio:** Ian Maskell.
Coach: Kelvin Alexis. **Press Officer:** Nick Quail (01235 832499)
Ground: Culham Road, Abingdon OX14 3BT (01235 521684).
Directions: On A415 road to Dorchester-on-Thames half a mile south of town centre. Nearest rail station is Culham. Main line: Didcot Parkway or Oxford. Bus service from Didcot and London.
Capacity: 3,000 **Cover:** 1,771 **Seats:** 271 **Floodlights:** Yes **Metal Badges:** £2
Club Shop: Yes, selling programmes, magazines, scarves, badges.
Colours: Yellow & green **Change colours:** Black+white. **Sponsors:** Morlands.
Previous Name: Abingdon FC (amalgamated with St Michaels in 1899).
Previous Leagues: Oxford & District/ West Berks/ Reading Temperance/ North Berks/ Reading & District 1927-50/ Spartan 50-53/ Hellenic 53-88/ London Spartan 88-89.
Midweek home matchday: Wednesday. **Reserve Team's League:** Suburban (West).
Best FA Cup season: 4th Qualifying Rd 60-61 (lost 0-2 v Hitchin), 89-90 (01-3 at home to Slough), 92-93 (lost 1-2 at Merthyr Tydfil after 0-0 draw).
Best FA Vase season: 5th Round replay 89-90.
Record Attendance: 1,400 v Oxford City, FA Cup September 1960.
Players progressing to Football League: Maurice Owen (Swindon Town), George Buck (Stockport County & Reading), Sammy Chung (Reading, Norwich City, Watford & Wolverhampton Wanderers).
Clubhouse: (01235 521684). 7.30-11pm. 6pm matchdays. 12.30-2.30, 4-11 on Saturdays. Hot food on matchdays. Pool, darts, jukebox, canteen.
Club record appearances: John Harvey-Lynch.
95-96 Top scorer: Howard Forinton.
Local Newspapers: Oxford Mail, Oxford Times, Abingdon Herald, South Oxon Guardian.
Honours: Berks & Bucks Senior Cup 58-59 (R-up 88-89 92-93), Isthmian League Div 2 (Sth) 90-91 (Associate Members Tphy R-up 90-91), London Spartan League 88-89 (League Cup SF 88-89), Hellenic League(4) 56-57 58-60 86-87 (R-up(3) 70-72 87-88, League Cup 57-58 70-71 81-82 (R-up 83-84 86-87), Div 1 75-76, Div 1 Cup 75-76, Res. Div(3) 69-71 86-87, Res. Div Cup 70-71 85-86, Res. Div Suppl. Cup 74-75), Oxford & District League(3) 1898-1901, Reading & District League 47-48, Berks & Bucks Jnr Cup 06-07, Abingdon Centenary Cup 58-59, Joan Lee Memorial Cup 69-70 70-71 86-87, Oxford I'mediate League (Reserves) 47-48, Newbury Graystoke Cup(Reserves) 92-93 94-95 (R-up 90-91).

PROGRAMME DETAILS:
Pages: 40 **Price:** 80p
Editor: Simon Element
(01235 520605)

ALDERSHOT TOWN

Formed: 1992 | The Shots

Back Row (L-R): Paul Priddy, Steve Wigley, Jamie Horton, Tony Cleeve, Andy Russell, Mark Watson, Errol Chambers, Andy Nunn, Stuart Udall, Asa Head, Claire Eastland, Paul Shrubb. Front Row: John Humphries, Danny Holmes, Jason Chewins, Mark Butler, Mark Anderson, Andy Parr, Nick Burton.

Photo - Ian Morsman.

Chairman: Terry Owens **Vice Chairman:** Karl Prentice
Company Secretary: Graham Brookland, c/o Aldershot Town FC.
Manager: Steve Wigley. **Asst Manager:** Paul Shrubb. **Physio:** Clare Eastland
Club Newsline: 0891 446 834. **Press Officer:** Nick Fryer.
Commercial Manager: Ian Crossley (01256 59313)
Ground: Recreation Ground, High Street, Aldershot, Hants GU11 1TW (01252 20211. Fax: 24347).
Directions: Ground situated on eastern end of High Street next to large multi-storey B.T. building. From M3 (jct 4) take A325 to Aldershot. After five miles at r'bout take 1st exit marked town centre (A323) into Wellington Ave. At Burger King r'bout take 2nd exit into High Street - ground on left, large car park adjacent. 5 mins walk from Aldershot (BR).Clubhouse Steward:David McClounan (club tel.no.)
Capacity: 7,500 **Cover:** 6,850 **Seats:** 1,800 **Metal Badges:** Yes
Colours: Red shirts with blue trim and sleeves. **Change colours:** White & black trim/black/black & wh
Club Shop: Yes. Range of souvenirs, programmes, replica kits. Open matchdays or contact Ian Crossley(01252-20211) for mail order.
Sponsors: Datrontech Plc **Previous Leagues:** None.
Midweek home matchday: Tuesday
Reserve Team's League: Suburban.
Record win: 7-0 v Gosport Borough (H), FA Vase Preliminary Round 2/10/93,vDorking,Diadora League.94-95.
Record defeat: 1-5 v Gloucester City, FA Trophy Nov 1995
Record Attendance: 5,961 v Farnborough Town, Hants Senior Cup SF 16/3/93. *Ground record: 19,138 Aldershot FC v Carlisle United, FA Cup 4th Rd replay 28/1/70.*
Record Fees - Paid: £5,000 to Basingstoke Tn.for Paul Chambers 94-95.
Received: £3,000 for Daren O'Neill from Kingstonian 94
Clubhouse: 7-11pm every evening and matchdays except Wednesday. Pool, darts, satellite TV & skittles alley. Steward: David McClounan via the club.
Club record scorer: Mark Butler 131.
Club record appearances: Mark Butler 213.
95-96 Captain:
95-96 Top scorer: Mark Butler 33.
95-96 P.o.Y.:
Local Newspapers: Aldershot News (01252 28221), Farnham Herald (01252 725224).
Local Radio: County Sound (203m m/w, 1476 khz), BBC Radio Surrey (104.6 fm), Radio 210 (210m m/w).
Hons: Isthmian League Div 3 92-93, Simpsonair Trophy 92-93, Skol Invitation Trophy 92-93, FA Vase QF 94-95, Hants Senior Cup SF 92-93, Suburban League Western Division champions 1994-95, Allied Counties Youth League Champions 1994-95.

PROGRAMME DETAILS:
Pages: 40 **Price:** £1
Editor: Karl Prentice/ Graham Brookland

1898 # BARTON ROVERS Rovers

Barton Rovers celecbrate winning the Bedfordshire Premier Cup for the first time, following their 1-0 win over Bedford Town.

Chairman: S.J.Harris. **Vice Chairman:** T Capon. **President:** P Howarth.
Secretary: Owen Clark, 108 Manor Road, Barton-le-Clay, Bedford MK45 4NS (01582 882398).
Manager: Gordon Taylor **Asst Manager:** Paul Burgess **Coach:** Gordon Guile.
Press Officer: N Rhodes (01582 881865) **Physio:** Roy Cullis.
Ground: Sharpenhoe Road, Barton-le-Clay, Bedford MK45 4SD (01582 882607).
Directions: M1 Jct 12, from London exit turn right, take 2nd right through Harlington and Sharpenhoe. Ground on right entering village. Four and a half miles from Harlington (BR), 6 miles from Luton (BR), good bus service from Luton.
Capacity: 4,000 **Seats:** 160 **Cover:** 1,120 **Floodlights:** Yes
Colours: All blue **Change colours:** All red. **Club Shop:** No.
Midweek Matchday: Tuesday **Kit Sponsors:** **Metal Badges:** Yes
Previous Ground: Church Pitch 1898-1912; Barton Cutting 1912; Sharpenhoe Rd 12-33; Faldo Rd 33-38; Barton Rec. 46-75.
Reserves' Lg: None **Previous Leagues:** Luton & Dist. 47-54/ Sth Midlands 54-79.
Record Gate: 1,900 v Nuneaton, FA Cup 4th Qual. Rd 1976.
Best FA Cup year: 1st Rd. 80-81 (lost 0-2 at Torquay United).
Record win: 17-1 v Flitwick Athletic (H), S Midlands Lge Div 1 55-56.
Record defeat: 1-11 v Leighton United (H), S Midlands Lge Prem Div 62-63.
Record Fees - Paid: £1,000 for B Baldry (Hitchin Town, 1980).
Received: £1,000 for B Baldry (Bishop's Stortford, 1981).
Players progressing to Football Lge: Kevin Blackwell (Huddersfield, Torquay, Notts Co., Scarborough, Plymouth).
Clubhouse: Noon-3pm weekends (no football), noon-11pm (matchdays), 7-11pm weekdays. Real ale, hot & cold snacks, pool, darts, gaming machines.
Local Press: Luton News, Herald, Beds on Sunday.
Local Radio: Radio Chiltern, Radio Beds.
Record Scorer: Richard Camp 138, 1989-96.
Club Record Appearances: Bill Goodyear 475, 1982-93.
95-96 Captain: Danny Turner
95-96 P.o.Y.: Steve Hunt.
95-96 Top scorer: Gordon Guile.
Honours: FA Vase R-up 77-78 (SF 76-77 81-82, QF 75-76 78-79), Sth Mids Lg(8) 70-73 74-79 (R-up 67-68, Div 1 64-65 (R-up 55-56), Div 2 54-55, Lg Shield 57-58 60-61 68-69, Chal. Tphy 71-72 74-75 77-78 78-79), Beds Snr Cup (5) 71-73 80-82 89-90 (R-up(3) 74-76 82-83 90-91 95-96), Beds Premier Cup 95-96, R-up 81-82 83-84 88-89, Beds Intermediate Cup 53-54, Luton & Dist. Lg Div 3 47-48, North Beds Charity Cup 72-73 74-75 76-77 77-78 79-80 80-81 (R-up 70-71), Isthmian Lg Associate Members Tphy R-up 92-93. Diadora(Isthmian) Div.2 R-Up. 94-95.

PROGRAMME DETAILS:
Pages: 64 **Price:** £1
Editor: Nick Rhodes
(01582 881865)

BASINGSTOKE TOWN

1896 Stoke

Basingstoke Town FC 1995-96. *Photo - Andrew Chitty*

Chairman: David Knight **President:** Rafi Pazzak
Secretary: Richard Trodd, 5 Lemar Close, Brighton Hill, Basingstoke RG22 4HT (01256 413076)
Manager: Ernie Howe **Asst Manager:** Steve Richardson **Physio:** Ian McKarg.
Press Officer: David Knight
Commercial Manager: Chris Richardson.
Ground: Camrose Road, Western Way, Basingstoke RG24 6HW (01256 25063).
Directions: Exit 6 off M3 and follow A30 west, ground off Winchester Road. Two miles from bus and rail stations.
Capacity: 6,000 **Cover:** 1,500 **Seats:** 651 **Metal Badges:** Yes
Colours: Blue & gold stripes **Change colours:** Red & Black Stripes. **Sponsors:** Centerprise International & Panacea
Previous Leagues: Hants 1900-40 45-71/ Southern 71-87.
Previous Ground: Castle Field 1896-1947.
Midweek home matchday: Tuesday **Reserve Team's League:** Suburban.
Club Shop: Yes, selling programmes, books, scarves, shirts etc. Contact Neil Tysoe.
Record Attendance: 4,091 v Northampton, FA Cup 1st Rd 1971.
Best FA Cup season: 2nd Rd 89-90 (lost 2-3 at home to Torquay). Also 1st Rd 71-72.
League clubs defeated in FA Cup: None.
Record win: 10-0 v Chichester City (H), FA Cup 1st Qualifying Round, September 1976.
Record defeat: 0-8 v Aylesbury United, Southern League, April 1979.
Record Fees - Paid: £4,750 for Steve Ingham (Gosport Borough)
Received: £6,750 for Steve Ingham (Bashley)
Players progressing to Football League: Tony Godfrey (Southampton 1958), John Neale (Exeter 1972), Mike Doherty (Reading 1982), Micky Cheetham (Ipswich 1988), Matt Carmichael (Lincoln), Tony Franklin (Exeter), Steve Welsh (Peterborough 1990).
Clubhouse: Open every day (including lunchtime)(01256 464353)
Steward: Cheryl Fox.
Club Record Goalscorer: Unkown
Club Record Appearances: Billy Coombs
95-96 Captain: Paul Coombs.
95-96 P.o.Y.: Paul Coombs.
95-96 Top scorer: Paul Coombs.
Local Newspapers: Basingstoke Gazette (461131).
Local Radio Stations: Radio 210 (01734 413131)
Honours: Southern League Southern Div 85-86, Isthmian League Div 1 R-up 88-89, Hants League 67-68 69-70 70-71 (R-up 65-66 66-67 68-69, North Div 11-12 19-20), Hants Senior Cup 70-71 89-90 95-96

PROGRAMME DETAILS:
Pages: 40 **Price:** £1
Editor: Michael Edwards

1895 BERKHAMSTED TOWN Lilywhites

Berkhamsted defence clear their lines during the first half at Broadwater. *Photo - Martin Wray.*

Chairman: Brian McCarthy. **President:** Dennis Wright **Secretary:** Mrs Christine Sims, 18 Chiltern Park Avenue, Berkhamsted, Herts HP4 1EU (01442 873413).
Manager: Roy Butler **Coach:** Howard Cowley.
Press Officer: Bob Sear **Physio:** Kevin Burke.
Ground: Broadwater, Lower Kings Road, Berkhamsted, Herts HP4 2AA (01442 862815).
Directions: Adjacent to Berkhamsted station (Euston-Birmingham line). A41 to Berkhamsted town centre traffic lights, left into Lower Kings Road.
Capacity: 2,000 **Seats:** 120 **Cover:** 200 **Floodlights:** Yes **Founded:** 1895
Colours: White/black/black **Change:** Green & white halves. **Metal Badges:** Yes.
Club Shop: Old programmes and club scarves, ties, boot bags, and baseball hats available. See Graham Hastie.
Previous Ground: Sunnyside Enclosure 1895-1919/ Sports Ground 1919-83.
Previous Leagues: W Herts & Herts Co. 95-22/ Spartan 22-51 66-75/ Delphian 51-63/ Athenian 63-66 83-84/ London Spartan 75-83.
Midweek Matchday: Tuesday
Sponsors: C D Wright Electrical Wholesalers.
Reserve Team's League: Essex & Herts Border Combination.

Record Gate: 1,163 v Barnet, FA Cup 3rd Qual. Rd 1987.
Best FA Cup year: 3rd Qual Rd 87-88
Players progressing to Football League: Frank Broome, Maurice Cook, Keith Ryan (Wycombe).
Clubhouse: Open 7 days a week. Pool & darts.
Club Record Goalscorer:
Club Record Apps:
95-96 Top scorer: Ian Rutherford
Local Press: Berkhamsted Herald, Berkhamsted Gazette.
Local Radio Stations: Chiltern Radio, Radio Beds.
Honours: Hertfordshire Senior Cup 52-53, London Spartan League 79-80 (Div 2 26-27), Herts Charity Shield 73-74 79-80 84-85 90-91 50-51(jt), Herts Senior County League Aubrey Cup 52-53, St Marys Cup(12), Apsley Senior Charity Cup(9), Wallspan Southern Combination 84-85 (Floodlit Cup 84-85).

PROGRAMME DETAILS:
Pages: 32 **Price:** 70p
Editor: Bob Sear
(01442 864547)

Formed: 1880

BILLERICAY TOWN

The Town

Back Row (L-R): J Kendall (Mgr), G Waters, J Collins, M Sinfield, N Munson, G Howard, P Reed, J Turnbull, A Skinner, K Varney (Coach), J Kelly (Physio). Front: P Battram, T Caines, M Brewer, J Prue, C Payne, P Shirt, J Purdie, P Brown (Asst Coach). *Photo - Evening Echo*

Chairman: Rod Moore **Vice Chairman:** Len Willis. **President:** Barry Spall
Secretary: Len Dewson, 14 Graham Close, Billericay, Essex CM12 0QW (01277 622375).
Manager: John Kendall **Coach:** Ken Varney **Asst Coach:**
Press Officer: Phil Heady (01277 626560). **Physio:** John Kelly.
Ground: New Lodge, Blunts Wall Road, Billericay CM12 9SA (01277 652188).
Directions: From Shenfield (A129) turn right at 1st lights then 2nd right. From Basildon (A129) proceed over 1st lights in town, then left at next lights and 2nd right. Half mile from Billericay (BR) station (London Liverpool Str.-Southend line). Ground 5 mins walk from buses 222, 251, 357, 255, 551.
Capacity: 3,500 **Seats:** 238 **Cover:** 850 **Metal Badges:** Yes
Colours: All Royal Blue withwhite trim. **Change colours:** All white with red trim.
Club Shop: Yes, open matchdays for souvenirs, metal badges, old progs,etc.Programme swaps with other clubs encouraged. Contact Nigel Harris (01268 558114).
Midweek Matches: Tuesday. **Previous Ground:** Laindon Road (pre-1971)
Previous Leagues: Romford & Dist. 1890-1914/ Mid Essex 18-47/ South Essex Comb. 47-66/ Essex Olympian 66-71/ Essex Snr 71-77/ Athenian 77-79.
Sponsors: Imation (Borne of 3m Innovation) **Reserves' Lge:** Essex & Herts Border Comb.
Best FA Cup year: 4th Qual Rd 77-78 **Best FA Vase year:** Winners 3 times
Record Gate: 3,841 v West Ham Utd, Floodlight opener 77. Comp match: 3,193 v Farnborough Tn, FA Vase SF 1st leg 76.
Record win: 11-0 v Stansted (A), Essex Senior League 5/5/76.
Record defeat: 3-10 v Chelmsford City (A), Essex Senior Cup 4/1/93.
Record Fees - Paid: Undisclosed.
Received: £22,500 for Steve Jones (West Ham, Nov. 1992).
Players progressing to Football League: D Westwood (QPR & Gillingham) 75, A Hull, D Carter (Peterborough, Orient), D Cass (Orient) 88, D Ludden (Orient &Watford) 92, S Jones (West Ham Utd/Bournemouth/West Ham Utd) 92.
Clubhouse: Open every evening 8-11pm (except Monday)(1pm-11pm Sat) and weekend lunchtimes noon-2.30pm. Discos, live entertainment.
Rec Goalscorer: F Clayden 273 **Rec Appearances:** J Pullen 418.
95-96 Captain: Gary Howard.
95-96 P.o.Y. & Top scorer: Leon Gutzmore 27 in 38 games
Players & Supporters' P.o.Y. 95-96: Leon Gutzmore
Local Press: Evening Echo (01268 522792), Billericay Gazette 01245 262421).
Local Radio: BBC Radio Essex (01268 522792), Essex Radio (01702 33311).
Hons: FA Vase (3 - a record) 75-77 78-79, Essex Snr Lg(3) 72-73 74-75 75-76 (R-up 71-72 73-74, Lg Cup(4) 71-74 76-77 (R-up 74-75), Challenge Cup 72-73), Isthmian Lg Div 2 79-80 (Div 1 R-up 80-81), Athenian Lg(2) 77-79 (Lg Cup 77-78), East Anglian Cup R-up 79-80 84-85, Essex Snr Cup 75-76 (R-up 85-86 93-94 94-95 95-96), Essex Snr Tphy 77-78 79-80, Essex Thameside Tphy 86-87 91-92 (R-up 90-91), Essex F'lit Tphy 77-78, Phillips F'lit Tphy 76-77, Rothmans Merit Award 1978.

PROGRAMME DETAILS:
Pages: 36 **Price:** TBA
Editor: Steve Lewis.
(01277 625679)

1883 **BOGNOR REGIS TOWN** The Rocks

BOGNOR REGIS TOWN

Back Row (L-R); R Pearce, G Marriner, M Rice, T Mallesa, C Matthews, A Miles, D Kilpatrick, R Eastland, G Rutherford. Front; P Lewis, I Ford, D Pearce, A Beazeley, P Pullen, M Birmingham, M Pullen, L Cormack, J Quinlan.
Photo - Martin Denyer

Chairman: Jack Pearce **Vice Chairman:** **President:** S Rowlands
Secretary: Paul Harwood c/o The Club. (01243 587554(H)).
Manager: Jack Pearce. **Asst Manager:** Neil Hider **Physio:** Martin James.
Press Officer: Martin Denyer **Comm. Manager:** Maurice Warner **Gen. Manager:** Jack Pearce
Ground: Nyewood Lane, Bognor Regis PO21 2TY (01243 822325).
Directions: West along seafront from pier, past Aldwick shopping centre, and right into Nyewood Lane.
Capacity: 6,000 **Cover:** 3,800 **Seats:** 243 **Floodlights:** Yes **Metal Badges:** Yes
Club Shop: Yes, selling programmes and normal club items.
Colours: White (green trim)/green/white **Change colours:** All yellow
Previous Leagues: W Sussex Lge 1896-1926/ Brighton, Hove & District Lge 26-27/ Sussex County Lge 27-72/ Southern Lge 72-81
Midweek home matchday: Monday **Reserve's League:** None.
Record Attendance: 3,642 v Swansea FA Cup 1st Rd replay, 84. **Sponsors:** Reynolds Furnishing Ltd
Best FA Cup season: 2nd Rd 84-85 (lost 2-6 at Reading), 85-86 (1-6 at Gillingham), 88-89 (lost 0-1 at home to Cambridge). 1st Rd 72-73 86-87 87-88.
League clubs beaten in FA Cup: Swansea 84-85, Exeter 88-89.
Record Fees - Paid: None
Received: £10,500 for John Crumplin & Geoff Cooper (Brighton & Hove Albion, 1987) & Simon Rodger (Crystal Palace, 1989).
Players progressing to Football League: E Randall (Chelsea 50), J Standing (Brighton 61), A Woon (Brentford 72), J Crumplin & G Cooper (Brighton 87), Simon Rodger (C Palace 89).
Clubhouse: Open every night, matchdays and Sunday lunchtimes. Hot food available.
Club Record Goalscorer: Kevin Clements
Club Record Appearances: Mick Pullen, 914.
95-96 P.o.Y.: **95-96 Top scorer:** Adie Miles.
Local Newspapers (+Tel.Nos.): Bognor Regis Joural & Guardian (865421), Bognor Observer (827111), Brighton Argus (544544), Portsmouth News (64488).
Local Radio Stations: Radio Sussex, Ocean Sound, Radio Solent, Southern Sound.
Hons: Isthmian Lg Div 1 R-up 81-82, (Lg Cup 86-87), Southern Lg R-up 80-81 (Lg Cup R-up 80-81, Merit Cup 80-81), Sussex Lg 48-49 71-72 (R-up 38-39 51-52, Div 2 70-71, Invitation Cup 40-41 49-50 62-63 71-72), Brighton Lg R-up 26-27, W Sussex Lg(5) 20-25 (R-up 1896-97, 25-26), W Sussex Jnr Lg 10-11 13-14, Southern Co's Comb 78-79, Sussex Snr Cup(9) 54-56 79-84 86-87 94-95 (R-up 51-52 58-59 84-85), Sussex Prof. Cup 73-74, Sussex RUR Cup 71-72, Sussex I'mediate Cup 52-53, Littlehampton Hosp. Cup 29-30 33-34, Bognor Charity Cup(8) 28-29 30-31 32-33 37-38 47-48 58-59 71-73, Gosport War Mem. Cup(2) 81-83 (R-up 86-87), Snr Midweek F'lit Cup R-up 74-75, FA Amtr Cup 1st Rd 71-72, FA Tphy 1st Rd 80-81 90-91.

PROGRAMME DETAILS:
Pages: 36 **Price:** £1
Editor: Maurice Warner

1926

CANVEY ISLAND

Gulls

Canvey Island's Chris Blakebraigh celebrates with scorers Alan Brett & Steve Porter

Photo - Richard Brock

Chairman: Ray Cross **Manager:** Jeff King.
Secretary: Mrs Frances Roche, 56 Harvest Road, Canvey Island SS8 9RP (01268 698586).
Ground: Park Lane, Canvey Island (01268 682991).
Directions: A130 from A13 or A127 at Sadlers Farm r'bout, 1 mile right through town centre, first on right past old bus garage. Bus 3 or 151 from Benfleet (BR) to stop after Admiral Jellicoe (PH).
Seats: 165 **Cover:** 250 **Capacity:** 2,500 **Floodlights:** Yes
Colours: Yellow **Change cols:** Red
Record Gate: 3,250 v Tiverton, FA Vase SF 27/3/93
Previous Lges: Southend & Dist.; Thurrock & Thameside Comb.; Parthenon; Metropolitan; Gtr London 64-71; Essex Senior.
Best FA Cup season: Fourth Qualifying Round 93-94, lost 1-3 at Kettering Town.
Players progressing to Football League: Peter Taylor (Spurs, Crystal Palace & England).
Hons: Isthmian Lg Div 2 95-96, Div 3 R-up 94-95, Carlton Trophy 95-96, FA Vase SF 92-93, Essex Snr Lg 86-87 92-93 (Lg Cup 83-84 92-93, Harry Fisher Memorial Trophy 93-94, Sportsmanship Award 83-84, Reserve Shield 91-92, Reserve Cup R-up 93-94), Essex Senior Trophy R-up 93-94, Essex Thameside Trophy 93-94, Gtr London Lg(2) 67-69 (Lg Cup 68-69).

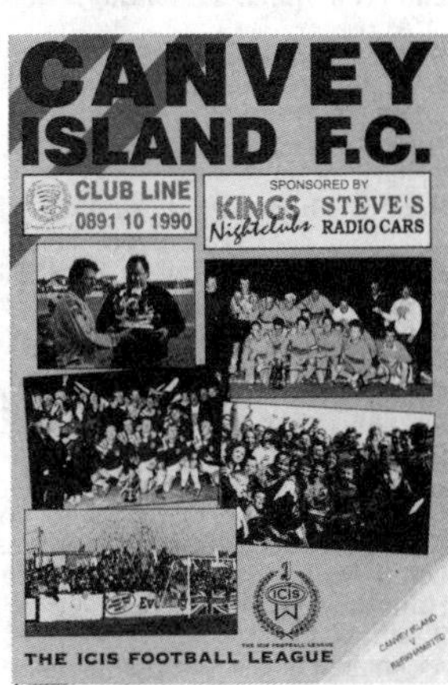

PROGRAMME DETAILS:
Pages: 32 **Price:** 70p
Editor: Rod Hall
(01268 697348)

CHESHAM UNITED

Formed: 1886

The Generals

Action between Chesham United & Aldershot Town *Photo - Eric Marsh*

President: Bill Wells **Chairman:** David Pembroke **Vice-Chairman:** Dennis Bone.
Secretary: Ronald Campion c/o Chesham United FC.
Manager: Paul O'Reilly **Assistant Manager:** Mickey Barnes **Physio:** Ann Wheeler
Press Officer: Ken Ambrose Tel. 01494 873250. **Commercial Manager:** Ken Ambrose.
Ground: Meadow Park, Amy Lane, Amersham Road, Chesham HP5 1NE (01494 783964 - ground clubhouse. 0494 791608 - fax. 0891 884580 - match information service).
Directions: M25 junction 18, A404 to Amersham, A416 to Chesham - go down to r-about at foot of Amersham Hill, then sharp left. 10 mins walk from Chesham station (Metropolitan Line).
Capacity: 5,000 **Cover:** 2,500 **Seats:** 224 **Floodlights:** Yes **Metal Badges:** Yes
Club Shop: Yes. Open matchdays - Manager: Peter Annetts (01296 87615).
Colours: Claret & blue **Change colours:** Yellow & black. **Sponsors:** MFI.
Previous Leagues: Spartan 17-47/ Corinthian 47-63/ Athenian 63-73.
Midweek home matchday: Wednesday **Reserve Team's League:** N/A.
Record Attendance: 5,000 v Cambridge Utd, FA 3rd Rd 5/12/79.
Best FA Cup season: 3rd Rd as above (lost 0-2). Also 1st Rd 66-67 68-69 76-77 82-83.
Best FA Trophy season: 3rd Rd 92-93 (lost 1-3 at home to Sutton United).
Record Fees - Paid: Undisclosed (club policy)
Received: Undisclosed (club policy).
Players progressing to Football League: Bill Shipwright & Jimmy Strain (Watford 1953 & 55), Stewart Scullion (Charlton 1965), John Pyatt (L'pool 1967), Brian Carter (Brentford 1968), Kerry Dixon (Spurs 1978), Tony Currie (Torquay 1984).
Clubhouse: Open every evening & matchdays. Bar snacks. Available for hire (business training meetings, weddings etc).
Club Record Goalscorer: John Willis.
Club Record Appearances: Martin Baguley (600+).
Local Newspapers: Bucks Examiner (01494 792616), Bucks Advertiser (01895 632000), Bucks Free Press (01494 21212).
Local Radio Stations: Radio Chiltern (01582 666001).
Honours: FA Amtr Cup R-up 67-68, Isthmian Lg 92-93 (Div 1 90-91, Div 2 Nth 86-87, Associate Members Cup R-up 90-91, Charity Shield 94-95), Athenian Lg Div 1 Cup 63-64 68-69, Corinthian Lg R-up(2) 60-62 (Lg Cup 60-61), Spartan Lg(4) 21-23 24-25 32-33 (R-up 26-27 29-30 33-34), Berks & Bucks Snr Cup 21-22 25-26 28-29 33-34 47-48 50-51 64-65 66-67 75-76 92-93 (R-up 94-95).

PROGRAMME DETAILS:
Pages: 36 **Price:** £1.20
Editors: J & S Chambers

1953

CROYDON

Croydon FC 96-97 *Photo - Andrew Chitty*

Chairman: Ken Jarvie.
Secretary: Mrs.J.R.Jarvie, 2 Spa Close, London SE25 6DS. Tel. 0181 6537250.
Manager: Ken Jarvie **Press Officer:** Russell Chandler.
Ground: Croydon Sports Arena, Albert Road, South Norwood SE25 4QL (081 654 3462).
Directions: Train to East Croydon or Norwood Junction, then bus 12 to either Belmont or Dundee Road. Walk down either - ground at bottom. 5 mins walk from Woodside (BR).
Capacity: 8,000 **Cover:** 450 **Seats:** 450 **Club Shop:** Yes **Metal Badges:** Yes
Colours: Sky blue/blue **Change colours:** All red **Sponsors:** Philips.
Reserve Team's League: Suburban.
Previous Leagues: Surrey Senior 53-63/ Spartan 63-64/ Athenian 64-74.
Midweek home matchday: Monday **Previous Name:** Croydon Amateurs 1953-74.
Record Attendance: 1,450 v Wycombe, FA Cup 4th Qualifying Rd 1975.
Best FA Cup season: 2nd Rd replay 79-80 (lost 2-3 to Millwall after 1-1 draw).
Record Fees - Paid: Steve Brown **Received:** Peter Evans (to Sutton Utd).
Players progressing to Football League: Alan Barnett (Plymouth 1955), Peter Bonetti (Chelsea), Leroy Ambrose (Charlton 1979), Steve Milton (Fulham - via Whyteleafe), Murray Jones (Crystal & Exeter - via Carshalton).
Clubhouse: (081 654 8555). Open every evening and lunchtime, holds 250, snacks available. Dancing, discos, bingo. Lounge bar available for private hire.
Club Record Appearances: Alec Jackson (400+)
Newspapers: Croydon Advertiser, Croydon Midweek Post, Croydon Times, Croydon Guardian.
Hons: F.A. Amateur Cup 3rd Rd 71-72, F.A. Tphy 2nd Rd(2) 81-83, Isthmian Lg Div 2 R-up 75-76 95-96, Surrey Snr Cup 81-82 (R-up 76-77), Surrey Prem Cup 86-87, Spartan Lg 63-64, Athenian Lg R-up 71-72 (Div 2 65-66 (R-up 70-71)), Surrey Snr Lg R-up 56-57 60-61 62-63 (Lg Cup 60-61, Charity Cup 53-54 62-63, Res Section 57-58), London Snr Cup R-up 78-79, Suburban Lg South 86-87 (Lg Cup(2)), Southern Yth Lg 85-86 (Lg Cup 85-86 87-88), Berger Yth Cup 78-79.

PROGRAMME DETAILS:
Pages: 28 **Price:** 70p
Editor: Russell Chandler
(0181 6542603)

HAMPTON

1920 Beavers

Back Row (L-R): Chick Botley (Mgr), Kevin Duffell, Lyndon Buckwell, Warren Bayliss, Jim Wigmore, Mark Russell, Darren Smith, Dave Rattue, Robin Lewis, Barry Barnes (Asst Mgr). Front Row: Mark Wilson, Steve Cheshire, Barry Moore, Danny Collyer, Warren Drew, Richard Sell, Matthew Stark (Mascot).

Chairman: Robert Hayes **Vice Chairman:** Ken Gazzard **President:** Alan Simpson
Secretary: Adrian Mann, 30 Burniston Court, Manor Rd, Wallington, Surrey SM6 0AD (0181 773 0858).
Manager: Chick Botley. **Assistant Manager:** Barry Barnes. **Physio:** Bob Morford.
Press Officer: Les Rance
Ground: Beveree Stadium, Beaver Close, off Station Rd, Hampton TW12 2BX (0181 979 2456-Club; 0181 941 4936-Boardroom; 0181 941 2838-Office matchdays only)
Directions:
A3 out of London, fork left (signed Staines/Esher/Sandown Pk) onto A243, A309 Staines exit to Hampton Ct at 'Scilly Isles' r'bout, left at r'bout after Hampton Court Bridge onto A308, after 1 mile right into Church St (A311), left after White Hart after 200yds into High St, Station Rd on right just before junction with A308.
Capacity: 3,000 **Seats:** 200 **Cover:** 800 **Floodlights:** Yes
Colours: Red & blue/white/blue **Change:** White/tangerine/white. **Metal Badges:** Yes
Club Shop: Yes, selling various club souvenirs and programmes. Contact Stefan Rance (0181 287 4682).
Sponsors: Saft-Nife Ltd. **Midweek Matchday:** Tuesday **Reserve Team's League:** Suburban
Previous Leagues: Kingston & District 21-33/ South West Middx 33-59/ Surrey Snr 59-64/ Spartan 64-71/ Athenian 71-73.
Previous Grounds: Hatherop Rec (until 1959).
Record win: 11-1 v Eastbourne Utd, Isthmian Lge Div 2 (S), 90-91
Record defeat: 0-13 v Hounslow Town, Middlesex Senior Cup 62-63.
Record Fees - Paid: £400 for Peter Shodiende (Hendon, 1981)
Received: £2,500 from APOP (Cyprus) for Ricky Walkes (June 1989).
Best F.A. Cup year: 4th Qualifying Round 77-78 (lost 1-2 v Barnet).
Clubhouse: (0181 979 2456). Lounge bar and Hall, open on matchdays and training nights. Hall available for hire.
Steward: Steve Penny.
Players progressing to Football League: Andy Rogers (Southampton, Plymouth, Reading), Dwight Marshall (Plymouth,Luton Town),Paul Rogers(Sheffield Utd.)
Club Record Goalscorer: Peter Allen
Club Record Appearances: Tim Hollands
95-96 Captain: Steve Cheshire **95-96 P.o.Y.:** Dave Rattue.
95-96 Top scorer: Warren Bayliss 23
Local Newspapers: Middx Chronicle, Surrey Comet, Richmond & Twickemham Times, The Informer.
Hons: London Snr Cup(2) 86-88, Spartan Lg(4) 64-67 69-70 (R-up 67-68, Lg Cup(4) 64-68 (R-up(2) 68-70), Surrey Snr Lg 63-64 (Lg Cup R-up 60-61, Middx Charity Cup 69-70 95-96 (R-up 68-69 71-72 89-90 94-95), Middx Snr Cup R-up 71-72 76-77 95-96, Athenian Lg Div 2 R-up 72-73, Southern Comb. Cup 68-69 71-72 76-77 81-82 83-84 85-86 (R-up 77-78 79-80), Isthmian Lge Div 3 winners 91-92, Isthmian Lge Div 2 winners 95-96.

PROGRAMME DETAILS:
Pages: 28 **Price:** £1
Editor: Secretary

LEYTON PENNANT

Formed: 1868 Lilywhites

Back Row (L-R): Christie Keane, Paul Salmon, John Varney, David Flint, Marc Baker, Joe Harley, Ben Barnett, Alex Welsh (Coach), Paul Taylor (Player Mgr). Front; Richard Chick, Pat Staunton, Barry Popplewell, Phil Lovell, Tery O'Neil, Ropy Edwards, Mick Cole.

Chairman: John Stacey **President:** George Cross **Jt Vice-Chairmen:** David Ward/ Dave Crabb
Secretary: Andy Perkins, 4 Chestnut Drive, Wanstead, London E11 2TA, (0181 530 4551)
Manager: Paul Taylor **Gen. Manager:** Kevin Moran **Coach:** Trevor Harvey
Press Officer: Charlie Ward (01295 780639) **Physio:** Christie Keene
Ground: Wadham Lodge,Kitchener Road,Walthamstow E17 4JP (0181 527 2444)
Directions: North Circular Road to Crooked Billet,turn into Chingford Road,then into Brookscroft Road,first on left.Walthamstow Central (Victoria Line tube) one mile away,then buses W21 or 256.
Capacity: 2,000 **Cover:** 600 **Seats:** 200 **Floodlights:** Yes **Metal Badges:** No.
Club Shop: Sells programmes, pennants, scarves, badges etc. Contact Ian Wells c/o the club.
Colours: White/navy/white **Change colours:** All navy **Sponsors:** Kay Sports.
Previous Leagues: Leyton & District Alliance/ South Essex/ Southern 05-11/ London 20-26/ Athenian 27-82/ Spartan Lge as Walthamstow Pennant.
Midweek home matchday: Tuesday **Reserve Team League:** Essex & Herts Border Comb.
Record Attendance: 676 v Aldershot Icis Lge 10/2/96, *(100,000 saw Leyton v Walthamstow Avenue, FA Amateur Cup final at Wembley, April 26th 1952).*
Record win: 10-2 v Horsham 82 **Record defeat:** 1-11 v Barnet 46.
Best FA Trophy season: 3rd Rd 86-87.
Best FA Vase season: 6th Rd 83-84.
Best FA Cup season: 3rd Rd in 09-10
Record Fees - Paid: £200 for Dwight Marshall (Hampton)
Received: £6,000 for T Williams (Redbridge Forest).
Players progressing to Football League: C Buchan (Sunderland) 10, Casey (Chelsea) 52, K Facey (Orient 52), M Costello (Aldershot 56), D Clark (Orient 61).
Clubhouse: (0181 527 2444). Open 11am-11pm Mon-Sat, 12-3 & 7-10.30pm Sun. Pool, darts, music. No hot food - hot snacks are sold at tea bar on matchdays.
Club Record Goalscorer: Steve Lane 118
Club Record Appearances: Steve Hamberger 387.
95-96 Captain: Stuart McLean **95-96 P.o.Y.:**
95-96 Top scorer:
Local Press: Waltham Forest Guardian, Hackney Gazette
Local Radio Stations: LBC.
Honours: Isthmian Lg Div 1 R-up 86-87 (Div 2 North 84-85), Essex Snr Tphy R-up 84-85, Thorn EMI National Floodlight Cup 84-85, FA Amateur Cup 26-27 27-28 (R-up 28-29 33-34 36-37 51-52), London Senior Cup 03-04 (R-up 33-34 37-38 45-46), London Charity Cup 34-35 36-37 (R-up 32-33 46-47 66-67 70-71), London Lg 23-24 24-25 25-26 (R-up 26-27, Lg Cup 56-57), Athenian Lg 28-29 65-66 66-67 76-77 81-82 (R-up 45-46 64-65 77-78, Div 2 Cup R-up 69-70), London Challenge Cup R-up 09-10 27-28 95-96, East Anglian Cup R-up 45-46 72-73, Essex Thameside Trophy 64-65 66-67 81-82 (R-up 63-64), Leyton & Dist. All 1892-93 94-95

PROGRAMME DETAILS:
Pages: 32 **Price:** 80p
Editor: John Stacey
(0181 527 8116)

MAIDENHEAD UNITED

1869 Magpies

Back Row (L-R); R Coombs (Tres), R Bannister (Sec), A Swan (Comm Mgr), J Swan (Vice Chr), P McDonald, R Popejoy, R Jackson, R Hussey, S Payne, J Coombs, D Jones (Committee). Second Row; T Kingham, M MacLeod (Comm), V Pratt, P Mckinnon, K Brown, T Roffey, M Harrison, L Knott, P Dadson, A Ross (Prog), R Dawson (Soc). Third Row; C Tate, A Norman, P McNamee, J Watt (Mgr), J Parsons (Chr), D Sweetman (Asst Mgr), D Harrison, R Gold, A Dell. Front; J Barrs (Physio), M Sciaraffa, T Houston, M Creighton, R McDowell, F Araguez, A Smith, J Pritchard.

Chairman: Jim Parsons **Vice Chairman:** Jon Swan **President:** Cliff West.
Secretary: Roy Bannister, 24 Queensway, Maidenhead, Berks SL6 7SD (011628 36314).
Managers: Martyn Busby & Alan Devonshire **Physio:** Jim Barrs.
Press Off.: John Swan (01628 473411) **Commercial Manager:** Aviva Swan(011628 36314).
Ground: York Road, Maidenhead, Berks SL6 1SQ (01628 24739).
Directions: From Maidenhead BR station proceed eastwards down Bell St - grd 300yds. From bus station southwards down Bridge Ave to York Rd, turn right, grd 200yds on left.
Capacity: 3,000 **Cover:** 900 **Seats:** 220 **Floodlights:** Yes **Metal Badges:** Yes
Club Shop: Yes, wide range of programmes and club souvenirs. Contact Mark Smith (01753 854674).
Cols: White & black stripes/black/red. **Change colours:** All blue. **Sponsors:** Whichford International.
Previous Leagues: Southern 1894-1902/ West Berks 02-04/ Great Western Suburban 04-22/ Spartan 22-39/Great Western Combination 39-45/ Corinthian 45-63/ Athenian 63-73.
Midweek matchday: Tuesday **Reserve Lge:** Suburban.
Record Attendance: 7,920 v Southall, FA Amateur quarter-final 7/3/36.
Best FA Cup season: Quarter Finals 1873-74 74-75 75-76.
Record win: 14-1 v Buckingham Town (H), FA Amateur Cup 6/9/52.
Record defeat: 0-14 v Chesham United (A), Spartan League 31/3/23.
Record transfer fee paid: £500 to Wycombe for Derek Harris, 1978.
Record fee received: £5,000 from Norwich for Alan Cordice, 1979.
Players progressing to Football League: L Allum (Chelsea 33), D Barley (Arsenal 51), R Barrett (Grimsby 58), A Cordice (Norwich 79), P Priddy (Brentford 72), D Kemp (Plymouth), L Sanchez (Reading, Wimbledon), E Kelsey, J Palethorpe (Reading 30), B Laryea, R Davies.
Clubhouse: Open some evenings & matchdays. Some hot food. Regular darts & pool matches.
Record Scorer: George Copas 270, 1924-35.
Record scorer in season: Jack Palethorpe 66, 1929-30.
Club Record Appearances: Bert Randall 532, 1950-64.
95-96 Top scorer: Paul McKinnon. **95-96 P.o.Y.:** Vernon Pratt.
Local Newspapers: Maidenhead Advertiser, Reading Evening Post.
Local Radio Stations: Radio 210, Star FM.
Hons: FA Amtr Cup SF 35-36, Isthmian Lg Div 2 Sth R-up 90-91; Spartan Lg(3) (R-up [2]); Corinthian Lg 57-58 60-61 61-62 (R-up 58-59 59-60, Mem. Shield 56-57 61-62 (R-up(4) 48-49 50-51 59-61), Neale Cup 48-49 57-58 60-61; Gt Western Suburban Lg 19-20 (R-up 20-21), Berks & Bucks Snr Cup(16) Berks & Bucks Benev. Cup(6) (R-up [2]); Mithras Cup R-up 63-64 66-67 68-69 78-79, Southern Comb. Cup R-up 81-82.

PROGRAMME DETAILS:
Pages: 36 **Price:** 80p
Editor: Jon Swann
(01628 473411)

MARLOW

Formed: 1870 The Blues

Marlow FC *Photo: The Maidenhead Advertiser*

Chairman: Terry Staines. **Vice-Chairman:** Michael Watson **President:** Herbie Swadling.
Secretary: Paul Burdell,69 Wycombe Rd., Marlow, High Wycombe (01628 483722)
Manager: Graham Wilkins. **Coach:** Steve Roberts. **Physio:** Sarah Cripps.
Press Officer/Commercial Manager: Terry Staines.
Information Line (local call rates): 01628 477032).
Ground: Alfred Davis Memorial Ground, Oak Tree Road, Marlow SL7 3ED (01628 483970).
Directions: A404 to Marlow (from M4 or M40), then A4155 towards town centre. Turn right into Maple Rise (by ESSO garage), ground in road opposite (Oak Tree Rd). Half mile from Marlow (BR) station. Quarter mile from Chapel Street bus stops.
Capacity: 3,000 **Cover:** 600 **Seats:** 250 **Floodlights:** Yes **Metal Badges:** Yes
Club Shop: Yes, selling programmes, badges, ties, pens, videos etc.
Colours: Royal blue **Change colours:** Orange & black
Sponsors: The Marlow Building Company
Previous Leagues: Reading & Dist./ Spartan 1908-10 28-65/ Great Western Suburban/ Athenian 65-84.
Previous Name: Great Marlow.
Previous Grounds: Crown Ground 1870-1919)/ Star Meadow 19-24.
Midweek home matchday: Tuesday
Reserve Team's League: Suburban Premier.
Record Attendance: 8,000; Slough Town v Wycombe Wanderers, Berks & Bucks Snr Cup Final, 1972. For Marlow game: 3,000 v Oxford United, FA Cup 1st Round 1994.
Best FA Cup season: Semi-Finals 1882. Also 3rd Rd 92-93 (lost 1-5 at Tottenham) and 1st Rd on 19 other occasions: 1871-85 86-88 92-93 1991-92 94-95.
Record Fees - Paid: £5,000 for Richard Evans (Sutton Utd. 94)
Received: £8,000 for David Lay from Slought Town 94.
Players progressing to Football League: Leo Markham (Watford 1972), Naseem Bashir (Reading).
Clubhouse: Open matchdays & most evenings. Snack bar open matchdays.
Club Record Goalscorer: Kevin Stone 31.
Club Record Appearances: Mick McKeown 500+.
95-96 Captain: Colin Ferguson.
95-96 P.o.Y.: Micky Floyd.
95-96 Top scorer: Matthew McDonnell.
Local Newspapers: Bucks Free Press (01494 521212), Maidenhead Advertiser (01628 771155), Evening Post (01734 575833).
Local Radio Stations: Eleven 70, Radio Berkshire, Radio 210
Honours: Isthmian Lg Div 1 87-88 (Div 2 South R-up 86-87, Lg Cup 92-93), Spartan Lg Div 1 37-38 (Div 2 West 29-30), Berks & Bucks Senior Cup 1880-81 82-83 84-85 85-86 87-88 88-89 89-90 94-95 96-97 98-99 99-1900 90-91 94-95, FA Trophy 1st Rd 1987-88 91-92, FA Vase 5th Rd replay 74-75.

PROGRAMME DETAILS:
Pages: 40 **Price:** £1
Editor: Terry Staines.
John Addaway

MOLESEY

Formed: 1950 | The Moles

Molesey's Marvin Bates No 9 shields the ball from Steve Young the Hitchen goalkeeper, 17/2/96
Photo - Garry Letts

Chairman: T.B.A. **President:** Fred Maynard
Secretary: Martyn Cole, 1 Elm Tree Avenue, Esher, Surrey. KT10 8JG. (0181 398 1751 Fax 0181 224 5515 (H) 0181 247 7015 (B).
Manager: Mick Browne **Physio:** Clive Martland **Coach:** Ged Murphy
Commercial Manager: TBA **Press Officer:** Ben O'Connor (c/o the clun).
Ground: 412 Walton Road, West Molesey, Surrey KT8 0JG (0181 979 4823).
Directions: A3 from London to Hook, then A309 to Marquis of Granby pub, right to Hampton Court station, turn right for West Molesey, ground one mile on left.
Capacity: 4,000 **Cover:** 600 **Seats:** 400 **Floodlights:** Yes **Metal Badges:** Yes
Colours: White/black/black **Change colours:** All Red
Club Shop: Yes, contact John Chambers at the club.
Previous Leagues: Surrey Intermediate 53-56/ Surrey Snr 56-59/ Spartan 59-72/ Athenian 72-77.
Sponsors: T.B.A. **Previous Name:** Molesey St Pauls 1950-53.
Midweek home matchday: Wednesday **Reserve Team's League:** Suburban.
Record Attendance: 1,255 v Sutton United, Surrey Senior Cup Semi-Final 1966.
Best FA Vase season: 6th Rd 81-82 **Best FA Trophy season:** 1st Rd replay 90-91.
Best FA Cup season: First Round Proper 94-95 (lost 0-4 at home to Bath City).
Record Fees - Paid: £500 for Chris Vidal (Leatherhead, 1988)
Received: £5,000 for Chris Vidal (Hythe Town, 1989).
Players progressing to Football League: John Finch (Fulham), Cyrille Regis (WBA, Coventry & England).
Clubhouse: Open every evening and weekend lunchtimes. 2 bars, discos, live artists, darts, bingo, pool.
Steward: John Chambers
Club Record Goalscorer: Michael Rose, 130
Club Record Appearances: Frank Hanley, 453
Local Newspapers: Surrey Comet, Surrey Herald, Molesey News.
Local Radio: County Sound, Capital.
95-96 Captain: Mick Dalton.
95-96 P.o.Y.: Micky Ndah.
95-96 Top Scorer: Trevor McCoy.
Honours: Isthmian Lg Div 1 R-up 92-93 (Div 2 South R-up 89-90, Lg Cup R-up 92-93), Surrey Senior Lg 57-58, (Lg Charity Cup 56-57), Spartan Lg R-up 59-60 (Lg Cup 61-62 (R-up 63-64)), Surrey Senior Shield R-up 74-75, Southern Combination Cup 90-91 94-95.

PROGRAMME DETAILS:
Pages: 26 **Price:** 80p
Editor: Peter Bowers
c/o the club

THAME UNITED

1883 United

Back Row (L-R): Andy Cooper, Phil Rodney, Lee Bastable, Matthew Webb, Steve Mayhew, Lee Perkins, Danny Mann, Andy Shildrick, Robbie Carlisle, Dennis Gascoyne, Graham Tollervey, Declan Cuddy. Middle Row Standing: Brett Chowns Patrick Baptiste, Dave Southam, Justin Merritt, Greg Williams, Kenny Cox, Dave Tregurtha, Julio Barresi, Chris Johnson, Julian Dark. Middle Row Seated: Chris Perkins, Malcom McIntosh, Robert Pratley, Sally Turner, Dave North, Jim Tite, Paul Smith, Philip Caulfield, Neil Crocker, Mark Gee, Andy Thomas, Malcolm Grant. Front Row: Nigel Mott Jason Clifford, Pat McCoy, Michael Robson, Andy Mason, Keith Handsley, Alan Rourke, Anthony Wise.

Chairman: Jim Tite **Vice Chairman:** Paul K Smith
Secretary: Dave North, 35 Oregon Avenue, Tilehurst, Reading, Berks. RG3 6RZ4 (01734 423537)
Manager: Bob Pratley **Asst Manager:** Malcolm McIntosh **Physio:** Chris Perkins
Press Officer: Neil Crocker
Ground: Windmill Road, Thame, Oxon OX9 2DR (01844 213017).
Directions: Into Nelson Street from Market Square. 3 miles from Haddenham & Thame Parkway (BR). Nearest bus stop at Town Hall (half mile away).
Capacity: 2,500 **Seats:** 230 **Cover:** 400 **Floodlights:** Yes
Colours: Red & black Halves/White/Red and Black Hoops. **Change colours:** Black & white
Midweek Matchday: Tuesday **Club Shop:** No
Sponsors: Tennents Extra
Previous Leagues: Oxon Senior; Hellenic 1959-87; South Midlands 1987-91.
Previous Grounds: None
Previous Name: Thame FC
Record Gate: 1,035 v Aldershot, Isthmian Div 2 4/4/94.
Reserves' League: Suburban (West)
Record win: 9-0 v Bracknell, 31/10/92
Record defeat: 2-11 v Hungerford, FA Cup Prelim. Rd 1984.
Best FA Cup year: Third Qualifying Round 91-92 (lost 0-4 to Salisbury).
Clubhouse: Open every evening and weekend lunchtimes. Banquetting facilities for 200 (weddings, dinners, dances etc).
Record Scorer: Not known
Record appearances: Steve Mayhew.
95-96 Captain:
95-96 P.O.Y. & Top scorer:
Local Press: Oxford Mail, Thame Gazette, Bucks Free Press.
Local Radio: BBC Radio Oxford, Fox FM.
Honours: Isthmian Lg Div 3 R-up 92-93, Isthmian Lg Div 2 winners 94-95, Hellenic Lg 61-62 69-70 (Premier Div Cup(4)), Sth Mids Lg 90-91, Oxon Snr Cup 1894-95 05-06 08-09 09-10 75-76 80-81 92-93, Oxon Intermediate Cup 76-77 78-79 91-92, Oxon Charity Cup.

PROGRAMME DETAILS:
Pages: 24 **Price:** £1
Editor: Sally Turner
(C/o Club)

1932 **TOOTING & MITCHAM UTD** Terrors

Tooting may soon be leaving their famous old ground at Sandy Lane. *Photo - Gordon Whittington*

Chairman: John Buffoni **Vice Chairman:** Alan Simpson **President:** Cliff Bilham
Secretary: Les Roberts, 91 Fernlea Road, Mitcham, Surrey CR4 2HG (01816 465275)
Manager: John Langford **Coach:** Peter Shaw **Physio:** Danny Keenan
Press Officer: Jim Silvey. **Commercial Mgr:** John Pollard.
Ground: Sandy Lane, Mitcham, Surrey CR4 2HD (0181 648 3248).
Directions: Tooting (BR) quarter mile. Sandy Lane is off Streatham Road near Swan Hotel.
Capacity: 8,000 **Cover:** 1,990 **Seats:** 1,990 **Floodlights:** Yes **Metal Badges:** Yes
Club Shop: Yes, selling souvenirs and confectionary, etc.
Colours: Black & White stripes/Black/Red. **Change colours:** All red.
Sponsors: Claremont Coaches. **Midweek matchday:** Tuesday **Reserve League:** Suburban.
Prevs Lgs: London 32-37/ Athenian 37-56. **Record Gate:** 17,500 v QPR, FA Cup 2nd Rd 56-57.
Best FA Trophy season: 2nd Qualifying Rd Replay 71-72 81-82.
Best FA Amateur Cup season: 1st Rd replay 22-23.
Best FA Cup season: 4th Rd 75-76 (lost 1-3 at Bradford City). Also 3rd Rd 58-59, 2nd Rd 56-57 76-77, 1st Rd 48-49 50-51 63-64 74-75 77-78.
Record win: 11-0 v Welton Rovers, FA Amateur Cup 62-63.
Record defeat: 1-8 v Kingstonian, Surrey Snr Cup 66-67 & v Redbridge F. (H), Loctite Cup 3rd Rd 19/2/91.
League clubs defeated in FA Cup: Bournemouth & Boscombe Ath, Northampton 58-59, Swindon 75-76.
Record Fees - Paid: £9,000 for Dave Flint (Enfield)
Received: £10,000 for Herbie Smith (Luton).
Players progressing to Football League: Trevor Owen (Orient 1958), Dave Bumpstead (Millwall 1958), Paddy Hasty (Aldersot 1958), Walter Pearson (Aldershot 1961), Richie Ward & Alex Stepney (Millwall 1962 & 63), Vic Akers (Watford 1975), Paul Priddy (Wimbledon 1978), Carlton Fairweather & Brian Gayle (Wimbledon 1984).
Clubhouse: Open every evening and weekend lunchtimes. Wide variety of food available.
Club Record Goalscorer: Alan Ives 92 (1972-78)
Club Record Appearances: Danny Godwin 470.
95-96 P.o.Y.: **95-96 Top scorer:** Mark Tompkins.
Local Newspapers: Mitcham News (0181 672 1077), South London Press (0181 769 4444), South London Guardian (0181 644 4300).
Local Radio Stations: Capital.
Honours: Isthmian League 57-58 59-60 (Full Members Cup 92-93), Athenian League 49-50 54-55, London Challenge Cup R-up 59-60, Surrey Senior Cup 37-38 43-44 44-45 52-53 59-60 75-76 76-77 77-78, London Senior Cup 42-43 48-49 58-59 59-60 (R-up 43-44 44-45), South Thames Cup 69-70, Surrey Senior Shield 51-52 60-61 61-62 65-66.

PROGRAMME DETAILS:
Pages: 24 **Price:** 80p
Editor: Jim Silvey.

UXBRIDGE

Formed: 1871 The Reds

Back Row (L-R): George Talbot (Mgr), Sean Dawson, Mark Gill, Steve Toms, Gary Williams, Phil Granville, Kevin Cleary, Gavin Bamford, Raoul Sam, Bobby Ropr (Coach), Ernie Kempster (Physio). Front Row: John Regan, Gareth Thomas, Nicky Ryder, Leon Latty, Jamie Cleary, Chris Yeardley, Micky Perry.

Chairman: Alan Holloway **Vice-Chairman:** Tom Barnard **Joint President:** Tom Barnard & Alan Odell.
Secretary: Graham Hiseman, 96 New Peachey Lane, Cowley, Uxbridge, Middx UB8 3SY (01895 237195).
Manager: George Talbot **Asst Mgr:** T.B.A. **Coach:** Micky Nicks.
Press Officer: Andy Peart (01895 444686) **Physio:** Ernie Kempster
Ground: Honeycroft, Horton Road, West Drayton, Middx UB7 8HX (01895 445830).
Directions: From West Drayton (BR) turn right then 1st right (Horton Road). Ground 1 mile on left. From Uxbridge (LT) take 222, U3 or U5 bus to West Drayton station, then follow as above. By road, ground 1 mile north of M4 jct 4 taking road to Uxbridge and leaving by first junction and turning left into Horton Rd - ground 600yds on right.
Capacity: 4,500 **Cover:** 480 **Seats:** 201 **Floodlights:** Yes **Metal Badges:** Yes.
Club Shop: Yes, selling club badges, ties, pennants, mugs, T-shirts, jumpers, programmes (League & non-League), pens, key-rings etc. Contact secretary.
Colours: Red/white/red **Change colours:** All blue or white and black
Previous Leagues: Southern 1894-99/ Gt Western Suburban 1906-19 20-23/ Athenian 1919-20 24-37 63-82/ Spartan 37-38/ London 38-46/ Gt Western Comb. 39-45/ Corinthian 46-63.
Prev. Name: Uxbridge Town (23-45) **Prev. Grnds:** RAF Stadium 23-48/ Cleveland Rd 48-78.
Midweek home matchday: Tuesday **Reserve Team's League:** Suburban (North Division).
Record Attendance: 1,000 v Arsenal, floodlight opening 1981.
Best FA Cup season: 2nd Rd 1873-74. 1st Rd on three other occasions 1883-84 84-85 85-86.
Best FA Trophy season: 1st Rd replay 88-89
Best FA Vase season: 4th Rd 83-84.
Players progressing to Football League: William Hill (QPR 1951), Lee Stapleton (Fulham 1952), Gary Churchouse,Tony Witter and Michael Meaker
Clubhouse: (01895 443557). Large clubhouse with bar and function room available for hire. Open every evening and weekend/bank holiday lunchtimes. Hot & cold snacks available on matchdays.
Club Record Scorer: Danny Needham, 125
Club Record Appearances: Roger Nicholls, 1054.
95-96 Captain: Gary Downes **95-96 Top Scorer:** Mark Gill 23.
95-96 P.o.Y.: Mark Gill.
95-96 Players' P.o.Y.: Mark Gill.
95-96 Supporters P.o.Y.: Steve Toms
95-96 Most Appearances: Sean Dawson 55, Phil Granville & Mark Gill 53
Local Newspapers: Uxbridge Gazette & Leader (01895 627000).
Local Radio Stations: Capital, G L R, Star FM.
Honours: FA Amateur Cup R-up 1897-98, London Challenge Cup 93-94, Isthmian League Div 2 South R-up 84-85 (League Cup R-up 85-86), Athenian League Cup R-up 81-82, Reserve Section 69-70, Reserve Cup 68-69), Corinthian League 59-60 (R-up 48-49, League Memorial Shield 50-51 52-53), Middx Senior Cup 1893-94 95-96 1950-51, Middx Senior Charity Cup 07-08 12-13 35-36 81-82 (R-up 69-70 82-83 85-86), Middx Prem Cup R-up 95-96, Allied Counties Yth League 92-93 (League Cup R-up 86-87, League Shield 88-89 92-93), AC Delco Cup R-up 85-86, Sub Lge North Div Champions 95-96.

PROGRAMME DETAILS:
Pages: 48-56 **Price:** 80p
Editor: A Peart & M.Bodman
(01895 444686+01895 813445)

1896 **WALTON & HERSHAM** Swans

WALTON & HERSHAM

Back Row (L-R): Dean Callagham, Mark Hill, Matt Edwards, John Power, Richard Smart, John Gasson, George Worley, Gerry Soloman. Front Row: Grant Hutchinson, Lee Brownlie, Tommy Mason, Graham Westley, Justin Mitchell Jason Davey. Photo - Andrew Chitty

Chairman: Theo Paphitis **President:** W Bigmore.
Secretary: Mark Massingham, 7b Sidney Rd., Walton-on-Thames, Surrey. KT12 2NP (01932 885814).
Manager: Dave Russell. **Asst Manager:** Laurie Craker **Physio:** Chris Channon.
Press Officer: Brian Freeman (01932 560738) **Commercial Manager:**
Ground: Sports Ground, Stompond Lane, Walton-on-Thames (01932 245263-club, 247565-boardroom).
Directions: From North: Over Walton Bridge & along New Zealand Ave., down 1-way street and up A244 Hersham Road - ground 2nd right. From Esher: Down Lammas Lane then Esher Rd, straight over 1st r'bout, 4th exit at next r'bout (West Grove) 2nd left at end of Hersham Rd and Stompond Lane is half mile on left. Ten minutes walk fron Walton-on-Thames (BR). Bus 218 passes ground.
Capacity: 6,500 **Cover:** 2,500 **Seats:** 500 **Floodlights:** Yes **Metal Badges:** Yes.
Club Shop: Yes, open matchdays. Contact Richard Olds, c/o the club.
Colours: White with red band/white/red. **Change colours:** Yellow/Blue/White.
Previous Leagues: Surrey Senior/ Corinthian 45-50/ Athenian 50-71.
Midweek home matchday: Tuesday **Reserve Team's League:** Suburban. **Sponsors:** T.B.A.
Record win: 10-0 v Clevedon, FA Amateur Cup 1960.
Record Gate: 6,500 v Brighton, FA Cup First Round 73-74.
Best FA Cup season: 2nd Rd 72-73 (v Margate), 73-74 (v Hereford).
League clubs defeated in FA Cup: Exeter 72-73, Brighton 73-74.
Players progressing to Football League: Denis Pacey (Orient 1951), John Whitear (Aston Villa 1953), Andy McCulloch (QPR 1970), Mick Heath (Brentford 1971), Paul Priddy (Brentford 1972), Richard Teale (Queens Park Rangers 1973), Steve Parsons (Wimbledon 1977), Stuart Massey (Crystal Palace), Ross Davidson (Sheffield Utd).
Clubhouse: (01932 244967). Open most nights. Bar, TV, darts, pool, refreshments on matchdays.
Club record scorer: Brian Jenkins.
Club record appearances: Terry Keen.
95-96 Captain: David Lay. **95-96 P.o.Y.** George Worley.
95-96 Top Scorer: Grant Hutchinson.
Local Newspapers: Surrey Herald, Surrey Comet.
Local Radio Stations: County Sound, BBC Southern Counties.
Honours: FA Amateur Cup 72-73 (SF 51-52 52-53), Isthmian Lg R-up 72-73, Barassi Cup 73-74, Athenian Lg 68-69 (R-up 50-51 69-70 70-71, Lg Cup 69-70), Corinthian Lg(3) 46-49 (R-up 49-50), Premier Midweek F'lit Lg(3) 67-69 70-71 (R-up 71-72), Surrey Snr Cup 47-48 50-51 60-61 61-62 70-71 72-73 (R-up 46-47 51-52 59-60 69-70 71-72 73-74), London Snr Cup R-up 73-74, Southern Combination Cup 82-83 88-89 91-92, Surrey Combination Cup 49-50 91-92, John Livey Memorial Trophy 91-92.

SWANS
Review
£1.20
Centenary Year
ICIS LEAGUE PREMIER DIVISION
WALTON & HERSHAM
versus
BOREHAM WOOD
Saturday 27th April 1996
Kick off 3.00pm
Match Sponsor: WEST LONDON TIMBER
MAIN SPONSOR
West London Timber Ltd.
THE ICIS FOOTBALL LEAGUE

PROGRAMME DETAILS:
Pages: 40 **Price:** £1.20
Editor: Brian Freeman/ Nick Swindley

WHYTELEAFE

Formed: 1946 Leafe

Back Row (L-R); Nigel Smith (Coach), Ian Paterson, Steve Milton, Gary Richards, Gary Fisher, Danny Rose, Dean Howland, Neil Pearson. Front; Malcom Smart, Gary Wilgoss, Eddy Dixon, Mark Dodman, Dean Davenport, Nigel Skeet. *Photo - J D Fountain.*

President: A F Lidbury **Chairman:** Paul Owens **Vice-Chairman:**
Secretary: Ian Robertson (01883 622096).
Manager: Lee Richardson. **Coach:** Bernie Donnelly
Press Officer: Warren Filmer (181 660 3255)
Commercial Manager: Paul Owens.
Ground: 15 Church Road, Whyteleafe, Surrey CR3 0AR (0181 660 5491).
Directions: Five minutes walk from Whyteleafe (BR) - turn right from station, and left into Church Road.
Capacity: 5,000 **Cover:** 600 **Seats:** 200 **Floodlights:** Yes **Metal Badges:** Yes
Colours: Green & white/green/green **Change colours:** Yellow/green.
Sponsors: Sunday Sport.
Previous Leagues: Caterham & Edenbridge/ Croydon/ Thornton Heath & Dist./ Surrey Intermediate (East) 54-58/ Surrey Senior 58-75/ Spartan 75-81/ Athenian 81-84.
Midweek matchday: Tuesday **Reserve Team's League:** Suburban.
Record Attendance: 780.
Best FA Vase season: 5th Rd 80-81 85-86
Best FA Trophy season: 3rd Qualifying Rd 89-90
Best FA Cup season: Third Qualifying Round replay (lost 1-2 after 1-1 draw at Wokingham Town).
League clubs defeated in FA Cup: None.
Record Fees - Paid: £1,000 for Gary Bowyer (Carshalton)
Received: £25,000 for Steve Milton.
Players progressing to Football League: Steve Milton (Fulham).
Clubhouse: Open every lunchtime and evening. Hot and cold food, pool, darts, gaming machines.
95-96 Captain: Steve Milton.
95-96 Player of the Year: Danny Rose.
95-96 Clubman of the Year: Lee Richardson
95-96 Top scorer: Neil Pearson **Local Press:** Croydon Advertiser.
Local Radio Stations:
Honours: Isthmian League Div 2 South R-up 88-89; Surrey Senior League 68-69 (League Cup R-up 68-69, League Charity Cup 71-72, Reserve Section 62-63 (Challenge Cup 62-63 (R-up 59-60); Surrey Senior Cup 68-69 (R-up 87-88); Surrey Premier Cup R-up 84-85; East Surrey Charity Cup 79-80 (R-up 76-77 77-78); Thornton Heath & Dist League 51-52 (League Cup 51-52, Div 4 R-up 51-52); Edenbridge Charity Cup 51-52; Caterham & Purley Hospital Cup 51-52; Surrey County Intermediate League East Section 1 55-56; Surrey Junior Cup R-up 51-52; Caterham & Edenbridge League Div 3 51-52; Borough of Croydon Charity Cup 56-57; Southern Yth League 89-90 (R-up 88-89, League Cup 88-89 89-90); Southern Count Midweek Floodlit cup 95-96.

PROGRAMME DETAILS:
Pages: 36 **Price:** 70p
Editor: Tony Lidbury

Formed: 1875

WOKINGHAM TOWN

The Town

Wokingham FC: Back Row (L-R); Dave Prior, Jason Walkington, Barry Miller, Matt Ward, Steve Darlington, Tony Gribben, Andy Russell. Front; Craig Osborne, Ian Savage, Andy Leader, John Crouch, Iain Duncan
Photo - Andrew Chitty

Chairman: P Walsh **Vice Chairman:** R Harrison **President:** G Gale.
Secretary: John Aulsberry, 8 Paice Green, Wokingham RG40 1YN (01189 790441).
Managers: Derek Cottrell & Wayne Wanklyn. **Physio:** Dave Lane
Commercial Manager: Roy Merryweather (01189 780253).
Ground: Town Ground, Finchampstead Road, Wokingham, Berks RG11 2NR (01189 780377).
Directions: Half mile from town centre on A321 (signed Camberley & Sandhurst) Finchampstead Rd - walk down Denmark Street to swimming pool and straight on onto Finchampstead Rd. Half mile from Wokingham (BR) - turn right out of station, walk along Wellington Rd to swimming pool, right into Finchampstead Rd - ground entrance on right immediately after railway bridge.
Capacity: 3,500 **Cover:** 1,500 **Seats:** 300 **Floodlights:** Yes **Metal Badges:** Yes.
Club Shop: Progs, scarves, magazines & club souvenirs. Contact Brian & Sue McKeown at club
Colours: Yellow & black/black/black **Change colours:** Red/white/red.
Previous Leagues: Reading & Dist./ Great Western Comb 07-54/ Metropolitan 54-57/ Delphian 57-59/ Corinthian 59-63/ Athenian 63-73.
Previous Grounds: Oxford Road 1875-1883/ Wellington Road 83-96/ Langborough Rd 96-1906.
Midweek matchday: Tuesday **Sponsors:** Higgs & Hill Homes.
Record Attendance: 3,473 v Norton Woodseats, FA Amateur Cup 57-58.
Best F.A. Cup season: 1st Rd replay 82-83 (lost 0-3 at Cardiff after 1-1 draw).
League clubs defeated in F.A. Cup: None.
Record Fees - Paid: £5,000 for Fred Hyatt (Burnham, 1990)
Received: £25,000 for Mark Harris (C Palace 88).
Players progressing to Football League: Ian Kirkwood (Reading 53), John Harley (Hartlepool 76), Kirk Corbin (Cambridge 78), Phil Alexander (Norwich 81), Doug Hatcher (Aldershot 83), Steven Butler & George Torrance (Brentford 84), Mark Harris (C Palace 88), Gary Smart (Oxford 88), Darren Barnard (Chelsea 90), Paul Holsgrove (Luton Town 91), Darron Wilkinson (Brighton) 92.
Clubhouse: Mon-Sat 12-3 & 7-11pm (12-3 & 4.30-11pm Sat matchdays), Sun 12-2.30pm. Hot & cold food & snacks.
Club Record Goalscorer: Dave Pearce, 79.
Club Record Appearances: Dave Cox, 533.
95-96 Captain: John Crouch. **95-96 P.o.Y.:** Steve Darlington.
95-96 Top scorer: Steve Darlington 41.
Local Newspapers: Wokingham Times (782000), Wokingham News (Bracknell 20363), Reading Evening Post (55875).
Local Radio Stations: 210 FM
Honours: Isthmian Lg R-up 89-90 (Div 1 81-82, Full Members Cup R-up 94-95), Berks & Bucks Snr Cup 68-69 82-83 84-85 95-96, Berks & Bucks Intermediate Cup 52-53, FA Tphy SF 87-88, FA Amtr Cup 4th Rd 57-58.

PROGRAMME DETAILS:
Pages: 32 Price: £1
Editor: Mrs Anne Gale (c/o the club)

WORTHING

Formed: 1886 | The Rebels

Back Row: (L-R): Phil Ashnell (Physio), Horst, Richard Maynard, Alan Scannell, Alan Carter, Dean Beal, Tim Read, Spencer Mintram, Rich Thomas, Peter Gamble, Kevin Dinan (Coach). Front Row: John Robson (Mgr), Scott Robson, Steve Poulton, Steve Riley, Umberto Oliva, Jack Dineen, Sandy Brown, McArthur.
Photo: Andrew Chitty.

Chairman: Beau Reynolds **Vice Chairman:** Ray Smith **President:** Morty Hollis.
Secretary: Paul Damper, 19 Fletcher Road, Worthing, West Sussex BN14 8EX.
Managers: Mark Falco **Physio:** Phil Ashwell **Coach:** John Pratt
Press Officer: Morty Hollis **Commercial Manager:** David Groom.
Ground: Woodside Road, Worthing, West Sussex BN14 7HQ (01903 239575).
Directions: Follow A24 to town, at end of Broadwater Rd having gone over railway bridge, take 1st right into Teville Rd, take right into South Farm RD, 2nd left into Pavilion Rd, Woodside Rd is first right. Half a mile from Worthing (BR).
Capacity: 4,500 **Seats:** 450 **Cover:** 1,000 **Midweek matches:** Tuesday.
Colours: Red with blue & white trim/white/red. **Change colours:** All blue
Shop: Yes, selling T-shirts, sweatshirts, scarves, mugs, pens, progs etc.
Previous Leagues: West Sussex/ Sussex County 20-48/ Corinthian 48-63/ Athenian 63-77.
Record Gate: 4,500 v Depot Battalion Royal Engineers, FA Amtr Cup 07-08.
Best FA Vase season: 5th Rd 78-79 **Best FA Trophy season:** 3rd Rd Replay 85-86
Best FA Amateur Cup season: Quarter-Final replay 07-08.
Best FA Cup season: 2nd Rd 82-83, (0-4 to Oxford Utd), 1st Rd 36-37, 94-95, (1-3 v AFC Bournemouth).
Record Fees - Paid: £1,000 for Steve Guille (Bognor Regis Tn 89)
Received: £7,500 for Tim Read (Woking, 1990).
Record win: 25-0 v Littlehampton (H) West Sussex Lge 1911-12
Record defeat: 0-14 v Southwick (A), Sussex County Lge 1946-47.
Clubhouse: Open two hours before kick-off and closes 11pm. Hot & cold food available.
Players progressing to Football League: Ken Suttle (Chelsea 1948), Alan Arnell & Fred Perry (Liverpool 1954), Craig Whitington (Scarborough, via Crawley Town) 1993, Darren Freeman (Gillingham), Paul Musselwhite (Scunthorpe,Port Vale), Trevor Wood (Port Vale,Walsall), Richard Tiltman (Brighton).
Club Record Scorer: Mick Edmonds 275
Club Record Appearances: Geoff Raynsford
95-96 Captain: Steve Riley **95-96 P.o.Y.:** Steve Riley
95-96 Top scorer: Gary Joseph 8
Local Press: Evening Argus, Worthing Gazette & Herald.
Local Radio: Radio Sussex.
Hons: Isthmian Lg R-up(2) 83-85 (Div 1 82-83, Div 2 81-82 92-93), Athenian Lg Div 1 R-up 63-64 (Div 2 R-up 71-72, Lg Cup R-up 72-73, Mem. Shield 63-64), Sussex Snr Cup (19); Sussex RUR Char. Cup (14); Sussex Co. Lg(8) 20-22 26-27 28-29 30-31 33-34 38-40, W Sussex Lg (7); Brighton Char. Cup(9) 29-31 34-35 62-63 69-71 73-74(jt) 80-82, Worthing Char. Cup (10); AFA Invit. Cup 63-64 68-69 73-74 75-76 (Snr Cup R-up 36-37 46-47 48-49), Corinth. Lg Mem. Shield R-up 49-50 (Neale Tphy 58-59), Roy Hayden Mem. Tphy 75(jt), 1977 1978, Don Morecraft Tphy 72 73 76 81 82, Sussex F'lit Cup(2) 88-90, Sussex I'mediate Cup 34-35 64-65, Brighton Chal. Shield 29-30 31-32.

PROGRAMME DETAILS:
Pages: 32 **Price:** £1
Editor: Secretary

ICIS (Isthmian) LEAGUE Division Two Ten Year Records

(N - Denotes Division Two (North), S - Denotes Division Two (South))

	86/7	87/8	88/9	89/0	90/1	91/2	92/3	93/4	94/5	95/6
Abingdon Town	-	-	-	3S	1S	-	-	-	-	-
Aldershot Town	-	-	-	-	-	-	-	3	-	-
Aveley	5N	21N	9N	2N	-	-	-	10	21	-
Banstead Athletic	17S	21S	16S	11S	11S	14	13	9	8	4
Barton Rovers	7N	15N	8N	5N	10N	11	18	4	2	-
Basildon United	-	-	-	7N	18N	-	-	-	-	-
Bedford Town	-	-	-	-	-	-	-	-	-	8
Berkhamsted Town	16N	4N	15N	17N	5N	18	3	-	-	-
Billericay Town	-	-	6N	15N	3N	3	-	-	-	-
Bracknell Town	-	-	-	-	-	-	-	-	4	9
Camberley Town	15S	19S	14S	17S	22S	-	-	-	-	-
Canvey Island	-	-	-	-	-	-	-	-	-	1
Chalfont St Peter	8S	1S	-	-	-	-	-	-	10	13
Chertsey Town	6S	6S	12S	13S	14S	-	7	2	-	-
Chesham	1N	-	-	-	-	-	-	-	-	-
Cheshunt	22N	-	-	-	-	-	-	-	15	16
Clapton	19N	13N	7N	12N	20N	-	-	-	-	-
Collier Row	9N	2N	-	8N	12N	-	-	21	-	5
Cove	-	-	-	-	19S	-	-	-	-	-
Croydon	-	-	-	-	-	-	-	-	7	2
Dorking Town	3S	3S	1S	-	-	-	-	-	-	21
Eastbourne United	11S	12S	11S	16S	20S	-	-	-	-	-
Edgware Town	-	-	-	-	14N	-	11	11	13	10
Egham Town	14S	14S	10S	10S	3S	6	12	14	17	18
Epsom & Ewell	-	5S	9S	14S	13S	-	-	-	-	-
Feltham	4S	4S	8S	18S	18S	-	-	-	-	-
Finchley	-	12N	3S	18N	21N	-	-	-	-	-
Flackwell Heath	16S	20S	13S	8S	16S	-	-	-	-	-
Hampton	-	-	-	-	12S	-	10	18	6	3
Harefield United	10S	13S	5S	12S	7S	19	21	-	-	-
Haringey Borough	3N	20N	-	-	-	-	-	-	-	-
Harlow Town	17N	5N	1N	-	-	-	-	-	-	-
Hemel Hempstead	20N	19N	12N	14N	9N	9	4	13	18	17
Hertford Town	15N	22N	10N	3N	15N	-	-	-	-	-
Heybridge Swifts	4N	9N	5N	1N	-	-	-	-	-	-
Hornchurch	14N	14N	16N	16N	19N	-	-	-	-	-
Horsham	13S	15S	20S	21S	15S	-	-	-	-	-
Hungerford Town	9S	8S	6S	9S	9S	10	19	16	19	20
Kingsbury Town	-	-	-	-	13N	-	-	-	-	-
Leatherhead	-	-	-	-	10S	4	14	19	12	14
Letchworth G City	6N	11N	21N	22N	-	-	-	-	-	-
Lewes	-	-	-	-	-	2	-	20	-	-
Maidenhead United	-	11S	17S	5S	2S	-	-	-	-	-
Malden Vale	-	-	-	15S	4S	15	6	6	22	-
Marlow	2S	-	-	-	-	-	-	-	-	-
Metropolitan Police	7S	2S	-	-	-	7	5	8	5	7
Molesey	19S	17S	4S	2S	-	-	-	-	-	-
Newbury Town	20S	18S	19S	7S	8S	22	9	1	-	-
Oxford City	-	-	-	-	-	-	-	-	3	-
Petersfield	18S	22S	21S	20S	21S	-	-	-	-	-
Purfleet	-	-	2N	-	7N	1	-	-	-	-
Rainham Town	18N	16N	19N	21N	8N	16	20	22	-	-
Royston Town	21N	17N	18N	9N	16N	-	-	-	-	-
Ruislip Manor	5S	9S	7S	4S	5S	5	2	-	-	-
Saffron Walden Town	11N	18N	20N	10N	11N	8	8	12	9	15
Southall	21S	16S	18S	6S	6S	20	22	-	-	-

	86/7	87/8	88/9	89/0	90/1	91/2	92/3	93/4	94/5	95/6
Southwick Borough	-	-	-	-	-	21	-	-	-	-
Stevenage Borough	-	-	4N	4N	1N	-	-	-	-	-
Thame United	-	-	-	-	-	-	-	7	1	-
Tilbury	-	3N	17N	6N	17N	-	17	17	14	11
Tring Town	8N	10N	3N	19N	22N	-	-	-	-	-
Vauxhall Motors	13N	8N	14N	11N	2N	-	-	-	-	-
Ware	10N	6N	11N	13N	4N	17	15	15	16	12
Whyteleafe	12S	7S	2S	-	-	-	-	-	-	-
Windsor & Eton	-	-	-	-	-	-	-	-	20	-
Witham Town	-	7N	13N	20N	6N	13	16	5	11	19
Wivenhoe Town	12N	1N	-	-	-	-	-	-	-	6
Woking	1S	-	-	-	-	-	-	-	-	-
Wolverton Town	2N	-	22N	-	-	-	-	-	-	-
Worthing	-	-	-	-	-	12	1	-	-	-
Yeading	-	10S	15S	1S	-	-	-	-	-	-
No of clubs competing	22N	22N	22N	22N	22N	22	22	22	22	21
	21S	22S	21S	21S	22S					

DIVISION TWO FINAL LEAGUE TABLE 1995/96

		P	*W*	*D*	*L*	*F*	*A*	*Pts*
1.	Canvey Island	40	25	12	3	91	36	87
2.	Croydon	40	25	6	9	78	42	81
3.	Hampton	40	23	10	7	74	44	79
4.	Banstead Athletic	40	21	11	8	72	36	74
5.	Collier Row	40	21	11	8	73	41	74
6.	Wivenhoe Town	40	21	8	11	82	57	71
7.	Met Police	40	18	10	12	57	45	64
8.	Bedford Town	40	18	10	12	67	59	64
9.	Bracknell Town	40	18	8	14	69	50	62
10.	Edgware Town	40	16	9	15	72	67	57
11.	Tilbury	40	12	11	17	52	62	47
12.	Ware	40	13	8	19	55	80	47
13.	Chalfont St P	40	11	13	16	58	63	46
14.	Leatherhead	40	12	10	18	71	77	46
15.	Saffron Walden	40	11	12	17	56	58	45
16.	Cheshunt	40	10	12	18	56	90	42
17.	Hemel Hempstead	40	10	10	20	46	62	40
18.	Egham Town	40	12	3	25	42	74	39
19.	Witham Town	40	8	10	22	35	68	34
20.	Hungerford Town	40	9	7	24	44	79	34
21.	Dorking	40	8	5	27	44	104	29

LEADING LEAGUE GOALSCORERS:

Andy Jones	Canvey Island	24
Jason Reed	Bedford Town	23
Simon Liddle	Banstead Athletic	16
Alan Brett	Canvey Island	16

ICIS DIVISION TWO CLUBS 1996-97

BANSTEAD ATHLETIC

Chairman: Terry Molloy **President:**
Secretary: Gordon Taylor, 116 Kingston Avenue, North Cheam, Surrey SM3 9UF (0181 641 2957).
Manager: Bob Langford. **Coach:** **Physio:** Kevin Taylor
Ground: Merland Rise, Tadworth, Surrey KT20 5JG (01737 350982).
Directions: Follow signs to Tattenham Corner (Epsom racecourse), then to Banstead Sports Centre. Ground adjacent to swimming pool. Half a mile from Tattenham Corner (BR). Bus 420 from Sutton stops outside ground. Also buses 406 & 727 from Epsom.
Capacity: 3,500 **Seats:** 250 **Cover:** 800 **Floodlights:** Yes **Club Shop:** No.
Programme: 38 pages, 50p **Editor/Press Officer:** Colin Darby (0181 643 5437)
Colours: Amber/black/black **Change colours:** Red & white
Sponsors: PDM Marketing **Nickname:** A's. **Founded:** 1944
Reserve Team's League: Suburban **Midweek Matchday:** Tuesday
Record Gate: 1,400 v Leytonstone, FA Amateur 1953.
Best FA Cup year: 3rd Qual.Rd. 86-87
Previous Leagues: Surrey Int./Surrey Snr 49-65/ Spartan 65-75/ London Spartan 75-79/ Athenian 79-84.
Players progressing to Football League: W Chesney & B Robinson (Crystal Palace).
Clubhouse: Mon-Sat noon-11pm, noon-2 & 7.30-11pm Sun. 2 bars, real ale, bar snacks.
95-96 Captain: Steve Shaw. **95-96 P.o.Y.:** Steve Shaw. **95-96 Top scorer:** Simon Liddle.
Club Record Scorer: Harry Clark **Club Record Appearances:** Dennis Wall.
Hons: FA Vase QF 92-93, Surrey Snr Lg(6) 50-54 56-57 64-65 (R-up(5) 49-50 54-56 57-59, Lg Cup 57-58, Charity Cup 52-53 58-59), London Spartan Lg R-up 77-78 (Lg Cup(2) 65-67), Surrey Prem. Cup R-up 91-92, 95-96, Surrey Snr Shield 55-56, Gilbert Rice F'lit Cup 81-82 86-87 (R-up(4) 82-86), Athenian Lg Cup(2) 80-82 (R-up 82-83 (SF 79-80)), Surrey Int. Lg(2) 47-49, Surrey Int. Cup 46-47 54-55, E. Surrey Charity Cup(4) 59-60 66-67 76-78 (R-up 79-80, I'mediate Sect. 75-76 (R-up 76-77), Jnr Sect. 81-82), Southern Comb. Cup R-up 69-70, Suburban Lg R-up 86-87, Carlton T.V. Trophy R-Up 95-96.

BARKING

Chairman: Stephen Ward. **Vice-Chairman/President:**
Secretary: Roger Chilvers, 50 Harrow Rd, Barking, Essex IG11 7RA (0181 591 5313).
Manager: Paul Downes **Asst Manager.** T.B.A. **Physio:** T.B.A.
Ground: Mayesbrook Park, Lodge Avenue, Dagenham RM8 2JR (0181 595 6511).
Directions: Off A13 on A1153 (Lodge Ave), and grd 1 mile on left. Bus 162 from Barking station. Nearest tube Becontree.
Capacity: 2,500 **Cover:** 600 **Seats:** 200 **Floodlights:** Yes **Club Shop:** No
Programme: 28 50p **Editor:** Peter Pendle **Press Officer:** Terry Horgan (0181 478 4150)
Colours: Blue & white **Change colours:** Red & white. **Midweek home matchday:** Tuesday
Previous Leagues: London 1896-98 1909-26/ South Essex/ Athenian 23-52.
Previous Names: Barking Rovers, Barking Institute, Barking Woodville, Barking Town.
Record Attendance: (At Mayesbrook) 1,972 v Aldershot FA Cup 2nd Rd 1978.
Best FA Cup season: 2nd Rd replay 81-82 (lost 1-3 at Gillingham after 1-1 draw). Also 2nd Rd 78-79 79-80 83-84, and 1st Rd 26-27 28-29 78-80.
Players progressing to Football League: Don Colombo (Portsmouth 1953), Wally Bellet (Chelsea 1954), John Smith (Millwall 1956), Peter Carey (Orient 1957), Lawrie Abrahams (Charlton 1977), Kevin Hitchcock (Nottm Forest 1983), Dennis Bailey (Fulham 1986), Alan Hull (Orient 1987).
Clubhouse: 2 large bars, open daily 11am-11pm (Sundays Noon-11pm). Hot & cold food and drinks.
95-96 Captain: Gary Seymour **95-96 P.o.Y.:** Marc Baker **95-96 Top Scorer:** Jeff Wood & Tim Hope
Record Goalscorer: Micky Guyton 135 (1924-30) **Record Appearances:** Bob Makin 566
Honours: FA Amateur Cup R-up 26-27, Isthmian Lg 78-79 (Lg Cup R-up 76-77), Athenian Lg 34-35 (R-up 24-25), London Lg 20-21 (Div 1 (A) 09-10), South Essex Lg Div 1 1898-99 (R-up 08-09, Div 2 1900-01 01-02 04-05 05-06), London Senior Cup 11-12 20-21 26-27 78-79 (R-up 19-20 75-76 79-80), Essex Senior Cup 1894-95 95-96 1919-20 45-46 62-63 69-70 89-90, Dylon Shield 79-80, Eastern Floodlit R-up 85-86, London Intermediate Cup 85-86.

BEDFORD TOWN

Chairman: David Donnelly. **Vice Chairman:** John Laing. **President:** Allen J Sturgess
Secretary: Barry Stephenson, 9 Aspen Ave., Bedford, Beds MK41 8BX (01234 342276).
Manager: Mick Foster **Asst Manager:** Neal Rodney **Physio:** Mick Dilley
Ground: Meadow Lane, Cardington, Beds.
Directions: On A603 Bedford to Sandy rd. Come off A1 at Sandy following signs to Bedford - grd on right. From Bedford take Cardington Rd out of town signed Biggleswade and Sandy.On Saturdays only an'Eagles Special' bus picks up at various points in town and arrives at grd 20 minutes before kick-off, leaving 15 minutes after game.
Capacity: 3,000 **Seats:** 150 **Cover:** 500 **Floodlights:** Yes **Founded:** 1908
Colours: Blue & white **Change Colours:** yellow & black **Reformed:** 1989.
Programme: 40 pages, 75p **Editor:** Matt Webb (01234 364191) **Press Officer:** Ian Slater (01234 871122)
Midweek Matchday: Tuesday **Sponsors:** Allen Sturges Travel **Nickname:** Eagles.

Club Shop: Yes, selling scarves, t-shirts, sweatshirts, mugs, badges, key-rings, programmes. Contact Les Usher (01234 303595).
Record Attendance: 3,000 v Peterborough Utd, ground opening 6/8/93. At Allen Park: 1,227 v Bedford Utd, South Midlands League Division One, 26/12/91.
Previous Leagues: South Midlands 91-94.
Reserves' Lge: Sth Mids Lge Res. Div **Clubhouse:** Open matchdays. Bar meals and snacks.
Players progressing to Football League: Bill Garner (Southend) 1969, Nicky Platnaeur (moved to Bristol Rovers when Bedford Town folded in 1977).Ray Bailey 5/66,Derek Bellotti 7/66,Billy Brown 2/66,Bert Carberry 7/56,Peter Hall 11/67,Dave Quirke 7/66 Bobby Fold 11/61 all to Gillingham, Phil Driver (Wimbledon) 12/78,Joe Dubois (Grimsby T) 7/53 ,Ted Duggan (Luton T)2/56 , Harry Duke (Noprwich C) 9/46 ,John Fahy (Oxford U) 1/64 ,Ken Flint (Spurs) 7/47 ,Joe Hooley(Accrington) 10/61 ,Joe Kirkup (Reading) 8/55,Graham Moxon (Exeter C) 7/75 ,Bela Olah (Northampton) 12/58 , Gary Sergeant (Peterborough U) 7/77,Neil Townsend (Southend U) 7/73.
Captain 95-96: **Top Scorer 5-96:** **P.o.Y. 95-96:**
Club record scorer: Jason Reed **Club record appearances:** Jason Reed.
Hons: South Mids Lg 94-95 (Div 1 92-93, Floodlit Cup 94-95), Hinchingbrook Cup 94-95 94-95 *(predecessors: Southern Lg 58-59 (Div 1 69-70), Utd Co's Lg 30-31 32-33 33-34 (R-up 11-12 12-13 13-14 29-30 31-32 34-35 36-37), FA Cup 4th Rd 63-64 65-66, FA Tphy SF 74-75).*Beds.Sen.Cup 94-95.

BRACKNELL TOWN

Chairman: Dave Mihell **Vice Chairman:** Paul Broome **President:**Jack Quinton.
Secretary: Cliff McFadden, 15 Goodways Drive, Bracknell, Berks RG12 9AU (01344 640349.
Manager: Brian Broome **Asst Manager:** Chris Hodge. **Physio:** Jeff Jones.
Ground: Larges Lane, Bracknell RG12 9AN (01344 412305club,01344 300933 office) **Directions:** Off A329 just before Met Office r'bout by Bracknell College, ground 200 yards. From Bracknell (BR)/bus station - right out of station, follow path over bridge, left down steps and follow cycle path ahead, after 300yds follow curve over footbridge, right and follow lane to end, left and ground on left after bend.
Capacity: 2,500 **Seats:** 190 **Cover:** 400 **Floodlights:** Yes **Founded:** 1896
Programme: 32 pages, 50p **Editor:Press Officer:** Robert Scully (01344 640721).
Colours: Red & white stripes/red/red **Change colours:** All blue **Nickname:** Robins
Club Shop: Yes, selling metal badges, programmes, scarves, club sweaters, club ties.
Previous Grounds: None **Midweek Matchday:** Tuesday **Sponsors:** Panasonic
Previous Leagues: Great Western Comb./ Surrey Snr 63-70/ London Spartan 70-75.
Reserve's League: Suburban (west) **Record Gate:** 2,500 v Newquay, FA Amateur Cup 1971.
Best FA Cup season: 4th Qual Rd 88 (lost 1-2 v Cheltenham Tn), 4th Qual Rd 96 (lost 3-1 v Burton Albion)
Players progressing to Football League: Willie Graham (Brentford).
Clubhouse: Members' bar open 11am-11pm Mon-Sat, 12-3 & 7-10.30pm Sun. Function hall bookable.
Club Record Scorer: Richard Whithy **Club Record Appearances:** James Woodcock.
95-96 Captain: Alan Williams **95-96 P.o.Y:** Alan Williams/Mark Franks(joint)
Hons: Isthmian Lg Div 3 94-95 (Div 2 Sth R-up), Berks & Bucks Snr Cup R-up, Spartan Lg 82-83 (R-up(2)), Surrey Snr Lg 69-70 (Lg Cup 68-69 69-70).

CHALFONT St PETER

Chairman: Ray Franks **President:**
Secretary: Mr G Lester, 38 Orchard Rd, Seer Green, Bucks HP8 2XU (0494 675034).
Manager: TBA **Asst Manager:** **Physio:**
Ground: The Playing Fields, Amersham Road, Chalfont St Peter SL9 7BQ (0753 885797).
Directions: A413 from Uxbridge (London) to Chalfont. Turn left 100 yds after 2nd major roundabout (between Ambulance station and Community Centre. Two miles from Gerrards Cross (BR), regular buses from Slough.
Capacity: 4,500 **Cover:** 220 **Seats:** 220 **Floodlights:** Yes **Club Shop:** Yes.
Programme: 30 pages 50p **Editor:** **Press Officer:** Mal Keenan.
Colours: Green Shirts,Red shorts **Change colours:** Yellow/blue/blue
Previous Leagues: Great Western Combination 1948-58/ Parthenon 58-59/ London 60-62/ Spartan 62-75/ London Spartan 75-76/ Athenian 76-84.
Midweek home matchday: Tuesday **Reserve League:**
Record Attendance: 2,55 v Watford,benefit match.1985.
Best F.A. Cup season: 3rd Qualifying Rd 85-86 (wins over Banbury, King's Lynn and Barking).
Players progressing to Football League: None.
Clubhouse: Open every evening, Saturday afternoons and Sunday lunchtimes.
95-96 Captain: Richard Carr. **95-96 P.o.Y.:** Richard Carr. **95-96 Top scorer:** Lance Cadogan.
Club Record Goalscorer: Unknown. **Club Record Appearances:** Colin Davies.
Honours: Isthmian Lg Div 2 87-88, Athenian Lg R-up 83-84 (Lg Cup 76-77 82-83), London Spartan Lg Div 2 75-76, Berks & Bucks Intermediate Cup 52-53, FA Tphy 3rd Qualifying Rd 89-90 91-92, FA Vase 4th Rd 87-88, Berks & Bucks Benevolent Cup 64-65.

CHESHUNT

Chairman: George Norman **Vice Chairman:** Paul Cully **President:** Mr Roy Burt.
Secretary: Mr Richard Cotterell, 46 Friends Ave, Cheshunt, Herts EN8 8LX
Manager: John Ward. **Assistant Manager:** Ernie Ford. **Physio:** Lou Dedman.
Ground: The Stadium, Theobalds Lane, Cheshunt, Herts (01992 26752).
Directions: M25 to junction 25, A10 north towards Hertford, next roundabout third exit to next roundabout, turn left proceed under railway bridge, turn left, ground approx 400 yards on right. 400yds from Theobalds Grove BR station, Buses 279,310 to Theobalds Grove station.
Seats: 285 **Cover:** 600 **Capacity:** 2,500 **Floodlights:** Yes **Club Shop:** No.
Programme: 20 pgs 50p **Editor:** A Timpson (01707 874028) **Press Officer:** N Harrison (01992 423678)
Colours: Yellow/blue **Change colours:** All blue
Sponsors: Flex Limited **Nickname:** Ambers **Founded:** 1946.
Midweek matchday: Tuesday **Reserve team's League:** None.
Record Attendance: 7,000 v Bromley, London Senior Cup 1947.
Best FA Vase season: Qtr Final 81-82 **Best FA Cup season:** 4th Qual. Rd(4)
Previous Leagues: Athenian 19-20 21-31 64-77/ London 20-21 24-25 46-51 55-59/ Delphian 51-55/ Aetolian 59-62/ Spartan 62-64/ Isthmian 77-87.
Players progressing to Football League: Ian Dowie, Ruben Abgula, Steve Sedgeley, Lee Hodges, Paul Marquis, Steve Terry, Neil Prosser, Mario Walsh. **Clubhouse:** Yes.
95-96 Captain: Matt Barlow **95-96 P.o.Y.:** Trevor Lake. **95-96 Top Scorer:** Matt Barlow 16
Honours: Athenian Lg 75-76 (R-up 73-74, Div 1 67-68, Div 2 R-up 65-66, Lg Cup 74-75 75-76), Spartan Lg 62-63 (Lg Cup 63-64 92-93 (R-up 89-90)), London Lg 49-50 (R-up 56-57, Div 1 47-48 48-49 (R-up 46-47), Div 1 Cup 46-47, Lg Cup R-up 58-59), Park Royal Cup 46-47), Isthmian Lg Div 2 R-up 81-82 (Div 3 R-up 94-95), Herts Snr Cup 23-24 (R-up 6), Herts Charity Cup 00-01 05-06 (R-up 70-71 74-75 80-81), Herts Charity Shield 46-47 65-66 (R-up 5), Herts Snr Centenary Tphy 91-92, East Anglian Cup 74-75 (R-up 75-76), Mithras Floodlit Cup 69-70 (R-up 75-76), London Charity Cup 73-74, Roy Bailey Tphy 90-91 94-95 .

COLLIER ROW & ROMFORD

Chairman: Bradley Goodwin **Vice-Chairman:** Steve Gardener. **Life President:** Ron Walker
Secretary: Anne Rogers, 11 Witham Road, Dagenham, Essex RM10 8JL (0181 593 2182)
Manager: Donal McGovern **Asst Mgr:** Alan Marson **Coach:** Don Calder
Ground: 'Sungate', Collier Row Rd, Collier Row, Romford, Essex (01708 722766).
Directions: A12 from London, left at Moby Dick (PH) traffic lights, right at next r'bout, ground entrance signposted 200 yards on right. London bus 247 passes ground.
Capacity: 2,000 **Seats:** **Cover:** 150 **Floodlights:** Yes **Club Shop:** Yes
Editor/Press Officer: David Fletcher (01956 528829) **Programme:** 48 pages, £1.20
Colours: Blue & Gold/blue/blue **Change colours:** Blue & black/black/black
Sponsors: TBA **Nickname:** The Boro **Reformed:** 1992.
Midweek Matchday: Wednesday **Reserve League:** Essex & Herts Border West
Record Attendance: 412 v East Ham 15.8.92 **Best FA Cup Season:** £rd Qual Rd 94-95, 95-96.
Previous Leagues: Essex Senior 92-96 **Clubhouse:** Open 7 days a week 11.30 -11.00
95-96 Captain: Paul Evans **95-96 Top Scorer:** **95-96 P.o.Y.:** Danny Benstock
Club Record Goalscorer: Micky Ross **Club Record Appearances:** Micky Ross
Honours: Essex Sen Lge 95-96

DORKING

Chairman: Jack Collins. **President:** Ingram Whittingham **Vice-Chairman:** Ray Collins
Secretary (& Press Off.): David Short, 29 Bennett Close, Cobham, Surrey KT11 1AH (01932 866496)
Manager: Terry Eames. **Asst Manager:** Steve Osgood **Physio:** Bob Hemstead.
Ground: Meadowbank, Mill Lane, Dorking, Surrey RH4 1DX (01306 884112).
Directions: Mill Lane off Dorking High St. next to Woolworths & M & S opp White Horse. Fork right in Mill Lane past Malthouse pub. 1/2 mile from both Dorking & Deepdene (BR) stations.
Capacity: 3,600 **Cover:** 800 **Seats:** 200 **Floodlights:** Yes **Club Shop:** Yes
Programme: 48 pages 80p **Editor:** Paul Mason/Bryan Bletso **Press Officer:**
Colours: Green & white hoops/green & yellow. **Change colours:** All blue
Midweek home matchday: Tuesday **Reserve League:** Suburban
Sponsors: **Formed:** 1880 **Nickname:** The Chicks
Record Attendance: 4,500 v Folkestone Town, FA Cup 1st Qualifying Round 1955.
Best FA Cup season: 1st Round Proper 92-93 (lost 2-3 at home to Plymouth Argyle).
Previous Leagues: Surrey Senior 22-56 77-78/ Corinthian 56-63/ Athenian 63-74 78-80/ Southern 74-77.
Players progressing to Football Lge: Steve Scrivens & John Finch (Fulham), Andy Ansah (Brentford 89).
Clubhouse: Open matchdays, weekends and training nights. Hot & cold food on matchdays. Pool, bar billiards, widescreen TV, Fruit Machines.
95-96 Captain: **95-96 P.o.Y.:** Terry Gale/Malcolm Shevlin **95-96 Top scorer:** Kevin Glavey
Club Record Goalscorer: Andy Bushnell. **Club Record Appearances:** Steve Lunn.
Honours: Isthmian Lge Div 2 Sth 88-89 (Full Members Cup R-up 92-93), Surrey Sen Cup R-up 1885-86 1989-90, Surrey Sen Shield(2) 58-60 (R-up 07-08 10-11 60-61), Surrey Senior League(4) 28-30 54-56 (R-up 51-52 53-54, League Cup 48-49 50-51 53-54, League Charity Cup(4) 48-49 53-54(jt), 54-56 (R-up(5) 28-30 46-47 50-51 77-78)), Gilbert Rice F'lit Cup 87-88 (R-up 89-90), Surrey I'mediate Cup 56-57 (R-up 54-55), Southern Comb. Chall Cup 92-93, FA Trophy 2nd Rd 91-92, FA Vase 3rd Rd(3) 83-84 86-88.

Barking FC: Photo - Andrew Chitty

Bedford Town FC:

Bracknell Town: Back Row (L-R); Justin Day, Paul Mulvaney, Mark Tallentire, Brian Broome,Paul Maynard. Middle; Jeff Dennis (Coach), Ken Wilson, Andy Mackenzie, Alan Henly, Jason Day, Warren Hatt, Mark Franks, Nick Collier (Mgr). Fronr Row; Phil Alexander (Asst Mgr), Alan Williams (Capt), Ritchie Moore, Micky Parker, Mark Murphy, Bobby Hodge, Phil Norville, Geoff Jones (Physio).

EDGWARE TOWN

Chairman: Michael Flynn. **President:** Mr V Deritis **Patron:** Russell Grant.
Secretary: Barry Boreham, 28 St Brides Ave., Edgware, Middx HA8 6BS (0181 952 1685).
Manager: Jim McGleish. **Asst Manager:** Peter Grant **Physio:** Sarah Gow
Ground: White Lion Ground, High Street, Edgware HA8 5AQ (0181 952 6799).
Directions: Turn left out of Edgware tube station (Northern Line), turn left again at crossroads and ground 300yds on right in Edgware High Street behind White Lion pub. Buses 32, 288 and 142.
Capacity: 5,000 **Seats:** 220 **Cover:** 1,500 **Floodlights:** Yes **Club Shop:** No
Programme: 16 pages, 50p **Editor:** Kevin Brown (0181 950 8065). **Press Officer:** Tom Hooks
Colours: Green & white Qtrs **Change colours:** All yellow
Sponsor: **Nickname:** Wares. **Founded:** 1939
Midweek Matchday: Tuesday **Reserve League:** Suburban
Record Attendance: 8,500 v Wealdstone, FA Cup 1948.
Players progressing to Football League: Brian Stein (Luton), Dave Beasant (Wimbledon), Scott McGleish (Charlton 1994).
Clubhouse: Open nightly and Fri, Sat, Sun lunchtimes. Hot & cold food matchdays, cold food lunchtimes.
95-96 Top scorer: S Newing **95-96 Captain:** S Finnerty **95-96 P.o.Y.:** J Coleman
Club Record Appearances: John Mangan. **Club Record Goalscorer:**
Honours: FA Vase 5th Rd 91-92, Isthmian Lg Div 3 91-92, London Spartan Lg 87-88 89-90 (Lg Cup 87-88), Corinthian Lg R-up 53-54 (Memorial Shield 52-53 61-62), Athenian Lg R-up 81-82, Middx Snr Lg 40-41 41-42 42-43 43-44 44-45, Middx Snr Cup 47-48 (R-up 73-74 94-95), London Snr Cup R-up 47-48, Middx Border Lg Cup 79-80, Suburban Lg Div R-up 89-90.

EGHAM TOWN

Chairman: Pat Bennett **Vice Chairman:** Peter Barnes **President:** Peter Barnes.
Secretary: Chris Thompson,138A Thorpe Lea Rd.,Egham,Surrey.TW20 8BL(01784 463562)
Manager: Steve Webb. **Asst Manager:** Peter Lliott. **Physio:** Alan Maynard.
Ground: Tempest Road, Pooley Green, Egham, Surrey TW20 9DW (01784 435226).
Directions: M25 jct 13, follow signs to Egham, under M25 at r'bout, left to end, left at mini-r'bout, over railway crossing, left to end (Pooley Green Rd), right, ground on right after 'Compasses' and 'Robin Hood' pubs. Bus 441 from Staines to Poolley Green. Forty mins walk from Egham (BR) station.
Capacity: 3,000 **Seats:** 230 **Cover:** 1,120 **Floodlights:** Yes **Club Shop:** Yes
Programme: 12 pages, 60p **Editor/Press Officer:** Mark Ferguson (01784 258656).
Colours: White/blue/white **Change colours:** Yellow & blue
Club Sponsors: TBA **Nickname:** Sarnies/Swans/Town. **Founded:** 1877
Reserve Team's League: Suburban **Midweek Matches:** Tuesday.
Record Gate: 2,000 - Egham XI v Select XI, Billy King Memorial match 1981. Competitive: 1,400 v Wycombe Wanderers, FA Cup 2nd Qualifying Rd 1972.
Previous Leagues: Hounslow & District 1896-1914/ Surrey Intermediate 19-22/ Surrey Senior 22-28 65-67/ Spartan 29-33 67-74/ Parthenon 64-65/ Athenian 74-77.
Best FA Cup year: 4th Qual Rd 90-91 (lost 0-2 at Telford United.
Clubhouse: (0784 435226) 7-11pm and weekend lunchtimes. Members bar, function hall and pool room.
95-96 Captain: Malcolm Dickinson **95-96 P.o.Y.:** Julian Burrows **95-96 Top scorer:** Daren Howell.
Record Scorer: Mark Butler 50 (91-92). Career record scorer too.
Record Appearances: Dave Jones 850+.
Hons: Isthmian Lg Associate Members Tphy R-up 91-92, Spartan Lg 71-72 (Lg Cup R-up 67-68), Athenian Lg R-up 75-76 (Div 2 74-75), Surrey Snr Cup R-up 91-92, Surrey Snr Lg 22-23 (Lg Charity Cup 22-23 (R-up 26-27 34-35)), Surrey Intermediate Lg 20-21, Surrey Intermediate Charity Cup 19-20 20-21 (R-up 26-27), North West Surrey Charity Cup 20-21, Egham Twinning Tournament 67-68 71-72 74-75 75-76 76-77 80-81, Southern Comb. Floodlit Cup 77-78 (R-up 83-84).

HEMEL HEMPSTEAD

Chairman: Mike Pearson **President:** Tom Abbott. **Vice President:** Dave Lloyd.
Secretary: Mrs Vivienne Herbert, 2 Montgomery Ave, Hemel Hempstead HP2 4HD. (01442 395633)
Manager: Steve Ringrose. **Asst Manager:** Mark Pearson. **Physio:** Chris Hewitt
Ground: Vauxhall Road, Adeyfield, Hemel Hempstead HP2 4HW (01442 259777)
club).
Directions: Euston to Hemel Hempstead Station. H2 or H3 bus to Windmill Rd, Longlands.
Capacity: 3,000 **Seats:** 100 **Cover:** Yes **Floodlights:** Yes **Founded:** 1885
Colours: All red **Change colours:** All blue
Club Shop: Yes **Metal Badges:** No **Sponsors:** Dexion.
Programme: 36 pages, 50p **Editor/Press Officer:** Steve Watson **Midweek Matchday:** Tuesday
Previous Leagues: Spartan 22-52/ Delphian 52-63/ Athenian 63-77.
Previous Grounds: Crabtree Lane (til '71).
Reserve Team's League: Essex & Herts Border Combination **Nickname:** Hemel

Record Gate: 2,000 v Watford 1985 (at Crabtree Lane: 3,500 v Tooting, FA Amtr Cup 1st Rd 1962).
Best FA Cup year: Never past Qualifying Rounds.
Clubhouse: (01442 259777). 7-11pm weekends, noon-11pm weekends and Bank Holidays. Pool, darts. Bingo Tuesday. Race nights. Dancing Fri, Sat & Sun nights. Tea bar open matchdays;
Players progressing to Football League: Colin and Ernie Bateman (Watford).
Club Record Goalscorer: Dai Price **Club Record Apps:** John Wallace, 1012.
95-96 Captain: **95-96 P.O.Y.:** **95-96 Top scorer:**
Hons: Herts Snr Cup 05-06 07-08 08-09 25-26 61-62 65-66 91-92, Herts Charity Cup/Shield 25-26 34-35 51-52 63-64 76-77 83-84 (R-up 90-91), Spartan Lg 33-34, Herts Intermediate Cup 54-55 65-66 83-84, West Herts St Mary Cup 70-71 75-76 82-83 85-86 90-91 91-92 93-94, Athenian Lg Div 1 R-up 64-65 (Reserves Cup 65-66), Delphian Lg(reserves) 54-55 (Reserves Cup 54-55 61-62).

HORSHAM

Chairman: Frank King **Vice Chairman:** Jeff Barratt **President:** Geoff Holtom
Secretary: Eric Mallard, 6 Morrell Avenue, Horsham, West Sussex RH12 4DD (01403 267687 H; 0181 643 6406 B)
Manager: Mark Dunk **Asst Mgr/Coach:** Sam Chapman. **Physio:** Geoff Britta1n.
Ground: Queen Street, Horsham RH13 5AD (01403 252310).
Directions: From the station turn left into North Street. Pass the Arts Centre to the traffic lights and turn left. At the next set of lights (200 yards) turn left again into East Street. East Street becomes Queen Street after the Iron Bridge and the ground lies opposite Queens Head public house.
Capacity: 4,500 **Seats:** 300 **Cover:** 3,000 **Floodlights:** Yes **Club Shop:** Yes.
Programme: 40 pages, £1 **Editor:** Adam Hammond (01403 217316). **Press Officer:**
Colours: Yellow & green halves/green/yellow. **Change colours:** White/blue/white
Founded: 1885 **Nickname:** Hornets **Club Sponsors:** Persimmon Homes.
Midweek Matchday: Tuesday **Reserve League:** Sussex County.
Record Attendance: 8,000 v Swindon, FA Cup 1st Rd, November 1966.
Best FA Cup year: 1st Rd 47-48 (lost 1-9 at Notts County), 66-67 (lost 0-3 v Swindon).
Previous Leagues: W Sussex Sen/ Sussex County 26-51/ Metropolitan 51-57/ Corinthian 57-63/ Athenian 63-73.
Players progressing to Football League: Jamie Ndah (Torquay Utd), Darren Freeman (Gillingham), Paul Smith (Barnet).
Clubhouse: Normal licensing hours. Hot and cold snacks. Dancehall.
95-96 Captain: Steve Breach. **95-96 P.O.Y.:** Rodney Prosper. **95-96 Top scorer:** Rodney Prosper
Hons: Sussex Snr Cup 33-34 38-39 49-50 53-54 71-72 73-74 75-76, Sussex RUR Cup 1899-1900 30-31 31-32 33-34(jt with Worthing) 34-35 35-36 36-37 37-38(jt with Southwick) 45-46 48-49(jt with Worthing) 50-51 51-52 56-57. Sussex Floodlight Cup 77-78. Sussex County Lg 31-33 34-38 46-47 (R-up 29-30 30-31 47-48 48-49, Lg Cup 45-46 46-47), Metropolitan Lg 51-52, Athenian Lg Div 1 72-73, Div 2 69-70 72-73. West Sussex Sen Lge 1899-90 1900-01 01-02 25-26. ICIS Div 3 95-96.

HUNGERFORD TOWN

Chairman: Alan Holland. **Vice Chairman:** Ron Tarry **President:** Sir Seton Wills.
Secretary: Eric Richardson, 3 Windermere Way, Thatcham, Berks RG13 4UL (01536 868674).
Manager: Gerald Smith. **Asst Manager:** **Physio:** Steve Puffet.
Ground: Town Ground, Bulpit Lane, Hungerford RG17 0AY (01488 682939-club, 684597-boardroom).
Directions: M4 jct 14 to A4, right and left at Bear Hotel, through town centre on A338, left into Priory Rd, second left into Bulpit Lane, over crossroads, ground on left. Three quarters of a mile from Hungerford BR station.
Capacity: 3,000 **Seats:** 172 **Cover:** 200 **Floodlights:** Yes **Club Shop:** Yes.
Colours: White/blue/white **Change colours:** All red. **Metal Badges:** Yes
Programme: 24 pages, 50p **Editor/Press Officer:** M Wiltshire (01488 682818).
Founded: 1886 **Nickname:** Crusaders. **Club Sponsors:** Below Stairs of Hungerford.
Midweek Matchday: Tuesday **Reserve Team's League:** Suburban (West)
Record Attendance: 1,684 v Sudbury Town, FA Vase SF 1st leg 88-89 (20,000 v Modena in Italy 1981).
Best FA Cup year: 1st Rd 79-80 (lost 1-3 at Slough Town).
Previous Legues: Newbury & D./ Swindon & D./ Hellenic 58-78.
Players progressing to Football League: Steve Hetzke (Reading, Blackpool, Sunderland), Bruce Walker (Swindon, Blackpool), Des McMahon (Reading), Brian Mundee (Bournemouth, Northampton), Darren Anderson.
Clubhouse: Open every evening and lunchtimes including Sunday. 2 bars, dancehall, boardroom/committee room, darts, pool, fruit machines. Hot & cold snacks. Stewards: Bob & Sandra Ponsford, (01488 682939).
95-96 Captain: Mal Ford **95-96 P.O.Y.:** Mark Brown **95-96 Top scorer:** Peter Horwat 15
Club Record Scorer: Ian Farr (268) **Club Record Appearances:** Dean Bailey (approx 400)
Hons: FA Vase SF 77-78 79-80 88-89, Berks & Bucks Snr Cup 81-82 (R-up 75-76 76-77), Hellenic Lg Div 1 70-71 (Prem Div Cup 77-78, Div 1 Cup 70-71, Benevolent Cup 60-61).

LEATHERHEAD

Chairman: Keith Wenham **Vice Chairman:** B Ashi **President:** Gerald Darby.
Secretary: Mike Bailey, c/o Leatherhead FC (01372 360151).
General Manager: Mike Bailey. **Physio:** Ted Richards. **Press Officer:** Mike Bailey.
Ground: Fetcham Grove, Guildford Rd, Leatherhead, Surrey KT22 9AS (01372 360151).
Directions: M25 jct 9 to Leatherhead; follow signs to Leisure Centre, ground adjacent. Half mile from Leatherhead (BR). London Country Buses 479 and 408 - ground opposite bus garage.
Capacity: 3,400 **Seats:** 200 **Cover:** 445 **Floodlights:** Yes **Founded:** 1946
Colours: Green and White. **Change colours:** All yellow **Nickname:** Tanners
Programme: 20+ pages, 50p **Editor:** Keith Wenham (0181 4611369) **Club Shop:** No
Midweek Matchday: Tuesday **Sponsors:** Marchant Construction.
Prevs Lgs: Surrey Snr 46-50/Metrop 50-51/Delphian 51-58/Corinthian 58-63/ Athenian 63-72.
Reserve's League: Suburban (South) **Record Gate:** 5,500 v Wimbledon, 1976.
Record win: Unknown **Record defeat:** 1-11 v Sutton United.
Best FA Cup year: Fourth Round 74-75 (lost 2-3 at Leicester City).
Players progressing to Football League: Chris Kelly (Millwall), B Friend (Fulham), L Harwood (Port Vale), John Humphrey (Millwall).
Record Fees - Paid: £1,500 to Croydon (B Salkeld) **Rec'd:** £1,500 from Croydon (B Salkeld)
Clubhouse: (0372 360151) Licensed bar open noon-11pm matchdays. Burgers, hot dogs, tea & coffee etc on matchdays.
Club Record Scorer: Not known **Club record appearances:** P Caswell.
95-96 Top Scorer: Ray Arnett **95-96 P.o.Y.:**
Hons: Isthmian Lg Cup 77-78, Corinthian Lg 62-63, Athenian Ld Div 1 63-64, Surrey Snr Cup 68-69 (R-up 64-65 66-67 74-75 78-79), Surrey Snr Lg 46-47 47-48 48-49 49-50 (Lg Cup 49-50, Charity Cup 46-47 49-50), East Surrey Charity Cup 68-69 (R-up 67-68), Surrey Snr Shield 68-69, FA Amateur Cup SF 70-71 73-74 (QF 65-66 66-67 71-72), FA Trophy R-up 77-78, London Snr Cup R-up 74-75 77-78, Surrey Inter. Cup, Southern Comb. Cup 89-90.

LEIGHTON TOWN

Chairman: Bill Harrison **President:** Mike Hide.
Secretary: Alec Irvine, 12 Rowley Furrows, Linslade, Leighton Buzzard, Beds LU7 7SH (01525 376475).
Manager: Peter Lawrence. **Physio:** George Lathwell
Ground: Bell Close, Lake Street, Leighton Buzzard, Beds (01525 373311).
Directions: From bypass (A505) take A4146 (Billington Rd) towards Leighton Buzzard, straight over mini-r'bout & 1st left into car park - ground behind Camden Motors just before town centre. Half mile from Leighton Buzzard (BR) station. Buses from Luton, Aylesbury and Milton Keynes.
Capacity: 2,500 **Seats:** 155 **Cover:** 300 **Floodlights:** Yes **Club Shop:** Yes
Colours: Red & white **Change colours:** All blue
Programme: 50p **Editor:** Ian McGregor (01525 370142). **Press Officer:** Ian McGregor (01525 370142).
Sponsors: Camden Motors. **Nickname:** Reds. **Founded:** 1885
Midweek Matchday: Tuesday **Reserve Team's League:** Suburban
Record Attendance: 1,522 v Aldershot T., Isthmian Lg Div 3, 30/1/93
Best FA Cup year: Third Qualifying Rounds 70-71, lost 1-2 at St Albans City.
Previous Leagues: Leighton & District/ South Midlands 22-24 26-29 46-54 55-56 76-92/ Spartan 22-53 67-74/ United Counties 74-76.
Clubhouse: Normal licensing hours. Snack/refreshment bar on matchdays
95-96 Captain: Craig Johnstone **95-96 P.o.Y.:** Tony McGuinness **95-96 Top scorer:** Bradley Anderson
Hons: Sth Midlands Lg 66-67 91-92 (Lg Cup 90-91, O'Brien Tphy 90-91, Reserve Div 1 87-88 91-92 94-95, Reserve Div 2 76-77, Reserve Challenge Cup 93-94,94-95 Beds Snr Cup 26-27 67-68 68-69 69-70 92-93 Bucks Charity Cup 94-95, Spartan Lg Div 2 23-24 27-28, Leighton & District Lg, Beds Intermediate Cup(res) 90-91, Beds Yth Cup 91-92 92-93 94-95,Chiltern Youth Lg.94-95, Chiltern Yth Lg Cup 93-94 East Anglian Yth.Cup 94-95. Isthmian Lge Div 3 R-up 95-96.

METROPOLITAN POLICE

Chairman: Des Flanders QPM. **Vice Chairman:** Terry Siggs QBE **President:** Sir Paul Condon QPM
Secretary: Tony Brooking, 15 Westmoreland Avenue, Hornchurch, Essex. RM11 2EJ.(01708 450715)
Manager: John Cottam. **Physio:** Dick Pierce
Ground: Metropolitan Police Sports Ground, Imber Court, East Molesey (0181 398 7358).
Directions: From London: A3 then A309 to Scilly Isles r'bout, right into Hampton Court Way, left at 1st r'bout into Imber Court Rd - ground faces in 300yds. From M25 jct 10: A3 towards London for 1 mile, A307 through Cobham, left immediately after Sandown Park into Station Rd - ground 1 mile on left. Half mile from either Thames Ditton or Esher BR stations.
Capacity: 3,000 **Seats:** 297 **Cover:** 1,800 **Floodlights:** Yes **Club Shop:** No
Colours: All blue **Change colours:** All yellow
Programme: 10 pages, 50p **Editor/Press Officer:** Cliff Travis (01932 782215).
Founded: 1919 **Nickname:** Blues. **Club Sponsors:** McDonalds.
Midweek Matchday: Tuesday **Reserve Team's League:** Suburban **Metal Badges:** No
Record Attendance: 4,500 v Kingstonian, FA Cup 1934.
Best FA Cup year: 1st Rd 32-33 (0-9 at Northampton Town), 84-85 (0-3 at home to Dartford), 94-95 (0-3 at home to Crawley Town).
Previous Leagues: Spartan 28-60/ Metropolitan 60-71/ Southern 71-78.
Clubhouse: (0181 398 1267). Four bars, dancehall, cafeteria open 9am-11pm. Hot & cold food.
95-96 Captain: Adam Wickens. **95-96 P.o.Y:** Jason Prins. **95-96 Top Scorer:** Mario Russo.
Club Record Scorer: Mario Russo **Club Record Appearances:** Pat Robert.
Hons: Isthmian Lg Div 2 R-up 77-78 87-88, Spartan Lg 28-29 29-30 36-37 38-39 45-46 53-54 54-55 (R-up 47-48, Lg Cup 59-60 (R-up 57-58)), Middx Snr Cup 27-28, Surrey Snr Cup 32-33, Surrey Charity Shield 38-39, Metropolitan Lg Cup 68-69 (Amtr Cup 68-69 69-70), London Snr Cup R-up 34-35 40-41, Herts & Middx Comb. 39-40.Diadora Lg., Carlsberg Trophy Winners 94-95.

Horsham ICIS Division 3 Champions: Back Row (L-R); Mark Dunk, Sam Chapman (Coach), Marcus Cooke, Geoff Ward, Richard Knight, Duncan Green, Chris May, Paul Smith, John Waters, Martin Gray, Geoff Brittain (Physio). Front Row; Roger Barnes, Phil Soamers, Wayne Wren, Mark Stepney, Steve Breach, Mark Chaplin, Zac Newman, Mark Pulling, Rodney Prosper.

Hungerford Town FC:

Leatherhead FC: Back Row (L-R); Terry Mills (Mgr), Hugh Mann, Robin Welch, Gerald Dawson, Tony Webb, Kevin Glavey, David D'Rozario, Ray Arnett, Nigel Webb. Front Row; Tony Leslie, Lawrence Ennis, Paul Bertley, Alf Winyard, Andy Jepson, Simon Jones. *Photo - Tim Edwards*

TILBURY

Chairman: R Nash **Vice Chairman:** T.Harvey. **President:** J B Wilson.
Secretary: L. Brown, 52 Lionel Oxley House, New Road, Grays, Essex RM17 6PP (01375 377427)
Manager: Paul Armstrong **Asst Manager:** Roger Hutton **Physio:** Roger Hutton
Ground: Chadfields, St Chad's Rd, Tilbury, Essex RM18 8NL (01375 23093).
Directions: M25 (jct 30 or 31) - A13 Southend bound, Tilbury Docks turn off after 4 miles, Chadwell St Mary turn off (left) after another one and a half miles, left again after 400 metres, right at r'bout (signed Tilbury), right into St Chad's Rd after half mile, 1st right into Chadfields for ground.
Capacity: 3,500 **Seats:** 250 **Cover:** 1,000 **Floodlights:** Yes **Founded:** 1900
Colours: Black & white stripes/black/black **Change colours:** All red.
Programme: Min 32 pages, 50p **Editor:** Lloyd Brown. **Club Shop:** No.
Midweek Matchday: Tuesday **Sponsors:** None. **Nickname:** Dockers
Previous Leagues: Grays & Dist. + Sth Essex (simultaneously)/ Kent 27-31/ London 31-39 46-50 57-62/ Sth Essex Comb. (war-time)/ Corinthian 50-57/ Delphian 62-63/ Athenian 63-73.
Reserve Team's League: Essex & Herts Border Comb.
Record Gate: 5,500 v Gorleston, FA Cup 4th Qual. Rd 19/11/49 (won 2-0).
Best FA Cup year: 3rd Rd Proper 77-78 (lost 0-4 at Stoke City). Also 1st Rd 49-50 (01-4 at Notts Co.)
Clubhouse: Open every evening, all day Friday & Saturday, and Sunday lunchtimes.
Players progressing to Football League: L Le May, T Scannell, T Oakley, J Evans.
Club Record Scorer: Ross Livermore 305 (in 282 games, 1958-66).
Club Record Appearances: Nicky Smith 424 (1975-85).
Hons: FA Amtr Cup QF, Isthmian Lg Div 1 75-76 (Div 1 Cup 74-75), Essex Snr Cup 4, (R-up 5).

WARE

Chairman: W J Luck
Secretary: I Bush, 42 Burnett Squ, Hertford, Herts SG14 2HD (01992 587334).
Manager: John Godleman. **Coach:** Dermot Drummy **Physio:** Frank Roberts
Ground: Wodson Park, Wadesmill Road, Ware Herts SG12 0HZ (01920 463247).
Directions: A10 off at junction A602 & B1001 (Ware North), turn right at roundabout 300yds, and follow Ware sign, past Rank factory, turn left at main roundabout onto A1170 (Wadesmill Rd). After 3/4 mile stadium on right.
Capacity: 3,300 **Seats:** 312 **Cover:** 500 **Floodlights:** Yes **Club Shop:** Yes
Programme: 24 pages, 50p **Editor/Press Officer:** Secretary
Colours: Blue & white stripes/blue/red **Change colours:** Amber/black
Sponsors: Charvill Bros Ltd. **Nickname:** Blues. **Founded:** 1892
Midweek Matchday: Tuesday **Reserve League:** Essex & Herts Border Comb.
Record Attendance: 3,800 v Hendon Amt Cup 56-57
Best FA Cup year: First Round Proper 68-69 (lost 6-1 to Luton Town).
Previous Leagues: East Herts/ North Middx 07-08/ Herts County 08-25/ Spartan 25-55/ Delphian 55-63/ Athenian 63-75.
Players progressing to Football League: Derek Saunders (Chelsea), Ken Humphrey (QPR).
Clubhouse: Licensed bar open matchdays. Light snacks at refreshment bar.
Club Record Scorer: M Hibbert 229 **Club Record Appearances:** Gary Riddle 654.
Honours: Herts Snr Cup 5, Herts Charity Shield 5, Herts Charity Cup R-up 4, Spartan Lg 52-53 (Div 1 Sect.B 51-52, Div 2 Sect.A 26-27), Athenian Lg Div 2 Cup 65-66 72-73, E Anglian Cup 73-74, Herts Co. Lg 08-09 21-22, East Herts Lg 04-05 06-07 (Lg Cup 06-07), Perry Cup 7, Dunkels Cup 52-53, Rolleston Cup 39-40 51-52.

WEMBLEY

Formed: 1946. The Lions
Chairman: Brian Gumm **Vice Chairman:** Eric Stringer **President:** Jim Bryan, BEM
Secretary: Mrs Jean Gumm, 14 Woodfield Avenue, North Wembley, Middx HA0 3NR (0181 908 3353).
General Manager: Tony Simpson. **Manager:** Glen Charles **Assistant Manager:** Paul Shields.
Ground: Vale Farm, Watford Road, Sudbury, Wembley HA0 4UR (0181 908 8169).
Directions: Sudbury Town station (Underground) 400 yds, or 10 mins walk from North Wembley (BR) station. Buses 18, 92, 245 & 182.
Capacity: 2,000 **Cover:** 350 **Seats:** 350 **Floodlights:** **Club Shop:** No
Programme: 28 pages £1 **Editor/Press Officer:** R Markiewicz (0181 902 0541).
Colours: Red & white **Change colours:** Yellow & Navy.
Midweek matchday: Tuesday **Reserve Team's League:** Sub Prem **Sponsors:** G & B Builders.
Record Attendance: 2,654 v Wealdstone, FA Amateur Cup 52-53.
Best season in FA Cup: 1st Round Proper 1980-81 (lost 0-3 at Enfield).
Previous Leagues: Middx 46-49/ Spartan 49-51/ Delphian 51-56/ Corinthian 56-63/ Athenian 63-75.
Players progressing to Football League: Ken Coote (Brentford 1949), Keith Cassells (Watford 1977), Mike O'Donague (Southampton 1979), A McGonigle (Olympiakos), Gary Roberts (Brentford 1980), Richard Cadette (Orient 1984).
Clubhouse: (0181 904 8169). Open every night & weekend lunchtimes. Hot food on matchdays.
95-96 Captain: Ian Bates. **95-96 P.o.Y:** Shaun Fleming. **95-96 Top Scorer:** Jon-Barrie Bates.
Club Record Goalscorer: Bill Handrahan 105 (1946-52) **Club Record Apps:** Spud Murphy 505 (78-88).
Honours: FA Amat Cup 2nd Rd 66-67 68-69, FA Tphy 1st Rd Prop 91-92, Middx Sen Cup 83-84 86-87 (R-up 6,), Middx Lge 47-48 (Lge Cup 46-47), Middx Charity Cup 67-68(jnt) 80-81(jnt) 82-83 86-87 94-95,(R-up 83-84 87-88), Middx Invitation Cup 56-57, Athenian Lge R-up 74-75 (Div 1 R-up 67-68), Corinthian Lge

Mem Shield R-up 58-59, Delphian Lge R-up 55-56, Spartan Lge Div 1 West 50-51 (Dunkel Trophy 50-51(joint)), London Sen Cup R-up 55-56, Hitachi Cup SF 83-84, Suburban Lge North 85-86 (Lge Cup 84-85 (R-up 83-84)).

WINDSOR & ETON

Chairman: Peter Simpson **Vice-Chairman:** Fred Atkins **President:** Sir David Hill-Wood, Bt
Secretary: Steve Rowland,91 Duke St, WQindsor, Berks. SL4 1SJ.(01753 774528)
Manager: Alan Davies. **Asst Manager:** Alan Rowe **Physio:** Des Hunt
Ground: Stag Meadow, St Leonards Road, Windsor, Berkshire SL4 3DR (01753 860656).
Directions: A332 from M4 junct 6. Left at r'bout (B3173), left into St Leonards Rd at lights on T-junction, ground 500 yards on right on B3022 opposite Stag & Hounds PH. 1 mile from town centre, Windsor Central or Windsor Riverside BR
Capacity: 4,500 **Cover:** 650 **Seats:** 400 **Floodlights:** Yes **Founded:** 1892
Club Shop: Yes
Colours: Red (green trim)/red/red **Change colours:** White/black/black. **Nickname:** Royalists
Sponsors: Murex Welding Products. **Previous Ground:** Ballon Meadow 1892-1912.
Programme: 28 pages **Editor:** Eric Richford.
Midweek home matchday: Tuesday **Reserve Team's League:** Suburban (North)
Record Gate: 8,500 (Charity match). **Best FA Cup season:** 2nd Rd replay 83-84. 1st Rd on seven occasions; 25-26 80-81 82-86 91-92.
Clubhouse: (01753 860656). Juke-box, Sky TV, licensed bar, darts, pool, contact Alan Baker
Club record appearances: Kevin Mitchell.
Hons: Isthmian Lg Div 1 83-84 (Div 2 R-up 82-83), Athenian Lg 79-80 80-81 (Lg Cup 79-80 (R-up 78-79 80-81), Div 2 Cup 63-64 (R-up 68-69)), Spartan Lg R-up 36-37 37-38 (Div 1 30-31), Metropolitan Lg R-up 53-54 (Lg Amtr Cup 51-52 52-53, Lg Cup 52-53 (R-up 53-54 54-55)), Gt Western Suburban Lg R-up 21-22, Berks & Bucks Snr Cup(11) (R-up 6), Berks & Bucks Benev. Cup 4, (R-up 3), FA Amtr Cup 4th Rd 21-22, FA Vase SF 80-81 (QF 79-80), FA Tphy 3rd Rd 88-89.

WITHAM TOWN

Chairman: Mr A Marshall **Vice Chairman:** Reg Wright **President:** Mr B Olley.
Secretary: Reg Wright, 28 Mersey Rd, Witham, Essex CM8 1LJ (01376 512990).
Manager: Spencer Pratten **Asst Mgr:** George Young **Physio:** Elaine Hume
Ground: Spa Road, Witham, Essex CM8 1UN (01376 511198-lounge, 500146-reception, 520996-boardroom).
Directions: From Witham BR (network S.E.) station; through pub car park and follow road to Faulkbourne, at main r'bout turn left and ground is on the right. By road; Off A12 at Witham sign, left at 1st lights (Spinks Lane), right at end of road, follow road under railway bridge - ground 100yds on left.
Capacity: 2,500 **Seats:** 150 **Cover:** 300 **Floodlights:** Yes **Club Shop:** No.
Programme: 24 pages, 60p **Editor:** Alison Gray **Press Officer:** G Vale (01376 513861)
Colours: Red & black stripes/black/black **Change colours:** Green & yellow.
Sponsor: **Nickname:** Town **Founded:** 1947
Midweek Matchday: Tuesday **Reserve's League:** Essex & Herts Border Comb.
Record Attendance: 800 v Billericay Town, Essex Senior League, May 1976.
Best FA Cup year: 2nd Qual. Rd 87-88 (v Gravesend), 88-89 (v B. Stortford), 89-90 (v Dartford).
Previous Leagues: Mid Essex/ Essex & Suffolk Border/ Essex Senior 71-87.
Clubhouse: Open every night and weekend lunctimes. Hot bar snacks
95-96 Captain: **95-96 P.O.Y.:** Dean Braybrock **95-96 Top scorer:** C J Emmanuel
Club Record Goalscorer: Colin Mitchell **Club Record Appearances:** Keith Dent (16 years)
Honours: Essex Snr Lg 70-71 85-86 (R-up 84-85 86-87), Essex Snr Tphy 85-86 (R-up 88-89), FA Vase 5th Rd 85-86, Loctite Tphy SF 90-91.

WIVENHOE TOWN

Formed: 1925 The Dragons
Chairman: Dave Whymark **President:** Harry Welsh.
Secretary/Press Officer: Mike Boyle, 15 Daniell Drive, Colchester, Essex (01206 573223).
Manager: Steve Dowman. **Physio:** Barry Wreford **Commercial Manager:** Phil Reeve.
Ground: Broad Lane Ground, Elmstead Road, Wivenhoe CO7 7HA (01206 823416).
Directions: Coming out of Colchester towards Clacton take first turning (right) towards Wivenhoe, first left and ground clearly visible on right at cross-roads. 1 mile from Wivenhoe (BR).
Capacity: 3,000 **Cover:** 1,300 **Seats:** 250 **Floodlights:** Yes **Club Shop:** Yes
Programme: 44 pages £1 **Editor:** Mr M Boyle
Colours: All Royal Blue. **Change colours:** Yellow/royal/yellow. **Midweek matchday:** Tuesday
Previous Leagues: Brighlingsea & District 1927-50/ Colchester & East Essex 50-71/ Essex & Suffolk Border 71-79/ Essex Senior 79-86.
Prevs Name: Wivenhoe Rangers. **Res Lge:** Essex & Herts Border Comb.
Record Attendance: 1,912 v Runcorn, FA Trophy 1st Rd, Feb 1990.
Best FA Cup season: 4th Qual Rd 89-90 (lost 2-3 at Halesowen Town), 94-95 (1-2 at home to Enfield).
Clubhouse: (01206 825380). Open normal pub hours.
Club Record Goalscorer: Paul Harrison, 258 in 350 games. **Club Record Appearances:** Keith Bain, 536.
Hons: FA Tphy 2nd Rd replay 89-90, FA Vase 5th Rd 82-83, Isthmian Lg Div 1 89-90 (Div 2 Nth 87-88), Essex Snr Lg R-up 3, Harry Fisher Tphy 83-84 85-86, Essex & Suffolk Border Lg 78-79 (Div 1 72-73, Div 2 71-72, Lg Cup R-up(2) 75-77), Essex Snr Tphy 87-88, Amos Charity Cup(7)

ICIS DIVISION THREE FINAL LEAGUE TABLE 1995/96

		P	W	D	L	F	A	Pts
1.	Horsham	40	29	5	6	95	40	92
2.	Leighton	40	28	5	7	95	34	89
3.	Windsor & Eton	40	27	6	7	117	46	87
4.	Wealdstone	40	23	8	9	104	39	77
5.	Harlow Town	40	22	10	8	85	62	76
6.	Northwood	40	20	9	11	76	56	69
7.	Epsom & Ewell	40	18	14	8	95	57	68
8.	Kingsbury Town	40	15	16	9	61	48	61
9.	E Thurrock Utd	40	17	8	15	61	50	59
10.	Aveley	40	16	10	14	62	53	58
11.	Wingate & Finch	40	16	7	17	74	70	55
12.	Lewes	40	14	7	19	56	72	49
13.	Flackwell Heath	40	14	5	21	60	84	47
14.	Hornchurch	40	11	8	21	55	77	41
15.	Harefield United	40	11	7	22	49	89	40
16.	Tring Town	40	10	8	22	40	78	38
17.	Camberley Town	40	9	9	22	45	81	36
18.	Hertford Town	40	10	5	25	72	103	35
19.	Cove	40	8	10	22	37	89	34
20.	Clapton	40	9	6	25	48	89	33
21.	Southall	40	9	5	26	34	104	32

LEADING LEAGUE GOALSCORERS;

Bradley Anderson	Leighton Town	33
Stafford Browne	Lewes	28
David Whitehead	Hertford Town	28
Andy Boxall	Epsom & Ewell	27

DIVISION THREE RESULTS CHART 1995-96

HOME TEAM	1	2	3	4	5	6	7	8	9	10	11	12	13	14	15	16	17	18	19	20	21
1. Aveley	*	3-2	3-0	0-0	2-1	0-2	1-1	3-2	0-1	0-0	1-1	0-2	1-1	0-1	2-1	4-0	0-1	1-0	1-1	0-0	4-3
2. Camberley Town	1-2	*	1-0	0-1	0-4	0-2	2-0	1-2	1-3	4-3	0-1	0-2	1-1	1-5	2-1	0-1	0-0	0-3	1-2	1-1	0-2
3. Clapton	0-3	1-3	*	0-1	3-2	2-4	0-2	2-1	0-0	3-0	1-2	1-3	2-2	1-2	2-0	0-2	4-2	5-0	1-10	0-5	3-0
4. Cove	0-2	0-0	1-0	*	0-2	2-2	1-2	1-1	1-1	2-0	2-0	0-5	0-0	0-3	1-0	0-2	3-0	1-1	1-9	0-4	3-1
5. E Thurrock Utd	0-1	4-1	5-1	3-0	*	1-1	2-1	4-1	2-2	0-2	3-0	3-0	2-2	1-1	2-0	1-0	2-0	0-1	0-3	1-4	4-2
6. Epsom & Ewell	2-2	4-0	2-1	6-0	1-1	*	4-3	2-0	2-2	1-1	1-4	1-2	2-2	1-2	0-0	3-0	5-0	11-1	0-2	4-1	7-1
7. Flackwell Heath	1-0	1-4	1-1	3-2	1-1	1-2	*	3-0	0-1	2-3	1-3	2-1	1-2	1-0	2-4	1-2	4-2	1-0	0-0	0-3	1-2
8. Harefield Utd	1-3	2-1	1-0	2-1	2-0	0-0	2-4	*	1-3	1-3	1-0	0-6	0-1	1-4	0-1	2-2	0-0	0-2	1-2	1-3	4-3
9. Harlow Town	4-3	2-2	2-1	3-1	1-0	1-1	2-3	1-1	*	8-4	2-1	2-3	3-2	3-0	4-3	1-1	0-2	3-0	3-0	3-3	2-0
10. Hertford Town	0-2	1-3	5-2	3-1	2-3	1-4	3-4	0-2	1-3	*	2-4	1-3	0-4	0-3	1-2	2-3	5-0	5-0	1-2	1-4	1-7
11. Hornchurch	2-2	1-3	0-0	1-1	0-0	0-1	2-2	1-2	3-5	2-1	*	1-4	0-2	1-2	2-1	2-2	1-2	6-1	1-1	1-4	0-2
12. Horsham	3-1	6-0	2-1	5-1	1-1	3-1	1-3	5-2	3-0	1-0	2-1	*	0-1	1-3	2-0	1-0	3-1	2-0	2-1	1-1	1-0
13. Kingsbury Town	3-2	2-2	2-2	1-0	1-3	1-1	5-0	0-0	2-1	0-2	0-1	3-3	*	1-0	1-1	3-1	2-0	1-0	0-0	1-1	4-0
14. Leighton Town	2-1	6-0	1-0	3-0	2-3	3-1	3-1	5-1	2-1	4-1	5-0	3-3	2-0	*	3-0	5-0	5-0	2-0	0-2	4-3	0-1
15. Lewes	3-2	2-3	4-2	1-1	1-0	2-3	3-0	3-3	1-2	4-2	1-0	2-1	1-1	0-3	*	0-2	1-0	2-1	0-4	2-0	2-2
16. Northwood	3-1	2-2	6-1	3-2	3-0	4-2	2-1	3-1	4-0	1-1	7-1	1-1	4-1	0-0	1-2	*	2-1	0-2	0-5	1-1	2-2
17. Southall	2-1	2-1	0-3	2-1	0-1	1-1	1-3	3-2	0-2	2-6	1-2	2-6	3-1	0-3	1-1	0-3	*	0-0	0-7	0-3	1-2
18. Tring Town	0-0	2-2	0-0	1-1	2-0	1-1	3-1	1-2	1-2	1-1	2-6	0-1	1-3	0-1	5-1	0-2	0-1	*	1-0	0-3	3-1
19. Wealdstone	3-4	0-0	2-1	4-0	3-0	1-1	4-0	3-1	0-2	7-0	4-0	0-1	2-0	1-1	3-2	0-4	9-0	3-1	*	1-5	1-1
20. Windsor & Eton	2-1	3-0	0-1	5-3	2-0	7-2	7-0	7-0	5-2	2-5	2-1	0-2	2-1	2-0	5-1	2-0	6-1	4-0	0-2	*	3-1
21. Wingate & Finch	1-3	1-0	7-0	8-1	0-2	1-4	3-2	2-3	2-2	2-2	1-0	0-1	1-1	1-1	1-0	2-0	3-0	2-3	2-0	1-2	*

AVELEY

Chairman: Bill Taylor **President:** Ken Clay
Secretary: Ken Sutliff, 9 Westlyn Close, Rainham, Essex RM13 9JP (01708 555271).
Manager: Craig Johnson. **Asst Mgr/Coach:** John Kerslake **Physio:** Phil Hunter
Ground Address & Tel: 'Mill Field', Mill Road, Aveley, Essex RM15 4TR (01708 865940).
Directions: London - Southend A13, turn into Sandy Lane at Aveley. Rainham or Purfleet BR stations then bus No. 723 to the ground.
Capacity: 8,000 **Cover:** 400 **Seats:** 400 **Floodlights:** Yes **Shop:** No
Colours: Royal blue/white/royal blue **Change colours:** All yellow.
Sponsors: Dagenham Motors. **Shop:** No
Midweek home matchday: Tuesday **Reserve Lge:** Essex & Herts Border Comb.
Record Attendance: 3,741 v Slough Town, FA Amateur Cup 27/2/71.
Best F.A. Cup season: 1st Rd 70-71 (lost 0-1 to Yeovil).
Clubhouse: Normal pub hours. All kinds of bar snacks and hot food.
95-96 Top scorer: Micky Waite.
Honours: Isthmian Lg Div 2 (North) R-up 89-90 (Lg (AC Delco) Cup 89-90),FA Amateur Cup QF 70-71, FA Tphy 3rd Qualifying Rd replay 74-75, FA Vase 3rd Rd 89-90.

BRAINTREE TOWN

Chairman: George Rosling **Vice Chairman:** Ivan Kibble **President:** R F Webb.
Secretary: T A Woodley, 19a Bailey Bridge Road, Braintree, Essex CM7 5TT (01376 326234).
Manager: Keith Martin **Ass.Mans.:** Tony Hall **Physio:** Tony Last.
Ground: Cressing Road Stadium, Clockhouse Way, Braintree, Essex (01376 345617).
Directions: All routes Braintree by-pass & turn to Braintree at McDonalds r'bout signs for E Braintree Ind Est on left half mile into town opp Orange Tree Pub ent next left Clockhouse Way, left again.
Capacity: 4,000 **Cover:** 1,500 **Seats:** 292 **Floodlights:** Yes **Shop:** Yes
Programme: 40pages £1 **Editor:** **Press Officer:** R F Webb (01376 325338)
Colours: Navy Blue with yellow stripes/Navy/Yellow. **Change colours:** All White.
Reserves' Lg: Essex/Herts Border Comb. **Sponsors:** Yellow Line Taxis.
Midweek home matchday: Tuesday **Best FA Cup season:** 4th Qual. Rd 69-70 85-86 94-95
Record Attendance: 6,000 - Saffron Walden v Rainham, Essex Jnr Cup final 1926. For Braintree game: 4,000 v Spurs, charity challenge match, May 1952.
Clubhouse: Open every evening 7-11pm, Saturday & Sunday lunchtimes noon-2pm
95-96 Captain : Adrian Owers. **95-96 Top scorer:** Wade Falana 46 **95-96 P.o.Y.:** Shane Bailey
Honours: E Counties Lg 3, (R-up 4); Lg Cup 87-88 (R-up 35-36 74-75)); Essex County Lg R-up 37-38; E Anglian Cup 46-47 68-69 95-96; Essex Senior Trophy 86-87 (R-up 90-91); Essex Snr Cup 95-96:

CAMBERLEY TOWN

Chairman: Ian Waldren **Vice Chairman:** Gordon Foss **President:** Paul Prentice
Secretary: Dave Slater, 33 Blythwood Drive, Frimley, Camberley, Surrey GU15 1SD 01276 23096).
Manager: Danny McGranaghan. **Asst Manager:** Paul Xiberras **Physio:** Julia Richards.
Ground: Krooner Park, Krooner Road, off Frimley Rd, Camberley, Surrey GU15 2QP (01276 65392).
Directions: M3 Jct 4, follow signs to Frimley, follow B3411 towards Camberley, ground on left opposite 'The Standard' pub.
Capacity: 3,000 **Seats:** 195 **Cover:** 195 **Floodlights:** Yes **Club Shop:** Yes
Colours: Red/white/red. **Change colours:** All yellow
Programme: 24 pages, 50p **Sponsors:** Zip Print **Founded:** 1896
Midweek Matchday: Tuesday
Res's Lge: Suburban **Nickname:** Krooners/Reds/Town **Best F.A. Cup:** 3rd Qual Rd 79
Record Gate: Comp: 2,066 v Aldershot Town, Isthmian Lge Div 3, 92.
Clubhouse: Open matchdays and 2 evenings per week.
Hons: FA Vase QF 85-86, Isthmian Lg Div 2 R-up 78-79,

CLAPTON

Chairman: Ken Harris. **President:** Mike Gliksten
Secretary: Steven Walters,10 Buttfield Close,Dagenham Village,Essex.RM10 8TJ. (0181 596 0424).
Manager: Lyndon Lynch **Coach:** John Simmonds **Physio:** M Roberts
Ground: The Old Spotted Dog, Upton Lane, Forest Gate, London E7 9NP (0181 472 0822).
Directions: BR to Forest Gate, tube to Plaistow (District Line), or bus 278 passes ground. Official entrance in Upton Lane. Docklands Light Railway to Prince Regent then 325 bus to ground.
Capacity: 2,000 **Seats:** 100 **Cover:** 180. **Floodlights:** Yes **Club Shop:** Yes
Colours: Red & white stripes/black/black **Change colours:** Yellow/blue.
Programme: 12-16 pages 60p. **Editor:** Secretary. **Press Officer:** Chairman.
Midweek Matchday: Tuesday **Nickname:** Tons **Sponsors:** Mullalley Const.
Reserves' Lge: Essex/Herts Border Com.
Record Attendance: 12,000 v Tottenham Hotspur, FA Cup 1898-99.
Best FA Cup year: 3rd Rd Proper 25-26 (lost 2-3 to Swindon at Upton Park).
Clubhouse: Open most evenings & match day. Light snacks available.
95-96 Captain: **95-96 P.o.Y.:** **95-96 Top scorer:**
Hons: FA Amtr Cup 5,(R-up 04-05), Isthmian Lg 2, (R-up 5);

EAST THURROCK UNITED

Chairman: Brian Grover **Vice Chairman:** Harry Caine. **President:** Alan Gower
Secretary: Malcolm Harris, 14 Colne Valley, Upminster, Essex RM14 1QA (017082 2818).
Manager: Tommy Lee. **Physio:** Pat Thompson
Ground: Rookery Hill, Corringham, Essex (01375 644166-club, 641009-boardroom).
Directions: A13 London-Southend, take 1014 at Stanford-le-Hope for two and a half miles - ground on left. Two miles from Stanford-le-Hope and Basildon BR stations.
Seats: 160 **Cover:** 360 **Capacity:** 3,000 **Floodlights:** Yes **Club Shop:** Yes
Programme: 24 pages, 50p **Editor:** Tony Smith (01268 292142) **Press Officer:** Secretary
Colours: Amber/black/black **Change colours:** Blue/white/white
Founded: 1969. **Nickname:** Rocks
Midweek Matchday: **Reserves' Lge:** Essex/Herts Border Com.
Record Attendance: 947 v Trevor Brooking XI, May 1987. Competitive: 845 v Bashley, FA Vase 1989.
Clubhouse: Open all day seven days a week. Hot and cold snacks.
95-96 Captain: Gary Lynch. **95-96 P.o.Y.:** Steve Carter. **95-96 Top Scorer:** Lee Antoniou.
Honours: Essex Snr Tphy R-up 91-92 95-96, Fred Budden Tphy R-up 89-90, Essex & Herts Border Comb. 89-90 (Lg Cup 89-90).

EPSOM & EWELL

Chairman: Peter Atkins **Vice Chairman:** Stella Lamont. **President:**
Secretary: David Wilson, 33 Delaporte Close, Epsom, Surrey KT17 4AF (01372 729817).
Manager: Adrian Hill **Coach:** John Wood **Physio:** Jo Morgan.
Ground: As Banstead Athletic FC. **Club Shop:** No
Programme: 28/32 pages, 35p **Editor/Press Officer:** Stella Lamont (01737 356245).
Colours: Royal & white **Change colours:** All yellow.
Sponsors: TBA **Nickname:** E's. **Founded:** 1917
Midweek Matches: Tuesday **Reserve Team's League:** Suburban
Record Attendance: 5,000 v Kingstonian, F.A. Cup Second Qualifying Rd, 15/10/49.
Best F.A. Cup year: 1st Rd Proper 33-34, lost 2-4 at Clapton Orient.
Best FA Vase year: Finalists 74-75
Best FA Trophy year: 2nd Rd Proper 81-82.
Clubhouse: Normal licensing hours, food available.
95-96 Captain: Graham Meakin. **95-96 Top Scorer:** Andy Boxall 29 **95-96 P.o.Y.:** Dave Hyatt
Hons: F.A. Vase R-up 74-75, Isthmian Lg Div 2 77-78 (Div 1 R-up 83-84).

FLACKWELL HEATH

Chairman: A.Lee. **Vice Chairman:** T Glynn. **President:** Ken Crook
Secretary: Mrs Christine Hobbs, 23 Southfield Rd., Flackwell Heath, Bucks. HP10 9BT (01628-521051)
Ground: Wilks Park, Heath End Rd, Flackwell Heath, High Wycombe, Bucks HP10 9EA (01628 523892).
Directions: M40 jct 4, follow A404 towards High Wycombe, 1st turning into Daws Hill Lane, continue for 2 miles until you see signs for the club, left into Magpie Lane, ground at rear of Magpie (PH).
Capacity: 2,000 **Seats:** 150 **Cover:** Yes **Floodlights:** Yes **Club Shop:** No
Programme: 18 pages 50p **Editor:** Jonathon Lee(01628 850440).
Colours: Red/white/red **Change colours:** Yellow/black/yellow **Sponsors:** TBA
Midweek Matches: Tuesday. **Reserve Team's League:** Suburban. **Founded:** 1907
Record Attendance: 4,500 v Oxford U., charity game 1986 (competitive: 700 v Aldershot Town, 27/10/92).
Best F.A. Cup season: 2nd Qualifying Round replay 1990-91 (lost 0-3 at Grays after 2-2 draw).
Clubhouse: Open every night 6.30-11pm and before and after matches. Hot food in tea bar.
Hons: Gt Western Combination 57-58 62-63, Hellenic Lg Div 1 R-up 76-77, Berks & Bucks Snr Cup SF 85-86.

HARLOW TOWN

Chairman: John Taylor
Secretary: Ron Bruce, 26 Monksbury, Harlow, Essex CM18 7TA (01279 431883).
Manager: David Greene. **Physio:** Malcolm Roddy **Press Officer:** G Perkins (01372 273982).
Ground: Harlow Sports Centre, Hammarskjold Rd, Harlow CM20 2JF (01279 445319).
Directions: Near town centre, 10 mins walk from Harlow (BR) station.
Capacity: 10,000 **Cover:** 500 **Seats:** 400 **Floodlights:** Yes **Founded:** 1879.
Cols: Red white flash/white/white. **Change colours:** White/black/white. **Nickname:** Hawks.
Programme: 32 pages, 70. **Editor:** Phil Tuson (01279 416743) **Club Shop:** No.
Midweek matchday: Wednesday. **Reserve's League:** Essex & Herts Border Comb.
Record Attendance: 9,723 v Leicester, FA Cup 3rd Rd replay 8/1/80.
Best FA Cup season: 4th Rd 79-80 (lost 3-4 at Watford). Also 1st Rd 80-81 81-82.
Clubhouse: Open daily 11am-11pm (10.30 Sundays).
Sponsors: Harlow Sporting Club.Britsec.Int.Ltd. **Top Scorer 95-96:** David Greene.
Honours: FA Amtr Cup 2nd Rd 72-73, FA Tphy 2nd Rd(2) 80-82, FA Vase 3rd Rd 88-89, Isthmian Lg Div 1 78-79 (R-up 82-83, Div 2 Nth 88-89).

HERTFORD TOWN

President: Bernard Molloy **Chairman:** John Hedley **Vice Chairman:** Graham Wood.
Secretary: Stephen Hedley, 28 Cherry Tree Green, Hertford SG14 2HP (01992 587011).
Manager: Dave Whitehead. **Coach:** **Physio:** Ray Price
Ground: Hertingfordbury Park, West Street, Hertford (0992 5837011).
Directions: Rail to Hertford Nth (from Moorgate) or Hertford East (Liverpool Str.); both 15 mins walk. Green Line bus to town centre then 10 mins walk. By road; off bypass heading east, turn off at Ford garage.
Capacity: 6,500 **Seats:** 200 **Cover:** 1,500 **Floodlights:** Yes **Founded:** 1908
Colours: Blue & White, blue with white trim **Change colours:** All red **Club Shop:** Yes
Midweek Matches: Tuesday. **Nickname:** The Blues **Sponsors:** None
Programme: 28 pages, 40p **Editor:** Martin Climpson:(01992 589972)
Reserve Team's League: Essex & Herts Border Comb.
Best FA Cup year: Fourth Qualifying Rd 73-74 (lost 1-2 at Hillingdon Borough).
Record Gate: 5,000 v Kingstonian, F.A. Amateur Cup 2nd Rd 55-56.
Clubhouse: Old clubhouse burnt down in 1992. New clubhouse due to open at start of 1994-95 season.
95-96 Top Scorer: David Whitehead. **Hons:** Herts Charity Cup 72-73, Herts Snr Cup 66-67, Herts Charity Shield 6; Eastern Co's Lg Cup 72-73, E Anglian Cup 62-63 69-70, Southern Co's Comb F/lit Cup 94-95, Mithras Cup SF 85-86.

Flackwell Heath FC:

Northwood Town: back Row (L-R); George Price (Physio), Richard Coppinger, Vladimir Lazic, Jon Pettifer, Simon Walsh, Colin Robinson, Andre Delisser, Sean Glynn, Steve Emmanuel (Mgr). Front Row; Paul Webb, Steve Jones, Kevin Dodson, Chris Gell, Lee Carroll, John Carter, Gavin MacPherson, Paul Halbert.
Photo - Paul Evans

HORNCHURCH

Chairman: Brian Davie. **Vice Chairman:** K Nicholls.
Secretary: Ted Harris, 13 Claremont Gdns, Upminster, Essex RM14 1DW (01708 227891).
Manager: Dave Cox. **Asst Mgr & Coach:** Richard Gray **Physio:** D Edkins.
Ground: The Stadium, Bridge Avenue, Upminster, Essex RM14 2LX (01708 220080).
Directions: Bridge Avenue is off A124 between Hornchurch and Upminster. Buses 248, 348, 370, 373 from Romford or Upminster BR stations.
Capacity: 3,000 **Seats:** 300 **Cover:** 350 **Floodlights:** Yes **Club Shop:** Yes
Colours: Broad red and white stripes,red,red. **Change colours:** Purple & Yellow **Founded:** 1923
Programme: 16-20 pages with admission **Programme Editor/Press Officer:** Rob Monger(01268 490847).
Midweek Matchday: Tuesday **Reserve League:** Essex & Herts Border Comb.
Sponsors: Premier Snacks **Nickname:** Urchins. **Record Attendance:** 3,000 v Chelmsford, FA Cup 66-67.
Best FA Cup year: 4th Qualifying Rd 66-67, lost 0-4 at home to Chelmsford City.
Clubhouse: Mon-Fri 7.30-11pm, Sat noon-11pm, Sun noon-3pm. Bar snacks only
Hons: Carlsberg Trophy (R-up) 93-94.

KINGSBURY TOWN

Chairman: Allan J Davies **Vice Chairman:** Paul Blackman.
Secretary: Dave Thomas, 9 Hillview Gardens, Kingsbury, London NW9 0TE (0181 205 2047).
Manager: Dave Finn & Peter Blain. **Press Officer:** Allan Davies (01895 443761) **Physio:** Margaret Romer
Ground: Silver Jubilee Park, Townsend Lane, Kingsbury, London NW9 0DE (0181 205 1645-club).
Directions: Underground to Kingsbury, cross road and take bus 183 to Townsend Lane (2 miles) - ground in far left-hand corner of Silver Jubilee Park.
Capacity: 4,000 **Seats:** 165 **Cover:** 250 **Nickname:** Kings **Founded:** 1927
Colours: Royal/white/royal **Change colours:** Yellow/navy/yellow.
Programme: 16-20 pages, 50p **Editor:** Allan Davies. **Club Shop:** Yes
Midweek Matchday: Tuesday **Sponsors:** VPA Entertainment Technology.
Reserve League: Suburban **Record Gate:** 1,300 v Wealdstone, FA Amateur Cup 1971.
Best FA Cup year: 3rd Qualifying Round 87-88 (lost 0-1 at home to Leytonstone-Ilford).
Clubhouse: (0181 205 1645). Mon-Fri 7-11pm, Sat noon-11pm, Sun noon-2.30 & 7-10.30.
Hons: FA Vase 4th Rd 74-75, Isthmian Lg Div 2 Nth R-up 85-86, Spartan Lg Cup R-up 59-60 64-65, London Snr Cup R-up 95-96.

LEWES

Chairman: D.Southouse **President:** W.D.Carr
Secretary: John Lewis, Marshlands, Kingston Rd, Lewes, East Sussex BN7 3NB (01273 472822).
Manager: Terry Parris **Asst Manager:** **Physio:** Sue Bowen.
Ground: The Dripping Pan, Mountfield Road, Lewes BN7 1XN (01273 472574). **Directions:** Two minute walk from Lewes (BR) - turn left out of station and left into Mountfield Road. Ground 100 yards on right.
Capacity: 2,600. **Cover:** 400 **Seats:** 400 **Club Shop:** Yes.
Colours: Blue & Black stripes/Black/Black. **Change colours:** Yellow/green
Programme: 32 pages, 50p **Editor:** Secretary.
Nickname: Rooks **Founded:** 1885 **Sponsors:** T.B.A.
Midweek home matchday: Wednesday **Reserve Team's League:** Sussex Co. reserve section.
Record Attendance: 2,500 v Newhaven, Sussex County Lg 26/12/47.
Best F.A. Cup season: 4th Qualifying Rd (lost to Harwich & Parkeston)
Clubhouse: (01273 472100). Bar, tea bar, pool, table tennis. **Steward:** P Brook.
94-95 Captain: **94-95 P.o.Y.:** Adrian Richards. **94-95 Top scorer:**
Honours: Isth. Lg Div 2 R-up 79-80 91-92, FA Tphy 1st Rd 82-83, FA Amtr Cup 2nd Rd 67-68, FA Vase 1st Rd 79-80.

NORTHWOOD

Chairman: Andy Johnson **Vice Chairman:** Geoff Foster **President:** Lothar Hahn
Secretary: Steve Williams, 35 Evelyn Drive, Hatch End, Pinner, Middx HA5 4RL (0181 428 1533 H).
Manager: Steve Emmanuel **Physio:** George Price **Coach:** T Benning/J Toogood.
Ground: Northwood Park, Chestnut Avenue, Northwood (01923 827148).
Directions: A404 (Pinner-Rickmansworth) - Chestnut Ave. on left by large grey iron railway bridge and Shell petrol station.
Capacity: 2,000 **Seats:** 150 **Cover:** 200 **Floodlights:** Yes **Club Shop:** No
Programme: 52 pgs 70p **Editor:** A Evans (0181 566 2880) **Press Off:** M Russell (01923 827690)
Colours: All red **Change colours:** All Yellow.
Sponsors: IFS Freight Forwarding **Nickname:** Woods. **Founded:** 1902.
Midweek Matches: Tuesday **Reserve League:** Suburban **Rec Gate:** 1,324 v Chelsea Friendly 95
Best F.A. Cup year: 2nd.Qual.Rd.94-95. **Best F.A. Vase year:** 4th Rd 91-92.94-95.
Clubhouse: Weekends and most evenings from 6pm. Bar. Hot and cold food.
95-96 Captain: Sean Glynn **95-96 P.o.Y:** Chris Gell **95-96 Top Scorer:** Chris Gell 19
Honours: Isthmian Lg Ass Memb Cup 92-93, Lndn Spartan Lg 91-92 (R-up 89-90, Lg Cup 89-90 91-92), Middlesex Prem Cup 94-95

Windsor & Eton 95-96: *Photo - Andrew Chitty*

Wingate & Finchley 95-96:
Back Row (L-R); Paul Davis (Res Team Coach), Darren Carr, Barry Greenstreet, Adam Solomons, Joel Redgrave, Russell Brill, Ron Franklyn (Physio).
Centre Row; Jeff Bookman (Mgr), Andy Myers, Mason Fisk, Steve Cobb, David Newman, Andy Yetzes, Tim Becker, Martin Burt (Res Team Mgr).
Front Row; Danny Piler, Nigel Portman, Spencer Fenton, Darren Curtis, Marc Morris, John Bolle, Mark Lennard.

SOUTHALL

Chairman: J J Loftus **President:** R E Fowler
Secretary: Maria Smith, 22 Barchester Rd, Harrow Weald, Middx HA3 5HH (0181 933 9699)
Manager: Keith Chamberlin **Asst Manager:** TBA **Physio:** George Richardson
Ground: Tring Town FC, Pendley Sports Centre, Cow Lane, Tring, Herts. HP23 5NS (014428 23075).
Ground directions & details: As Tring Town
Colours: Red & white stripes,white,red. **Change colours:** Grey & white **Nickname:** Fowlers
Club Shop: No **Sponsors:** Longwood Builders **Founded:** 1871
Programme: 6 pages, 50p **Editor:** Secretary
Midweek Matchday: Tuesday **Reserve League:** Middx County.
Record Gate: 17,000 v Watford, FA Cup 3rd Rd 1935.
Best F.A. Cup year: 3rd Round 35-36 (lost 1-4 at home to Watford).
Clubhouse: Normal pub hours. Hot snacks available on matchdays.
Hons: FA Amtr Cup R-up 24-25 (SF 25-26 52-53), FA Vase R-up 85-86, Isthmian Lg Div 2 R-up 74-75.

TRING TOWN

Chairman: Martin Jones **Secretary:** Ian Brading, c/o Club.
Manager: John Arnold **Asst Manager:** Micky Connolly **Physio:** Stuart McCorkindale
Ground: Pendley Sports Centre, Cow Lane, Tring, Herts HP23 5NS (01442 823075).
Directions: One mile from Tring centre on A41 - direct connection to M25 (jct 20) via new A41 bypass. One and a half miles from Tring (BR).
Capacity: 2,500 **Seats:** 150 **Cover:** 250 **Floodlights:** Yes **Club Shop:** No
Programme: 24 pages 50p **Editor:** Alan Lee. **Press Officer:** Alan Lee
Colours: Red & white stripes/red/red **Change colours:** Yellow & blue stripes/blue/blue
Sponsors: None. **Nickname:** T's. **Founded:** 1904
Midweek Matchday: Monday **Reserve Team's League:** No reserve team.
Record Attendance: 2,500 v West Ham Utd friendly
Best FA Cup year: 3rd Qualifying Rd replay 84-85, lost 0-5 at Fisher after 1-1 draw.
Clubhouse: All licensing hours. Dancehall, pool, darts, kitchen.
95-96 Captain: Del Deanus **Club Record Scorer & Appearances:** Gary Harthill
Hons: Spartan Lg 66-67, R-up 68-69.

WEALDSTONE

Formed: 1899. The Stones

Chairman: Paul Rumens **Vice Chairman:** Nick Dugard.
Secretary: Steve Hibberd, 17 Brancaster Rd, Newbury Park, Ilford, Essex IG2 7ER (0181 597 7534).
Manager: Gordon Bartlett. **Asst Mgr:** Leo Morris. **Physio:** Alan Wharton
Ground: As Edgware Town F.C.(Wealdstone club office 0181 381 1671)
Programme: 30 pages £1 **Editor:** Roy Couch (0181 907 4421) **Press Officer:** Graham Sharpe
Colours: Blue & white quarters **Change colours:** all yellow.
Midweek home matchday: Wednesday **Reserve League:** None. **Shop:** No
Record Attendance: 13,504 v Leytonstone FA Amateur Cup Fourth Round replay 5/3/49.
Best FA Cup season: 3rd Rd 77-78 (01-4 at Q.P.R.). 1st Rd on 13 occasions 49-50 65-67 68-69 75-80 82-84 85-87.
Clubhouse: Yes, normal licensing hours.
95-96 Captain: Steve Croad. **95-96 P.o.Y.:** Chris Walton. **95-96 Top scorer:** Paul Sheldrick 36
Honours: FA Tphy 84-85, FA Amateur Cup 65-66 , GMV Conference 84-85,

WINGATE & FINCHLEY

Chairman: Peter Rebak **Vice Chairman:** **President:** H Whidden.
Secretary: Richard Cooper, c/o Club Tel,0181 446 2217 Fax 0181 343 8194
Manager: Martin Burt. **Coach:** Bobby Fisher **Physio:** Amos Shanaan
Ground: The Abrahams Stadium, Summers Lane, Finchley, London N12 0PD.(0181 446 2217)
Directions: North Circular (A406) to jct with High Road Finchley (A1000), go north & Summers Lane 200 yards right. Tube East Finchley Station (Northern Line) & 263 bus.
Capacity: 8,500 **Seats:** 500 **Cover:** 500 **Floodlights:** Yes **Club Shop:** No.
Colours: Blue/white/blue **Change Colours:** All red
Programme: 24 pages, 50p **Editor:** Marc Morris (0181 371 6008) **Press Off.:** Harvey Ackerman.
Founded: 1991 **Nickname:** Blues **Club Sponsors:** None
Midweek matchday: Tuesday **Reserve's Lge:** Sub Lge under 18, S Counties F/light Youth
Record Attendance: 9,555 - Finchley v Bishop Auckland, F.A. Amateur Cup QF 49-50.
Clubhouse: Open during matches. Also tea-bar selling most refreshments.
95-96 Captain: **95-96 P.o.Y.:** **95-96 Top Scorer:** Andy Myers
Hons: FA Amtr Cup SF.

COMBINED COUNTIES LEAGUE

Chairman: Bill Lale.
20 Beverley Gardens, Rustington, Sussex BN16 3LT, (01903 770551)
Hon. Secretary: Clive Tidey,
22 Silo Road, Farncombe, Godalming, Surrey GU7 3PA (01483 428453)

Once again a long, and tiring, season came to a coclusion with the final games being played on the last Saturday in May. This season proved to be difficult for more than the usual weather-affected reason. Firstly this season saw the deadline for clubs to reach the new minimum ground improvement standards by 31st May, and secondly, events at the turn of the year saw dramatic changes to the formation of the League Management Committe. These reasons, coupled with the weather causing havoc to the fixture lists, resulted in a traumatic few months from January through to May. However, it was to everyone's credit that only one League game was not played from the 924 scheduled games at the beginning of the season.

Ashford Town (middx) were the Champions for the second successive year with Chipstead finishing as runners-up. The Reseve scetion was won by Godalming & Guildford with Ashford Town in second place. The Challenge Cup was won by Farnham Town in the final played at Woking's refurbished ground against Netherne. Merstham were successful in winning the Reserve Challenge Cup from Godalming & Guildford in the final played at Ashford Town's ground.

This season saw the departure of Horley Town, leaving to return to Junior football, DCA Basingstoke, Eton Wick and Peppard returning to the Chiltonian League. However the relegation of Cove from the ICIS Division three, and the transfer of Corinthian Casuals from the London Spartan League will result in a constitution of 20 members for next season. With both Cobham and Reading Town completing their floodlight installations during the close season the League is steadily moving towards its target of being fully floodlit by 1999 with two of the remaining clubs completing their installations by April 97.

FINAL LEAGUE TABLES 1995/96

Div One	P	W	D	L	F	A	Pts
1. Ashford Tn	42	32	7	3	111	36	103
2. Chipstead	42	30	4	8	102	44	94
3. Peppard	42	23	8	11	86	58	77
4. Merstham	42	22	9	11	89	66	75
5. Farnham Tn	42	20	12	10	71	52	72
6. Godalming	42	19	10	13	80	56	67
7. Reading Tn	42	20	6	16	76	69	66
8. Feltham	42	18	10	14	94	86	63
9. Bedfont	42	18	6	18	67	64	63
10. Ash United	42	17	12	13	74	73	63
11. Westfield	42	17	11	14	69	67	62
12. Sandhurst Tn	42	18	7	17	77	89	61
13. Netherne	42	16	12	14	78	64	60
14. DCA B/stoke	42	15	6	21	56	73	51
15. Eton Wick	42	13	11	18	71	81	50
16. Hartley Witney	42	13	6	23	47	88	45
17. Viking Sports	42	11	9	22	58	85	43
18. Cranleigh	42	11	8	23	70	94	41
19. Cobham	42	12	4	26	59	84	40
20. Walton Casuals	42	10	8	24	46	67	38
21. Raynes P V	42	10	7	25	58	97	34
22. Horley Tn	42	6	9	27	49	95	27

Reserve Div	P	W	D	L	F	A	Pts
1. Godalming	36	26	4	6	89	29	82
2. Ashford Tn	36	24	4	8	88	44	76
3. Cobham	36	19	8	9	82	45	65
4. Netherne	36	17	10	9	77	47	61
5. Bedfont	36	17	8	11	74	58	59
6. Ash United	36	18	4	14	72	64	58
7. Reading Tn	36	16	9	11	77	63	57
8. Farnham Tn	36	16	8	12	82	76	56
9. Peppard	36	17	4	15	68	50	55
10. Eton Wick	36	16	3	17	62	70	51
11. Viking Spts	36	14	8	14	58	73	50
12. DCA B/stoke	36	13	9	14	57	62	48
13. Cranleigh	36	12	7	16	71	79	46
14. Sandhurst Tn	36	10	11	15	57	63	41
15. Horley Tn	36	11	6	18	53	71	39
16. Merstham	36	9	9	18	54	80	36
17. Westfield	36	7	8	21	33	76	29
18. Walton Cas	36	6	7	23	44	82	28
19. Hartley Witney	36	9	3	24	49	109	27

Premier Division;
Feltham 1 point deducted.
Raynes Park Vale 3 points deducted

Viking Sports 1 point awarded.
Bedfont 3 points awarded.

PREMIER DIVISION RESULTS CHART 1995-96

HOME TEAM	1	2	3	4	5	6	7	8	9	10	11	12	13	14	15	16	17	18	19	20	21	22
1. Ash United	*	0-0	0-2	1-7	5-0	4-0	4-2	1-0	1-1	2-4	1-6	1-0	1-1	1-2	2-2	2-0	0-0	2-1	2-0	2-0	1-1	1-1
2. Ashford Tn	3-1	*	2-1	2-2	4-1	4-2	1-0	2-1	3-2	6-0	1-0	6-0	5-2	2-0	2-0	1-1	5-0	1-1	6-2	3-0	5-3	4-1
3. Bedfont	0-2	1-0	*	0-0	2-1	0-0	0-1	2-2	2-2	2-1	3-1	3-0	4-1	1-1	1-0	3-2	0-1	1-2	2-0	1-2	4-2	2-0
4. Chipstead	3-2	0-1	2-1	*	1-1	3-0	4-1	3-2	3-1	2-1	0-1	6-0	0-0	2-0	2-0	1-4	2-2	3-1	5-1	4-2	2-1	5-1
5. Cobham	0-2	0-0	0-2	0-4	*	1-2	2-0	3-5	0-1	4-4	0-1	2-0	3-0	0-1	1-2	5-1	2-0	1-3	6-3	2-0	1-2	4-0
6. Cranleigh	4-0	1-4	1-2	2-5	1-2	*	2-1	2-2	3-2	1-2	1-1	6-2	1-4	2-2	3-1	0-2	6-0	1-3	1-2	2-5	3-1	1-1
7. Basingstoke	5-0	0-2	1-0	1-2	1-0	5-2	*	1-2	0-0	1-1	3-0	1-2	1-0	2-3	1-2	1-0	3-1	2-2	1-2	2-2	3-2	1-3
8. Eton Wick	3-3	1-3	2-1	1-3	1-0	0-0	6-0	*	1-2	2-4	3-2	3-2	2-2	2-0	2-2	2-2	1-0	2-1	0-1	2-2	0-0	1-3
9. Farnham Tn	1-1	0-2	2-0	0-3	6-4	2-1	0-1	3-2	*	3-2	3-0	1-1	4-0	1-1	2-2	3-1	3-3	1-0	3-3	2-0	2-0	1-0
10. Feltham	5-4	1-6	2-1	2-1	4-1	1-0	2-3	1-1	0-1	*	2-1	4-1	6-1	2-3	3-2	2-4	0-2	8-2	3-3	4-2	0-2	2-2
11. Godalming	3-0	1-0	3-2	1-2	3-1	1-0	0-2	1-1	0-2	4-1	*	4-0	0-0	2-3	2-0	1-1	2-4	1-1	5-0	1-1	1-0	1-2
12. Hartley Wit	0-3	0-2	2-5	1-0	2-1	5-3	3-2	2-0	2-0	0-0	1-7	*	3-0	1-1	1-3	2-0	0-0	0-3	0-1	1-1	0-2	1-4
13. Horley Tn	1-2	1-1	0-0	2-3	0-3	1-3	2-2	4-2	1-3	3-1	2-5	0-2	*	3-1	2-2	0-3	3-2	1-2	1-2	0-0	0-2	0-1
14. Merstham	0-1	3-5	3-5	1-0	4-1	1-1	6-1	2-1	3-1	1-3	2-2	5-2	3-1	*	1-0	1-3	3-0	2-6	2-2	2-0	3-1	4-1
15. Netherne	6-1	0-2	4-3	1-2	1-2	1-0	1-1	5-0	0-2	1-1	3-2	1-2	3-2	1-1	*	1-1	5-3	2-2	4-0	3-0	2-3	0-0
16. Peppard	2-2	1-0	4-0	2-1	3-0	7-1	2-0	4-3	1-0	3-2	2-2	1-0	4-1	1-3	2-4	*	1-1	3-1	1-2	3-0	1-0	5-3
17. Raynes Park	0-8	1-2	4-3	1-5	0-1	2-2	4-1	0-1	1-2	1-2	2-3	1-3	4-2	2-2	1-3	1-2	*	0-2	0-4	3-1	3-1	1-2
18. Reading Tn	0-1	0-3	1-2	0-1	3-0	3-2	2-0	3-1	0-0	2-2	1-4	1-0	1-0	1-3	2-3	2-0	2-3	*	2-0	1-0	3-2	3-2
19. Sandhurst Tn	3-2	3-3	5-0	3-2	3-1	1-2	0-1	3-1	2-2	1-4	0-0	2-1	1-0	0-3	1-0	1-3	1-3	1-4	*	5-3	4-1	1-1
20. Viking Sport	2-3	2-3	2-1	1-2	2-0	3-2	2-0	2-5	2-1	1-1	0-1	2-0	3-2	1-3	0-2	1-1	2-1	4-2	3-5	*	0-3	1-3
21. Walton Cas	1-1	0-2	2-0	0-1	2-2	1-2	2-0	1-2	0-3	1-2	1-2	0-0	0-2	0-3	1-1	0-1	0-0	2-1	2-1	0-0	*	1-2
22. Westfield	1-1	0-2	1-2	0-3	3-0	4-1	0-1	3-0	0-0	2-2	1-1	0-2	4-1	2-1	2-2	2-1	4-1	2-3	3-2	1-1	1-0	*

LEADING GOALSCORERS 1995-96

Premier Division;

L May	Chipstead	41
P German	Ashford Town	38
P Edghill	Feltham	28
G Price	Sandhurst Town	28
P McKay	Chipstead	27
P Warner	Farnham Town	26
P Otway	Netherne	26
B Cook	DCA Basingstoke	25
L Holman	Ashford Town	25

Reserve Division;

C Nobbe	Cobham	28
D Logie	Bedfont	20
I Gascoigne	Ashford Town	20
G Elliott	Farnham Town	19
S Monaghan	Reading Town	19
M Occomorme	Cobham	16
A Warner	Farnham Town	16
R McDonald	Ashford Town	15

PREMIER DIVISION CHALLENGE CUP 1995-96

First Round;

Ash United v Ashford Town 0-4
Eton Wick v Sandhurst Town 0-1
Viking Sports v Cobham 3-2
DCA Basingstoke v Walton Casuals 1-2
Feltham v Raynes Park Vale 2-1
Reading Town v Peppard 3-3, 3-2 (aet)

Second Round;

Ashford Town v Viking Sports 5-1
Farnham Town v Sandhurst Town 2-1
Horley Town v Netherne 1-3
Merstham v Bedfont 1-2
Chipstead v Feltham 5-4 (aet)
Godalming & Guildford v Cranleigh 1-0
Hartley Witney v Reading Town 2-2, 2-1
Walton Casuals v Westfield 3-2

Third Round;

Ashford Town v Farnham Town 1-2
Netherne v Hartley Witney 1-0
Godalming & Guildford v Chipstead 1-0
Walton Casuals v Bedfont 1-3

Semi-Finals;

Godalming & Guildford v Farnham Town 0-2
Netherne v Bedfont 4-0

Final; Farnham Town v Netherne 3-0

Farnham Town 95-96: After winning the Premier Challenge Cup by beating Netherne 3-1 in the final at Woking.

Chipstead F C: Runners-up in the Combined Counties League Photo- G Whittingham

CLUB DIRECTORY 1996-97

ASH UNITED

President: Mrs B Wallman **Chairman:** R J Atkins
Secretary: Mr Alan Haberle, 30 Longfield Rd, Ash, nr Aldershot, Hants GU12 6NA (01252 310092)
Ground: Youngs Drive, off Shawfield Rd, Ash, Nr Aldershot (01252 20385).
Directions: A323 towards Ash, left into Shawfield Rd, right into Ash Church Rd, right at crossroads into Shawfield Rd. 1 mile from both Ash and Ash Vale BR stations.
Seats: None **Cover:** Overhang **Capacity:** 1,500 **Floodlights:** No **Founded:** 1911
Colours: Green/white/red. **Change colours:** All blue or all red.
Programme: 36 pages, 50p with admission. Editor: Gareth Watmore.
Midweek Matchday: Tuesday

ASHFORD TOWN (MIDDX)

President: E Britzman **Chairman:** R Parker **Vice Chairman:** Peter Hefferman
Secretary: A B J Constable, 30 Marlborough Rd, Ashford, Middx TW15 3QA (01784 885092).
Manager: Dave Kent **Asst Manager:** TBA **Physio:** D Hanks
Ground: Short Lane, Stanwell, Staines, Middx (01784 245908).
Directions: M25 jct 13, A30 towards London, 3rd left at footbridge after Ashford Hospital crossroads - ground signposted after quarter of a mile on right down Short Lane. Two miles from Ashford (BR) and Hatton Cross (tube) stations. Bus route 116.
Seats: None **Cover:** 75 **Capacity:** 2,000 **Floodlights:** Due **Club Shop:** No
Colours: Tangerine & white/white/tangerine. **Change colours:** All blue
Programme: 24 pages, 50p **Editor:** Secretary **Press Secretary:** D Baker
Formed: 1964 **Nickname:** Ash Trees **Sponsors:** Courage PLC
Midweek matchday: Tuesday **Record Gate:** 750 v Brentford, friendly 86.
Clubhouse: Open 7 days a week. Refreshments always available - hot food on matchdays.
95-96 Captain: Jim Heggarty **95-96 Top Scorer:** Paul German 51 **95-96 P.o.Y.:** Gary Cambridge
Honours: Combined Co's Lg R-up 94-95 (Chall. Cup R-up 92-93 94-95, Lg Vase Cup R-up 91-92 94-95)

BEDFONT

President: Jack Newman **Vice Pres.:** F Nichols/W Feltz **Chairman:** Alan Hale.
Secretary: Geoff Knock, 187 Northumberland Cres., Bedfont, Middlesex TW14 9SR (0181 890 6233).
Manager: Alan Humphries **Asst Manager:** Bob Barnes
Physio: Paul Donworth.
Ground: The Orchard, Hatton Rd, Bedfont, Middx (0181 890 7264).
Directions: Turn down Faggs Rd opp Hatton Cross (Tube) station on Grt Sth Western Rd (A30), sharp right Hatton Rd. Grnd opp Duke of Wellington pub.
Seats: None **Cover:** 50 **Capacity:** **Floodlights:** Yes **Founded:** 1968.
Colours: Yellow/blue/blue **Change colours:** Blue/yellow/yellow.
Midweek matchday: Tuesday. **Clubhouse:** Yes.
Programme: 28 pages, 50p. Editors: Alan Humphries (01932 563548) and Colin McNeill (0181 384 8410).
Captain 94-95:
Hons: Combined Counties Lg Chall. Vase 92-93

CHIPSTEAD

President: B Nicholls **Chairman:** Keith Rivers
Secretary: Geoff Corner, 20 Sunnymede Avenue, Carshalton Beeches, Surrey SM5 4JF (01816 420827)
Manager: John Sears **Coach:** Paul Duffield.
Ground: High Road, Chipstead, Surrey (01737 553250).
Directions: Brighton Rd north left into Church Ln, left Hogcross Ln, right into High Rd. 1.5 miles Chipstead (BR).
Seats: 30 **Cover:** 100 **Capacity:** 2,000 **Floodlights:** Yes **Founded:** 1906
Midweek matchday: Tuesday.
Colours: Green/green/white. **Change cols:** All Yellow. **Programme:** 44 pages
Nickname: Chips
Hons: Combined Co's Lg 89-90 (R-up 90-91 92-93, Lg Cup 86-87 90-91 92-93)

COBHAM

Chairman: E Strange **President:** E Strange **Secretary:** K Reed.
Manager: R Rembridge **Coach:** M Dickerson **Physio:** C Bird
Ground: Leg O'Mutton Field, Anvil Lane, Downside Bridge Rd, Cobham, Surrey (01932 865959).
Directions: A3 turnoff A245, A307 (Portsmouth Road) towards Leatherhead, right into Between Sts, right Downside Rd, right opp car park. 2 miles Cobham & Stoke D'Abernon (BR).
Seats: None **Cover:** Yes **Capacity:** 2,000 **Floodlights:** No **Shop:** No
Programme: Yes **Editor:** No
Colours: All red **Change colours:** All Blue.
Sponsor: Dawson/Strange Photography. **Nickname:** Hammers **Founded:** 1892
Midweek matchday: Tuesday.
Record Gate: 2,000 v Showbiz team, charity match 1975.
Honours: Combined Counties Lge Cup, Res Lge (3).

CORINTHIAN-CASUALS

President: Sir Maurice Coop **Chairman:** D G Harrison **Manager:** Roger Steer.
Secretary: Brian Wakefield, 5 Martingales Close, Ham Common, Richmond, Surrey (01181 940 9208).
Match Secretary : G.Young,227 Lynmouth Avenue,Morden,Surrey. SM4 4RX.
Ground: King George's Field, Hook Rise, South Tolworth, Surrey KT6 7NA (01181 397 3368).
Directions: A3 to Tolworth r'bout (The Toby Jug). Hook Rise is slip road immediately after the Toby Jug pub. Turn left under railway bridge after a quarter mile - ground immediately on right. Half mile from Tolworth (BR); turn left, continue to Toby Jug, then as above. K2 Hoppa bus from Kingston passes ground.
Seats: 126 **Cover:** 250 **Capacity:** 1,700 **Floodlights:** Yes **Founded:** 1939.
Previous Leagues: Isthmian 39-84 **Programme:** 24-48 pages, £1
Colours: White/navy/navy **Change colours:** Chocolate & Pink/navy/navy
Best FA Cup season: 1st Rd replay 85-86 **Reserve Team's League:** Suburban.
Players progressing to Football League: Andy Gray, Tony Finnegan, Alan Pardew to Crystal Palace.
Clubhouse: Evenings, matchdays, Sunday lunchtimes. Darts, pool, hot & cold snacks on matchdays.
Hons: FA Amateur Cup R-up 55-56 (SF 56-57), London Spartan Lg R-up 92-93 (Lg Cup R-up 91-92).

COVE

Chairman: Alan Stansbury. **President:** Ron Brown
Secretary: Graham Brown, 126 Prospect Road,Cove,Farnborough, Hants GU14 9QX (01252 541152)
Manager/Press Officer: Chris Penney. **Asst Manager:** Steve Hibbins
Ground: Oak Farm, off Romayne Close, Cove, Farnborough, Hants GU14 8LB (01252 543615).
Directions: Farnborough (BR) 2 miles; right into Union Street, right at lights into Prospect Rd, left into West Heath Rd, right into Romayne close and follow signs to Cove FC.
Capacity: 3,500 **Seats:** 75 **Cover:** 475 **Floodlights:** Yes **Founded:** 1897
Colours: Amber & black/black/amber & black **Change cols:** Red/blue/red & blue **Nickname:** None.
Programme: 30 pages, 50p **Editor:** Graham Brown (01252 541152). **Club Shop:** No
Midweek Matchday: Tuesday **Sponsors:** Oasis soft drinks
Reserve Team's League: Suburban **Record Gate:** 1,798 v Aldershot, Isthmian Lg Div 3, 1/5/93.
Best FA Cup year: First Qualifying Round replay 91-92 (lost 0-4 at Burgess Hill Town).
Clubhouse: Mon-Fri 7-11pm, Sat noon-11pm, Sunday noon-3pm & 7-11pm.
Hons: Combined Co's Lg Cup 81-82,

CRANLEIGH

Chairman: Vic Simmonds **Vice Chairman:** Roy Kelsey **President:** Alan Pavia.
Secretary: Mark Edwards, 15 High Town Rd, Maidenhead, Berks. SL6 1PA (01628 783 922).
Manager: Roy Kelsey **Asst Manager:** Paul Jones. **Coach:** Andy Clements.
Ground: Snoxall Playing Fields, Knowle Lane, Cranleigh (01483 275295).
Directions: A281 from Guildford towards Horsham, at Shalford take B2128 to Cranleigh High Street, right opposite Onslow Arms into Knowle Lane, ground half mile on left. Public transport: Guildford (BR) then bus 273 or 283.
Seats: None **Cover:** 50 **Capacity:** 450 **Floodlights:** No **Club Shop:** No.
Programme: £1.50 **Editor:** Peter Slater (01483 894245) **Press Officer:**
Colours: Blue/blck/white **Change colours:** Yellow/green/yellow
Sponsors: Roger Coupe, Est. Agents **Founded:** 1893. **Nickname:** Cranes.
Midweek matchday: Tuesday
Record Gate: 450 v C Palace, friendly 89. Comp: 285 v Hailsham, F.A. Vase 3rd Rd 92.
Clubhouse: Licensed bar. Hot food on matchdays.
95-96 Captain: Andy Dear **95-96 Top Scorer:** Chris Lamboll. **95-96 P.o.Y.:** Matt Butcher
Honours: W Sussex County Times Cup 92-93; F.A. Vase 3rd Rd 92-93.

FARNHAM TOWN

Chairman: N Harrington **President:** J Butters.
Secretary: Mrs Barbara Fripp, 70 Lower Farnham Rd., Aldershot, Hampshire. GU12 4EA (01252 28055)
Manager: Peter Browning **Asst Manager:** Roy Atkin **Coach:** A Wyciechowski/A Metcalfe
Ground: Memorial Ground, Babbs Mead, West Street, Farnham, Surrey (01252 715305).
Directions: Take A31, direction Winchester. Take second turning into town at Coxbridge roundabout. Follow West Street until you come to new mini roundabout - The Memorial Ground is on the right.
Capacity: 2,000 **Seats:** None **Cover:** 150 **Floodlights:** Yes **Club Shop:** No
Programme: 32 pgs 50p **Editor:** Ann Butters **Press Officer:** Charlie White
Colours: All Claret & Blue. **Change colours:** All yellow
Sponsors: Frazer Freight. **Nickname:** The Town **Founded:** 1921
Midweek Matchday: Tuesday **Reserve League:** Comb Counties Res Div
Record Attendance: 500 v Kingstonian, Surrey Snr Cup 1960.
Best FA Cup year: Never past Qualifying Rounds
Clubhouse: Open every evening and match days. One bar, committee room.
95-96 Captain: Shaun Dowling **95-96 Top Scorer:** Paul Warner 28
95-96 P.o.Y.: Paul Warner & Clive Ventham
Honours: Comb Cnts Lg 90-91 91-92, Chall Cup Prem Div 95-96, Chall Tphy 91-92 (R-up 89-90).

FELTHAM

Chairman: W F P Seuke **President:**
Secretary: John Cronk, 37 Ruskin Ave, Feltham, Middlesex. TW14 9HY. (01817 513663)
Manager: Carl Taylor. **Asst Manager:** **Physio:**
Ground: Feltham Arena, Shakespeare Avenue, Feltham, Middx TW14 9HY (0181 384 5048-club, 0181 890 6905-ground). **Nb- the club have an artificial pitch.*
Directions: M3, M4, A312 Staines road towards Bedfont, 2nd left is Shakespeare Ave.
Capacity: 10,000 **Seats:** 650. **Cover:** 1,500 **Floodlights:** Yes **Club Shop:** No
Programme: 20 pages, 50p **Editor/Press Officer:** John Cronk (0181 751 3663).
Colours: Royal blue & white halves/blue/blue. **Change colours:** Red & blue strips.
Sponsors: Cowley Security Locksmiths/Damar Glass **Nickname:** **Founded:** 1946.
Midweek Matchday: Wednesday **Reserve Team's League:** Suburban.
Record Attendance: 1,938 v Hampton,Middlesex Senior Cup 1968.
Best FA Cup year:3rd Qual.Rd.77-78 (lost 1-4 tp Tilbury) 82-83(0-1 v Chesham U)
Clubhouse: Open 7 days a week.2 bars, dancehall available for hire. Pool,Darts.
95-96 Captain: Darren Girvan **95-96 P.o.Y.:** Paul Edghill **95-96 Top scorer:** Paul Edghill 33
Hons: Surrey Snr Lg R-up 65-66 (Lg Cup 65-66, Charity Cup 63-64 65-66), Isthmian Div 2 80-81.

Feltham FC: Back Row (L-R); P Edgehill, A Humphries, C Ryder, N Rice, P Heggie, T Moody. Front Row; L Hadj, L Kehal, S Whitecombe, K Cherles, S Christophe, A Clerke. *Photo - Martin Wray*

GODALMING & GUILDFORD

Chairman: Ron Rawlings **Vice-Chairman:** C J Keen **President:** W Kyte
Secretary: Eddie Russell, 75 Drummond Road, Guildford, Surrey GU1 4NX (01483 35287)
Manager: Mick Wollen **Asst Manager:** Chris Hatchwell **Physio:** Len Brown
Ground: Weycourt, Meadrow, Godalming, Surrey (01483 417520).
Directions: A3100 from Guildford - carry on past Godalming Rugby Club & grd on right after Burmah garage. 3/4 mile Farncombe BR station.
Seats: Yes **Cover:** 200 **Capacity:** 1,500 **Floodlights:** Yes **Club Shop:** No
Programme: Yes **Editor:** **Press Officer:** Secretary.
Colours: Green & yellow/green/green. **Change colours:** Red & Blue/blue/blue.
Sponsors: **Nickname:** The Weys **Founded:** 1971
Midweek matchday: Tuesday/Thursday.
Record Attendance: 600+ - Ex-Guildford City XI v Ex-Football Lg XI. Tony Burge benefit 1991.
Clubhouse: Open Tues,Wed,Thurs even, matchdays & Sunday lunch. Hot & cold food & snacks etc.
Honours: Combined Co's Lg 83-84 (Challenge Trophy 82-83, Res Challenge Cup 91-92 (R-up 92-93)).

HARTLEY WINTNEY

President: W A Mitchell **Chairman:** F Humphreys
Secretary: Ross Hillair, 17 Rye Close, Cove, Farnborough, Hampshire GU14 9LU (01252 516174)
Ground: Memorial Playing Fields, Green Lane, Hartley Wintney, Hants (0251 263586).
Directions: A30 west through Camberley, left at shops at beginning of village then sharp right - grd on right. 2 miles Winchfield (BR).
Seats: None **Cover:** No **Capacity:** 2,000 **Floodlights:** No **Founded:** 1897
Colours: Tangerine/black/tangerine **Change colours:** White/blue/blue **Programme:** Yes
Nickname: The Row **Midweek matchday:** Tuesday.

MERSTHAM

Chairman: Stan Baker **Vice Chairman:** **President:** Stan Baker
Secretary: Matthew Boardman, 49 Orpin Road, Merstham,Surrey.RH1 3EX (01737 212543)
Manager: Joe McElligott **Asst Manager:** Martin Rosser **Physio:** Steve D'arcy
Ground: Merstham Rec., Weldon Way, Merstham, Redhill, Surrey (01737 644046)
Directions: Leave Merstham village (A23) by School Hill, take 5th right (Weldon Way), clubhouse and car park 100m on right. 10 mins Merstham (BR).
Seats: 100 **Cover:** 100 **Capacity:** 2,000 **Floodlights:** Yes **Club Shop:**
Press Officer: Roger Peerless. **Programme:** **Editor:**
Colours: Amber/black/amber. **Change colours:** Purple/white/purple
Sponsors: Whitbread **Founded:** 1892. **Midweek matchday:** Tuesday/Thursday
Reserve League:
Clubhouse: Across adjacent footpath. Open daily (am & pm). Snacks available.
95-96 Captain: Andy Renton **95-96 P.o.Y.:** Andy Renton **95-96 Top Scorer:** Steve Elliott
Honours: Combined Co's Lg R-up 87-88 89-90 (Elite Class Cup 89-90 (R-up 90-91), Res Sect 90-91).

NETHERNE

Chairman: Steve Clark **President:** Noel Duffy
Secretary: Steve Clark, 28 Lackford Road, Chipstead, Surrey, CR5 3TA, (01737 552200)
Manager Graeme Crawford **Asst Manager:** John Fullick **Physio:** Dermot Hennessy
Ground: Netherne Sports Club, Woodplace Lane, Hooley, Coulsdon, Surrey CR5 1YE (01737 553580).
Ground: 1 mile end of M23. Right off Brighton Rd into Woodplace Lane, follow up hill half mile, grd on left. 20 mins Coulsdon South (BR) station.
Capacity: 2,000 **Seats:** None **Cover:** 50 **Floodlights:** No **Club Shop:** No
Programme: 20 pages, 50p **Editor:** Steve Clark (01737 552200). **Press Officer:** Tony Hermitage.
Change Colours: Green **Colours:** Blue & black stripes
Sponsor: **Nickname:** None **Founded:** 1968
Midweek Matchday: **Reserve Team's League:** Combined Co's Res Div.
Clubhouse: Open matchdays with hot food available over bar.
95-96 Captain: Steve Parker **95-96 Top Scorer:** Paul Otway 26 **95-96 P.o.Y.:** Andy Kiff.
Honours: Surrey Co. Prem. Lg 93-94 (Lg Cup 92-93), Surrey Sth East Interm Comb. 88-89.

Netheren FC: *Photo - Eric Marsh*

RAYNES PARK

Secretary: Paul Armour, 6 Woodstock Rise, Sutton, Surrey SM3 3JE (081 644 2444).
Ground: Raynes Park Sports Ground, Taunton Avenue, Raynes Park SW20 (081 946 8385).
Colours: Red & black stripes/black/black. **Change colours:** White/black.black.

READING TOWN

Chairman: Mr N Milne **Manager:** Mr R Ford.
Secretary: M Chatfield, 11 Goddard Close, Shinfield Village, Reading, Berks RG2 9DR.
Ground: Reading Town Spts Ground, Scours Lane, Tilehurst, Reading, Berks (0734 453555).
Directions: Out of Reading on Oxford road (A329), past Battle Hosp. Scours Lane 1st right after r'bout.
Seats: Yes **Cover:** Yes **Programme:** Yes **Sponsors:** None **Founded:** 1968.
Colours: Black & red halves/black **Change colours:** Sky/white.
Clubhouse: Yes
Honours: Chiltonian Lg Res Div 1 R-up 93-94.

SANDHURST TOWN

Chairman: Brian Levy. **President:** M.Watts.
Secretary: J E Parker, 24 Florence Rd, College Town, Camberley, Surrey GU15 4QD (01276 32308).
Manager: Tony O'Connor **Coach:** Steve Atkins.
Ground: Memorial Ground, Yorktown Rd, Sandhurst (01252 873767).
Directions: A30 westwards through Camberley, right at r-bout with traffic lights, past superstore turning right, left at next r'bout. Ground next to Town & Council offices and Community Sports Centre.
Seats: None **Cover:** No **Floodlights:** No **Programme:** Yes **Nickname:** Fizzers
Colours: Red/black/black **Change colours:** Yellow/white/yellow.
Midweek matchday: Tuesday.
Hons: Combined Co's Lg Chal. Vase R-up 92-93

VIKING SPORTS

Chairman: Brian Lown **President:** Roy Bartlett
Secretary: John Bennett, 6 Bridge House, Boston Manor Rd, Brentford TW8 9LH (0181 568 9047).
Manager: Terry Cross. **Asst Manager:** Jim Curran **Physio:** Terry Cross
Ground: Avenue Park, Western Avenue, Greenford, Middx (0181 578 2706).
Directions: On London-bound carriageway of A40, 300 yds before Greenford flyover and slip road to A4127. 12 mins walk from Greenford (Central Line) station
Seats: 50 **Cover:** 100 **Capacity:** 450 **Floodlights:** Yes **Club Shop:** No.
Programme: 12 pages, 50p **Editor:** Secretary **Press Officer:**
Colours: Tangerine/black/tangerine. **Change colours:** Sky/maroon
Sponsors: Measham Self-Drive **Nickname:** Vikings. **Founded:** 1945
Midweek matchday: Tuesday
Record Attendance: 180 v Lambourn, Hellenic Lg 1982
Clubhouse: Open every evening except Sunday. Hot & cold snacks on matchdays.
95-96 Captain: Lynton Humphries **95-96 Top Scorer:** Dave Hewing. **95-96 P.o.Y.:** Dave Hewing
Honours: Hellenic Lg Div 1 85-86 (Div 1 Cup R-up 90-91).Co.Counties Lg.(R-Up. 94-95).

WALTON CASUALS

Chairman: Graham James **President:** Mr D Pullin
Secretary: Stuart Roberts, 47 Foxholes, Weybridge KT13 0BN (01932 845923).
Ground: Franklyn Road Sports Ground, off Waterside Drive, Walton-on-Thames (01932 247318).
Colours: Orange & white/white/white **Change colours:** White/blue/white

WESTFIELD

Chairman: S P Perkins **President:** Mr R Hill **Manager:** John Martin.
Secretary: Michael L:awrence, 19 Ash Road, Barnsbury Est, Woking, Surrey. GU22 0BJ (01483 722184)
Ground: Woking Park, Kingfield, Woking, Surrey (01483 771106).
Directions: Adjacent to Woking FC (see GMV Conference section).
Seats: None **Cover:** No **Capacity:** 1,000 **Floodlights:** No **Programme:** No
Colours: Yellow/black/yellow. **Change colours:** White/navy/navy. **Clubhouse:** Yes.

ESSEX SENIOR LEAGUE

FEEDER TO: ICIS LEAGUE

President: Arthur Dimond

Chairman: Robert Errington

Secretary: David Wingrove, 8 Oak Piece, North Weald, Epping, Essex CM16 6JJ (01992 522147)

Romford Rise Again at the Double

The season belonged to the new Romford, only re-formed in 1992 and without their own home, they marched through the League programme continuing to break attendance records all over the league with their magnificent support and to top it all, won the Challenge Cup on a hot day at Burnham with a 2-0 win over Southend Manor, then, in order to qualify for the ICIS League merged with Collier Row and will play in that competition's second division. As Champions, Romford showed a clean pair of heels for most of the season but all credit to the previous winners, Great Wakering Rovers who put up a brave fight and took the runners-up spot with a close 3-2 win over Ford United at Rush Green.

The season was dominated by the quite extraordinary events involving the Pyramid of football and Maldon Town, they applied to play their football across the pyramid in the Jewson League, a situation previously not granted under the Charter and not even possible in our own half of the Pyramid, yet, after aa appeal and a re-hearing at the FA, Maldon were granted their wish and, along with other clubs moving the same or opposite ways in other parts of the country, the Charter as we know it was left in tatters and we all await the deliberations of the FA on the whole matter which should make for a very interesting new season and a possible freedom of movement.

The most improved club was probably Concord Rangers who endeavour to compete with the success of fellow Islanders, Canvey Island , who continue to show how success can be achieved in the Pyramid. Brentwood, as ever, one of the hardest clubs to beat, won the Harry Fisher Trophy at Barking on a baking holiday Monday with a penalty shoot-out against Ford United. Sawbridgeworth Town were successful once again, in the Herts Charity Shield. Brentwood reached the FA Vase 3rd Round and Romford, the 3rd Qualifying Round of the FA Cup. A record 9 clubs were entered in this season's competition. We lose the aforementioned Maldon Town,after 24 years membership, and Romford, but have gained, in their place, another grand old name of Amateur football -Ilford, playing at Cricklefield Stadium. Also, previous members, Saffron Walden return to the fold, so the season should be very competitive. The Reserve Division has been dissolved due to decreasing numbers but the whole future could be very interesting and the aims of this League to encompass All Essex clubs may well bear fruit. Congratulations to Vernon Sitch, our Vice Chairman who received a Long Service Award from the Essex County FA, having first come into football with Witham Town in 1960. Paul Burch of Basildon United brought back memories of the mid-eighties Glory in Match Programme writing with his 11th place Nationally in the Wirral Awards, and, on the retirement of David Pond as President we are delighted that Arthur Dimond, a former chairman and Football League Referee has taken over that position. The Sportsmanship Award went to the very go-ahead Great Wakering Rovers who are slowly building up their ground and facilities and hope to be the success side of the future but, whoever it is, The Essex Senior League will give every encouragement to teams that, wish to progress knowing full well that others may just wish to play good class County Football - we hope that their loyalty will be rewarded sooner than later.
Robert Errington

FINAL LEAGUE TABLES 1995/96

	Division One	*P*	*W*	*D*	*L*	*F*	*A*	*Pts*
1.	Romford	28	23	2	3	91	27	71
2.	Great Wakering Rovers	28	20	4	4	67	28	64
3.	Concord Rangers	28	20	3	5	67	31	63
4.	Maldon Town	28	16	4	8	87	47	52
5.	Ford United	28	14	6	8	59	53	48
6.	Sawbridgeworth Tn	28	13	5	10	59	43	44
7.	Stansted	28	12	8	8	47	34	44
8.	Southend Manor	28	12	7	9	50	49	43
9.	Burnham Ramblers	28	13	3	12	63	48	42
10.	Brentwood	28	13	2	13	56	53	41
11.	Basildon United	28	5	8	15	31	52	23
12.	Bowers United	28	5	6	17	28	57	18
13.	Eton Manor	28	4	6	18	32	72	18
14.	Hullbridge Sports	28	4	5	19	30	88	17
15.	East Ham United	28	0	3	25	18	103	3

ESSEX SENIOR LEAGUE RESULTS CHART 1995-96

HOME TEAM	1	2	3	4	5	6	7	8	9	10	11	12	13	14	15
1. Basildon United	*	1-0	1-3	2-1	0-0	1-1	3-0	0-1	0-4	3-1	0-2	1-3	0-0	3-3	1-1
2. Bowers United	1-1	*	0-1	2-1	1-1	2-1	2-0	2-3	0-2	1-1	0-1	0-3	3-4	0-2	2-2
3. Brentwood	2-0	5-0	*	2-3	0-1	5-1	5-1	1-3	5-0	3-3	2-1	0-2	0-1	2-3	0-7
4. Burnham Rangers	1-0	4-2	0-0	*	1-3	5-0	2-0	1-3	0-2	3-2	2-3	2-5	4-1	4-3	4-0
5. Concord Rangers	3-1	4-1	3-0	2-1	*	5-1	2-0	1-2	0-1	4-0	4-0	2-5	3-2	1-0	0-1
6. East Ham United	2-2	0-3	0-3	0-4	1-2	*	1-2	1-2	1-5	2-2	1-7	0-4	1-9	0-3	0-3
7. Eton Manor	1-3	0-0	1-3	1-1	0-2	6-1	*	3-4	2-2	1-1	1-3	2-2	1-4	2-1	2-1
8. Ford United	4-3	1-1	6-4	1-4	3-4	1-0	1-1	*	2-3	3-0	6-5	2-3	0-4	4-1	0-1
9. Great Wakering Rovers	3-1	2-0	5-0	4-2	0-0	3-0	3-2	1-1	*	2-0	3-2	2-1	0-1	2-2	1-0
10. Hullbridge Sports	2-0	0-3	3-6	0-2	1-7	3-0	2-0	0-1	1-5	*	1-8	1-6	2-1	1-4	1-3
11. Maldon Town	6-3	2-0	0-3	3-3	1-0	6-1	6-0	3-1	4-3	5-0	*	3-4	0-0	1-2	6-1
12. Romford	3-0	2-0	4-1	3-1	2-3	6-0	7-1	3-1	2-0	9-0	2-1	*	3-1	1-0	0-0
13. Sawbridgeworth Town	2-0	6-0	1-3	3-1	1-4	1-0	3-0	1-1	3-0	3-0	1-4	1-0	*	2-3	1-1
14. Southend Manor	2-1	3-0	1-0	0-6	3-4	3-2	4-1	2-2	0-5	1-1	1-1	1-2	1-1	*	0-0
15. Stansted	0-0	3-2	1-0	1-0	1-2	5-0	3-0	0-0	1-3	2-1	2-2	1-4	6-1	0-1	*

LEADING PREMIER DIVISION GOALSCORERS 1995-96

Neil Harris	Maldon Town	26	Des Charlery	Brentwood	25
Paul Flack	Great Wakering Rovers	25	Steve Harding	Burnham Ramblers	19
Tony Macklin	Concord Rangers	19	M Lawrence	Maldon Town	17
Kevin Rendell	Romford	16	Lee Rush	Southend Manor	16
Scott Witney	Maldon Town	16	Dean Calcutt	Romford	14
Steve West	Formerly Concord Rangers	14	D Benstock	Romford	13
Dean Francis	Burnham Ramblers	12	David Hope	Southend Manor	12
Mark Mower	Sawbridgeworth Town	12	Steve Portway	Formerly Romford	11
Reg Gardiner	Ford United	10	Billy Herbert	Burnham Ramblers	10
Gary Hart	Stansted	10	Micky Ross	Romford	10
R Stapleton	Sawbridgeworth Town	10			

LEADING RESERVE DIVISION GOALSCORERS 1995-96

Peter Zielinski	Sawbridgeworth Town R	27	Mark Smith	Brentwood Res	23
Steve Harding	Burnham Ramblers R	11	Dave Green	Canvey Island Res	11
Rob Stewart	Brentwood Res	11	Rob Jones	Southend Manor Res	11
Andy Green	Gt Wakering Rovers Res	10	Dave Jenkins	Canvey Island Res	10

HARRY FISHER MEMORIAL TROPHY 1995-96

First Round;

East Ham United v Brentwood 0-6

Stansted v Concord Rangers 3-2

Eton Manor v Hullbridge Sports 2-2, 3-1 (aet)

Ford United Bye

Second Round; 1st Leg;

Eton Manor v Brentwood 1-3

Replay: Brentwood v Eton Manor 3-2

Stansted v Ford United 1-3

2nd Leg;

Brentwood v Eton Manor 2-4, **(5-5 agg)**

Ford United v Stansted 2-2, **(5-3 agg)**

Final; Brentwood v Ford United 1-1 (aet), 4-2 penalties

CHALLENGE CUP 1995-96

First Round;

Hullbridge Sports v Southend Manor	0-4	Basildon United v Eton Manor	4-1
Stansted v Burnham Ramblers	0-0, 1-3	Maldon Town v Brentwood	2-0
Concord Rangers v Gt Wakering Rovers	0-1	East Ham United v Bowers United	1-4
Romford v Ford United	3-1		
Sawbridgeworth Town (Holders) Bye to 2nd Round			

Second Round;

Southend Manor v Basildon United	3-1	Burnham Ramblers v Sawbridgeworth Town	2-0
Maldon Town v Gt Wakering Rovers	1-2	Bowers United v Romford	0-1

Semi-Finals; 1st Leg;		**2nd Leg;**	
Southend Manor v Burnham Ramblers	0-0, 0-1	Southend Manor v Burnham Ramb	2-1, **(3-0 pen)**
Gt Wakering Rovers v Romford	0-2	Gt Wakering Rovers v Romford	0-2, **(0-4agg)**

Final; Romford v Southend Manor 2-0

THE RESERVE CUP 1995-96

First Round;

Burnham Ramblers v Bowers United	4-1	Brentwood Res v Basildon United	1-2

Second Round;

Hullbridge Sports v Burnham Ramblers	1-3	Gt Wakering Rovers v Canvey Island	3-4 (aet)
Eton Manor v Basildon United	1-2	Sawbridgeworth Town v Southend Manor	1-4

Semi-Finals; 1st Leg		**2nd Leg;**	
Burnham Ramblers v Canvey Island	0-1	Burnham Ramblers v Canvey Island	0-1. **(0-2 agg)**
Basildon United v Southend Manor	2-5	Basildon United v Southend Manor	1-0, **(3-5 agg)**

Final; Canvey Island Reserves v Southend Manor Reserves 1-0

Romford FC: 1995-96 Essex Senior League Premier Division Champions.
Back Row (L-R); Michael Taylor, Peter Shea, Marvin Rufus, Kevin Rendell, Simon Livett, Michael Milton, Micky Ross, Dean Callcut, Dave Spittle.
Front Row; Troy Braham, Allen McKnight, Danny Benstock, Paul Evans, Terry Beck, Mark Reed.
Photo - Steve Gedge

BASILDON UNITED

President: J Oakes **Chairman:** J.Rayment. **Vice-Chairman:** M.Carter
Secretary: Trevor Thomas, 100 Littlecroft, South Woodham Ferrers, Essex CM3 5GQ (01245 323645).
Manager: Cliff Moorcroft **Asst Manager:** **Press Officer:** Frank Ford (01268 552994
Ground: Gardiners Close, Gardiners Lane, Basildon, Essex SS14 3AW (01268 520268).
Directions: A176 off Southend arterial (A127), left at r'bout into Cranes Farm Road, proceed to end of duel carriageway, left at lights, Gardiners Close is 1st left (Football Club signed). Two and a half miles from Basildon BR station.
Seats: 400 **Cover:** 1,000 **Capacity:** 2,000 **Floodlights:** Yes **Founded:** 1963.
Colours: Amber & black stripes **Change:** Sky & navy **Sponsors:** Beesbar
Prevs Lgs: Grays & Thurrock/ Gtr London 68-70/ Essex Snr 70-80/ Athenian 80-81/ Isthmian 81-91.
Reserves' Lge: Essex Bus Users **Record Gate:** 4,000 v West Ham, ground opening 11/8/70
Programme: 16 pages, Free. **Editor:** F.Ford (01268 552994). **Club Shop:** No.
Midweek Matches: Tuesday
Clubhouse: Open lunchtimes, evenings, weekends. Hot food sold.
Players progressing to Football League: Jeff Hull (Colchester), Alan Hull (Orient), David Matthews & Steve Tilson (Southend), Jonathan Gould (Coventry City), Ken Charlery (Watford), Steve Jones (West Ham (via Billericay)).
95-96 Captain: **95-96 Top Scorer:** Ricky Bond. **95-96 P.o.Y.:**
Hons: Isthmian Lg Div 2 82-83, Essex Snr Lg(5) 76-80 94-95 (Lg Cup 77-78 94-95, Reserve Cup 92-93), Essex Senior Trophy 78-79. Reserve League & Shield 94-95.

BOWERS UNITED

Chairman: P Felfam **Manager:** Steve Wheeler
Secretary: E D Brown, 92 Quilters Straight, Fryerns, Basildon, Essex SS14 2SJ (01268 521201).
Ground: Crown Avenue, off Kenneth Rd, Pitsea, Basildon (01268 452068).
Directions: Turn into Rectory Rd from Old London Rd (B1464) at Pitsea Broadway into Kenneth Rd, right at top Crown Ave. 1.25 miles Pitsea (BR). Bus 523 to Rectory Rd, Bowers Guild.
Seats: 200 **Stand:** Yes **Capacity:** 2,000 **Floodlights:** Yes **Founded:** 1946.
Colours: Red & black stripes/black. **Change colours:** Blue/white/white.
Previous Leagues: Thurrock & Thameside Comb./Olympian. **Clubhouse:** Open every night.
Players progressing to Football League: Steve Tilson (Southend Utd).
Record Gate: 1,800 v Billericay Town, FA Vase. **Midweek Matches:** Wednesday.
95-96 Top Scorer: Terry Barrett
Hons: Thurrock & Thameside Comb. 58-59/ Essex Snr Lg 80-81 (Div 1 Cup 90-91, Harry Fisher Mem. Tphy 91-92, Reserve Div R-up 92-93).

BRENTWOOD

Chairman: K J O'Neale **Manager:** Derek Stittle
Secretary: C Harris, 56 Viking Way, Brentwood, Essex CM15 9HY (01277 219564).
Ground: Brentwood Centre, Doddinghurst Rd, Brentwood, Essex.
Directions:
Cover: Yes **Seats:** **Capacity:** **Floodlights:** No **Founded:** 1955.
Colours: Blue & White Stripes,White,White. **Change colours:** All amber.
Programme: Free with admission
Midweek Matches: Tuesday **Nickname:** Blues
Previous Leagues: Romford & District/ Sth Essex Combination/ London & Essex Border/ Olympian.
Top Scorer 94-95:
Hons: Olympian Lg Cup 67-68, Essex Intermediate Cup 76-77, Essex Lg Cup 75-76 78-79 90-91

BURNHAM RAMBLERS

Chairman: Gordon Brasted **Vice-Chairman:** Ron Hatcher **President:** R J Cole, Esq.
Secretary: Gordon Brasted, 6 Ramblers Way, Burnham-on-Crouch, Essex CM0 8LR (01621 782785).
Manager: Colin Wallington. **Asst Manager:** Paul Bolton **Physio:** Cyril Tennant
Ground: 'Leslie Field', Springfield Rd, Burnham-on-Crouch CM0 8TE (01621 784383).
Directions: On B1010 from South Woodham Ferrers, turn right half mile before town. 15 mins from Burnham (BR).
Seats: 300 **Stand:** Yes **Capacity:** 5,000 **Floodlights:** Yes
Programme: 36 pages, 40p **Editor:** Ron Bush (01621 783706). **Press Officer:** Secretary
Colours: Royal blue **Change colours:** Red
Nickname: Ramblers **Founded:** 1900
Midweek matches: Tuesday. **Reserves' Lge:** Essex Snr Div 1 **Record Gate:** 1,500.
Players progressing to Football League: I Woolf (West Ham) 1911, Gordon Brasted (Arsenal) 1953, John Warner (Colchester) 1990.
Clubhouse: Open Mon-FRi 7-11pm, Sat noon-3 & 5-11pm, Sun noon-3 & 7-9.30pm. Hot meals & snacks available.
95-96 Captain: Shaun Tracey. **95-96 P.o.Y:** Billy Herbert/Tony Wilkin. **95-96 Top Scorer:** Steve Harding
Honours: Olympian Lg 65-66, Essex I'mediate Cup R-up 81-82, Essex Snr Lg Cup R-up 86-87 89-90 (Reserve Cup 89-90 (R-up 92-93), Reserve Shield R-up 90-91).

FA Cup Preliminary Round: Burnham Ramblers (Blue) 1 v Holbeach (Yellow Strip) 3

Photo - Martin Wray

Brentwood FC:

Photo - R Brock

CONCORD RANGERS

President: Albert Lant **Chairman:** Grant Beglan **Manager:** C Crerie/Alan Howard
Secretary: Mrs Carol McKenna, 285 Link Road, Canvey Island, Essex SS8 9YU (01268 515048).
Ground: Thames Road, Canvey Island (0268 691780). **Midweek Matches:** Tuesday.
Seats: No **Capacity:** 1,500 **Cover:** Yes **Floodlights:** Yes **Founded:** 1967.
Colours: Yellow/blue **Change colours:** Blue
Club Sponsor: Aspect Contracts. **Prev. Lges:** Southend & D. All./ Essex I'mediate (pre-1991)
Programme: 10 pages, 50p **Editor:**
Record Gate: 1,500 v Lee Chapel North, FA Sunday Cup 89-90
Record win: 7-0 v Bowers Utd (A), Essex Snr Lge 20/11/93.
Clubhouse: Evenings & weekends.
95-96 Top Scorer: **95-96 Captain:** **95-96 P.o.Y.:**
Hons: Essex I'mediate Lg Div 2 & Lg Cup, Southend Alliance, Wirral Programme Award 93-94.

EAST HAM UNITED

Chairman: E H Whatmough
Mamager/Secretary/Comm. Mgr: Reuben Gane, 108 Beccles Drive, Barking IG11 9HZ (0181 594 7861).
Physio: Regan Cavanagh. **Press Officer:** Roland Clooge **Coach:**
Ground: Ferndale Spts Grnd, East Ham Manorway, Beckton E6 4NG (0171 476 5514).
Directions: East Ham Manorway - Cyprus Place - Beckton off A13 Newham Way from east or west. Nearest tube is East Ham thence bus 101 to ground.Or Cyprus Station(Docklands Light Railway).
Seats: 150 **Cover:** 300 **Capacity:** 2,500 **Floodlights:** Yes **Founded:** 1933.
Colours: Green, white & gold **Change colours:** Gold/green **Programme:** Yes.
Previous Lges: Spartan, Metropolitan **Previous Name:** Storey Ath. 1933-53 **Nickname:** Hammers.
Clubhouse: Evenings & weekends. **Midweek Matchday:** Tuesday
Record Gate: 4,250 - East Ham (inc George Best) v West Ham, friendly 15/2/76 at Terrance McMillan Stadium. 2,400 v Sutton United, FA Amateur Cup 14/11/53.
Players progressing to Football League: Lee Holmes (Brentford 1972), Miguel de Souza (Birmingham City 1988 via Charlton Athletic).Buck Ryan (Charlton).
Record scorer: David Norris **Record appearances:** Ken Bowhill, 1964-84.
Captain 95-96: **Top Scorer 95-96:** Eva Zaal **P.o.Y. 95-96:** Eddie Nwachukwv.
Hons: Metropolitan Lg, FA Vase QF, Essex Snr Tphy 76-77, Gtr London Lg Cup 69-70, London Jnr Cup 46-47, Bob Murrant Memorial Trophy 94-95, Carpathian Charity Cup 94-95.Harry Fisher Memorial Trophy R-U 1994-95.

ETON MANOR

Chairman: D McCann.
Secretary: George E Whiting, 20 Old South, Fairfield Est, Kings Lynn, Norfolk PE30 4RN (01553 773866)
Manager: Mark Downes **Coach:** C Drane **Physio:** F Rose.
Ground: Shared with East Ham United
Colours: Sky & navy/white **Change colours:** Black and Yellow/white/black **Nickname:** The Manor
Midweek Matches: Tuesday **Reserves' League:** Ilford & Dist. **Founded:** 1901
Programme: 12 pages with entry **Editor:** Secretary
Record Gate: 600 v Leyton Orient, opening of floodlights at Roding Lane.
Previous Grounds: Wildness, Hackney/ GUS Sports Ground, Clapton/ Walthamstow Avenue FC/ Norwegian Ground, Barking.
Previous Leagues: London 33-59/ Aetolian 59-64/ Greater London 64-69/ Metropolitan 69-75.
Clubhouse: Evenings (except Mondays), matchdays & Sunday mornings. Bar snacks.
Club record scorer: Dave Sams **Top Scorer 95-96:**
Captain 95-96: Mark Downes **P.o.Y. 95-96:** Dean Protain
Hons: Essex Snr Cup R-up 37-38, London Lg 33-34 37-38 52-53 53-54 (R-up 48-49 57-58, Lg Cup 55-56 (R-up 46-47 54-55)), Greater London Lg 64-65, Essex Intermediate Cup 64-65, London Intermediate Cup R-up 33-34 66-67, Essex Snr Lg Sportsmanship Award 75-76 (Div 1 Cup 90-91, Reserve Div 76-77, Reserve Div Cup 91-92).

FORD UNITED

Chairman: J M Rowe **Vice-Chairman:** George Adams **President:** Stuart J Harmer
Secretary: Michael Ewen, 215 Rush Green Road, Romford, Essex RM7 0JR, (01708 724178)
Manager: TBA **Asst Manager:** **Physio:**
Ground: Ford Spts & Soc. Club, Rush Green Rd., Romford (01708 745678). **Directions:** On the A124 (Rush Green road) on left going towards Hornchurch. 2 miles from Romford (BR). Buses 173, 175 87, 106, 23.
Seats: 800 **Cover:** Yes **Capacity:** 2,500 **Floodlights:** Yes **Club Shop:**
Programme: Yes **Editor:** John Powe **Press Officer:**
Colours: D/blue & red stripe/blue/blue **Change:** All dark green
Sponsor: **Founded:** 1958 **Nickname:** Motormen
Midweek Matchday: **Reserve Team's League:** Essex & Herts Border Combination.
Record Attendance: 58,000 Briggs Sports v Bishop Auckland, at St James Park, Newcastle, FA Amateur Cup.

Previous Leagues: Spartan, Aetolian, Metropolitan
Players progressing to Football League: Les Allen (Spurs), Mick Flanagan (QPR, Charlton, Crystal Palace), Jim Stannard (Fulham, Southend, Millwall), Nicky Hammond (Arsenal, Swindon), Laurie Abrahams (Charlton), Doug Barton (Reading, Newport).
Clubhouse: 4 bars, 2 dance halls, tea bar, snooker room.
95-96 Captain: **95-96 Top Scorer:** Reg Gardiner **95-96 P.o.Y.:**
Club Record Appearances: Roger Bond. **Club Record Goalscorer:**
Hons: FA Amateur Cup SF 53-54, London Snr Cup 55-56 56-57 94-95, Essex Snr Trophy 90-91 91-92, Essex Snr Cup 39-40 49-50 50-51 51-52, Spartan Lg 49-50 50-51 55-56 56-57 57-58, London Lg 36-37 38-39, Essex Elizabethan 59-60 60-61 70-71, Gtr London Lg 70-71, Essex Snr Lg 91-92 (R-up 94-95, Lg Cup 85-86, Sportsmanship Award 77-78 79-80 80-81), Essex & Herts Border Comb.(res) 94-95 (Lg Cup 94-95).

GREAT WAKERING ROVERS

Chairman: Fred Smith. **Vice-Chairman:** Barry Beadle. **President:** Eddie Ellis
Secretary: Roger Sampson, 37 Lee Lotts, Gt Wakering, Southend-on-Sea, Essex SS3 0HA (01702 218794).
Manager: Kevin Maddocks **Assistant Manager:** Eddie Nash. **Physio:** Cleave Taylor.
Ground: Burroughs Park, Little Wakering Hall Lane, Gt Wakering, Southend-on-Sea SS3 0HQ (01702 217812).
Directions: 4a bus from Shoeburyness (BR), 4a or 4b from Southend - alight at British Legion in Gt Wakering alongside which runs Little Wakering Hall Lane. A127 past Southend signposted Gt Wakering. In Gt Wakering, half mile past large Esso garage is along High Street is Little Wakering Hall Lane, ground 250 yds along on left.
Seats: **Cover:** 300 **Capacity:** 1,500 **Floodlights:** Yes **Club Shop:** No
Programme: 24-32 pages, 50p **Editor/Press Officer:** Nobby Johnson (01702 611964).
Colours: Green & white stripes/white/green **Change colours:** Blue & yellow stripes/blue/blue
Sponsors: PAX (CCTV) **Founded:** 1919 **Nickname:** Rovers
Midweek Matchday: Tuesday **Reserves' League:** Essex & Herts Border Comb
Record Attendance: 500 v Leyton Orient, friendly 18/7/92.
Previous Leagues: Southend & District 19-81/ Southend Alliance 81-89/ Essex Intermediate 89-92.
Players progressing to Football League: Les Stubbs (Southend, Chelsea) 1947, Jackie Bridge (Southend Utd) 1948, Kevin Maddocks (Maidstone Utd).
Clubhouse: Open weekday evenings, Sat 11am-11pm, Sun noon-3 & 7.30-10.30pm. Hot meals, snacks, rolls, tea, coffee available matchdays.
95-96 Captain: John Heffer. **95-96 P.o.Y.:** Lee Maddocks. **95-96 Top Scorer:** Paul Flack.
Honours: Essex I'mediate Cup 91-92, Essex I'mediate Lg Div 2 91-92 (Div 3 90-91, Lg Cup 91-92), Southend Charity Shield 90-91 91-92, Essex Snr Lg. Champions 94-95,Lg Reserve Section 94-95 (Wirral Programme Essex Sen.Lg.Award 92-93 94-95).

HULLBRIDGE SPORTS

Chairman: Brian Lloyd **Manager:** John Bacon
Secretary: Bob Cheesewright, 85 Bardfield Way, Rayleigh, Essex. SS6 9HE (01268 782937)
Ground: Lower Road, Hullbridge, Essex SS5 6BJ (01702 230420).
Directions: Turn into Rawreth Lane from A130 (left if arriving from Chelmsford), down to mini-r'bout, left, across next mini-r'bout, up hill, ground signed on right just past garage.
Seats: No **Cover:** Yes **Capacity:** **Floodlights:** No **Founded:** 1945
Colours: Blue & white stripes/white/blue **Change colours:** Yellow/Blue/Yellow
Midweek matches: Tues/Thursday. **Prog. Editor:** Mrs Lynne Ward. **Sponsor:** Thermo Shield
Prev. Grounds: Pooles Lane Rec. **Prev. Lges:** Southend & Dist./ Alliance/ Essex I'mediate
Clubhouse details: Lounge bar, function hall with bar & changing rooms - set in 16 acre land.
Top Scorer 95-96: Derek Foster
Honours: Essex Intermediate Snr Div Cup 87-88, Southend & District Lg Div 1 65-66 (Div 2 51-52, Div 3 56-57), French Cup 51-52, Essex Snr Lg Sportsmanship Award 91-92 92-93 94-95.

ILFORD FC

Secretary: Michael Roberts, 168 Dawlish Drive, Ilford, Essex, IG3 9EG (0181 599 2384)
Fixtures Sec: Clifford Nowell.

SAFFRON WALDEN TOWN

Chairman: Paul Diggons. **Vice Chairman:** Peter Walker.
Secretary: H J Harvey, 1 New Willow Cottage, Langley, Saffron Walden, Essex CB11 4RC (01799 550615).
Manager: Phil Hopkins. **Assistant Manager:** Marc Das **Physio:** Peter White.
Ground: Catons Lane, Saffron Walden, Essex CB10 2DU (01799 22789).
Directions: In Saffron Walden High Street turn into Castle Street, left at T-junction, 1st left by Victory pub.
Capacity: 5,000 **Seats:** 500 **Cover:** 2,000 **Floodlights:** Yes **Club Shop:** Yes
Programme: 24 pages, 40p **Editor:** R Smith (01799 500061) **Press Officer:** D Lightning
Colours: Red/black/white **Change colours:** All yellow.
Club Sponsors: Tolly Cobbold. **Nickname:** Bloods. **Founded:** 1872
Midweek Matchday: Tuesday **Reserve Team's League:** Essex & Herts Comb.
Record Attendance: 6,000 v Rainham Ath., Essex Junior Cup Final 1926 (played at Crittals, Braintree).
Best F.A. Cup year: Second Qualifying Round replay 84-85 (lost 1-2 at King's Lynn).

Previous Leagues: Haverhill & Dist./ Stansted & Dist./ Cambridgeshire/ Nth Essex/ Herts Co./ Spartan 33-49 50-54/ Parthenon 49-50/ Essex Snr 71-74/ Eastern Co's 74-84.
Clubhouse: Yes.
95-96 Captain: **95-96 P.o.Y.:** Julian Bedford **95-96 Top scorer:** Marc Das
Club Record Scorer: John Tipputt **Club Record Appearances:** Les Page, 700+.
Hons: Essex Snr Lg 73-74, Eastern Co's Lg 82-83, Spartan Lg Eastern Div 2 36-37, Essex Snr Tphy 82-83 83-84 84-85, Eastern F'lit Competition 91-92 (R-up 88-89, Nth Thames Group B 82-83), Essex Jnr Cup 1896-97 (R-up 25-26), Cambs Lg R-up 22-23, Essex & Herts Border Lg R-up 25-26(joint), Stansted & Dist. Lg 07-08 08-09 09-10 11-12 20-21 22-23 23-24, Haverhill & Dist. Lg 08-09 22-23 23-24 29-30 33-34.

SAWBRIDGEWORTH TOWN

Chairman: Barry Mutimer **President:** Ron Alder
Secretary: Gary Bennett, 21 Sayesbury Road, Sawbridgeworth, Herts, CM21 0EB (01279 830306)
Manager: Louis Molds **Coach:** Brian Pidgeon **Physio:** Brian Latchford
Ground: Crofters End, West Road, Sawbridgeworth (01279 722039).
Directions: Three quarters of a mile from station; up Station Road then West Road.
Seats: No **Capacity:** 1,500 **Cover:** 250 **Floodlights:** Yes **Club Shop:**
Programme: Yes **Editor:** R Alder (01279 722360) **Press Officer:** Micky Phillips
Colours: Red & black **Change colours:** Green and White Hoops.
Sponsor: **Nickname:** Robins. **Founded:** 1890.
Record Attendance: 610 v Bishop's Stortford.
Previous Leagues: Essex Olympian, Spartan 36-53.
Clubhouse:
95-96 Captain: **95-96 Top Scorer:** Richard Stapleton 18 **95-96 P.o.Y.:**
Honours: Essex Olympian Lg 71-72; Essex Snr Lg R-up 92-93 94-95; Harry Fisher Mem. Cup 87-88; Lg Cup 94-95 R-up 92-93 93-94, Reserve Div 91-92 92-93 (R-up 93-94), Reserve Shield R-up 92-93); Herts Snr Tphy 90-91 93-94 (R-up 92-93); Herts Charity Shield 92-93 94-95 95-96; Uttlesford Charity Cup 92-93; Herts Intermediate Cup R-up 93-93(res); South Midlands Floodlit Cup R.Up.94-95; Reserve Sect S.M Lge & Lg.Cup R-Up 94-95:

SOUTHEND MANOR

Chairman: Robert Westley. **Vice-Chairman:**John Hughes.
Secretary: Dave Kittle, 15 Seymour Rd, Hadleigh, Benfleet, Essex SS7 2HB (01702 559581)
Manager: Ian Ness. **Coach:** Alan Braylee. **Physio:** Paul Brooks.
Ground: Southchurch Park Arena, Lifstan Way, Southend-on-Sea. (01702 615577)
Directions: A127 then A1159 for 1 mile turn right at second roundabout by Rusty Bucket PH, due south for 1 mile, ground on right near sea front.
Seats: 500 **Cover:** Yes **Capacity:** 2,000 **Floodlights:** Yes **Club Shop:**
Programme: 10 pages, 50p **Editor/Press Officer:** Paul Docherty.
Colours: Yellow, red & black **Change colours:** Black & white
Sponsors: Hi-Tech. **Nickname:** The Manor **Founded:** 1955
Midweek Matchday: Tuesday. **Reserves League:** Essex & Suffolk Border Comb.
Record Attendance: 1,521 v Southend Utd, 22/7/91, floodlight opener.
Previous Leagues: Southend Borough Combination, Southend Alliance
Clubhouse: Open every evening
95-96 Captain: Slott Syrett **95-96 Top Scorer:** Lee Rush. **95-96 P.o.Y.:**
Honours: Essex Snr Trophy 92-93, Essex Intermediate Cup 78-79, Essex Snr Lg 90-91 (Lg Cup 87-88, ESL Challenge Cup 89-90, Harry Fisher Mem. Tphy 90-91 92-93 (R-up 91-92)).

STANSTED

Chairman: Terry Shoebridge **General Manager;** Alan Russell. **President:** P Heal
Secretary: Mrs D Murnane, Appletree Hse, Fullers End, Elsenham, Bishops S/ford, Herts, CM22 6DU. (01279 815404)
Manager: M Simpson, S Atkinson **Asst Manager:** **Coach:**
Ground: Hargrave Park, Cambridge Road, Stansted (01279 812897).
Directions: B1383 north of Bishops Stortford on west side of Cambridge Rd. Stansted (BR) – 1/2 mile
Seats: 200 **Cover:** Yes **Capacity:** 2,000 **Floodlights:** Yes **Club Shop:**
Programme: Yes **Editor:** Secretary **Press Officer:**
Colours: Blue & yellow/blue/yellow **Change:** Blue & black/black/blue
Sponsor: Sharpes Builders Ltd **Nickname:** The blues
Founded: 1902
Midweek matches: Tuesday. **Reserves League:** B.Stortford,Stansted & District
Record Attendance: 828 v Whickham (FA Vase 83-84).
Previous Leagues: Spartan, London, Herts Co.
Clubhouse: Open matchdays to 11pm. Sandwiches available.
95-96 Captain: S Atkinson. **95-96 Top Scorer:** G Hart. **95-96 P.o.Y.:** P Munn.
Honours: FA Vase 83-84; Essex Snr Lg R-up 82-83; Essex Snr Lg Cup 83-84, (R-up 72-73 94-95); Harry Fisher Mem Cup 82-83 84-85 (R-up 92-93 93-94); East Anglian Cup 83-84; Courage East F/lit Cup 83-84; Uttlesford Char. Cup 93-84 86-87 88-89 94-95:

LONDON SPARTAN LEAGUE

FEEDER TO: ICIS LEAGUE

FOUNDED: 1974

[Merger of the London League (1896) and the Spartan League (1907)]

President: K G Aston **Chairman:** Basil Stallard

Hon. Scretary: Dennid Cordell,

44 Greenleas, Waltham Abbey, Essex, EN9 1SZ (01992 712428)

In the 21st year of the combined London-Spartan League, St Margaretsbury at their fourth attempt, won the Premier Division title. And the reformed Hillingdon Borough had their best season to date, back in Senior football, finishing a close second.

In national competitions no club past the FA Cup First Qualifying Round and in the FA Vase ony Barkingside reached the First Round Proper. In Senior County Cup honours, Tottenham Omada in their first season as a Senior Club, collected the London Senior Cup.

Intermediate football, and Leyton County must be congratulated on achieving the Division One and the League Intermediate Cup double, they are only the third team in eight years to do this, the other two were Metrogas in 93 and Newmont Travel in 89.

In County honours, St Mary's Islington lifted the London Junior Cup for the third time running, and they have been granted Senior status from the London FA, ground-sharing at Haringey Borough.

Metpol Chigwell one of the longest serving Imtermediate clubs in our League, are leaving for pastures new in the Essex Intermediate League next season, they had a successful run in the Essex FA Intermediate Cup this year, being knocked out in the Fourth Round.

In Division Two AFC Blackheath did put a dent in Leyton County shoes in someway, as Blackheath's Reserves drew with County's Reserves in their last league game, to deny Leyton County Res the Div Two title. AC Milla faltered at the final hurdle after leading for so long, but Classic Inter came in at the death and topped the table, sitting and waiting on other teams to complete their fixtures just proves that points in the bag, are sometimes better than games in hand.

With two merger prospects hopefully behind us, this League can now build on its strengths and continue to be a leading force in London Football.

St Margaretsbury celebrate their Spartan League Title after victory at Tufnell Park *Photo - G Whittington*

FINAL LEAGUE TABLES 1995/96

Premier Div		P	W	D	L	F	A	Pts	Div One		P	W	D	L	F	A	Pts
1.	St Margaretsbury	30	18	7	5	51	29	61	*1.*	Leyton County	24	20	1	3	68	25	61
2.	Hillingdon Boro	30	17	8	5	55	28	59	*2.*	AFC Blackheath	24	18	3	3	68	26	57
3.	Corinthian Cas	30	15	6	9	49	30	51	*3.*	St Mary's	24	15	6	3	60	28	51
4.	Brimsdown Rov	30	14	9	7	55	38	51	*4.*	Old Roan	24	10	10	4	45	26	40
5.	Cockfosters	30	14	7	9	61	43	49	*5.*	Woodford Tn	24	11	5	8	46	37	38
6.	Tottenham Omada	30	13	6	11	67	53	45	*6.*	Craven	24	10	3	11	66	49	33
7.	Croydon Ath	30	13	6	11	50	51	45	*7.*	Walthamstow T	24	7	7	10	35	34	28
8.	Barkingside	30	11	6	13	48	46	39	*8.*	Cray Valley	24	7	6	11	39	49	27
9.	Brook House	30	10	8	12	29	37	38	*9.*	Bridon Ropes	24	8	3	13	44	59	27
10.	Tufnell Park	30	11	4	15	38	55	37	*10.*	Beckton Utd	24	8	3	13	39	64	27
11.	Hanwell Town	30	10	6	14	41	60	36	*11.*	Metpol	24	7	5	12	46	45	26
12.	Woolwich Town	30	9	7	14	42	48	34	*12.*	Catford Wand	24	5	3	16	31	67	18
13.	Waltham Abbey	30	8	10	12	27	45	34	*13.*	Lewisham	24	2	1	21	22	100	7
14.	Beaconsfield	30	8	6	16	42	56	30									
15.	Willesdon	30	7	7	16	37	44	28									
16.	Amersham Town	30	7	7	16	29	58	28									

LONDON SPARTAN LEAGUE SENIOR CUP 1995-96

First Round;

Beaconsfield SYCOB v Waltham Abbey 2-1

Waltham Abbey awarded tie as Beaconsfield used an ineligible player.

Second Round;

Barkingside v Hillingdon Boro 0-0, 0-1
Corinthian Casuals v Waltham Abbey 1-0, 1-0
Hanwell Town v Woolwich Town 1-0, 0-0
Tottenham Omada v Woodford Town 2-0, 1-1
Cockfosters v Brimsdown Rovers 0-0, 2-3
Croydon Ath v Tufnell Park 2-1, 0-1, (2-4pen)
St Margarets. v Amersham Tn 2-0, 1-3, (4-3pen)
Willedon Hawkeye v Brook House 0-2, 1-0

Third Round;

Corinthian Casuals v Hillingdon Boro 2-1, 1-1
Tufnell Park v Brook House 1-1, 2-1
Brimsdown Rovers v Tottenham Omada 3-0, 1-0
St Margaret. v Hanwell Tn 1-2, 4-1 (aet)

Semi-Final;

Brimsdown Rovers v Corinthian Cas 3-1, 3-3
St Margarets. v Tufnell Park 9-1, 0-1

Final; St Margaretsbury v Brimsdown Rovers 2-2 (aet), 0-1

LONDON SPARTAN LEAGUE INTERMEDIATE CUP 1995-96

First Round;

Craven v AFC Blackheath 3-3, 1-2
Beckton United v Woodford 94 1-2
Faweh v Long Lane 4-0
Walthamstow Trojans v Clapham 1-1, 2-1
Catford Wanderers v Cray Valley PM 1-0

Second Round;

Leyton County v Bridon Ropes 3-0
Metpol Chigwell v Crofton Albion 2-0
Catford Wanderers v Walthamstow Trojans 0-3
Chingford United v Faweh 3-4
Holland Park v Old Roan 2-3
St Mary's Islington v Woodford 94 3-1
AFC Blackheath v AC Milla 5-1
Lewisham Elms v Classic Inter 2-1

Third Round;

Walthamstow Trojans v St Mary's 0-3 (aet)
Faweh v Metpol Chigwell 2-1
Leyton County v Lewisham Elms 8-1
AFC Blackheath v Old Roan 2-1

Semi-Final;

Faweh v Leyton County 0-3
AFC Blackheath v St Mary's 2-1

Final; Leyton County v A.F.C. Blackheath 2-0

LONDON SENIOR CUP COMPETITION 1995-96

Quarter Finals;

Thamesmead Town v Kingsbury Town 1-3
Tottenham Omada v Wingate & Finchley 2-1
Hoddesdon Town v Willesdon Hawkeye 1-2
Hanwell Town v St Margaretsbury 1-3

Semi-Final;

Willedon Hawkeye v Kingsbury Town 1-1, 1-3
Tottenham Omada v St Margartsbury 4-2 (aet)

Final; Tottenham Omada v Kingsbury Town 2-1

AMERSHAM TOWN

Chairman: Howard Lambert **Vice Chairman:** David Holdcroft **President:** Graham Taylor
Secretary: Richard Phillips, 16 Cameron Rd, Chesham, Bucks HP5 3BS (01494 784469).
Manager: Paul Pitfield **Coach:** Oscar Ringsell
Ground: Spratley's Meadow, School Lane, Amersham (01494 727428).
Directions: A413 London to Aylesbury road, right into Mill Lane at end of Amersham old town, left into School Lane at top of Hill Lane, ground on left 200yds past school. 1 mile from Amersham Station - BR & underground Metropolitan Line.
Seats: None **Cover:** No **Capacity:** 1,500 **Floodlights:** No **Club Shop:** No.
Programme: With admission **Editor/Press Officer:** David Rake (01844 290176).
Colours: Black & white stripes/black/black **Change colours:** Tangerine/black/black
Founded: 1890 **Nickname:** Magpies.
Midweek home matches: Tuesday **Reserve's League:** Middx Co.
Clubhouse: Open matchdays. Bar facilities. Teas, coffees and light snacks
Hons: Hellenic Lg 63-64 (R-up 64-65 65-66, Div 1 62-63, Cup 53-54), Ldn Spartan Lg R-up 79-80

BARKINGSIDE

President: A Smith **Chairman:** K Harris.
Secretary/Press Officer: N A Ingram, 45 Cheneys Rd, Leytonstone, London E11 3LL (0181 555 1447).
Manager: C Edwards. **Asst Manager:** W Roche. **Physio:** G.Thompson.
Ground: Oakside, Station Road, Barkingside, Ilford, Essex (0181 550 3611). **Club Shop:** No.
Directions: London A12 Eastern Ave to Green Gate, left into Hurns Rd to Barkingside, right into Craven Gardens, right again Carlton Dr leading to Station Rd, under bridge & grd on right. Adjacent to Barkingside station (Central Line), 3 miles Ilford station (BR).
Seats: 60 **Cover:** 60 **Capacity:** 1,000 **Floodlights:** Yes **Founded:** 1898.
Cols: White/blue/yellow **Change cols:** All Red **Sponsors:** Directa
Programme: 12 pages with admission **Programme Editor:** J Brown (0181 500 5125).
Midweek matchday: Tuesday **Reserve's lge:** Ess. & Herts Border Comb.
Clubhouse: Saturdays 1pm-12. midweek matchnights 6.30-11pm. Rolls, hotdogs, hamburgers.
1995-96 Captain: N Simmonds **1995-96 P.o.Y.** L Lennon **1995-96 Top-scorer:** I Duley
Hons: L'don Spartan Lg R-up 90-91

BEACONSFIELD S.Y.C.O.B.

President: T Keylock **Chairman:** Fred Deanus **Manager:** Ian Dare.
Secretary: Ken Barrett, 31 Stockley End, Abbingdon, Oxon OX14 2HF (01235 526832)
Ground: Holloway Park, Slough Road, Beaconsfield, Bucks (01494 676868).
Directions: M40 (Jct 2), 1st exit to A355. Club 100yds on right. One and a miles from Beaconsfield (BR). Bus 441 Slough/ High Wycombe.
Seats: None **Cover:** 60 **Capacity:** 1,000 **Floodlights:** Yes **Founded:** 1994.
Colours: Red & white/black/black **Change colours:** White/black/black.
Best FA Vase season: Beaconsfield: 1st Rd 83-84 85-86 87-88.
Clubhouse: Open evenings and matchdays. Bar, Committee Room, Hall, Kitchen, Changing Room
Hons: *Slough YCOB: Chiltonian Lg Rup 93-94 (Lg Cup 92-93), Slough Town Cup R-up 91-92.*

BRIMSDOWN ROVERS

Chairman/Secretary: Graham Dodd, 57 Roundmoor Drive, Cheshunt, Herts EN8 9HU (01992 626820)
Manager: Tony Faulkner **Match Secretary:** Tony Beasley
Ground Brimsdown Sports & Social Club, Goldsdown Road, Enfield, Middlesex (0181 804 5491).
Directions: BR from Liverpool Street to Brimsdown (half mile away but not open Saturdays) or Southbury Road. By road off Green Street, itself off Hertford Road (A1010). Buses 191 or 307.
Seats: None **Cover:** 50 **Capacity:** 1,000 **Floodlights:** Yes **Founded:** 1948.
Colours: Black & white stripes/black/black **Change colours:** All yellow
Programme: Yes with Admission £1.50 **Editor:** Peter Wade
Best FA Vase season: 2nd Rd rep. 84-85 **Best FA Cup season:** 3rd Qual. replay 91-92
Clubhouse: Large lounge & clubroom, games room & stage. 3 bars (300 capacity)
95-96 Captain: Noel Lenihan **95-96 Top Scorer:** **94-95 P.o.Y.:** Dave Burke
Honours: Spartan Lg 92-93. Spartan Lg Cup 95-96.

BROOK HOUSE

President: G Waddock **Chairman:** M Ralph **Vice-Chairman:** B Crump.
Secretary: Barry Crump, 19 Bradenham Road, Hayes, Middlesex UB4 8LP (0181 841 3959)
Manager: Dermot Jackson **Assy Manager:** Frank Lutt **Press Officer:** Frank Lamb.
Ground: Farm Park, Kingshill Avenue, Hayes, Middlesex (0181 845 0110).
Directions: A40 Western Avenue to Target roundabout, turn left towards Hayes (A312), over White Hart r'bout towards Hayes, turn right at traffic lights in to Kingshill Ave, grd 1 mile on right. Nearest BR station is Hayes & Harlington.
Seats: None **Cover:** 75 **Capacity:** 250 **Floodlights:** Yes **Founded:** 1974
Cols: Blue & white stripes/white/white. **Change:** All green.
Programme: 10 pages, £1.50 with entry **Editor:** Frank Lamb **Club Shop:** No
Midweek matchday: Monday **Reserve League:** Middlesex County
Best FA Vase season: Prel Rd 90-91 91-92 93-94. **Best FA Cup season:** 1st Qual Round 93-94.
Clubhouse: Open weekdays 7-11pm, Sat noon-11pm, Sun noon-3 & 7-10.30pm

COCKFOSTERS

Chairman: Frank Brownlie **Vice Chairman:** T.B.A. **President:** Vic Bates
Secretary: Graham Bint, 15 Chigwell Park, Chigwell, Essex IG7 5BE (0181 500 7369).
Manager: Derek Townsend **Asst Manager:** T.B.A. **Physio:** Derek Carlisle
Ground: Cockfosters Sports Ground, Chalk Lane, Cockfosters, Barnet (0181 449 5833).
Directions: Ground on A111. M25 Jct 24 (Potters Bar), take A111 signed Cockfosters - ground 2 miles on right. Next to Cockfosters tube (Picadilly Line).
Seats: None **Cover:** 50 **Capacity:** 1,000 **Floodlights:** No **Club Shop:** No.
Programme: 12 pages, £2 with entry. **Editor:** A Simmons (0181 440 7998) **Press Off.:** F Brownlie
Colours: All Red **Change colours:** All White
Sponsors: T.S.I. Design. **Nickname:** Fosters **Founded:** 1921.
Midweek matchday: Tuesday **Reserve League:** Middx County.
Clubhouse: 7-11pm Tues & Thurs, 4-11pm Sat, noon-3pm Sunday. Hot and cold food on matchdays.
95-96 Captain: David Lee **95-96 P.o.Y.:** David Finch **95-96 Top Scorer:**
Hons: London Intermediate Cup 70-71 89-90, F.A. Vase 2nd Rd 91-92.

CROYDON ATHLETIC

Chairman: Keith Tuckey **Vice Chairman:** Clive Thompson.
Secretary: Dean Fisher, 9 Kelvin Gardens, Croydon Surrey CR0 4UU, (0181 667 1049 H)
Manager: Micky Taylor **Asst Manager:** Leon Maxwell. **Physio:** Mick Reed.
Ground: Mayfields, off Mayfield Road, Thornton Heath, Surrey CR7 6DN (0181-664-8343/ 0181 684 4851)
Directions: From Thornton Road, turn right into Silverleigh Rd, take left fork into Trafford Rd which continues into Mayfield Rd, follow road/path to ground. One mile from Norbury (BR). Buses 109, 154.
Seats: 120 **Cover:** 300 **Capacity:** 3,000 **Floodlights:** Yes **Shop:** Yes.
Programme: 38 pages, £1 **Editor:** Secretary **Press Officer:** Clive Thompson
Colours: Maroon & white **Change colours:** All white **Nickname:** Rams.
Sponsors: T.C.S. Media **Midweek matchday:** Wednesday
Reserve League: Suburban (South) **Club Shop:** Yes
Best FA Vase season: 3rd Rd 94-95 **Best FA Cup season:** 2nd Qual. Rd 94-95
Clubhouse: Open matchdays (inc Reserve & Youth) and Sun noon-3pm, Monday to Friday 7-11pm.
95-96 P.o.Y.: Simon Rollison. **95-96 Captain:** Paul Muir **95-96 Players P.o.Y.:** Paul Muir.
Hons: London Spartan Lg 94-95, R-up 88-89 93-94, London Snr Cup R-up 91-92.

HANWELL TOWN

Chairman/Press Officer: Bob Fisher(01819 524142) **President:** Dave Iddiols
Secretaryr: J A Wake, 38 Warwick Ave., South Harrow HA2 8RD (0181 422 1048).
Manager: Roy Nairn **Asst Manager:** Arthur Rowlands **Physio:** Catherine Horne
Ground: Reynolds Field, Perivale Lane, Perivale, Greenford, Middx (0181 998 1701).
Directions: A40 Oxford road from London, exit B456 for Ealing, ground on corner of junction approached immediately via left turn into Perivale Lane.
Seats: None **Cover:** 200 **Capacity:** 2,000 **Floodlights:** Yes **Club Shop:** No.
Programme: 16 pages, £2 including entry **Editor:** Julie Soutar, C/O The club.
Founded: 1948 **Nickname:** The Town
Colours: Black & white stripes/Black/Black & White. **Change colours:** All red.
Midweek home matchday: Tuesday **Reserves' League:** Middx County
Clubhouse: Saturday matchdays 2-11pm, Tuesdays 6-11pm, Non-matchdays 7.30-11pm.
95-96 Captain: Andy Paull **95-96 Top Scorer:** **95-96 P.o.Y.:**
Honours: London Spartan Lg 83-84 (Lg Cup finalists 93-94, London Snr Cup 91-92 92-93 (R-up 93-94).

HAREFIELD UNITED

Chairman: David West **President:** Mr Ivor Mitchell
Secretary: Terry Devereux, 72 Williamson Way, Rickmansworth,Herts WD3 "GL (01923 711451).
Manager: **Asst Manager:** **Physio:** Alan Carpenter, John Godfrey.
Ground: Preston Park, Breakespeare Rd, North Harefield, Middx UB9 6DG (01895 823474).
Directions: M25 jct 17, follow signs to Swakely corner then to Harefield A40. Denham (BR).
Capacity: 2,000 **Seats:** 150 **Cover:** Yes **Floodlights:** Yes **Founded:** 1868
Colours: Blue & yellow/blue/blue **Change colours:** White/black/black
Club Shop: No **Programme:** 12-40 pages, 30p **Editor:** Eric Findall.
Midweek Matchday: Tuesday **Reserve Team's League:** Suburban **Nickname:** Hares.
Best FA Cup year: 2nd Qual. Rd replay 80-81 (lost 1-5 at Maidenhead), 86-87 (1-2 at Aylesbury).
Clubhouse: (01895 823474). Lunchtimes and evenings. Two bars, cold snacks (hot on matchdays).
Hons: Middx Premier Cup 85-86, Athenian Lg R-up 83-84, Parthenon Lg 64-65 (Div 1 Cup 65-66),

HARINGEY BOROUGH

Chairman: Peter Lawlor **Vice-Chairman:** T O'Connell.
Secretary: George Kilikita, Unit 12A, 16/22 Seven Sisters Rd, London N7 6AE (0181 368 2783)
Ground: Coles Park, White Hart Lane, Wood Green N22 (081 881 9184).
Directions: Wood Green (Picadilly Line). BR (Eastern Region) to White Hart Lane, W3 bus passes ground A105 or A10 from Nth. Circular to Wood Green.
Seats: 280 **Cover:** Yes **Capacity:** 2,500 **Floodlights:** Yes **Founded:**
Cols: Green & white/white/green & white **Change colours:** Yellow & black/black/black.
Clubhouse: Open 7 days a week

Hanwell's David Salive leaves Beaconfield's Adam Bridge grounded. *Photo Ray Pruden*

Hanwell Town FC: *Photo - Martin Wray*

Beckton's Nicholas Hawtrey holds the ball from Cray Valley's Thomas Heathcote. *Photo - Ray Pruden*

HILLINGDON BOROUGH

Chairman: Roy Lovell.
Secretary: Graham Bundy, 43 Heatherwood Drive, Hayes, Middlesex UB4 8TN (0181 845 7355).
Manager: John Morris **Asst Manager:** John Toogood **Coach:** Dave Silman.
Physio: Dave Pook **Commercial Mgr:** Ken Rogers **Press Officer:** John Mason.
Ground: Middlesex Stadium, Breakspear Road, Ruislip, Middx HA4 7SB (01895 639544).
Directions: A40 take B467 (signed Ickenham), left at 2nd r'bout into Breakspear Rd South, right after 1 mile by Breakspear pub - grd 1/2 mile left. Nearest station Ruislip.
Seats: 150 **Cover:** 150 **Capacity:** 1,500 **Floodlights:** Yes **Founded:** 1990
Midweek Matches: Wednesday **Sponsors:** Airport Motor Radiator Co. **Nickname:** Boro.
Colours: White/blue/blue **Change colours:** Red & white stripes/white/red.
Programme: 20 pages **Editor:** John Mason (081 868 7551) **Club Shop:** No.
Clubhouse: Mon-Fri 7.30-11pm, Sat & Sun lunchtime & 7.30-10.30pm.

ISLINGTON St MARYS

Chairman: Ian Myclam (0171 359 6112)
Secretary: Nick Adams, 5 Hambledon Chase, 58 Crouch Hill London N4 4AH (0171 263 1530 H)
Match Secretary: Eddie Webb, 34 Bidwell Gardens, Bounds Green, London, N11 2AU (0181 881 0538)
Ground: Coles Park, White Hart Lane, Tottenham N17 (0181 889 1495)
Directions: N Circular Rd to White Hart Lane, turn right or left, (left is opposite B D C) 500 yds going to Wood Green, grd 300 yards from New River Sports ground.
Colours: Black & red/white/white **Change Colours:** Black & white/black/white

RUISLIP MANOR

Chairman: Mick Connors **Vice Chairman:** Jim Evans **President:**
Secretary: Mrs Avice Horne, 49 Evelyn Close, Whitton, Twickenham, Middx TW2 7BL (0181 898 3581).
Manager: Andy Waddock **Asst Manager:** Gary Farrant **Physio:** Gary Strudwick
Ground: Grosvenor Vale, off West End Road, Ruislip, Middx (01895 637487-office, 676168-boardroom)
Directions: A40 to Ruislip, turn off on A4180, right at r'bout into West End Rd, right into Grosvenor Vale after a 1 1/2 miles - ground at end.
Capacity: 3,000 **Seats:** 100 **Cover:** 300 **Floodlights:** Yes **Club Shop:** Yes
Programme: 32 **Price:** 60p **Editor:** Victor Klarfeld **Press Officer:** S Szymanski (01895 637933)
Colours: Black & White/black/black **Change colours:** Yellow & blue/yellow/yellow
Sponsors: Golf Course Management **Founded:** 1938 **Nickname:**The Manor
Clubhouse: Mon-Fri noon-3.30 & 5.30-11pm, noon-3 & 7.30-10.30.
95-96 Captain: Steve Scott **95-96 P.o.Y.:** Keith Cooper **95-96 Top scorer:** Tery Flaherty
Honours: Isthmian Lg Div 2 R-up 92-93 Middx Charity Cup R-up 90-91 95-96.

St MARGARETSBURY

Chairman: T I Blacktin **President:** R L Groucott
Secretary: K.Myall, 30 Crib St, Ware, Herts. SG12 9EX (01920 830356(H) 01920 658502(W).)
Manager: Kelvin Hart **Asst Manager:** Colin Richards **Physio:** Derek Ridgewell.
Ground: Station Road, Stanstead St Margarets, Nr Ware, Herts (01920 870473).
Directions: Harlow/Chelmsford exit from A10 to A414, take B181 at Amwell after 300yds towards Stanstead Abotts, ground quarter mile on right. 300yds from St Margaretsbury BR
Seats: 60 **Cover:** 60 **Capacity:** 1,000 **Floodlights:** No **Club Shop:** No
Programme: £2.00 with entry **Editor:** Jane Free (01920 870431) **Press Officer:**
Colours: Red & black/black/black & red. **Change colours:** All white
Sponsors: Universal Office Automation **Nickname:** The Bury. **Founded:** 1894
Midweek matchday: Tuesday **Reserve League:** Hertford & District.
Clubhouse: Bar open 7-11pm + Sat noon-2, Sun noon-3pm. Bar snacks available.
95-96 Captain: Paul Letts **95-96 Top Scorer:** Darren White **95-96 P.o.Y.:** Russell Ling.
Honours: Herts Snr Cent Tphy 92-93; Spartan Lge 95-96; Roy Bailey Mem Trophy 95-96.

TOTTENHAM(OMADA)

Chairman: George William
Secretary: Lindsay Boyaram, 33 Adlington Close, off Ploughman Close, Edmonton N18 1XJ.(011813 455902(H),01956 888582(W).)
Ground & Directions: As Barking FC (see Icis League).
Colours: Gold/blue/white **Change Colours:** All white **Honours:** Spartan Lg Div 2 93-94.

WALTHAM ABBEY

Chairman: Phil Morris **President:** Dennis Cordell. **Manager:** Joe Collins & John Ward
Secretary: Mr Alec Myers, 88 The Weymarks, Weir Hall Road, Tottenham N17 8LD (0181 808 2706)
Ground: Capershotts, Sewardstone Road, Waltham Abbey, Essex (01992 711287).
Directions: Just off M25 jct 26. Waltham Cross (BR Eastern Region) station three miles distant. 242 Bus.
Seats: None **Cover:** 400 **Capacity:** 2,000 **Floodlights:** Yes **Club Shop:** No.
Programme: 8 pages.50p . **Editor:** David Hodges (01992 652594)
Colours: Green & white hoops/white/green **Change colours:** Red & black hoops/red/red.
Nickname: The Abbey **Founded:** 1948.
Midweek matchday: Tuesday. **Reserve's League:** Essex & Herts Border Combination
Best FA Cup season: Prel. Rd 90-91 **Best FA Vase season:** Prel. Rd 87-88 88-89 89-90
Clubhouse: 7-11pm Mon-Fri, 11am-11pm Sat, noon-3pm Sun. Cold snacks, pool, darts.

WOODFORD TOWN

Chairman: Mrs. Robertson.
Secretary: Mr W Robertson, 2 Humphrey Close, Clayhill, Ilford, Essex IG5 0RW (0181 550 6680).
Ground & Directions: As East Ham United FC (see page 804).
Colours: Royal blue/black/black **Change Colours:** White & black stripes/white/white.

SOUTH MIDLANDS LEAGUE

FEEDER TO: ICIS LEAGUE

FOUNDED: 1922

President: B Smith, **Chairman:** P Burns,

Hon. Secretary: M Mitchell, 26 Leighton Court, Dunstable, Beds, LU6 1EW. (01582 667291)

FINAL LEAGUE TABLE 1995/96

Premier Division	*P*	*W*	*D*	*L*	*F*	*A*	*Pts*
1. Arlesey Town	32	24	2	6	64	27	74
2. Hatfield Town	32	22	5	5	79	31	71
3. London Colney	32	21	5	6	88	34	68
4. Brache Sparta	32	20	8	4	56	24	68
5. Toddington Rovers	32	14	9	9	50	45	51
6. Royston Town	32	13	11	8	48	36	*47
7. Hoddesdon Town	32	12	8	12	49	44	44
8. Milton Keynes	32	13	4	15	55	70	43
9. Potters Bar Town	32	11	9	12	56	63	42
10. Biggleswade Town	32	12	5	15	51	50	41
11. Welwyn Garden City	32	11	7	14	53	62	40
12. Langford	32	10	8	14	30	48	38
13. Buckingham Ath	32	9	6	17	43	63	33
14. Harpenden Town	32	8	8	16	42	56	32
15. Dunstable Utd	32	6	7	19	33	71	25
16. Shillington	32	5	9	18	42	60	24
17. Letchworth	32	1	9	22	33	88	12

** Royston Town 3 points deducted*

PREMIER DIVISION RESULTS CHART 1995-96

HOME TEAM	**1**	**2**	**3**	**4**	**5**	**6**	**7**	**8**	**9**	**10**	**11**	**12**	**13**	**14**	**15**	**16**	**17**
1. Arlesey Town	*	2-0	0-1	3-1	2-1	2-2	2-1	1-0	2-0	2-0	1-0	3-0	4-2	1-3	2-1	2-1	4-0
2. Biggleswade Town	2-3	*	1-2	1-3	1-0	3-1	2-0	0-1	1-1	4-1	2-0	2-2	1-3	3-1	1-3	2-3	2-1
3. Brache Sparta	0-0	3-2	*	2-0	6-1	1-0	3-1	1-1	1-1	6-1	2-0	2-3	2-1	0-0	1-0	3-0	1-0
4. Buckingham Athletic	0-4	0-0	2-1	*	5-1	4-1	0-4	2-3	0-1	4-0	1-4	3-2	1-1	0-0	0-3	1-4	2-1
5. Dunstable	0-1	1-0	0-1	2-0	*	4-2	0-0	1-0	0-1	2-0	2-5	0-3	2-5	1-1	3-4	2-2	1-1
6. Harpenden Town	1-2	0-1	1-3	1-1	0-0	*	0-2	1-2	3-1	3-1	0-1	3-2	4-2	1-2	5-1	1-2	2-1
7. Hatfield Town	2-1	3-0	2-0	2-0	1-0	3-0	*	4-2	5-1	2-2	4-1	6-1	3-0	1-0	6-1	1-1	3-0
8. Hoddesdon Town	1-2	2-1	1-1	0-2	0-1	0-1	1-3	*	0-0	3-1	1-1	2-1	2-0	1-2	2-2	2-2	6-2
9. Langford	2-1	2-0	1-2	2-2	1-0	0-0	0-3	1-3	*	2-1	0-2	2-0	1-1	1-2	1-0	0-1	1-2
10. Letchworth Garden City	1-3	0-4	0-1	1-4	2-2	2-0	0-2	1-4	1-2	*	1-6	0-1	2-2	2-2	2-2	1-1	2-2
11. London Colney	2-0	6-0	1-1	3-0	6-1	2-2	1-1	2-2	3-1	3-0	*	7-1	6-1	1-2	1-2	4-1	2-1
12. Milton Keynes	1-2	1-1	1-2	2-0	4-3	3-1	1-5	1-0	2-0	4-2	1-5	*	1-2	3-0	4-3	2-1	3-4
13. Potters Bar Town	0-2	0-3	0-0	4-2	4-1	1-1	4-2	1-3	2-2	2-2	1-2	4-2	*	2-1	0-0	1-1	3-1
14. Royston Town	0-2	1-1	1-1	3-0	6-0	2-2	1-3	1-0	3-0	2-1	0-3	1-1	0-1	*	3-0	1-1	1-2
15. Shillington	0-2	1-2	0-1	1-1	5-0	1-1	2-2	1-2	1-1	3-3	0-2	0-2	2-3	1-2	*	1-2	0-0
16. Toddington Rovers	0-3	2-1	1-0	2-1	1-1	1-2	1-2	3-1	0-1	3-0	1-4	4-0	2-1	0-0	2-1	*	3-2
17. Welwyn Garden City	0-5	1-7	1-5	4-1	1-0	3-0	3-0	1-1	4-0	5-0	1-2	0-0	5-2	2-2	1-0	1-1	*

FINAL LEAGUE TABLES 1995/96

Senior Div		P	W	D	L	F	A	Pts
1.	Holmer Green	26	19	5	2	71	31	62
2.	Leverstock Gr	26	17	6	3	63	26	57
3.	Bedford Utd	26	16	3	7	57	32	51
4.	N Bradwell S P	26	14	5	7	69	43	47
5.	Totternhoe	26	13	6	7	52	44	45
6.	Tring Ath	26	13	4	9	66	37	43
7.	Houghton Tn	26	9	8	9	40	33	35
8.	Winslow Utd	26	7	8	11	43	57	29
9.	Risborough R	26	7	7	12	35	56	28
10.	A.C.D.	26	7	6	13	46	42	27
11.	Ampthill Tn	26	7	6	13	39	62	27
12.	Stony Stratford	26	6	5	15	39	67	23
13.	61 FC	26	5	4	17	28	71	19
14.	Kent Athletic	26	3	5	18	31	78	14

** Bridger Packaging 3 points deducted, Old Bradwell United 1 point deducted.*

Div One		P	W	D	L	F	A	Pts
1.	Mercedes Benz	32	21	7	4	69	25	70
2.	De-Haviland	32	21	6	5	86	44	69
3.	Walden Rang	32	21	5	6	72	41	68
4.	Leighton Ath	32	18	5	9	87	50	59
5.	Crawley Gr SS	32	16	6	10	52	42	54
6.	Bridger Pack.	32	14	8	10	77	57	*47
7.	Caddington	32	13	8	11	57	54	47
8.	Bow Brickhill	32	13	6	13	46	55	45
9.	Buckingham U	32	14	1	17	58	53	43
10.	Emberton	32	10	11	11	58	55	41
11.	Flamstead	32	9	13	10	47	55	40
12.	Abbey National	32	11	5	16	53	70	38
13.	Scot	32	9	10	13	50	63	37
14.	O Dunstonians	32	7	7	18	43	70	28
15.	Pitstone & Iv.	32	5	8	19	36	85	23
16.	O Bradwell Utd	32	5	8	19	63	93	*22
17.	Cranfield U	32	6	4	22	45	87	22

LEADING LEAGUE GOALSCORERS 1995-96

Premier Division:

M Swaysland	London Colney	24
Dave Cutmore	London Colney	20
Barry Dellar	Arlesey Town	22
P McCormack	Welwyn Garden City	18

Senior Division;

K Millington	New Bradwell St Peter	23
Shaun Martin	Holmer Green	17
PatBooden	New Bradwell St Peter	19

Division One;

John Fogarty	Walden Rangers	25
Nick Edgar	Bridger Packaging	22
M Carrozza	Leighton Athletic	19
Paul Clarke	De Haviland	22
Grant Carney	Crawley Green	19
A Spencer	Buckingham United	19

O'BRIEN/McKENZIE BUTCHERS CHALLENGE TROPHY 1995-96

First Round;

Leighton Athletic v Kent Athletic	5-3
Abbey National v Buckingham Utd	1-3
Walden Rangers v Toddington	1-4
Bedford United v Shillington	3-1
Houghton v Hatfield	4-0
Flamstead v Caddington	0-1
London Colney v Bow Brickhill	5-0
Buckingham Ath v Holmer Green	2-3
Arlesey	Bye
Langford v Risborough	2-0
Cranfield v Ampthill	2-2, 0-2
Old Bradwell v Hoddesdon	3-3, 0-4
Scot v Winslow	4-1
Pitsone & Iv v De Haviland	2-3
The 61 FC v Mercedes Benz	1-1, 0-3
Brache Sparta v Letchworth	5-2
Biggleswade v ACD	3-1

Second Round;

De Haviland v New Bradwell	4-5
Potters Bar v Mercedes Benz	5-3
Bridger Packaging v Bedford United	2-1
Leverstock v London Colney	3-2
Dunstable United v Caddington	3-0
Holmer Green v Totternhoe	2-0
Biggleswade v Langford	1-0
Scot v Harpenden	1-2
Ampthill v Dunstablians	3-2
Brache Sparta v Welwyn Garden City	3-1
Arlesey v Tring Athletic	5-2
Houghton v Emberton	4-2
Hoddesdon v Royston	0-2
Crawley Green v Buckingham Utd	1-2
Milton Keynes v Leighton Ath	2-1
Stony Stratford v Toddington	4-2

Third Round;

Houghton v Brache Sparta	1-2	Harpenden v Buckingham Utd	1-1, 4-0
Biggleswade v Potters Bar	2-1	Leverstock Green v Milton Keynes	1-0
Ampthill v Arlesey	1-3	Holmer Green v Dunstable Utd	1-0
Royston v Stony Stratford	4-0	Bridger Packaging v New Bradwell	2-1

Fourth Round;

Leverstock Green v Harpenden	2-0	Royston v Brache Sparta	1-0
Biggleswade v Bridger Packaging	4-1	Holmer Green v Arlesey	0-1

Semi-Final;

Royston v Arlesey	1-0 (aet)	Biggleswade v Leverstock Green	3-1

Final; Royston v Biggleswade 3-1, 1-0, (4-1 agg)

O'BRIEN/McKENZIE BUTCHERS PREMIER DIVISION CUP 1995-96

Quarter Finals;

Shillington v Bigglewade	1-2	Biggleswade v Shillington	1-1, **(3-2 agg)**
Hatfield v Langford	3-1	Langford v Hatfield	0-4, **(1-7 agg)**
Toddington v Harpenden	4-0	Harpenden v Toddington	0-2, **(0-6 agg)**
Arlesey v London Colney	0-4	London Colney v Arlesey	3-2, **(7-2 agg)**

Semi-Finals;

Hatfield v Biggleswade	3-0	London Colney v Toddington	0-2

Final; Toddington v Hatfield 2-1

DIVISION ONE CUP 1995-96

Semi-Final;

Bow Brickhill v Buckingham United	1-2	Cranfield United v De Haviland	0-6

Final; Buckingham United v De Haviland 2-1

PREMIER DIVISION CLUBS 1996-97

ARLESEY TOWN

Chairman: John Milton **Vice-Chairman:** Scott Geekie **President:** Maurice Crouch.
Secretary: John Albon, 13 St Johns Rd, Arlesey, Beds SG15 6ST (01462 731318).
Manager: Robbie O'Keefe **Asst Manager:** **Physio:** Jim Anderson.
Ground: Lamb Meadow,Hitchin Rd, Arlesey (01462 731448).
Directions: On main road thru village. From Hitchin, ground 200 yds past Biggs Wall on left.
Capacity: 8,000 **Seats:** 120 **Cover:** 1,000 **Floodlights:** Yes **Club Shop:**
Programme: Yes, 50p **Editor:** Pete Brennan (01462 834455). **Press Officer:**
Colours: Sky & navy **Change Colours:** All white.
Founded: 1891. **Nickname:** Blues. **Sponsors:** Milcutt Goldstar
Midweek matchday: Tuesday **Reserve Team's League:** South Midlands Lge Res Div
Record Attendance: 2,000 v Luton Res, Beds Snr Cup 1906
Best FA Vase Season: Winners 94-95
Clubhouse: Open daily 6-11.30, Sat noon-11.30, Sin noon-2.30 & 6-11.30.
95-96 Captain: Pete Gonsalves. **95-96 Top Scorer:** Barry Dellar **95-96 P.o.Y.:** Barry Dellar
Club Record Appearance: Gary Marshall
Honours: F.A.Vase Winners: 1994-5, Premier Champions: 94-95, Prem Div Cup 94-95.

BEDFORD UNITED

Chairman: John Cleverley **Vice Chairman:** Jim McMullen **President:** D Rostron
Secretary: Graham Ford, 59 Southville Road, Bedford MK42 9PS (01234 401159).
Manager: Bob Bell **Assistant Manager:** Trevor Barnett **Coach:** Colin Hoyland
Ground: Hillgrounds, Kempston.(01234 841065)
Directions: M1 jct 13, A421 to Bedford, follow signs to Kempston at 1st r'bout, 2nd r'bout keep left, 3rd r'bout turn right, Hillgrounds is 1st left, ground half mile on left.
Capacity: 1,000 **Seats:** 25 **Cover:** 100 **Floodlights:** No **Founded:** 1957
Colours: Blue & White/blue/blue **Change cols:** All Red. **Nickname:** United
Midweek matches: Tuesday **Clubhouse:** Open matchdays.
Programme: 24 pages, £1 **Editor:** Geoff Seagrave (01234 856117).
Club Sponsors: Grant Thornton **Reserve Team's League:** South Midlands Lge Reserve section.
Record Gate: (at Fairhill) 852 v Bedford Town, South Midlands League Division One 26/12/92.
Hons: Bedford & Dist Lg Premier Division & Division One.

BIGGLESWADE TOWN

Chairman: M Dorrington **Vice Chairman:** M.Quin. **President:** R Dorrington.
Secretary: G Arkwright, 21 Willsheres Road, Biggleswade, Beds SG18 0BU (01767 316992).
Manager: D Earl **Physio:** R Ashcroft.
Ground: 'Fairfield', Fairfield Road, Biggleswade, Beds (01767 312374).
Directions: A1 North r'bout, left immediately after metal bridge into car park. 10 mins walk from Biggleswade (BR).
Capacity: 2,400 **Seats:** 250 **Cover:** 400 **Floodlights:** Yes **Club Shop:** No.
Programme: 32 pages, with admission
Colours: Green/black **Change:** Tangerine/Black.
Club Sponsors: Mantles Ford. **Nickname:** Waders **Founded:** 1874
Clubhouse: Open all matchdays.
95-96 Captain: S Pearson **95-96 Top Scorer:** S.Pearson. **95-96 P.o.Y.:**
Honours: Sth Mids Lg Res Div 2 87-88, Res Chall Trophy 88-89.

BRACHE SPARTA

Chairman: Roy Standring **President:** Doug Smith.
Secretary: Maurice Franklin, 62 Katherine Drive, Dunstable LU5 4NU (01582 661177).
Manager: Steve Brinckman. **Physio:** Phil Toyer.
Ground: Foxdell Spts Ground, Dallow Rd, Luton LU1 1UP (01582 20751).
Directions: Left off A505 to Dunstable into Chaul Lane at r'bout. Proceed across new relief road - ground entrance adjacent to Foxdell Junior School.
Cover: 100 **Seats:** 25 **Capacity:** 400 **Floodlights:** Yes **Founded:** 1960
Colours: White/navy/white **Change Colours:** All royal **Nickname:** None.
Midweek home maches: Wednesday **Previous League:** Luton & Dist.
Programme: 30 pages, £1 **Club Sponsors:** A & E Engineering.
Clubhouse: Open daily noon-3 & 7.30-11pm. Light snacks
Hons: South Mids Lg R-up 92-93 (Div 1 R-up 83-84 87-88, Lg Cup R-up 75-76 80-81 92-93

BUCKINGHAM ATHLETIC

Chairman: Alex Miller **President:**J.Burgess.
Secretary: Chris Forman, 10 Elm Drive, Deanshanger, Milton Keynes, MK19 6JS (01908 563526)
Manager: Malcolm East.
Ground: Stratford Fields, Stratford Rd, Buckingham (01280 816945).
Directions: From Milton Keynes take the A422 Stony Stratford-Buckingham road – ground on left just before town centre. From Aylesbury, turn right at 1st r-about, across 2nd r-bout, left at 3rd – ground at bottom of hill on left.
Capacity: 1,500 **Seats:** No **Cover:** 200 **Floodlights:** Yes **Founded:** 1933
Colours: Sky & navy/navy/navy **Change Cols:** Red & white/white/red **Nickname:** Swans
Midweek home matchday: Wednesday **Programme:** 10 pages, 50p
Hons: Sth Mids Lg Div 1 85-86 90-91 (R-up 88-89, Div 1 Cup 90-91).

HARPENDEN TOWN

Chairman: Alan King **Manager:** Mark Nicholls Paul Woolfrey
Secretary: Stephen Whiting, 169 Grove Rd, Harpenden, Herts AL5 1SY (01582 761606).
Ground: Rothamsted Park, Amenbury Lane, Harpenden (01582 715724).
Directions: A1081 to Harpenden. Turn left/right at George Hotel into Leyton Rd. Turn left into Amenbury Rd, then left again (50yds) into 'Pay and Display' car park - entrance is signposted thru car park to opposite corner.
Capacity: 1,500 **Seats:** 25 **Cover:** 100 **Floodlights:** Yes
Programme: 50p **Editor:** Secretary
Colours: Yellow/blue/blue **Change Colours:** Red and Blue stripes/yellow/yellow
Founded: 1891 **Nickname:** The Town
Midweek matchday: Tuesday **Previous Leagues:** Mid-Herts/ Herts County.
Hons: Sth Mids Lg 61-62 64-65 (Champ Shield 67-68, Lg Cup 70-71, Div 1 89-90, Prem Div Tphy 89-90.

HODDESDON TOWN

President: Peter Haynes **Chairman:** Roger Merton. **Deputy Chairman:** Srewart Edwards.
Secretary: Brenda Timpson, 82 Tolmers Road, Cuffley, Potters Bar, Herts EN6 4JY (01707 874028)
Manager: Ray Greenall **Asst Manager:** Jim Briggs **Coach:** John Walton.
Ground: 'Lowfield', Park View, Hoddesdon, Herts (0992 463133).
Directions: A10, A1170 and follow signs to town centre until left-hand fork signposted Broxbourne, right at 1st mini r-about into Cock Lane and 1st right is Park View. Ground on 200yds left opposite Park Rd. Nearest BR station is Broxbourne.
Capacity: 3,000 **Seats:** 250 **Cover:** 250 **Floodlights:** Yes **Founded:** 1879
Midweek matchday: Tuesday **Nickname:** Lilywhites/ Lowfielders **Club Shop:** No.
Colours: White/black/white **Change Colours:** All yellow.
Record Gate: 3,500 v West Ham, friendly 1975.
Programme: 72-100 pages 60p. **Editor:** Mrs Jane Sinden (01767 631297).
Clubhouse: Bar and well-stocked tea bar with hot food open at every game.
Hons: FA Vase 74-75 (1st winners), Sth Mids Lg Lg Cup 85-86 86-87 91-92 (Prem Div Tphy R-up 92-93)

Leverstock Green FC *Photo - Martin Wray*

Harpenden Town FC *Photo - Martin Wray*

Ampthill Town FC *Photo - Martin Wray*

LANGFORD

Chairman: Mick Quinlan **President:** Ted Rutt.
Secretary: Frank Woodward, 2 North Lane, Gamlingay, Sandy, Beds SG19 3NT (0767 51022).
Manager: Pete Hayes **Asst Mgr:** Eric Cumberbatch **Coaches:** Bob Wright & Steve Ward.
Press Officer: Secretary **Commercial Manager:** David Binks.
Ground: Forde Park, Langford Road, Henlow SG16 6AF (0426 816106).
Directions: Halfway between Langford and Henlow on A6001 Hitchin to Biggleswade road. Bus 177 on main Hitchin-Biggleswade route stops right outside ground.
Capacity: 4,000 **Seats:** 100 **Cover:** 250 **Floodlights:** Yes **Founded:** 1910.
Cols: Red & white **Change Colours:** Blue &white
Record Gate: 450 v Q.P.R., 75th Anniversary and clubhouse opening, 22/8/85.
Programme: With admission. **Editor:** Barry Dellar. **Club Shop:** Yes
Sponsors: Fine Stamps Ltd, A.H. Printers **Midweek home matchday:** Tuesday **Nickname:** Reds.
Clubhouse: Weekday evenings, matchdays 11am-11pm, Sun 12-3pm. Hot food on matchdays only.
Hons: S Mids Lg 88-89 (Lg Cup 73-74 75-76, Prem Div Tphy 88-89 94-95. O'Brien Div 1 Tphy 84-85).

LETCHWORTH GARDEN CITY

Chairman: Adrian Earl **President:** Anthony Burrows **Manager:** Mick Clements.
Secretary: June Earl, 92 Bilberry Road, Clifton, Shefford, Beds SG17 5HD (01462 816683)
Ground: Baldock Road, Letchworth, Herts SG6 2GN (01462 684691).
Directions: Jct 9 (A6141) off A1M straight over large r-about, right at next r-about, ground on right. From Luton (A505) thru Hitchin, ground 3 miles after Hitchin. 2 miles from Letchworth (BR).
Capacity: 3,200 **Cover:** 400 **Seats:** 200 **Floodlights:** Yes **Founded:** 1906
Colours: All Blue **Change Colours:** Red and White stripes/Red/Red **Nickname:** Bluebirds.
Programme: 24 pages, 50p (Keith Brown 01707 251854) **Midweek matchday:** Tuesday
Hons: Herts Charity Shield 22-23 47-48 87-88 91-92:

LONDON COLNEY

Chairman: Bill Gash **Vice Chairman:** P Light **President:** I Holt.
Secretary: David Brock,50 Seymour Rd., St Albans, Herts. AL3 5HW (01727 761644)
Manager: S Seabrook/ M Wright **Physio:** J Burt
Ground: Cotslandswick, London Colney (01727 822132).
Directions: From London Colney r'bout (junc A414/A1081), A414 towards Watford, after layby (300yds) turn left (hidden turning marked 'Sports Ground') and follow around. 3 miles St Albans (BR).
Capacity: 1,000 **Cover:** 100 **Seats:** 30 **Floodlights:** Yes **Club Shop:**
Programme: £1 with entry **Editor:** **Press Officer:**
Colours: All royal **Change Colours:** All Red
Sponsors: Harris Mortgage & Finance **Nickname:** Blueboys **Founded:** 1907.
Clubhouse: Open after games. Hot food available.
95-96 Captain: Paul Vye **95-96 Top Scorer:** Mick Swaysland **95-96 P.o.Y.:**
Hons: Sth Mids Lg Snr 94-95, R-up 93-94 (Chall Trophy 93-94, Div 1 R-up 92-93)

MILTON KEYNES

Chairman: John Wisson **President:** None.
Secretary: Mr Neasham Galloway, 22 Bascote, Tinkers Bridge, Milton Keynes, MK6 3DW (01908 374022).
Manager: Alan Blackman **Asst Manager:** Riki Barry **Physio:** John Butcher
Ground: Manor Fields, Bletchley, Milton Keynes (01908 375256)
Directions: Old A5 to Fenny Stratford, about 500yds on left go over bridge opposite Belvedere Nursuries into Manor Fields - ground on right.
Capacity: 3,000 **Seats:** 160 **Cover:** 1,000 **Floodlights:** Yes **Founded:** 1993.
Colours: Red and Black/Black/Black. **Change Colours:** Blue/white/blue. **Nickname:** None.
Programme: 16 pages, 40p **Editor:** **Club Shop:** No.
Record Gate: 250 v Bedford Town, S. Mids Lge 30/4/94.
Midweek home matchday: Tuesday **Reserves' Lge:** Minerva Sth Mids Reserve Div 1A.
Clubhouse: Two bars. Upstairs bar open every evening. Snacks available.
Record scorer: Andy McCabe **Record appearances:** Paul Joyce. **Hons:** None.

POTTERS BAR TOWN

Chairman: Peter Waller. **Vice Chairman:** Alan Bolt. **President:** Bert Wright
Secretary: Carol Waller, 26 Queen Annes Grove, Bush Hill Park, Enfield, Middx EN1 2JR (0181 360 7859).
Manager: Ray Kierstenson **General Manager:** Les Eason **Physio:** Brian Gaymer.
Ground: Parkfield Centre, The Walk, Potters Bar, Herts EN6 1QN (01707 654833
Directions: M25 jct 24, enter Potters Bar along Southgate Rd (A111), at 1st lights right into the High St (A1000), half mile left into The Walk, ground 200 yds on right (opp. Potters Bar Cricket Club). BR Potters

Bar - The Walk is directly opp station
Capacity: 2,000 **Seats:** 25 **Cover:** 100 **Floodlights:** Yes **Club Shop:** Yes
Programme: 48 pages, £1 **Editor/Press Officer:** Robert Brassett (01707 661795).
Colours: Red & royal stripes/royal/royal **Change colours:** White/red/red
Sponsors: Century 21 Estates **Nickname:** The Grace or The Scholars. **Founded:** 1960
Midweek matchday: Tuesday or Wednesday
Record Attendance: 387 v Barnet, floodlight opener 8/12/93. Comp: 200 v Cockfosters, Herts Snr
Best FA Vase season: Third Round, 90-91.
Clubhouse: Sat 12.30-11pm, Sun noon-5pm, Tues & Thurs 7.30-11pm, midweek matchnights 6-11pm.
95-96 Captain: Lee Johnson **95-96 Top Scorer:** Paul Weaver **95-96 P.O.Y.:** Grahame Garrett
Club Record Goalscorer: Micky Gray 260 **Club Record Appearances:** Mick Holson 708 (60-89).
Honours: Herts Co. Lg 90-91 (Div 1 73-74 81-82); Potters Bar Charity Cup 76-77 95-96; Herts Snr Centenary Tphy SF 91-92; Herts Charity Shield SF 74-75 75-76 95-96; Bingham Cox Cup 94-95:

ROYSTON TOWN

Chairman: Tony Moulding **Vice-Chairman:** Bernard Brown **President:** Bill Cosgrove
Secretary/Press Officer: Trevor Glasscock, 39 Poplar Drive, Royston, Herts. SG8 (01763 230783)
Manager: Paddy Butcher **Asst Mgr:** Bernard Brown **Physio:** Colin Mardell
Ground: Garden Walk, Royston, Herts SG8 7HP (01763 241204).
Directions: From Baldock, A505 to Royston bypass, right at 2nd island onto A10 towards London, 2nd left is Garden Walk; ground 100 yds on left. From A11, exit 10 turning left onto A505, left at 1st island, 2nd left is Garden Walk. Ten mins walk from Royston (BR).
Capacity: 4,000 **Seats:** 300 **Cover:** 300 **Floodlights:** Yes **Club Shop:** Yes
Programme: 16 pages, 30p **Editor:** Steve Langridge (01438 356661)
Colours: White/black/black **Change colours:** Red/white/white
Sponsors: ABA Consultants. **Nickname:** Crows. **Founded:** 1875
Midweek Matchday: Tuesday **Record Attendance:** 876 v Aldershot, 13/2/93
Best FA Cup year: Second Qualifying Round 59-60 (lost 0-9 at Barnet), 89-90 (lost 0-3 at Bromley).
Clubhouse: Mon-Thurs 7-11pm, Fri 11am-3 & 7-11pm, Sat 11am-3 & 4-11pm, Sun noon-3pm.
Club Record Scorer: Trevor Glasscock 289 (1968-82) **Club Record Appearances:** Fred Bradley 713.
Hons: Sth Mids Lg R-up 79-80 (Div 1 78-79, Chall. Cup R-up 78-79, Res Div 1 79-80 (Div 2 78-79).

TODDINGTON ROVERS

Chairman: Hugh Geddes **Vice Chairman:** Brian Horne **President:** Peter Turner.
Secretary: Barry Hill, 9 Fairfield Rd, Dunstable,Beds. LU5 4JT (01582 471150)
Manager: Steve Loasby **Asst Manager:** Alan Loeasby **Coach:** Roger King.
Physio: John Cullen **Press Officer:** Colin Bryson.
Ground: Dunstable F.C. ,Creasey Park, Brewers Hill Rd., Dunstable.(01582 606691)
Directions: 1 mile to Toddington village centre from M1, take one-way st signed Luton, grd 150yds left.
Seats: No **Cover:** 100 **Nickname:** Rovers **Floodlights:** No **Founded:** 1894
Colours: Black & white stripes **Change Colours:** All Blue. **Club Shop:** No.
Programme: 36 pages, 75p (incl entry & raffle) **Editor:** Andrew Parker (01582 599158) **Nickname:** Rovers
Sponsors: O'Neill Plant Hire **Record Gate:** 160 v Silsoe, Luton & D. Lg 26/1/23.
Midweek home matchday: Tuesday
Clubhouse: Club use Toddington Social & Services Club 600 yds - cold food available
Club record scorer: David Ashby **Club record appearances:** George Stewart, 1050.
Hons: South Midlands Lg Snr Div 94-95 (Snr Div Cup 94-95).

WELWYN GARDEN CITY

Chairman: John Newman **Manager:** Ian Priest. **Physio:** Arthur Wood
Secretary: Keith Browne, 12 Lemsford Road, Hatfield, Herts AL10 0DH (01707 251854)
Ground: Herns Lane, Welwyn Garden City (01707 328470).
Directions: From A1 follow signs for industrial area. Take one-way system opposite Avdel Ltd (signed Hertford B195), take 2nd exit off one-way system. Ground 400 yards on left. One and a half miles from Welwyn GC (BR).
Capacity: 1,500 **Seats:** 40 **Cover:** 120 **Floodlights:** Yes **Founded:** 1921
Cols: Maroon & blue/royal/royal **Change Colours:** Yellow/blue/yellow
Midweek Matches: Tuesday **Club Shop:** Yes **Nickname:** Citzens.
Programme: 24 pages, 50p **Editor:** Keith Browne (01707 251854).
Record Gate: 600 v Welwyn Garden United.
Best FA Vase year: 1st Rd 86-87. **Best FA Cup year:** First Qual.Rd. 94-95.
Clubhouse: Open every night and weekend lunchtimes. Members Bar, Hall. Steward: Dave Parham.
Hons: Herts Charity Shield 27-28 86-87 87-88 94-95, Sth Mids Lg 73-74 (R-up 85-86, Div 1 69-70 81-82, Lg Cup R-up 74-75 81-82 88-89, Reserve Cup 85-86).

SENIOR DIVISION

AMPTHILL TOWN

Chairman: Richard Brown **President:** Gary Williams.
Secretary: Eric Turner, 34 Dunstable Street, Ampthill, Beds MK45 2JT (01525 403128).
Manager: Neil Rodney.
Ground: Woburn Road, Ampthill (01525 404440)
Directions: From Ampthill Town Centre follow signs to Woburn then 1st right into Ampthill Park.
Capacity: 1,500 **Seats:** 30 **Cover:** 400 **Floodlights:** No **Founded:** 1888.
Colours: Yellow+Navy/Blue/Blue. **Change Colours:** Yellow+Red/Red/Red **Nickname:** Town
Midweek home matchday: Tuesday **Programme:** 16 pages, 50p with admission.
Hons: Sth Mids Lg 59-60 (C'ship Shield 58-59 59-60), North Beds Charity Cup 84-85.

A.C.D.

Chairman: Martin O'Brien
Secretary: Terry Owen, 29 Elm Partk Close, Houghton Regis, Dunstable, Beds LU5 5PN. (01582 863273).
Ground: A.C.D. Sports Ground, High Street North, Dunstable (01582 678668)
Directions: On A5 trunk Road to the north of Dunstable. Entrance to ground 150 yards south of traffic lights at chalk cutting.
Colours: Red & white/red/red **Change cols:** White/red/white
Programme Editor: Martin Johnson (01582 603931)

HOLMER GREEN

Chairman/Match Secretary: Bill Scholes
Secretary: John Anderson, The Brambles, Penfold Lane, Holmer Green Bucks HP15 6XS (01494 713867)
Ground: Watchet Lane, Holmer Green (01494 711485)
Directions: From Amersham on A404 High Wycombe Road, after approx 2 miles turn right into Sheepcote Dell Road. Continue until end of road by Bat & Ball PH. Turn right then immediate left, continue approx 1/2 mile until 2 mini roundabouts, turn left in front of the Mandarin Duck into Watchet Lane, grd 150 yards right.
Colours: All Green **Programme:** Yes **Editor:** Bill Scholes

HOUGHTON TOWN

Chairman: D McMorrow **Manager:** P Rowe.
Secretary: Ken Dye, 9 Luxembourg Close Luton, Beds LU3 3TD (01582 563378)
Ground: Houghton Town Associated Club, Park Rd North, Houghton Regis (01582 866128)
Directions: M1 jct 11, head towards Dunstable, right at island into Poynters Rd, straight over next island keeping left at small r'bout onto Park Rd North - ground on left 10yds before pelican crossing.
Capacity:200. **Seats:** None **Cover:** yes. **Floodlights:** No **Founded:** 1993
Colours: Blue & white/blue/blue **Change Colours:** All red
Programme: 50p **Midweek home matchday:** Tuesday.
Hons: S Mid Lg Chall Trophy R-up 93-94 (Div 1 Cup R-up 93-94), S Mid Div 1 94-95,Div 1 Cup 94-95

KENT ATHLETIC

Secretary: Felix Macquire, 79 Roman Road, Luton, LU4 9DL (01582 584170)
Ground: Tenby Drive, Leagrave, Luton (01582 582723)
Directions: M1 jct 11 take A505 towards Luton. Take the first turning on the left (Stoneygate Road), straight over at the roundabout and turn right at traffic lights into Beechwood Road. Take the first road on the left and then the first right into Tenby Drive. Ground and car park 100 yards on left.
Colours: Black & white/black/black **Change cols:** Green & white/white/green
Pragramme: Yes **Editor:** Eric Smith (01582 482165).

LEVERSTOCK GREEN

Chairman: W.Dawes. **President:** L Bolino
Secretary: S D Robinson, 11 Connaught Close, Hemel Hempstead, Herts HP2 7AB (0442 65734)
Manager: M Vipond **Asst Manager:** D.Johnson.
Ground: Pancake Lane, Leverstock Green, Hemel Hempstead (0442 246280).
Directions: From M1 leave at A4147 to 2nd r-about. 1st exit to Leverstock Green, Pancake Lane is on left 300 yrds past the 'Leather Bottle' pub.
Capacity: **Seats:** 25 **Cover:** 100 **Floodlights:** No **Club Shop:**
Programme: 24 pages, 50p **Editor:** **Press Officer:** B Barter.
Colours: Green & white/black/green **Change Colours:** Green & black/white/black
Sponsor: **Founded:** 1907 **Nickname:** The Green.
Clubhouse: Yes.
95-96 Captain: **95-96 Top scorer:** Rob Smith. **95-96 P.o.Y.:** Wayne Cogswell
Hons: South Midlands Lg Snr Div Cup R-up 93-94, Herts Centenary Tphy R-up 91-92, Herts Charity Shield R-up 91-92, Frank Major Tphy 1991.

MERCEDES BENZ

Chairman: Martin Parlett **President:** Nigel Wells
Sec.: Bob Flight, Mercedes (UK) Ltd, Mercedes Benz Centre, Tongwell, Milton Keynes MK15 8BA (011604 764433).
Manager: Cliff Peters. **Assistant Manager:** Mark Collender.
Coach: Kevin England **Physio:** Nick Booth.
Ground: The Barn, Pannier Place, Downs Barn, Milton Keynes, Bucks (01908 245158).
Directions: M1 jct 14, A509 for Milton Keynes, right onto H5 Portway at 1st island, right onto V9 Overstreet at 3rd island, 1st left into Downs Barn Boulevard, 2nd left into Pannier Place, ground at top of hill.
Capacity: 300 **Cover:** No **Seats:** None **Floodlights:** No **Founded:** 1967.
Colours: Royal/navy/navy **Change Colours:** All white **Nickname:** Blues.
Programme: 16 pages, 50p **Editor:** Stuart Collard. **Club Shop:** No.
Midweek matches: Wednesday **Sponsors:** Mercedes-Benz (UK) Ltd
Reserve team's league: South Midlands Reserve Div.
Clubhouse: Not on ground, but the Mercedes-Benz Sports & Social Club is situated one mile from the ground and is open normal licensing hours.
Record scorer: Stuart Collard 132. **Record appearances:** Stuart Collard 206.
Hons: Nth Bucks Lg Div 1 90-91 (Premier Div Cup 92-93, Intermediate Tphy 91-92), Daimler-Benz Austrian International Tournament R-up 1990.

NEW BRADWELL ST PETER

Chairman: J E Haynes **Vice-Chairman:** K Felce **President:** J P Booden.
Secretary: L Smith, 47 Rowle Close, Stantonbury, Milton Keynes MK14 6BJ (01908 319522).
Manager: S.Spooner. **Press Officer:** P Smith.
Ground: Recreation Ground, Bradwell Road, New Bradwell, Milton Keynes MK13 7AT (01908 313835)
Directions: From M1 Jnt 14 go towards Newport Pagnell, left at 1st r-about into H3 (A422 Monks Way). Over 5 r-abouts, right at 6th island into V6 (Grafton St.), go right the way round (back on yourself) 1st island, 1st left, left at mini-roundabout, ground half mile on left (before bridge).
Nickname: Peters **Seats:** 30 **Cover:** 100 **Floodlights:** No **Founded:** 1902
Colours: Maroon & blue stripes/maroon/maroon **Change:** Green & yellow halves/green/yellow.
Programme: 32 pages, £1 with entry **Editor:** P.Smith (01908 315766).
Midweek home matchday: Wednesday **Sponsors:**New Bradwell St Peter V-Presidents.
Clubhouse: Members only (a member can sign in 2 guests). Open every evening and weekend lunchtimes. No food available.
Hons: Sth Mids Lg Div 1 76-77 83-84 (Reserve Div 2 R-up 76-77)

RISBOROUGH RANGERS

Chairman: Malcolm Drysdale
Secretary: Derrick J Wallace, 42 Ash Rd, Princes Risborough, Bucks HP27 0BQ (01844 345179)
Manager: Dave Dunsworth **Asst Manager:** Mark Avery **Physio:** Ken Sheppard
Ground: Windsor, Horsendon Lane, Princes Risborough (01844 274176)
Directions: Rear of Princes Risborough BR Station (Chiltern Line). A4010 from Aylesbury thru Princes Risborough, fork right onto A4009, left by thatched cottage, over railway bridge, immediate right ground 150 yds on right.
Capacity: 2,000 **Seats:** 25 **Cover:** 100 **Floodlights:** No **Founded:** 1971
Colours: Red & black/black/black. **Change Colours:** Blue & white stripes/white/white.
Programme: 20+ pages, £1 with entry **Editor:** Andrew Woodward (01844 342202) **Club Shop:** No.
Midweek home matchday: Tuesday. **Clubhouse:** Yes. Snacks available matchdays.
Record Gate: 1,200 v Showbiz XI. **Club Sponsors:** Systems 3R **Club record scorer:** Craig Smith.
Hons: Berks & Bucks Jnr Cup 85-86, Wycombe & District Lg Div 2 85-86 (Div 3 84-85).

STONY STRATFORD TOWN

Chairman: Roger Taylor **Manager:** Perry Mercer
Secretary: Maurice J Barber, 26 Boundary Cres., Stony Stratford, Milton Keynes MK11 1DF (0908 567930).
Ground: Sports Ground, Ostlers Lane, Stony Stratford (0908 562267)
Directions: From Dunstable old A5, Watling Street, on approaching Bletchley continue on A5 loop road (Hinkley) to end of dual c'way to A422/A508 r'bout. First exit, thru lights, 2nd right into Ostlers Lane. From M1 jct 13 pick up A421 and join A5 (Hinkley) and proceed as above.
Capacity: 500+ **Seats:** None **Cover:** No **Floodlights:** No **Reformed:** 1953
Previous Leagues: North Bucks & Dist./ Northampton Combination.
Colours: Sky/navy/navy **Change Colours:** Red/black/red
Programme: 10 pages, £1 with entry **Midweek matchday:** Tuesday.
Honours: Sth Mids Lg R-up 70-71 71-72 (Div 1 93-94, Div 1 Cup 93-94).

THE 61 F.C. (LUTON)

Chairman: Mark Davie. **Vice Chairman:** Ms.Nicki Rowley. **President:** G B Mapp.
Secretary/Manager: R Everitt, 44 Somersby Close, Luton LU1 3XB (01582 485095).
Asst Manager: P Miller **Physio:** N.McNully. **Comercial Mgr:** Andrew Rowley.
Ground: Kingsway, Beverley Road, Luton, Beds. (01582 582965)
Directions: M1 jct 11, A505 to Luton centre, right at 1st island, 1st left, Beverley Rd is 3rd left, entrance in Beverley Rd, exactly 1 mile junction 11. All Luton to Dunstable buses pass ground - alight at Beech Hill Bowling Club. One mile from both Leagrave and Luton BR stations.
Capacity: 2,500 **Cover:** 150 **Seats:** 100 **Floodlights:** No **Formed:** 1961
Colours: Sky/royal/royal **Change:** Red/black/red **Nickname:** Two Blues
Club Sponsors: Quality Homecrafts. **Record Gate:** 265 v Selby, SML Tphy final 1st leg, 16/4/88.
Programme: 8 pages **Editor:** Andrew Rowley (01582 611292) **Club Shop:** No.
Midweek home matchday: Wednesday
Clubhouse: Open every evening and weekend lunchtimes. Hot and cold snacks.
Club record scorer: Sandor Simon **Club record appearances:** Roger Smith 620.
Hons: Beds Snr Cup 83-84.

TOTTERNHOE

Chairman: Jim Basterfield **Vice Chairman:** John Power **President:** Alf Joyce.
Secretary: Jim Basterfield, 41 Park Avenue, Totternhoe, Dunstable, Beds LU6 1QF (01582 667941)
Manager: Alex Butler **Assistant Manager:** Paul Simmonds
Physio: Roy Mackerness.
Ground: Totternhoe Recreation Ground, Dunstable (01582 606738).
Directions: Turn off the main Dunstable to Tring Road B489. Ground on right as you enter the Totternhoe. Five miles from Leighton Buzzard (BR), 7 miles from Luton. Bus 61 Luton-Aylesbury.
Capacity: 1,000 **Seats:** 30 **Cover:** 200 **Floodlights:** No **Founded:** 1906
Colours: All red. **Change Colours:** White/blue/blsack.
Record Gate: 300 v Luton Town, clubhouse opening 13/10/82
Programme: 16 pages, 80p with entry **Sponsors:** Building Conservations **Shop:** No.
Midweek home matchday: Tuesday **Club Nickname:** Totts.
Clubhouse: Open evenings 8pm, Saturday after games, Sunday lunchtime. Sweets, confectionary, tea, coffee, soups at matches.
Club record scorer: John Waites, 48 **Club record appearances:** John Binding, 631.
Hons: Sth Mids Lg Div 1 61-62 (R-up 68-69 85-86).

TRING ATHLETIC

Chairman: Steve Thomas **President:** Paul Nichols
Secretary: Ralph Griffiths, 42 Bedgrove, Aylesbury, Bucks HP21 7BD (01296 26425).
Manager: Mick Eldridge **Asst Manager:** Ray Brimson **Physio:** Jean Adams
Ground: Miswell Lane, Tring, Herts.(01442 828331)
Directions: Through Tring on main road towards Aylesbury, right just after Anchor PH into Miswell Lane, pitch approximately 500yds on right opposite Beaconsfield Road. Tring railway station is several miles outside town, but ground can be reached by bus or taxi.
Seats: 25+ **Cover:** 100+ **Floodlights:** No **Founded:** 1958 **Nickname:** Athletic
Colours: Red & black/Black/Black. **Change colours:** Blue & Yellow/Blue/Blue **Sponsors:** Heygates
Programme: 36 pages, 50p **Programme Editor:** Secretary **Club Shop:** No.
Midweek matchday: Wednesday **Previous League:** West Herts 58-88.
Clubhouse: Bar, open matchdays, training nights & Sunday lunchtimes.
Club record scorer: Ian Butler **Club record appearances:** Alan Sheppard.
Hons: West Herts Lg R-up 72-73 (Lg Cup 65-66, Div 1 61-62 64-65 65-66 (R-up 71-72 85-86).

WINSLOW UNITED

Chairman: J B Robins **Manager:** L Lamb.
Secretary: David F Ward, 29 Avenue Rd, Winslow, Buckingham MK18 3DH (01296 713202).
Ground: Winslow Recreation Ground, Elmfields Gate, Winslow (01296 713057)
Directions: A413 from Aylesbury to Winslow, in High Street turn right into Emerald Gate, ground 100yds on left opposite car park. From Milton Keynes take A421 to Buckingham, turn left thru Gt Horwood to Winslow, turn left off High Street into Emerald Gate.
Capacity: 2,000 **Seats:** 25 **Cover:** 100 **Floodlights:** Yes **Founded:** 1891.
Colours: Yellow/blue/blue **Change Colours:** Red/white/white **Club Shop:** No.
Record Gate: 720 v Aylesbury Utd, Berks & Bucks Snr Cup.
Programme: 16 pages, £1 with entry **Editor:** J Robins (01296 714206).
Midweek home matchday: Tuesday
Clubhouse: Open every eveining except Wednesday. Full weekend opening.
Hons: Sth Mids Lg R-up 75-76 (Div 1 74-75), Leighton Challenge Cup 92-93.

DIVISION ONE

ABBEY NATIONAL (M.K.)

Secretary: Michael Burnside, 32 Falcon View, Greens Norton, Northants NN12 8BT (01327 352095).
Ground: Loughton Sports & Social Club, Linceslade Grove, Loughton, Milton Keynes (01908 690668)
Directions: From M1 Jct 14 follow H6, Childs Way for 5 miles until V4 Watling Way (Knowlhill r-about), right to Loughton r-about, right along H5 Portway - 1st right Linceslade Grove.
Capacity: 550 **Cover:** 40 **Seats:** 25 **Floodlights:** No **Founded:** 1947.
Cols: All Green & white **Change Colours:** Black & white stripes/white/black.
Programme: Yes **Midweek matchday:** Doug Sinclair (01525 376952).

BEDFORD EAGLES

Chairman: David Donnelly
Secretary: Barry Stephenson, 9 Aspen Avenue, Putnoe, Bedford, MK41 8BX (01234 342276)
Ground: The New Eyrie, Meadow Lane Cardington, Bedford MK44 3SB (01234 838448)
Directions: A1 come off at Sandy, follow signs for Bedford, thr Willington, ground on right.
Colours: Blue & white/blue/blue **Programme Editor:** Matt Webb (01234 364191)

BIGGLESWADE UNITED

Chairman: David Lee
Secretary: Tracey James, 17 Havelock Road, Biggleswade, Beds SG18 0DB (01767 316270)
Ground: Second Meadow, Fairfield Road, Biggleswade, (01767 600408)
Directions: From A1 Sainsbury's roundabout, cross over iron bridge and take first left into Sun Street. Take next turn left into Fairfield Road ground at bottom of road in lane
Colours: Blue & black/black/black **Programme Editor:**

BRIDGER PACKAGING

Chairman: Lawrence Bridger
Secretary: Laurence Jack, 8 Lambsmeadow, Arlesey, Beds SG15 6RY (01462 835661)
Ground: Letchworth Corner Sports Club, Muddy Lane, Letchworth, Herts.
Directions: A1M junc 9 towards Letchworth, over large roundabout, turn left at next roundabout A505 Hitchin, thr lights, turn left at pelican crossing into Muddy Lane.
Colours: Yellow/sky/yellow **Programme Editor:** John Furness (01462 673402)

BUCKINGHAM UNITED

Chairman: Tony Diston
Secretary: Stuart Mackey, 10 Gawcott Fields, Buckingham, Bucks MK18 1TL (01280 816903)
Ground: Ford Meadow, Ford Street, Buckingham (01280 816257)
Directions: A421 Buckingham Road, right aty roundabout. At next 'T' junction you are opposite The New Inn Public House and Phillips Rover dealership, go between, ground on left.
Colours: All royal blue
Programme Editor: Stuart Mackey

CADDINGTON

Chairman: David Mark **Manager:** Leigh Glenister
Secretary: Leigh Glenister,14 Elaine Gardens, Woodside,Luton.LU1 4Dl.(01582 477557)
Ground: Caddington Recreation Club, Manor Road, Luton (01582 450151).
Directions: On entering village turn into Manor Road (adjacent to shops and village green), proceed 500 metres: Clubhouse and ground on left side next to Catholic Church.
Capacity: Unknown **Seats:** Not yet **Cover:** Due **Floodlights:** No **Founded:** 1971.
Colours: Red & black/black/black **Programme:** No
Record Gate: 150 v Barton Rvrs, Beds Snr Cup.
Nickname: The Oaks **Midweek matchday:** Tuesday or Thursday.
Hons: Beds Intermediate Cup 85-86 92-93

CRAWLEY GREEN SPORTS & SOCIAL

Chairman: John Symonds
Secretary: Neil Ludlow, 159 Cutenhoe Road, Luton, LU1 3NQ (01582 486802)
Ground: Crawley Green Road Recreation Ground (01582 451058).
Directions: M1 junction 10 continue straight on at the roundabout at the end of the motorway slip road into Airport way. At the 4th roundabout turn right into Crawley Green Road, the ground is 800 yards on the left just past Ashcroft.
Colours: Black & blue/black/black **Programme Editor:** Robert Freeman (01582 616640)

DE HAVILLAND

Chairman: M J Hollis **Manager:** P Long.
Secretary: Roy Ridgway, 85 Garden Ave., Hatfield, Herts AL10 8LH (01707 267327).
Ground: Comet Way, Hatfield (01707 263204/ 262665).
Directions: From south leave A1(M) at Hatfield turn, A1001 to Birchwood r'bout, 1st exit into car park. From north leave A1(M) at Welwyn G.C., A1001 to Birchwood r'bout and 4th exit into car park.
Capacity: **Seats:** None **Cover:** No **Floodlights:** No **Founded:** 1934.
Colours: Blue & white halves/white/blue. **Change colours:** Red & white halves/black/red.
Programme: Sometimes, 30p **Editor:** Nigel Upson (01707 272711)

EMBERTON

Chairman/Secretary: R L Dugdale, 9 Stone Court, West Lane, Emberton, Nr Olney, Bucks MK46 5ND (0234 711004).
Manager: P Bone. **Asst Manager:** B.Chapman. **Coach:** C Beard/N Bunker
Ground: Hulton Drive, Emberton, Nr Olney, Bucks.
Directions: M1 jct 14 to Newport Pagnell, right onto A422 at 1st r'bout straight on north towards Olney. Emberton lies before Olney. Turn left at 2nd turning into village and 1st right Hulton Drive. Buses from Northampton, Bedford and Milton Keynes.
Capacity: 400 **Seats:** No **Cover:** No **Floodlights:** No **Reformed:** 1968
Colours: Navy & white/navy/navy **Change colours:** Navy/white **Nickname:** Rams
Programme: No. **Editor:** Bob McKain (01908 604856) **Club Shop:** No.
Sponsors: Dugdale Builders **Record Gate:** 180 v Bedford T., Sth Mids Lg Div 1.
Clubhouse: Matchdays. Tea, coffee, soft drinks, confectionary.Bar after Games.
Club record scorer: D Maloney 54 **Club record appearances:** R L Dugdale.
Hons: Stantonbury Cup R-up 92-93 (SF 91-92).

FLAMSTEAD

Chairman: Colin Hayward **Manager:** Tony Dumingan
Secretary: Susan Hayward, Greenways, Old Watling Street, Flamstead, St Albans, Herts. AL3 8HL (01582 841213)
Ground: Friendless Lane, Flamstead, St Albans, Herts (0582 841307).
Ground Directions: From Dunstable Town Centre travel south on A5 Trunk Road towards the M1. Follow for approximately 3 miles then turn right opposite Hertfordshire Moat House Hotel. Ground and parking approximately half a mile on the corner of the first right turn.
Seats: None **Cover:** None **Floodlights:** No **Founded:** 1962. **Nickname:** None
Colours: Red & white/red/red. **Change Colours:** Orange/black/black.
Programme: 4 pages, 25p **Midweek home matchday:** Tuesday.

LEIGHTON ATHLETIC

Chairman: Robin Bradburn
Secretary: Lin Scott, 1 Meadow Way, Leighton Buzzard, Beds, LU7 8XN.
Ground: Mentmore Road, Linslade, Leighton Buzzard, Beds (01525 370469)
Directions: On A5 north of Dunstable travelling towards Hockliffe turn left on to A505 Leighton Buzzard bypass. At end of bypass turn right towartds Leighton Buzzard and take the first right immediately after the railway bridge into Cedars Way. At 'T' Junction turn left into Mentmore Road, ground 300 yards on right
Colours: Red/black/red **Programme Editor:** Mike Parker (01525 854960)

LUTON OLD BOYS

Chairman: Graham Bailey
Secretary: Roland Dodge, 5 Brunel Road, Luton, LU4 0RX (01582 601705)
Ground: Luton Old Boys, Dunstable Road, Lutopn (01582 582060)
Directions: On the A505 Luton to Dunstable Road between junction 11 of the M1 and Lex Vauxhall Luton.
Colours: Red & white/white/red **Programme Editor:** Secretary.

MURSLEY UNITED

Chairman: Alan Knowles
Secretary: Roger Gurnett, 6 Station Road, Mursley, Milton Keynes MK17 0SA (01296 720505)
Ground: Station Road, Mursley
Directions: A421 Bletchley to Buckingham Road, first right in village
Colours: All Red & white **Programme Editor:** Lena Witkowski (01296 720469)

OLD BRADWELL UNITED

Chairman: Christopher Button
Secretary: David Bird, 24 Loughton Road, Bradwell Village, Milton Keynes MK13 9AA (01908 315947)
Ground: Abbey Road, Bradwell Village, Milton Keynes (01908 312355)
Directions: M1 junction 14 go towards Newport Pagnell. Turn left at first roundabout into H3 Honks Way. Go six roundabouts then turn left onto V6 Grafton Street. Take first right at mini-roundabout into Rawlins Road and then second left into Loughton Road.Take first right into Primrose Road and at the 'T' junction turn right into Abbey Road
Colours: Red & navy/navy/navy **Programme Editor:** Secretary

OLD DUNSTABLIANS

Chairman: Simon Bullard
Secretary: Craig Renfrew, 75B Princes Street. Dunstable Beds LU6 3AS
Ground: Lancot Park. Dunstable Road, Totternhoe (01582 663735)
Directions: From Dunstable Town Centre take the B489 Tring Road. At the 4th roundabout turn right, signposted Totternhoe. The pitch is located withion Dunstable Town Cricket Club which is on the right just before entering the village of Totternhoe.
Colours: White & blue/navy/navy **Programme Editor:** Craig Renfrew

PITSTONE & IVINGHOE

Chairman: Harry Bowden
Secretary: Jay Adlem, 22 Maud Janes Close, Ivinghoe, Leighton Buzzard, Beds LU7 9ED (01296 668663).
Manager: Dave Fox. **Assistant Manager** H.Bowden & R.Adlem.
Ground: Pitstone Recreation Ground, Vicarage Road, Pitstone, Bucks (01296 661271)
Directions: Tring Rd from Dunstable, turn right for Ivinghoe, and continue through to Pitstone r-about; ground left then right. From Aylesbury - left at 'Rising Sun' in Aston Clinton, keep on that road to Pitstone r'bout; ground right then right. Bus 61 from Luton or Aylesbury. Nearest BR stations are Tring or Cheddington.
Cover: 100 **Seats:** 25 **Capacity:** 500 **Floodlights:** No **Founded:** 1958
Colours: Red & black stripes/black/black **Change Colours:** Blue/blue/white.
Midweek home matches: Tuesday
Programme: 16 pages £1 with admission **Editor:** Laurie McPharland (01442 401704)
Clubhouse: Open after every match 3.30pm until late. Snacks available.
Hons: Sth Mids Lg 89-90 (Div 1 87-88, Lg Cup 88-89, Div 1 Cup 87-88).

SCOT

Chairman: Peter Soper **Manager:** Peter Soper
Secretary: Ann Land, 18 Coleridge Close, Bletchley, Milton Keynes. MK3 5AF (01908 372228)
Ground: Selbourne Ave., Bletchley, Milton Keynes (01908 368881).
Directions: Main roads to Bletchley then A421 Buckingham road, at Glen Garage right into Newton Rd, 2nd left into Selbourne Ave., through railway bridge to bottom of road.
Capacity: **Seats:** None **Cover:** No **Floodlights:** No **Founded:** 1968.
Colours: Blue & white/blue/blue **Change Colours:** Yellow/Blue/Yellow.
Programme: Yes **Editor:** Drew Dias (01908 379877) **Nickname:** Scots.
Midweek home matches: Wednesday **Hons:** Nth Bucks & Dist. Lg 91-92.

WALDEN RANGERS

Chairman: Alan Curran **Manager:** Cliff Bailey.
Secretary: Irene Oodian, 9 Garfield Court, Handcross Rd, Luton, Beds LU2 8JZ (0582 483090).
Ground: Breachwood Green Rec., Chapel Rd, Breachwood Green, Herts (0438 833332).
Directions: From Luton Airport roundabout (Eaton Green Rd)(away from Vauxhall/ IBC direction) take country road to Breachwood Green (2 miles). From Hitchin on A602, take country road to Preston (6 miles to Breachwood Green).
Floodlights: No **Founded:** 1966
Colours: Blue & black/black/black **Programme Editor:** Alan Clark (01582 451202)

BEDFORDSHIRE F.A.

Secretary: Peter D Brown,
19 Lambs Close, Dunstable LU5 4QA (01582 668013)
01582 565111 (County Office) Fax: 01582 565222

BEDFORDSHIRE SENIOR CUP
(FOUNDED 1894–95)

RECENT FINALS

1990–91	Electrolux	v	Barton Rovers	3–3 (4–2 Pens)
1991–92	Kempston Rovers	v	Totternhoe	1–0
1992–93	Leighton Town	v	Kempston Rovers	2–1
1993–94	Potton United	v	Stotfold	2–1
1994–95	Bedford Town	v	Toddington Rovers	5–3 (AET)

MOST WINS Waterlows 10 Dunstable 9 Luton Clarence 8

1995–1996

BEDFORDSHIRE PREMIER CUP

14 CLUBS **HOLDERS: POTTON UNITED**

FIRST ROUND

Kempston Rovers	v	Brache Sparta	0–2	Dunstable United	v	Shillington	0–4
Biggleswade Town	v	Langford	1–2	Bedford Town	v	Wootton Blue Cross	3–1
Potton United	v	Arlesey Town	1–4	Stotfold	v	Luton Town	2*3

2 Clubs with Byes Barton Rovers & Leighton Town

SECOND ROUND

Leighton Town	v	Brache Sparta	3p4 0*0	Barton Rovers	v	Luton Town	2*1
Arlesey Town	v	Bedford Town	0*1	Shillington	v	Langford	2–1

SEMI-FINALS

Brache Sparta	v	Bedford Town	0*3	Barton Rovers	v	Shillington	2–1

FINAL (Two legs)
BEDFORD TOWN v BARTON ROVERS 0–0
BARTON ROVERS v BEDFORD TOWN 1–0

BEDFORDSHIRE SENIOR CUP

20 CLUBS **HOLDERS: BEDFORD TOWN**

PRELIMINARY ROUND

Wootton B Cross	v	61 FC Luton	5–1	Stotfold	v	Dunstable United	4–2
Potton United	v	Biggleswade Town	1–0	Langford	v	Houghton Town	0–1

FIRST ROUND

Kempston Rovers	v	Totternhoe	0–2	Potton United	v	Wootton Blue Cross	0–1
Houghton Town	v	Toddington Rovers	1–4	Stotfold	v	Barton Rovers	2*4
ACD FC	v	Ampthill Town	1–3	Shillington	v	Bedford United	0A0 0–1
Bedford Town	v	Brache Sparta	2–1	Leighton Town	v	Arlesey Town	1–2

SECOND ROUND

Wootton B Cross	v	Ampthill Town	1–3	Totternhoe	v	Barton Rovers	1–3
Bedford United	v	Bedford Town	0–4	Toddington Rovers	v	Arlesey Town	1–2

SEMI-FINALS

Bedford Town	v	Ampthill Town	2–1	Barton Rovers	v	Arlesey Town	2–0

at Kempston Rovers FC. Tuesday 5th March 1996 — at Stotfold FC. Wednesday 6th March 1996

FINAL
BARTON ROVERS v BEDFORD TOWN 0–1 at Kenilworth Road, Luton Town FC

BERKS & BUCKS F.A.

Secretary: W J Gosling,
15a London Street, Faringdon, Oxon SN7 8AG
(01367 242099 County Office) Fax: (01367) 242158

BERKS & BUCKS SENIOR CUP (FOUNDED 1878–79)

RECENT FINALS

1990–91	Marlow	v	Wycombe Wanderers	3–2
1991–92	Chesham United	v	Windsor & Eton	3–1
1992–93	Chesham United	v	Abingdon Town	1–0
1993–94	Marlow	v	Chesham United	1–0
1994–95	Reading	v	Slough Town	1–0

MOST WINS Wycombe 24 Maidenhead United 15 Marlow 13

1995–1996

BERKS & BUCKS SENIOR CUP

18 CLUBS **HOLDERS: READING**

2nd QUALIFYING ROUND (1st Not Used)

Burnham	v	Flackwell Heath	3–2	Thatcham Town	v	Newport Pagnell Tn	7–0

FIRST ROUND PROPER

Maidenhead Utd	v	Bracknell Town	1–0	Abingdon Town	v	Buckingham Town	2-1
Marlow	v	Thatcham Town	0–2	Wycombe Wand'rs	v	Aylesbury United	1–2
Reading	v	Slough Town	3–2	Chesham United	v	Hungerford Town	0–2
Chalfont St Peter	v	Windsor & Eton	0–1	Burnham	v	Wokingham Town	1–5

SECOND ROUND Tuesday 20th February 1996

Abingdon Town	v	Reading	1–3	Wokingham Town	v	Hungerford Town	3–0
Thatcham Town	v	Aylesbury United	0–2	Windsor & Eton	v	Maidenhead United	0–2

SEMI-FINALS March/April 1996

Reading	v	Wokingham Town	0–2	Maidenhead Utd	v	Aylesbury United	2–2 0–4

FINAL Monday 6.5.96.
AYLESBURY UNITED v WOKINGHAM TOWN 0–1 at Buckingham Road, Aylesbury United FC.

BERKS & BUCKS SENIOR TROPHY

44 CLUBS **HOLDERS; LAMBOURN SPORTS**

SECOND QUALIFYING ROUND Saturday 16th December

Holmer Green	v	Mortimer	1–0	Wantage Town	v	Old Paludians	3–0
Reading Town	v	Winslow United	4–1	Stocklake	v	Risborough Rangers	1•1 3–1
Amersham Town	v	Forest Old Boys	2–1	New Bradwell St P	v	Prestwood	10–1
Milton Keynes	v	Finchamstead	1–0	Pitstone & Iv	v	Beaconsfield SYCOB	1–4
Didcot Town	v	Wooburn Athletic	0–1	Binfield	v	Sandhurst Town	1*1 3–2
Wraysbury	v	Kintbury Rangers	2–1	Abingdon United	v	Milton United	2-0
Reading Exiles	v	Chalfont Wasps	4–1	Letcombe	v	Broadmoor Social	1–2

2 Clubs exempt Eton Wick, Lambourn Sports into the

FIRST ROUND PROPER

Amersham Town	v	Lambourn Sports	2–4	Holmer Green	v	Wooburn Athletic	3–0
Reading Exiles	v	Beaconsfield SYCOB	1–0	Abingdon United	v	Broadmoor Social	1–4
Wraysbury	v	Reading Town	0–1	Milton Keynes	v	Eton Wick	2–0
Stocklake	v	Binfield	3–2	Wantage Town	v	N Bradwell St Peter	0–1

SECOND ROUND Saturday 24th February 1996

Broadmoor Social	v	Holmer Green	1–4	Lambourn Sports	v	New Bradwell St Peter	1–0
Stocklake	v	Milton Keynes	1–2	Reading Exiles	v	Reading Town	2–3

SEMI-FINALS Saturday 30th March 1996

Milton Keynes	v	Lambourn Sports	1–3	Reading Town	v	Holmer Green	3–1

FINAL Saturday 27th April 1996 3.00pm
LAMBOURN SPORTS v READING TOWN 1–2 at Waterside Park, Thatcham Town FC.

CHILTONIAN FOOTBALL LEAGUE

Hon. Secretary: A R Ford, Pennings Cottage, Aldershot Road, Guildford, Surrey. Tel (01483) 567284, Mobile 0378 628547

FINAL LEAGUE TABLES 1995/96

Premier Div	P	W	D	L	F	A	Pts
1. Binfield	30	25	1	4	97	30	76
2. Denham Utd	30	22	6	2	94	28	72
3. Quarry Nomads	30	19	4	7	64	40	61
4. AFC Wallingford	30	18	6	6	89	53	60
5. Wraysbury	30	18	5	7	79	40	59
6. Stocklake	30	13	8	9	65	53	47
7. Old Paludians	30	14	1	15	58	50	43
8. Iver	30	13	3	14	43	44	42
9. Finchampstead	30	11	5	14	51	53	38
10. Martin Baker S	30	10	7	13	48	51	37
11. Penn & Tylers	30	10	7	13	40	57	37
12. Broadmoor Spt	30	11	1	18	49	98	34
13. Henley Town	30	7	8	15	52	68	29
14. Wooburn Ath	30	5	6	19	36	75	21
15. Prestwood	30	4	4	22	41	90	16
16. Chalfont Wasps	30	3	2	25	31	107	11

Div One	P	W	D	L	F	A	Pts
1. Vansittart Wand	20	16	1	3	61	23	49
2. Finchampstead	20	13	6	1	61	28	45
3. Slough Heating	20	14	3	3	45	15	45
4. Wraysbury Res	20	13	2	5	52	35	41
5. Denham Utd R	20	10	3	7	45	33	33
6. Binfield Res	30	9	3	8	43	39	30
7. Drayton Wand	20	9	0	11	37	35	27
8. Iver Res	20	4	3	13	24	54	15
9. Beaconsfield R	20	2	5	13	30	49	11
10. M Baker Sp R	20	2	5	13	27	55	11
11. Cippenham	20	0	5	15	22	81	5

SENIOR LEAGUE CUP FINAL 1995-96: **Holders; Holmer Green**

Denham United v AFC Wallingford 1-1, (6-7 pen)

PREMIER DIVISION CLUBS 1995-96

AFC WALLINGFORD

Secretary: Mr E Gniadek, 17 Offas Close, Benson, Wallingford, Oxon OX10 6NR (01491 838540).
Ground: Hithercroft, Wallingford, Oxon.
Colours: Red & black/black **Change colours:** Green & yellow/green

BINFIELD

Secretary: Paul Hammerstone, 3 Knox Green, Binfield, Berks RG12 5HZ (01344 427179).
Ground: Stubbs Hill, Binfield, Berks.
Colours: All red **Change colours:** Blue/black

BROADMOOR SOCIAL

Secretary: Mr M A Roberts, 14 Hone Hill, Sandhurst, Camberley, Surrey (01252 879513).
Ground: Cricket Field Grove, Broadmoor Est., Crowthorne, Berks (01344 772612).
Colours: Red/white/white. **Change colours:** Green/black.

D.C.A. BASINGSTOKE

Secretary: D J Brand, 128 Stratfield Rd, Oakridge, Basingstoke, Hants RG21 2SA (01256 57309).
Ground: Whiteditch Playing Field, Sherbourne Rd, Basingstoke, Hants (01256 844866).
Colours: Maroon/Navy/Navy

DENHAM UNITED

Secretary: Colin Stevens, 18 The Dene, West Molesey, Surrey KT8 2HL (0181 783 0433).
Ground: Oxford Road, Denham, Bucks (01895 238717).
Colours: Blue & white/blue **Change colours:** Red & Black/black

ETON WICK

Secretary: Mr Joe Bussey, 50 Tilestone Close, Eton Wick, Windsor, Berks SL4 6NG (01753 859493).
Ground: Haywards Mead, Eton Wick, Windsor (01753 852749).
Colours: Amber/black **Change colours:** All white

FINCHAMPSTEAD

Secretary: Mr R Bradley, 37 Alpha Rd, Chobham, Surrey GU24 8NE (01276 855367).
Ground: Memorial Ground, Finchampstead (01734 732890).
Colours: Blue & white stripes/blue **Change colours:** All red.

HENLEY TOWN

Secretary: Mr A Kingston, 50 Birdhill Ave., Reading, Berks RG2 7JU.
Ground: The Triangle Ground, Mill Lane, Henley-on-Thames, Oxon (0491 576463).
Colours: White/black/black **Change colours:** Claret & blue/black.

IVER

Secretary: Mr S Law, 59 Grange Way, Iver, Bucks SL0 9NT (01753 819780).
Ground: Lee Barton, High Street, Iver, Bucks (01753 651248).
Colours: Yellow & navy stripes/navy **Change colours:** White & blue halves/blue.

MARTIN BAKER SPORTS & SOCIAL

Secretary: W Wright, Hillside Cottage, Tilehouse Lane, Denham, Bucks UB9 5DD (01895 832977).
Ground: Martin's Field, Tilehouse Lane, Denham, Bucks (01895 833077).
Colours: Blue & black/black **Change colours:** White/blue.

OLD PALUDIANS

Secretary: D Aslett, 14 Cornwall Close, Eton Wick, Windsor, Berks SL4 6NB (01628 31176).
Ground: Stanley Jones Field, Berry Hill, Taplow, near Maidenhead (01628 21745).
Colours: Sky/navy **Change colours:** Maroon/white.

PENN & TYLERS GREEN

Secretary: Mr R Dalling, 28 Baring Rd, Beaconsfield, Bucks HP9 2NE (01494 671424).
Ground: French School Meadow, Elm Road, Penn, Bucks (01494 815346).
Colours: Blue & white stripes/blue. **Change colours:** Yellow/blue.

PEPPARD

Secretary: Chris Boyles, 14 Redwood Ave, Woodley, Reading, Berks RG5 4DR (0118 969 9488)
Ground: Bishopswood Sports Centre, Horsepond Rd, Sonning Common, nr Reading (01734 712265).
Colours: All red **Change colours:** Sky/navy/navy

PRESTWOOD

Secretary: Mr G Stansbury, 31 Colne Rd, High Wycombe, Bucks (01494 521792).
Ground: Prestwood Sports Centre, Honor End Lane, Prestwood, Great Missenden, Bucks (01240 65946).
Colours: Claret & sky/white **Change colours:** Sky/white.

QUARRY NOMADS

Secretary: K Dalton, 58 Pitts Rd, Headington, Oxon (01865 65332).
Ground: St Margarets Road, Headington, Oxford.
Colours: Black & white stripes/black **Change colours:** Red & white stripes/white.

STOCKLAKE

Secretary: Mr Tom Exton, 116 Narbeth Drive, Aylesbury, Bucks HP20 1PZ (01296 415780).
Ground: Stocklake Sports & Social Club, Hayward Way, Aylesbury, Bucks (01296 23324).
Colours: Yellow/blue **Change colours:** Coral/purple

WOOBURN ATHLETIC

Secretary: Mr B Nash, 10 Philip Drive, Flackwell Heath, Bucks HP10 9JB (01628 523293).
Ground: Wooburn Park, Town Lane, Wooburn Green, Bucks (01628 819201/520772).
Colours: Red & white/red **Change colours:** Green/white

WRAYSBURY-COOPERS

Secretary: Mr J Rice, 77 Grange Way, Iver, Bucks (01753 652780).
Ground: Memorial Ground, Wraysbury, Bucks (01784 482155).
Colours: Red/black **Change Colours:** Claret & Blue/red

READING FOOTBALL LEAGUE

President: Leon Summers
Chairman: John Dell
Secretary: David Jeanes, 6 Hawkesbury Drive, Fords Farm, Calcot, Reading RG3 5ZP (01734 413926)

FINAL LEAGUE TABLES 1995/96

SENIOR DIVISION

		Home			Away						
	P	W	D	L	W	D	L	F	A	GD	Pts
1. Reading Exiles	22	10	1	0	7	1	3	49	18	31	53
2. Mortimer	22	9	2	0	7	2	2	56	23	33	53
3. Forest	22	9	1	1	5	5	1	48	22	26	48
4. Checkendon	22	7	2	2	5	2	4	55	34	21	40
5. Sutton Exiles	22	7	2	2	4	3	4	52	45	7	38
6. South Reading	22	6	2	3	2	0	9	45	50	-5	26
7. AFC Maidenhead	22	5	0	6	2	5	4	38	44	-6	26
8. Woodley Yeoman	22	4	4	3	2	1	8	53	47	6	23
9. West Reading	22	3	3	5	3	2	6	38	45	-7	23
10. Cookham Dean	22	2	3	6	3	2	6	29	50	-21	20
11. Marlow	22	3	3	5	1	1	9	29	46	-17	16
12. Reading Old Blues	22	1	2	8	0	1	10	21	89	-68	6

PREMIER DIVISION

		Home			Away						
	P	W	D	L	W	D	L	F	A	Gd	Pts
1. Unity	22	7	3	1	8	1	2	67	25	42	49
2. Roundhead	22	9	1	1	4	4	3	54	39	15	44
3. REME	22	7	4	0	5	3	3	70	25	45	43
4. Emmbrook Sports	22	6	2	3	5	2	4	54	37	17	37
5. Ibis	22	6	2	3	4	1	6	55	53	2	33
6. SEB Reading	22	5	2	4	4	3	4	55	58	-3	32
7. Cox Green	22	5	3	3	3	3	5	49	43	6	30
8. Earlbourne	22	4	2	5	3	3	5	56	50	6	26
9. Cantely Manor	22	3	1	7	4	1	6	45	69	-24	23
10. Reading University	22	4	0	7	2	4	5	30	62	-32	22
11. Berks CS	22	3	2	6	2	0	9	30	69	-39	17
12. Forst OB Reserves	22	0	4	7	3	1	7	33	68	-35	14

SENIOR DIV.

A.F.C. MAIDENHEAD

Secretary: Mrs D Saunders, 63 Furze Road, Maidenhead, SL6 7NF (01628 35994)
Ground: Cox Green School, Highfield Lane, Maidenhead
Colours: Green/white/green **Reserves colours:** Red/black/black

CHECKENDON SPORTS

Secretary: Ernie Smith, 10 Emmens Close, Checkendon, Reading RG8 0TU (01491 681575).
Ground: Checkendon PF
Colours: Blue & white/black/white **Reserve colours:** Red & blue/red/red & blue

COOKHAM DEAN

Secretary: Rory Gavin, 14 Northfield Rd, Maidenhead SL6 7JP (01628 832997)
Ground: Alfred Major Rec., Hillcrest Ave., Cookham Rise, Maidenhead.
Colours: Red & black/black/red. **Reserve colours:** Red & black/black/red

FOREST OLD BOYS

Secretary: Bob Hulett, 10 Ramsbury Drive, Earley, Reading RG6 2RT (01734 663514).
Ground: Holme Park, Sonning (01734 690356)
Colours: Yellow & blue/blue/blue. **Reserve coloures:** Red & black/red/red

MORTIMER

Secretary: Steve Dell, 30 Croft Rd, Mortimer, nr Reading RG7 3TS (01734 333821).
Ground: Alfred Palmer Mem. P.F., West End Rd, Mortimer.
Colours: Amber/black/black **Reserve Colours:**

READING EXILES

Secretary: M J Aust, 24 Aylsham Close, Tilehurst, Reading RG3 4XG (01734 421453).
Ground: Palmer Park Sports Stadium, Wokingham Road Reading
Colours: Royal & white stripes/royal/royal **Reserve Colours:** Navy & white stripes/navy/navy

ROUNDHEAD

Secretary: Eric Wise, 63 St Saviours Rd, Reading RG1 6EJ (01734 588426).
Ground: Prospect Park, St Saviours Rd, Coley, Reading.
Colours: Green & yellow/black/black **Reserve Colours:** Green/black/black

SOUTH READING

Secretary: David Spiller, 5 Village Close, Whitley Wood, Reading (01734 864989).
Ground: Whitley Wood Recreation Ground, Basingstoke Rd, Reading
Colours: Red & black/black/black. **Reserve Colours**

SUTTON EXILES

Secretary: Michael Charles, 32 Eastwood Rd, Woodley, Reading RG5 3PY (01734 448130).
Ground: Cantley Park, Milton Road, Wokingham (01734 793188)
Colours: All blue **Reserve Colours:**

UNITY

Secretary: Trevor Lowe, 161 Cotswold Way, Tilehurst, Reading RG31 6ST (01734 455133)
Ground: Cintra Park
Colours: Amber/black/black **Reserve Colours:**

WEST READING

Secretary: Mrs Susan Porton, 6 Hampstead Court, Grovelands Rd, Reading RG3 2QQ (01734 504034).
Ground: Victoria Recreation Ground.
Colours: Amber/black/black & amber **Reserve Colours:**

WOODLEY YEOMAN

Secretary: Bob Brodrick, 44 Hilltop Road, Earley, Reading RG6 1OA (01734 342478)
Ground: Woodford Park, Haddon Drive, Woodley
Colours: Green/black/black **Reserves colours:** Green/green/white

PREMIER DIVISION

COX GREEN

Secretary: Mrs Janet Gilbert, 6 Anstey Place, Burghfield Common RG7 3NQ (01734 835473).
Ground: Desborough Pk, The Croft, Norden Rd, Maidenhead.

EARLBOURNE

Secretary: Andrew Beach, 24 Quentin Road, Woodley, Reading RG5 3NE (01734 697162).
Ground: Woodford Park, Haddon Drive, Woodley, Reading RG5 4LY (01734 690356).

EMMBROOK SPORTS CLUB

Secretary: Steve Haynes, 15 Tilney Way,Lower Earley RG6 4AD (01734 670459).
Ground: Emmbrook Sports Ground, Lowther Road, Emmbrook, Wokingham (01734 780209).

IBIS

Secretary: Tony McGrath, 25 Luscombe Close, Caversham, Reading RG4 0LG (01734 478161).
Ground: IBIS Sports Club, Scours Lane, Reading RG3 6AY (01734 424130).

LOWER EARLEY

Secretary: Steve Price, 50 Faygate Way, Lower Earley, Reading RG6 4DA (01734 611652)
Ground: Laurel Park, Marefield, Lower Earley

MARLOW UNITED

Secretary: Rae Flint, 30 Dean Street, Marlow, Bucks SL7 3AE (01628 476611).
Ground: Gossmore Park, Gossmore Lane, Marlow.

PEGASUS

Secretary: Barry Hoy, 24 Hadleigh Rise, Caversham Park Village, Reading RG4 0RW (01734 476434)
Ground: Emmer Green Recreation Ground

R.E.M.E. ARBORFIELD

Secretary: Peter Davies, 73 Chestnut Cres., Shinfield, Reading RG2 9HA (01734 884107).
Ground: Sports Pavilion, Biggs Lane, Princess Marina College, Arborfield

READING OLD BLUES

Secretary: Andrew Davies, 74 Hemdeon Road, Caversham RG4 7ST (01734 474621)
Ground: Sol Joel Playing Field, Church Rd, Earley, Reading.

S.E.B. (READING)

Secretary: George Walker, 9 Springdale, Lower Earley, Reading RG6 5PR (01734 670846)
Ground: Christchurch Meadows, George Street, Caversham, Reading

SHINFIELD

Secretary: Nigel Blunt, 6 Mayfields, Sindlesham RG41 5BY (01734 772791)
Ground: Millworth Lane, Shinfield, Reading

SONNING COMMON

Secretary: Steve Hill, 52 Loxwood, Lower Earley, Reading RG6 5QZ (01734 752753)
Ground: The Pavilion, King George VI Memorial Playing Fields, Pound Lane Sonning

BIRMINGHAM F.A.

Secretary: M Pennick FFA,
Ray Hall Lane, Great Barr, Birmingham B43 6JF
Tel: (01213) 574278 (County Office) Fax: 01213 581661

BIRMINGHAM SENIOR CUP (FOUNDED 1875–76)

RECENT FINALS

1990–91	West Bromwich Alb	v	Nuneaton Borough	2–0
1991–92	VS Rugby	v	Birmingham City	3–1
1992–93	Nuneaton Borough	v	VS Rugby	2–0
1993–94	Walsall	v	Hednesford Town	3–0
1994–95	Solihull Borough	v	Aston Villa	2–0

MOST WINS Aston Villa 19 Birmingham City 7 Kidderminster Harriers 7 Wolverhampton Wanderers 7

1995–1996

BIRMINGHAM SENIOR CUP

45 CLUBS **HOLDERS: SOLIHULL BOROUGH**

FIRST ROUND

Halesowen Harrs	v	Racing Club Warwick	0–2
Knowle	v	Tividale	4–3
Oldbury United	v	Redditch United	4–0
Gornal Athletic	v	Atherstone United	0–0 2–4
Brierley Hill Tn	v	Darlaston	2–0
Lye Town	v	Paget Rangers	1–1 2–1
Wednesfield	v	Highgate United	1–1 3–1
Sutton Coldfield Tn	v	Moor Green	2–4
Northfield Town	v	West Midlands Police	1–3
Boldmere St Mich'	v	Tamworth	1–4
Willenhall Town	v	Stourbridge	1–0
Banbury United	v	Evesham United	1–2
Cradley Town	v	Dudley Town	1–4

19 Clubs with Byes into the

SECOND ROUND Saturday 2nd December 1995

Bolehall Swifts	v	Lye Town	0–4
Bedworth United	v	Brierley Hill Town	5–0
Worcester City	v	West Midlands Police	3–1
Sandwell Borough	v	Birmingham City	1–2
Walsall	v	Kings Heath	1–0
Evesham United	v	Wednesfield	2–3
Burton Albion	v	Nuneaton Borough	2–1
Tamworth	v	Halesowen Town	1–1 2–1
Knowle	v	Racing Club Warwick	2–1
VS Rugby	v	Willenhall Town	3–1
Coleshill Town	v	Solihull Borough	1–3
Wolverhampton W	v	Oldbury United @OU	2–0
Aston Villa	v	Stratford Town @ST	2–1
Atherstone United	v	Coventry City	0–3
Moor Green	v	Dudley Town	1–3
Hednesford Town	v	West Bromwich Albion	2–3

THIRD ROUND by 6th January 1996

Wednesfield	v	Bedworth United	0–3
Wolverhampton	v	Lye Town @LT	1–0
Dudley Town	v	Birmingham City	0–3
Burton Albion	v	Walsall @BA	0–0 0–3
Aston Villa @WC	v	Worcester City	2–1
VS Rugby	v	Coventry City	1–2
Knowle	v	West Bromwich A	0–0 0–2
Solihull Borough	v	Tamworth	1–0

FOURTH ROUND by 17th February 1996

Solihull Borough	v	West Bromwich Albion	0–2
Walsall	v	Coventry City	2–1
W'hpton Wanderers	v	Birmingham City	2–3
Bedworth United	v	Aston Villa	1–2

SEMI-FINALS

Aston Villa	v	West Bromwich Albion	3–1
Walsall	v	Birmingham City	0–1

FINAL Monday 6th May 1996, 7.30pm.
BIRMINGHAM CITY v ASTON VILLA 2–0 at St Andrews Stadium, Birmingham City FC

CAMBRIDGESHIRE F.A.

Secretary: Roger Pawley,
3 Signet Court, Swanns Road, Cambridge CB5 8LA
(01223) 576770 (County Office) Fax: (01223) 576780

CAMBRIDGESHIRE INVITATION CUP (FOUNDED 1950–51)

RECENT FINALS

1990–91	Soham Town Rangers	v	March Town United	4–1
1991–92	Wisbech Town	v	Cambridge City	2–0
1992–93	Cambridge City	v	Wisbech Town	3–1
1993–94	Chatteris Town	v	Wisbech Town	3–1
1994–95	Wisbech Town	v	Cambridge City	4–2

MOST WINS Wisbech Town 9 Cambridge City 8 Chatteris Town 7

1995–1996

CAMBRIDGESHIRE INVITATION CUP

12 CLUBS **HOLDERS: WISBECH TOWN**

PRELIMINARY ROUND 31st October–1st November

March Town Utd	v	Great Shelford	0–2	Chatteris Town	v	Soham Town Rangers	0–1
Histon	v	Foxton	1–5	Newmarket Town	v	Leverington Sports	4–2

FIRST ROUND

Mildenhall Town	v	Cambridge City	2–1	Chatteris Town	v	Foxton	1–5
Ely City	v	Newmarket	5p4 0*0 1*1	Wisbech Town	v	Great Shelford	5–2

(Wisbech Town are removed from the Competition and Great Shelford Re-instated)

SEMI-FINALS (Both at Histon FC)

Foxton	v	Ely City	3–2	Great Shelford	v	Mildenhall Town	1–2

FINAL Friday 3rd May 7.30pm
FOXTON v MILDENHALL TOWN 0–3 at Bridge Road, Impington, Cambridge, Histon FC.

CAMBRIDGESHIRE CHALLENGE CUP (FOUNDED 1922–23)

RECENT FINALS

1990–91	Whittlesey United	v	Levrington Sports	2–0
1991–92	Godmanchester R	v	Wisbech Town Res	2–1
1992–93	Philips UK	v	Wisbech Town Res	2–0
1993–94	Levrington Sports	v	Fulbourn Institute	2–0
1994–95	Great Shelford	v	Foxton	2–0

MOST WINS Great Shelford 8 Chatteris Town 5 Ely City 4 Parson Drove 4
Soham Town Rangers 4 Whittlesey United 4

CAMBRIDGESHIRE FOOTBALL ASSOCIATION

Hon Secretary: M L North, 25 Fleet Close,
Littleport, Ely, Cambs CB6 1PG (01353 861742, Fax 01353 863331)

FINAL LEAGUE TABLES 1995/96

KERSHAW PREMIER LEAGUES:

Prem A	P	W	D	L	F	A	Pts
1. Foxton	28	19	3	6	78	32	60
2. Over Sports	28	16	9	3	64	33	57
3. Bassingbourn	28	18	3	7	62	34	57
4. Great Shelford	28	17	5	6	68	31	56
5. Waterbeach	28	11	8	9	55	50	41
6. Girton United	28	11	7	10	47	51	40
7. West Wratting	28	10	9	9	60	61	39
8. Comberton Utd	28	9	10	9	53	51	37
9. Cherry Hinton	28	9	7	12	48	56	34
10. Godmanchester	28	8	8	12	48	48	32
11. Newmarket T R	28	9	5	14	52	56	32
12. St Bumpstead	28	7	7	14	38	63	28
13. Fulborn Inst.	28	8	3	17	45	67	27
14. Philips UK	28	6	7	15	51	88	25
15. Gamlingay	28	4	5	19	32	80	17

Prem B	P	W	D	L	F	A	Pts
1. Cottenham Utd	28	19	5	4	98	54	62
2. Debden	28	18	7	3	69	29	61
3. Linton Granta	28	17	5	6	70	41	56
4. Mildenhall T R	28	14	5	9	63	50	47
5. Ashdon Villa	28	14	2	12	65	49	44
6. Soham Tn Res	28	14	1	13	59	48	43
7. Bluntisham Ran	28	12	7	9	50	49	43
8. Gt Shelford R	28	12	2	14	46	63	38
9. Longstanton	28	11	3	14	52	54	36
10. Histon Res	28	11	5	12	48	57	*35
11. Whittlesford U	28	9	8	11	60	71	35
12. Balsham	28	9	7	12	45	49	34
13. Somersham TR	28	9	6	13	66	68	33
14. Haddenham R	28	4	5	19	37	64	17
15. Sawston Rovers	28	1	4	23	27	109	*4

** Clubs with points adjustments*

Pearl Asssurance Peterborough & District:

Premier Div	P	W	D	L	F	A	Pts
1. Leverington Sports	30	21	5	4	63	24	68
2. Deeping Rangers	30	18	6	6	71	39	60
3. Ortonians	30	17	5	8	75	36	56
4. Hotpoint	30	16	7	7	66	23	55
5. Perkins Sports	30	17	4	9	71	45	55
6. Oundle Town	30	16	6	8	69	40	54
7. Moulton Harrox	30	15	4	11	65	47	49
8. Whittlesey United	30	12	6	12	53	58	42
9. Brotherhoods	30	11	7	12	44	53	37
10. Pinchbeck United	30	10	6	14	47	75	36
11. Wisbech Town Res	30	10	5	15	45	60	35
12. Eye United	30	10	5	15	50	69	35
13. Pearl Assurance	30	8	5	17	53	70	29
14. Stamford Belvedere	30	9	1	20	39	86	28
15. March Tn Utd Res	30	8	2	20	47	69	26
16. Alconbury	30	2	6	22	29	93	12

Div One	P	W	D	L	F	A	Pts
1. Ortonians Rs	26	18	4	4	68	26	58
2. Ryhall Utd	26	17	4	5	57	34	55
3. Gedney Hill	26	16	4	6	59	34	52
4. Manea United	26	12	6	8	65	42	42
5. Kings Cliffe	26	12	5	9	57	41	41
6. Perkins Spts R	26	11	8	7	53	46	41
7. Deeping Rgr R	26	11	5	10	53	52	38
8. Ketton	26	11	4	11	59	59	37
9. Outwell Swifts	26	11	2	13	62	58	35
10. March T U A	26	8	6	12	40	60	30
11. Newage	26	6	7	13	39	51	25
12. Holbeach U R	26	5	7	14	38	57	22
13. Oundle Res	26	6	3	17	31	78	18
14. Chatteris Res	26	3	5	18	39	89	14

Div Two	P	W	D	L	F	A	Pts
1. Hotpoint R	26	20	4	2	92	35	64
2. Leverington R	26	18	3	5	85	45	57
3. Ramsey T R	26	16	4	6	63	40	52
4. Oakham Tn	26	16	2	8	83	50	50
5. Bell Walsoken	26	14	7	5	59	39	49
6. Stilton	26	11	6	9	49	35	39
7. Deeping A	26	12	2	12	48	43	38
8. Eye Utd R 3	26	12	3	11	55	58	36
9. ICA Juventus	26	10	3	13	51	58	33
10. Pinchbeck R	26	9	4	13	40	53	31
11. Pearl Ass Res	26	9	3	14	49	60	30
12. Whittlesey Res	26	5	1	20	31	78	16
13. Sawtry 3	26	5	3	18	34	78	15
14. Crowland Tn	26	1	3	22	23	100	6

CHESHIRE F.A.

Secretary: Alan Collins,
The Cottage, Hartford Moss Rec Centre, Winnington, Northwich, Cheshire CW8 4BG
(01619) 804706 (H) (01606) 871166 (County Office) Fax: 01606 871292

CHESHIRE SENIOR CUP (FOUNDED 1879–80)

RECENT FINALS

1990–91	Macclesfield Town	v	Witton Albion	2–0
1991–92	Macclesfield Town	v	Witton Albion	1–1 (Rep 2–0)
1992–93	Winsford United	v	Witton Albion	3–0
1993–94	Northwich Victoria	v	Runcorn	1–0
1994–95	Witton Albion	v	Altrincham	2–1

MOST WINS Macclesfield Town 18 Northwich Victoria 16 Crewe Alexandra 12 Runcorn 12

1995–1996 CHESHIRE SENIOR CUP

13 CLUBS **HOLDERS: WITTON ALBION**

FIRST ROUND Tuesday 26th September

Winsford United	v	Hyde United	1–4	Congleton	v	Stalybridge Celtic	2–6
Vauxhall GM	v	Cheadle Town	3–0	Warrington Town	v	Nantwich Town	6–1
Northwich Victoria	v	Runcorn	3–1				

3 Clubs with Byes Altrincham, Macclesfield Town, Witton Albion into the

SECOND ROUND 21st November 1995

Vauxhall GM	v	Macclesfield Town	0–4	Stalybridge Celtic	v	Hyde United	0–3
Altrincham	v	Warrington Town	4–0	Witton Albion	v	Northwich Victoria	2–0

SEMI-FINALS (Two Legs)

Hyde United	v	Macclesfield T	2–1 1–1=3–2	Witton Albion	v	Altrincham	1–1 2–1=3–2

FINAL Monday 6th May 1996
HYDE UNITED v WITTON ALBION 1–3 at Moss Lane, Altrincham FC.

Witton Albion – Cheshire Senior Cup Winners. Photo: Keith Clayton.

FINAL LEAGUE TABLES 1995/96

Altrincham Saturday League; Founded 1974

Div One	P	W	D	L	F	A	Pts
1. Partington	24	20	3	1	127	30	63
2. Timperley W	24	19	5	0	95	19	62
3. Pelican Rov	24	14	2	8	82	48	44
4. Brooklands Alb	24	13	4	7	63	46	43
5. Timperley	24	12	4	8	47	54	40
6. Atlantic	24	11	4	9	52	47	37
7. Old York Vict	24	9	8	7	55	39	35
8. Knutsford	24	10	3	11	41	54	33
9. Broadheath Ct	24	6	5	13	46	64	23
10. Radbrooke Hall	24	5	5	14	34	61	20
11. Railway Inn	24	5	3	16	29	92	18
12. Wythenshawe	24	5	3	16	36	81	15
13. Knutsford Wan	24	0	5	19	37	109	5

Div Two	P	W	D	L	F	A	Pts
1. The Bowler	26	18	4	4	80	38	58
2. Wellgreen	26	18	2	6	73	46	56
3. Partington Res	26	15	4	7	97	59	49
4. Kartel Spts	26	14	7	5	68	48	48
5. Silks	26	13	4	9	69	59	43
6. Wythenshawe T	26	13	3	10	84	44	42
7. Trafford	26	12	6	8	66	56	42
8. Whalley Range	26	13	2	11	89	70	38
9. Wythenshawe A	26	9	3	14	44	59	30
10. Sale Amt.	26	8	4	14	46	55	28
11. Styal	26	7	4	15	36	67	24
12. United Services	26	7	2	17	31	69	22
13. YMOB FC	26	6	1	19	40	89	19

League Challenge Cup:	Old York Victoria	v Wythenshawe Amateurs	1-0 (aet)
Broadheath Central Cup:	Timperley Wanderers Res	v St Peters	0-1
Altrincham & District Senior Cup:	Knutsford	v Atlantic	3-2

Altrincham Sunday League: Founded 1967

Dave Jordan Motor Body Repairers

Premier Div	P	W	D	L	F	A	Pts
1. Southern Hotel	26	18	5	3	92	36	59
2. Melville Hotel	26	17	3	6	72	48	54
3. Bowdon Vale	26	15	8	3	59	30	53
4. King William	26	15	7	4	63	36	52
5. Packet House	26	16	3	7	56	29	51
6. Brooklands Tap	26	15	4	7	74	40	49
7. Jacksons Boat	26	11	4	11	49	44	37
8. Stamford Lads	26	9	4	13	48	62	31
9. Chorlton RS	26	9	4	13	43	57	31
10. Unicorn Tn	26	9	3	14	50	62	30
11. Lisbon St Ant	26	6	4	16	50	67	22
12. DeTrafford	26	6	4	16	47	71	19
13. Cock Robin	26	4	4	18	41	89	16
14. Star Inn	26	3	1	22	44	117	10

Irwin Rangers

Div One	P	W	D	L	F	A	Pts
1. Partington Soc	22	18	4	0	80	32	58
2. Station Flixton	22	15	5	2	60	26	50
3. Ladybarn	22	13	5	4	64	31	44
4. Urmston Mens	22	12	3	7	50	41	39
5. Cheshire Cheese	22	9	5	8	47	42	32
6. Hale Barn Utd	22	8	5	9	33	38	29
7. Broadheath Cen	22	8	4	10	34	43	28
8. Stonemasons	22	6	5	11	51	63	23
9. Partington WMC	22	7	2	13	53	72	23
10. Bollington Park	22	6	2	14	49	63	20
11. Old Cock	22	4	3	15	38	69	15
12. Wagon & Horse	22	4	1	17	38	77	13

Manchester United Memorial Cup:	DeTrafford	v De La Salle	2-2 (aet), 2-4pen
Kevan Guiney Newagents Cup:	Cheshire Cheese	v Hale Barn United	0-1
Dave Rundle Auto Eng Lge Cup:	Melville Hotel	v Packet House	0-2
Altrincham & Dist FA Sun Sen Cup:	Packet House	v Temple Inn	3-3 (aet), 0-3

Altrincham Youth League

Under 17	P	W	D	L	F	A	Pts
1. Urmston Med	14	10	1	3	63	24	31
2. Cheadle Tn	14	8	3	3	49	25	27
3. Hale Barns Utd	14	7	4	3	53	41	25
4. Marple Ath	14	6	5	3	41	35	23
5. Northwich Tn	14	7	1	6	47	34	22
6. Cheadle Hth N	14	6	3	5	42	36	21
7. Broadheath Cen	14	2	2	10	29	55	8
8. Frodsham	14	0	1	13	21	95	1

Under 18	P	W	D	L	F	A	Pts
1. Wythenshawe A	12	10	0	2	52	17	30
2. Chadderton	12	7	1	4	37	18	22
3. Sale United	12	7	0	5	44	32	21
4. Priory Cty	12	6	1	5	27	34	19
5. Flixtonians	12	6	0	6	34	33	18
6. Glossop Jun	12	4	0	8	20	34	12
7. Lymm Rovers	12	1	0	11	11	57	3

CORNWALL F.A.

Secretary: J M Ryder,
Penare, 16 Gloweth View, Truro, Cornwall TR1 3JZ

CORNWALL SENIOR CUP
(FOUNDED 1892–93)

RECENT FINALS

1990–91	Saltash United	v	Falmouth Town	4–1
1991–92	Newquay	v	Falmouth Town	1–0
1992–93	Saltash United	v	Launceston	3–2
1993–94	Liskeard Athletic	v	Bodmin Town	2–1
1994–95	Truro City	v	Liskeard Athletic	2–1

MOST WINS Truro City 12 St Austell 11 Penzance 10 St Blazey 10 Torpoint Athletic 10

1995–1996

CORNWALL SENIOR CUP

42 CLUBS **HOLDERS: TRURO CITY**

FIRST ROUND Saturday 28th October

Bude	v	Helston Athletic	5–1	Pendeen Rovers	v	Foxhole Stars	2–0
Ludgvan	v	Mousehole	1–5	Roche	v	Illogan RBL	0–0 1–1
Marazion Blues	v	Perranwell	0–5	St Agnes	v	St Breward	4–0
Mullion	v	St Ives Town	0–0 3–2	Sticker	v	St Cleer	3–5
Nanpean Rovers	v	RNAS Culdrose	6–1	Troon	v	St Just	1–1 1–2

8 Clubs with Byes and 14 Clubs Exempt to

SECOND ROUND

Bude	v	Millbrook	0–5	Nanpean Rovers	v	Falmouth Town	0–9
Bugle	v	Padstow United	0–2	Newquay	v	St Cleer	4–0
Callington	v	Penryn Athletic	3–1	Pendeen Rovers	v	St Dennis	0–2
Camelford	v	RAF St Mawgan	7–3	Penzance	v	Bodmin Town	0–1
Launceston	v	Truro City	0–0 1–2	Riveria Coasters	v	St Austell	1–4
Liskeard Ath	v	Perranwell	0–0 4–1	St Blazey	v	Roche	4–0
Mousehole	v	Porthleven	0–5	St Just	v	Torpoint Athletic	1–5
Mullion	v	St Agnes	3–4	Wadebridge Town	v	Saltash United	1–4

THIRD ROUND

Falmouth Town	v	Millbrook	4–1	St Agnes	v	Porthleven	1–2
Liskeard Athletic	v	St Dennis	1–2	Saltash United	v	Bodmin Town	4–3
Newquay	v	Callington	3–2	Torpoint Athletic	v	St Austell	3–2
Padstow United	v	St Blazey	0–1	Truro City	v	Camelford	10–2

QUARTER FINALS Saturday 17th February & Replay

Falmouth Town	v	Truro City	4–0	St Blazey	v	Porthleven	1–1 0–5
Newquay	v	St Dennis	1–0	Saltash United	v	Torpoint Athletic	1–3

SEMI-FINALS

Falmouth Town	v	Torpoint Athletic	1–2	Newquay	v	Porthleven	0–1
at St Blazey FC.				at Falmouth Town FC.			

FINAL Monday 8th April 1996
PORTHLEVEN v TORPOINT ATHLETIC 1*1 at Blaise Park, St Blazey FC.

FINAL Thursday 11th April 1996
PORTHLEVEN v TORPOINT ATHLETIC 0–2 at Blaise Park, St Blazey FC.

CORNISH GUARDIAN EAST CORNWALL PREMIER LEAGUE

FINAL LEAGUE TABLES 1995/96

			Home					Away					
		P	*W*	*D*	*L*	*F*	*A*	*W*	*D*	*L*	*F*	*A*	*Pts*
1.	Saltash United	36	14	2	2	65	16	15	2	1	61	18	91
2.	Torpoint Athletic	36	14	1	3	43	14	11	2	5	41	31	78
3.	Nanpean Rovers	36	12	0	6	50	32	13	2	3	48	20	77
4.	St Dennis	36	13	3	2	45	16	9	3	6	35	24	72
5.	Padstow United	36	11	4	3	51	27	9	5	4	47	29	69
6.	Wadebridge Town	36	12	2	4	41	20	10	0	8	51	35	68
7.	Callington	36	10	4	4	50	35	11	1	6	41	23	68
8.	Roche	36	12	2	4	39	29	9	1	8	34	18	66
9.	Foxhole	36	11	1	6	40	32	5	7	6	38	35	56
10.	Bodmin Town	36	9	1	8	29	31	8	3	7	37	37	47
11.	Camelford	36	5	7	6	29	24	7	3	8	33	30	46
12.	St Cleer	36	7	5	6	41	36	4	5	9	30	50	43
13.	Bude	36	9	4	5	35	28	3	2	13	21	40	42
14.	Liskeard Athletic	36	7	2	9	39	34	6	1	11	29	49	42
15.	Sticker	36	6	3	9	38	52	2	2	14	21	55	29
16.	Bugle	36	5	4	9	21	35	1	4	13	24	49	26
17.	St Blazey	36	2	4	12	30	65	1	5	12	16	49	18
18.	St Breward	36	1	2	15	19	59	3	3	12	24	44	17
19.	Riviera Coasters	36	2	0	16	14	63	2	0	16	12	61	6

LEAGUE CUP FINAL: Nanpean Rovers v Saltash United 1-0 (aet).

SUPPLEMENTRY CUP: St Cleer v St Dennis 1-4.

Leading Goalscorers:

		Lge	Cups	Tot
Colin Barrett	Saltash United	41	3	44
Chris Truscott	Callington	26	-	26
Gary Dyer	Nanpean Rovers	16	8	24
Lee Rowsell	Bude	21	2	23
Paul Rowe	Wadebridge Town	19	4	23
Dean Tongue	St Cleer	18	4	22
Martin Polatch	Saltash United	26	6	32
Brett Elliott	St Dennis	18	7	25
Karl Daley	Wadebridge Town	23	-	23
Anthony Hurst	Padstow United	21	2	23
Mikle Yelland	Camelford	20	2	22
Carl Mallett	Foxhole	20	1	21

JOLLYS CORNWALL COMBINATION

			Home					Away					
		P	*W*	*D*	*L*	*F*	*A*	*W*	*D*	*L*	*F*	*A*	*Pts*
1.	Penryn Athletic	38	17	1	1	66	15	14	3	2	47	14	97
2.	Perranwell	38	18	0	1	71	13	12	6	1	55	23	96
3.	Truro City	38	14	3	2	62	23	12	3	4	52	26	84
4.	St Ives	38	13	2	4	52	18	12	2	5	50	23	79
5.	Falmouth Town	38	10	6	3	55	18	11	3	5	43	22	72
6.	Helston	38	12	3	4	42	15	9	4	6	43	33	70
7.	Mullion	38	8	5	6	34	20	8	4	7	29	23	57
8.	Newquay	38	8	5	6	39	23	6	6	7	34	36	53
9.	St Agnes	38	9	4	6	43	30	6	4	9	23	30	53
10.	Penzance	38	7	7	5	39	29	7	3	9	29	38	52
11.	Porthleven	38	8	6	5	42	33	6	6	7	28	29	*51
12.	Troon	38	6	5	8	37	32	8	2	9	35	38	49
13.	Illogan RBL	38	8	4	7	35	32	4	8	7	24	31	48
14.	Mousehole	38	6	6	7	28	22	4	7	8	26	31	43
15.	Pendeen Rovers	38	7	2	10	33	32	4	4	11	25	53	39
16.	St Just	38	5	6	8	28	43	4	2	13	18	54	35
17.	Culdrose	38	5	5	9	35	42	3	3	13	20	51	32
18.	RAF St Mawgan	38	3	2	14	22	68	3	1	15	17	69	21
19.	Ludgvan	38	2	2	15	22	50	3	3	13	19	65	20
20.	Marazion	38	1	2	16	9	72	1	2	16	12	105	10

** Points adjusted*

CUMBERLAND F.A.

Secretary: R Johnson,
72 Victoria Road, Workington, Cumbria CA14 2QT (01900 603979) (County Office)

CUMBERLAND SENIOR CUP
(FOUNDED 1960–61)

RECENT FINALS

1990–91	Marchon	v	Cleator Moor Celtic	3–1
1991–92	Gretna	v	Penrith	1–0
1992–93	Carlisle United Res	v	Gretna	0–0 (Rep 3–1)
1993–94	Gretna	v	Carlisle United Res	3–0
1994–95	Gretna	v	Penrith	2–0

MOST WINS Penrith 10 Gretna 8 Haig Colliery 3

1995–1996

CUMBERLAND SENIOR CUP

38 CLUBS **HOLDERS: GRETNA**

FIRST ROUND14.10.95

Sporting Museum	v	Windscales	1–2
Maryport	v	Windscales Res	WRs W–O
Cumbria Police	v	Carlisle United Res	0–1
Whitehaven Soc.	v	Gillford Park	1–3
Wigton Harriers	v	Whitehaven Rangers	2–3
Whitehaven Amtrs	v	Penrith	0–7

SECOND ROUND Saturday 4th November 1995

Braithwaite	v	British Steel	1–2
Gretna	v	Gillford Park	3–2
Parton United	v	Silloth	3–2
Penrith	v	Aspatria Spartans	5–0
Windscales	v	Langworthy	1–0
Whitehaven Rgrs	v	Silloth Vets	3–3 5–3
Keswick	v	Alston Town	7–1
Windscales Res	v	Workington Res	0–2
Cleator Moor Cel	v	New Victoria	5–2
Kirkoswald	v	Whitehaven Amtrs	0–5
Greystoke	v	Northbank	2–5
Whitehaven S Res	v	Carlisle Utd Res	W W–O
Wetheriggs	v	St Bees	6–1
Longtown	v	Egremont St Mary's	3–1
Mirehouse	v	Carlisle City	1–8
Abbeytown	v	Workington	2–5

THIRD ROUND Saturday 9th December

Parton United	v	Longtown	1–2
Wetheriggs	v	Windscales	3–5
Gretna	v	Workington Res	1–0
British Steel	v	Whitehaven S Res	5–0
Whitehaven Amtrs	v	Workington	0–3
Carlisle City @P	v	Penrith	2–1
Whitehaven Rgrs	v	Keswick	0–3
Cleator Moor Celtic	v	North Bank	5–3

FOURTH ROUND Saturday 20th January 1996

Carlisle City	v	British Steel	5–0
Longtown	v	Keswick	1–2
Workington	v	Gretna	2–1
Cleator Moor Celtic	v	Windscales	2–1

SEMI-FINALS Saturday 10th February 1996

Cleator Moor Celtic	v	Carlisle City	3–2
Keswick	v	Workington	1–3

FINAL Wednesday 1st May 6.45pm
CLEATOR MOOR CELTIC v WORKINGTON 1–4 at Falcon Field, Egremont BNFL FC. att; 397

DERBYSHIRE F.A.

Secretary: K Compton,
The Grandstand, Moorways Stadium,
Moor Lane, Derby DE2 8FB (01332 361422)

DERBYSHIRE SENIOR CUP
(FOUNDED 1883–84)

RECENT FINALS

1990–91	Gresley Rovers	v	Barrowash Victoria	7–1 (Agg)
1991–92	Matlock Town	v	Stapenhill	3–1 (Agg)
1992–93	Ilkeston Town	v	Alfreton Town	1–1 (Agg) 7–6 (Pens)
1993–94	Gresley Rovers	v	Matlock Town	4–1 (Agg)
1994–95	Alfreton Town	v	Ilkeston Town	8–1 (Agg)

MOST WINS Derby County 15 Ilkeston Town 11 Buxton 8 Chesterfield 8 Heanor Town 8

1995–1996

DERBYSHIRE SENIOR CUP

25 CLUBS **HOLDERS: ALFRETON TOWN**

FIRST ROUND by 7th October

Glapwell	v	Shardlow St James	1–3	Mickleover Sports	v	Long Eaton United	3–0

SECOND ROUND by 2nd December

Graham St Prims	v	Sheepbridge	8–2	Newhall United	v	Shardlow St James	1–1 2–1
Heanor Town	v	Rolls Royce	2–0	Sandiacre Town	v	Blackwell MW	2–0
Mickleover Sports	v	Shirebrook Town	3–2	Staveley MW	v	Stanton Ilkeston	3–1
Mickleover RBL	v	Sth Normanton Ath	2–5				

9 Clubs Exempt Alfreton Town, Belper Town, Borrowash Victoria, Buxton, Glossop North End, Gresley Rovers, Ilkeston Town, Matlock Town, Stapenhill to the

THIRD ROUND

Mickleover Sports	v	Glossop North End	4–4 1–3	Alfreton Town	v	Heanor Town	9–1
Sth Normanton Ath	v	Belper Town	1–8	Borrowash Vics	v	Graham Street Prims	0–1
Staveley MW	v	Gresley Rovers	1–4	Stapenhill	v	Buxton	0–0 0–1
Newhall @ Gresley	v	Ilkeston Town	1–0	Matlock Town	v	Sandiacre Town	8–2

FOURTH ROUND by Saturday 10th February 1996

Belper Town	v	Alfreton Town	4–3	Glossop North End	v	Newhall United	6–1
Gresley Rovers	v	Buxton	2–0	Graham St Prims	v	Matlock Town	1–0

SEMI-FINALS

Gresley Rovers	v	Glossop North End	3–0	Belper Town	v	Graham Street Prims	2–0

FINAL (Two Legs) Thursday 9th May
GRESLEY ROVERS v BELPER TOWN 0–0

FINAL Monday 13th May
BELPER TOWN v GRESLEY ROVERS 1–2

Keyline Derby Senior League

Premier Div		P	W	D	L	F	A	Pts
1.	Santos	26	21	3	2	76	20	66
2.	Melbourne Dyn	26	20	3	3	100	40	63
3.	Alvaston R	26	19	4	3	86	33	61
4.	Alvaston & B	26	16	4	6	85	40	52
5.	Little Eaton	26	17	1	8	68	38	52
6.	Qualcast	26	11	6	9	64	50	39
7.	Stanley Comm	26	11	5	10	72	72	38
8.	Allestree	26	11	2	13	64	68	35
9.	Henington	26	9	4	13	66	65	31
10.	Grenville Ath	26	8	1	17	36	70	25
11.	Allenton Ath	26	6	6	14	40	59	24
12.	Aston	26	6	1	19	46	94	19
13.	Chellaston	26	3	1	22	17	90	10
14.	Meadows	26	2	3	21	43	124	9

Gresley lift the Derbyshire Senior Cup for the sixth time in nine seasons.
Captain Richard Denby shows off the Trophy after their victory over Belper Town.
Photo: Derrick Kinsey

The Chesterfield & Distict Mansfield Bitter Sunday League

Division One Winners Doe Lea FC; Runners-Up Staveley Miners Welfare.

Doe Lea FC; *Back Row (L-R): Guy Rosewarne, Stuart Bargh, Andy Kirk, Paul Morgan, Neil Etheridge, Wayne Turner, Paul Beardsmore, Mick Simpson, Cusimo De Girulamo, Kevin Letherday. Front Row: Paul Bexton, Brendon Yates, Chris Tansley, Steve Pell, Mark Bexton, Paul Murcott.*

DEVON F.A.

Secretary: Colin Squirrell,
Coach Road, Newton Abbot, Devon TQ12 1EJ
Tel: 1626 332077 (County Office) Fax: 01626 336814

DEVON ST LUKES CHALLENGE CUP (FOUNDED 1981–82)

RECENT FINALS

1992–93	Tiverton Town	v	Clyst Rovers	3–0
1993–94	Tiverton Town	v	Bideford	1–0
1994–95	Tiverton Town	v	Bideford	5–1

MOST WINS Tiverton Town 5 Bideford 3 Exmouth Town 3

1995–1996

DEVON ST LUKES COLLEGE CUP

11 CLUBS **HOLDERS: TIVERTON TOWN**

FIRST ROUND on or before Saturday 20th January 1996

Clyst Rovers	v	Exmouth Town	6–3	Ilfracombe	v	Elmore	1–2
Heavitree United	v	Torrington	1–3				

FOURTH ROUND by Saturday 17th February 1996

Barnstaple Town	v	Bideford	2–3	Torrington	v	Elmore	3–1
Clyst Rovers	v	Crediton	6p7 2*2	Tiverton Town	v	Dawlish	4–2

(Crediton were found to have fielded ineligible players in the above match and were removed from the competition with Clyst Rovers being re-instated).

SEMI-FINALS by Saturday 23rd March 1996

Clyst R/Crediton	v	Torrington	0–2	Tiverton Town	v	Bideford	1–2

FINAL Bank Holiday Monday 6th May 3.00pm
BIDEFORD v TORRINGTON 2–1 at The Sports Ground, Kingsley Road, Bideford FC.

DEVON PREMIER CUP (FOUNDED 1969–70)

RECENT FINALS

1990–91	Newton Abbot Spurs	v	Exeter St Thomas	2–0
1991–92	Upton Athletic	v	Stoke Gabriel	2–1
1992–93	Devon & Cornwall Pol	v	Exeter Civil Service	2–0 (AET)
1993–94	Stoke Gabriel	v	Tavistock	4–2
1994–95	Devon & Cornwall Pol	v	Budleigh Salterton	2–1

MOST WINS Upton Athletic 4 Dawlish 3

DEVON SENIOR CUP (FOUNDED 1889–90)

RECENT WINNERS

1990–91	Newton Abbot Spurs	1993–94	Cheriton Fitzpaine
1991–92	St Martins	1994–95	Barnstaple Town
1992–93	Barnstaple Town		

MOST WINS Plymouth 6 Green Waves 4 Tavistock 4

WESTWARD DEVELOPEMENTS DEVON COUNTY LEAGUE

Chairman: Brian Williams

Hon. Secretary: Roger Lowe, Panorama, Lamerton, Tavistock, Devon PL19 8SD (01822 613516)

FINAL LEAGUE TABLE 1995/96

		P	*W*	*D*	*L*	*F*	*A*	*Pts*
1.	Budleigh Salterton	36	21	10	5	96	41	73
2.	Stoke Gabriel	36	22	7	7	91	36	73
3.	Willand Rovers	36	22	6	8	73	41	72
4.	Dartmouth United	36	22	6	8	80	52	72
5.	Alphington	36	19	6	11	86	47	63
6.	Topsham Town	36	17	9	10	87	69	60
7.	Teignmouth	36	19	3	14	93	67	60
8.	Newton Abbott	36	16	8	12	66	55	56
9.	Plymouth Command	36	16	6	14	68	58	54
10.	Buckfastleigh	36	12	11	13	62	66	47
11.	Elburton Villa	36	13	7	16	56	81	46
12.	Cullompton Rgrs	36	13	7	16	46	57	46
13.	Plymouth Parkway	36	11	12	13	72	77	45
14.	Plymstock United	36	12	8	16	54	63	44
15.	Newton St Cyres	36	9	7	20	51	89	34
16.	Ivybridge Town	36	10	4	22	55	95	34
17.	W Mill Oak Villa	36	9	6	21	55	90	33
18.	Ottery St Mary	36	8	6	22	43	111	30
19.	Chagford	36	4	5	27	48	95	17

LEAGUE CHALLENGE CUP:

Sponsored by Throgmorton. **Holders:** Elburton Villa.

Semi-finals:	Dartmouth United	v Newton Abbott	0-0, 1-2
	Topsham Town	v Teignmouth	2-1
Final:	**Topsham Town**	**v Newton Abbott**	**1-1, 1-0**

Newton St Cyres clear their lines during this end of season fixture that they lost 2-5 to Plymouth Command.
Photo - Tim Lancaster

ALPHINGTON

Secretary: Keith Phare, 23 Sussex Close, Exeter EX4 1LP (01392 58636).
Ground: The Chronicles, Church Road, Alphington (01392 79556)
Cover: Yes **Clubhouse:** Yes **Floodlights:** No **Programme:** Yes
Colours: Amber/black/black **Change colours:** Blue & black/white/blue.
Previous League: Devon & Exeter. **Hons:** Devon County Lg Cup 93-94.

BUCKFASTLEIGH RANGERS

Secretary: T Crimp, 8 West End, Buckfastleigh, South Devon, TQ11 0DJ. (01364 642449).
Ground: Ducks Pond Playing Fields, Buckfastleigh, Devon
Directions: On east side of 3380, just off main A38, to south of Buckfastleigh village centre.
Cover: No **Clubhouse:** Yes **Floodlights:** Yes.
Colours: All green & white **Change colours:** Red & blue/blue/blue
Hons: Devon County Lg 92-93.

BUDLEIGH SALTERTON A.F.C.

Secretary: Nick Pannell, 33 Armytage Road, Budleigh Salterton, Devon, EX9 6SD, (01395 445877).
Ground: Greenway Lane, Budleigh Salterton (01395 443850).
Colours: All Red **Change colours:** All Light blue

CHAGFORD

Secretary: Michelle Accia Carelli, 13 Orchard Meadow, Chagford, Devon TQ13 8BP (01647 432219).
Ground: Padley Common, Chagford.
Colours: Royal & sky stripes/navy/sky **Change colours:** All white.

CULLOMPTON RANGERS

Secretary: K Norman, 78 Langlands Rd, Cullompton (01884 33539).
Ground: Speeds Meadow, Duke Street, Cullompton, Devon.
Directions: M5 jct 28, head for town centre, turn left, through thru town centre for 1 mile, left into Meadow Lane, past sports centre, right at T-junction, left after 100yds and follow signs.
Colours: Red & black **Change colours:** Royal blue **Nickname:** Rangers
Hons: Devon & Exeter Lg 61-62 63-64 (Snr Div 59-60 78-79, Int Div 1 R-up 93-94(res), Jnr Div 3 49-50 59-60(res)), East Devon Snr Cup 83-84, Devon Premier Cup R-up 84-85, Axminster Hosp. Cup 92-93, Golesworthy & Grange Cup(res) 92-93 93-94.

DARTMOUTH UNITED F.C.

Secretary: Debbie Smith, 3 Archway Drive, Dartmouth, Devon, TQ6 9TE, (01803 833791)
Ground: Longcross, (01803 832902).
Colours: Black & white/black/white **Change colours:** Green/black/black

ELBURTON VILLA

Secretary: Linda Tope, 27 Villiers Close, Plymstock, Plymouth PL9 7QP, (01752 493105).
Ground: Haye Road, Elburton, Plymouth. (01752 480025).
Colours: Red & black/black/red **Change colours:** Grey/white/white.

IVYBRIDGE TOWN

Secretary: Garfield Goodwin, 36 Longland Close, Plympton, Plymouth PL7 3HD (01752 344364)
Ground: Erme Playing Fields, Ivybridge (01752 892584). **Directions:** Coming from Plymouth on A38 take Ivybridge turn, double back over A38 and take 1st left - ground entrance quarter mile on right after Industrial Estate.
Colours: Green & white/green/green & white **Change colours:** Navy & white/navy/navy & white

NEWTON ABBOT

Secretary: Mr Roy Perkins, 21 Prospect Terrace, Newton Abbot, Devon, TQ12 2LN (01626 61596).
Ground: The Playing Fields, Coach Rd, Newton Abbot (01626 335011).
Directions: Half mile off the Torquay Road leading to Newton Abbot centre, past Ford Park tennis courts.
Colours: Red & black/black/black **Change colours:** Black & white/black or white/white
Hons: Devon Co. Lg 93-94 (R-up 92-93, Lg Cup 92-93), Devon Prem. Cup R-up 82-83 87-88 (Snr Cup R-up 90-91.

NEWTON St CYRES

Secretary: Roger Dymond, 12 New Estate, Newton St Cyres, Devon (01392 851719).
Ground: The Recreation Ground, Station Rd, Newton St Cyres, Devon (01392 851546).
Directions: A377 from Exeter towards Crediton, on reaching Newton Cyres proceed to village centre, and turn right (signposted BR station) - ground half mile on right. Trains to Exeter Central station or buses from Exeter coach station.
Colours: Sky blue/blue/blue **Change:** Red & white/white/red**Nickname:** Saints
Hons: Devon Premier Cup 88-89 (Snr Cup 74-75, I'mediate Cup 72-73), Devon & Exeter Lg 88-89 (Lg Cup 88-89), East Devon Snr Cup 88-89 89-90 90-91 92-93.

OTTERY St MARY

Secretary: Ray Dack, 13 Vaughan Rise, Whipton, Exeter, Devon EX1 3UD (01392 422190).
Ground: Washbrook Meadows, Butts Road, Ottery St Mary, Devon EX11 1EL (01404 813539).
Directions: From main town square, turn left following road around church, 2nd right into Butts Rd. Or, B3177 to Ottery from A30 Honiton by-pass - ground on left past Otter workshops.
Colours: All Dark Blue **Change colours:** Yellow/black/red **Nickname:** The Otters
Hons: East Devon Snr Cup, Devon & Exeter Lg, Western Lg Div 1 89-90

PLYMOUTH PARKWAY

Secretary: S Cadmore, 25 Dudley Gdns, Plymouth, Devon PL6 5PE (01752 782661).
Ground: Parkway Sports Club, Tamar Vale, Ernesettle Lane, Ernesettle, Plymouth (01752 363080).
Directions: Take Ernesettle exit off A38 & follow signs to Ernesettle Industrial Estate - ground on right halfway down steep hill.
Hons: Plymouth & Dist. Lg Div 2 90-91 (Div 4 Cup 88-89 (R-up 91-92(res)), Div 3 Cup R-up 89-90 84).

PLYMOUTH COMMAND FC

Secretary: M.A.Launce, 57 Chaucer Way, Brake Farm, Plymouth, PL5 3EQ, (01752 700168)
Ground: T B A
Colours: Blue & white/white/blue & white **Change colours:** Red/black/red

PLYMSTOCK UNITED

Secretary: Alan Demuth, 35 Treveneague Gdns, Manadon, Plymouth PL2 3SX (01752 782807).
Ground: Deans Cross, Plymstock, Plymouth, Devon (01752 406776).
Directions: Local bus service to Plymstock Broadway.
Colours: Red/white/red **Change colours:** Gold/black/gold **Nickname:** Reds.
Hons: Plymouth & Dist Lg 66-67 74-75 84-85 (R-up 75-76 76-77 90-91), Devon Snr Cup R-up 87-88, Victory Cup 67-68 74-75 78-79 86-87 (R-up 62-63 69-70 71-72 76-77 77-78 83-84).

STOKE GABRIEL

Secretary: Mr Barry Prowse, 269 Teignmouth Rd, St Marychurch, Torquay TQ1 4RT (01803 327930).
Ground: G J Churchward Mem. Grnd, Broadley Lane, Stoke Gabriel, (01803 78223)
Directions: Turn right into Broadley Lane just before Four Crosses crossroads approaching from Paington.
Colours: Blue & black/black/black **Change colours:** Light blue & white/white/white
Hons: Devon Premier Cup 93-94 (R-up 91-92), Devon County Lg R-up 93-94, Torbay Herald Cup 83-84 88-89, South Devon Lg 87-88 88-89 (Belli Cip 90-91),

TEIGNMOUTH

Secretary: Brian Barnden, 37 Eastlands, Hemyock, Cullompton, Devon EX1 53QP, (01823 680981).
Ground: Coombe Valley, Lower Combe Lane, Teignmouth, Devon (01626 776688).
Directions: From Newton Abbot: Turn left into Mill Lane 100yds past lights at Shaldon Bridge, right after 100yds into Fourth Ave., 2nd right, car park down hill on left. From Exeter: Turn right (past cemetary) into Higher Combe Lane, 1st left down Deer Park Ave., right at bottom & follow road round to left, turn right & right again - ground down hill on left. Rail to Teignmouth (BR).
Colours: White/black/black **Change colours:** Red/white/red **Nickname:** Teigns
Hons: Torbay Herald Cup 58-59 79-80 80-81, Sth Western Lg Cup R-up 85-86, Sth Devon Lg Div 1 85-86(res) 89-90, Devon County Lg Cup SF 93-94.

TOPSHAM TOWN

Secretary: Mr D G Marks, 66 Gloucester Rd, Exeter EX4 2EE (01392 58896).
Ground: Coronation Field, Exeter Road, Topsham (01392 873678).
Colours: All Blue **Change colours:** White/black/black

WESTON MILL OAK VILLA

Secretary: Mr John Davey, 5 Westciuntry Close, Weston Mill, Plymouth, PL2 2BJ, (01752 365587).
Ground: WMOV Sports Ground, Ferndale Rd, Weston Mill, Plymouth (01752 363352).
Colours: Green & white/ black/green **Change colours:** Red/black/black
Hons: Devon County Lg Cup SF 93-94

WILLAND ROVERS

Secretary/Press Officer: Andrew Jarrett, 2 College Court, Uffculme, Cullompton Devon, EX15 3EQ (01884 841210).
Ground: Silver Street, Willand, nr Cullompton, Devon (01884 33885).
Directions: Ground situated on east side of B3181, halfway between M5 jcts 27 & 28. 2 miles from Tiverton Parkway BR station. Regular buses from Exeter via Cullompton.
Colours: White/black/black **Change colours:** Blue/blue & white/blue & white **Nickname:** Rovers
Hons: Devon Snr Cup 85-86 (I'mediate Cup 66-67), Devon Co. Lg Cup R-up 92-93 93-94, Exeter & Dist. Lg Snr Div 1 70-71 (Jnr Div 1 67-68, Jnr Div 2 64-65, Jnr Div 3 65-66, Premier Lg Cup 79-80), East Devon Snr Cup 72-73 91-92 93-94.

FINAL LEAGUE TABLES 1995/96

DEVON & EXETER LEAGUE

Premier Div	P	W	D	L	F	A	Pts
1. Cheriton Fitz	26	19	6	1	95	31	63
2. Exeter Civ Ser	26	19	5	2	101	33	62
3. Exeter St Th	26	16	1	9	60	40	49
4. Buckland Ath	26	14	5	7	77	41	47
5. Sidmouth Tn	26	14	4	8	54	43	45
6. Exmouth Amt	26	13	2	11	66	48	41
7. Ex Univ	26	13	3	10	66	53	40
8. Feniton	26	9	8	9	44	35	35
9. St Martins	26	9	5	12	43	56	32
10. Honiton Tn	26	10	2	14	48	70	32
11. Morchard Bish	26	8	4	14	45	65	28
12. Culm Utd	26	6	4	16	40	77	22
13. Clyst Vall	26	2	5	19	33	104	11
14. Beer Albion	26	2	2	22	24	100	8

Div One	P	W	D	L	F	A	Pts
1. Budleigh Salt	28	25	1	2	108	32	76
2. Pinhoe	28	19	2	7	75	41	59
3. Witheridge	28	18	3	7	71	41	57
4. Dawlish Villa	28	17	5	6	69	25	56
5. Seaton Tn	28	18	2	8	72	37	56
6. Lapford	28	16	4	8	55	47	52
7. Exeter Civ Ser	28	16	2	10	75	49	50
8. Dunkeswell Rov	28	8	7	13	47	54	31
9. East Budleigh	28	8	5	15	58	73	29
10. North Tawton	28	9	3	16	50	72	29
11. E University	28	7	4	17	55	90	25
12. Westexe Rovers	28	6	6	16	35	69	24
13. Lympstone	28	6	4	18	48	88	22
14. Tedburn St Mary	28	6	3	19	45	83	21
15. Sidbury Utd	28	4	3	21	32	94	15

NORTH DEVON LEAGUE:

Premier Div	P	W	D	L	F	A	Pts
1. Appledore BAAC	34	21	10	3	115	36	73
2. Braunton	34	21	8	5	85	45	71
3. Combe Martin	34	17	10	7	88	58	61
4. Willand	34	18	6	10	89	53	60
5. Bradworthy	34	15	11	8	62	43	56
6. Morwenstow	34	15	9	10	60	43	54
7. Putford	34	15	7	12	49	52	52
8. Ilfracombe Tn	34	14	8	12	58	60	50
9. Torrington	34	14	7	13	70	68	49
10. Holsworthy	34	14	3	17	57	68	45
11. Fremington Fox	34	14	3	17	77	97	45
12. Torr Admirals	34	11	6	17	60	64	39
13. Shamwickshire	34	11	6	17	75	91	39
14. Chittlehampton	34	10	5	19	56	75	35
15. Barnstable	34	9	7	18	63	70	34
16. Dolton	34	9	5	20	48	80	32
17. Kilkhampton	34	9	5	20	46	127	32
18. Parkhead	34	9	4	21	63	91	31

Senior Div	P	W	D	L	F	A	Pts
1. Georgeham	22	16	2	4	62	22	50
2. Appledore	22	15	3	4	64	32	48
3. Northam Lions	22	15	1	6	56	24	46
4. South Molton	22	11	2	9	47	34	35
5. Golden Lion	22	11	2	9	53	54	35
6. North Molton	22	10	2	10	48	47	32
7. Lynton & Lyn	22	9	3	10	49	46	30
8. Bratton Flem	22	8	3	11	43	54	27
9. Bradworthy	22	7	4	11	40	51	25
10. Bridgerule	22	6	5	11	35	47	23
11. Hartland	22	5	7	10	41	43	22
12. Rolle Quay	22	2	0	20	21	105	6

MOD DEC SOUTH DEVON LEAGUE

Premier Div	P	W	D	L	F	A	Pts
1. N Abbott Spurs	26	20	3	3	94	40	43
2. N Abbott 66	26	18	3	5	79	40	39
3. Kingsteignton	26	15	3	8	76	46	33
4. Upton Ath	26	16	1	9	75	58	33
5. Galmpton	26	11	7	8	75	52	29
6. Stoke Gabriel R	26	11	7	8	44	42	29
7. Hele Rovers	26	9	8	9	52	46	26
8. D/tmouth YMRC	26	10	5	11	49	59	25
9. Brixham Villa	26	10	4	12	46	55	24
10. Waldon Ath	26	9	5	12	50	64	23
11. Brixham Tn	26	7	5	14	29	77	19
12. Dartington U	26	6	5	15	54	64	17
13. Brixham Utd	26	7	1	18	45	82	15
14. Newton Town	26	2	5	19	29	81	9

Div One	P	W	D	L	F	A	Pts
1. Kingskerswell	26	20	2	4	81	34	42
2. N Abbott Sp R	26	19	3	4	60	27	41
3. Liverton Utd	26	16	5	5	79	30	37
4. Loddiswell	26	14	7	5	74	56	35
5. Watts Blake B	26	14	5	7	80	45	33
6. Buckfastleigh R	26	11	4	11	70	49	26
7. South Brent	26	10	5	11	54	66	25
8. Victoria Rgrs	26	10	3	13	44	53	23
9. Bovey Tracey	26	7	6	13	54	81	20
10. Paignton Tn	26	7	5	14	64	72	19
11. Combined 89	26	7	5	14	39	78	19
12. Babbacombe C	26	6	6	14	48	73	18
13. Newton Rgrs	26	4	7	15	36	67	15
14. Teign Vill	26	3	5	18	42	94	11

DORSET F.A.

Secretary: P S Hough,
County Ground, Blandford Close, Hamworthy, Poole BH15 4BF
Tel: 01202 682375 (County Office) Fax: 01202 666577

DORSET SENIOR CUP
(FOUNDED 1887–88)
RECENT FINALS

1990–91	Weymouth	v	Swanage T & Herston	5–1
1991–92	Wimborne Town	v	Bridport	1–0
1992–93	Weymouth	v	Poole Town	4–0
1993–94	Dorchester Town	v	Poole Town	1–0
1994–95	Hamworthy Eng	v	Poole Town	4–1

MOST WINS Weymouth 24 Portland United 10 Bridport 9 Poole Town 9

1995–1996

DORSET SENIOR CUP

23 CLUBS **HOLDERS: HAMWORTHY ENGINEERING**

FIRST ROUND Saturday 7th October 1995

Holt United	v	Portland United	0–2
Wareham Rangers	v	Verwood Town	1–1 1–3
Hamworthy United	v	Blandford United	1–1 1–2
Flight Refuelling	v	Bournemouth Sports	0–1
Gillingham Town	v	Sturminster Newton	1–1 1–4
Parley Sports	v	Shaftsbury	0–7
Hamworthy Eng	v	Weymouth Sports	4–1

SECOND ROUND Saturday 4th November 1995 (Inc 9 Byes)

Dorchester Town	v	Sturminster Newton	10–0
Verwood Town	v	Wimborne Town	0–3
Allendale	v	Shaftsbury	3–0
Weymouth	v	Poole Town	5–1
Swanage T&H	v	Sherborne Town	1–3
St Pauls Jersey	v	Hamworthy Eng	1–0
Bournemouth Sp	v	Portland United	2–1
Hamworthy United	v	Bridport	0–2

THIRD ROUND Saturday 2nd December 1995

Weymouth	v	Dorchester Town	0–2
Sherborne Town	v	Wimborne Town	0–1
Bridport	v	St Pauls Jersey	3–3 1–3
Bournemouth Sp	v	Allendale	2–1

SEMI-FINALS Saturday 2nd March 1996

Wimborne Town	v	St Pauls Jersey	0–2
Dorchester Town	v	Bournemouth Sp	0–0 2–2 1–0

FINAL Tuesday 16th April 1996
DORCHESTER TOWN v ST PAULS 3–1 at Cuthbury, Cowgrove Road, Wimborne Town FC. att:362.

Dorset Combination; Portland United's smart new ground at Grove Road. *Photo - Tim Lancaster*

BLACKMORE VALE SUNDAY LEAGUE:

FINAL LEAGUE TABLES 1995/96

Div One	P	W	D	L	F	A	Pts
1. Templecombe	12	10	1	1	44	22	31
2. Stour Provost	12	7	2	3	38	19	23
3. Half Moon	12	6	1	5	38	39	*16
4. Childe Okeford	12	4	2	6	33	38	14
5. Milborne Port	12	4	2	6	27	44	14
6. Thornford	12	4	0	8	34	36	12
7. S Cheriton	12	3	0	9	21	50	9

** 3 points deducted*

Henstridge & Sherborne withdrew.

Div Two	P	W	D	L	F	A	Pts
1. Maiden Bradley	16	14	1	1	68	33	43
2. Palace Court	16	9	5	2	55	35	32
3. Iwerne Minister	16	9	3	4	57	29	30
4. Plume	16	6	6	4	48	34	24
5. Bruton	16	7	2	7	56	54	23
6. Shaftsbury Corr	16	6	3	7	56	54	21
7. Kings Arms	16	4	4	8	38	51	16
8. Great Lyde	16	2	3	11	28	71	9
9. Stur Rovers	16	0	3	13	25	70	3

Div Three	P	W	D	L	F	A	Pts
1. Yetminster	16	13	0	3	62	35	39
2. Queens Head	16	11	4	1	78	33	37
3. Torpedo Stoke	16	9	2	5	58	41	29
4. Greyhound	16	9	0	7	56	51	27
5. Templecombe R	16	8	0	8	41	47	24
6. Mitre	16	5	32	8	39	49	18
7. Donhead	16	5	2	9	32	52	17
8. George	16	4	2	10	42	51	14
9. Shaston Spts	16	1	1	14	28	79	4

Div Four	P	W	D	L	F	A	Pts
1. Zeals	14	10	2	2	43	18	32
2. Lamb	14	9	2	3	47	29	29
3. S Cheriton Res	14	8	2	4	34	29	26
4. White Horse	14	7	0	7	46	37	21
5. Sherborne Yth	14	6	1	7	32	39	19
6. Palace Ct Res	14	4	2	8	19	32	14
7. Shaston Anarch	14	3	2	9	22	42	14
8. Bear Rgrs	14	2	3	9	18	35	9

Barber Shop withdrew.

CUP FINAL RESULTS:

Open Cup:	Queens Head	v Thornford	2-2 (aet), 1-0
Challenge Cup:	Stour Provost	v Templecombe	1-1 (aet), 3-2
Charity Cup:	Stour Provost	v Thornford	2-1
McCreery Cup	Iwerne Minster	v Shaftsbury Corr	1-1 (aet), 4-2 (aet)
Merthyr Guest Cup:	Iwerne Minster	v Queens Head	6-1
Division One & Two Cup:	Half Moon	v Stour Provost	3-2
Division Three & Four Cup:	Mitre	v South Cheriton Res	3-0

DURHAM F.A.

Secretary: J R Walsh,
'Codeslaw', Ferens Park, Durham DH1 1JZ (091 384 8653)
Fax: (01367) 242158

DURHAM CHALLENGE CUP
(FOUNDED 1883–84)

RECENT FINALS

1990–91	Billingham Syntonia	v	Ellpeton CW	1–0
1991–92	Hebburn	v	Billingham Synthonia	2–1
1992–93	Murton	v	Bishop Auckland	2–1
1993–94	Spennymoor United	v	Bishop Auckland	2–2 (Rep 3–2)
1994–95	Spennymoor United	v	South Shields	1–1 (Rep 3–0)

MOST WINS Sunderland 21 Spennymoor United 15 Bishop Auckland 11

1995–1996

DURHAM CHALLENGE CUP

45 CLUBS **HOLDERS: SPENNYMOOR UNITED**

FIRST PRELIMINARY ROUND by14th October

Billingham Town	v	Darlington CS	5–0
Shotton Comrades	v	Annfield Plain	2–1
Consett	v	Jarrow FC	6–1
Boldon CA	v	Norton-Stockton Anc	3–1
Hartlepool BWOB	v	Seaham Red Star	0–5
Easington Colliery	v	Willington	1–0
Ryhope CA	v	Whickham	0–1
Evenwood Town	v	Dunston FB	0–1
Horden CW	v	Stanley United	3–2
Wolvistion	v	Birtley Town	2–3
Brandon United	v	South Shields Cleadon	2–0
Washington	v	South Tyneside Utd	1–3
Peterlee	v	Murton AFC	1–2

3 Clubs with Byes Sunderland Ryhope CW, Esh Winning, Jarrow Roofing, 16 Clubs Exempt to First Round.

FIRST ROUND PROPER 4th November 1995

Hebburn	v	Shotton Comrades	0–1
South Shields	v	Cockfield	3–1
Ryhope CW	v	West Auckland Town	0–4
Spennymoor Utd	v	Birtley Town	3–2
Eppleton CW	v	Brandon United	4–5
Murton	v	Shildon	1–1 2–0
Boldon CA	v	Easington CW	3–1
Whickham	v	Durham City	0–4
Crook Town	v	South Tyneside Utd	1–1 2–0
Tow Law Town	v	Kennet Roker	4–0
Consett	v	Washington Nissan	3–0
Dunston FB	v	Billingham Synthonia	2–1
Esh Winning	v	Bishop Auckland	2–3
Ferryhill Athletic	v	Billingham Town	3–4
Jarrow Roofing	v	Horden CW	5–1
Seaham Red Star	v	Chester Le St Tn	1–3

SECOND ROUND PROPER Saturday 25th November 1995

Brandon United	v	Billngham Town	0–3
West Auckland Tn	v	Bishop Auckland	1–5
South Shields	v	Spennymoor United	0–3
Jarrow Roofing	v	Durham City	0–1
Crook Town	v	Dunston FB	0–1
Chester Le St Tn	v	Consett	3–2
Boldon CA	v	Tow Law Town	0–7
Murton	v	Shotton Comrades	2–1

THIRD ROUND by Saturday 13th January 1996

Spennymoor Utd	v	Tow Law Town	2–0
Bishop Auckland	v	Murton	2–0
Billingham Town	v	Durham City	0–2
Chester Le St Tn	v	Dunston	2–5

SEMI-FINALS

Bishop Auckland	v	Durham City	DC W–O
Dunston FB	v	Spennymoor United	0–1

(Bishop Auckland removed from the Competition for fielding an ineligible player).

FINAL Monday 6th May 1996
DURHAM CITY v SPENNYMOOR UNITED 0*1 at The New Ferens Park, Belmont, Durham City FC.

EAST RIDING F.A.

Secretary: D R Johnson,
52 Bethune Avenue., Hull HU4 7EJ
Tel: 01482 641458 Fax: 01482 647512

EAST RIDING SENIOR CUP (FOUNDED 1903–04)

RECENT FINALS

1990–91	North Ferriby Utd	v	Hull City	0–0
			Replay Never Played	
1991–92	Bridlington Town	v	Schultz YC	2–1
1992–93	Bridlington Town	v	North Ferriby United	3–1
1993–94	Hall Road Rangers	v	Sculcoates Amateurs	1–0
1994–95	Sculcoates Amt	v	Hall Road Rangers	2–1

MOST WINS Hull City 25 Bridlington Town 12 Bridlington Trinity 5 North Ferriby United 5

1995–1996

EAST RIDING SENIOR CUP

20 CLUBS **HOLDERS: SCULCOATES AMATEURS**

SECOND ROUND 11th November 12 Clubs with Byes

Ideal Standard	v	Bulmans	1A1 2–1
Hull City	v	Sculcoates Amts	1–5
Anlaby United	v	Youngs	3–3 1–4
Westella & Willerby	v	Cottingham Sports	1–3
Hall Road Rgns	v	Hedon United	7–0
AFC Reckitts	v	Malet Lambert YC	3–2
Beverley OG's	v	Leconfield	BOG W–O
North Ferriby Utd	v	Haltemprice	4–0

THIRD ROUND Saturday 10th February 1996

Ideal Standard	v	Youngs FC	3–2
Beverley Old G's	v	Hall Road Rangers	0–1
Cottingham Sports	v	Sculcoates Amts	1–1 4V3
AFC Reckitts	v	North Ferriby United	3–1

SEMI-FINALS April 1996

Sculcoates Amts v Ideal Standard
Tuesday 16th at Dene Park, Hall Road Rangers FC.

AFC Reckitts v Hall Rd Rangers
Thursday 18th at Northern Foods Sports Ground, via Cottingham

(Cottingham Sports removed from the Competition for fielding an unregistered player in the Third Round and their opponents Sculcoates Amateurs re-instated)

FINAL Monday 13th May 1996 Kick off 7.00pm
RECKITTS v SCULCOATES AMATEURS 3*3 at Boothferry Park, Hull City AFC.

FINAL Replay Thursday 16th May
RECKITTS v SCULCOATES AMATEURS 1–2 at Dene Park, Hall Road Rangers FC.

EAST RIDING COUNTRY CUP

HOLDERS: WARD

SECOND ROUND Saturday 11th November 1995

South Cave Utd	v	Kingburn Athletic	2–4
Brandesburton	v	Viking Panthers**	0–1
Rudston Utd 2nd	v	Rudston United	1–4
Tickton	v	North Cave	1–4
Holme Rovers	v	Hunmanby United	9–0
Ward**	v	Withernsea	10–0
Bridlington Tn**	v	Little Driffield**	9–0
Bridlington Tn Res**	v	Hilderthorpe AFC	0–6

THIRD ROUND Saturday 10th February 1996

Hilderthorpe	v	Rudston United	2–1
Holme Rovers	v	Kingburn Athletic	4–2
Bridlington Tn	v	Viking Panthers	2–0
North Cave	v	Ward FC	2–2 1–6

SEMI-FINALS April 1996

Hilderthorpe v Bridlington Town 3–8
at Queensgate, Bridlington Town FC.

Holme Rovers v Ward FC 2–5
at Stamford Bridge, Stamford Bridge FC. Via York.

FINAL Saturday 4th May 1996, Kick off 6.30pm
BRIDLINGTON TOWN v WARD 0–2 at Queensgate, Bridlington Town FC.

EAST RIDING COUNTY FOOTBALL LEAGUE

FINAL LEAGUE TABLES 1995/96

Premier Div	P	W	D	L	F	A	Pts
1. Sculcoates Amt	18	13	4	1	52	20	30
2. AFC Reckitts	18	12	4	2	66	29	28
3. Haltemprice	18	10	6	2	46	19	26
4. North Cave	18	11	3	4	55	32	25
5. Anlaby Utd	18	5	7	6	44	43	17
6. Westella & Will	18	6	2	10	40	48	14
7. Holme Rovers	18	5	4	9	29	42	14
8. Woodlands	18	4	2	12	30	49	10
9. Beverley O G	18	3	4	11	37	60	10
10. Rudston Utd	18	2	2	14	19	76	6

Div One	P	W	D	L	F	A	Pts
1. Bridlington T	24	18	4	2	88	30	40
2. South Cave U	24	14	7	3	85	41	35
3. Sculcoates II	24	11	9	4	53	25	31
4. Brandesburton	24	12	5	7	53	39	29
5. Mkt Weighton U	24	12	5	7	61	65	29
6. Howden Amt	24	10	7	7	50	53	27
7. Skidby Millers	24	10	4	10	55	62	24
8. Holmpton Utd	24	7	6	11	44	56	20
9. Tickton	24	8	4	12	49	71	20
10. Westella II	24	7	4	13	32	44	18
11. Easington Utd	24	6	5	13	38	55	17
12. North Cave II	24	6	4	14	41	47	16
13. Hook Amateurs	24	1	4	19	32	93	6

Division Two: **Champions:** Beverley Town **Runners-up:** Haltemprice II
Division Three: **Champions:** Creykes Arms **Runners-up:** Beverley OG II
Division Four: **Champions:** Easington Utd II **Runners-up:** Cross Keys

DIFFIELD & DISTRICT A.F.L.

Premier Div	P	W	D	L	F	A	Pts
1. Brid Labour Cl	22	19	3	0	93	27	41
2. Viking Panthers	21	17	2	2	90	18	36
3. Crown AFC	22	12	5	5	58	47	29
4. Full Measure	22	9	9	4	56	47	27
5. Driffield El	22	11	3	8	54	43	25
6. Hilderthorpe	21	9	4	8	50	52	22
7. Middleton Rov	22	9	3	10	47	61	21
8. Hornsea Town	22	8	3	11	46	49	19
9. Rudston Utd	22	8	2	12	53	63	18
10. Brid Town Res	22	5	2	15	30	55	12
11. Brid Rovers	22	4	0	18	27	85	8
12. Little Driffield	22	1	2	19	21	78	4

Top Scorer; L Johnstone (Viking Panthers) 32

Div One	P	W	D	L	F	A	Pts
1. Shiptonthorpe	20	14	3	3	85	24	31
2. Charles Dickens	20	14	3	3	68	26	31
3. Brid Labour II	20	13	2	5	80	37	28
4. Full Measure II	20	11	4	5	51	36	26
5. AFC Tavern	20	12	2	6	54	47	26
6. Htn. Cranswick	20	11	3	6	48	30	25
7. Ship Inn	20	6	5	9	44	41	17
8. Royal Oak	20	5	3	12	34	52	13
9. Hornsea Tn II	20	4	3	13	19	53	11
10. Sledmere	20	2	5	13	21	59	9
11. Rose & Crown	20	1	1	18	23	122	3

Top Scorer: A Thompson (Brid Labour Club II) 20

Division Two: **Champions:** Nafferton AFC **Runners-up:** Globe
Top Scorer: A Stbler (Nafferton) 35
Division Three: **Champions:** FC Quay Leisure **Runners-up:** Beaconsfield AFC
Top Scorer: J Wallis (FC Quay Leisure) 22
Division Four: **Champions:** Brummells **Runners-up:** H/Cranswick United
Top Scorer: M Colley (North Burton) 46

Cup Winners:

Challenge Cup Viking Panthers
Senior Cup Skiptonthorpe
Blind Cup Burton Agnes
Don Bemrose Viking Panthers
Legion Cup Globe
Bryan Pannhausen Harbor Lights II

HUMBERSIDE LEAGUE

Division One: **Champions:** Rover Cars **Runners-up:** Schooner B
Division Two: **Champions:** Wallis Cars **Runners-up:** Kinloss FC

CLUB DIRECTORY Premier & Division One 1995-96

ANLABY UNITED
Secretary: Steve Smith, 12 Hawkshead Green, Malham Ave., Hull HU4 7SZ (01482 562925).
Ground: King George V PF, Beverley Rd, Hull **Colours:** Sky Blue.

BEVERLEY TOWN
Secretary: Paul Garwood, 7 Eden Close, Beverley,HU17 7HE (01482 870805)
Ground: Beverley Leisure Centre, Flemingate, Beverley **Colours:** Sky & claret stripes.

BRANDESBURTON
Secretary: Les Watts, 'Towyn'Foston Lane, North Frodingham, Driffield YO25 8JZ (01262 488543)
Ground: Catwick Lane, Brandesburton **Colours:** Black & amber stripes.

BRIDLINGTON TOWN A.F.C.
Secretary: Chris Bemrose, 16 North Back Lane, Bridlington YO16 5BA (01262 604036)
Ground: Queensgate Bridlington **Colours:** Blue & black/black

EASINGTON UNITED
Secretary: Mrs Judith Foster, 5 Humber Lane, Patrington, Hull HU12 0PJ.
Ground: Low Farm, Easington **Colours:** Navy & sky/sky.

HALTEMPRICE
Secretary: Keith Failey, 77 Beech Rd, Ellhoughton, HU15 1JY (01482 666994)
Ground: King George V PF, Beverley Rd, Kirkella **Colours:** White and Black

HOLME ROVERS
Secretary: Paul Harrison, 4 Hawthorn Drive, Holme-on-Spalding Moor, York YO4 4AP (01430 861140)
Ground: Village Hall, High Str., Holme-on-Spalding Moor **Colours:** White & blue/blue.

HOLMPTON UNITED
Secretary: Wayne Christie, 20 Garrick Close, Pocklington YO4 2YX (01759 306796)
Ground: Welwick Rd, Patrington **Colours:** Green & black stripes.

HOOK AMATEURS
Secretary: Kevin Young, 'Mandavale', High Str., Hook, Goole DN14 5NY (01405 760322)
Ground: Church Lane, Hook **Colours:** Green & Yellow.

HOWDEN AMATEURS
Secretary: Brian Stevens, 15 Derwent Ave., Howden, nr Goole DN14 7AJ (01430 431185)
Ground: Ashes Park, Playing Field, Howden **Colours:** Red & black.

MARKET WEIGHTON UNITED
Secretary: Stephen P Denness, Holly Tree Farm, Holme-on-Spalding Moor, York YO4 4HE (01430 860413)
Ground: Goodmanham Rd, Market Weighton **Colours:** Green & white.

NORTH CAVE
Secretary: Cliff Robson, 6 Blanshards Lane, North Cave HU15 2LN (01430 422071)
Ground: Church Street PF, North Cave **Colours:** Blue/white.

A.F.C. RECKITTS
Secretary: Alan Hitchcock, 9 Ashgate Road, Willerby HU10 6HH (01482 654286)
Ground: Chamberlain Road Hull. **Colours:** Blue & black.

SCULCOATES AMATEURS
Secretary: Tony Exton, 9 32nd Avenue, Hull HU6 9SD (01482 802600)
Ground: Pitch No.1 Oak Rd Playing Fields, Hull **Colours:** White and Black.

SKIDBY MILLERS
Secretary: Ron Leveridge, 121 Main Str., Skidby, Cottingham, Hull HU16 5TX (01482 847289)
Ground: Skidby PF, Manor Garth, Skidby **Colours:** Black and white.

SOUTH CAVE UNITED
Secretary: Norman Elliott, 41 Church Str., South Cave, Brough HU15 2EP (01430 422577)
Ground: Church Street, South Cave **Colours:** All blue.

TICKTON
Secretary: Alan Hayton, 54 Churchfields, Tickton, Beverley HU17 9RQ (01964 542040)
Ground: Playing Fields, Main St., Tickton, Beverley **Colours:** Blue and white

WESTELLA & WILLERBY
Secretary: John Walker, 174 Maplewood Avenue,Goole DN14 6ND (01482 572462)
Ground: Hull & ER Ath. Club, Chanterlands Ave Hull **Colours:** Black & white stripes/white

WOODLANDS
Secretary: George Clark, 87 Westfield Avenue,Goole,DN14 6ND (01405 761047)
Ground: Parkside School, Western Rd, Goole **Colours:** Orange/purple.

ESSEX F.A.

Secretary: T Alexander,
31 Mildmay Road, Chelmsford CM2 0DN (01245 357727)

ESSEX SENIOR CUP
(FOUNDED 1883–84)

RECENT FINALS

1990–91	Southend United	v	Leyton Orient	1–1 (Rep 2–1)
1991–92	Redbridge Forest	v	Chelmsford City	3–0
1992–93	Chelmsford City	v	Wivenhoe Town	1–0
1993–94	Grays Athletic	v	Billericay Town	1–0
1994–95	Grays Athletic	v	Billericay Town	1–0

MOST WINS Ilford 13 Walthamstow Avenue 12 Grays Athletic 8 Leyton 8

1995–1996

ESSEX SENIOR CUP

45 CLUBS **HOLDERS: GRAYS ATHLETIC**

PRELIMINARY ROUND

Brightlingsea Utd	v	Southend Manor	2–3	Clackton Town	v	Brentwood	0–1
Concord Rangers	v	East Ham United	4–0	Maldon Town	v	Hullbridge Sports	9–0

FIRST ROUND

Burnham Ramblers	v	Woodford Town	BR W–O	Ford United	v	Maldon Town	1–0
Concord Rangers	v	Romford	1–0	Stanway Rovers	v	Waltham Abbey	3–1
Basildon United	v	Harwich & Parkeston	1–2	Gt Wakering Rvrs	v	Stanstead	0–1
Halstead Town	v	Brentwood	1–0	Southend Manor	v	Barkingside	0–2
Bowers United	v	Tiptree United	0–3				

23 Clubs seeded into the

SECOND ROUND by Saturday 9th December 1995

Wivenhoe Town	v	Billericay Town	3*3 1*2	Heybridge Swifts	v	Tiptree United	5–1
Southend United	v	Canvey Island	6–0	Aveley	v	Purfleet	0–3
Chelmsford City	v	Tilbury	3–0	Harwich Parkeston	v	Grays Athletic	2–3
Collier Row	v	Harlow Town	4–0	Burnham Ramblers	v	Barkingside	0–1
Stanway Rovers	v	Stansted	2–3	Dagenham & R'dge	v	Leyton Orient	1–3
Concord Rangers	v	Colchester United	2*1	Witham Town	v	Hornchurch	2–1
Leyton Pennant	v	Saffron Walden Town	2–1	Barking	v	Ford United	2*3
Clapton	v	Halstead Town	1–4	Braintree Town	v	East Thurrock United	2–1

THIRD ROUND Saturday 13th January 1996

Barkingside	v	Southend Utd	1–5	Collier Row	v	Purfleet	0–1
Grays Athletic	v	Ford United	3–2	Concord Rangers	v	Leyton Orient	2–0
Halstead Town	v	Heybridge Swifts	0–3	Leyton Pennant	v	Billericay Town	3V2
Braintree Town	v	Chelmsford City	3–2	Stansted	v	Witham Town	3*4

(Leyton Pennant removed from Competition for fielding an ineligible player Billericay Town re-instated)

FOURTH ROUND by Saturday 17th February

Heybridge Swifts	v	Billericay Town	1–3	Grays Athletic	v	Witham Town	4–0
Purfleet	v	Southend United	2–4	Braintree Town	v	Concord Rangers	3–0

SEMI-FINALS March

Braintree Town	v	Southend United	1*1 1–0	Grays Athletic	v	Billericay Town	0–2

FINAL Monday 22nd April 1996 7.30pm
BILLERICAY TOWN v BRAINTREE TOWN 1–2 at Victoria Road, Dagenham & Redbridge FC.

ESSEX THAMES-SIDE TROPHY
(FOUNDED 1945–56)

RECENT FINALS

1990–91	Grays Athletic	v	Billericay Town	1–0
1991–92	Billericay Town	v	Ford United	2–2 (4–2 Pens)
1992–93	Leyton	v	Rainham Town	5–4
1993–94	Canvey Island	v	Grays Athletic	2–2 (4–3 Pens)
1994–95	Purfleet	v	Chelmsford City	2–0

MOST WINS Ilford 13 Walthamstow Avenue 12 Grays Athletic 8 Leyton 8

1995–1996

ESSEX THAME-SIDE TROPHY

25 CLUBS **HOLDERS: PURFLEET**

FIRST ROUND

Witham Town	v	Barkingside	2–1	Romford	v	Ford United	3–1
Collier Row	v	Hornchurch	3p2 1*1	Tilbury	v	Gt Wakering Rovers	0–5
Waltham Abbey	v	Basildon United	0–1	Burnham Ramblers	v	Aveley	2–1
East Thurrock Utd	v	Canvey Island	1*2	Southend Manor	v	Bowers United	1–0
Clapton	v	Concord Rangers	0–3				

4 Clubs with Byes Barking, Billericay Town, Leyton Pennant, Tiptree United and 3 Clubs Exempt Purfleet, Chelmsford City, Grays Athletic into the

SECOND ROUND

Concord Rangers	v	Southend Manor	1A0 2–1	Witham Town	v	Chelmsford City	2–1
Gt Wakering Rvrs	v	Barking	3–2	Leyton Pennant	v	Collier Row	2–1
Billericay Town	v	Purfleet	0–2	Basildon United	v	Canvey Island	1–3
Grays Athletic	v	Romford	3–0	Tiptree United	v	Burnham Ramblers	2–3

The above match Great Wakering Rovers v Barking was the first full game under floodlights at the Borough Park home of Rovers.

THIRD ROUND

Grays Athletic	v	Gt Wakering Rvrs	2–1	Witham Town	v	Burnham Ramblers	1–0
Leyton Pennant	v	Purfleet	6–2	Canvey Island	v	Concord Rangers	1–0

SEMI-FINALS

Witham Town @LP	v	Leyton Pennant	3–1	Grays Athletic	v	Canvey Island	0*2

FINAL Sunday 12th May 1996 Kick off 3.00pm
CANVEY ISLAND v WITHAM TOWN 5–0 at Park Lane, Canvey Island FC.

ESSEX SENIOR TROPHY
(FOUNDED 1976–77)

RECENT FINALS

1990–91	Ford United	v	Braintree Town	1–0
1991–92	Ford United	v	East Thurrock United	3–0
1992–93	Southern Manor	v	Harwich & Parkeston	1–0
1993–94	Halstead Town	v	Canvey Island	2–0
1994–95	Billericay Town Res	v	Halstead Town Res	1–0

MOST WINS Leytonstone 8 Dagenham 6 Walthamstow Avenue 6

1995–1996

EAST ANGLIAN CUP

56 CLUBS **HOLDERS: HEYBRIDGE SWIFTS**

GROUP 1 FIRST ROUND by 15th November 1995

Hadleigh United	v	Stowmarket Town	4p5 2*2	Woodbridge Town	v	Sudbury Town	0–1
Felixstowe P&Tn	v	Ipswich Wanderers	3–6				

SECOND ROUND by 31st December **Bye to this Round

Stowmarket Town	v	Sudbury Town	1–2	Cornard United**	v	Ipswich Wanderers	1–3

GROUP FINAL

Sudbury Town	v	Ipswich Wanderers	2–0

GROUP 2 FIRST ROUND

Fakenham Town	v	March Town Utd	2–1	Stamford AFC	v	Spalding United	6p7 3*3
Downham Town	v	Holbeach Utd	1–2				

SECOND ROUND

Fakenham Town	v	Spalding United	1–0	Bourne Town**	v	Holbeach United	0–2

GROUP FINAL

Fakenham Town	v	Holbeach United	2–1

GROUP 3 FIRST ROUND

Ely City	v	Soham Town Rangers	1–3	Watton United	v	Thetford Town	1–3
Diss Town	v	Mildenhall Town	2–0				

SECOND ROUND

Soham Tn Rangers	v	Thetford Town	4p3 4*4	Bury Town**	v	Diss Town	2–0

GROUP FINAL

Soham Tn Rangers	v	Bury Town	4–0

GROUP 4 FIRST ROUND

Royston Town	v	Sawbridgeworth Tn	4–1	Ware	v	Stansted	5–1
Letchworth	v	Saffron Walden Tn	0–6				

SECOND ROUND

Royston Rown	v	Ware	0–2	Harlow Town**	v	Saffron Walden Tn	6p5 2*2

GROUP FINAL **A=Fog**

Ware	v	Harlow Town	0A0 1–0

GROUP 5 FIRST ROUND

Fynesbury Rovers	v	Potton United	7p8 1*1	Somersham Town	v	St Ives Town	0–2
Cambridge City	v	Histon	6–0	Warboys Town	v	Biggleswade Tn	1A1 3–1

SECOND ROUND

Potton United	v	St Ives Town	2–0	Warboys Town	v	Cambridge City	2–4

GROUP FINAL

Potton United	v	Cambridge City	0–2

GROUP 6 FIRST ROUND

Harpenden Town	v	Hoddesdon Town	2–0	St Albans City	v	Romford	2–0
Barkingside	v	Hertford Town	5–1				

SECOND ROUND

Harpenden Town	v	St Albans City	1-2	Barking**	v	Barkingside	4–0

GROUP FINAL

St Albans City	v	Barking	1–0

GROUP 7 FIRST ROUND

Concord Rangers	v	Maldon Town	4–2	Tiptree United	v	Southend Manor	5–2
Burnham Ramblers	v	Heybridge Swifts	0–3				

SECOND ROUND

Concord Rangers	v	Tiptree United	2–0	Aveley**	v	Heybridge Swifts	3–2

GROUP FINAL

Concord Rangers	v	Aveley	2*0

GROUP 8 FIRST ROUND

Colchester United	v	Harwich & Parkeston	5–0	Clacton Town	v	Halstead Town	1–2

SECOND ROUND

Colchester United	v	Witham Town**	2–1	Braintree Town**	v	Halstead Town	2–1

GROUP FINAL

Colchester United	v	Braintree Town	3–4

COMPETITION PROPER QUARTER FINALS

Braintree Town	v	Ware	5–4	Fakenham Town	v	Sudbury Town	1–2
Concord Rangers	v	Cambridge City	1–0	St Albans City	v	Soham Tn Rangers	1–0

SEMI-FINALS

Concord Rangers	v	Sudbury Town	0–2	Braintree Town	v	St Albans City	2–0

FINAL Tuesday 7th May 1996
BRAINTREE TOWN v SUDBURY TOWN 3–0 at Cressing Road, Braintree Town FC. att: 643.

Resignations were received from 6 Clubs; Boston Town, Chatteris Town, Long Sutton Athletic, Swaffham Town, Wisbech Town, Wroxham, 4 New Entrants accepted: Concord Rangers, Ipswich Wanderers, Maldon Town, Potton United. 1994/5, 58 - 6 = 52 + 4 = 56. 1995/6.

Braintree Town FC: Essex Senior Cup Winners & East Anglian Cup Winners; seen here with the Senior Cup. Photo - Jon Weaver

GLOUCESTERSHIRE F.A.

Secretary: E J Marsh, 46 Douglas Road, Horfield, Bristol BS7 0JD (0117 951 9435)

GLOUCESTERSHIRE SENIOR TROPHY (FOUNDED 1978–79)

RECENT FINALS

1990–91	Mangotsfield Utd	v	Bristol Manor Farm	6–0
1991–92	Cheltenham Saracens	v	Vikings (Stroud)	6–5
1992–93	Hallen	v	Cinderford Town	4–1
1993–94	Mangotsfield Utd	v	Moreton Town	3–1 (AET)
1994–95	Shortwood United	v	Fairford Town	2–1

MOST WINS Mangotsfield United 4 Moreton Town 3 Shortwood United 2

1995–1996

GLOUCESTERSHIRE SENIOR TROPHY

33 CLUBS **HOLDERS: SHORTWOOD UNITED**

FIRST ROUND Saturday 21st October 2.30pm

Mangotsfield Utd	v	Shirehampton	1–3
Endsleigh @P	v	Pucklechurch Sports	3–1
Broad Plain Hs	v	Wotton Rovers	3–1
Bishops Cleeve	v	Tuffley Rovers	0–3
Stapleton/Brock'th	v	DRG (FP)	0*0 1–3
Broadwell Amt	v	Ellwood	0–2
Bitton	v	Hallen	1*1 3–1
Longwell Grn Abb	v	Winterbourne Utd	0–1
Harrow Hill	v	St Marks CA	1–2
Cirencester Utd	v	Cheltenham Saracens	2–3
Patchway Town	v	Old Georgians	0–1
Almondsbury Tn	v	Cirencester Town	2–6
Totterdown Ath	v	Cadbury Heath	1–3
Shortwood Utd	v	Bristol Manor Farm	2*1
Frampton Athletic	v	Smiths Athletic	1–0
Henbury Old Boys	v	Fairford Town	1–3

SECOND ROUND Saturday 2nd December 1995

Old Georgians	v	Fairford Town	1–3
Ellwood	v	Frampton Athletic	3–1
Bitton	v	Tuffley Rovers	3–1
DRG	v	Endsleigh	0–2
Shortwood United	v	Cirencester Town	0–3
Cheltenham S'cens	v	Broad Plain House	2–1
Winterbourne Utd	v	Shirehampton	2–1
Cadbury Heath	v	St Marks CA	3*3 2–4

THIRD ROUND

Cirencester Town	v	Fairford Town	3*2
St Marks CA @B	v	Bitton	1–3
Cheltenham S'cens	v	Winterbourne Utd	1–3
Ellwood	v	Endsleigh	0–2

SEMI-FINALS

Winterbourne Utd v Cirencester Town 0–1
at Shortwood United AFC Tuesday 5th March

Endsleigh v Bitton 2–0
at Almondsbury Town FC Tuesday 19th March

FINAL Monday 6th May 7.30pm
CIRENCESTER TOWN v ENDSLEIGH 2*1 at Meadow Park, Gloucester City AFC.

GLOUCESTERSHIRE SENIOR CUP (FOUNDED 1936–37)

RECENT FINALS

1990–91	Gloucester City	v	Cheltenham Town	2–1
1991–92	Cheltenham Town	v	Gloucester City	4–2 (AET)
1992–93	Gloucester City	v	Yate Town	3–2 (AET)
1993–94	Newport AFC	v	Gloucester City	1–0
1994–95	Cheltenham Town	v	Yate Town	1–1 (5–4 Pens)

MOST WINS Cheltenham Town 29 Gloucester City 18 Forest Green Rovers 3

GLOUCESTERSHIRE SENIOR CUP

5 CLUBS **HOLDERS: CHELTENHAM TOWN**

SEMI-FINALS **A=Fog**

Gloucester City	v	Cinderford Town	2A0 3–2
Cheltenham Town	v	Yate Town	2–0

FINAL Tuesday 2nd April 7.30pm
CHELTENHAM TOWN v GLOUCESTER CITY 0*0 (3p1) at Waddon Road, Cheltenham Town FC.

GLOUCESTERSHIRE NORTHERN SENIOR LEAGUE

FOUNDED: 1922

Chairmam: R Davis

Hon Secretary: W N Pember, 11 Linworth Road, Bishops Cleeve, Cheltenham GL52 4PF (01242 673800)

FINAL LEAGUE TABLES 1995/96

Div One		P	W	D	L	F	A	Pts
1.	Dursley Town	28	18	5	5	50	19	41
2.	Kings Stanley	28	16	6	6	78	34	38
3.	Frampton United	28	13	10	5	52	30	36
4.	Lydney Town	28	15	4	9	69	53	34
5.	Barnwood Utd	28	16	2	10	56	51	34
6.	Crescent Utd	28	15	3	10	68	41	33
7.	Stonehouse	28	13	6	9	64	48	*30
8.	Shortwood U R	28	10	7	11	51	54	27
9.	Hardwicke	28	10	6	12	49	55	26
10.	Longford	28	8	9	11	48	47	25
11.	Lydbrook Ath	28	9	5	14	45	57	23
12.	Viney St Swiths	28	8	7	13	42	62	23
13.	Sharpness	28	5	9	14	34	58	19
14.	Berkeley Town	28	5	4	19	32	65	14
15.	Ellwood Res	28	5	5	18	33	97	*13

* 2 points deducted

Yate Town A record expunged.

Div Two		P	W	D	L	F	A	Pts
1.	Tuffley R R	28	22	6	0	108	27	50
2.	Eagle Star	28	22	2	4	109	43	46
3.	Brimscombe	28	16	5	7	58	29	37
4.	R Hill Rangers	28	16	5	7	61	39	37
5.	Longlevens	28	13	5	10	64	46	31
6.	Charfield	28	14	6	8	55	54	*30
7.	Nuclear Elec	28	11	5	12	49	58	27
8.	Harrow Hill R	28	10	6	12	46	51	26
9.	Taverners	28	10	5	13	47	50	25
10.	Coleford Utd	28	8	9	11	26	37	25
11.	Worrall Hill	28	9	4	15	41	52	22
12.	Eastcombe	28	7	6	15	33	46	20
13.	Cam Bulldogs	28	7	6	15	32	58	20
14.	Bilbury	28	6	4	18	37	82	16
15.	Newent Town	28	1	2	25	22	11	4

* 4 points deducted

FIRST DIVISION CLUBS 1996-97

BARNWOOD UNITED

Secretary: S A Brown, 60 Haunton Road, Coney Hill, Gloucester GL4 7RD (01452 310788)
Colours: Green/navy/navy **Change colours:** Orange/black/black
Ground: Walls Social Club. Hammond Way, Barnwood (01452 610277)

BRIMSCOMBE & THRUPP

Secretary: B F Roberts, Elmcroft, Old Horsley Rd., Nailsworth, Glos. GL6 OJW (01453 836311)
Colours: White/navy/red **Change colours:** Red/navy/red
Ground: The Meadow, London Rd, Brimscombe, Nr Stroud, Glos.

CRESCENT UNITED

Secretary: C Beale, 17 Cleeveland Street, Cheltenham (01242 514323)
Colours: All green **Change colours:** Blue/white/blue
Ground: Whaddon Recreation Ground, Whaddon Road, Cheltenham

EAGLE STAR

Secretary: P Cotton, 48 Glynbridge Gardens, Cheltenham, GL51 0BZ (01242 571624)
Ground: Eagle Star Sports & Social Club, Quat Goose Lane, Swindon Village, Cheltenham (01242 522208)
Colours: Blue & black/black/black **Change Colours:** Green & white/black/black

FRAMPTON UNITED

Secretary: H G Tudor, 'Ad Extremum', Frampton-upon-Severn, Glos GL2 7EA (01452 740224).
Colours: Royal & white stripes/white/blue **Change colours:** Yellow/white/blue
Ground: Bell Field, Frampton-on-Severn

HARDWICKE

Secretary: Ms P Langley, 13 Merchants Mead, Quedgeley. Gloucester, GL2 4FA (01452 723063)
Colours: Blue/blue/red **Change colours:** Yellow/blue/red
Ground: Green Lane, Hardwicke (01452 720587).

KINGS STANLEY

Secretary: R K Bassett, 8 Guildings Way, Kings Stanley, Stonehouse, Glos GL1 3LF (01453 824012).
Colours: Blue & Black stripes/black/blue **Change colours:** Black & white stripes/black/black
Ground: Marling Close, Kings Stanley (01453 828975).

LONGFORD

Secretary: T Godwin, 2 Abbotts Cottage, Sandhurst, Gloucester GL2 9NW (01452 730727).
Colours: Sky+white stripes/navy/sky **Change colours:** Red & white stripes/white/red
Ground: Longford Playing Fields, Longford Lane.

LYDBROOK

Secretary: A.Brain, Fairless, Hangerberry,Lydbrook, Glos GL17 9QG (01594 861079)
Colours: Black & white/black/black **Change colours:** Gold/black/black
Ground: Reeds, Lower Lydbrook.

LYDNEY TOWN

Secretary: R A Sansom, 17 Woodland Rise, Lydney, Glos GL15 5LH (01594 843210).
Colours: White & royal/royal/royal **Change colours:** Yellow/black/black
Ground: Lydney Recreation Trust Ground (01594 844523).

SHARPNESS

Secretary: J Thomas, 3 Severn View Parade, Newtown, Berkeley, Glos. GL13 9ND (01453 511510)
Colours: Red/white/red **Change colours:** All white or all blue.
Ground: Berkeley Vale Community School.

SHORTWOOD UNITED RESERVES

Secretary: Mark Webb, 1 The Bungalow, Shortwood, Nailsworth, Glos GL6 0SD (01453 833204)
Colours: All red **Change Colours:** All blue
Ground: Meadow Bank Shortwood (01453 833936)

SMITHS ATHLETIC

Secretary: Peter Jurd, 11 Shaw Green Lane, Prestbury, Cheltenham GL52 3BS (01242 529188)
Colours: Blue & black/black/black **Change Colours:** Green & white/black/black
Ground: The Newlands, Bishops Cleeve (01242 672752)

STONEHOUSE FREEWAY

Secretary: M Smith, 2 The Cottage, The Cross, Eastington, Stonehouse, Glos GL10 3AB (01453 824214).
Colours: White/black/black **Change colours:** Black & White/black/red
Ground: Oldends Lane, Stonehouse, Glos.

TUFFLEY ROVERS RESERVES

Secretary: Graham Moody, 50 Giles Cox, Quedgeley, Gloucester GL2 4YL (01452 724083)
Colours: All Claret **Change colours:** Yellow/blue/blue
Ground: Glevum Park, Lower Tuffley Lane, Gloucester (01452 423402)

VINEY St SWITHINS

Secretary: A R Thomas, 'Ravenscoft', 28 Allaston Rd, Lydney, Glos GL15 5ST (01594 843634).
Colours: Red/black/Red **Change colours:** Blue & white/Blue/Blue
Ground: Viney St Swithins Sports & Social Club, Viney Hill (01594 510658).

SECOND DIVISION CLUBS 1996-97

BERKELEY TOWN

Secretary: Mrs C Fulton, The Saplings, Ham, Berkeley, GL13 9Qn (01453 810840)
Colours: Yellow/green/yellow **Change colours:** Black & white/black/black
Ground: Station Rd, Berkeley.

CAM BULLDOGS

Secretary: R.Brady, 12 New Road, Cam, Nr Dursley, Glos. GL11 6PN (01453 542388)
Colours: Black & white/black/black **Change colours:** Green & yellow/black/black
Ground: Cam Sports Club, Everlands, Cam (01453 546736).

CHARFIELD

Secretary: C.Somerton, 7 Newtown, Charfield, Wotton under Edge, GL12 8TF (01454 260559)
Colours: Red/black/red **Change Colours:** Blue & white/black/red
Ground: Charfield Memorial Playing Fields, Wotton Rd, Charfield (01454 260204).

CHELTENHAM CIVIL SERVICE

Secretary: Geoff Trott, 7 Oakhurst Rise, Charlton Kings, Cheltenham GL52 6JU (01242 576645)
Colours: Blue & black/black/black **Change Colours:** Red & black/black/black
Ground: Civil Service Sports Ground, Tewkesbury Road, Cheltenham (01242 680424)

COLEFORD UNITED

Secretary: T Smith, 3A Lower Palmers Flat, Coalway, Coleford, Glos GL16 7LT (01594 834791).
Colours: Yellow/green/yellow **Change colours:** White/black/black
Ground: King George V Playing Fields, Victoria Rd, Coleford.

ELLWOOD RESERVES

Secretary: Ian Edwards, 24 Forest Road, Milkwall, Coleford, GL56 7LB (01594 833585)
Colours: Blue & yellow/blue/blue **Change Colours:** Red.blue/blue
Ground: Bromley Road, Ellwood, Nr Coleford (01594 832927)

EASTCOMBE

Secretary: John Pollard, Newholme, Middle Hill, Chalford Hill, Stroud, Glos (01453 884704).
Colours: Blue & Yellow stripes/blue/blue **Change Colours:** Orange/blue/blue
Ground: The Recreation Ground, Eastcombe

HARROW HILL RESERVES

Secretary: Geoff Tuffley, 9 Danby Close, Hilldene, Cinderford,GL14 2RL (01594 825274)
Colours: Claret & blue/sky/sky
Change Colours: Black & white/black/black
Ground: Larksfield Road, Harrow Hill (01594 543873)

LONGLEVENS

Secretary: B.Davis, 28 Simon Road, Longlevens, Gloucester GL2 0TP (01452 422450).
Colours: Red/black/black **Change colours:** Blue/black/black
Ground: The Pavilion, Longford Lane, Longlevens, Gloucester (01452 308152).

NUCLEAR ELECTRIC

Secretary: Gregory Smith, 19 Sydney Street Gloucester, GL1 4DB (01452 410452)
Colours: White/white/red **Change colours:**
Ground: Woodlawns Sports & Social Club, Green Street, Brockworth, Glos (01452 617112)

RUARDEAN HILL RANGERS

Secretary: G Meek, 31 Hazel Road, Drybrook, Glos GL17 9HQ, (01594 542032)
Colours: Red/black/black **Change colours:** Black & white/black/black
Ground: Hillview Road, Ruardean Hill (01594 544871)

SOUTH CERNEY

Secretary: Mrs Kay Allen, 22 Broadway Lane, South Cerney, Cirencester GL7 5UH (01285 860168)
Colours: Yellow/black/black **Change Colours:** Blue/black/black
Ground: Walnut Tree, Upper Up, South Cerney (01585 529946)

TAVERNERS

Secretary: P.Shiers, 29 Blackwater Way, Longlevens,Glos GL2 OXN (01452 388195)
Colours: All Blue **Change colours:** White/blue/white
Ground: Nailsworth Rec Centre, Nympsfield Road, Nailsworth.

WHITECROFT

Secretary: Roland Elsmore, Oakwood, Charleswood Road, Whitecroft, Lydney GL15 4QH (01594 563111)
Colours: Green & black/black/black & red **Change Colours:** Blue & Black/black/Blue & black

WHITMINSTER

Secretary: Dave Herbert, 4 High Street, Arlingham, Gloucester GL2 7JN (01452 740627)
Colours: Sky/maroon/maroon **Change Colours:** All Royal
Ground: School Lane Whitminster

WORRALL HILL

Secretary: B Wadley, 9 Hillside Terrace, Joys Green, Lydbrook, Glos GL17 9DY (01594 860587).
Colours: Yellow/green/green **Change colours:** Blue & white/blue/blue
Ground: Worrall Hill, Lydbrook, Glos (01594 860532).

HAMPSHIRE F.A.

Secretary: R G Barnes,
8 Ashwood Gardens, off Winchester Road, Southampton SO16 7PW (01703 79110)

HAMPSHIRE SENIOR CUP
(FOUNDED 1887–88)

RECENT FINALS

1990–91	Farnborough Town	v	Waterlooville	1–0
1991–92	Waterlooville	v	Havant Town	1–0
1992–93	Fareham Town	v	Farnborough Town	4–1
1993–94	Havant Town	v	Farnborough Town	1–0
1994–95	Havant Town	v	Farnborough Town	1–0

MOST WINS Southampton 13 Newport 7 Cowes 6

1995–1996

HAMPSHIRE SENIOR CUP

49 CLUBS **HOLDERS: HAVANT TOWN**

PRELIMINARY ROUND by Saturday 7th October

Aerostructures	v	Hartley Wintney	4–0
AFC Lymington	v	Hayling Islane	4–0
AFC Totton	v	Eastleigh	0–4
Bashley	v	Paulsgrove	5–1
Basingstoke Town	v	Pirelli General	8–0
Bass Alton Town	v	Fleetlands	1–0
Bemerton HH	v	Romsey Town	RT W–O
Brockenhurst	v	AC Delco	3–1
Christchurch	v	Ecchinswell	0–1
Cove	v	Liss Athletic	4–2
East Cowes Vics	v	Petersfield Town	2–1
Fareham Town	v	Malshanger	5–4
Fleet Town	v	Overton United	6–1
New Milton Tn	v	Gosport Borough	1–2
New Street	v	Cowes Sports	7–0
Sylvans Sports	v	BAT Sports	6–0
Whitchurch Utd	v	Netley Central Sports	0–3

15 Clubs with Byes into the

FIRST ROUND by Saturday 4th November 1995

Aerostructures	v	Moneyfields	2–1
Lymington AFC	v	Sylvans Sports	2–1
Aldershot Town	v	East Cowes Vic Ath	5–0
Andover	v	Colden Common	3–1
Brockenhurst	v	Winchester City	1–4
Cove	v	Bashley	1–7
DCA Basingstoke	v	Ecchinswell	5–1
Eastleigh	v	Bass Alton Town	2–1
Fareham Town	v	Basingstoke Town	1–3
Farnborough Town	v	New Street	6–1
Fleet Town	v	Blackfield & Langley	4–1
Gosport Borough	v	Newport IOW	1–5
Horndean	v	Bournemouth	0–1
Portsmouth RN	v	Netley Central Sports	1–0
Romsey Town	v	Havant Town	1–5
Waterlooville	v	Ryde	4–0

SECOND ROUND by 6th January 1996

AFC Lymington	v	Winchester City	4–0
Bashley	v	Newport IOW	1–0
Basingstoke Town	v	Havant Town	1A0
Bournemouth	v	Andover	2–1
Eastleigh	v	Aldershot Town	2–3
Farnborough Town	v	DCA Basingstoke	1–4
Portsmouth RN	v	Aerostructures	1–2
Waterlooville	v	Fleet Town	2–1

The above match between Basingstoke Town and Havant Town was Abandoned after 87 minutes with Havant down to 7 players. A County FA Committee will decide whether the result shall be allowed to stand or the match ordered to be re-played.**
(**Reanet stands)

THIRD ROUND

Aerostructures	v	Bashley	0–1
AFC Lymington	v	Bournemouth	2–3
Basingstoke Town	v	DCA Basingstoke	4–1
Waterlooville	v	Aldershot Town	3–1

SEMI-FINALS

Bashley v Waterlooville 0–1
at Eastleigh FC Wednesday 13th March 1996

Bournemouth v Basingstoke Town 1*3
at Waterlooville FC Wednesday 6th March 1996

FINAL Tuesday 23rd April 1996. Kick off 7.30pm
BASINGSTOKE TOWN v WATERLOOVILLE 2–0 at The Dell, Southampton FC. att: 850

FINAL LEAGUE TABLES 1995/96

Portsmouth League

		P	W	D	L	F	A	Pts
1.	Stockheath Rov	22	17	2	3	80	28	53
2.	Wicor Mill	22	13	6	3	83	44	45
3.	George Dragon	22	12	7	3	70	24	43
4.	Jubilee Utd	22	12	4	6	51	47	40
5.	Ventnor	22	11	5	6	70	45	38
6.	Clanfield	22	9	4	9	47	52	31
7.	Mayflower Res	22	8	5	9	46	47	29
8.	P/mouth RN R	22	7	4	11	44	59	25
9.	St Mary's Res	22	7	4	11	37	73	25
10.	Hayling Is	22	5	4	13	33	52	19
11.	Paulsgrove	22	4	1	17	31	87	13
12.	Portchester	22	3	2	17	34	68	11

Portsmouth North End League

Div One		P	W	D	L	F	A	Pts
1.	Falcon	16	13	2	1	79	31	28
2.	George Dragon	16	10	2	4	69	25	22
3.	Kingston Arr	16	10	1	5	57	43	21
4.	Belle Vue	16	10	0	6	57	35	20
5.	Stag	16	7	1	8	30	33	15
6.	Grant Thornton	16	7	0	9	33	32	14
7.	Somerstown 90	16	6	0	10	21	51	12
8.	Curlew Exiles	16	5	0	11	37	54	10
9.	Sparta 81	16	1	0	15	30	109	2

Portsmouth Sunday League

Prem Div		P	W	D	L	F	A	Pts
1.	Sheourer	22	16	2	4	108	44	50
2.	Wicor Mill	22	15	2	5	78	43	47
3.	Admiral	22	15	2	5	77	43	47
4.	Denmead	22	11	6	5	68	43	39
5.	Havant Rov	22	10	5	7	66	57	35
6.	Devonshire	22	10	3	9	57	45	33
7.	Transfreight	22	10	3	9	53	64	33
8.	Harvest Home	22	8	6	8	48	46	30
9.	Drayton	22	6	2	14	47	75	20
10.	Trafalgar Arms	22	5	1	16	35	69	16
11.	Manor Court	22	4	3	15	33	82	15
12.	Kingsway	22	4	1	17	42	101	13

Bognor Sunday Promotional League

		P	W	D	L	F	A	Pts
1.	Walberton	20	20	0	0	136	24	40
2.	Waterlooville	20	13	2	5	78	28	28
3.	Barclays Bank	20	11	3	6	77	34	25
4.	Chichester H B	20	11	3	6	65	28	25
5.	Southbourne	20	10	2	8	80	32	22
6.	Woodmancote	20	10	1	9	46	39	21
7.	Hunston	20	9	0	11	65	57	18
8.	AFC Tangmere	20	5	4	11	33	72	14
9.	Barley Mow	20	4	3	13	37	74	11
10.	King Edward	20	3	3	14	34	99	9
11.	West Meods	20	0	3	17	18	178	3

Gosport & Fareham Sat Lge

		P	W	D	L	F	A	Pts
1.	Rowner RC	20	15	4	1	106	25	34
2.	Foresters Arms	20	16	2	2	98	22	34
3.	Bridgemary	20	15	3	2	113	16	33
4.	Fareport Ath	20	13	3	4	84	29	29
5.	Turnpike	20	10	3	7	66	43	23
6.	Stokeselect	20	10	2	8	73	46	22
7.	Phoenix 89	20	8	0	12	51	44	16
8.	Royal FC	20	7	2	11	37	51	*14
9.	Three Tuns	20	3	1	16	20	107	7
10.	Abbey Works	20	2	0	18	45	153	4
11.	AC Middlecroft	20	0	2	18	22	180	2

** 2 points deducted*

Meon Valley League

Div One		P	W	D	L	F	A	Pts
1.	Sportique	20	17	2	1	123	25	53
2.	AFC Clanfield	20	16	2	2	98	28	50
3.	Buccanneer	20	14	0	6	82	43	42
4.	Wickham Dyn	20	11	3	6	84	32	36
5.	Elite	20	10	2	8	76	51	32
6.	Soberton Utd	20	9	3	8	52	49	30
7.	Inter Northam	20	8	3	9	54	49	27
8.	Kennett Bros	20	7	2	11	70	78	23
9.	Mainline Taxis	20	7	1	12	67	71	22
10.	Burridge AFC	20	1	0	19	19	157	3
11.	FC Timberland	20	1	0	19	20	167	3

Worthing & District League

Prem Div		P	W	D	L	F	A	Pts
1.	Sompting	22	18	1	3	81	27	55
2.	Northbrook	22	14	5	3	56	22	47
3.	Eurotherm	22	13	4	5	62	35	43
4.	Mapleleafe	22	13	2	7	58	33	41
5.	Royal Mail	22	12	3	7	48	36	39
6.	West Tarring	22	7	8	7	45	61	29
7.	APC Lion	22	8	4	10	46	52	28
8.	Russell Bourne	22	6	5	11	32	52	23
9.	St Theresa's	22	6	3	13	35	61	21
10.	Worthing Utd	22	5	3	14	34	55	18
11.	Inland Rev	22	4	5	13	39	56	17
12.	Worthing Civic	22	3	3	16	34	80	12

Chichester & W Sussex Sunday

Div One		P	W	D	L	F	A	Pts
1.	White Horse	12	9	2	1	37	11	20
2.	Wittering RBL	12	8	2	2	31	16	18
3.	Havant	12	5	2	5	41	39	12
4.	Epreston YC	12	4	2	6	20	22	10
5.	Forsters	12	4	2	6	28	32	10
6.	Berkeley Arms	12	4	2	6	22	29	10
7.	Chourta	12	1	2	9	15	45	4

HEREFORDSHIRE F.A.

Secretary: E R Prescott,
7 Kirkland Close, Hampton Park, Hereford HR1 1XP

HEREFORDSHIRE COUNTY CUP
(FOUNDED 1973–74)
RECENT FINALS

1990–91	Fownhope	v	Ewyas Harold	5–2
1991–92	Westfields	v	Pegasus Juniors	5–0
1992–93	Hinton	v	Westfields	3–1
1993–94	Hinton	v	Pegasus Juniors	1–1 (Rep 3–2)
1994–95	Hinton	v	Pegasus Juniors	4–1

1995–1996

HEREFORDSHIRE SENIOR CUP

17 CLUBS **HOLDERS: HINTON**

PRELIMINARY ROUND

Kington Town	v	Pegasus Juniors	0–5

FIRST ROUND Saturday 21st October 1995

Leominster	v	Ross Town	1–3
Colwall Rangers	v	Westfields	W W–O
Ewyas Harold	v	Conquest	1–3
Golden Valley	v	Pegasus Juniors	0–7
Hereford Lads Club	v	Hinton	0–5
Ledbury Town	v	Fownhope	2–5
Wellington	v	Woofferton	1–2
Weston	v	Bromyard Town	1–5

SECOND ROUND Saturday 25th November 1995

Conquest	v	Ross Town '93	2–4
Hinton	v	Woofferton	0–3
Fownhope	v	Westfields	1–4
Bromyard Town	v	Pegasus Juniors	3–6

SEMI-FINALS

Westfields	v	Woofferton	1*0
Ross Town	v	Pegasus Juniors	1–0

FINAL Monday 8th April 1996 11.00am
ROSS TOWN v WESTFIELDS 2p4 2*2 at Edgar Street, Hereford United FC.

Westfields FC with the Herefordshire Senior Cup:

HERTFORDSHIRE F.A.

Secretary: R G Kibble,
4 The Wayside, Leverstock Green,
Hemel Hempstead HP3 8NR

HERTFORDSHIRE SENIOR CUP (FOUNDED 1886–87)

RECENT FINALS

1990–91	Barnet	v	Watford	5–2
1991–92	Barnet	v	Hemel Hempstead	4–1
1992–93	Barnet	v	Watford	4–2
1993–94	Watford	v	Stevenage Borough	3–1
1994–95	Watford	v	St Albans City	4–0

MOST WINS Hitchin Town 19 Barnet 16 Watford 14

1995–1996 HERTFORDSHIRE SENIOR CUP

23 CLUBS **HOLDERS: WATFORD**

FIRST ROUND Tuesday 24th October

Sawbridgeworth Tn	v	London Colney	1–4	Cheshunt	v	Ware	1–2
Royston Town	v	Hoddesdon Town	1–0	Hertford Town	v	Tring Town	2–0
Welwyn Gdn City	v	Hatfield Town	0–4	Harpenden Town	v	Letchworth	2–3
Potters Bar Town	v	Hemel Hempstead	4–3				

SECOND ROUND Tuesday 5th December

Barnet	v	St Albans City	3–0	Bishops Stortford	v	Berkhamsted Town	2–0
Royston Town	v	Boreham Wood	0–2	Stevenage Borough	v	Watford @SB	0*0 3*4
London Colney	v	Ware	3–1	Baldock Town	v	Hatfield Town	3*1
Letchworth	v	Potters Bar Town	2–3	Hertford Town	v	Hitchin Town	0–6

THIRD ROUND Tuesday 30th January 1996

Hitchin Town	v	Bishops Stortford	4–1	Boreham Wood	v	Barnet	2–3
Watford	v	Potters Bar Town	4–0	Baldock Town	v	London Colney	4–3

SEMI-FINALS March 1996

Barnet	v	Hitchin Town	1–0	Watford @BT	v	Baldock Town	2–1

FINAL Monday 22nd April. Kick off 7.30pm
BARNET v WATFORD 2–1 at Clarence Park, St Albans City FC.

HERTFORDSHIRE CHARITY SHIELD (FOUNDED 1919–20)

RECENT FINALS

1990–91	Berkhamstead Town	v	Hemel Hempstead	1–0
1991–92	Letchworth Gdn City	v	Leverstock Green	1–0
1992–93	Sawbridgeworth Tn	v	Leverstock Green	1–1 (6–5 Pens)
1993–94	London Colney	v	Hoddesdon Town	2–0
1994–95	Sawbridgeworth Tn	v	Welwyn Garden City	2–2 (4–2 Pens)

MOST WINS Hertford Town 6 Ware 6 Berkhamstead Town 5

HERTFORDSHIRE CHARITY SHIELD

14 CLUBS **HOLDERS: SAWBRIDGEWORTH TOWN**

FIRST ROUND

Harpenden Town	v	Letchworth FC @L	4–0	Sun Sports	v	Sandridge Rovers	0–1
London Colney	v	St Margaretsbury	0–5	Hatfield Town	v	Tring Athletic	2–1
Royston Town	v	Sawbridgeworth Tn	0–4	Welwyn Gdn City	v	Hoddesdon Town	0–2

2 Clubs with Byes Leverstock Green, Potters Bar Town.

SECOND ROUND by 31st October

Potters Bar Town	v	Leverstock Green	4–0	Harpenden Town	v	Hoddesdon Town	1*2
Hatfield Town	v	Sandridge Rovers	1–2	Sawbridgeworth Tn	v	St Margaretsbury	2–1

SEMI-FINALS by 31st January 1996

Potters Bar Town	v	Hoddesdon Town	4–0	Sandridge Rovers	v	Sawbridgeworth Tn	0–3

(Played at London Colney FC).

FINAL Thursday 9th May 1996 7.30pm
POTTERS BAR TOWN v SAWBRIDGEWORTH TOWN 2–4 at Crofters End, West Road, Sawbridgeworth Town FC.

HERTFORDSHIRE CHARITY CUP (FOUNDED 1900–01)

RECENT FINALS

1990–91	Hitchin Town	v	Boreham Wood	1–0
1991–92	Baldock Town	v	Boreham Wood	2–1
1992–93	St Albans City	v	Boreham Wood	1–0
1993–94	Baldock Town	v	Stevenage Borough	2–1
1994–95	St Albans City	v	Boreham Wood	2–1

MOST WINS Barnet 27 St Albans City 26 Hitchin Town 16

HERTFORDSHIRE CHARITY CUP

12 CLUBS **HOLDERS: ST ALBANS CITY**

FIRST ROUND

Boreham Wood	v	Bishops Stortford @BS	2*0	Cheshunt	v	Tring Town	0–2
Hertford Town	v	Hemel Hempstead	1*3	Baldock Town	v	Berkhamsted Town	2–0

SECOND ROUND by 31st October

St Albans City	v	Ware	4–2	Boreham Wood	v	Baldock Town	BW W–O
Stevenage Town	v	Hitchin Town	3–0	Hemel Hempstead	v	Tring	1–0

SEMI-FINALS by 31st January 1996

Stevenage Borough	v	Hemel Hempstead	0A0 2–1	St Albans City	v	Boreham Wood	2–0

FINAL Held over to pre-season
STEVENAGE BOROUGH v ST ALBANS CITY

HERTFORDSHIRE SENIOR TROPHY (FOUNDED 1984–85)

RECENT FINALS

1990–91	Sawbridgeworth Town	v	London Colney	3–1
1991–92	Cheshunt	v	Leverstock Green	2–1
1992–93	St Margaretsbury	v	Sawbridgeworth Town	2–1
1993–94	Sawbridgeworth Town	v	Bushey Rangers	2–1
1994–95	London Colney	v	Sandridge Rovers	2–2 (Rep 1–0)

MOST WINS London Colney 2 Sawbridgeworth Town 2 Selby 2

HERTFORDSHIRE CENTENARY TROPHY

20 CLUBS **HOLDERS: LONDON COLNEY**

FIRST ROUND Saturday 4th November 2.15pm

Somersett A V&E	v	Leverstock Green	1–4	St Peters	v	Kings Langley	4–2
Bovingdon	v	Wormley Rovers	0–2	Sun Postal Sports	v	Tring Athletic	2–0

SECOND ROUND Saturday 2nd December 1.45pm

St Peters	v	Cuffley	2–1	Sandridge Rovers	v	Chipperfields Co's	1A1 1*2
Colney Heath	v	Leverstock Green	3–1	Bedmond Sports	v	Agrevo Sports	0–4
Oxhey Jets	v	Welwyn	0–1	Sun Postal Sports	v	Elliott Star	1–2
Met Police Bushey	v	St Margaretsbury	4–1	Wormley Rovers	v	Bragbury Athletic	4–3

THIRD ROUND Saturday 17th February 2.30pm

Wormley Rovers	v	Chipperfield Corinthians	3–1	Welwyn	v	Met Police Bushey	3–2
Agrevo Sports	v	Elliott Star	2–1	St Peters	v	Colney Heath	2p4 2*2 3*3

SEMI-FINALS Saturday 9th March 2.30pm

Welwyn @CH	v	Colney Heath	0–2	Wormley Rovers	v	Agrevo 'Sports	1–3

FINAL Saturday 20th April 3.00pm
AGREVO SPORTs v COLNEY HEATH 1–4 at Wadson's Close, (A10), Ware FC.

HERTS SENIOR COUNTY LEAGUE

President: W J R Veneear
Chairman: C T Hudson
Secretary: Mr E H Dear,
48 Wilshere Road, Welwyn, Herts

FINAL LEAGUE TABLES 1995/96

Premier Div	*P*	*W*	*D*	*L*	*F*	*A*	*Pts*
1. Elliott Star	32	25	4	3	103	40	79
2. Met Police Bus	32	19	7	6	79	49	64
3. Colney Heath	32	20	2	10	78	52	62
4. Somerset AV&E	32	19	3	10	71	55	60
5. Kings Langley	32	18	4	10	67	45	58
6. Sun Postal Sp	32	14	6	12	47	42	48
7. Chipperfield C	32	13	8	11	49	38	47
8. Agrevo Spts	32	13	7	12	73	68	46
9. Sandridge Rov	32	13	5	14	62	57	44
10. Welwyn	32	12	5	15	35	45	41
11. Cuffley	32	12	4	16	46	61	40
12. St Peters	32	10	7	15	57	67	37
13. Oxhey Jets	32	10	5	17	41	55	35
14. Bedmond Soc	32	9	8	15	40	57	35
15. Wormley Rov	32	11	2	19	40	66	35
16. Bovingdon	32	9	2	21	33	64	29
17. Bragbury Ath	32	2	7	23	38	98	13

Div One	*P*	*W*	*D*	*L*	*F*	*A*	*Pts*
1. North Mymms	30	21	6	3	91	35	69
2. MMS Dynamics	30	20	2	8	79	43	62
3. Walkern	30	18	5	7	63	31	59
4. Emeralds	30	16	6	8	66	41	54
5. Bushey Rgrs	30	16	5	9	74	44	53
6. Malex	30	16	5	9	47	41	53
7. Allenburys Spts	30	16	4	10	73	53	52
8. Kimpton Rov	30	14	5	1	58	59	47
9. Standon Puck	30	13	4	13	67	64	43
10. Cox Guild Ast	30	12	4	14	76	64	40
11. Giffen Valmar	30	11	4	15	72	72	37
12. Evergreen	30	10	5	15	53	63	35
13. Kodak Hemel	30	10	1	19	44	73	31
14. Serrett	30	6	5	19	41	69	23
15. Codicote	30	5	7	18	31	64	22
16. St Ippolyte	30	1	2	27	25	144	5

Bedmond Social's James Bree about to go round Elliott Star goal keeper Terranc Dicks.

Photo - Ray Pruden

HUNTINGDONSHIRE F.A.

Secretary: Maurice Armstrong,
1 Chapel End, Gt Gidding, Huntingdon, Cambs PE17 5NP
Tel: (01832 293262 County Office)

HUNTINGDONSHIRE SENIOR CUP
(FOUNDED 1888–89)

RECENT FINALS

1990–91	Eynesbury Rovers	v	Somersham Town	1–0
1991–92	Eynesbury Rovers	v	Ramsey Town	3–0
1992–93	Eynesbury Rovers	v	Warboys Town	4–2
1993–94	Somersham Town	v	Ortonians	1–0
1994–95	Warboys Town	v	Godmanchester Rovers	2–1

MOST WINS

St Neots Town 33 Eynesbury Rovers 12 Huntingdon Town 12

1995–1996

HUNTINGDONSHIRE SENIOR CUP

12 CLUBS **HOLDERS: WARBOYS TOWN**

FIRST ROUND Saturday 7th October 1995

Somersham Town	v	Warboys Town	0–2	Ramsey Town	v	Hotpoint	1–0
Godm'chester Rvs	v	Yaxley	0–2	St Ives Town	v	Eynesbury Rovers	2–3

SECOND ROUND Saturday 4th November 1995

Alconbury	v	Eynesbury Rvs	0–3	Yaxley	v	Warboys Town	0–2
Ramsey Town	v	Bluntisham Rngs	3–1	St Neots Town	v	Ortonians	6–1

SEMI-FINAL Saturday 2nd March 1996

Eynesbury Rvs	v	St Neots Town	2–0	Ramsey Town	v	Warboys Town	0–2

FINAL Monday 6th May 3.00pm
EYNESBURY ROVERS v WARBOYS TOWN 3*2 at Rowley Park, Cambridge Rd, St Neots Town FC.

Godmanchester Rovers FC – Photograph of ground of Judith's Field, Godmanchester.

KENT F.A.

Secretary: K T Masters,
69 Maidstone Road, Chatham, Kent ME4 6DT (01634 843824)

KENT SENIOR CUP
(FOUNDED 1888–89)

RECENT FINALS

1990–91	Dover Athletic	v	Gravesend & Northfleet	1–0
1991–92	Bromley	v	Hythe Town	3–1
1992–93	Ashford Town	v	Bromley	3–2
1993–94	Margate	v	Dover Athletc	3–2
1994–95	Charlton Athletic	v	Gillingham	4–2

MOST WINS Maidstone United 15 Dartford 9 Northfleet United 9

1995–1996

KENT FACIT SENIOR CUP

14 CLUBS **HOLDERS: CHARLTON ATHLETIC**

FIRST ROUND

Tonbridge AFC	v	Fisher	1–2
Dover Athletic	v	Ashford Town	1–2
Bromley	v	Millwall	1*1 4–1
Gravesend & Nfleet	v	Margate	2–1
Welling United	v	Deal Town	1–0
Sittingbourne	v	Erith & Belvedere	3–3 5–2

2 Clubs with Byes Charlton Athletic and Gillingham

SECOND ROUND by 20th January 1996

Gillingham @B	v	Bromley	4p3 1*1
Welling United	v	Ashford Town	2*3
Sittingbourne	v	Charlton Atheltic	1–3
Fisher	v	Gravesend & Nfleet	2–0

SEMI-FINALS

Ashford Town	v	Gillingham	3–1
Fisher	v	Charlton Athletic	4*8

FINAL Monday 6th May 1996 3.00pm
ASHFORD TOWN v CHARLTON ATHELTIC 3–0 at Central Park, Sittingbourne FC. att; 1,200

KENT SENIOR TROPHY
(FOUNDED 1874–75)

RECENT FINALS

1990–91	Hythe Town	v	Deal Town	1–0
1991–92	Slade Green	v	Tunbridge Wells	3–1
1992–93	Cray Wanderers	v	Whitstable Town	1–0
1993–94	Alma Swanley	v	Folkestone Invicta	3–1
1994–95	Deal Town	v	Folkestone Invicta	2–2 (5–4 Pens)

MOST WINS Alma Swanley 2 Corinthians 2 Faversham Town 2 Fisher Athletic 2 Ramsgate 2

KENT PLAAYA SENIOR TROPHY

26 CLUBS **HOLDERS: DEAL TOWN**

FIRST ROUND Saturday 14th October 1995

Beckenham Town	v	Stansfeld O&B	0–0 3–2	Thamesmead Tn	v	Hythe United	4–2
Greenwich Boro	v	West Wickham	4–2	Tunbridge Wells	v	Corinthian	2–1
Sheppey United	v	Woolwich Town	2–0	Midland Bank	v	VCD Athletic	1–4
Cray Wanderers	v	Whitstable Town	1–2	Chatham Town	v	Crockenhill	4–2
Kent Police	v	Canterbury City	0–4	Ramsgate	v	Furness	0–4

SECOND ROUND 2nd December 1995

VCD Athletic	v	Furness	0–2	Canterbury City	v	Herne Bay	0–1
Folkestone Invicta	v	Dartford	0–1	Slade Green	v	Thamesmead Tn	1–3
Chatham Town	v	Thames Polytechnic	9–2	Beckenham Tn	v	Tunbridge Wells	1–3
Whitstable Town	v	Faversham Town	3–0	Greenwich Boro	v	Sheppey United	3–1

THIRD ROUND 13th January 1996

Thamesmead Tn	v	Tunbridge Wells	2–1	Whitstable Tn	v	Dartford	1*2
Chatham Town	v	Herne Bay	2*1	Furness	v	Greenwich Boro	2–0

SEMI-FINALS 9th March 1996 No8p21

Dartford	v	Furness	1–0	Thamesmead Tn	v	Chatham Town	0–4

FINAL Saturday 13th April 1996

DARTFORD v CHATHAM TOWN 3–0 at Park View Road, Welling United FC.

Dartford Celebrate with the Kent Senior Trophy, Dartford 3 Chatham 0. Photo Roger Turner.

KENT COUNTY LEAGUE

President: Bill Manklow
Chairman: C T C Windiate
Press Officer: J C Mugridge, 14 Cherry Tree Road, Tunbridge Wells, Kent TN2 5QA (01892 521578)

Two clubs, Lordswood and Teynham & Lynsted, having worked hard on their grounds since 1994 were awarded senior status during the season and this has led to Lordswood being elected into the Winstonlead Kent League. Teynham & Lynsted decided that they would remain in the Nuclear Electric Kent County League taking the next step forward in the pyramid at a more appropriate time. Three sides took part in the Kent Senior Trophy, in the first round VCD Athletic beat Midland Bank 4-1 with Stansfeld Oxford and Bermondsey drawing 0-0 away to Beckenham Town only to lose by the odd goal in five after extra time in the replay. Thames Poly had a bye in the First Round and in the second round played Chatham only for a weakened team to go down by a colossal 9-2 whilst VCD were having a much closer game at home to Furness eventually losing 2-0. Two Nuclear Electric sides won their way to the Kent Intermediate Challenge Shield final with AFC Egerton last season's losing finalists coming away with the Cup following an entertaining match against Milton Athletic. It took extra time before AFC Egerton won 2-1. Central Park Sittingbourne was the venue for both the Kent Intermediate Challenge Shield and the Inter Regional Challenge Cup which for the first time in its history was played for by two Eastern based sides. The Premier Division Championship was close run this year with Sevenoaks Town needing to win their last game on 11th May to clinch the championship by three points over Lydd Town who had pursued them all the way. This is the second time in four years that Sevenoaks have been champions of the League. Two well established sides withdrew from the competition during the season, Empire, formed in 1910, joined the Kent County League for the 1991\92 season, were the first to go and Wellcome (Saturday) formed in 1985 were the second side to drop out.

Friday 24th May, 1996 saw the Nuclear Electric Kent County League celebrating the end of their season with a very successful presentation Dinner and Dance at the Jarvis Great Danes Hotel & Country Club, Hollingbourne. Principle guests Nigel Dixon, Human Resources Manager of Nuclear Electric and Peter Taylor current manager of Dover and formerly of Crystal Palace, Spurs and England presented the winners and runners-up with their awards. During the evening Long Service Awards were presented to Wendy Whitehead of Tynham & Lynsted, Bill Warner of Tonbridge Invicta, Mike Bennett of Borough United, Mark Ashworth of Teynham and Lynsted, John Edginton of Broomfield United and last but certainly not least to Archie Boulden of New Romney who was 99 years old last February and is still active with New Romney following seventy five-years service with the club. Referee of the Year was Greg Brown of Sidcup and the Most Promising Referee Award was presented to Adam Bowey of Swalecliffe. At the annual general meeting, University of Kent secretary Irene Simmonds collected the Fair Play Award and a cheque for £250 on behalf of the club. this was for being the team with best disciplinary record over the entire competition. Ray Miles of Premier Division winners Sevenoaks Town was Manager of the Year and received his award from President Bill Manklow. John Marsh retiring Western Section Registration Secretary received an inscribed silver salver to commemorate 16 years with the League, eight of which have been as registration secretary, this was also presented by President Bill Manklow. This coming season sees Scott Sports & Social renamed Beauwater, Maidstone Invicta now Maidstone United (96) and Bond Sports playing as Sheerness East. New clubs elected into the competition at the annual general meeting were Leaves Green and Wittersham. It is understood that there is one casualty prior to the commencement of the new season and that is Nomads who have announced their intention to withdraw before a ball is kicked.

Sevenoaks Town F C; Premier Division Campions 1995-96: Back Row (L-R); Ray Miles, John Harrison, David Norburn, Mick Miles, Jamie Brady, Ian Garston, Kevin Marsh, Steve McKenzie, Barry Wickenden. Front Row; Neil Bell, Kevin Crickett, Peter Harrington, Tony Diment, Michael Stirling, Neil Impazzi.

Photo: John Mugridge.

FINAL LEAGUE TABLES 1995/96

Premier Division	P	W	D	L	F	A	Pts
1. Sevenoaks Town	28	19	4	5	75	32	61
2. Lydd Town	28	17	4	7	69	41	55
3. AFC Egerton	28	15	5	8	74	42	50
4. Milton Athletic	28	15	5	8	61	44	50
5. VCD Athletic	28	14	8	6	54	40	50
6. Greenways	28	14	4	10	48	36	46
7. Lordswood	28	13	5	10	52	51	44
8. Stansfeld O&B	28	13	4	11	48	46	43
9. Aylesford P M	28	11	8	9	48	49	41
10. Teynham & Lyn	28	10	7	11	30	28	37
11. Knatchbull	28	10	7	11	36	39	37
12. Thames Poly	28	8	6	14	56	60	30
13. Oakwood	28	7	7	14	29	55	28
14. Ten Em Bee	28	2	6	20	28	71	12
15. Knockholt	28	0	4	24	16	90	4

PREMIER DIVISION RESULTS CHART 1995-96

HOME TEAM	1	2	3	4	5	6	7	8	9	10	11	12	13	14	15
1. AFC Egerton	*	1-1	0-2	3-1	5-0	6-1	3-3	2-1	1-2	5-0	4-2	4-0	1-2	3-1	1-4
2. Aylesford P M	0-3	*	3-4	1-1	1-0	1-3	1-3	3-1	4-1	2-2	3-3	3-0	2-2	2-1	1-2
3. Greenways	0-2	0-1	*	0-1	3-0	0-2	0-1	2-3	4-0	1-0	1-1	2-1	0-1	3-2	2-1
4. Knatchbull	2-3	2-0	2-4	*	3-0	1-1	1-1	0-2	1-1	3-1	0-1	0-0	2-0	1-0	1-1
5. Knockholt	1-5	1-5	1-1	0-4	*	1-2	0-3	2-2	0-0	1-7	1-5	1-1	0-1	2-3	1-3
6. Lordswood	1-0	4-2	1-3	3-1	3-1	*	1-2	4-1	1-0	2-3	5-1	1-3	1-0	2-2	0-3
7. Lydd Town	1-2	5-0	2-0	4-2	8-0	4-2	*	4-1	2-0	3-1	1-1	7-2	AW	2-2	3-5
8. Milton Ath	3-3	3-4	2-2	3-1	4-0	3-1	2-1	*	3-0	0-1	2-0	3-0	0-0	4-3	4-0
9. Oakwood	1-1	2-3	0-5	0-3	3-0	0-0	1-0	1-1	*	0-4	2-3	3-2	0-0	4-1	0-2
10. Sevenoaks Town	1-0	0-1	5-1	4-0	4-1	4-2	3-0	4-1	5-1	*	3-0	5-1	2-2	3-2	1-1
11. Stansfeld O & B	3-6	0-1	0-1	1-0	4-0	3-1	2-3	0-1	1-0	2-3	*	2-0	1-3	1-0	2-1
12. Ten Em Bee	1-5	2-2	1-4	1-2	1-0	1-1	1-2	0-2	3-3	0-3	1-2	*	1-1	1-2	0-2
13. Teynham & Lynsted	4-2	2-0	1-2	0-1	2-0	1-1	0-1	0-3	0-1	0-0	1-2	3-1	*	0-1	4-2
14. Thames Poly	2-2	1-1	1-1	4-0	7-2	2-3	3-2	3-4	4-1	1-5	0-3	2-0	1-2	*	4-4
15. VCD Athletic	2-1	0-0	1-0	0-0	AW	2-3	5-1	3-2	1-2	1-1	2-2	4-3	0-0	2-1	*

AW - Awarded games **VCD Athletic** v Knockholt; **Lydd Town** v Teynham & Lynsted

FINAL LEAGUE TABLES 1995/96

Div One East	P	W	D	L	F	A	Pts
1. Tenterden	24	19	3	2	86	31	60
2. Snowdown CW	24	14	6	4	60	38	48
3. Bond Sports	24	13	4	7	60	40	43
4. New Romney	24	13	1	10	51	45	40
5. Bishopsbourne	24	12	1	11	62	54	37
6. Woodnesboro.	24	10	4	10	53	46	34
7. Kennington	24	10	3	11	52	52	33
8. Bromley Green	24	9	5	10	46	51	32
9. Uni of Kent	24	8	3	13	40	57	27
10. Rye United	24	7	5	12	44	44	26
11. Broomfield Utd	24	7	4	13	41	54	22
12. Lydd Town R	24	6	5	13	40	78	20
13. St Margarets	24	4	4	16	32	77	16

Div One West	P	W	D	L	F	A	Pts
1. Ex Blues	20	16	3	1	53	16	51
2. Bearsted	20	14	2	4	48	20	44
3. Scott S & S	20	13	3	4	61	27	42
4. Phoenix Spts	20	9	5	6	49	33	32
5. Rusthall	20	10	1	9	39	39	31
6. Platt United	20	7	5	8	41	47	26
7. Maidstone Inv	20	6	6	8	44	51	24
8. Eynesford	20	5	5	10	35	34	20
9. Sutton Ath	20	4	5	11	38	70	17
10. Westerham	20	4	1	15	19	50	13
11. Swanscombe U	20	2	4	14	22	62	10

Division Two East:	**Champions:** Broomfield Reserves	**Runners-up:** Iden
Division Two West:	**Champions:** Snodland	**Runners-up:** Paddock Wood Town
Division Three West:	**Champions:** Hawkenbury	**Runners-up:** Farnborough O B
Reserve Division One West:	**Champions:** Lordswood Reserves	**Runners-up:** Sevenoaks Tn Res
Reserve Division Two West:	**Champions:** Bearsted Reserves	**Runners-up:** Eynsford Reserves

Snodland FC, Champions Division Two West 1995-96; Back Row (L-R); M Harris, J Barden, P Sutton, J Smith (capt), G Moseley, R Thorogood, G Morgan, G Duffus (Mgr). Front Row; N Sims, W Watson, S Wall, K Gooda, D Hill, T Reeves.

Photo - John Mugridge.

INTER REGIONAL CHALLENGE CUP

RECENT FINALS	Winners;	Runner-up;
1987-88	New Romney	Otford United
1988-89	Greenways	Lordswood
1989-90	Stansfeld Oxford & Bermondsey	Vickers Crayford/Dartford Ath
1990-91	Bearsted	Scott Sports & Social
1991-92	Stansfeld O B	Oakwood
1992-93	Oakwood	Teynham & Lynsted
1993-94	Bearsted	Rye United
1994-95	Vickers Crayford	Teynham & Lynsted

First Round;

Ex Blues v Swanscombe United	2-0	Platt United v Oakwood	4-4 (aet)
Scott Sports & Social v Knockholt	4-0	Sevenoaks Town v Phoenix Sports	6-1
Sutton Athletic v Rusthall	3-2 (aet)	VCD Athletic v Empire	5-0
Bearsted v Stansfeld O & B	4-0	Ten Em Bee v Eynsford	1-2 (aet)

Second Round;

Aylesford Paper Mills v Oakwood	1-3	Bond Sports v University of Kent	7-1
Kennington v Snowdown C W	7-0	Knatchbull v Bishopsbourne	3-2
Milton Athletic v Broomfield United	4-2	Rye United v New Romney	1-2
Tenterden v Lydd Town	0-3	Teynham & Lynsted v Bromley Green	5-1
Thames Polytechnic v AFC Egerton	2-3	Woodnesborough v St Margarets	6-0

Third Round;

Bearsted v Scott Sports & Social	4-3	Eynesford v Ex Blues	4-2 (aet)
Kennington v Woodnesborough	1-0	Knatchbull v Teynham & Lynsted	0-3
Lydd Town v Bond Sports	3-0	New Romney v Milton Athletic	1-3
Oakwood v AFC Egerton	2-4 (aet)	VCD Athletic v Westerham	5-1

Quarter Finals;

AFC Egerton v Kennington	5-2	Lydd Town v Bearsted	3-1
Teynham & Lynsted v Milton Athletic	2-1 (aet)	VCD Athletic v Eynesford	3-0

Semi-Finals;

Lydd Town v AFC Egerton	3-1	VCD Athletic v Teynham & Lynsted	1-2

Final: Lydd Town v Teynham & Lynsted 2-2 (aet), 3-4 penalties.

CLUB DIRECTORY 1996-97

Premier & Division One East & West

A.F.C. EGERTON

Secretary: Mr S Parkes, 48 Oakdene Road, St Mary Cray, Orpington, Kent BR5 2AN (01689 818382)
Ground: St Marys Cray Rec Grd, Park Rd, St Marys Cray **Founded:** 1971
Colours: Royal/royal/white **Change Colours:** Green & white/white/green & white

AYLESFORD PAPER MILL

Secretary: Mrs L Casey, 41 Cobdown Close, Ditton, Aylesford, Kent ME20 6SZ (01732 849476)
Ground: Cobdown, Station Road, Ditton, Nr Maidstone (01622 717771) **Founded:** 1979
Colours: Black & white/black/black **Change Colours:** Yellow & blue/black/black

BEARSTED

Secretary:M J Scannel, 24 Fauchons Lane, Bearsted, Maidstone, Kent ME14 4AH (01622 739072)
Ground: The Green, The Street, Bearsted **Founded:** 1895
Colours: White/white/blue **Change Colours:** Blue & green/navy/navy

BEAUWATER

Secretary: Mr R Taylor, 24 Sun Lane, Gravesend, Kent DA12 5HG (01474 332208)
Ground: Beauwater Leisure Club, Nelson Road, Northfleet (01474 336456) **Founded:** 1927
Colours: Black & red/black/red **Change Colours:** Black & white/black/black

BISHOPSBOURNE

Secretary: Mr N Carter, 43 Palm Tree Way, Lyminge, Folkstone, Kent CT18 8JN (01303 862687)
Ground: Canteen Meadow, The Street, Bishopsbourne, Nr Canterbury, Kent **Founded:** 1963
Colours: Royal/white/royal & white **Change Colours:** Red & white/black/black

BROMLEY GREEN

Secretary: Mr C McQuillan, 42 Falcon Way, Singleton Farm, Ashford, Kent TN23 5UR (01233 642941)
Ground: The Swan Centre, South Willesborough, Ashford, Kent **Founded:** 1930
Colours: White/green/white **Change Colours:** All green

BROOMFIELD UNITED

Secretary: Mr R Cork, Flat 17, Francis Court, 117 High Street, Herne Bay, Kent CT6 5LA (01227 742480)
Ground: Bridge Rec Ground, Patrixbourne Road, Bridge, Nr Canterbury **Founded:** 1925
Colours: Azure & black/black/black & azure) **Change Colours:** Red/red/red & white

Ex BLUES

Secretary: Mr M Harvey, 29 Crown Lane, Bromley, Kent, BR2 9PG (0181 464 4815)
Ground: Wellcome Sports Club, Langley Court, South Eden Park Road, Beckenham, Kent **Founded:** 1945
Colours: Yellow & blue/blue/blue **Change Colours:** All blue

EYNESFORD

Secretary: Mr E Walking, 76 Pollyhaugh, Eynesford, Nr Dartford, Kent DA4 0HF (01322 863673)
Ground: Harrow Meadow, Rear of Castle Hotel, Bower Lane, off Eynesford High Street. **Founded:** 1894
Colours: Black & white/black/black **Change Colours:** All purple

GREENWAYS

Secretary: Mr W Miller, 14 Cygnet Gardens, Northfleet, Kent DA11 7DN (01474 560913)
Ground: Beauwater Leisure Centre, Nelson Road, Northfleet, (01474 359222) **Founded:** 1965
Colours: All green **Change Colours:** Orange/black/black

IDEN

Secretary: Mr G Say, 18 Parkwood, Iden, Rye, East Sussex TN31 7XE (01797 280495)
Ground: Iden Playing Field, Iden, Rye, East Sussex **Founded:** 1965
Colours: Tangerine/white/tangerine **Change Colours:** Green/black/black

KENNINGTON

Secretary: Mr M Smith, The Gables, Sandyhurst Lane, Ashford, Kent TN25 4PE (01233 628586)
Ground: Kennington Cricket Club Pav. Ulley Road, Kennington, Ashford, Kent **Founded:** 1888
Colours: All yellow **Change Colours:** All red

KNATCHBULL

Secretary: Mr D Howle, 13 Charminster, Washford Farm, Ashford, Kent TN23 2UH (01233 611207)
Ground: Hatch Park, Off A20, Mersham, Nr Ashford, (01585 663171) **Founded:** 1981
Colours: Claret & blue/white/white **Change Colours:** All white

KNOCKHOLT

Secretary: Mr R Thurlow, 37 Whitethorne Ave, Coulsdon Surrey CR5 2PQ (0181 668 1418)
Ground: The Pound, Ivy Farm Lane, Knockholt **Founded:** 1967
Colours: D/Blue & Black/black/black **Change Colours:** Red & black/black/black

LYDD TOWN

Secretary: Mr P Sisley, 21 The Fairway, Littlestone, Romney Marsh, Kent TN28 8 PJ, (01797 366101)
Ground: The Rype, Manor Road, Lydd. **Founded:** 1885
Colours: Red & green/green/green **Change Colours:** All green

MAIDSTONE UNITED

Secretary: Mr G Gray, 6 Morella Walk, Lenham, Maidstone, Kent ME17 2JX (01622 859964)
Ground: The Athletic Ground, London Road, Maidstone. **Founded:** 1992
Colours: Gold/black/black **Change Colours:** Yellow & black/black/black

MILTON ATHLETIC

Secretary: Mr P Duffin, 18 Hales Road, Tunstall, Sittingbourne, Kent ME10 1SR (01795 471260)
Ground: UK Paper Sports Ground, Gore Court Road, Sittingbourne, Kent **Founded:** 1926
Colours: White & navy/navy/navy **Change Colours:** Red & white/white/white

NEW ROMNEY

Secretary: Mr D Masters, 44 Fernbank Cres, Folkstone, Kent CT19 5SF (01303 253961)
Ground: Station Road, New Romney **Founded:** 1895
Colours: Blue & white/blue/blue **Change Colours:** All white

OAKWOOD

Secretary: Mr P Mannering, 24 Ellenswood Close, Otham Maidstone Kent ME15 8SG (01622 862482)
Ground: Honey Lane, Otham, Maidstone **Founded:** 1924
Colours: All Red **Change Colours:** White/black/black

PADDOCK WOOD TOWN

Secretary: Mrs J Inhester, 17 Newton Gardens, Paddock Wood, Kent TN12 6AJ (01892 833766)
Ground: Memorial Playing Field, Maidstone Road, Paddock Wood, Nr Tonbridge **Founded:** 1907
Colours: Green & white/white/white **Change Colours:** All white

PHOENIX SPORTS

Secretary: Mr M Cole, 91 Hurst Road, Northumberland Heath, Erith, Kent DA8 3EW (01322 350750)
Ground: Phoenix Sports Club, Mayplace Road East, Bexleyheath, Kent DA7 6JT **Founded:** 1935
Colours: Red & white/black/red **Change Colours:** Yellow/black/black

PLATT UNITED

Secretary: Mr G Broad, The Lilacs, Rowhill Road, Hextable, Kent BR8 7RL (01322 662452)
Ground: Stonehouse Field, off A25, Longmill Lane, Platt **Founded:** 1920
Colours: Red/black/red **Change Colours:** White/black/red

RUSTHALL

Secretary: Mr K Brownson, 13 Bretland Road, Rusthall, Tunbridge Wells, Kent TN4 8PS (01892 536544)
Ground: Jockey Farm, Nellington Road, Rusthall, Tunbridge Wells **Founded:** 1899
Colours: Green/white/green **Change Colours:** Claret & blue/blue/claret

RYE UNITED

Secretary: Mr B Goodsell, 15 Spring Hill, Northian, Nr Rye, East Sussex TN31 6PX (01797 253028)
Ground: Sydney Allnut Pav. Rye Cricket & Football Salts, Rye, East Sussex **Founded:** 1938
Colours: White & red & black/black/black & red **Change Colours:** Red & black/black/black

SEVENOAKS TOWN

Secretary: Mr E Diplock, 23 Holly Bush Lane, Sevenoaks, Kent TN13 3TH (01732 454280)
Ground: Greatness Park, Seal Road, Sevenoaks, (01732 741987) **Founded:** 1883
Colours: Azure & black/black/azure **Change Colours:** Red & black/black/black

SHEERNESS EAST

Secretary: Mr J Longhurst, 5 Weekes Court, Mountfield, Queenborough, Sheppey, Kent ME11 5DB (01795 667758)
Ground: Sheerness East Working Mens Club, 47 Queenborough Road, Halfway, Sheerness **Founded:** 1982
Colours: Blue & white/blue/blue **Change Colours:** Red & black/black/black

SNODLAND

Secretary: Mr T Reeves, 136 Townsend Road, Snodland, Kent ME6 5RN (01634 240076)
Ground: Potyn's Field, Paddlesworth Road, Snodland **Founded:** 1940
Colours: White/royal/royal **Change Colours:** Navy & sky/navy/navy

SNOWDOWN COLLIERY WELFARE

Secretary: Mr A Jones, 121 St Radigunds Road, Dover, Kent CT17 0LA (01304 211856)
Ground: Spinney Lane, Aylesham, Canterbury CT3 3AF **Founded:** 1907
Colours: Black & white/black/black **Change Colours:** All green

St MARGARETS

Secretary: Mr W Hay, 28 The Freedown, St Margarets at Cliffe, Nr Dover, Kent CT15 6BD (01304 852386)
Ground: The Alexander Field, Kingsdown Road, St Margarets at Cliffe, Nr Dover **Founded:** 1993
Colours: Yellow & black/black/yellow & black **Change Colours:** Blue & black/black/black

STANSFELD OXFORD & BERMONDSEY CLUB

Secretary: Me E Ellis, 40 Tilbrook Road, Kidbrooke, London SE3 9QE (0181 319 0903)
Ground: St James Squash & Leisure Club, 35 Marvels Lane, Grove Park, SE12. **Founded:** 1897
Colours: Yellow/blue/blue **Change Colours:** All red

SUTTON ATHLETIC

Secretary: Mr J Willis, 6 Somerset Road, Dartford, Kent DA1 3DP (01322 222540)
Ground: The Roaches, Parsonage Lane, Sutton at Hone, Nr Dartford. **Founded:** 1904
Colours: Green & white/green/green **Change Colours:** Red & white/red/red

TENTERDEN ST MICHAELS UNITED

Secretary: Mr S Stevens, Kent House, Ashford Road, St Michaels, Tenterden, Kent TN30 6PY (01580 762703)
Ground: Recreation Ground, Tenterden High Street, Tenterden **Founded:** 1890
Colours: Blue & white/blue/blue **Change Colours:** All maroon

TEN EM BEE

Secretary: Mr C Rhule, 6 Waddan Close, Croydon, Surrey CR0 4JT (0181 680 6893)
Ground: Ladywell Runing Track, Silvermere Road, Catford SE6 **Founded:** 1975
Colours: All blue **Change Colours:** Yellow/blue/blue

TEYNHAM & LYNSTED

Secretary: Mr C Page, 2 Foxgrove, Milton Regis, Sittingbourne, Kent ME10 2DW (01795 426675)
Ground: Central Park, Eurolink Way, Sittingbourne. **Founded:** 1961
Colours: Yellow & blue/blue/yellow **Change Colours:** Sky & white/black/white

THAMES POLYTECHNIC

Secretary: Mrs S Jarvis, 31 Monkton Road, Welling, Kent DA16 3JU (0181 854 5509)
Ground: Thames Polytechnic, Kidbrooke Lane, Eltham, London SE9 **Founded:** 1888
Colours: Green & yellow/green/yellow **Change Colours:** White & green/green/yellow

UNIVERSITY OF KENT

Secretary: Mrs I Simmonds, Sports Federation, Sports Centre, University of Kent Canterbury, Kent CT2 7NL
Ground: The Playing Fields, University of Kent, Canterbury **Founded:** 1967
Colours: Black & white/black/black **Change Colours:** Red & black/black/black

VICKERS CRAYFORD/DARTFORD ATHLETIC

Secretary: Mr Gary Dillon, 5 Ladds Way, Swanley, Kent BR8 8HN (01322 669057)
Ground: VCD Sports & Soc Club, Oakwood, Old Road, Crayford (01322 524262) **Founded:** 1916
Colours: Green & white/white/white **Change Colours:** Yellow/blue/blue

WESTERHAM

Secretary: Mr D Sayers, 16A The Green, Westerham, Kent TN16 1AX (01959 563163)
Ground: King George Playing Fields, Costells Meadow, off Quebec Avenue, Wetserham **Founded:** 1888
Colours: Red/black/black **Change Colours:** Green/black/black

WOONESBOROUGH

Secretary: Mr G Hunt, Hillcross Farm, Eastry, Sandwich, Kent CT13 0NY (01304 611311)
Ground: Hillborough, Woodnesborough Road, Eastry **Founded:** 1962
Colours: Red/black/black **Change Colours:** Yellow/black/black

LANCASHIRE F.A.

Founded: 28th September 1878
Hon. Secretary: J Kenyon, ACIS,
Northbank, 31a Wellington Street (St Johns), Blackburn BB1 8AU
(01254 24433 (County Office) Fax: (01254) 260095

LANCASHIRE CHALLENGE TROPHY (FOUNDED 1885–86)

RECENT FINALS

1990–91	Marine	v	Gt Harwood Town	1–0
1991–92	Gt Harwood Town	v	Southport	3–2
1992–93	Southport	v	Chorley	5–2 (AET)
1993–94	Morecambe	v	Southport	4–3 (AET)
1994–95	Bamber Bridge	V	Morecambe	2–1

LANCASHIRE ATS TROPHY

24 CLUBS **HOLDERS: BAMBER BRIDGE**

FIRST ROUND w/e 27th November 1995

Atherton LR	v	Bacup Borough	7–0	Holker OB	v	Blackpool Mech	6–0
Barrow	v	Fleetwood	3–1	Leigh RMI	v	Atherton Collieries	1–0
Burscough	v	Marine	3*3 0–2	Radcliffe Borough	v	Great Harwood Town	3–1
Daisy Hill	v	Nelson	2–1	Rossendale United	v	Blackpool Rovers	0–3

8 Clubs with Byes Accrington Stanley, Bamber Bridge, Chorley, Lancaster City, Clitheroe, Darwen, Morecambe, Southport, into the

SECOND ROUND Monday 15th to Saturday 20th January

Accrington Stanley	v	Radcliffe Borough	1*1 1–2	Clitheroe	v	Darwen	1A1 2–0
Atherton L Rovers	v	Chorley	1–2	Holker Old Boys	v	Barrow	1–2
Bamber Bridge	v	Lancaster City	4*3	Morecambe	v	Leigh RMI	2–0
Blackpool Rovers	v	Daisy Hill	1–2	Southport	v	Marine	1–0

THIRD ROUND by Saturday 10th February 1996

Bamber Bridge	v	Daisy Hill	3–1	Morecambe	v	Radcliffe Borougg	3–1
Clitheroe	v	Chorley	2–3	Southport	v	Barrow	3–1

SEMI-FINALS

Bamber Bridge	v	Chorley	3–0	Morecambe	v	Southport	2–1

FINAL Wednesday 24th April 1996
BAMBER BRIDGE v MORECAMBE 0–1 at Deepdale, Preston North End FC. att; 1,708

Morecambe FC winners of Lancashire ATS Trophy 95-96. *Photo Michael R Williamson*

WEST LANCASHIRE LEAGUE

FOUNDED:1905

President: H Johnstone **Chairman:** D Proctor

Hon. Secretary: W Carr, 60 Selby Avenue, Blackpool.

The League Championship was won by Springfields FC , their first success in the Senior Division since 1976 although they have figured prominently in off field honours in recent seasons. Burnley United finished a point behind the Champions when they gained the runners-up Shield on the last day of the season by goal difference only, from last seasons champions Fulwood Amateurs. Leyland Motors Athletic, only four points behind the Champions were in fourth place.

The Second Division had its usual close fight for promotion places and again it took the final games to decide the top three clubs, Lansil Lancaster were champions just three points ahead of Kirkham & Wesham who had the consolation of beating the Champions in the final of the Presidents Cup, although they were taken to the last minutes of extra time in a replayed Cup Final. The Kirkham club also won the treasured Fair Play Trophy for good measure. Tempest United in third place enter the Senior Division for the first time since joining the League, the popularity of this well run club was rewarded by winning the Carradus Trophy for Hospitality. Hesketh Bank were very dissapointed inmissing out on promotion after all their hard work both on and off the field, the competition is tough but 97 could finally be their year which they well deserve.

Both the Richardson and Houston Cup finals were a repeat of the previous season and with the same result, Lancashire Constabulary winning the senior division's Richardson Cup against Leyland Motors. The Motors Reserve team gained some consolation by retaing the Houston Cup by beating the Turton reserve team.

It is sad to record the loss of three fine clubs at the end of the season, all have been lost to the gamethrough ground problems not of their own making, Colne Legion who took over the Dynamoes Stadium at Holt House finally fell victims of the vandals, Vernon Carus (originally Penwortham Hill Rovers) could not raise the required finance, whilst the saddest of them all, Chorley Motors had to leave their private ground at St james Park, home for 77 years, after it was bought by Chorley Football Club.

The League is indeed fortunate to be able to recruit suitable replacements from our wide catchment area, so we are pleased to welcome back two previous members, Glazo S C from Ulverston and Corinthians of Milnthorpe, Haslingden St Mary's take up the third vacancy and have a long and successful history, all have excellent grounds and fscilities which will maintain the reputation and standards of the League.

FINAL LEAGUE TABLES 1995/96

Div One		*P*	*W*	*D*	*L*	*F*	*A*	*Pts*
1.	Springfields	32	22	3	7	74	45	69
2.	Burnley Utd	32	21	5	6	101	47	68
3.	Fulwood Amt	32	21	5	6	76	35	68
4.	Leyland Motors	32	20	5	7	83	34	65
5.	Charnock Ric	32	18	7	7	69	28	61
6.	Lancs Constab.	32	16	2	14	71	54	50
7.	Eagley	32	15	5	12	73	74	50
8.	Turton	32	13	5	14	61	62	44
9.	Poulton Tn	32	11	9	12	51	53	42
10.	Vickers S C	32	11	6	15	49	56	39
11.	Freckleton	32	11	5	16	53	74	38
12.	Wyre Villa	32	9	9	14	50	54	36
13.	Dalton Utd	32	7	10	15	43	71	31
14.	Blackrod Tn	32	9	4	19	47	82	31
15.	Feniscowles	32	8	6	18	51	67	30
16.	BAE Canberra	32	8	4	20	35	87	28
17.	Vernon Carus	32	6	2	24	53	117	20

** Clubs with points adjusted*

Div Two		*P*	*W*	*D*	*L*	*F*	*A*	*Pts*
1.	Lansil	34	25	6	3	96	40	81
2.	Kirkham & Wh	34	23	9	2	75	22	78
3.	Tempest Utd	34	24	4	6	85	38	*73
4.	Hesketh Bank	34	21	8	5	85	30	71
5.	Fleetwood Hes	34	16	9	9	84	48	57
6.	Garstang	34	15	9	10	73	59	*51
7.	Whinney Hill	34	14	5	15	58	60	47
8.	Blackpool Wren	34	12	10	12	65	62	46
9.	BAC Preston	34	13	5	16	75	84	44
10.	Carnforth R	34	11	10	13	42	43	43
11.	Lytham S A	34	10	11	13	49	51	41
12.	West End	34	9	11	14	58	85	38
13.	Thornton Inter	34	8	6	20	52	77	30
14.	Chorley M	34	9	3	22	58	103	30
15.	Wigan College	34	9	5	20	47	75	*29
16.	Norcross & W	34	8	4	22	53	101	28
17.	Barrow Wand	34	10	3	21	63	104	*27
18.	Padiham	34	6	8	20	50	86	26

DIVISION ONE CLUBS 1995-96

BRITISH AEROSPACE CANBERRA

Ground British Aerospace Samlesbury (01254 813088) **Sec:** Mr S P Halse (01254 772687).

BLACKROD TOWN

G: Blackrod Community Centre, Vicarage Rd, Blackrod (01204 692614) **Sec:** Mr D Almond (01942 818663).

BURNLEY UNITED

Ground Barden Lane Spts Grnd, Burnley. **Sec:** Mr R Greenwood (01282 34739).

CHARNOCK RICHARD

G: Charter Lane, off Chorley Lane, Charnock Richard (01257 794288) **Sec:** Mr G S Randle (01772 747129).

COLNE BRITISH LEGION

Ground Holt House (top of Harrison Drive), Colne (01282 863313) **Sec:** Mr W Alexander (01282 866638).

DALTON UNITED
Grd Railway Meadow, Beckside Rd, Dalton-in-Furness (01229 462799) **Sec:** Mr D Lacey (01229 464202).

EAGLEY
Grd Eagley Sports Complex, Dunscar Bridge, Bolton (01204 304181) **Sec:** Mr M Hackin (01204 595863).

FENISCOWLES
Ground Livsey Branch Road, Feniscowles, Blackburn (01254 208210) **Sec:** Mr A Akeroyd (01254 706931).

FRECKLETON
G: Hodgson Mem. Grnd, Bush Lane, Freckleton, Preston (01772 679139) Mrs L O'Reilly (01772 634773).

FULWOOD AMATEURS
Ground Close to M6 jct 32 on M6 and A6-M55 junction **Sec:** Mr A Wilson (01772 798256).

LANCASHIRE CONSTABULARY
G: Police HQ, Saunders Lane, off A59 at Hutton, nr Preston **Sec:** E.Thistlethwaiten (01253 700153).

LEYLAND MOTORS ATHLETIC
Ground Thurston Road, Leyland, Lancs (01772 422400) **Sec:** Mr K Pownall (01772 431066)

POULTON TOWN
Ground Cottam Hall PF, Blackpool Old Rd, Poulton-le-Fylde **Sec:** Mr M Sponder (01253 890284).

SPRINGFIELDS
G: S.S.R.A. Spts Grnd, Dodney Drive, Lea, Preston (01772 726131) **Sec:** Mr T Threlfall (01772 718959).

TURTON
Ground Moorfield, Edgworth. **Sec:** Mr E.Charnock (01204 852608)

VERNON CARUS
Ground Factory Lane, Penwortham (01772 744006) **Sec:** Paul Lees (01942 248313).

VICKERS SPORTS CLUB
Ground Hawcoat Lane, Barrow-in-Furness (01229 825296) **Sec:** Mrs B Knagg (01229 831785).

WYRE HILL
Ground: Stalmine Village, nr Knott End (01253 701468) **Secretary:** Mr G Bradley (01253 810637).

DIVISION TWO CLUBS 1995-96

BRITISH AIRCRAFT CORPORATION PRESTON
Grd Riverside Spts Grnd, Sth Meadow Lane, Preston (01772 51009) **Sec:** Mr F Heaton (01772 724751).

BARROW WANDERERS
Ground Lesh Lane, off Abbey Rd, Barrow-in-F. (01229 825224) **Sec:** Mr M Poole (01229 839148).

BLACKPOOL (WREN) ROVERS RESERVES (see N.W.Co Section)

CARNFORTH RANGERS
Ground Quarry Road,close to town centre **Sec:** Mr K Webster (01524 735322).

CHORLEY MOTORS
Ground St Georges Park, Duke Street, Chorley (01257 270103) **Sec:** Mr D Jolly (01257 270518).

FLEETWOOD HESKETH
Ground Fylde Road, Southport (01704 27968) **Sec:** Mr B Charnock (01704 895588).

GARSTANG
Ground: Off High St,Garstang town centre.(01995 601586) **Sec:** Mr M Gornall (01995 605678).

HESKETH BANK
Ground Hesketh Spts Field, Station Rd, Hesketh Bank **Sec:** Mr D Hand (01772 813247).

KIRKHAM & WESHAM
Ground Coronation Rd Recreation Ground, Kirkham **Sec:** Mr E Pickton (01772 686264).

LANSIL
Ground Lansil Sports Ground, Caton Rd, Lancaster **Sec:** Mr M E Miller (01524 33962).

LYTHAM St ANNES
G: Lytham Cricket & Spts Club, Church Rd, Lytham St A. (01253 734137) Mr M.E.Miller (01524 33962).

NORCROSS & WARBRECK
G: Anchorsholme Lane, Thornton Cleveleys, Blackpool (01253 852415) **Sec:** Mr J.Moore (01253 824627).

PADIHAM
Grd The Arbouries, Holland Street, Padiham (01282 773742) **Secretary:** Mr C D Barker (01282 452395).

TEMPEST UNITED
Ground: Tempest Rd, Chow Moor Village, Lostock (01942 811938) **Sec:** Mrs L Laird (01942 812772).

THORNTON INTERNATIONAL
Prev. Name: ICI Thornton **G:** Gamble Road, Thornton Cleveleys **Sec:** Mr J F Wright (01253 868430).

WEST END
Ground Fishwick Bottoms, off London Rd, Preston (01772 715907) **Sec:** Mr S Robinson (01772 715907).

WHINNEY HILL
Ground **Sec:** Mr D W Keely (01254 387938)

WIGAN COLLEGE
Ground Christopher Park, Standish (01942 41140) **Sec:** Mr G T Reid (01942 208147).

EAST LANCASHIRE LEAGUE

President: H Waddington
Chairman: R A Little
Vice Chairman: K Dean
Secretary: J Constable, 66 Dukes Meadow, Ingol, Preston PR2 7AT (01772 727135)

NORTHERN PLANT HIRE FINAL LEAGUE TABLES 1995/96

Division One	P	W	D	L	F	A	Pts
1. Oswaldtwistle	26	23	1	2	94	22	70
2. Gargrave	26	21	1	4	92	31	64
3. Mill Hill St Peters	26	19	4	3	66	30	61
4. Clitheroe Res	26	16	4	6	67	36	52
5. Worsthorne	26	11	4	11	70	49	37
6. Helmshore Utd	26	10	5	11	49	59	35
7. Sabden	26	10	4	12	57	85	34
8. Crosshills	26	9	5	12	62	60	32
9. Stacksteads SJ	26	9	4	13	50	59	31
10. Barnoldswick Utd	26	8	3	15	43	54	27
11. Whalley	26	7	2	17	53	66	23
12. Rimington	26	6	5	15	46	68	23
13. Settle Utd	26	4	7	15	35	86	19
14. Colne Utd	26	1	7	18	29	108	10

Div Two	P	W	D	L	F	A	Pts
1. Rist Rangers	20	16	3	1	101	28	51
2. Trawden Celtic	20	16	1	3	68	25	49
3. Whinney Hill	20	13	2	5	55	32	41
4. Langho	20	12	2	6	59	42	38
5. Hurst Green	20	10	3	7	38	34	33
6. Rock Rovers	20	10	2	8	66	59	32
7. Read United	20	6	2	12	51	62	20
8. Nelson & FOB	20	6	0	14	39	63	18
9. Pendle Forest	20	5	2	13	41	88	17
10. Oswaldtwistle Tr	20	4	4	12	43	49	16
11. Chatburn	20	1	1	18	18	97	4

Reserve Div	P	W	D	L	F	A	Pts
1. Barnoldswick	22	14	6	2	55	25	48
2. Settle Utd	22	14	4	4	68	39	46
3. Mill Hill St P	22	13	5	4	65	28	44
4. Helmshore U	22	12	5	5	53	26	41
5. Hurst Green	22	12	4	6	56	32	40
6. Rock Rovers	22	11	3	8	82	53	36
7. Worsthorne	22	8	4	10	49	57	28
8. Sabden	22	8	3	11	48	64	27
9. Read United	22	8	2	12	53	59	26
10. Trawden Celtic	22	8	1	13	60	49	25
11. Pendle Forest	22	1	4	17	26	129	7
12. Colne Utd	22	1	3	18	24	78	6

DIVISION ONE

BARNOLDSWICK UNITED

Secretary: Mrr L.James, 37 Long Inn Lane,Barnoldswick,Lancs BB8 6BJ (01282 815361).
Ground: West Close, Victory Park, Barnoldswick.
Colours: Blue & Black/black/black **Reserves colours:** Blue & Yellow

CLITHEROE

Secretary: Mr C Wilson 4 Moss Street, Clitheroe, Lancs BB7 1DP (01200 24370)
Ground: Shawbridge, Pendle Road, Clithroe
Colours: Blue & white/blue/blue **Change Colours:** Red & blue/blue/blue

COLNE UNITED

Secretary: Mr S Bannister, 41 Derby St,Colne. Lancs.BB8 9AA (01282 869995)
Ground: Sough Park, Kelbrook, Earby, Colne.
Colours: Black and white **Change colours:** Tangerine

CROSSHILLS

Secretary: Mr A Knox, 33 Ash Grove, Sutton-in-Craven, Keighley, West Yorks (01535 632088).
Ground: Sutton Fields, Sutton-in-Craven, Keighley, West Yorkshire.
Colours: red and black **Change colours:** Blue and maroon

GARGRAVE

Secretary: Mr M Barrett 31 Neville Road, Gargrave, Skipton N Yorks BD23 3RE (01756 749426)
Ground: Skipton Road, Gargrave
Colours: Blue/white **Change Colours:** Red & black/white

HELMSHORE UNITED

Secretary: Mr I Walkden, 13 Piccadilly Str., Haslingden, Rossendale BB4 5LU (01706 226753).
Ground: Marl Pitts, Newchurch Rd, Rawtenstall.
Colours: Red & blue/red/red. **Change colours:** Blue & white/blue.

MILL HILL St PETERS

Secretary: Mr J.V.Fleming, 24 Feniscliffe Drive, Blackburn, Lancs BB2 2UF (011254 209101)
Ground: Mill Hill St Peters, Queen Victoria St.,Mill Hill,Blackburn.
Colours: Black & White **Change colours:** All Green

OSWALDTWISTLE TOWN

Ground: Heys Playing Field, Heron Way, Oswaldtwistle.
Secretary: Mrs M.Riley, 11A Polar Close, Oswaldtwistle,Lancs.BB5 3AY (011254 382830)
Colours: Blue and Black **Change colours:** Green and Yellow

RIMINGTON

Secretary: Mr L Whittaker, 2 Dorset Drive, Clitheroe, Lancs BB7 2BQ (01200 29112).
Ground: Coulthurst Memorial Field, Back Lane, Rimington (behind Black Bull).
Colours: Tangerine/black **Change colours:** Green/black.

SABDEN

Secretary: Mrs A Weir, 59 Whalley Rd., Sabden ,Clitheroe, Lancs.BB7 9EA (01282 774829)
Ground: Nutter Barn Field, Sabden, Blackburn.
Colours: Red & blue/blue/blue **Change colours:** Red & black/black/red.

SETTLE UNITED

Secretary: Mr J Dinsdale, 3 Goldielands Settle N Yorks (01729 823738)
Ground: Bridge End Ground, Goggleswick, Settle.

STACKSTEAD ST JOSEPH'S

Secretary: Mr P Hopkinson, 19 Branch Street, Stacksteads, Bacup, Lancs OL13 0TX (01706 874643)
Ground: Stacksteads Recreation Ground.
Colours: All Blue **Change Colours:** Green & white/green/green

WHALLEY

Secretary: Mrs A Bury, 59 Lord Str., Oswaldtwistle, Accrington, Lancs BB5 3EF (01254 235443).
Ground: Queen Elizabeth Playing Field, Mitton Rd, Whalley.
Colours: Red and Black **Change colours:** Green and Black.

WORSTHORNE UNITED

Secretary: Mrs W.Hughes, 11 Mayfair Rd., Burnley,Lancs. BB10 4HW (01282 411195)
Ground: Worsthorne, Lennox St.
Colours: Yellow & green/green/yellow **Change colours:** Blue/black/black.

LEICESTERSHIRE F.A.

Hon. Secretary: Ron E Barston,
Holmes Park, Dog & Gun Lane, Whetstone LE8 3LJ (0116 288 0312) – Home
(0116 286 7828) County Office Fax: (0116 286 7828)

LEICESTERSHIRE SENIOR CUP (FOUNDED 1887–88)

RECENT FINALS

1990–91	Hinckley Town	v	Newfoundpool WMC	5–2
1991–92	Friar Lane Old Boys	v	Lutterworth Town	1–0
1992–93	Friar Lane Old Boys	v	Birstall United	2–1 (AET)
1993–94	Ibstock Welfare	v	St Andrews SC	2–1
1994–95	Anstey Nomads	v	Holwell Sports	2–0

MOST WINS Leicester City 26 Enderby Town 6 Shepshed Dynamo 6

1995–1996

LEICESTERSHIRE 'JELSON HOMES' SENIOR CUP

42 CLUBS **HOLDERS: ANSTEY NOMADS**

FIRST ROUND Saturday 7th October

Earl Shilton Alb	v	Kirby Muxloe	1–6
Cotesmore Amt	v	Ayleston Park OB	0–1
Narboro & L'thorpe	V	Asfordby Amateurs	2*3
Oadby Town	v	Hemington	10–2
Blaby & Whetstone	v	Holwell Sports	1–2
Saffron Dynamo	v	Barlestone St Giles	4–1
Syston St Peters	v	Downes Sports	2–3
United Collieries	v	Burbage OB	1–6
Newfoundpool	v	Friar Lane OB	2–1
North Kilworth	v	Anstey Nomads	1*5

SECOND ROUND 4th November **22 Clubs with Byes

St Andrews**	v	Fosse Imps**	4–0
Anstey Town**	v	Barwell**	0–1
Coalville Town**	v	Harborough Town**	7–1
Slack & Parr**	v	Thringstone MW**	0–1
L'boro**Dynamo	v	Houghton Rngs**	6–0
Burbage OB	v	Kirby Muxloe	1–3
Huncote S&S**	v	Sileby Town	3–1
Newfoundpool**	v	Birstall United**	1–2
Saffron Dynamo	v	Quorn**	2–1
Bardon Hill**	v	Barrow Town**	0–2
Lutterworth**Tn	v	Highfield Rangers**	0–3
Holwell Sports	v	Hillcroft**	2–3
Oadby Town	v	Anstey Nomads	4–1
Asfordby Amt	v	Ibstock Welfare**	2–1
Downes Sports	v	Stoney Stanton**	3–2
Leics**Constab	v	Aylestone Park OB	2–1

THIRD ROUND

Huncote SSC	v	Highfield Rangers	1–3
Thringstone MW	v	Saffron Dynamo	2–1
Downes Sports	v	Barwell	1–3
L'boro Dynamo	v	Leics Constab	2–1
Oadby Town	v	St Andrews	1–0
Birstall United	v	Barrow Town	3–1
Kirby Muxloe	v	Coalville	5–0
Asfordby Amt	v	Hillcroft	4–1

FOURTH ROUND 6th January 1996

Barwell	v	Highfield Rangers	3–0
Oadby Town	v	Asfordby Amt	6–2
Thringstone MW	v	Kirby Muxloe	1–5
Birstall United	v	L'boro Dynamo	4–2

SEMI-FINALS

Barwell v Oadby Town 0–1
at Leicester United FC Tuesday 13th February 1996

Kirby Muxloe v Birstall United 2–3
at Quorn FC Tuesday 27th February 1996

FINAL Tuesday 2nd April
BIRSTALL UNITED v OADBY TOWN 1*0 at Holmes Park, Whetstone.

LEICESTERSHIRE WESTERBY CHALLENGE CUP

12 CLUBS **HOLDERS: LEICESTER CITY**

FIRST ROUND on or before 19th October

Hinckley Athletic	v	Oadby Town	0–3
Anstey Nomads	v	Shepshed Dynamo	0–2
Holwell Sports	v	Leicester Utd	1–4
Friar Lane OB	v	Barrow Town	5–0

SECOND ROUND ** 4 Clubs with Byes

Barwell**	v	St Andrews**	2–3
Friar Lane OB	v	Leicester United	2–1
Shepshed Dynamo	v	Hinckley Town**	1–0
Leicester City**	v	Oadby Town	5–0

SEMI-FINALS March at Holmes Park, Whetstone

St Andrews	v	Shepshed Dynamo	3–1
Friar Lane OB	v	Leicester City	0–6

FINAL Monday 22nd April 1996
LEICESTER CITY v ST ANDREWS 2–1 at Filbert Street, Leicester City FC.

FINAL LEAGUE TABLES 1995/96

TMS MOTORS LEICESTERSHIRE & DISTRICT LEAGUE

Premier Div	P	W	D	L	F	A	Pts
1. Cosby United	24	20	2	2	85	26	62
2. Pedigree Pet	24	17	3	4	105	35	54
3. G E C	24	15	1	8	80	36	46
4. Birstall RBL	24	14	2	8	71	44	44
5. D C E	24	12	5	7	58	32	41
6. Magna 73	24	11	3	10	70	57	36
7. Leic YMCA	24	10	4	10	64	58	34
8. Grace Dieu U	24	8	7	9	51	52	31
9. Blaby Utd	24	8	2	14	32	56	26
10. Uppingham Tn	24	6	6	12	40	56	24
11. Glenfield Tn	24	6	5	13	44	64	23
12. British Shoe	24	6	4	14	40	61	22
13. Dunton Bassett	24	1	0	23	17	180	3

Div One	P	W	D	L	F	A	Pts
1. Thurnby Rgrs	22	19	2	1	83	20	59
2. City Gas	22	16	3	3	59	21	51
3. New Parks	22	15	4	3	77	22	49
4. Epworth	22	12	0	10	67	49	36
5. Syston Town	22	9	3	10	50	52	30
6. Lutterworth A	22	9	2	11	43	40	29
7. County Hall	22	8	5	9	31	51	29
8. Winstanley	22	8	4	10	42	42	28
9. Wreake Valley	22	8	2	12	53	63	26
10. Stoke Golding	22	6	2	14	31	83	20
11. Sapcote Utd	22	4	1	17	25	79	13
12. Glen Villa	22	3	2	17	27	66	11

Div Two	P	W	D	L	F	A	Pts
1. Grange AFC	22	18	2	2	69	16	56
2. Kibworth Tn	22	17	1	4	89	37	52
3. Loughboro Ath	22	15	5	2	85	26	50
4. Ratby Sports	22	11	5	6	63	39	38

NORTH LEICESTERSHIRE LEAGUE:

Premier Div	P	W	D	L	F	A	Pts
1. Ingles	18	14	2	2	71	17	44
2. Hillside Rgrs	18	11	5	2	65	34	38
3. Ashby Ivanhoe	18	10	4	4	57	23	34
4. West End Utd	18	9	2	7	31	35	29
5. Shepshed Amt	18	8	4	6	35	38	28
6. Hethern	18	8	3	7	48	41	27
7. Measham Imp	18	6	4	8	36	35	22
8. L/ghborough T	18	6	3	9	35	46	21
9. Belton Villa	18	3	1	14	25	63	10
10. Mountsorrell	18	1	0	17	15	86	3

Div One	P	W	D	L	F	A	Pts
1. Woodhouse Im	20	18	2	0	74	17	56
2. West End U R	20	10	1	9	34	30	31
3. Sileby Saints	20	8	6	6	38	29	30
4. Quorn Utd	20	9	2	9	46	42	29
5. Ingles Res	20	8	4	8	47	46	28
6. Kegworth Wand	20	8	4	8	38	47	28
7. L'boro Tn Res	20	8	3	9	45	43	27
8. L'boro Dynamo	20	6	4	10	38	64	22
9. Bagworth	20	5	6	9	34	39	21
10. Markfield L	20	5	4	11	38	52	19
11. Old Dalby	20	5	4	11	31	54	19

ELTON & RUTLAND LEAGUE

Div One	P	W	D	L	F	A	Pts
1. Ashwell Ath	12	10	2	0	53	16	22
2. Asfordby Vill	12	8	2	2	40	17	18
3. AB Kettleby	12	9	2	1	33	13	18
4. Toy Soldiers	12	4	1	7	25	33	9
5. Cottesmore	12	2	3	7	21	37	7
6. Boulton & P	12	3	1	8	16	40	7
7. Melton BS	12	0	1	11	13	45	1

CITY LEAGUE

Terjon Prem Div	P	W	D	L	F	A	Pts
1. Oadby BCOB	18	15	2	1	55	14	47
2. G N G	18	12	4	2	55	24	40
3. FC Blaby	18	11	0	7	57	40	33
4. Anstey United	18	10	3	5	43	35	30
5. Bharat	18	9	2	7	47	37	29
6. St Patricks	18	8	3	7	41	49	27
7. Kirkland	18	5	2	11	39	57	17
8. Last Straw	18	4	2	12	33	56	14
9. Rothley Imps	18	4	1	13	39	48	13
10. Goodwins	18	1	3	14	23	72	6

LINCOLNSHIRE F.A.

Hon. Secretary: Mr F S Richardson,
PO Box 26, 12 Dean Road, Lincoln LN2 4DP (01522 524917) County Office
Fax: (01522 528859)

LINCOLNSHIRE SENIOR CUP
(FOUNDED 1935–36)

RECENT WINNERS

1990–91 Lincoln City
1991–92 Grimsby Town
1992–93 Grimsby Town
1993–94 Grimsby Town
1994–95 Grimsby Town

MOST WINS Grimsby Town 13 Lincoln City 12 Boston United 5

1995–1996

LINCOLNSHIRE SENIOR CUP

6 CLUBS **HOLDERS: GRIMSBY TOWN**

SECTION 'A' ****Won on the toss of a coin**

Grimsby Town	v	Scunthorpe United	3–0
Gainsboro Trinity	v	Scunthorpe United	3–0
Gainsboro Trinity	v	Grimsby Town	0–0

FINAL TABLE	P	W	D	L	G\F	A	Pts	GD
Grimsby Town**	2	1	1	0	3	0	5	+ 3
Gainsboro Trinity	2	1	1	0	3	0	5	+ 3
Scunthorpe United	2	0	0	2	0	6	0	– 6

SECTION 'B'

Boston United	v	Lincoln City	0–0
Grantham Town	v	Lincoln City	1–2
Grantham Town	v	Boston United	0–2

FINAL TABLE	P	W	D	L	G\F	A	Pts	GD
Boston United	2	1	1	0	2	0	4	+ 2
Lincoln City	2	1	1	0	2	1	4	+ 1
Grantham Town	2	0	0	2	1	4	0	– 3

FINAL Tuesday 6th November 1995
BOSTON UNITED v GRIMSBY TOWN 1–4 at York Road, Boston United FC.

LINCOLNSHIRE SENIOR 'A' CUP
(FOUNDED 1968–69)

RECENT FINALS

1990–91	Gainsborough Town	v	Louth United	2–1
1991–92	Nettleham	v	Lincoln United	3–1
1992–93	Mirrlees Blackstone	v	Bourne Town	1–1 (AET)
1993–94	Brigg Town	v	Lincoln United	5–2
1994–95	Holbeach United	v	Boston Town	1–0

MOST WINS Boston Town 6 Holbeach United 4 Skegness Town 4

LINCOLNSHIRE SENIOR 'A' CUP

12 CLUBS **HOLDERS: HOLBEACH UNITED**

PRELIMINARY ROUND Saturday 14th October ****Won on the toss of a coin**

Bourne Town	v	Mirrlees Blackstone	0–2	Brigg Town	v	Spalding United	3–0
Immingham Town	v	Boston Town	0–4	Stamford AFC	v	Holbeach United	1–1 SW–O

FIRST ROUND ** 4 Clubs with Byes

Mirrlees Blackstone	v	Brigg Town	0–3	Boston Town	v	Stamford AFC	3–1
Louth United**	v	Nettleham**	1–2	Lincoln United**	v	Winterton Rangers**	4–0

SEMI-FINALS

Lincoln United	v	Brigg Town	4–0	Boston Town	v	Nettleham	2–1

FINAL Tuesday 16th April 1996

LINCOLN UNITED v BOSTON TOWN 2*1 at Ashby Avenue, Lincoln United FC.

LINCOLNSHIRE SENIOR 'B' CUP
(FOUNDED 1949–50)

RECENT FINALS

1990–91	Harrowby United	v	Grimsby Borough	4–2
1991–92	Harrowby United	v	Hykeham Town	3–0
1992–93	Appleby Frod Ath	v	Humberside Utd	1–1 (11–10 Pens)
1993–94	Wyberton	v	Hykeham Town	2–2 (4–1 Pens)
1994–95	Immingham Blos Way	v	Limestone Rangers	3–0

MOST WINS Brigg Town 5
Appleby Frodingham Athletic 4

LINCOLNSHIRE SENIOR 'B' CUP

HOLDERS: IMMINGHAM BLOSSOM WAY

FIRST ROUND Saturday 4th November 1995

Limestone Rng	v	Deeping Rangers	4–1	Harrowby United	v	Ruston Sports	0–3
Louth OB	v	Appleby Frod Ath	0–3	Skegness Town	v	Lincoln Moorlands	2–3
Hykeham Town	v	Sleaford Town	4–1	Barton Town OB	v	Epworth Town	2–0
Grimsby Amateurs	v	Bottesford Town	4–1	Wyberton	v	Spilsby Town	W W–O

SECOND ROUND

Appleby Frod Ath	v	Ruston Sports	2–1	Grimsby Amateurs	v	Lincoln Moorlands	1–2
Wyberton	v	Barton Town OB	2–2 1–2	Hykeham Town	v	Limestone Rangers	2–0

SEMI-FINALS

Appleby Frod Ath	v	Lincoln Morlands	2–0	Barton OB	v	Hykeham Town	3–0

FINAL Wednesday 13th March 1996

APPLEBY FRODINGHAM ATHLETIC v BARTON OLD BOYS 0–2 at West Street, Scunthorpe, Winterton Rangers FC.

TSW PRINTERS (SCUNTHORPE)
LINCOLNSHIRE LEAGUE

President: Mr R Jackson

Hon. Secretary: Mr R Hewson

219 Scotter Road, Scunthorpe, South Humberside, DN15 7EJ (01724 846166)

FINAL LEAGUE TABLES 1995/96

		P	*W*	*D*	*L*	*F*	*A*	*Pts*
1.	Lincoln United	36	29	3	4	107	25	*87
2.	Boston Utd Res	36	23	7	6	85	38	76
3.	Limestone Rangers	36	23	5	8	89	52	74
4.	Barton Town OB	36	22	6	8	97	47	72
5.	App Frod Ath	36	20	8	8	79	44	68
6.	Grimsby Ath	36	17	7	12	72	55	61
7.	Sleaford Town	36	17	7	12	74	60	*58
8.	Wyberton	36	17	6	13	84	64	56
9.	Hykeham Town	36	17	4	15	77	71	55
10.	Lincoln Moorlands	36	15	5	16	79	71	50
11.	Skegness Town	36	15	4	17	60	72	49
12.	Bottesford Town	36	13	8	15	73	58	47
13.	Epworth Town LC	36	14	5	17	62	78	47
14.	Grantham Tn Res	36	13	5	18	57	81	41
15.	Ruston Sports	36	10	6	20	75	98	36
16.	BRSA Retford	36	8	2	26	56	101	*29
17.	Louth Utd Amt	36	6	9	21	50	98	*29
18.	Louth Old Boys	36	4	8	24	43	109	20
19.	Nettleham Res	36	5	3	28	29	126	18

** points adjusted: Grimsby Amt, BRSA Retford; + 3: Lincon Utd, Grantham T Res; - 3: Louth Utd Amt + 2:*

Barry Fenton & Partners Insurance League Cup:

Semi-finals;	Grimsby Amateurs	v App-Frd Athletcic	0-2
	Grantham Town Reserves	v Lincoln Moorlands	0-1
Final:	Appleby Frodingham Athletic	v Lincon Moorlands	0-2

BOSTON FOOTBALL LEAGUE

Premier Div		*P*	*W*	*D*	*L*	*F*	*A*	*Pts*
1.	Coningsby	26	20	2	4	81	33	62
2.	Horncastle Town	26	15	4	7	84	54	49
3.	Wyberton Res	26	14	5	7	64	41	47
4.	Fishtoft	26	12	8	5	65	38	44
5.	Billinghay Ath	26	13	5	7	59	40	44
6.	Swineshead	26	123	6	8	65	47	42
7.	Spilsby Town	26	12	3	11	48	40	39
8.	Wrangle United	26	10	5	11	48	39	35
9.	Lutton Marsh	26	10	5	10	52	62	35
10.	CFC Boston	26	9	4	13	65	75	31
11.	Cowbridge Rangers	26	10	1	15	45	58	31
12.	Wainfleet United	26	7	7	12	54	62	28
13.	Old Leake	26	6	5	15	34	73	23
14.	Holbeach St Marks	26	0	0	25	18	120	0

LINCOLNSHIRE LEAGUE CLUBS 1995-96

APPLEBY FRODINGHAM ATHLETIC

Chairman: G Keena **Manager:** Mr Walker
Secretary: Mr M D Mumby, 21 Messingham Rd, Scunthorpe, South Humbs DN17 2LL (01724 840117).
Ground: Brumby Hall, Ashby Rd, Scunthorpe (01724 843024).
Directions: A18 turn right at 2nd circle, 2nd left, left at next lights, strght on at next circle, 2nd left after circle.
Colours: Purple (thin white stripe)/purple **Change colours:** Red & blue stripes/blue

BOTTESFORD TOWN

Chairman: A Reeve **Manager:** P Ashworth
Secretary: Mr P Herrick, 22a Rooklands, Scotter, Gainsborough, Lincs DN21 3TT (01724 764183).
Ground: Ontario Road, Bottesford, Scunthorpe (01724 871883).
Directions: Berkeley Circle, Scotter Road South, Asda Circle, straight across 2nd left past Darby Glass Factory, turn right into Goodwood, turn right to Club.
Colours: Yellow & blue trim/blue **Change colours:** White/white

BOSTON UNITED RESERVES

Chairman: P Malkinson **Manager:** C Cook/D Creasey
Secretary: Mr J Blackwell, 14-16 Span Place, Boston PE21 6HN (01205 365652).
Ground: York Street, Boston (01205 365524/5)
Directions: A52 Sleaford-Boston Rd., 2nd left Brothertoft Rd., Argyle St. to Argyle Sluice Bridge. Immediately over bridge turn left Tattershall Rd., ground three quarters of a mile.
Colours: Amber/black **Change colours:** White/green

B.R.S.A. RETFORD

Chairman: S Pringle **Manager:** D Whalley
Secretary: Mr M Keeling, 18 Rutland Road, Retford, Notts DN22 7HF (01777 703929).
Ground: British Rail, Badworth Road, Retford.
Directions: Into centre of Retford, follow signs for Worksop A620. After crossing railway bridge, turn 1st left. Ground entrance on left under bridge.
Colours: Blue & black stripes/white **Change colours:** White/white

EPWORTH TOWN

Chairman: T Pyle **Manager:** P Deno
Secretary: Mr G Yeardley, 9 Hayfield Close, Haxey, Doncaster DN9 2NT (01427 753257).
Ground: Leisure Centre, Burnham Road, Epworth (01427 873945).
Directions: Main Road through village A161 Goole/Gainsborough Road becomes Burnham Road, ground behind South Axholme School access via Leisure Centre adj.
Colours: White/blue **Change colours:** Red/blue

GRANTHAM TOWN RESERVES

Chairman: A Prince **Manager:** T Eldred
Secretary: Mr P S Nixon, 72 Huntingtower Road, Grantham, Lincs NG31 7AU (01476 64408).
Ground: Trent Road, Grantham (01476 62011).
Directions: A1 leave at A52 Nottingham. Turn, take 1st right after Nissan Garage in Barrowby Gate. At T junction turn right then left into Trent Rd. From A607 Lincoln-Sleaford. Right at 3rd lights. Sign post A52 Nottingham. Over next lights on outskirts of town, turn right into Springfield Rd, over next lights into Trent Rd.
Colours: Black & white stripes/black **Change colours:** Yellow & blue or Red & white

GRIMSBY AMATEURS

Chairman: M Duckworth **Manager:** N Shackleton
Secretary: Mrs P Shackleton, 42 Campden Cres., Cleethorpes, S. Humbs DN35 2UL (01472 698351).
Ground: The Club, Wilton Road, Humberston (01472 872936).
Directions: A16 Toll Bar circle, right for Cleethorpes, left when road forks. Next circle right Wilton Rd, 1st right from A46 Nuns Corner College right at lights. Next circle 2nd exit. Next circle 2nd exit 1st right Wilton Rd, Grd on left
Colours: White/navy **Change colours:** Yellow/navy

HYKEHAM TOWN

Chairman: M Clayton **Manager:** M Poucher
Secretary: Mr C Edwards, 5 Landsdowne Road, Lincoln (01522 520857).
Ground: Memorial Playing Fields, North Hykeham (01522 680193)
Directions: Off A46 opposite Kesteven Sports Centre - Memorial Playing Fields.
Colours: Blue/blue **Change colours:** Red/white

IMMINGHAM BLOSSOM WAY SPORTS

Chairman: N Day **Manager:** H Jacklin
Secretary: Mrs C Jacklin, 272 St. Nicholas Drive, Grimsby DN37 9RP (01472 882690).
Ground: Blossom Way, Immingham (01472 572612).
Directions: Enter Immingham from A180 -Blossom Way on right hand side.
Colours: White (black trim)/black **Change colours:** Red & white halves/red

LIMESTONE RANGERS

Chairman: P Wray **Manager:** D Andrews
Secretary: M Harty, 3 Brook Street, Hemswell, Gainsborough, Lincs DN21 5UT (01427 668382).
Ground: Willoughton.
Directions: Half way down Willoughton Hill, down Hollowgate Hill.
Colours: Red/black **Change colours:** Blue/black

LINCOLN MOORLANDS

Chairman: S Gordon **Manager:** S Gordon
Secretary: T Walshaw, 19 Spilsby Close, Hartsholme Field, Lincoln LN6 3YX (01522 501229).
Ground: Moorland Sports Ground, Newark Road, Lincoln (01522 520184)
Directions: The Moorland Club, Newark Road. Lincoln from Lincoln City Centre along A1434 towards Newark, Ground quarter mile passed Rooker Lane.
Colours: Red & white stripes/red **Change colours:** Blue/royal blue

LINCOLN UNITED COLTS

Chairman: K Roe **Manager:** P Tittcombe
Secretary: K Weaver, 22 Grainsby Close, Lincoln LN6 7QF (01522 531832).
Ground: Ashby Av., Hartsholme, Lincoln (01522 843024).
Directions: A46 Lincoln by-pass-circle exit marked Birchwood - 1 mile 30 mph sign turn right into Ashby Av., ground 200 yards on right.
Colours: White/white stripe **Change colours:** Yellow/yellow

LOUTH OLD BOYS

Chairman: A Roberson **Manager:** M Shackleton
Secretary: M Shackleton, 12 Tudor Drive, Louth, Lincs (01507 602929).
Ground: London Rd., Louth (01507 603928).
Directions: A16 road, ground one mile south of main church, sports ground.
Colours: Red & black stripe/black **Change colours:** Blue/blue

LOUTH UNITED AMATEURS

Chairman: C Horton **Manager:** T Porter
Secretary: P Smith, 84 Scartho Road, Grimsby DN33 2BG (01472 879356).
Ground: Park Avenue, Louth (01507 607351).
Directions: A16 from North or South to main Church traffic lights. Turn right or left into Eastgate - follow road through seeking ambulance/fire station on right, next turning on right Park Av. Grd at end of Ave, right, left
Colours: Royal blue/royal blue **Change colours:** Black & red stripes/black

NETTLEHAM RESERVES

Chairman: C Mason **Manager:** R Mason
Secretary: S W Timms, 5 Ash Tree Ave., Nettleham, Lincoln LN2 2TQ (01522 751140).
Ground: Mulsanne Park, Nettleham (01522 750007).
Directions: From A46 turn onto Washdyke Lane, name change to High Street, Mill Hill and Sudbrook Road, 2nd left into Greenfields, turn right into Field Close to Mulsanne Park.
Colours: Royal & white stripes/blue **Change colours:** Red/red

RUSTON SPORTS

Chairman: G Curtis **Manager:** B Linnicor
Secretary: P Dickson, 42 Fontwell Crescent, Lincoln LN6 7LE (01522 684738).
Ground: RMSC Club, Newark Road, Lincoln (01522 680057).
Directions: A46 road to Newark, left hand side of road approx 250 meters before City boundary.
Colours: Blue/white **Change colours:** White/white

SKEGNESS TOWN

Chairman: K Brearley **Manager:** B Ferguson
Secretary: M Brown, 10 Thames Meadow Drive, Hogsthorpe, Skegness, Lincs PE24 5PU (01754 73678).
Ground: Burgh Road, Skegness. (01754 4385).
Directions: A158 Road into Skegness, ground on the right hand side.
Colours: White/red **Change colours:** Green/white

SLEAFORD TOWN

Chairman: M Cameron **Manager:** B Rowland
Secretary: Miss J Muxlow, 7 Milton Way, Boston Road, Sleaford, Lincs NG34 7HX (01529 304502).
Ground: Boston Road, Sleaford.
Directions: A15 Lincoln to Sleaford centre, left at Hanley monument to Boston Rd, Grd 800 yds right.
Colours: Green & white stripes/white **Change colours:** Red/white

SPILSBY TOWN

Chairman: J Skinner **Manager:** D Wilkinson
Secretary: C Tempest, 59 Boston Road, Spilsby, Lincs PE25 5HQ (01790 53185).
Ground: Ancaster Ave., Spilsby.
Directions: Town centre for A16, Church Turn right, 2nd right Ancaster Ave., 100 mtrs grd.
Colours: Black & white stripes/black **Change colours:** Red (black trim).

WYBERTON

Chairman: I Smith **Manager:** M Scrupps
Secretary: Mrs C Scrupps, 52 Deldale Road, Wyberton, Boston, Lincs PE21 7BT (01205 367756).
Ground: Causeway, Wyberton (01522 353525).
Directions: From Boston take Spalding road, A16 to 1st circle, turn right onto B1397 Kirton end and proceed 1 mile to cross roads just before Pin Cushion Inn. Turn left into Saunder Gate Lane and turn immediately left again into the Causeway.
Colours: Black & white/black (white trim) **Change colours:** Red & blue stripes/blue

LIVERPOOL COUNTY F.A.

Secretary: Fred Hunter,
23 Greenfield Road, Liverpool L13 3BN. Tel: (01514) 27179
(01512) 206089 (County Office) Fax: 0151 2200573

LIVERPOOL SENIOR CUP
(FOUNDED 1977–78)

RECENT FINALS

1990–91	Southport	v	Marine	4–0
1991–92	Tranmere Rovers	v	Marine	4–1
1992–93	Southport	v	Burscough	2–1
1993–94	Marine	v	Southport	2–1
1994–95	Tranmere Rovers	v	Marine	2–0 (AET)

MOST WINS Marine 5 Liverpool 3 South Liverpool 3

1995–1996

LIVERPOOL SENIOR CUP

11 CLUBS **HOLDERS: TRANMERE ROVERS**

FIRST ROUND

Bootle	v	Prescot Cables	5–3	Knowsley United	v	Skelmersdale Utd	2–0
Burscough	v	St Helens Town	1–2				

SECOND ROUND

Knowsley Utd	v	Bootle	4–0	Marine	v	St Helens Town	1–0
Southport	v	Everton	3–3 0–2	Tranmere Rovers	v	Liverpool	3–1

SEMI-FINALS by Saturday 30th March

Knowsley United	v	Everton	0–2	Marine	v	Tranmere Rovers	1–4

FINAL held over to pre season (First XI"s)
EVERTON v TRANMERE ROVERS at Prenton Park, Transmere Rovers FC.

Liverpool Challenge Cup Semi-final between Garswood United & Waterloo Dock.
Photo- Rob Ruddock

FRANK ARMITT LIVERPOOL COMBINATION FINAL LEAGUE TABLES 1995/96

Division One	P	W	D	L	F	A	Pts
1. Stockbridge	30	21	2	7	75	40	65
2. Waterloo Dock	30	20	4	6	89	36	64
3. Crawfords U B	30	20	4	6	55	38	64
4. Electric Supply	30	16	12	2	75	44	60
5. St Dominics	30	17	4	9	66	38	55
6. South Liverpool	30	16	4	10	61	32	52
7. York CT	30	13	7	10	69	50	46
8. Ayone	30	13	7	10	48	49	46
9. Mossley Hill	30	11	5	14	60	64	38
10. Ford Motors	30	11	4	15	43	56	37
11. Royal Seaforth	30	10	5	15	58	62	35
12. Lucas Sports	30	7	9	14	49	66	30
13. Earle	30	5	9	16	47	85	24
14. G P T Plessey	30	6	5	19	54	95	23
15. Crystal Villa	30	6	1	23	38	79	19
16. BRNESC 3	30	6	2	22	42	95	17

Division Two	P	W	D	L	F	A	Pts
1. Eldonians	26	17	4	5	81	30	55
2. Selwyn	26	16	6	4	71	32	54
3. Bootle Res	26	16	2	8	77	42	50
4. Halewood Tn	26	16	2	8	71	46	50
5. Speke	26	15	3	8	61	39	48
6. Camadale	26	14	5	7	69	50	47
7. Rainhill Town 3	26	12	3	11	56	41	36
8. Cheshire Lines	26	10	1	15	55	58	31
9. Beesix	26	8	5	13	56	67	29
10. El Supply R	26	8	4	14	40	58	28
11. Maghull Res 3	26	8	6	12	38	41	27
12. BRNESC Res 3	26	8	1	17	40	85	22
13. Y C T Res	26	7	1	18	31	98	22
14. Avon Athleyic	26	4	3	19	42	100	15

DIVISION ONE CLUBS 1996-97

(Tel. codes 0151 unless stated)

AYONE

Ground: Edinburgh Park (263 5267) **Secretary:** J Doyle (207 1437)
Colours: White/blue/blue

CRAWFORDS U.B.

Ground: As Cheshire Lines (above) **Secretary:** V Goodman (475 1563)
Colours: Yellow/blue/blue

EARLE

Ground: Arncliffe Leisure Centre, Arncliffe Rd, Halewood (428 1929). **Secretary:** W Hollerhead (489 9103)
Colours: All red

ELDONIANS

Ground: Edinburgh Park (263 5185) **Secretary:** J Shea (207 1907)

ELECTRIC SUPPLY (MANWEB)

Ground: Thingwall Road **Secretary:** J Shimmin (523 5593)
Colours: White/navy/navy

FORD MOTORS

Ground: Ford Spts & Soc Club, Cronton Lane, Widnes (424 7078) **Secretary:** T Doyle (01928 568329)
Colours: Blue & black/black/blue

LUCAS SPORTS

Ground: Edenhurst Ave (nr Coronation Hotel) Liverpool (480 6365) **Secretary:** A Brodrick (423 4615)
Colours: Yellow/sky/yellow

MOSSLEY HILL

Ground: Mossley Hill Athletic Club, Mossley Hill Rd (724 4377) **Secretary:** R Fitzpatrick (475 1934)
Colours: Maroon & Sky

PLESSEY (GPT)

Ground: 'Whitfield', Roby Rd, Huyton (489 1031) **Secretary:** I Scholes (728 9848)
Colours: Black & blue/blue/blue

ROYAL SEAFORTH

Ground: Edinburgh Park (263 5185) **Secretary:** A Stanton (489 9980)
Colours: Black & white/black/black

SELWYN

Ground: Bootle Stadium (523 4213). **Secretary:** S Spencer (256 8255)

SOUTH LIVERPOOL

Ground: Blessed John Almond School, Horrocks Avenue, Liverpool L19 **Secretary:** J Stanway (733 1286)
Colours: White/black/red

St DOMINICS

Ground: St Dominics School, Lordens Rd, Huyton (489 2798) **Secretary:** M Donohue (220 8180)
Colours: Green/black/green

STOCKBRIDGE

Ground: Stockbridge Comprehensive School **Secretary:** P Shaw (226 5857)
Colours: Red/black/red

WATERLOO DOCK

Ground: Edinburgh Park (263 5267) **Secretary:** J Davies (264 8179)
Colours: All blue

YORKSHIRE COPPER TUBE

Ground: Factory Site, East Lancashire Rd, Kirkby (545 5133) **Secretary:** J Murray (228 6112)
Colours: All blue

LONDON F.A.

Secretary: Ron Ashford,
Aldworth Grove, Lewisham, London SE13 6HY
Tel: 01816 909626 (County Office) Fax: 01816 909471

LONDON CHALLENGE CUP
(FOUNDED 1990–91)

RECENT FINALS

1990–91	Carshalton Ath	v	Welling United	4–2
1991–92	Welling United	v	Dulwich Hamlet	2–0
1992–93	Leyton Orient	v	Barnet	3–2
1993–94	Uxbridge	v	Welling United	3–0
1994–95	St Albans City	v	Fisher	6–0

1995–1996

LONDON CHALLENGE CUP

16 CLUBS **HOLDERS: ST ALBANS CITY**

FIRST ROUND 30th October–4th November 1995

Uxbridge	v	Hampton	0–2
Leyton Pennant	v	Boreham Wood	5*5 3–2
Barking	v	Fisher	2–1
Erith & Belvedere	v	Tooting & Mitchem	1–6
Dulwich Hamlet	v	Bromley	1–2
Welling United	v	Southall	12–0
Met Police	v	Croydon	2–1
Collier Row	v	St Albans City	2–1

SECOND ROUND 8th–13th January 1996

Bromley	v	Barking	Bromley W–O
Tooting & Mitcham	v	Welling United	2–1
Met Police	v	Hampton	1–3
Leyton Pennant	v	Collier Row	3–3 2*1

SEMI-FINALS

Leyton Pennant	v	Hampton	2–1
Tooting & Mitcham	v	Bromley	0–1

FINAL Wednesday 1st May 7.30pm
BROMLEY v LEYTON PENNANT 3*2 at The New Den, Millwall FC.

Bromley FC – Winners 1995/96 London Challenge Cup.

LONDON SENIOR CUP
(FOUNDED 1887–88)

RECENT FINALS

1990–91	Haringey Borough	v	Walthamstow Pennant	1–0
1991–92	Hanwell Town	v	Croydon Athletic	4–3
1992–93	Hanwell Town	v	Brimsdown Rovers	4–3
1993–94	Ford United	v	Hanwell Town	2–1
1994–95	Wingate & Finchley	v	Tower Hamlets	4–3

MOST WINS Walthamstow Avenue 9 Ilford 7 Enfield 6

LONDON SENIOR CUP

25 CLUBS **HOLDERS: WINGATE & FINCHLEY**

FIRST ROUND 30th October–4th November 1995

Woolwich Town	v	Hillingdon Borough	1*2	Civil Service	v	Barkingside	2–0
Tufnell Park	v	East Ham United	5–0	Brimsdown Rovers	v	Kingsbury Town	2–3
Cray Wand @F	v	Ford United	2*2 1–2	Hanwell Town	v	Croydon Ath	4–1
Thames Poly	v	Cockfosters	3–2	Clapton	v	Woodford Town	3–1
Bedfont	v	St Margaretsbury	2*3				

SECOND ROUND 27th November–2nd December 1995

Willesden Hawkeye	v	Corinthian Casuals	3–0	Tufnell Park	v	Tottenham Omada	0–1
Hoddesdon Town	v	Thames Poly	3–2	Eton Manor	v	Hanwell Town	0–2
Kingsbury Town	v	Hillingdon Borough	1–0	Thamesmead Tn	v	Ford United	2–0
Wingate & Finch	v	Civil Service	2–0	St Margaretsbury	v	Clapton	2*1

THIRD ROUND 5th–10th February 1996

Thamesmead Tn	v	Kingsbury	1–3	Tottenham Omada	v	Wingate & Finch	2–1
Hoddesdon Town	v	Willesden Hawkeye	1–2	Hanwell Town	v	St Margaretsbury	1–3

SEMI-FINALS

Willesden Hawkeye	v	Kingsbury Town	1–1 1–3	St Margaretsbury	v	Tottenham Omada	2*4

FINAL Saturday 20th April 3.00pm

KINGSBURY TOWN v TOTTENHAM OMADA 1–2 at Champion Hill Stadium, Dulwich Hamlet FC.

Tottenham Omada show off the London Senior Cup to their supporters.

MANCHESTER F.A.

Secretary: Fred Brocklehurst,
Sports Complex, Branthingham Road, Chorlton, Manchester M21 1TG
(01619) 984839 (Home) (01618) 810299 (County Office) Fax: (01618) 816833

MANCHESTER PREMIER CUP
(FOUNDED 1979–80)

RECENT FINALS

1990–91	Mossley	v	Droylesden	3_2
1991–92	Ashton United	v	Flixton	2–1
1992–93	Droylsden	v	Curzon Ashton	2–0 (AET)
1993–94	Hyde United	v	Droylsden	4–1
1994–95	Hyde United	v	Trafford	2–1

MOST WINS Curzon Ashton 5 Ashton United 3 Droylsden 2 Hyde United 2 Mossley 2

1995–1996

13 CLUBS **HOLDERS: HYDE UNITED**

FIRST ROUND

Chadderton @SC	v	Salford City	2–3	Droylsdon	v	Flixton	2–4
Radcliffe Borough	v	Glossop North End	2–1	Maine Road	v	Ashton United	1–0
Curzon Ashton	v	Mossley	2–1				

3 Clubs with Byes Hyde United, Oldham Town, Trafford.

SECOND ROUND between 17th & 31st Janaury 1996

Trafford	v	Flixton	1*3	Curzon Ashton	v	Oldham Town	2–1
Salford City	v	Radcliffe Borough	0–4	Maine Road	v	Hyde United	1*2

(Trafford are re-instated as Flixton were found to have fielded an ineligible player in the above match).

SEMI-FINALS

Curzon Ashton	v	Trafford	6–2	Hyde United	v	Radcliffe Borough	2–0

FINAL Tuesday 7th May 1996
CURZON ASHTON v HYDE UNITED 3p4 2*2 at Burnden Park, Bolton Wanderers FC.

Hyde United enjoyed an excellent season: Here we see manager Mike Mckenzie and goalkeeper Arthur Williams after another victory. *Photo - Colin Stevens*

MANCHESTER FOOTBALL LEAGUE

President: A Booth
Secretary: F Fitzpatrick, 102 Victoria Road,
Stretford, Manchester M32 0AD (0161 865 2726)

MANCHESTER LEAGUE FINAL LEAGUE TABLES 1995/96

Premier Div	P	W	D	L	F	A	Pts
1. Little Hulton Utd	30	22	4	4	78	37	70
2. Springhead	30	18	7	5	61	36	61
3. Abbey Hey	30	19	3	8	62	38	60
4. Highfield United	30	17	5	8	59	39	56
5. B I C C	30	14	10	6	60	43	52
6. WQythenshawe T	30	16	4	10	50	33	52
7. Woodley Sports	30	12	8	10	49	41	44
8. M Shackelton	30	11	10	9	55	48	43
9. Wythenshawe Am	30	12	7	11	50	44	43
10. E Manchester	30	10	12	8	54	51	42
11. Alberton Town	30	12	5	13	54	53	41
12. Dukinfield Tn	30	9	6	15	39	58	33
13. Stockport Geo	30	5	5	20	45	74	20
14. Monton Amt	30	5	5	20	37	73	20
15. Prestwich Hey	30	4	7	19	37	75	19
16. Sacred Heart	30	3	4	23	34	81	13

Div One	P	W	D	L	F	A	Pts
1. Stand Athletic	26	18	5	3	83	25	59
2. Elton Fold	26	15	5	6	75	38	50
3. Manchester Roy	26	14	3	9	77	58	45
4. Breightnet Utd	26	12	9	5	59	42	45
5. Pennington	26	11	8	7	50	52	41
6. Whitworth Vall	26	11	7	8	68	66	40
7. Hollinwood	26	10	8	8	55	47	38
8. Old Altrinchams	26	9	7	10	52	46	34
9. Ashton Athletic	26	7	9	10	37	48	30
10. Whalley Range	26	8	5	13	58	83	29
11. Coldhurst Utd	26	7	6	13	53	79	27
12. Milton	26	6	7	13	51	66	25
13. New Mills	26	6	6	14	54	85	24
14. Gt Man Police	26	2	7	17	33	70	13

STOCKPORT LEAGUE

Premier Div	P	W	D	L	Pts
1. Norris Villa	16	15	0	1	30
2. Brinnington Celtic	16	14	0	2	28
3. Bridge Street	16	8	2	6	18
4. Offerton Georgians	16	7	2	7	16
5. Victoria Park	16	6	3	7	15
6. Barcelona	16	5	2	9	12
7. Adswood United	16	4	2	10	10
8. George N Dragon	16	3	3	10	9
9. Grapes	16	2	2	12	6

Division One:	**Champions;**	Houldsworth FC
Division Two:	**Champions;**	Stockport Allied
Division Three:	**Champions;**	Hillgate FC
Division Four:	**Champions;**	Carousel FC

MIDDLESEX F.A.

Secretary: Peter Clayton,
39 Roxborough Road, Harrow, Middlesex HA1 1NS
Tel: (01819) 093124 (H) – (01812) 008300 (B) –
(01814) 248524 (City Office) Fax: 0181 862062 (County Office)

MIDDLESEX CHARITY CUP
(FOUNDED 1901–02)

RECENT FINALS

1990–91	Hayes	v	Ruislip Manor	2–1
1991–92	Chelsea	v	Edgware Town	3–1
1992–93	Harrow Borough	v	Hanwell Town	3–1 (AET)
1993–94	Staines Town	v	Northwood	4–0
1994–95	Wembley	v	Hampton	2–0

MOST WINS Wealdstone 11 Hayes 10 Southall 10

1995–1996

MIDDLESEX SENIOR CHARITY CUP

18 CLUBS **HOLDERS: WEMBLEY**

FIRST ROUND by Thursday 2nd November

Tufnell Park	v	Waltham Abbey	0–1	Feltham	v	Rayners Lane	2–0

SECOND ROUND by Thursday 14th December

Ruislip Manor	v	Viking Sports	4–0	Brimsdown Rovers	v	Wealdstone	0–1
Kingsbury Town	v	Potters Bar Town	3–0	Willesden Hawkeye	v	Feltham	3–2
Bedfont	v	Hillingdon Borough	3*2	Harefield United	v	Waltham Abbey	3–1
Brook House	v	Ashford Town (Mx)	1–2	Southall	v	Cockfosters	1–2

THIRD ROUND by Thursday 25th January 1996

Uxbridge	v	Ashford Town	0–1	Staines Town	v	Edgware Town	0A0 1*0
Northwood	v	Bedfont	5–1	Hanwell Town	v	Wealdstone	2–0
Wembley	v	Brentford	0–1	Cockfosters	v	Willesden Hawkeye	0–1
Kingsbury Town	v	Ruislip Manor	1–2	Hampton	v	Harefield United	3–2

FOURTH ROUND by 29th February 1996

Northwood	v	Ruislip Manor	2*5	Staines Town	v	Willesden	1–0
Ashford Town	v	Brentford	1–3	Hampton	v	Hanwell Town	3–2

SEMI-FINALS

Ruislip Manor	v	Brentford	4–0	Staines Town	v	Hampton	2–3

FINAL Friday 10th May 1996 7.30pm
HAMPTON v RUISLIP MANOR 3–2 at White Lion Ground, High Street, Edgware Town FC. att: 260

MIDDLESEX SENIOR CUP
(FOUNDED 1888–89)

RECENT FINALS

1990–91	Enfield	v	Yeading	1–0
1991–92	Yeading	v	Wembley	2–1
1992–93	Harrow Borough	v	Wembley	1–0
1993–94	Staines Town	v	Edgware Town	2–1
1994–95	Yeading	v	Staines Town	2–0

MOST WINS Enfield 13 Southall 12 Wealdstone 11

MIDDLESEX SENIOR CUP

29 CLUBS **HOLDERS: YEADING**

PRELIMINARY ROUND

Potters Bar Town	v	Hillingdon Borough	1–2	Ruislip Manor	v	Harefield United	4–3
Southall	v	Viking Sports	3–0	Hanwell Town	v	Rayners Lane	4–3
Waltham Abbey	v	Cockfosters	0–3				

FIRST ROUND (11 Clubs Exempt to this Round)**

Brook House**	v	Ashford Town(Mx)**	0–3	Cockfosters @H	v	Hayes**	2*3
Bedfont**	v	Hampton**	0–2	Feltham**	v	Wealdstone**	2*1
Hendon**	v	Ruislip Manor	2–5	Hanwell Town	v	Southall	3–0
Hillingdon Borough	v	Wingate & Finchley**	2–0	Brimsdown Rovers**	v	Kingsbury Town**	2–4

8 Clubs Exempt Edgware Town, Enfield, Harrow Borough, Northwood, Staines Town, Uxbridge, Wembley, Yeading to the

SECOND ROUND 9th January 1996

Kingsbury Town	v	Hayes	0–4	Uxbridge	v	Yeading	2*1
Harrow Borough	v	Wembley 2*2 1A1	3–2	Northwood	v	Feltham	1–2
Hillingdon Borough	v	Ashford Town (Mx)	4–1	Staines Town	v	Ruislip Manor	1–0
Enfield	v	Hanwell Town	3–1	Hampton	v	Edgware Town	2–1

THIRD ROUND Tuesday 13th February 1996

Hayes	v	Feltham	6–2	Harrow Borough	v	Uxbridge	1–0
Hillingdon Borough	v	Hampton	1–6	Enfield	v	Staines Town	3–2

SEMI-FINALS w/e 11th March 1996

Hampton	v	Enfield	3*1	Hayes	v	Harrow Borough	2–1

FINAL Monday 8th April 1996

HAMPTON v HAYES 2*3 at Beaconsfield Road, Hayes, Yeading FC att; 813

Hayes are seen here celebrating the ICIS title and they also won the Middlesex Senior Cup.

Photo - Eric Marsh

PREMIER DIVISION CLUBS 1996-97

BROADWATER UNITED

Secretary: Godfrey Lowe, 53 Rochford Griffin Road, Tottenham N17 6HX (0181 801 7616).
Ground: Lordship Lane Recreation Ground, Lordship Lane, Tottenham, London N17 (0181 880 3944).
Colours: Black & white/black/black **Change colours:** All blue.

HANWORTH VILLA

Secretary: David Brown, 104 Park Road Kingston Surrey KT2 5JZ (0181 546 5979)
Ground: Rectory Meadows, Sunbury Road, Hanworth, Middlesex.
Colours: Blue & white/white/blue **Change colours:** White & sky/sky

HOUNSLOW TOWN '91

Secretary: Irene Ambrose, 171 Heath Rd, Hounslow, Middx TW3 2NR (0181 568 9635).
Ground: Ingwood Park, Ingwood Road, Hounslow, Middx.
Colours: White/orange/black **Change colours:** Red & black hoops/red/red.

NEW HANFORD

Secretary: Jerry Scanlon, 70 Bridge Avenue, Hanwell W7 3DJ (0181 575 0113).
Ground: Drayton Manor Playing Fields, Greenford Ave., Hanwell, London W7 (0181 578 5831).
Colours: Sky/navy/navy **Change Colours:** Green & white

NORTHFIELD C.A.V.

Secretary: Pauline Jones, 6 Siverst Close, Northolt, Middx UB5 4NJ (0181 422 8012).
Ground: The Annexe, Yeading FC *(see page 458).*
Colours: Yellow/black/yellow **Change Colours:** Blue/navy/navy.

NORTH GREENFORD UNITED

Secretary: Reg Johnson, 63 Berkeley Ave. Greenford, Middx.UB6 0NY (0181 864 2645)
Ground: Berkeley Fields, Berkeley Ave, Greenford Middx (0181 422 8923)
Colours: Royal & white/royal **Change colours:** Yellow/black/yellow

OSTERLEY

Secretary: C Clapham, 2 Minehead House, 25 Hanson St W1P 7LQ (0171 436 9208)
Ground: The White Lodge Club, Syon Lane, Osterley, Middx (0181 758 1191).
Colours: Royal & white/blue/blue **Change Colours:** Red & white/red/red

PITSHANGER

Secretary: Chris Green, 14 Silver Birch Close, Ickenham, Middx UB10 8AP (01895 231796).
Ground: Pitshanger Park, Scotch Common, Ealing, London W13 (0181 991 9826).
Colours: Tangerine/black/tangerine **Club Colours:** White/white/orange.

SHAMROCK

Secretary: Danny Gallagher, 32 Beaumont Avenue,Wembley Middx HA0 3BZ (0181 902 3591)
Ground: Shamrock Club House, Horn Lane, Acton, London W3 (0181 993 1270).
Colours: Green/white/green. **Change colours:** White/green/white.

SOUTHGATE

Secretary: Kevin Cullen, 39 Hill Rise, Potters Bar, Herts EN6 2RX (01707 656136).
Ground: Tottenhall Rd Spts Ground, Tottenhall Rd, Palmers Green, London N13 (0181 888 1542).
Colours: Amber/black/amber **Change Colours:** All blue.

SPELTHORNE SPORTS

Secretary: Ron Ford, 35 Walton Gardens, Feltham, Middx TW13 4QY (0181 890 8346).
Ground: Spelthorne Spts Ground, 296 Staines Rd West, Ashford Common, Middx (01932 783625).
Colours: Sky/navy/navy **Club Colours:** All green

WILLESDEN (CONSTANTINE)

Secretary: Dwight John, 29 Tangmere Gardens, Northolt UB5 6LS (0181 845 9887).
Ground: Alperton Spts Ground, Alperton Lane, Alperton, Middx.
Colours: Gold/yellow/yellow **Club Colours:** Red & white/white/white

NORFOLK F.A.

Secretary: Ray W Kiddell JP, ACII,
153 Middletons Lane, Hellesdon, Norwich NR6 5SF (0603 488222)

NORFOLK SENIOR CUP
(FOUNDED 1881–82)

RECENT FINALS

1990–91	Thetford Town	v	St Andrews	4–3
1991–92	Fakenham Town	v	Gorleston	2–2 (Rep 2–1)
1992–93	Wroxham	v	Watton United	3–0
1993–94	Fakenham Town	v	Kings Lynn	4–0
1994–95	Fakenham Town	v	Gorleston	2–1

MOST WINS Kings Lynn 19 Great Yarmouth Town 14 Gorleston 13

1995–1996

NORFOLK SENIOR CUP

31 CLUBS **HOLDERS: FAKENHAM TOWN**

FIRST ROUND Saturday 16th September 1995

Anglian Windows	v	Stalham Town	2–1	Mattishall	v	Coltishall	1–5
North Walsham Tn	v	Loddon United	0–1	Bradenham Wdrs	v	Hellesdon	0–2

2 Clubs with Byes and 16 Clubs Exempt to the

SECOND ROUND Saturday 21st October

Norwich United	v	Madra United	2–1	Downham Town	v	St Andrews	0–3
Wortwell	v	Horsford United	0–7	Hellesdon	v	Coltishall HV	1–7
Poringland Wdrs	v	Gorleston	1–7	Loddon United	v	Kings Lynn Res	0–0 3–3
Thetford Town	v	Swaffham Town	0–1	Thorpe Village	v	Blofield United	0–1
Newton Flotman	v	Mulbarton Utd	2–4	Wymondham Tn	v	Lakeford Rangers	2–1
Anglian Windows	v	Dereham Town	2–1				

5 Clubs Exempt to

THIRD ROUND Saturday 25th November

Wroxham	v	Blofield United	2–1	St Andrews	v	Wymondham Town	1–2
Horsford United	v	Coltishall HV	1–4	Mulbarton Utd	v	Anglian Windows	3–2
Loddon United	v	Swaffham Town	3–1	Diss Town	v	Gt Yarmouth Town	5–2
Norwich United	v	Watton United	2–0	Fakenham Town	v	Gorleston	3–1

FOURTH ROUND Saturday 6th January 1996

Coltishall HV	v	Diss Town	2*2 1–4	Wroxham	v	Loddon United	2–0
Mulbarton Utd	v	Fakenham Town	2–3	Wymondham Town	v	Norwich United	1–4

SEMI-FINALS

Diss Town	v	Norwich United	2–1	Fakenham Town		Wroxham	1–6

FINAL Monday 15th April Kick off 7.00pm
DISS TOWN v WROXHAM 4–0 at Carrow Road, Norwich City FC.

LOVEWELL BLAKE ANGLIAN COMBINATION

(Amalgamated East Anglian, Norfolk and Suffolk Leagues)

President: B A R Hansell

Chairman: A J Dickerson

Hon.Secretary: J C Harpley, 4 Harlington Avenue, Hellesdon, Norwich NR6 5LJ (01603 408803)

FINAL LEAGUE TABLES 1995/96

Premier Div	P	W	D	L	F	A	Pts
1. Horsford Utd	30	22	4	4	68	31	70
2. Madra Utd	30	22	2	6	76	28	68
3. Wroxham Res	30	19	6	5	70	32	63
4. Diss Tn Res	30	19	2	9	62	35	59
5. Dereham Tn	30	15	8	7	44	37	53
6. Ashlea	30	15	4	11	56	52	49
7. Lowestoft T R	30	14	3	13	52	47	45
8. Blofield Utd	30	12	4	14	70	55	40
9. Mulbarton Utd	30	10	7	13	57	66	37
10. St Andrews	30	9	8	13	47	54	35
11. Thorpe Vill	30	10	4	16	38	53	34
12. Lakeford Rang	30	8	5	17	48	74	29
13. Kirkley	30	8	4	18	33	78	28
14. Wymondham T	30	6	9	15	49	61	27
15. Beccles Tn	30	7	5	18	38	65	26
16. Newton Flotman	30	4	5	21	21	61	17

Div One	P	W	D	L	F	A	Pts
1. Loddon Utd	30	18	6	6	71	34	60
2. Stalham Tn	30	17	8	5	76	42	59
3. Fakenham Res	30	14	10	6	62	35	52
4. N Walsham Tn	30	14	8	8	67	41	50
5. Coltishall HV	30	13	8	9	61	43	47
6. Oulton Broad	30	14	5	11	62	46	47
7. Gorleston Res	30	13	6	11	54	45	45
8. Poringland W	30	13	6	11	33	47	45
9. Brandon Tn	30	12	8	10	49	50	44
10. Wortwell	30	10	7	13	43	57	37
11. Angl Windows	30	9	8	13	43	51	35
12. Hellesdon	30	9	5	16	34	80	32
13. Mattishall	30	8	7	15	39	50	31
14. Yarmouth T R	30	8	7	15	31	46	31
15. Watton U R	30	6	7	17	31	65	25
16. Bradenham W	30	6	6	18	28	52	24

SENIOR KNOCK-OUT CUP 1995-96

First Round;

North Walsham v Diss Town Res 2-1
Blofield United v Gorleston Res 6-1
Beccles Town v Yarmouth Res 4-1
Wymondham Town v Fakenham Res 1-3
Newton Flotman v Stalham Town 4-1
Horsford United v Thorpe Village 1-0
Brandon Town v Oulton Broad & LR 2-3
Dereham Town v Mattishall 1-0
Madra United v Bradenham Wanderers 5-0
Hellesdon v Coltishall HV 0-4
Kirkley v Poringland Wands 3-3, 1-0
Anglian Windows v Watton United Res 3-1
Loddon United v Mulbarton United 1-1, 1-2
St Andrews v Lowestoft Res 0-2
Lakeford Rangers v Wortwell 3-2
Ashlea v Wroxham Res 0-3

Kirkley withdrawn played ineligible player.

Second Round;

Dereham Town v Lowestoft Res 4-0
Wroxham Res v Horsford United 3-3, 6-1
Beccles Town v Newton Flotman 0-1
Poringland Wands v Fakenham Res 1-4
Oulton Broad v Mulbarrow United 2-4
Madra United v Coltishall HV 6-0
North Walsham v Blofield United 0-3
Lajeford Rangers v Anglian Windows 2-4

Quarter Finals;

Madra United v Blofield United 0-4
Dereham Town v Wroxham Res 0-1
Anglian Windows v Fakenham Res 2-3
Molbarton United v Newton Flotman 2-1

Semi-Finals;

Wroxham Res v Blofield United 4-1
Fakenham Res v Mulbarton United 5-1

Final: Wroxham Reserves v Fakenham Reserves 1-0

RECENT KNOCK OUT CUP CHAMPIONS

1985-86	Watton United	1986-87	St Andrews
1987-88	Wroxham	1988-89	Bradenham
1989-90	Bradenham	1990-91	Lakeford Rangers
1991-92	Overstrand	1992-93	Blofield United
1993-94	Dereham Town	1994-95	Wroxham Reserves

PREMIER DIVISION CLUBS 1995-96

ASHLEA
Secretary: S Gilder, 5 Back Lane Lowestoft Suffolk NR32 5NE, (01502 731052)
Ground: Pitch 1, Normanston Park, Lowestoft. **Colours:** Yellow/blue/yellow

BECCLES TOWN
Secretary: J Humby, 11 Station Rd,Beccles Suffolk, NR34 9Qh (01502 713776)
Ground: College Meadow, (01502 712016) **Colours:** Black & white/black

BLOFIELD UNITED
Secretary: P Stevens, 25 Medeswell Close, Brindall, Norwich NR13 5Qg (01603 717406)
Ground: Gt Yarmouth Rd, Blofield. (01603 712576) **Colours:** Red/black/black

DEREHAM TOWN
Secretary: M Henman, 17 Hillcrest Ave, Toftwood, Dereham, Norfolk NR19 1NF (01362 692242)
Ground: Aldiss Park, Norwich Rd, Dereham **Colours:** White & black/black

DISS TOWN
Secretary: Mr R Upson, Bamburgh Hse, Brewers Green Lane, Diss, Norfolk IP22 3QP (01379 642923)
Ground: Brewers Green Lane, Diss **Colours:** Tangerine/navy

HORSFORD UNITED
Secretary: Mr G Soanes, 5 Bulwer Road, Buxton, Norwich NR10 5HG (01603 278156)
Ground: Horsford Village Hall Rec Ground. **Colours:** Jade/black/white

KIRKLEY FC
Secretary: Mr G Reynolds, 79 May Road, Lowestoft, Suffolk, NR32 2DJ (01502 566867)
Ground: Kirkley Rec Ground, Walmer Rd, Lowestoft. **Colours:** Blue/white/blue

LAKEFORD RANGERS 94
Secretary: Mr R J Watling, 6 Cressener Close, Hellesdon, Norwich NR6 5RF (01603 405032)
Ground: Marlingsford Spts Grd, Easton Rd, Marlingsford. **Colours:** Red & black/black/black

LOWESTOFT TOWN
Secretary: Mr M Pearce, 46 Teesdale Rd, Carlton Colville, Lowestoft NR33 8TG (01502 519229)
Ground: Crown Meadow, Lowestoft (01502 573818) **Colours:** Blue/white/blue.

MADRA UNITED
Secretary: Mr P Bugdale, 101 Colindeep Lane, Sprowston, Norwich NR7 8EQ (01603 483283)
Ground: Madra Spts Field, Knapton, North Walsham (01263 721630) **Colours:** Red/white

MULBARTON UNITED
Secretary: Mr J Eastell, ! Cuckoofield Lane, Mulbarton, Norwich NR14 8AZ (01508 570832)
Ground: Mulberry Park **Colours:** Black & blue/black

NEWTON FLOTMAN
Secretary: Mr N Harrod, 158 Norwich Rd, New Costessey, Norwich NR5 0EH (01603 746507)
Ground: Newton Flotman Village Centre, Grove Way **Colours:** Yellow & Black/black

ST ANDREWS
Secretary: Mr V Hatchett, 53 Cheyney Ave, Salhouse, Norwich NR13 6SA (01603 721286)
Ground: Thorpe Rec Grd, Laundry Lane, Thorpe **Colours:** Blue/black/black

THORPE VILLAGE
Secretary: Mr A Meek, 8 Birchwood, Thorpe, Norwich NR7 0RL (01603 435985)
Ground: Thorpe Rec Grd, Laundry Lane, Thorpe **Colours:** Claret & sky/sky

WROXHAM
Secretary: Mr C Green, 24 Keys Drive, Wroxham, Norwich NR12 8SS (01603 783936)
Ground: Trafford Pk, Skinners Lane, Wroxham **Colours:** Royal & white

WYMONDHAM TOWN
Secretary: Mr M Utting, 52 Mill Lane, Attleborough, Norfolk NR17 2NW (01953 453146)
Ground: Kings Head Meadow, Wymondham **Colours:** Red & black/black

NORTHAMPTONSHIRE F.A.

Secretary: Brian Walden, 2 Duncan Close, Red House Road, Moulton Park
Northampton NN3 6WL Tel: (01604) 670741 (County Office) Fax: (01604) 670742

NORTHAMPTONSHIRE SENIOR CUP
(FOUNDED 1883–84)

RECENT FINALS

1990–91	Raunds Town	v	Rushden Town	1–0
1991–92	Kettering Town	v	Corby Town	1–0
1992–93	Kettering Town	v	Rushden & Diamonds	2–1
1993–94	Rushden & Diamonds	v	Northampton Spencer	5–0
1994–95	Kettering Town	v	Rushden & Diamonds	2–2(Rep 2–2)(3–1 Pens)

MOST WINS Kettering Town 27 Northampton Town 11 Peterborough United 11

1995–1996

NORTHAMPTONSHIRE 'HILLIER' SENIOR CUP

12 CLUBS **HOLDERS: KETTERING TOWN**

FIRST ROUND by 28th October 1995

Desborough Tn	v	Long Buckby	1–2	Corby S&L	v	N'pton Spencer	3–3 3–1
Wellingborough Tn	v	Rothwell Town	0–3	Brackley Town	v	Corby Town	1–0

2 Clubs with Byes Raunds Town, Congenhoe United
2 Clubs Exempt Kettering Town, Rushden & Diamonds

SECOND ROUND – QUARTER FINALS

Cogenhoe United	v	Rothwell Town	0–1	Long Buckby @RD	v	Rushden & Diam	0–4
Corby S&L	v	Kettering Town	1–2	Brackley Town	v	Raunds Town	0–4

SEMI-FINALS

Rushden & Diam	v	Raunds Town	1–0	Rothwell Town	v	Kettering Town	5–0

FINAL Tuesday 26th March
ROTHWELL TOWN v RUSHDEN & DIAMONDS 1–0 at Home Close, Cecil Street att; 511

DR MARTENS EAST MIDLANDS FOOTBALL ALLIANCE

Chairman: John Shooter,
Secretary: Walter Morris, 30 Exeter Street, Kettering

County Div	P	W	D	L	F	A	Pts
1. Cy Danesholme	22	18	2	2	87	22	56
2. Kettering Gen	22	15	3	4	45	19	48
3. Kettering Nom	22	12	3	7	51	35	39
4. Weldon	22	12	3	7	56	46	39
5. Gretton	22	11	2	9	60	48	35
6. Corby Strip M	22	9	6	7	35	36	33
7. Cy St Brendans	22	8	6	8	53	40	30
8. Corby Pegasus	22	9	2	11	51	50	29
9. Cy Darleydale	22	8	5	9	39	39	29
10. Wilbarston	22	6	2	14	34	52	20
11. Wellingboro Gr	22	3	3	16	35	74	12
12. Corby Fisher	22	2	1	19	27	111	7

Intermediate	P	W	D	L	F	A	Pts
1. Geddington	24	19	2	3	82	29	59
2. Corby Danes R	24	18	0	6	77	38	54
3. Kettering Briars	24	15	3	6	70	47	48
4. Corby Peg Res	24	11	1	12	54	57	34
5. Corby Loco	24	9	5	10	52	55	32
6. Corby Strip R	24	9	4	11	38	38	31
7. Burton Utd	24	9	4	11	38	54	31
8. Stanwick Rov	24	7	8	9	44	35	29
9. Barton Seagr	24	7	8	9	44	49	29
10. Medbourne	24	9	2	13	41	46	29
11. Weldon Res	24	7	5	12	42	61	26
12. Gretton Res	24	7	3	14	49	70	24
13. Kett Orchard P	24	6	1	17	33	85	19

NORTH RIDING F.A.

Secretary: P Kirby,
284 Linthorpe Road, Middlesbrough TS1 3QU (10642 224585)

NORTH RIDING SENIOR CUP (FOUNDED 1881–82)

RECENT FINALS

1990–91	Guisborough Town	v	South Bank	1–0
1991–92	Scarborough	v	Guisborough Town	3–2 (AET)
1992–93	Guisborough Town	v	Rowntrees	2–0
1993–94	Guisborough Town	v	Pickering Town	2–0
1994–95	Marske United	v	Pickering Town	5–2

MOST WINS Middlesbrough 45 Scarborough 17 South Bank 8 Stockton 8

1995–1996

NORTH RIDING SENIOR CUP

19 CLUBS **HOLDERS: MARSKE UNITED**

FIRST PRELIMINARY ROUND

Tees Components	v	Loftus West Rd	3p4 3*3	Mannion Park	v	South Bank '95	2–1
Fishburn Park	v	Stokesley	3–0				

SECOND PRELIMINARY ROUND Saturday 25th November

Northallerton Anb'y	v	Mannion Park	3–2	Loftus West Rd	v	Dormans Athletic	2–1
Fishburn Park	v	New Marske SC	7–0	Nunthorpe Athletic	v	Grangetown BC	2–3

THIRD PRELIMINARY ROUND Saturday 27th January 1996

Loftus West Rd	v	Grangetown BC	1–2	Fishburn Park	v	N'allerton Ainderby	4–0

FIRST QUALIFYING ROUND by Saturday 24th February

Fishburn Park	v	Guisborough Tn	7p6 1*1	Grangetown	v	Marske United	3–1
Northallerton '94	v	Pickering Town	6–2	Stockton	v	Whitby Town	2–4

SECOND QUALIFYING ROUND

Northallerton '94	v	Guisborough Tn	2–6	Whitby Town	v	Grangetown BC	4–0

THIRD QUALIFYING ROUND

Whitby Tn @GT	v	Guisborough Tn	0–2

SEMI-FINALS PROPER

Guisborough Tn	v	Scarborough	York City	v	Middlesborough

The completion of the competition is scheduled for pre season 1996–97.

TEESSIDE STRONGARM FOOTBALL LEAGUE

Founded: 1891

President: K P Moore **Chairman:** L Crossman

Secretary: R D Marsay, 12 Aislaby Court, Wilton Lane, Guisborough, Cleveland TS14 6TG (01287 637087)

FINAL LEAGUE TABLE 1995/96

		P	W	D	L	F	A	Pts
1.	Acklam SW	30	23	6	1	92	31	75
2.	Fishburn Park	30	18	8	4	69	38	62
3.	Grangetown BC	30	16	7	7	62	51	55
4.	Nunthorpe Ath	30	16	8	6	79	43	*53
5.	Stockton Supp	30	14	6	10	60	57	48
6.	Tees Comp	30	14	4	12	84	71	46
7.	Dormans Ath	30	14	3	13	67	45	45
8.	Thornaby YC	30	12	8	10	66	49	44
9.	Mannion Park	30	11	5	13	67	62	41
10.	Stokesley SC	30	12	5	13	59	62	41
11.	Beads FC	30	11	5	14	54	61	*35
12.	Guisb Town Res	30	7	6	17	41	77	27
13.	Loftus WR	30	10	3	17	47	85	#27
14.	BSC Redcar	30	7	2	21	40	74	23
15.	New Marske SC	30	6	4	20	41	90	22
16.	Richmond Town	30	4	8	18	45	78	20

** 3 points deducted; 6 points deducted*

Recent League Champions:

1987-88	New Marske Sports Club	1988-89	Hemlington Sports Club
1989-90	Nunthorpe Athletic	1991-91	ICI Wilton FC
1991-92	Billingham Cassel Mall	1992-93	Rowntrees
1993-94	Rowntrees	1994-95	Tees Components

MacMillan Bowl Final:

1995-96 **Acklam SW v Stockton Supporters** **2-0**

1987-88	Teesside Polytechnic	1988-89	I C I Wilton
1989-90	Nunthorpe Athletic	1990-91	Tees Components FC
1991-92	Thornaby Youth Club	1992-93	Rowntrees
1993-94	Thornaby Youth Club	1994-95	BSC Redcar

R. T. Raine Trophy Final:

1995-96 **BSC Redcar v Stokelsey** **1-0**

1991-92	Tees Components	1992-93	Stockton Supporters
1993-94	Fishburn Park	1994-95	Stokesley SC

North Riding County Cup Final:

1995-96 **Acklam Steelworks v Fishburn Park** **2-3**

J V Madden Cup

1995-96 **BSC Redcar v Tees Components** **1-4**

1993-94	Rowntrees	1994-95	Rowntrees

Strongarm Player of the Year:

1995-96 **D Gallagher** **Mannion Park**

CLUB DIRECTORY

ACKLAM STEELWORKS

Secretary: Peter Conley, 53 Roseberry Road, Longlands, Middlesbrough, Cleveland TS4 2LJ (01642 224266)
Ground: Acklam Steelworks Club, Park Road South, Middlesbrough (01642 818717)
Directions: Marton Road A172, follow route to Middlesbrough centre, follow signs to County Sports Stadium, entrance opposite Sports Stadium.
Sponsor: Upsall Vending
Colours: Red/blue/red **Change Colours:** Blue & black/black/blue

B.E.A.D.S.

Secretary: Dave Kane, 27 Edgeworth Court, Hemlington, Middlesbrough, Cleveland TS8 9EP (01642 596559)
Ground: Beechwood & Easterside SC, Marton Road, Middlesbrough. (01642 311304)
Directions: Follow A172 into Middlesbrough centre down Marton Road, ground behind Social Club.
Sponsor: Classic Trophies UK
Colours: Red & black/black/black **Change Colours:** Yellow/blue/blue

BSC REDCAR

Secretary: David Collins, 23 Welland Road, Redcar, Cleveland TS10 1NR (01642 491547)
Ground: BSC Sports & Social Club, Dormanstown, Redcar (01642 486691)
Directions: Approaching Redcar from Middlesbrough, enter Dormanstown at BSC Steel House Works rounabout, turn 1st right then 1st left, ground behind club.
Sponsor: Area Electrical Projects
Colours: Sky/black/black **Change Colours:** White/black/black

DORMANS ATHLETIC

Secretary: Don Hall, 52 Westbourne Road, Linthorpe, Middlesbrough, Cleveland TS5 5BJ (01642 817771)
Ground: Dormans Athletic Club, Oxford Road, Middlesbrough. (01642 817099)
Directions: Follow the A1032 down Acklam Road towards Middlesbrough Centre, turn right onto Oxford Road, ground on right before the garage.
Sponsor: MSV Technics
Colours: Blue & black/black/black **Change Colours:** All red

FISHBURN PARK

Secretary: Ian Landers, 9 Pinewood Close, Whitby, N Yorks YO21 1LR (01947 600066)
Ground: Turnbull Ground, Upgang Lane, Whitby, (01947 603193)
Directions: Follow coast road into Whitby, ground on left (Home of Whitby Town FC)
Sponsor: Phil Burton
Colours: Gren/white/green **Change Colours:** White/blue/blue

GRANGETOWN BOYS CLUB

Secretary: Brian Honeywell, 11 Ambleside Road, Normanby, Middlesbrough, Cleveland TS6 0DY (01642 458208)
Ground: Grangetown YCC, Trunk Road, Grangtown, Midlesbrough (01642 455435)
Directions: Follow the trunk road into Redcar from M'bro, ground on right after roundabout leading over bridge.
Sponsor: Grangetown Youth & Community Centre
Colours: Blavk & Amber/black/black **Change Colours:** All red

GUISBOROUGH TOWN RESERVES

Secretary: Keith Smeltzer, 55 Thames Avenue, Guisborough, Cleveland TS154 8AR (01287 638993)
Ground: King George V Playing Fields, Howlbeck Road, Guisborough (01287 636925)
Directions: Follow A171 into Guisborough, turn left at 2nd traffic lights opposite Moorcock Hotel, turne 3rd left follow signs for swimming baths.
Sponsor: Bells Stores
Colours: Red & white/black/red **Change Colours:** Yellow/black/yellow

LOFTUS WEST ROAD SC

Secretary: Simon Whitwell, 10 Harebell Close, Skelton, Saltburn, Cleveland TS12 2FE (01287 652135)
Ground: Rosecroft School, Rosedale Lane, Loftus.
Directions: A173/174 into Loftus, at traffic lights turn right to Liverton Mines B1366. then 1st left up Rosedale Lane to ground.
Sponsor: Camerons Brewery/ Special Sections British Steel.
Colours: All Blue **Change Colours:** Green & white/white/green

MANNION PARK

Secretary: Mike Andrew, 12 Fieldview Close, Port Clarence, Middlesbrough, Cleveland, TS2 1TN (01642 564363)
Ground: Mannion Park Recreation Club, Broadway, Grangetown, Middlesbrough (01642 453701)
Directions: Follow trunk road from middlesbrough, past Grangetown YCC over roundabout to ICI works roundabout, turn back to Middlesbrough on trunk road, take 1st turn left to ground.
Sponsor: B Turner & Son
Colours: Blue/navy/navy **Change Colours:** White/sky/sky

NEW MARSKE SPORTS CLUB

Secretary: Peter Whitaker, 28 High Street, Marske, Redcar, Cleveland TS11 7BE (01642 489441)
Ground: New Marske Sports Club, New Marske, Redcar (01642 479808)
Directions: From M'bro A174 to rounabout junc with Longbeck Lane turn right, ground on left.
Sponsor: Car Care
Colours: Yellow/blue/white **Change Colours:** Blue & white/blue/blue

NUNTHORPE ATHLETIC

Secretary: Kevin Levitt, 131 Burlam Road, Middlesbrough, Cleveland, TS5 5AX (01642 824332)
Ground: Recreation Ground, Guisborough Road, Nunthorpe (01642 313251)
Directions: Leaving Middlesbrough on A172, turn left into Nunthorpe ground 300 yards on right.
Sponsor: Val Reeve & Chis Elvin at Paws
Colours: Blue/white/blue **Change Colours:** Red/white/red

RICHMOND TOWN

Secretary: Geoff Hunter, 49 Willance Grove, Richmond, N Yorks DL10 4HA (01748 822657)
Ground: Earls Orchard Playing Fields,Sleegill, Richmond
Directions: Entering Richmond on A6108, over 2 roundabouts turn right at third, 2nd left follow downhill and cross Green Bridge on road to Hudswell village, ground on left immediately after bridge.
Sponsor: Poperty Management Services
Colours: Blue & black/black/black **Change Colours:** Yellow/blue/blue

STOCKTON SUPPORTERS

Secretary: Susan Gardner, 25 Brotton Road, Thornaby, Stockton, Cleveland TS17 8EP (01642 646032)
Ground: Teesdale Park, Acklam Road, Thornaby (01642 606803)
Directions: Leaving A19 at Thornaby interchange, follow road through traffic lights towards Stockton Centre, turn right when in dip at sign for Teesdale Park
Sponsor: Bob Scott & Son
Colours: Red & black/black/red **Change Colours:** All sky

STOKESLEY SC

Secretary: Peter Grainge, 77 Darnton Drive, Easterside, Middlesbrough, Cleveland TS4 3RF (01642 316691)
Ground: Stokesley Sports Club, Broughton Road, Stokesley (01642 710051)
Directions: Follow signs for Stokesley. Take B1257 to Great Broughton at roundabout junc A172/A173, ground on left next to cricket field.
Sponsor: The Stokesley Sports Shop
Colours: Red/black/red **Change Colours:** White/blue/blue

TEES COMPONENTS

Secretary: Bryan Kichen, 151 Guisborough Road, Nunthorpe, Middlesbrough, Cleveland TS7 0JQ (01642 311358)
Ground: Recreation Ground, Machine Lane, North Skelton.
Directions: Follow A173 into Skelton, then into North Skelton. Ground off North Skelton High Street, follow the lane between Esso garage and church
Sponsor: Tees Components Ltd
Colours: Yellow/navy/navy **Change Colours:** L & D blue/d blue/l blue

THORNABY YOUTH CLUB

Secretary: Geoffrey Kirk, 9 Tipton Close, Thornaby, Stockton, Cleveland TS17 9QF (01642 676516)
Ground: Dene School, Baysdale Road, Thornaby.
Directions: Leave A19 at Thornaby interchange. turn left at the Roundel Pub onto Mitchell Ave, proceed towards Thornaby Town centre, turn right at Baysdale Road, follow road round to entrance.
Sponsor: Thornaby Youth Club
Colours: Claret/claret/sky **Change Colours:** Blue/black/black

NORTHUMBERLAND F.A.

Secretary: Roland Maughan, Seymour House,
10 Brenkley Way, Blezard Business Park,
Seaton Burn, Newcastle NE13 6DT (0191 236 8020)

NORTHUMBERLAND SENIOR CUP
(FOUNDED 1883–84)

RECENT FINALS

1990–91	North Shields	v	Whitley Bay	1–0
1991–92	Blyth Spartans	v	North Shields	2–1
1992–93	Newcastle Blue Star	v	Newcastle Utd Reserves	2–1
1993–94	Blyth Spartans	v	Newcastle Blue Star	1–0
1994–95	Blythe Spartans	v	Newcastle Utd Reserves	6–2

MOST WINS Blyth Spartans 21 Newcastle United 18 North Shields 12

1995–1996

NORTHUMBERLAND SENIOR CUP

12 CLUBS **HOLDERS: NEWCASTLE UNITED RESERVES**

FIRST ROUND week 6th November

Whitley Bay	v	Morpeth Town	2–4	RTM Newcastle	v	Alnwick Town	1–0
Benfield Park	v	Ashington	3–1	West Allotment C	v	Seaton Delaval Amt	3–2

4 Clubs with Byes Newcastle United Reserves, Blyth Spartans, Bedlington Terriers, Prudhoe Town

SECOND ROUND

Bedlington Terriers	v	RTM Newcastle	1–2	Prudhoe Town	v	West Allotment C	3–0
Blyth Spartans	v	Morpeth Town	5–0	Benfield Park	v	Newcastle Utd Res	0–3

SEMI-FINALS by 23rd March 1996

Newcastle Utd Res	v	Prudhoe Town	3–1	Blyth Spartans	v	RTM Newcastle	3–2

FINAL Wednesday 8th May 7.30pm
BLYTH SPARTANS v NEWCASTLE UNITED 0–3 at Hillheads Park, Whitley Bay FC.

NORTHUMBERLAND SENIOR BENEVOLENT BOWL
(FOUNDED 1975–76)

RECENT FINALS

1990–91	Westerhope Hillheads	v	Walker	2–0
1991–92	Newcastle Benfield Pk	v	Blyth Kitty Brewster	1–0
1992–93	West Allot Celtic	v	Walker	4–3
1993–94	Spittal Rovers	v	Longbenton	1–1 (Rep 2–1)
1994–95	Westerhope	v	North Shields St Columbas	2–0

MOST WINS Morpeth Town 2 Stobswood Welfare 2

NORTHUMBERLAND BENEVOLENT BOWL Sponsored by 'Brother'

16 CLUBS **HOLDERS: WESTERHOPE HILLHEADS**

FIRST ROUND Saturday 21st October

Haltwhistle C-P	v	NS St Columbas	2–1	Hexham Swinton	v	Westerhope	0–2
Orwin Rosehill	v	Walker Central	2–6	Amble Town	v	Longbenton	4–0
Ponteland Utd	v	Newbiggin Central W	1–0	Ashington Hirst P	v	Spittal Rovers	4–2
Percy Main Amt	v	Heaton Stannington	0–4	Blyth Seahorse	v	North Shields Ath	1–4

SECOND ROUND Saturday 10th February 1996

North Shields Ath	v	Heaton Stannington	9–0	Amble Town	v	Ashington Hirst Prog	5*4
Haltwhistle C-P	v	Walker Central	3–1	Ponteland Utd	v	Westerhope	3–1

SEMI-FINALS Saturday 2nd March

Amble Town	v	Ponteland United	0–3	Haltwhistle C-P	v	North Shields Ath	3–0

FINAL Wednesday 1st May Kick off 7.00pm
HALTWHISTLE v PONTELAND UNITED 1–2 at Wentworth Park, Hexham, Swinton FC.

HEXHAM & NORTH TYNE FOOTBALL LEAGUE

Chairman: David Tiffin

Secretary: Colin Smith, 32 Sidgate, Newbrough, Northumberland (01434 674338)

Alston Town won the first play off for the Championship of the League for twenty years 4-2, when they beat Corbridge United, who had led the table for the majority of the season. Alston went on to complete the double when Nev McHahon's hat-trick saw them beat Haydon Bridge 3-2 in the final of the Matthew Charlton League Cup.

It was a season of change for Corbridge United who had finished in bottom spot the previous season, they fielded a team of youngsters mixed with experience. The bend nearly worked as Corbridge came near to clinching their first title since 1990.

Haydon Bridge reached all three Cup Finals and were able to call on the services of former Sunderland & England 'B' defender Shaun Elliott who took his place in the side along side his brothers Paul & Scott. Elliott himself scored the winning goal in the Just Sport Clayton Cup Final against Hexhamshire. Haydon Bridge also won the Azco League Knock-out Cup Final, also against Hexhamshire.

Haltwhistle Crown Paints A quit the league because of high running costs. Newcomers Newcastle Deaf who struggled for most of the season showed some good spirit dispite poor results, their highlight was in the last game of the season when they held Alston to a 2-2 draw and denied the Cumbrians the Championship outright.

Whitfield made history when they played Haydon Bridge in a League Cup game, they turned out one of the oldest teams ever to play a first class game in the area. Dennis Spark (58), Reg Dover (56), Stan Jackson (52) and Alan white turned out because of a shortage of players. It was no surprise when the visitors won 7-0, apart from Spark all still play regular Sunday football a great example to the youngsters of the area.

With the membership down to seven teams it is hoped that new teams join the league for the coming season which in 1995-96 was more evenly contested for some years.

FINAL LEAGUE TABLES 1995/96

	P	W	D	L	F	A	Pts
1. Corbridge Utd	12	9	0	3	44	19	27
2. Alston United	12	8	3	1	43	20	27
3. Haydon Bridge	12	6	2	4	33	20	20
4. Haltwhistle RS	12	6	2	4	22	20	20
5. Hexhamshire	12	5	1	6	31	23	16
6. Newcastle D	12	1	2	9	20	52	5
7. Whitfield	12	1	2	9	22	62	5

Results	1	2	3	4	5	6	7
1. Alston Tn	*	4-3	1-2	4-0	4-2	5-2	4-1
2. Corbridge U	2-6	*	2-0	2-0	2-1	6-2	7-1
3. Haltwhistle	1-1	1-0	*	1-0	0-4	4-2	5-2
4. Haydon Brd	1-1	1-4	1-1	*	2-0	8-1	5-0
5. Hexhamshire	0-1	1-5	3-1	3-4	*	8-0	3-3
6. Newcastle D	2-2	1-3	3-2	1-3	0-4	*	5-5
7. Whitfield	4-10	1-8	1-4	1-8	1-2	2-1	*

League Championship Play Off; Alston Town v Corbridge Unitd 4-2

JUST SPORT CLAYTON CUP 1995-96

First Round;

Alston Town v Haltwhistle R S 6-2
Whitfield v Haydon Bridge 0-6
Hexhamshire v Newcastle Deaf 8-0

Semi-Finals;

Hexhamshire v Corbridge Utd 2-1
Haydon Bridge v Alston Town 2-1 (aet)

Final; Haydon Bridge v Hexhamshire 1-0

MATTHEW CHARLTON LEAGUE CUP 1995-96

Semi-Finals;

Alston Town v Whitfield 4-3
Haydon Bridge v Corbridge Utd 4-0

Final: Alston Town v Haydon Bridge 3-2

AZKO LEAGUE KNOCKOUT CUP 1995-96

Semi-Finals;

Hexhamshire v Whitfield 5-1
Haydon Bridge v Newcastle Deaf 8-0

Final; Hexhamshire v Haydon Bridge 0-3

NOTTINGHAMSHIRE F.A.

Secretary: W T Annable,
7 Clarendon Street, Nottingham NG1 5HS
Tel: (01602) 418954 (County Office) Fax: (01705) 724923

NOTTINGHAMSHIRE SENIOR CUP
(FOUNDED 1883–84)

RECENT FINALS

1990–91	Hucknall Town	v	Clipstone Welfare	3–0
1991–92	Eastwood Town	v	Nottinghamshire Police	2–0
1992–93	Arnold Town	v	Rainworth Miners Welfare	3–1
1993–94	Clipstone Welfare	v	Boots Athletic	3–2
1994–95	Oakham United	v	Clipstone Welfare	3–0

MOST WINS Nottingham Forest 17 Sutton Town 17 Notts County 11

1995–1996

NOTTINGHAMSHIRE SENIOR CUP

32 CLUBS **HOLDERS: OAKHAM UNITED**

FIRST ROUND Saturday 7th October 1995

Dunkirk	v	Wollaton	0–2
BRSA Retford	v	Radford	2–4
Pelican	v	Southwell City	3p4 2*2
Hucknall Town	v	Eastwood Town	3–1
Hucknall RRW	v	Thoresby CW	1–0
Sneinton	v	Nuthall	4–2
City&Sherwood H	v	Rainworth MW	1–3
Bldworth W	v	Cotgrave CW	5–3
Boots Athletic	v	Greenwood Meadows	6–1
Kimberley Town	v	Welbeck Colliery	1–3
Ruddington Utd	v	Clipstone Welfare	0–2
Oakham United	v	Ashfield United	1–0
Priory Eastwood	v	Gedling Town	GT W-O
GPT FC	v	Notts Police	1–4
W'gton Simpson	v	Basford United	3-2
Arnold Town	v	John Player FC	4–2

SECOND ROUND Saturday 2nd December

Radford	v	Arnold Town	2–3
Boots Athletic	v	Blidworth Welfare	4–1
Hucknall Town	v	Welbeck Colliery	5–0
Notts Police	v	Rainworth MW	1–2
Clipstone Welfare	v	Worthington Simps	1–0
Gedling Town	v	Sneinton	2–3
Oakham United	v	Hucknall RR Welfare	3–0
Southwell City	v	Wollaton	5–0

THIRD ROUND Saturday 13th January 1996

Sneinton	v	Boots Athletic	1–2
Arnold town	v	Southwell City	3–0
Oakham United	v	Hucknall Town	0–1
Rainworth MW	v	Clipstone MW	1–2

SEMI-FINALS Saturday 9th March 1996

Boots Athletic	v	Clipstone Welfare	1–0
Arnold Town	v	Hucknall Town	2–1

FINAL Tuesday 30th April 1996
ARNOLD TOWN v BOOTS ATHLETIC 2–0 at Coronation Park, Eastwood Town FC.

NOTTS FOOTBALL ALLIANCE

ESTABLISHED: 1894

President: R J Leafe

Chairman: A Wright. **Vice Chairman:** Bryn Richards

Secretary: Godfrey Stafford,
7 The Rushes, Gotham, Nottingham NG11 0HY (0115 9830576)

NOTTS ALLIANCE SENIOR DIVISION 1996-97

AWSWORTH VILLA

Secretary: Keith Slaney, 24 Attewell Road, Awsworth, Nottm NG16 2SY (0602 302514).
Ground: Attewell Road, Awsworth. **Colours:** Red & white & black/black

BOOTS ATHLETIC

Secretary: Ian Whitehead, 21 Rosthwaite Close, West Bridgford, Nottingham NG2 6RA (01159 812830).
Ground: Lady Bay, West Bridgford, Nottingham (01159 822392). **Colours:** White/black.
Hons: Notts Alliance Div 1 91-92 (Lg Cup 91-92), Notts Snr Cup R-up 93-94, Notts Inter R-up 91-92.

COTGRAVE COLLIERY WELFARE

Secretary: Kevin Whitehead, 51 Cross Hill, Cotgrave, Nottinham. (0115 9894043)
Ground: Cotgrave Miners Welfare. **Colours:** Yellow/black.

GREENWOOD MEADOWS

Secretary: Brian Hall, 35 Sullivan Close, Marmion Estate, Nottingham NG3 2HX (0115 958 2459)
Ground: Lenton Lane, Clifton Bridge, Nottm (01159 630134). **Colours:** Green & White/green/green

HUCKNALL ROLLS ROYCE WELFARE

Secretary: Adrian Ward, 7 Redwood Court, Hucknall, Nottm (01159 538491).
Ground: Sports and Social Club, Entrance Watnall Road (01159 635724).
Colours: All Blue. **Hons:** Notts I'mediate Cup 92-93

JOHN PLAYER

Secretary: Ron Walton, 27 St Margarets Ave., Aspley Lane, Nottm NG8 5GD (01159 292027).
Ground: Aspley Lane, Nottm (01159 292027)
Directions: Corner of Nottingham ring road B690 turn towards City Centre.
Colours: Yellow & navy/navy
Hons: Notts Alliance 21-22 22-23 23-24 24-25 25-26 26-27 67-68 68-69 69-70 85-86 89-90 (Div 1 93-94).

KEYWORTH UNITED

Secretary: M Simpson, 25 Waddington Drive, Wilford Hill, West Bridgford, Nottm NG2 7GT (0602 232921).
Ground: Platt Lane, Keyworth (0607 375998). **Colours:** Green/black

NOTTINGHAMSHIRE POLICE

Secretary: John Beeston, 17 Alandene Ave, Watnall, Nottingham NG16 1HH (0115 938 2110)
Ground: Force Training School, Epperstone Manor, Notts.
Directions: On A60 Mansfield Road, on right from City Centre (2 miles).
Colours: White/navy.
Hons: Notts Snr R-up 91-92, Notts All. Div 1 & Lge Snr Cup R-up 85-86, PAAN Nat. K-O Comp 63-64.

OLLERTON TOWN

Secretary: Jack Graham 73 Petersmith Drive, New Ollerton, Mansfield, Notts NG22 9SD (01623 863127)
Ground: Walesby Lane, New Ollerton, Notts
Colours: Red & black/black

PELICAN

Secretary: Dave Eastwood, 42 Chetwin Road, Bilborough, Nottm NG8 4HN (01159 138345).
Ground: John Pearson Spts Ground, Lenton Lane, Nottm (01159 868255)
Colours: All Blue. **Hons:** Notts Alliance Lg Cup 90-91 (R-up 91-92 93-94).

RAINWORTH MINERS WELFARE

Secretary: Alan Wright, 10 Faraday Road, Mansfield NG18 4ES (01632 24379).
Ground: Kirklington Road, Rainworth.
Directions: On A617 Mansfield - Newark Road. **Colours:** All White
Hons: Notts Alliance 77-78 78-79 79-80 80-81 81-82 82-83 (R-up 93-94, Lg Cup 81-82), Notts Snr Cup 80-81 81-82 (R-up 82-83 92-93), FA Vase R-up 82-82, Thorn EMI F'lit Cup R-up 82-83 83-84 84-85.

RUDDINGTON UNITED

Secretary: John Fisk, 3 Savages Road, Ruddington, Nottm NG11 6EW (01159 842552).
Ground & Directions: The Elms Park Ground, Loughborough Road, Ruddington (01159 844976. On A60 Nottm to Loughborough, 5 miles out of Nottingham.
Colours: Red & blue stripes/blue. **Honours:** Notts Comb. Lg 79-80 (Lg Cup 70-71 76-77 80-81).

SOUTHWELL CITY

Secretary: P K Johnson, 63 The Ropewalk, Southwell, Notts NG25 0AL (0636 814386).
Ground: War Memorial Ground, Southwell (0636 4386) **Colours:** Black & white stripes/black

THORESBY COLLIERY WELFARE

Secretary: Brian Wathall, 29 First Ave., Edwinstowe, Nr Mansfield NG21 9NZ (01636 812594).
Ground: Thoresby Colliery, Fourth Avenue, Edwinstowe, Nr Mansfield. **Colours:** Blue/white.

WELBECK COLLIERY

Secretary: Mr Ron Turner, 75 Hamilton Drive, Warsop, Mansfield, Notts NG20 0EY (01623 847738).
Ground: Welbeck Colliery Pit (0623 842611). **Colours:** Black & yellow/black.
Hons: Notts Alliance Div 2 93-94 (Intermediate Cup 93-94), Chesterfield & District Lg 92-93.

WOLLATON

Secretary: Andrew Moon, 150 Wollaton Vale, Wollaton, Nottm NG8 2PL (01159 281215).
Ground: Wollaton Sports Club, Wollaton Village, Nottm (01159 289748).
Colours: Sky/maroon **Hons:** Notts All. Div 1 R-up 92-93 (Div 2 91-92 (I'mediate Cup R-up 91-92)).

FINAL LEAGUE TABLES 1995/96

	Div One	*P*	*W*	*D*	*L*	*F*	*A*	*Pts*
1.	Ollerton Town	30	19	7	4	66	28	64
2.	Awsworth Villa	30	16	7	7	71	52	55
3.	City & Sherwood	30	15	4	11	51	44	49
4.	Abacus	30	14	6	10	46	43	48
5.	Retford United	30	12	10	8	43	40	46
6.	Linby CW	30	11	10	9	49	50	43
7.	Boots Ath Res	30	10	11	9	65	63	41
8.	Teversal Grange	30	10	11	9	56	54	41
9.	Rainsworth MWR	30	11	7	12	72	63	40
10.	Bilsthorpe CW	30	11	6	13	58	68	39
11.	Bestwood MW	30	11	5	14	53	58	38
12.	Gedling MW	30	8	11	11	46	48	35
13.	W'ton Simpsons	30	9	8	13	63	70	35
14.	Clifton	30	9	4	17	51	72	31
15.	Pelican Res	30	7	8	15	54	65	29
16.	Radcliffe Oly	30	4	11	15	39	65	23

	Div Two	*P*	*W*	*D*	*L*	*F*	*A*	*Pts*
1.	Beeston Town	30	23	4	3	92	41	73
2.	Attenborough	30	22	4	4	82	42	70
3.	Carlton DC	30	21	4	5	105	33	67
4.	Wollaton Res	30	19	4	7	69	50	61
5.	Kimberley MW	30	15	6	9	68	55	51
6.	Southwell C R	30	15	3	12	77	54	48
7.	Ruddington UR	30	14	4	12	61	69	46
8.	John Player R	30	12	7	11	61	54	43
9.	East Lake Ath	30	11	6	13	47	56	39
10.	Calverton Tn	30	11	4	15	63	61	37
11.	Grnw'd Meadows	30	10	5	15	53	64	35
12.	Basford Utd	30	8	3	19	56	75	27
13.	W'ton Simpsons	30	8	2	20	48	99	26
14.	Thoresby CWR	30	7	4	19	53	97	25
15.	Hucknall RR R	30	6	4	20	48	77	22
16.	GPT Res	30	4	4	22	39	95	16

NOTTS ALLIANCE DIVISION ONE CLUBS 1996-97

ABACUS

Secretary: Mr Stephen Bingley, 6 Brisbane Close, Mansfield Woodhouse NG19 8QZ (0623 23072).
Ground: Sherwood Colliery Sports Ground, Debdale Lane, Mansfield Woodhouse, Notts.
Colours: Black & white stripes.

ATTENBOROUGH

Secretary: Terry Allen, 3 Firth Close, Arnold, Nottingham NG5 8RU (0602 200698).
Ground & Directions: The Village Green, The Strand, Attenborough, Beeston, Nottingham. Midway between Beeston & Long Eaton on A6005 - adjacent to Nature Reserve (via Attenborough Lane).
Colours: All blue **Change cols:** White/black/black.

BASFORD UNITED

Secretary: Paul Dobson, 26 Chevin Gardens, Top Valley, Nottm NG5 9ES (01159 274790

Ground: Greenwich Ave, Sports Ground, Bagnall Road, Basford, Nottm (01159 423918).

Directions: M1 (J26) follow signs 'A610 Nottingham' then 'B6004 Arnold' into Mill Street.

Colours: Yellow/black **Hons:** Notts Snr Cup 46-47 87-88, Notts Alliance Div 1 R-up 71-72 84-85 93-94.

BEESTON TOWN

Secretary: Andy Meakin, 26 Redland Drive, Chilwell, Nottingham NG9 5LE (0115 967 7520

Ground: University Ground, Nottingham **Colours:** Red & black/black

BESTWOOD MINERS WELFARE

Secretary: Mrs Alana Jackson, 9 Derwent Drive, Hucknall, Nottm NG15 6DS (0602 630189).

Ground: Bestwood Workshops, Park Rd, Bestwood (0602 273711) **Colours:** White/blue.

BILSTHORPE COLLIERY WELFARE

Secretary: Mr Les Lee, 42 Chapel Lane, Ravenshead, Mansfield NG15 9DA (0623 794442).

Ground: Bilsthorpe CW Ground, Eakring Road, Bilsthorpe. **Colours:** White/navy/navy.

CITY & SHERWOOD HOSPITALS

Secretary: Mr Alan Bird, 72 Bilborough Rd, Nottm NG8 4DW (0602 285507).

Ground: COD Military Ground, Chilwell (0602 254811). **Colours:** All Royal blue

CLIFTON

Secretary: Keith Elliott, 61 Greencroft, Clifton Est., Nottm NG11 8GT (0602 215401).

Ground: Green Lane, Clifton Est., Nottm (0602 844903). **Colours:** All white

GEDLING COLLIERY WELFARE

Secretary: Mrs Maureen Chambers, 8 Fraser Road, Carlton, Nottm NG4 1NJ (0602 612994).

Ground: Gedling Colliery Welfare, Plains Road, Mapperley (0602 266300) **Colours:** Yellow/blue

G.P.T.

Secretary: Roger Marshall, Sports Office, GPT, Beeston, Nottm NG9 1LA (01159 433669)

Ground: Trent Vale Rd, Beeston, Nottm (01159 258695). **Colours:** Black & Blue stripes/Black.

Hons: Notts Alliance 66-67 91-92 (R-up 92-93, Lg Cup 92-93).

LINBY COLLIERY MINERS WELFARE

Secretary: D G Dickens, 4 Old Mill Close, Bestwood, Nottingham, NG6 8TA (0602 276598).

Ground: Church Lane, Linby **Colours:** Red/White

RETFORD UNITED

Secretary: Jeff Lamb, 18 Northumbria Drive, Retford, Notts, DN22 7PR (0602 705833).

Ground: Oaklands Lane (Off London Road), Retford. **Colours:** Black & white stripes/black

TEVERSAL GRANGE

Secretary: Kevin Newton, 8 Vere Ave., Sutton in Ashfield, Notts NG17 2ES (0623 511402).

Ground: Carnarvon Street, Sutton in Ashfield. **Colours:** Red & black hoops/red/red.

WORTHINGTON SIMPSONS

Secretary: Alan Toule, 54 Elterwater Drive, Gamston, Nottingham NG2 6PX (0602 810258).

Ground: Lowfields, off Hawton Lane, New Baldeton, Newark, Notts (0636 702672).

Colours: Maroon/sky **Hons:** Notts Alliance Lg Cup (Intermediate Cup(res) 92-93 (R-up 93-94)).

This Division also includes the Reserve sides of: Boots Athletic, Rainworth MW.

OXFORDSHIRE F.A.

Hon. Secretary: Mr P J Ladbrook,
3 Wilkins Road, Cowley, Oxford OX4 2HY

OXFORDSHIRE SENIOR CUP (FOUNDED 1884–85)

RECENT FINALS

1990–91	Oxford United Res	v	Carterton Town	5–0
1991–92	Oxford United Res	v	Witney Town	3–1
1992–93	Thame United	v	Banbury United	2–1
1993–94	Witney Town	v	Peppard	1–0
1994–95	Witney Town	v	North Leigh	1–0

MOST WINS Oxford City 28 Witney Town 9 Oxford United 8

1995–1996

OXFORDSHIRE SENIOR CUP

29 CLUBS **HOLDERS: WITNEY TOWN**

FIRST ROUND 18th November 1995

AP Sports & S	v	Checkendon Sports	0–2	Chipping Norton T	v	Woodstock Town	2–2 1–3
Garsington	v	Watlington	3–4	Chinnor	v	Old Woodstock	3–4
Worcs College OB	v	Rover Cowley	4–1	Headington Amt	v	Eynsham AFC	5–5 2–3
Henley Town	v	Launton Sport	4–0	Wheatley United	v	Yarnton	0–4
Kidlington	v	Easington Sports	8–1				

7 Clubs with Byes Ardley United, Banbury United, Bicester United, Carterton Town, Clanfield, Peppard, Quarry Nomads to the

SECOND ROUND Saturday 9th December 1995

Ardley United	v	Peppard	0–2	Yarnton	v	Clanfield	0–1
Banbury United	v	Old Woodstock	2–0	Watlington	v	Woodstock Town	6–1
Bicester Town	v	Kidlington	3–1	Worc's College OB	v	Quarry Nomads	0–2
Carterton Town	v	Checkendon Sports	6–0	Eynsham AFC	v	Henley Town	3–1

THIRD ROUND 13th January 1996

Peppard	v	Clanfield	2–1	Quarry Nomads	v	Bicester Town	1–1 1–3
Banbury United	v	Eynsham AFC	4–3	Watlington	v	Carterton Town	0–2

4 Clubs Exempt Thame United, Witney Town, Oxford City, North Leigh to

FOURTH ROUND 10th February 1996

Carterton Town	v	Witney Town	0–1	Thame United	v	Banbury United	7–0
Bicester Town	v	Peppard	1–0	Oxford City	v	North Leigh	3–1

SEMI-FINALS on or before 24th March 1996

Bicester Town	v	Oxford City	1–2	Thame United	v	Witney Town	3–0
at Thame United FC				at Oxford City FC			

FINAL Wednesday 8th May 1996
THAME UNITED v OXFORD CITY 1–2 at Windmill Road, Thame United FC.

SHEFFIELD & HALLAMSHIRE F.A.

Secretary: G Thompson JP,
Clegg House, 5 Onslow Road, Sheffield S11 7AF (01742 670068)

SHEFFIELD & HALLAMSHIRE SENIOR CUP (FOUNDED 1876–77)

RECENT FINALS

1990–91	Emley	v	Worksop Town	1–1 (4–3 Pens)
1991–92	Emley	v	Frickley Athletic	1–0
1992–93	Stocksbridge Pk Steels	v	Worksop Town	5–3 (Agg.)
1993–94	Sheffield	v	Worksop Town	1–1 (6–5 Pens)
1994–95	Worksop Town	v	Emley	1–0

MOST WINS Sheffield 10 Frickley Athletic 9 Sheffield Wednesday 9

1995–1996

SHEFFIELD & HALLAMSHIRE CUP

52 CLUBS **HOLDERS: WORKSOP TOWN**

FIRST QUALIFYING ROUND 9th September 1995

Sheffield Bankers	v	Mexborough Main St	3–2
Wath Saracens A	v	Clifton Rovers	1–3
Kiveton Park	v	Caribbean Sports	2–3
Ash Hse Phoenix	v	Sheffield Abbeydale	2–1
Denaby & Cadeby	v	Case Sports	1–2
ABM FC	v	Wickersley OB	2–1
Wombwell Town	v	Grapes Nthn General	8–1
S&H Univ Union	v	Harworth C Institute	4–2
Parramores Sports	v	Yorkshire Main	3–1
Thurcroft DB	v	Grimethorpe MW	0–2
Old Edwardians	v	Swinton Athletic	0–5
Frecheville CA	v	Mexboro Ath Oakhse	4–2
Hemsworth Town	v	Sheffield Centralians	4–0
Avesta Sheffield	v	Peniston Church	1–4
Elsecar Market H	v	Killamarsh AFC	2–2 0–2
Throstles Ridgeway	v	High Green Villa	1–5
Ecclesfield RR	v	Woodsetts Sports	3–0
Treeton Welfare	v	NCB Maltby MW	0–5
Oughtibridge WM	v	Davy FC	2–0
Rossington FC	v	The Wetherby	0–1

12 Clubs with Byes Brodsworth, Denaby United, Emley, Frickley Athletic, Hallam, Maltby MW, Parkgate, Rossington Main, Sheffield, Stocksbridge Park Steels, Worksop Town, Worsbrough Bridge MW, into the

FIRST ROUND PROPER Saturday 11th November

Hallam	v	Clifton Rovers	5–1
Denaby United	v	Hemsworth Town	3–1
Case Sports	v	Ecclesfield Red Rose	0–3
Maltby MW	v	Swinton Athletic	3–1
Sheffield Bankers	v	Peniston Church	2–1
Grimethorpe MW	v	Wombwell Town	5*1
Oughtibridge WMC	v	Parkgate	2–1
Brodsworth	v	Caribbean Sports	0*0 1–0
Worsbrough Br	v	Ash Hse Phoenix	0–2
Killamarsh	v	Sheff-Hallam Univ Un	5*4
Emley AFC	v	Worksop Town	2–1
High Green Villa	v	Stocksbridge Pk St	0*0 2–5
Frecheville CA	v	NCB Maltby MW	2–1
Parramore Sports	v	Sheffield	2–5
Rossington Main	v	Frickley Athletic	2–8
The Wetherby	v	ABM	2–1

SECOND ROUND PROPER Saturday 9th December

The Wetherby	v	Frickley Athletic	1–3
Ecclesfield Red R	v	Hallam	1–4
Frecheville CA	v	Emley	1–0
Brodsworth	v	Sheffield	1–0
Maltby MW	v	Killamarsh Juniors	2–1
Grimethorpe MW	v	Ash Hse Phoenix	4–2
Sheffield Bankers	v	Oughtibridge WMC	1–2
Denaby United	v	Stocksbridge Pk Steels	2–3

THIRD ROUND

Brodsworth	v	Maltby MW	0–3
Frecheville CA	v	Grimethorpe MW	1–3
Frickley Athletic	v	Stocksbridge Pk	2*2 0–2
Hallam	v	Oughtibridge WMC	3–2

SEMI-FINALS (Two Legs)

Grimethorpe MW	v	Hallam	0–1 2–0 2–1
Maltby MW	v	Stocksbridge PS	1–1 2–4 3–5

FINAL Wednesday 17th April 7.30pm
GRIMETHORPE MW v STOCKSBRIDGE PARK STEELS 0–1 at Welfare Sports Ground, Huddersfield, Emly FC.

BEEFEATER COUNTY SENIOR FOOTBALL LEAGUE

Secretary; Bob Bowler, 1 Holbein Close, Dronfield Woodhouse, Sheffield S18 6QH (01246 410739)

Publicity Officer; David Shepherd, 8 Broomhill Avenue, Worksop, S81 7Qp (01909 484568)

Forty-one teams competed in the League ans League Cup Competitions. The Premier Division, consisting of 14 contenders, wasw won by High Green Villa FC who boasted a full 100% home win record with Grimethorpe MW finishing runners-up, an unfortunate record additionally experienced in the Sheffield & Hallamshire County FA Senior Challenge Cup, the Beefeater League Cup and the Carlsberg Club Knockout Competitions although a Wembley appearance in the last named event and a Civic Reception at Barnsley Town Hall brought some consolation.

Ecclesfield Red Rose and Pargate respectively filled the top two berths in a 13 strong Division One, Red Rose's unbeaten League record being the first such feat in four seasons.

The Division Two contest proved to be the tightest with Wickersley OB pipping The Wetherby by one point with the season's leading goalscorers, Clifton Rovers, having to content themselves with fifth position in a scetion of 14. The League Management Committee's selection policy proved to be successful again with all three teams promoted to Division One being participants for no more than two seasons.

Worsbrough Bridge MW & Athletic won the Beefeater League Cup Competition by three poals to two after trailing 0-2 to Grimethorpe MW at fogbound Bracken Moor on 11th April in front of a crowd approaching 400 in number.

Kiveton Park who, along with Grimethorpe MW and Sheffield Abbeydale, will no longer be League members next season, won the Arnold Kettell sporting award. The Hague & Ibbotson Cup, awarded to the League's highest goalscorer, went to Grimethorpe MW for the third successive year, Glenn Wilson acquiring 23 of his team's 63 league goals.

FINAL LEAGUE TABLES 1995/96

	Premier Division	P	W	D	L	F	A	Pts
1.	High Green V	26	21	3	2	74	20	66
2.	Grimethorpe MW	26	17	4	5	63	21	55
3.	Ash Hse Phoenix	26	15	4	7	54	36	49
4.	A.B.M.	26	14	5	7	57	45	47
5.	Denaby & Cadeby	26	12	6	8	58	39	42
6.	Frecheville C A	26	11	5	10	64	50	38
7.	Parramore Spts	26	12	2	12	46	56	38
8.	Worsbrough Bdge	26	9	8	9	43	40	35
9.	Oughtibr WMSC	26	9	7	10	38	41	34
10.	Mexborough M St	26	7	9	10	46	46	30
11.	Stocksbridge PS	26	8	5	13	44	46	*23
12.	Caribbean Spts	26	6	4	16	40	79	22
13.	Penistone Church	26	6	1	19	37	62	19
14.	Throstles Ridge	26	3	1	22	23	106	10

PREMIER DIVISION RESULTS CHART 1995-96

HOME TEAM	1	2	3	4	5	6	7	8	9	10	11	12	13	14
1. A.B.M.	*	2-1	4-2	4-4	2-2	1-4	1-3	3-2	0-2	2-0	3-1	0-5	0-1	0-2
2. Ash House Phoenix	2-2	*	1-0	1-2	2-1	0-1	1-1	3-1	2-3	2-1	2-3	3-1	6-2	3-1
3. Caribbean Sports	0-9	2-3	*	1-4	0-3	0-3	2-2	3-2	1-1	1-3	4-1	1-2	4-1	3-1
4. Denaby & Cadeby	1-3	2-0	4-1	*	3-0	1-2	0-3	3-3	2-2	5-0	2-0	2-1	6-0	1-1
5. Frecheville & C.A.	1-3	0-2	1-1	3-1	*	1-4	1-2	5-2	2-1	3-1	6-0	3-2	9-0	2-2
6. Grimethorpe M W	2-2	1-2	1-2	3-0	4-1	*	1-0	2-1	0-2	6-0	5-1	3-0	2-0	1-0
7. High Green Villa	3-0	2-0	7-1	3-0	2-1	1-0	*	2-1	4-0	4-1	2-1	3-1	5-0	2-1
8. Mexborough M St	1-1	1-3	3-3	1-2	5-2	0-0	1-1	*	0-2	0-0	3-1	1-2	3-1	1-1
9. Oughtibr W M S C	1-3	0-4	3-1	1-1	1-1	0-4	0-2	2-2	*	0-0	3-1	0-1	4-0	1-2
10. Parramore Sports	1-4	1-3	2-1	2-1	0-4	3-2	1-3	1-3	1-3	*	3-1	2-1	8-2	2-1
11. Penistone Church	1-2	1-2	6-1	0-2	4-1	0-4	1-2	0-2	3-0	1-3	*	0-0	5-1	0-3
12. Stocksbridge P S	2-3	1-1	6-0	2-1	3-5	2-2	1-2	1-1	0-3	3-4	3-0	*	1-2	0-0
13. Throstles Ridgeway	0-1	2-3	0-5	1-7	1-4	0-5	0-11	1-4	2-2	0-3	0-3	3-0	*	2-3
14. Worsbrough Bridge	1-2	2-2	6-0	1-1	2-2	1-1	3-2	1-2	2-1	0-3	3-2	1-3	2-1	*

FINAL LEAGUE TABLES 1995/96

Div One	P	W	D	L	F	A	Pts
1. Ecclesfield R R	24	19	5	0	76	22	62
2. Parkgate	24	15	3	6	67	42	48
3. Wombwell Tn	24	13	5	6	47	26	44
4. Thurcroft D B	24	12	4	8	68	42	40
5. Swinton Ath	24	11	5	8	42	31	38
6. Grapes N Gen	24	12	4	8	64	64	*38
7. Treeton Wel	24	8	7	9	48	58	31
8. Davy	24	9	3	12	48	56	30
9. Sheffield Bank	24	6	11	7	40	45	29
10. Wath S/ens A	24	7	7	10	30	37	28
11. Hallam	24	7	3	14	34	49	24
12. Woodsetts Spts	24	3	5	16	31	77	14
13. Yorkshire Main	24	2	2	20	24	70	8

** 2 points deducted*

Div Two	P	W	D	L	F	A	Pts
1. Wickersley OB	26	18	7	1	83	32	61
2. The Wetherby	26	19	3	4	81	18	60
3. Worksop Town	26	18	4	4	71	27	58
4. Maltby M W	26	17	3	6	71	33	54
5. Clifton Rovers	26	16	4	6	88	32	52
6. Elsecar Mkt Htl	26	14	2	10	65	50	44
7. Avesta Sheffield	26	14	1	11	76	64	43
8. Rossington Mn	26	11	5	10	47	57	38
9. Sheff Central	26	7	5	14	29	52	26
10. Penistone C R	26	6	6	14	37	59	24
11. Sheff Abbeydale	26	5	3	18	41	81	18
12. Harworth C I	26	5	3	18	33	80	18
13. Kiveton Park	26	4	1	21	36	106	13
14. Old Edwardians	26	3	3	20	30	97	12

DIVISION ONE RESULTS CHART 1995-96

HOME TEAM	1	2	3	4	5	6	7	8	9	10	11	12	13
1. Davy	*	3-4	2-1	1-2	5-6	1-4	1-5	0-3	3-1	0-4	3-3	4-2	2-0
2. Ecclesfield Red Rose	1-1	*	3-0	3-2	1-0	3-3	2-2	5-4	2-1	3-1	2-2	4-1	8-0
3. Grapes Nth General	1-3	1-10	*	3-2	6-2	0-2	0-3	2-4	4-4	3-0	1-1	5-3	3-1
4. Hallam	3-6	0-3	2-7	*	1-4	0-0	1-2	3-2	5-0	2-0	1-0	1-2	1-3
5. Parkgate	2-1	1-2	2-2	3-2	*	4-1	2-0	2-2	6-0	2-2	1-0	5-2	5-4
6. Sheffield Bankers	1-2	1-1	4-7	1-1	0-3	*	2-2	1-7	3-3	1-1	0-1	2-1	4-0
7. Swinton Athletic	1-1	0-5	3-4	0-2	0-1	1-0	*	0-2	0-0	1-1	0-1	3-0	2-1
8. Thurcroft D Barrel	1-2	1-1	1-3	2-1	3-1	3-4	2-3	*	1-2	4-5	2-2	2-0	2-1
9. Treeton Welfare	4-2	0-4	3-4	3-0	4-0	1-1	0-6	3-3	*	1-1	3-3	2-3	3-1
10. Wath Saracens Athletic	2-0	1-1	1-3	2-0	1-5	0-2	0-0	0-2	0-1	*	0-2	1-1	3-0
11. Wombwell Town	1-0	1-2	6-0	1-0	2-1	0-0	1-2	1-2	4-1	2-0	*	3-1	4-2
12. Woodsetts Sports	3-2	0-5	2-2	0-0	0-4	2-2	2-6	0-10	1-4	1-3	0-2	*	1-1
13. Yorkshire Main	1-3	0-1	0-1	1-2	1-5	1-1	0-2	0-3	1-4	0-1	1-6	4-3	*

BEEFEATER LEAGUE CUP COMPETITION 1995-96

First Round;

A.B.M. v Oughtibr W M S C	1-0
Frecheville C A v Swinton ASthletic	2-0
Old Edwardians v Elsecar Market Htl	0-3
Wombwell Town v Hallam	3-0
Worsbrough Bridge v Treeton Welfare	2-1
Ash House Phoenix v Sheff Centralians	2-1
NCB Maltby M W v Parkgate	3-1
Penistone Ch Res v Caribbean Sports	2-0
Woodsetts Sports v Ecclesfield Red Rose	1-2

Second Round:

A B M v Denaby & Cadeby	3-0
Davy v Sheffield Bankers	2-0
Elsecar Market Htl v Ash House Phoenix	1-4
Grimethorpe M W v Clifton Rovers	3-1
High Green Villa v Rossington Main	5-1
Stocksbridge P S v Mexborough M St	0-3
Throstles Ridgeway v Thurcroft D Barrel	3-2
Wickersley OB v Yorkshire Main	3-2
Avesta Sheffield v Kiveton Park	4-3
Ecclesfield Red Rose v Penistone Church Res	4-0
Frecheville C A v Wombwell Town	1-0
Harworth Coll Inst v Worsbrough Bridge	0-3
Penistone Church v Grapes Nth General	3-2
The Wetherby v Parramore Sports	3-1
Wath Saracens Ath v Sheff Abbeydale	5-1
Worksop Town v Maltby M W	3-1

Third Round;

Ash House Phoenix v Penistone Church	4-3
Ecclesfield Red Rose v Avesta Sheffield	2-1
Grimethorpe MW v Worksop Town	1-0
The Wetherby v Wickersley OB	5-3
Davy v Wath Saracens Ath	3-1
Frechiville C A v ABM	2-1
Mexborough M St v Worsbrough Bridge	3-5 *
Throstes Ridgeway v High Green Villa	1-2

** Match ordered to be replayed*

Worsbrough Bridge v Mexborough M St *3-3, (3-2pen)*

Fourth Round;

Davy v Ecclesfield Red Rose	2-1	Grimethorpe M W v The Wetherby	2-0
High Green Villa v Frencheville CA	0-0, 2-1	Worsbrough Bridge v Ash House Phoenix	1-0

Semi-Finals;

Grimethorpe M W v Davy	2-0	Worsbrough Bridge v High Gren Villa	1-0

Final; Worsbrough Bridge v Grimethorpe Miners Welfare 3-2

PREMIER DIVISION CLUBS 1995-96

A.B.M.

Secretary: Mr M Newton, 1 Skelton Way, Woodhouse, Sheffield S13 7Qw (0114 269 7900)
Ground: Sheffield Transport, Meadowfield, Sheffield.

Ash House Phoenix

Secretary: T Cottam, 41 Pleasant Road, Sheffield S12 2BD (0114 239 0897)
Ground: As ABM above

Caribbean Sports

Denaby & Cadeby Miners Welfare

Secretary: Mr D Steer, 27 Tickhill Square, Denaby Main, Doncaster DN12 4AW (01709 867824)
Ground: Denaby United FC, Ticknell Square, Denaby Main, Doncaster

Frechiville Community Association

Secretary: Mr R Davenport, 45 Aspen Close, Killamarsh, Sheffield S31 8TA, (0114 247 0937)
Ground: Silkstone Road, Frecheville, Sheffield

Grimethorpe Miners Welfare

Secretary: Mr A Gill, 7 Duke Street, Grimethorpe, Barnsley S72 7NJ (01226 712863)
Ground: Cemetry Road, Grimethorpe, Barnsley

High Green Villa

Secretary: T Staples, 41 Woodburn Drive, Chapeltown, Sheffield S30 4YT (0114 246 8560)
Ground: High Green Playing Fields, Mortomley Close.

Mexborough Main Street

Secretary: Mr A A Hough, 4 Cranswick Way, Conisborough, Doncaster DN12 3Ay (01709 866479)
Ground: Hampden Road, Mexborough

Oughtibridge W.M.S.C.

Secretary: Mr K Dewsbury, 11 Footgate Close, Oughtibridge, Sheffield S30 3JA (0114 286 2948)
Ground: Station Lane, Oughtibridge

Parramore Sports

Secretary: Mr R Blagden, 15 Moor Farm Avenue, Mosborough Moor, Sheffield S19 5JP (0114 247 6025)
Ground: Davy Sports Club, Prince of Wales Road, Sheffield

Penistone Church

Secretary: Mr D Hampshire, 36 Park Avenue, Penistone, Sheffield S30 6DN (01226 764689)
Ground: Church View Road, Penistone

Stocksbridge Park Steel Reserves

Secretary: M Grimmer, 48 Hole House Lane, Stocksbridge, Sheffield S30 5BP (0114 2886470)
Ground: Bracken Moor Lane, Stocksbridge, Sheffield

Throstles Ridgeway

Secretary: Mr P Crookes, Oak House, The Ford, Ridgeway, Sheffield S12 3YD (01246 434646)
Ground: Ridgeway Sports Ground, Main Road, Ridgeway, Sheffield

Worsbrough Bridge Miners Welfare & Athletic Reserves

Secretary: D Smith, 18 Shield Avenue, Worsbrough Bridge, Barnsley S70 5Bq (01226 243418)
Ground: Park Road, Worsbrough Bridge, Barnsley.

FINAL LEAGUE TABLES 1995/96

Doncaster Senior League:

Premier Div	P	W	D	L	F	A	Pts
1. S Kirby Coll	24	18	4	2	82	25	58
2. Carcroft Vill	24	18	2	4	59	17	56
3. Northgate WMC	24	13	7	4	47	26	46
4. Plant Works	24	12	7	5	62	34	43
5. Kinsley Boys	24	12	7	5	51	28	43
6. Sutton Rov	24	12	5	7	61	37	41
7. Hemsworth SP	24	11	4	9	64	56	37
8. Scawthorpe S	24	10	3	11	40	42	33
9. Skellow Gran	24	7	2	15	43	65	23
10. Upton & Hare	24	7	2	15	35	62	23
11. Hemsworth MW	24	4	2	18	29	88	14
12. Askern Wel	24	3	4	17	26	76	13
13. Ings Lane	24	2	5	17	35	78	11

Div One	P	W	D	L	F	A	Pts
1. Ackworth	24	14	6	4	70	36	48
2. Yorkshire M	24	13	4	7	54	34	48
3. Highfields MW	24	12	4	8	53	37	40
4. Bentley Coll	24	11	3	10	66	60	36
5. Edlington	24	11	3	10	56	50	36
6. Lodge	24	10	3	11	53	57	33
7. White Hart U	24	7	6	11	46	61	27
8. Kinsley Boys	24	8	2	14	49	91	26
9. S Kirkby Coll	24	4	5	15	47	68	17

Doncaster & District FA Cup:

Quarter Finals:

Plant Works	v	Scawthorpe Social	1-0
South Kirkby Coll A	v	Edlington Brit Leg	1-3
Sutton Rovers	v	Lindholme	3-0
Hemsworth MW A	v	Northgate WMC	2-2, 4-2

Semi-Finals:

Plant Works	v	Edlington Brit Leg	4-0
Sutton Rovers	v	Hemsworth MW A	0-2

Final;

Plant Works	v	Hemsworth MW A	1-1, 1-3pen

Rotherham Association Football League

Premier Div	P	W	D	L	F	A	Pts
1. Brinsworth Ath	18	13	1	4	54	32	27
2. Thorpe Hesley	18	9	4	5	40	28	26
3. Mexborough S	18	9	4	5	47	30	22
4. Queens Hotel	18	9	3	6	63	30	21
5. Albion Road	18	8	3	7	47	47	19
6. Roland Arms	18	8	1	9	51	46	17
7. New Life	18	6	3	9	55	46	15
8. Brinsworth	18	6	3	9	38	59	15
9. BSM D/bridge	18	4	3	11	36	59	11
10. Kimberworth	18	3	1	14	33	77	7

Div One	P	W	D	L	F	A	Pts
1. Crown NB	16	14	2	0	68	22	30
2. Canklow	16	12	1	2	99	19	27
3. The Rats	16	12	1	3	78	22	25
4. Eastwood View	16	10	0	5	48	40	20
5. Maltby Sheppey	16	7	1	8	63	36	15
6. Queens R/msh	16	5	3	8	40	47	13
7. Master Brewer	16	3	2	11	41	72	8
8. Cranworth Hot	16	0	0	16	9	153	0

Canklow 2 points awarded
Eastwood View 2 points deducted

South Yorkshire Amateur League

Premier Div	P	W	D	L	F	A	Pts
1. Burncross	20	17	0	3	57	19	51
2. Elm Tree	20	16	2	2	70	25	50
3. Market Inn	20	14	2	4	50	24	44
4. Kings Ch	20	10	4	6	48	37	34
5. De La Salle	20	8	5	7	50	46	29
6. Records	20	8	4	8	48	48	28
7. Phoenix A	20	7	5	8	46	59	26
8. Midland Bank	20	6	4	10	56	52	22
9. Centralians	20	4	2	14	25	64	14
10. Windsor 89	20	3	4	13	41	60	13
11. Castle Coll	20	1	1	18	18	75	4

Div One	P	W	D	L	F	A	Pts
1. Oughtibridge	22	17	1	4	81	28	52
2. Hollinsend Alb	22	13	6	3	66	40	47
3. Gate 13	22	12	5	5	63	34	41
4. Hollinsend	22	10	8	4	62	40	38
5. Davy	21	10	5	6	57	54	35
6. SWD Survey	22	9	6	7	51	31	33
7. Cumberland	22	7	9	6	45	46	29
8. Sh Bankers	22	8	4	10	40	56	28
9. Medic A	21	5	6	10	32	43	21
10. Moorfoot	22	4	2	16	48	75	14
11. Vermeer	20	3	3	14	26	80	12
12. Bradway	22	2	5	15	38	82	11

SHROPSHIRE F.A.

Secretary: A W Brett,
10-11 High Street, Shrewsbyry SY1 1SG
Tel: 01743 362769 Fax: (Home) 01743 236145

SHROPSHIRE SENIOR CUP (FOUNDED 1877–78)

RECENT FINALS

1990–91	Shrewsbury Town	v	Telford United	3–1
1991–92	Telford United	v	Shrewsbury Town	1–0
1992–93	Telford United	v	Shrewsbury Town	2–0
1993–94	Telford United	v	Shrewsbury Town	2–1
1994–95	Shrewsbury Town	v	Telford United	5–1

MOST WINS Shrewsbury Town 50 Telford United 34 Oswestry Town 11

1995–1996

SHROPSHIRE SENIOR CUP

5 CLUBS **HOLDERS: SHREWSBURY TOWN**

FIRST ROUND

Ludlow Town v Shifnal Town 0–3

SEMI-FINALS

Bridgnorth Town v Telford United 1–2
Shifnal Town v Shrewsbury Town 0–4

FINAL

TELFORD UNITED v SHREWSBURY TOWN 0–2 at Buck's Head, Telford United FC.

SHROPSHIRE COUNTY CUP (FOUNDED 1966–67)

RECENT FINALS

1990–91	Shifnal Town	v	Newport Town	5–2
1991–92	Little Drayton Rngs	v	Shifnal Town	3–0
1992–93	Oakengates Town	v	Albrighton S&S	1–0
1993–94	Ludlow Town	v	Morda United	1–0
1994–95	Ludlow Town	v	Bridgnorth Town Res	3–1

MOST WINS GKN Sankey 6 Bridgnorth Town 5 Whitchurch Alport 4

SHROPSHIRE COUNTY CUP

23 CLUBS **HOLDERS: LUDLOW TOWN**

FIRST ROUND Saturday 23rd September

Wellington Amt v Madeley Town 1–3
Newport v Belle Vue OB 3–4
Lt Drayton Amt v Snailbeach WS 3–1
Springvale Rovers v Oakengates Town 0–3
Bandon Arms v Bridgenorth Tn Res 7–3
Tibberton v Church Stretton 2–3
Hadley Keys v Wem Town WT W–O
9 Clubs with Byes into

SECOND ROUND

Meole Brace v Ellesmere Rngs 5–2
Bandon v Ludlow Town Colts 3–2
Highley Welfare v St Martins 6–0
Oakengates Tn v Morda United 3–1
L Drayton Rngs v Belle Vue OB 0–1
Whitchurch Alport v Star Aluminium 2–1
Madeley Town v Wem Town 2–3
Church Stretton v Broseley 2–5

THIRD ROUND

Bandon v Meole Brace 4–2
Belle Vue OB v Oakengates Town 3–3 2–1
Wem Town v Broseley 4–1
Highley Welfare v Whitchurch Alport 2–3

SEMI-FINALS

Whitchurch Alport v Wem Town 4–1
Bandon v Belle Vue OB 0–0 4–1

FINAL Thursday 4th April 1996

BANDON v WHITCHURCH ALPORT 3–1 at Gay Meadow, Shrewsbury Town FC.

SOMERSET F.A.

Hon. Secretary: Mrs H Marchment,
30 North Road, Midsomer Norton, Bath, Somerset BA3 2QQ (01761) 410280

SOMERSET SENIOR CUP
(FOUNDED 1895–96)

RECENT FINALS

1990–91	Brislington	v	Bridgwater Town	3–1
1991–92	Odd Down	v	Portishead	4–2
1992–93	Brislington	v	Saltford	1–0
1993–94	Bridgwater Town	v	Brislington	1–0
1994–95	Brislington	v	Bridgwater Town	0–0 (5–4 Pens)

MOST WINS Paulton Rovers 12 Radstock Town 12 Welton Rovers 9

1995–1996

SOMERSET SENIOR CUP

HOLDERS: BRISLINGTON

FIRST ROUND

Hengrove Ath	v	Weston-s-Mare	1–0	Westland Sports	v	Castle Cary	0–1
Long Sutton	v	Ilminster Town	1–0	Burnham United	v	Clutton	4–0
Nailsea Town	v	Hartcliffe Comm Cen	5*3	Wellington	v	Hartcliffe OB	3–1
Highridge Utd	v	CTK Southside	3–0	Paulton Rovers	v	Bishop Sutton	0–6
Weston St John	v	Portishead	1–0	Clevedon United	v	Radstock Town	2–4
Cheddar	v	St George E in G	2–1	Wells City	v	Westland United	1–5
Bristol Spartak	v	Nailsea United	4–6	Frome Town	v	Backwell United	3*3 0–6
Imperial	v	Clandown	4–2	Temple Cloud	v	Larkhall Ath	0–7
Welton Rovers	v	Shepton Mallet Tn	0–2	Keynsham Town	v	Street	2–7
Peasedown Ath	v	Keynsham Cricketers	4–2	Fry's Club	v	Dundry Athletic	4–0
Brislington	v	Congresbury	2p4 2*2 1*1	Tunley Athletic	v	Clevedon Town	1–4
Wrington-Redhill	v	Glastonbury	1*1 2–4	Cleeve West Tn	v	Teyfant Athletic	3–2
Winscombe	v	P&W United	5*3				

7 Clubs with Byes Timsbury Athletic, Watchet Town, Odd Down, Peasedown MYCOR, Saltford, Bridgwater Town, Stockwood Green into the

SECOND ROUND Saturday 2nd December

Backwell United	v	Glastonbury	2–0	Bishop Sutton	v	Nalsea United	1–2
Larkhall Athletic	v	Peasedown Athletic	1–2	Castle Cary	v	Hengrove Athletic	0–2
Brislington	v	Street	3–2	Peasedown MYC	v	Timsbury Athletic	0–2
Saltford	v	Winscombe	3–4	Westland United	v	Radstock Town	2–3
Long Sutton	v	Nailsea United	1–0	Burnham United	v	Cleeve West Town	1–4
Weston St John	v	Stockwood Green	1–1 6–4	Watchet Town	v	Odd Down	3–1
Imperial	v	Cheddar	1–2	Highridge United	v	Wellington Res	2–0
Bridgwater Town	v	Clevedon Town	2–1	Shepton Mallet Tn	v	Fry's Club	0–1

THIRD ROUND 6th January 1996

Winscombe	v	Cheddar	2–3	Watchet Town	v	Nailsea United	0–2
Timsbury Athletic	v	Hengrove Athletic	1–2	Peasedown Ath	v	Highridge United	1–1 3–0
Weston St John	v	Brislington	2–1	Backwell United	v	Fry's Club	3*3 0–2
Bridgwater Town	v	Long Sutton	5–0	Radstock Town	v	Cleeve West Town	3–1

FOURTH ROUND Saturday 3rd February 1996

Radstock Town	v	Hengrove Athletic	0A0 0–3	Bridgwater Town	v	Nailsea United	3–2
Weston St John	v	Fry's Club	4–3	Peasedown Ath	v	Cheddar	14–1

SEMI-FINALS

Hengrove Athletic	v	Peasedown Ath	0*2	Bridgwater Town	v	Weston St John	8–1

FINAL Monday 6th May 1996 3.00pm
BRIDGWATER TOWN v PEASEDOWN ATHLETIC 2–0 at Winterfield Road, Paulton Rovers FC.

SOMERSET PREMIER CUP
(FOUNDED 1948–49)

RECENT FINALS

1990–91	Bristol City	v	Weston-super-Mare	4–3 (Agg.)
1991–92	Bristol Rovers	v	Yeovil Town	3–2 (Agg.)
1992–93	Bristol Rovers Res	v	Taunton Town	5–1 (Agg.)
1993–94	Bath City	v	Bristol Rovers Res	5–4 (Agg.)
1994–95	Bath City	v	Taunton Town	2–0 (Agg.)

MOST WINS Bath City 17 Yeovil Town 13 Bristol City 5

SOMERSET PREMIER CUP

HOLDERS: BATH CITY

FIRST ROUND

Chard Town	v	Yeovil Town	0–2	Wellington	v	Keynsham Town	1–2

SECOND ROUND 14th November 1995

Taunton Town	v	Welton Rovers	4-1	Odd Down	v	Frome Town	4–2
Bath City	v	Keynsham Town	3–0	Weston-s-Mare	v	Clevedon Town	5p3 2*2
Minehead	v	Paulton Rovers	0–4	Brislington	v	Yeovil Town	2–1
Mangotsfield Utd	v	Backwell United	3–1	Glastonbury	v	Bristol City	0–2

THIRD ROUND w/c 27th January 1996

Paulton Rovers	v	Taunton Town	0–2	Bristol City	v	Bath City	3*2
Odd Down	v	Brislington	0–3	Weston-s-Mare	v	Mangotsfield Utd	3–4

SEMI-FINALS w/c 25th March 1996

Bristol City	v	Mangotsfield Utd	0–1	Brislington	v	Taunton Town	1–0

FINAL Monday 6th May Kick off 7.30pm
BRISLINGTON v MANGOTSFIELD UNITED 6p5 1*1 at Hand Stadium, Davis Lane, Clevedon Town FC.

Somerset Senior League Division Three action; Clutton v Robinsons Reserves

Photo - Tim Lancaster

STAFFORDSHIRE F.A.

Secretary: G S Brookes,
County Showground, Weston Road, Stafford ST18 0DB
Tel: 01785 56994 (County Office) Fax: 01785 224334

STAFFORDSHIRE SENIOR CUP
(FOUNDED 1877–78)

RECENT FINALS

1990–91	Redditch United	v	Northwich Victoria	4–3 (Agg.)
1991–92	Stafford Rangers	v	Chasetown	4–2 (Agg.)
1992–93	Stoke City Res	v	Hednesford Town	6–1 (Agg.)
1993–94	Macclesfield Town	v	Wednesfield	10–3 (Agg.)
1994–95	Stoke City Res	v	Paget Rangers	4–2 (Agg.)

MOST WINS Stoke City 17 Aston Villa 16 West Bromwich Albion 13

1995–1996
STAFFORDSHIRE SENIOR CUP

29 CLUBS **HOLDERS: STOKE CITY**

FIRST ROUND

Bolehall Swifts	v	Halesowm Harriers	1–2	Eastwood Hanley	v	Newcastle Town	1–5
Bilston Town	v	Stourport Swifts	4–1	Armitage	v	Knypersley Victoria	3–1
Stoke City	v	Leek Town	2–3	Chasetown	v	Stourbridge	1–1 0–4
Dudley Town	v	Rocester	0–1	Tamworth	v	Lye Town	9–3
Kidsgrove Ath	v	Walsall Wood	2–0	Stafford Rangers	v	Rushall Olympic	0–2
Shifnal Town	v	Oldbury United	0–4	Hednesford Tn	v	Willenhall Town	6–1
Macclesfield Tn	v	Pelsall Villa	1–1 1–0				

3 Clubs with a Bye Boldmere St Michaels, Paget Rangers, Port Vale, into

SECOND ROUND

Halesowen Harriers	v	Kidsgrove Athletic	7*3	Armitage	v	Hednesford Town	1–3
Bilston Town	v	Oldbury United	4–0	Paget Rangers	v	Stourbridge	3–2
Rocester	v	Leek Town	2–3	Rushall Olympic	v	Newcastle Town	0–4
Macclesfield Tn	v	Boldmere St Michaels	5–2	Port Vale @T	v	Tamworth	1–4

THIRD ROUND

Macclesfield Tn	v	Bilston Town	1–2	Paget Rangers	v	Hednesford Town	2*1
Leek Town	v	Halesowen Harriers	3–2	Tamworth	v	Newcastle Town	0–0 1–3

SEMI-FINALS

Bilston Town	v	Leek Town	0–1	Newcastle Town	v	Paget Rangers	2–1

FINAL First Leg Tuesday 16th April 1996
NEWCASTLE TOWN v LEEK TOWN 1–0 att; 221

FINAL Second Leg Monday 29th April 1996
LEEK TOWN v NEWCASTLE TOWN 4*2 att; 204

SUFFOLK F.A.

Secretary: William M Steward,
2 Millfields, Haughley, Stowmarket IP14 3PU
Tel: 01449 673481

SUFFOLK SENIOR CUP
(FOUNDED 1885–86)

RECENT FINALS

1990–91	Sudbury Wanderers	v	BT Research	5–1
1991–92	Whitton United	v	Long Melford	2–0
1992–93	Woodbridge Town	v	Stonham Aspal	5–2 (AET)
1993–94	Woodbridge Town	v	Saxmundham Sports	4–0
1994–95	Grundisburgh	v	Whitton United	2–0

MOST WINS Ipswich Town 16 Lowestoft Town 10 Stowmarket Town 8

1995–1996

SUFFOLK SENIOR CUP

32 CLUBS **HOLDERS: GRUNDISBURGH**

SECOND ROUND Saturday 25th November 1995

Framlingham Tn	v	Whitton United	1–0
Brantham & S Utd	v	Bury Town Res	0–0 3–5
Needham Market	v	Achilles	4–4 5–2
Mildenhall Town	v	BS Fonnereau Ath	2–2 1–3
Ashlea	v	Sudbury Wdrs Res	1–1 1–2
Stonham Aspal	v	Grundisburgh	1–2
Ipswich Wanderers	v	Oulton B&L Rail	4–1
Walton United	v	BT Research	2–2 4–2

THIRD ROUND Saturday 6th January 1996

Sudbury Wds Res	v	Ipswich Wanderers	1–4
BS Fonnereau Ath	v	Bury Town Res	3–1
Grundisburgh	v	Walton United	3*3 1*1 5p4
Framlingham Tn	v	Needham Market	1*1 3–2

SEMI-FINALS Saturday 24th February 1996

BS Fonnereau Ath v Grundisburgh 0–5
at Stowmarket Town FC.

Framlingham Tn v Ipswich Wanders 4–2
at Woodbridge Town FC.

FINAL Tuesday 16th April 1996 Kick off 7.30pm
FRAMLINGHAM TOWN v GRUNDISBURGH 0–3 at Portman Road, Ipswich Town FC.

SUFFOLK PREMIER CUP
(FOUNDED 1958–59)

RECENT FINALS

1990–91	Stowmarket Town	v	Haverhill Rovers	3–2
1991–92	Sudbury Town	v	Stowmarket Town	1–0
1992–93	Sudbury Town	v	Brantham Athletic	2–1
1993–94	Newmarket Town	v	Sudbury Town	2–1
1994–95	Newmarket Town	v	Felixstowe Town	1–1 (Rep 1–0)

MOST WINS Sudbury Town 12 Bury Town 10 Lowestoft Town 5

SUFFOLK PREMIER CUP

11 CLUBS **HOLDERS: NEWMARKET TOWN**

FIRST ROUND on or before 14th October

Sudbury Town	v	Bury Town	1–2
Lowestoft Town	v	Felixstowe P&Town	1–0
Sudbury Wanderers	v	Newmarket Town	0–1
Woodbridge Town	v	Stowmarket Town	5–1

SEMI-FINALS by March 1996

Bury Town	v	Lowestoft Town	2–1
Woodbridge Town	v	Newmarket Town	2–2 3–0

FINAL Monday 6th May 1996 Kick off 3.00pm
WOODBRIDGE TOWN v BURY TOWN 0*0

Replay Thursday 9th May 1996
BURY TOWN v WOODBRIDGE TOWN 5p4 0*0

SURREY F.A.

(Est. 1877)
Secretary: Peter Adams,
321 Kingston Road, Leatherhead, Surrey KT22 7TU
Tel: 01372 373543

SURREY SENIOR CUP
(FOUNDED 1882–83)

RECENT FINALS

1990–91	Woking	v	Kingstonian	3–0
1991–92	Carshalton Ath	v	Egham Town	3–1
1992–93	Sutton United	v	Carshalton Athletic	2–1
1993–94	Woking	v	Sutton United	3–1
1994–95	Sutton United	v	Carshalton Athletic	3–1

MOST WINS Dulwich Hamlet 16 Sutton United 13 Kingstonian 9

1995–1996

SURREY SENIOR CUP

39 CLUBS **HOLDERS: SUTTON UNITED**

SECOND QUALIFYING ROUND by 18th October

Raynes Park Vale	v	Shene Old Gramm	3–2
Dorking	v	Leatherhead	0–4
Chipstead	v	Ash United	6–0
Croydon	v	Camberley Town	0–1
Netherne	v	Old Suttonians	2–0
Cobham	v	Farnham Town	2–3
Cranleigh	v	Mersham	2–0
Walton Casuals	v	Corinthian Casuals	0–2
Ashford Tn (Mx)	v	Merton	3–1
Redhill	v	Nat West Bank	3–1
Westfield	v	Kew Association	2–1

THIRD QUALIFYING ROUND by 4th November

Corinthian-Cas	v	Ashford Tn (Mx)	2*2 5–2
Redhill	v	Carshalton	2–3
Horley Town	v	Cranleigh	0–1
Netherne	v	Farnham Town	0–1
Camberley Town	v	Godalming & G'dfd	1–3
Raynes Park Vale	v	Leatherhead	1–4
Westfield	v	Chipstead	2–2 3–4

3 Clubs with Byes Banstead Athletic, Epsom & Ewell, Tooting & Mitcham United into the

FOURTH QUALIFYING ROUND by 25th November

Corinthian-Cas	v	Farnham Town	0–0 1A0 2–0
Godalming & G'dfd	v	Banstead Athletic	0–0 1–6
Carshalton @EE	v	Epsom & Ewell	0–3
Horley Town	v	Tooting & Mitch Utd	1–4
Leatherhead	v	Chipstead	1–0

11 Clubs Exempt Carshalton Athletic, Chertsey Town, Crystal Palace, Egham Town, Kingstonian, Metropolitan Police, Molesey, Sutton United, Walton & Hersham, Whyteleafe, Woking to the

FIRST ROUND by 16th December 1995

Egham Town	v	Chertsey Town	2–4
Molesey	v	Leatherhead	3–1
Tooting & Mitch Utd	v	Sutton United	2–1
Carshalton Ath	v	Kingstonian	1–1 2–1
Banstead Athletic	v	Metropolitan Pol	1–2
Walton & Hersham	v	Crystal Palace	0–3
Woking	v	Epsom & Ewell	6–0
Corinthian Casuals	v	Whyteleafe	1–0

SECOND ROUND by 27th January 1996

Chertsey Town	v	Tooting & Mitch Utd	1–3
Corinthian Cas	v	Carshalton Ath	2–3
Metropolitan Pol	v	Crystal Palace	1–3
Woking	v	Molesey	8–1

SEMI-FINALS by 2nd March 1996

Tooting & Mitch Utd	v	Carshalton Ath	4–2
Crystal Palace @W	v	Woking	0–0 1–4

FINAL Tuesday 23rd April 1996 7.30pm
TOOTING & MITCHAM UNITED v WOKING 0–2 at Kingston Road, Kingstonian FC.

SURREY COUNTY PREMIER FINAL LEAGUE TABLE 1995/96

		P	W	D	L	F	A	Pts
1.	Chobham	30	22	3	5	71	28	69
2.	Worcester Park	30	19	6	5	56	31	63
3.	Coney Hall	30	15	8	7	47	33	53
4.	Holmsdale	30	14	6	10	60	51	48
5.	Bisley	30	13	6	11	61	53	45
6.	Bookham	30	11	11	8	48	37	44
7.	Shottermill	30	13	4	13	72	64	43
8.	Virginia Water	30	11	8	11	45	40	41
9.	Croydon MO	30	11	8	11	50	57	41
10.	Chessington	30	11	7	12	54	52	40
11.	Vandyke	30	11	6	13	44	53	39
12.	Burpham	30	10	8	12	51	55	38
13.	Sheerwater	30	10	7	13	44	54	37
14.	Ottershaw	30	6	9	15	34	53	27
15.	Hersham RBL	30	7	5	18	41	66	26
16.	Farleigh Rovers	30	2	6	22	30	81	12

WIMBLEDON & DISTRICT FOOTBALL LEAGUE

FINAL LEAGUE TABLES 1995/96

Premier Div

		P	W	D	L	F	A	Pts
1.	Bradshaw Webb	15	12	2	1	68	22	38
2.	Seven Seals Utd	16	9	5	2	53	21	32
3.	Putney Corin.	14	7	2	5	39	26	23
4.	Wilf Kroucher U	16	7	1	8	42	47	22
5.	Notvry Ath	16	6	2	8	40	32	20
6.	Nascimento	14	5	3	6	31	38	18
7.	Sportif Iviorien	12	5	3	4	21	30	18
8.	Putney Celtic	15	4	3	8	25	40	15
9.	Cosmos Utd	14	0	1	13	6	69	1

Div One

		P	W	D	L	F	A	Pts
1.	La Delizia	16	12	2	2	53	22	38
2.	Rusmill	16	11	0	5	43	24	33
3.	Stapleton	16	10	2	4	42	23	32
4.	Clapham Tn	16	8	2	6	66	44	29
5.	Balham Celtic	16	6	2	8	30	52	23
6.	Gladstone	15	6	3	6	37	29	18
7.	Union 200	16	4	3	9	36	53	17
8.	Liam Og's	16	3	1	12	34	72	9
9.	Campbell	15	3	1	11	38	60	4

JUBILEE CUP 95-96

Winners: Putney Corinthians **Runners up:** Stapleton

WIMBLEDON TROPHY 95-96

Winners: Notvry Athletic **Runners up:** Nascimento

Sheerwater FC; Surrey Premier League: *Photo - Eric Marsh*

Reigate Priory FC; one of the oldest clubs (125 years old) in Surrey

Photo - Eric Marsh

Saltdean United finalist's in the Sussex Royal Ulster Charity Cup 95-96:
Back Row (L-R); G Green (Mgr), C Deane, C Strange. M Silsby, M Hammond, J Scriven, M Tester, P Berry, D Lightwood, D Burnett (Coach).
Front; S Baker, M Shaw, T Towner, D Stevens, M Hamilton, M Sayers.

Photo - Roger Turner

Chicester City FC: *Photo - Eric Marsh*

SUSSEX F.A.

Secretary: Mr D Worsfold,
Culver Road, Lancing, West Sussex BN15 9AX (01903) 753547

SUSSEX SENIOR CUP (FOUNDED 1882–83)

RECENT FINALS

1990–91	Crawley Town	v	Littlehampton Town	2–1
1991–92	Brighton&Hove Alb Res	v	Langney Sports	1–0
1992–93	Wick	v	Oakwood	3–1
1993–94	Brighton&Hove Alb Res	v	Peacehaven & Telscombe	1–0
1994–95	Brighton&Hove Alb Res	v	Bognor Regis Town	2–0

MOST WINS Worthing 19 Eastbourne Town 12 Southwick 10

1995–1996 SUSSEX SENIOR CUP

44 CLUBS **HOLDERS: BRIGHTON & HOVE ALBION**

SECOND ROUND Saturday 25th November 1995

Pagham	v	Eastbourne	2–0
Stamco	v	Three Bridges	4–0
Bognor Regis Tn	v	Sidley United	5–1
Saltdean United	v	East Preston	1–1 0–2
Brighton & Hove	v	Newhaven	6–1
Peacehaven & T	v	Hastings Town	1–2
Chichester City	v	Wick	0–3
Langney Sports	v	Whitehawk	6–0
Lancing	v	Crawley Town	0–4
Burgess Hill Tn	v	Shoreham	2–1
Worthing	v	Oakwood	7–0
Ringmer	v	Crowborough Ath	2*1
Selsey	v	Bexhill Town	3–2
Lewes	v	Hailsham Town	3–2
Horsham	v	Portfield	2–1
Mile Oak	v	Arundel	2–0

THIRD ROUND Saturday 13th January 1996

Brighton & Hove	v	Bognor Regis Tn	2*3
Pagham	v	Worthing	1*2
Selsey	v	Crawley Town	1–3
Horsham	v	Ringmer	2–1
Hastings Town	v	Stamco	2–1
Wick	v	East Preston	1–0
Mile Oak	v	Burgess Hill Town	0–4
Langney Sports	v	Lewes	4–0

QUARTER-FINALS Saturday 10th February 1996

Hastings Town	v	Burgess Hill Town	4–0
Horsham	v	Wick	0–1
Langney Sports	v	Bognor Regis Town	2–1
Worthing	v	Crawley Town	1–4

SEMI-FINALS March 1996

Crawley Town v Wick 4–1
at Culver Road, Lancing FC.

Hastings Town v Langney Sports 6–0
at The Dripping Pan, Mountfield Road, Lewes FC.

FINAL Monday 6th May 1996 3.00pm
CRAWLEY TOWN v HASTINGS TOWN 0–1 at Woodside Road, Worthing FC.

Hastings Town, Sussex Senior Cup Winners. Photo Roger Turner.

SUSSEX ROYAL ULSTER RIFLES CHARITY CUP
(FOUNDED 1896–97)

RECENT FINALS

1990–91	Whitehaak	v	Peacehaven & Tels	2–1
1991–92	Burgess Hill Tn	v	Ringmer	2–1 (AET)
1992–93	Peacehaven & Tels	v	Lancing	2–1
1993–94	Newhaven	v	Pagham	4–0
1994–95	Peacehaven & Tels	v	Stamco	1–0

MOST WINS Horsham 13 Worthing 12 Southwick 10

SUSSEX ROYAL ULSTER RIFLES CHARITY CUP

37 CLUBS **HOLDERS: PEACEHAVEN & TELSCOMBE**

PRELIMINARY ROUND

Whitehawk	v	Eastbourne Town	3–1
Withdean	v	Newhaven	3–6
Steyning Town	v	East Preston	0–0 0–3
Wick	v	Littlehampton Tn	3–0
Selsey	v	Broadbridge Heath	4–1

FIRST ROUND Saturday 23rd September

East Grinstead	v	Oakwood	5–0
Three Bridges	v	Ringmer	1–2
Burgess Hill Tn	v	Newhaven	4–1
Peacehaven & T	v	Sidley United	4–1
Eastbourne Utd	v	Crowborough Athletic	4–3
Hailsham Town	v	Saltdean United	0–2
Stamco	v	Langney Sports	3–1
Bexhill Town	v	Whitehawk	2*3
Chichester City	v	Midhurst & Easeb'ne	0–2
Southwick	v	Pagham	1*1 1–0
Bosham	v	Wick	2–4
Mile Oak	v	Selsey	2–1
Hassocks	v	Worthing United	4*2
Horsham YMCA	v	Portfield	1–5
Shoreham	v	Lancing	2–0
Arundel	v	East Preston	3–1

SECOND ROUND Saturday 4th November 1995

Ringmer	v	Burgess Hill Town	0–1
Saltdean United	v	Whitehawk	4–3
East Grinstead	v	Eastbourne United	2–1
Stamco	v	Peacehaven & Tels	0–1
Southwick	v	Wick	0*2
Portfield	v	Arundel	0*2
Midhurst&Easeb'ne	v	Hassocks	2–1
Shoreham	v	Mile Oak	6–1

QUARTER-FINALS Saturday 6th January 1996

Burgess Hill Town	v	Arundel	2–4
East Grinstead	v	Peacehaven & Tels	0–3
Midhurst&Easeb'ne	v	Saltdean United	3*3 0–10
Wick	v	Shoreham	1–5

SEMI-FINALS 10th February 1996

Peacehaven & Tels	v	Arundel	5–1
Shoreham	v	Saltdean United	0–1

FINAL Tuesday 5th March 1996

PEACEHAVEN & TELSCOMBE v SALTDEAN UNITED 1–0 at Culver Road, Lancing FC. att; 482

WESTMORLAND F.A.

Founded: 1897

Secretary: Mr J B Fleming,
Beezon Chambers, off Sandes Avenue, Kendal, Cumbria
(01539) 730946 (County Office)

WESTMORLAND SENIOR CUP (FOUNDED 1896–97)

RECENT FINALS

1990–91	Netherfield	v	Burton Thistle	4–0
1991–92	Coniston	v	Kendal United	4–1
1992–93	Coniston	v	Ambleside	4–2
1993–94	Kendal United	v	Keswick	2–0
1994–95	Kendal United	v	Staveley United	2–1

MOST WINS Corinthians 11 Netherfield 8 Burneside 7 Windermere 7

1995–1996

'WESTMORLAND GAZETTE' SENIOR CHALLENGE CUP

23 CLUBS

HOLDERS: KENDAL UNITED

FIRST ROUND Saturday 16th September

Burton Thistle	v	Appleby	0–3
Burneside	v	Ambleside United	1–4
Grange Amt	v	Kirkby Stephen	3–0
Milnthorpe Cor'ian	v	Coniston	3–1
Staveley United	v	Wetheriggs	2–1
Kendal County	v	Lunesdale United	4–1
Shap	v	Arnside	0–2

SECOND ROUND 7th October

Staveley United	v	Kendal United**	2–3
Keswick**	v	Milnthorpe Cor'ian	2–3
Sedburgh**	v	Arnside	7–0
Braithewaite**	v	Kirkby Lonsdale**	1–2
Grange Amateur	v	Windermere SC**	3–0
Endmoor KGR**	v	Kendal County	5–0
Kirkoswald**	v	Netherfield Res**	3–3 0–3
Appleby	v	Ambleside United	2–4

**9 Clubs with Byes

THIRD ROUND Saturday 18th November 1995

Ambleside United	v	Kendal County	2–1
Milnthorpe Cor'ian	v	Kirkby Lonsdale	4–1
Grange Amt	v	Netherfield Res	1–1 3–1
Kendal United	v	Sedburgh	1–1 3–1

SEMI-FINALS Saturday 2nd March 1996 2.30pm

Ambleside United	v	Netherfield Res	5–5 0–5
Milnthorpe Cor'ian	v	Kendal United	3–0

FINAL Saturday 13th April
NETHERFIELD RESERVES v MILNTHORPE CORINTHIANS 0–0 at Parkside Road, Kendal,Netherfield FC.

FINAL REPLAY Saturday 20th April 1996
MILNTHORPE CORINTHIANS v NETHERFIELD RESERVES 2–1 at Milnthorpe Corinthians FC.

WEST RIDING F.A.

Secretary: Roy Carter JP,
Fleet Lane, Woodlesford, Leeds LS26 8NX (0113) 231 0101 (County Office)

WEST RIDING SENIOR CUP
(FOUNDED 1924–25)

RECENT FINALS

1990–91	Bradford Park Ave	v	Pontefract Collieries	5–1
1991–92	Goole Town	v	Bradley Rangers	3–2
1992–93	Glasshoughton Welfare	v	Selby Town	4–2
1993–94	Guiseley	v	Goole Town	1–0
1994–95	Farsley Celtic	v	Thackley	2–1

MOST WINS Goole Town 11 Farsley Celtic 7 Guiseley 5

1995–1996

WEST RIDING COUNTY CUP

20 CLUBS **HOLDERS: FARSLEY CELTIC**

FIRST ROUND by Saturday 11th November 1995

Liversedge	v	Glasshoughton Welf	0–1
Goole Town	v	Guiseley	0–3
Garforth Town	v	Ossett Albion	0–3
Yorkshire Amateur	v	Selby Town	2–1

SECOND ROUND by Saturday 9th December 1995

Pktefract Coll's	v	Glasshoughton Welf	0–2
Bradford Park Ave	v	Ossett Albion	3–1
Guiseley	v	Hatfield Main	3*3 2–0
Yorkshire Amt	v	Thackley	0–2
Farsley Celtic	v	Harrogate Town	3–2
Harrogate Rly	v	Tadcaster Alb	8p7 1*1 2*2
Armthorpe Welf	v	Eccleshill Utd Sp Cl	1–2
Halifax Town	v	Ossett Town	5–1

FOURTH ROUND Tuesday 6th February unless stated

Harrogate Rly	v	Eccleshill Utd Sp	tba
Thackley	v	Guiseley	1*2
Glasshoughton MW	v	Bradford Park Ave	0–2
Farsley Celtic	v	Halifax Town	1–0

SEMI-FINALS

Harrogate Rly	v	Guiseley	1–3
Farsley Celtic	v	Bradford Park Ave	2A1 1–0

FINAL Wednesday 3rd April 1996 Kick off 7.30pm
FARSLEY CELTIC v GUISELEY 0–0 at West Riding Co FA Ground, Fleet Lane, Leeds att; 598

FINAL REPLAY Wednesday 10th April 1996
FARSLEY CELTIC v GUISELEY 2–3 at West Riding Co FA Ground, Fleet Lane, Leeds att; 440

WEST RIDING COUNTY AMATEUR LEAGUE

Founded: 1922
President: J Jones
Hon. Secretary: Mr D H Humpleby,
1 The Leys, Baildon, Shipley, Bradford BD17 5PR

Brighouse Town maintained their domination of the League, last seasons champions making it a league and cup double this time. Brighouse always had games in hand on their rivals and despite strong challenges from Altofts, Golcar and Bradford based Fields,(who hope to move up to Northern Counties East football in the near future), they finished a full seven points clear by the season close.

Despite winning over a third of their league games, Campion and Otley Town both return to Division One after brief spells in the Premier Division- although their points totals would have ensured survival in most other seasons.

The race for the First Division title was a four horse race. Newcomers Storthers Hall and Hemsworth made the early running, along with Keighley based Phoenix. Storthers Hall's repeat performance in reaching the County Cup Final (lost 1-2 to Boroughbridge in a repeat of last seasons final) did not affect their league form however, and it was they who took the titlt, winning their games in hand late in the season

Meanwhile Dudley Hill seem to have turned the tide. The Bradford side dominated the league in the 1970's-80's have had a lean time recently, but a late run saw them pip their rivals for second place and promotion to the premier division. Poor Phoenix narrowly missed promotion for the second year in succession. At the wrong end of the table TS Harrison were relegated for the second year in succession. Spen Valley champions Oventhorpe won division two at a canter, with Wakefield side Eastmoor squeezing out ex-premier outfit Littletown for second place. What a difference a season made to Keighley Shamrocks! Despite finishing one of the bottom last season, the resurrgent club led the division three almost all season and despite the strong challenge of several premier division reserve sides held on to take the division title. Newcomers Bradford Celtic and Rawdon found the going hard, finishing well down the table.

HORTON PRINT FINAL LEAGUE TABLES 1995/96

Div One	P	W	D	L	F	A	Pts
1. Brighouse Tn	26	17	3	6	79	30	37
2. Altofts	26	14	4	8	46	46	32
3. Field	26	14	3	9	65	48	31
4. Tyersal	26	10	9	7	67	56	29
5. Marsden	26	11	6	9	51	42	28
6. Golcar Utd	26	11	6	9	56	54	28
7. Ovenden W Rid	26	12	3	11	65	63	27
8. Crag Rd Utd	26	10	4	12	49	39	24
9. Halifax Irish	26	10	4	12	52	79	24
10. Salts	26	9	4	13	48	58	22
11. Wibsey	26	8	6	12	46	56	22
12. Farnley	26	8	6	12	44	60	22
13. Campion	26	9	3	14	57	61	*19
14. Otley Tn	26	9	0	17	36	67	18

** 2 points deducted*

Div Two	P	W	D	L	F	A	Pts
1. Storthes Hall	30	23	5	2	100	34	51
2. Dudley Hill	30	21	5	4	78	35	47
3. Hemsworth	30	20	6	4	85	33	46
4. Phoenix	30	22	2	6	81	42	46
5. Greetland	30	12	8	10	58	51	32
6. Pontefract	30	12	7	11	49	52	31
7. Morley Tn	30	10	9	11	46	53	29
8. Brighouse T R	30	11	6	13	62	63	28
9. Rawdon O B	30	11	6	13	45	64	28
10. Aberford A	30	11	4	15	55	57	26
11. Ardsley Cel	30	9	7	14	58	74	25
12. Ventus Y C	30	8	6	16	45	73	22
13. Bowling Cel	30	8	4	18	50	75	20
14. Lower Hopton	30	6	7	17	35	64	19
15. Hall Grn Utd	30	8	2	20	46	70	18
16. TS Harrison	30	4	5	21	51	99	13

Div Two	P	W	D	L	F	A	Pts
1. Overthorpe SC	26	20	2	4	99	36	42
2. Eastmoor Alb	25#	17	0	8	68	34	34
3. Littletown	26	13	5	8	66	53	31
4. Holmewood Ath	26	13	4	9	70	56	30
5. Selby RSSC*	26	13	3	10	68	50	29
6. Steeton	26	13	3	10	64	56	29
7. Heckmondwike	26	12	4	10	72	69	28
8. Salts GSOB	25#	10	4	11	58	58	24
9. Pudsey Lib	25#	10	4	11	56	58	24
10. Wibsey A	26	10	4	12	64	68	24
11. Westbrook W	26	6	6	14	49	79	18
12. Trinity Ath	26	7	3	16	40	75	17
13. Ovendon Res	26	7	2	17	46	95	16
14. Allerton*	25#	5	4	16	49	82	14

** Withdrawn*

 # Remaining fixtures declared void

Div Three	P	W	D	L	F	A	Pts
1. Keighley Sham	28	22	3	3	100	32	47
2. Campion Res	28	19	6	3	92	44	44
3. Field Res	28	19	4	5	88	46	42
4. Altofts Res	28	18	3	7	82	54	39
5. Dynamoes	28	15	4	9	95	76	34
6. Low Moor	27#	15	2	10	77	62	32
7. Salts Res	28	13	4	11	61	49	30
8. Aberford A R	27#	9	9	9	55	64	27
9. Bowling	28	7	8	13	72	90	22
10. Hunsworth	28	7	6	15	68	86	20
11. Bradford Cel	28	8	4	16	60	108	20
12. Tyersal Res	28	7	5	16	59	73	19
13. Crag Rd U Res	28	8	3	17	59	86	19
14. Rawdon	28	4	5	19	41	93	13
15. Green Lane	28	4	2	22	38	83	10

 # Remaining fixtures declared void

WAKEFIELD & DISTRICT

Div One	P	W	D	L	F	A	Pts
1. Stanley Utd	24	18	2	4	87	29	56
2. Walton	24	12	5	7	60	50	41
3. Royal Oak	24	12	4	8	45	44	40
4. Elephant & C	24	11	4	9	60	51	37
5. Shepherds A	24	9	5	10	54	63	32
6. St Oswalds A	24	9	4	11	42	49	31
7. Fieldhead Hosp	24	4	10	10	45	51	22
8. Nestell MW R	24	5	6	13	25	48	21
9. Cherry Tree	24	5	6	13	32	70	21

Div Two	P	W	D	L	F	A	Pts
1. Gardeners A	22	19	2	1	92	21	59
2. Queens	22	15	2	5	93	54	47
3. Flanshaw Htl	22	12	6	4	86	39	42
4. Bay Horse W	22	13	32	6	70	42	42
5. Snydale Ath	22	12	5	5	83	34	41
6. Hall Grn OB	22	7	4	11	52	71	25
7. Normanton S J	22	7	3	12	39	45	24
8. Henry Boons	22	6	4	12	45	78	22
9. Vine Tree	22	6	3	13	32	65	21
10. Kettlethorpe	22	6	2	14	43	71	20
11. Shepherds A R	22	4	5	13	36	89	17
12. British Oak	22	4	3	15	29	90	15

PREMIER DIVISION CLUBS 1995-96

ALTOFTS

Secretary: M Bell, 67 Churchfield Croft, Altofts, Normanton WF6 2QB (01924 893507)
Ground: Altofts Sports Club, Lock Lane, Altofts (01924 892708)
Colours: Red & white/black/black **Change Colours:** Blue/white

BRIGHOUSE TOWN

Secretary: N Wilson,Lundy House, Limes Avenue, Halifax HX3 0NT (01422 345057)
Ground: St Giles Road, Hove Edge, Brighouse.
Colours: Tangerine/black/black **Change Colours:** White/navy/navy

CAMPION

Secretary: A Shepherd, 1 Avocet Close, Bradford BD8 0RB (01274 884152)
Ground: Manningham Mills CC, Scotchman Rd, Heaton, Bradford (01274 546726)
Colours: Black & Yellow/black/black **Change Colours:** All blue

CRAG ROAD UNITED

Secretary: R Knight, 23 Easthorpe Court, Eccleshill, Bradford BD2 2PB (01274 635889)
Ground: Apperley Bridge, Greengats, Bradford
Colours: Red & black/black **Change Colours:** All white

FARNLEY

Secretary: Steve Coulson, Lane Side Farm, Tong Road, Farnley, Leeds LS12 5HF (0113 257 3992)
Ground: Lawns Lane, Farnley (0113 2638826)
Colours: White/black **Change Colours:** Yellow/black/black

FIELD A F C

Secretary: C Clough, 8 Hospital Road, Riddlesdon, Keighley BD20 5EP (01535 603782)
Ground: Hollingwood Lane, Lidget Green, Bradford (01274 571750)
Colours: All Blue **Change Colours:** Green & white/green/green

GOLCAR UNITED

Secretary: Margaret Whitaker, 8 Burcott Drive, Outlane, Huddersfield HD3 3FY (01422 378901)
Ground: Longfield Rec. Golcar.
Colours: Blue & white/blue **Change Colours:** Yellow/black/black

HALIFAX IRISH CLUB

Secretary: R Stephenson, 10 Marldon Road, Nothowram, Halifax HX3 7BP (01422 201594)
Ground: Natty Lane, Illingworth, Halifax (01422 360134)
Colours: Green/white/gold **Change Colours:** Black & White

MARSDEN

Secretary: D Warwick, 44 Western Road, Cowlersley, Huddersfield HD7 5TH (01484 647807)
Ground: Fall Lane, Marsden, Huddersfield (01484 844191)
Colours: Black & White stripes/black **Change Colours:** All blue

OTLEY TOWN

Secretary: G W Jones, 5 Cambridge Drive, Otley, Leeds, LS21 1DD (01943 462380)
Ground: Old Show Field, Pool Road, Otley (01943 461025)
Colours: Yellow/blue **Change Colours:** Blue & White/white/blue

OVENDEN WEST RIDING

Secretary: S Smith, 192 Illingworth Road, Bradshaw, Halifax HX2 9XH (01422 248753)
Ground: Natty Lane,Illingworth, Halifax (01422 360134)
Colours: Black & jade/black **Change Colours:** Red & blue stripes

SALTS

Secretary: Brian Parker, 14 Northedge Meadow, Doctor Hill, Idle, Bradford BD10 8SF (01274 621167)
Ground: Salts Playing Fields, Hirst Lane, Shipley (01274 587427)
Colours: White/blue/blue **Change Colours:** All blue

TYERSAL

Secretary: H Foster, 5 Norwood House, Sticker Lane, Bradford Bd4 8DR (01274 667773)
Ground: Arkwright Street, off Dick Lane, Bradford 4
Colours: Red & white/red/white **Change Colours:**

WIBSEY

Secretary: D Nolan, 21 Glendale Drive, Bradford Bd6 2LT (01274 602934)
Ground: Harold Park
Colours: Blue & white/blue **Change Colours:**

FIRST DIVISION CLUBS 1995-96

ABERFORD ALBION
Secretary: P A Walton, 18 Highfield Road, Aberford, Leeds LS25 (01532 813206)
Ground: The Willows off A1 Bypass, Aberford (01532 813248)
Colours: Yellow/yellow/red **Change Colours:** All green

ARDSLEY CELTIC
Secretary: Stuart Scott, 31 Clifton Avenue, Stanley, Wakefield WF3 4HB (01924 870993)
Ground: White Horse, Main Street, East Ardsley.
Colours: Green & white/white/green **Change Colours:** Blue & white/white/blue

BOWLING CELTIC
Secretary: Stewart Delaney, 557 Huddersfield Road, Wyke, Bradford BD12 (01274 605423)
Ground: Avenue Road P F, Bowling Park, West Bowling, Bradford
Colours: Yellow & blue/blue/blue **Change Colours:** Blue & white/black/black

DUDLEY HILL ATHLETIC
Secretary: C Cook, 12 Richardson Street, Oakenshaw, Bradford BD12 7EH (01274 604561)
Ground: Hunsworth Lane, East Bierley.
Colours: Red & navy/navy/navy **Change Colours:** Green/black/green

GREETLAND
Secretary: Peter Walker, 15 Sunnybank Drive, Greetland, Halifax HX4 8NB (01422 378203)
Ground: Greetland Community Centre, Rochdale Road, Greetland, Halifax (01422 370140)
Colours: White/green **Change Colours:** Green/white

HALL GREEN UNITED
Secretary: S Marsden, 28 Church View, Crigglestone, Wakefield WF4 3PF (01924 253095)
Ground: Haslegrove Sports Ground, Criggleston (01924 254544)
Colours: Green & white/green/green **Change Colours:** Red/black/black

HEMSWORTH MINERS WELFARE
Secretary: Barry Turner, 20 Rockingham St, Fitzwilliam, Pontefract WF9 5AB (01977 616707)
Ground: Fitzwilliam Sports Complex, Wakefield Road, Fitzwilliam
Colours; All blue

LOWER HOPTON
Secretary: Graham Preston, 14 Leonards Place, Bingley, Bradford BD16 1AD (01274 567239)
Ground: Woodend Road, Lower Hopton, Mirfield (01924 492048)
Colours: Sky/blue/sky **Change Colours:** All gold

MORLEY TOWN
Secretary: Melvyn Hudson, 20 Brayshaw Road, East Ardsley nr Wakefield WF3 2JJ (01924 825833)
Ground: Brookes PF, Nepshaw Lane, Morley
Colours: Blue & red/blue **Change Colours:** All blue

PHOENIX
Secretary: M Breeze, 17 Green Avenue, Silsden, Keighley BD20 9LD (01535 669940)
Ground: Utley, Keighley.
Colours: Black & white stripes/black/black & white **Change Colours:** Grey & green

PONTEFRACT
Secretary: Mark Scott, 6 Avenue Terrace, Halfpenny Lane, Pontefract WF8 4BE (01977 703141)
Ground: Pontefract Park (01977 702228)
Colours: Black & blue/black/black **Change Colours:** Grey/black/black

RAWDON OLD BOYS
Secretary: D Saynor, 10 West Lea Grove, Yeadon, Leeds, LS19 7EF (01532 506037)
Ground: Hanson Field, Rawdon
Colours: White/purple/purple **Change Colours:**

STORTHERS HALL
Secretary: M Brooks, 16 Cockley Meadows, Kirkheaton, Huddersfield HD5 0LA (01484 426211)
Ground: Woodfield Park, Police Sports Ground, Lockwood
Colours: White/blue/white

T.S.HARRISON
Secretary: R Fisher, 32 Berwick Avenue, Heckmondwike WF16 9AE (01924 402206)
Ground: T S Harrison Sports & Social Club, Healey Lane, Batley (01924 475859)
Colours: All Red **Change Colours:**

VENTUS & YEADON CELTIC
Secretary: Frank Veto, 120 Pullan Avenue, Eccleshill, Bradford BD2 3RN (01274 779361)
Ground: Dam Lane, Yeadon, Leeds
Colours: Black & White stripes/black/black **Change Colours:** White & black

CRAVEN & DISTRICT FOOTBALL LEAGUE FINAL TABLES 1995/96

Skipton Bulldogs made history in becoming the first team to remain unbeaten in two consecutive seasons. Oxenhope and Embsay pushed the Skipton side all the way, Oxenhope needing to beat Bulldogs by 10 goals in their final match of the season; a 1-1 draw was the result.
Top teams in thie League progress to the East Lancashire League or the West Riding League

Skipton Building Society

Premier Div	*P*	*W*	*D*	*L*	*F*	*A*	*Pts*
1. Skipton B/dogs	20	12	8	0	66	19	32
2. Oxenhope Rec	20	13	4	3	54	25	30
3. Cononley Sp	20	13	3	4	65	31	29
4. Embsay	20	12	4	4	71	25	28
5. Keighley Lifts	20	10	4	6	42	31	24
6. Crosshill	20	6	5	9	30	42	17
7. Earby Tn	20	7	3	10	39	48	17
8. Carleton	20	6	3	11	40	62	15
9. Haworth	20	6	3	11	47	69	15
10. Barnoldswick	20	3	3	14	28	65	9
11. Nelson F/ridge	20	2	0	18	14	79	4

Dalesway Caravan Park

Div One	*P*	*W*	*D*	*L*	*F*	*A*	*Pts*
1. Skipton Tn	20	15	3	2	69	24	33
2. Skipton LMS	20	15	2	3	73	40	32
3. Rimington	20	12	4	4	50	31	28
4. Cowling	20	12	0	8	55	54	24
5. Rolls Royce	20	9	2	9	48	54	20
6. Intake	20	7	5	8	56	44	19
7. Colne Cricket	20	7	2	11	38	47	16
8. Oxenhope R R	20	6	4	10	33	50	16
9. Bronte Wand	20	5	5	10	39	49	15
10. Grindelton	20	4	1	15	41	63	9
11. Bradley	20	3	2	15	42	88	8

SPEN VALLEY & DISTRICT LEAGUE

Top teams in this league progress to the West Riding County Amateur, or the West Yorkshire League.

FINAL LEAGUE TABLES 1995/96

Premier Div	*P*	*W*	*D*	*L*	*F*	*A*	*Pts*
1. Yorkshire Rose	20	16	2	2	71	22	50
2. White Rose	20	16	1	3	114	47	49
3. Hightown	20	12	4	4	91	34	40
4. Batley WMC	20	12	2	6	59	45	38
5. Howden Clough	20	10	6	4	66	40	36
6. Barclays A	20	6	4	10	48	80	22
7. Saville Tn	19	6	3	10	53	60	21
8. Shoulder	20	5	4	11	34	59	19
9. Overthorpe	19	2	7	10	27	58	13
10. Bl Labrador	20	4	0	16	33	108	12
11. Mirfield Tn	20	1	5	14	27	73	8

Old Oak & Airedale Celtic both resigned records expunged

Div One	*P*	*W*	*D*	*L*	*F*	*A*	*Pts*
1. Wellington	20	20	0	0	96	27	60
2. Ravensthorpe	20	13	2	5	75	36	41
3. Barclays B	20	12	5	3	79	43	41
4. Scholes	20	10	3	7	74	58	33
5. White Horse	20	10	2	8	65	40	32
6. Fountain	20	9	3	8	72	53	30
7. Howden Cl Res	20	8	1	11	47	62	25
8. Rising Sun	20	7	3	10	60	84	24
9. Thornhill	20	6	2	12	45	68	20
10. Bosnia	20	4	1	15	38	83	13
11. Inter Batley	20	0	0	20	24	138	0

Flyers resigned record expunged

SELBY & DISTRICT FOOTBALL LEAGUE

FINAL LEAGUE TABLES 1995/96

Div One	*P*	*W*	*D*	*L*	*F*	*A*	*Pts*
1. Kippax Utd	20	15	4	1	79	21	49
2. Thorpe Utd	20	13	3	4	72	28	42
3. Hensall Ath	20	13	3	4	48	27	42
4. Crimea Tav	20	10	3	7	40	40	33
5. John O'Gaunts	20	7	5	8	24	43	26
6. Redhill SS	20	6	7	7	39	46	25
7. Barlby	20	6	5	9	47	54	23
8. Knottingley	20	6	4	10	43	52	22
9. Pollington	20	5	5	10	39	54	20
10. Altofts A	20	5	2	13	25	65	17
11. Fox Inn	20	1	5	14	22	55	8

Div Two	*P*	*W*	*D*	*L*	*F*	*A*	*Pts*
1. Riccall Coll	20	16	1	3	75	28	49
2. Kippax Wel	20	14	3	4	62	24	45
3. Normanton	20	10	5	5	45	28	35
4. Real Cliffe	20	10	3	7	49	49	33
5. Thorpe U R	20	8	5	7	50	57	32
6. S Milford	20	9	1	10	53	60	28
7. Monk Fryston	20	7	4	9	47	57	25
8. Ferrybridge	20	7	2	11	39	40	23
9. Four Ferrets	20	5	4	11	39	50	19
10. Drax PS	20	6	0	14	33	67	18
11. Eggborough	20	4	1	15	40	74	13

HALIFAX & DISTRICT FOOTBALL LEAGUE FINAL TABLES 1995/96

Last seasons division one champion Halifax Kestrels led throughout the season, finishing 8 points clear of a strong Hebden Royd team. At the other end of the table Ruburn and Mixenden were both relegated after poor seasons.
Queensbury 72 made it four championship titles on the trot as they sped to the Division One title. Since leaving the West Riding County Amateur League at the end of the 1991-92 season they have been champions in each of their subsequent seasons, winning their way from Division Four to next season the Premier Division. The side also reached the final of the Bradford & District Cup for the first team, meeting County Amateur opponents Tyersal FC.

Premier Div	P	W	D	L	F	A	Pts
1. Halifax Kest	22	17*	4	0	81	24	40
2. Hebden Royd	22	15	2	5	75	37	32
3. Stump Cross	22	15	2	5	53	24	32
4. St Andrews	22	13	5	4	51	26	31
5. Sowerby Brdge	22	9	5	8	53	42	23
6. Midgley Utd	22	8	3	11	41	48	19
7. Denholme Utd	22	7	4	11	42	43	18
8. Shelf Utd	22	6	6	10	36	55	18
9. Peacock	22	6	4	12	37	56	16
10. Salem	22	5	4	13	47	75	14
11. Ryburn Utd	22	4	3	15	30	75	11
12. Mixenden Utd	22	4	2	15*	31	72	10

** Halifax Kestrels awarded 2 points*

Div One	P	W	D	L	F	A	Pts
1. Queensbury	22	17	3	2	112	39	38
2. Shant Holmfield	22	13	7	2	66	38	32
3. Greetland	22	11	5	6	52	51	27
4. Wheatley	22	12	2	8	81	56	26
5. Wadsworth	22	10	5	7	77	72	25
6. Warley Tn	22	9	5	8	63	65	23
7. Trafalgar 86	22	8	6	8	61	60	22
8. Halifax IDC	22	9	3	9	62	66	21
9. Junction Inn	22	8	4	10	51	62	20
10. Sowerby Utd	22	5	5	12	57	76	15
11. Boothtown	22	2	4	15	35	70	10
12. Calder 76	22	2	1	19	42	104	5

BRADFORD GRATTAN LEAGUE FINAL TABLES 1995/96

Premier Division	P	W	D	L	F	A	Pts
1. Thornton FC	18	15	0	3	58	32	45
2. Woodend Rangers	18	14	1	3	94	22	43
3. Fagley FC	18	9	2	7	68	59	29
4. British Queen	18	9	2	7	50	50	29
5. Pakistan C C	18	4	3	11	38	75	15
6. Bierley County	18	3	2	13	31	64	11
7. Holme Wood Ath Res	18	2	4	12	44	81	10

Division One: **Winners:** Holme Wood Athletic A **Runners-up:** Wrose FC
Division Two: **Winners:** Royds United **Runners-up:** Ryecroft Rangers

LRP BRIGHOUSE SUNDAY LEAGUE

FINAL LEAGUE TABLES 1995/96

Div One	P	W	D	L	F	A	Pts
1. Star	18	17	0	1	85	25	34
2. Elland	18	16	0	2	69	19	32
3. Crown	18	12	2	4	68	23	26
4. Windmill	18	7	2	9	52	52	16
5. Top Club	18	6	3	9	41	46	15
6. Rastrick CC	18	6	3	9	42	72	15
7. Whitehall	18	6	0	12	40	91	12
8. Greyhound	18	4	3	11	43	65	11
9. Thornhill Briggs	18	4	3	11	44	68	11
10. Eastfield	18	3	2	13	24	61	8

Div Two	P	W	D	L	F	A	Pts
1. Sun Inn	18	11	5	2	64	38	27
2. Holywell Gr	18	11	4	3	54	32	26
3. Hove Edge	18	12	1	5	83	43	25
4. Pond	18	10	4	4	57	38	24
5. Rastrick OB	18	9	3	6	48	34	*19
6. Northowram	18	8	0	10	54	67	16
7. Pop Inn	18	6	2	10	36	49	14
8. Town Hall	18	4	1	13	44	66	9
9. Triangle	18	2	5	11	32	59	9
10. Travellers	18	4	2	12	22	81	9

** 2 points deducted*

YORKSHIRE OLD BOYS ASSOCIATION LEAGUE

FINAL LEAGUE TABLES 1995/96

Senior Div A	P	W	D	L	F	A	Pts
1. Wakefield C	22	15	3	4	74	29	48
2. M Murray FP	22	13	4	5	52	29	43
3. Almondburians	22	13	1	8	66	48	40
4. Leeds Univ Un	22	10	7	5	54	31	37
5. Yorkshire Bank	22	12	1	9	44	47	37
6. Roundhegians	22	11	1	10	45	44	34
7. O Modernians	22	9	6	7	59	47	33
8. O Centralians	22	9	4	9	46	50	31
9. Sandal Wand	22	8	3	11	40	57	27
10. Leeds Medics	22	3	6	13	27	54	15
11. Trinity AS Col	22	4	3	15	49	89	15
12. Academicals	22	3	5	14	37	68	14

Senior Div B	P	W	D	L	F	A	Pts
1. Ealadians	20	16	1	3	73	21	49
2. Abbey Grange	20	15	2	3	60	34	47
3. Wheelwright	20	11	2	7	57	42	35
4. O Batelians	20	11	1	8	77	48	34
5. Yorkshire B Res	20	9	1	10	44	51	28
6. Salendine Nook	20	8	4	8	41	57	28
7. Wakefield C R	20	7	3	10	36	52	24
8. Modernians R	20	7	2	11	37	44	23
9. O Thornesians	20	6	4	10	42	56	22
10. O Collegians	20	5	6	9	39	60	21
11. Hartshead Moor	20	1	2	17	20	61	5

HUDDERSFIELD & DISTRICT FOOTBALL LEAGUE

Possibly the second strongest league in the West Riding behind the West Riding County Amateur League. Top teams progress to the West Riding Amateur if desired.

FINAL LEAGUE TABLES 1995/96

Div One	P	W	D	L	F	A	Pts
1. Scholes	22	14	5	3	57	30	33
2. Brackenhall	22	13	5	4	62	46	31
3. Kirkburton	22	12	4	6	61	37	28
4. Bay Athletic	22	10	8	4	50	34	28
5. Kirkheaton	22	10	3	9	40	35	23
6. Hepworth	22	9	5	8	41	39	23
7. Storthers Hall R	22	9	3	10	38	44	21
8. Almondsbury	22	8	4	10	41	36	20
9. Honley	22	7	5	10	33	39	19
10. Heywood Sp	22	4	10	8	31	42	18
11. Meltham	22	6	2	14	39	54	14
12. Brittannia Sp	22	2	2	18	33	90	6

Div Two	P	W	D	L	F	A	Pts
1. Skelmanthorpe	26	21	2	3	79	14	44
2. Wooldale	26	19	4	3	85	33	42
3. Shepley	26	17	3	6	52	44	37
4. Slaithwaite	26	17	0	9	75	42	34
5. Rawthorpe	26	14	3	9	71	50	31
6. Upperthong	26	11	7	8	61	58	29
7. Marsden	26	11	5	10	48	44	27
8. Grange Moor	26	7	6	13	49	55	20
9. Cartworth Moor	26	9	2	15	64	79	20
10. Lepton	26	8	2	16	60	81	18
11. Netherton	26	6	6	14	40	71	18
12. Black Stars	26	6	5	15	34	71	17
13. Cravens	26	7	2	17	42	73	16
14. Berry Brow	26	5	1	20	42	87	11

Division Three	P	W	D	L	F	A	Pts
1. Sovereign	26	20	2	4	86	32	42
2. Uppermill	26	20	2	4	81	38	42
3. Golcar Res	26	16	5	5	73	35	37
4. Netherthong	26	15	5	6	78	53	35
5. Diggle	26	15	3	8	70	38	33
6. Lockwood	26	14	3	9	67	51	31
7. Little John	26	11	5	10	64	52	27
8. Flockton	26	12	2	12	64	62	26
9. Peters Hotel	26	9	6	11	62	57	24
10. Scissett	26	8	6	12	45	60	22
11. Academicals	26	7	6	13	46	59	20
12. KKS	26	7	2	17	46	82	16
13. Lindley	26	2	4	20	41	85	8
14. Linthwaite	26	0	1	25	19	138	1

LEEDS RED TRIANGLE LEAGUE

FINAL LEAGUE TABLES 1995/96

Premier Div	P	W	D	L	F	A	Pts
1. Seacroft WMC	22	18	1	3	88	28	55
2. Wykebeck Arms	22	18	0	4	107	45	54
3. Beeston Spin	22	14	5	3	83	28	47
4. Torre Soc Ath	22	11	6	5	55	34	39
5. Farnley WMC	22	11	4	7	76	51	37
6. Victoria	22	11	4	7	50	41	37
7. Belle Isle	22	8	6	8	59	51	30
8. Wagon & Horses	22	6	3	13	43	75	21
9. Merlins	22	5	4	13	54	75	19
10. Crossgates	22	4	4	14	29	82	16
11. Meanwood	22	3	2	17	32	84	11
12. W Shaftsbury	22	3	1	18	22	104	10

Senior Div	P	W	D	L	F	A	Pts
1. Corpus Christi	22	20	2	0	134	32	62
2. Cavalier	22	14	5	3	126	33	47
3. Griffin Head	22	14	3	5	108	54	45
4. Oddfellows	22	14	1	7	91	47	43
5. Pudsey Boro	22	12	5	5	117	67	41
6. Dragon Rovers	22	10	2	10	82	77	32
7. Woodhouse	22	10	1	11	75	74	31
8. Royal Hotel	22	9	3	10	81	98	30
9. Morley Dashers	22	5	5	12	70	86	20
10. Mazz United	22	6	1	15	58	99	19
11. Beulah Hotel	22	3	0	19	42	135	9
12. Wanderers	22	1	0	21	31	213	3

The Tay Homes Challenge Cup: **Winner:** Beeston Spinning Wheel **Runners-up:** Wykebeck Arms
Senior Cup: **Winner:** Torre Social Athletic **Runners-up:** Beeston Spinn Wheel
Ronnie Walker Trophy Final: **Winner:** Griffin Head **Runners-up:** Pudsey Borough
Y.E.News Cup Final: **Winner:** Hobby Horse **Runners-up:** Railway Tavern

---

Brighouse Town: *Celebrate winning the West Riding County Amateur League Premier Division Cup 95-96, they also won the Premier Division League title.*

WEST YORKSHIRE LEAGUE

FOUNDED: 1928 (Formerley The Leeds League)

President: W Keyworth **Chairman:** J Hill

Secretary: Kevin Parkinson, 9 Lake Lock Drive, Stanley, Wakefield WF3 4HN

The Premier Division had its highest ever membership with the introduction of promoted clubs Nostell Miners Welfare and Horbury Town and new clubs Magnet Sports and Rowntrees (York), the former N.C.E. club. With 30 league games in all it meant a mid August start and night matches early in the season, as none of the clubs had grounds with floodlights. Early season results saw Charlton Athletic and Wakefield making the early running with Rowntrees and Beeston St. Anthony's keeping in contention.

Magnet Sports started well with two high scoring wins over Swillington Miners Welfare and Nostell. This early season burst of fine form however vanished by Christmas as the club lost their leading scorers and eventually finished just below midtable. Swillington had a poor start to the season, but following the demise of Unibond League club Goole Town, the Miners recruited a number of their ex-players and they began to move away from the bottom of the table. Featherstone, the perrenial league strugglers continued in the same vein and by the end of the season had only one win to show for their efforts, this was against Whitkirk Wanderers, who started smartly but fell away following two defeats by Carlton. Two long standing Premier League sides, Horsforth St. Margaret's and East End Park also found the going difficult, particularly the 'Park'. The previous season they had done the League and Premier Cup double but early results together with increasing ground grading problems was to see their downfall. Horsforth with a council ground was another of the teams to face re-election, after a run of extremely poor results culminated in a 12-1 defeat at Wakefield saw them entrenched in the bottom four. Another club fighting re-election was Robin Hood Athletic whose spirited efforts against near neighbours Carlton saw them in the bottom four. Rothwell Athletic's second season in the top flight saw them heavily involved in Cup competitions, reaching the semi-finals of the District and Leagues Cups, but in doing so their league form suffered and a back log of fixtures also saw them in a mid table position. Knaresborough Town had an 'in and out' season and never seriously challenged the top four and Sherburn White Rose internal problems hindered their league form, although they reached the League Cup Final. Nostell were reasonably happy with their position, having been promoted from 4th in Division One, but the top four clubs found themselves ten points clear of everyone else. Beeston began to climb back to the top but were still three players short of a championship side, and Rowntrees although winning the Premier League Cup against Sherburn 1-0 and beating champions Carlton 4-1 lacked consistency and finished third with over a hundred goals to their credit. Wakefield had started the season low key with a number of narrow wins which took them into the top two and after sharing the points with rivals Carlton on both occasions they were on course for their first championship win. Having a superior goal difference they saw Carlton beat Beeston 6-1 and the following week Wakefield travelled to Leeds for the all important match. An early set piece error by the visiting 'keeper gave the Saints the edge and although Wakefield equalised they lost in the first six minutes of the game.

This meant that Carlton had to win their last two matches to win the title by a point. The championship duly arrived at Town Street after a delay when they overcame Sherburn 3-1 to take the title in early June.

Bramley the Division One champions from the previous season saw their Premiership hopes dashed because of ground requirements and therefore had to defend their title. The season started slowly and they suffered a couple of early season defeats. The pace makers were newly promoted Garforth W M C but a lack of goals saw their hopes slowly diminish. Newcomers Bardsley, former champions of the Harrogate League also found things difficult in the early stages and only found themselves in mid-table at Christmas. They recovered and ended in a top four position. Great Preston had improved their facilities and this encouraged their performance on the field. They had a great chance of the League title but a number of low par performances inkey games ended their hopes. GN Prince Phillips, former champions and Cup Winners in this Division, also found the going hard and they also found themselves in a mid table position. Armley Athletic under new manager Stuart Walker started the season in fine form and at one stage looked likely to take the title. But again inconsistancy saw them lose out.

The relegation battle began early in the season with Beeston Reserves, Pontefract Town and Upper Armley in the frame. In Beeston's case loosing their first eight games put them down even though a late revival just saw them 3 points from safety. Pontefract Town only collected 5 points throughout the season. Rothwell Reserves and Wakefield Reserves found early season points to find the safety margin and Upper Armley proved to be the team with the great escape expertise. After suffering a 4-0 defeat at Beeston they then hit 12 goals and 4 ppoints against the champions Bramley, and high riding Armley Athletic to avoid relegation. The team of the season turned out to be Barwick under the influence of Phil Mathews the former N.C.E. player. They reached the League Cup final against Bramley and took the runners-up spot in the division. Bramley though, did the double to prove their outstanding ability yet again. But facilities would be their drawback in trying to obtain promotion

FINAL LEAGUE TABLES 1995/96

PREMIER DIVISION	P	Home W	D	L	F	A	Away W	D	L	F	A	Pts
1. Carlton Athletic	30	11	2	2	43	21	12	2	1	50	20	50
2. Wakefield	30	12	2	1	51	11	9	5	1	41	11	49
3. Rowntrees	30	9	3	3	58	18	10	3	2	44	19	44
4. Beeston St Anthony	30	11	2	2	39	12	6	5	4	27	24	41
5. Whitkirk Wanderers	30	5	6	4	34	29	6	3	6	29	24	31
6. Horbury Town	30	5	3	7	20	29	7	4	4	32	29	31
7. Rothwell Athletic	30	3	5	7	23	30	9	1	5	36	19	30
8. Knaresborough Tn	30	6	6	3	25	21	5	2	8	24	33	30
9. Swillington M W	30	4	3	8	23	40	6	5	4	26	21	28
10. Sherburn W Rose	30	5	4	6	22	18	4	5	6	21	26	27
11. Magnet Sports	30	5	2	8	21	35	6	2	7	36	37	26
12. Nostell M W	30	6	1	8	31	42	3	5	7	21	36	24
13. Horsforth S M	30	3	3	9	20	35	3	6	6	23	42	21
14. East End Park	30	5	1	9	29	37	4	1	10	17	36	20
15. Robin Hood Athletic	30	3	4	8	23	48	4	1	10	19	44	19
16. Featherstone Coll	30	1	5	9	23	48	0	2	13	12	56	9

Horbury Town v East End Park - Not Played - 2 points awarded to Horbury Town
Beeston v Rothwell Athletic - Not Played - 2 points awarded to Beeston

DIVISION ONE	P	Home W	D	L	F	A	Away W	D	L	F	A	Pts
1. Bramley	22	7	1	3	37	21	8	2	1	39	17	33
2. Barwick	22	6	3	2	28	19	7	1	3	21	16	30
3. Great Preston	22	7	1	3	20	18	6	2	3	22	9	29
4. Bardsey	22	5	4	2	26	15	6	2	3	27	14	28
5. Armley Athletic	22	6	2	3	25	17	6	2	3	22	17	28
6. GN Prince Phillip	22	5	2	4	30	25	5	3	3	39	25	25
7. Garforth WMC	22	6	2	3	10	10	4	3	4	16	21	25
8. Rothwell Ath Res	22	5	2	4	11	9	3	2	6	17	24	20
9. Wakefield Res	22	2	2	7	15	32	4	2	5	21	23	16
10. Upper Armley OB	22	2	4	5	24	34	2	2	7	17	25	14
11. Beeston SA Res	22	2	2	7	18	30	1	3	7	15	30	11
12. Pontefract Town	22	1	1	9	11	37	0	2	9	11	34	5

Great Preston v Beeston SA Res - Not played - 2 points awarded to Great Preston
Wakefield Res v Upper Armley OB - Not played _ 2 points awarded to Wakefield Res.

PREMIER DIVISION RESULTS CHART 1995-96

HOME TEAM	1	2	3	4	5	6	7	8	9	10	11	12	13	14	15	16
1. Whitkirk Wanderers	*	2-2	3-1	1-1	1-1	2-4	2-3	1-1	3-1	2-3	3-3	3-0	4-0	3-4	2-1	2-0
2. Swillington WM	4-1	*	5-0	2-2	1-1	0-3	0-5	0-2	0-3	4-3	0-3	4-2	0-4	0-7	0-1	3-3
3. Knaresboro Town	3-2	2-4	*	1-0	0-3	2-2	1-0	2-1	1-1	1-1	0-0	1-1	0-3	6-2	5-1	0-0
4. Sherburn White Rose	0-1	1-3	1-1	*	0-0	2-1	0-1	1-1	2-1	5-1	1-1	2-0	0-1	3-3	1-2	2-0
5. Wakefield	0-0	2-1	5-1	7-1	*	2-2	2-1	0-2	5-1	4-1	11-1	4-0	1-0	2-0	3-0	3-0
6. Carlton Athletic	2-1	1-0	3-2	3-1	2-2	*	3-2	0-2	6-1	2-0	4-0	6-1	2-4	4-3	5-1	1-1
7. Rothwell Athletic	2-2	0-1	0-2	1-2	1-1	0-3	*	4-5	1-1	2-0	2-2	2-1	0-5	2-2	1-2	5-1
8. Horbury Town	1-7	1-4	2-1	1-1	0-2	1-3	0-3	*	0-3	4-0	4-0	4-0	3-0	2-2	*	0-0
9. Beeston St Anthony	3-1	2-0	1-2	0-0	2-1	2-5	*	4-1	*	6-0	3-1	3-0	1-1	3-0	2-0	7-0
10. Robin Hood Athletic	1-2	1-1	0-0	1-0	1-5	1-2	0-1	0-1	0-3	*	0-4	1-1	2-7	4-2	2-1	1-1
11. Horsforth S M	1-2	0-0	1-3	2-4	0-2	0-6	1-1	3-3	0-2	0-2	*	4-0	1-4	1-0	2-3	4-3
12. Featherstone Coll	3-2	1-1	2-4	0-5	1-4	1-3	0-8	3-3	2-2	2-3	2-2	*	2-3	1-2	1-1	2-5
13. Rowntrees	1-1	3-1	3-1	2-2	1-2	1-1	6-3	4-1	2-2	6-0	8-0	9-1	*	1-2	6-0	5-0
14. Magnet Sports	0-2	4-4	3-2	1-0	0-6	0-1	0-2	2-4	1-1	3-2	0-4	3-1	0-2	*	3-2	1-2
15. East End Park	1-3	0-1	3-2	4-0	0-8	2-6	1-2	1-3	0-2	2-0	2-2	7-1	1-2	5-0	*	0-5
16. Nostell M W	2-1	0-3	1-1	0-2	1-3	4-7	3-4	4-2	1-3	1-3	3-0	4-3	3-2	1-6	3-2	*

PREMIER DIVISION CLUBS 1996-97

BARDSEY

Secretary: M Furlong, 7 The Drive, Crossgate, Leeds LS15 8ER (0113 26456963)
Ground: The Sportsfield, Keswick Lane, Bardsey (01937 574286)
Colours: White/black/black **Change Colours:** All navy

BARWICK

Secretary: B J Kollescoff, 3 Leeds Road, Barwick-in-Elmet, LS15 4JE (0113 2812683)
Ground: Back of village Hall, Chapel Lane
Colours: Yellow/blue/blue **Change Colours:** Blue & black/black/blue

BEESTON ST ANTHONY

Secretary: M Browne, 42 Old Lane, Beeston, Leeds LS11 8AA (0113 2708408)
Ground: Beggars Hill, Beeston Road, Leeds 11, (0113 2707223)
Colours: Green & black/black/green **Change Colours:** Red/black/red

CARLTON ATHLETIC

Secretary: R Hargreaves, 11 Newton Drive, Outwood, Wakefield WF1 3HZ (01924 826141)
Ground: Carlton Cricket Club, Town Street, Carlton (0113 2821114)
Colours: Red/navy/navy **Change Colours:** Yellow & Blue/blue/blue

G.N.KHALSA

Secretary: A Wisdom, 17 Bayswater Terrace, Leeds LS8 5QI (0113 2351445)
Ground: Prince Phillip Centre, Scott Hall Avenue, Leeds 7
Colours: All blue **Change Colours:** Yellow/green/green

HORBURY TOWN

Secretary: J Mosalski, 21 Blake Hall Drive, Mirfield, West Yorks, WF14 9NL (01924 492346)
Ground: Slazenger Sports Complex, Horbury
Colours: Red/black/red **Change Colours:** Amber/black/black

KNARESBOROUGH TOWN

Secretary: I J Pickles, 3 Farndale Road, Knaresborough, N Yorks HG5 0NY (01483 862073)
Ground: Manse Lane
Colours: Red & white/black/red **Change Colours:** White/black/white

MAGNET SPORTS

Secretary: M Howcroft, 45 Willow Rise, Tadcaster, N York LS24 9LG (01937 833756)
Ground: Rear of Magnet Sports & Social Club
Colours: Navy & white/navy/white **Change Colours:** Tangerine & purple/purple

NOSTELL MINERS WELFARE

Secretary: R Winfield, 13 Edward Drive, Outwood, Wakefield WF1 2LL (01924 826408)
Ground: Nostell Miners Welfare, New Crofton, Wakefield
Colours: Yellow/black/yellow **Change Colours:** Red/white/red

ROBIN HOOD ATHLETIC

Secretary: G Hart, 16 Belfry Court, Outwoode, Wakefield WF1 3TY (01924 820635)
Ground: Rear of Coach & Horses Hotel, Rothwell Haigh (0113 2821021)
Colours: Blue & black/black/black **Change Colours:** Green & black/black/black

ROTHWELL ATHLETIC

Secretary: D Amann, 28 Haigh Road, Rothwell, Leeds LS26 0NH (0113 2827322)
Ground: Royds Lane, Rothwell
Colours: Red & black/black/red **Change Colours:** Sky/navy/navy

SHERBURN WHITE ROSE

Secretary: Mrs S Inglis, 21 Deighton Avenue, Sherburn-in-Elmet, Leeds LS25 6BR (01977 683089)
Ground: Recreation Ground, Finkle Hill, Sherburn-in-Elmet.
Colours: White/black/black **Change Colours:** Yellow/blue/yellow

SWILLINGTON MINERS WELFARE

Secretary: F Boon, 39 Neville Grove, Swillington, Leeds LS26 8QN (0113 2867833)
Ground: Welfare Sports Ground, Wakefield Road, Swillington.
Colours: Red & white/white/red **Change Colours:** All blue

WAKEFIELD

Secretary: Mrs S Dean, 2 Malham Road, Eastmoor, Wakefield WF1 4HN (01924 383792)
Ground: Woolley Colliery (01226 385095)
Colours: Blue & white/blue/blue **Change Colours:** Red/navy/red

WHITKIRK WANDERERS

Secretary: D J Nutter, 17 The Crescent, Leeds LS15 7SL (0113 2945408)
Ground: Next to Whitkirk Social & Sports Club
Colours: All light blue **Change Colours:** All white

YORK R.I.

Secretary: S M Alford, 12 St Gilesway, Copmanthorpe, York YO2 3XT (01904 702407)
Ground: York R I, New Lane, Acomb, York
Colours: Blue & white/blue/blue **Change Colours:** Blue & red/red/red

FIRST DIVISION CLUBS 1996-97

ARMLEY ATHLETIC

Secretary: P Lofts, 6 Halliday Mount, Leeds LS12 3Pf (0113 2794251)
Ground: Western Flatts Park, Wortley, Leeds 12
Colours: Maroon/navy/maroon **Change Colours:** All royal

BRAMLEY

Secretary: J Earl, 6 Ashlea Gate, Bramley Leeds, LS13 2EE (0113 2573607)
Ground: Hough Side Playing Fields, Hough Top, Bramley
Colours: Yellow & black/black/black **Change Colours:** All Blue

EAST END PARK W.M.C.

Secretary: P Makler, 18 Newlay Lane Place, Bramley, Leeds LS13 2BB (0113 2557159)
Ground: Skelton Road
Colours: Blue/black/black **Change Colours:** Green & white/green/green

FEATHERSTONE COLLIERY

Secretary: M Smith, 11A Jardine Avenue, Featherstone, W Yorks WF7 6LA (01977 796395)
Ground: Featherstone Miners Welfare, Creesey's Corner, Green Lane, Featherstone
Colours: All maroon **Change Colours:** White & blue/navy/navy

GARFORTH W.M.C.

Secretary: Mrs W Webster, 4 Knightsway, Garforth, Leeds LS25 1BG (0113 2866797)
Ground: Micklefield Welfare Ground
Colours: Red & white/white/red **Change Colours:** Green & gold/green/gold

GREAT PRESTON

Secretary: V Donnelly, 51 Hollinhurst, Allerton Bywater, Castleford WF10 2HY (0113 2871713)
Ground: Berry Lane, Great Preston
Colours: All navy **Change Colours:** White/blue/blue

HORSFORTH ST MARGARETS

Secretary: S Elgen, 14 Prospect Avenue, Pudsey, Leeds LS28 7HN (0113 2550792)
Ground: Cragg Hill Recreation Ground, Horsforth
Colours: Yellow/blue/blue **Change Colours:** Red/blue/red

PONTEFRACT LABOUR

Secretary: M Downes, 36 Rookhill Road, Pontefract WF8 2BY (01977 790187)
Ground: Willow Park Playing Fields, Pontefract
Colours: Red & white/red/red **Change Colours:** Green & black/black/green

ROTHWELL ATHLETIC RESERVES

As First Team Premier Division
Colours: Sky/navy/navy **Change Colours:** Red & black/black/red

SELBY R.S.S.C.

Secretary: R Webb, 25 Abbotts Road, Selby, N York YO8 8AS (01757 709079)
Ground: Dennison Road, Selby
Colours: Yellow/black/yellow **Change Colours:** White/black/red

UPPER ARMLEY OLD BOYS

Secretary: J Plowright, 29 Armley Grange View, Leeds LS12 3QP (0113 2797134)
Ground: Moorfield Road, Leeds 12
Colours: Blue & red/blue/blue **Change Colours:** White/blue/blue

WAKEFIELD RESERVES

All Details as First Team Premier Division

WHITKIRK WANDERERS RESERVES

All Details as First Team Premier Division

WILLOWFIELD CELTIC

Secretary: A Buckley, 58 Green Park Road, Skircoat Green, Halifax HX3 0SW (01422 350249)
Ground: Holmes Park, Luddendenfoot
Colours: Red & black/black/red **Change Colours:** All white

WILTSHIRE F.A.

Secretary: Mr E M Parry
44 Kennet Avenue, Swindon, Wiltshire SN2 3LG

WILTSHIRE SENIOR CUP
(FOUNDED 1886–87)

RECENT FINALS

1990–91	Pewsey Vale	v	Swindon Athletic	2–1
1991–92	Wollen Sports	v	Dowton	3–1
1992–93	Bemerton Heath Harl	v	Wollen Sports	3–1
1993–94	Amesbury Town	v	Swindon Supermarine	2–1
1994–95	Purton	v	Downton	1–0

MOST WINS Devizes Town 14 Swindon Town 10 Chippenham Town 8

1995–1996
WILTSHIRE SENIOR CUP

20 CLUBS **HOLDERS: PURTON**

FIRST ROUND Saturday 25th November 1995

Wroughton	v	Aldbourne Park	3–3 5–2
Burmah Castrol	v	Amesbury Town	0–2
Biddestone	v	Bromham	4–2
Highworth Town	v	Tisbury United	2–1

12 Clubs with a Bye into the

SECOND ROUND 6th January 1996

Purton	v	Marlborough Town	7–1
Pewsey Vale	v	Corsham Town	4–3
Highworth Town	v	Bradford Town	4–0
Shrewton Town	v	Biddestone	1–1 1–2
Dunbar Athletic	v	Plessey Semics	2–0
Pinehurst	v	Wootton Bassett Town	0–3
Malmesbury Vics	v	Amesbury Town	1–3
Sanford	v	Wroughton	2–3

THIRD ROUND

Wootton Basset Tn	v	Wroughton	2–0
Highworth Town	v	Pewsey Vale	1–0
Amesbury Town	v	Purton	3–1
Biddestone	v	Dunbar Athletic	0–1

SEMI-FINALS

Amesbury Town v Dunbar Athletic 3–1
at Pewsey Vale FC Saturday 16th March1996

Highworth Town v Wootton Basset Town 3–1
at Swindon Supermarine FC Saturday 23rd March 1996

FINAL Wednesday 24th April 7.30pm
AMESBURY TOWN v HIGHWORTH TOWN 0–3 at The Conigre, Melksham Town FC.

WILTSHIRE PREMIER SHIELD
(FOUNDED 1926–27)

RECENT FINALS

1991–92	Trowbridge Town	v	Salisbury City	2–1
1992–93	Trowbridge Town	v	Westbury United	1–0
1993–94	Trowbridge Town	v	Chippenham Town	3–0
1994–95	Trowbridge Town	v	Swindon Supermarine	1–0

MOST WINS Swindon Town 26 Salisbury City 10 Trowbridge Town 9

WILTSHIRE PREMIER SHIELD

11 CLUBS **HOLDERS: TROWBRIDGE TOWN**

FIRST ROUND by Saturday 5th November 1995

Warminster Town	v	Bemerton Heath H	1–1 1–3
Calne Town	v	Chippenham Town	1–2
Devizes Town	v	Trowbridge Town	0–2

SECOND ROUND by Sunday 7th January 1996

Melksham Town	v	Trowbridge Town	0–3
Chippenham Town	v	Downton	2–0
Swindon Supermar	v	Bemerton Heath H	3–4
Salisbury City	v	Westbury United	3–2

SEMI-FINALS

Chippenham Town	v	Bemerton Heath H	2–1
Salisbury City	v	Trowbridge Town	2–1

FINAL Wednesday 1st May 7.30pm
CHIPPENHAM TOWN v SALISBURY CITY 0–2 at Meadow Lane, Westbury United FC.

SKURRAYS WILTSHIRE LEAGUE

FINAL LEAGUE TABLES 1995/96

Div One	P	W	D	L	F	A	Pts
1. Pinehurst	26	20	1	5	55	29	61
2. Biddestone	26	13	8	5	43	27	47
3. Albourne	26	14	3	9	60	46	45
4. Tisbury Utd	26	12	6	8	53	40	42
5. Melksham T R	26	11	3	10	39	31	38
6. Corsham Town	26	10	8	8	34	34	38
7. Devizes T Res	26	10	6	10	34	29	36
8. Sauford	26	10	4	12	39	41	34
9. Bradford Town	26	9	6	11	36	38	33
10. Shrewton Utd	26	9	6	11	36	39	33
11. Burmah Castrol	26	6	13	7	38	38	31
12. Malmesbury V	26	7	8	11	32	37	29
13. Marlborough T	26	8	5	13	40	53	29
14. Pewsey Vale R	26	3	1	22	29	86	10

Div Two	P	W	D	L	F	A	Pts
1. Southbrook Wal	27	20	4	3	82	22	64
2. Purton Res	27	18	4	5	63	41	58
3. Wroughton	27	15	7	5	63	29	52
4. Chippenham T R	27	14	4	9	43	34	46
5. Warminster T R	27	12	4	11	48	40	39
6. W Bassett T R	27	9	4	14	44	53	31
7. Bromham	27	8	5	14	35	41	29
8. Dunbar Ath	27	8	3	16	35	55	27
9. Plessey Set	27	7	2	18	20	53	23
10. Amesbury T R	27	4	3	20	24	79	15

WORCESTERSHIRE F.A.

Secretary: M R Leggatt,
'Fermain', 12 Worcester Road, Evesham, Worcs WR11 4JU
(01905) 612336

WORCESTERSHIRE SENIOR CUP
(FOUNDED 1893–94)

RECENT FINALS

1990–91	Kidderminster Har	v	Sutton Coldfield Tn	5–1 (Agg.)
1991–92	Bromsgrove Rovers	v	Sutton Coldfield Tn	4–1 (Agg.)
1992–93	Kidderminster Har	v	Solihull Borough	3–1 (Agg.)
1993–94	Bromsgrove Rovers	v	Kidderminster Har	5–1 (Agg.)
1994–95	Bromsgrove Rovers	v	Moor Green	4–1 (Agg.)

1995–1996

12 CLUBS **HOLDERS: BROMSGROVE ROVERS**

FIRST ROUND by 18th November 1995

Evesham United	v	Solihull Borough	2–2 1–2
Bridgnorth Town	v	Halesowen Town	0–3
Stourbridge	v	Redditch United	1–0
Sutton Coldfield Tn	v	Dudley Town	0–1

SECOND ROUND by Saturday 27th January 1996

Worcester City	v	Solihull Borough	0–2
Stourbridge	v	Halesowen Town	1–0
Kidderminster Har	v	Dudley Town	2–1
Bromsgrove Rovers	v	Moor Green	5–0

SEMI-FINALS

Solihull Borough	v	Bromsgrove Rovers	2–2 1–3
Kidderminster Har	v	Stourbridge	1–2

FINAL First Leg Monday 22nd April 1996
STOURBRIDGE v BROMSGROVE ROVERS 2–1

FINAL Second Leg Thursday 9th May 1996
BROMSGROVE ROVERS v STOURBRIDGE 3*1

Bromsgrove Rovers after winning the Worcestershire Senior Cup
Bach Row (L-R): Fergus Dowling, Chris Taylor, Andy Marlowe, Recky Carter. Front Row; Mark Crisp, Ward Troman, Richard Gardener, Kevin Richardson, Adie Smith, Craig Gaunt, Andy Dale.

Don't Lose your head son!

Erith's goal keeper John Whitehouse fails to stop a Braintree shot. *Photo - K Gillard.*

The same keeper looks much the same in prematch practice. *Photo - K Gillard*

THE FOOTBALL LEAGUE OF WALES

President: B Fear **Chairman:** J E Lloyd.
Secretary: J C Deakin, Plymouth Chambers, 3 Westgate Street Cardiff CF1 1DD, Tel; (01222) 372325, Fax; (01222) 343961

BARRY TOWN WALK AWAY WITH LEAGUE TITLE

Barry Town stormed to the League of Wales title with a fantastic season in which they lost just three League games, accumulating 97 points in the process. Yet amazingly, manager Paul Giles was dismissed from the club just weeks later after a fall out with the Barry board.

Brian Coyne's Newtown side did well in the second half of the season to land the runners-up spot and a place in the UEFA Cup Preliminary Round.

Defending champions Bangor City were always on the parameters of the title race and suffered managerial difficulties of their own. Player-boss Nigel Adkins was sacked just before Christmas, only to be re-instated again a few days later. However, after Christmas he was dismissed again and former Witton Albion manager Bryan Griffiths took up the Farrar Road reins.

Conwy United clinched the third European spot in the Inter-Toto Cup by finishing third, just edging out Flint Town United, who marked an impressive first season in management for Stef Rush by finishing fourth. Conwy boss John Hulses must have been delighted with his strikeforce of 'thirty-somethings' Chris Camden and Ken McKenna, with the latter running away with the golden boot and finishing as Europe's top scorer with 49 League and Cup goals.

Connah's Quay Nomads edged out Eddw Vale in a tense League of Wales Cup final but the 11 games in the competition played by the finalists did little to aid their progress in the League and the format of the competition has been revised for the 1996/97 season.

A little romance was provided by Llansantffraid in the Welsh Cup. The small village side from mid-Wales upset the form book by defeating Barry Town on penalties in the Cardiff Arms Park final to scupper the Linnets hopes of a league and cup double. As well as landing the coveted trophy, Llansantffraid were rewarded with a European tie against Ruch Chorzow.
WILLIAM HUGHES

FINAL LEAGUE TABLES 1995/96

The League of Wales		Home					Away					
	P	*W*	*D*	*L*	*F*	*A*	*W*	*D*	*L*	*F*	*A*	*Pts*
1. Barry Town	40	17	2	1	50	10	13	5	2	42	13	97
2. Newtown	40	12	5	3	32	7	11	6	3	37	18	80
3. Conwy United	40	11	7	2	53	23	10	6	4	48	35	76
4. Bangor City	40	12	5	3	40	27	9	1	10	32	38	69
5. Flint Town United	40	9	6	5	35	28	10	3	7	41	29	66
6. Caernarfon Town	40	9	7	4	38	23	7	6	7	39	36	61
7. Cwmbran Town	40	8	6	6	30	24	6	9	5	28	25	57
8. Inter Cardiff	40	11	6	3	41	27	3	6	11	21	35	54
9. Caersws	40	10	3	7	46	46	5	6	9	35	51	54
10. Connahs Quay No	40	9	6	5	46	32	4	8	8	22	31	53
11. Ebbw Vale	40	7	5	8	35	28	7	6	7	24	28	53
12. Llansantffaid	40	9	3	8	36	29	5	7	8	30	28	52
13. CPD Porthmadog	40	7	7	6	34	28	6	4	10	22	34	50
14. Aberystwyth Town	40	7	7	6	32	30	6	2	12	28	38	48
15. Cemaes Bay	40	11	5	4	45	28	2	2	16	18	52	46
16. Holywell Town	40	8	3	9	32	34	4	4	12	21	40	43
17. Briton Ferry Athletic	40	8	5	7	38	35	3	4	13	26	56	42
18. Rhyl	40	6	5	9	23	31	5	4	11	24	52	42
19. Ton Pentre	40	4	8	8	25	29	4	8	8	21	36	40
20. Afan Lido	40	7	2	11	21	33	2	7	11	12	38	36
21. Llanelli	40	5	5	10	31	38	3	4	13	19	50	33

LEAGUE OF WALES Ten Year Record

(includes Welsh League National Division prior to 1992-93)

	86/7	87/8	88/9	89/0	90/1	91/2	92/3	93/4	94/5	95/6
Abergavenny Thursday	-	-	7	3	1	1	20	-	-	-
Aberystwyth	-	4	2	2	2	3	3	10	17	14
Afan Lido	-	-	-	-	12	8	12	16	2	20
AFC Cardiff	-	7	13	7	-	-	-	-	-	-
Ammanford Town	-	-	-	14	16	-	-	-	-	-
Bangor City	-	-	-	-	-	-	5	1	1	4
Barry Town	1	2	1	-	-	-	-	-	7	1
Blaenrhondda	12	18	-	-	-	-	-	-	-	-
Brecon Corinthians	10	12	5	12	8	14	-	-	-	-
Bridgend Town	7	15	6	10	11	15	-	-	-	-
Briton Ferry Athletic	8	8	11	6	7	2	17	20	-	17
Caerau Athletic	17	-	-	-	-	-	-	-	-	-
Caerleon	14	16	16	-	-	-	-	-	-	-
Caernarfon Town	-	-	-	-	-	-	-	-	-	6
Caersws	-	-	-	-	-	-	11	17	14	9
Caldicot Town	-	-	-	-	-	13	-	-	-	-
Cemaes Bay	-	-	-	-	-	-	-	-	-	15
Connahs Quay Nomads	-	-	-	-	-	-	8	7	15	10
Conwy United	-	-	-	-	-	-	7	13	12	3
Cwmbran Town	3	5	14	4	9	7	1	8	5	7
Ebbw Vale	6	1	4	16	-	11	4	9	13	11
Ferndale Athletic	-	-	-	-	13	16	-	-	-	-
Flint Town United	-	-	-	-	-	-	16	4	6	5
Haverfordwest County	5	6	3	1	3	4	10	15	-	-
Holywell Town	-	-	-	-	-	-	6	5	8	16
Inter Cardiff	-	-	-	-	6	12	2	2	10	8
Llanelli	13	14	-	5	14	10	14	12	18	21
Llanidloes Town	-	-	-	-	-	-	19	-	-	-
Llansantffraid	-	-	-	-	-	-	-	18	9	12
Maestag Park Ath	4	10	10	13	5	6	15	19	20	-
Milford United	11	17	17	-	-	-	-	-	-	-
Mold Alexandra	-	-	-	-	-	-	13	14	19	-
Newtown	-	-	-	-	-	-	18	6	4	2
Pembroke Borough	16	9	9	8	10	9	-	-	-	-
Pontllanfraith	9	13	15	15	-	-	-	-	-	-
Porthmadog	-	-	-	-	-	-	9	11	16	13
Port Talbot Athletic	15	11	12	11	15	-	-	-	-	-
Rhyl	-	-	-	-	-	-	-	-	11	18
Ton Pentre	2	3	8	9	4	5	-	3	3	19
No of Clubs Competing	17	18	17	16	16	16	20	20	20	21

LEAGUE OF WALES LEAGUE CUP FINAL

Peter Hughes, who at one time looked likely to be Connah's Quay Nomads third choice striker, turned match winner with the only goal of an exciting League Cup Final at Caersws late in the game.

Ebbw Vale began on top with Steve Woods and Simon Tyler both going close inside the opening five minutes. A physical encounter saw several bookings as both sides tried to gain the upper hand.

Connah's Quay's first attack saw acting skipper Marc Limbert head wide after good approach play from Stuart Rain and Darren Wynne.

Ebbw were frustrated by a spectacular save from Nomads 'keeper Phil Collister in the 28th minute when Lee Walker's right-wing raid ended in a cross being flicked on by Woods towards Tyler whose shot on the turn seemed destined for the net before the Nomads 'keeper intervened.

The turning point of the game came within two minutes of the second period when Woods caught Mike Carroll with a flailing forearm and Newport referee P.L. Scott produced the red card.

Nomads began to make their advantage in personnel count, and they should have taken the lead 20 minutes from time when player-boss Nev Powell sent Danny McGoona skipping away down the left-wing and his centre provided Hughes with a golden chance but, perhaps sensing glory, he snatched at his shot and blazed the ball wildly over the crossbar. Yet he was given the chance to make amends eight minutes from time and he responded with a cracker.

Vernon Keep won the ball on the right flank and hooked it on towards Rain. A cheeky backheel created space for Hughes on the right-hand edge of the penalty area and he hit a ferocious angled drive beyond the dive of Kevin Creedon and into the top corner of the net.

It was Connah's Quay's greatest success since winning the Welsh Intermediate Cup in 1981 and just reward for a gritty performance

Ebbw Vale 0 Connah's Quay Nomads 1
Sunday May 12 1996 at the Recreation Ground, Caersws

MATCHFACTS:
Ebbw Vale: Creedon: Walker, (Williams 82), Graham, Cable, Needs, Mitchell, Dicks, Pengelly, L Powell, Woods, Tayler. Subs not used - Cooper, Gummer.
CQNomads: Collister: Smyth, G Wynne, Carroll, D Wynne, Keep, N Powell, Limbert, McGoona, Rain (Morris 87), Hughes. Subs not used - Roberts, N Davies.
Referee: P.L. Scott (Newport) - Attendance: 500

Connahs Quay Nomads League of Wales, League Cup Winners 1995-96: *Photo - Andy Dakin*

WELSH CUP FINAL

The entire village of Llansantffraid journeyed down to Arms Park and their trip was rewarded as they saw their team become the first Mid Wales team to lift the Welsh Cup. They did so against all the odds, overcoming a Barry Town side packed with full time players and chasing a league and cup double.

But Llansantffraid were good value for their win - even if they had to go through the drama of a penalty shoot-out before earning the right to lift the silverware.

Barry had dominated the opening 20 minutes but failed to breakthrough the Saints' defence and on 28 minutes player\boss Tommy Morgan gave the villagers a dream start, running onto a pass from Chris Whelan before slipping the ball beyond Mark Ovendale in the Linnets goal.

But the lead was to last just seven minutes as Barry left-back Gary Lloyd fired home a free-kick from 25 yards after Garry Evans was adjudged to have fouled Barry front runner Tony Bird. However, Evans made amends nine minutes after the break when he hit a tremendous volley from 25 yards to defeat a surprised Ovendale.

Once again Barry came roaring back, equalising with a bizarre goal. Chris Pike flicked on Dave O'Gorman's cross but Mike Brown appeared to have the situation under control, incredibly his clearance hit goalkeeper Andy Mulliner and rebounded into the net.

Former Northwich Victoria players O'Gorman and Simon Abercrombie had chances to win the game late on for their respective sides but the game went into extra time.

Once again the Saints took the lead. Abercrombie's free kick presented Chris Whelan with the chance to dive in and head them in front from eight yards. As the game ticked towards its conclusion Saints became visibly jittery at the prospect of what they were about to achieve and Mulliner needlessly conceded a corner with just three minutes remaining. The flag kick was half cleared but the ball fell to Bird who returned it with interest to smash home a stunning equaliser and put Barry on terms once again.

If Mulliner had been the villain, he was soon to become the hero. Pike and Gary Lloyd's penalties were both stopped by the Saints 'keeper while John Wheland and Morgan slotted theirs away and they seemed to have the trophy in the bag. But once again the drama was not over in an enthralling final, Garry Evans and Tim Nunnerley both missed their spot kicks, while Bird and 'keeper Ovendale scored for Barry to put them on level terms for the fourth time in the game.

Full-back Gary Curtis kept his head to fire Llansantffraid ahead and then Mulliner won his moment of fame by blocking Dave Withers kick to earn Saints victory and a place in the European Cup Winners' Cup.

BARRY TOWN 3 LLANSANTFFRAID 3 At Cardiff Arms Park
Llansantffraid won 3-2 on penalties

Matchfacts:
LLANSANTFFRAID: Mulliner, J Whelan, Curtis, Brown, A Jones, O'Brien (Watt 113), I Evans (Nunnerley 113), G Evans, Morgan, C Whelan, Abercrombie. Sub not used - Barrett.
BARRY TOWN: Ovendale, Evans, Lloyd, Mayer, Batchelor, Barnett (Griffith 105), P Giles (Withers 97), Bird, Hunter (Pike 57), R Jones, O'Gorman.
REFEREE: R Gifford (Llanbradach)

Honours 1995-96

Competition:	Winner:	Runners-up:
FAW Trophy	Rhydymwyn	Penrhyncoch
Welsh Youth Cup	Wrexham	Swansea City
Welsh Womens Cup	Newport Strikers	Bangor City Ladies
Welsh Schools Cup	Ysgol Mold Alun	Penglais
Cymru Alliance Cup	Oswestry Town	Llandudno
Cyril Rogers Cup	Carmarthen Town	Maesteg Park Athletic
Central Wales Floodlit Cup	Aberystwyth Town	Newtown
North Wales Coast Challenge Cup	Colwyn Bay	Porthmadog
Fitlock Cookson Cup	Denbigh Town	Halkyn United
Fitlock Alves Cup	Glantraeth	Locomotive Llanberis
Tyn Lon Volvo Barritt Cup	Halkyn United	Llandyrnog
Clwyd Cup	Rhuddlan New Pines	Trefnant Village
North East Wales Cup	Brymbo	Lex XI
WR Nedin Cup	Merlins Bridge	Trostre
Gwent Senior Cup	Cwmbran Town	Risca United
WNL (Wrexham) Premier Cup	New Broughton	Llay Welfare
WNL (Wrexham) Div One Cup	Llangollen	Bala Town
WNL (Wrexham) Div Two Cup	Pentre Broughton	LLanuwychllyn
John Smiths Cwpan Gwynedd	Conwy United	Y Felinheli
Gwynedd League Presidents Cup	Pwllheli	Conwy United
Eryri Shield	Penrhyndeudraeth	Conwy United

Competition:	Winner:	Runners-up:
Anglesey Dargie Cup	Holyhead Hotspur	Gwalchmai
Anglesey Megan Cup	Holyhead Hotspur	Bryngwran Buls
Angelsey Elias Cup	Holyhead Hotspur	Llanerchymedd Bulls
Tanners Wines Amateur Lge Cup	Kerry	Waterloo Rovers
Derek Mills Cup	Dyffryn Banw	Llanrhaeadr
Cardigan Bay Cup	Llandysul	Dewi Stars
Greyhound Cup	Barry Athletic	Hopkinstown
CW Bruty Cup	Penydarren BC	Llangynwyd Rangers
Astoria Sports Cup	Swansea Youth	Aberaman Youth
L & J Newman Memorial Trophy	Aberysrwyth Town	Bont
Ron Jones Trophy	Machno United	Inter Cerrig
J Hughes Challenge Cup	Llandudno Cricketers	Llanrwst Reserves
T&GWU Cup	Talysarn Celts	Llanystumdwy
Pems Junior Cup	Merlins Bridge	Narbeth
F Tyldesley Cup	Llandudno Reserves	Llansannan

FINAL LEAGUE TABLES 1995/96

The PA Rowlands Cymru League

		P	W	D	L	F	A	Pts
1.	Oswestry Town	36	25	3	8	84	41	76
2.	Welshpool	36	23	7	6	83	40	76
3.	Brymbo	36	23	4	9	81	57	73
4.	Llandudno	36	21	9	6	94	42	72
5.	Rhydymwyn	36	21	8	7	73	40	71
6.	Rhayador Tn	36	20	5	11	66	44	65
7.	Penrhycoch	*35	18	10	7	74	45	64
8.	Cefn Druids	36	19	4	13	82	57	61
9.	Lex X1	36	18	4	14	67	49	58
10.	Penycae	36	13	8	15	58	71	47
11.	Llandrindod W	36	11	11	14	50	58	44
12.	Mostyn	36	13	4	19	78	78	43
13.	Rhos Aelwyd	*35	10	5	20	47	74	35
14.	Knighton Town	36	11	2	23	52	83	35
15.	Mold Alexandra	36	10	6	20	61	90	33
16.	Ruthin Town	36	9	6	21	42	71	33
17.	Llanidloes Tn	36	8	5	23	34	70	29
18.	Buckley Town	36	7	6	2	38	107	27
19.	Carno	36	6	3	27	42	89	21

Office Visions Welsh League

Div One		P	W	D	L	F	A	Pts
1.	Carmarthen Tn	34	25	7	2	101	37	82
2.	Haverfordwest	34	23	7	4	116	34	76
3.	Maesteg Park	34	20	8	6	73	47	68
4.	Cardiff Civ Ser	34	19	6	9	82	47	63
5.	Treowen	34	18	6	10	67	46	60
6.	Llanwern	34	15	7	12	57	56	52
7.	Penrhiwceiber	34	14	9	11	69	58	51
8.	Taffs Well	34	14	9	11	66	63	51
9.	Caldicot Tn	34	14	4	16	60	68	46
10.	AFC Porth	34	11	10	13	57	67	43
11.	Pontypridd Tn	34	12	7	15	58	73	43
12.	Risca	34	12	6	16	50	67	42
13.	Cardiff Corries	34	11	7	16	46	56	40
14.	Aberaman	34	11	7	16	64	79	40
15.	Abergavenny T	34	10	8	16	50	62	38
16.	Brecon Corries	34	8	3	23	48	90	27
17.	Ammanford	34	6	5	23	43	105	23
18.	Caerleon	34	2	6	26	30	82	12

Fitlock Welsh Alliance

		P	W	D	L	F	A	Pts
1.	Denbigh Town	28	20	3	5	60	30	63
2.	Prestatyn Town	28	19	3	6	70	31	60
3.	Llanfairpwll	28	18	4	6	74	41	58
4.	Glantreath	28	17	2	9	66	50	53
5.	Porthmadog R	28	16	4	8	62	42	52
6.	Loco Llanberis	28	15	2	11	46	35	47
7.	Llandymog Utd	28	14	4	10	53	48	46
8.	Llangefn Tn	28	13	3	12	55	51	42
9.	Bangor City R	28	12	5	11	45	38	41
10.	Nantile Vale	28	9	6	13	53	56	33
11.	Halkyn United	28	10	3	15	46	50	33
12.	Connahs Qu R	28	6	3	19	48	80	21
13.	Caernafon T R	28	6	3	19	27	60	21
14.	Nefyn United	28	5	4	19	38	86	19
15.	Rhyl	28	4	3	21	28	80	15

Welsh National League Wrexham Area.

		P	W	D	L	F	A	Pts
1.	Gresford Ath	26	21	3	2	81	23	66
2.	Rhoat/Bersham	26	19	5	2	83	27	62
3.	Chirk	26	18	3	5	69	21	57
4.	New Broughton	26	17	3	6	80	22	54
5.	Penley	26	16	2	8	107	46	50
6.	Corwen	26	14	2	10	67	52	44
7.	Llay Welfare	26	11	5	10	48	44	38
8.	Ruthin T R	26	9	4	13	50	56	31
9.	Lex XI Res	26	9	2	15	58	82	29
10.	Cefn Dr Res	26	8	3	15	48	64	24
11.	New Brighton	26	7	1	18	25	67	22
12.	Rhosddu	26	6	3	17	55	87	21
13.	Buckley T R	26	4	5	17	40	80	17
14.	Brymbo Res	26	2	1	23	36	176	7

LEAGUE OF WALES IN EUROPE 1995-96

UEFA Cup Preliminary Round:

Afan Lido v RAF Riga	1-2, 0-2, (1-4agg)
Bangor City v Widzew Lodz	0-4, 0-1, (0-5agg)

Following Llansantffraid's success in the Welsh Cup, Wales won three representatives into European competition for 1996-97, as Barry Town had already qualified for the UEFA Cup by virtue of winning the League of Wales.

The draw was as follows;

UEFA Cup Preliminary Round:

Newtown v Skonto (Latvia)	1-4, 0-3, (1-7agg)
Barry Town v Dinaburg (Latvia)	0-0, 2-1, (2-1agg)

Cup Winners Cup Qualifying Round:

Llansantffraid v Ruch Chorzow (Poland)

THE INTER-TOTO CUP

Although the competition has been much maligned, a place in the Inter-Toto Cup has certainly given clubs hovering around the top five in the League of Wales something to play for.
Ton Pentre were the first representatives and found the going tough, losing all four of their group matches, conceding 16 goals in the process.
However, this season's ambassadors, Conwy United produced a tremendous performance at The Racecorse Ground. Wrexham in their first game in the competition, holding Charleroi, a team who finished seventh in the Belgian first Division and boasting several internationals, to a goalless draw on 29th June to the delight of manager John Hulse.

Ton Pentre v Heerenveen	0-7	Beakescsaba v Ton Pentre	4-0
Ton Pentre v Uniao Leiria	0-3	Nasteved v Ton Pentre	2-0
Conwy United v Royal Charleroi	0-0	Zaglubie Lubin v Conwy United	3-0
Conwy United v S V Marc O'Polo Ried	1-2	Silkeborg v Conwy United	4-0

Dave Withers of Barry Town clears away from Timmy Williams of Flint. *Photo - Don Fowler*

ABERYSTWYTH TOWN

Chairman: Derek Dawson. **President:** Mr D Jones **Vice-Chairman:**
Secretary: Mr D Steeds, Glenrosa, Brynymor Road, Aberystwyth, Dyfed (01970 623520)
Manager: Meirion Appleton **Asst Manager:** **Physio:**
Ground: Park Avenue, Aberystwyth, Dyfed (01970 612122).
Directions: From south: A487, 1st right at Trefachan Bridge to r'bout, 1st right with Park Avenue being 3rd right. From north: A487 and follow one-way system to railway station, at r'bout 1st left with Park Avenue being 3rd right. 5 mins walk from Aberystwyth (BR) - follow as above.
Seats: 300 **Cover:** 1,200 **Capacity:** 4,500 **Floodlights:** Yes **Shop:** Yes
Programme: 24 pages, 60p. **Editor:** Steve Moore (01970 617705)**Press Officer:** David Thomas
Colours: Green & black stripes/black/black. **Change colours:** Yellow/blue/blue
Sponsors: Continental Cambria Tyres. **Nickname:** Seasiders **Founded:** 1884.
Midweek Matcheday: Wednesday **Reserves League:** Mid-Wales
Record Attendance: 4,500 v Hereford, Welsh Cup 1971.
Previous League: Welsh 1896-97/ Nth Wales Comb. 99-1900/ Montgomeryshire & Dist. 04-20/ Central Wales 21-25 81-87/ Mid-Wales 26-32 51-81/ Cambrian Coast 32-51/ Welsh Lg South 51-63/ Abacus 87-92.
Clubhouse: Open daily noon-3 & 7-12pm. Snacks available.
95-96 Top Scorer: Kevin Morrison **95-96 Captain:** Mark Devereux. **95-96 P.o.Y.:** Donald Kane
Club Record Scorer: David Williams 476, 66-83. **Club Record Appearances:** David P Whitney 572, 62-81.
Hons: Welsh Cup 1899-1900; Welsh I'mediate Cup 85-86 87-88; Mid Wales Lg(11) (Lg Cup(7); Welsh Amtr Cup (3); Welsh Lg Div 2 Sth 51-52; Cambrian Coast Lg(8) Central Wales Chal. Cup(6)

BANGOR CITY

President: Lady Pennant **Chairman:** Gwyn Pierce Owen **Vice Chairman:** David Gareth Jones.
Secretary: Alun Griffiths, 12 Lon-Y-Bryn, Menai Bridge, Anglesey, Gwynedd LL57 5NM (01248 712820).
Manager: Bryan Griffiths **Asst Manager:** Paul Lodge **Physio:** Arwel Jones
Ground: The Stadium, Farrar Road, Bangor, Gwynedd (01248 355852)
Directions: Old A5 into Bangor, 1st left before railway station, ground on left by garage.
Seats: 700 **Cover:** 1,200 **Capacity:** 5,000 **Floodlights:** Yes **Shop:** Yes
Programme: 32 pages, 70p **Editor:** Anthony Evans **Press Officer:** Alun Griffiths
Colours: All blue **Change colours:** All red
Sponsors: Pentraeth Mazda **Nickname:** Citizens **Founded:** 1876
Midweek Matchedays: Tuesday **Reserve League:** Welsh Alliance.
Record Attendance: 10,000 v Wrexham, Welsh Cup final 78-79.
Previous Leagues:: N Wales Coast 1893-98 1911-12/The Comb 1898-1910/N Wales Comb 30-33/W Mids 32-38/Lancs Comb 38-39 46-50/Ches Co 50-68/NPL 68-79 81-82 84-92/Alliance Prem 79-81 82-84.
Clubhouse: Not on ground
95-96 Captain: Dave Barnett. **95-96 P.o.Y.:** Frank Mottram. **95-96 Top Scorer:**
Honours: FA Tphy R-up 83-84; Northern Prem. Lg 81-82 (R-up 86-87, Lg Cup 68-69, Presidents Cup 88-89, Chal. Shield 87-88), Cheshire Co. Lg R-up 53-54 58-59, Lancs Comb. R-up 30-31, League of Wales 94-95 (Lg Cup R-up 94-95), Welsh National Lg 27-28 (R-up 26-27), Nth Wales Coast Lg 1895-96, Welsh Cup 1888-89 95-96 1961-62 (R-up 27-28 60-61 63-64 72-73 77-78 84-85), Nth Wales Chal. Cup 26-27 35-36 36-37 37-38 46-47 51-52 57-58 64-65 67-68, Welsh Amtr Cup 1894-95 96-96 97-98 98-99 1900-01 02-03 04-05 05-06 11-12, Welsh Jnr Cup 1995-96 97-98 1919-20, Welsh All. Alves Cup 49-50 59-60 (Cookson Cup 61-62 68-69 84-85 86-87).

BARRY TOWN

Chairman: Paula O'Halloran **Player Manager:** Gary Barnett
Secretary: Alan Whelan, 166 Jenner Road, Barry, South Glam. CF62 7HR (01446 737188).
Ground: Jenner Park, Barry (01446 735858)
Directions: M4 jct 33 via Wenvoe (A4050) to Barry. Left at 1st 2 r'bouts to Jenner Park. Nearest rail station is Cadoxton.
Capacity: 3,000 **Floodlights:** Yes **Cover:** Yes **Seats:** 800 **Programme:** Yes
Colours: Yellow/Blue/Blue. **Change:** Red & white/white/white
Sponsors: **Nickname:** Linnets **Founded:** 1923.
Midweek Matchedays: Tuesday.
Record Attendance: 7,400 v Queens Park Rangers, FA Cup 1st Rd 1961.
Previous Leagues: Western 08-13/ Southern 13-82 89-93/ Welsh 82-89 94-95.
Best FA Cup season: 2nd Rd 29-30.
Best FA Trophy season: 3rd Qualifying Rd replay 90-91.
Players progressing to Football League: C Simmonds (Millwall) 47, J Brown (Ipswich) 48, D Tennant (Brighton) 48, T Elwell (Swansea) 48, R McLaren (Cardiff) 50, R Howells (Cardiff) 50, C Cairney (Bristol Rovers) 53, D Tapscott (Arsenal) 53, D Ward (Bristol Rovers) 54, J McGhee (Newport) 54, T Quigley (Portsmouth) 55, B Keating (Crewe) 56, J Hartnett (Hartlepool) 57, R Twigg (Notts County) 57, K Webber (Everton) 60, P Issac (Northampton) 1962, L Sheffield (Newport) 62, G Fraser (Newport) 66, R Ferguson (Newport) 69, R Delgado (Luton) 70, G Jones (Luton) 72, R Green (Newport) 72, M Coslett (Newport) 78, P Green (Newport) 84, C Pike (Fulham) 85, I Love (Swansea) 86.
Clubhouse: Open normal licensing hours.
95-96 Captain: Andy Beattie **95-96 Top Scorer:** Paul Hunter **95-96 P.o.Y.:**
Club Record Goalscorer: Clive Ayres **Club Record Appearances:** Basil Bright.
Honours: Welsh Cup (2); Welsh Trophy 94-95; Southern Lg R-up 20-21; Western Lg R-up 11-12, Welsh Lg (7), Lg Cup (4); South Wales Senior Cup (13); SA Brain Cup (3); League of Wales 95-96.

BRITON FERRY ATHLETIC

President: D Prosser **Chairman:** Graham Jenkins **Vice Chairman:** Len Thomas
Secretary: G Jenkins, 262 Neath Road, Briton Ferry, West Glamorgan SA11 2SL (01639 814762).
Manager: Paul Burrows **Asst Manager:** Ian Frazer. **Physio:** Alan Bramhall
Commercial Manager: I Morgan.
Ground: Old Road, Briton Ferry, West Glamorgan (01639 812458).
Directions: M4 onto A48 at r'bout (3rd exit) signed Briton Ferry, right at 1st traffic lights - grd half mile on right.
Seats: 150 **Cover:** 1,000 **Capacity:** 2,500 **Floodlights:** Yes **Shop:** No
Programme: 30 pages, 50p **Editor:** Chris Bearzi
Colours: Green & red quarters/white/white **Change colours:** Gold/green/gold
Sponsors: Howard & Palmet Photoshop **Nickname:** The Athletic **Founded:** 1925.
Midweek Matchday: Wednesday. **Reserve League:** Abacus Reserve Division.
Record Attendance: 1,090 v Abergavenny Thursdays, Abacus Welsh Lge National Div 91
Previous League: Abacus
Clubhouse: Every evenings 7-11pm, and weekend lunchtimes.
95-96 Captain: **95-96 P.o.Y.:** **95-96 Top Scorer:** Paul Burrows
Honours: Abacus Lg R-up 91-92 (Div 2 71-72); Welsh Lg Div 2 37-38 38-39 39-40 46-47.

CAERNARFON TOWN

President: Jack F Thomas. **Chairman:** G.Lloyd Owen. **Vice-Chairmen:**
Secretary: W.Gray-Thomas, ' Dorwyn', Bethel Road, Caernarfon,Gwynedd.LL55 1EB (01286 674482)
Player Manager: John Aspinall. **Coach:** Jimmy Williams **Physio:** Ian Humphreys
Ground: The Oval, Marcus Street, Caernarfon, Gwynedd (01286 675002).
Directions: A55 coast road to A487 bypass to Caernarfon. At inner relief road r'bout follow Beddlegert sign, then 2nd right - ground opposite. Nearest BR station is 9 miles distant at Bangor. Local buses to Hendre estate.
Capacity: 3,678 **Seats:** 178 **Cover:** 1,500 **Floodlights:** Yes **Club Shop:** Yes
Programme: 44pgs 50p **Editor:** Wyn Gray Thomas **Press Officer:** Dr Emrys Price-Jones (01286 830631).
Colours: Yellow & green/green/green **Change colours:** Claret/sky/claret
Sponsors: TBA **Nickname:** Canaries **Founded:** 1876
Midweek Matchday: Wednesday. **Reserve Team:** None.
Record Attendance: 6,002 v Bournemouth, FA Cup 2nd Rd 1929.
Best FA Trophy season: 1st Round replay 87-88.
Best FA Cup season: 3rd Rd replay 86-87 (lost 0-1 at Barnsley). Also 2nd Rd 29-30.
Previous Leagues: North Wales Coast 06-21/ Welsh National 26-30/ North Wales Combination 32-33/ Welsh Lg (North) 37-76 77-80/ Lancs Combination 80-82/ North West Counties 82-85.
Players progressing to Football League: Ernie Walley (Spurs), Gwyn Jones (Wolves 1955), Wyn Davies & Haydn Jones (Wrexham 1960 & 64), Tom Walley (Arsenal 1964), Paul Crooks (Stoke 1986), David Martindale & Steve Craven & David Higgins (Tranmere 1987).
Clubhouse: Yes. 2 snooker tables, darts, pool, fruit machines and live entertainment.
95-96 Top scorer: Eifon Williams **95-96 Captain:** **95-96 P.o.Y.:** Eifon Williams
Club Record Goalscorer: W Jones 255 (1906-26) **Club Record Appearances:** Walter Jones 306.
Honours: N West Co's Lg R-up 84-85 (Div 2 R-up 82-83), Lancs Comb 81-82 (Lg Cup 80-81), Welsh Lg (North)(4) 46-47 65-66 77-79 (R-up(4) 56-58 72-73 79-80, Alves Cup(4) 38-39 74-75 77-79, Cookson 56-57 77-78, N Wales Combination 32-33, Welsh National Lg 26-27 29-30 (R-up 28-29), N Wales Coast Lg 11-12.

CAERSWS

Chairman: Gareth Williams **Vice Chairman:** Hadyn Jones **President:** G Williams
Secretary: T M B Jones, 3 Hafren Terrace, Caersws, Powys SY17 5ES (01686 688103).
Manager: Mickey Evans **Asst Manager:** Barry Harding **Physio:** John Wilden
Ground: The Recreation Ground, Caersws, Powys.(01686 688753)
Directions: Entering Caersws (between Newtown & Llanidloes on A470) grd entrance on left by bridge.
Seats: 150 **Cover:** 300 **Capacity:** 3,250 **Floodlights:** Yes **Shop:** No.
Programme: 44 pages, 50p **Editor:** Graham Burrows. **Press Officer:** Ivor Williams
Colours: Blue/white/blue **Change colours:** Orange/black/black
Sponsor: **Nickname:** Bluebirds **Founded:** 1887.
Midweek Matchday: Tuesday **Reserve League:** Mid-Wales.
Record Attendance: 2,795 v Swansea City, Welsh Cup 1990.
Previous Leagues: Mid-Wales (pre-1989)/Cymru Alliance 90-92.
Players progressing to Football League: P Woosnam (Leyton Orient, West Ham United, Aston Villa, Atalanta), M Evans (Wolverhampton Wanderers, Wrexham),K.Lloyd (Hereford U).
Clubhouse: Not on ground, but in village centre. Normal licensing hours. Food served.
95-96 Captain: **95-96 P.o.Y.:** Paul Jones **95-96 Top Scorer:** Stuart Aubrey
Club Record Scorer: Gareth Davies. **Club Record Appearances:**
Hons: Welsh Amtr Cup 60-61 (I'mediate Cup 88-89 (R-up 91-92)), Mid-Wales Lg(8) 59-61 62-63 77-78 82-83 85-86 88-90 (Lg Cup 79-80 82-83 87-88 89-90), Cent. Wales Challenge Cup 77-78 82-83 87-88 89-90 (Yth Cup 69-70 72-73), Montgomeryshire Challenge Cup(17) 52-53 59-60 62-63 69-72 74-75 76-78 83-89 90-91 94-95 94-95, Montgomeryshire Lg 77-78.

The Stadium Farrar Road, Bangor Photo - Don Fowler

Park Avenue, Aberystwth. Photo - Andy Darin

The Recreation Ground, Caersws Photo - Andy Darin

CARMARTHEN TOWN

Chairman: Malcolm Williams **President:** Anthony Jenkins
Secretary: Alan Latham, 3 Maesdolau, Idole, Carmarthen SA32 8DQ (01267 232432 H), Fax (01267 220116).
Manager: Wyndham Evans **Asst Manager:** Denley Morgan **Physio:** T Poynton/A Underwood
Ground: Richmond Park, Priory Street, Carmarthen Dyfed (01267 232101)
Directions: Proceed into Carmarthen on A48, pich up 440 to Llandaild at the 1st rounabout and follow signs for 1/2 mile. The ground is on left in Priory Street.
Seats: 120 **Cover:** 750 **Capacity:** 3,000 **Floodlights:** Yes **Club Shop:** Yes
Programme: Yes **Editor:** Alvn Charles
Colours: Gold/black/black **Change colours:** Blue & black/black/blue
Sponsors: Jewson Carmarthen **Nickname:** The Town **Founded:** 1948
Midweek Matchday: Wednesday **Reserve League:** Carmarthenshire Lge
Record Attendance: 3,000
Previous Leagues: Welsh League
Clubhouse: Yes
95-96 Captain: Dudley Lewis **95-96 P.o.Y.:** Mike Lewis **95-96 Top Scorer:** Mike Lewis
Hons: Welsh Lge Div 2 59-60, Div 1 95-96, Cup Winners 95-96.

CEMAES BAY

Chairman: Mr I Clews **President:** Mr E Brownlee
Secretary: Mrs N Hughes, 12 Maes Garnedd, Tregele, Cemaes Bay, Anglsey LL67 0DR (01407 710297)
Manager: Bryn Howes **Asst Manager:** Stephen Edwards **Physio:**
Ground: School Lane Stadium, Cemaes Bay, Anglesey (01407 710600)
Directions: A5025 from Brittania Bridge into Anglsey
Seats: 25 **Cover:** 600 **Capacity:** 3,000 **Floodlights:** **Club Shop:** Yes
Programme: 30 pages 50p **Editor:**
Colours: Yellow/black/yellow **Change colours:** All red
Sponsors: King Scaffolding **Nickname:** Seasiders **Founded:**
Midweek Matchday: Wednesday **Reserve League:**
Record Attendance: 721 v Bangor City 95-96
Previous Leagues: Welsh Alliance, Cymru Alliance
Clubhouse: No
95-96 Captain: **95-96 P.o.Y.:** Peter Daley **95-96 Top Scorer:** Kevin Hagan
Hons: Cookson Cup 91-92, 92-93; Welsh Alliance 92-93; Cymru Alliance 94-95

CONNAH'S QUAY NOMADS

Chairman: Mr R Morris **President:** Mr R Jones.
Secretary/Press Officer: Mr Robert Hunter, 40 Brookdale Avenue, Connah's Quay, Deeside, Clywd CH5 4LU (01244 831212(h)/ 520299(b)).
Managers: Neville Powell **Asst Manager:** Gary Wynne **Physio:** Mr M Latter.
Ground: Halfway Ground, Connah's Quay, Deeside, Clwyd.
Directions: On main coast road (A548) from Chester to Rhyl west end of Connah's Quay behind Halfway Hotal.
Seats: 105 **Cover:** 500 **Capacity:** 1,500 **Floodlights:** Yes **Club Shop:** No
Programme: 26 pages, 50p **Editor:** Rachel Morgan
Colours: White/navy/White. **Change colours:** Yellow/blue/yellow
Sponsors: Hallows Associatres Solicitors **Nickname:** Westenders **Founded:** 1946
Midweek Matchday: Tuesday. **Reserve League:** Sealink Welsh Alliance.
Record Attendance: 1,500 v Rhyl, Welsh Cup SF 29/3/93.
Previous Leagues: Clywd/ Welsh Alliance/ Cymru Alliance 90-92.
Clubhouse: No, but Halfway Hotel is adjacent
95-96 Captain: **95-96 P.o.Y.:** Peter Hughes **95-96 Top Scorer:** Stuart Rain
Hons: Welsh Amtr Cup 52-53 54-55, Nth Wales FA Amtr Cup 52-53 54-55, North Wales Coast Challenge Cup, Welsh Intermediate Cup 80-81, Welsh Alliance Cookson Cup 87-88, Welsh Youth Cup 47-48.

CONWY UNITED

Chairman: Graham Rees. **Vice Chairman:** G Evans **President:** K Davies
Secretary: Mr Cecil Jones, 'Iolyn', Iolyn Park, Conwy, Gwynedd LL32 8UX (01492 593496).
Manager: John Hulse. **Asst Manager:** Steve Myers **Coach:** Chris Camden.
Ground: Morfa Ground, Conwy, Gwynedd (01492 593860).
Directions: Leave A55 on 1st slip road after river tunnel and turn left towards Conwy. Sharp left immediately after overhead railway bridge - ground 400yds on left of Penmaen Rd.
Seats: 150 **Cover:** 400 **Capacity:** 2,500 **Floodlights:** Yes **Shop:** Yes
Programme: 32 pages, 75p **Editor:** Dylan Evans **Press Officer:** G Rees
Colours: Tangerine/black/black. **Change colours:** All white
Sponsors: Carlsberg Tetley. **Nickname:** Musselmen **Founded:** 1977.
Midweek Matches: Tuesday. **Reserves League:** Gwynedd League
Record Attendance: 600 v Bangor City, Ton Lon Barritt Cup 88
Previous Leagues: Vale of Conwy/ Gwynedd/ Welsh Alliance/ Cymru Alliance.
Players progressing to Football League: Neville Southall (via Winsford to Bury, Everton), Carl Dale (via Rhyl and Bangor to Chester City, Cardiff City).
Clubhouse: Yes,at Ground.
95-96 Captain: Kenny McKenna. **95-96 Top Scorer:** Kenny McKenna.**95-96 P.o.Y.:** Kenny McKenna
Club Record Goalscorer: Carl Dale **Club Record Appearances:** Gwyn Williams.
Honours: Welsh Alliance 84-85 85-86; Barritt Cup 84-85; Welsh Intermediate Cup 81-82.

CWMBRAN TOWN

Chairman: T B A **Vice Chairman:** **President:** John Colley
Secretary: Mr P Dauncey, 36 Gregory Close, Pencoed, Bridgend, Mid Glam CF35 6RF (01656 861274 H), (0831 264343 B), Fax (01656 861274)
Manager: Tony Wilcox **Coach:** Roger Gibbons. **Physio:** Roy Langley.
Ground: Cwmbran Stadium, Henllys Way, Cwmbran, Gwent (01633 866192).
Directions: M4 jct 26, follow signns to Cwmbran on A4042 & A4051, bear right after 3rd r'bout on A4051 to stadium. One and a half miles from Cwmbran (BR).
Seats: 3,200 **Cover:** 4,700 **Capacity:** 13,200 **Floodlights:** Yes **Shop:** Yes
Programme: 28 pages, 50p. **Programme Editor/Press Officer:** Maurice Salway (01633 430065).
Colours: White/blue/white. **Change colours:** Blue/white/white
Sponsors: B.I.G. Batteries **Nickname:** The Town **Founded:** 1951.
Midweek Matches: Wednesday. **Reserves League:** None
Record Attendance: 3,582 v Cork City Euro Cup Prelim 1st leg 1994
Previous Leagues: Monmouthshire Snr 51-59/ Welsh 60-92.
Players progressing to Football League: Simon King (Newport 1984), Mark Waite (Bristol Rovers 1984), Nathan Wigg (Cardiff 1993), Chris Watkins (Swansea 1993).
Clubhouse: Pub hours, on ground. Catering facilities.
95-96 Captain: **95-96 P.o.Y.:** **95-96 Top Scorer:**
Club Record Scorer: Graham Reynolds **Club Record Appearances:** Mostyn Lewis.
Hons: Lg of W. 92-93; Welsh Lg Div 1 66-67, Welsh Lg Cup 85-86 90-91.

EBBW VALE

President: J S Harrison **Chairman:** J.Hopkins. **V-Chairmanm** M.Carini.
Secretary: D Couglin, 107 Mount Pleasant Rd, Ebbw Vale, Gwent NP3 6JL (01495 305993 H), (01633 290288 ex 243 B)
Manager: John Lewis **Asst Manager:** Mick Martin. **Physio:**
Ground: Eugene Cross Park, Ebbw Vale, Gwent (01495 302995).
Directions: From A465 follow signs to Ebbw Vale, 1st left at next two r'bouts - ground on left.
Seats: 1,200 **Cover:** 1,200 **Capacity:** 10,000 **Floodlights:** Yes **Shop:** No
Programme: 26 pages, 50p **Editor:**
Change colours: Sky/navy/grey. **Colours:** Amber/black/amber.
Sponsor: **Nickname:** Cowboys **Founded:** 1950
Midweek matches: Wednesday
Record Attendance: 1,762 v Wrexham, Welsh Cup 1989.
Previous League: Abacus
Clubhouse: Yes open daily share with Rugby Club
95-96 Captain: **95-96 Top Scorer:** **95-96 P.o.Y.:**
Hons: Abacus Lg 87-88 (Div 1 64-65, Southern Div 52-53, Div 2 East 60-61), Sth Wales Lg 03-04, Welsh Cup 25-26, South Wales Snr Cup 04-05, Gwent Snr Cup 24-25 26-27 28-29 32-33 45-46 50-51.

FLINT TOWN UNITED

Chairman: A Baines **Vice Chairman:** **President:** David Hough.
Secretary: G.M.Davies, 45 Bron y Wern, Bagillt, Flintshire, CH6 6BS (01352 763571 H), (01352 730982 B), Fax (01352 763571)
Manager: Stef Rush **Asst Manager:** Steve Jones **Physio:** Ray Marshall
Ground: Cae-Y-Castell, Marsh Lane, Flint, Clywd CH6 5JP (01352 730982).
Directions: Approaching Flint on A548 from Chester, turn right at signpost for Flint Castle. Ground to right of car park. Flint BR station and bus stops are adjacent to ground.
Seats: 300 **Cover:** 500 **Capacity:** 6,000 **Floodlights:** Yes **Shop:** Yes
Programme: 36 pages, 80p **Editor:** Graham George (01352 7351**P8)ess Officer:** Nigel Sheen
Colours: Black & white stripes/black/black. **Change colours:** Yellow/black/yellow
Sponsors: Procter Johnsen **Nickname:** Silkmen **Founded:** 1886
Midweek matchday: Tuesday **Reserves League:** Clywd
Previous Leagues: Clwyd/ Welsh Alliance/ Cymru Alliance 90-92.
Clubhouse: Yes open every evening and matchdays.
95-96 Captain: **95-96 Top Scorer:** Steve Jones **95-96 P.o.Y.:** Glen Graham
Hons: Cymru Alliance 90-91, Welsh Cup 53-54, Welsh Amtr Cup 47-48, Welsh All.(4) 54-57 89-90 (Alves Cup 53-54 89-90, Cookson Cup 52-53 88-89), Welsh Championship Cup 90-91, N. Wales Coast Chal. Cup 90-91, Nth Wales Coast Amtr Cup(8) 09-10 30-36 68-69.

HOLYWELL TOWN

Chairman: Emile Moore **Vice Chairman:** Ian Ross **President:** Charles Meredith
Secretary: Mrs Carolyn Hughes, Bryn Awel, St James Place, Holway Rd, Holywell, Flintshire, CH8 7NH (01352 714216).
Manager: Mark Jones. **Asst Manager:** John Mahoney **Physio:** Glyn Owen
Ground: Halkyn Road, Holywell (01352 711411).
Directions: A55 Expressway to A5026 Holywell turn, turn right for ground just after Stanford Gate Hotel. Coming from town centre, turn left off ringroad at Victoria Hotel, pass Police Station and turn left for ground at the surgery.
Capacity: 3,000 **Seats:** 300 **Cover:** 500 **Floodlights:** Yes **Shop:** Yes
Programme: 32 pages, 60p **Editor:** Sean Elliott **Press Officer:** Dylan Ellis
Colours: Red & white/red/red **Change colours:** Yellow/blue/yellow
Sponsors: Shotblast Engineering **Nickname:** Wellmen **Founded:** 1946
Midweek Matchday: Tuesday **Reserve League:** Clwyd.
Previous Leagues: Welsh League North 50-60/ Clwyd 84-88/ Cymru Alliance 89-92.
Clubhouse: No - use Springfields Hotel, Pentre Halkyn..Snack bar at ground.
95-96 Captain: **95-96 Top Scorer:** Neil Davies/Tommy Jones **95-96 P.o.Y.:** Stuart Jones
Club Record Goalscorer: Neil Davies **Club Record Appearances:**
Hons: North Wales Coast Amtr Cup 13-14 21-22 57-58, North Wales Coast Jnr Cup 76-77, North Wales Coast Chal. Cup 86-87, Clywd Lg Presidents Cup 86-87 (Lg Cup 87-88, Yth Cup 92-93, Yth Auxiliary Cup 92-93), North Wales Coast Yth Cup 75-76.

INTER-CARDIFF

Chairman: Max James **President:** Len Carroll.
Secretary: C.Hicks, 48 Radyr Court Close, Llandaff, Cardiff. CF5 2OG (01222 552679)
Manager: George Wood **Asst Manager:** Phil Holme **Physio:** Roy Langley
Ground: Cardiff Athletic Ground, Leckwith Road, Cardiff (01222 225345)
Directions: M4 Junc 33 to Barry A4232 past Culverhouse Cross take right after 2 miles onto Leckwith Road, grd on right.
Capacity: 7,500 **Covered:** 5,000 **Seats:** 5,000 **Floodlights:** Yes **Shop:** No
Programme: 24 pages, £1 **Editor:** Terry Martin. **Press Officer:** Clive Harry
Colours: White/black/red **Change colours:** All Yellow
Sponsors: Cabletel **Nickname:** Seagulls **Founded:** 1990.
Midweek Matchedays: Tuesday.
Record Attendance: 1,500 v Cardiff City, Sth Wales Snr Cup 1974.
Previous Leagues: Barry & District/ South Wales Amateur/ Abacus
Clubhouse: Tues/Thurs/Sat 7-11pm at old ground (Cwrt-yr-Ala).
95-96 Captain: **95-96 Top Scorer:** Nathan Johnson 13 **95-96 P.o.Y.:** Nathan Johnson
Hons: League of Wales R-up 92-93 93-94, Abacus Lg Div 1 86-87, Sth Wales Amtr Lg 84-85 85-86. *As Sully: Sth Wales Amtr Lg Coronation Cup 69-70, Corinthian Cup 78-79, Abacus Lg Div 1 83-84 85-86 89-90 (Div 2 80-81), Sth Wales Snr Cup 80-81 81-82.*

Flint's Steve Jones faces up to Simon Bremmer of Holywell *Photo - Don Fowler*

LLANSANTFFRAID

President: Mike Hughes. **Chairman:** Edgar Jones **Vice-Chairman:** Roger Moreton
Secretary: A F Williams, 5 Maes y Garreg, Llansantffraid, Powys SY22 6BD (01691 828535 H), (01691 828441 B), Fax (01691 828862)
Manager: Tommy Morgan **Asst Manager:** **Physio:** Gordon Evans.
Ground: Recreation Park, Treflan, Llansantffraid (01691 828112).
Directions: A470 between Welshpool and Oswestry, left for Llansantffraid at Llynclys, follow signs to village.Turn opposite Silos towards Community Centre.Ground is adjacent.
Seats: 120 **Cover:** 250 **Capacity:** 1,500 **Floodlights:** Yes **Shop:** Yes
Programme: 24 pages, 50p **Editor:** Tony Williams.
Colours: Green/white/white. **Change:** White/black/black.
Sponsors: Mike Hughes Construction. **Nickname:** The Saints. **Founded:**
Midweek Matchedays: Wednesday **Reserves League:** Mid-Wales
Record Attendance: 475 v Rhyl, Welsh Cup '93
Previous League: Mid-Wales/ Cymru Alliance (pre-1993)
Clubhouse: Normal licensing hours.
95-96 Captain: Gary Evans. **95-96 P.o.Y.:** Andy Mullinor. **95-96 Top Scorer:** Tommy Morgan.
Club Record Goalscorer: Andy Oakley **Club Record Appearances:** Derek Arthur.
Honours: Cymru Alliance 92-93, Welsh Intermediate Cup 92-93, Central Wales Cup 92-93 (R-up 94-95), Central Wales Lg R-up 90-91,94-95,Montgomeryshire Amtr Lg 68-69 69-70 70-71 82-83 86-87 91-92 92-93 (R-up 72-73 73-74 74-75, Div 2 80-81, Lg Cup 62-63 65-66 69-70 70-71 73-74 75-76 91-92 92-93 (R-up 59-60 65-66 77-78 80-81 85-86 87-88 88-89)), J Emrys Morgan Cup 72-73 81-82 82-83 92-93, Montgomeryshire Cup R-up 82-83, Presteigne-Otway Cup 92-93, Tommy Jarman Cup 91-92 92-93.League of Wales Lg.Cup 94-95.

Action between Barry Town and Flint Town *Photo - Don Fowler*

NEWTOWN

President: Trevor Jones **Chairman:** Keith Harding **Manager:** Brian Coyne
Secretary: Mr S Reynolds, 19 Brynwood Drive, Milford Rd, Newtown, Powys (01686 628089 H), (01686 626965 B), Fax (01681 623813)
Manager: Brian Coyne **Asst Manager:** Jake King. **Physio:** Elwyn Morgan
Ground: Latham Park, Newtown, Powys (01686 623813).
Directions: A43 to Newtown, right at 1st lights into Back Lane & town centre - 400yds left into Park St., 500yds right (at Library) into Park Lane - ground at end.
Seats: 200 **Cover:** 700 **Capacity:** 5,000 **Floodlights:** Yes **Shop:** Yes.
Programme: 36 pages, 50p **Editor:** Keith Harding/ Nigel Bevan. **Press Officer:** John Annerean.
Colours: All Red **Change colours:** White/red/white
Sponsors: Shell Gas **Nickname:** Robins **Founded:** 1875.
Midweek Matchdays: Tuesday. **Reserves League:** Central Wales
Record Attendance: 5,002 v Swansea City, Welsh Cup 1954.
Previous Leagues: The Combination/ Central Wales/ Northern Premier.
Best FA Trophy year: 3rd Qual. 89-90
Best FA Cup year: 2nd Rd 1884-85. Also 1st Rd 1885-86.
Players progressing to Football League: C Lloyd (Orient), J Lovent (C Palace & Exeter), M Bloor (Stoke & Lincoln), I Woan (Nottm Forest), J Hill (Rochdale), R Newlands (Plymouth), M Williams (Shrewsbury).
Clubhouse: Open every evening. Hot/cold snacks, pool, darts.
95-96 Captain: **95-96 P.o.Y.:** **95-96 Top Scorer:** Mark Williams
Hons: Welsh Cup 1878-79 94-95 (R-up 85-65 87-88 96-97), Welsh Amtr Cup 1954-55, Central Wales Lg 75-76 78-79 81-82 86-87 87-88 (R-up 51-52 52-53 55-56 56-57 74-75 82-83, Lg Cup 54-55 56-57 74-75 75-76 81-82 83-84), Arthur Barritt Cup 86-87, Central Wales Cup 74-75 80-81 92-93, Emrys Morgan Cup 80-81.

PORTHMADOG

Chairman: R.J.Havelock **President:** William Pike
Secretary: Mr R I Griffiths, Llyn-yr-Eryr, Ynys, Cricieth, Gwynedd LL52 0PH (01766 810349).
Manager: Colin Hawkins **Physio:** Ifor Roberts
Ground: Y Traeth, Porthmadog, Gwynedd,(01766 514687).
Directions: At town centre crossroads (by Woolworths) into Snowdon Str., pass RBL/Craft Centre onto unmade track, over railway line - ground on right.
Seats: 100 **Cover:** 400 **Capacity:** 4,000 **Floodlights:** Yes **Club Shop:** No.
Programme: 28 pages, 50p **Editor:** Dylan Ellis. **Press Officer:**
Colours: Red & black/black/black & red. **Change:** Yellow & green/sky/white.
Sponsor: **Nickname:** Porth. **Founded:** 1884.
Midweek Matchday: Wednesday. **Reserve League:** Gwynedd.
Record Attendance: 3,500 v Swansea, Welsh Cup 64-65.
Prevoius Leagues: N Wales/Gwynedd/Bangor & Dist/Lleyn & Dist/Cambrian Coast/Welsh All/Cymru All
Clubhouse: Not on ground (use Midland Hotel), but matchday refreshments available.
95-96 Captain: **95-96 Top Scorer:** **95-96 P.o.Y.:**
Hons: Welsh Amtr Cup(3) 55-58, N. Wales Amtr Cup 37-38 56-57 58-59 62-63, Lge of Wales Cup R-up 92-93, N. Wales Coast Chal. Cup(5) 55-56 73-75 76-78, Welsh All.(8) 02-03 37-38 66-69 74-76 89-90 (Cookson Cup 75-76 89-90, Barritt Cup 77-78, Alves Cup 65-66 73-74 76-77).

RHYL

Chairman: E.Davies. **President:**
Secretary: Mr D Williams, 81A Dyserth Road, Rhyl, LL18 4DT (01745 354773 H), Fax (01745 354773)
Ground: Belle Vue, Grange Road, Rhyl, Clwyd (01745 338327).
Directions: A55 Expressway to Rhyl turn-off and follow signs thru Rhuddlan. Follow signs for Sun Centre along Pendyffryn Rd and turn left at junction - ground 200 yards on left.
Capacity: 4,000 **Floodlights:** Yes **Cover:** 1,200 **Seats:** 200 **Shop:** Yes
Programme: 40 pages 80p **Editor:** Andrew Wilson **Press Officer:** John Daley
Colours: White and blue /navy/navy. **Change:** Red/black/red
Sponsors: **Nickname:** Lilywhites **Founded:** 1883.
Midweek matches: Tuesday.
Record Attendance: 10,000 v Cardiff City, Welsh Cup 1953.
Previous Leagues: Cheshire County/ North West Counties/ Northern Premier/ Cymru Alliance 92-94.
Best FA Cup season: 4th Rd Proper 56-57 (lost 0-3 at Bristol City).
Players progressing to Football League: Ian Edwards, Grenville Millington, Brian Lloyd, Andy Holden, Barry Horne, Andy Jones.
Clubhouse:
Club record scorer: Don Spendlove. **Club record appearances:** Not known.
Honours: Welsh Cup 51-52 52-53 (R-up 29-30 36-37 92-93), Welsh Amateur Cup 72-73, Northern Premier Lg Presidents Cup 84-85, North West Counties Lg R-up 82-83, North Wales Coast Challenge Cup, Cheshire County Lg 47-48 50-51 71-72 (R-up 48-49 49-50 51-52 55-56, Div 2 R-up 81-82, Lg Cup 48-49 51-52 70-71, Div 2 Shield 81-82), Cymru Alliance 93-94 (R-up 92-93, Lg Cup 92-93).

TON PENTRE

Chairman: Jeff Orrells **Vice Chairman:** Trevor Lowe **President:** Kirit Patel.
Secretary: Paul Willoughby, 37 Bailey Street, Ton Pentre, Rhondda CF41 7EN (01443 438281), Fax (01443 442625)
Manager: John Emmanuel
Ground: Ynys Park, Ton Row, Ton Pentre, Rhondda (01443 432813).
Directions: A4058 Pontypridd to Treorchy Plain road, left at Thames Rico Garage then first left again. Ton Pentre (BR) station 400yds from ground.
Seats: 400 **Cover:** 800 **Capacity:** 2,750 **Floodlights:** Yes **Club Shop:** Yes
Programme: 28 pages, 50p **Editor:**
Colours: All red **Change colours:** All blue
Sponsors: Patel V.G. Stores Gelli. **Nickname:** Ton **Founded:** 1935
Midweek Matchday: Wednesday **Reserve League:** None.
Record Attendance: 2,900 v Cardiff City, F.A. Cup 1st Rd 1986.
Previous Leagues: Welsh (Abacus) pre-1993.
Clubhouse: Open daily snacks available.
95-96 Captain: **95-96 Top Scorer:** **95-96 P.o.Y.:**
Hons: Welsh League 57-58 60-61 73-74 81-82 92-93, Welsh Amateur Cup 51-52, South Wales Senior Cup 47-48 60-61 61-62 63-64 83-84 92-93.

WELSHPOOL

Chairman: M G Edwards. **President:**
Secretary: Mr J A Bartley, 24 Bryn Glas, Welshpool, Powys SY21 7TL (01938 552131 H), (01686 626246 B).
Manager: Gareth Cadwallader **Asst Manager:** **Physio:**
Ground: Maesydre Recreation Ground, Welshpool, Powys.
Directions:
Seats: **Cover:** 100 **Capacity:** **Floodlights:** **Club Shop:**
Programme: **Editor:**
Colours: White/black/white **Change colours:** Red/black/black
Sponsors: **Nickname:** Seasiders **Founded:** 1878
Midweek Matchday: Wednesday **Reserve League:**
Record Attendance:
Previous Leagues:
Clubhouse:
95-96 Captain: **95-96 P.o.Y.:** **95-96 Top Scorer:**
Hons:

Flint Town v Barry Town *Photo - Don Fowler*

SCOTTISH FOOTBALL

'O.V.D. RUM' SCOTTISH JUNIOR CUP

FIRST ROUND

Arbroath SC	v	Bishopmill U.	1–0
Baillieston	v	Port Glasgow	4–0
Bankfoot Athletic	v	Broxburn Ath.	2–1
Bathgate Th.	v	Broughty Ath.	3–2
Benburb	v	Inverurie Jnrs.	16–0
Bonnyrigg Rose	v	Jeanfield	2–2 3–0
Camelon	v	G.Perthshire	5–0
Dundonald B.	v	Bo'ness Utd.	1–2
Dyce Juniors	v	Coltness Utd.	0–1
Glenrothes	v	Haddington Ath.	4–1
Irvine Victoria	v	Aberdeen E.End	2–0
Lugar Boswell Th.	v	RAF Lossiemouth	4–2
Muirkirk	v	Blantyre Vics	4–3
Oakley Utd	v	Montrose R.	3–1
Pumpherston	v	Inverurie Locos	3–4
Royal Albert	v	Musselburgh A.	2–4
Thorniewood Utd	v	Johnston Burgh	2–1
Turriff United	v	Downfield	4–1
Whitburn	v	Forfar Albion	4–0
Wishaw	v	Parkvale	1–0
Arthurlie	v	Lossiemouth Utd.	9–0
Bankfoot Ath.	v	Broxburn Athletic	2–1
Banks O'Dee	v	Ashfield	0–0 1–0 (aet)
Bellshill Ath.	v	Linlithgow	1–1 0–6
Blairgowrie	v	Elmwood	1–1 1–0
Burghead Th.	v	Armadale Thistle	0–10
Dalkeith Th.	v	Dundee N.End	2–2 0–3
Dunipace	v	Bonnybridge	2–1
Ellon United	v	St Josephs	0–3
Hurlford Utd.	v	Arbroath Vics	2–3
Kilwinning R.	v	Buchanhaven Hearts	6–0
Maryhill	v	Pollok	1–1 1–2
Newburgh	v	Fochabers	7–1
Portgordon U.	v	St Rochs	0–5
Renfrew	v	East Craigie	3–3 1–2
Tayport	v	Banchory St T.	6–0
Tulliallan Th.	v	New Elgin	2–2 3–1
Vale of Clyde	v	Brechin Vics	3–1
Whitletts Vics	v	Coupar Angus	6–2

SECOND ROUND

Aberdeen L. Club	v	Arbroath SC	0–2
Arthurlie	v	Linlithgow R.	2–0
Beith	v	Armadale Th.	3–0
Blackburn Utd.	v	Livingston Utd	1–4
Bonnyrigg Rose	v	Kilwinning R	2–3
Carnoustie Panmure	v	Lugar Boswell T.	2–0
Crombie Sports	v	Carluke Rovers	2–4
Cumbernauld U.	v	Cambuslang R.	3–2
Deveronside	v	Buckie Rovers	2–0
East Kilbride Th.	v	Islavale	5–1
Fauldhouse Utd.	v	Annbank Utd.	0–1
Forfar West End	v	Lewis United	2–3
Hall Russell Utd.	v	Maud	6–0
Hill of Beath H.	v	Newburgh	2–1
Irvine Meadow	v	Oakley Utd.	4–1
Kilbirnie Ladeside	v	Arbroath Vics	5–1
Kinnoull	v	Pollok	1–2
Kirrie Thistle	v	Whitburn	1–5
Lesmahagow	v	Arniston R.	1–1 0–2
Lochee United	v	Forth W.	3–3 1–1 4p5 (aet)
Maybole	v	Coltness United	1–2
Musselburgh	v	Ormiston Primrose	1–2
Neilston	v	St Andrews Utd.	1–3
Rosyth Rec.	v	Lanark Utd.	3–0
Sauchie	v	Dundee Violet	3–4
Shettleston	v	Dunipace	1–1 1–2
St Josephs	v	Kinloss (Kinloss failed to raise a team)	
Steelend Vics	v	West Calder Utd.	2–5
Stoneyburn	v	Tranent	2–2 0–2
Sunnybank	v	Thornton Hibs	4–0
Thorniewood	v	Rob Roy	1–4
Turriff United	v	Greenock	0–1
Ardeer Thistle	v	Auchinleck T.	0–2
Baillieston	v	Stonehouse Violt	4–1
Benburb	v	Glenafton Ath.	1–5
Bo'ness Utd.	v	Yoker A	1–1 0–0 5p6 (aet)
Camelon	v	Luncarty	10–0
Craigmark B.	v	Dunbar Utd.	4–2
Cruden Bay	v	Crossgates P.	3–2
Cumnock	v	Bankfoot Ath.	9–0
East Craigie	v	Larkhall Th.	0–3
Edinburgh U.	v	Dundee North End	3–4
FC St'wood	v	Longside	2–0
Glenrothes	v	Bathgate Th.	0–0 1–0
Hermes	v	Bon Accord	0–2
Inverurie LW	v	Kello Rovers	2–2 4–2
Irvine Victoria	v	R. Glencairn	2–1
Kilsyth R.	v	Newtongrange Star	2–1
Kirkcaldy YM	v	Fraserburgh U.	3–3 2–7
Largs Thistle	v	Culter	6–0
Lochee Harp	v	Tulliallan Thistle	0–1
Lochore Welfare	v	Balbeggie	2–0
Muirkirk	v	Harthill Royal	2–1
Nairn St Ninians	v	Ardrossan WR	6–2
Petershill	v	Formatine Utd.	4–1
Saltcoats Vics	v	Kelty H.	1–1 0–3
Scone Thistle	v	Vale of Clyde	2–0
St Anthonys	v	Forres Th. 0–0 (abandoned after 3 mins.)	
St Rochs	v	Vale of Leven	0–3
Stonehaven	v	Blairgowrie	9–0
Strathspey Th.	v	Darvel	0–3
Tayport	v	Lochgelly Albert	6–0
Troon	v	Banks O'Dee	2–3
Whitletts Vics	v	Wishaw	2–2 2–1

THIRD ROUND

Arbroath SC	v	Whitburn	1–1 1–3
Coltness Utd.	v	Vale of Leven	1–4
Cumnock	v	Beith	5–1
Dunipace	v	St Andrews Utd	0–1
Forth Wand.	v	St Anthonys	6–0
Hall Russell Utd	v	FC Stoneywood	0–4
Inverurie LW	v	Kilbirnie	1–1 2–1
Irvine Victoria	v	Dev'side	0–0 5–2 (aet)
Kilwinning R.	v	Kelty Hearts	1–0
Larkhall Th.	v	Livingston Utd	1–2
Ormiston P.	v	Bon Accord	0–2
Rob Roy	v	Banks O'Dee	1–0
St Josephs	v	Stonehaven	4–0
Stonehaven	v	Lewis United	3–1
Tayport	v	Baillieston	1–1 3–0
Tulliallan Thistle	v	Petershill	1–4
Carnoustie P.	v	Whitletts Victoria	4–2
Cruden Bay	v	Glenafton Ath.	1–5
Darvel	v	Camelon	3–3 0–1
East Kilbride	v	Auchinleck Talbot	0–2
Glenrothes	v	West Calder Utd.	5–0
H. of Beath H.	v	Arniston R.	1–1 3–2
Irvine Meadow	v	Dundee Violet	4–1
Kilsyth R.	v	Cumbernauld Utd.	3–2
Largs Th.	v	Muirkirk	5–0
Nairn St N.	v	Greenock	1–3
Pollok	v	Craigmark B.	2–0
Rosyth Rec.	v	Carluke R.	3–3 1–2
Scone Thistle	v	Lochore Welfare	3–0
Sunnybank	v	Dundee North End	5–1
Tranent	v	Annbank United	1–2
Yoker Athletic	v	Arthurlie	0–0 1–2

FOURTH ROUND

Annbank United	v	Kilwinning R.	0–2
Carluke Rovers	v	Greenock	2–1
Cumnock	v	Pollok	1–5
Glenrothes	v	Scone	2–2 2–1 (aet)
Irvine Meadow	v	Bon Accord	2–3
Kilsyth Rangers	v	Glenafton	2–2 1–3
Sunnybank	v	Livingston Utd.	1–2
Vale of Leven	v	H. of Beath H.	2–0
Camelon	v	Largs Thistle	3–1
Carnoustie P.	v	Rob Roy	1–4
Forth Wand.	v	St Josephs	2–3
Inverurie LW	v	St Andrews U.	1–1 2–0
Irvine Victoria	v	Auchinleck	1–1 0–5
Petershill	v	Stonehaven	3–0
Tayport	v	FC Stoneywood	1–1 3–1
Whitburn	v	Arthurlie	0–2

FIFTH ROUND

Arthurlie	v	Petershill	1–1 2–1
Camelon	v	Inverurie LW	3–0
Kilwinning Rangers	v	V of Leven	0–0 1–0
St Josephs	v	Pollok	0–4
Auchinleck	v	Gl'rothes	0–0 1–1 6p5 (aet)
Carluke Rov.	v	Glenafton	0–0 0–3
Rob Roy	v	Livingston Utd	2–1
Tayport	v	Bon Accord	2–0

SIXTH ROUND

Auchinleck T.	v	Glenafton	1–1 2–0
Pollok	v	Arthurlie	1–1 1–0
Camelon	v	Kilwinning R.	1–1 2–1
Tayport	v	Rob Roy	2–1

SEMI FINALS

Tayport v Auchinleck Talbot 2–0 *April 12 at Motherwell FC*
(Ross, Stewart) *Att: 3016*

Camelon v Pollok 0–0 4p3 (aet) *April 15 at St Mirren FC*
Att: 3951

FINAL *(May 12 at Motherwell FC Att: 4652)*

Tayport v Camelon 2–0 (aet)
(Stephen Ross 95, 112)

OVD Scottish Cup 5th Round Auchinleck Talbot c Glenrothes. Photo: J. B. Vass.

OVD Scottish Cup 5th Round Replay. Grethafton Athletic (white shirts) v Carluke Rovers. Photo: J. B. Vass.

JUNIOR INTERNATIONALS

This season saw the International side playing again in the Quadrangular Tournament, the only competitive outing of the season. Several warm-up matches were played : winning 3–0 v Hamilton Accies (Linlithgow, February 28), losing 2–1 to St Mirren (Bathgate, March 4) and winning 10–2 at Troon (March 31).

The Guinness Cup Quadrangular Tournament was played on the Isle of Man on Friday/Saturday 19th/20th April. In the semi final, they lost 1–0 to Northern Ireland before hammering the Republic of Ireland side 4–0 in the 3rd/4th place match the next day.

Scorers were Ian Ashcroft (Pollok), Robert Anderson (Arthurlie), Billy Spence (Hill of Beath Hawthorn) and Gary Graham (Auchinleck Talbot).

Teams (v N. Ireland): Jamie Picken (Dalry Th.), Gavin Duncan (Arthurlie), Grant Paterson (Tayport), Ian Ashcroft (Pollok), Robert Anderson (Arthurlie), Sean Bonnar (Camelon), Gary Graham (Auchinleck T.), David Fulton (Arthurlie), Norman Montgomery (Cumnock), Billy Spence (Hill of Beath Hawthorn), David Walker (Glenafton Ath). (v Rep. of Ireland): Kevin Budinaikas (Armadale Thistle), Duncan, Douglas Todd (Linlithgow Rose), Ashcroft, Anderson, Stewart, Graham, Fulton, Montgomery, Spence, McKenzie (Camelon)

Substitutes for both games are unknown.

Northern Ireland beat Isle of Man 2–1 in the final. Previous finals:

93/4	Scotland	1–0	N. Ireland
94/5	N.Ireland	3–2	Scotland

Ashton United and Tayport line up before their International Challenge Match. In the foreground is the Scottish Junior Cup won by Tayport last season. Photo: Colin Stevens.

AYRSHIRE REGIONAL LEAGUE TABLES 1995–96

DIVISION ONE

	P	W	D	L	F	A	Pts
Cumnock Juniors	20	16	1	3	56	24	49
Glenafton Athletic	20	10	7	3	42	29	37
Auchinleck Talbot	20	10	5	5	40	17	35
Kilwinning Rangers	20	8	6	6	34	31	30
Largs Thistle	20	8	5	7	27	30	29
Kilbirnie Ladeside	20	8	3	9	38	31	27
Dalry Thistle	20	8	3	9	32	30	27
Irvine Meadow XI	20	7	6	7	32	30	27
Beith Juniors	20	7	4	9	36	49	25
Ardrossan Win. R.	20	4	3	13	22	58	15
Ardeer Thistle	20	2	1	17	23	52	7

DIVISION TWO

	P	W	D	L	F	A	Pts
Lugar Boswell Th.	22	18	1	3	50	20	55
Maybole Juniors	22	14	3	5	56	32	45
Craigmark Burnt	22	13	1	8	39	29	40
Troon	22	11	4	7	47	27	37
Muirkirk Juniors	22	10	3	9	43	35	33
Kello Rovers	22	9	5	8	44	47	32
Annbank United	22	9	4	9	43	34	31
Saltcoats Victoria	22	8	7	7	34	33	31
Irvine Victoria	22	9	4	9	48	48	31
Darvel Juniors	22	6	3	13	41	47	21
Whitletts Victoria	22	4	7	11	47	62	19
Hurlford United	22	0	0	22	10	88	0

'JACKIE SCARLETT' LEAGUE CUP

FINAL *(Oct 2 at Ayr United FC Att: 1741)*

Cumnock v Ardeer Thistle 3–1
(Wilson, Robertson, Montgomery) *(Stewart)*

'IRVINE TIMES' AYRSHIRE DISTRICT CUP

FINAL *(Dec 17 at Meadow Park, Irvine)*

Kilwinning Rngs v Ardeer Thistle 3–0
(Peline, Adams, Mullin)

'ARDROSSAN & SALTCOATS HERALD' AYRSHIRE CUP

FINAL *(June 8 at Beechwood Park, Auchinleck)*

Auchinleck Talbot v Cumnock 3–1
(Ellis 2, MacDonald) *(Wilson)*

EAST AYRSHIRE CUP

FINAL *(May 30 atTownhead Park, Cumnock)*

Cumnock v Auchinleck Talbot 0–0 4p2

SOUTH AYRSHIRE CUP

FINAL *(May 8 at Portland Park, Troon)*

Troon v Maybole 2–3
(Harvey, Clark) *(Dunn, Robertson, Gallagher)*

AYRSHIRE SUPER CUP

FINAL *(June 3 at Townhead Park, Cumnock)*

Cumnock v Maybole 4–0
(Montgomery 2, Irving, Lamont)

Cumnock – Ayrshire Division One Champions. Photo: J. B. Vass.

Kilw... 1995/9... of the No... Ayrshire Cu... Photo: J. B. V...

Lugar Boswell Thistle – Division Two Champions 95/96. Photo: J. B. Vass.

Maybole – Winners of the South Ayrshire Cup. Photo: J. B. Vass.

'WHYTE & MACKAY' WEST OF SCOTLAND CUP

…entral Region clubs. 1995/96 was the 21st consecutive season with the current sponsor)

		Blantyre V.	1–0
		Vale of Leven	2–6
		Port Glasgow	5–1
		Darvel	4–3
		Lesmahagow	2–3
Irvine Victoria	v	St Anthonys	5–1
Kello Rovers	v	East Kilbride Th.	5–1
Kilsyth Rangers	v	Lanark U.	0–0 3–3 3p2 (aet)
Larkhall Thistle	v	Irvine Meadow	0–4
Maryhill	v	Beith	2–1
Petershill	v	Largs Th.	1–1 4–2
Royal Albert	v	Stonehouse V.	3–1
Shettleston	v	Ashfield	3–2
Troon	v	Renfrew	4–2
Yoker Athletic	v	Benburb	0–2
Ardeer Thistle	v	Forth Wanderers	3–0
Auchinleck Talbot	v	St Rochs	3–2
Craigmark B.	v	Vale of Clyde	1–3
Glenafton Athletic	v	Carluke Rovers	0–1
Hurlford United	v	R. Glencairn	1–9
Johnstone Burgh	v	Dunipace	2–1
Kikbirnie Ladeside	v	Dalry Thistle	2–1
Kilwinning Rangers	v	Maybole	3–1
Lugar Boswell Th.	v	Neilston	2–0
Muirkirk	v	G. Perthshire	3–0
Pollok	v	Whitletts Vics	2–0
Saltcoats Vics	v	Rob Roy	1–1 2–1
Thorniewood Utd.	v	Arthurlie	1–4
Wishaw	v	Cumnock	0–5

Byes: Baillieston, Bellshill Athletic, Coltness United

SECOND ROUND

Annbank United	v	Arthurlie	1–1 2–2 3p4 (aet)
Cambuslang R'gers	v	Johnstone	3–3 3–1
Coltness Utd.	v	Cumbernauld U.	1–3
Irvine Meadow	v	Maryhill	1–1 1–3
Kilsyth Rangers	v	Lugar Boswell T.	0–1
Muirkirk	v	Pollok	3–3 0–2
Saltcoats Vics	v	Vale of Leven	0–3
Troon	v	Kello Rovers	5–1
Benburb	v	Baillieston	10–0
Carluke Rovers	v	Petershill	1–2
Cumnock	v	Auchinleck T.	0–2
Kilbirnie Ladeside	v	Bellshill Athletic	3–1
Kilwinning Rangers	v	Royal Albert	5–0
R. Glencairn	v	Lesmahagow	0–1
Shettleston	v	Irvine Victoria	4–3
Vale of Clyde	v	Ardee	3–3 2–3 (aet)

THIRD ROUND

Arthurlie	v	Kilbirnie L.	4–0
Cambuslang R.	v	Auchinleck T.	1–0
Maryhill	v	Kilwi'ng R.	0–0 1–0
Pollok	v	Lesmahagow	3–0
Benburb	v	Troon	4–1
Lugar Boswell Th.	v	Cumbernauld U.	1–3
Petershill	v	Vale of Leven	2–1
Shettleston	v	Ardeer Thistle	3–1

FOURTH ROUND

Maryhill	v	Cumbernauld U.	8–1
Pollok	v	Benburb	2–2 1–2 (aet)
Petershill	v	Cambuslang R.	2–0
Shettleston	v	Arthurlie	0–4

SEMI FINALS

Petershill v Arthurlie 2–0
at Newlandsfield Park, Pollok

Maryhill v Benburb 5–1
at Greenfield Park, Shettleston

FINAL

Petershill v Maryhill 0–0 2p0 (aet)
at Somervell Park, Cambuslang

NB . . . this was the first time since 1983 that there had been no Ayrshire Region representation in the quarter finals of the competition.

CENTRAL REGION

PREMIER DIVISION (Reebok)

Pollok	20	15	3	2	50–18	49
Petershill	20	13	7	0	40–14	46
Arthurlie	20	14	3	3	50–21	45
Maryhill	20	8	7	5	31–28	31
Shettleston	20	6	10	4	39–34	28
Larkhall Thistle	20	7	5	8	41–40	26
Benburb	20	5	5	10	26–34	20
Kilsyth Rangers	20	6	2	12	24–33	20
Baillieston	20	2	8	10	30–44	14
Dunipace	20	2	6	12	20–54	12
Cambuslang R'gers	20	2	3	15	17–48	9

FIRST DIVISION

Blantyre Victoria	26	21	3	2	59–26	66
Vale of Leven	26	12	8	6	54–38	44
Rob Roy	26	12	8	6	41–27	44
Yoker Athletic	26	10	9	7	40–31	39
Lesmahagow	26	10	8	8	40–34	38
Rutherglen Glencairn	26	10	7	9	43–57	37
Ashfield	26	8	12	6	44–41	36
Cumbernauld United	26	10	3	13	38–48	33
East Kilbride Thistle	26	8	8	10	44–49	32
Vale of Clyde	26	8	4	14	38–44	28
Forth Wanderers	26	7	7	12	36–47	28
Neilston	26	7	4	15	34-35	25
St Rochs	26	6	7	13	32-51	25
Port Glasgow	26	6	6	14	34-57	24

'ABERCORN BUILDERS' SECTIONAL LEAGUE CUP

FINAL *(September 25 at Motherwell FC)*

Blantyre Victoria v Pollok 1–0

'EVENING TIMES' CUP WINNERS CUP

FINAL *(June 8 at Somervell Park, Cambuslang)*

Maryhill v Blantyre Victoria 3–0

EAST REGION

DIVISION ONE

Whitburn	22	13	5	4	41–22	44
Arniston Rangers	22	13	4	5	43–28	43
Linlithgow Rose	22	12	5	5	45–32	41
Nrewtongrange Star	22	12	4	6	40–25	40
Armadale Thistle	22	11	6	5	46–36	39
Camelon	22	11	3	8	42–32	36
Dunbar United	22	17	6	9	39–45	27
Bo'ness United	22	7	4	11	31–32	25
Harthill Royal	22	7	4	11	33–44	25
Bonnyrigg Rose	22	6	5	11	33–42	23
Ormiston Primrose	22	5	4	13	26–46	19
Fauldhouse United	22	1	4	17	22–57	7

DIVISION TWO

Tranent	26	18	5	3	52–20	59
Bonnybridge	26	18	4	4	57–28	58
Musselburgh Athletic	26	17	5	4	71–31	56
Haddington Athletic	26	16	7	3	63–32	55
Livingston United	26	13	4	9	46–36	43
Bathgate Thistle	26	13	3	10	56–45	42
Pumpherston	26	12	5	9	32–26	41
Stoneyburn	26	10	6	10	49–42	36
Edinburgh United	26	9	6	11	35–50	33
Blackburn United	26	8	5	13	45–48	29
Sauchie	26	6	5	15	45–69	23
Dalkeith Thistle	26	3	4	19	29–65	13
Broxburn Athletic	26	2	6	18	22–62	12
West Calder United	26	2	5	19	25–73	11

'SKOL' LEAGUE CUP

FINAL *(January 6 at Forresters park, Tranent)*

Whitburn v Ormiston Primrose 2–1

CALDERS 70/- CUP

FINAL *(June 12 at Newton Park, Bo'ness)*

Linlithgow Rose v Camelon 3–0

PENDRICH STEEPLEJACKS CUP

FINAL *(June 1 at Broxburn Athletic FC)*

Linlithgow Rose v Livingston United 2–1

'WHYTE & MACKAY' FIFE & LOTHIANS CUP

FINAL *(May 25 at Prestonfield, Linlithgow)*

Hill of Beath Hawthorn v Whitburn 1–0

FIFE REGION

(JOHN FYFE LEAGUE)

Hill of Beath Hawthorn	28	14	3	1	131–27	51
Kelty Hearts	28	20	3	5	99–35	43
Glenrothes	28	18	5	5	84–25	41
Dundonald Bluebell	28	19	3	6	86–36	41
St Andrews United	28	16	7	5	96–34	39
Newburgh	28	13	8	7	79–52	34
Oakley United	28	12	6	10	78–59	30
Rosyth Recreation	28	12	6	10	59–40	30
Crossgates Primrose	28	10	6	12	57–57	26
Lochgelly Albert	28	8	6	14	54–67	22
Thornton Hibs	28	6	9	13	42–60	21
Tulliallan Thistle	28	6	8	14	30–62	20
Kirkcaldy YM	28	4	3	21	56–117	11
Lochore Welfare	28	3	1	24	30–177	7
Steelend Vics	28	2	0	26	22–155	4

PEDDIE SMITH MALOCO CUP

FINAL *(October 8 at Rosyth Recreation FC)*

Hill of Beath Hawthorn v Kelty Hearts 1–0

JOHN FYFE CUP

FINAL *(May 4 at Kelty Hearts FC)*

Oakley United v Hill of Beath Hawthorn 1–0

NORTH REGION
East Section

PREMIER DIVISION (BON ACCORD GLASS)

Team	P	W	D	L	Goals	Pts	
Inverurie Loco Works	22	16	4	2	58–26	52	
Turriff United	22	14	1	7	49–33	43	
Sunnybank	22	13	4	5	51–30	40	(-3)
FC Stoneywood	22	11	7	4	57–38	40	
Longside	22	9	5	8	48–48	32	
Bon Accord	22	9	4	9	34–40	31	
Hall Russell United	22	8	5	9	44–43	26	(-3)
Culter	22	6	6	10	28–37	24	
East End	22	9	2	11	35–41	23	(-6)
Stonehaven	22	5	7	10	32–41	22	
Hermes	22	4	6	12	39–60	18	
Formartine United	22	1	3	18	27–65	6	

FIRST DIVISION

Team	P	W	D	L	Goals	Pts	
Banks O'Dee	24	16	3	5	62–21	51	
Banchory St Ternan	24	15	6	3	58–24	51	
Lewis United	24	14	7	3	54–24	46	(-3)
Buchanhaven Hearts	24	14	3	7	51–29	45	
Parkvale	24	12	3	9	34–30	39	
Cruden Bay	24	10	6	8	58–40	36	
Lads Club	24	10	6	8	52–37	36	
Crombie Sports	24	10	5	9	49–47	35	
Fraserburgh United	24	8	4	12	38–41	28	
Maud	24	7	3	14	31–53	24	
Ellon United	24	4	7	13	18–48	19	
Dyce Juniors	24	5	3	16	28–54	18	
Inverurie Juniors	24	2	2	20	22–108	8	

NORTH SECTION (SCOTSCOUP)

Team	P	W	D	L	Goals	Pts
Deveronside	26	20	3	3	70–30	63
Islavale	26	17	4	5	69–29	55
Forres Thistle	26	14	5	7	63–45	47
Buckie Rovers	26	13	7	6	58–40	46
Nairn St Ninian	26	13	5	8	60–43	44
New Elgin	26	11	10	5	58–34	43
Kinloss	26	13	2	11	62–54	41
RAF Lossiemouth	26	10	5	11	60–60	35
Bishopmill United	26	7	10	9	57–52	31
Lossiemouth Utd.	26	8	3	15	41–59	27
Burghead Thistle	26	6	7	13	43–69	25
Strathspey Thistle	26	7	2	17	48–78	23
Portgordon Utd.	26	5	4	17	40–84	19
Fochabers	26	3	3	20	30–82	12

'GREAT NORTHERN TROPHIES' NORTH REGIONAL CUP

FINAL *(April 27 at Spain Park, Aberdeen)*
Inverurie Loco Works v Bon Accord 3–1

'THE GRILL' LEAGUE CUP

FINAL
Bon Accord v Inverurie Loco Wks2-2 3–1 (pens) (aet)
(Stephen, Keith) (Findlay, Yule)

ABERDEEN CABLE TV CUP

FINAL *(May 31 at Spain Park, Aberdeen)*
FC Stoneywood v Sunnybank 2–1
(England, Collins) (Troup)

ACORN HEATING CUP

FINAL *(June 12 at North Lodge Park, Pitmedden)*
Banks O'Dee v Inverurie Loco Wks 2–1
(Irvine, Lockhead) (Alexander)

ARCHIBALD CUP

FINAL *(June 13 at Spain Park, Aberdeen)*
Sunnybank v FC Stoneywood 2–0
(Brebner 2)

GORDON CAMPBELL CONSTRUCTION TROPHY

FINAL *(June 10 at New Advocates Park, Aberdeen)*
Sunnybank v Banks O'Dee 3–1
(Davidson 2, Thomson) (Montgomery-pen)

MORRISON TROPHY

FINAL *(June 7 at Denmore Park, Aberdeen)*
Banchory St Ternan v Buchanhaven Hearts 2–1
(Cole, Ewan) (Christie)

JIMMY GIBB MEMORIAL TROPHY

FINAL *(June 14 at Heathryfold Park, Aberdeen)*
Inverurie Loco Works v Banks O'Dee 3–0
(Alexander, Nicol, Coll)

STEWART MEMORIAL TROPHY

FINAL *(May 12 at Mosset Park, Forres)*
Nairn St Ninian v Losiemouth Utd. 2–1

GORDON WILLIAMSON CUP

FINAL *(May 26 at Gordon Park, Portgordon)*
Deveronside v Islavale 1–0

TOM GORDON CUP

FINAL *(May 25 at Pinefield, Elgin)*
Nairn St Ninian v Forres Thistle 7–2

MATTHEW CUP

FINAL *(April 28 at Princess Royal Park, Banff)*
RAF Lossiemouth v New Elgin 2–1 (aet)

ROBERTSON CUP

FINAL *(October 15 at Mosset Park, Banff)*
Buckie Rovers v Forres Thistle 5–1
(Johnston, Mackie 2, Wood, Innes) (Duncan)

NICHOLSON CUP

FINAL *(November 26 at Kynoch Park, Keith)*
Islavale v New Elgin 2–0

NORTH REGIONAL CHAMPIONSHIP PLAY OFF

June 8 at Canal Park Banff
Deveronside v Inverurie Loco Wks. 1–4
(Bruce (Coll, Findlay, Reid, Reed)

ARCHIE COOK MEMORIAL TROPHY

April 7 at Davidson Park, Longside
East Section XI v North Section XI 3–0
(McLeadog, Findlay, Walker)

HAROLD PETRIE MEMORIAL TROPHY

May 5 at Harlaw Park, Inverurie
North Region XI v Tayside Region XI 3–2

NORTH END CENTENARY TROPHY

FINAL *(May 25 at North End Park, Dundee)*
St Josephs v Downfield 2–1
(Graham, Devine) (Cameron)

TAYSIDE REGION

FIRST DIVISION (A.T. & T. LEAGUE)

Tayport	26	23	2	1	87–17	48
Downfield	26	17	6	3	66–28	40
St Josephs	26	15	5	6	57–29	35
Lochee United	26	14	6	6	59–34	34
North End	26	15	3	8	63–45	33
Carnoustie Panmure	26	8	9	9	61–54	25
Arbroath SC	26	9	5	12	38–52	23
Kinnoull	26	10	2	14	38–48	22
Scone Thistle	26	7	8	11	41–54	22
Violet	26	8	5	13	39–58	21
Forfar Albion	26	6	6	14	35–58	17
Broughty Athletic	26	4	9	13	33–58	17
Forfar West End	26	5	6	15	38–67	16
Montrose Roselea	26	4	2	20	30–83	10

SECOND DIVISION

Jeanfield Swifts	22	17	2	3	69–21	36
Bankfoot Athletic	22	16	4	2	59–24	36
East Craigie	22	13	4	5	63–30	30
Lochee Harp	22	12	4	6	64–41	28
Arbroath Vics	22	10	8	4	48–28	28
Kirrie Thistle	22	10	4	8	40–45	24
Elmwood	22	8	6	8	34–37	22
Brechin Vics	22	8	5	9	52–45	21
Coupar Angus	22	4	7	11	53–61	15
Balbeggie	22	5	2	14	47–68	12
Blairgowrie	22	4	2	16	48–61	10
Luncarty	22	0	2	20	19–135	2

TAYCARS TROPHY

FINAL *(June 1 at Warout Stadium, Glenrothes)*
Hill of Beath Hawthorn v Dundonald Bluebell 2–1
(Ritchie, Wright) *(Cochrane)*

WHYTE & MACKAY CUP

FINAL *(June 5 at Downfield Park, Dundee)*
St Josephs v North End 3–0
(Kopel, McLaren, Cree (OG))

PERTHSHIRE ADVERTISER CUP

FINAL *(May 1 at McDiarmid Park, Perth)*
Tayport v North End 1–0
(Ross)

D.J. LAING HOMES TROPHY

FINAL *(June 11 at Westfield Park, Carnoustie)*
Downfield v Scone Thistle 1–0
(Ferrie)

INTERSPORT CUP

FINAL *(June 6 at Downfield Park, Dundee)*
Jeanfield Swifts v East Craigie 2–1
(Pymm, Walker) *(Gormley)*

DOWNFIELD S.C. LEAGUE CUP

FINAL *(May 23 at Downfield Park, Dundee)*
Kirrie Thistle v Bankfoot Athletic 1–0
(Kilcoyne)

SCOTTISH QUALIFYING CUP NORTH

ROUND ONE

Peterhead	v	Clachnacuddin	4–3

ROUND TWO

Brora Rangers	v	Elgin City	0–0 1–3
Deveronvale	v	Fort William	3–1
Fraserburgh	v	Forres Mechanics	4–0
Golspie Sutherland	v	Buckie Thistle	1–3
Huntly	v	Rothes	4–0
Lossiemouth	v	Nairn County	0–0 4–1
Peterhead	v	Cove Rangers	7–2
Wick Academy	v	Keith	0–2

ROUND THREE

Buckie Thistle	v	Lossiemouth	1–2
Elgin City	v	Deveronvale	1–2
Huntly	v	Fraserburgh	0-2
Keith	v	Peterhead	3–2

SEMI FINALS

Keith	v	Deveronvale	2–1
Lossiemouth	v	Fraserburgh	1–1 1–1 5p3 (aet)

FINAL *(November 11 at Christie Park, Huntly)*
Fraserburgh v Keith 4–3
(Keith, Thomson, McCafferty, Geddes) *(S. Taylor, Wilson 2 1 a penalty)*
(After extra time, 3–3 after 90 minutes)

Teams: Fraserburgh — Gordon, Clark, Michie, Young, Milne, Thomson, McCafferty, Killoh (Murray), Keith, Hunter (Geddes), Stephen
Keith — Thain, G. Taylor (Woolley), Wilson, Watt, Slinger, Gibson, Thomson, S. Taylor, Lavelle (Nicol), Will, Allan

SCOTTISH QUALIFYING CUP SOUTH

ROUND ONE

Dalbeattie Star	v	Burntisland Shipyard	0–2
Gala Fairydean	v	Preston Athletic	1–0
Newton Stewart	v	Wigtown & Bladnoch	1–0
St Cuthbert Wand.	v	Spartans	0–4

ROUND TWO

Civil Service Stroll.	v	Edinburgh Univ.	0–1
Coldstream	v	Selkirk	0–0 4–0
Glasgow Univ.	v	Threave Rovers	5–1
Hawick Ryl. Albert	v	Annan Athletic	1–4
Newton Stewart	v	Vale of Leithen	2–6
Spartans	v	Gala Fairydean	0–0 1–1 5p4
Tarff Rovers	v	Burntisland Shipyard	1–1 1–3
Whitehill Welfare	v	Girvan	10–0

ROUND THREE

Burntisland Shipyd	v	Annan Athletic	0–0 1–4
Coldstream	v	Spartans	0–2
Edinburgh Univ.	v	Whitehill Welfare	0–3
Vale of Leithen	v	Glasgow Univ.	0–1

SEMI FINALS

Annan Athletic	v	Glasgow Univ.	0–0 4–2
Spartans	v	Whitehill Welfare	0–1

FINAL *(November 18 at Palmerstone Park, Dumfries)*
Whitehill Welfare v Annan Athletic 4–2

HIGHLAND LEAGUE

Huntly	30	27	0	3	103–84	81
Cove Rangers	30	20	5	5	74–35	65
Lossiemouth	30	18	3	9	55–37	57
Peterhead	30	16	7	7	74–51	55
Fraserburgh	30	14	9	7	85–46	51
Keith	30	14	6	10	59–40	48
Elgin City	30	15	3	12	59–55	48
Brora Rangers	30	12	5	13	40–50	41
Deveronvale	30	12	3	15	47–53	39
Wick Academy	30	11	5	14	42–63	39
Clachnacuddin	30	9	7	14	45–51	34
Buckie Thistle	30	8	8	14	45–61	32
Forres Mechanics	30	6	8	18	38–51	26
Fort William	30	8	2	20	27–72	26
Rothes	30	4	8	18	39–74	20
Nairn County	30	4	5	21	26–85	17

TOP 5 SCORERS

32 Craig Yeats (Huntly)
29 Paul Hunter (Fraserburgh), Gary White (Huntly)
28 Martin Stewart (Huntly)
25 Paul Bridgeford (Deveronvale)

TENNENTS HIGHLAND LEAGUE CUP

DISTRICT ONE

Huntly	3	3	0	0	6–2	9
Keith	3	1	0	2	5–5	3
Peterhead	3	1	0	2	4–6	3
Rothes	3	1	0	2	3–5	3

DISTRICT TWO

Cove Rangers	3	2	0	1	13–9	6
Fraserburgh	3	1	1	1	6–4	4
BuckieThistle	3	1	1	1	6–7	4
Deveronvale	3	1	0	2	4–9	3

DISTRICT THREE

Elgin City	3	2	1	0	7–2	7
Lossiemouth	3	1	1	1	9–5	4
Nairn County	3	1	1	1	4–5	4
Forres Mech.	3	0	1	2	1–9	1

DISTRICT FOUR

Clachnacuddin	3	2	0	1	5–2	6
Fort William	3	1	1	1	6–2	4
Wick Academy	3	1	1	1	4–8	4
Brora Rangers	3	0	2	1	1–3	2

SEMI FINALS

Cove Rangers v Elgin City 3–0
Huntly v Clachnacuddin 1–0

FINAL *(September 16 at Kynoch Park, Keith. Att: 1200)*

Cove Rangers v Huntly 1–2
(Walker) *(Copland, de Barros)*
(aet, 1–1 after 90 mins)

Teams: Cove Rangers — Charles, Morrison, Whyte, Ritchie, Paterson, Gibson (Leslie), Megginson (Lorimer), Park, Stephen (Lefevre), Walker, MacRonald
Huntly — Gardiner, Grant, Allan, Copland (Gray), Rougvie, Moreland, Yeats, Stewart (Whyte), Thomson, Selbie, de Barros (Scott)

McEWANS LAGER NORTH OF SCOTLAND CUP

FINAL *(March 23 at Mosset Park, Forres)*

Lossiemouth v Clachnacuddin 1–0
(Patterson)

JARLAW ABERDEENSHIRE CUP

FINAL *(March 30 at Kynoch Park, Keith. Att.: 850)*

Huntly v Deveronvale 2–1
(Stewart, Yeats) *(Humphries)*

JARLAW ABERDEENSHIRE SHIELD

FINAL *(Nov 28 at Christie Park, Huntly. Att.: 900)*

Fraserburgh v Peterhead 2–1
(Clark, Hunter) *(Shepherd)*

H.O.E. INVERNESS CUP

FINAL *(Dec 9 at Grant Street Park, Inverness. Att.: 2495)*

Caledonian Thistle v Ross County 5–2
(Stewart 3, Christie, Teasdale) *(MacPherson, Milne)*

SCOTTISH F.A. CUP
NON-LEAGUE wins over League opposition

1989–90	09/12/89	One	Elgin City	Arbroath	H	2–1
1989–90	24/01/90	Three Replay	Inverness Caledonian	Airdrie	H	1p1
1990–91	15/12/90	One	Ross County	Alloa Athletic	A	3–2
1990–91	28/01/91	Two Replay	Ross County	Queen of the South	A	6–2
1991–92	04/01/92	Two	Inverness Caledonian	Stenhousemuir	A	4–1
1991–92	25/01/92	Three	Inverness Caledonian	Clyde	H	3–1
1991–92	25/01/92	Three	Huntly	Dumbarton	A	2–0
1992–93	05/12/92	One	Huntly	Stranraer	H	4–2
1992–93	19/12/92	Two	Cove Rangers	Montrose	H	2–0
1992–93	04/01/93	Two	Huntly	Queen of the South	H	2–1
1993–94	15/01/94	One Replay	Huntly	Albion Rovers	H	5–3
1993–94	08/01/94	Two	Ross County	Forfar Athletic	A	4–0
1994–95	07/01/95	Two	Cove Rangers	Cwdenbeath	H	2–1
1995–96	16/12/95	One	Deveronvale	Albion Rovers	A	2–0

EAST OF SCOTLAND LEAGUE

PREMIER DIVISION

Whitehill Welfare	18	16	0	2	71–14	48
Gala Fairydean	18	10	4	4	37–25	34
Annan Athletic	18	9	6	3	41–30	33
Spartans	18	8	2	8	24–32	26
Craigroyston	18	6	4	8	33–37	22
Pencaitland	18	5	6	7	25–28	21
Preston Athletic	18	4	7	7	29–42	19
Edinburgh University	18	3	6	9	18–31	15
Vale of Leithen	18	3	6	9	28–50	15
Civil Service Strollers	18	3	5	10	24–41	14

FIRST DIVISION

Edinburgh City	22	14	5	3	67–33	47
Manor Thistle	22	14	4	4	58–29	46
Lothian Thistle	22	12	3	7	46–34	39
Peebles Rovers	22	11	3	8	46–38	36
Easthouses Lily	22	11	3	8	58–51	36
Selkirk	22	10	4	8	44–42	34
Tollcross Utd.	22	9	4	9	41–40	31
Eyemouth Utd.	22	8	3	11	40–55	27
Hawick Ryl. Albert	22	7	5	10	45–50	26
Kelso United	22	7	2	13	31–50	23
Coldstream	22	3	8	11	30–47	17
Heriot Watt Univ.	22	3	2	17	32–69	11

'CONFEDERATION LIFE' LEAGUE CUP

FINAL *(April 17 at Gala Fairydean FC)*
Whitehill Welfare v Annan Athletic 3–2 (aet)

'IMAGE PRINTERS' EAST OF SCOTLAND QUALIFYING CUP

FINAL *(April 30 at Preston Athletic FC)*
Spartans v Edinburgh City 3–1

KING CUP

FINAL *(May 14 at Tynecastle Park, Edinburgh)*
Whitehill Welfare v Civil Service Strollers 3–0

ALEX JACK CUP

FINAL *(December 3 at Whitehill Welfare FC)*
Lothian Thistle v Manor Thistle 0–2

SOUTH OF SCOTLAND LEAGUE

St Cuthbert Wanderers	24	20	2	2	91–33	62
Stranraer Athletic	24	15	4	5	73–27	49
Dumfries High Sch.FP	24	11	7	6	55–35	40
Girvan	24	11	6	7	79–59	39
Wigtown & Bladnoch	24	11	5	8	52–42	38
Annan Athletic	24	9	10	5	64–54	37
Blackwood Dynamos	24	10	3	11	61–55	33
Maxwelltown HSFP	24	18	6	10	60–64	30
Threave Rovers	24	8	5	11	59–70	29
Dalbeattie Star	24	8	4	12	49–66	28
Tarff Rovers	24	7	3	14	39–64	24
Creetown	24	5	5	14	33–70	20
Newton Stewart	24	1	4	19	33–109	7

LEAGUE CUP

FINAL
First leg
Maxwelltown HSFP v St Cuthbert Wanderers 2–2
(Telfer 2, 1 a penalty) *(Tweedie, Baker)*

Second leg Att.: 400
St Cuthbert Wand. v Maxwelltown HSFP 2–1
(Tweedie, Muirhead) *Hannah)*
Aggregate: St Cuthbert Wanderers 4–3

SOUTHERN COUNTIES CHALLENGE CUP

FINAL *(May 6 at Galabank, Annan)*
Annan Athletic v Stranraer Athletic 4–0
(Docherty 2, Telfer 2)

POTTS CUP

FINAL *(May 11 at Stair Park, Stranraer)*
Stranraer Athletic v Dumfries HSFP 2–1
(Carnochan 2) *(Glendinning)*

HAIG GORDON MEMORIAL TROPHY

FINAL *(April 24 at Barbour Hall, Glencaple)*
Dumfries HSFP v Annan Athletic 0-5
(Docherty 3, Telfer, Paterson)

CREE LODGE CUP

FINAL *(May 4 at Stair Park, Stranraer)*
Annan Athletic v Stranraer Athletic 3–2
(Docherty 2, Telfer) *(Duffy 2)*

TWEEDIE CUP

FINAL *(April 27 at Galabank, Annan)*
Annan Athletic v Stranraer Athletic 3–1 (aet)
(Docherty, Telfer, Elliot penalty) *(Duffy)*

AYRSHIRE CUP

FINAL *(May 6 at Rugby Park, Kilmarnock)*
Kilmarnock v Ayr United 1–0
(Roberts)

'FAMOUS GROUSE' SCOTTISH AMATEUR CUP

ROUND SIX

Bannockburn	v	Stanley	1–0
Campsie Thistle	v	Redbrae	1–1 3–2
Colville Park	v	Bellshill YMCAs	2–6
Dailly	v	Wellhouse	1–3
Kettle United	v	Dunipace	2–0
Knockentiber	v	Heathside	2–2 2–1
Stirling University	v	Bo'ness Fisons	3–3 1–1 4p2
Symington Tinto	v	NCR	1–0
Bourtreehill	v	Plains Arms	1–1 0–4
Coatbridge CC	v	St Ninians Th.	5–0
Cowglen	v	Kemnay Youth	4–3
Echt	v	Norton House	3–1
Kilsyth	v	Hunter Clark	0–0 2–1 (aet)
Riverside Ath.	v	Glentyan	4–2
Strathclyde Police	v	Dyce Ams.	1–3
Woodside	v	Port Glasgow Hibs	3–2

ROUND SEVEN

Coatbridge CC	v	Wellhouse	3–1
Echt	v	Symington	2–2 3–2
Knockentiber Ams.	v	Campsie Th.	3–0
Stirling University	v	Dyce Ams.	3–1
Cowglen	v	Bellshill YMCA	2–3
Kilsyth Ams.	v	Kettle United	0–3
Plains Ams.	v	Bannockburn	0–2
Woodside	v	Riverside Athletic	1–6

ROUND EIGHT

Coatbridge CC	v	Bellshill YMCA	0–1
Knockentiber	v	Echt	1–1 1–0
Kettle Utd.	v	Ban'burn	0–0 1–1 4p5
Riverside Ath.	v	Stirling University	1–0

SEMI FINALS

Bellshill YMCA	V	Knockentiber	1–0
Riverside Ath.	v	Bannockburn	1–0 (aet)

FINAL *(May 25 at Hampden Park)*

Bellshill YMCA v Riverside Ath. 1–0 (aet)
(Grant)

NOTE: Ronnie Kenneth of Riverside Athletic missed the final. The previous Saturday he had scored the winner for the Scottish Amateur side against Northern Ireland, but was jailed for three months on the eve of the final, for a breach of the peace offence at a Dundee Utd v Airdrie match in September 1995.

WINNERS

1986–87	Bannockburn Ams FC
1987–88	Coatbridge Com. C. AFC
1988–89	Norton House AFC
1989–90	St Patrocks FP AFC
1990–91	Bannockburn Ams FC
1991–92	Heathside Amateurs FC
1992–93	Bankhall Villa AFC
1993–94	Bannockburn Ams FC
1994–95	Heathside Amateurs FC
1995–96	Bellshill YMCA AFC

AMATEUR FOOTBALL ALLIANCE

Secretary: W P Goss,
55 Islington Park Street, London N1 1QB
0171-359 3493 Fax: 0171 359 5027

AFA SENIOR CUP 1995–96

FIRST ROUND PROPER

Match		Result
Southbank v Old Owens		1–0
Old Camdenians v Old Actonians Association		1–2
Ibis v Old Suttonians		2–1
Winchmore Hill v Old Salvatorians		0–4
Old Foresters v Norsemen		6*–4*
Old Vaughanians v Old Tiffinian		1–2
Old Wilsonians v Carshalton		1*–2*
Old Kingsburians v Old Hamptonians		1*–4*
Old Lyonian v Shene Old Grammarians		6–0
Enfield Old Grammarians v Crouch End Vampires		3–1
Mill Hill Village v Old Cholmeleians		1–3
Wake Green v Old Elizabethans		5–1
Hampstead Heathens v Witan		2–0
Old Meadonians v St Mary's College		1–2
Cardinal Manning Old Boys v Hale End Athletic		4*–5*
Old Tennisonians v Old Westhamians	3*–3*	2–1
Ulysses v London Airways		1–0
Corinthian-Casuals 'A' v Wandsworth Borough		1–0
Old Manorians v Broomfield		2*–3*
Civil Service v Old Chigwellians		2–1
Lloyds Bank v Old Stationers		3–1
Pegasus Inner Temple v Nottsborough		2–5
Midland Bank v West Wickham		1–4
Southgate Olympic v Alleyn Old Boys		1–3
Old Isleworthians v Barclays Bank		2–4
Old Salesians v Old Tollingtonians		3–2
Parkfield v Ealing Association		5*–2*
Polytechnic v Glyn Old Boys		1–0
Old Parkonians v Bank of England	0–0	0–3
Cuaco v William Fitt		5–1
Old Ignatians v Old Alpertonians		7–0
Westerns v East Barnet Old Grammarians		0–2

SECOND ROUND PROPER

Match		Result
South Bank v Old Actonians Association		2*–3*
Old Suttonians v Winchmore Hill		4–1
Old Foresters v Old Tiffinian		0–4
Carshalton v Old Hamptonians		2–1
Old Lyonian v Enfield Old Grammarians		7–1
Old Cholmeleians v Wake Green		1–2
Hampstead Heathens v St Mary's College		3–2
Hale End Athletic v Old Tenisonians		3–6
Ulysses v Corinthian-Casuals 'A'		3–1
Broomfield v Civil Service		1–3
Lloyds Bank v Nottsborough		2–1
West Wickham v Alleyn Old Boys		3–0
Barclays Bank v Old Salesians		6–2
Parkfield v Polytechnic		2–5
Bank of England v Cuaco	2*–2*	1*–0*
Old Ignatians v East Barnet Old Grammarians		3–2

THIRD ROUND PROPER

Match	Result
Old Actonians Association v Old Suttonians	2–0
Old Tiffinian v Carshalton	1–0
Old Lyonian v Wake Green	2*–3*
Hampstead Heathens v Old Tenisonians	0–4
Ulysses v Civil Service	2–3
Lloyds Bank v West Wickham	1–0
Barclays Bank v Polytechnic	3–0
Bank of England v Old Ignatians	0–2

FOURTH ROUND PROPER

Match	Result
Old Actonians Association v Old Tiffinian	2–0
Wake Green v Old Tenisonians	1–2
Civil Service v Lloyds Bank	2–0
Barclays Bank v Old Ignatians	1–3

SEMI-FINALS

Match	Result
Old Actonians Association v Old Tenisonians	1–0
Civil Service v Old Ignatians	5–1

FINAL TIE: Old Actonians Association v Civil Service4–0

(* — after extra time)

AFA CUP RESULTS SEASON 1995–96

SENIOR: Old Actonians Association 4 Civil Service 0
INTERMEDIATE: Crouch End Vampires Res. 4 Old Actonians Association Res. 2
JUNIOR: Winchmore Hill 3rd 1 Old Actonians Association 3rd 1–0
MINOR: Polytechnic 4th 1 v Old Meadonians 4th 0
SENIOR NOVETS: Civil Service 5th 0 Old Suttonians 5th 1
INTERMEDIATE NOVETS: Old Finchleians 6th 2 Old Tollingtonians 6th 3
JUNIOR NOVETS: Norsemen 8th 0 Old Suttonians 7th 2
VETERANS: City of London Veterans 2 Winchmore Hill Veterans 4
OPEN VETERANS: Tate & Lyall Veterans 1 Port of London Authority Veterans 2
ESSEX SENIOR: Old Foresters 2 Old Chigwellians 1
MIDDLESEX SENIOR: Crouch End Vampires 3 Old Ignatians 2
SURREY SENIOR: Carshalton 1 South Bank 2
ESSEX INTERMEDIATE: Old Chigwellians Res. 4 Old Parkonians Res. 0
KENT INTERMEDIATE: West Wickham Res. 1 Old Addeyans 1st 0
MIDDLESEX INTERMEDIATE: Cardinal Manning Old Boys Res 2 Crouch End Vampires Res. 1
SURREY INTERMEDIATE: Old Dorkinians Res. 4 Kew Association Res. 2
W E GREENLAND MEMORIAL: Old Chigwellians 2* Witan 1*

(* — after extra time)

SOUTHERN AMATEUR LEAGUE 1995–6

SENIOR SECTION:

FIRST DIVISION	P	W	D	L	F	A	Pts
Old Actonians	22	17	3	2	54	20	35*
Crouch End Vamps	22	12	6	4	46	30	30
South Bank Poly	22	12	5	5	45	32	29
Nat West Bank	22	11	6	5	42	31	28
Old Esthameians	22	9	7	6	38	29	25
Civil Service	22	9	4	9	47	42	22
West Wickham	22	7	6	9	37	39	20
Carshalton	22	6	8	8	29	37	20
East Barnet OG	22	4	8	10	25	43	16
Norsemen	22	4	5	13	22	43	13
Kew Association	22	3	6	13	30	47	12
Winchmore Hill	22	4	4	14	24	46	12

SECOND DIVISION	P	W	D	L	F	A	Pts
Old Parmiterians	22	15	5	2	52	31	35
Polytechnic	22	14	4	4	55	34	32
Barclays Bank	22	12	2	8	51	39	26
Lloyds Bank	22	10	5	7	35	28	25
Alexandra Park	22	10	3	9	42	39	23
Old Lyonians	22	11	1	10	43	41	23
Old Parkonians	22	8	5	9	26	25	21
Old Latymerians	22	7	6	9	42	40	20
Lensbury	22	8	4	10	40	43	20
Old Stationers	22	6	7	9	25	38	19
Midland Bank	22	8	1	13	36	47	17
Old Bromleians	22	1	1	20	23	65	3

THIRD DIVISION	P	W	D	L	F	A	Pts
Old Salesians	20	15	3	2	64	20	33
Cuaco	20	12	6	2	43	19	30
Bank of England	20	12	2	6	56	28	26
Alleyn Old Boys	20	9	5	6	47	30	23
Brentham	20	9	3	8	45	46	21
Merton	20	8	4	8	46	49	20
Broomfield	20	7	5	8	43	44	19
Southgate Olympic	20	8	2	10	38	41	18
Ibis	20	4	4	12	29	55	12
Reigate Priory	20	4	3	13	19	53	11
Old W'minster C'zens	20	3	1	16	21	66	7
Winchmore Hill	22	4	4	14	24	46	12

(* — points deducted breach of rule)

RESERVE TEAMS SECTION:
Div 1: 12 teams, won by Old Actonians Ass. Res.
Div 2: 12 teams, won by Crouch End Vamps Res.
Div 3: 11 teams, won by Old Lyonians Res.

THIRD TEAMS SECTION:
Div 1: 12 teams, won by Winchmore Hilll 3rd
Div 2: 12 teams, won by Carshalton 3rd
Div 3: 11 teams, won by Lensbury 3rd

FOURTH TEAMS SECTION:
Div 1: 12 teams, won by Polytechnic 4th
Div 2: 12 teams, won by Old Stationers 4th
Div 3: 11 teams, won by Old Salesians 4th

FIFTH TEAMS SECTION:
Div 1: 10 teams, won by Old Actonians Ass. 5th.
Div 2: 10 teams, won by Old Latymerians 5th
Div 3: 11 teams, won by Kew Association 5th

SIXTH TEAMS SECTION:
Div 1: 8 teams, won by Civil Service 6th
Div 2: 9 teams, won by Midland Bank 6th
Div 3: 8 teams, won by Broomfield 6th

SEVENTH TEAMS SECTION:
Div 1: 8 teams, won by Nat. West. Bank 7th
Div 2: 8 teams, won by Carshalton 7th

8th, 9th & 10th TEAMS SECTION:
Div 1: 8 teams, won by Nat. West. Bank 8th
Div 2: 8 teams, won by Norsemen 8th
Div 3: 8 teams, won by Old Actonians Ass. 9th

SOUTHERN OLYMPIAN LEAGUE

SENIOR SECTION:

FIRST DIVISION	P	W	D	L	F	A	Pts
Old Owens	18	14	2	2	56	24	30
Southgate County	18	11	3	4	42	28	25
Hale End Athletic	18	11	3	4	48	39	25
Parkfield	18	8	3	7	40	33	19
Witan	18	6	6	6	43	32	18
Albanian	18	5	7	6	29	35	17
Nottsborough	18	5	4	9	33	35	14
Ulysses	18	5	2	11	36	38	12
St Mary's College	18	4	3	11	21	48	11
Old Grammarians	18	3	3	12	26	62	9

SECOND DIVISION	P	W	D	L	F	A	Pts
Old Finchleians	20	16	3	1	87	31	35
Wandsworth Borough	20	11	4	5	62	39	26
City of London	20	11	2	7	46	37	24
Old Woodhouseians	20	11	2	7	50	43	24
Corinthian-Casuals 'A'	20	9	4	7	39	36	22
Hon Artillery Co	20	7	3	10	45	52	17
UCL Academicals	20	7	3	10	31	46	17
Hadley	20	7	3	10	30	51	17
Mill Hill Village	20	6	3	11	40	55	15
Ealing Association	20	5	3	12	36	49	13
Old Bealonians	20	5	0	15	38	65	10

THIRD DIVISION	P	W	D	L	F	A	Pts
Old Simmarobians	20	15	3	2	70	18	33
Westerns	20	15	3	2	69	21	33
Fulham Compton OB	20	14	3	3	74	19	31
Hampstead Heathens	20	15	1	4	64	18	31
B.B.C.	20	12	0	8	52	47	24
Old Fairlopians	20	6	3	11	42	56	15
Duncombe Sports	20	5	4	11	33	38	14
London Welsh	20	5	3	12	42	71	13
Birkbeck College	20	4	4	12	37	69	12
Old Monovians	20	5	1	14	25	70	11
Pollygons	20	0	3	16	22	103	3

FOURTH DIVISION	P	W	D	L	F	A	Pts
Pegasus (Inner Tple)	18	14	0	4	50	23	28
Old Colfeians	18	13	0	5	40	21	26
Mayfield Athletic	18	10	3	5	45	37	23
Inland Revenue	18	9	4	5	40	34	22
London Airways	18	9	3	6	51	49	21
Brent	18	6	5	7	22	23	17
New Scot Yard Comets	18	5	4	9	24	32	14
Centymca	18	4	3	11	26	37	11
Cardinal Pole OB	18	3	3	12	28	39	9
Economicals	18	3	3	12	27	58	9

INTERMEDIATE SECTION:
Div 1: 10 teams, won by Nottsborough Res.
Div 2: 10 teams, won by Southgate County Res.
Div 3: 11 teams, won by Honourable Artillery Co. Res.
Div 4: 9 teams, won by Westerns Res.

JUNIOR SECTION:
Div 1: 10 teams, won by Old Finchleians 3rd
Div 2: 10 teams, won by Albanian 4th
Div 3: 10 teams, won by Old Woodhouseians 3rd
Div 4: 10 teams, won by Fulham Compton Old Boys 3rd

MINOR SECTION:
Div 'A': 10 teams, won by B.B.C. 4th
Div 'B': 11 teams, won by Ealing Association 5th
Div 'C': 10 teams, won by Old Owens 6th
Div 'D': 9 teams, won by Brent 4th
Div 'E': 9 teams, won by Old Fairlopians 3rd

Senior Challenge Bowl: Won by Witan
Senior Challenge Shield: Won by Ealing Association
Intermediate Challenge Cup: Won by Nottsborough Res.
Intermediate Challenge Shield: Won by Albanian Res.
Junior Challenge Cup: Won by Old Finchleians 3rd.
Junior Challenge Shield: Won by Hampstead Heathens 3rd.
Mander Cup: Won by Albanian 4th.
Mander Shield: Won by Old Finchleians 4th.
Burntwood Trophy: Won by Parkfield 5th.
Burntwood Trophy: Won by Albanian 5th.
Thomas Parmiter Cup: Won by Old Finchleians 6th.
Thomas Parmiter Shield: Won by Old Bealonians 7th.
Veterans' Challenge Cup: Won by City of London Vets.
Veterans' Challenge Shield: Won by Parkfield Vets.

Southern Amateur League XI v Reigate Priory XI 125th Anniversary. Photo: Eric Marsh.

Above: West Wickham F.C. '95–'96 Team v Herne Bay. (F.A. Vase – 1st Round – 28-10-95 at Corkscrew Hill. Photo: Dennis Nicholson.

Left: The Captains before the Southern Amateur League XI v Reigate Priory game to commemorate 125 years of football at the same ground. Photo: Eric Marsh.

OLD BOYS' LEAGUE

PREM. DIV.	P	W	D	L	F	A	Pts
Old Aloysians	20	15	1	4	56	16	31
Glyn Old Boys	20	11	5	4	42	23	27
Cardinal Manning OB	20	11	5	4	44	29	27
Old Meadonians	20	12	2	6	41	20	26
Old Tenisonians	20	9	5	6	50	34	23
Old Hamptonians	20	9	2	9	43	27	20
Latymer Old Boys	20	7	6	7	42	38	20
Old Ignatians	20	6	6	8	41	31	18
Clapham O Xaverians	20	6	3	11	28	42	15
Old Isleworthians	20	5	1	14	29	56	11
Old Danes	20	1	0	19	10	110	2

SEN. DIV. ONE	P	W	D	L	F	A	Pts
Old Kingsburians	20	14	3	3	44	28	31
Old Vaughanians	20	12	6	2	44	23	30
Old Suttonians	20	11	4	5	39	28	26
Old Tiffinians	20	10	1	9	36	35	21
Old Wilsonians	20	9	2	9	34	40	20
Old Salvatorians	20	9	1	10	39	41	19
Old Manorians	20	6	5	9	41	47	17
Chertsey O Salesians	20	7	2	11	39	48	16
Phoenix Old Boys	20	7	1	12	34	37	15
Old Tenisonians Res.	20	5	4	11	36	40	14
Shene O Grammarians	20	5	1	14	37	56	11

SEN. DIV. TWO	P	W	D	L	F	A	Pts
Enfield O Grammarians	20	14	1	5	60	29	29
Old Westhamians	20	12	2	6	46	26	26
Old Camdenians	20	10	6	4	43	28	26
Old Minchendenians	20	11	4	5	43	33	26
Old Tollingtonians	20	11	2	7	52	36	24
Latymer OB Res.	20	8	5	7	33	31	21
Old Wokingians	20	7	6	7	41	44	20
Old Meadonians Res.	20	7	2	11	34	39	16
Mill Hill County OB	20	4	5	11	28	49	13
Phoenix OB Res.	20	5	1	14	27	61	11
Old Southallians	20	3	2	15	20	51	8

SEN. DIV. THREE	P	W	D	L	F	A	Pts
Old Buckwellians	20	13	3	4	64	29	29
Old Reigatians	20	12	5	3	47	23	29
Old Grocers	20	12	4	4	65	39	28
Old Dorkinians	20	10	4	6	62	30	24
Old Vaughanians Res.	20	8	5	7	41	41	21
Old Hamptonians Res.	20	8	3	9	42	45	19
Old Salvatorians Res.	20	6	6	8	32	45	18
Glyn OB Res.	20	6	3	11	38	47	15
John Fisher OB	20	5	5	10	28	46	15
Old Tollingtonians Res.	20	5	5	10	31	57	15
Old Ignatians Res.	20	2	3	15	22	70	7

Int. Div. North: 12 teams, won by Wood Green OB.
Int. Div. South: 11 teams, won by Old Addeyans.
Div. 1 North: 10 teams, won by Old Highburians.
Div. 1 South: 12 teams, won by Old Tenisonians 3rd.
Div. 1 West: 11 teams, won by Old Uffingtonians.
Div. 2 North: 11 teams, won by Old Grocers Res.
Div. 2 South: 11 teams, won by Old Suttonians 3rd.
Div. 2 West: 9 teams, won by Old Alpertonians Res.
Div. 3 North: 10 teams, won by Davenant Wand OB.
Div. 3 South: 12 teams, won by Old Suttonians 4th.
Div. 3 West: 11 teams, won by Old Alpertonians 3rd.
Div. 4 North: 10 teams, won by Leyton County OB 4th.
Div. 4 South: 11 teams, won by Old St Mary's Res.
Div. 4 West: 10 teams, won by Old Uffingtonians 3rd.
Div. 5 North: 11 teams, won by Old Tollingtonians 6th.
Div. 5 South: 12 teams, won by Old Tenisonians 5th.
Div. 5 West: 10 teams, won by Old Manorians 5th.
Div. 6 North: 10 teams, won by Wood Green OB 5th.
Div. 6 South: 10 teams, won by Old Suttonians 7th.
Div. 6 West: 8 teams, won by Holland Park OB Res.
Div. 7 North: 7 teams, won by Old Egbertians 5th.
Div. 7 South: 10 teams, won by Old Meadonians 8th.
Div. 7 West: 9 teams, won by Old Magdalenians Res.
Div. 8 South: 9 teams, won by Clapham O. Xaverians 6th.
Div. 8 West: 9 teams, won by Holland Park OB 3rd.
Div. 9 South: 10 teams, won by Holland Park OB 5th.

MIDLAND AMATEUR ALLIANCE

DIV. ONE	P	W	D	L	F	A	Pts
Old Elizabethans	22	17	3	2	77	25	37
Lady Bay	22	16	4	2	77	30	36
Magdala Amateurs	22	15	3	4	85	36	33
Racing Toton	22	13	1	8	55	52	27
Bassingfield	22	11	2	9	65	52	24
Kirton B.W.	22	10	3	9	42	45	23
Beeston Town 'A'	22	7	5	10	28	47	19
Derbyshire Amateurs	22	8	2	12	32	48	18
Old Bemrosians	22	5	5	12	38	51	15
County Nalgo	22	5	3	14	38	72	13
Arnold & Carlton Coll	22	4	2	16	33	55	10
Brunts Old Boys	22	4	1	17	28	85	9

DIV. TWO	P	W	D	L	F	A	Pts
Old Eliz. Res.	20	13	3	4	48	23	29
Magdala Amtrs. Res.	20	12	4	4	50	25	28
Nottingham Univ. Post.	20	11	4	5	63	36	26
Ilkeston Rangers	20	11	3	6	47	38	25
Tibshelf Old Boys	20	10	3	7	38	40	23
Chilwell	20	9	4	7	40	40	22
Nottinghamshire	20	6	6	8	44	41	18
Beeston OB Assn.	20	8	2	10	32	40	18
Woodborough United	20	5	5	10	35	44	15
Keyworth A.F.C.	20	2	4	14	29	48	8
Bassingfield Res.	20	2	4	14	26	77	8

DIV. THREE	P	W	D	L	F	A	Pts
South Forest	18	12	5	1	61	18	29
Lady Bay Res.	18	13	2	3	62	22	28
Old Elizibethans 3rd	18	10	3	5	43	25	23
Brunts OB Res.	18	8	4	6	43	37	20
Derbyshire Amtrs. Res.	18	8	3	7	35	36	19
Old Bemrosians Res.	18	6	3	9	34	40	15
A&C College Res.	18	5	3	10	37	52	13
West-Clif	18	6	0	12	32	60	12
Nottinghamshire Res.	18	3	5	10	18	36	11
Tibshelf OB Res.	18	5	0	13	27	66	10

DIV. FOUR	P	W	D	L	F	A	Pts
Magdala Amateurs 3rd	16	13	0	3	80	23	26
Beeston OB Assn. Res.	16	10	0	6	42	29	20
Derbyshire Amtrs 3rd	16	10	0	6	47	40	20
Ilkeston Rangers Res.	19	9	0	7	48	35	18
Old Elizabethans 4th	16	8	1	7	29	39	17
Racing Toton Res.	16	7	0	9	49	53	14
West-Clif Res.	16	5	1	10	35	51	11
Old Bemrosians 3rd	16	4	2	10	32	53	10
Nottinghamshire 3rd	16	3	2	11	29	68	8

LEAGUE CUPS

Senior: Lady Bay 2* Old Elizabethans 1*
Inter.: Lady Bay Res. 1 Old Elizabethans Res. 0
Minor: Old Elizabethans 3rd 5 Nottinghamshire 3rd 3
Chall. Trophy: Lady Bay 1*:4p Old Bemrosians 1*:2p
Div. Two Chall.: Bassingfield Res. 1 Magdala Amtrs. Res. 7
Div. Three Chall.: West-Clif 3* Old Elizabethans 3rd 2*
Div. Four Chall.: Derbyshire Amtrs. 3rd 1*:4p Old Elizabethans 4th 1*:2p
Div. Three Supp.: Lady Bay Res. 2 South Forest 3
Div. Four Supp.: Beeston O.B.A. Res. 2 Magdala Amtrs. 3rd 1
H.B. Poole Trophy: Lady Bay 0 Magdala Amateurs 2

OLD BOYS' INVITATION CUPS

Senior: Old Lyonians 2 Old Owens 0
Junior: O Finchle'ns Res. 3* E Barnet O Gramm'ns Res.3*:wp
Minor: Old Finchleians 3rd 1 Glyn Old Boys 3rd 3
4th XI: Old Stationers 4th 2* Old Suttonians 4th 2*:wp
5fh XI: Old Finchleians 5th 2 Old Suttonians 5th 1
6fh XI: Old Owens 6ths 4 Old Finchleians 6th 1
7th XI: Old Latymerians 7th 3 Old Suttonians 7th 0
Veterans' XI: Old Tenisonians Vets 3 Old Finchleians Vets 0
(* — after extra time; wp — won on spot kicks)

LONDON OLD BOYS' CUPS

Senior: Phoenix OB 3 Old Meadonians 1
Int: Old Tenisonians 1 Cardinal Manning OB Res. 4
Junior: Old Tenisonians 3rd 2 Phoenix OB 3rd 1
Minor: Old Actonians 4th 2 Albanian 4th 1
Novets: O Suttonians 5th 4*:6* O Tollingtonians 5th 4*:3*
Drummond: Old Tollingtonians 6th 9 Old Suttonians 6th 1
Nemean: Old Addeyans 6th 2 Old Salvatorians 8th 1
Veterans': O Isleworthians Vets 2 Old Tenisonians Vets 1
(* — after extra time)

UNIVERSITY OF LONDON INTER-COLLEGIATE LEAGUE

PREM. DIV.	P	W	D	L	F	A	Pts
Q. Mary Westfield Coll.	14	11	1	2	47	18	34
Goldsmiths' College	14	10	3	1	39	7	33
L'don Sch of Econ.	14	8	1	5	31	22	25
Ryl Holloway College	14	6	2	6	31	19	20
King's College	14	5	1	8	21	36	16
Imperial College	14	4	3	7	27	37	15
University College	14	2	4	8	19	44	10
Char X/W'min HMS	14	2	1	11	13	45	7

DIV. ONE	P	W	D	L	F	A	Pts
Ryl Holloway Coll. Res.	18	15	0	3	53	18	45
Univ. Coll & Middx HMS	18	14	2	2	63	19	44
QM Westfield Coll. Res.	18	13	2	3	54	17	41
Ryl Holloway Coll. 3rd	18	11	0	7	44	26	33
Univ. College Res.	18	7	0	11	31	51	21
St George's HMS	18	4	6	8	25	41	18
L'don Sch of Econ. Res.	18	5	1	12	39	68	16
R.L'don & St Barts HMC	18	4	3	11	29	43	15
Imperial Coll. Res.	18	3	5	10	23	45	14
Royal Free HMS	18	3	3	12	20	53	12

DIV. TWO	P	W	D	L	F	A	Pts
King's Coll.HMS	18	14	1	3	65	19	43
U.M.D.S.	18	14	0	4	57	20	42
L'don Sch of Econ 3rd	18	11	0	7	45	33	33
Ryl Veterinary Coll.	18	11	0	7	41	37	33
St Mary's HMS	18	10	2	6	54	31	32
King's Coll. Res.	18	10	1	7	38	42	31
Imperial Coll. 3rd	18	5	2	11	27	44	17
Ryl Holloway Coll. 4th	18	5	1	12	30	47	16
Sch. Slav/E.Euro Stud.	18	3	1	14	21	51	10
Univsity Coll. 3rd	18	2	2	14	21	75	8

Div. 3: 10 teams, won by Goldsmiths' College Res.
Div. 4: 10 teams, won by St George's Hospital MS Res.
Div. 5: 8 teams, won by University College 6th.
Div. 6: 9 teams, won by Wye College, Kent.

Challenge Cup: Goldsmiths' College 1*:5p London School of Economics 1*:4p
Upper Reserves Cup: Royal Holloway College 3rd 1* Queen Mary Westfield College Res. 2*
Lower Reserves Cup: London School of Economics 5th 1 Royal Holloway College 5th 2
(* — after extra time)

United Hospitals Senior Cup: St Mary's Hospital Medical School 6 Charing Cross & Westminster Hospital Medical School 4
Junior Cup: Middlesex & University College Hospital Res. 6 U.M.D.S. 3rd 1

LONDON UNIVERSITY REPRESENTATIVE MATCH RESULTS

Ulysses	Won	4–1
Old Boys' League	Lost	0–3
Southern Amateur League	Lost	2–3
Royal Navy	Lost	0–4
Arthurian League	Won	1–0
London Legal League	Lost	1–3
Lloyds Insurers	Won	3–0
Cambridge University	Won	2–1*
Oxford University	Won	2–0*
Amateur Football Alliance	Drawn	1–1

(* — Lloyds' Shield Competition — Won by London)

ARTHUR DUNN CUP

Old Brentwoods 1 Lancing Old Boys 4

ARTHURIAN LEAGUE

PREM. DIV.	P	W	D	L	F	A	Pts
Old Foresters	16	14	0	2	67	26	25~
Old Chigwellians	16	11	3	2	39	23	25
Lancing Old Boys	16	10	3	3	54	25	23
Old Carthusians	16	8	2	6	41	30	18
Old Reptonians	16	7	1	8	33	35	15
Old Cholmeleians	16	6	1	9	45	43	13
Old Etonians	16	5	2	9	32	44	12
Old Malvernians	16	4	1	11	25	47	9
Old Aldenhamians	16	0	1	15	10	73	1

DIV. ONE	P	W	D	L	F	A	Pts
Old Brentwoods	16	14	1	1	63	18	29
Old Witleians	16	11	3	2	57	25	25
Old Salopians	16	10	3	3	44	24	23
Old Wellingburians	16	7	4	5	41	49	16~
Old Bradfieldians	16	6	3	7	33	37	15
Old Harrovians	16	5	2	9	30	43	12
Old Haileyburians	16	4	2	10	40	56	10
Old Haberdashers	16	2	3	11	22	51	7
Old Wykehamists	16	2	1	13	25	52	5

DIV. TWO	P	W	D	L	F	A	Pts
Old Chigwellians Res.	16	13	1	2	74	22	27
Old Cholmeleians Res.	16	8	4	4	39	24	20
Old Etonians Res.	16	7	3	6	36	28	17
Old Carthusians Res.	16	7	3	6	31	32	17
Old Foresters Res.	16	9	0	7	32	38	15~
Old Cholmeleians 3rd	16	5	3	8	33	35	13
Lancing Old Boys Res.	16	6	3	7	36	44	13~
Old Chigwellians 3rd	16	4	4	8	18	36	12
Old Salopians Res.	16	2	1	13	25	65	3~

DIV. THREE	P	W	D	L	F	A	Pts
Old Etonians 3rd	16	10	5	1	52	21	25
Old Harrovians Res.	16	9	3	4	41	27	21
Old Brentwoods Res.	16	8	4	4	37	29	20
Old Haberdashers Res.	16	7	2	7	30	45	16
Old Aldenhamians Res.	16	6	3	7	45	50	15
Old Westminsters	16	7	1	8	37	40	13~
Old Eastbournians	16	5	1	10	28	36	11
Old Malvernians Res.	16	3	5	8	26	40	11
Old Reptonians Res.	16	4	2	10	38	46	8~

(~ — points deducted — breach of rule)

Div. 4: Won by Old Cholmeleians 4th.
Div. 5: Won by Old Haileyburians Res.

Junior League Cup: Old Chigwellians Res. 3 Old Brentwood Res. 0
Lady Bay 2* Old Elizabethans 1*
Derrik Moore Veterans Cup: Old Cholmeleians Vets 1* Old Carthusians Vets 0*
(* — after extra time)

BOODLE & DUNTHORPE CUP (Public Schools Knockout)

Quarter Finals:

Ardingly	0	Bury GS.	1
Lancing	2*3	Latymer Upper	2*4
Brentwood	2	Hulme GS, Oldham	1
Manchester GS	1	QEGS Blackburn	2

(* — won on penalties after extra time)

Semi Finals:

QEGS Blackburn	2	Latymer Upper	1
Bury GS.	1	Brentwood	1

(Bury GS won on penalties)

Cup Final (at Chester City F.C.):

Queen Elizabeth GS	1	Bury GS	0

LONDON LEGAL LEAGUE

DIV. ONE	P	W	D	L	F	A	Pts
Grays Inn	18	17	0	1	73	13	34
Wilde Sapte	18	14	2	2	58	25	30
Pegasus (Inner Tple)	18	9	4	5	46	34	22
Linklaters & Paines	18	7	5	6	31	37	19
Gouldens	18	6	4	8	27	42	16
Nabarro Nathanson	18	4	7	7	37	44	15
Cameron Markby Hewitt	18	6	2	10	33	48	14
Clifford Chance	18	6	1	11	26	38	13
D.J. Freeman & Co	18	4	1	13	28	46	9
Slaughter & May	18	3	2	13	24	56	8

DIV. TWO	P	W	D	L	F	A	Pts
Lovell White Durrant	18	15	3	0	74	20	33
Herbert Smith	18	9	5	4	45	26	23
Rosling King	18	9	3	6	63	35	21
S.J. Berwin	18	9	3	6	59	57	21
Macfarlanes	18	8	3	7	48	43	19
Norton Rose	18	8	3	7	40	42	19
Freshfields	18	8	2	8	48	38	18
Allen & Overy	18	4	3	11	30	78	11
Stephenson Harwood	18	5	0	13	38	54	10
Wat. Farley & Williams	18	2	1	15	21	63	5

DIV. THREE							
Baker & McKenzie	14	13	1	0	67	16	27
Taylor Joynson Garrett	14	9	3	2	39	31	21
McKenna & Co.	14	6	2	6	35	37	14
Simmons & Simmons	14	6	2	6	28	32	14
Titmuss Sainer	14	5	2	7	31	25	12
Denton Hall	14	4	4	6	25	36	12
Barlow Lyde & Gilbert	14	3	3	8	25	41	9
Richards Butler	14	0	3	11	16	48	3

League Challenge Cup: Gray's Inn 1 Stephenson Harwood 0
Weavers Arms Cup: Wilde Sapte 4* Taylor Joynson Garrett 3*
Invitation Cup: Allen & Overy 2 Titmuss Sainer 1
Division 3 Cup: Barlow Lyde & Gilbert 3 Taylor Joynson Garrett 4

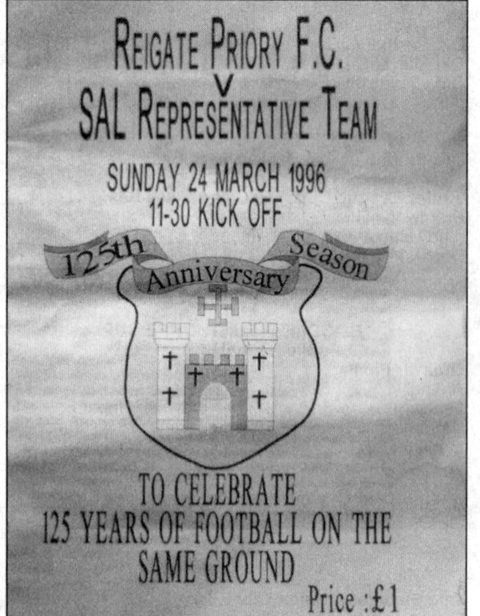

LONDON FINANCIAL F.A.

DIV. ONE	P	W	D	L	F	A	Pts
Sun Alliance	18	11	6	1	53	14	28
Royal Bank of Scotland	18	12	2	4	77	23	26
Morgan Stanley Int.	18	11	1	6	50	26	23
Bank America	18	9	5	4	38	24	23
Kleinwort Benson	18	8	5	5	49	26	21
Coutts	17	9	2	7	49	28	20
Chemical Bank	18	6	4	8	43	72	16
Citibank	18	4	2	12	29	64	10
Temple Bar	18	2	3	13	21	91	7
Liverpool Victoria	18	2	2	14	30	71	6

DIV. TWO	P	W	D	L	F	A	Pts
Morgan Guaranty	14	12	2	0	54	13	26
Churchill Insurance	14	10	1	3	40	11	21
Allied Irish Bank	14	7	4	3	51	34	18
Granby	14	8	1	5	48	34	17
Eagle Star	14	5	2	7	30	33	12
Sedgwick	14	4	2	8	30	50	10
Salomon Brothers	14	2	1	11	20	67	5
Bardhill	14	0	3	11	14	45	3
Invesco	Withdrew after 11 matches						

DIV. THREE	P	W	D	L	F	A	Pts
Bowring	16	14	1	1	62	25	29
Ryl Bank of Scot. Res.	16	9	0	7	45	39	18
United Bank of Kuwait	16	8	1	7	52	45	17
Chase Manhattan Bank	16	5	5	6	49	46	15
Un. Bank of Switzerland	16	8	2	6	37	31	14~
Sdgwk Noble Lowndes	16	6	1	9	39	40	13
Direct Line Insurance	16	5	3	8	41	54	13
ANZ Banking Group	16	5	2	9	24	43	12
Coutts Res.	16	3	3	10	31	57	9

DIV. FOUR							
Vantage	18	14	2	2	75	23	30
Bankers Trust	18	13	3	2	56	26	29
Citibank Res.	18	7	8	3	28	15	22
Granby Res.	18	8	3	7	51	41	19
Bank America Res.	18	8	3	7	49	40	19
Lincoln National	18	7	4	7	39	45	18
Ryl Bk of Scotland 3rd	18	7	2	9	37	41	16
Asphalia	18	5	3	10	30	47	13
U.C.B. Home Loans	18	1	6	11	20	52	8
Temple Bar Res.	18	2	2	14	28	83	6

(~ — points deducted — breach of rule)

Div. 5: 9 teams, won by Credit Suisse Financial Products
Div. 6: 8 teams, won by Bowring Res.

Challenge Cup: Lensbury 2 Barclays Bank 1
Senior Cup: Ryl Bank of Scotland 6 Morgan Guaranty 1
Senior Plate: Chemical Bank 3* Liverpool Victoria 1*
Junior Cup: United Bank of Kuwait 4 Royal Bank of Scotland 3rd 0
Junior Plate: Citibank Res. 2 Vantage 1
Minor Cup: Sun Alliance 3rd 5 St Paul International 2
Minor Plate: British Gas (Bromley) 7* Standard Chartered Bank 5*
Veterans' Cup: Lensbury 4 Bank of America 2
Veterans' Plate: Sedgwick 5 Coutts Bank 4
W A Jewell Memorial: Chemical Bank 5-a-side
Saunders Shield: Morgan Guaranty 5-a-side
Sportsmanship Shield: Kleinwort Benson

Representative Matches:

v Southern Olympian League	Lost	0–2
v Royal Marines	Won	5–2
v Southern Amateur League 'B'	Won	2–1
v Old Boys' League	Lost	1–3
v Stock Exchange F.A.	Won	3–1
v Bristol Insurance Institute	Lost	0–3

VARSITY MATCH

OXFORD UNIVERSITY 2 CAMBRIDGE UNIVERSITY 1

BUSA CHAMPIONSHIP 1995–6

Round 1 — 7th Feb.

Leicester 1 Birmingham FTC 0; Leeds Met 4 Newcastle 2; Loughborough 3 Liverpool Inst 1; Staffs (Stoke) 3 Keele 4; Warwick 6 Liverpool 0; Liverpool JM 2 Salford 1; Worcester 2 Nottingham 3; Northumbria 2 Central England 0; Bradford 3 Wolverhampton 4; Hull W/O Edge Hill; Cheltenham & Glos 4 Teesside 3; Leeds 2 Crewe & Alsagar 1; TASC 1 Sheffield Hallam 5; Birmingham 8 Sunderland 7; Scot Scot; Scot Scot; St Mark & St John 5 Goldsmiths 2; Westminster 2 Charing X & West 1; Bristol 2 Luton 1; Essex 2 UW Swansea 3; RHBNC 2 UW Cardiff 0; Swansea Inst 1 Bath 3; Bath College 0 Bangor Normal 1; Cardiff Inst 3 Southampton 1; Brunel UC 6 Glamorgan 1; East Anglia 2 St Mary's College 3; QMW 0 Greenwich 1; Exeter 0 Canterbury CCC 2; Chichester 2 Wye College 0; UCL 2 Brunel 5; Roehampton Inst 3 Bucks College 1; Cranfield (Shriven) v R London/St Barts W/O.

Round 2 — 14th Feb.

Keele 1 Leicester 4; Liverpool JM 3 Nottingham 1; Leeds Met 2 Loughborough 1; Chelt & Glos 3 Hull 4; Sheffield Hallam 4 Northumbria 5; Warwick 2 Leeds 0; Birmingham 4 Notts Trent 1; Roehampton 2 Bath 0; Royal London/St Barts 2 Canterbury 5; Bangor Normal 2 UW Swansea 4; Westminster 2 Greenwich 4; Chichester 0 Cardiff Inst 3; RHBNC 5 St Mary's College 6; Brunel 0 Marjons 4; BUC 4 Bristol 0; Edinburgh won the Round 2 Scottish match.

Round 3 — 21st Feb.

Leeds Met. 2 Liverpool JM 3; Roehampton 5 Greenwich 3; Hull 1 Warwick 2; Cardiff Institute 4 Northumbria 2; St Mary's College 0 BUC 6; Edinburgh 5 Birmingham 0; Canterbury 5 Marjons 3; UW Swansea 3 Leicester 0.

Quarter Finals 28th Feb.		**Semi Finals** 6th March.		**Final** 7th May at Walsall FC K.O. 7.30pm	
Canterbury	0				
Roehampton	2	Roehampton	1		
Cardiff Institute	3	Cardiff Institute	0	Roehampton	2
AUW Swansea	1				
Liverpool JM	3				
Warwick	1	Liverpool JM	0		
				Edinburgh	1
Edinburgh	1	Edinburgh	2		
BUC	0				

INTER SERVICES

Royal Navy	3	RAP	0
Army	1	Royal Navy	1
RAF	0	Army	2

KENTISH CUP

Combined Services	1	Netherlands Services	1
Netherlands Services	0	Belgian Forces	4
(At Home)			
Belgian Forces	1	Combined Services	2

JUBILEE CUP (SINGLE SERVICES CUP WINNER 1994–5)

HMS Neptune	3	RAF Coltishall	2
RAF Coltishall	0	1 Cheshire Regiment	5
1 Cheshire Regiment	0	HMS Neptune	4

28 Eng Regt win Army Cup (95–96) at Aldershot. Photo: Eric Marsh.

THE ENGLISH SCHOOLS' F.A.

Secretary: M.R. Berry, 1-2 Eastgate St., Stafford ST16 2NO
Tel: 01785 251142
Publicity: Mike Simmonds. Tel: 0115 931 3299

THE INTERNATIONAL SEASON UNDER 18's

The overall record for the season of P4 W1 L1 D2 does not really give a true picture of the season. The 2 draws were gained against the most difficult opponents, both of whom choose from the full age cohort, whereas the England Schools' squad is chosen only from those still in full-time education.

Against Belgium, pre-match preparations were ruined by the worst weather of the winter, culminating in the arrival of the England team at 3am on the day of the match. Despite this, the team recovered from a 2–0 deficit with 10 minutes remaining to force a 2–2. An even more spectacular recovery came against the young Dutch professionals with 3 goals in the last 15 minutes, shocking the visitors after they had appeared to be coasting home.

The real disappointment was the 3–1 defeat in the Heinz Centenary Shield at the hands of Switzerland when England had sufficient chances to win and go through to the final. Instead, they had to be satisfied with third place thanks to the comfortable victory over Wales.

RESULTS

Belgium	v	England (Own goal, Sadler)	2–2
(at Oostduinkerke)			
England	v	Holland	3–3
(Innes 2, Sadler) (at Carlisle United F.C.)			
Switzerland	v	England (Fotiadis)	31
Heinz Centenary Shield semi-final (at Gland F.C.)			
England	v	Wales	4–0
(Sutton 2, Fotiadis, Innes)			
Heinz Centenary Shield 3rd place play-off			
N.Ireland	v	Switzerland	1–0
Centenary Shield Final (Belfast)			

Team Manager: P. Brackwell (Northants)
Assistant Team Manager: D. Cook (London)
Physiotherapist: F. Melia (Merseyside)
Doctor: D. Baron

APPEARANCES AND GOALSCORERS

S. Adams	Humberside	3	
M. Burrow	Worcestershire	4	
R. Clarke	Avon	0	(+ 4 sub)
A. Clementson	Northumberland	4	
A. Fotiadis	Hertfordshire	4	(2 goals)
G. Innes	Durham	4	(3 goals)
S. Langrish	Dorset	4	
A. O'Brien	Northumberland	1	
R. Penn	Essex	3	
A. Potter	Essex	4	
J. Preston	Dorset	0	(+ 3 sub)
C. Riley	Worcestershire	4	
D. Sadler	Somerset	2	(+ 2 sub) (1 goal)
M. Simpson	Northumberland	4	
P. Sutton	Worcestershire	2	(+ 1 sub) (3 goals)
M. Stevens	Wiltshire	2	(+ 1 sub)
R. Walker	Somerset	1	(+ 2 sub)

England Schools's Under 15 International Squad 1995–97.

THE INTERNATIONAL SEASON UNDER 15's

After 2 excellent seasons, it was perhaps inevitable that the 1995–6 Under 15 squad should struggle, winning only 2 of their 8 matches. They did, however, retain the adidas Victory Shield to complete a hat-trick of successes in this Home International Championship. The foreign opposition, however, generally proved too strong with new opponents in Spain and Hungary both returning home with 3–2 victories. England did, however, retain their stranglehold over Holland who have never won a match at this level between the 2 countries, despite the much-vaunted Dutch training methods.

RESULTS

England	v	Wales	2–1
(Wheatcroft, Taylor) (at Fratton Park, Portsmouth)			
adidas Victory Shield			
England	v	Northern Ireland	0–0
(at Cellnet Stadium, Middlesbrough)			
adidas Victory Shield			
England	v	Spain	2–3
(Standing, Jeffers) (at Wembley Stadium)			
England	v	Hungary	2–3
(Parker, Foster) (at Molineux, Wolverhampton)			
Scotland	v	England (Wheatcroft)	1–1
(at Kilmarnock) adidas Victory Shield			
England	v	Holland	1–0
(Parker) (at Old Trafford)			
Germany	v	England	3–0
(Olympic Stadium, Berlin)			
France	v	England (Wheatcroft)	2–1
(at Epernay)			

APPEARANCED AND GOALSCORERS

Anthony Allman	Maidstone SFA*	3	(+ 4 sub)
Lee Cannoville	Watford SFA*	8	
Ian Fitzpatrick	Bury SFA*	2	(+ 6 sub)
Stephen Foster	Warrington SFA	6	(1 goal)
Matthew Ghent	Tamworth SFA*	6	(+ 1 sub)
Alex Higgins	Sheffield*	7	(+ 1 sub)
Peter Holmes	Bishop Auckland SFA*	6	(+ 1 sub)
Francis Jeffers	Liverpool SFA	5	(+ 2 sub) (1 goal)
Ray Johnston	North Avon SFA	2	(+ 3 sub)
Mark Maley	Newcastle SFA	5	(+ 1 sub)
Kevin Nicholson	Derby SFA*	8	(Captain)
Scott Parker	Blackheath SFA*	7	(2 goals)
Michael Standing	Brighton SFA	5	(+ 3 sub) (1 goal)
Perry Taylor	Wirral SFA	8	(1 goal)
Rhys Weston	Woking SFA*	6	
Paul Wheatcroft	Bolton SFA*	4	(+ 4 sub) (3 goals)

* Indicates player also attending F.A. National School

Team Manager: J. Owens (St Helens)
Assistant Team Manager: D. Parnaby (Spennymoor)
Physiotherapist: M. Dickinson (Bootle)
Doctor: A Tabor
F.A. Advisor: J. Peacock

adidas VICTORY SHIELD FINAL TABLE

	P	W	D	L	F	A	Pts
England	3	1	2	0	3	2	4
Scotland	3	1	1	1	5	3	3
N. Ireland	3	1	1	1	2	2	3
Wales	3	1	0	2	4	7	2

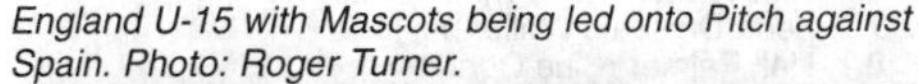

England U-15 with Mascots being led onto Pitch against Spain. Photo: Roger Turner.

INTER-ASSOCIATION COMPETITIONS

E.S.F.A. FUJI FILMS TROPHY 1995–96

Final: (First leg) (at Gigg Lane, Bury) : Bury 1 Walsall 0
(Second leg) (at Bescot Stadium, Walsall) : Walsall 1 Bury 1

Bury won 2–1 on aggregate

ROUTES TO THE FINAL

Bury

Round 1	–	Bye		
Round 2	v	Blackburn & Darwen	A	4–0
Round 3	v	Wrexham	A	4–1
Round 4	v	Leeds	H	3–0
Round 5	v	East Northumberland	H	2–1 (aet)
Round 6	v	West Bromwich	A	0–0
Replay	v	West Bromwich	H	3–1
Semi-final	v	Hackney & Tower Hamlets	A	2–1

Walsall

Round 1	v	Aston	H	7–0
Round 2	v	Halesowen & Stourbridge	A	4–3
Round 3	v	Stoke-on-Trent	A	3–0
Round 4	v	Warley	H	1–0
Round 5	v	Burnley	A	3–2
Round 6	v	Wirral	H	1–0
Semi-final	v	East Berkshire	H	1–0

For the second season in succession, the premier English Schools' F.A. competition, the Fuji Films Trophy was contested by 2 teams which had never reached the final before. An attractive Bury side entered the first leg with a 24 match unbeaten record and dominated the game with Gardiner going close in the 2nd minute and Hutchinson hitting the woodwork soon afterwards. The Walsall keeper, Calvin Dixon pulled off 2 important saves but there was little he could do when minutes after Reilly had headed against the bar, midfielder Stephen Newall finished a fine move with an inch-perfect shot from 18 yards. Bury's victory was well deserved but Walsall's gallant defence gave them a chance in the second leg.

In fact, they pulled the aggregate score level with 10 minutes of the home leg remaining when Phil Lewis stabbed the ball in from close range after Pemberton was unable to hold Beckett's cross. Walsall's joy was short-lived because 6 minutes later striker Lee Buggie headed the equaliser which gave Bury their 2–1 aggregate victory.

THE SQUADS:

Bury:

1. John Pemberton (Elton)
2. Paul Hayes (Broad Oak)
3. Ian Hutchinson (St Gabriel's)
4. Stephen Halford (St Gabriel's) (Captain)
5. James Sharples (Woodhey)
6. Dale Fielding (Derby)
7. Gareth Gardiner (St Gabriel's)
8. Steven Newall (Prestwich)
9. Darren Wardle (Elton)
10. Lee Connell (Derby)
11. Lee Buggie (St Gabriels)
12. Jimmy Reilly (St Gabriel's)
13.
14. Ian Newton (Castlebrook)
15. Dean Speight (Prestwich)
16. Andrew Chapman (St Gabriel's)
17. Stuart Brown (St Monica's)
18. John Tuffield (Tottington)
19 Martin Diggle (Elton)
GK Simon Hargreaves (Broad Oak)

Walsall

1. Calvin Dixon (Sneyd)
2. Robert Pearce (St Thomas More)
3. Angelo Brunetti (St Thomas More)
4. Darren Read (Shelfield)
5. Stuart Birt (Pool Hayes) (Captain)
6. Karl Wheeler (Brownhills)
7. Leon Drysdale (Willenhall)
8. Neil Palmer (Blue Coat)
9. Phil Lewis (Aldridge)
10. Ryan Meath (Willenhall)
11. Grant Beckett (Streetly)
12. Mark Swann (Willenhall)
13. Jamie Hayward (Sneyd)
14. Martin Cooper (Sneyd)
15. Chris Yates (Streetly)
16. Roger Adams (Aldridge)
17. Sean Edwards (Sneyd)
18.
19
GK Stephen Spittle (Darlaston)

MANAGERS

Mr A. Barnett (Sneyd) — Mr A. Smith
Mr R. Beech (Shire Oak) — Mr N. Parkinson

PHYSIOTHERAPIST: Mr D. Spittle

Phil Lewis of Walsall Schools follows his shot into the Bury net for hiss equaliser in the 2nd leg of the English Schools' F.A. Fuji Films Trophy.

E.S.F.A. PREMIER LEAGUE UNDER 16 INTER-COUNTY COMPETITION

Semi-Finals: Hertfordshire 5 Devon 0
West Midlands 5 Humberside 3

Final: (played at Sixfields Stadium, Northampton)
Hertfordshire 2 West Midlands 0

This was Hertfordshire's first ever national title.

West Midlands County Schools – Runners up in the E.S.F.A. Premier League U16 County Championship.

E.S.F.A. PREMIER LEAGUE UNDER 19 INTER-COUNTY COMPETITION

Semi-Finals: Hampshire 2 Essex 3
Northumberland 5 Merseyside 3

Final: Essex 1 Northumberland 1

(Played at Upton Park, West Ham United F.C.) (Trophy shared)

E.S.F.A. PREDATOR PREMIER 7-a-side TROPHY

Semi-Finals: Vale of White Horse 2 East Riding 0
Sutton 2 Wakefield 0

3rd Place: Wakefield 1 East Riding 0

Final: Sutton 2 Vale of White Horse 0

(Played at Wembley Stadium, 9th March)

THE INDIVIDUAL SCHOOLS' COMPETITIONS

E.S.F.A. SNICKERS UNDER 19 COMPETITION
(In association with Channel 4)

Semi-Finals: Ridge Danyers College, Stockport 2 Franklin College Grimsby 0
Palmers College, Grays 2 Fareham College 1

Final: (played at Stockport County F.C.)
Ridge Danyers College 2 Palmers College 3

Palmers College from Grays in Essex not only won the English Schools Snickers' Championship for the first time but through the co-operation of Channel 4 had the magnificent experience of a week-end in Genoa to meet an Under 20 Sampdoria side as a curtain-raiser to the Sampdoria v AC Milan game.

In the final, Palmers fell behind after 8 minutes but Captain Steve Billton equalised from the penalty spot before Ridge Danyers went ahead for the second time. Billton made it 2–2 this time with a 75th minute free-kick and he completed his hat-trick with the winning goal soon afterwards.

E.S.F.A. GOODYEAR UNDER 16 CHAMPIONSHIP

Final: (at Molineux, Wolverhampton Wanderers F.C.)
St Francis Xavier School (Liverpool) 0 Larkmead School (Abingdon) 2

Larkmead School became the first holders of the Goodyear Trophy played at Molineux because of the new sponsor's association with the Wolverhampton club. A crowd of over 2000 saw Larkmead beaten only once in 4 years, take an early lead through Kevin Kogel who ran on to a through ball by Greg Lester. Despite the presence of Michael O'Brien, an England Schools' international, the Liverpool side rarely threatened and it came as no surprise when Larkmead clinched the title when Kogel's cross was met by Tom Larman 6 yards out.

THE SQUADS:

St Francis Xavier's College Liverpool, Merseyside

1. Joseph Bickerton (Goalkeeper)
2. John Jackson
3. Gavin Wenham
4. Lee Andrews
5. Steven Duggan
6. Gary Howard
7. Martin Battle
8. Michael O'Brien
9. Christopher McGrath
10. Scott Sloan (Captain)
11. Michael Ness
12. Gary Dunning
14. Daniel Omar
15. Owen McGinn
16. David O'Leary
17. Jonjo Swinnerton

Team Manager — Mr Tom Brophy

Larkmead School Abingdon, Oxfordshire

1. Aaron Deadman (Goalkeeper)
2. Jason Thomas
3. Graham Freeman
4. Daniel Webber
5. Kenny Rogers (Captain)
6. Greg Lester
7. Gavin Best
8. Craig Antcliffe
9. Kevin Kogel
10. Richard Twine
11. Tom Larman
12. James Pickard
13. David Bayliss
14. Tom Finch
15. Craig Whitehead
16. Chris Spayes

Team Manager — Mr Roy Lewis

ROUTES TO THE FINAL

Larkmead:

Round 1	v	Dr Challoners (Bucks)	H	2–1
Round 2	v	Court Moor (Hants)	A	3–0
Round 3	v	St Cyres (S. Glam)	H	3–0
Round 4	v	St Joseph's (Wilts)	H	3–0
Semi-final	v	Bungay H.S. (Suffolk)	H	1–1
Replay	v	Bungay H.S. (Suffolk)	A	3–0

St Francis Xavier

Round 1	v	St Chads (Cheshire)	H	4–2
Round 2	v	Burnage (G.Manchester)	H	3–1
Round 3	v	Lacon Childe (Shropshire)	H	2–1
Round 4	v	Darland (Clywd)	A	2–2
		(St Francis Xavier won on penalties)		
Semi-final	v	George Stephenson (Northumberland	H	3–1

Captain Kenny Rodgers Lifts the Goodyear Trophy for Larkmead School.

St. Fracis Xavier School, Runners-Up in English Schools' Goodyear U16 Championship.

E.S.F.A. VIMTO UNDER 16 GIRLS' CHAMPIONSHIP

Final: (at Meadow Lane, Notts County F.C.)
West Bridgford School (Notts) 3 St John Bosco School (Merseyside) 2

West Bridgford School from Nottinghamshire became only the third school to retain a national E.S.F.A. title when they defeated Liverpool opposition in the final for the second year running. Late arrivals missed the first 2 goals with Julie Spencer putting St Bosco ahead after only 55 seconds and Helen Carver equalising within 2 minutes. A simdsilar start to the second period saw Helen Richardson score Bridgford's second goal straight from the kick-off. Hazel Savage seemed to have settled the match with a good finish after a corner but within 3 minutes Liz Maher had made it 3–2 and only some good saves by Gillian Davies and the crossbar kept Bridgford ahead.

THE SQUADS:

The West Bridgford School

1. Gillian Davies
2. Jo Lappin
3. Chloe Fortescue
4. Lindsay Hillyard (Captain)
5. Andi Pissaridou
6. Sam Lea
7. Emma Davies
9. Helen Reesby
10. Helen Carver
11. Hazel Savage
12. Helen Richardson

Substitutes:
Jane Carver
GK Satveer Nijjar
Elaine Crossley
Philipa Hogg

Team Manager — Ray Moore
Sponsor — Halifax Building Society

St John Bosco High School

1. Nicola Lea
2. Rachel Wilson
3. Terrie Smith
4. Arainne Goodwin
5. Kate McGlory
6. Leanne Henshaw
7. Gillian Quinn
8. Amanda Morris
9. Julie Spencer
10. Liz Maher
11. Collette Dwyer
12. Caroline Davies
14. Erika Todd
15. Maria Dagnall
16. Lindsey Matthews
17. Donna Swift

Team Manager — Pam McFarlane
Team Coach — Sue Hussey

ROUTES TO THE FINAL

West Bridgford

Round 1	v	Uppingham Comm Coll (Leics)	11–0
Round 2	v	Meadowhead Sch (S.Yorks)	5–3
Round 3	v	Tytherington High Sch, Macclesfield (Ches)	3–0
Semi-final	v	Archbishop Grimshaw Sch Birmingham (W.Midlands)	4–2

St John Bosco's

Round 1	v	Blacon High Sch, Chester (Ches)	3–0
Round 2	v	Harlescott Sch, Shrewsbury (Shropshire)	4–0
Round 3	v	Willenhall Sch (W. Midlands)	3–0
Semi-final	v	Corfe High School (Dorset)	1–1

(aet St John Bosco won on penalties)

The Under 16 Girls of West Bridgford School celebrate their 3-2 victory int he Vimto Trophy at Meadow Lane, Nottingham.

E.S.F.A. PREDATOR 6-a-side TROPHY

Semi-Finals: Kingsmoor Junior School (Carlisle) 1 Field End Junior School (Ruislip) 1 (Field End won on corners)
Grange Junior School (Swindon) 0 Sneyd Green Primary School (Stoke) 2

3rd Place: Kingmoor Junior School 3 Grange Junior School 0

Final: Sneyd Green Junior School 3 Field End Junior School 0 (Played at Old Trafford)

E.S.F.A. WAGON WHEELS 5-a-side COMPETITION

Girls' Final: Queen's Park Community School, Brent 3 George Abbott School, Guildford 2

Boys' Final: Bradon Forest School, Swindon 2 Westwood School, Newham 2 (Played at Aston Villa)

'SPICE FC'

One interesting, and hopefully, productive promotional idea has been launched jointly with Peter and Colleen Grove's Real Curry Guide. The two well respected journalists in the world of eastern cuisine and I were discussing the link between most sportsmen and their liking for Indian food when we thought of the idea of a 'Sponsored Twinning' between Rugby Union and Non-League Football clubs and their recommended local Indian restaurants.

Providing the restaurant owners accept the invitation to 'twin', we are sure the scheme would help:-

The Restaurants through:-

1. Mentions on match days in the programme or over the loudspeakers.
2. Club members regularly bringing parties for meals.
3. Increasing involvement with the local community.

The Football Club through:-

1. Receiving possible discounts, or special offers for club members when visiting the restaurant.
2. Possible help from the Indian restaurateurs at club functions.
3. Possible sponsorship of future events etc.

The Sponsor will be Cobra Lager - A very tasty Indian bottled lager which will be offered to twinned club and restaurants at competitive rates.

Cobra will supply twinning posters for the Football Club notice boards and window stickers for restaurants to announce their involvement with the local club.

It is also hoped that all the restaurants who join the twinning will welcome all Twinning Football Club members, whether they live in their part of the country or are just visiting.

A number of other money saving schemes may also be offered to twinning members of 'Spice FC' and I can certainly recommend the sponsor's Cobra lager as a start, in a scheme which we hope will benefit everyone involved, while also boosting community spirit.

Tony Williams

AFC LYMINGTON	Dynasty
ALDERSHOT	Cove Tandoori
ARLESEY TOWN	Maharajah Tandoori
ASHFORD TOWN	Ancient Raj
ASHFORD TOWN	Curry Garden
ASHINGTON	Only Takeaways available
ATHERSTONE UNITED	Star Tandoori
BACKWELL UNITED	Backwell Takeaway
BALDOCK TOWN	Viceroy of India
BAMBER BRIDGE	Naaz
BARKINGSIDE	India Passage
BARTON ROVERS	Passage To India
BARWELL TOWN	Leeja Tandoori
BASHLEY	India Cottage
BASINGSTOKE	Chineham Indian
BAT SOUTHAMPTON	Gandhi's
BEDWORTH UNITED	Kushiara
BIGGLESWADE FC	Biggles Tandoori
BIGGLESWADE FC	Viceroy of India
BILLERICAY TOWN	Shamiana
BISHOP SUTTON	Sagars
BLOXWICH	Gulshan
BRACKNELL TOWN	Passage To India
BRIDGNORTH	Punjab Terrace
BRIDGWATER TOWN	Taste of India
BRIGG TOWN	Rahman Restaurant
BRIGHTLINGSEA UNITED	The Indian
BRISTOL MANOR FARM	British Raj
BROMLEY	Suruchi
BROMSBROVE ROVERS	The Tandoori
BUCKINGHAM TOWN	Dipalee
BURGESS HILL	Shapla
BURNHAM	Akash Tandoori
BURNHAM RAMBLERS	The Polash
BURSCOUGH	Taste of Bengal
CANTERBURY CITY	Gandhi Tandoori
CARSHALTON ATHLETIC	Haweli
CHALFONT ST PETER	Tripti Tandoori

CHARD TOWN	Taj Tandoori
CHELMSFORD CITY	Alladin
CHESHUNT	Cheshunt Tandoori
CLITHEROE	Shah Tandoori
COCKFOSTERS FC	Tandoori Nights
CONGLETON TOWN	Al Amin Tandoori
CORINTHIAN FC	Mahatma Cote
CRANLEIGH FC	Curry Inn
CRAY WANDERERS	Omar Khayyam
CREDITON TOWN	Crediton Tandoori
CROYDON ATHLETIC	Taj Mahal
DAISY HILL	Sagar Indian
DARLASTON	Jewel Balti
EAST GRINSTEAD TOWN	Shapla Tandoori
EAST THURROCK UNITED	New Curry Centre
EGHAM TOWN	Egham Tandoori
ELMORE FC	Gate of India
EMLEY	Balooshal
EPSOM & EWELL	Curry House 2
ESH WINNING	Belmont Tandoori
FARSLEY CELTIC	Aagrah
FELTHAM	Yum Yum Tree Chinese
FLACKWELL HEATH	Tuptim Thai
GARFORTH TOWN	Aagrah
GATESHEAD	The Rupali
GRESLEY ROVERS	Sohni Mehiwaal Tandoori
GT YARMOUTH TOWN	Shah Indian
GUISBOROUGH TOWN	Indian Cottage
HAILSHAM TOWN	Rajdhutt
HALESOWEN	High Court Indian
HALESOWEN WARRIORS	Vakas
HALIFAX TOWN	Mumtaz Paan House
HALLAM	New Bengal Tandoori
HAMPTON	Monaf's
HANWELL	Madhu's Brilliant
HARPENDEN TOWN	New Taj Mahal
HARROGATE TOWN	Star of India
HARROW BOROUGH	Rayners Tandoori
HASLINGDEN	Nila
HEYBRIDGE SWIFTS	Maidon Tandoori
HISTON	India House
HORNCHURCH	Raj of India
HORSHAM FC	Marrakesh
HYDE UNITED	Jalsa
JARROW ROOFING BCA	Eastern Touch
KETTERING TOWN	The Raj
KEYNSHAM TOWN	Eastern Eye
KIDDERMINSTER HARRIERS	New Sher-e-Punjab
KIDSGROVE ATHLETIC	Rozey Balti
KNYPERSLEY VICTORIA	Shaffers Balti
LAGNEY SPORTS	Rajdutt
LEEK TOWN	Shapla Tandoori
LEIGH R.M.I.	Sagars
LEIGHTON TOWN	Indian Pavilion
LEWES	Light of Bengal
LISKEARD ATHLETIC	Liskeard Balti
MAGHULL	La Quila
MARINE	Arong
MERTHYR TYDFIL	Shapla Balti
NANTWICH TOWN	Bombay
NETHERFIELD	Flavour of India
NEWCASTLE TOWN	Al Sheiks
NEWMARKET TOWN	Newmarket Indian
NEWPORT AFC	The Kohinoor
NEWPORT I.O.W.	Curry Garden
NORTH FERRIBY UNITED	Naseeb
NORTHWOOD FC	Bina
NUNEATON BOROUGH	Agra Palace
OSSETT TOWN	Star of India
OXFORD CITY	Aziz
PAGET RANGERS	Balti Delight
PEACEHAVEN/TELSCOMBE	Tandoori Nights
PENRITH	Cagneys
PONTEFRACT COLLIERY	Roti
POTTERS BAR TOWN	Pubali Tandoori
R.T.M. NEWCASTLE	New Bengal
RADCLIFFE BOROUGH	Shahbaaz
REDHILL	Viceroy of India
ROTHWELL TOWN	Taste of India
ROYSTON TOWN	Prince of India
ROYSTON TOWN	Taste of India
RUSHALL OLYMPIC	Rose of Bengal
RUSHDEN & DIAMONDS	Eastern Spice
SALISBURY CITY	Shah Jahan
SAWBRIDGEWORTH TOWN	Star of India
SHIFNAL TOWN	Shifnal Balti
SHILDON	The Rajah
SHORTWOOD	Passage To India
SLADE GREEN	Jafflong Tandoori
SOUTHEND MANOR	Tandoori Parlour
STAINES TOWN	Staines Tandoori
STAMFORD	Bombay Cottage
STANSTED	Sonargaon
STEVENAGE BOROUGH	Raja Tandoori
STEYNING TOWN	Maharajah
STOURBRIDGE	India House
STRATFORD TOWN	Usha
SUTTON UNITED	Indus
THETFORD TOWN	Brandon Tandoori
TIVIDALE	Dilshad Tandoori
TONBRIDGE ANGELS	Afsana Tandoori
TRAFFORD FC	Deccan Restaurant
TRING TOWN	Jubraj
TUNBRIDGE WELLS	Lalipu
UPTON TOWN	Anarkali Tandoori
UXBRIDGE	Yiewsley Tandoori
WANTAGE TOWN	Prince of India
WARE TOWN	Ware Tandoori
WEALDSTONE	Bobby's Tandoori
WELLINGTON	Taste of India
WEMBLEY	Bollywood Nights
WHYTELEAFE	Royal Tandoori
WICK	Jewel in the Crown
WIMBORNE TOWN	Wimborne Tandoori
WITHAM TOWN	Dhaka Brasserie
WOODBRIDGE TOWN	Royal Bengal
WROXHAM	Star of India
YEOVIL TOWN	The Viceroy

CHANNEL ISLAND FOOTBALL

FINAL LEAGUE TABLES 1995/96

GUERNSEY

Barclays Priaulx League:

	P	W	D	L	F	A	Pts
1. Sylvans	21	18	2	1	84	15	56
2. Northerners	21	12	6	3	75	29	42
3. Belgrave's	21	13	3	5	52	32	42
4. St Martins	21	11	3	7	49	46	36
5. Rangers	21	8	2	11	49	63	26
6. Vale Recreation	21	6	3	12	41	53	21
7. Port City	21	4	4	13	31	61	16
8. Rovers	21	0	1	20	13	95	1

Barclays Jackson League:

	P	W	D	L	F	A	Pts
1. St Martins	16	12	3	1	58	13	39
2. Sylvans	16	11	2	3	45	13	35
3. Belgrave's	16	9	3	4	49	16	30
4. Port City	16	8	1	7	34	44	25
5. Vale Recreation	16	7	1	8	34	37	22
6. Rovers	16	5	1	10	24	47	16
7. Rangers	16	5	1	10	27	52	16
8. Northerners	16	3	6	7	28	33	15
9. Aurigny Nom	16	1	4	11	165	60	7

Barclays Railway League:

	P	W	D	L	F	A	Pts
1. St Martins	16	11	3	2	46	19	36
2. Rovers	16	11	1	4	35	18	34
3. Northerners	16	9	4	3	37	18	31
4. Sylvans	16	9	3	4	44	29	30
5. Belgrave's	16	7	1	8	37	41	22
6. Vale Recreation	16	5	3	8	24	30	18
7. Police	16	5	2	9	27	39	17
8. Port City	16	3	4	9	29	49	13
9. Rangers	16	0	3	13	21	57	3

JERSEY

European Football Combination:

Div One	P	W	D	L	F	A	Pts
1. Jersey Scottish	16	12	4	0	48	7	40
2. Portuguese CI	16	10	4	2	44	12	34
3. St Peter	16	8	3	5	35	14	27
4. First Tower Utd	16	7	3	6	31	21	24
5. Roxel Rovers	16	6	5	5	25	18	23
6. Jersey Wands	16	6	5	5	21	20	23
7. St Pauls	16	6	4	6	32	28	22
8. Springfield	16	3	0	13	21	47	9
9. Sporting Club	16	0	0	16	3	93	0

Div Two	P	W	D	L	F	A	Pts
1. Magpies	16	14	2	0	63	15	44
2. St Martin	16	10	2	4	36	22	32
3. LMJ Northeners	16	9	2	5	30	18	29
4. Oaklands/St Sav.	16	6	4	6	32	29	22
5. Beeches O B	16	6	3	7	31	29	21
6. St Lawrence	16	4	6	6	18	26	18
7. St Clement	16	5	2	9	13	31	17
8. St John	16	3	3	10	21	35	12
9. St Quen	16	2	2	12	22	51	8

Div Three	P	W	D	L	F	A	Pts
1. Grands Vaux	18	12	2	4	48	26	38
2. Sporting Acad.	18	10	4	4	44	23	34
3. St Brelade	18	9	4	5	44	31	31
4. St Helier	18	6	5	7	42	49	23
5. Sylvans	18	6	3	9	25	40	21
6. Trinity	18	5	5	8	35	44	20
7. Grouville	18	1	5	12	20	45	8

Barclays Fair Play League (overall):

	C	SO	Pts
Sylvans	8	0	28
Belgrave's	10	0	34
Northerners	13	1	58
Rangers	10	4	58
Port City	17	4	93
Vale Recreation	23	4	124
St Martins	28	4	134
Rovers	30	3	136

Barclays Priaulx Fair Play League:

	C	SO	Pts
Northerners	3	0	9
Sylvans	4	0	15
Belgrave's	5	0	16
Rangers	3	3	28
Port City	7	2	35
Vale Recreation	11	4	77
St Martins	17	2	79
Rovers	16	2	81

MURATTI FINAL RESULTS
(CHANNEL ISLANDS INTERNATIONAL CHAMPIONSHIP)

Previous Winners:

1990	Jersey 2 Guernsey 1	**1991**	Guernsey 3 Jersey 0
1992	Jersey 2 Guernsey 3	**1993**	Guernsey 1 Jersey 2
1994	Jersey 3 Guernsey 1	**1995**	Guernsey 1 Jersey 2

1996: Jersey 0 Guernsey 0. Replay: Guernsey 0 Jersey 1.

Total Wins (since 1905): Jersey 41, Guernsey 36, Alderney 1. Once shared Jersey & Guernsey:

Team Members:

Guernsey: Paul De Garis, Daryl Yeates, John Nobes, Joel Avery, Chris Dyer, Mark Coutanche, Michael de la Haye, Mark Culverhouse (Kevin Le Tissier), Grant Chalmers (Craig Allen), Adrian Exall, Paul Nobes. Other subs; Gary de Carteret, Martin Gauvain, Paul Ozanne.

Jersey: Steve Carlyon, Martin Cassidy, Craig Ferey, Ricky Muddyman, Trevor Le Maistre, Ian Daly (John Kellett), Nelio De Freitas (Mark Brown), Andy Barker, Craig Morton, Adam Greig (Michael Steigenberger), Chris Hamon. Other subs; Damon Pih, Paulo Campos.

Referee: Martin Bodenham (Cornwall). **Linesmen:** Geoff Ogler, Eric Graham (both Guernsey).

UPTON PARK CUP
(Guernsey Champions v Jersey Champions)

Previous Winners:

1990	Northeners 4 Jersey Wanderers 0	**1991**	Sporting Academics 3 Northerners 1
1992	Northeners 1, 0 Jersey Scottish 1, 2	**1993**	Jersey Scottish 5 Vale Recreation 4
1994	Sylvans 0 First Tower United 1	**1995**	First Tower United 1 Sylvans 0

1996: Sylvans 1 Jersey Scottish 0

Total Wins (since 1907): Jersey 42, Guernsey 36.

ISLE OF MAN FOOTBALL 1995-96

FINAL LEAGUE TABLES

Taylor Woodrow League

Div One	P	W	D	L	F	A	Pts
1. St Marys	22	18	2	2	85	15	56
2. DHSOB	22	17	1	4	103	29	52
3. St George	22	12	5	5	86	41	41
4. Rushen United	22	12	3	7	52	39	39
5. Castletown	22	11	4	7	43	35	37
6. Douglas Royal	22	11	3	8	60	42	36
7. Gymnasium	22	11	1	10	49	50	34
8. Pulrose United	22	7	4	11	60	83	25
9. Laxey	22	7	1	14	33	68	22
10. Braddon	22	4	4	14	30	92	16
11. Foxdale	22	3	4	15	32	65	13
12. Ronaldsway	22	3	0	19	31	110	9

Record Victory:
Braddon 1, DHSOB 13
Most Goals in a Game 14:
Braddon 1, DHSOB 13: Ronaldsway 4, Pulrose 10

Most League Goals 32:
Chris Bass (DHSOB)
Hat Tricks 44:
Most Hat Tricks 6:
Chris Bass (DHSOB)
Most Goals in a Game 5:
Rob Wakenshaw (St Georges) v Ronaldsway

Bowling League:

Div Two	P	W	D	L	F	A	Pts
1. Police	26	18	2	6	93	48	56
2. Ayre United	26	17	4	5	82	41	55
3. Colby	26	17	3	6	80	45	54
4. Corinthians	26	16	4	6	87	42	52
5. Peel	26	13	7	6	68	47	46
6. RYCOB	26	12	4	10	73	46	40
7. Marown	26	13	1	12	76	73	40
8. Onchan	26	11	6	9	59	50	39
9. Ramsey	26	12	3	11	54	55	39
10. Union Mills	26	8	4	14	49	74	28
11. Michael United	26	7	4	15	47	73	25
12. Malew	26	6	3	17	60	95	21
13. St John's Utd	26	5	5	16	40	62	20
14. Jurby	26	1	2	23	21	138	5

Record Victory:
Police 11, Jurby 0
Most Goals in a Game 11:
Jurby 1, Marown 10: Police 11, Jurby 0: Corinthians 10, Union Mill 1

Most League Goals 32:
Nick Cray (Police)
Hat Tricks 35:
Most Hat Tricks 4:
Nick Cray (Police)
Most Goals in a Game 5:
Alan Agrew (Rycob) v Jurby

Manx Football:
The 1996 Manx football season was dominated by a resurgent St Marys, the Douglas side under new coach Richard Hodgson, won the Manx First Division title for the first time in over 60 years and in the process their defence marshalled by Island keeper Colin McMullin have conceded just 15 goals. In addition the Saints won the Hospital Cup final with a win over St Georges.
They clinched the title in spectacular fashion coming back to defeat Old Boys 6-4 after being behind by two goals with just fifteen minutes left. One of their most satisfactory moments came when they beat local rivals Pulrose United 10-0 in a local derby match. That was due revenge for the Pulrose 5-0 victory in the 1993 Railway Cup Final.
The season started with two clubs at new grounds with excellent facilities, Foxdale, who have only been in the league for four years, after playing in the frozen North at Jurby, now play at the quaintly named Billy Goat Park at the back of the Moon near Foxdale. The other side to get a new ground and clubhouse were Braddan who have been going a good deal longer, winning their first league title back in 1930. Neither Foxdale nor Braddan however, had much success on the field, battling each other for the second relegation spot with Foxdale going down with Ronaldsway, whose first division sojourn lasted just one season.
Back at the top St Marys who have won the Railway Cup just once and that last year, lost in the semi-finals to Douglas High School Old Boys, who went on to defeat Rushen United in the final. In the other semi-final Rushen had defeated their southern rivals Castletown.
Old Boys made up their disappointment in losing out on the championship by collecting the other two major trophies, adding the FA Cup to their Railway Cup truimph. In the final they beat second division Ramsey Youth Centre who upset all the odds by defeating St Georges to reach the final.
Chris Bass from Old Boys led the league scorers after netting four in his last match to pip Peter Langridge from St Marys, who had one spell of scoring in seven succesive matches. The disappointing side undoubtedly was the last league champions St Georges who despite adding two Island goalscorers to their ranks failed to qualify for the Railway Cup and were only third in the league despite a better second half.
Division Two now also has a halfway playoff and up to ten teams had chances to make the top four in a topsy turvy season where any consistency was almost an accident. Eventually it was Ayre United who took the honours defeating the Police in the final at Peel.
Ayre United were the surprise packet with a prolific young strike force of Nigel Corkill, Martin Torr and James Teare scoring over 80 goals between them. Peel in their first ever visit to the lower ranks were undoubtedly the biggest disappointments never really challenging for promotion or cup honours. Ayre and the Police took the promotion spots. For the Police promotion puts them into the top flight for the first time in their history.
Dave Phillips.

Champions St Mary's AFC with The Hospital Cup.

D.H.S.O.B. (Isle of Man) celebrate the I.O.M. FA Cup win with their young following.

UK LIVING WOMEN'S F.A. CUP 1995-96

Preliminary Round (10-9-95)

Hull City	4-2	Blackburn Rangers
Blackpool Wren Rovers	0-4	Scunthorpe Ironesses
Manchester Rangers	v	Winsford United
(walkover for Winsford United - Manchester Rangers withdrawn)		
Deans	0-4	Runcorn
Royal Strikers	v	Lowestoft Town
(walkover for Lowesoft Town - Royal Strikers withdrawn)		
West Ham	5-0	Great Wakering Rovers
Dulwich Hamlet	8-1	Hackney
Drayton Wanderers	0-4	Chelsea
Chesham United	2-5	Thames Valley
Sherborne	12-0	Tuffley Athletic
Hereford United	1-5	Cable-Tel (Newport)

First Round (17-9-95)

Preston Rangers	3-2	Hull City
Amble Town	7-0	Cleveland
Sheffield & Hallam	4-1	Haslingden
Sunderland	2-1	Leeds United
Darlington Spraire	3-13	Newcastle
Accrington Stanley	1-2	Doncaster Rovers
Brighouse	3-5	Wakefield
Kirklees	4-4	Barnsley
(after extra time)		
Barnsley	1-0	Kirklees
Middlesbrough	v	South Shields
Lincoln United	0-4	Kilnhurst
Scunthorpe Ironesses	1-1	Bradford City
(after extra time)		
Bradford City	5-1	Scunthorpe Ironesses
Rochdale	4-1	Wigan
Manchester Belle Vue	10-1	Newsham PH
Radcliffe Borough	12-0	Chester City
Manchester United	7-0	Vernon-Carus
Leek Town	2-3	Bangor City
Blackburn Rovers	4-2	Derby County
Winsford United	1-5	Whalley Rangers
Highfield Rangers	4-2	Calverton MW
Nettleham	1-2	Wrexham
Warrington	1-2	Chesterfield
(after extra time)		
Manchester City	0-1	Oldham Athletic
Newcastle Town	4-5	Stockport County
Liverpool Feds	4-3	Rainworth MW
Stockport	10-1	Runcorn
Milton Keynes Athletic	1-1	Dunstable
(after extra time)		
Dunstable	3-0	Milton Keynes
Rugby	0-12	Coventry City
Bedford Bells	4-1	Lowestoft Town
Cambridge City	2-4	Birmingham City
Rea Valley Rovers	1-4	Cambridge United
Tamworth	1-2	Leicester City
Leighton Linslade	v	Atherstone
(walkover for Leighton Linslade - Atherstone failed to fulfil the tie)		
Canary Racers	4-0	Pye
Chelsea	8-0	Hassocks
Watford	1-4	Fulham
Collier Row	4-2	Abbey Rangers
Tottenham Hotspur	9-0	Winchester & Ealing
Charlton	2-5	Whitehawk
Dulwich Hamlet	2-1	Surbiton Town
Colchester	3-2	Romford
Mill Hill United	6-0	Redbridge Wanderers
Crowbrough Athletic	2-3	Barnet
Enfield	2-0	Sutton United
Palace Eagles	1-0	West Ham
Sittingbourne	0-7	Newham
(abandoned after 86 mins, tie awarded to Newham)		
Edenbridge Town	3-4	Colchester Royals
Clacton	v	Crystal Palace
(walkover for Clacton - Crystal Palace failed to fulfil the tie)		
Gillingham	3-7	Harlow Town
St Georges	5-0	Teynham Gunners
Thames Valley	v	Sturminster Newton
(walkover for Thames Valley - Sturminster Newton withdrawn)		
Bournemouth	3-0	Bow Brickhill
Leatherhead	4-1	Aylesbury United
Gosport Borough	2-5	Thame United
Binfield	3-0	Portsmouth
Reading Royals	1-2	Farnborough Town
Bracknell Town	6-2	Slough Town
Winchester City	0-9	Camberley Town
Denham United	3-1	Newbury
Cable-Tel (Newport)	1-5	Plymouth Pilgrims
Elmore Eagles	0-7	Frome
Inter Cardiff	15-0	Clevedon
Newton Abbot	1-3	Barry
Swindon Town	v	Cardiff Institute
(walkover for Swindon Town - Cardiff Institute withdrawn)		
Clevedon United	0-6	Swindon Town Spitfires
Brislington	2-8	Sherborne
Truro City	1-0	Yate Town
Cheltenham YMCA	12-1	Freeway (3.00)
Exeter Rangers	2-8	Worcester City

10 clubs exempt to Fourth Round (FA Women's Premier League National Division)

Arsenal, Croydon, Doncaster Belles, Everton, Ilkeston Town Rangers, Liverpool, Millwall Lionesses, Villa Aztecs, Wembley, Wolverhampton Wanderers

20 clubs exempt to Second Round (FA Women's Premier League Northern & Southern Divisions)

Northern Division

Bronte, Garswood/St Helens, Huddersfield Town, Kidderminster Harriers, Langford, Notts County, RTM Newcastle Kestrels, Sheffield Wednesday, Tranmere Rovers

Southern Division

Berkhampstead Town, Brentford, Brighton & Hove Albion, Leyton Orient, Ipswich Town, Oxford United, Southampton Saints, Three Bridges, Town & County, Wimbledon

Bristol City - Losing Semi-Finalist not in FA Women's Premier League

Second Round (15-10-95)

Doncaster Rovers	0-3	Middlesbrough
Killnhurst	5-1	Barnsley
RTM Newcastle Kestrels	0-1	Newcastle
Bronte	3-2	Preston Rangers
Amble Town	1-5	Huddersfield Town
Sheffield Wednesday	6-0	Sheffield Hallam United
Sunderland	0-2	Wakefield
Wrexham	1-3	Manchester United
Radcliffe Borough	1-4	Bangor City Girls
Leicester City	1-5	Oldham Athletic
Whalley Rangers	0-4	Highfield Rangers
Coventry City	2-1	Chesterfield
Garswood/St Helens	3-0	Bradford City
Liverpool Feds	7-5	Birmingham City
(after extra time)		

Dunstable 2-4 Blackburn Rovers
Stockport County 2-1 Stockport
Rochdale 0-9 Tranmere Rovers
Notts County 1-3 Manchester Belle Vue
Mill Hill United 4-2 Colchester Royals
Colchester 3-7 Langford
Cambridge Town 1-7 Dulwich Hamlet
Denham United 14-0 Leighton Linslade
Barnet 4-3 St Georges
Brentford 2-3 Leyton Orient
Palace Eagles 3-1 Leatherhead
Cambridge United 0-1 Newham
Tottenham Hotspur 5-4 Enfield
Whitehawk 1-0 Wimbledon
(after extra time)
Town & County 3-4 Chelsea
(after extra time)
Bedford Bells 3-1 Collier Row
Clacton 1-5 Brighton & Hove Albion
Canary Racers 6-0 Harlow Town
Berkhamsted 5-0 Fulham
Ipswich Town 3-1 Three Bridges
Plymouth Pilgrims 3-0 Swindon Town
AFC Bournemouth 0-2 Thame United
Sherborne 18-0 Worcester City
Bracknell Town 1-7 Binfield
Swindon Town Spitfires 3-1 Farnborough Town
Swindon Town Spitfires 3-1 Farnborough Town
Bristol City 2-3 Southampton Saints
(after extra time)
Truro City 0-1 Oxford United
Frome 3-0 Thames Valley
Cheltenham YMCA 2-2 Barry
(after extra time)
Barry 2-1 Cheltenham YMCA
Inter Cardiff 2-1 Kidderminster Harriers

Third Round (12-11-95)

Oldham Athletic 1-0 Liverpool Feds
Bangor City Girls 1-6 Huddersfield Town
Bronte 1-3 Stockport County
Blackburn Rovers 1-3 Manchester United
Middlesbrough 2-1 Manchester Belle Vue
Newcastle 2-1 Wakefield
Coventry City 0-2 Sheffield Wednesday
Kilnhurst 2-4 Highfield Rangers
Tranmere Rovers 2-3 Garswood/St Helens
Leyton Orient 2-3 Langford
Ipswich Town 7-3 DenhamUnited
Canary Racers 2-1 Mill Hill United
Bedford Bells 0-6 Berkhamsted Town
Chelsea 3-1 Palace Eagles
Brighton & Hove Albion 6-0 Dulwich Hamlet
Barnet 0-4 Whitehawk
Newham 0-6 Tottenham Hotspur
Oxford United 3-0 Thame United
Swindon Town Spitfires 2-3 Southampton Saints
Plymouth Pilgrims 1-1 Barry
(after extra time)
Barry 4-3 Plymouth Pilgrims
Inter Cardiff 3-0 Sherborne
Frome 1-4 Binfield

Fourth Round (3-12-95)

Oxford United 3-6 Everton
Millwall Lionesses 5-0 Langford
Arsenal 10-0 Manchester United
Binfield 0-9 Doncaster Belles
Chelsea 0-0 Newcastle
(after extra time)
Newcastle 3-0 Chelsea
Huddersfield Town 2-1 Berkhamsted Town
Liverpool 3-0 Garswood/St Helens
Oldham Athletic 2-4 Croydon
Ilkeston Town Rangers 5-0 Highfield Rangers
Southampton Saints 1-2 Whitehawk
(after extra time)
Tottenham Hotspur 3-4 Villa Aztecs
(after extra time)
Stockport County 0-9 Wembley
Sheffield Wednesday 2-3 Middlesbrough
Brighton & Hove Albion 0-1 Ipsiwch Town
Inter Cardiff 1-0 Wolverhampton Wanderers
Canary Racers 2-2 Barry
(after extra time)
Barry 1-4 Canary Racers (7 Jan)

Fifth Round (21-1-96)

Liverpool 7-1 Middlesbrough
Croydon 2-0 Inter Cardiff
Canary Racers 1-3 Ipswich Town
Ilkeston Town 2-0 Millwall Lionesses
Arsenal 2-1 Wembley
Whitehawk 1-0 Newcastle
Huddersfield Town 5-5 Everton
(after extra time)
Everton 1-2 Huddersfield Town
Villa Aztecs 1-5 Doncaster Belles

Sixth Round (18-2-96)

Ilkeston Town 1-2 Arsenal
Huddersfield Town 0-9 Liverpool
Whitehawk 2-2 Ipswich Town
(after extra time)
Ipswich Town 2-1 Whitehawk
Croydon 1-0 Doncaster Belles
(after extra time)

Semi-Finals (24-3-96)

Liverpool 0-0 Arsenal
(after extra time)
(at Runcorn FC)
(Liverpool won 5-4 on kicks fromt he penalty mark)
Croydon 5-0 Ipswich Town
(at Dulwich Hamlet FC)

Final (28-4-95)

Croydon 1-1 Liverpool
(after extra time)
(attendance 2500)
(Croydon won on kicks from the penalty mark, 3-2)

FA WOMEN'S PREMIER LEAGUE

FINAL TABLES

NATIONAL DIVISION	P	W	D	L	For	Agt	Pts	G.D.
CROYDON	18	13	5	0	58	17	**44**	+41
DONCASTER BELLES	18	14	2	2	57	19	**44**	+38
ARSENAL	18	11	4	3	54	12	**37**	+42
EVERTON	18	10	1	7	44	40	**31**	+4
LIVERPOOL	18	9	2	7	36	27	**29**	+9
WEMBLEY	18	7	5	6	43	21	**26**	+22
MILLWALL LIONESSES	18	5	3	10	20	32	**18**	-12
ILKESTON TOWN	18	4	3	11	21	46	**15**	-25
VILLA AZTECS	18	4	1	13	22	51	**13**	-29
WOLVERHAMPTON WANDERERS	18	0	0	18	8	98	**0**	-90

SOUTHERN DIVISION	P	W	D	L	For	Agt	Pts	G.D.
SOUTHAMPTON SAINTS	18	13	2	3	52	21	**41**	+31
BERKHAMSTED TOWN	18	13	1	4	42	26	**40**	+16
WIMBLEDON	18	12	1	5	53	36	**37**	+17
THREE BRIDGES	18	11	1	6	47	24	**34**	+23
IPSWICH TOWN	18	8	1	9	36	35	**25**	+1
BRIGHTON & HOVE ALBION	18	5	4	9	35	47	**19**	-12
TOWN & COUNTY	18	6	1	11	27	48	**19**	-21
LEYTON ORIENT	18	5	2	11	33	45	***16**	-12
OXFORD UNITED	18	4	4	10	24	46	**16**	-22
BRENTFORD	18	3	3	12	29	50	**12**	-21

* Leyton Orient deducted 1 point for playing an ineligible player.

NORTHERN DIVISION	P	W	D	L	For	Agt	Pts	G.D.
TRANMERE ROVERS	16	14	2	0	73	11	**44**	+62
HUDDERSFIELD TOWN	16	12	3	1	60	23	**39**	+37
GARSWOOD / ST HELENS	16	9	4	3	51	23	**31**	+28
SHEFFIELD WEDNESDAY	16	9	3	4	41	22	**30**	+19
LANGFORD	16	6	2	8	27	44	***17**	-17
RTM NEWCASTLE KESTRELS	16	3	4	9	21	43	**13**	-22
NOTTS COUNTY	16	4	1	11	18	43	**13**	-25
KIDDERMINSTER HARRIERS	16	4	1	11	27	53	**13**	-26
BRONTE	16	0	2	14	11	67	**2**	-56

* Langford deducted 3 points.

Doncaster Belles

Doncaster Belles finished second in the National Division, only losing out in the title chase on goal difference. Photo: Eric Marsh.

Ipswich Town

Ipswich Town ladies ended their season in a comfortable mid-table position in the Southern Division. Photo: Roger Turner.

WIRRAL PROGRAMME CLUB AWARDS 1995-96

Secretary: I. R. W. Runham
3 Tansley Close, Newton, West Kirby, Wirral, Merseyside L48 9XH (0151-625-9554)

NON-LEAGUE PROGRAMME SURVEY 1995-96 SPECIALS SECTION

267 programmes were received for this part of the survey made up as follows:- 66 entries from cup finals, semi finals, representative, charity games etc., 201 from clubs – of these 82 just entered this part of the survey so the total number of clubs represented in this seasons survey was 1298, a new record. Marks in the survey were awarded on the following sections:- Cover design and details, page size, team layout and position within the programme, paper quality, artwork and printing, contents, price, photographs, originality, and value for money. The last section included the ratio of adverts to articles, the use of colour etc. As a result of the survey the:-

Best Non-League Special 1995-1996. Gravesend & Northfleet v Aston Villa. FA Cup
2nd Hoddesdon Town v Willesden Hawkeye. London Senior Cup
3rd Rushden & Diamonds v Cardiff City. FA Cup
4th Clitheroe v Mangotsfield United. FA Vase Semi Final
5th Bideford v Barnstaple Town. League
6th Bognor Regis Town v Ashford Town. FA Cup
7th East Bergholt United v Paul Goddard XI. Centenary/Yateley Cream (Green) v Fleetlands. League
9th Sutton United v Kidderminster Harriers. FA Cup
10th Heybridge Swifts v Whyteleafe. League (Promotion Special)

21st NON-LEAGUE FOOTBALL PROGRAMME OF THE YEAR SURVEY

Some clubs only issue for Saturday games, some for special games, some change their style, format, editor, price etc. during the season; some have special connections with printers etc.; usually we are not aware of most of these circumstances, obviously we can only survey the programmes we receive. Some are from early in the season, others from just before the closing date, most from in between. The results always create a lot of interest with varying points being expressed, some of those we hear second or third hand but most miss our ears, if you have any comments on the survey please let us know. I am sure the day will never come when there is complete agreement on the results, however the more discussion there is over the survey the better, it will keep programmes to the forefront and hopefully maintain or even improve the standards, better still it may encourage more clubs to issue next season.

The club with the winning programme will receive a framed certificate, the winners of each league will also receive a certificate. Please note the programmes have been surveyed, not as many assume voted upon. Marks are awarded to each programme as follows (the maximum marks are given for each section):- Cover 15 (design 10, match details 5), Page size 10, Team Layout and position within the programme 10, Results 10, League Tables 10, Price 15, Printing and Paper Quality 20, Frequency of issue 20, Value for money 20 (this takes into account the ratio of adverts to content, the clubs league etc.), Contents 105 (other than those listed) taking into account their relevance to the club, its league, environs etc., the size of the print used, the spacing between lines, the size of the margins, and if the contents are original or reproduced (from league bulletins, newspapers etc.). To gain full marks in the Frequency of Issue section programmes from 10 different matches were required for each team entered (allowences were made if 10 home games had not been played by the closing date and that we were informed of this). As many programmes varied from issue to issue all the programmes received were surveyed, the marks in each section were totalled and divided by the number of issues received to get the final mark for each section. The marks from each section were then totalled to get the final score. A new standard of marks is set each season so this seasons totals should not be compared with those of previous seasons as the comparison will almost certainly be inaccurate, a programme identical to last seasons will almost certainly have gained different marks.

The results of this seasons survey are as follows:-

Best Non-League Programme Nationally 1995-1996. NORTHWOOD 185points
2nd LANGEY SPORTS 182 points
3rd HODDESDON TOWN & NORTH SHIELDS ATHLETIC 173 points

NATIONAL TOP 30 1 Northwood 185. 2 Langey Sports 182. 3= Hoddesdon T, N Shields A 173. 5 Raunds T 167. 6 Sutton U 165. 7 Aldershot T 164. 8 Lancaster C 163. 9= Witney T, ICL U 161. 11= Basildon U, Denbigh T 158. 13 Lancing 155. 14= Gorleston, Lincoln Moorlands 154. 16= Pelsall Villa, S Normanton A 153. 18= Denaby U, Stamco 152. 20 Thame U 150. 21 Peppard 148. 22= Chelsford C, Wealdstone, Somerton T 147. 25 Andover 146. 26 Newcastle T 145. 27= Kettering T, Swindon Supermarine 144. 29 Blyth Spartans 143. 30 Truro C 142.

INDIVIDUAL LEAGUE RESULTS TOP 3

LEAGUE (No. of entries)	1st	Pts	2nd	Pts	3rd	Pts
Vauxhall Conference (22)	Kettering T	144	Southport	133	Kidderminster H	128
Beazer Homes Overall (66)	Witney T	161	Chelmsford C	147	Ilkeston T/Weymouth =	138
Prem. Div. (22)	Chelsford C	147	Ilkeston T	138	Newport	136
Div 1M (22)	Paget R	121	Rothwell T	118	Nuneaton B	108
Div 1S (22)	Witney T	161	Weymouth	138	Bashley	136
ICIS Overall (77)	Northwood	185	Sutton U	165	Aldershot T	164
Prem Div (22)	Sutton U	165	= Bishops Stortford	126	= Worthing	126
Div 1 (21)	Aldershot T	164	Thame U	150	Bognor Regis T/Uxbridge =	126
Div 2 (17)	Collier Row	131	Calfont St Peter	99	Bracknell T	93
Div 3 (17)	Northwood	185	Wealdstone	147	Wingate & Finchley	130
Unibond Overall (40)	Lancaster C	163	Blyth Spartans	143	Lincoln U	140
Prem Div (20)	Blyth Spartans	143	Barrow	130	Bamber Bridge	126
Spartan (13)	Cockfosters	129	Metpol Chigwell	124	Corinthian Casuals	144
Combined Counties (12)	Peppard	148	Walton Casuals	123	Ashford T	110
Essex Senior (10)	Basildon U	158	= Gt Wakering R	115	= Romford	115
Winstonlead Kent (18)	Dartford	133	Folkstone Invicta	126	Thamesmead T	121
Jewson Wessex (17)	Andover	146	Lymington	127	Bournemouth	88
Unijet Overall (42)	Langney Sports	182	Lancing	155	Stamco	152
Sussex Div 1 (15)	Langney Sports	182	Stamco	152	Burgess Hill T	120
County Div 2 (14)	Lancing	155	Broadbridge Heath	123	E Grinstead	120
Div 3 (13)	Ifield	133	Buxted	96	Haywards Heath T	90
Charrington Overall (13)	Penn & Tylers G	126	Quarry Nomads	125	Finchampstead	119
Chiltonian Prem Div (10)	Penn & Tylers G	126	Quarry Nomads	125	Finchampstead	119
Div 1/Res (3)	= Finchampstead Res	103	= Quarry Nomads Res	103	Chippenham Village	53

League	1st	Pts	2nd	Pts	3rd	Pts
Jewson Overall (35)	Gorleston	154	Somersham T	147	Sudbury T Res	127
Eastern Prem Div (22)	Sudbury T Res	127	Stowmarket T	120	Diss T	119
Counties Div 1 (13)	Gorleston	154	Somersham T	147	Downham T	114
Great Mills Overall (30)	Paulton R	129	Mangotsfield U	125	Bridport	115
Western Prem Div (15)	Paulton R	129	Mangotsfield U	125	Bridport	115
Div 1 (15)	Bridgwater T	113	Amesbury T	108	Glastonbury	101
Hellenic Overall (20)	Swindon Supermar	144	Harrow Hill	105	Purton	102
Prem Div (10)	Swindon Supermar	144	Carterton T	89	Brackley T	88
Div 1 (10)	Harrow Hill	105	Purton	102	Wantage T	101
Hereward Overall (25)	Raunds T	167	Newport Pagnell T	133	Yaxley	120
Sports Prem Div (18)	Raunds T	167	Newport Pagnell T	133	Northampton Spencer	105
United Co. Div 1 (7)	Yaxley	120	Thrapston	90	Cottingham	79
Minerva Overall (44)	Hoddesdon T	173	Arlesey T	138	Mecedes Benz	135
South Prem Div (17)	Hoddesdon T	173	Arlesey T	138	Welwyn Ganden C	103
Midlands Sen Div (14)	= Leverstock Green	106	= Tring A	106	Holmer Green	95
Div 1 (13)	Mercedes Benz	135	Walden R	85	Old Dunstablians	78
Interlink Express (20)	Knypersley Vics	137	Halesowen Harriers =	135		
Midland Alliance			Willenhall T =	135		
Endsleigh Overall (33)	Meir K A	119	Hams Hall	92	Badsey R	89
Midland Prem Div (12)	Meir K A	119	Coventry Sphinx	86	Bloxwich T	84
Combination Div 1 (11)	Hams Hall	92	Badsey R	89	Bilston Community College	64
Div 2 (5)	Cheslyn Hay	80	Bromsgrove Rangers	78	Earlswood T	72
Div 3 (5)	Dudley Sports Res	73	Feckenham	57	Richmond Sports Res	47
Banks Overall (19)	Pelsall Villa	153	Cheadle R	124	Walsall Wood	114
Brewery Prem Div (14)	Pelsall Villa	153	Walsall Wood	114	Westfields	96
W Midlands Div 1 (5)	Cheadle R	124	Goodyear	83	Morda U	65
North West Overall (39)	Newcastle T	145	St Helens T	138	Maine Road	126
Counties Div 1 (21)	Newcastle T	145	St Helens T	138	Maine Road	126
Div 2 (18)	Blackpool Mechanics	119	Formby	114	Daisy Hill	105
Northern Overall (33)	Denaby U	152	Hucknall T	137	Belper T	133
Counties Prem Div (20)	Denaby U	152	Hucknall T	137	Belper T	133
East Div 1 (13)	Selby T	127	Borrowash Victoria	116	Garforth T	104
Federation Overall (32)	Chester le Street T	115	Consett =	109		
Brewery			Shildon	109		
Northern Div 1 (15)	Chester le Street T	115	= Consett	109	= Shildon	109
Div 2 (17)	Billingham T	92	S Shields	88	Ashington	78
Middlesex County (5)	= Osterley	96	= Technicolour Sports	96	Spelthorne Sports	67
Dorset Combination (8)	Weymouth Sports	129	Blandford U	81	Hamworthy U	77
Gloucestershire County (11)	Henbury Old Boys	118	Winterbourne U	103	Totterdown P O B	100
Jewson South Western (11)	Truro C	142	Wadebridge T	118	Holsworthy	116
Westward Develop Devon (8)	Stoke Gabriel	110	Plymouth Parkway	100	Budleigh Salterton	84
Clubsaver Overall (14)	Colden Common	130	Yateley Green	107	Fleetlands	85
Hampshire Div 1 (7)	Colden Common	130	Fleetlands	85	Blackfield & Langley	82
Div 2 (4)	Arlesford T	72	Broughton	67	Hythe & Dibden	60
Div 3 (3)	Yateley Green	107	Sherborne St John	55	Four Marks	53
Kershaw Cambridgeshire (3)	Linton Granta	127	Debden	95	Cottenham U	59
Gloucestershire Northern (3)	Ruardean Hill R	84	= Bibury	72	= Taverners	72
Longwell Overall (14)	Attleborough	96	Loddon U	88	N Walsham T	81
Blake Prem Div (3)	Wymondham T	79	DerehamT	64	Blofield U	62
Anglian Div 1 (5)	Loddon U	88	N Walsham T	81	Stalham T	63
Combination Divs 2, 3 (6)	Attleborough	96	Holt U	69	Aylsham W	65
Refuge Assurance Midland (7)	Eccleshall	109	Brocton	99	Norton U	72
Somerset (4)	= Portishead	99	= Shirehampton	99	Shepton Mallet	86
Herts Senior County (4)	= Bovingdon	112	= Sandridge R	112	Malex	79
Nuclear Electric Kent Co (4)	Tonbridge R	100	Maidstone Invicta	96	V C D Athletic	86
West Hertfordshire (3)	= Kings Sports	98	= Kings Sports 3rd XI	98	Kings Sports Res	95
Essex Overall (10)	Broomfield	133	Springfield Res	88	Runwell Hospital	84
Intermediate Divs 1, 2, 3 (7)	Broomfield	133	Runwell Hospital	84	Upminster	82
Res Divs (3)	Springfield Res	88	Gt Baddow Res	78	Upminster Res	57
B Sugar Suffolk/Ipswich (12)	Needham Market	104	Haughley U	93	Bramford U	91
John Smiths Overall (33)	S Normanton A	153	Sandiacre T	120	Rossington	110
Bitter Sup Div (17)	S Normanton A	153	Sandiacre T	120	Rossington	110
Central Mids Prem Div (16)	Mickleover R B L	105	Radford	97	Sneinton	88
Everards Overall (9)	Anstey Nomads	81	Loughborough Dynamo	80	Earl Shilton Albion	78
Brewery Prem Div (6)	Anstey Nomads	81	Kirby Muxloe	56	Asfordby Amateurs	53
Leics Senior Div 1 (3)	Loughborough Dynamo	80	Earl Shilton Albion	78	Harborough Town Imperial	75
Vaux Wearside (5)	N Shields A	173	Nissan	75	Birtley T	68
Northern Alliance (10)	Rutherford	113	W Allotment Celtic	98	Carlisle Gillford Park =	95
					N Shields St Columbus =	95
Green Ins Mid Cheshire (5)	Rylands	132	Rylands Res	114	Garswood/Wilmslow A =	104
Manchester (5)	G Manchester Police	93	= Prestwich Heys	84	= Woodley Sports	84
TSW Printers Lincolnshire (4)	Lincoln Moorlands	154	Wyberton	101	Grimsby Amateurs	65
Lancs Overall (9)	Hesketh Bank	94	Poulton T Res	84	Poulton T	82
Evening Post Div 1 (4)	Poulton T	82	Turton	70	Fulwood Amateur	65
W Lancs Div 2/Res (5)	Hesketh Bank	94	Poulton T Res	84	Lytham St Annes	79
West Yorkshire (7)	= Carlton A	119	= Knaresborough T	119	Carlton A Res	103
West Riding Co Amateur (7)	Brighouse T	119	Wibsey	114	Wibsey Res	96
Other English Leagues (41)	Ifield Res	133	Colden Common Res	130	Easterborough	119
Youth Clubs (7)	= St Andrews U11	129	= St Andrews U11	129	Walton	123

The closing date for next seasons survey is January 31st 1997, and for the Specials section May 31st 1997. The minimum entry to the survey is one programme but to gain full marks in the Frequency of Issue section please send programmes from at least ten different matches for each team entered, these can be league, cup etc. If ten games have not been played by the closing date please let us know with your entries so that allowances can be made. Details of next seasons survey will be sent to League Secretaries in Sept/Oct for hopeful onward delivery to clubs, if you would like information to be sent directly to you could you please let us have a stamped sae by the end of September. Thank you.

The closing date for this seasons Specials section is now July 4th 1996. We hope to have the results out by the end of July, if you would like a copy please send us a stamped sae. Thank you. **Ian Runham,** Secretary

Top non-League Transfers 1995-96

Alford, Carl	Kettering T - Rushden & D	(£85,000)
Stott, Steve	Kettering T - Rushden & D	(£30,000)
McDonald, Martin	Macclesfield T - Southport	(£20,000)
Ross, Brian	Marine - Chorley	(£16,000)
Arnold, Ian	Kettering T - Stalybridge C	(£15,000)
Ashby, Nick	Kettering T - Rushden & D	(£14,000)
Cuggy, Steve	Margate - Hastings T	(£13,000)
Grocutt, Darren	Burton Alb - Bromsgrove R	(£12,500)
Mayers, Kenny	Bamber B - Chorley	(£12,000)
Tinson, Darren	Northwich V - Macclesfield T	(£12,000)
Sayer, Andy	Slough T - Enfield	(£11,000)
Smith, Neil	Cheltenham T - Rushden & D	(£11,000)
Birkby, Dean	Bath C - Yeovil T	(£10,000)
Hercules, Cliff	Aylesbury U - Slough T	(£10,000)
Humphreys, Delwyn	Kidderminster H - Northwich V	(£10,000)
Laws, David	Bishop Auckland - Weymouth	(£9,000)
Harvey, Lee	Aylesbury U - Slough T	(£8,000)
Newbery, Richard	Wokingham T - Gravesend	(£8,000)
Yates, Jason	Bridgnorth T - Clevedon T	(£8,000)
Freeman, Mark	Hednesford T - Gloucester C	(£7,500)
Freeman, Mark	Gloucester C - Cheltenham T	(£7,500)
Wingfield, Phil	Kingstonian - Farnborough T	(£7,500)
Browne, Corey	Dover Ath - Stevenage B	(£7,000)
Prindiville, Steve	Halifax T - Dagenham & Red	(£7,000)
Statham, Gary	VS Rugby - Nuneaton B	(£6,500)
Pye, Mark	Enfield - Slough T	(£5,500)
Brown, Dereck	Walton & Hersham - Welling U	(£5,000)
Caton, Colin	Colwyn Bay - Witton A	(£5,000)
Dobson, Paul	Gateshead - Bishop Auckland	(£5,000)
Hannigan, Al-James	Enfield - Rushden & D	(£5,000)
Johnson, David	Rushden & D - Gloucester C	(£5,000)
Mintram, Spencer	Worthing - Farnborough T	(£5,000)
Russell, Keith	Atherstone U - Hednesford T	(£5,000)
Trundle, Lee	Burscough - Chorley	(£5,000)
Vernon, Deion	Bath C - Gloucester C	(£5,000)
Wilson, Paddy	Knowsley U - Stalybridge C	(£5,000)
Hallam, Mark	Gloucester C - Ilkeston T	(£4,500)
Evans, Keith	Ashton U - Hyde U	(£3,500)
Stanborough, Nick	Gresley R - Hinckley Ath	(£3,500)
Jones, Steve.M	Leek T - Stalybridge C	(£3,250)
Mackenzie, Stuart	Yeading - Farnborough T	(£3,250)
Dixon, Tony	Dover Ath - Margate	(£3,000)
Pearson, Neil	Crawley T - Whyteleafe	(£3,000)
Wood, Jeff	Barking - Aldershot T	(£3,000)
Saunders, Neil	Tiverton T - Bath C	(£2,500)
Taylor, David	Gresley R - Ilkeston T	(£2,500)
Clayton, Paul	Stalybridge C - Northwich V	(£2,000)
McBean, Peter	Bridgnorth T - Hinckley T	(£2,000)
Pope, Neil	Cambridge C - Kettering T	(£2,000)
Sugrue, Jimmy	Aldershot T - Hayes	(£2,000)
Titterton, David	Hednesford T - Burton Alb	(£2,000)
Williams, Karl	Macclesfield T - Curzon Ashton	(£2,000)
Symonds, John	Nuneaton B - Bedworth U	(£1,800)
Wileman, Matthew	Atherstone U - Bedworth U	(£1,600)
Bullock, Tony	Northwich V - Leek T	(£1,000)
Dudley, Derek	Halesowen T - Telford U	(£1,000)
Kirkham, Paul	Stalybridge C - Ashton U	(£1,000)
Lynch, Tony	Stevenage B - Yeovil T	(£1,000)
Shirley, Mark	Ashton U - Lancaster C	(£1,000)

Some other transfers involved undisclosed fees)

The Top Transfers non-League to non-League

(Only those still playing are featured and original fees shown)

Leworthy, David	Farnborough T - Dover A	(£50,000)	1993
Abbott, Gary	Barnet - Enfield	(£40,000)	1989
Abbott, Gary	Enfield - Welling U	(£30,000)	1990
Alford, Carl	Macclesfield T - Kettering T	(£25,000)	1994
Fergusson, Steve	Worcester C - Gloucester C	(£25,000)	1990
Thomas, Karl	South Liverpool - Colne Dynamoes	(£25,000)	1989
Butterworth, Gary	Dag & Red - Rushden & Diamonds	(£20,000)	1994
Casey, Kim	Kidderminster H - Cheltenham T	(£20,000)	1990
Collins, Darren	Enfield - Rushden & Diamonds	(£20,000)	1994
Lee, Andy	Telford U - Colne Dynamoes	(£20,000)	1989
Wilmot, Richard	Scunthorpe U - Halifax T	(£20,000)	1994
Fielder, Colin	Farnborough T - Slough T	(£18,000)	1991
Jones, Gary	Grantham T - Kettering T	(£17,500)	1990
Portway, Steve	Gravesend - Gloucester C	(£17,500)	1994
Webb, Paul	Bromsgrove R - Kidderminster H	(£17,500)	1994
Golley, Mark	Sutton U - Maidstone U	(£16,000)	1988
Abbott, Gary	Welling U - Barnet	(£15,000)	1987
Creaser, Glyn	Barnet - Wycombe W	(£15,000)	1988
Doherty, Mick	Yeovil T - Runcorn	(£15,000)	1989
Golley, Mark	Maidstone U - Welling U	(£15,000)	1991
Greene, Dennis	Chelmsford C - Wycombe W	(£15,000)	1992
Lynch, Tony	Wealdstone - Barnet	(£15,000)	1990
Sherwood, Jeff	Yeovil T - Gloucester C	(£15,000)	1990
Warrilow, Tommy	Crawley T - Hythe T	(£15,000)	1990
Whale, Leroy	Bashley - Enfield	(£15,000)	1993
Conning, Peter	Weymouth - Yeovil T	(£13,000)	1989
Doherty, Mick	Maidstone U - Yeovil T	(£13,000)	1988
Ross, Jeff	Ashford T - Hythe T	(£12,500)	1990
Bancroft, Paul	Burton A - Kidderminster H	(£12,000)	1988
Bancroft, Paul	Kidderminster H - Kettering T	(£12,000)	1990
Blackford, Gary	Fisher A - Barnet	(£12,000)	1991
Burke, Brendan	Witton A - Stalybridge C	(£12,000)	1993
Ricketts, Tony	Bath C - Yeovil T	(£12,000)	1985
Kurila, Alan	Stafford R - Kidderminster H	(£11,000)	1990
Arnold, Ian	Carlisle U - Kettering T	(£10,000)	1994
Beech, Glenn	Boston U - Kettering T	(£10,000)	1988
Cooper, Richard	Weymouth - Yeovil T	(£10,000)	1989
Doherty, Mick	Weymouth - Maidstone U	(£10,000)	1987
Grainger, Paul	Telford U - Kidderminster H	(£10,000)	1992
Hadley, Dave	Moor Green - Kidderminster H	(£10,000)	1993
Harlow, David	Kingstonian - Farnborough T	(£10,000)	1994
Holmes, David	Gresley R - Gloucester C	(£10,000)	1995
Horwood, Neil	Spalding U - Kettering T	(£10,000)	1990
Humphreys, Delwyn	Bridgnorth T - Kidderminster H	(£10,000)	1990
Hyde, Paul	Hayes - Wycombe W	(£10,000)	1991
Kelly, Tony	Hayes - Wealdstone	(£10,000)	1989

Mogg, David	Bath C - Cheltenham T	(£10,000)	1987
Murphy, Frank	Kettering T - Barnet	(£10,000)	1987
Nuttell, Mick	Wycombe W - Boston U	(£10,000)	1991
O'Connor, Malcolm	Hyde U - Northwich V	(£10,000)	1988
Pearson, Jon	Kidderminster H - Burton A	(£10,000)	1989
Ricketts, Tony	Yeovil T - Bath C	(£10,000)	1988
Scott, Keith	Boston U - Wycombe W	(£10,000)	1991
Simpson, Wayne	Stafford R - Hednesford T	(£10,000)	1995
Smith, Jimmy	Salisbury C - Cheltenham T	(£10,000)	1992
Sowerby, Colin	Dartford - Redbridge F	(£10,000)	1991
Thomas, Karl	Colne Dynamoes - Witton A	(£10,000)	1990
Townsend, Chris	Gloucester C - Dorchester T	(£10,000)	1990
Watkins, Dale	Grantham T - Rushden & Diamonds	(£10,000)	1993
Westley, Graham	Barnet - Wycombe W	(£10,000)	1987
Whitby, Steve	Wycombe W - Slough T	(£10,000)	1991
Whitehouse, Mark	Burton A - Kidderminster H	(£10,000)	1989
Robbins, Terry	Crawley T - Welling U	(£8,000)	1986
Browne, Steve	Wealdstone - Sutton U	(£9,000)	1992
Casey, Kim	Cheltenham T - Wycombe W	(£9,000)	1992
Higginbotham, Paul	Barrow - Stalybridge C	(£9,000)	1994
Rudge, Simon	Hyde U - Runcorn	(£9,000)	1989
Rudge, Simon	Runcorn - Altrincham	(£9,000)	1991
Benbow, Ian	Telford U - Merthyr Tydfil	(£8,000)	1993
Coe, Paul	Rushden & Diamonds - Cambridge C	(£8,000)	1994
Hemmings, Tony	Rocester - Northwich V	(£8,000)	1989
Hughes, Mark	Irlam T - Altrincham	(£8,000)	1989
Nuttell, Mick	Peterborough - Cheltenham T	(£8,000)	1989
Hedges, Ian	AFC Bournemouth - Bath C	(£7,500)	1991
Singleton, Dave	Taunton T - Weymouth	(£7,500)	1979
Abbott, Gary	Welling U - Enfield	(£7,000)	1994
Cavell, Paul	Stafford R - Boston U	(£7,000)	1989
Essex, Steve	Aylesbury U - Stafford R	(£7,000)	1990
Hutchinson, Simon	Eastwood T - Wycombe W	(£7,000)	1990
Kurila, Alan	Burton A - Stafford R	(£7,000)	1989
Nuttell, Mick	Dag & Red - Rushden & Diamonds	(£7,000)	1994
Evans, Richard	Harrow B - Windsor & Eton	(£6,500)	1986
Blewden, Colin	Gravesend - Dover A	(£6,000)	1991
Boyle, Martin	Bath C - Cheltenham T	(£6,000)	1992
Carroll, Dave	Ruislip Manor - Wycombe W	(£6,000)	1988
Doherty, Mick	Runcorn - Farnborough T	(£6,000)	1990
Essex, Steve	Burton A - Aylesbury U	(£6,000)	1988
Fergusson, Steve	Gloucester C - Telford U	(£6,000)	1991
Golley, Mark	Welling U - Sutton U	(£6,000)	1992
Killick, Tommy	Wimborne T - Bashley	(£6,000)	1990
Killick, Tommy	Wimborne T - Dorchester T	(£6,000)	1994
Murphy, Frank	Nuneaton B - Kettering T	(£6,000)	1986
Nuttell, Mick	Cheltenham T - Wycombe W	(£6,000)	1991
Payne, Chris	Billericay T - Dageenham & Red	(£6,000)	1994
Shepherd, George	Hyde U - Macclesfield T	(£6,000)	1989
Beech, Glenn	Kettering T - Boston U	(£5,000)	1989
Bimson, Stuart	Southport - Macclesfield T	(£5,000)	1991
Bradder, Gary	Atherstone U - Gloucester C	(£5,000)	1988
Bradder, Gary	Gloucester C - Atherstone U	(£5,000)	1989
Bradshaw, Mark	Stafford R - Macclesfield T	(£5,000)	1995
Carroll, Robbie	Fareham T - Yeovil T	(£5,000)	1989
Casey, Paul	Lincoln C - Boston U	(£5,000)	1991
Cavell, Paul	Goole T - Stafford R	(£5,000)	1986

Northampton T - Aylesbury U	Collins, Darren	(£5,000)	1990
Duffield, Martin	Hendon - Sutton U	(£5,000)	1991
Duffield, Martin	Sutton U - St.Albans C	(£5,000)	1992
Hone, Mark	Crystal Palace - Welling U	(£5,000)	1989
Hughes, Mark	Altrincham - Witton A	(£5,000)	1991
Lambert, Colin	Macclesfield T - Halifax T	(£5,000)	1993
Lee, David	Ashford T - Hythe T	(£5,000)	1990
Murphy, Frank	Kettering T - Nuneaton B	(£5,000)	1984
Pearson, Jon	Burton A - Stafford R	(£5,000)	1990
Ridings, Dave	Lincoln C - Ashton U	(£5,000)	1994
Scott, Ian	Hinckley T - Kettering T	(£5,000)	1995
Shail, Mark	Worcester C - Yeovil T	(£5,000)	1989
Sherwood, Jeff	Bath C - Yeovil T	(£5,000)	1988
Stringfellow, Ian	Mansfield T - Kettering T	(£5,000)	1994
Duffield, Martin	Enfield - Hendon	(£4,800)	1988
Emms, Roger	Newbury T - Andover	(£4,000)	1991
Pearce, David	Harrow B - Barnet	(£4,000)	1984
Pearce, David	Wokingham T - Kingstonian	(£4,000)	1990
White, Terry	Hastings T - Hythe T	(£4,000)	1990
Bradder, Gary	Atherstone U - VS Rugby	(£3,500)	1991
Bushay, Ansil	St.Albans C - Slough T	(£3,500)	1994
Conner, Steve	Dartford - Redbridge F	(£3,500)	1990
Robson, Darren	Basingstoke T - Gosport B	(£3,250)	1990
Broom, Jason	Billericay T - Redbridge F	(£3,000)	1990
Casey, Kim	Gloucester C - Kidderminster H	(£3,000)	1983
Crowley, Richard	Cheltenham T - Bath C	(£3,000)	1990
Culley, Mark	Sutton T - Gainsborough T	(£3,000)	1992
Dowson, Alan	Slough T - Gateshead	(£3,000)	1994
Ferns, Phil	Poole T - Yeovil T	(£3,000)	1991
Filson, Martin	Stalybridge C - Halifax T	(£3,000)	1993
Graham, Jon	Boston U - Kettering T	(£3,000)	1993
Grant, Brendan	Marine - Colne Dynamoes	(£3,000)	1990
Griffiths, Tony	Leek T - Telford U	(£3,000)	1985
Keast, Doug	Corby T - Rushden & Diamonds	(£3,000)	1993
Kelly, Tony	Wealdstone - Hayes	(£3,000)	1992
Kerr, Andy	Telford U - Wycombe W	(£3,000)	1988
Lyons, Darren	Bury - Southport	(£3,000)	1993
McGinty, John	VS Rugby - Telford U	(£3,000)	1985
Pearce, David	Barhet - Dagenham	(£3,000)	1986
Pearce, David	Dagenham - Wokingham T	(£3,000)	1988
Shearer, Mick	Gloucester C - Halesowen T	(£3,000)	1995
Shoemake, Kevin	Chelmsford C - Welling U	(£3,000)	1986
Biggins, Mark	Windsor & Eton - Woking	(£2,500)	1987
Jackson, Steve	Bedworth U - Atherstone U	(£2,500)	1988
Mogg, David	Cheltenham T - Gloucester C	(£2,500)	1989
Anderson, Stewart	Witton A - Morecambe	(£2,000)	1992
Bradder, Gary	Bedworth U - Atherstone U	(£2,000)	1985
Conner, Steve	Tilbury - Dartford	(£2,000)	1986
Edwards, Mark	Chorley - Witton A	(£2,000)	1988
Evans, Richard	Windsor & Eton - Sutton U	(£2,000)	1991
Grimshaw, Andy	Witton A - Morecambe	(£2,000)	1992
Lee, Andy	Altrincham - Telford U	(£2,000)	1987
Mings, Adie	Chippenham T - Bath C	(£2,000)	1988
Murphy, Frank	Desborough T - Kettering T	(£2,000)	1982
O'Reilly, Paul	St.Albans C - Hayes	(£2,000)	1991
Sawyer, Paul	Margate - Dartford	(£2,000)	1991
Warmington, Curtis	Yeovil T - Carshalton A	(£2,000)	1987

DIRECTORY OF NON-LEAGUE MAGAZINES

BUREAU OF NON-LEAGUE FOOTBALL

Non-League tables, cup results and news from the Conference to local leagues. FA Competitions results and draws, County Senior Cups. Founded 1981. Editor Mike Ford. 1996/97 subscription (11 issues) £17.95 from 173 Leytonstone Road, London. E15 1LH.

PYRAMID FOOTBALL MAGAZINE

Founded 1984. The magazine for non-League fans by non-League fans. News, offbeat stories and excellent photos from the non-League scene. Editor Tony Incenzo. 1996/97 subscription £6.50, sample copy £2.20, from PO Box 10184, London N12 8JF.

NON-LEAGUE TRAVELLER MAGAZINE

Published weekly throughout the season containing fixtures for around 90 leagues, plus news, club focuses, cup draws etc. Founded 1987. Editor Bill Berry. Subscription rate for 1996/97 is £39 or £20 for half year to Christmas, from: Non-League Traveller, Top O'The Bank, Evesham Road, Broadway, Worcs. WR12 7DG.

TEAM TALK

Founded 1991. Editor Tony Williams. Glossy A4 magazine, 64 pages. Featuring Conference to County League football. Extensive coverage of FA competitions. On sale at newsagents price £2.20. Six months subscription £14, 12 months £27 from: Team Talk, Freepost, Taunton TA3 6BR.

GRASSROOTS

The best from the non-League scene. Founded 1994. Editor Steve Hardy. Club focus, programme notes, etc. £2 per issue incl p&p. £12 for six issues, £23 for full year. From: 9 Bishops Orchard, East Hagbourne, Didcot. OX11 9JS.

NON-LEAGUE NEWSDESK

First for results and tables. Delivered every Wednesday containing results and up-to-date tables from 40 major Pyramid leagues. Also results/draws from FA competitions, transfer activity and managerial appointments. All for 60p per week plus 25p postage. Founded 1995. Editor James wright. For sample copy, send SAE to James Wright, 26 Stephen Street, Taunton. TA1 1LD.

GROUNDTASTIC

The Grounds Magazine. The only magazine devoted to football grounds. Founded 1995. Editors Paul Claydon, Jon Weaver & Vince Taylor. For latest issue, send a £2.50 cheque made payable to Groundtastic to: 26 Doulton Way, Ashingdon, Rochford, Essex. SS4 3BX.

The Top Transfers non-League to League

(Only those still playing are featured and original fees shown)

Clarke, Andy	Barnet - Wimbledon	£250,000	1991
Emblem, Neil	Sittingbourne - Millwall	£175,000	1993
Gridelet, Phil	Barnet - Barnsley	£175,000	1990
Willis, Roger	Barnet - Watford	£175,000	1992
Harper, Lee	Sittingbourne - Arsenal	£150,000	1994
Hunt, Andy	Kettering T - Newcastle U	£150,000	1991
Furlong, Paul	Enfield - Coventry C	£130,000	1991
Collymore, Stan	Stafford R - Crystal Palace	£100,000	1991
Ekoku, Efan	Sutton U - AFC Bournemouth	£100,000	1990
Finnan, Steve	Welling U - Birmingham C	£100,000	1995
Nolan, Ian	Marine - Tranmere R	£100,000	1991
Taylor, Steve	Bromsgrove R - Crystal Palace	£90,000	1995
Woan, Ian	Runcorn - Nottingham F	£80,000	1990
Barnes, Steve	Welling U - Birmingham C	£70,000	1995
Charles, Lee	Chertsey T - QPR	£67,500	1995
Hessenthaler, Andy	Redbridge F - Watford	£65,000	1991
Harding, Paul	Barnet - Notts Co	£60,000	1990
Lake, Mike	Macclesfield T - Sheffield U	£60,000	1989
Lilwall, Steve	Kidderminster H - WBA	£60,000	1992
Bullock, Darren	Nuneaton B - Huddersfield T	£55,000	1993
Barnard, Darren	Wokingham T - Chelsea	£50,000	1990
Dodd, Jason	Bath C - Southampton	£50,000	1989
Forsyth, Richard	Kidderminster H - Birmingham C	£50,000	1995
Hanson, Dave	Hednesford T - Leyton O	£50,000	1995
Harle, Michael	Sittingbourne - Millwall	£50,000	1994
Little, Colin	Hyde U - Crewe A	£50,000	1996
Moody, Paul	Waterlooville - Southampton	£50,000	1991
Morah, Ollie	Sutton U - Cambridge U	£50,000	1994
Richardson, Ian	Dagenham & Red - Birmingham	£50,000	1995
Scott, Andrew	Sutton U - Sheffield U	£50,000	1992
Sharp, Lee	Lincoln U - QPR	£50,000	1995
Smith, Paul	Hastings T - Nottingham F	£50,000	1994
Teale, Shaun	Weymouth - AFC Bournemouth	£50,000	1989
Whittington, Craig	Crawley T - Scarborough	£50,000	1993
Brabin, Gary	Runcorn - Doncaster R	£45,000	1994
Farrell, Dave	Redditch U - Aston Villa	£45,000	1992
Forbes, Steve	Sittingbourne - Millwall	£45,000	1994
Shail, Mark	Yeovil T - Bristol C	£45,000	1993
Angell, Brett	Cheltenham T - Derby Co	£40,000	1988
Devlin, Paul	Stafford R - Notts Co	£40,000	1992
Doherty, Neil	Barrow - Birmingham C	£40,000	1994
Jones, Paul	Kidderminster H - Wolves	£40,000	1991
Rammell, Andy	Atherstone U - Manchester U	£40,000	1989
Agana, Tony	Weymouth - Watford	£35,000	1987
Cox, Ian	Carshalton A - Crystal Palace	£35,000	1994
Dalton, Paul	Brandon U - Manchester U	£35,000	1988

Impey, Andy	Yeading - QPR	£35,000	1990
McRobert, Lee	Sittingbourne - Millwall	£35,000	1995
Marshall, Dwight	Grays Ath - Plymouth A	£35,000	1991
Pugh, David	Runcorn - Chester C	£35,000	1989
Rogers, Paul	Sutton U - Sheffield U	£35,000	1992
Townsend, Andy	Weymouth - Southampton	£35,000	1985
Comyn, Andy	Alvechurch - Aston Villa	£34,000	1989
Cotterill, Steve	Burton Alb - Wimbledon	£30,000	1989
Dowie, Ian	Hendon - Luton T	£30,000	1988
Garner, Darren	Dorchester T - Rotherham	£30,000	1995
Gayle, John	Burton Alb - Wimbledon	£30,000	1989
Jones, Tom	Weymouth - Aberdeen	£30,000	1987
Landon, Richard	Bedworth U - Plymouth A	£30,000	1994
McGorry, Brian	Weymouth - AFC Bournemouth	£30,000	1991
Morrison, Dave	Chelmsford C - Peterborough U	£30,000	1994
O'Reilly, Justin	Gresley R - Port Vale	£30,000	1996
Pethick, Robbie	Weymouth - Portsmouth	£30,000	1993
Spink, Dean	Halesowen T - Aston Villa	£30,000	1989
Williams, Gareth	Gosport B - Aston Villa	£30,000	1988
Peake, Trevor	Nuneaton B - Lincoln C	£27,750	1979
Burns, Chris	Cheltenham T - Portsmouth	£25,000	1991
Clarke, Tim	Halesowen T - Coventry C	£25,000	1990
Cooksey, Scott	Bromsgrove R - Peterborough U	£25,000	1993
DeSouza, Miguel	Dagenham & Red - Birmingham C	£25,000	1994
Harris, Mark	Wokingham T - Crystal Palace	£25,000	1988
Hemmings, Tony	Northwich V - Wycombe W	£25,000	1993
Holsgrove, Paul	Wokingham T - Luton T	£25,000	1991
Jones, Gary	Boston U - Southend U	£25,000	1993
Jones, Steve	Cheltenham T - Swansea C	£25,000	1995
Leworthy, Dave	Fareham T - Tottenham H	£25,000	1984
Macauley, Steve	Fleetwood T - Crewe A	£25,000	1992
Martin, Dean	Fisher A - West Ham U	£25,000	1991
O'Connor, Martyn	Bromsgrove R - Crystal Palace	£25,000	1992
Pearce, Stuart	Wealdstone - Coventry C	£25,000	1983
Piggott, Gary	Dudley T - WBA	£25,000	1991
Regis, David	Barnet - Notts County	£25,000	1990
Clarkson, Phil	Fleetwood T - Crewe A	£22,500	1991
Jobson, Richard	Burton Alb - Watford	£22,000	1982
Jones, Steve	Billericay T - West Ham U	£22,000	1992
Crosby, Gary	Grantham T - Nottingham F	£20,000	1987
Dixon, Kerry	Dunstable - Reading	£20,000	1980
Farrelly, Steve	Macclesfield T - Rotherham	£20,000	1995
Flynn, Sean	Halesowen T - Coventry C	£20,000	1991
Heald, Greg	Enfield - Peterborough U	£20,000	1994
James, Tony	Gainsborough T - Lincoln C	£20,000	1988
Liburd, Richard	Eastwood T - Middlesbrough	£20,000	1993
McFarlane, Andy	Cradley T - Portsmouth	£20,000	1990
Massey, Stuart	Sutton U - Crystal PalacE	£20,000	1992
Milner, Andy	Netherfield - Rochdale	£20,000	1990
Morley, Trevor	Numeaton B - Northampton T	£20,000	1985
Murphy, Matt	Corby T - Oxford U	£20,000	1993
Naylor, Tony	Droylsden - Crewe Alexandra	£20,000	1990
Ndah, Jaimme	Kingstonian - Torquay U	£20,000	1995
Parrish, Sean	Telford U - Doncaster R	£20,000	1994
Parsley, Neil	Witton Alb - Leeds U	£20,000	1988
Roberts, Darren	Burton Alb - Wolves	£20,000	1992
Scott, Robert	Sutton U - Sheffield U	£20,000	1993

Nuneaton B - Oxford U	Smithers, Tim	£20,000	1980
Williams, Andy	Solihull B - Coventry C	£20,000	1985
Wilson, Kevin	Banbury U - Derby Co	£20,000	1979
Pickering, Ally	Buxton - Rotherham U	£18,500	1990
Angus, Terry	VS Rugby - Northampton T	£15,000	1990
Bodin, Paul	Bath C - Newport Co	£15,000	1988
Bullock, Martin	Eastwood T - Barnsley	£15,000	1993
Dennis, Tony	Slough T - Cambridge U	£15,000	1989
Ferdinand, Les	Hayes - QPR	£15,000	1987
Gayle, Mark	Worcester C - Walsall	£15,000	1991
Gorman, Paul	Fisher A - Charlton A	£15,000	1991
Heathcote, Mick	Spennymoor U - Sunderland	£15,000	1987
Hitchcock, Kevin	Barking - Nottingham F	£15,000	1983
Lyons, Andy	Fleetwood T - Crewe A	£15,000	1992
Pearce, Andy	Halesowen T - Coventry C	£15,000	1990
Pritchard, Dave	Telford U - Bristol R	£15,000	1994
Robertson, Paul	Runcorn - Doncaster R	£15,000	1995
Taylor, Ian	Moor Green - Port Vale	£15,000	1992
Taylor, Scott	Staines T - Millwall	£15,000	1995
Unsworth, Lee	Ashton U - Crewe A	£15,000	1994
Vowden, Colin	Cambridge C - Cambridge U	£15,000	1995
Wilcox, Russell	Frickley A - Northampton T	£15,000	1986
Claridge, Steve	Weymouth - Aldershot	£14,000	1988
Bimson, Stuart	Macclesfield T - Bury	£12,500	1995
Lyttle, Des	Worcester C - Swansea C	£12,500	1992
Austin, Dean	St.Albans C - Southend U	£12,000	1990
Dale, Carl	Bangor C - Cardiff C	£12,000	1988
Groves, Paul	Burton Alb - Leicester C	£12,000	1988
Williams, Paul A.	Woodford T - Charlton A	£12,000	1987
Freeman, Clive	Bridlington T - Swansae C	£10,500	1990
Alcide, Colin	Emley - Lincoln C	£10,000	1995
Bailey, Jon	Enfield - AFC Bournemouth	£10,000	1995
Barton, Warren	Leyt & Ilf - Maidstone U	£10,000	1989
Black, Tony	Bamber Bridge - Wigan A	£10,000	1995
Chalk, Martyn	Louth U - Derby Co	£10,000	1990
Collins, Wayne	Winsford U - Crewe A	£10,000	1993
Daws, Nicky	Altrincham - Bury	£10,000	1992
Eyres, David	Rhyl - Blackpool	£10,000	1989
Freestone, Chris	Arnold T - Middlesbrough	£10,000	1994
Gittens, Jon	Paget Rangers - Southampton	£10,000	1985
Helliwell, Ian	Matlock T - York C	£10,000	1987
Illman, Neil	Eastwood T - Plymouth A	£10,000	1996
Jones, Graeme	Bridlington T - Doncaster R	£10,000	1993
Jones, Nathan	Merthyr Tydfil - Luton T	£10,000	1995
Jones, Vinny	Wealdstone - Wimbledon	£10,000	1986
Love, Mickey	Hinckley Ath - Wigan Ath	£10,000	1995
McGoldrick, Eddie	Nuneaton B - Northampton T	£10,000	1986
Norbury, Mike	Bridlington T - Cambridge U	£10,000	1992
Phillips, Kevin	Baldock T - Watford	£10,000	1994
Quinn, Jimmy	Oswestry T - Swindon T	£10,000	1981
Richards, Carl	Enfield - AFC Bournemouth	£10,000	1986
Royce, Simon	Heybridge Swifts - Southend U	£10,000	1991
Sheridan, Darren	Winsford U - Barnsley	£10,000	1993
Shoemake, Kevin	Welling U - Peterborough U	£10,000	1986
Simkin, Darren	Blakenall - Wolves	£10,000	1991

Talboys, Steve	Gloucester C - Wimbledon	£10,000	1992
Tester, Paul	Cheltenham T - Shrewsbury T	£10,000	1983
Todd, Andrew	Eastwood T - Nottingham F	£10,000	1996
Toman, Andy	Bishop Auckland - Lincoln C	£10,000	1985
Whitlow, Mike	Witton Alb - Leeds U	£10,000	1988
Whitney, Jon	Winsford U - Huddersfield T	£10,000	1993
Williams, Marc	Bangor C - Stockport Co	£10,000	1995
Witter, Tony	Grays Ath - Crystal Palace	£10,000	1990
Young, Eric	Slough T - Brighton	£10,000	1982
Taylor, Ian	Bridlington T - Carlisle U	£9,000	1990
Jeffrey, Andy	Cambridge C - Cambridge U	£8,500	1993
Hathaway, Ian	Bedworth U - Mansfield T	£8,000	1989
McKinnon, Paul	Sutton U - Blackburn R	£8,000	1986
Puttnam, David	Leicester U - Leicester C	£8,000	1989
Barber, Phil	Aylesbury U - Crystal Palace	£7,500	1984
Bennett, Frank	Halesowen T - Southampton	£7,500	1993
Brook, Gary	Frickley A - Newport Co	£7,500	1987
Jones, Lee	AFC Porth - Swansea C	£7,500	1994
Pardew, Alan	Yeovil T - Crystal Palace	£7,000	1987
Hurlock, Terry	Leyt & Ilf - Brentford	£6,000	1980
Roberts, Graham	Weymouth - Tottenham H	£6,000	1979
Southall, Neville	Winsford U - Bury	£6,000	1980
Elliott, Matt	Epsom & Ewell - Charlton A	£5,000	1988
Flack, Steve	Cambridge C - Cardiff C	£5,000	1995
Hulme, Kevin	Radcliffe B - Bury	£5,000	1989
Milton, Simon	Bury T - Ipswich T	£5,500	1987
Ford, Jon	Cradley T - Swansea C	£5,000	1991
Gee, Phil	Gresley R - Derby Co	£5,000	1985
Hone, Mark	Welling U - Southend U	£5,000	1994
Hooker, Jon	Hertford T - Brentford	£5,000	1994
Pearson, Nigel	Heanor T - Shrewsbury T	£5,000	1981
Rattray, Kevin	Woking - Gillingham	£5,000	1995
Regis, Cyrille	Hayes - WBA	£5,000	1977
Tilley, Darren	Yate T - York C	£5,000	1992
Williams, John	Cradley T - Swansea C	£5,000	1991
Baker, Paul	Bishop Auckland - Southampton	£4,000	1984
Spink, Nigel	Chelmsford C - Aston Villa	£4,000	1977
Turley, Billy	Evesham U - Northampton T	£4,000	1995
Aldridge, John	Sth Liverpool - Newport Co	£3,500	1979
Holden, Andy	Rhyl - Chester C	£3,000	1983
Collins, Darren	Petersfield U - Northampton T	£2,500	1989
Berry, Greg	East Thurrock U - Leyton O	£2,000	1989
Williams, Dean P.	Tamworth - Brentford	£2,000	1993
Windass, Dean	North Ferriby U - Hull C	£2,000	1991
Penney, David	Pontefract Coll. - Derby Co	£1,500	1985
Austin, Kevin	Saffron Walden T - Leyton O	£1,000	1993
Beasant, Dave	Edgware T - Wimbledon	£1,000	1979
Davison, Bobby	Seaham CW - Huddersfield	£1,000	1980
Griffiths, Gareth	Rhyl - Port Vale	£1,000	1993
Nixon, Eric	Curzon Ashton - Manchester C	£1,000	1983
Rodger, Simon	Bognor Regis T - Crystal Palace	£1,000	1990
Waddle, Chris	Tow Law T - Newcastle U	£1,000	1980

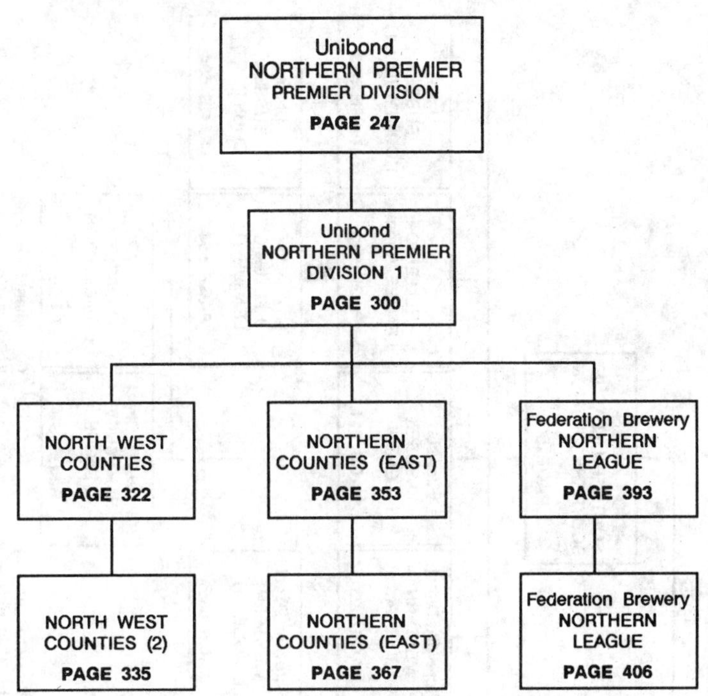

FEEDER LEAGUES

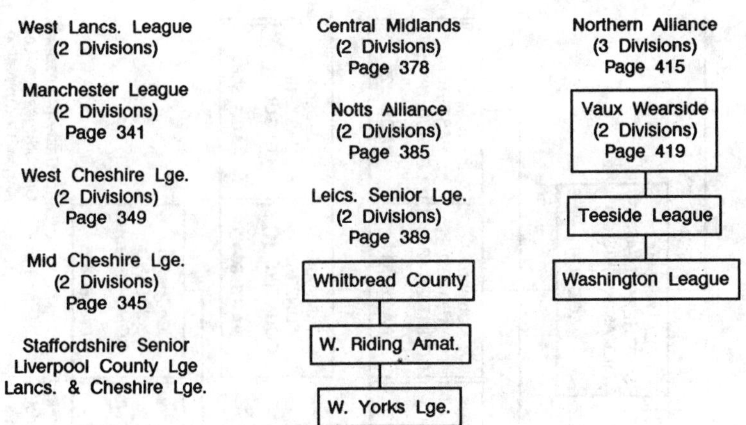

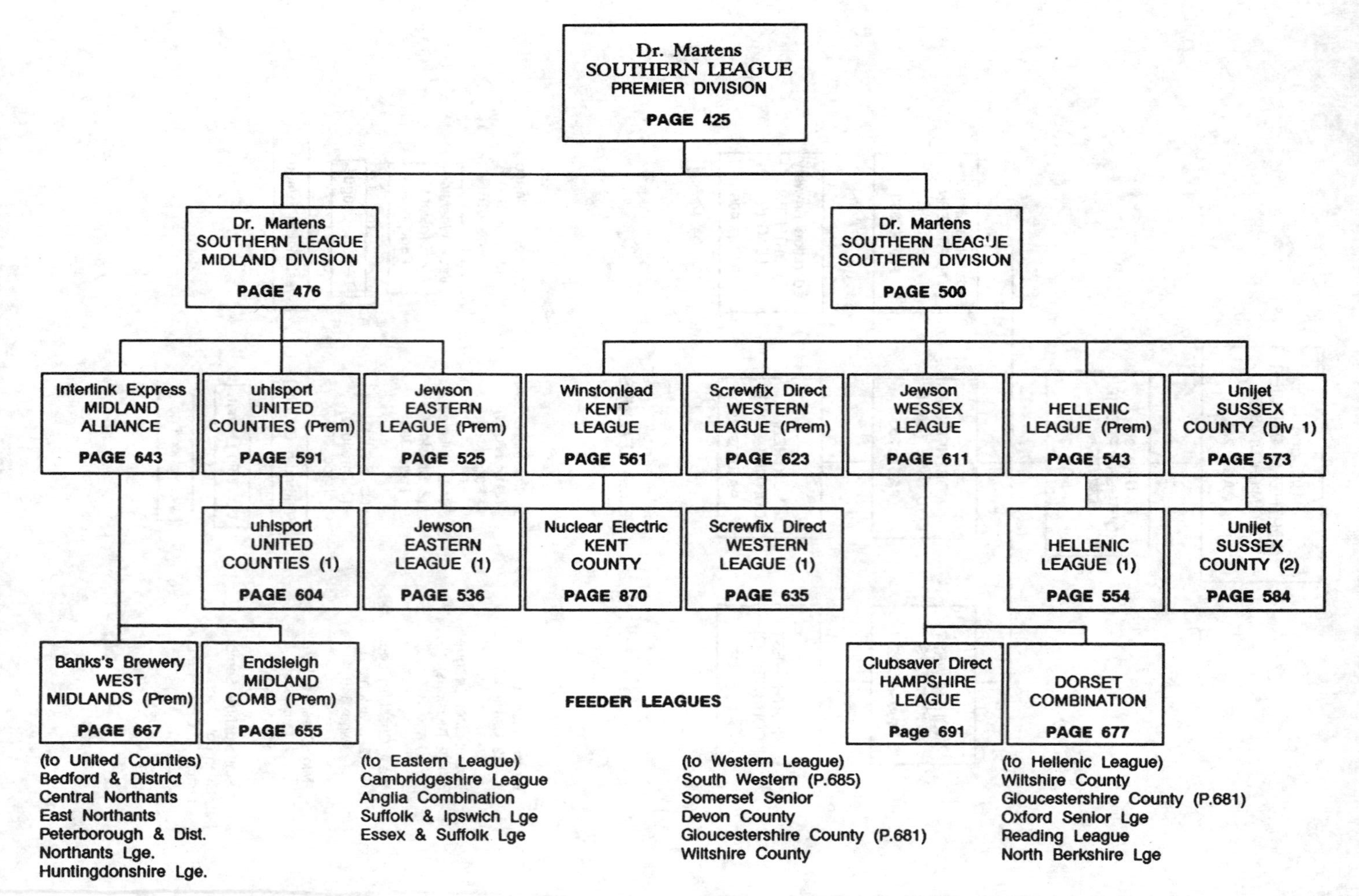

Dr. Martens SOUTHERN LEAGUE PREMIER DIVISION PAGE 425
Dr. Martens SOUTHERN LEAGUE MIDLAND DIVISION PAGE 476
Dr. Martens SOUTHERN LEAGUE SOUTHERN DIVISION PAGE 500
Interlink Express MIDLAND ALLIANCE PAGE 643
uhlsport UNITED COUNTIES (Prem) PAGE 591
Jewson EASTERN LEAGUE (Prem) PAGE 525
Winstonlead KENT LEAGUE PAGE 561
Screwfix Direct WESTERN LEAGUE (Prem) PAGE 623
Jewson WESSEX LEAGUE PAGE 611
HELLENIC LEAGUE (Prem) PAGE 543
Unijet SUSSEX COUNTY (Div 1) PAGE 573
uhlsport UNITED COUNTIES (1) PAGE 604
Jewson EASTERN LEAGUE (1) PAGE 536
Nuclear Electric KENT COUNTY PAGE 870
Screwfix Direct WESTERN LEAGUE (1) PAGE 635
HELLENIC LEAGUE (1) PAGE 554
Unijet SUSSEX COUNTY (2) PAGE 584
Banks's Brewery WEST MIDLANDS (Prem) PAGE 667
Endsleigh MIDLAND COMB (Prem) PAGE 655
FEEDER LEAGUES
Clubsaver Direct HAMPSHIRE LEAGUE Page 691
DORSET COMBINATION PAGE 677
(to United Counties)
Bedford & District
Central Northants
East Northants
Peterborough & Dist.
Northants Lge.
Huntingdonshire Lge.
(to Eastern League)
Cambridgeshire League
Anglia Combination
Suffolk & Ipswich Lge
Essex & Suffolk Lge
(to Western League)
South Western (P.685)
Somerset Senior
Devon County
Gloucestershire County (P.681)
Wiltshire County
(to Hellenic League)
Wiltshire County
Gloucestershire County (P.681)
Oxford Senior Lge
Reading League
North Berkshire Lge

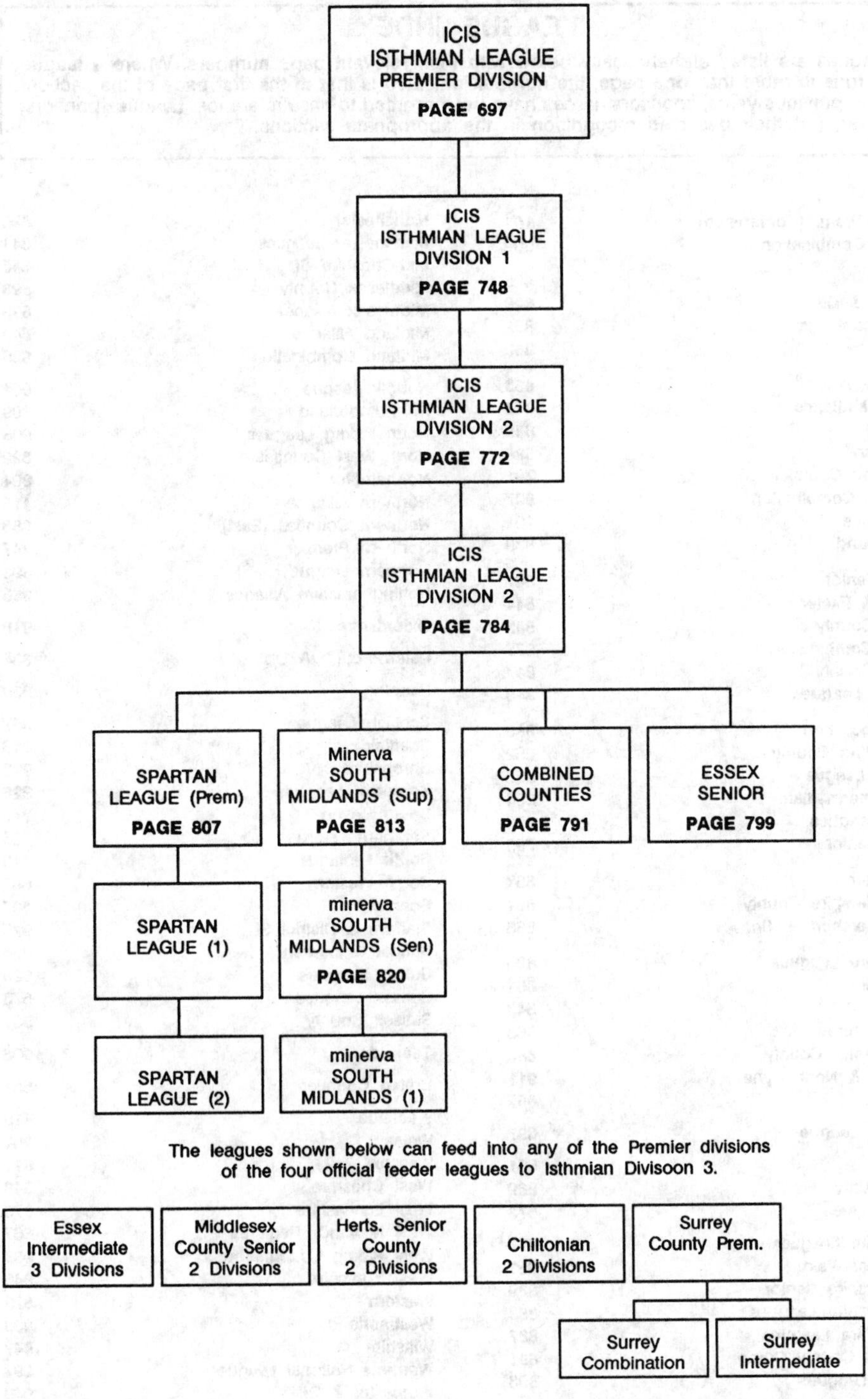

ICIS ISTHMIAN LEAGUE PREMIER DIVISION PAGE 697
ICIS ISTHMIAN LEAGUE DIVISION 1 PAGE 748
ICIS ISTHMIAN LEAGUE DIVISION 2 PAGE 772
ICIS ISTHMIAN LEAGUE DIVISION 2 PAGE 784
SPARTAN LEAGUE (Prem) PAGE 807
Minerva SOUTH MIDLANDS (Sup) PAGE 813
COMBINED COUNTIES PAGE 791
ESSEX SENIOR PAGE 799
SPARTAN LEAGUE (1)
minerva SOUTH MIDLANDS (Sen) PAGE 820
SPARTAN LEAGUE (2)
minerva SOUTH MIDLANDS (1)
The leagues shown below can feed into any of the Premier divisions of the four official feeder leagues to Isthmian Divisoon 3.
Essex Intermediate 3 Divisions
Middlesex County Senior 2 Divisions
Herts. Senior County 2 Divisions
Chiltonian 2 Divisions
Surrey County Prem.
Surrey Combination
Surrey Intermediate

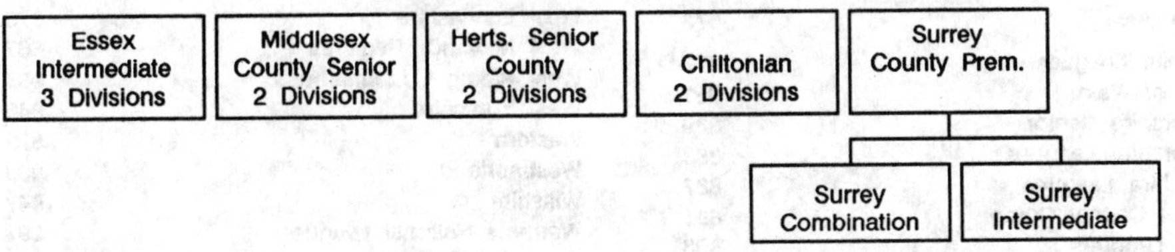

LEAGUE INDEX

Leagues are listed alphabetically below with their relevant page numbers. Where a league entry runs to more than one page, the number indicated is that of the first page of the section.

As in previous years, sponsors names have been omitted to ease reference. League sponsors, however, get their deserved recognition in the appropriate sections.

Clubs playing in the lower level pyramid leagues are not listed separately in this index.

CLUB INDEX

CLUB INDEX

CLUB INDEX

CLUB INDEX

* * *

A SPECIAL THANK YOU

NON LEAGUE CLUB DIRECTORY 1998

(20th Edition)

SAVE

£5

or

£2.50

Our special offer of discounts announced through Team Talk for this season's Directory were so popular we are certainly going to repeat them.

However as our lifeblood for the publications comes from Team Talk subscribers, who are probably regular Directory readers as well, we are announcing now that anyone taking out a 12 issue Team Talk subscription between August 1996 and August 1997 (inclusive) will be offered next year's Directory at a £5 discount off the cover price. Anyone taking out a 6 issue Team Talk subscription will be offered a £2.50 discount.

In this way we can say a special thank you to those of you who have invested in our efforts.

A 12 issue subscription costs £27 A 6 issue subscription costs £14

These rates include postage and packing in the U.K. (Overseas rates on application)

If you would like to subscribe to Team Talk you can either:

1. Use the form found in Team Talk each month.
2. Write to us, giving us your name, address including postcode, a telephone number for contact and tell us when you would like to start your subscription. You need to include payment - you can pay by cheque, postal order or credit card (Access, Visa or Mastercard).
3. If intending to pay by credit card you can call us on 01823 490080 and we can do the transaction over the telephone.